Visit classzone.com and get connected

Online resources provide instruction, practice, and learning support correlated to your text.

- **Online examples** offer extra at-home support.
- **State test practice** prepares students for assessments.
- **Self-scoring quizzes** provide comprehension checks.
- **Flashcards and crosswords** help students review vocabulary.
- **Teaching resources** offer answer keys and other support.

You have immediate access to *ClassZone's* teacher resources.

MCDTKASTMSMZ

Use this code to create your own username and password.

Also visit *ClassZone* to learn more about these innovative online resources.

- eEdition Plus Online
- eTutorial Plus Online
- eWorkbook Plus Online
- EasyPlanner Plus Online

ILLINOIS TEACHER'S EDITION

McDougal Littell Middle School

COURSE 3

Math

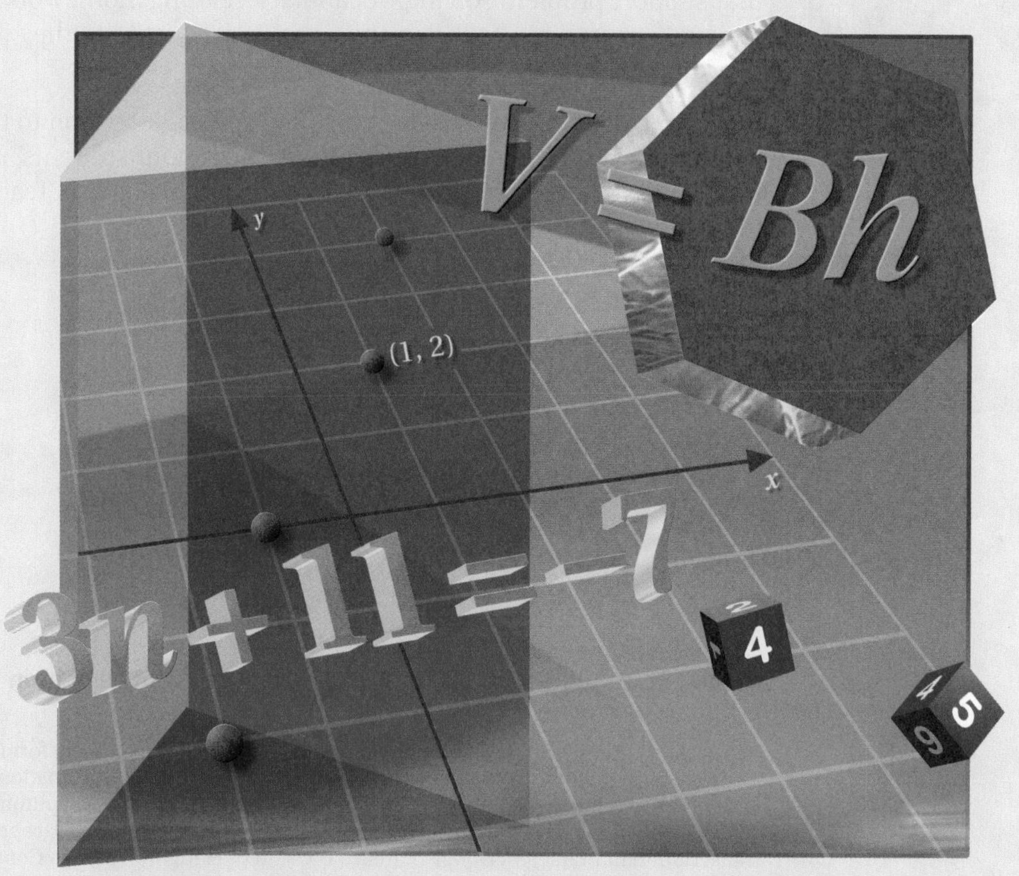

Larson Boswell Kanold Stiff

McDougal Littell
A HOUGHTON MIFFLIN COMPANY
Evanston, Illinois • Boston • Dallas

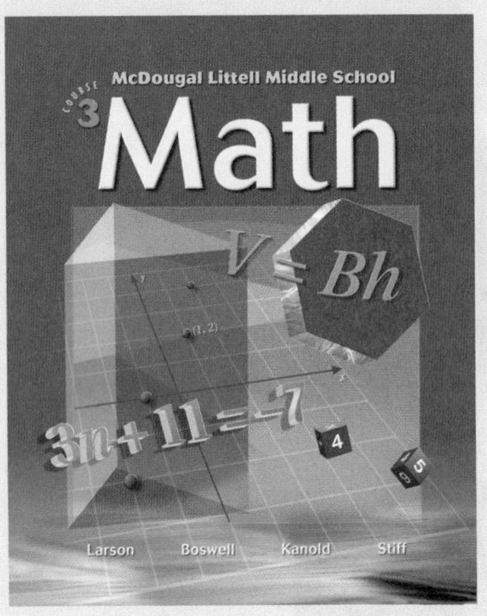

About Middle School Math: Course 3

McDougal Littell Middle School Math will help your students be successful in this course. The clearly written lessons with frequent step-by-step examples make even difficult math concepts and methods easier to understand. The number and variety of problems, ranging from basic to challenging, give your students the practice they need to develop their math skills. This book will also help them develop their notetaking and problem-solving skills. Look for notetaking strategies and Help Notes that support problem solving, vocabulary, reading, homework, technology, and review. Your students will also enjoy the Brain Games — they will challenge their thinking skills!

In writing this textbook, the authors paid special attention to the Illinois Learning Standards for mathematics. To help you check your students' progress in learning this Illinois content, there are margin notes in this Illinois Teacher's Edition indicating the learning standards they will study.

ISBN: 0-618-29372-8 123456789–DWO–07 06 05 04 03

Internet Web Site: http://www.classzone.com

Illinois Teacher's Edition Contents

Using the Illinois Teacher's Edition IL4

Illinois Teacher Support IL7

Overview of ISAT Reporting Sets IL9

Correlation to Illinois Learning Standards IL15

Lesson-by-Lesson Correlation to Illinois Learning Standards IL20

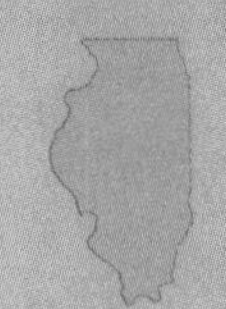

Overview of Illinois Correlations

The Illinois Student Edition and the Illinois Teacher's Edition for McDougal Littell Middle School Math, Course 3 *provide students and teachers with content that addresses the Illinois Learning Standards for mathematics.*

Illinois Learning Standards

The correlation charts on pages IL15–IL19 of this Illinois Teacher's Edition indicate lesson and page numbers where each learning standard for Grade 8 is covered in the textbook.

Correlation to Illinois Learning Standards *Continued*

ILLINOIS LEARNING STANDARD			STUDENT EDITION/TEACHER'S EDITION
STATE GOAL 7	Estimate, make and use measurements of objects, quantities and relationships and determine acceptable levels of accuracy.		
STANDARD A:	*Measure and compare quantities using appropriate units, instruments and methods.*		
	7.A.3a	Measure length, capacity, weight/mass and angles using sophisticated instruments (e.g., compass, protractor, trundle wheel).	pp. **396, 721, 722**
	7.A.3b	Apply the concepts and attributes of length, capacity, weight/mass, perimeter, area, volume, time, temperature and angle measures in practical situations.	pp. **375–379;** 199 (Exs. 45-48), 204 (Exs. 27-31), 382-385, 386-389, 390-393, 484 (Ex. 20)
STANDARD B:	*Estimate measurements and determine acceptable levels of accuracy.*		
	7.B.3	Select and apply instruments including rulers and protractors and units of measure to the degree of accuracy required.	pp. **720;** 274 (Ex. 25), 293 (Exs. 9-11), 488 (Ex. 23)
STANDARD C:	*Select and use appropriate technology, instruments and formulas to solve problems, interpret results and communicate findings.*		
	7.C.3a	Construct a simple scale drawing for a given situation.	pp. **321, 322–326;** 484 (Exs. 27, 28)
	7.C.3b	Use concrete and graphic models and appropriate formulas to find perimeters, areas, surface areas and volumes of two- and three-dimensional regions.	pp. **32, 33–37, 91–95, 132–133, 134–139, 178, 278–281, 288–289, 290–294, 402–403, 442, 443–447, 450–453, 478–479, 481–485, 486–490, 502–506, 507–511, 512, 513–517, 518, 519–523;** 82 (Ex. 13), 233 (Exs. 26-28), 274 (Exs. 35, 36), 431 (In-lesson Activity), 661-665 (Example 4; Exs. 29, 38)

Boldface Key page references are indicated in boldface type.

IL16

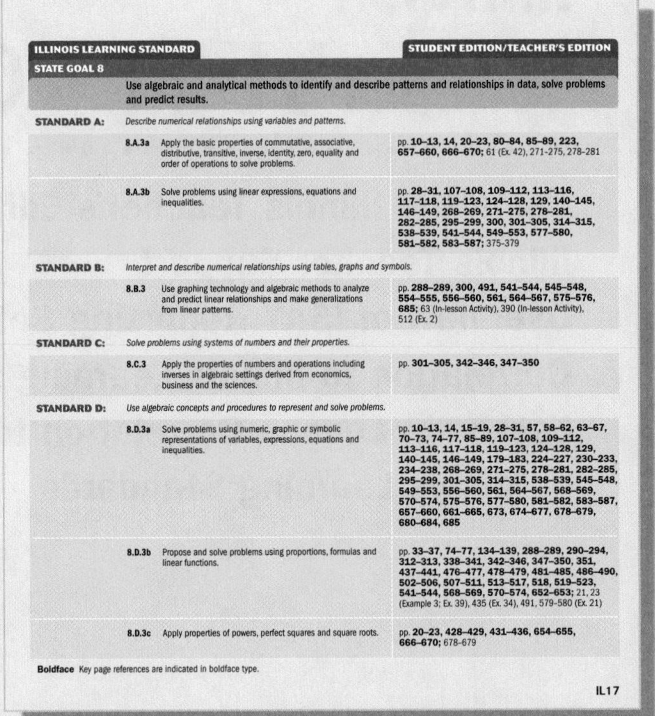

ILLINOIS LEARNING STANDARD			STUDENT EDITION/TEACHER'S EDITION
STATE GOAL 8	Use algebraic and analytical methods to identify and describe patterns and relationships in data, solve problems and predict results.		
STANDARD A:	*Describe numerical relationships using variables and patterns.*		
	8.A.3a	Apply the basic properties of commutative, associative, distributive, transitive, inverse, identity, zero, equality and order of operations to solve problems.	pp. **10–13, 14, 20–23, 80–84, 85–89, 223, 657–660, 666–670;** 61 (Ex. 42), 271-275, 278-281
	8.A.3b	Solve problems using linear expressions, equations and inequalities.	pp. **28–31, 107–108, 109–112, 113–116, 117–118, 119–123, 124–128, 129, 140–145, 146–149, 268–269, 271–275, 278–281, 282–285, 295–299, 300, 301–305, 314–315, 538–539, 541–544, 549–553, 577–580, 581–582, 583–587;** 375-379
STANDARD B:	*Interpret and describe numerical relationships using tables, graphs and symbols.*		
	8.B.3	Use graphing technology and algebraic methods to analyze and predict linear relationships and make generalizations from linear patterns.	pp. **288–289, 300, 491, 541–544, 545–548, 554–555, 556–560, 561, 564–567, 575–576, 685;** 63 (In-lesson Activity), 390 (In-lesson Activity), 512 (Ex. 2)
STANDARD C:	*Solve problems using systems of numbers and their properties.*		
	8.C.3	Apply the properties of numbers and operations including inverses in algebraic settings derived from economics, business and the sciences.	pp. **301–305, 342–346, 347–350**
STANDARD D:	*Use algebraic concepts and procedures to represent and solve problems.*		
	8.D.3a	Solve problems using numeric, graphic or symbolic representations of variables, expressions, equations and inequalities.	pp. **10–13, 14, 15–19, 28–31, 57, 58–62, 63–67, 70–73, 74–77, 85–89, 107–108, 109–112, 113–116, 117–118, 119–123, 124–128, 129, 140–145, 146–149, 179–183, 224–227, 230–233, 234–238, 268–269, 271–275, 278–281, 282–285, 295–299, 301–305, 314–315, 538–539, 545–548, 549–553, 556–560, 561, 564–567, 568–569, 570–574, 575–576, 577–580, 581–582, 583–587, 657–660, 661–665, 673, 674–677, 678–679, 680–684, 685**
	8.D.3b	Propose and solve problems using proportions, formulas and linear functions.	pp. **33–37, 74–77, 134–139, 288–289, 290–294, 312–313, 338–341, 342–346, 347–350, 351, 437–441, 476–477, 478–479, 481–485, 486–490, 502–506, 507–511, 513–517, 518, 519–523, 541–544, 568–569, 570–574, 652–653;** 21, 23 (Example 3; Ex. 39), 435 (Ex. 34), 491, 579-580 (Ex. 21)
	8.D.3c	Apply properties of powers, perfect squares and square roots.	pp. **20–23, 428–429, 431–436, 654–655, 666–670;** 678-679

Boldface Key page references are indicated in boldface type.

IL17

Lesson-by-Lesson Correlation

The correlation charts on pages IL20–IL24 of this Illinois Teacher's Edition are organized by lesson and they list the learning standards covered by each lesson.

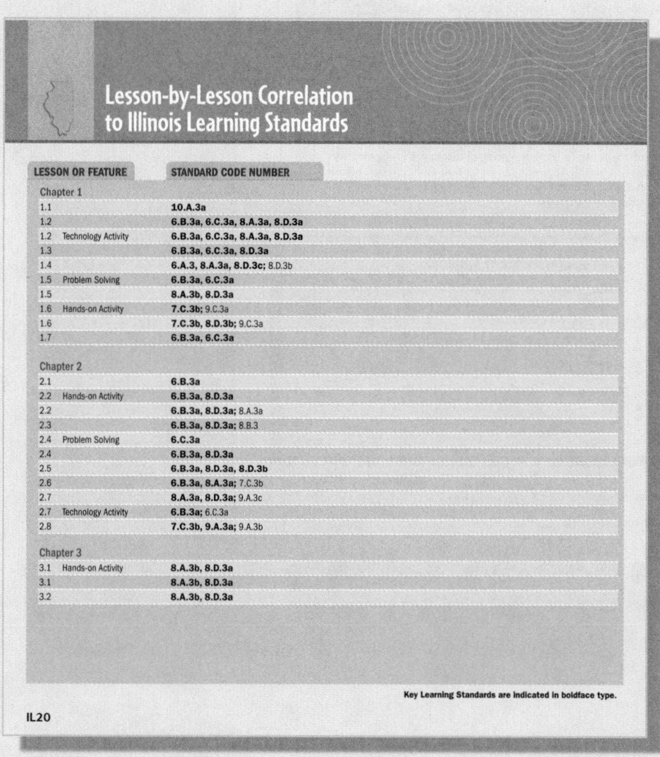

Lesson-by-Lesson Correlation to Illinois Learning Standards

LESSON OR FEATURE	STANDARD CODE NUMBER
Chapter 1	
1.1	**10.A.3a**
1.2	**6.B.3a, 6.C.3a, 8.A.3a, 8.D.3a**
1.2 Technology Activity	**6.B.3a, 6.C.3a, 8.A.3a, 8.D.3a**
1.3	**6.B.3a, 6.C.3a, 8.D.3a**
1.4	**6.A.3, 8.A.3a, 8.D.3c;** 8.D.3b
1.5 Problem Solving	**6.B.3a, 6.C.3a**
1.5	**8.A.3b, 8.D.3a**
1.6 Hands-on Activity	**7.C.3b;** 9.C.3a
1.6	**7.C.3b, 8.D.3b;** 9.C.3a
1.7	**6.B.3a, 6.C.3a**
Chapter 2	
2.1	**6.B.3a**
2.2 Hands-on Activity	**6.B.3a, 8.D.3a**
2.2	**6.B.3a, 8.D.3a;** 8.A.3a
2.3	**6.B.3a, 8.D.3a;** 8.B.3
2.4 Problem Solving	**6.C.3a**
2.4	**6.B.3a, 8.D.3a**
2.5	**6.B.3a, 8.D.3a, 8.D.3b**
2.6	**6.B.3a, 8.A.3a;** 7.C.3b
2.7	**8.A.3a, 8.D.3a;** 9.A.3c
2.7 Technology Activity	**6.B.3a;** 6.C.3a
2.8	**7.C.3b, 9.A.3a;** 9.A.3b
Chapter 3	
3.1 Hands-on Activity	**8.A.3b, 8.D.3a**
3.1	**8.A.3b, 8.D.3a**
3.2	**8.A.3b, 8.D.3a**

Key Learning Standards are indicated in boldface type.

IL20

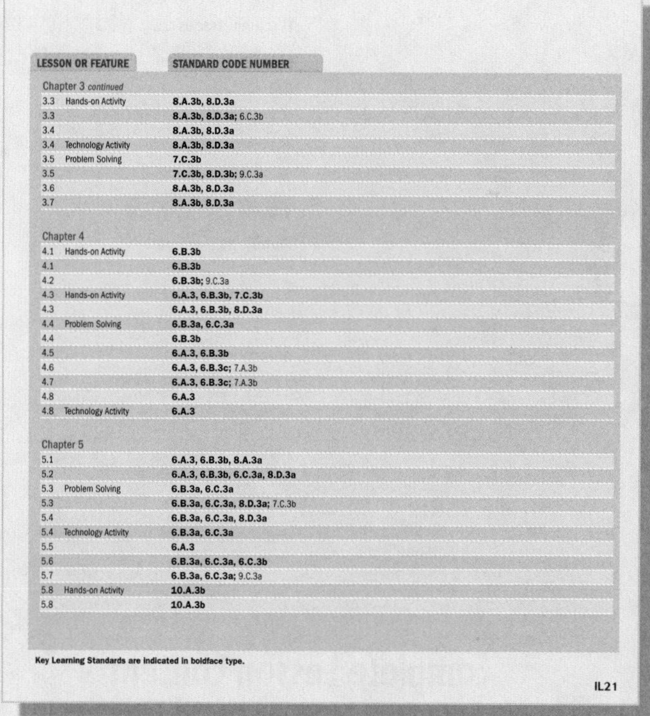

LESSON OR FEATURE	STANDARD CODE NUMBER
Chapter 3 *continued*	
3.3 Hands-on Activity	**8.A.3b, 8.D.3a**
3.3	**8.A.3b, 8.D.3a;** 6.C.3b
3.4	**8.A.3b, 8.D.3a**
3.4 Technology Activity	**8.A.3b, 8.D.3a**
3.5 Problem Solving	**7.C.3b**
3.5	**7.C.3b, 8.D.3b;** 9.C.3a
3.6	**8.A.3b, 8.D.3a**
3.7	**8.A.3b, 8.D.3a**
Chapter 4	
4.1 Hands-on Activity	**6.B.3b**
4.1	**6.B.3b**
4.2	**6.B.3b;** 9.C.3a
4.3 Hands-on Activity	**6.A.3, 6.B.3b, 7.C.3b**
4.3	**6.A.3, 6.B.3b, 8.D.3a**
4.4 Problem Solving	**6.B.3a, 6.C.3a**
4.4	**6.B.3b**
4.5	**6.A.3, 6.B.3b**
4.6	**6.A.3, 6.B.3c;** 7.A.3b
4.7	**6.A.3, 6.B.3c;** 7.A.3b
4.8	**6.A.3**
4.8 Technology Activity	**6.A.3**
Chapter 5	
5.1	**6.A.3, 6.B.3b, 8.A.3a**
5.2	**6.A.3, 6.B.3b, 6.C.3a, 8.D.3a**
5.3 Problem Solving	**6.B.3a, 6.C.3a**
5.3	**6.B.3a, 6.C.3a, 8.D.3a;** 7.C.3b
5.4	**6.B.3a, 6.C.3a, 8.D.3a**
5.4 Technology Activity	**6.B.3a, 6.C.3a**
5.5	**6.A.3**
5.6	**6.B.3a, 6.C.3a, 6.C.3b**
5.7	**6.B.3a, 6.C.3a;** 9.C.3a
5.8 Hands-on Activity	**10.A.3b**
5.8	**10.A.3b**

Key Learning Standards are indicated in boldface type.

IL21

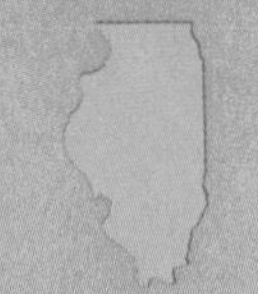

Lesson Correlations

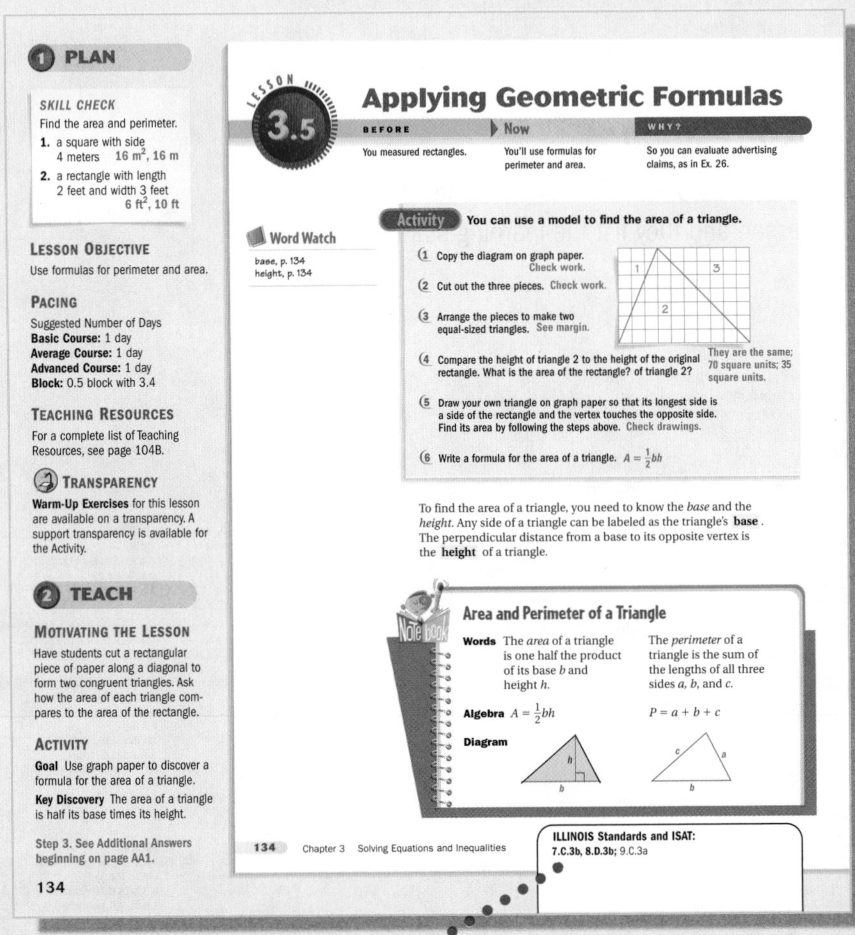

1 PLAN

SKILL CHECK

Find the area and perimeter.

1. a square with side 4 meters 16 m^2, 16 m
2. a rectangle with length 2 feet and width 3 feet 6 ft^2, 10 ft

LESSON OBJECTIVE

Use formulas for perimeter and area.

PACING

Suggested Number of Days
Basic Course: 1 day
Average Course: 1 day
Advanced Course: 1 day
Block: 0.5 block with 3.4

TEACHING RESOURCES

For a complete list of Teaching Resources, see page 104B.

TRANSPARENCY

Warm-Up Exercises for this lesson are available on a transparency. A support transparency is available for the Activity.

2 TEACH

MOTIVATING THE LESSON

Have students cut a rectangular piece of paper along a diagonal to form two congruent triangles. Ask how the area of each triangle compares to the area of the rectangle.

ACTIVITY

Goal Use graph paper to discover a formula for the area of a triangle.

Key Discovery The area of a triangle is half its base times its height.

Step 3. See Additional Answers beginning on page AA1.

134

LESSON 3.5

Applying Geometric Formulas

BEFORE	Now	WHY?
You measured rectangles.	You'll use formulas for perimeter and area.	So you can evaluate advertising claims, as in Ex. 26.

Word Watch

base, p. 134
height, p. 134

Activity You can use a model to find the area of a triangle.

1. Copy the diagram on graph paper. Check work.
2. Cut out the three pieces. Check work.
3. Arrange the pieces to make two equal-sized triangles. See margin.
4. Compare the height of triangle 2 to the height of the original rectangle. What is the area of the rectangle? of triangle 2? They are the same; 70 square units; 35 square units.
5. Draw your own triangle on graph paper so that its longest side is a side of the rectangle and the vertex touches the opposite side. Find its area by following the steps above. Check drawings.
6. Write a formula for the area of a triangle. $A = \frac{1}{2}bh$

To find the area of a triangle, you need to know the *base* and the *height*. Any side of a triangle can be labeled as the triangle's **base**. The perpendicular distance from a base to its opposite vertex is the **height** of a triangle.

Notebook

Area and Perimeter of a Triangle

Words The *area* of a triangle is one half the product of its base *b* and height *h*. The *perimeter* of a triangle is the sum of the lengths of all three sides *a*, *b*, and *c*.

Algebra $A = \frac{1}{2}bh$ $P = a + b + c$

Diagram

134 Chapter 3 Solving Equations and Inequalities

ILLINOIS Standards and ISAT:
7.C.3b, 8.D.3b; 9.C.3a

Complete Lesson Content

At point-of-use in this Illinois Teacher's Edition is a list of all the learning standards being covered in the lesson or activity.

Illinois Teacher Support

The Preparing for the Grade 8 Illinois Standards Achievement Test, Mathematics *book that accompanies* McDougal Littell Middle School Math, Courses 1–3 *provides test and practice materials to help you prepare middle school students for the ISAT.*

The book includes:

- *Two practice tests*
- *A prescriptive scoring sheet allowing for student-specific and standard-specific remediation*
- *Extensive practice worksheets that address the Illinois Learning Standards*
- *Scoring rubrics and exemplary answers for open-ended items*

ISAT Reporting Sets

The Illinois Standards Achievement Test (ISAT) measures student performance relative to the Illinois Learning Standards. The ISAT results are divided into eight Reporting Sets. Each reporting set encompasses certain of the Illinois Learning Standards. The chart on pages IL10 and IL11 shows which Illinois Learning Standards correspond to each Reporting Set. The charts on pages IL15–IL24 show how McDougal Littell Middle School Math, Course 3 *correlates to the Illinois Learning Standards.*

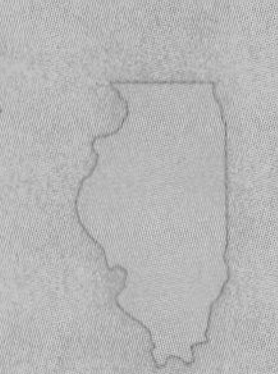

ISAT and Illinois Learning Standards

ISAT REPORTING SETS		ILLINOIS LEARNING STANDARDS
ESTIMATION/NUMBER SENSE/COMPUTATION		
Demonstrating an understanding of numbers, their representations, and number operations of addition, subtraction, multiplication, division, percentages and fractions as appropriate to grade level.	**6.A**	Demonstrate knowledge and use of numbers and their representations in a broad range of theoretical and practical settings.
	6.B	Investigate, represent and solve problems using number facts, operations (addition, subtraction, multiplication, division) and their properties, algorithms and relationships.
	6.C	Compute and estimate using mental mathematics, paper-and-pencil methods, calculators and computers.
	6.D	Solve problems using comparison of quantities, ratios, proportions and percents.
	8.C	Solve problems using systems of numbers and their properties.
ALGEBRAIC PATTERNS AND VARIABLES		
Identifying, describing, and extending algebraic, geometric and numeric patterns and constructing and solving problems using variables.	**8.A**	Describe numerical relationships using variables and patterns.
	8.C	Solve problems using systems of numbers and their properties.
	8.D	Use algebraic concepts and procedures to represent and solve problems.
ALGEBRAIC RELATIONSHIPS/REPRESENTATIONS		
Representing and interpreting algebraic concepts with words, diagrams, tables, coordinate graphs, equations, and inequalities.	**8.B**	Interpret and describe numerical relationships using tables, graphs and symbols.
	8.C	Solve problems using systems of numbers and their properties.
GEOMETRIC CONCEPTS		
Identifying and describing points, lines, two-and three-dimensional shapes and their properties, such as parallel; symmetry; perpendicular; and number of sides, faces and vertices.	**8.C**	Solve problems using systems of numbers and their properties.
	9.A	Demonstrate and apply geometric concepts involving points, lines, planes and space.

ISAT REPORTING SETS		ILLINOIS LEARNING STANDARDS
GEOMETRIC RELATIONSHIPS		
Sorting, classifying, comparing and contrasting geometric figures. This may include properties such as similarity and congruency.	**8.C**	Solve problems using systems of numbers and their properties.
	9.B	Identify, describe, classify and compare relationships using points, lines, planes and solids.
	9.D	Use trigonometric ratios and circular functions to solve problems.
MEASUREMENT		
Estimating, measuring and comparing quantities using appropriate units and acceptable levels of accuracy. At higher grades, this may include conversions within measurement systems.	**7.A**	Measure and compare quantities using appropriate units, instruments and methods.
	7.B	Estimate measurements and determine acceptable levels of accuracy.
	7.C	Select and use appropriate technology, instruments and formulas to solve problems, interpret results and communicate findings.
	8.C	Solve problems using systems of numbers and their properties.
DATA ORGANIZATION AND ANALYSIS		
Creating, analyzing, displaying, and interpreting data using a variety of graphs such as pictures; tallies; tables; charts; bar graphs; Venn diagrams; and computing the mean, median, mode, and range of given data.	**8.C**	Solve problems using systems of numbers and their properties.
	10.A	Organize, describe and make predictions from existing data.
	10.B	Formulate questions, design data collection methods, gather and analyze data and communicate findings.
PROBABILITY		
Determining, describing, and applying the probability of an event and using fundamental counting principles. At higher grades, may involve combinations and permutations of simple and complex events.	**8.C**	Solve problems using systems of numbers and their properties.
	10.C	Determine, describe and apply the probabilities of events.

Illinois Correlations

The material on pages IL15–IL24 will help you coordinate your teaching of McDougal Littell Middle School Math, Course 3 *with the Illinois Learning Standards.*

The charts on pages IL15–IL19 contain a correlation of Course 3 *to the learning standards for Grade 8. The first column of the charts lists the learning standards. The second column identifies pages in the Student and Teacher's Editions that teach the material included in the learning standards. Key page references appear in boldface type.*

The charts on pages IL20–IL24 are organized by chapter and they list the learning standards covered by each lesson or feature in the textbook.

Correlation to Illinois Learning Standards

ILLINOIS LEARNING STANDARD			STUDENT EDITION/TEACHER'S EDITION
STATE GOAL 6			
	Demonstrate and apply a knowledge and sense of numbers, including numeration and operations (addition, subtraction, multiplication, division), patterns, ratios and proportions.		
STANDARD A:	*Demonstrate knowledge and use of numbers and their representations in a broad range of theoretical and practical settings.*		
	6.A.3	Represent fractions, decimals, percentages, exponents and scientific notation in equivalent forms.	pp. **20–23, 178, 179–183, 192–195, 196–200, 201–204, 205–208, 209, 216–217, 219–223, 224–227, 241–246, 327–330, 331–335, 428–429, 437–441, 654–655, 704, 707**
STANDARD B:	*Investigate, represent and solve problems using number facts, operations (addition, subtraction, multiplication, division) and their properties, algorithms, and relationships.*		
	6.B.3a	Solve practical computation problems involving whole numbers, integers and rational numbers.	pp. **2–3, 10–13, 14, 15–19, 26–27, 38–43, 50–51, 53–56, 57, 58–62, 63–67, 70–73, 74–77, 80–84, 90, 104–105, 164–165, 184–185, 228–229, 230–233, 234–238, 239, 247–250, 251–254, 276–277, 437–441, 500–501, 554–555, 616–617, 706;** 402-403
	6.B.3b	Apply primes, factors, divisors, multiples, common factors and common multiples in solving problems.	pp. **164–165, 167, 168–172, 173–177, 178, 179–183, 186–189, 192–195, 216–217, 219–223, 224–227**
	6.B.3c	Identify and apply properties of real numbers including pi, squares, and square roots.	pp. **196–200, 201–204, 431–436**
STANDARD C:	*Compute and estimate using mental mathematics, paper-and-pencil methods, calculators and computers.*		
	6.C.3a	Select computational procedures and solve problems with whole numbers, fractions, decimals, percents and proportions.	pp. **2–3, 10–13, 14, 15–19, 26–27, 38–43, 50–51, 68–69, 104–105, 164–165, 184–185, 224–227, 228–229, 230–233, 234–238, 239, 247–250, 251–254, 276–277, 314–315, 327–330, 331–335, 338–341, 342–346, 347–350, 500–501, 554–555, 616–617, 709, 710, 712, 713, 714, 715, 717;** 90 (Exs. 10, 11), 402-403
	6.C.3b	Show evidence that computational results using whole numbers, fractions, decimals, percents and proportions are correct and/or that estimates are reasonable.	pp. **247–250, 705, 711, 716;** 122 (Ex. 23), 416-421, 489 (Ex. 33), 678-679 (Exs. 4, 6)
STANDARD D:	*Solve problems using comparison of quantities, ratios, proportions and percents.*		
	6.D.3	Apply ratios and proportions to solve practical problems.	pp. **317–320, 322–326, 327–330, 416–421, 708;** 352-353

Boldface Key page references are indicated in boldface type.

ILLINOIS LEARNING STANDARD			STUDENT EDITION/TEACHER'S EDITION
STATE GOAL 7			
	Estimate, make and use measurements of objects, quantities and relationships and determine acceptable levels of accuracy.		
STANDARD A:	*Measure and compare quantities using appropriate units, instruments and methods.*		
	7.A.3a	Measure length, capacity, weight/mass and angles using sophisticated instruments (e.g., compass, protractor, trundle wheel).	pp. **396, 721, 722**
	7.A.3b	Apply the concepts and attributes of length, capacity, weight/mass, perimeter, area, volume, time, temperature and angle measures in practical situations.	pp. **375–379;** 199 (Exs. 45-48), 204 (Exs. 27-31), 382-385, 386-389, 390-393, 484 (Ex. 20)
STANDARD B:	*Estimate measurements and determine acceptable levels of accuracy.*		
	7.B.3	Select and apply instruments including rulers and protractors and units of measure to the degree of accuracy required.	pp. **720;** 274 (Ex. 25), 293 (Exs. 9–11), 488 (Ex. 23)
STANDARD C:	*Select and use appropriate technology, instruments and formulas to solve problems, interpret results and communicate findings.*		
	7.C.3a	Construct a simple scale drawing for a given situation.	pp. **321, 322–326;** 484 (Exs. 27, 28)
	7.C.3b	Use concrete and graphic models and appropriate formulas to find perimeters, areas, surface areas and volumes of two- and three-dimensional regions.	pp. **32, 33–37, 91–95, 132–133, 134–139, 178, 278–281, 288–289, 290–294, 402–403, 442, 443–447, 450–453, 478–479, 481–485, 486–490, 502–506, 507–511, 512, 513–517, 518, 519–523;** 82 (Ex. 13), 233 (Exs. 26–28), 274 (Exs. 35, 36), 431 (In-lesson Activity), 661-665 (Example 4; Exs. 29, 38)

Boldface Key page references are indicated in boldface type.

ILLINOIS LEARNING STANDARD		STUDENT EDITION/TEACHER'S EDITION
STATE GOAL 8		
	Use algebraic and analytical methods to identify and describe patterns and relationships in data, solve problems and predict results.	
STANDARD A:	*Describe numerical relationships using variables and patterns.*	
	8.A.3a Apply the basic properties of commutative, associative, distributive, transitive, inverse, identity, zero, equality and order of operations to solve problems.	pp. **10–13, 14, 20–23, 80–84, 85–89, 223, 657–660, 666–670;** 61 (Ex. 42), 271-275, 278-281
	8.A.3b Solve problems using linear expressions, equations and inequalities.	pp. **28–31, 107–108, 109–112, 113–116, 117–118, 119–123, 124–128, 129, 140–145, 146–149, 268–269, 271–275, 278–281, 282–285, 295–299, 300, 301–305, 314–315, 538–539, 541–544, 549–553, 577–580, 581–582, 583–587;** 375-379
STANDARD B:	*Interpret and describe numerical relationships using tables, graphs and symbols.*	
	8.B.3 Use graphing technology and algebraic methods to analyze and predict linear relationships and make generalizations from linear patterns.	pp. **288–289, 300, 491, 541–544, 545–548, 554–555, 556–560, 561, 564–567, 575–576, 685;** 63 (In-lesson Activity), 390 (In-lesson Activity), 512 (Ex. 2)
STANDARD C:	*Solve problems using systems of numbers and their properties.*	
	8.C.3 Apply the properties of numbers and operations including inverses in algebraic settings derived from economics, business and the sciences.	pp. **301–305, 342–346, 347–350**
STANDARD D:	*Use algebraic concepts and procedures to represent and solve problems.*	
	8.D.3a Solve problems using numeric, graphic or symbolic representations of variables, expressions, equations and inequalities.	pp. **10–13, 14, 15–19, 28–31, 57, 58–62, 63–67, 70–73, 74–77, 85–89, 107–108, 109–112, 113–116, 117–118, 119–123, 124–128, 129, 140–145, 146–149, 179–183, 224–227, 230–233, 234–238, 268–269, 271–275, 278–281, 282–285, 295–299, 301–305, 314–315, 538–539, 545–548, 549–553, 556–560, 561, 564–567, 568–569, 570–574, 575–576, 577–580, 581–582, 583–587, 657–660, 661–665, 673, 674–677, 678–679, 680–684, 685**
	8.D.3b Propose and solve problems using proportions, formulas and linear functions.	pp. **33–37, 74–77, 134–139, 288–289, 290–294, 312–313, 338–341, 342–346, 347–350, 351, 437–441, 476–477, 478–479, 481–485, 486–490, 502–506, 507–511, 513–517, 518, 519–523, 541–544, 568–569, 570–574, 652–653;** 21, 23 (Example 3; Ex. 39), 435 (Ex. 34), 491, 579-580 (Ex. 21)
	8.D.3c Apply properties of powers, perfect squares and square roots.	pp. **20–23, 428–429, 431–436, 654–655, 666–670;** 678-679

Boldface Key page references are indicated in boldface type.

ILLINOIS LEARNING STANDARD		STUDENT EDITION/TEACHER'S EDITION
STATE GOAL 9	**Use geometric methods to analyze, categorize and draw conclusions about points, lines, planes and space.**	
STANDARD A:	*Demonstrate and apply geometric concepts involving points, lines, planes and space.*	
9.A.3a	Draw or construct two- and three- dimensional geometric figures including prisms, pyramids, cylinders and cones.	pp. **91–95, 372–373, 380–381, 396, 404–408, 448–449, 492–495, 496–497, 538–539;** 570-574
9.A.3b	Draw transformation images of figures, with and without the use of technology.	pp. **404–408, 409–413, 414–415;** 94 (Ex. 31)
9.A.3c	Use concepts of symmetry, congruency, similarity, scale, perspective, and angles to describe and analyze two- and three-dimensional shapes found in practical applications (e.g., geodesic domes, A-frame houses, basketball courts, inclined planes, art forms, blueprints).	pp. **404–408, 409–413, 416–421;** 88 (Ex. 33)
STANDARD B:	*Identify, describe, classify and compare relationships using points, lines, planes and solids.*	
9.B.3	Identify, describe, classify and compare two- and three-dimensional geometric figures and models according to their properties.	pp. **382–385, 386–389, 390–393, 397–401, 416–421, 428–429, 492–495, 718, 719**
STANDARD C:	*Construct convincing arguments and proofs to solve problems.*	
9.C.3a	Construct, develop and communicate logical arguments (informal proofs) about geometric figures and patterns.	pp. 32 (Ex. 4), 37 (Ex. 32), 102 (Ex. 4), 138 (Exs. 27-30), 164-165 (Ex. 2), 177 (Ex. 34), 254 (Ex. 35), 268–269 (Ex. 2), 517 (Exs. 30-31)
9.C.3b	Develop and solve problems using geometric relationships and models, with and without the use of technology.	pp. **288–289, 416–421, 456–460**
STANDARD D:	*Use trigonometric ratios and circular functions to solve problems.*	
9.D.3	Compute distances, lengths and measures of angles using proportions, the Pythagorean theorem and its converse.	pp. **442, 443–447, 450–453, 461–462, 463–468, 469, 476–477;** 448-449

Boldface Key page references are indicated in boldface type.

ILLINOIS LEARNING STANDARD		STUDENT EDITION/TEACHER'S EDITION
STATE GOAL 10		
	Collect, organize and analyze data using statistical methods; predict results; and interpret uncertainty using concepts of probability.	
STANDARD A:	*Organize, describe and make predictions from existing data.*	
	10.A.3a Construct, read and interpret tables, graphs (including circle graphs) and charts to organize and represent data.	pp. **5–9, 102–103, 594–595, 597–600, 601–604, 605–609, 610–611, 612–613, 723, 724, 725, 726;** 334–335 (Exs. 45–48, 58)
	10.A.3b Compare the mean, median, mode and range, with and without the use of technology.	pp. **255–256, 257–261;** 601-604
	10.A.3c Test the reasonableness of an argument based on data and communicate their findings.	pp. **612–613, 644–645;** 605-609
STANDARD B:	*Formulate questions, design data collection methods, gather and analyze data and communicate findings.*	
	10.B.3 Formulate questions (e.g., relationships between car age and mileage, average incomes and years of schooling), devise and conduct experiments or simulations, gather data, draw conclusions and communicate results to an audience using traditional methods and contemporary technologies.	pp. **352–353, 637–638;** 354-357
STANDARD C:	*Determine, describe and apply the probabilities of events.*	
	10.C.3a Determine the probability and odds of events using fundamental counting principles.	pp. **354–357, 618–622, 623–626, 627–631, 632–636, 637–638, 639–643, 652–653**
	10.C.3b Analyze problem situations (e.g., board games, grading scales) and make predictions about results.	pp. **352–353, 354–357**

Boldface Key page references are indicated in boldface type.

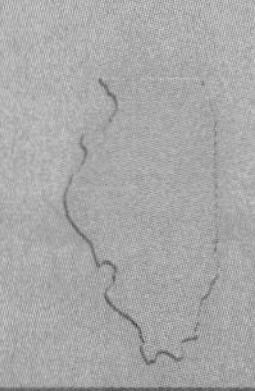

Lesson-by-Lesson Correlation to Illinois Learning Standards

LESSON OR FEATURE	STANDARD CODE NUMBER
Chapter 1	
1.1	**10.A.3a**
1.2	**6.B.3a, 6.C.3a, 8.A.3a, 8.D.3a**
1.2 Technology Activity	**6.B.3a, 6.C.3a, 8.A.3a, 8.D.3a**
1.3	**6.B.3a, 6.C.3a, 8.D.3a**
1.4	**6.A.3, 8.A.3a, 8.D.3c;** 8.D.3b
1.5 Problem Solving	**6.B.3a, 6.C.3a**
1.5	**8.A.3b, 8.D.3a**
1.6 Hands-on Activity	**7.C.3b;** 9.C.3a
1.6	**7.C.3b, 8.D.3b;** 9.C.3a
1.7	**6.B.3a, 6.C.3a**
Chapter 2	
2.1	**6.B.3a**
2.2 Hands-on Activity	**6.B.3a, 8.D.3a**
2.2	**6.B.3a, 8.D.3a;** 8.A.3a
2.3	**6.B.3a, 8.D.3a;** 8.B.3
2.4 Problem Solving	**6.C.3a**
2.4	**6.B.3a, 8.D.3a**
2.5	**6.B.3a, 8.D.3a, 8.D.3b**
2.6	**6.B.3a, 8.A.3a;** 7.C.3b
2.7	**8.A.3a, 8.D.3a;** 9.A.3c
2.7 Technology Activity	**6.B.3a;** 6.C.3a
2.8	**7.C.3b, 9.A.3a;** 9.A.3b
Chapter 3	
3.1 Hands-on Activity	**8.A.3b, 8.D.3a**
3.1	**8.A.3b, 8.D.3a**
3.2	**8.A.3b, 8.D.3a**

Key Learning Standards are indicated in boldface type.

LESSON OR FEATURE		STANDARD CODE NUMBER
Chapter 3 *continued*		
3.3	Hands-on Activity	**8.A.3b, 8.D.3a**
3.3		**8.A.3b, 8.D.3a;** 6.C.3b
3.4		**8.A.3b, 8.D.3a**
3.4	Technology Activity	**8.A.3b, 8.D.3a**
3.5	Problem Solving	**7.C.3b**
3.5		**7.C.3b, 8.D.3b;** 9.C.3a
3.6		**8.A.3b, 8.D.3a**
3.7		**8.A.3b, 8.D.3a**
Chapter 4		
4.1	Hands-on Activity	**6.B.3b**
4.1		**6.B.3b**
4.2		**6.B.3b;** 9.C.3a
4.3	Hands-on Activity	**6.A.3, 6.B.3b, 7.C.3b**
4.3		**6.A.3, 6.B.3b, 8.D.3a**
4.4	Problem Solving	**6.B.3a, 6.C.3a**
4.4		**6.B.3b**
4.5		**6.A.3, 6.B.3b**
4.6		**6.A.3, 6.B.3c;** 7.A.3b
4.7		**6.A.3, 6.B.3c;** 7.A.3b
4.8		**6.A.3**
4.8	Technology Activity	**6.A.3**
Chapter 5		
5.1		**6.A.3, 6.B.3b, 8.A.3a**
5.2		**6.A.3, 6.B.3b, 6.C.3a, 8.D.3a**
5.3	Problem Solving	**6.B.3a, 6.C.3a**
5.3		**6.B.3a, 6.C.3a, 8.D.3a;** 7.C.3b
5.4		**6.B.3a, 6.C.3a, 8.D.3a**
5.4	Technology Activity	**6.B.3a, 6.C.3a**
5.5		**6.A.3**
5.6		**6.B.3a, 6.C.3a, 6.C.3b**
5.7		**6.B.3a, 6.C.3a;** 9.C.3a
5.8	Hands-on Activity	**10.A.3b**
5.8		**10.A.3b**

Key Learning Standards are indicated in boldface type.

Lesson-by-Lesson Correlation to Illinois Learning Standards *Continued*

LESSON OR FEATURE	STANDARD CODE NUMBER
Chapter 6	
6.1	**8.A.3b, 8.D.3a;** 7.B.3, 7.C.3b, 8.A.3a
6.2 Problem Solving	**6.B.3a, 6.C.3a**
6.2	**7.C.3b, 8.A.3b, 8.D.3a;** 8.A.3a
6.3	**8.A.3b, 8.D.3a**
6.4 Hands-on Activity	**7.C.3b, 8.B.3, 8.D.3b, 9.C.3b**
6.4	**7.C.3b, 8.D.3b;** 7.B.3
6.5	**8.A.3b, 8.D.3a**
6.5 Technology Activity	**8.A.3b, 8.B.3**
6.6	**8.A.3b, 8.C.3, 8.D.3a**
Chapter 7	
7.1	**6.D.3**
7.2 Hands-on Activity	**7.C.3a**
7.2	**6.D.3, 7.C.3a**
7.3	**6.A.3, 6.C.3a, 6.D.3**
7.4	**6.A.3, 6.C.3a;** 10.A.3a
7.5	**6.C.3a, 8.D.3b**
7.6	**6.C.3a, 8.C.3, 8.D.3b**
7.7	**6.C.3a, 8.C.3, 8.D.3b**
7.7 Technology Activity	**8.D.3b**
7.8 Problem Solving	**10.B.3, 10.C.3b;** 6.D.3
7.8	**10.C.3a, 10.C.3b;** 10.B.3
Chapter 8	
8.1	**7.A.3b;** 8.A.3b
8 Special Topic #1	**9.A.3a**
8.2	**9.B.3;** 7.A.3b
8.3	**9.B.3;** 7.A.3b
8.4	**9.B.3;** 7.A.3b, 8.B.3
8.5 Hands-on Activity	**7.A.3a, 9.A.3a**
8.5	**9.B.3**
8.6 Problem Solving	**7.C.3b;** 6.B.3a, 6.C.3a
8.6	**9.A.3a, 9.A.3b, 9.A.3c**
8.7	**9.A.3b, 9.A.3c**
8 Special Topic #2	**9.A.3b**
8.8	**6.D.3, 9.A.3c, 9.B.3, 9.C.3b;** 6.C.3b

Key Learning Standards are indicated in boldface type.

LESSON OR FEATURE		STANDARD CODE NUMBER
Chapter 9		
9.1		**6.B.3c, 8.D.3c;** 7.C.3b, 8.D.3b
9.2		**6.A.3, 6.B.3a, 8.D.3b**
9.3	Hands-on Activity	**7.C.3b, 9.D.3**
9.3		**7.C.3b, 9.D.3**
9.4	Problem Solving	**9.A.3a;** 9.D.3
9.4		**7.C.3b, 9.D.3**
9.5		**9.C.3b**
9.6	Hands-on Activity	**9.D.3**
9.6		**9.D.3**
9.6	Technology Activity	**9.D.3**
Chapter 10		
10.1		**7.C.3b, 8.D.3b;** 7.A.3b, 7.C.3a
10.2		**7.C.3b, 8.D.3b;** 7.B.3, 6.C.3b
10.2	Technology Activity	**8.B.3;** 8.D.3b
10.3		**9.A.3a, 9.B.3**
10	Special Topic	**9.A.3a**
10.4	Problem Solving	**6.B.3a, 6.C.3a**
10.4		**7.C.3b, 8.D.3b**
10.5		**7.C.3b, 8.D.3b**
10.6	Hands-on Activity	**7.C.3b;** 8.B.3
10.6		**7.C.3b, 8.D.3b;** 9.C.3a
10.7	Hands-on Activity	**7.C.3b, 8.D.3b**
10.7		**7.C.3b, 8.D.3b**
Chapter 11		
11.1		**8.A.3b, 8.B.3, 8.D.3b**
11.2		**8.B.3, 8.D.3a**
11.3		**8.A.3b, 8.D.3a**
11.4	Problem Solving	**6.B.3a, 6.C.3a, 8.B.3**
11.4		**8.B.3, 8.D.3a**
11.4	Technology Activity	**8.B.3, 8.D.3a**
11.5		**8.B.3, 8.D.3a**
11.6	Hands-on Activity	**8.D.3a, 8.D.3b**
11.6		**8.D.3a, 8.D.3b;** 9.A.3a

Key Learning Standards are indicated in boldface type.

LESSON OR FEATURE	STANDARD CODE NUMBER
Chapter 11 *continued*	
11.7 Hands-on Activity	**8.B.3, 8.D.3a**
11.7	**8.A.3b, 8.D.3a;** 8.D.3b
11 Special Topic	**8.A.3b, 8.D.3a**
11.8	**8.A.3b, 8.D.3a**
Chapter 12	
12.1	**10.A.3a**
12.2	**10.A.3a;** 10.A.3b
12.3	**10.A.3a;** 10.A.3c
12.3 Technology Activity	**10.A.3a**
12 Special Topic #1	**10.A.3a, 10.A.3c**
12.4 Problem Solving	**6.B.3a, 6.C.3a**
12.4	**10.C.3a**
12.5	**10.C.3a**
12.6	**10.C.3a**
12.7	**10.C.3a**
12.8 Hands-on Activity	**10.B.3, 10.C.3a**
12.8	**10.C.3a**
12 Special Topic #2	**10.A.3c**
Chapter 13	
13.1	**8.A.3a, 8.D.3a**
13.2	**8.D.3a;** 7.C.3b
13.3	**8.A.3a, 8.D.3c**
13.4 Hands-on Activity	**8.D.3a**
13.4	**8.D.3a**
13.5 Problem Solving	**8.D.3a;** 8.D.3c, 6.C.3b
13.5	**8.D.3a**
13.5 Technology Activity	**8.B.3, 8.D.3a**

Key Learning Standards are indicated in boldface type.

McDougal Littell Middle School

COURSE 3

Math

Teacher's Edition

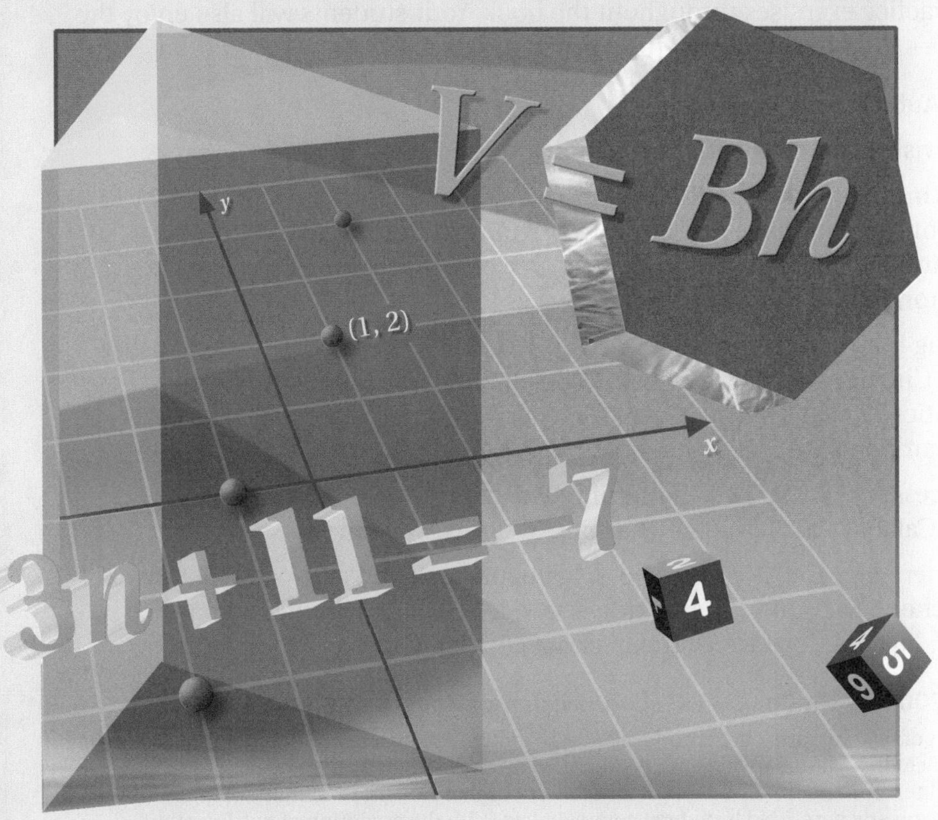

Larson Boswell Kanold Stiff

McDougal Littell
A HOUGHTON MIFFLIN COMPANY
Evanston, Illinois • Boston • Dallas

Contents

About the Authors	T3
Advisers and Reviewers	T4
Table of Contents	T6
Course Overview	T20
Teacher's Resources	T28
Using the Teacher's Edition	T34
Pacing the Course	T38
Professional Articles	T40
Correlation to NAEP Objectives	T56
Correlation to NCTM Standards	T57
Scope and Sequence	T58
Student Handbook	T68
Pre-Course Test	T74
Pre-Course Practice	T76
Content and Assessment	T80
Student Edition	1
Teacher's Edition Index	IN1
Additional Answers	AA1

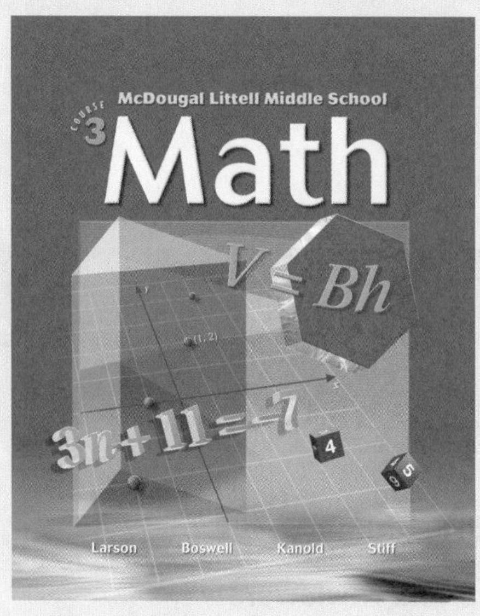

About Middle School Math Course 3

McDougal Littell Middle School Math will help your students be successful in this course. The clearly written lessons with frequent step-by-step examples make even difficult math concepts and methods easier to understand. The number and variety of problems, ranging from basic to challenging, give your students the practice they need to develop their math skills. This book will also help them develop their notetaking and problem-solving skills. Look for notetaking strategies and Help Notes that support problem solving, vocabulary, reading, homework, technology, and review. To help your students get ready for tests, there are test-taking strategies and test-taking practice exercises throughout the book. Your students will also enjoy the Brain Games — they will challenge their thinking skills!

Contributing Authors and Reviewers

The authors wish to thank the following individuals for their contributions.

Reading, Writing, Notetaking; CRISS *(pp. T45–T47)*—Joan Smathers, National CRISS Trainer, Former Language Arts Supervisor, Brevard County, FL; Marie Pettet, Reading and Language Arts Curriculum Specialist, Former K–12 Language Arts Coordinator, Fulton County, GA

Differentiating Instruction *(pp. T35, 1E–1F)*—Donna Foley, Curriculum Specialist for Math, Chelmsford Middle School, Chelmsford, MA; Mark Johnson, Mathematics Education Consultant, Teacher of Mathematics, Gardner High School, Gardner, MA

Universal Access *(pp. T50–T53)*—Catherine Barkett, Vice President, Director of Training, Calabash Professional Learning Systems, Sacramento, CA

English Learners *(pp. T54–T55, 1E–1F)*—Olga Bautista, Vice Principal, Will C. Wood Middle School, Sacramento, CA; Judy Lewis, Director, State and Federal Programs, Folsom Cordova Unified School District, CA

ISBN: 0-618-25002-6 23456789–DWO–07 06 05 04 03

Internet Web Site: http://www.classzone.com

Ron Larson

Ron Larson is a professor of mathematics at Penn State University at Erie, where he has taught since receiving his Ph.D. in mathematics from the University of Colorado. Dr. Larson is well known as the author of a comprehensive program for mathematics that spans middle school, high school, and college courses. Dr. Larson's numerous professional activities keep him in constant touch with the needs of teachers and supervisors. He closely follows developments in mathematics standards and assessment.

Laurie Boswell

Laurie Boswell is the mathematics department chair at Profile Junior-Senior High School in Bethlehem, New Hampshire. A recipient of the Presidential Award for Excellence in Mathematics Teaching, she has also been a Tandy Technology Scholar. She serves on the National Council of Teachers of Mathematics Board of Directors. She speaks frequently on topics related to instructional strategies and course content.

Timothy Kanold

Timothy Kanold is the superintendent of Adlai E. Stevenson High School District 125, where he served as a teacher and the Director of Mathematics for 16 years. He recently received his Ph.D. from Loyola University Chicago. Dr. Kanold is a recipient of the Presidential Award for Excellence in Mathematics and Science Teaching and served on The Academy Services Committee for NCTM. He is a frequent speaker at mathematics meetings where he shares his in-depth knowledge of mathematics teaching and curriculum.

Lee Stiff

Lee Stiff is a professor of mathematics education in the College of Education of North Carolina State University at Raleigh. His extensive experience in mathematics education includes teaching at the middle school and high school levels. He has received the W. W. Rankin Award for Excellence in Mathematics Education, and was Fulbright Scholar to the Department of Mathematics of the University of Ghana. He served as President of the National Council of Teachers of Mathematics (2000–2002).

Curriculum Advisers and Reviewers

Donna Foley
Curriculum Specialist for Math
Chelmsford Middle School
Chelmsford, MA

Wendy Loeb
Mathematics Teacher
Twin Groves Junior High School
Buffalo Grove, IL

Barbara Nunn
Secondary Mathematics Specialist
Broward County Schools
Fort Lauderdale, FL

Tom Scott
Resource Teacher
Duval County Public Schools
Jacksonville, FL

Teacher Panels

Florida Panel

Kathy Adams
Mathematics Teacher
Allapattah Middle School
Miami, FL

Sue Carrico-Beddow
Mathematics Teacher
Bayonet Point Middle School
New Port Richey, FL

Melissa Grabowski
Mathematics Teacher
Stone Middle School
Melbourne, FL

Micki Hawn
Mathematics Teacher
Pompano Beach Middle School
Pompano Beach, FL

Pat Powell
Mathematics Department Chair
Stewart Middle School
Tampa, FL

Barbara Schober
Mathematics Department Chair
Okeeheelee Middle School
West Palm Beach, FL

Laurie St. Julien
Mathematics Teacher
Oak Grove Middle School
Clearwater, FL

Kansas and Missouri Panel

Linda Cordes
Department Chair
Paul Robeson Middle School
Kansas City, MO

Linda Dodd
Mathematics Department Chair
Argentine Middle School
Kansas City, KS

Melanie Dowell
Mathematics Teacher
Raytown South Middle School
Raytown, MO

Rhonda Foote
Mathematics Department Chair
Maple Park Middle School
North Kansas City, MO

Cas Kyle
District Math Curriculum Coordinator
Richard A. Warren Middle School
Leavenworth, KS

Jan Rase
Mathematics Teacher
Moreland Ridge Middle School
Blue Springs, MO

Dan Schoenemann
Mathematics Teacher
Raytown Middle School
Kansas City, MO

Texas Panel

Judy Carlin
Mathematics Teacher
Brown Middle School
McAllen, TX

Judith Cody
Mathematics Teacher
Deady Middle School
Houston, TX

Lisa Hiracheta
Mathematics Teacher
Irons Junior High School
Lubbock, TX

Kay Neuse
Mathematics Teacher
Wilson Middle School
Plano, TX

Louise Nutzman
Mathematics Teacher
Sugar Land Middle School
Sugar Land, TX

Clarice Orise
Mathematics Teacher
Tafolla Middle School
San Antonio, TX

Wonda Webb
Mathematics Teacher
William H. Atwell Middle School
and Law Academy
Dallas, TX

Karen Young
Mathematics Teacher
Murchison Elementary School
Pflugerville, TX

Field Test Teachers

Kathryn Chamberlain
McCarthy Middle School
Chelmsford, MA

Sheree Daily
Canal Winchester Middle School
Canal Winchester, OH

Deborah Kebe
Canal Winchester Middle School
Canal Winchester, OH

Jill Leone
Twin Groves Junior High School
Buffalo Grove, IL

Wendy Loeb
Twin Groves Junior High School
Buffalo Grove, IL

Melissa McCarty
Canal Winchester Middle School
Canal Winchester, OH

Deb Mueth
St. Aloysius School
Springfield, IL

Gail Sigmund
Charles A. Mooney Middle School
Cleveland, OH

Teacher Reviewers

Susanne Artiñano
Bryn Mawr School
Baltimore, MD

Lisa Barnes
Bishop Spaugh Academy
Charlotte, NC

Beth Bryan
Sequoyah Middle School
Oklahoma City, OK

Jennifer Clark
Mayfield Middle School
Oklahoma City, OK

Lois Cole
Pickering Middle School
Lynn, MA

Louis Corbosiero
Pollard Middle School
Needham, MA

James Cussen
Candlewood Middle School
Dix Hills, NY

Kristen Dailey
Boardman Center Middle School
Boardman, OH

Shannon Galamore
Clay-Chalkville Middle School
Pinson, AL

Tricia Highland
Moon Area Middle School
Moon Township, PA

Myrna McNaboe
Immaculate Conception
East Aurora, NY

Angela Richardson
Sedgefield Middle School
Charlotte, NC

James Richardson
Booker T. Washington Middle School
Mobile, AL

Dianne Walker
Traverse City Central High School
Traverse City, MI

Stacey Wood
Cochrane Middle School
Charlotte, NC

Variables and Equations

Chapter Warm-Up Games 2

Getting Ready to Learn 4

1.1 Interpreting Graphs 5

1.2 Order of Operations 10
Technology Activity: Using Order of Operations, 14

1.3 Variables and Expressions 15

1.4 Powers and Exponents 20

1.5 Equations and Solutions 28
Problem Solving Strategies: Guess, Check, and Revise, 26

1.6 Variables in Familiar Formulas 33
Hands-On Activity: Modeling Area, 32

1.7 A Problem Solving Plan 38

Assessment
Test-Taking Practice, 9, 13, 19, 23, 31, 37, 43
Review Quiz, 25, 45
Chapter Review, 46
Chapter Test, 48
Chapter Standardized Test, 49

Notetaking and Student Help
Notetaking, 4, 10, 21, 24, 33 34, 39, 44
Reading, 16, 29, 33, 39
Solving, 10
Review, 6
Technology, 14
Vocabulary, 34
Watch Out, 11

Vacation Views, 2
Next Stop, 3
Find the Key, 19
What's Happening?, 43

Internet Resources
- eEdition Plus Online
- eWorkbook Plus Online
- eTutorial Plus Online
- State Test Practice
- More Examples

Pre-Course Assessment
Pre-Course Test, xxvi
Pre-Course Practice, xxviii

Student Handbook, xx

Exercise 29, p. 31

Integer Operations

Chapter Warm-Up Game 50

Getting Ready to Learn 52

2.1 **Integers and Absolute Value** 53

2.2 **Adding Integers** 58
Hands-On Activity: Adding Integers, 57

2.3 **Subtracting Integers** 63

2.4 **Multiplying Integers** 70
Problem Solving Strategies: Look for a Pattern, 68

2.5 **Dividing Integers** 74

2.6 **Number Properties** 80

2.7 **The Distributive Property** 85
Technology Activity: Using Integer Operations, 90

2.8 **The Coordinate Plane** 91

Assessment
Test-Taking Practice, 56, 62, 67, 73, 77, 84, 89, 95
Review Quiz, 79, 97
Chapter Review, 98
Chapter Test, 100
Chapter Standardized Test, 101

Exercise 44, p. 89

Notetaking and Student Help
Notetaking, 52, 59, 63, 70, 71, 74, 78, 80, 81, 85, 86, 96
Reading, 54
Vocabulary, 82
Solving, 56, 71, 81, 87, 92
Review, 81
Watch Out, 74, 90

Four in a Row, 50
Argyle Arithmetic, 67
Spatial Delivery, 95

Internet Resources
- eEdition Plus Online
- eWorkbook Plus Online
- eTutorial Plus Online
- State Test Practice
- More Examples

EXPLORING MATH IN SCIENCE

Life Science Supercool Squirrels, 102

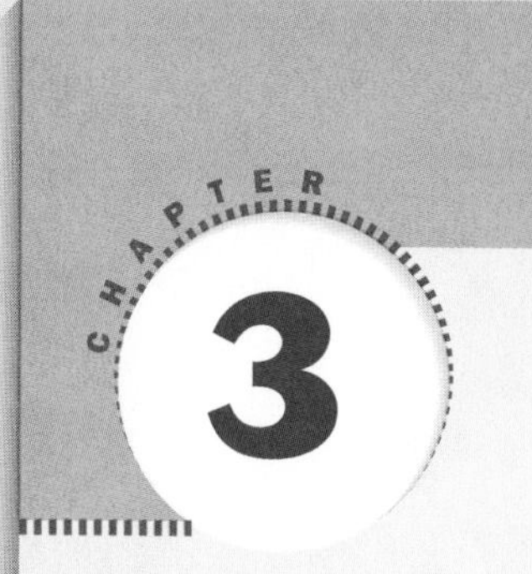

Solving Equations and Inequalities

Chapter Warm-Up Games 104

Getting Ready to Learn 106

3.1 **Solving Equations Using Addition or Subtraction** 109
Hands-On Activity: Modeling One-Step Equations, 107

3.2 **Solving Equations Using Multiplication or Division** 113

3.3 **Solving Two-Step Equations** 119
Hands-On Activity: Modeling Two-Step Equations, 117

3.4 **Writing Two-Step Equations** 124
Technology Activity: Searching for Information, 129

3.5 **Applying Geometry Formulas** 134
Problem Solving Strategies: Draw a Diagram, 132

3.6 **Solving Inequalities Using Addition or Subtraction** 140

3.7 **Solving Inequalities Using Multiplication or Division** 146

Assessment

Test-Taking Practice, 112, 116, 123, 128, 139, 145, 149
Review Quiz, 131, 151
Chapter Review, 152
Chapter Test, 154
Chapter Standardized Test, 155

Example 3, p. 110

Notetaking and Student Help

Notetaking, 106, 109, 110, 113, 114, 120, 130, 134, 141, 146, 147, 150
Solving, 113, 120, 125, 141
Review, 120, 135
Watch Out, 110, 114

Name that Planet!, 104
Planet Pinball, 105
Behind the Magic, 128
Prized Positions, 145

- eEdition Plus Online
- eWorkbook Plus Online
- eTutorial Plus Online
- State Test Practice
- More Examples

Unit 1 Assessment

Building Test-Taking Skills: Multiple Choice, 156
Practicing Test-Taking Skills, 158
Cumulative Practice, 160

Factors, Fractions, and Exponents

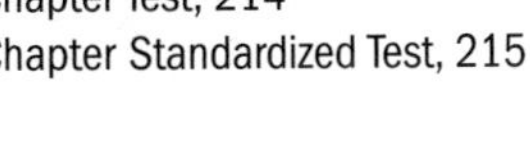

Chapter Warm-Up Game 164

Getting Ready to Learn 166

4.1 **Factors and Prime Factorization** 168
Hands-On Activity: Investigating Factors, 167

4.2 **Greatest Common Factor** 173

4.3 **Simplifying Fractions** 179
Hands-On Activity: Equivalent Fractions, 178

4.4 **Least Common Multiple** 186
Problem Solving Strategies: Make a List, 184

4.5 **Comparing Fractions and Mixed Numbers** 192

4.6 **Rules of Exponents** 196

4.7 **Negative and Zero Exponents** 201

4.8 **Scientific Notation** 205
Technology Activity: Using Scientific Notation, 209

Assessment
Test-Taking Practice, 172, 177, 183, 189, 195, 200, 204, 208
Review Quiz, 191, 211
Chapter Review, 212
Chapter Test, 214
Chapter Standardized Test, 215

Notetaking and Student Help

Notetaking, 166, 181, 190, 196, 197, 201, 202, 205, 210
Vocabulary, 173
Solving, 180, 192, 195, 205
Review, 169, 193
Technology, 209
Watch Out, 197, 198, 202, 206

Bicycle Math, 164
Marble Mystery, 177
Mix and Match, 200

- eEdition Plus Online
- eWorkbook Plus Online
- eTutorial Plus Online
- State Test Practice
- More Examples

Exercise 10, p. 194

Rational Number Operations

Chapter Warm-Up Games 216

Getting Ready to Learn 218

5.1 **Fractions with Common Denominators** 219

5.2 **Fractions with Different Denominators** 224

5.3 **Multiplying Fractions** 230
Problem Solving Strategies: Act It Out, 228

5.4 **Dividing Fractions** 234
Technology Activity: Operations with Fractions, 239

5.5 **Fractions and Decimals** 242

5.6 **Adding and Subtracting Decimals** 247

5.7 **Multiplying and Dividing Decimals** 251

5.8 **Mean, Median, and Mode** 257
Hands-On Activity: Collecting and Analyzing Data, 255

Assessment

Test-Taking Practice, 223, 227, 233, 238, 246, 250, 254, 261
Review Quiz, 241, 263
Chapter Review, 264
Chapter Test, 266
Chapter Standardized Test, 267

Notetaking and Student Help

Notetaking, 218, 219, 230, 234, 240, 244, 251, 252, 257, 262
Solving, 220, 235
Review, 224, 230
Watch Out, 225, 231, 258

Scale the Cliff, 216
Tangled Fractions, 217
Who's in First?, 238
The Prize is Right!, 261

- eEdition Plus Online
- eWorkbook Plus Online
- eTutorial Plus Online
- State Test Practice
- More Examples

Exercise 20, p. 226

Multi-Step Equations and Inequalities

Chapter Warm-Up Game 268

Getting Ready to Learn 270

6.1 **Solving Multi-Step Equations** 271

6.2 **Solving Equations with Variables on Both Sides** 278
Problem Solving Strategies: Work Backward, 276

6.3 **Solving Equations Involving Fractions and Decimals** 282

6.4 **Solving Equations Involving Circumference** 290
Hands-On Activity: Diameter and Circumference, 288

6.5 **Solving Multi-Step Inequalities** 295
Technology Activity: Solving Inequalities, 300

6.6 **Problem Solving and Inequalities** 301

Assessment

Test-Taking Practice, 275, 281, 285, 294, 299, 305
Review Quiz, 287, 307
Chapter Review, 308
Chapter Test, 310
Chapter Standardized Test, 311

Exercise 23, p. 298

Notetaking and Student Help

Notetaking, 270, 282, 286, 290, 306
Reading, 302
Solving, 283, 291
Review, 272, 292, 295
Technology, 300
Watch Out, 279

Treasure Hunt, 268
Going Bananas, 287
City Solutions, 299

- eEdition Plus Online
- eWorkbook Plus Online
- eTutorial Plus Online
- State Test Practice
- More Examples

EXPLORING MATH IN SCIENCE

Physical Science
The Physics of Basketball, 312

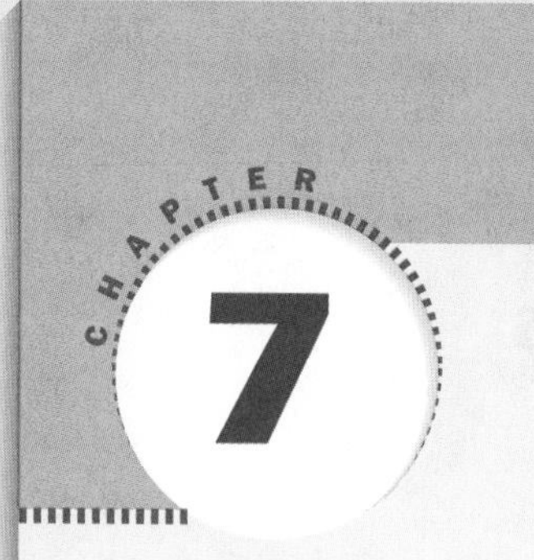

Ratio, Proportion, and Percent

Chapter Warm-Up Games 314

Getting Ready to Learn 316

7.1 Ratios and Rates 317

7.2 Writing and Solving Proportions 322
Hands-On Activity: Making a Scale Drawing, 321

7.3 Solving Percent Problems 327

7.4 Fractions, Decimals, and Percents 331

7.5 Percent of Change 338

7.6 Percent Applications 342

7.7 Using the Percent Equation 347
Technology Activity: Compound Interest, 351

7.8 Simple Probability 354
Problem Solving Strategies: Perform an Experiment, 352

Assessment

Test-Taking Practice, 320, 326, 330, 335, 341, 346, 350, 357
Review Quiz, 337, 359
Chapter Review, 360
Chapter Test, 362
Chapter Standardized Test, 363

Example 1, p. 327

Notetaking and Student Help

Notetaking, 316, 323, 327, 328, 336, 338, 347, 348, 354, 358
Vocabulary, 348, 351
Solving, 322, 332, 343, 355
Review, 318, 338
Watch Out, 339

Video Maze, 314
Find the Path, 315
Balancing Act, 326
Shrink Ray, 346

Internet Resources

- eEdition Plus Online
- eWorkbook Plus Online
- eTutorial Plus Online
- State Test Practice
- More Examples

Unit 2 Assessment

Building Test-Taking Skills: Short Response, 364
Practicing Test-Taking Skills, 366
Cumulative Practice, 368

Polygons and Transformations

Chapter Warm-Up Game 372

Getting Ready to Learn 374

8.1 Angle Pairs 375
Special Topic: Constructions, 380

8.2 Angles and Triangles 382

8.3 Quadrilaterals 386

8.4 Polygons and Angles 390

8.5 Congruent Polygons 397
Hands-On Activity: Copying a Triangle, 396

8.6 Reflections and Symmetry 404
Problem Solving Strategies: Make a Model, 402

8.7 Translations and Rotations 409
Special Topic: Tessellations, 414

8.8 Similarity and Dilations 416

Assessment

Test-Taking Practice, 379, 385, 389, 393, 401, 408, 413, 421
Review Quiz, 395, 423
Chapter Review, 424
Chapter Test, 426
Chapter Standardized Test, 427

Example 1, p. 416

Notetaking and Student Help

Notetaking, 374, 377, 382, 386, 391, 394, 405, 410, 411, 416, 418, 422
Reading, 383, 390, 398, 410
Vocabulary, 411
Solving, 377, 381
Review, 413, 417
Watch Out, 418, 419

Find the Flags, 372
Buy Oval Car, 389
Deep Reflections, 408

- eEdition Plus Online
- eWorkbook Plus Online
- eTutorial Plus Online
- State Test Practice
- More Examples

Real Numbers and Right Triangles

Chapter Warm-Up Games 428

Getting Ready to Learn 430

9.1 Square Roots 431

9.2 Rational and Irrational Numbers 437

9.3 The Pythagorean Theorem 443
Hands-On Activity: Modeling the Pythagorean Theorem, 442

9.4 Using the Pythagorean Theorem 450
Problem Solving Strategies: Draw a Diagram, 448

9.5 Special Right Triangles 456

9.6 Using Trigonometric Ratios 463
Hands-On Activity: Exploring Trigonometric Ratios, 461
Technology Activity: Finding an Angle Measure, 469

Assessment

Test-Taking Practice, 436, 441, 447, 453, 460, 468
Review Quiz, 455, 471
Chapter Review, 472
Chapter Test, 474
Chapter Standardized Test, 475

Notetaking and Student Help

Notetaking, 430, 443, 454, 456, 457, 463, 470
Reading, 433
Solving, 431, 435, 444, 457, 463
Review, 437, 451
Technology, 464, 469
Watch Out, 438

Spin Your Wheels, 428
Ramp Match, 429
X-cellent Birthday, 436
A Real Winner, 471

Internet Resources

- eEdition Plus Online
- eWorkbook Plus Online
- eTutorial Plus Online
- State Test Practice
- More Examples

EXPLORING MATH IN SCIENCE

Earth Science
Viewing the Stars, 476

Example 5, p. 465

Measurement, Area, and Volume

Chapter Warm-Up Game 478

Getting Ready to Learn 480

10.1 Areas of Parallelograms and Trapezoids 481

10.2 Areas of Circles 486
Technology Activity: Comparing Radii of Circles, 491

10.3 Three-Dimensional Figures 492
Special Topic: Sketching Solids, 496

10.4 Surface Areas of Prisms and Cylinders 502
Problem Solving Strategies: Break into Parts, 500

10.5 Surface Areas of Pyramids and Cones 507

10.6 Volumes of Prisms and Cylinders 513
Hands-On Activity: Exploring Volume, 512

10.7 Volumes of Pyramids and Cones 519
Hands-On Activity: Comparing Volumes, 518

Assessment
Test-Taking Practice, 485, 490, 495, 506, 511, 517, 523
Review Quiz, 499, 525
Chapter Review, 526
Chapter Test, 528
Chapter Standardized Test, 529

Example 1, p. 519

Notetaking and Student Help

Notetaking, 480, 481, 482, 486, 492, 498, 503, 504, 507, 508, 513, 514, 519, 520, 524
Reading, 482, 515
Vocabulary, 492, 493
Solving, 497, 507, 514
Technology, 504
Watch Out, 513

Measure Match, 478
What's the Score?, 490

- eEdition Plus Online
- eWorkbook Plus Online
- eTutorial Plus Online
- State Test Practice
- More Examples

Unit 3 Assessment

Building Test-Taking Skills: Context-Based Multiple Choice, 530
Practicing Test-Taking Skills, 532
Cumulative Practice, 534

Linear Equations and Graphs

	Chapter Warm-Up Games	538
	Getting Ready to Learn	**540**
11.1	**Relations and Functions**	**541**
11.2	**Scatter Plots**	**545**
11.3	**Equations in Two Variables**	**549**
11.4	**Graphs of Linear Equations** Problem Solving Strategies: Make a Table, 554 Technology Activity: Graphing Linear Functions, 561	**556**
11.5	**Using Intercepts**	**564**
11.6	**Slope** Hands-On Activity: Finding the Slope of a Line, 568	**570**
11.7	**Slope-intercept Form** Hands-On Activity: Slope-Intercept Form, 575 Special Topic: Systems of Equations, 581	**577**
11.8	**Graphs of Linear Inequalities**	**583**

Assessment

Test-Taking Practice, 544, 548, 553, 560, 567, 574, 580, 587
Review Quiz, 563, 589
Chapter Review, 590
Chapter Test, 592
Chapter Standardized Test, 593

Exercise 32, p. 586

Notetaking and Student Help

Notetaking, 540, 558, 562, 564, 565, 570, 572, 577, 584, 588
Vocabulary, 570, 584
Solving, 542, 550, 557, 582, 583, 584, 585
Review, 571, 577
Watch Out, 541, 558, 571

Sidewalk Scramble, 538
Plot the Picture, 539
Late Night Show, 553

- eEdition Plus Online
- eWorkbook Plus Online
- eTutorial Plus Online
- State Test Practice
- More Examples

Data Analysis and Probability

Chapter Warm-Up Game 594

Getting Ready to Learn 596

12.1 Stem-and-Leaf Plots 597

12.2 Box-and-Whisker Plots 601

12.3 Using Data Displays 605
Technology Activity: Making Data Displays, 610
Special Topic: Misleading Graphs, 612

12.4 Counting Methods 618
Problem Solving Strategies: Solve a Simpler Problem, 616

12.5 Permutations 623

12.6 Combinations 627

12.7 Probability and Odds 632

12.8 Independent and Dependent Events 639
Hands-On Activity: Probability and Simulations, 637
Special Topic: Samples, 644

Assessment

Test-Taking Practice, 600, 604, 609, 622, 626, 631, 636, 643
Review Quiz, 615, 647
Chapter Review, 648
Chapter Test, 650
Chapter Standardized Test, 651

Example 1, p. 627

Notetaking and Student Help

Notetaking, 596, 606, 614, 619, 624, 628, 629, 640, 646
Reading, 633
Solving, 598, 601, 605, 608, 612, 623, 624, 632
Review, 620

Galapagos Graphs, 594
Safe Cracker, 615
Lucky Numbers, 643

- eEdition Plus Online
- eWorkbook Plus Online
- eTutorial Plus Online
- State Test Practice
- More Examples

EXPLORING MATH IN SCIENCE

Measurement
Investigating Robins, 652

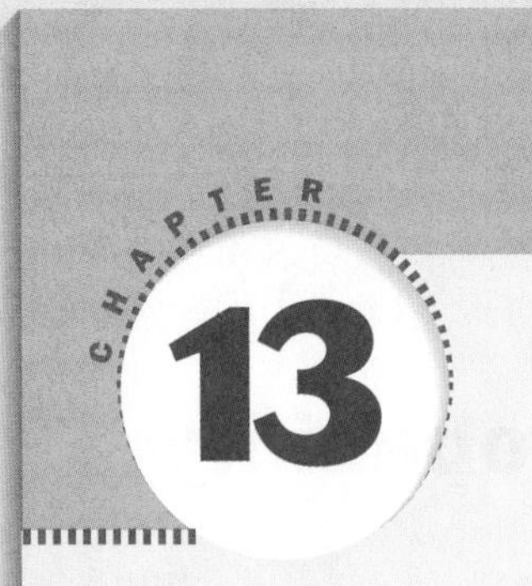

Polynomials and Functions

Chapter Warm-Up Games 654

Getting Ready to Learn 656

13.1 Polynomials 657

13.2 Adding and Subtracting Polynomials 661

13.3 Monomials and Powers 666

13.4 Multiplying Binomials 674
Hands-On Activity: Multiplying Binomials, 673

13.5 Non-Linear Functions 680
Problem Solving Strategies: Draw a Graph, 678
Technology Activity: Graphing Non-Linear Functions, 685

Assessment

Test-Taking Practice, 660, 665, 670, 677, 684
Review Quiz, 672, 687
Chapter Review, 688
Chapter Test, 690
Chapter Standardized Test, 691

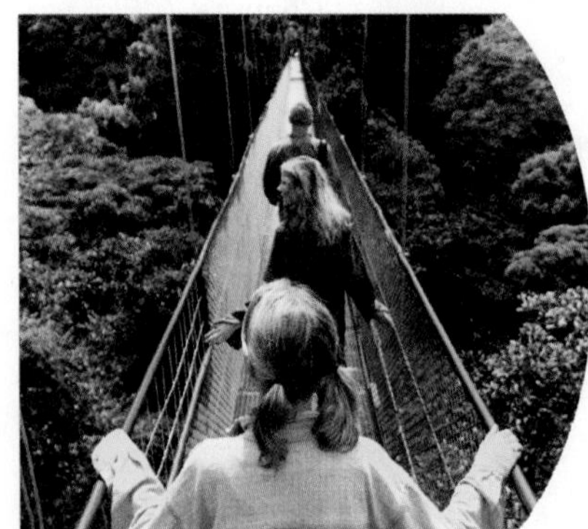

Example 3, p. 658

Notetaking and Student Help

Notetaking, 656, 667, 668, 671, 674, 686
Reading, 681
Vocabulary, 675
Solving, 662
Review, 658, 665, 666
Watch Out, 657
Technology, 685

Piñata Break, 654
Unmasking Expressions, 655
Polynomial Potions, 665
Number Crunch, 684

- eEdition Plus Online
- eWorkbook Plus Online
- eTutorial Plus Online
- State Test Practice
- More Examples

Unit 4 Assessment

Building Test-Taking Skills: Extended Response, 692
Practicing Test-Taking Skills, 694
Cumulative Practice, 696

End-of-Course Assessment

End-of-Course Test, 699

Contents of Student Resources

Skills Review Handbook 704

Number Sense

- Place Value, *704*
- Rounding, *705*
- Divisibility Tests, *706*
- Mixed Numbers and Improper Fractions, *707*
- Ratio and Rate, 708

Number Operations

- Adding and Subtracting Decimals, *709*
- Adding and Subtracting Fractions, *710*
- Estimation in Addition and Subtraction, *711*
- Solving Problems Using Addition and Subtraction, *712*
- Multiplying Fractions, *713*
- Multiplication of a Decimal by a Whole Number, *714*
- Dividing Decimals, *715*
- Estimation in Multiplication and Division, *716*
- Solving Problems Using Multiplication and Division, *717*

Measurement and Geometry

- Points, Lines, and Planes, *718*
- Angles, *719*
- Using a Ruler, *720*
- Using a Protractor, *721*
- Using a Compass, *722*

Data Analysis

- Reading and Making Line Plots, *723*
- Reading and Making Bar Graphs, *724*
- Reading and Making Line Graphs, *725*
- Venn Diagrams and Logical Reasoning, *726*

Extra Practice 727

Chapters 1–13

Tables 740

Symbols, Measures, Formulas, Properties, Squares and Square Roots, Equivalent Fractions, Decimals, and Percents

Glossary 747

Index 773

Credits 796

Selected Answers SA1

McDougal Littell Middle School

COURSE 3

Math

The right math, the right way, the right results

Our middle school program provides the math your students need to know in a way that they can understand. Fully integrated problem solving, notetaking, and assessment strategies help your students succeed.

Understand

Give your students math they can read, understand, and practice with built-in learning support, clear examples, and engaging review games that emphasize critical thinking.

Organize

Help your students organize their approach to new concepts with fully integrated notetaking and study strategies, as well as stepped-out examples.

Achieve

Prepare your students for success on local and state tests with frequent assessment strategies and practice opportunities.

Accessible Content

Our middle school program provides clear, concise math in a student-friendly voice.

EXPLORE IT!

Quick, hands-on activities help build conceptual understanding before the lesson begins.

THINK ABOUT IT!

Critical-thinking questions ask students to reflect on the exploration.

2.2 Hands-on Activity

GOAL
Model integer addition on a number line.

MATERIALS
- pencil
- paper

Adding Integers

You can model addition of integers by using a number line.

Explore **Find the sum $-15 + 11$.**

1. Draw a number line, place a pencil at 0, and move 15 units to the left to show -15.
2. Move 11 units to the right to show the addition of 11.

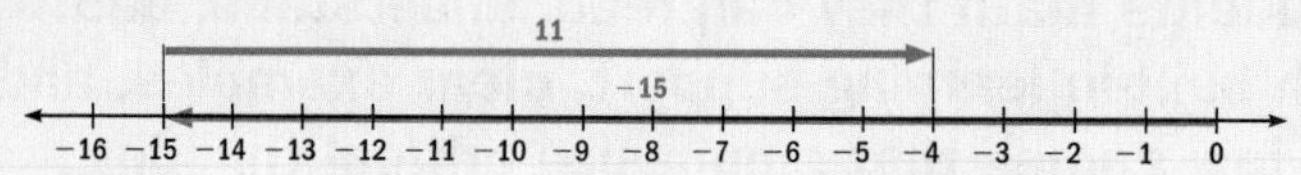

3. The final position is -4. So, $-15 + 11 = -4$.

Your turn now **Write an addition expression to represent the figure. Then evaluate the expression.**

1.

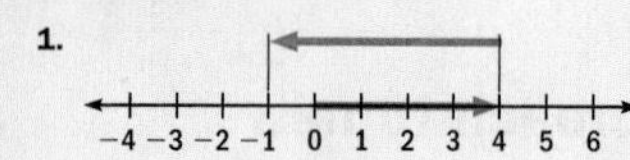

2.

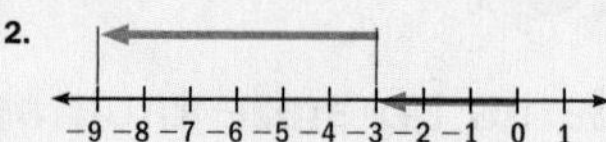

Use a number line to find the sum.

3. $-7 + (-14)$ **4.** $20 + (-50)$ **5.** $-10 + 65$ **6.** $-7 + (-33)$

7. $41 + (-25)$ **8.** $-23 + 52$ **9.** $-18 + (-34)$ **10.** $35 + (-37)$

Stop and Think

11. The sum of two positive integers is always positive. What is the sign of the sum of two negative integers? Use a number line to explain.

12. **Critical Thinking** How can you predict the sign of the sum of a positive and a negative integer before you add the numbers?

13. **Writing** Write the steps you use to evaluate $25 + (-13) + 5 + (-20)$. Then evaluate the expression.

Lesson 2.2 Adding Integers 57

Multiplying Integers

BEFORE	Now	WHY?
You added and subtracted integers.	You'll multiply integers.	So you can find the worth of a coin in a game, as in Ex. 32.

Word Watch

Review Words
integer, p 53
product, p. 713

In the Real World

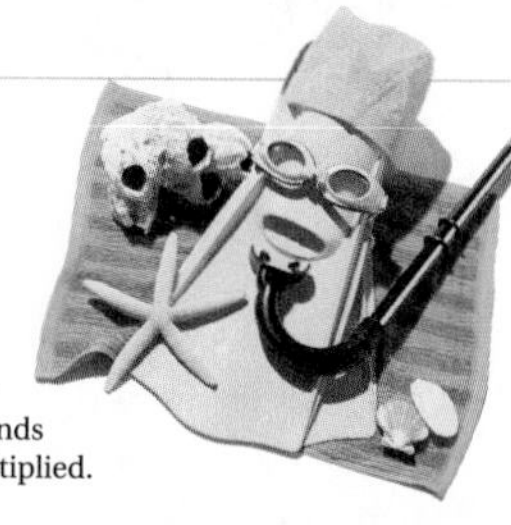

Diving A diver is exploring a coral reef. The diver's depth is changing by −6 feet per second. If the diver started at sea level, what is the diver's position after 10 seconds?

To find the position, you can multiply integers. When you multiply integers, the sign of the product depends on the signs of the integers being multiplied.

Multiplying Integers

Words	Numbers
The product of two integers with the same sign is positive.	$4 \cdot 2 = 8$ $-3 \cdot (-7) = 21$
The product of two integers with different signs is negative.	$4 \cdot (-2) = -8$ $-3 \cdot 7 = -21$

EXAMPLE 1 Multiplying Integers

To find the diver's position relative to sea level after 10 seconds, use the distance formula $d = rt$.

$d = rt$ Write the distance formula.

$d = -6(10)$ Substitute −6 for r and 10 for t.

$d = -60$ Different signs, so product is negative.

ANSWER The diver's position relative to sea level is −60 feet.

Your turn now Use the information above.

1. Find the diver's position relative to sea level after 13 seconds.

SEE IT!
Clear, stepped-out examples help students understand concepts.

TRY IT!
Practice opportunities, closely linked to examples, provide a quick check for understanding.

Multiplication Properties

Multiplication Property of Zero

Words The product of an integer and 0 is 0.

Numbers $-4 \cdot 0 = 0$ **Algebra** For any value of a, $a \cdot 0 =$

Identity Property of Multiplication

Words The product of an integer and 1 is the integer.

Numbers $4(1) = 4$ **Algebra** For any value of a, $a(1) = a$.

When you multiply a number by −1, the product is the *opposite* of the original number.

HELP with Solving

When you multiply more than two positive or negative integers:

- If there is an *even* number of negative factors then the product is *positive*.
- If there is an *odd* number of negative factors then the product is *negative*.

EXAMPLE 2 Multiplying Two or More Integers

a. $-1(6) = -6$ Different signs, so product is negative.

b. $-8(-2) = 16$ Same sign, so product is positive.

c. $-15(0) = 0$ Product of an integer and 0 is 0.

d. $4(-10)(-12) = -40(-12)$ Multiply from left to right.

$= 480$ Multiply.

EXAMPLE 3 Evaluating an Expression with Integers

Evaluate $a^2 + 3b$ when $a = -5$ and $b = -11$.

$a^2 + 3b = (-5)^2 + 3(-11)$ Substitute −5 for a and −11 for b.

$= 25 + 3(-11)$ Evaluate the power.

$= 25 + (-33)$ Multiply.

$= -8$ Add.

Your turn now Find the product.

2. $-1(4)$ 3. $7(0)$ 4. $-6(-11)$ 5. $-1(-12)(-9)$

Evaluate the expression when $a = 3$, $b = -4$ and $c = -8$.

6. $ac - b$ 7. $ac + b$ 8. $a^2 + bc$ 9. $ab - c^2$

READ IT!
The built-in tutor provides margin notes with reading and solving tips.

Study Strategies

Integrated notetaking and study strategies support the development of learning skills.

PREPARE FOR IT!

Prerequisite-skills review opens each chapter and prepares students for the chapter.

Getting Ready to Learn

Word Watch

Review Words

variable, p. 15
variable expression, p. 15
perimeter, p. 33
area, p. 33

Review What You Need to Know

Using Vocabulary **Copy and complete using a review word.**

1. A symbol that represents one or more numbers is called a(n) _?_.

2. The surface covered by a figure is called the _?_.

Round the decimal to the nearest whole number. *(p. 705)*

3. 10.61 **4.** 134.7 **5.** 0.25 **6.** 12.86

Evaluate the expression. *(p. 10)*

7. $32 - 27 + 14$ **8.** $4 \cdot 12 \div 6$ **9.** $6 + 34 \div 2$

Evaluate the expression when $s = 4$ and $t = 16$. *(p. 15)*

10. $(t - 9) + s$ **11.** $s(t - 5)$ **12.** $\frac{1}{4}t - 4$

Solve the equation using mental math. *(p. 28)*

13. $3x = 39$ **14.** $x - 6 = 12$ **15.** $x + 13 = 17$

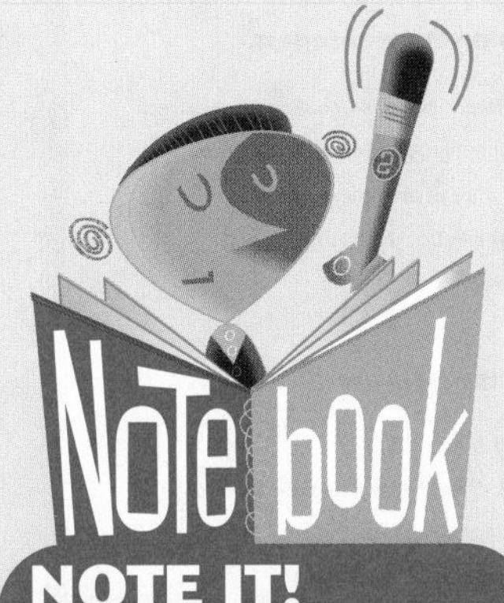

NOTE IT!

Notebook strategies provide examples of how to take good notes.

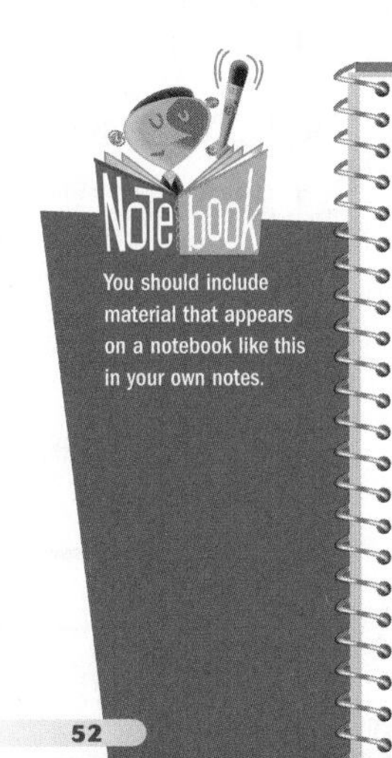

You should include material that appears on a notebook like this in your own notes.

Know How to Take Notes

Including Vocabulary Notes When you write down new vocabulary words, you should also write examples of how they are used. Label the examples with the new words.

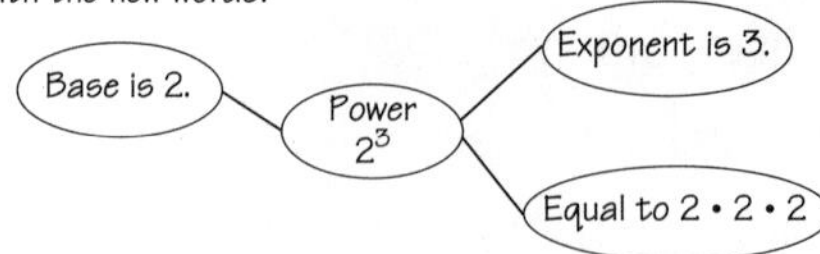

5^2 is read "five squared."

5^3 is read "five cubed."

5^4 is read "five to the fourth power."

As you work through Chapter 2, label examples of new vocabulary in your notes.

52

Number Properties

BEFORE	Now	WHY?
You evaluated expressions.	You'll use properties to evaluate expressions.	So you can find your weekly pay, as in Ex. 39.

Word Watch

Review Words
sum, p. 709
product, p. 713

In the Real World

Tour Biking You are going on a 400 mile bike trip. You plan to cycle at an average speed of 12 miles per hour for 7 hours a day. Can you complete the trip in 5 days?

The commutative properties of addition and multiplication can be used to make evaluating expressions using mental math easier.

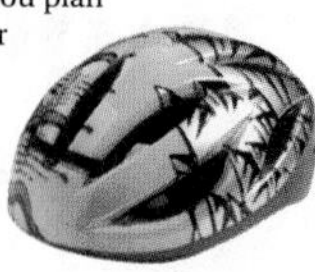

The Commutative Property

	Addition	Multiplication
Words	You can add numbers of a sum in any order.	You can multiply factors of a product in any order.
Numbers	$3 + (-8) = -8 + 3$	$5(-6) = -6(5)$
Algebra	$a + b = b + a$	$ab = ba$

EXAMPLE 1 **Using the Commutative Property**

To find if you can complete the bike trip in 5 days, find the total distance you plan to cycle. Then compare that distance to the length of the trip.

Total distance = Average speed · Hours per day ·

$= 12 \cdot 7 \cdot 5$ Substitute known

$= 12 \cdot 5 \cdot 7$ Commutative pro

$= 60 \cdot 7$ Multiply.

$= 420$ Multiply.

The unit for the result is miles. $\frac{\text{miles}}{\text{hour}} \cdot \frac{\text{hours}}{\text{day}} \cdot$ d

ANSWER Because 400 miles is less than the 420 mi 5 days, you can complete the trip in 5 days.

WRITE IT!

Integrated notetaking features remind students to write new concepts in their notebooks.

REVIEW IT!

Mid- and end-of-chapter reviews help students review notes and prepare for tests.

USE IT!

Vocabulary exercises give students an opportunity to use key terms.

Lessons 2.6 to 2.8 Notebook Review

Review the vocabulary definitions in your notebook.

Copy the review examples in your notebook. Then complete the exercises.

Check Your Definitions

distributive property, p. 85	constant term, p. 86	quadrant, p. 91
terms, like terms, p. 86	coordinate plane, p. 91	ordered pair, p. 91
coefficient, p. 86	x-axis, y-axis, p. 91	x-coordinate, p. 91
	origin, p. 91	y-coordinate, p. 91

Use Your Vocabulary

1. What is the y-coordinate of the point $(5, -5)$?

2.6 Can you use commutative and associative properties?

EXAMPLE Evaluate the expression.

$(-3 + 5) - 7 = (-3 + 5) + (-7)$ Change subtraction to addition.

$= [5 + (-3)] + (-7)$ Commutative property of addition

$= 5 + [-3 + (-7)]$ Associative property of addition

$= 5 + (-10)$ Add inside grouping symbols.

$= -5$ Add.

Use mental math to evaluate the expression. Justify.

2. $-5(19 \cdot 2)$ 3. $-25 \cdot 13 \cdot 4$ 4. $-42 + (-18 - 23)$

2.7 Can you use the distributive property?

EXAMPLE Simplify the expression.

$6(2x + 7) - 9x = 12x + 42 - 9x$ Distributive property

$= 12x + 42 + (-9x)$ Change subtraction to addition.

$= 12x + (-9x) + 42$ Commutative property of addition

$= 3x + 42$ Combine like terms.

Use the distributive property to simplify the expression.

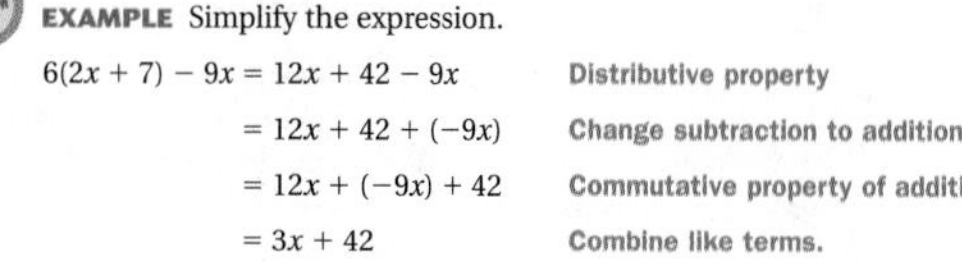

5. $9(3a + 11) - 4$ 6. $-8b + 12(7b + 3)$ 7. $2c - 8(9c - 5)$

Assessment Preparation

Assessment tips and practice opportunities help students achieve their goals.

UNIT 2 Chapters 4–7

BUILDING **Test-Taking Skills**

Strategies for Answering
Short Response Questions

Scoring Rubric

Full credit
- answer is correct, *and*
- work and reasoning are included

Partial credit
- answer is correct, but reasoning is incorrect, *or*
- answer is incorrect, but reasoning is correct

No credit
- no answer is given *or*
- answer makes no sense

Problem

You work for your uncle this summer. He pays you $20 on your first day. Each day after that, you will get a raise. You can choose from 2 payment plans. With Plan A, you earn a $5 raise each day. With Plan B, you earn a 20% raise each day. Which plan is a better deal?

Full credit solution

Plan B is a better deal if you work more than 5 days.

Data is used to justify the solution.

Day	1	2	3	4	5	6
Plan A pay	20.00	25.00	30.00	35.00	40.00	45.00
Plan A total	20.00	45.00	75.00	110.00	150.00	195.00
Plan B pay	20.00	24.00	28.80	34.56	41.47	49.76
Plan B total	20.00	44.00	72.80	107.36	148.83	198.59

The question is answered clearly and in complete sentences.

Plan A is better if you work 5 days or less, but Plan B is better if you work more than 5 days. By day 6, the pay with a 20% increase is more than the pay with a $5 raise, so it will continue to be the better plan.

Partial credit solution

I think Plan B is better than Plan A.

The calculations are correct.

Day	1	2	3	4	5	6
Plan A	20.00	25.00	30.00	35.00	40.00	45.00
Plan B	20.00	24.00	28.80	34.56	41.47	49.76

The reasoning is faulty, because the total amount earned was not considered.

The first 4 days, Plan A is better. The next 2 days, Plan B is better. By day 5 Plan B pays you more money, so it is the better plan.

364 Unit 2 Algebra and Rational Numbers

PLAN IT!

Test-taking strategies help students perform well on assessments.

EXPRESS IT!

Sample solutions help students analyze problems and write full-credit solutions.

Chapter Standardized Test

Test-Taking Strategy **Be careful about choosing an answer that seems obvious. Carefully read the problem and all the choices before answering.**

Multiple Choice

1. Which number is a prime number?

A. 51 **B.** 67 **C.** 82 **D.** 93

2. What is the greatest common factor of 420 and 385?

F. 5 **G.** 15 **H.** 35 **I.** 4620

3. Which fraction is written in simplest form?

A. $\frac{3}{16}$ **B.** $\frac{4}{10}$ **C.** $\frac{9}{21}$ **D.** $\frac{15}{33}$

4. Two toy cars begin at the starting line of a circular track at the same time. Car A goes around the track every 20 seconds. Car B goes around the track every 8 seconds. In how many seconds will the two cars reach the starting line at the same time?

F. 4 seconds **G.** 24 seconds

H. 40 seconds **I.** 160 seconds

5. Which list is *not* in order from least to greatest?

A. $\frac{1}{4}, \frac{3}{8}, \frac{7}{12}, \frac{2}{3}$

B. $\frac{1}{2}, \frac{3}{4}, \frac{13}{16}, \frac{7}{8}$

C. $1\frac{5}{18}, 1\frac{7}{9}, \frac{17}{12}, \frac{11}{6}$

D. $2\frac{4}{21}, 2\frac{5}{14}, \frac{18}{7}, \frac{17}{6}$

6. Which expression is *not* equal to 5^4?

F. $5^3 \cdot 5$ **G.** $5^2 \cdot 5^2$

H. $\frac{5^8}{5^4}$ **I.** $\frac{5^8}{5^2}$

7. Which number is equal to $\frac{2^9}{2^3}$?

A. 8 **B.** 64 **C.** 520 **D.** 4096

8. Write $\frac{-5x^{-6}}{x^3}$ using only positive exponents.

F. $\frac{-5}{x^9}$ **G.** $\frac{1}{5x^9}$ **H.** $-5x^6$ **I.** $30x^3$

9. Simplify $(5 \times 10^{-7}) \times (3.6 \times 10^4)$.

A. 1.8×10^{-4} **B.** 1.8×10^{-3}

C. 1.8×10^{-2} **D.** 18×10^{-3}

Short Response

10. **Planting Trees** A conservation group wants to plant 48 trees in a rectangular arrangement so that each row has the same number of trees. How many trees can be planted in each row? List all possibilities. Of the possible arrangements, which one is closest to having a length three times its width?

Extended Response

11. **History** The Orb of 1661 is a gold sphere set with 365 diamonds, 363 pearls, 18 rubies, 9 emeralds, 9 sapphires, and 1 amethyst. What is the total number of jewels? What fraction of jewels are rubies? What fraction are emeralds? Write each fraction in simplest form. Jane estimates that about half of the jewels in the Orb are diamonds. Do you agree with this estimate? Explain.

PRACTICE IT!

Multiple-choice, short-response, and extended-response questions prepare students for a variety of test-taking experiences.

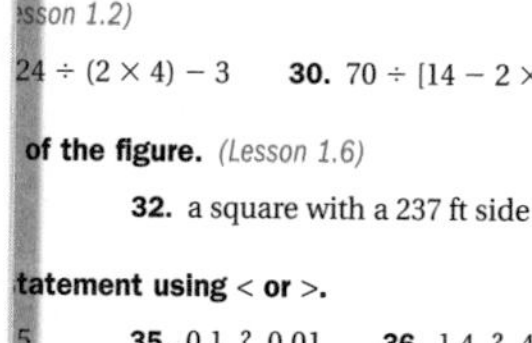

...sson 1.2)

...24 ÷ (2 × 4) − 3 **30.** 70 ÷ [14 − 2 × 2]

...**of the figure.** (Lesson 1.6)

32. a square with a 237 ft side

...**tatement using < or >.**

...5 **35.** 0.1 ? 0.01 **36.** 1.4 ? 4.1

Test-Taking Practice

INTERNET
State Test Practice
CLASSZONE.COM

37. **Multiple Choice** You are trying to earn 400 points in a game. In the first round you get 154 points. The next round you get 78 points. How many more points do you need?

A. 76 **B.** 168 **C.** 176 **D.** 268

38. **Multiple Choice** Which picture represents the next arrow in the pattern?

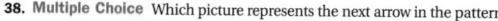

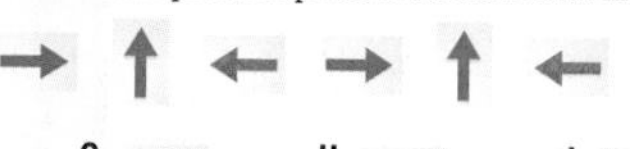

F. 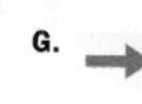 **G.** **H.**  **I.**

What's Happening?

Scott, John, Annie, and Rebecca are each doing a different activity. Who is doing what?

- Scott and John are not at the debate.
- Scott can't go to the student council meeting.
- Annie is not going to student council or to art club.
- Rebecca is not a member of the student council.
- Annie and Rebecca do not tutor.

SOLVE IT!

Test-Taking Practice with every lesson and frequent Brain Games provide ongoing assessment.

Connect to it!

CLASSZONE.COM

- ***eEdition Plus Online*** provides an interactive, online version of the text that engages students and facilitates teaching.
- ***eWorkbook Plus Online*** includes interactive practice opportunities that correspond to the text.
- ***eTutorial Plus Online*** offers an Internet tutorial that makes it easier than ever to help students master skills and concepts.
- ***State Test practice*** helps support students as they prepare to achieve their goals on state tests.
- ***More Examples*** include additional, online support that helps students master new concepts.
- ***Online Quizzes*** help students assess their own progress.
- ***Vocabulary Support*** provides interactive practice with vocabulary.
- ***Activities*** help students become engaged with the mathematics.

Teacher's Resource Package

This package is conveniently organized and includes a variety of materials to help you adapt the program to your teaching style and to the specific needs of your middle school students!

Teacher's Resource Package includes:

Chapter Resource Books
(one for each chapter, organized by lesson)

Assessment Book

Notetaking Guide Teacher's Edition

Practice Workbook Teacher's Edition

Teacher Survival Kit
(includes the Professional Development Book, the Special Activities Book, and Posters)

Warm-Up Transparencies with Daily Homework Quiz

Worked-Out Solution Key

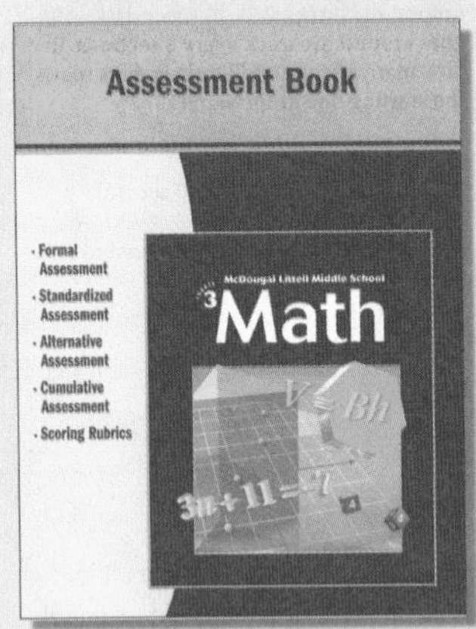

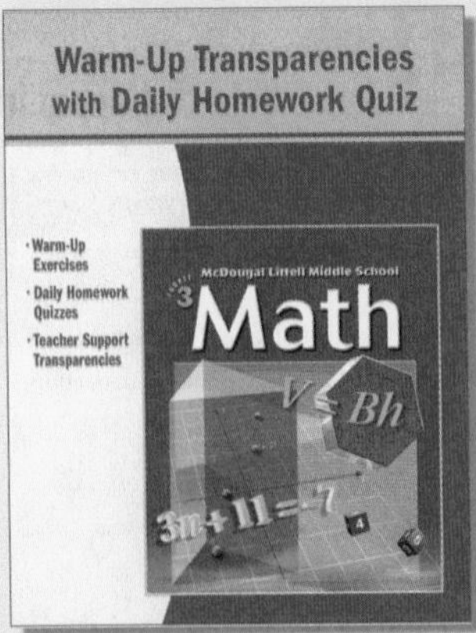

Complete daily resources, organized to save you time!

Chapter Resource Books

Chapter Resource Books allow you to carry the resources you have for a chapter in one manageable book. The materials in each Chapter Resource Book are organized by lesson so that you can easily see everything you have available.

Chapter Resource Books include:

- Tips for New Teachers
- Parents as Partners
- Games Support Master
- Lesson Plans
- Lesson Plans for Block Scheduling
- Activity Masters
- Technology Activities and Keystrokes
- Practice (Levels A, B, and C)
- Study Guide
- Real-World Problem Solving
- Challenge Practice
- Chapter Review Games and Activities
- Real Life Project with Teacher's Notes
- Cooperative Project with Teacher's Notes
- Independent Extra Credit Project with Teacher's Notes
- Cumulative Practice
- Resource Book Answers

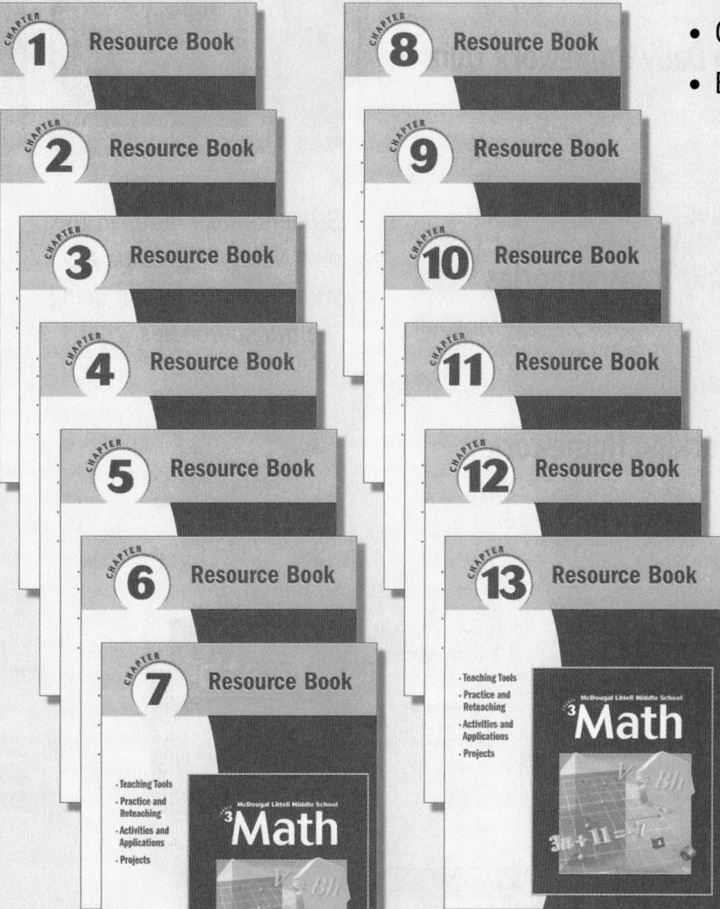

Assessment Book

- Diagnostic Pre-Course Test
- Quizzes
- Chapter Tests (Levels A, B, and C)
- Standardized Tests
- Alternative Assessment with Math Journal and Rubric
- Unit Tests
- Cumulative Tests
- End-of-Course Test

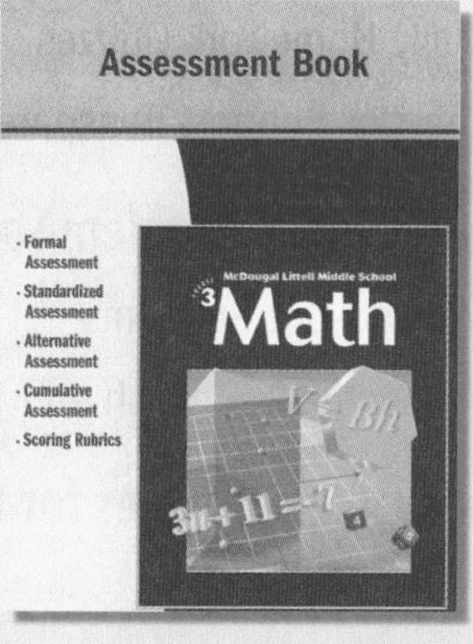

Transparency Packages

The transparency packages give you many easy-to-use options for reviewing homework, starting class, and teaching notetaking and problem solving strategies.

Notetaking Guide Transparencies

- Promote notetaking skills
- Reinforce key concepts

Warm-Up Transparencies with Daily Homework Quiz

- Warm-Up Exercises
- Daily Homework Quizzes
- Teacher Support Transparencies

English-Spanish Problem Solving Transparencies

- Worked-Out Problems
- Presented in English and Spanish

Answer Transparencies for Checking Homework

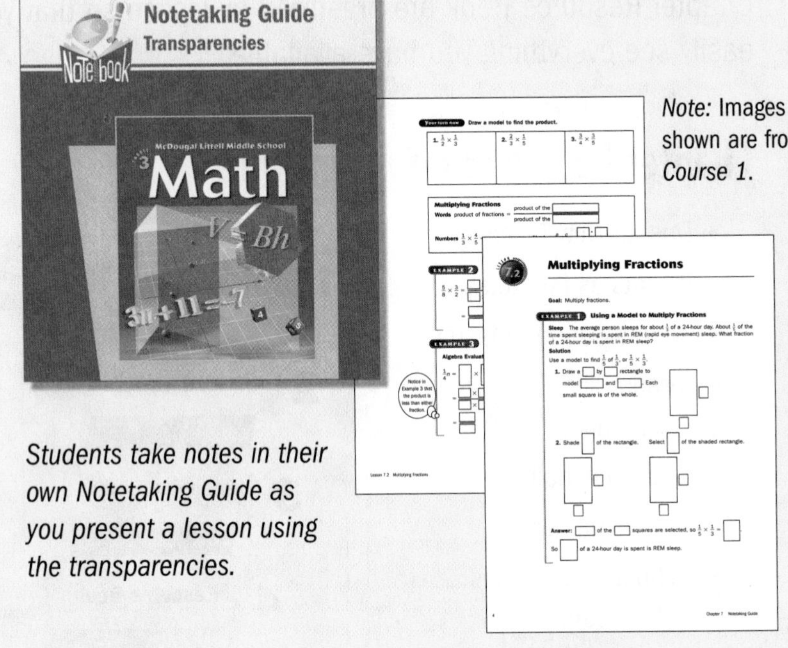

Note: Images shown are from *Course 1*.

Students take notes in their own Notetaking Guide as you present a lesson using the transparencies.

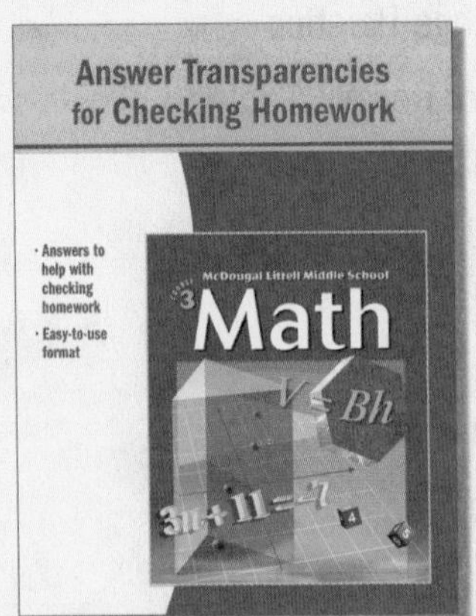

Teacher Survival Kit

This kit provides professional development ideas, helpful activities, and materials to enhance your classroom environment.

Teacher Survival Kit includes:

- Professional Development Book
- Special Activities Book
- Posters

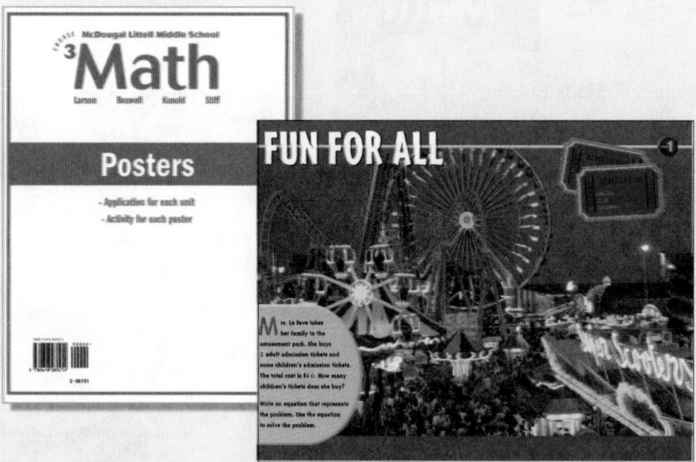

Math Tutor Place

Math Tutor Place helps students practice and master essential math topics. The instruction and practice are provided by 104 cards divided into five main categories:

- Whole Numbers and Decimals
- Fractions
- Ratio, Proportion, and Percent
- Geometry and Measurement
- Algebra

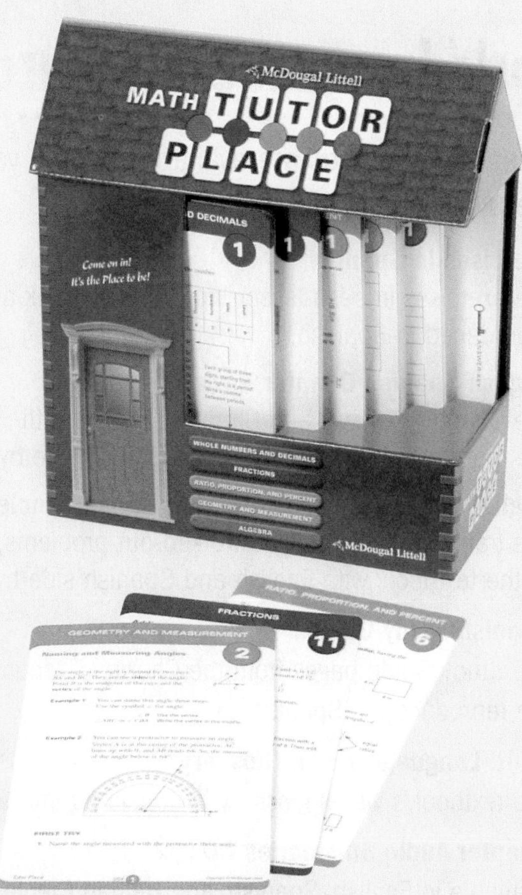

Notetaking Guide

This workbook promotes notetaking skills and helps build understanding by providing students with a framework for recording the key concepts of every lesson. This workbook is also useful in helping students review and prepare for tests.

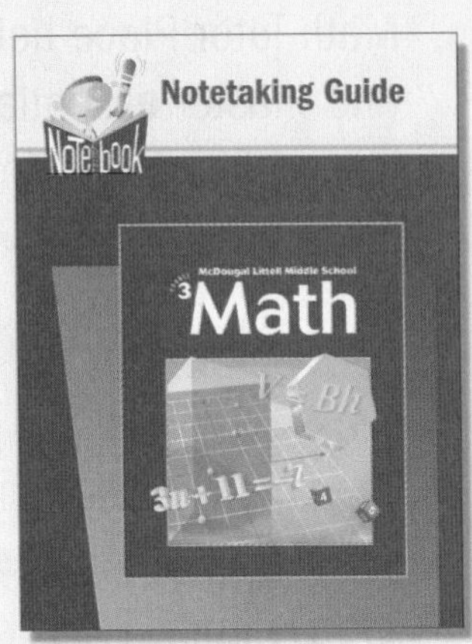

Practice Workbook

The Practice Workbook includes practice exercises for every lesson.

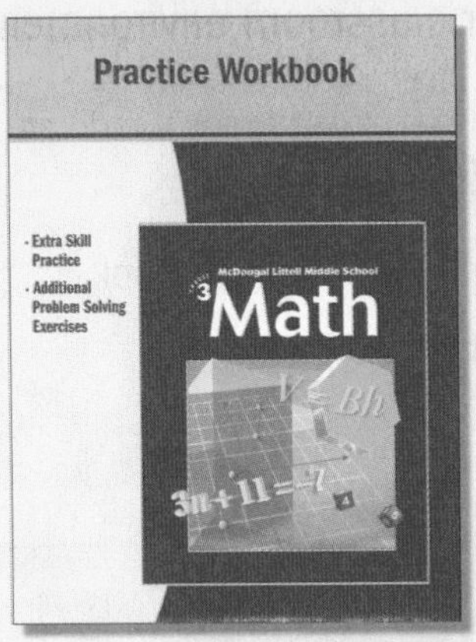

World Languages Resources

A variety of resources are available to help you address the needs of English learners.

Exercises in Spanish
The exercises in each lesson from the textbook are reproduced in Spanish.

English-Spanish Chapter Reviews and Tests
The Chapter Reviews and Chapter Tests from the textbook are reproduced with English and Spanish side-by-side.

English-Spanish Problem Solving Transparencies
The transparencies provide worked-out problems, correlated to the textbook, with English and Spanish side-by-side.

Spanish Study Guide
The Study Guide pages from the Chapter Resource Books are reproduced in Spanish.

Multi-Language Visual Glossary
The textbook's visual glossary is translated into 9 languages.

Chapter Audio Summaries CDs
Available in English, Spanish, and Haitian Creole.

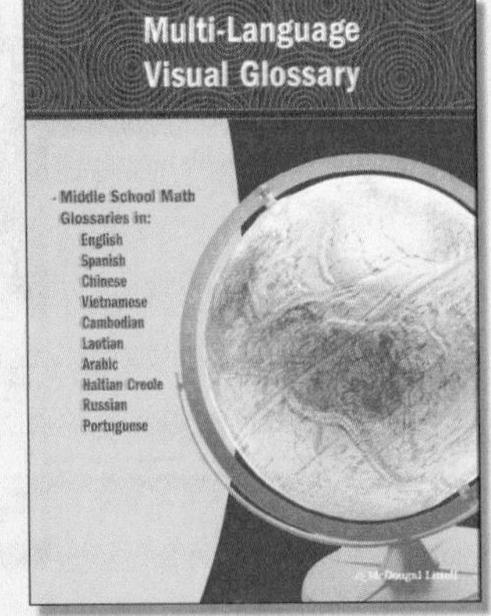

Technology Resources

McDougal Littell offers resources online and on CD-ROM to enhance lessons and help students build understanding.

Online Resources:

Online resources at www.classzone.com are linked together and provide instruction, practice, and learning support.

- **eEdition Plus Online** This electronic version of the book is enhanced by interactive extensions that allow students to explore concepts and self-assessment questions that check understanding. Reports on individual student performance help you track student progress.
- **eWorkbook Plus Online** This interactive software presents students with algorithmically generated problems correlated directly to the lessons and tracks their performance for your review. The problems can be accessed straight from the eEdition or directly from the Web site.
- **eTutorial Plus Online** An interactive program provides students additional material and reinforces key skills. The tutorial can be accessed straight from the eEdition or directly from the Web site.
- **Chapter-Based Support** State test practice, vocabulary support, self-quizzes, and other engaging student activities are provided online.
- **EasyPlanner Plus Online** This planner provides you access to all materials that come along with the program. It allows you to organize them into lesson plans and provides correlations to your state standards.

Other CD-Rom Resources include:

- **Chapter Audio Summaries CDs** These CDs summarize the key concepts of each chapter in English, Spanish, and Haitian Creole.
- **eEdition CD-ROM**
- **eTutorial CD-ROM**
- **EasyPlanner CD-ROM**
- **Electronic Lesson Presentations** PowerPoint™ slides help you walk through key concepts in a stepped out presentation.
- **Test and Practice Generator** The power of the Internet and the computer lab are available to you with this new generation of software.

eEdition Plus Online

Note: Images shown are from *Course 1* Technology Resources.

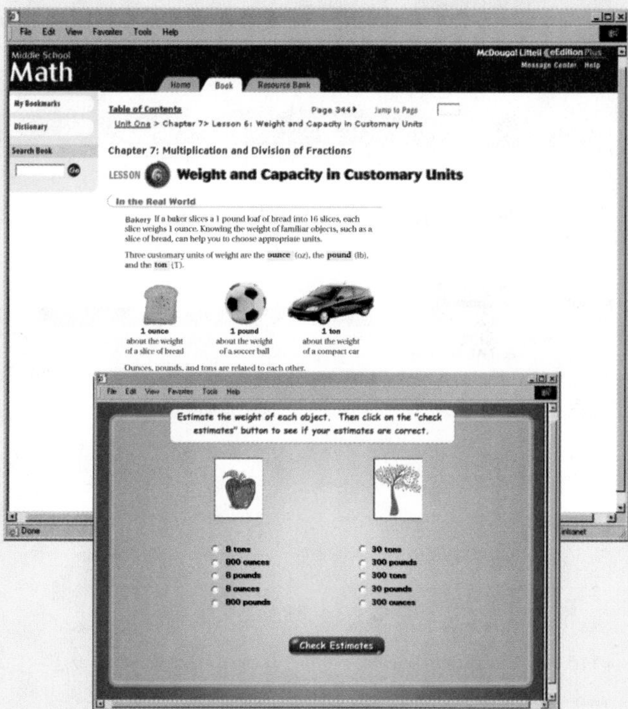

eTutorial Plus Online

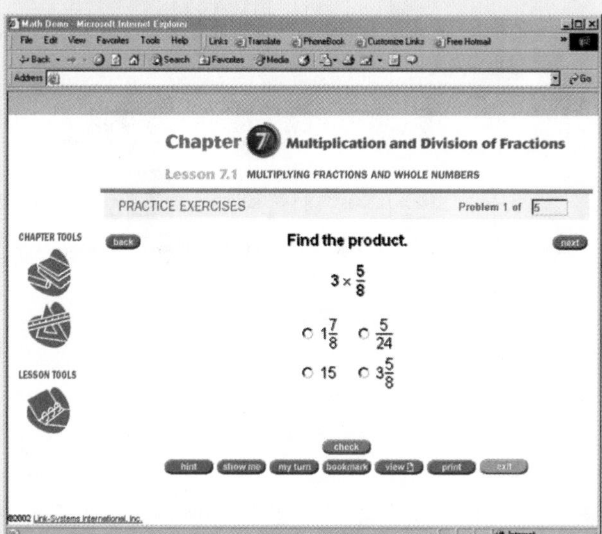

Planning the Chapter

- Regular and Block schedules for pacing the course

- A handy guide for integrating resource materials into your lessons

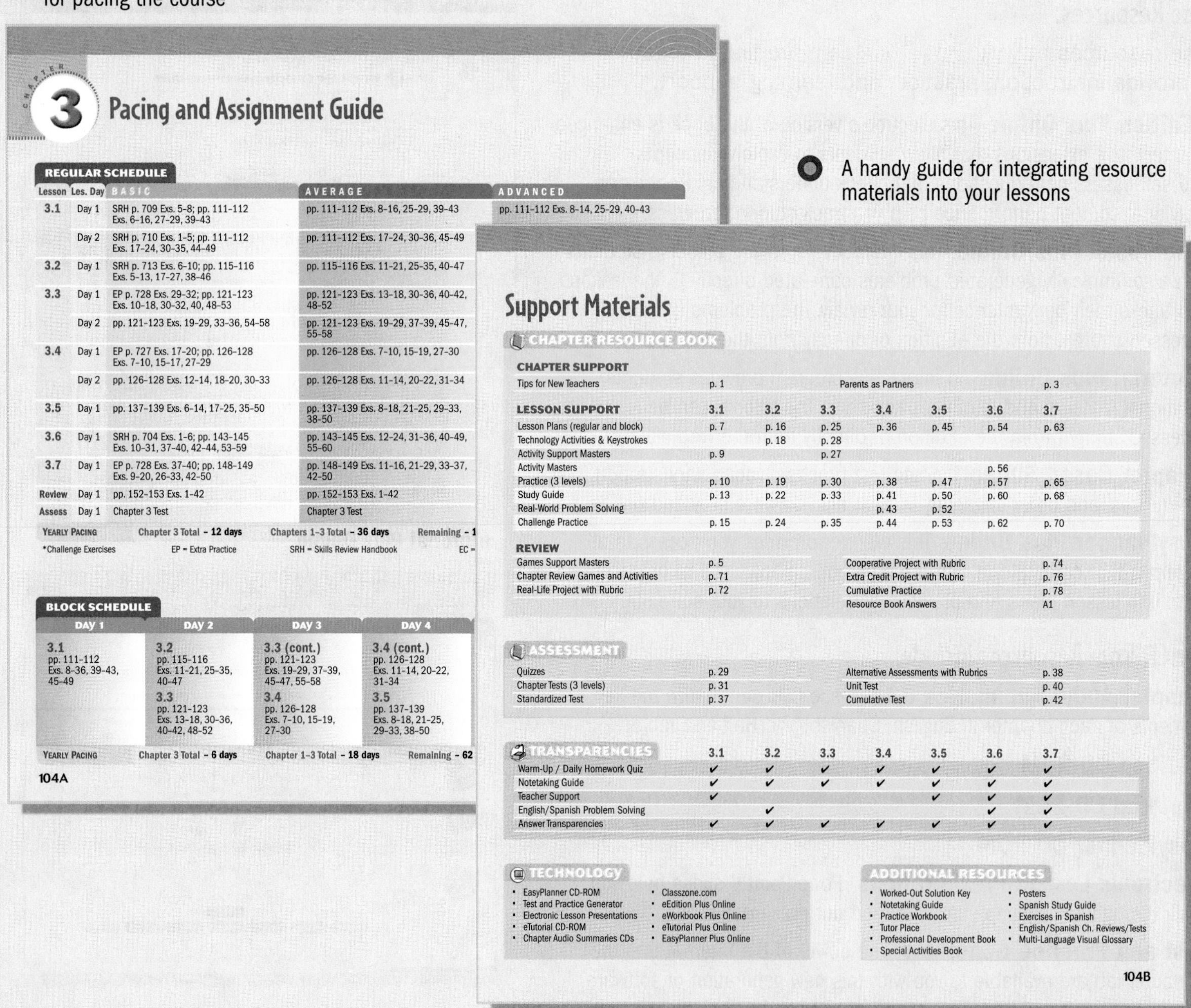

CHAPTER 3 Pacing and Assignment Guide

REGULAR SCHEDULE

Lesson	Les. Day	BASIC	AVERAGE	ADVANCED
3.1	Day 1	SRH p. 709 Exs. 5-8; pp. 111-112 Exs. 6-16, 27-29, 39-43	pp. 111-112 Exs. 8-16, 25-29, 39-43	pp. 111-112 Exs. 8-14, 25-29, 40-43
	Day 2	SRH p. 710 Exs. 1-5; pp. 111-112 Exs. 17-24, 30-35, 44-49	pp. 111-112 Exs. 17-24, 30-36, 45-49	
3.2	Day 1	SRH p. 713 Exs. 6-10; pp. 115-116 Exs. 5-13, 17-27, 38-46	pp. 115-116 Exs. 11-21, 25-35, 40-47	
3.3	Day 1	EP p. 728 Exs. 29-32; pp. 121-123 Exs. 10-18, 30-32, 40, 48-53	pp. 121-123 Exs. 13-18, 30-36, 40-42, 48-52	
	Day 2	pp. 121-123 Exs. 19-29, 33-36, 54-58	pp. 121-123 Exs. 19-29, 37-39, 45-47, 55-58	
3.4	Day 1	EP p. 727 Exs. 17-20; pp. 126-128 Exs. 7-10, 15-17, 27-29	pp. 126-128 Exs. 7-10, 15-19, 27-30	
	Day 2	pp. 126-128 Exs. 12-14, 18-20, 30-33	pp. 126-128 Exs. 11-14, 20-22, 31-34	
3.5	Day 1	pp. 137-139 Exs. 6-14, 17-25, 35-50	pp. 137-139 Exs. 8-18, 21-25, 29-33, 38-50	
3.6	Day 1	SRH p. 704 Exs. 1-6; pp. 143-145 Exs. 10-31, 37-40, 42-44, 53-59	pp. 143-145 Exs. 12-24, 31-36, 40-49, 55-60	
3.7	Day 1	EP p. 728 Exs. 37-40; pp. 148-149 Exs. 9-20, 26-33, 42-50	pp. 148-149 Exs. 11-16, 21-29, 33-37, 42-50	
Review	Day 1	pp. 152-153 Exs. 1-42	pp. 152-153 Exs. 1-42	
Assess	Day 1	Chapter 3 Test	Chapter 3 Test	

YEARLY PACING Chapter 3 Total – **12 days** Chapters 1–3 Total – **36 days** Remaining – 1

*Challenge Exercises EP = Extra Practice SRH = Skills Review Handbook EC =

BLOCK SCHEDULE

DAY 1	DAY 2	DAY 3	DAY 4
3.1 pp. 111-112 Exs. 8-36, 39-43, 45-49	**3.2** pp. 115-116 Exs. 11-21, 25-35, 40-47 **3.3** pp. 121-123 Exs. 13-18, 30-36, 40-42, 48-52	**3.3 (cont.)** pp. 121-123 Exs. 19-29, 37-39, 45-47, 55-58 **3.4** pp. 126-128 Exs. 7-10, 15-19, 27-30	**3.4 (cont.)** pp. 126-128 Exs. 11-14, 20-22, 31-34 **3.5** pp. 137-139 Exs. 8-18, 21-25, 29-33, 38-50

YEARLY PACING Chapter 3 Total – **6 days** Chapter 1–3 Total – **18 days** Remaining – 62

104A

Support Materials

CHAPTER RESOURCE BOOK

CHAPTER SUPPORT

Tips for New Teachers	p. 1	Parents as Partners	p. 3

LESSON SUPPORT	3.1	3.2	3.3	3.4	3.5	3.6	3.7
Lesson Plans (regular and block)	p. 7	p. 16	p. 25	p. 36	p. 45	p. 54	p. 63
Technology Activities & Keystrokes		p. 18	p. 28				
Activity Support Masters	p. 9		p. 27				
Activity Masters						p. 56	
Practice (3 levels)	p. 10	p. 19	p. 30	p. 38	p. 47	p. 57	p. 65
Study Guide	p. 13	p. 22	p. 33	p. 41	p. 50	p. 60	p. 68
Real-World Problem Solving				p. 43	p. 52		
Challenge Practice	p. 15	p. 24	p. 35	p. 44	p. 53	p. 62	p. 70

REVIEW

Games Support Masters	p. 5	Cooperative Project with Rubric	p. 74
Chapter Review Games and Activities	p. 71	Extra Credit Project with Rubric	p. 76
Real-Life Project with Rubric	p. 72	Cumulative Practice	p. 78
		Resource Book Answers	A1

ASSESSMENT

Quizzes	p. 29	Alternative Assessments with Rubrics	p. 38
Chapter Tests (3 levels)	p. 31	Unit Test	p. 40
Standardized Test	p. 37	Cumulative Test	p. 42

TRANSPARENCIES	3.1	3.2	3.3	3.4	3.5	3.6	3.7
Warm-Up / Daily Homework Quiz	✔	✔	✔	✔	✔	✔	✔
Notetaking Guide	✔	✔	✔	✔	✔	✔	✔
Teacher Support	✔				✔	✔	✔
English/Spanish Problem Solving		✔				✔	✔
Answer Transparencies	✔	✔	✔	✔	✔	✔	✔

TECHNOLOGY

- EasyPlanner CD-ROM
- Test and Practice Generator
- Electronic Lesson Presentations
- eTutorial CD-ROM
- Chapter Audio Summaries CDs
- Classzone.com
- eEdition Plus Online
- eWorkbook Plus Online
- eTutorial Plus Online
- EasyPlanner Plus Online

ADDITIONAL RESOURCES

- Worked-Out Solution Key
- Notetaking Guide
- Practice Workbook
- Tutor Place
- Professional Development Book
- Special Activities Book
- Posters
- Spanish Study Guide
- Exercises in Spanish
- English/Spanish Ch. Reviews/Tests
- Multi-Language Visual Glossary

104B

Complete planning support preceding each chapter

Math background and teaching strategies provide suggestions to help you present each lesson and to increase student understanding

Math Background and Teaching Strategies

Lesson 3.1

MATH BACKGROUND

SOLVING EQUATIONS The key to solving an equation is to perform operations that produce successively simpler **equivalent equations**, with the goal of isolating the variable on one side of the equation. For a simple equation involving only addition or subtraction, this means applying the same **inverse operation** to each side: subtraction to undo addition, or addition to undo subtraction. The subtraction and addition properties of equality ensure that the result is an equivalent equation.

TEACHING STRATEGIES

Stress the following keys to solving an equation:

(1) You must perform the same operation on each side of an equation to keep it in "balance."
(2) Choose operations that undo what is done to the variable.
(3) The goal is to get the variable alone on one side of the equation.

For the simple equations of this lesson, students should be able to verbalize the operation to be undone and how to undo it. For example, "In the equation $x + 8 = 11$, 8 is added to the variable, so to get the variable alone I must subtract 8 from each side of the equation."

Lesson 3.2

MATH BACKGROUND

MULTIPLICATION/DIVISION EQUATIONS Solving a simple equation involving only multiplication or division is similar to solving an equation involving only addition or subtraction. Again, this involves performing the inverse operation on each side of the equation that undoes the given operation: multiplication to undo division, and division to undo multiplication. The multiplication and division properties of equality ensure that the result is an equivalent equation. Multiplying or dividing both sides of an equation by zero is not permitted, since doing so does not produce an equivalent equation.

TEACHING STRATEGIES

Point out that the three keys given in the Teaching Strategies for Lesson 3.1 also apply to solving equations involving multiplication or division. Encourage students again to verbalize the operation to be undone and how to undo it. For example, "In the equation $4x = -52$, the variable is multiplied by 4, so to get the variable alone I must divide each side of the equation by 4."

Lesson 3.3

MATH BACKGROU

TWO-STEP EQUA
an addition or sul
division operatio
will lead to solvin
one or both sides
have variable terr
at this step is the
properties of equ

TEACHING STRATE

Point out to stude
properties to lear
before still guide
applying two pro
the use of algebra
not only stresses
operation to each
students learn to
multiplication or
impossible to firs

Lesson 3.4

MATH BACKGROU

Even math teach
"word problems,"
two-step equatio
four-step process
strategy, solving
ful. To aid compr

Strategies for enabling all students to learn mathematics

3 Differentiating Instruction

Strategies for Underachievers

USE MODELS

MANIPULATIVES Hands-on Activity 3.1 and Hands-on Activity 3.3, which use algebra tiles to solve equations, will be of special benefit to underachievers. Provide each student her or his own set of algebra tiles to manipulate. Students should have access to algebra tiles for as long as the tiles are helpful to them.

USE CALCULATORS

PROPERTIES OF EQUALITY When learning how to use the properties of equality to solve equations in Lessons 3.1–3.3, some students may benefit from the use of calculators. These students should still be required to show each step used in the equation solving process. This process should be the focus of the lesson, with the calculator used only to keep the focus on solving equations and away from computation.

USE REPETITION

After completing the Activity at the beginning of Lesson 3.5, some students may have the feeling that the result is some kind of "magic." Have them repeat this activity with several different triangles so that they become comfortable with the result. Students should also be allowed to view the work of other students for even more reinforcement.

SIMPLIFY

OPPOSITES/RECIPROCALS In Lesson 3.3, the Help with Solving tip in the left margin on page 120 suggests that students *add the opposite* to undo either addition or subtraction and *multiply by the reciprocal* to undo either division or multiplication. This tip may help some underachievers by reducing the number of inverse operations they have to choose from when solving an equation. Before suggesting this to a student, however, make sure that the student is comfortable with the concepts of opposites and reciprocals.

USE SCAFFOLDING

In Lesson 3.1, the equations involve only addition or subtraction. You may suggest to students that after they identify such an equation, they can use the method shown below as a template to guide them and help them show the steps of their work. First, the equation is written, in this case $x + 33 = 87$. Next, lines are drawn under each side of the equation, leaving space above the lines to add the same number to each side or subtract the same number from each side. Then an equal sign is placed in the next line, aligned with the original equal sign, to prompt students to write the result of the addition or subtraction.

$$\begin{array}{c} x + 33 = 87 \\ \underline{\quad\quad} \quad \underline{\quad} \\ = \end{array}$$

Notice in Example 1 of Lesson 3.3 on page 119 that a vertical addition or subtraction format can also be used as a template for the first step in a two-step equation, but in this case additional lines are required for the steps involving multiplication or division. Some students may benefit from using grid paper to keep their equation-solving work organized and aligned both horizontally and vertically.

In Lesson 3.3, you may wish to provide underachievers with additional scaffolded examples in the style of Exercise 9 on page 121.

IDENTIFY KEY TERMS

WRITING EQUATIONS In Lessons 3.1–3.3, and especially in Lesson 3.4, students will be writing equations to model situations that are presented verbally, that is, they will be solving "word problems." Underachievers may benefit from reviewing the vocabulary cards created for the Strategies for Underachievers from Chapter 1. As they encounter new words or phrases that model mathematical operations, have them create new vocabulary cards, or have them create a poster identifying key terms and language, updating it as necessary.

Planning the Lesson

SKILL CHECK

Solve the equation.

1. $\frac{x}{8} = 2$ 16
2. $6 = -\frac{n}{6}$ −36
3. $-4j = 56$ −14
4. $-91 = -13k$ 7

LESSON OBJECTIVE

Solve inequalities using multiplication or division.

PACING

Suggested Number of Days
Basic Course: 1 day
Average Course: 1 day
Advanced Course: 1 day
Block: 0.5 block with 3.6

TEACHING RESOURCES

For a complete list of Teaching Resources, see page 104B.

TRANSPARENCY

Warm-Up Exercises for this lesson are available on a transparency.

MOTIVATING THE LESSON

Ask students what they know about bats. You may point out that in Austin, Texas, a colony of up to one and one-half million Mexican free-tail bats lives under the Congress Avenue bridge, and that the colony will eat from 10,000 to 30,000 pounds of insects in a single night.

146

Solving Inequalities Using Multiplication or Division

BEFORE: You solved equations using multiplication or division.

Now: You'll solve inequalities using multiplication or division.

WHY? So you can find how many students must attend a dance, as in Ex. 26.

In the Real World

Word Watch

Review Words
inequality, p. 140
solution of an inequality, p. 140
equivalent inequalities, p. 141

Bats About 15,000 fruit-eating bats live on Panama's Barro Colorado Island. Every year they consume up to 61,440,000 grams of fruit. About how many grams of fruit does each bat consume in a year? You will use an inequality to solve this in Example 3.

There is one important difference between solving inequalities and solving equations. When multiplying or dividing each side of an inequality by a negative number, you must *reverse the direction of the inequality symbol.*

Multiplication Property of In

Words

Multiplying each side of an inequality by a *positive* number makes an equivalent inequality.

Multiplying each side of an inequality by a *negative* number and *reversing the direction of the inequality symbol* makes an equivalent inequality.

HELP with Notetaking

You might want to use a table to organize this information about reversing the inequality symbol.

EXAMPLE 1 Solving an Inequa

$-\frac{1}{8}n \geq 2$ Original ine

$-8 \cdot \left(-\frac{1}{8}\right)n \leq -8 \cdot 2$ Multiply ea Reverse ine

$n \leq -16$ Simplify.

146 Chapter 3 Solving Equations and Inequalities

TEACH

- A Motivating the Lesson note at the beginning of each lesson
- Extra Example for each example in the book
- Concept Check question at the end of each lesson
- Teaching Tips, Common Error notes ... AND MORE

PLAN

- Skill Check
- Lesson Objective
- Pacing Summary
- Teaching Resources

Division Property of Inequality

Words	Algebra
Dividing each side of an inequality by a *positive* number makes an equivalent inequality.	If $2x < 10$, then $\frac{2x}{2} < \frac{10}{2}$.
Dividing each side of an inequality by a *negative* number and *reversing the direction of the inequality symbol* makes an equivalent inequality.	If $-5x < 15$, then $\frac{-5x}{-5} > \frac{15}{-5}$.

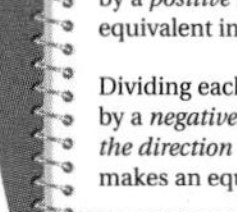

EXAMPLE 2 Solving an Inequality Using Division

$15 > -3m$ Original inequality

$\frac{15}{-3} < \frac{-3m}{-3}$ Divide each side by −3. Reverse inequality symbol.

$-5 < m$ Simplify.

Your turn now Solve the inequality.

1. $\frac{t}{6} > 4$ $t > 24$
2. $-\frac{1}{2}x \leq 10$ $x \geq -20$
3. $27 > -3t$ $t > -9$
4. $9n < 63$ $n < 7$

Fruit Bats

Fruit bats help forests regrow by spreading the seeds from the figs that they eat each night. One kind of fruit bat is about 25 grams and can eat 2.5 times its body mass in figs in one night. How many grams of figs can one of these bats eat? 62.5

EXAMPLE 3 Using the Division Property of Inequality

Bats You can find how much each fruit-eating bat eats annually as described on the previous page as follows.

Solution

Write a verbal model. Let g represent the number of grams one bat eats in a year.

Number of bats • Grams each bat eats ≤ Maximum amount eaten annually

$15{,}000g \leq 61{,}440{,}000$ Write an algebraic model.

$\frac{15{,}000g}{15{,}000} \leq \frac{61{,}440{,}000}{15{,}000}$ Divide each side by 15,000.

$g \leq 4096$ Simplify.

ANSWER Each bat eats as much as 4096 grams of fruit in a year.

Lesson 3.7 Solving Inequalities Using Multiplication or Division 147

TIPS FOR NEW TEACHERS

To illustrate why an inequality is reversed when multiplying or dividing by a negative number, use the inequality $-x < 0$, or "the opposite of a number is less than zero." For this to be true, the original number must be greater than zero. See Tips for New Teachers in the *Chapter 3 Resource Book.*

EXTRA EXAMPLES

Example 1 Solve $-\frac{2}{3}k \geq 8$. $k \leq -12$

Example 2 Solve $60 > -5a$. $a > -12$

Example 3 Each lunchtime in a school, students consume up to 3000 ounces of milk. If there are 250 students, write and solve an inequality to find the average amount of milk per student consumed each lunchtime. $250m \leq 3000$; $m \leq 12$ oz

MATH REASONING

Because the graph of 3 is to the right of the graph of 2, 3 > 2. Multiplying both numbers by −1 gives −3 and −2. Because the graph of −3 is to the left of the graph of −2, −3 < −2, that is, the inequality is reversed.

CONCEPT CHECK

When is it necessary to reverse the direction of the inequality symbol when solving an inequality? when you multiply or divide each side of an inequality by a negative number

The perimeter of a square is x meters and the area of the square is x square meters. What is x? 16

147

Convenient, point-of-use support for each lesson

3 APPLY

ASSIGNMENT GUIDE

Basic Course
Day 1: EP p. 728 Exs. 37–40; pp. 148–149 Exs. 9–20, 26–33, 42–50

Average Course
Day 1: pp. 148–149 Exs. 11–16, 21–29, 33–37, 42–50

Advanced Course
Day 1: pp. 148–149 Exs. 11–16, 21–29, 33–45*, 50

Block
pp. 148–149 Exs. 11–16, 21–29, 33–37, 42–50

EXTRA PRACTICE
- Student Edition, p. 729
- Chapter 3 Resource Book, pp. 65–67
- Test and Practice Generator

TRANSPARENCY
Even-numbered answers are available on transparencies. A support transparency is available for Exercises 4–7, 13–24, and 27–32.

HOMEWORK CHECK
When you review students' homework for this lesson, go over the following exercises to check understanding of key concepts.
Basic: 9, 13, 15, 18, 26
Average: 11, 13, 15, 21, 26
Advanced: 11, 14, 16, 22, 26

TEACHING TIP
In Exercises 14, 15, 19, and 22–24, where an inequality is to be reversed, it may help students to take an extra step. For example, in Exercise 14, students can multiply both sides by 7 to obtain $-t \geq 21$, then multiply by -1 and reverse the inequality.

4–7, 13–24. See Additional Answers beginning on page AA1.

3.7 Exercises
More Practice, p. 729

INTERNET eWorkbook Plus CLASSZONE.COM

Getting Ready to Practice

1. **Vocabulary** Copy and complete: When you multiply both sides of an inequality by a negative number, you need to _?_ the inequality symbol. reverse

Decide whether the solution strategy will require reversing the inequality symbol.

2. $\frac{1}{3}x < 18$ Multiply each side by 3. no
3. $-6x \geq 24$ Divide each side by -6. yes

Solve the inequality. Then graph its solution. 4–7. See margin for art.

4. $\frac{1}{2}x < 4$ $x < 8$ 5. $\frac{m}{-7} \geq 6$ $m \leq -42$ 6. $9 \leq -3z$ $z \leq -3$ 7. $30 > -6p$ $p > -5$

8. **Fundraising** The diving club is selling lessons to raise money. The profit is $15 per lesson. The diving club wants to raise at least $300. How many lessons must be sold? at least 20 lessons

Practice and Problem Solving

Solve the inequality. Match the inequality with the graph of its solution.

A 9. $\frac{1}{4}x \leq 8$ D 10. $-4x \geq 8$ C 11. $4x \geq -8$ A 12. $-\frac{1}{4}x \leq 8$ B

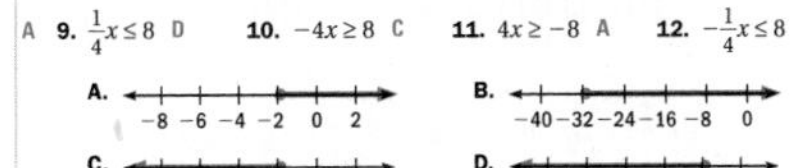

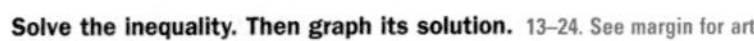

HELP with Homework

Example	Exercises
1	9–24
2	9–24
3	26

Online Resources CLASSZONE.COM
- More Examples
- eTutorial Plus

Solve the inequality. Then graph its solution. 13–24. See margin for art.

13. $\frac{1}{4}x > 1$ $x > 4$ 14. $-\frac{1}{7}t \geq 3$ $t \leq -21$ 15. $-\frac{1}{5}b \geq 72$ $b \leq -360$ 16. $\frac{1}{3}d < -33$ $d < -99$

17. $4g < 24$ $g < 6$ 18. $12 \geq -3s$ $s \geq -4$ 19. $-9c \leq 54$ $c \geq -6$ 20. $5z < -15$ $z < -3$

21. $7 > -\frac{1}{8}r$ $r > -56$ 22. $-6t \geq 36$ $t \leq -6$ 23. $-39 \leq -13k$ $k \leq 3$ 24. $-\frac{1}{7}a < 54$ $a > -378$

25. **Critical Thinking** Is it possible to list every number in the solution set of an inequality? Explain your answer. No; there are infinitely many solutions.

APPLY

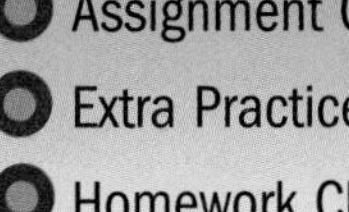

- Assignment Guide
- Extra Practice references

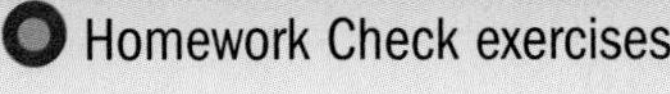

- Homework Check exercises

ASSESS AND FOLLOW-UP

- Assessment Resources
- Mini-Quiz for each lesson
- Reteaching/Remediation
- Challenge/Enrichment
- English Learner Support

…e The student council must pay a DJ $275 to work at a dance. …et to the dance costs $5.50. The amount of money received from …sales must at least cover the cost of the DJ. Write and solve an …ality that gives the number of students that must attend the …in order to pay the $275 for the DJ. $5.5s \geq 275$; $s \geq 50$ students

…inequality. Then graph its solution. 27–32. See margin for art.

…$-2x$ $x > -3$ 28. $3y - 4 < 2y + 5$ $y < 9$ 29. $4p - 9 \geq -1$ $p \geq 2$

…$t) \leq 4(3 - t)$ $t \geq -7$ 31. $4d < -2(33 + d)$ $d < -11$ 32. $7z + 3 \leq 5z - 1$ $z \leq -2$

…g How is solving an inequality like solving an equation? …s solving an inequality different from solving an equation? See margin.

…wing Money You borrow $200 from your aunt to buy a new …oard. If you pay her back at a rate of $12 per week, when will …we her less than $60? in 12 wk

…inequality.

…$20) \geq 3x + 60$ $x \geq 80$ 36. $4(12 - 5x) \geq -4$ $x \leq 2.6$ 37. $2(3 - x) \leq 10x$ $x \geq \frac{1}{2}$

…Solve the compound inequality.

…$2x < 10$ $< x < 5$ 39. $-35 \leq 7x \leq -14$ $-5 \leq x \leq -2$ 40. $10 < 5x < 100$ $2 < x < 20$

…tor The height of a rectangular computer screen is 20 centimeters …an twice the width. The perimeter is at least 53 centimeters. Find the minimum dimensions of the screen if each dimension is an integer. 12 cm by 16 cm

reverse the direction of the inequality.

Mixed Review

Use mental math to solve the equation. *(Lessons 2.2, 2.4)*

42. $-4x = 0$ 0 43. $11a = 11$ 1 44. $z + (-12) = -12$ 0

Solve the inequality. Then graph its solution. *(Lesson 3.6)* 45–47. See margin for art.

45. $c + 7 \leq 11$ $c \leq 4$ 46. $3 < 12 + s$ $s > -9$ 47. $x - 12 > 17$ $x > 29$

Basic Skills Find the missing number.

48. 7 hours = _?_ minutes 420 49. 3 days = _?_ hours 72

Test-Taking Practice

INTERNET State Test Practice CLASSZONE.COM

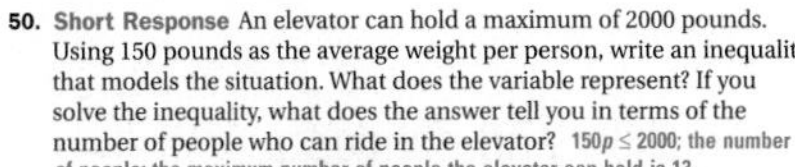

50. **Short Response** An elevator can hold a maximum of 2000 pounds. Using 150 pounds as the average weight per person, write an inequality that models the situation. What does the variable represent? If you solve the inequality, what does the answer tell you in terms of the number of people who can ride in the elevator? $150p \leq 2000$; the number of people; the maximum number of people the elevator can hold is 13.

4 ASSESS

ASSESSMENT RESOURCES
For more assessment resources, see:
- Assessment Book
- Test and Practice Generator

MINI-QUIZ
Solve the inequality. Then graph its solution.

1. $\frac{1}{7}d > 2$
$d > 14$
11 12 13 14 15 16 17

2. $-\frac{2}{3}e \geq 4$
$e \leq -6$
-9 -8 -7 -6 -5 -4 -3

3. $-96 < -8h$
$h < 12$
9 10 11 12 13 14 15

5 FOLLOW-UP

RETEACHING/REMEDIATION
- Study Guide in Chapter 3 Resource Book, pp. 68–69
- Tutor Place, Algebra Cards 15, 16
- eTutorial Plus Online
- Extra Practice, p. 729
- Lesson Practice in Chapter 3 Resource Book, pp. 65–67

CHALLENGE/ENRICHMENT
- Challenge Practice in Chapter 3 Resource Book, p. 70
- Teacher's Edition, p. 104F

ENGLISH LEARNER SUPPORT
- Spanish Study Guide
- Multi-Language Glossary
- Chapter Audio Summaries CDs

27–32, 45–47. See Additional Answers beginning on page AA1.

Pacing the Course

The Pacing Chart below shows the number of days allotted for each chapter. The Regular Schedule requires 160 days. The Block Schedule requires 80 days. These time frames include days for review and assessment: 2 days per chapter for the Regular Schedule and 1 day per chapter for the Block Schedule. Semester and trimester divisions are indicated by green and blue rules, respectively.

	Semester 1							Semester 2					
Chapter	1	2	3	4	5	6	7	8	9	10	11	12	13
Regular Schedule	12	12	12	12	12	10	10	14	10	12	16	16	12
Block Schedule	6	6	6	6	6	5	5	7	5	6	8	8	6
	Trimester 1				Trimester 2					Trimester 3			

Assignments are provided with each lesson for a basic course, an average course, an advanced course, and a block-schedule course. Each of the four courses covers all thirteen chapters.

Basic Course

The basic course is intended for students who enter with below-average mathematical and problem-solving skills. Assignments include:

- spiral review of pre-course and on-level topics through Skills Review Handbook and Extra Practice references
- substantial work with the skills and concepts presented in the lesson
- straightforward applications of these skills and concepts
- test preparation and mixed review exercises

Average Course

The average course is intended for students who enter with typical mathematical and problem-solving skills. Assignments include:

- substantial work with the skills and concepts presented in the lesson
- applications of these skills and concepts
- test preparation and mixed review exercises

Advanced Course

The advanced course is intended for students who enter with above-average mathematical and problem-solving skills. Assignments include:

- substantial work with the skills and concepts presented in the lesson
- more complex applications and challenge exercises
- test preparation and mixed review exercises
- optional extra challenge exercises provided in the Teacher's Edition and in the Chapter Resource Books

Block-Schedule Course

The block-schedule course is intended for schools that use a block schedule. It covers the same content as the regular-schedule course. The exercises assigned are comparable to the exercises for the average course.

Pacing and daily assignments for 4 courses

The Pacing and Assignment Guide for each chapter is located on the interleaved pages preceding the chapter. Part of the Pacing Chart for Chapter 3 is shown here.

Regular-Schedule Chart

This chart provides pacing for the basic, average, and advanced courses.

Lesson	Les. Day	BASIC	AVERAGE	ADVANCED
3.1	Day 1	SRH p. 709 Exs. 5-8; pp. 111-112 Exs. 6-16, 27-29, 39-43	pp. 111-112 Exs. 8-16, 25-29, 39-43	pp. 111-112 Exs. 8-14, 25-29, 40-43
	Day 2	SRH p. 710 Exs. 1-5; pp. 111-112 Exs. 17-24, 30-35, 44-49	pp. 111-112 Exs. 17-24, 30-36, 45-49	pp. 111-112 Exs. 19-24, 33-39*, 46-49
3.2	Day 1	SRH p. 713 Exs. 6-10; pp. 115-116 Exs. 5-13, 17-27, 38-46	pp. 115-116 Exs. 11-21, 25-35, 40-47	pp. 115-116 Exs. 11-21, 28-39*, 44-47

*Challenge Exercises EP = Extra Practice SRH = Skills Review Handbook EC = Extra Challenge

Block-Schedule Chart

This chart provides pacing for the block-schedule course.

Day 1	Day 2	Day 3	Day 4	Day 5	Day 6
3.1 pp. 111-112 Exs. 8-36, 39-43, 45-49	**3.2** pp. 115-116 Exs. 11-21, 25-35, 40-47 **3.3** pp. 121-123 Exs. 13-18, 30-36, 40-42, 48-52	**3.3 (cont.)** pp. 121-123 Exs. 19-29, 37-39, 45-47, 55-58 **3.4** pp. 126-128 Exs. 7-10, 15-19, 27-30	**3.4 (cont.)** pp. 126-128 Exs. 11-14, 20-22, 31-34 **3.5** pp. 137-139 Exs. 8-18, 21-25, 29-33, 38-50	**3.6** pp. 143-145 Exs. 12-24, 31-36, 40-49, 55-60 **3.7** pp. 148-149 Exs. 11-16, 21-29, 33-37, 42-50	**Review** pp. 152-153 Exs. 1-42 **Assess** Chapter 3 Test

YEARLY PACING **Chapter 3 Total** – 6 days **Chapters 1–3 Total** – 18 days **Remaining** – 62 days

Assignment Guide

An assignment guide for each lesson is provided at the beginning of the exercise set. Assignments are given for basic, average, advanced, and block-schedule courses.

Basic Course

Day 1: pp. 111-112 Exs. 6-16, 27-29, 39-43

Day 2: pp. 111-112 Exs. 17-24, 30-35, 44-49

Average Course

Day 1: pp. 111-112 Exs. 8-16, 25-29, 39-43

Day 2: pp. 111-112 Exs. 17-24, 30-36, 45-49

Advanced Course

Day 1: pp. 111-112 Exs. 8-14, 25-29, 40-43

Day 2: pp. 111-112 Exs. 19-24, 33-39*, 46-49

Block

pp. 111-112 Exs. 8-36, 39-43, 45-49

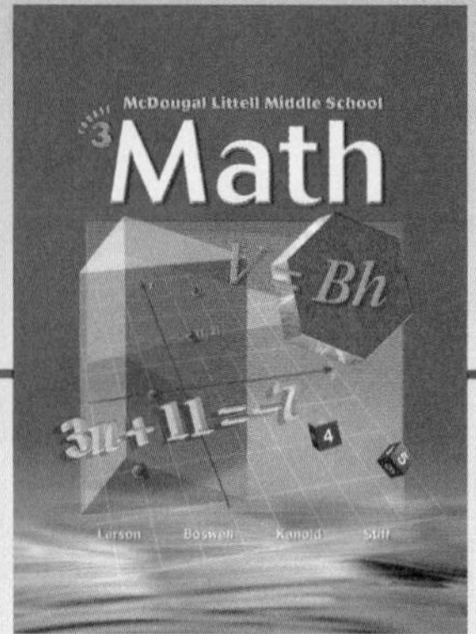

A Program *you can* trust

The right math, presented in the right way.

McDougal Littell Middle School Math, Course 3, is a program you can count on to teach the mathematical concepts and methods that your students need to know in order to meet high curriculum standards and succeed on high-stakes tests. Including the appropriate content, however, is not enough. The math must be presented in a way that students can understand and that will motivate them to learn. The distinguished author team of *McDougal Littell Middle School Math* and the thorough, research-based planning and development process ensure that this program both includes the right math and teaches the math in the right way, so that students gain conceptual understanding and achieve success on important assessments.

DISTINGUISHED AUTHOR TEAM

The experienced, expert author team of Ron Larson, Laurie Boswell, Timothy Kanold, and Lee Stiff brings a wealth of mathematical expertise, writing talent, and classroom teaching and curriculum planning experience from middle school through college to the creation of this new program. Lead author Ron Larson has been writing highly-respected and widely-used textbooks for more than 20 years, and each new book benefits from the comments of the many teachers and students who used earlier editions.

STANDARDS-BASED INSTRUCTION AND ASSESSMENT

State and National Standards In planning the outlines and writing the textbook, the authors paid careful attention to state curriculum standards and state assessment objectives from all states to make sure that the important mathematical concepts and skills were included and given appropriate emphasis. The authors also made sure that the outline and course content fully addressed the standards of national organizations such as the National Council of Teachers of Mathematics (NCTM) and the National Assessment of Educational Progress (NAEP). A correlation to the NAEP objectives appears on page T56 and a correlation to the NCTM Standards can be found on page T57.

SUPPORTING BEST PRACTICES FROM RESEARCH

Educational and Cognitive Research Recent research studies have confirmed strategies for increasing student achievement. These strategies, which reflect the best practices of successful teachers, can help all students learn more effectively. The authors kept this research in mind as they planned and wrote *Middle School Math,* so that the content, organization, and instructional strategies in the program would make it easy for you to implement best-practice instruction in your classroom.

...validated by research

COMPREHENSIVE RESEARCH, REVIEW, AND FIELD-TESTING

About three years prior to the publication of this book, the authors and teams of editors, consultants, graphic designers, professional researchers, and experts in content, instruction, and technology began gathering and analyzing the extensive data on which the plans for this program are based. Data were gathered in a variety of ways, starting with school visits and concluding with field testing.

- **Classroom Visits** Discussions and classroom observations took place in schools throughout the country to determine the key needs of teachers and students, the obstacles that they face in achieving their goals, and the types of materials that can help them achieve success.

- **Nationwide Research Surveys** Comprehensive mail surveys on middle school math curriculum needs, instructional practices, student achievement levels, and teacher preferences regarding instructional materials were conducted early in the development process to guide the planning of the program.

- **Teacher Panels** Panels of expert teachers from different areas of the country participated in the development of the program by identifying instructional and curriculum needs, reviewing prototype outlines and sample materials for both print and electronic materials, and providing suggestions for teaching-support publications.

- **Student Discussion Groups** Discussion groups were held with middle school students to determine the textbook characteristics that make it easy or hard for them to learn and the extent to which they have access to and feel comfortable using electronic products.

- **Focus Tests** Focus tests in which teachers discussed their instructional goals and evaluated sample student and teacher materials were held in different areas of the country. The teachers participating in the focus groups were chosen to represent the wide range of types of schools, philosophies of instruction, and teacher characteristics (like number of years of teaching) in the teaching population. The feedback from these diverse groups of teachers was used to revise and refine the project plans prior to writing.

- **Curriculum Advisers and Reviewers** The Curriculum Advisers and Reviewers listed on page T4 participated in planning the program and read all the proof for the student edition in detail with regard to clarity, accuracy, and appropriateness for classroom use. Other teacher reviewers read selected chapters for these characteristics.

- **Field-Testing** Selected chapters from each grade level were taught in the classroom to test how successful students were in learning from the textbook. Some of the aspects tested were student achievement as measured by pre- and post-test scores, students' ease of learning from the material, and students' interest in the material.

Reaching *All* students

No Child Left Behind

The new federal law known as *No Child Left Behind* (NCLB) highlights the need to ensure that all students, whether they are struggling, average, or advanced learners, have opportunities to make continuing progress in developing the skills they need to become successful adults. This law charges the states with the responsibility of establishing statewide accountability systems based on challenging standards, annual assessment in Grades 3–8, and annual statewide progress objectives.

Intervention begins with diagnosis.

McDougal Littell Middle School Math supports the goals of NCLB. The program is based on challenging state curriculum standards and assessment objectives *(see page T40)*. It provides you with helpful materials for diagnosing how well students understand the material, for differentiating instruction to reach all students, for assessing student progress, and for providing remediation. It also emphasizes important test-taking skills and problem-solving strategies.

ONGOING DIAGNOSIS

Materials to diagnose student understanding are provided before, during, and following each chapter and lesson.

- **Pre-Course Tests** in the Student Edition and the Assessment Book help you diagnose how well students have mastered key prerequisite skills for the course.
- **Chapter Warm-Up Games** and **Getting Ready to Learn** exercises at the beginning of each chapter provide two different mechanisms for reviewing pre-chapter skills and vocabulary.
- **Skill Check** exercises in the Teacher's Edition and **Warm-Up** exercises on transparencies provide practice with prerequisite skills for the upcoming lesson.
- **Your Turn Now** and **Getting Ready to Practice** exercises in the Student Edition, along with **Concept Check** items in the Teacher's Edition, help you monitor how well students are grasping the vocabulary, skills, and concepts as you present each lesson.
- **Homework Check** boxes in the Teacher's Edition identify exercises from the homework assignment that you can use to determine whether or not students have mastered the key skills and concepts.
- You can also use the **Test and Practice Generator** to create online practice sheets and see a report of the results to monitor individual progress.

...in your diverse classroom

DIFFERENTIATED INSTRUCTION AND PRACTICE

Being able to differentiate instruction and practice can help you reach all students. The list below highlights a few components of *Middle School Math* that are designed to help you in this effort. You can use **EasyPlanner Plus Online** to preview and select the resources as you develop your lesson plans. *(See also pages T50–T55 and the E and F pages preceding each chapter.)*

INSTRUCTION

- Hands-On Activities in the Student Edition and a Special Activities Book
- Visualize and Multiple Representation notes in the Teacher's Edition
- Notetaking Guide workbook and transparencies
- English-Spanish Problem Solving Transparencies
- Chapter Audio Summaries CDs (in English, Spanish, and Haitian Creole)
- Electronic Lesson Presentations
- Online Activities and Vocabulary Support

PRACTICE

- Leveled exercises labeled in the Teacher's Edition; leveled homework assignments; leveled practice worksheets
- Challenge exercises in the Student Edition; Daily Puzzlers in the Teacher's Edition; and Challenge Practice masters in the Chapter Resource Books
- Math Tutor Place cards with practice on essential math topics
- Cooperative Learning Projects in the Chapter Resource Books
- Textbook exercises in Spanish
- Spanish Study Guide

ASSESSMENT

Middle School Math provides diagnostic, formative, and summative assessment resources for measuring student progress on an ongoing basis.

- The **Student Edition** has test-practice questions at the end of every exercise set, including multiple choice, short response, and extended response items. Also included are quizzes, reviews, traditional and standardized chapter tests, and an end-of-course test.
- The **Teacher's Edition** has a quiz for every lesson. An alternate quiz is available on a transparency.
- The **Assessment Book** has alternate forms of all the quizzes and tests in the textbook, PLUS leveled chapter tests, alternative assessments, unit tests, and cumulative tests.
- You can use the **Test and Practice Generator** to create your own customized quizzes and tests. **Online quizzes** and **State Test Practice** are available at www.classzone.com.

Students need practice with the various types of questions on standardized tests.

BUILDING TEST-TAKING SKILLS

It is more important than ever for students to build strong test-taking skills in order to be successful on annual assessments required by the NCLB Act. *Middle School Math* provides instruction and practice with test-taking skills at the end of every unit in the textbook.

- **Multiple Choice Questions** Students are encouraged to use number sense and estimation skills to decide whether answer choices are reasonable.
- **Short Response Questions** Students are given guidance about how to write complete answers and show their work.
- **Context-Based Multiple Choice Questions** Students practice answering multiple-choice questions that involve interpreting diagrams and graphs.
- **Extended Response Questions** Students learn how to write complete answers to multi-step problems.

Continued

RETEACHING AND REMEDIATION

Students sometimes need reteaching in order to understand concepts better or additional practice in order to master key skills. *Middle School Math* provides a variety of resources to help students achieve success. Some of these same resources can also be used by absent students to help them catch up.

Strong problem solving skills help students become successful adults.

- **Student Edition** Includes **Help with Review** notes that direct students to appropriate review materials, **Notebook Reviews** after every three or four lessons that summarize and practice key vocabulary and skills, **Chapter Reviews** with more vocabulary and skill practice, **Cumulative Practice** at the end of every unit, a **Skills Review Handbook** with reteaching and practice for pre-book skills, and **Extra Practice** for every lesson.
- **Teacher's Edition** Includes **Extra Examples** and **Common Error** notes that can be used to help clarify understanding.
- **Chapter Resource Books** Include **Practice** masters (Levels A, B, C), **Challenge Practice** masters, **Cumulative Practice** masters, **Study Guide** masters with worked-out examples, and **Chapter Review Games and Activities.**
- **Math Tutor Place** Includes 104 cards organized by mathematical strand to give students reteaching and practice on important concepts.
- **Technology Resources** Include a variety of interactive and engaging materials for reteaching and practice. *(See page T33 for descriptions.)*

PROBLEM SOLVING STRATEGIES

Questions on state and national tests are often posed as word problems. In order for students to demonstrate mastery of computational skills, they must be able to read and interpret word problems and apply appropriate strategies to solve them. *Middle School Math* incorporates problem solving throughout the textbook to help students learn to apply computational skills in context. *(See also the Professional Development Book, the Chapter Resource Books, and the English-Spanish Problem Solving Transparencies.)*

- **Problem Solving Plan** A four-step problem solving plan, where students read, plan, solve, and look back, is introduced in Chapter 1.
- **Problem Solving Strategies** A familiar or new problem solving strategy is featured in every chapter. Each feature includes practice on that strategy as well as mixed practice. The strategy is then applied in the lesson that follows. Choose a Strategy exercises provide ongoing review.
- **Word Problems at All Levels** Word problems appear at all three exercise levels and in the Getting Ready to Practice section.
- **Multi-Step Problems** Guided Problem Solving and Extended Problem Solving exercises help students prepare for multi-step problems on state and national tests.
- **Test Practice** Test-practice exercises at the end of each lesson, chapter, and unit are stated in words.

Reading, *Writing*, Notetaking

Vital Skills for Today and the Future

Vital Skills Today more than ever, students need strong skills in reading, writing, and notetaking in mathematics in order to understand course content, be successful on important state and national assessments, and develop the ability to become independent learners. Acquiring these skills in middle school will build an important foundation for more advanced courses and for adult life. *McDougal Littell Middle School Math* provides many opportunities in the textbook and in the teacher's materials to help students develop their reading, writing, and notetaking skills.

Recent Research Recent brain research and classroom research in reading and writing have provided new insights into learning and also confirmed the value of well-known practices of successful teachers. Although the focus of this research is often on reading in language arts and social studies, many of the strategies also help those reading mathematical material. Two important aspects of reading addressed by research are vocabulary development and reading comprehension. *McDougal Littell Middle School Math* offers substantial learning support in these core areas.

VOCABULARY DEVELOPMENT

The textbook provides strong support to students in learning, practicing, and reviewing vocabulary. On the Getting Ready to Learn page at the start of each chapter, the important review words are listed and practiced in the Using Vocabulary exercises. Then, at the beginning of each lesson, the key vocabulary for the lesson appears under the Word Watch list, and new vocabulary in the lesson is emphasized by boldface type with yellow highlighting. The Help Notes in the margin serve as a built-in vocabulary, reading, and problem solving tutor. *See pp. 52, 173, 322, 431.*

HELP
with Vocabulary
The GCF is sometimes called the greatest common divisor (GCD) because it is the largest common factor that can be divided evenly into the given numbers.

In the Exercises, the Getting Ready to Practice exercises (which provide guided practice prior to homework) include vocabulary as well as computational and problem solving practice. The Notebook Review pages (two per chapter) and the Chapter Reviews also list key vocabulary and include vocabulary exercises. In addition, there is a complete Glossary that includes examples and diagrams at the back of the book. *See pp. 30, 240–241, 526–527, 748.*

The teacher's materials give specific suggestions for helping students understand and remember vocabulary. ***See, in particular, the Professional Development Book, pp. 13–20.***

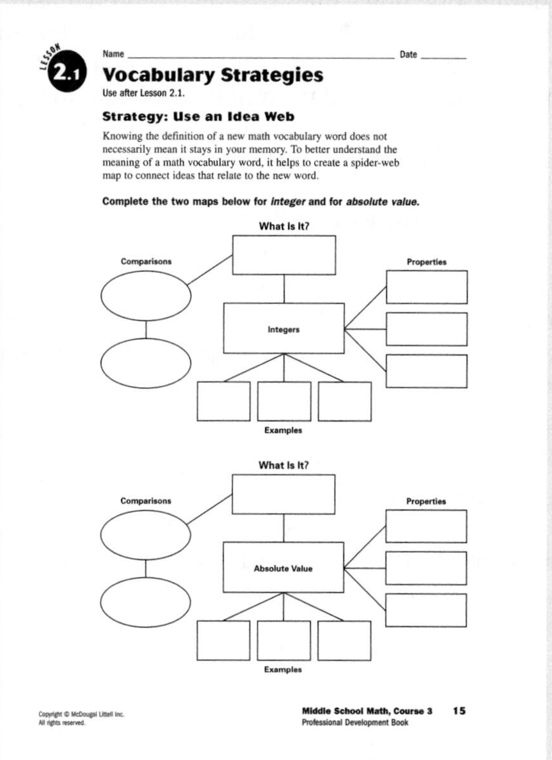
LESSON 2.1

Name ________________________ Date ________

Vocabulary Strategies

Use after Lesson 2.1.

Strategy: Use an Idea Web

Knowing the definition of a new math vocabulary word does not necessarily mean it stays in your memory. To better understand the meaning of a math vocabulary word, it helps to create a spider-web map to connect ideas that relate to the new word.

Complete the two maps below for *integer* and for *absolute value.*

Middle School Math, Course 3 15
Professional Development Book

Continued

READING COMPREHENSION

The Student Handbook on pp. xx–xxv gets students off to a good start with reading the textbook by giving tips for identifying the main idea, understanding the vocabulary, knowing what's important in a lesson, being an active reader, and reading word problems.

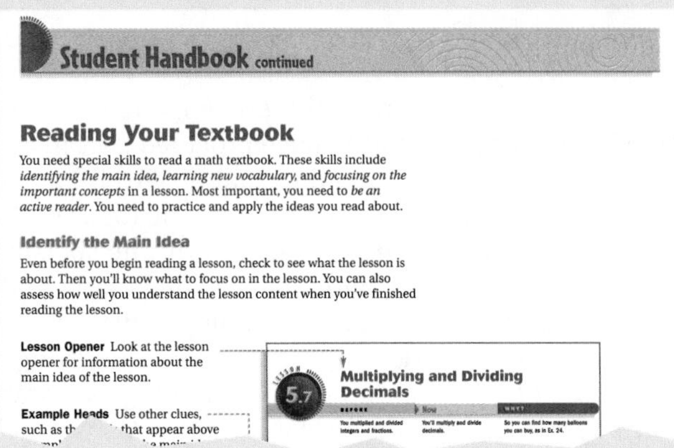

Student Handbook continued

Reading Your Textbook

You need special skills to read a math textbook. These skills include *identifying the main idea, learning new vocabulary,* and *focusing on the important concepts* in a lesson. Most important, you need to *be an active reader*. You need to practice and apply the ideas you read about.

Identify the Main Idea

Even before you begin reading a lesson, check to see what the lesson is about. Then you'll know what to focus on in the lesson. You can also assess how well you understand the lesson content when you've finished reading the lesson.

Lesson Opener Look at the lesson opener for information about the main idea of the lesson.

Example Heads Use other clues, such as th... that appear above ...

Establishing a Context A useful comprehension strategy supported by both brain and classroom research is connecting new learning to prior knowledge. This strategy is incorporated throughout *Middle School Math* in the Before/Now/Why lists at the beginning of chapters and the beginnings of lessons; in the chapter-opening games that review prerequisite skills; and in the Getting Ready to Learn pages at the start of each chapter. Also, each lesson starts with either a real world example, a short activity, or a visual presentation of a math idea in order to set the stage for the new concepts in the lesson. ***See pp. 104, 270, 375, 545, 618.***

Facilitating Understanding In order to create a student-friendly book, the authors kept these principles in mind as they wrote: Students can learn new concepts more easily when they are presented in short sentences that use simple syntax and are accompanied by appropriate tables, charts, and diagrams.

Clear definitions that enable students to determine easily whether a particular mathematical object fits the definition or not are essential for comprehension. Students need special help in understanding the symbols of mathematics and knowing how to use them in writing algebraic expressions. ***See pp. 16, 382, 386.***

Reflecting on Learning An effective strategy for increasing both reading comprehension and thinking skills is reflection on what has been read or learned (metacognition). The Stop and Think questions throughout the book, the worked-out examples that encourage students to consider whether an answer is reasonable, and the exercises that ask students to explain their reasoning all help students develop metacognitive skills. ***See pp. 105, 252, 263, 544.***

Using Graphic Organizers Graphic organizers such as charts, Venn diagrams, or concept maps can be especially helpful for classifying mathematical objects such as types of numbers or types of geometric figures. These organizers are used throughout the textbook, and suggestions on how to use them are given to students in the Know How to Take Notes sections. ***See pp. 374, 390, 437.***

WRITING OPPORTUNITIES

In order to become good writers, students need frequent opportunities to practice their writing skills. These opportunities occur throughout the textbook in the Exercises; in the Stop and Think questions in the chapter-opening games, the activities, and the Notebook Reviews; and in the Exploring Math in Science sections. ***See pp. 83, 178, 217, 312–313, 471.***

EFFECTIVE NOTETAKING

Taking effective notes is an important reading, learning, and review strategy, and yet math teachers throughout the country report that many students enter middle school with few if any notetaking skills. Thus, the authors identified the goal of helping students develop their notetaking skills as an important objective of the program, and they have incorporated many notetaking aids into the program. See, especially, the Getting Ready to Learn pages and the Notebook Reviews in the textbook, and the Notetaking Guide workbooks and overhead visuals in the teacher's materials. ***See pp. 270, 524–525.***

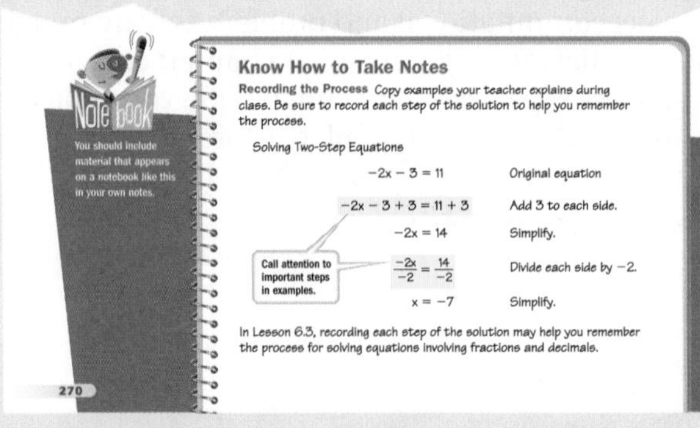

CRISS: CReating Independence through Student-owned Strategies

Project CRISS was founded to help develop thoughtful, independent readers and learners through instruction based on strategies arising from scientifically-based cognitive and social learning research of the past 25 years. The chart below lists the key CRISS principles, together with examples from *McDougal Littell Middle School Math, Course 3* that support them.

Background Knowledge Background knowledge is a powerful determinant of reading comprehension. Look for introductory material that both builds upon and provides background knowledge.	Chapter Warm-up Games, 2–3, 164–165, 216–217, 314–315; Getting Ready to Learn, 4, 52, 218, 430; Stop and Think, 57, 108, 178, 287; Help with Review, 81, 120, 230, 272
Active Involvement Good readers are actively involved with the text and in their learning. Look for methods and activities that show students how to be active and that provide ways for them to be active.	Know How to Take Notes, 52, 166, 218, 316; Notebook, 39, 141, 196, 338, 410; Notebook Review, 24, 210, 306; Chapter Review, 46, 212, 360, 526; Worked-out Examples, 124, 271, 322, 410
Discussion Students need many opportunities to talk with one another about their reading and about what they are learning. Look for activities that open doors for discussion, in pairs, in groups, and with the whole class.	Chapter Warm-Up Games, 50–51, 104–105, 268–269, 372–373; Brain Games, 200; Hands-On Activity, 107, 255–256, 512; Activity, 196; What Do You Think? 144, 246, 298
Metacognition Good readers are metacognitive. They are goal-directed, and they know how to interact with print to construct meaning. Look for opportunities to help students become more aware of and to discuss the *how* and *why* of their learning.	Help with Review, 81, 169, 230; Help with Solving, 56, 120, 141, 180, 332; Help with Homework, 36, 115, 259, 446; Help with Notetaking, 146, 181, 328, 386; Help with Reading, 29, 33, 383, 410; Help with Technology, 209, 300, 469; Help with Vocabulary, 34, 82, 173, 675; Watch Out, 74, 206, 225, 339; Building Test-Taking Skills, 530
Writing Students need multiple opportunities to write about what they are learning. Look for activities that occur naturally throughout the textbook and activities in teacher's materials that are correlated to the textbook.	Know How to Take Notes, 52, 218, 270; Notebook, 10, 120, 196, 290; Notebook Review, 24, 190, 240, 336; Help with Notetaking, 86, 244, 328; Short Response, 116, 189, 227; Extended Response, 9, 128, 172, 413; Stop and Think, 57, 108, 167, 256, 442; Writing, 23, 42, 189, 227; Exploring Math in Science, 312, 652
Organizing for Learning Good readers know a variety of ways to organize information for learning. Look for suggestions for use of tables, charts, graphic organizers, and other devices that help students organize and interpret their learning.	Know How to Take Notes, 4, 106, 374, 430; Problem Solving Strategies, 26, 68, 184, 352, 402; Help with Notetaking, 21, 146, 386
Explanation and Modeling Students become strategic when teachers model processes. Look for modeling that explains the *why* of a method or strategy.	Worked-out Examples, 38–40, 110, 244, 318; Problem Solving Strategies, 26, 68, 184, 352, 402; Technology Activities, 129, 239, 300, 351, 469; Special Topic, 496
Teaching for Understanding Students come to understand by doing a variety of activities. Look for a rich variety and choice of activities, exercises, and projects.	Extended Problem Solving, 94, 245, 325; Stop and Think, 57, 108, 167, 256, 442; Critical Thinking, 25, 37, 45, 183, 462; Challenge, 62, 172, 223, 320; Brain Games, 177, 200, 287; Activity, 28, 63, 234, 317, 431; Hands-On Activity, 32, 57, 107, 255–256; Writing, 23, 42, 189, 227; Short Response, 116, 189, 227; Extended Response, 9, 128, 172, 413

Further reading: A helpful reference is *Teaching Reading in Mathematics*, by Mary Less Barton and Clare Heidema, published by Mid-continent Research for Education and Learning (MCREL), Aurora, Colorado.

Research-Based *Solutions*

The *McDougal Littell Middle School Math* program reflects current research in education. The student editions (**SE**), teacher's editions (**TE**), Chapter Resource Books (**CRB**), and other ancillary materials provide opportunities for teachers and students to experience a number of different learning strategies both in school and at home.

Research supports a variety of learning strategies.

One group of instructional strategies used in this program are the instructional strategies presented in *Classroom Instruction that Works**, a publication from the Association for Supervision and Curriculum Development. The nine strategies discussed in that publication are summarized below, along with some specific instances of the strategy's use in the *McDougal Littell Middle School Math, Course 3* program.

1. Identifying Similarities and Differences

This strategy includes comparing and classifying, and suggests representing comparisons in graphic or symbolic form.

Course 3 examples include *compare* exercises throughout the chapters, contrasting units of measure and types of geometric figures, and making concept maps and Venn diagrams.

See for example, SE192, SE437, SE492, TE374, TE377, TE435, TE444

2. Summarizing and Notetaking

This strategy includes deciding when to delete, substitute, or keep information when writing a summary and using a variety of notetaking formats — e.g., outlines, webbing, or a combination technique — and suggests encouraging students to use notes as a study guide for tests.

Course 3 examples include the entire Notetaking Guide; Know How to Take Notes, Help with Notetaking, Notebooks (SE); Notetaking Strategies, Notetaking (TE)

See, for example, SE146, SE328, SE480, TE316, TE324, TE596, CRB2 p. 3

3. Reinforcing Effort and Providing Recognition

This strategy includes making the connection between effort and achievement clear to students and providing recognition for attainment of specific goals to stimulate motivation.

Course 3 examples include Your Turn Now, Getting Ready to Practice, Guided Problem Solving (SE); Motivating the Lesson, Concept Check, Mini Quiz (TE)

See, for example, SE87, TE112, TE328, TE344, CRB4 p. 4

4. Homework and Practice

This strategy includes making the purpose of homework assignments clear to students and focusing practice assignments on specific elements of a complex skill.

Course 3 examples include Math Tutor Place; Homework Help, Practice and Problem Solving, Notebook Review, Extra Practice (SE); Diagnosis/Remediation, Homework Check, Skill Check (TE); Practice A, B, C (CRB)

See, for example, SE392, SE540, SE686, TE111, TE316, TE327, CRB2 pp. 9, 87–88

...for success in your classroom

5. Nonlinguistic Representations

This strategy includes creating nonlinguistic representations — including creating graphic organizers, making physical models, generating mental pictures, drawing pictures and pictographs, and engaging in kinesthetic activity — to help students understand content in a whole new way.

Course 3 examples include Know How to Take Notes, Problem Solving Strategies, Brain Games (SE); Differentiating Instruction, Visualize, Multiple Representations, Alt. Strategy (TE)

See, for example, SE228, SE278, SE496, TE107, TE142, TE383, TE619, CRB4 p. 41

6. Cooperative Learning

This strategy includes a description of the five defining elements of cooperative learning — positive interdependence, face-to-face interaction, individual and group accountability, interpersonal and group skills, and group processing — and gives suggestions for grouping techniques.

Course 3 examples include Chapter Warm-Up Games, Hands-On Activities, In-lesson Activities, Brain Games (SE); Grouping (TE); Cooperative Projects (CRB); see also the Special Activities Book

See, for example, SE50, SE105, SE616, TE107, TE461, CRB3 pp. 74–75

7. Setting Objectives and Providing Feedback

This strategy includes using instructional goals to narrow what students focus on and suggests providing feedback that is specific to a criterion and encouraging students to personalize their teacher's goals and to provide some of their own feedback.

Course 3 examples include Before/Why/Now lists in student lessons and scoring rubrics on Building Test-Taking Skills pages (SE); Lesson Objectives, Activity Goals, Assess rubrics (TE); goals and objectives given on Activity Master and Technology Activity pages and rubrics provided with projects (CRB); discussion of rubrics in the Professional Development Book; Online self-assessment quizzes

See, for example, SE271, SE692, TE364, TE431, TE477, CRB2 pp. 82, 84, 86

8. Generating and Testing Hypotheses

This strategy includes using a variety of structured tasks to guide students through generating and testing hypotheses, using induction or deduction, and suggests asking students to clearly explain their hypotheses and conclusions to help deepen their understanding.

Course 3 examples include Hands-On Act., Predict exercises throughout book (SE); Activity/Key Discovery, Math Reasoning (TE)

See, for example, SE103, SE461, TE118, TE387, TE462

9. Cues, Questions, and Advance Organizers

This strategy includes asking questions or giving explicit cues before a learning experience to provide students with a preview of what they are about to experience; using verbal and graphic advance organizers, or having students skim information before reading as an advance organizer.

Course 3 examples include Before/Why/Now lists at beginning of lessons, pre-reading lesson elements such as Word Watch lists and Example heads throughout book, problem solving plan (SE); Motivating the Lesson (TE); discussion of problem solving in the Professional Development Book

See, for example, SE53–54, TE119, TE331, TE375

*Marzano, Robert J., Debra J. Pickering, and Jane E. Pollock, *Classroom Instruction that Works: Research-Based Strategies for Increasing Student Achievement* and its accompanying handbook. Alexandria, Virginia: Association for Supervision and Curriculum Development, 2001

Providing *Universal Access*

DIVERSE STUDENTS

With careful planning, teachers can help <u>all</u> students reach a level of mathematical competence needed to continue their education in mathematics.

In most classrooms, students present a variety of achievement levels, skills, and needs. The goal for all students is the same: We want them to develop sufficient computational, procedural, and problem solving skills to provide a solid foundation for further study in mathematics. However, all students do not arrive at these competencies at the same time or in the same way. In this article we suggest research-based strategies teachers can use to modify curriculum and instruction for special needs students. The basic instructional plan in *Middle School Math* is designed for students who are achieving at near grade level; but just prior to each chapter we include specific suggestions for students who are achieving above and below grade level, and for students who are not fluent in English (see also the article titled "Adapting Curriculum and Instruction for English Learners").

Student Groups Teachers may find it helpful to view students as members of four basic groups, as shown on the facing page. (English learners can be found in all four groups.) Teachers do not need to place students in these groups; the categories are suggested so teachers can plan ahead to meet different needs of students. Note the use of the term *underachievers.* This term is not synonymous with special education. It may include some special education pupils but includes many more students whose low achievement levels are the result of inadequate prior schooling or attendance, high mobility rates, or a host of other reasons that have nothing to do with their abilities or disabilities. The term *underachievers* is not meant to be a negative term. On the contrary, we believe that students achieving below grade level can be successful in mathematics given carefully designed instruction.

SETTING THE RIGHT TONE

There are three key strategies recommended for teachers as they adapt any program to students' needs:

- Use frequent assessment as a way to determine what each student does or does not know, and use that assessment as the basis for planning.
- Plan modifications of curriculum and instruction ahead of time so that you are ready to differentiate as the need arises.
- Use a variety of grouping strategies to facilitate learning. A combination of whole class instruction and temporary groupings of students, with groups organized around students' needs, will facilitate management of the variety of achievement levels and learning needs in the classroom.

Assessment, planning, and flexible grouping are essential to ensuring that your students have the optimal chance for success. In addition to these three key strategies, general guidelines for establishing a classroom designed to meet students' needs are:

1. Establish an atmosphere where students feel comfortable asking questions and are rewarded for asking about things they don't understand.
2. Maintain the same goals for all students. Allow additional time and practice for students who need it, and provide challenging alternatives for those who are ready to move more quickly.
3. Clearly identify the skill, concept, or standards you are working on and measure progress toward those ends.
4. Have students show their work. It is much easier for teachers to understand where a student gets confused if they have evidence of the student's thought process.

5. Try small modifications in curriculum and instruction before more drastic ones.
6. Don't persist with a strategy that is not working. Try something else.
7. Encourage effort and persistence, and celebrate successes with your students.

VARYING CURRICULUM AND INSTRUCTION

1. **Time** Most students whose achievement is below grade level will need more time. Students who are not fluent in English will need more time. The contents of this book might be offered over a two-year period, or two periods a day. Perhaps the day can be extended through study hall, regular homework assignments, tutoring, or Saturday, summer, or "off track" catch-up sessions. Advanced students might "test out" of portions of the book and complete the material in half a year, or they may compact two courses into one.

2. **Presentation** Instructing in a variety of ways and taking a single concept and explaining it verbally and visually with concrete and abstract examples provide students multiple opportunities for understanding. Area, for example, is a key concept in geometry. In earlier grades students have found areas of simple objects, both by using tiles to cover an area, and by applying algorithms. Later, students practice with unusual shapes, dividing them into simpler ones. Finally, students tackle sophisticated examples like finding the shape with the maximum area given a fixed perimeter, using both trial and error and more abstract methods.

3. **Task parameters** Multi-step problems can be especially difficult for students. These types of problems are just combinations of simpler problems and can be broken down into those simpler steps, with additional help and practice at each step. Confusing elements can be minimized and extraneous material can be eliminated. For advanced students, simpler problems can be eliminated and more challenging ones (as suggested in each chapter) may be substituted.

4. **Methods of assessment** Students learning English may be able to demonstrate on paper what they cannot yet verbalize. Students with physical challenges may be unable to draw a graph but may be able to select the right graph from a series of options or verbally describe the graph so that someone else can draw it. Allow students to demonstrate their knowledge in a variety of ways while helping all students to master the skills and knowledge necessary to exhibit their understanding in standard ways.

Middle School Math is organized so that much of the differentiation for special needs students is built into the design of the program. Note that simpler concepts are introduced before

FOUR BASIC STUDENT GROUPS

Advanced Group

Advanced students have already completed some of the grade-level material. They make rapid progress and become bored with repetition. They may or may not have been formally identified as gifted or talented in the area of mathematics.

Suggested Plan

1. Assess what these students already know.
2. Allow these students to "test out" of chapters or assignments.
3. Substitute challenging assignments for easier ones.
4. Modify instruction so that it is more complex or more in-depth.

Grade Level Group

Students achieving at grade level may have minor, occasional difficulties but they can be assisted to maintain their progress with extra practice and individual or group assistance on an ad hoc basis.

Suggested Plan

1. Assess what these students already know.
2. Progress through *Middle School Math* at the recommended pace and sequence.
3. On an ad hoc basis, review or provide additional practice as needed.

Underachieving Group

These learners are not achieving at expected grade level but can, with a carefully designed program that provides targeted assistance. Systematic differentiation such as preteaching, reteaching, and additional instructional time should be planned for these students, as suggested in each chapter.

Suggested Plan

1. Assess what these students already know.
2. Provide additional scaffolding and the instructional variations suggested in this book.
3. Focus on the key concepts and present material systematically.
4. Vary the kinds of instruction so that students have several opportunities to understand.
5. Provide additional practice homework.

Intensive Needs Group

Intensive needs students are those whose performance is two or more standard deviations below the mean on standardized measures. These students will probably already be eligible for special education services. This is a very small percentage of the general population.

Suggested Plan

1. Assess what these students already know.
2. Determine if these students have an IEP.
3. Refer students for special education testing or child study team discussion; enlist the help of specialists.
4. Carefully consider each student's most appropriate placement in mathematics.
5. Use the specific suggestions for underachieving learners.

Continued

more complex ones. Ample practice is provided. Challenge exercises are included throughout the pupil text. Activities provide students with models for conceptual understanding of the mathematical reasoning behind each key concept. Mathematical reasoning is stressed throughout each chapter. Vocabulary words, examples, and Getting Ready to Practice exercises are standard features of each chapter. Each lesson includes Mixed Review exercises so that students recall and use skills and understandings from previous chapters. These features were designed to help you meet the needs of the students in your class.

FOR STUDENTS WHO HAVE TROUBLE PAYING ATTENTION

Some students in your classroom may be formally identified as having Attention Deficit Hyperactivity Disorder (ADHD) or Attention Deficit Disorder (ADD). Others may exhibit the same learning challenges but may not be formally identified. Whether formally identified or not, students who have trouble paying attention generally share the following characteristics:

- Trouble paying attention is not just occasional. It occurs most or all of the time, across content areas, and is inappropriate for the age of the child.
- Forgetfulness, memory problems, losing things, disorganization
- Restlessness, fidgeting
- Socially inappropriate behavior such as excessive talking, interrupting others, and difficulty waiting their turn

These students may be very bright and capable in mathematics but have a hard time staying focused for long periods of time. They need to be taught strategies for organizing their work and keeping track of where they are. In general, students with attention problems need to be helped to develop coping strategies. The teacher should approach the student in a problem solving mode: "Let's find ways to help you concentrate and organize your work," rather than using one of the following strategies in a punitive way.

1. **Present the work in smaller chunks over smaller time periods** and then gradually increase expectations. If students have trouble completing long tests, for example, break the material into smaller quizzes and increase the length of the quizzes as the year progresses.
2. **Use cumulative review and practice.** Have students periodically review what they learned in previous chapters and provide additional practice if they have forgotten.
3. **Make it more obvious what the student should focus on.** For example, use the test generator to put only four problems on each page; use a large font; or use an index card or piece of cardboard with a hole cut out of the middle to place on the page so that the student can focus on one problem at a time. A pencil, finger, highlighter, or sticky paper can also be used by the student to keep track of which problem he or she is working on.
4. **Have students race against the clock.** For some students, racing against the clock to see how many problems can be completed accurately within a five-minute time period is more motivating than doing the same number of problems at their leisure. The time period can be extended gradually.
5. **Help students develop simple strategies for bringing work to and from class.** A two-pocket folder, where homework goes home in the left pocket and comes back in the right, is a simple way to keep track of assignments.
6. **Allow movement and schedule breaks.**
7. **Minimize distractions by seating students that are easily distracted near the teacher** and away from hallway noise. Tables with several students at a table are more distracting than rows of desks. When students are to work quietly, offer headphones to block out noise. Headphones can be set to play quiet music, "white noise," or can be used just as earplugs to help block out noise.
8. **Graphic organizers** such as Venn diagrams, tree diagrams, lists, outlines, tables, and charts can all provide structures for organizing and remembering information. Mental images, choral responses, or even hand signals can help students remember. Highlighters can be used to make sure that decimal points are lined up. Graph paper is excellent for keeping homework problems neat, even when a graph is not required.
9. **Keep instructions simple and clear, especially at the beginning of the year.** Establish routines (e.g., the week's homework is always due on Thursday; assignments are written in a specific place on the board; the last ten minutes of class is used to make sure everyone understands what homework is expected and how to do it). Students who know the routine find it easier to work independently.

FOR STUDENTS WHO HAVE TROUBLE UNDERSTANDING THE CONCEPTS

Success in mathematics, as in music, sports, or other areas, comes for most students only with hard work and persistent effort. Concepts may seem difficult at first, but with repeated teaching and practice virtually all students can master the mathematics they need to graduate from high school, access a variety of jobs, and lay the foundation for further study in mathematics or a related field.

Several strategies can help students make steady progress in mathematics. These include:

1. Focus on key mathematical concepts.
2. Review key concepts and skills from earlier lessons, chapters, or years.
3. Preteach key concepts and vocabulary.
4. Anticipate problem areas.
5. Provide scaffolding (guided practice) for students who need extra help.
6. Think out loud to show hidden steps.
7. Provide a sample problem to which students can return when they get stuck.
8. Break problems into simpler components.
9. Explicitly teach students a variety of problem solving strategies and help them select one that fits the situation.
10. Present concepts in a variety of ways: visually, verbally, concretely, abstractly, etc.
11. Encourage students to draw a picture or use a visual aid such as a number line, graph, or diagram.
12. Provide sufficient practice.

Finally, good teachers are perpetual students themselves. They are always looking for ways to deepen their understanding of mathematics and for good ways to explain and teach mathematics to others.

FOR ADVANCED STUDENTS

Occasionally students can demonstrate mastery of all the mathematics expected to be learned in a given grade level. Repeating previously learned material for a year is deadly to these students. It can make them dislike mathematics. For these students, moving them up a grade level for math is a simple and cost-effective solution.

Most advanced students, however, are advanced in some areas but not in others. They tend to learn quickly and need more instructional material, as well as more difficult material. The student edition, teacher's edition, and ancillaries for this program provide challenging exercises that can be used when students have demonstrated competence in a particular area. These challenge exercises should be substituted for the easier exercises in a homework assignment or lesson. When they have the time and interest, all students should be encouraged to work the challenge exercises.

General strategies for differentiating the curriculum for advanced learners include:

1. **Vary the pacing.** Allow advanced students some flexibility in how they progress through the course. Students who can demonstrate mastery of the objectives for a given lesson or chapter can be working on challenge exercises. Advanced students may become fascinated with a particular aspect of mathematics and want to spend *more* time on it.
2. **Differentiate in terms of depth.** Encourage advanced students to delve more in depth into mathematics. Looking at the details and the patterns; studying the language of the discipline; and looking at trends, themes, properties, theorems, proofs, and unanswered questions can enrich the curriculum for advanced students.
3. **Differentiate in terms of complexity.** Advanced students may be ready to connect ideas across disciplines in ways characteristic of older students or adults. Encourage them to investigate relationships between mathematics and art, history, science, and music, and to look at the development of mathematics over time.

USING GROUPING TO BENEFIT ALL STUDENTS

Grouping advanced learners together for investigations of challenge problems can provide you with time to work more closely with a group of students who need help in a particular area. Alternatively, while students who need more help are working on additional reinforcement activities or practice, you can work with a group of advanced students on a challenge project. Groups can be organized and revised daily, weekly, or by lesson according to how proficient students are with the concepts and skills targeted for that day, week, or lesson. At times you may have only one student who is ready for a challenge problem; at other times the whole class may be ready. Flexible grouping is the key to ensuring that students do not become "tracked." Asking advanced students to report to the whole class on their progress on challenge problems can provide the opportunity for the whole class to engage in more abstract and theoretical thinking.

Adapting Curriculum and Instruction for *English Learners*

English learners come to the classroom with all the variety of English speakers in regard to mathematics achievement. They may be at, behind, or ahead of grade expectations in mathematics. They may be gifted or eligible for special education services. They may have been born in the United States, or they may have arrived in this country very recently. They may speak one or more languages, and they may be literate in one or more languages other than English. They may be nearly fluent in English or have beginning or intermediate levels of understanding and production. They have in common one characteristic: They are all learning English.

With careful planning, teachers can maximize success for English learners in the mathematics classroom. Assessing each student's competencies in mathematics and English will form a basis for program planning.

ENGLISH LEARNERS

	Low Mathematics Achievement		High Mathematics Achievement	
	Who is this student?	**What to do?**	**Who is this student?**	**What to do?**
Low Reading Achievement	Student may be new to the class, school, or country. Student may have had inadequate schooling. Student may have moved a lot. Student may be unmotivated or have test anxiety. Low reading achievement may be depressing mathematics scores. Student may have gaps and holes in knowledge. Student may need special education assistance.	Examine cumulative folder for other testing, notes, etc. Delay any testing for a week or two. Help student feel comfortable in the class during that period of time. Administer mathematics achievement test and reading test, preferably in an individual setting. Plan to assess this student at weekly intervals and closely monitor classroom work to determine if progress is being made. Look at the English Learners suggestions in each chapter.	Student has had good prior mathematics instruction. Mathematics is an area where this student can excel. Math achievement level may actually be higher than scores indicate. (Limited English reading skills affect mathematics achievement as well.) Word problems will be especially difficult.	Mathematics instruction should proceed at normal or near normal pace. Student should be involved in a systematic English language development program and intensive reading program outside of mathematics class. Spend part of each class period on mathematics vocabulary study. Provide a bilingual dictionary or math glossary and a grade-level mathematics text in the home language for home use. Look at the English Learners suggestions in each chapter for those that are most useful.
High Reading Achievement	**Who is this student?** Student may have been designated as an English learner because oral skills lag behind reading skills. Student may not test well in mathematics. Most students can make rapid progress in mathematics; a few may have learning difficulties that require the help of a specialist.	**What to do?** Assess mathematics achievement in a variety of ways. Concentrate on developing oral fluency. Focus on vocabulary specific to mathematics. Use a student's reading ability to improve his or her math scores.	**Who is this student?** May be a student who is ready for re-designation as a fluent English speaker. May need extra study in academic vocabulary, *i.e.*, the specialized vocabulary of mathematics. Given systematic instruction, this student should be able to achieve at or above grade level.	**What to do?** Scan all of the suggestions for English learners in each chapter and progress through the ones the student needs as quickly as possible. Monitor carefully to make sure this student continues to progress at a reasonable pace.

GETTING TO KNOW YOUR STUDENTS

Before school starts, check the cumulative folder on each student in your class to determine which ones are learning English. See if there is recent testing. Two types of testing are most useful: mathematics achievement and reading achievement levels. If no recent test information is available, you may instead administer a pre-course math test and ask English learners to write a dictated paragraph in English to assess their reading and writing skills. Use the chart on the facing page as a guide to understanding student assessment data.

SUGGESTIONS FOR MATHEMATICS TEACHERS OF ENGLISH LEARNERS

1. Allocate additional time for mathematics. Many students will be translating from English to their primary language and back again. The meaning of many words will not be immediately clear. When you ask questions, allow extra time for students to respond. Reading mathematics textbooks and understanding what is asked for in a word problem will be slower.
2. Use student's background knowledge. Some English learners will have developed substantial background in mathematics; others will have very little. Find out what students know and then build on that knowledge.
3. Reduce the amount and sophistication of the English language used. This may be done by reordering the lessons in each chapter to begin with key vocabulary, followed by problems with a minimum of written English, followed by at least one word problem each day. Choose word problems that don't rely on assumed background knowledge. Monitor and simplify the speech you use. Speak more slowly, avoid idioms and slang, be precise and concise, and use short sentences and simple vocabulary. Using hand gestures and pictures as well as words aids communication.
4. Introduce one concept per day. Keeping the focus of each day simple will aid students in understanding the point of the lesson. Focus on key concepts, and use mathematics instructional time well.
5. Use a variety of different methods for getting a point across. Presenting concepts verbally and visually, with concrete examples and in abstract mathematical symbols, and using pictures, graphs, diagrams, and charts will enhance the chance that students will understand at least one of the presentations. As you introduce a new word, rule, or property, write it down.
6. Provide opportunities for English learners to interact with their English-speaking peers. Students who are learning a language need to hear native speakers using the language, and they need opportunities to use their new mathematics vocabulary in their speech and in their writing.
7. Provide opportunities for English learners to discuss their understandings with each other, confirm the homework assignments, or ask questions of each other in whatever language they may have in common.
8. Allow English learners to demonstrate what they know in a variety of ways. When students first learn a language, they are usually shy about speaking. They generally understand spoken language before they can produce it. Students who have recently arrived from another country with good prior schooling may be able to read in English but not speak it. Allow students to point, nod, gesture, draw a picture, or work math problems without words as they learn English.
9. Extend mathematics instructional time through homework, an extra class period, summer school, or tutoring. Many of the language-related suggestions for English learners in this series can be carried out in collaboration with the language arts teacher.
10. Keep on hand picture dictionaries, foreign language dictionaries, multi-language math glossaries, and drawing materials.

SPECIFIC SUGGESTIONS

Prior to each chapter you will find suggestions to help you modify curriculum and instruction so that the content is accessible to English learners. You may want to collaborate with language arts teachers or other specialists, because many of the suggestions are well suited for discussion in a language arts class, English as a second language class, or in a tutorial. In these sections we will provide you suggestions and activities designed to (1) teach the vocabulary commonly used in mathematics; (2) explain mathematical concepts in a variety of ways; and (3) dissect the structure of word problems. Much of the vocabulary study in this book may be review for your students, and in that case, you should feel free to work as quickly as possible through the activities. For those students who need more systematic study, progressing through the activities as indicated will ensure that students have refreshed their understanding of basic terms prior to statewide testing that generally occurs toward the end of each school year. We recommend that if you have English learners in your classroom, you skim all the chapter suggestions for English learners so that you may use them as you need them.

NAEP: National Assessment of Educational Progress

The NAEP is used to assess student understanding of math across the nation. The chart below lists the topics assessed by the NAEP, and lessons and features from Middle School Math, Course 3 that address them.

Number Properties and Operations	
1) Number sense	1.4, 2.1, 2.2, 3.1 Act., 3.1, 3.3 Act., 4.1, 4.3, 4.5, 4.8, 5.3, 5.5, 7.1, 7.2 Act., 7.2, 7.3, 7.4, 7.5, 7.6, 9.1, 9.2, 9.3 Act., 9.3, Skills Review Handbook
2) Estimation	5.6, 6.3 (Ex. 17), 6.4 (Ex. 21), 7.6 (Ex. 30), 9.1, 10.1 (Exs. 27, 28), 10.2, 10.5, Skills Rev. Handbook
3) Number operations	1.2, 1.2 Tech. Act., 1.3, 1.4, 1.5, Ch. 2, Ch. 3, 4.6, 4.7, 5.1, 5.2, 5.5, 5.6, 5.7, 9.1, 9.2, 9.3, 9.4, 9.5, 13.3, Skills Review Handbook
4) Ratios and proportional reasoning	7.1, 9.6 Act., 9.6, 9.6 Tech. Act., Skills Review Handbook
5) Properties of number and operations	1.2, 1.2 Tech. Act., 1.5, 2.2 Act., 2.2, 2.6, 2.7, 4.1 Act., 4.1, 4.2, 4.4, 5.6, 5.7, 9.4, Skills Review Handbook

Measurement	
1) Measuring physical attributes	1.6 Act., 1.6, 2.3 (Exs. 26–28), 2.5, 3.5 Prob. Solving, 6.4 Act., 6.4, 7.2 Act., 8.1, 8.1 Special Topic, 8.2, 8.3, 8.4, 8.5 Act., 8.5, 8.8, 9.3 Act., 9.3, 9.4 Prob. Solving, 9.4, 9.5, 9.6 Act., 9.6, 9.6 Tech. Act., Ch. 10, Skills Review Handbook
2) Systems of measurement	1.6 Act., 1.6, 2.5 (Ex. 31), 3.5 Prob. Solving, 7.2 Act., 7.2, 10.6 Act., 10.6

Geometry	
1) Dimension and shape	1.6 Act., 1.7, 8.3, 8.4, 9.5, 10.3, 10.3 Special Topic, 10.5, 10.6 Act., 10.6, 10.7 Act., 10.7, Skills Review Handbook
2) Transformation of shapes and preservation of properties	7.2 Act., 8.6 Prob. Solving, 8.6, 8.7, 8.7 Special Topic, 8.8
3) Relationships between geometric figures	2.8, 3.5, 6.4 Act., 6.4, Ch. 8, 9.3, 9.4, 10.1, 10.2, 10.4, 10.5, 10.6, 10.7 Act., 10.7, 13.2
4) Position and direction	8.1, 8.1 Special Topic, 8.6, 8.7
5) Mathematical reasoning	8.4, 8.5 Act., 8.6, 8.7 Special Topic, 10.2 Tech. Act.

Data Analysis and Probability	
1) Data representation	1.1, 5.8, 7.4, 10.2 Tech. Act., 10.6 Act., 11.2, 12.1, 12.2, 12.3, 12.3 Tech. Act., 12.3 Special Topic, 13.5 Prob. Solving, Skills Review Handbook
2) Characteristics of data sets	2.5, 5.8 Act., 5.8, 11.2, 12.2
3) Experiments and samples	7.8 Act., 12.8 Act., 12.8 Special Topic
4) Probability	7.8, 12.4, 12.5, 12.6. 12.7, 12.8

Algebra	
1) Patterns, relations, and functions	2.4 Prob. Solving, 7.7 (Ex. 23), 8.6 Prob. Solving, 8.7, 8.7 Special Topic, 11.1, 11.4, 12.6 (Ex. 30), 13.4 (Ex. 21), 13.5
2) Algebraic representations	1.5, 1.6, 1.7, 2.4, 2.7, Ch. 3, 5.1, 6.1, 6.2, 6.3, 6.4, 6.5, 7.2, 7.6, 7.7, 8.6, 8.7, 11.4, 11.5, 11.6, 11.7, 11.8, 13.2 Act., 13.3 Act., 13.4 Act.
3) Variables, expressions, and operations	1.3, 1.6 Act., 1.6, 1.7, 2.4, 2.7, Ch. 3, 4.6, 4.7, 5.1, 5.2, 5.3, 5.4, 5.6, 5.7, 6.1, 6.2, 6.3, 6.4, 6.5, 6.6, 7.2, 7.5, 7.6, 7.7, 7.8, 8.1, 8.2, 9.1, 9.2, 9.3, 9.4, 9.5, 9.6, 10.1, 10.2, 10.4, 10.5, 10.6, 10.7, 13.1, 13.2, 13.3, 13.4
4) Equations and inequalities	1.5, 1.6, 2.4, Ch. 3, 6.1, 6.2, 6.3, 6.4 Act., 6.4, 6.5, 6.6, 7.2, 7.6, 7.7, 7.8, 8.1, 8.2, 9.1, 9.2, 9.3, 9.4, 9.5, 9.6, 9.6 Tech. Act., 10.1, 10.2, 10.4, 10.5, 10.6, 10.7, 11.3, 11.4, 11.7, 11.7 Special Topic, 11.8, 13.1, 13.2, 13.3, 13.4

NCTM: National Council of Teachers of Mathematics

The chart below lists the lessons and other features in the textbook that address the NCTM Standards.

Content Standards

Standard	Lessons
1) Number and Operations Understand numbers, ways of representing numbers, relationships among numbers, and number systems; understand meanings of operations and how they relate to one another; compute fluently and make reasonable estimates.	1.2 through 1.4, 2.1 through 2.3, 2.4, 2.5 through 2.7, 3.1 through 3.3, 3.4, 4.3 Act., 4.3, 4.5, 4.8, 4.8 Tech. Act., 5.1, 5.2, 5.3, 5.4 through 5.7, 7.1, 7.3 through 7.7, 9.1, 9.2, 11.8, 12.1, 13.1, 13.2, 13.3, 13.4
2) Algebra Understand patterns, relations, and functions; represent and analyze mathematical situations and structures using algebraic symbols; use mathematical models to represent and understand quantitative relationships; analyze change in various contexts.	1.3, 1.4, 1.5, 1.6, 1.7, 2.4 through 2.6, 2.7, 3.1 through 3.3, 3.4, 3.5, 3.6, 3.7, 4.1 Act., 4.1, 4.5, 4.6, 4.7, 5.2, 6.1, 6.2, 6.3, 6.4, 6.5, 6.5 Tech. Act., 6.6, 7.1, 7.2, 7.3, 7.5, 7.7, 8.2 through 8.5, 8.6, 8.7, 8.8, 8.8 Tech. Act., 9.1, 9.2, 9.3. 9.4 through 9.6, 10.1, 10.2, 10.2 Tech. Act., 10.6, 11.1, 11.3, 11.4, 11.4 Tech. Act., 11.5, 11.7 Act., 11.7, 11.7 Special Topic, 11.8, 12.5, 12.6, 13.2 through 13.4, 13.5
3) Geometry Analyze characteristics and properties of two- and three-dimensional geometric shapes and develop mathematical arguments about geometric relationships; specify locations and describe spatial relationships using coordinate geometry and other representational systems; apply transformations and use symmetry to analyze mathematical situations; use visualization, spatial reasoning, and geometric modeling to solve problems.	2.8, 7.2 Act., 8.1 through 8.8, 9.3 Act., 9.3, 9.4, 9.5, 9.6 Act., 9.6, 10.1, 10.2, 10.3, 10.3 Special Topic, 10.4, 10.5 through 10.7, 11.4, 11.4 Tech. Act., 11.5, 11.6 Act., 11.6, 11.7, 11.7 Special Topic
4) Measurement Understand measurable attributes of objects and the units, systems, and processes of measurement; apply appropriate techniques, tools, and formulas to determine measurements.	1.6 Act., 1.6, 2.8, 3.5, 6.4 Act., 6.4, 7.2, 10.1, 10.2, 10.2 Tech. Act., 10.4 Prob. Solving, 10.4, 10.5, 10.6, 10.7 Act., 10.7, 11.6
5) Data Analysis and Probability Formulate questions that can be addressed with data and collect, organize, and display relevant data to answer them; select and use appropriate statistical methods to analyze data; develop and evaluate inferences and predictions that are based on data; understand and apply basic concepts of probability.	1.1, 5.8 Act., 5.8, 7.8 Prob. Solving, 7.8, 11.2, 11.4 Prob. Solving, 12.1 through 12.3, 12.7, 12.8 Act., 12.8, 12.8 Special Topic, 13.5 Prob. Solving

Process Standards

Standard	Lessons
6) Problem Solving Build new mathematical knowledge through problem solving; solve problems that arise in mathematics and in other contexts; apply and adapt a variety of appropriate strategies to solve problems; monitor and reflect on the process of mathematical problem solving.	1.5 Prob. Solving, 1.7, 2.4 Prob. Solving, 3.1, 3.2, 3.3, 3.4 through 3.7, 4.1 Act., 4.2, 4.4 Prob. Solving, 4.4, 5.3 Prob. Solving, 5.8, 6.1 through 6.3, 6.5, 6.6, 7.2, 7.3, 7.6, 7.7, 7.7 Tech. Act., 8.6 Prob. Solving, 9.6, 9.6 Tech. Act., 10.4 Prob. Solving, 10.7, 11.4 Prob. Solving, 11.4, 12.4 through 12.7, 12.8 Act., 12.8, 13.5 Prob. Solving
7) Reasoning and Proof Recognize reasoning and proof as fundamental aspects of mathematics; make and investigate mathematical conjectures; develop and evaluate mathematical arguments and proofs; select and use various types of reasoning and methods of proof.	Occurs throughout. E.g.: Critical thinking exs.: 1.2, 4.6, 7.3, 10.1, 13.4; Error analysis exs.: 2.7, 5.7, 6.5, 8.2, 9.6, 11.7; Short/extended response exs.: 3.4, 6.4, 9.3, 12.4
8) Communication Organize and consolidate their mathematical thinking through communication; communicate their mathematical thinking coherently and clearly to peers, teachers, and others; analyze and evaluate the mathematical thinking and strategies of others; use the language of mathematical ideas precisely.	Occurs throughout. E.g.: Explain exs.: 1.1, 2.7, 3.7, 5.4, 6.3, 8.5, 9.4, 10.7; Notetaking help: 1.4, 3.7, 5.1, 7.3, 8.3, 11.5, 12.6; Writing exs.: 1.5, 2.5, 4.4, 5.4, 6.4, 8.8, 11.1, 13.4
9) Connections Recognize and use connections among mathematical ideas; understand how mathematical ideas interconnect and build on one another to produce a coherent whole; recognize and apply mathematics in contexts outside of mathematics.	4.1, 4.2, 4.3, 4.4, 4.6, 4.7, 13.5
10) Representation Create and use representations to organize, record, and communicate mathematical ideas; select, apply, and translate among mathematical representations to solve problems; use representations to model and interpret physical, social, and mathematical phenomena.	1.6 Act., 2.1 through 2.3, 7.2 Act., 9.3 Act., 9.4 Prob. Solving, 10.3, 11.2, 12.3 Tech. Act., 12.4, 13.4 Act.

SCOPE AND SEQUENCE FOR MIDDLE SCHOOL MATH, COURSES 1–3

TOPICS	Middle School Math Course 1	Middle School Math Course 2	Middle School Math Course 3	IN COURSE 3, SEE THE FOLLOWING KEY PAGES:
NUMBERS AND THEIR OPERATIONS				
Whole Numbers and Decimals				
Whole number concepts	■	■	■	pp. 704, 705
Whole number operations	▲ ■	■	■	pp. 712, 717
Order of operations	▲ ■	▲ ■	▲ ■	pp. 10-13, 14
Reading and writing decimals	● ▲ ■	▲ ■	■	p. 704
Expanded form for whole numbers and decimals	▲ ■	● ■	■	p. 704
Rounding decimals	▲ ■	▲ ■	■	p. 705
Comparing and ordering decimals	▲ ■	● ▲ ■	■	pp. 242-246, 437-441
Adding and subtracting decimals	● ▲ ■	● ▲ ■	▲ ■	pp. 247-250, 709
Multiplying and dividing decimals	● ▲ ■	▲ ■	▲ ■	pp. 251-254, 714, 715
Multiplying and dividing by powers of 10	● ▲ ■	▲ ■	■	pp. 205-208, 209
Equivalent forms of decimals and fractions	● ▲ ■	▲ ■	▲ ■	pp. 242-246, 746
Fractions and Mixed Numbers				
Meaning of a fraction or a mixed number	● ▲ ■	▲ ■	■	pp. 179, 707
Fractions as division	▲ ■	■	■	pp. 179, 707
Equivalent fractions including simplest form	● ▲ ■	● ▲ ■	● ▲ ■	pp. 178, 179-183
Equivalent forms of improper fractions and mixed numbers	▲ ■	▲ ■	▲ ■	pp. 192-195, 707
Common denominators	▲ ■	● ▲ ■	▲ ■	pp. 219-223
Comparing and ordering fractions	● ▲ ■	● ▲ ■	▲ ■	pp. 192-195, 242-246
Equivalent forms of fractions and decimals	● ▲ ■	▲ ■	▲ ■	pp. 242-246, 746
Adding and subtracting fractions, mixed numbers, and rational numbers	● ▲ ■	● ▲ ■	▲ ■	pp. 219-223, 224-227, 710
Multiplying and dividing fractions, mixed numbers, and rational numbers	● ▲ ■	● ▲ ■	● ▲ ■	pp. 234-238, 230-233, 234-238, 713
Ratio, Proportion, and Percent				
Modeling ratios and percents	● ▲	● ▲ ■	■	pp. 192, 331, 334
Writing and using ratios and rates	▲ ■	● ▲ ■	● ▲ ■	pp. 317-320, 354, 632, 708
Equivalent ratios	▲ ■	▲ ■	▲ ■	pp. 317-320
Equivalent rates and unit rates	▲ ■	▲ ■	▲ ■	pp. 317-320
Unit price and comparison shopping	▲	▲ ■	■	p. 320
Deciding whether ratios form a proportion	▲	■	■	pp. 322-326
Writing and solving proportions	▲ ■	● ▲ ■	▲ ■	pp. 322-326
Making a prediction in proportional situations	▲	▲ ■	▲ ■	pp. 322-326

Symbol Key

● Explore ▲ Teach and Assess ■ Maintain and Apply

TOPICS	Middle School Math Course 1	Middle School Math Course 2	Middle School Math Course 3	**IN COURSE 3, SEE THE FOLLOWING KEY PAGES:**
Scale drawings, including map scales	▲ ■	● ▲ ■	● ▲ ■	pp. 321, 324-326, 484
Similar figures		● ▲ ■	▲ ■	pp. 321, 416-421
Equivalent forms of percents, decimals, and fractions	● ▲ ■	▲ ■	▲ ■	pp. 331-335, 746
Percent of a number	● ▲ ■	● ▲ ■	▲ ■	pp. 327-330
Percent equations		▲ ■	▲ ■	pp. 327-330, 347-350
Interest	▲	▲ ■	▲ ■	pp. 347-350, 351
Consumer percent applications	▲ ■	▲ ■	▲ ■	pp. 327-330, 338-341, 342-346, 347-350
Percent of change		● ▲ ■	▲ ■	pp. 338-341
Ratios in right triangles			▲ ■	pp. 456-460, 461-462, 463-468
Trigonometric ratios			● ▲ ■	pp. 461-462, 463-468
Estimation				
Estimation strategies	▲ ■	▲ ■	▲ ■	pp. 711, 716
Checking reasonableness	▲ ■	▲ ■	▲ ■	pp. 156, 235, 251, 252
Estimating with whole numbers	● ▲ ■	■	■	pp. 711, 716
Estimating with decimals	▲ ■	▲ ■	▲ ■	pp. 432-436
Estimating with fractions	▲ ■			
Estimating with ratio and percent	▲ ■	■		
Integers				
Meaning of integers	▲	▲	▲	pp. 53-56
Integers on a number line	▲ ■	● ▲ ■	● ▲ ■	pp. 53-56, 57
Absolute value of a number	▲ ■	▲ ■	▲ ■	pp. 53-56
Ordering integers	▲ ■	▲ ■	▲ ■	pp. 53-56
Adding and subtracting integers	● ▲ ■	● ▲ ■	● ▲ ■	pp. 57, 58-62, 63-67, 90
Multiplying and dividing integers	● ▲ ■	● ▲ ■	▲ ■	pp. 70-73, 74-77, 90
Rational and Real Numbers				
Terminating and repeating decimals	▲ ■	▲	▲ ■	pp. 242-246, 437
Showing that a number is rational		▲ ■	▲ ■	pp. 437-441
Classifying real numbers as rational or irrational		▲ ■	▲ ■	pp. 437-441
Ordering rational or irrational numbers		▲ ■	▲ ■	pp. 437-441
Computing with rational numbers			▲ ■	pp. 437-441, 456-460
Evaluating square roots		▲ ■	● ▲ ■	pp. 431-436, 744-745

Symbol Key

● Explore ▲ Teach and Assess ■ Maintain and Apply

TOPICS	Middle School Math Course 1	Middle School Math Course 2	Middle School Math Course 3	**IN COURSE 3, SEE THE FOLLOWING KEY PAGES:**
Using Exponents				
Exponential notation	▲ ■	▲ ■	▲ ■	pp. 196–200, 201–204
Zero and negative exponents		▲	▲ ■	pp. 201–204
Scientific notation		▲ ■	▲ ■	pp. 205–208, 209
Properties of exponents			● ▲ ■	pp. 196–200, 666–670, 743
Computation involving powers		■	● ▲ ■	pp. 196, 666–670
Number Properties				
Commutative Properties of Addition and Multiplication	▲ ■	▲ ■	▲ ■	pp. 80–84, 743
Associative Properties of Addition and Multiplication	▲ ■	▲ ■	▲ ■	pp. 80–84, 743
Distributive Property	▲ ■	▲ ■	▲ ■	pp. 85–89, 743
Properties of 0 and 1	▲	▲ ■	▲ ■	pp. 59, 61, 71, 73, 743
Cross Products Property	▲ ■	▲ ■	▲ ■	pp. 322–326, 743
Number fact families and related equations	▲ ■	● ■		
Number Theory				
Factors of a number	▲	● ▲ ■	● ▲ ■	pp. 168–172, 173
Divisibility tests	● ▲ ■	▲ ■	■	p. 706
Prime and composite numbers	▲ ■	● ▲ ■	● ▲ ■	pp. 167, 169
Prime factorization	▲ ■	▲ ■	▲ ■	pp. 168–172
Common factors and greatest common factor	▲ ■	▲ ■	● ▲ ■	pp. 173–177
Multiples and least common multiple	▲ ■	● ▲ ■	▲ ■	pp. 186–189
MEASUREMENT				
Length, Weight, and Capacity				
Reading rulers and other measurement scales	● ▲ ■	● ▲ ■	■	pp. 720, 721
Customary units of length, weight, and capacity	● ▲ ■	▲ ■	■	p. 741
Metric units of length, mass, and capacity	● ▲ ■	● ▲ ■	■	p. 741
Benchmarks for customary and metric units	▲ ■	▲		
Choosing an appropriate unit of measure	▲ ■	▲		
Rewriting customary measurements	▲ ■	▲ ■	■	p. 741
Rewriting metric measurements	● ▲ ■	● ▲ ■	■	p. 741
Perimeter				
Perimeter of polygons	▲ ■	▲ ■	● ▲ ■	pp. 33–37, 317
Circumference of a circle	● ▲ ■	▲ ■	● ▲ ■	pp. 288–289, 290–294
Comparison of similar figures	▲	■	● ■	pp. 317, 321

Symbol Key

● Explore ▲ Teach and Assess ■ Maintain and Apply

TOPICS	Middle School Math Course 1	Middle School Math Course 2	Middle School Math Course 3	**IN COURSE 3, SEE THE FOLLOWING KEY PAGES:**
Area				
Square and rectangle	● ▲ ■	● ▲ ■	● ▲ ■	pp. 32, 33-37, 134-139
Triangle	● ▲ ■	● ▲ ■	● ▲ ■	pp. 134–139
Parallelogram	● ▲ ■	● ▲ ■	▲ ■	pp. 481–485
Trapezoid		● ▲ ■	▲ ■	pp. 481–485
Circle	▲ ■	▲ ■	● ▲ ■	pp. 486–490
Irregular figures	▲ ■	■	▲ ■	pp. 136–139, 483, 485
Comparison of similar figures	▲ ■	■	● ■	pp. 321, 511
Surface Area				
Prism	● ▲ ■	● ▲ ■	▲ ■	pp. 502-506
Cylinder		● ▲ ■	▲ ■	pp. 502-506
Pyramid			▲ ■	pp. 507–511
Cone			▲ ■	pp. 507–511
Volume				
Prism	▲ ■	● ▲ ■	● ▲ ■	pp. 512, 513–517, 518
Cylinder		▲ ■	● ▲ ■	pp. 513–517, 518
Pyramid			● ▲ ■	pp. 518, 519–523
Cone			● ▲ ■	pp. 518, 519–523
Time and Temperature				
Finding elapsed time	▲ ■	■	■	p. 66
Rewriting units of time	■	■	■	p. 259
Temperature	■	■	■	pp. 36, 66, 74, 75, 77, 84, 100, 101, 157, 523, 592, 613, 615, 650, 695
Indirect Measurement				
Scale drawings, including map scales	● ▲ ■	● ▲ ■	● ▲ ■	pp. 321, 324–326, 484
Pythagorean Theorem		● ▲ ■	● ▲ ■	pp. 442, 443–447, 450–453, 456–460
Using similar triangles		▲ ■	▲ ■	pp. 416–421
Ratios in right triangles			▲ ■	pp. 456–460, 461–462, 463–468
Trigonometric ratios			● ▲ ■	pp. 461–462, 463–468

Symbol Key

● Explore ▲ Teach and Assess ■ Maintain and Apply

TOPICS	Middle School Math Course 1	Middle School Math Course 2	Middle School Math Course 3	IN COURSE 3, SEE THE FOLLOWING KEY PAGES:
GEOMETRY				
Geometry of a Plane				
Points, lines, and planes	▲ ■	▲ ■	■	p. 718
Parallel lines	▲ ■	▲ ■	■	pp. 375-379
Angles formed by parallel lines and a transversal		▲ ■	▲ ■	pp. 375-379
Naming, measuring, and drawing angles	▲ ■	● ▲ ■	● ▲ ■	pp. 375-379, 396, 719
Acute, right, obtuse, or straight angles	▲ ■	▲ ■	▲ ■	pp. 375-379, 382-385
Vertical angles	▲ ■	● ▲	▲ ■	pp. 375-379
Supplementary and complementary angles	▲ ■	▲ ■	▲ ■	pp. 375-379
Classifying triangles, quadrilaterals, and other polygons	▲ ■	▲ ■	▲ ■	pp. 382-385, 386-389
Angle relationships in polygons	● ▲ ■	● ▲ ■	● ▲ ■	pp. 382-385, 386-389, 390-393
Congruent and similar figures	● ▲ ■	● ▲ ■	● ▲ ■	pp. 396, 397-401, 416-421
Properties of similar figures		● ▲ ■	▲ ■	pp. 321, 416-421
Tilings of a plane (Tessellations)	▲	▲	▲	pp. 414-415
Using algebra to solve geometry problems	▲ ■	▲ ■	▲ ■	pp. 375-379, 382-385, 386-389, 390-393
Pythagorean Theorem		● ▲ ■	● ▲ ■	pp. 442, 443-447, 450-453, 456-460
Geometry of Space				
Polyhedrons and their parts	▲ ■	● ▲ ■	▲	pp. 492-495
Cones, cylinders, spheres, and their parts	▲ ■	● ▲ ■	▲ ■	pp. 492-495
Surface area	● ▲ ■	● ▲ ■	▲ ■	pp. 502-506, 507-511
Volume	▲ ■	● ▲ ■	● ▲ ■	pp. 512, 513-517, 518, 519-523
Views of a solid	■	▲	▲ ■	pp. 496-497
Geometric Transformations				
Reflections, or flips	▲ ■	▲ ■	▲ ■	pp. 404-408
Rotations, or turns	▲ ■	● ▲ ■	▲ ■	pp. 409-413
Translations, or slides	▲ ■	▲ ■	● ▲ ■	pp. 409-413
Line and rotational symmetry	● ▲ ■	● ▲ ■	▲ ■	pp. 404-408, 409-413
Dilations			● ▲	pp. 321, 416-421
Coordinate Geometry				
Plotting ordered pairs	▲ ■	● ▲ ■	● ▲ ■	pp. 91-95, 556, 568-569, 583
Graphing equations with two variables	▲ ■	▲ ■	● ▲ ■	pp. 556-560, 575-576
Recognizing linear and non-linear graphs	▲	▲	■	pp. 556-560, 680-684

Symbol Key

● Explore ▲ Teach and Assess ■ Maintain and Apply

Topics	Middle School Math Course 1	Middle School Math Course 2	Middle School Math Course 3	**In Course 3, see the following key pages:**
Intercepts of a line			● ▲ ■	pp. 564-567, 575-576
Slope of a line		● ▲ ■	● ▲ ■	pp. 568-569, 570-574, 575-576, 577-580
Graphing systems of equations			▲	pp. 581-582
Transformations in a coordinate plane	▲ ■	▲ ■	● ▲ ■	pp. 409-413
Using a coordinate plane to represent data graphically	▲ ■	▲ ■	▲ ■	pp. 91-95, 545-548
Graphing linear inequalities			● ▲ ■	pp. 583-587
Spatial Visualization				
Visual patterns	▲ ■	▲ ■		
Visualizing plane and space figures	● ▲ ■	● ▲ ■	▲ ■	pp. 380-381, 496-497
Data Analysis and Probability				
Statistics				
Data in tables	● ▲ ■	▲ ■	▲ ■	pp. 38, 199, 243, 260, 288, 390, 545-548, 554-555, 557, 724, 725
Tallies	● ▲ ■	▲ ■	● ▲ ■	pp. 255-256, 637-638
Frequency table	● ▲ ■	● ▲ ■	● ▲ ■	pp. 5-9, 255-256, 637-638
Range of a set of data	▲ ■	▲ ■	▲ ■	pp. 257-261
Mean, median, and mode of a set of data	▲ ■	● ▲ ■	● ▲ ■	pp. 255-256, 257-261
Quartiles of a set of data	▲	▲ ■	▲ ■	pp. 601-604
Using percents to help organize data	▲ ■	▲ ■	▲ ■	pp. 605-609
Evaluating methods of sampling		▲	▲	pp. 644-645
Collecting data	● ■	● ■	●	pp. 255-256
Graphs				
Organizing data with a graph	▲ ■	■	▲ ■	pp. 605-609
Organizing data with a color-coded map	■	■	■	pp. 182, 608
Bar graphs	▲ ■	▲ ■	▲ ■	pp. 5-9, 724
Histograms		▲ ■	▲ ■	p. 5-9
Line graphs	▲ ■	▲ ■	▲ ■	pp. 605-609, 725
Circle graphs	▲ ■	▲ ■	▲ ■	pp. 605-609
Pictographs	■			
Line plots	▲ ■	■	■	p. 723
Scatter plots		● ▲ ■	▲ ■	pp. 545-548
Box-and-whisker plots	▲ ■	▲ ■	▲ ■	pp. 601-604

Symbol Key

● Explore ▲ Teach and Assess ■ Maintain and Apply

TOPICS	Middle School Math Course 1	Middle School Math Course 2	Middle School Math Course 3	IN COURSE 3, SEE THE FOLLOWING KEY PAGES:
Stem-and-leaf plots	▲ ■	▲ ■	▲ ■	pp. 597-600
Appropriate graphs	▲ ■	▲ ■	▲ ■	pp. 605-609, 612-613
Misleading graphs	● ▲	▲	▲	pp. 612-613
Comparing different graphs of the same data	▲ ■	▲ ■	▲	pp. 612-613
Probability				
Finding outcomes	▲ ■	● ▲ ■	▲ ■	pp. 354-357
Combinations and permutations	▲	● ▲ ■	▲ ■	pp. 618-622, 623-626, 627-631
Counting Principle		● ▲ ■	▲ ■	pp. 618-622
Simulating or conducting an experiment	● ▲	● ▲	●	pp. 354, 632, 637-638
Probability of a simple event and its complement	▲ ■	● ▲ ■	● ▲ ■	pp. 354, 632-636
Dependent and independent events	▲ ■	● ▲ ■	● ▲ ■	pp. 637-638, 639-643
Comparison of theoretical and experimental probabilities	▲	▲	● ▲	pp. 354-357, 637-638
Odds	■	■	▲	pp. 632-636
Geometric probability			▲	pp. 652-653
ALGEBRA				
Expressions				
Numerical expressions	● ▲ ■	● ▲ ■	● ▲ ■	pp. 15-19, 21-22, 85-87, 196
Variable expressions	● ▲ ■	● ▲ ■	▲ ■	pp. 15-19, 23, 33-36, 86-89, 657-677
Powers and square roots (exponents)	▲ ■	● ▲ ■	● ▲ ■	pp. 20-23, 196, 431
Order of operations	▲ ■	● ▲ ■	▲ ■	pp. 10-13, 14
Simplifying expressions		▲ ■	● ▲ ■	pp. 86-89, 666-670
Writing verbal phrases as algebraic expressions	▲ ■	▲ ■	▲ ■	pp. 15-19
Polynomials and standard form			▲ ■	pp. 657-660
Computing with monomials and polynomials			● ▲ ■	pp. 661-665, 666-670, 673, 674-677
Equations				
Checking a solution to an equation	▲ ■	● ▲ ■	▲ ■	pp. 28-31
Using mental math to solve	▲ ■	● ▲ ■	▲ ■	pp. 28-31
Using a letter to represent an unknown in an equation	▲ ■	▲ ■	▲ ■	pp. 15-19, 28-31
Addition and subtraction equations	● ▲ ■	● ▲ ■	● ▲ ■	pp. 28-31, 107-108, 109-112, 134-139
Multiplication and division equations	● ▲ ■	● ▲ ■	● ▲ ■	pp. 113-116, 134-139, 290-294

Symbol Key
● Explore ▲ Teach and Assess ■ Maintain and Apply

TOPICS	Middle School Math Course 1	Middle School Math Course 2	Middle School Math Course 3	**IN COURSE 3, SEE THE FOLLOWING KEY PAGES:**
Multi-step equations		● ▲ ■	● ▲ ■	pp. 117-118, 119-123, 124-128, 134-139, 271-275
Equations with variables on both sides			● ▲ ■	pp. 278-281
Percent equations		▲ ■	▲ ■	pp. 327-330, 347-350
Solving equations involving fractions and decimals			▲ ■	pp. 282-285
Equations whose solutions are square roots		▲ ■	▲ ■	pp. 431-436
Writing verbal sentences as algebraic equations	▲ ■	▲ ■	▲ ■	pp. 28-31
Formulating an equation from a problem situation	▲ ■	▲ ■	▲ ■	pp. 28-31, 33-37
Translating an equation into words	▲ ■	▲	▲ ■	pp. 113-116, 124-128, 301-305
Generating a formula	● ▲	● ▲	●	pp. 134, 317
Using a formula	▲ ■	● ▲ ■	● ▲ ■	pp. 33-37, 390-393, 575-576, 742
Equations with two variables	▲ ■	▲ ■	▲ ■	pp. 541-544, 549-553, 556-560, 564-567, 575-576
Systems of equations			▲	pp. 581-582
Inequalities				
Solving and graphing inequalities in one variable	▲	▲ ■	● ▲ ■	pp. 140-145, 146-149, 295-299, 301-305
Solving and graphing inequalities in two variables			● ▲ ■	pp. 583-587
Checking the solution to a linear inequality			▲ ■	pp. 583-587
Patterns and Functions				
Number patterns	● ▲ ■	● ▲ ■	● ▲ ■	pp. 63, 68-69, 72, 196, 295, 390
Geometric patterns	▲ ■	▲ ■	▲ ■	pp. 68, 69, 414-415, 617
Making and using function tables	● ▲ ■	▲ ■	● ▲ ■	pp. 541-544, 556-560
Writing a rule for a function	● ▲ ■	▲ ■	▲ ■	pp. 541-544
Evaluating a function	▲ ■	▲ ■	● ▲ ■	pp. 549-553, 556
Graphing a function	▲ ■	▲ ■	● ▲ ■	pp. 556-560, 564-567
MODELS AND MANIPULATIVES				
Set Models				
For representing fractions and ratios	▲ ■	▲ ■		
For multiplying	● ▲	▲		
Area Models				
For representing decimals and fractions	● ▲ ■	● ▲ ■	● ▲ ■	pp. 166, 178, 192, 234

TOPICS	Middle School Math Course 1	Middle School Math Course 2	Middle School Math Course 3	IN COURSE 3, SEE THE FOLLOWING KEY PAGES:
For adding and subtracting	● ▲ ■	● ▲ ■	▲ ■	p. 219
For multiplying and dividing	● ▲ ■	● ▲ ■	● ■	p. 234
For representing ratio, proportion, and percent	● ▲ ■	● ■	■	pp. 178, 331, 334, 652-653
Number-Line Models				
For whole numbers	▲ ■	■	■	p. 705
For decimals, fractions, or percents	▲ ■	▲ ■	▲ ■	pp. 243, 333, 705
For integers	▲ ■	● ▲ ■	● ▲ ■	pp. 53, 57, 58–62, 66, 78
For rational or irrational numbers		▲	▲	pp. 432, 438
For probability	▲	▲ ■		
For inequalities	▲	▲ ■	▲ ■	pp. 140–145
Problem Solving Models				
Using a diagram	▲ ■	● ▲ ■	▲ ■	pp. 132-133, 138, 448–449, 453
Using a graph	▲ ■	● ▲ ■	▲ ■	pp. 678–679, 683
Using a list or table	▲ ■	● ▲ ■	● ▲ ■	pp. 184, 186, 554, 557, 618
Using a model	▲ ■	● ▲ ■	● ▲ ■	pp. 402, 407, 512, 518
Using a verbal model	▲ ■	▲ ■	▲ ■	pp. 11, 14, 80, 110, 111, 114, 115, 119, 124–126, 132, 225, 236, 271, 276, 278, 282, 301, 303, 304, 578
Graphic Organizers				
Factor tree	▲ ■	▲ ■	▲ ■	pp. 169, 171
Tree diagram	▲ ■	● ▲ ■	● ▲ ■	pp. 618–622
Venn diagram	▲ ■	▲ ■	■	pp. 242, 437, 726
Concept map	▲	▲	▲	pp. 374, 386
Concept grid		▲	▲	p. 480
Flow chart	▲			
Manipulatives				
Algebra tiles	● ▲	● ▲	● ▲	pp. 28, 107-108, 117-118, 278, 661, 673
Base-ten pieces	● ▲	●		
Compass and straightedge	● ▲ ■	● ▲ ■	● ▲ ■	pp. 380–381, 396, 722
Geoboard	●			
Integer chips	●			
Number counters or tiles	●	●	●	pp. 32, 50-51, 268-269
Number cubes	●	●	●	pp. 255-256, 268-269, 352

Symbol Key

● Explore ▲ Teach and Assess ■ Maintain and Apply

Topics	Middle School Math Course 1	Middle School Math Course 2	Middle School Math Course 3	In Course 3, see the following key pages:
Paper folding and cutting	● ▲ ■	●	●	pp. 134, 442, 486, 518
Protractor	● ▲ ■	● ▲ ■	● ■	pp. 396, 461-462, 605, 721
Ruler	● ▲ ■	● ▲ ■	● ■	pp. 321, 461-462, 720
Unit cubes		▲	●	p. 512
Problem Solving				
Making Decisions				
Choosing an operation	▲ ■	■	■	pp. 109-112, 113-116
Choosing an appropriate form of a number	▲ ■	▲ ■	▲ ■	pp. 192-195, 242-246, 290-294, 331-335
Choosing a computation method	● ▲ ■	■		
Checking reasonableness	▲ ■	● ▲ ■	▲ ■	pp. 156, 235, 251, 252
Using Strategies				
Using a problem-solving plan	▲ ■	▲ ■	▲ ■	pp. 38-43
Guess, Check, and Revise	▲ ■	▲ ■	▲ ■	pp. 26-27, 31
Draw a Diagram or Graph	▲ ■	▲ ■	▲ ■	pp. 132-133, 138, 448-449, 453, 678-679, 683
Perform an Experiment	● ▲ ■	▲ ■	● ▲ ■	pp. 352-353, 354, 637-638
Make a List or Table	▲ ■	▲ ■	● ▲ ■	pp. 184-185, 186, 554-555, 557, 618
Work Backward	▲ ■	● ▲ ■	▲ ■	pp. 276-277, 280
Solve a Related/Simpler Problem	▲ ■	● ▲ ■	▲ ■	pp. 616-617, 622
Make a Model	▲ ■	● ▲ ■	▲ ■	pp. 402-403, 407
Break into Parts	● ▲ ■	▲ ■	▲ ■	pp. 500-501, 506
Look for a Pattern	▲ ■	▲ ■	▲ ■	pp. 68-69, 72
Act it Out	▲ ■	▲ ■	▲ ■	pp. 228-229, 232
Estimate	■	▲ ■		
Write an Equation		▲ ■	▲ ■	pp. 144, 124-128, 577-580
Using Technology				
Calculator	▲ ■	▲ ■	▲ ■	pp. 14, 90, 209, 239, 351, 469, 638
Graphing calculator	▲	▲	▲ ■	pp. 561, 610-611, 685
Spreadsheet	▲ ■	▲	▲ ■	pp. 300, 491
Internet	▲	▲	▲	p. 129

Symbol Key

● Explore ▲ Teach and Assess ■ Maintain and Apply

Student Handbook

Help with Taking Notes

One of the most important tools for success in mathematics is organizing what you have learned. Writing down important information in a notebook helps you remember key concepts and skills. You can use your notebook as a reference when you do your homework or when you study for a test.

Taking Notes

Your textbook displays important ideas and definitions on a notebook. You'll want to include this information in your notes.

Notetaking Strategies

You'll find a different notetaking strategy at the beginning of each chapter. Within the chapter, you'll find helpful hints about taking notes.

Notebook Review

Your textbook includes frequent notebook reviews. These reviews help you use your notebook to check your understanding of important skills and concepts.

LESSON 2.6

Number Properties

BEFORE: You evaluated expressions.
Now: You'll use properties to evaluate expressions.
WHY? So you can find your weekly pay, as in Ex. 39.

Word Watch
Review Words
sum, p. 709
product, p. 713

In the Real World

Tour Biking You are going on a 400 mile bike trip. You plan to cycle at an average speed of 12 miles per hour for 7 hours a day. Can you complete the trip in 5 days?

The commutative properties of addition and multiplication can be used to make evaluating expressions using mental math easier.

The Commutative Property

	Addition	Multiplication
Words	You can add numbers of a sum in any order.	You can multiply factors of a product in any order.
Numbers	$3 + (-8) = -8 + 3$	$5(-6) = -6(5)$
Algebra	$a + b = b + a$	$ab = ba$

EXAMPLE 1 Using the Commutative Property

To find if you can complete the bike trip in 5 days, find the total distance you plan to cycle. Then compare that distance to the length of the trip.

= Average speed • Hours per day • Number of days

$= 12 \cdot 7 \cdot 5$ Substitute known values.
$= 12 \cdot 5 \cdot 7$ Commutative property of multiplication
$= 60 \cdot 7$ Multiply.
$= 420$ Multiply.

result is miles. $\frac{\text{miles}}{\text{hour}} \cdot \frac{\text{hours}}{\text{day}} \cdot \text{days} = \text{miles}$

e 400 miles is less than the 420 miles you can travel in complete the trip in 5 days.

Know How to Take Notes

Including Vocabulary Notes When you write down new vocabulary words, you should also write examples of how they are used. Label the examples with the new words.

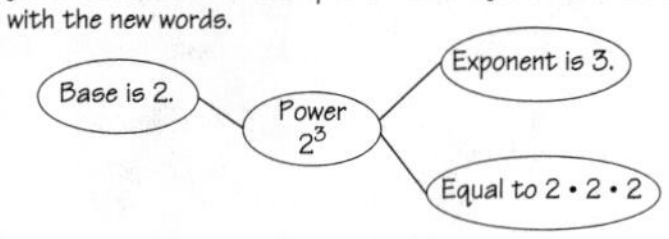

Base is 2. — Power 2^3 — Exponent is 3. — Equal to 2 • 2 • 2

5^2 is read "five squared."

5^3 is read "five cubed."

5^4 is read "five to the fourth power."

... through Chapter 2, label examples of new vocabulary in

LESSONS 3.5 TO 3.7

Notebook Review

Review the vocabulary definitions in your notebook.

Check Your Definitions

base, p. 134
height, p. 134
inequality, p. 140
solution of an inequality, p. 140
equivalent inequalities, p. 141

Use Your Vocabulary

Help with Learning Mathematics

Your textbook helps you succeed in mathematics. Keep your eye out for notes that help you with reading mathematics, learning vocabulary terms, solving problems, using technology, and doing your homework. Some examples of the types of notes you'll see are shown below.

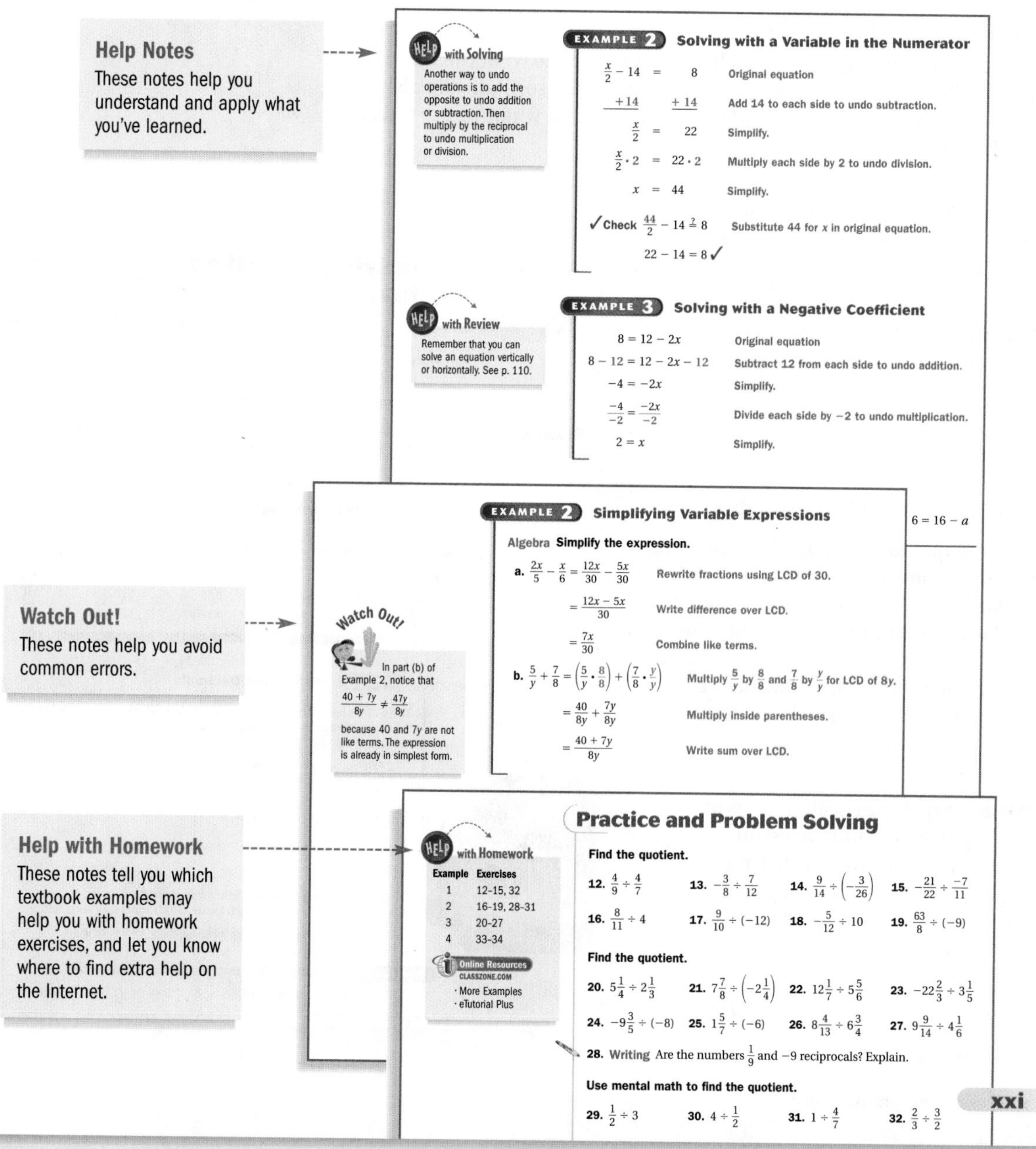

Help Notes
These notes help you understand and apply what you've learned.

HELP with Solving
Another way to undo operations is to add the opposite to undo addition or subtraction. Then multiply by the reciprocal to undo multiplication or division.

EXAMPLE 2 Solving with a Variable in the Numerator

$\frac{x}{2} - 14 = 8$	Original equation
$+14 \quad\; +14$	Add 14 to each side to undo subtraction.
$\frac{x}{2} = 22$	Simplify.
$\frac{x}{2} \cdot 2 = 22 \cdot 2$	Multiply each side by 2 to undo division.
$x = 44$	Simplify.
✓Check $\frac{44}{2} - 14 \stackrel{?}{=} 8$	Substitute 44 for x in original equation.
$22 - 14 = 8$ ✓	

HELP with Review
Remember that you can solve an equation vertically or horizontally. See p. 110.

EXAMPLE 3 Solving with a Negative Coefficient

$8 = 12 - 2x$	Original equation
$8 - 12 = 12 - 2x - 12$	Subtract 12 from each side to undo addition.
$-4 = -2x$	Simplify.
$\frac{-4}{-2} = \frac{-2x}{-2}$	Divide each side by -2 to undo multiplication.
$2 = x$	Simplify.

$6 = 16 - a$

Watch Out!
These notes help you avoid common errors.

Watch Out!
In part (b) of Example 2, notice that $\frac{40 + 7y}{8y} \neq \frac{47y}{8y}$ because 40 and $7y$ are not like terms. The expression is already in simplest form.

EXAMPLE 2 Simplifying Variable Expressions

Algebra **Simplify the expression.**

a. $\frac{2x}{5} - \frac{x}{6} = \frac{12x}{30} - \frac{5x}{30}$	Rewrite fractions using LCD of 30.
$= \frac{12x - 5x}{30}$	Write difference over LCD.
$= \frac{7x}{30}$	Combine like terms.
b. $\frac{5}{y} + \frac{7}{8} = \left(\frac{5}{y} \cdot \frac{8}{8}\right) + \left(\frac{7}{8} \cdot \frac{y}{y}\right)$	Multiply $\frac{5}{y}$ by $\frac{8}{8}$ and $\frac{7}{8}$ by $\frac{y}{y}$ for LCD of $8y$.
$= \frac{40}{8y} + \frac{7y}{8y}$	Multiply inside parentheses.
$= \frac{40 + 7y}{8y}$	Write sum over LCD.

Help with Homework
These notes tell you which textbook examples may help you with homework exercises, and let you know where to find extra help on the Internet.

HELP with Homework

Example	Exercises
1	12-15, 32
2	16-19, 28-31
3	20-27
4	33-34

Online Resources CLASSZONE.COM
- More Examples
- eTutorial Plus

Practice and Problem Solving

Find the quotient.

12. $\frac{4}{9} \div \frac{4}{7}$ 13. $-\frac{3}{8} \div \frac{7}{12}$ 14. $\frac{9}{14} \div \left(-\frac{3}{26}\right)$ 15. $-\frac{21}{22} \div \frac{-7}{11}$

16. $\frac{8}{11} \div 4$ 17. $\frac{9}{10} \div (-12)$ 18. $-\frac{5}{12} \div 10$ 19. $\frac{63}{8} \div (-9)$

Find the quotient.

20. $5\frac{1}{4} \div 2\frac{1}{3}$ 21. $7\frac{7}{8} \div \left(-2\frac{1}{4}\right)$ 22. $12\frac{1}{7} \div 5\frac{5}{6}$ 23. $-22\frac{2}{3} \div 3\frac{1}{5}$

24. $-9\frac{3}{5} \div (-8)$ 25. $1\frac{5}{7} \div (-6)$ 26. $8\frac{4}{13} \div 6\frac{3}{4}$ 27. $9\frac{9}{14} \div 4\frac{1}{6}$

28. Writing Are the numbers $\frac{1}{9}$ and -9 reciprocals? Explain.

Use mental math to find the quotient.

29. $\frac{1}{2} \div 3$ 30. $4 \div \frac{1}{2}$ 31. $1 \div \frac{4}{7}$ 32. $\frac{2}{3} \div \frac{3}{2}$

xxi

Reading Your Textbook

You need special skills to read a math textbook. These skills include *identifying the main idea, learning new vocabulary,* and *focusing on the important concepts* in a lesson. Most important, you need to *be an active reader*. You need to practice and apply the ideas you read about.

Identify the Main Idea

Even before you begin reading a lesson, check to see what the lesson is about. Then you'll know what to focus on in the lesson. You can also assess how well you understand the lesson content when you've finished reading the lesson.

Lesson Opener Look at the lesson opener for information about the main idea of the lesson.

Example Heads Use other clues, such as the heads that appear above examples, to identify the main idea.

Understand the Vocabulary

Reading mathematics involves learning and using new vocabulary terms. Refer to diagrams and worked-out examples to clarify your understanding of new terms. If you forget what a term you've already learned means, look back at previous lessons or use the Glossary, which starts on page 747.

Vocabulary New vocabulary terms are highlighted within a lesson. In addition, the *Word Watch* at the beginning of the lesson lists the important vocabulary terms in the lesson.

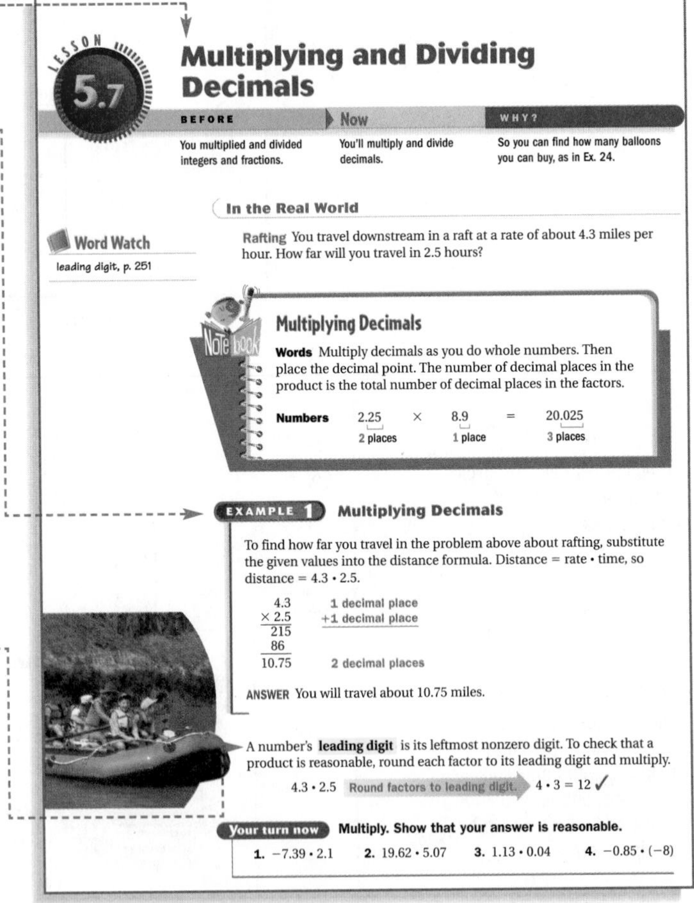

LESSON 5.7

Multiplying and Dividing Decimals

BEFORE	Now	WHY?
You multiplied and divided integers and fractions.	You'll multiply and divide decimals.	So you can find how many balloons you can buy, as in Ex. 24.

Word Watch

leading digit, p. 251

In the Real World

Rafting You travel downstream in a raft at a rate of about 4.3 miles per hour. How far will you travel in 2.5 hours?

Notebook

Multiplying Decimals

Words Multiply decimals as you do whole numbers. Then place the decimal point. The number of decimal places in the product is the total number of decimal places in the factors.

Numbers 2.25 (2 places) × 8.9 (1 place) = 20.025 (3 places)

EXAMPLE 1 **Multiplying Decimals**

To find how far you travel in the problem above about rafting, substitute the given values into the distance formula. Distance = rate • time, so distance = 4.3 • 2.5.

4.3	1 decimal place
× 2.5	+1 decimal place
215	
86	
10.75	2 decimal places

ANSWER You will travel about 10.75 miles.

A number's **leading digit** is its leftmost nonzero digit. To check that a product is reasonable, round each factor to its leading digit and multiply.

4.3 • 2.5 → Round factors to leading digit. → 4 • 3 = 12 ✓

Your turn now **Multiply. Show that your answer is reasonable.**

1. −7.39 • 2.1 2. 19.62 • 5.07 3. 1.13 • 0.04 4. −0.85 • (−8)

Know What's Important

Focus in on the important information in a lesson. Pay attention to highlighted vocabulary terms and definitions. Be on the lookout for definitions, properties, formulas, and other information displayed on a notebook. Make sure that you understand the worked-out examples.

Notebook Focus in on key ideas that are displayed on a notebook.

Worked-Out Examples Do the worked-out examples to make sure you know how to apply new concepts.

Be an Active Reader

As you read, keep a pencil in your hand and your notebook ready so that you can write down important information, practice new skills, and jot down questions to ask in class.

Your Turn Now Solve the *Your turn now* exercises to check your understanding.

Use Your Notebook As you solve the examples yourself, you may find it helpful to describe the steps you follow. Write down any questions you have so you can ask them in class.

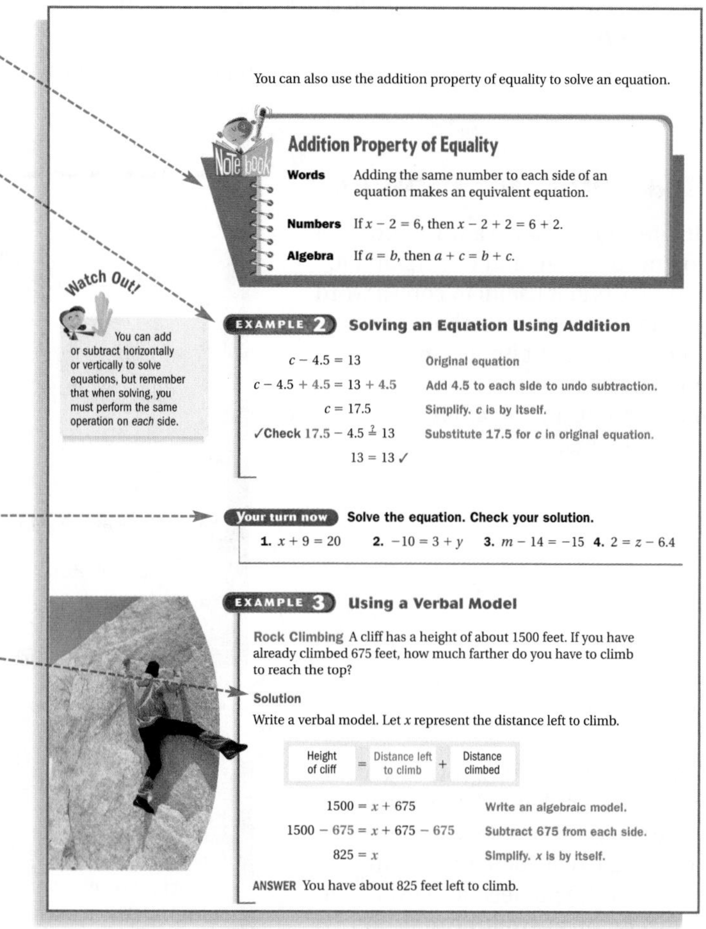

You can also use the addition property of equality to solve an equation.

Notebook

Addition Property of Equality

Words Adding the same number to each side of an equation makes an equivalent equation.

Numbers If $x - 2 = 6$, then $x - 2 + 2 = 6 + 2$.

Algebra If $a = b$, then $a + c = b + c$.

Watch Out! You can add or subtract horizontally or vertically to solve equations, but remember that when solving, you must perform the same operation on *each* side.

EXAMPLE 2 Solving an Equation Using Addition

$c - 4.5 = 13$	Original equation
$c - 4.5 + 4.5 = 13 + 4.5$	Add 4.5 to each side to undo subtraction.
$c = 17.5$	Simplify. c is by itself.
✓**Check** $17.5 - 4.5 \stackrel{?}{=} 13$	Substitute 17.5 for c in original equation.
$13 = 13$ ✓	

Your turn now Solve the equation. Check your solution.

1. $x + 9 = 20$ **2.** $-10 = 3 + y$ **3.** $m - 14 = -15$ **4.** $2 = z - 6.4$

EXAMPLE 3 Using a Verbal Model

Rock Climbing A cliff has a height of about 1500 feet. If you have already climbed 675 feet, how much farther do you have to climb to reach the top?

Solution

Write a verbal model. Let x represent the distance left to climb.

Height of cliff = Distance left to climb + Distance climbed

$1500 = x + 675$	Write an algebraic model.
$1500 - 675 = x + 675 - 675$	Subtract 675 from each side.
$825 = x$	Simplify. x is by itself.

ANSWER You have about 825 feet left to climb.

Reading and Problem Solving

The language in your math textbook is precise. When you do your homework, be sure to read carefully. For example, the direction line below asks you to do three different things for each of the exercises: sketch, measure, and compare.

> **Estimation** **Sketch a line segment of the given length without using a ruler. Then use a ruler to check your estimate. How close was your estimate?**
>
> **21.** 6.5 cm **22.** 45 mm **23.** 0.01 m **24.** 0.15 m

Reading Word Problems

Before you can solve a word problem, you need to read and understand it. You may find it useful to copy a word problem into your notebook. Then you can highlight important information, cross out unnecessary information, and organize your thinking.

You have a recipe that makes 24 cookies. The ingredients include 2 eggs, 1 cup of sugar, 1.5 cups of flour, ~~1 teaspoon of vanilla, and 1 teaspoon of baking soda~~. What is the greatest number of cookies you can make if you have 12 eggs, 4 cups of sugar, and 9 cups of flour?

	Needed (one batch)	Already have
Number of eggs	2	12
Cups of sugar	1	4
Cups of flour	1.5	9

Make sure that you've solved a word problem completely. For example, to solve the word problem at the right, you need to calculate how many more points you need for Levels 5, 6, and 7. But to answer the question, you must determine how many total points you need.

In a certain video game, when you reach 50 points, you reach Level 2. You need 70 more points to reach Level 3, and then you need 90 more points to reach Level 4. Suppose the pattern continues. How many points do you need to reach Level 7?

Level 5: 110 more, Level 6: 130 more, Level 7: 150 more

Total points:
$50 + 70 + 90 + 110 + 130 + 150 = 600$

Additional Resources in Your Textbook

Your textbook contains many resources that you can use for reference when you are studying or doing your homework.

Skills Review Handbook Use the Skills Review Handbook on pages 704–726 to review material learned in previous courses.

Tables Refer to the tables on pages 740–746 if you need information about mathematical symbols, measures, formulas, and properties.

Glossary Use the Glossary on pages 747–772 to look up the meanings of math vocabulary terms. Each glossary entry also tells where in your book a term is covered in more detail.

Index Use the Index on pages 773–795 as a quick guide for finding out where a particular math topic is covered in the book.

Selected Answers Use the Selected Answers starting on page SA1 to check your work or to see whether you are on the right track in solving a problem.

Textbook Scavenger Hunt

Get some practice using your textbook. Use the additional resources described above to answer each question. Give page numbers to show where you found the answer to the question.

1 What is a biased sample? **See p. 748.**

2 Tell what each of these symbols means: $\stackrel{?}{=}$, $\sim$, $\pm$. **See p. 740.**

3 How many square inches are there in one square foot? **See p. 741.**

4 On what page or pages of the book is the distributive property first discussed? **See p. 743.**

5 What is the normal body temperature in degrees Fahrenheit? in degrees Celsius? **See p. 741.**

6 What is a variable? **See p. 771.**

7 On what page can you review the skill of adding and subtracting decimals? **See p. 709.**

8 On what page of the book can you find selected answers for Lesson 1.1? **See p. SA1.**

9 What formula can you use to find the volume of a cylinder? **See p. 742.**

1. $3 \times 10{,}000 + 4 \times 1000 + 7 \times 100 + 7 \times 10 + 7 \times 1$

2. $8 \times 100 + 3 \times 10 + 7 \times 1 + 4 \times 0.1$

3. $5 \times 1000 + 4 \times 100 + 5 \times 10 + 9 \times 1$

4. $1 \times 1000 + 2 \times 1 + 3 \times 0.001$

Pre-Course Test

Number Sense and Operations

Place Value and Rounding *(Skills Review, pp. 704–705)*

Write the number in expanded form. 1–4. See margin.

1. 34,777 **2.** 837.4 **3.** 5459 **4.** 1002.003

Round the number to the place value of the red digit.

5. 3465 3470 **6.** 44,656 44,700 **7.** 66,789 66,790 **8.** 55.677 55.7

Operations with Decimals and Fractions *(Skills Review, pp. 707–715)*

Write the mixed number as an improper fraction or the improper fraction as a mixed number.

9. $4\frac{2}{3}$ $\frac{14}{3}$ **10.** $12\frac{1}{2}$ $\frac{25}{2}$ **11.** $\frac{13}{6}$ $2\frac{1}{6}$ **12.** $\frac{24}{5}$ $4\frac{4}{5}$

Find the sum, difference, product, or quotient. Simplify if possible.

13. $6.77 + 5.66$ 12.43 **14.** $77.555 - 34.55$ 43.005 **15.** $\frac{4}{12} - \frac{3}{12}$ $\frac{1}{12}$ **16.** $\frac{4}{5} + \frac{3}{5}$ $1\frac{2}{5}$

17. 3.4×45 153 **18.** $10\frac{2}{3} \times 5\frac{1}{4}$ 56 **19.** $14.49 \div 7$ 2.07 **20.** $2.1 \div 84$ 0.025

21. $\frac{3}{4} \times \frac{1}{4}$ $\frac{3}{16}$ **22.** 3.89×16 62.24 **23.** $1\frac{2}{3} \times 1\frac{4}{5}$ 3 **24.** $3 \times 4\frac{1}{2}$ $13\frac{1}{2}$

Problem Solving *(Skills Review, pp. 712, 717)*

25. The computer club has already raised $120.95 for new software. A math program costs $39.50, a game costs $24.75, and a reading program costs $66.29. How much more money does the club need to raise to pay for the software? $9.59

26. The soccer team had a car wash to raise money. They charged $3 for each car. If they washed 23 cars, how much money did they earn? $69

Estimation *(Skills Review, pp. 711, 716)*

Estimate the sum or difference. 27–29. Estimates may vary.

27. $666 + 453 + 123$ 1250 **28.** $45{,}768 - 23{,}409$ 23,000 **29.** $7666 + 4555 + 994$ 13,000

Find a low and high estimate for the product or quotient. 30–33. Estimates may vary.

30. 54×19 500; 1200 **31.** $788 \div 9$ 80; 90 **32.** 560×236 100,000; 180,000 **33.** $8557 \div 29$ 280; 430

 Geometry

Points, Lines, and Planes *(Skills Review, p. 718)*

In Exercises 34–36, use the diagram.

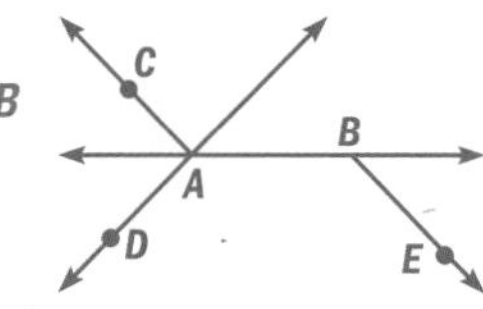

34. Name three points. ***Sample answer: C, A, and B***

35. Name two rays. ***Sample answer:*** $\overrightarrow{BE}$ **and** $\overrightarrow{AD}$

36. Name two lines. $\overleftrightarrow{AB}$ **and** $\overleftrightarrow{DA}$

Using a Protractor *(Skills Review, p. 721)*

Use a protractor to measure the angle.

37.

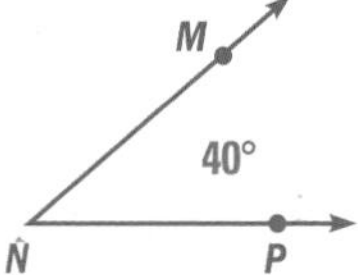

38.

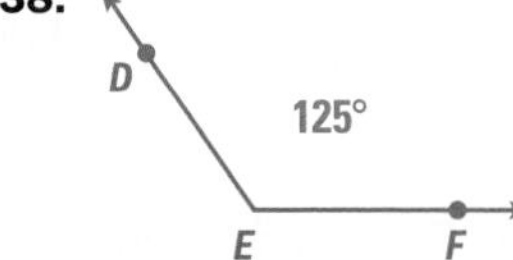

Use a protractor to draw an angle that has the given measure. **39–41. See margin.**

39. 125° **40.** 34° **41.** 90°

39.

40.

41.

Data Analysis

Reading Bar Graphs and Line Graphs *(Skills Review, pp. 724–725)*

In Exercises 42 and 43, use the bar graph.

42. Which sale made the least money? **book**

43. How much more money was made from the bake sale than the yard sale? **$20**

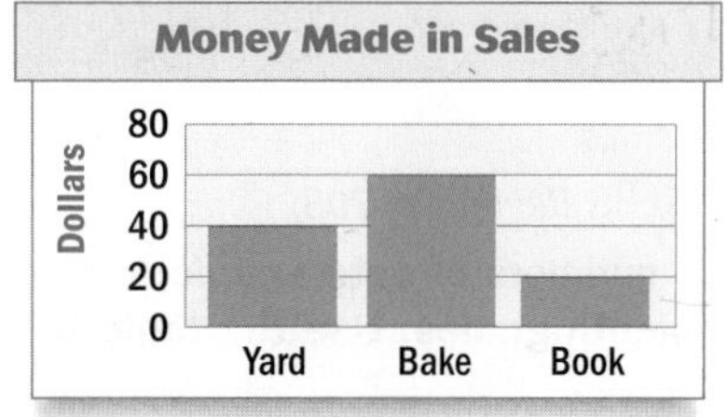

In Exercises 44 and 45, use the line graph.

44. Which month had the greatest concert attendance? **July**

45. What was the difference in concert attendance between June and May? **10,000**

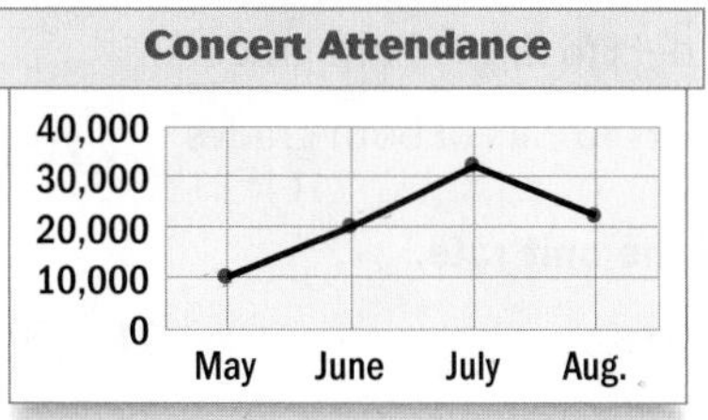

1. $4 \times 10{,}000 + 5 \times 1000 + 7 \times 100 + 8 \times 1$
2. $4 \times 1 + 5 \times 0.01 + 6 \times 0.001$
3. $1 \times 1000 + 3 \times 1 + 4 \times 0.01$
4. $4 \times 100 + 5 \times 1 + 3 \times 0.1 + 5 \times 0.001$

Pre-Course Practice

Number Sense and Operations

Place Value and Rounding *(Skills Review, pp. 704–705)*

Write the number in expanded form. 1–4. See margin.

1. 45,708 **2.** 4.056 **3.** 1003.04 **4.** 405.305

Write the number in standard form.

5. $4 \times 100{,}000 + 7 \times 10 + 8 \times 1 + 8 \times 0.001$ 400,078.008

6. $5 \times 100 + 8 \times 1 + 3 \times 0.1 + 4 \times 0.01$ 508.34

Round the number to the place value of the red digit.

7. 2234 2200 **8.** 48,139 48,100 **9.** 4.566 4.6 **10.** 33.86 30

11. 13.444 13.44 **12.** 556.78 560 **13.** 73.845 74 **14.** 546,888 546,900

Divisibility *(Skills Review, p. 706)*

Test the number for divisibility by 2, 3, 4, 5, 6, 8, 9, and 10.

15. 44 2, 4 **16.** 88 2, 4, 8 **17.** 385 5 **18.** 870 2, 3, 5, 6, 10

Mixed Numbers and Improper Fractions *(Skills Review, p. 707)*

Write the mixed number as an improper fraction.

19. $4\frac{1}{2}$ $\frac{9}{2}$ **20.** $2\frac{4}{5}$ $\frac{14}{5}$ **21.** $8\frac{4}{9}$ $\frac{76}{9}$ **22.** $9\frac{4}{7}$ $\frac{67}{7}$

Write the improper fraction as a mixed number.

23. $\frac{12}{7}$ $1\frac{5}{7}$ **24.** $\frac{18}{4}$ $4\frac{1}{2}$ **25.** $\frac{21}{5}$ $4\frac{1}{5}$ **26.** $\frac{33}{7}$ $4\frac{5}{7}$

Ratio and Rate *(Skills Review, p. 708)*

The table shows the numbers of cats and dogs owned by the students in the seventh and eighth grades. Use the table to write the ratio.

27. Cats of 8th graders to cats of 7th graders 12 to 11

28. Dogs of 7th graders to dogs of 8th graders 15 to 14

29. Cats of 7th graders to cats of both grades 11 to 23

	Cats	Dogs
8th Grade	12	14
7th Grade	11	15

Write the rate and the unit rate.

30. \$3.90 for 30 ounces $\frac{\$3.90}{30\text{ oz}}, \frac{\$.13}{1\text{ oz}}$

31. 250 miles in 4 hours $\frac{250\text{ mi}}{4\text{ h}}, \frac{62.5\text{ mi}}{1\text{ h}}$

32. \$4.50 for 30 minutes long distance $\frac{\$4.50}{30\text{ min}}, \frac{\$.15}{1\text{ min}}$

33. 329 miles on 14 gallons of gas $\frac{329\text{ mi}}{14\text{ gal}}, \frac{23.5\text{ mi}}{1\text{ gal}}$

Operations with Decimals and Fractions *(Skills Review, pp. 709–714)*

Find the sum or difference.

34. 8.4 − 3.3 5.1 **35.** 23.8 + 84.9 108.7 **36.** 38.6 + 4.7 43.3 **37.** 5.44 − 2.33 3.11

38. 4.67 + 3.85 8.52 **39.** 49.55 − 18.23 31.32 **40.** 66.77 + 3.45 70.22 **41.** 34.56 − 30.89 3.67

42. 5.329 + 8.455 13.784 **43.** 14.86 − 6.656 8.204 **44.** 888.66 − 56.88 831.78 **45.** 475.67 + 89.44 565.11

Find the sum or difference.

46. $\frac{1}{7} + \frac{4}{7}$ $\frac{5}{7}$ **47.** $\frac{14}{17} - \frac{11}{17}$ $\frac{3}{17}$ **48.** $\frac{7}{9} - \frac{5}{9}$ $\frac{2}{9}$ **49.** $\frac{9}{13} + \frac{8}{13}$ $1\frac{4}{13}$

50. $\frac{5}{12} + \frac{2}{12}$ $\frac{7}{12}$ **51.** $\frac{3}{9} + \frac{4}{9}$ $\frac{7}{9}$ **52.** $\frac{12}{13} - \frac{4}{13}$ $\frac{8}{13}$ **53.** $\frac{5}{8} - \frac{4}{8}$ $\frac{1}{8}$

54. $\frac{1}{4} + \frac{2}{4}$ $\frac{3}{4}$ **55.** $\frac{12}{14} - \frac{9}{14}$ $\frac{3}{14}$ **56.** $\frac{7}{8} - \frac{4}{8}$ $\frac{3}{8}$ **57.** $\frac{5}{11} + \frac{3}{11}$ $\frac{8}{11}$

Find the product. Simplify if possible.

58. $\frac{2}{9} \times \frac{1}{7}$ $\frac{2}{63}$ **59.** $\frac{1}{5} \times \frac{2}{3}$ $\frac{2}{15}$ **60.** $\frac{3}{4} \times \frac{1}{8}$ $\frac{3}{32}$ **61.** $\frac{1}{4} \times \frac{3}{7}$ $\frac{3}{28}$

62. $\frac{1}{4} \times \frac{3}{4}$ $\frac{3}{16}$ **63.** $\frac{4}{5} \times \frac{7}{8}$ $\frac{7}{10}$ **64.** $\frac{1}{8} \times \frac{4}{5}$ $\frac{1}{10}$ **65.** $3 \times 1\frac{1}{5}$ $3\frac{3}{5}$

66. $5\frac{1}{2} \times 6$ 33 **67.** $2 \times 3\frac{1}{7}$ $6\frac{2}{7}$ **68.** $4\frac{2}{3} \times 1\frac{3}{4}$ $8\frac{1}{6}$ **69.** $1\frac{3}{8} \times 4\frac{2}{3}$ $6\frac{5}{12}$

Find the product or quotient.

70. 2.3 × 67 154.1 **71.** 3.42 ÷ 3 1.14 **72.** 367.5 ÷ 5 73.5 **73.** 0.55 × 88 48.4

74. 7.54 × 88 663.52 **75.** 8.44 × 77 649.88 **76.** 2.934 ÷ 9 0.326 **77.** 584.85 ÷ 7 83.55

78. 555 × 34.3 19,036.5 **79.** 788 × 66.4 52,323.2 **80.** 0.48 ÷ 6 0.08 **81.** 45.905 × 78 3580.59

82. 16.68 ÷ 2 8.34 **83.** 12.32 ÷ 4 3.08 **84.** 345.88 × 55 19,023.4 **85.** 401.1 ÷ 7 57.3

Problem Solving *(Skills Review, pp. 712, 717)*

86. A middle school has three grades and 667 students total. The eighth grade has 216 students. The seventh grade has 229 students. How many students are in the sixth grade? 222 students

87. Maria bought a hamburger for $1.59 and juice for $.68. She paid with a $5 bill. How much change should Maria receive? $2.73

88. Lee spent $7.89 for a hammer, $2.26 for nails, and $3.55 for a stapler. What was the total cost of Lee's purchase? $13.70

89. A sweater costs $28, and a pair of boots costs $56. What is the total cost of the sweater and the boots? $84

90. You bought 98 trading cards and gave 45 to your brother. How many cards do you have left? 53 cards

91. Sue has 12 CDs, and Kate has 28 CDs. How many CDs do Sue and Kate have all together? 40 CDs

92. The recycling committee collected 2575 newspapers and tied them in bundles. Each bundle contained 25 newspapers. How many bundles of newspapers did they make? 103 bundles

93. Your school cafeteria has enough seats for 540 students. Each table seats 12 students. How many tables are in the cafeteria? 45 tables

94. A youth organization sold 132 books of carnival ride coupons. Each book contained 18 ride coupons. How many ride coupons were sold? 2376 ride coupons

95. Basketball tickets cost $35 each. The team sold 12,383 tickets to their first game. How much money did the team make for the first game? $433,405

Estimation *(Skills Review, pp. 711, 716)*

Estimate the sum or difference. 96–103. Estimates may vary.

96. $6845 + 2687$ 9500 **97.** $7356 - 4699$ 2700 **98.** $8999 + 3456$ 12,500 **99.** $4567 - 3499$ 1100

100. $1867 + 5409$ 7300 **101.** $7865 - 5433$ 2500 **102.** $6577 - 3444$ 3200 **103.** $6999 + 5987$ 13,000

Find a low and high estimate for the product or quotient. 104–111. Estimates may vary.

104. 44×18 400; 1000 **105.** 555×34 15,000; 24,000 **106.** $333 \div 8$ 40; 50 **107.** $6566 \div 8$ 800; 900

108. 434×56 20,000; 30,000 **109.** $344 \div 23$ 10; 18 **110.** $7656 \div 19$ 380; 770 **111.** 808×66 48,000; 63,000

Geometry

Points, Lines, and Planes *(Skills Review, p. 718)*

In Exercises 112–115, use the diagram.

B
C
A
E
D

112. Name three points. *Sample answer: A, E, D*

113. Name two rays. *Sample answer:* $\overrightarrow{EB}$ and $\overrightarrow{EC}$

114. Give two different names for the line. $\overleftrightarrow{AE}$ and $\overleftrightarrow{ED}$

115. Name a segment that has D as an endpoint. *Sample answer:* $\overline{ED}$

Using a Protractor *(Skills Review, p. 721)*

Use a protractor to measure the angle.

116.

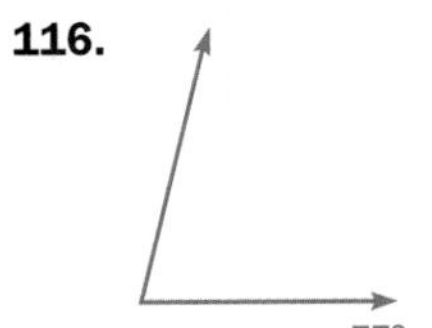

117.

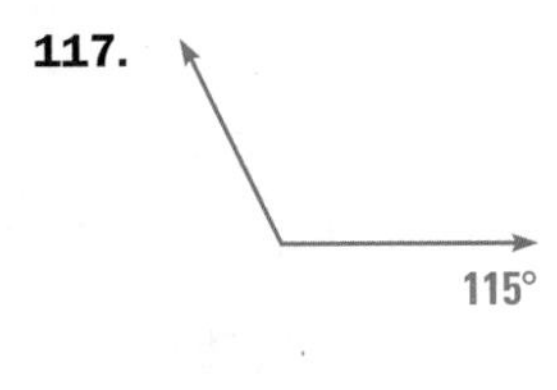

118.

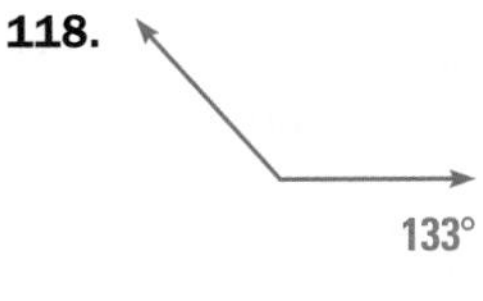

Use a protractor to draw an angle that has the given measure. 119–122. See margin.

119. 56° **120.** 125° **121.** 140° **122.** 15°

Data Analysis

Reading Bar Graphs and Line Graphs *(Skills Review, pp. 724–725)*

In Exercises 123–125, use the line graph. It shows the numbers of books sold on five different days.

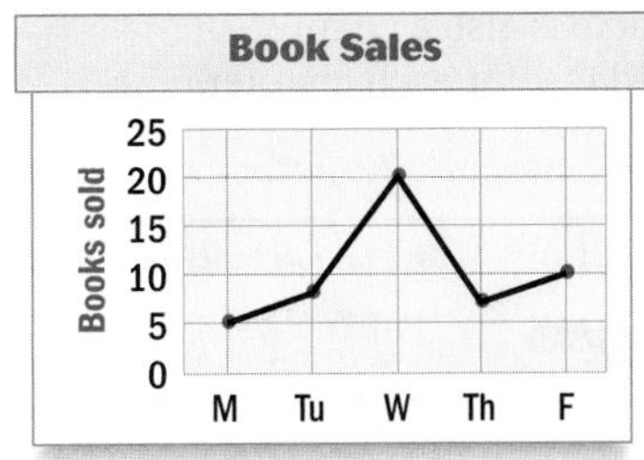

123. On what day were the fewest number of books sold? Monday

124. On what day were 8 books sold? Tuesday

125. How many more books were sold on Wednesday than on Monday? 15 books

In Exercises 126–128, use the bar graph. It shows the numbers of students that participate in school activities.

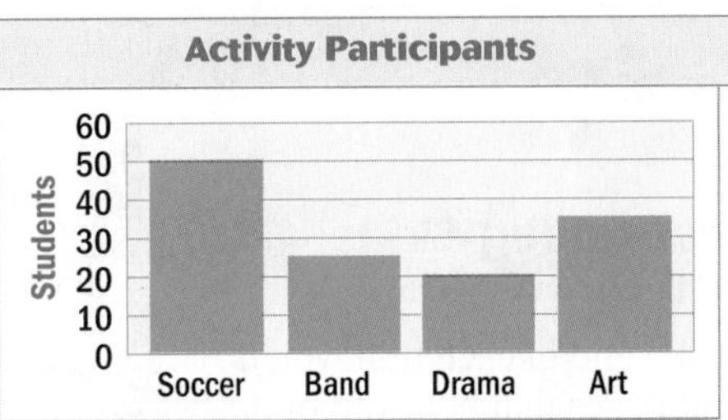

126. How many more students participate in the band than in drama? 5 students

127. In what activity do the greatest number of students participate? soccer

128. In what activity do 35 students participate? art

Venn Diagrams and Logical Reasoning *(Skills Review, p. 726)*

Draw a Venn diagram of the set described. 129–130. See margin.

129. Of the whole numbers less than 14, set A consists of numbers that are greater than 9, and set B consists of even numbers.

130. Of the whole numbers less than 12, set C consists of multiples of 2, and set D consists of odd numbers.

119.

120.

121.

122.

129.

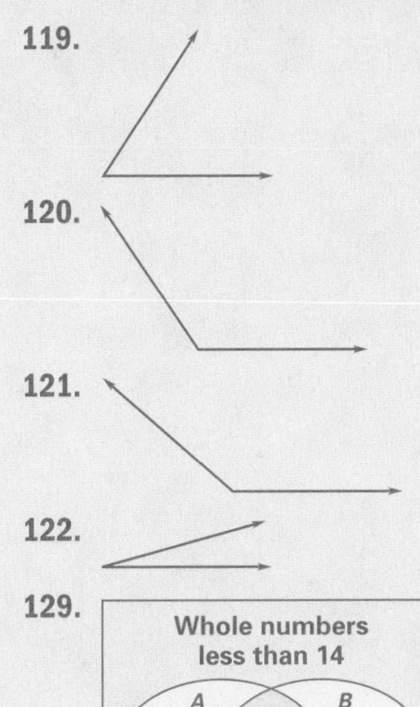

130.

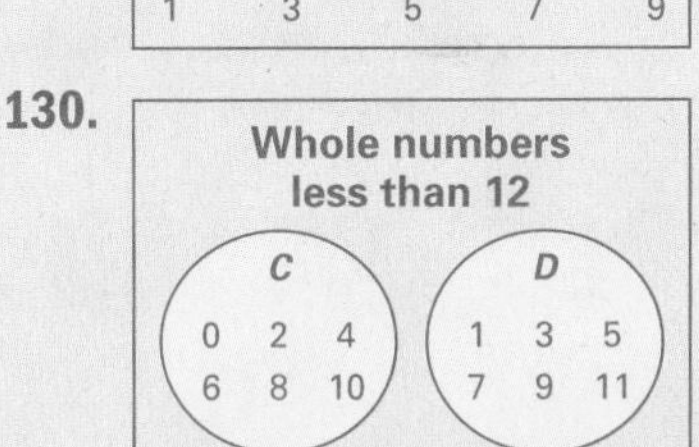

Content and Assessment

Course Content

The authors have developed a sequence of lessons that include all the concepts and skills you need in this course. What you learn is connected to prior knowledge and to your daily life.

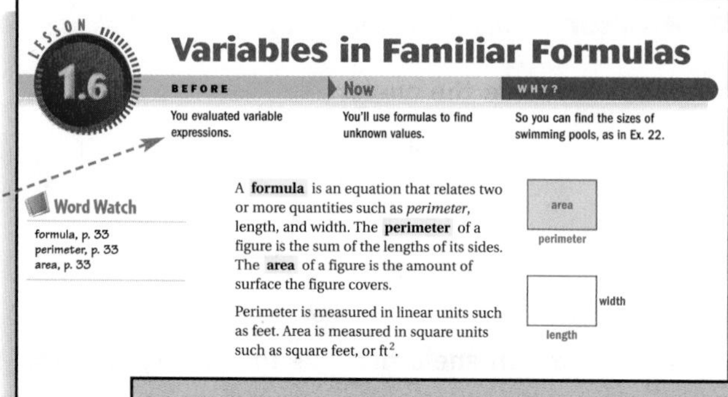

LESSON 1.6

Variables in Familiar Formulas

BEFORE: You evaluated variable expressions.

Now: You'll use formulas to find unknown values.

WHY? So you can find the sizes of swimming pools, as in Ex. 22.

Word Watch

formula, p. 33
perimeter, p. 33
area, p. 33

A **formula** is an equation that relates two or more quantities such as *perimeter*, length, and width. The **perimeter** of a figure is the sum of the lengths of its sides. The **area** of a figure is the amount of surface the figure covers.

Perimeter is measured in linear units such as feet. Area is measured in square units such as square feet, or ft^2.

Test-Taking Practice

Each lesson includes test-taking practice that helps you become comfortable with different formats of test questions. Additional practice is provided on the Internet. There is also a chapter standardized test for each chapter.

Chapter Standardized Test

Test-Taking Strategy **Avoid spending too much time on one question. Skip questions you have trouble with, and return to them after you have finished.**

Multiple Choice

1. Which ratio is *not* equivalent to $\frac{3}{7}$?

   A. $\frac{9}{21}$ **B.** $\frac{1.5}{3.5}$ **C.** $\frac{300}{700}$ **D.** $\frac{18}{39}$

2. Susan types at a speed of 54 words per minute. What is her typing speed in words per second?

   F. 5400 words per second
   G. 3240 words per second
   ...per second
   ...per second

...shows $\frac{10\text{ feet}}{4\text{ seconds}}$ correctly ...nit rate?

... $\frac{5\text{ ft}}{\text{sec}}$ **C.** $\frac{2.5\text{ ft}}{\text{sec}}$ **D.** $\frac{2\text{ ft}}{5\text{ sec}}$

...l of a school building is ...g and 3 inches high. The actual building is 231 feet long. How tall is the actual building?

F. 21 ft **G.** 33 ft

7. An item with a wholesale price of $8.40 is marked up 60%. What is the retail price?

   A. $3.36 **B.** $5.04 **C.** $13.44 **D.** $14.40

8. You and your friend are leaving a tip after eating dinner. The cost of the dinner is $15.35. You want to leave *about* an 18% tip. How much should you leave as a tip?

   F. $1.25 **G.** $2.75 **H.** $8.50 **I.** $18.00

9. You randomly draw a marble from a bag of 3 red, 8 yellow, and 13 blue marbles. What is the probability that the marble is yellow?

   A. $\frac{13}{24}$ **B.** $\frac{1}{2}$ **C.** $\frac{1}{3}$ **D.** $\frac{1}{8}$

Short Response

10. You deposit $1350 into a savings account that pays a simple annual interest rate of 2.8%. How much interest will you earn in 15 months? Compare this to the interest you would earn for the same amount of time in an account with a simple annual interest rate of 4%.

Extended Response

...random from a bag ...d yellow marbles ...ou record its color and ...ag of 75 marbles. The ...he table below. How ...arble do you predict ...n.

Green	Yellow
5	9

Test-Taking Practice

INTERNET State Test Practice CLASSZONE.COM

48. **Multiple Choice** What is the prime factorization of 72?

    A. $2^2 \cdot 3 \cdot 6$ **B.** $2 \cdot 6^2$ **C.** $2^3 \cdot 3^2$ **D.** $2^2 \cdot 3^2 \cdot 6$

49. **Short Response** A teacher can arrange a class into groups of 2, 5, or 6 students with no one left out. What is the least number of students that the teacher can have in class to do this? Explain how you found your answer.

Test-Taking Skills and Strategies

At the end of each unit, you'll find pages that help you build and practice test-taking skills and strategies.

UNIT 2 Chapters 4–7

BUILDING **Test-Taking Skills**

Strategies for Answering

Short Response Questions

Scoring Rubric

Full credit
- answer is correct, *and*
- work and reasoning are included

Partial credit
- answer is correct, but reasoning is incorrect, *or*
- answer is incorrect, but reasoning is correct

No credit
- no answer is given *or*
- answer makes no sense

Problem

You work for your uncle this summer. He pays you $20 on your first day. Each day after that, you will get a raise. You can choose from 2 payment plans. With Plan A, you earn a $5 raise each day. With Plan B, you earn a 20% raise each day. Which plan is a better deal?

Full credit solution

Plan B is a better deal if you work more than 5 days.

Data is used to justify the solution.

Day	1	2	3	4	5	6
Plan A pay	20.00	25.00	30.00	35.00	40.00	45.00
Plan A total	20.00	45.00	75.00	110.00	150.00	195.00
Plan B pay	20.00	24.00	28.80	34.56	41.47	49.76
Plan B total	20.00	44.00	72.80	107.36	148.83	198.59

The question is answered clearly and in complete sentences.

Plan A is better if you work 5 days or less, but Plan B is better if you work more than 5 days. By day 6, the pay with a 20% increase is more than the pay with a $5 raise, so it will continue to be the better plan.

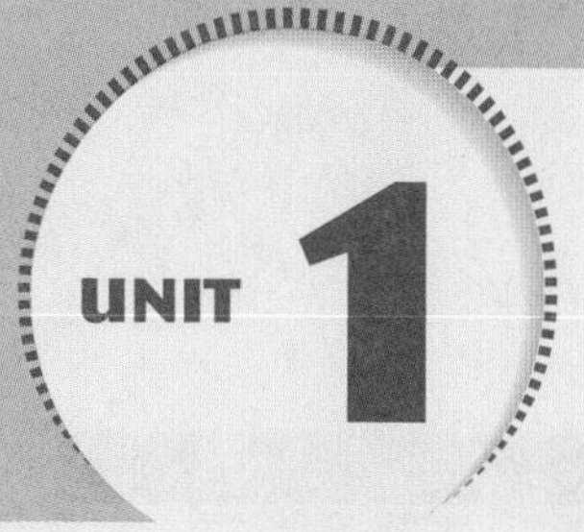

Algebra, Integers, and Equation Solving

Chapter 1 Variables and Equations

- Write and evaluate numerical and variable expressions.
- Use a variety of strategies to predict, find, and check results.
- Find lengths, perimeters, and areas in real-world situations.

Chapter 2 Integer Operations

- Use integers in numerical and variable expressions.
- Use number properties to solve problems.
- Plot points in a coordinate plane.

Chapter 3 Solving Equations and Inequalities

- Write and solve one- and two-step equations.
- Write and solve one-step inequalities.
- Model real-world situations with equations and inequalities.

From Chapter 3, p. 136
How fast can a polar bear swim?

Unit Resources

These resources are provided to help you prepare for the unit and to customize review materials:

 ***Chapter Resource Books***
- Chapter 1
- Chapter 2
- Chapter 3

 ***Assessment Book***
- Chapters 1–3, pp. 7–45

 ***Technology***
- EasyPlanner CD-ROM
- Test and Practice Generator
- Electronic Lesson Presentations CD-ROM
- eTutorial CD-ROM

 ***Internet***
- Classzone
- eEdition Plus Online
- eWorkbook Plus Online
- eTutorial Plus Online
- EasyPlanner Plus Online

English Learner Support

- Spanish Study Guide
- Multi-Language Glossary
- Chapter Audio Summaries CDs
- Teacher's Edition
  Chapter 1, pp. 2E–2F
  Chapter 2, pp. 50E–50F
  Chapter 3, pp. 104E–104F

Pacing and Assignment Guide

REGULAR SCHEDULE

Lesson	Les. Day	BASIC	AVERAGE	ADVANCED
1.1	Day 1	SRH p. 724 Exs. 1–4; pp. 7–9 Exs. 6–8, 10–16, 18, 21, 22, 25–31	pp. 7–9 Exs. 8–13, 16–22, 24–32	pp. 7–9 Exs. 8–14, 16–24*, 28–32
1.2	Day 1	pp. 12–13 Exs. 10–13, 21–26, 32, 37–39	pp. 12–13 Exs. 10–15, 21–23, 30–32, 37–39	pp. 12–13 Exs. 13–18, 27–31, 37–39
	Day 2	pp. 12–13 Exs. 14–19, 27–30, 34, 40–42	pp. 12–13 Exs. 16–20, 27–29, 33–35, 40–43	pp. 12–13 Exs. 19–23, 32–36*, 41–43
1.3	Day 1	SRH p. 709 Exs. 1–4; pp. 18–19 Exs. 11–16, 23–25, 29–32, 41–43	pp. 18–19 Exs. 13–18, 23–25, 31–34, 41–44	pp. 18–19 Exs. 13–18, 23–25, 33–36, 47–49
	Day 2	SRH p. 714 Exs. 1–5; pp. 18–19 Exs. 19–22, 26–28, 38, 39, 44–49	pp. 18–19 Exs. 19–22, 26–28, 35–39, 45–49	pp. 18–19 Exs. 19–22, 26–28, 37–43*
1.4	Day 1	pp. 22–23 Exs. 12–23, 27–29, 32–37, 44–49	pp. 22–23 Exs. 12–17, 21–23, 27–42, 46–49	pp. 22–23 Exs. 12–17, 24–43*, 47–49
1.5	Day 1	SRH p. 712 Exs. 1–3, p. 717 Exs. 1, 4; pp. 30–31 Exs. 11–22, 27, 29–31, 38–44	pp. 30–31 Exs. 11–22, 27–32, 37–40, 43–45	pp. 30–31 Exs. 11–16, 23–38*, 43–45
1.6	Day 1	SRH p. 713 Exs. 1–5; pp. 36–37 Exs. 7–15, 17–24, 27–29, 33–39	pp. 36–37 Exs. 9–16, 19–29, 32–40	pp. 36–37 Exs. 9–11, 14–18, 21–34*, 38–40
1.7	Day 1	SRH p. 715 Exs. 1–5; pp. 41–43 Exs. 4–12 even, 15–18, 28–33	pp. 41–43 Exs. 4–16 even, 17–21, 28–32	pp. 41–43 Exs. 4–16 even, 19–23, 30–32
	Day 2	pp. 41–43 Exs. 5–13 odd, 19–23, 34–38	pp. 41–43 Exs. 5–15 odd, 22–26, 33–38	pp. 41–43 Exs. 5–15 odd, 24–29*, 36–38
Review	Day 1	pp. 46–47 Exs. 1–35	pp. 46–47 Exs. 1–35	pp. 46–47 Exs. 1–35
Assess	Day 1	Chapter 1 Test	Chapter 1 Test	Chapter 1 Test
YEARLY PACING		Chapter 1 Total – **12 days**	Chapter 1 Total – **12 days**	Remaining – **148 days**

*Challenge Exercises   EP = Extra Practice   SRH = Skills Review Handbook   EC = Extra Challenge

BLOCK SCHEDULE

DAY 1	DAY 2	DAY 3	DAY 4	DAY 5	DAY 6
1.1 pp. 7–9 Exs. 8–13, 16–22, 24–32 **1.2** pp. 12–13 Exs. 10–15, 21–23, 30–32, 37–39	**1.2 (cont.)** pp. 12–13 Exs. 16–20, 27–29, 33–35, 40–43 **1.3** pp. 18–19 Exs. 13–18, 23–25, 31–34, 41–44	**1.3 (cont.)** pp. 18–19 Exs. 19–22, 26–28, 35–39, 45–49 **1.4** pp. 22–23 Exs. 12–17, 21–23, 27–42, 46–49	**1.5** pp. 30–31 Exs. 11–22, 27–32, 37–40, 43–45 **1.6** pp. 36–37 Exs. 9–16, 19–29, 32–40	**1.7** pp. 41–43 Exs. 4–26, 28–38	**Review** pp. 46–47 Exs. 1–35 **Assess** Chapter 1 Test

YEARLY PACING	Chapter 1 Total – **6 days**	Chapter 1 Total – **6 days**	Remaining – **74 days**

Support Materials

CHAPTER RESOURCE BOOK

CHAPTER SUPPORT							
Tips for New Teachers	p. 1			Parents as Partners			p. 3

LESSON SUPPORT	1.1	1.2	1.3	1.4	1.5	1.6	1.7
Lesson Plans (regular and block)	p. 5	p. 14	p. 24	p. 34	p. 43	p. 52	p. 62
Technology Activities & Keystrokes		p. 17	p. 26	p. 36			
Activity Support Masters					p. 45	p. 54	
Activity Masters		p. 16					
Practice (3 levels)	p. 7	p. 18	p. 28	p. 37	p. 46	p. 55	p. 64
Study Guide	p. 10	p. 21	p. 31	p. 40	p. 49	p. 58	p. 67
Real-World Problem Solving	p. 12					p. 60	
Challenge Practice	p. 13	p. 23	p. 33	p. 42	p. 51	p. 61	p. 69

REVIEW			
Games Support Masters	p. 70	Cooperative Project with Rubric	p. 74
Chapter Review Games and Activities	p. 71	Extra Credit Project with Rubric	p. 76
Real-Life Project with Rubric	p. 72	Cumulative Practice	p. 78
		Resource Book Answers	A1

ASSESSMENT

Quizzes	p. 7	Alternative Assessments with Rubrics	p. 16
Chapter Tests (3 levels)	p. 9	Unit Test	p. 40
Standardized Test	p. 15	Cumulative Test	p. 42

TRANSPARENCIES

	1.1	1.2	1.3	1.4	1.5	1.6	1.7
Warm-Up / Daily Homework Quiz	✔	✔	✔	✔	✔	✔	✔
Notetaking Guide	✔	✔	✔	✔	✔	✔	✔
Teacher Support					✔		
English/Spanish Problem Solving	✔	✔	✔		✔	✔	✔
Answer Transparencies	✔	✔	✔	✔	✔	✔	✔

TECHNOLOGY

- EasyPlanner CD-ROM
- Test and Practice Generator
- Electronic Lesson Presentations
- eTutorial CD-ROM
- Chapter Audio Summaries CDs
- Classzone.com
- eEdition Plus Online
- eWorkbook Plus Online
- eTutorial Plus Online
- EasyPlanner Plus Online

ADDITIONAL RESOURCES

- Worked-Out Solution Key
- Notetaking Guide
- Practice Workbook
- Tutor Place
- Professional Development Book
- Special Activities Book
- Posters
- Spanish Study Guide
- Exercises in Spanish
- English/Spanish Ch. Reviews/Tests
- Multi-Language Visual Glossary

Math Background and Teaching Strategies

Lesson 1.1

MATH BACKGROUND

A **bar graph** displays data that are divided into categories. The lengths of the bars represent the number of data values in each category. A bar graph may be horizontal or vertical. A *double bar graph* compares two data sets on the same graph. A **histogram** differs from a bar graph in that it displays data that fall into consecutive, non-overlapping, equal, numerical intervals. The heights of the bars represent the frequency of occurrence of data values in each interval.

TEACHING STRATEGIES

To help distinguish between bar graphs and histograms, have students create a bar graph of the classroom data about T-shirts shown below and a histogram of the data about height. Make sure they recognize the difference between data in categories and data in intervals.

What Size T-Shirt Do You Wear?	
Size	Number
S	5
M	9
L	6
XL	4
XXL	2

How Tall Are You to the Nearest Inch?	
Height (in.)	Frequency
60–62	5
63–65	7
66–68	9
69–71	3
72–74	2

Lesson 1.2

MATH BACKGROUND

ORDER OF OPERATIONS To ensure a unique answer to a calculation involving a sequence of two or more operations, mathematicians have agreed upon an order in which to do the operations. First evaluate expressions inside grouping symbols, then evaluate powers. Next, multiply and divide from left to right, and then add and subtract from left to right. When using a scientific or graphing calculator, consult the instruction manual for the built-in order of operations.

TEACHING STRATEGIES

Write expressions on the board or overhead for students to evaluate using the order of operations. Present the classic mnemonic device for the order of operations: "Please Excuse My Dear Aunt Sally," for *P*arentheses, *E*xponents, *M*ultiplication and *D*ivision, and *A*ddition and *S*ubtraction. (Note that this anticipates the introduction of exponents in Lesson 1.4.)

Lesson 1.3

MATH BACKGROUND

A **variable expression** includes numbers, variables, and operations to be performed between them, along with any grouping symbols. It does not include an equal sign or any inequality signs. A **variable** represents an unknown number, and is usually represented by a letter. To evaluate a variable expression for specific values of any variables, substitute those values and then simplify the resulting numerical expression.

TEACHING STRATEGIES

WRITING AND TRANSLATING EXPRESSIONS Students should see writing verbal and variable expressions, translating between them, and applying them as part of a single process that also includes evaluating them for different values of the variables and simplifying the resulting numerical expressions. To emphasize this, have students suggest verbal phrases and translate them into variable expressions. Then have them suggest different values to substitute for the variables and simplify the result. Emphasize that the numerical value depends upon the values that are substituted for the variables.

Lesson 1.4

MATH BACKGROUND

A **power** is a short-hand way to express the repeated multiplication of a **base**, which can be a number, variable, or expression in parentheses or brackets, a number of times indicated by the **exponent**. The power consists of both the base and the exponent together. Powers can be expressed verbally in different ways. For example, x^3 can be read as "the third power of x," "x to the third power," or "x cubed."

TEACHING STRATEGIES

Have students work in pairs. Each pair should have two number cubes and a calculator. Have students roll the number cubes successively, using the first value for the base of a power and the second for the exponent. Have students write each power both in exponential form and as a repeated multiplication. Then have them evaluate the power, using a calculator as needed for the higher powers. Students should realize that powers can become very large even for small values of the base and exponent. For example, $6^6 = 46{,}656$.

Lesson 1.5

MATH BACKGROUND

While a variable expression lacks an equal sign, an **equation** uses an equal sign to state that two expressions are equivalent. Because the expressions in an equation are not equivalent for all values of a variable (unless the equation is an *identity*), the equation must be *solved* to find any values of a variable that make the equation a true statement. Thus, while a variable expression is "open" in that its value can be changed at will by substituting a different value for the variable, an equation is "closed" in that it is true only when a certain value or values are substituted for the variable.

TEACHING STRATEGIES

MENTAL MATH In this chapter, only equations that can be solved by mental math will appear. Thus, stress to students the importance of being able to state and understand an equation verbally. This will allow students to ask themselves "What am I looking for?" For example, students should be able to translate $p \div 5 = 15$ as "a number p divided by 5 is equal to 15," which indicates to look for the number that will give a quotient of 15 when it is divided by 5. At this point, the student may also want to use the guess-and-check strategy to help find the solution.

Lesson 1.6

MATH BACKGROUND

Formulas are real-world equations, such as $I = Prt$, that express the equivalence of two or more quantities, in this case that of simple interest and the product of the principal, interest rate, and time. Some of the more commonly encountered elementary formulas are those for the perimeter, P, and area, A, of a rectangle of length l and width w, $P = 2l + 2w$ and $A = lw$, and the corollary formulas for the perimeter and area of a square with side length s, $P = 4s$ and $A = s^2$. The distance formula, $d = rt$, relates distance traveled, d, with the product of the rate of travel, r, and the time of travel, t.

TEACHING STRATEGIES

On the board or overhead, write the formula for the area of a rectangle or the distance formula. Make a table with columns for each of the three variables in the formula. In the rows, give values for two of the three variables, as shown below.

Distance (mi)	Rate (mi/h)	Time (h)
?	20	2
?	25	2
100	?	4
400	50	?

Have students find the missing values by substituting in the formula or by using mental math. This will give students a clearer picture of how the variables relate to each other.

Lesson 1.7

MATH BACKGROUND

PROBLEM SOLVING Just as you may use many means to get to work: by car, bus, train, bicycle, foot, or a combination, there are many ways to solve a mathematical problem. Whether getting to work or solving a problem, you must thoroughly understand the situation and the options available to you, make a plan, and carry out the plan. In the case of a mathematical problem, you should also look back to make sure that your answer is reasonable for the situation.

TEACHING STRATEGIES

Have students suggest a real-life problem similar to one they might actually use and apply the 4-step problem solving plan to its solution. Some examples might be to find how long it would take to get to a destination at a certain speed, what score is needed on a test to have a certain total test score, or how much money should be set aside each week to purchase an item. Students should realize that the general approach is the same in any of these situations.

Differentiating Instruction

At the start of each chapter, we will outline modifications of curriculum and instruction designed to address the unique needs of Underachieving Students, English Learners, and Advanced Learners. Underachievers are those whose mathematics achievement is below grade level who need strategic and sustained assistance in order to be successful in mathematics. English Learners are those who are not yet fluent in English. Advanced Learners are those whose mathematics achievement is above grade level. Each class of students is different, and you may find your whole class benefits from some of these suggestions. Most of the activities for Underachievers and English Learners would best be done in a second class period, as homework, or in a tutorial, since both groups of students need increased instructional time in mathematics. Some of the activities, particularly those involving vocabulary development, would fit nicely into a language arts period. The activities for Advanced Learners in these pages and throughout the text are meant as substitutes for easier problems in the text.

Strategies for Underachievers

USE TECHNOLOGY

GRAPHING In Lesson 1.1, all students, but especially those who have difficulty constructing bar graphs and histograms, may benefit by having access to computers and software such as spreadsheet software that will create graphs for entered data. This will give students instant feedback when they change data values, and will also allow them to change and experiment with the scale and other parameters of the graph. When students make a change in data or graph parameters, make sure that they can describe any change that they make and its result on the graph.

In Lesson 1.2, underachievers can benefit from the use of a calculator. Allow students who can understand order of operations but have difficulties with computation to use a simple calculator that does not follow the order of operations. That way, these students will still have to follow the order of operations to show their step-by-step computations. As always when using a calculator, students should check their answers for reasonableness.

In Lesson 1.4, the focus is on understanding powers. You may wish to allow students to use a calculator to evaluate higher powers, since numerical results can get large quickly. Using a calculator, students can also experiment to see how quickly powers grow as the exponent increases.

USE MODELS

In Hands-on Activity 1.6 and Lesson 1.6, you may want to provide students with graph paper to draw rectangles and squares and find perimeter and area. This will allow them to count as needed to reinforce the concepts of perimeter and area.

DECREASE COMPLEXITY

In Lesson 1.1, it may help some students to work with histograms using fewer intervals and with intervals involving only whole numbers.

USE SCAFFOLDING

Scaffolding is a pedagogical technique designed to help students build the understanding they need for solving complex and multi-step problems. It involves breaking down problems so that they can be solved by a step-by-step approach. In Lesson 1.2, some underachievers may benefit from scaffolding of complicated evaluations of expressions involving order of operations, such as the following:

$$\begin{aligned} &18 \div (8 + 4 - 9) \\ &= 18 \div (\underline{?} - 9) \\ &= 18 \div \underline{?} \\ &= \underline{?} \end{aligned}$$

This can help students learn to show all steps in their work, which is essential to evaluating expressions correctly.

In Lesson 1.5 and especially in Lesson 1.7, you may wish to enlist the assistance of a Reading Specialist to help some underachievers with strategies for selecting the important information out of word problems in order to set up accurate equations.

IDENTIFY KEY TERMS

In Lesson 1.3, on page 16, there is a vocabulary list of words and phrases that correspond to the mathematical operations of addition, subtraction, multiplication, and division. Students may benefit from organizing this list using note cards that list the word or phrase and the indicated operation. Encourage students to write verbal expressions that include each word or phrase, along with a mathematical translation of the expression.

Strategies for English Learners

EXPLAIN KEY WORDS

For students without a lot of mathematics vocabulary, sometimes the best explanation of a key word is a simple problem or illustration. For example, the word *variable* is used repeatedly in algebra and is often represented by the letter x, although any letter can be used. The letter stands for a number that changes, or varies. Later you will discuss with students the difference between a variable and a constant. Although using a letter to stand for an unknown number is a new concept for many students, most will be familiar with using an answer blank or a question mark for an unknown.

REWORD PROBLEMS

At the beginning of the year you may want to focus on using math problems that require little or no reading in English. As the year goes on, and the constant emphasis on vocabulary study results in improved reading skills, you can increase the number of problems that require reading and increase the length of word problems. Many math problems can be rewritten in an "if . . . then" format. For example, students could be asked to "Evaluate the variable expression when $x = 3$," and given four problems to solve. At the beginning of the year, the English can be minimized so that the student can do the mathematics if he or she can read the word *if*, understand the equal sign, and understand that a letter represents a number. It can read:

If $x = 3$, $7x = \underline{?}$

$5 + x = \underline{?}$

$\frac{12}{x} = \underline{?}$

$x - 2 = \underline{?}$

If the teacher works several of these problems for students in the "if . . . then" format, it will help them understand what they are asked to do.

Strategies for Advanced Learners

INCREASE DEPTH AND COMPLEXITY

CREATE SURVEYS Lesson 1.1 can provide an excellent opportunity to engage students in a project. Most students enjoy creating and administering survey questions. The data for Exercises 18–20 on page 8 provide an example of data that can be elicited by a survey question. Allow students to choose topics that are of interest to them. Then guide them in creating questions that will elicit data that can be used in bar graphs, tables, and histograms.

In Lesson 1.3, after completing Exercise 40 on page 19, advanced learners may wish to develop their own problems to challenge each other. Students should be able to answer their own problems before giving them to others.

USE CROSS-CURRICULAR CONNECTIONS

REAL-WORLD GRAPHS Students will encounter bar graphs and histograms in many other subjects. As students attend other classes, especially science and social science classes, ask them to pay special attention to the graphs they encounter. Their teachers in these classes may be able to suggest related information that students can research and display in a bar graph or histogram. Students may also be able to come up with survey questions that relate to other classes and then create graphs for the data produced.

Differentiating Instruction: Teaching Resources

Differentiating Practice

McDougal Littell *Middle School Mathematics* offers teachers a wide variety of practice for all levels of students. Pictured on these pages are facsimiles of the Level A, Level B, Level C, and Challenge Practice pages from the *Chapter 1 Resource Book*, pages from the *Practice Workbook*, and the *Test and Practice Generator*.

Resource Book

The *Chapter Resource Books* contain three levels of practice, A (Basic), B (Average), and C (Advanced), for each lesson in the textbook. Also included is a page of Challenge practice for each lesson for your most advanced students.

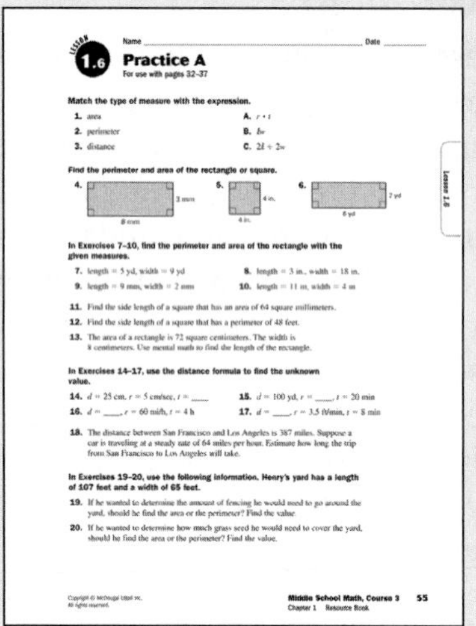

Lesson 1.6 Name ________ Date ________

Practice A
For use with pages 32–37

Match the type of measure with the expression.

1. area — A. $r \cdot t$
2. perimeter — B. lw
3. distance — C. $2l + 2w$

Find the perimeter and area of the rectangle or square.

4. 8 mm, 3 mm
5. 4 in., 4 in.
6. 8 yd, 7 yd

In Exercises 7–10, find the perimeter and area of the rectangle with the given measures.

7. length = 5 yd, width = 9 yd
8. length = 3 in., width = 18 in.
9. length = 9 mm, width = 2 mm
10. length = 11 m, width = 4 m
11. Find the side length of a square that has an area of 64 square millimeters.
12. Find the side length of a square that has a perimeter of 48 feet.
13. The area of a rectangle is 72 square centimeters. The width is 8 centimeters. Use mental math to find the length of the rectangle.

In Exercises 14–17, use the distance formula to find the unknown value.

14. d = 25 cm, r = 5 cm/sec, t = ____
15. d = 100 yd, r = ____, t = 20 min
16. d = ____, r = 60 mi/h, t = 4 h
17. d = ____, r = 3.5 ft/min, t = 8 min
18. The distance between San Francisco and Los Angeles is 387 miles. Suppose a car is traveling at a steady rate of 64 miles per hour. Estimate how long the trip from San Francisco to Los Angeles will take.

In Exercises 19–20, use the following information. Henry's yard has a length of 107 feet and a width of 65 feet.

19. If he wanted to determine the amount of fencing he would need to go around the yard, should he find the area or the perimeter? Find the value.
20. If he wanted to determine how much grass seed he would need to cover the yard, should he find the area or the perimeter? Find the value.

Lesson 1.6

Copyright © McDougal Littell Inc. All rights reserved.

Middle School Math, Course 3 Chapter 1 Resource Book 55

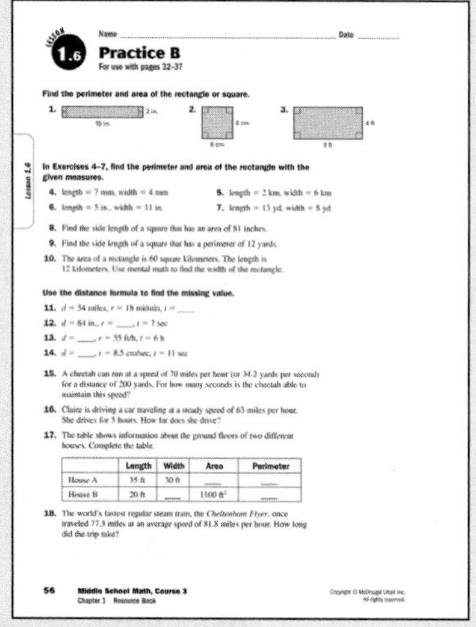

Lesson 1.6 Name ________ Date ________

Practice B
For use with pages 32–37

Find the perimeter and area of the rectangle or square.

1. 15 in., 2 in.
2. 8 cm, 8 cm
3. 9 ft, 4 ft

In Exercises 4–7, find the perimeter and area of the rectangle with the given measures.

4. length = 7 mm, width = 4 mm
5. length = 2 km, width = 6 km
6. length = 5 in., width = 11 in.
7. length = 13 yd, width = 8 yd
8. Find the side length of a square that has an area of 81 inches.
9. Find the side length of a square that has a perimeter of 12 yards.
10. The area of a rectangle is 60 square kilometers. The length is 12 kilometers. Use mental math to find the width of the rectangle.

Use the distance formula to find the missing value.

11. d = 54 miles, r = 18 mi/min, t = ____
12. d = 84 in., r = ____, t = 7 sec
13. d = ____, r = 55 ft/h, t = 6 h
14. d = ____, r = 8.5 cm/sec, t = 11 sec
15. A cheetah can run at a speed of 70 miles per hour (or 34.2 yards per second) for a distance of 200 yards. For how many seconds is the cheetah able to maintain this speed?
16. Claire is driving a car traveling at a steady speed of 63 miles per hour. She drives for 3 hours. How far does she drive?
17. The table shows information about the ground floors of two different houses. Complete the table.

	Length	Width	Area	Perimeter
House A	35 ft	30 ft	____	____
House B	20 ft	____	1100 ft^2	____

18. The world's fastest regular steam train, the *Cheltenham Flyer*, once traveled 77.3 miles at an average speed of 81.8 miles per hour. How long did the trip take?

Lesson 1.6

56 Middle School Math, Course 3 Chapter 1 Resource Book

Copyright © McDougal Littell Inc. All rights reserved.

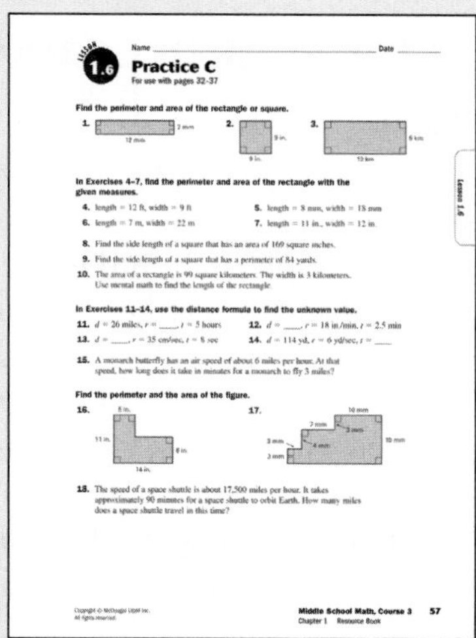

Lesson 1.6 Name ________ Date ________

Practice C
For use with pages 32–37

Find the perimeter and area of the rectangle or square.

1. 12 mm, 2 mm
2. 9 in., 9 in.
3. 12 km, 6 km

In Exercises 4–7, find the perimeter and area of the rectangle with the given measures.

4. length = 12 ft, width = 9 ft
5. length = 8 mm, width = 18 mm
6. length = 7 m, width = 22 m
7. length = 11 in., width = 12 in.
8. Find the side length of a square that has an area of 169 square inches.
9. Find the side length of a square that has a perimeter of 84 yards.
10. The area of a rectangle is 99 square kilometers. The width is 3 kilometers. Use mental math to find the length of the rectangle.

In Exercises 11–14, use the distance formula to find the unknown value.

11. d = 26 miles, r = ____, t = 5 hours
12. d = ____, r = 18 in./min, t = 2.5 min
13. d = ____, r = 35 cm/sec, t = 8 sec
14. d = 114 yd, r = 6 yd/sec, t = ____
15. A monarch butterfly has an air speed of about 6 miles per hour. At that speed, how long does it take in minutes for a monarch to fly 3 miles?

Find the perimeter and the area of the figure.

16. 8 in., 11 in., 8 in., 14 in.
17. 10 mm, 2 mm, 3 mm, 4 mm, 3 mm, 3 mm, 10 mm

18. The speed of a space shuttle is about 17,500 miles per hour. It takes approximately 90 minutes for a space shuttle to orbit Earth. How many miles does a space shuttle travel in this time?

Lesson 1.6

Copyright © McDougal Littell Inc. All rights reserved.

Middle School Math, Course 3 Chapter 1 Resource Book 57

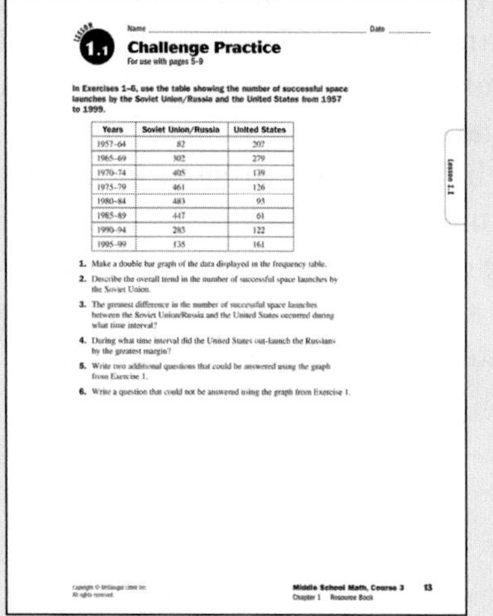

Lesson 1.1 Name ________ Date ________

Challenge Practice
For use with pages 5–9

In Exercises 1–6, use the table showing the number of successful space launches by the Soviet Union/Russia and the United States from 1957 to 1999.

Years	Soviet Union/Russia	United States
1957–64	82	207
1965–69	302	279
1970–74	405	139
1975–79	461	126
1980–84	483	93
1985–89	447	61
1990–94	283	122
1995–99	135	161

1. Make a double bar graph of the data displayed in the frequency table.
2. Describe the overall trend in the number of successful space launches by the Soviet Union.
3. The greatest difference in the number of successful space launches between the Soviet Union/Russia and the United States occurred during what time interval?
4. During what time interval did the United States out-launch the Russians by the greatest margin?
5. Write two additional questions that could be answered using the graph from Exercise 1.
6. Write a question that could not be answered using the graph from Exercise 1.

Lesson 1.1

Copyright © McDougal Littell Inc. All rights reserved.

Middle School Math, Course 3 Chapter 1 Resource Book 13

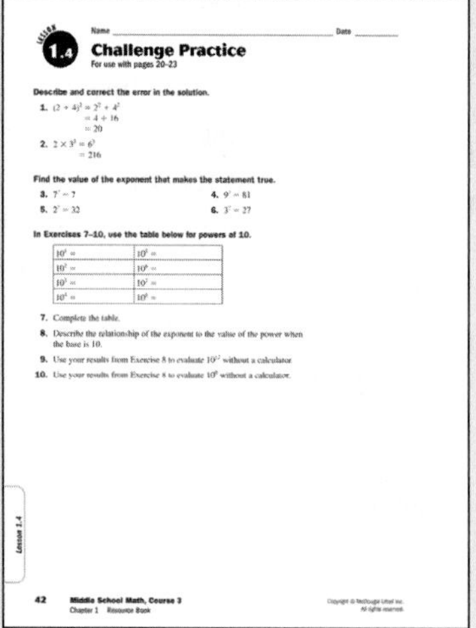

Lesson 1.4 Name ________ Date ________

Challenge Practice
For use with pages 20–23

Describe and correct the error in the solution.

1. $(2 + 4)^2 = 2^2 + 4^2$
   $= 4 + 16$
   $= 20$
2. $2 \times 3^3 = 6^3$
   $= 216$

Find the value of the exponent that makes the statement true.

3. $7^? = 7$
4. $9^? = 81$
5. $2^? = 32$
6. $3^? = 27$

In Exercises 7–10, use the table below for powers of 10.

10^1 =	10^5 =
10^2 =	10^6 =
10^3 =	10^7 =
10^4 =	10^8 =

7. Complete the table.
8. Describe the relationship of the exponent to the value of the power when the base is 10.
9. Use your results from Exercise 8 to evaluate 10^{12} without a calculator.
10. Use your results from Exercise 8 to evaluate 10^9 without a calculator.

Lesson 1.4

42 Middle School Math, Course 3 Chapter 1 Resource Book

Copyright © McDougal Littell Inc. All rights reserved.

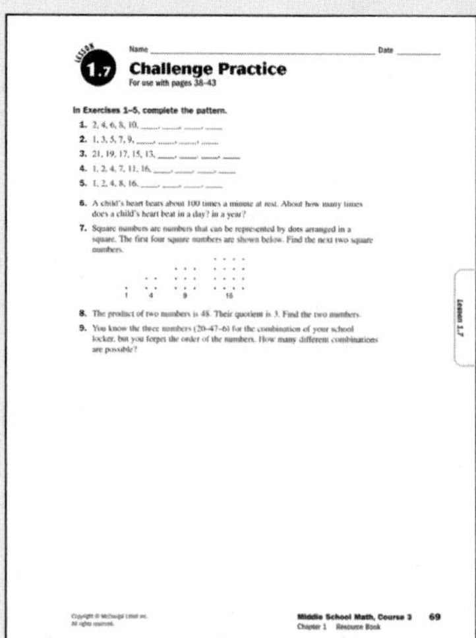

Lesson 1.7 Name ________ Date ________

Challenge Practice
For use with pages 38–43

In Exercises 1–5, complete the pattern.

1. 2, 4, 6, 8, 10, ____, ____, ____, ____
2. 1, 3, 5, 7, 9, ____, ____, ____, ____
3. 21, 19, 17, 15, 13, ____, ____, ____, ____
4. 1, 2, 4, 7, 11, 16, ____, ____, ____, ____
5. 1, 2, 4, 8, 16, ____, ____, ____, ____
6. A child's heart beats about 100 times a minute at rest. About how many times does a child's heart beat in a day? in a year?
7. Square numbers are numbers that can be represented by dots arranged in a square. The first four square numbers are shown below. Find the next two square numbers.

   1 4 9 16

8. The product of two numbers is 48. Their quotient is 3. Find the two numbers.
9. You know the three numbers (20-47-6) for the combination of your school locker, but you forget the order of the numbers. How many different combinations are possible?

Lesson 1.7

Copyright © McDougal Littell Inc. All rights reserved.

Middle School Math, Course 3 Chapter 1 Resource Book 69

Practice Workbook

The *Practice Workbook* contains the average B-level practice for each lesson reformatted in workbook form to allow students to show their work for each exercise.

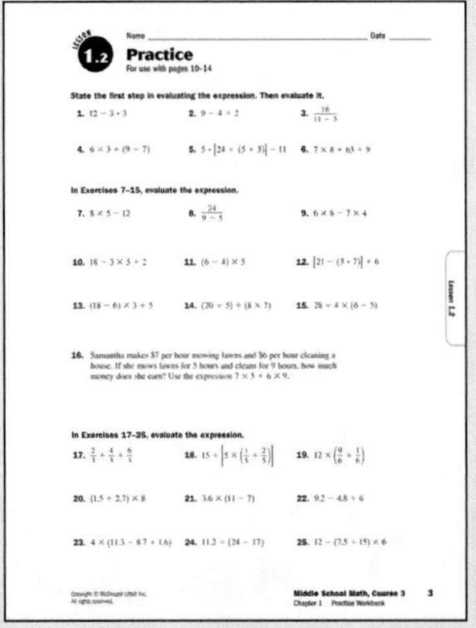

LESSON 1.2 Name ____ Date ____

Practice

For use with pages 10–14

State the first step in evaluating the expression. Then evaluate it.

1. $12 - 3 \cdot 3$
2. $9 - 4 \div 2$
3. $\frac{16}{11 - 3}$
4. $6 \times 3 + (9 - 7)$
5. $5 \cdot [24 \div (5 + 3)] - 11$
6. $7 \times 8 + 63 \div 9$

In Exercises 7–15, evaluate the expression.

7. $8 \times 5 - 12$
8. $\frac{24}{9 - 5}$
9. $6 \times 8 - 7 \times 4$
10. $18 - 3 \times 5 \div 2$
11. $(6 - 4) \times 5$
12. $[21 - (3 \cdot 7)] + 6$
13. $(18 - 6) \times 3 + 5$
14. $(20 \div 5) + (8 \times 7)$
15. $28 \div 4 \times (6 - 5)$
16. Samantha makes $7 per hour mowing lawns and $6 per hour cleaning a house. If she mows lawns for 5 hours and cleans for 9 hours, how much money does she earn? Use the expression $7 \times 5 + 6 \times 9$.

In Exercises 17–25, evaluate the expression.

17. $\frac{2}{3} + \frac{4}{3} + \frac{6}{3}$
18. $15 \div \left[5 \times \left(\frac{1}{5} + \frac{2}{5}\right)\right]$
19. $12 \times \left(\frac{9}{6} + \frac{1}{6}\right)$
20. $(1.5 + 2.7) \times 8$
21. $3.6 \times (11 - 7)$
22. $9.2 - 4.8 \div 6$
23. $4 \times (11.3 - 8.7 + 1.6)$
24. $11.2 \div (24 - 17)$
25. $12 - (7.5 \div 15) \times 6$

Lesson 1.2

Copyright © McDougal Littell Inc. All rights reserved.

Middle School Math, Course 3 3
Chapter 1 Practice Workbook

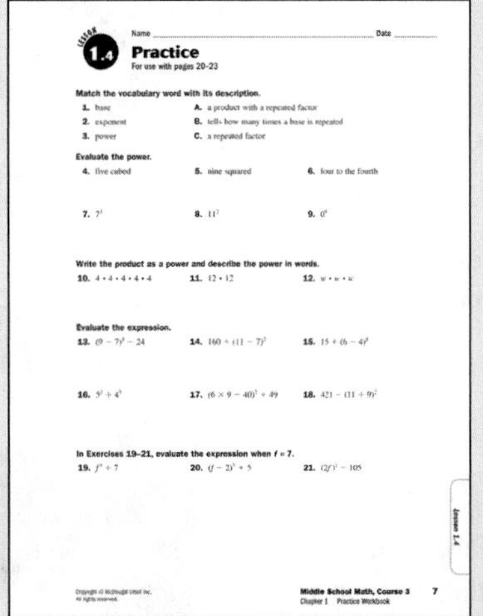

LESSON 1.4 Name ____ Date ____

Practice

For use with pages 20–23

Match the vocabulary word with its description.

1. base — A. a product with a repeated factor
2. exponent — B. tells how many times a base is repeated
3. power — C. a repeated factor

Evaluate the power.

4. five cubed
5. nine squared
6. four to the fourth
7. 7^3
8. 11^2
9. 0^6

Write the product as a power and describe the power in words.

10. $4 \cdot 4 \cdot 4 \cdot 4 \cdot 4$
11. $12 \cdot 12$
12. $w \cdot w \cdot w$

Evaluate the expression.

13. $(9 - 7)^5 - 24$
14. $160 \div (11 - 7)^2$
15. $15 + (6 - 4)^3$
16. $5^2 + 4^3$
17. $(6 \times 9 - 40)^2 + 49$
18. $421 - (11 + 9)^2$

In Exercises 19–21, evaluate the expression when $f = 7$.

19. $f^2 + 7$
20. $(f - 2)^3 + 5$
21. $(2f)^2 - 105$

Lesson 1.4

Copyright © McDougal Littell Inc. All rights reserved.

Middle School Math, Course 3 7
Chapter 1 Practice Workbook

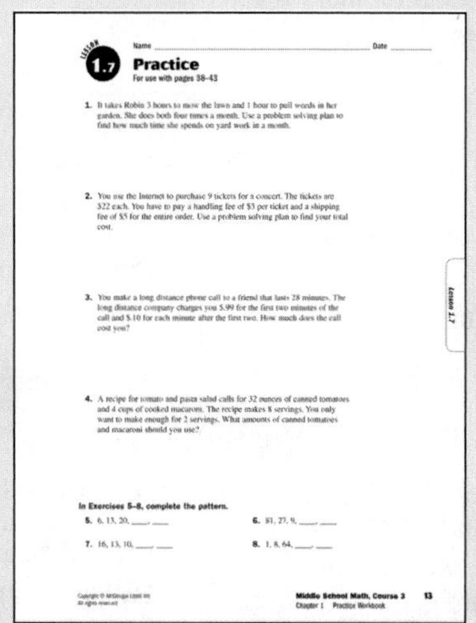

LESSON 1.7 Name ____ Date ____

Practice

For use with pages 38–43

1. It takes Robin 3 hours to mow the lawn and 1 hour to pull weeds in her garden. She does both four times a month. Use a problem solving plan to find how much time she spends on yard work in a month.
2. You use the Internet to purchase 9 tickets for a concert. The tickets are $22 each. You have to pay a handling fee of $3 per ticket and a shipping fee of $5 for the entire order. Use a problem solving plan to find your total cost.
3. You make a long distance phone call to a friend that lasts 28 minutes. The long distance company charges you $.99 for the first two minutes of the call and $.10 for each minute after the first two. How much does the call cost you?
4. A recipe for tomato and pasta salad calls for 32 ounces of canned tomatoes and 4 cups of cooked macaroni. The recipe makes 8 servings. You only want to make enough for 2 servings. What amounts of canned tomatoes and macaroni should you use?

In Exercises 5–8, complete the pattern.

5. 6, 13, 20, ___, ___
6. 81, 27, 9, ___, ___
7. 16, 13, 10, ___, ___
8. 1, 8, 64, ___, ___

Lesson 1.7

Copyright © McDougal Littell Inc. All rights reserved.

Middle School Math, Course 3 13
Chapter 1 Practice Workbook

Test and Practice Generator CD-ROM

The *Test and Practice Generator* allows you to create practice worksheets for each lesson using both static and algorithmic exercises.

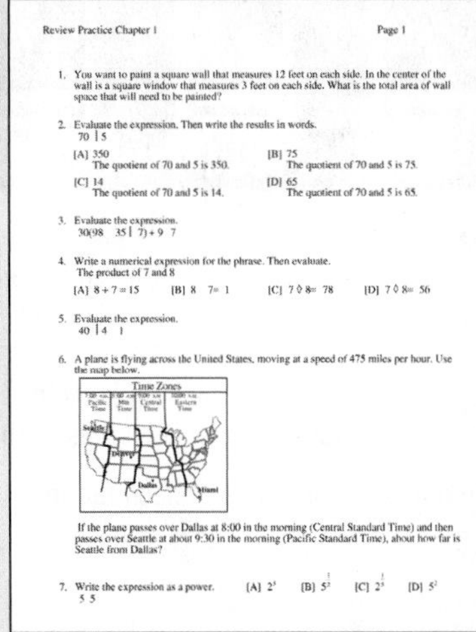

Review Practice Chapter 1 Page 1

1. You want to paint a square wall that measures 12 feet on each side. In the center of the wall is a square window that measures 3 feet on each side. What is the total area of wall space that will need to be painted?
2. Evaluate the expression. Then write the results in words.
   70 ∣ 5
   [A] 350 The quotient of 70 and 5 is 350.
   [B] 75 The quotient of 70 and 5 is 75.
   [C] 14 The quotient of 70 and 5 is 14.
   [D] 65 The quotient of 70 and 5 is 65.
3. Evaluate the expression.
   30(98 35 ∣ 7) + 9 7
4. Write a numerical expression for the phrase. Then evaluate.
   The product of 7 and 8
   [A] 8 + 7 = 15 [B] 8 7 = 1 [C] 7 ◊ 8 = 78 [D] 7 ◊ 8 = 56
5. Evaluate the expression.
   40 ∣ 4 1
6. A plane is flying across the United States, moving at a speed of 475 miles per hour. Use the map below.

   If the plane passes over Dallas at 8:00 in the morning (Central Standard Time) and then passes over Seattle at about 9:30 in the morning (Pacific Standard Time), about how far is Seattle from Dallas?
7. Write the expression as a power. 5 5
   [A] 2^5 [B] $5^{\frac{1}{2}}$ [C] $2^{\frac{1}{5}}$ [D] 5^2

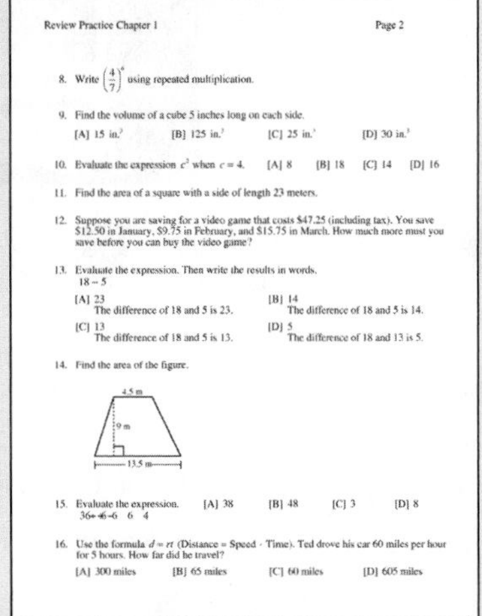

Review Practice Chapter 1 Page 2

8. Write $\left(\frac{4}{7}\right)^6$ using repeated multiplication.
9. Find the volume of a cube 5 inches long on each side.
   [A] 15 in.^{3} [B] 125 in.^{3} [C] 25 in.^{3} [D] 30 in.^{3}
10. Evaluate the expression c^2 when $c = 4$. [A] 8 [B] 18 [C] 14 [D] 16
11. Find the area of a square with a side of length 23 meters.
12. Suppose you are saving for a video game that costs $47.25 (including tax). You save $12.50 in January, $9.75 in February, and $15.75 in March. How much more must you save before you can buy the video game?
13. Evaluate the expression. Then write the results in words.
    18 − 5
    [A] 23 The difference of 18 and 5 is 23.
    [B] 14 The difference of 18 and 5 is 14.
    [C] 13 The difference of 18 and 5 is 13.
    [D] 5 The difference of 18 and 13 is 5.
14. Find the area of the figure.

15. Evaluate the expression. 36 ÷ 6 − 6 6 4
    [A] 38 [B] 48 [C] 3 [D] 8
16. Use the formula $d = rt$ (Distance = Speed · Time). Ted drove his car 60 miles per hour for 5 hours. How far did he travel?
    [A] 300 miles [B] 65 miles [C] 60 miles [D] 605 miles

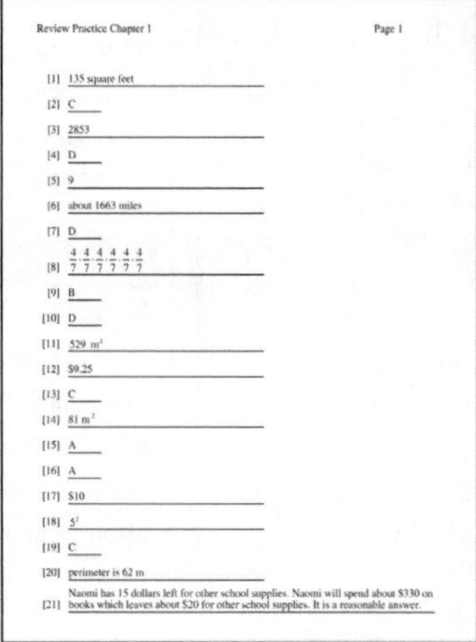

Review Practice Chapter 1 Page 1

[1] 135 square feet
[2] C
[3] 2853
[4] D
[5] 9
[6] about 1663 miles
[7] D
[8] $\frac{4}{7} \cdot \frac{4}{7} \cdot \frac{4}{7} \cdot \frac{4}{7} \cdot \frac{4}{7} \cdot \frac{4}{7}$
[9] B
[10] D
[11] 529 m^2
[12] $9.25
[13] C
[14] 81 m^2
[15] A
[16] A
[17] $10
[18] 5^2
[19] C
[20] perimeter is 62 m
[21] Naomi has 15 dollars left for other school supplies. Naomi will spend about $330 on books which leaves about $20 for other school supplies. It is a reasonable answer.

OVERVIEW

Main Ideas

In this chapter, students use bar graphs and histograms to analyze data. Students use order of operations to evaluate numerical and variable expressions, including expressions with powers. Students write variable expressions and write and solve equations using mental math. Students use formulas to find unknown values. Students also use a four-step solving plan.

Prerequisite Skills

The key skills reviewed in the games on these pages are:

- Finding sums of whole numbers and decimals
- Rounding
- Identifying place value

Additional practice with prerequisite skills can be found in the Review What You Need to Know exercises on page 4. Additional resources for reviewing prerequisite skills are:

- Skills Review Handbook, pp. 704–726
- Tutor Place
- eTutorial Plus

Managing the Games

Tips for Success

In *Lookout Tower*, point out that the sums are not numbers of rungs, because some sums are decimals, and the ladders all stretch the same distance. Students may want to think of the sums as times, so the person with the shortest time is the fastest climber.

Before starting *Next Stop*, ask students to name all place values in a number such as 964.357. Also make sure they realize that the blanks do not correspond to the letters of the answers horizontally opposite them.

Variables and Equations

BEFORE

In previous courses you've...

- Compared quantities
- Performed operations on numbers

Now

In Chapter 1 you'll study...

- Using graphs to analyze data
- Evaluating and writing numerical and variable expressions
- Solving equations using mental math
- A four-step problem solving plan

WHY?

So you can solve real-world problems about...

- volcanoes, p. 5
- cliff diving, p. 23
- tiger beetles, p. 35
- parachuting, p. 37

Internet Preview
CLASSZONE.COM

- eEdition Plus Online
- eWorkbook Plus Online
- eTutorial Plus Online
- State Test Practice
- More Examples

Chapter Warm-Up Games

Review skills you need for this chapter in these quick games.

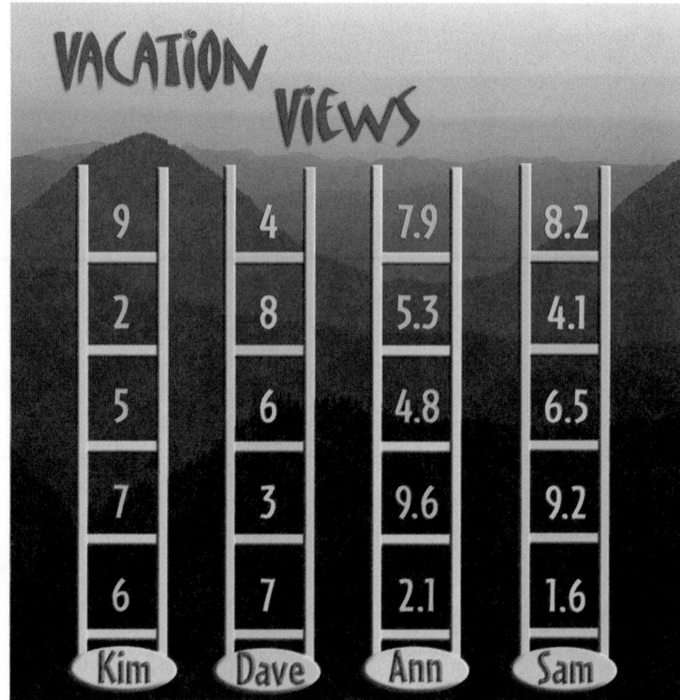

BRAIN GAME

Key Skill:
- Finding the sums of whole numbers and decimals

On a family vacation trip the first stop is a mountain lookout tower. The four ladders lead to the top of the tower. Which child gets to the top first?

- Find the sum of the numbers on the rungs of each ladder. **Kim: 29, Dave: 28, Ann: 29.7, Sam: 29.6**
- The ladder with the least sum is where the fastest person climbs. **Dave gets to the top first.**

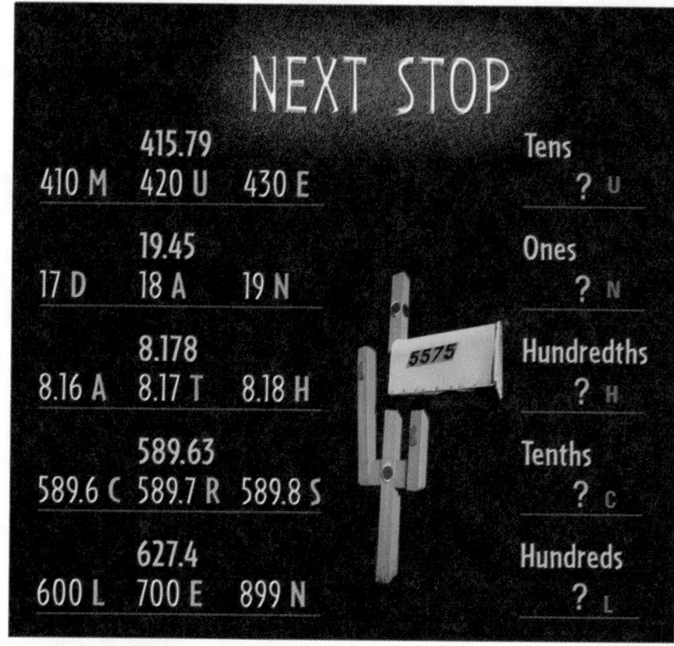

Key Skills:
- Rounding
- Identifying place value

Help the kids figure out what the next stop is on the family trip by solving the puzzle.

- Each number has been rounded to one of its digits. Select the answer that shows the number rounded correctly.
- On the right, write each letter below the place value it was rounded to. **See above.**
- Put letters in correct place value order to figure out the next stop. **LUNCH**

Stop *and* Think

1. **Critical Thinking** Order the names in *Vacation Views* from who gets to the top first to who gets there last (the least sum to the greatest). **Dave, Kim, Sam, Ann**
2. **Writing** In *Next Stop*, a student thinks that the result of rounding 8.178 is 8.17 because the last digit is removed. What is wrong with the student's reasoning? ***Sample Answer:* Since 8 > 5, you cannot just drop it. You need to round up the digit in the hundredths place. So, the correct answer is 8.18.**

3

Reflecting on the Games

After Stop and Think Question 2, ask students how they would round 8.175 to the nearest hundredth. Make sure they realize the convention that if the last digit is 5, and the number is being rounded to the preceding decimal place, then the number is rounded up. Also, let students see an example such as rounding 8.999 to the nearest hundredth (9.00), in which the rounding changes more than one digit.

Chapter Resources

These resources are provided to help you prepare for the chapter and to customize review materials:

Chapter 1 Resource Book
- Tips for New Teachers, pp. 1–2
- Lesson Plan, pp. 5, 14, 24, 34, 43, 52, 62
- Lesson Plan for Block Scheduling, pp. 6, 15, 25, 35, 44, 53, 63

Technology
- EasyPlanner CD-ROM
- Test and Practice Generator
- Electronic Lesson Presentations CD-ROM
- eTutorial CD-ROM

Internet
- Classzone
- eEdition Plus Online
- eWorkbook Plus Online
- eTutorial Plus Online
- EasyPlanner Plus Online

English Learner Support

- Spanish Study Guide
- Multi-Language Glossary
- Chapter Audio Summaries CDs
- Teacher's Edition, pp. 2E–2F

PREPARE

DIAGNOSIS/REMEDIATION

Review What You Need to Know
The Review What You Need to Know exercises can help you diagnose whether students have the following skills needed in Chapter 1:

- Using vocabulary (Exs. 1-2)
- Identifying place value (Exs. 3-6)
- Finding the sum, difference, product, or quotient of two numbers (Exs. 7-19)

Chapter 1 Resource Book

- Study Guide (Lessons 1.1-1.7)

Tutor Place

NOTETAKING STRATEGIES

Some students may not be familiar with keeping a math notebook. Stress that this notebook is for them and them alone; it will not be graded or evaluated. Students should record what is important specifically for them, organized in a consistent manner that will make it easy for them to review the material. Further suggestions for keeping a notebook can be found on page 21.

For more support on notetaking, see:

- Notetaking Guide Workbook
- Notetaking Transparencies

Getting Ready to Learn

Word Watch

Review Words
whole number, p. 704
sum, p. 709
difference, p. 709
product, p. 713
quotient, p. 715

Review What You Need to Know 

Using Vocabulary **Copy and complete using a review word.**

1. When you add two numbers, the result is called the _?_. sum
2. When you multiply two numbers, the result is called the _?_. product

Write the place value of the red digit. *(p. 704)*

3. 26.10 ones
4. 45.901 tenths
5. 139.07 hundreds
6. 6.394 thousandths

Find the sum, difference, product, or quotient. *(p. 709)*

7. 29 + 45 74
8. 103 + 8 111
9. 25 − 12 13
10. 72 − 56 16
11. 13 × 3 39
12. 27 × 8 216
13. 96 ÷ 6 16
14. 60 ÷ 12 5
15. 12.7 − 9.4 3.3
16. 17.8 + 26.3 44.1
17. 9.64 + 6.36 16
18. 20.24 − 16.5 3.74
19. You are shopping for new clothes for school. If you have $75.00 and buy a pair of jeans for $37.75, how much money do you have left? *(p. 709)* $37.25

You should include material that appears on a notebook like this in your own notes.

Know How to Take Notes

Keeping a Notebook Your math notebook is an important tool for learning and reviewing the topics of this course. Here are some tips for organizing your notes. Organize your notes in the same way for each lesson.

Start with the date and topic.

September 7 Decimals

To add decimals, line up the decimal points.

Copy examples shown in class.

Example: Adding Decimals

$$\begin{array}{r} 23.40 \\ +\ 36.15 \\ \hline 59.55 \end{array}$$

In Lesson 1.4, you should organize your notes by labeling the examples that you copy.

4

Interpreting Graphs

BEFORE	Now	WHY?
You compared quantities.	You'll use graphs to analyze data.	So you can make conclusions about mall businesses, as in Exs. 6–8.

Word Watch

bar graph, p. 5
data, p. 5
frequency table, p. 6
histogram, p. 6

In the Real World

Volcanoes The *bar graph* at the right shows the number of historically active volcanoes in four countries. Which country has the most historically active volcanoes?

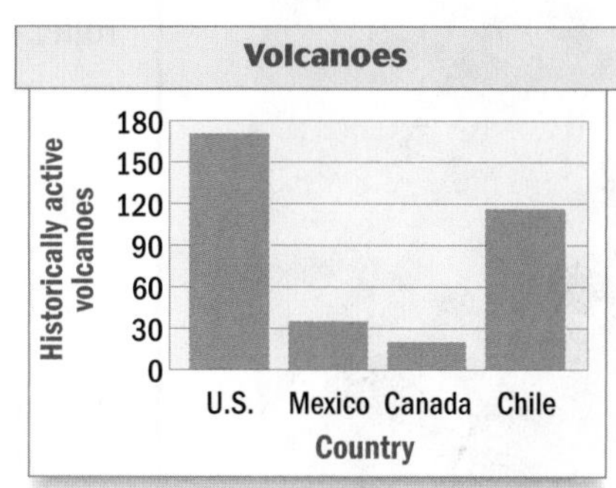

A **bar graph** is a type of graph in which the lengths of bars are used to represent and compare *data* in categories. **Data** are information, facts, or numbers that describe something.

EXAMPLE 1 Interpreting a Bar Graph

Use the bar graph above about volcanoes to answer the question or explain why you can't answer the question using the graph.

a. Which country has the most historically active volcanoes?

b. Which country has the most volcanic eruptions in a given year?

Solution

a. The vertical axis in the bar graph is labeled *Historically active volcanoes,* so the tallest bar represents the country with the most historically active volcanoes. Because the United States has the tallest bar, it has the most historically active volcanoes.

b. Having more historically active volcanoes doesn't necessarily mean having more eruptions, so you can't answer this question from the bar graph.

Your turn now **Use the bar graph about historically active volcanoes.**

1. About how many more historically active volcanoes does Chile have than Mexico? about 80

2. Which country has the least number of historically active volcanoes? Canada

ILLINOIS Standards and ISAT:
10.A.3a

1 PLAN

SKILL CHECK

1. List in order from least to greatest: 91.7, 90.9, 93.3
90.9, 91.7, 93.3

2. Which of the following numbers fall within the range 0.95 to 1.15? 1.05, 11, 1.2, 9.6, 1, 0.98, 1.09
1.05, 1, 0.98, 1.09

Lesson Objective

Use graphs to analyze data.

Pacing

Suggested Number of Days
Basic Course: 1 day
Average Course: 1 day
Advanced Course: 1 day
Block: 0.5 block with 1.2

Teaching Resources

For a complete list of Teaching Resources, see page 2B.

Transparency

Warm-Up Exercises for this lesson are available on a transparency.

2 TEACH

Motivating the Lesson

Ask an Earth Science teacher to talk to the class about volcanoes.

TIPS FOR NEW TEACHERS

After Example 3, have students discuss how bar graphs and histograms are similar and how they are different. See Tips for New Teachers in the *Chapter 1 Resource Book.*

EXTRA EXAMPLES

Example 1 Use the bar graph to answer the question or explain why you cannot answer the question using the graph.

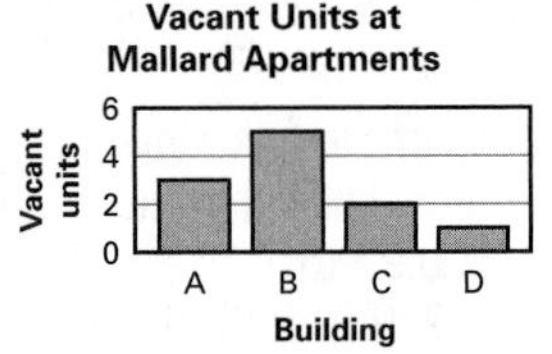

a. Which building has the most vacancies? **B**

b. How many units are occupied in building A? **Cannot answer; the graph does not tell you how many units are in each building.**

Example 2 The data show the heights in inches of tomato plants. Make a frequency table of the data using intervals of 10.
5, 21, 12, 22, 8, 14, 9, 17, 9

Height (in.)	Tally	Freq.
0–10	IIII	4
11–20	III	3
21–30	II	2

Example 3 Make a histogram of the data shown in the frequency table in Extra Example 2.

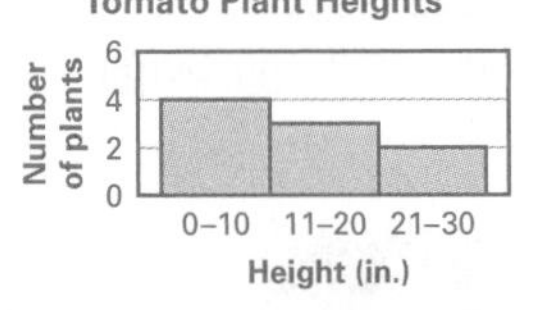

CONCEPT CHECK

How does a histogram help you analyze data? **Because the intervals are equal, you can see the "shape" of the data distribution.**

DAILY PUZZLER

If you write all the multiples of 7 from 7 to 98, which nonzero digit(s) do you write least often? **3, 5, 6**

Histograms When you have a large set of data to organize, you may be able to use a **frequency table** to group the data into *intervals*. The frequency of an interval is the number of values in the interval. You can graph data organized into equal intervals in a **histogram**. The height of each bar in a histogram indicates the frequency of an interval.

EXAMPLE 2 Making a Frequency Table

Roller Coasters The data show the heights, in meters, of the tallest roller coasters in the world. Make a frequency table of the data.

66.4, 94.5, 68.3, 115, 62.5, 97, 66.4, 126.5, 63.4, 74.7, 63.4, 70.1, 66.4, 64.9, 63.7, 79, 63.4, 63.1, 62.5, 61.9, 71.6

1. Choose intervals of equal size for the data.
2. Tally the data in each interval. Use tally marks to record each occurrence of a height in its interval.
3. Write the frequency for each interval by totaling the tally marks.

Height (m)	Tally	Frequency
60–69.9	~~IIII~~ ~~IIII~~ III	13
70–79.9	IIII	4
80–89.9		0
90–99.9	II	2
100–109.9		0
110–119.9	I	1
120–129.9	I	1

with Review

For help with data displays, see p. 724.

EXAMPLE 3 Making a Histogram

Make a histogram of the data shown in the frequency table in Example 2.

1. Draw and label the horizontal and vertical axes. Start the vertical scale at 0 and end at 15. Use increments of 3.
2. Draw a bar to represent the frequency of each interval. The bars of neighboring intervals should touch.
3. Write a title.

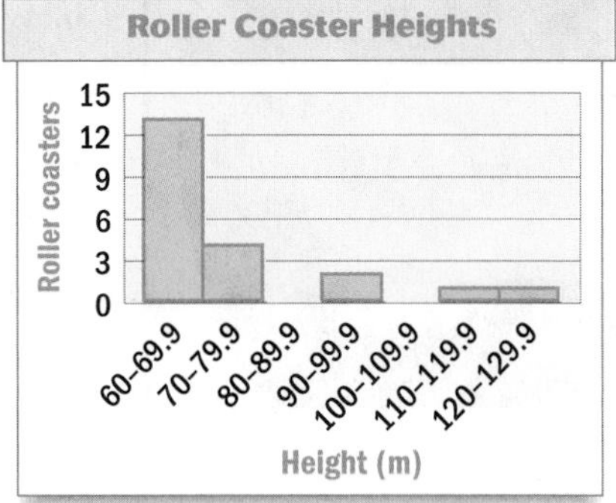

Your turn now

3. Which interval has the greatest number of roller coasters? **60–69.9**
4. When the next roller coaster between 60 and 130 meters tall is built, in what interval do you think it will be? Explain.

4. *Sample answer:* **The 60–69.9 interval; the most roller coasters fall in that interval.**

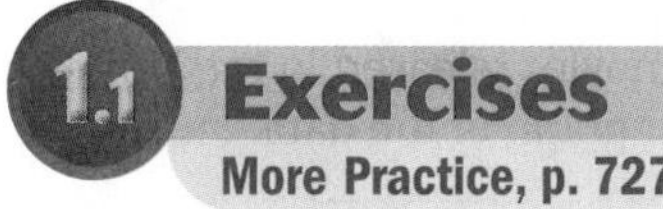

1.1 Exercises

More Practice, p. 727

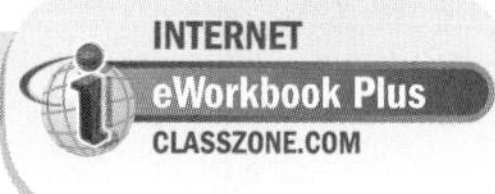

Getting Ready to Practice

1. **Vocabulary** Copy and complete: A histogram is a graph that shows data that are divided equally into _?_. intervals

In Exercises 2–4, use the graph at the right. It displays the number of times each country has won the World Cup in soccer.

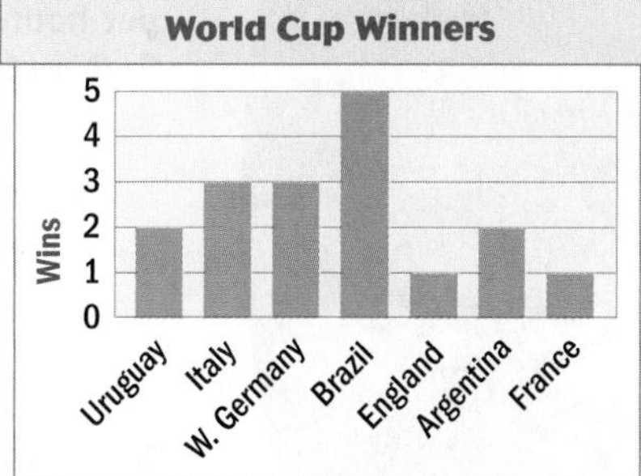

2. What type of graph is shown? bar graph
3. How many times has Italy won? 3 times
4. How many more times has Argentina won than France? 1 time
5. **Guided Problem Solving** The frequency table shows when new states were added to the United States. Use the frequency table to make a graph.

(1) Decide what kind of graph to use. histogram

(2) Draw and label horizontal and vertical axes. Steps 2–3. See margin.

(3) Draw bars. Write a title.

Years	States
1787-1836	25
1837-1886	13
1887-1936	10
1937-1986	2

9. No. *Sample answer:* The category with the most stores might not have the most floor space if each store is small, while a category with fewer stores might have the most floor space if each store is large.

Practice and Problem Solving

HELP with Homework

Example	Exercises
1	6-10, 15-17
2	12, 18-19
3	12-14, 18-20

- More Examples
- eTutorial Plus

Use the bar graph at the right. It shows the number of businesses at a mall in each category.

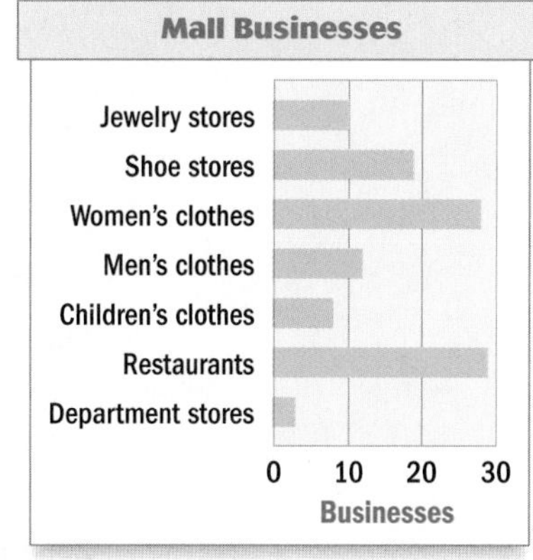

A 6. Which category has the greatest number of businesses? restaurants

7. Which category has the least number of businesses? department stores
8. About how many more shoe stores are there than jewelry stores? about 9 more
9. **Writing** Can you tell from the graph which category of businesses uses the most floor space in the mall? Explain. See margin.

3 APPLY

ASSIGNMENT GUIDE

Basic Course

Day 1: SRH p. 724 Ex. 1-4; pp. 7-9 Exs. 6-8, 10-16, 18, 21, 22, 25-31

Average Course

Day 1: pp. 7-9 Exs. 8-13, 16-22, 24-32

Average Course

Day 1: pp. 7-9 Exs. 8-14, 16-24*, 28-32

Block

pp. 7-9 Exs. 8-13, 16-22, 24-32 (with 1.2)

Extra Practice

- Student Edition, p. 727
- Chapter 1 Resource Book, pp. 7-9
- Test and Practice Generator

Transparency

Even-numbered answers are available on transparencies.

Homework Check

When you review students' homework for this lesson, go over the following exercises to check understanding of key concepts.

Basic: 6, 12, 13, 15, 18

Average: 8, 12, 13, 16, 20

Advanced: 8, 12, 14, 19, 20

Common Error

In Exercise 5, students may confuse bar graphs and histograms. Remind them that bar graphs are appropriate for data in *categories*, and histograms are appropriate for data in *intervals*.

5. Steps 2–3. See Additional Answers beginning on page AA1.

10.

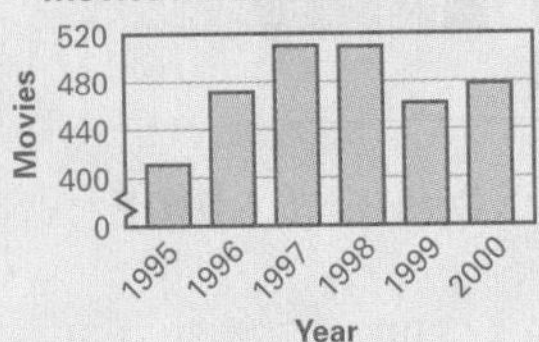

12.

Number of Meteors	Tally	Freq.
0–9	~~||||~~ ~~||||~~ |	11
10–19	~~||||~~ ~~||||~~ |||	13
20–29	~~||||~~ |||	8
30–39	||	2
40–49	|	1
50–59	|	1
60–69	|||	3

13.

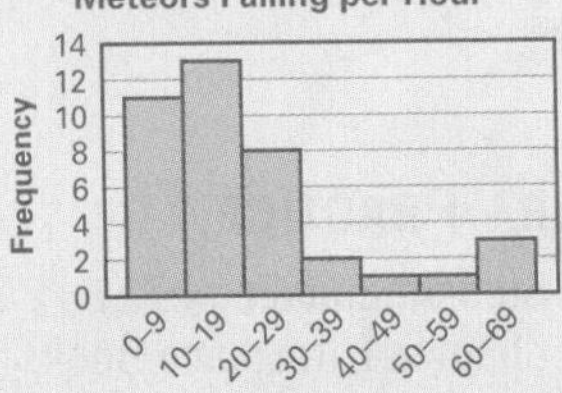

18.

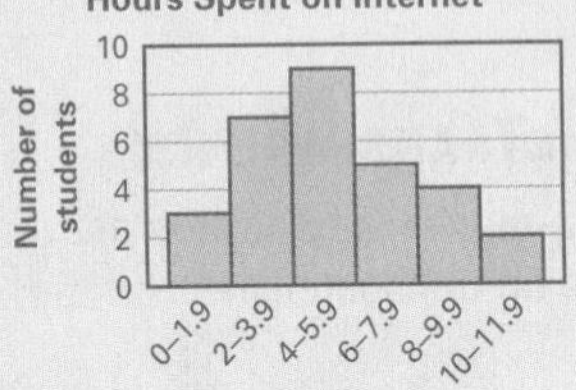

19.

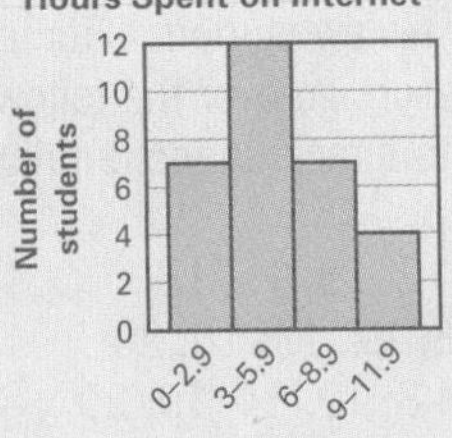

14. Frequency table; exact amounts are given in the frequency table but may be difficult to read from the bar graph.

16. No; the year is part of an interval, so the exact number in 1965 cannot be determined.

20. *Sample answer:* Exercise 18; the intervals are smaller.

10. Movies The table shows the numbers of movies released in the United States from 1995 through 2000. Make a bar graph of the data. **See margin.**

Year	1995	1996	1997	1998	1999	2000
Movies	411	471	510	509	461	478

11. Critical Thinking If you need to know an exact amount, is it easier to find this information from a table or a bar graph? Explain. **Table; exact amounts are given in a table but may be difficult to read from a bar graph.**

Meteors The data show the average numbers of meteors that fall per hour during 39 annual meteor showers. For example, in the first meteor shower, an average of 60 meteors fall each hour. **12–14. See margin.**

60, 4, 1, 5, 5, 1, 40, 4, 5, 20, 2, 15, 8, 6, 21, 15, 20, 30, 3, 15, 10, 62, 25, 26, 50, 12, 20, 12, 15, 30, 10, 10, 20, 12, 12, 60, 10, 12, 20

12. Make a frequency table to organize the data using intervals of 10, starting with 0–9.

13. Make a histogram of the data displayed in the frequency table.

14. Which display would you use to find the number of meteor showers that average 20 to 29 meteors falling per hour? Explain.

Hurricanes The histogram shows the numbers of hurricanes in the Atlantic Ocean from 1950 through 1999.

B **15.** About how many hurricanes were there in the Atlantic Ocean from 1980–1989? **52 hurricanes**

16. Can you determine the number of hurricanes there were in the Atlantic Ocean in 1965? Explain.

17. Can you use the histogram to predict the number of hurricanes in 2000–2009? Why or why not? **No; there does not appear to be a pattern in the data.**

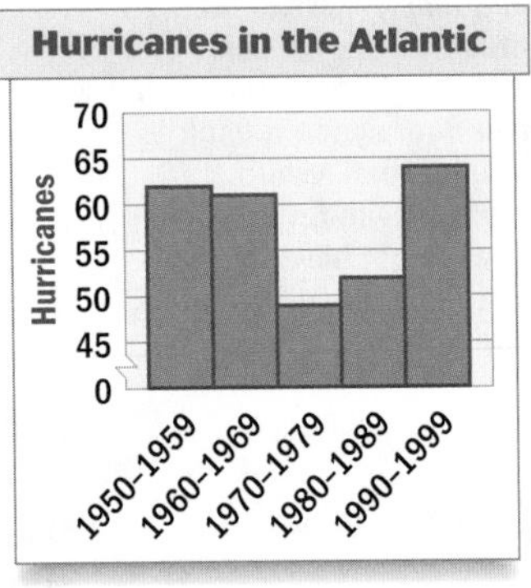

Extended Problem Solving The data show the numbers of hours 30 students in a class spent on the Internet in a week. **18–20. See margin.**

4, 2.5, 5.7, 1.8, 3.7, 5.4, 5.5, 11.6, 3.7, 6.5, 2, 10, 0.5, 4.5, 5, 9.5, 2.1, 4.5, 7.5, 2.5, 8, 1, 9, 4.2, 8, 7, 3, 7, 5, 6

18. Graph Make a histogram of the data using the intervals 0–1.9, 2–3.9, 4–5.9, 6–7.9, 8–9.9, and 10–11.9.

19. Graph Make a histogram of the data using the intervals 0–2.9, 3–5.9, 6–8.9, and 9–11.9.

20. Compare Does the histogram in Exercise 18 or in Exercise 19 give a clearer representation of the data? Explain your reasoning.

21. about 4000 schools

22. *Sample answer:* All of the activities except literary magazines went up slightly, with the greatest increase in radio/TV. Literary magazines showed a slight decrease.

23. It is increasing. *Sample answer:* Yes; more movies are now available on DVD.

24. *Sample answer:* For a histogram, ask students how many pets they have. For a bar graph, ask students what type of pets they have.

Media In Exercises 21 and 22, use the *double bar graph.* It shows the numbers of U.S. high schools with media activities in 1991 and 1998.

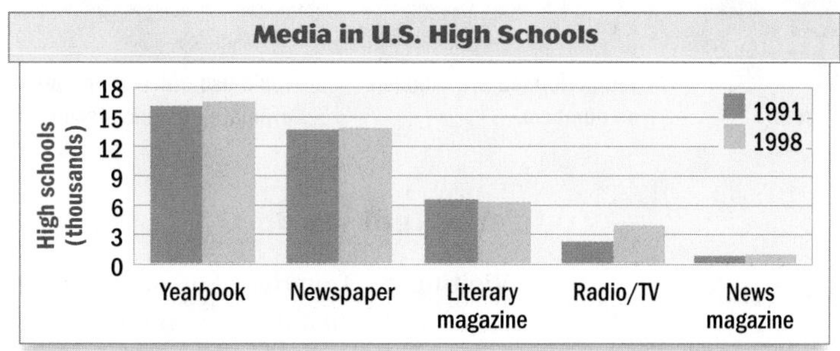

21. About how many of the schools offered radio or TV in 1998?

22. Describe the trends in media at the schools from 1991 to 1998.

C 23. **Challenge** What trend do you notice in the number of DVD players sold in the United States shown in the graph at the right? Do you think that this trend continued? Explain your reasoning.

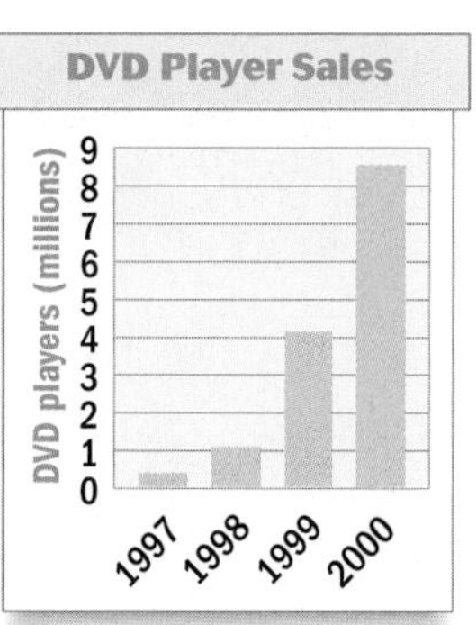

24. **Critical Thinking** You want to collect data about the pets students in your class have. What data would you collect to make a histogram? What data would you collect to make a bar graph?

Mixed Review 

Find the product or quotient. *(p. 713)*

25. 34×4 136 26. 6×15 90 27. $140 \div 20$ 7 28. $84 \div 7$ 12

Basic Skills Find the sum or difference.

29. $25.8 + 19.64$ 45.44 30. $106.58 - 56.33$ 50.25 31. $88.7 - 29.92$ 58.78

Test-Taking Practice 

32. **Extended Response** The data below are the number of medals the United States has won in each of the Winter Olympic Games since 1924.

4, 7, 12, 4, 9, 11, 7, 10, 6, 7, 8, 10, 12, 8, 6, 11, 13, 13, 34

Create a histogram of the data with intervals of 5 starting with 0–4 and a second histogram with intervals of 10 starting with 0–9. Tell which histogram you would use to predict how many medals the United States will win in the future and why. See margin for art.
Sample answer: I would use the second histogram because it shows a pattern: that frequency decreases as medal count increases.

4 ASSESS

Assessment Resources

For more assessment resources, see:
- Assessment Book
- Test and Practice Generator

Mini-Quiz

The bar graph shows absentees by grade one day from a school.

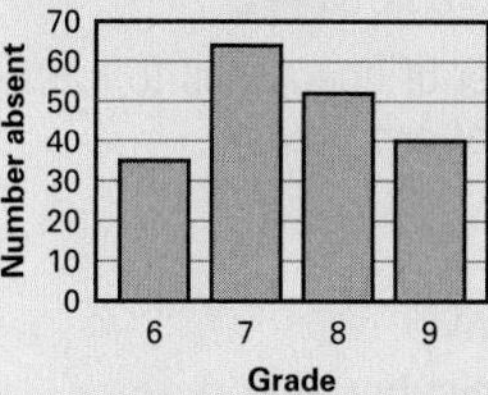

1. Which grade had the fewest absentees? 6
2. Estimate the difference in the absentees in the seventh and sixth grades. about 29

5 FOLLOW-UP

Reteaching/Remediation
- Study Guide in Chapter 1 Resource Book, pp. 10–11
- Tutor Place, Whole Numbers and Decimals Card 2
- eTutorial Plus Online
- Extra Practice, p. 727
- Lesson Practice in Chapter 1 Resource Book, pp. 7-9

Challenge/Enrichment
- Challenge Practice in Chapter 1 Resource Book, p. 13
- Teacher's Edition, p. 2F

English Learner Support
- Spanish Study Guide
- Multi-Language Glossary
- Chapter Audio Summaries CDs

32. See Additional Answers beginning on page AA1.

PLAN

SKILL CHECK

1. $16 \times 11 = \underline{?}$ 176
2. $\frac{18}{3} = \underline{?}$ 6
3. $119 \div 7 = \underline{?}$ 17
4. $15.3 - 6.7 = \underline{?}$ 8.6

LESSON OBJECTIVE

Use the order of operations to evaluate numerical expressions.

PACING

Suggested Number of Days
Basic Course: 2 days
Average Course: 2 days
Advanced Course: 2 days
Block: 0.5 block with 1.1
0.5 block with 1.3

TEACHING RESOURCES

For a complete list of Teaching Resources, see page 2B.

TRANSPARENCY

Warm-Up Exercises for this lesson are available on a transparency.

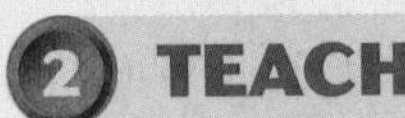

TEACH

MOTIVATING THE LESSON

Discuss options that might be available when purchasing admission to the aquarium. Ask students to give the cost for each option.

TIPS FOR NEW TEACHERS

Make sure students understand the term *evaluate* before continuing with the lesson. See Tips for New Teachers in the *Chapter 1 Resource Book.*

Order of Operations

BEFORE	Now	WHY?
You performed operations on numbers.	You'll use order of operations to evaluate numerical expressions.	So you can find how much money to raise for a team, as in Ex. 19.

Word Watch

numerical expression, p. 10
evaluate, p. 10
order of operations, p. 10
verbal model, p. 11

In the Real World

Visiting an Aquarium You and four friends visit an aquarium, but only three of you go to the movie at the aquarium. What is the total cost of the visit? You will find the total cost of the visit in Example 3.

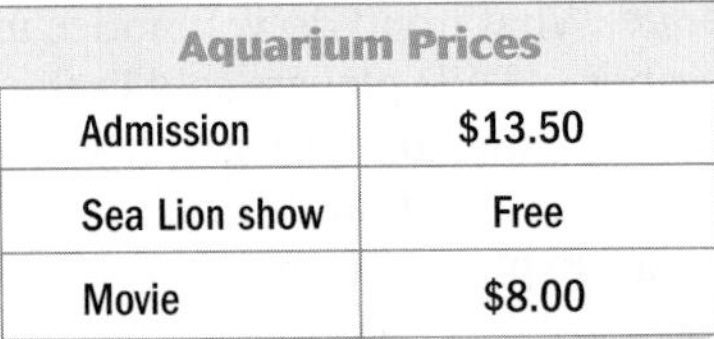

Aquarium Prices	
Admission	$13.50
Sea Lion show	Free
Movie	$8.00

Order of Operations A **numerical expression** consists of numbers and operations. To **evaluate** a numerical expression is to find its value. When a numerical expression has more than one operation, you must use a set of rules called the **order of operations**.

Order of Operations

To evaluate an expression that has more than one operation:

1. Evaluate expressions inside grouping symbols.
2. Multiply and divide from left to right.
3. Add and subtract from left to right.

HELP with Solving

You can express multiplication by using parentheses or the symbols • or ×.
3(4) = 12
3 • 4 = 12
3 × 4 = 12

EXAMPLE 1 **Using the Order of Operations**

Evaluate the expression $7 + 16 \cdot 3 \div 6$.

$7 + 16 \cdot 3 \div 6 = 7 + 48 \div 6$ **Multiply 16 by 3.**

$= 7 + 8$ **Divide 48 by 6.**

$= 15$ **Add 7 and 8.**

ILLINOIS Standards and ISAT:
6.B.3a, 6.C.3a, 8.A.3a, 8.D.3a

Watch Out!

You can express division using either the symbol ÷ or a fraction bar. To evaluate an expression with a fraction bar, evaluate the numerator and the denominator before you divide.

Grouping Symbols The most common grouping symbols are parentheses ( ), brackets [ ], and fraction bars.

EXAMPLE 2 Using Grouping Symbols

a. $(14 + 6) \cdot 8 = 20 \cdot 8$ **Add inside parentheses first.**

$= 160$ **Then multiply.**

b. $\frac{9 \times 8}{4 + 8} = \frac{72}{4 + 8}$ **Evaluate numerator.**

$= \frac{72}{12}$ **Evaluate denominator.**

$= 6$ **Divide.**

c. $45 \div [63 \div (56 \div 8)] = 45 \div [63 \div 7]$ **Divide inside the innermost set of grouping symbols.**

$= 45 \div 9$ **Divide inside brackets.**

$= 5$ **Divide.**

Your turn now **Evaluate the expression.**

1. $14 + 6 \div 2$ 17 **2.** $20 - 7 \times 2 + 1$ 7 **3.** $5 \cdot 7 - 2 \cdot 13$ 9

4. $35 \div (9 - 4)$ 7 **5.** $3 \cdot [(11 - 1) \div 5]$ 6 **6.** $\frac{45 + 19}{2 \times 8}$ 4

When you solve a problem, it may help to write a **verbal model** using symbols for operations and words to label necessary information.

EXAMPLE 3 Using a Verbal Model

To find the total cost of the visit to the aquarium described on the previous page, you can use a verbal model to write and evaluate an expression.

Total cost of visit = Admission price × Number of people + Movie price × Number of people

$= 13.50 \times 5 + 8 \times 3$ **Substitute values.**

$= 67.50 + 24$ **Multiply first.**

$= 91.50$ **Then add.**

ANSWER The total cost of the visit is \$91.50.

EXTRA EXAMPLES

Example 1 Evaluate the expression $9 - 3 \times 2 + 4$. 7

Example 2 Evaluate each expression.

a. $4 \times (6 - 3)$ 12

b. $\frac{5 \times 4}{5 - 3}$ 10

c. $12 - [6 + (19 - 14)]$ 1

Example 3 Penny bought two bananas costing 30 cents each and three carrots costing 10 cents each. Write and evaluate an expression for the total cost. **2 × 30 + 3 × 10 = 90¢, or \$.90**

CONCEPT CHECK

Explain the role of the fraction bar in the order of operations. **The fraction bar acts like a grouping symbol. It has the effect of placing parentheses or brackets around the numerator and around the denominator.**

DAILY PUZZLER

Replace each ? with +, −, ×, or ÷ to make the sentence true.

(5 ? 5) ? (5 ? 5) ? 5 = 55

(5 × 5) + (5 × 5) + 5 = 55

ASSIGNMENT GUIDE

Basic Course

Day 1: pp. 12-13 Exs. 10-13, 21-26, 32, 37-39

Day 2: pp. 12-13 Exs. 14-19, 27-30, 34, 40-42

Average Course

Day 1: pp. 12-13 Exs. 10-15, 21-23, 30-32, 37-39

Day 2: pp. 12-13 Exs. 16-20, 27-29, 33-35, 40-43

Average Course

Day 1: pp. 12-13 Exs. 13-18, 27-31, 37-39

Day 2: pp. 12-13 Exs. 19-23, 32-36*, 41-43

Block

pp. 12-13 Exs. 10-15, 21-23, 30-32, 37-39 (with 1.1)

pp. 12-13 Exs. 16-20, 27-29, 33-35, 40-43 (with 1.3)

EXTRA PRACTICE

- Student Edition, p. 727
- Chapter 1 Resource Book, pp. 18-20
- Test and Practice Generator

Even-numbered answers are available on transparencies.

HOMEWORK CHECK

When you review students' homework for this lesson, go over the following exercises to check understanding of key concepts.

Basic: 10, 13, 21, 27, 34

Average: 10, 14, 21, 28, 34

Advanced: 13, 15, 21, 29, 34

TEACHING TIP

In Exercises 10-18 and 21-29, remind students to write out every step.

1.2 Exercises

More Practice, p. 727

Getting Ready to Practice

1. **Vocabulary** Use the order of operations to list in order the steps needed to evaluate the following expression: $8 + 2 \times 5 - 4$. **Multiply 2 by 5. Add the result (10) to 8. Subtract 4 from this sum (18) to obtain the final result (14).**

State the first step in evaluating the expression. Then evaluate.

2. $10 \cdot 6 - 20$ **Multiply 10 by 6; 40.**
3. $5 \times 15 \div 3$ **Multiply 5 by 15; 25.**
4. $4 + 8 \div 2$ **Divide 8 by 2; 8.**
5. $2 \times 5 + (15 - 7)$ **Subtract 7 from 15; 18.**
6. $6 + 14 - 10 \div 2$ **Divide 10 by 2; 15.**
7. $10 \cdot [9 \div (5 - 2)]$ **Subtract 2 from 5; 30.**
8. **Fundraising Walk** Your friend pledges \$10 to you for a fundraising walk and \$.25 for each mile you walk. You walk 6 miles. How much money will your friend contribute? Use the expression $10 + 0.25(6)$. **\$11.50**
9. **Find the Error** Describe and correct the error in the solution. **In the second step, 63 must be divided by 9 before being added to 9: $3 \times 3 + 63 \div 9 = 9 + 63 \div 9 = 9 + 7 = 16$.**

$$3 \times 3 + 63 \div 9 = 9 + 63 \div 9$$
$$= 72 \div 9$$
$$= 8$$

Practice and Problem Solving

Example	Exercises
1	10-29, 33
2	10-18, 21-29
3	34

Online Resources CLASSZONE.COM
- More Examples
- eTutorial Plus

A Evaluate the expression.

10. $12 + 10 - 4$ **18**
11. $7 \cdot 3 + 2 \cdot 4$ **29**
12. $\frac{16}{7 - 3}$ **4**
13. $9 \times 3 + 2 - 5$ **24**
14. $16 - 6 + 2 \times 4$ **18**
15. $26 - 15 + 8 \div 2$ **15**
16. $8 + 2 \times (4 - 3)$ **10**
17. $120 \div [(6 + 2) \cdot 3]$ **5**
18. $18 \div (8 + 4 - 9)$ **6**
19. **Softball Uniforms** Your school softball team has 25 members. The school contributes \$30 toward each \$40 uniform. To find how much money the team needs to raise, evaluate the expression $40 \cdot 25 - 30 \cdot 25$. **\$250**
20. **Supplies** You buy 3 notebooks at \$2 each and 4 pens at \$1.50 each. What is the total cost? Use the expression $3 \times 2 + 4 \times 1.50$. **\$12**

Evaluate the expression.

B 21. $\frac{7}{4} - \frac{5}{4} + \frac{1}{4}$ **$\frac{3}{4}$**
22. $9 \div \left[3 \cdot \left(\frac{5}{3} + \frac{4}{3}\right)\right]$ **1**
23. $3 \cdot \left(\frac{7}{2} + \frac{1}{2}\right)$ **12**
24. $(1.5 - 0.5) \times 2$ **2**
25. $9.4 + 4.2 \div 6$ **10.1**
26. $6 \times (2.4 - 0.4 + 3)$ **30**
27. $7.8 \times (5 + 2)$ **54.6**
28. $8.4 \div (21 - 14)$ **1.2**
29. $4 + 3.9 \div 1.3$ **7**

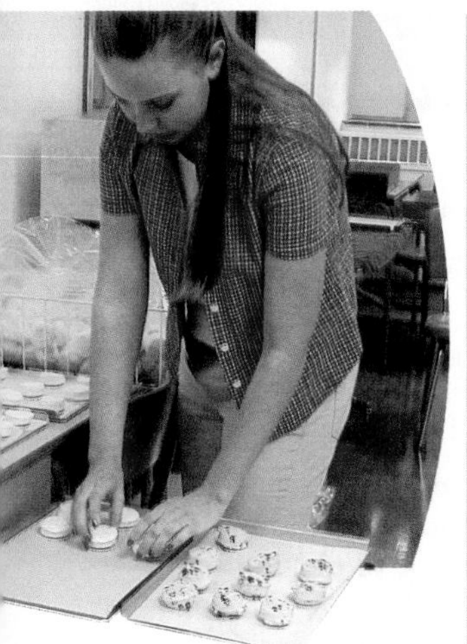

Critical Thinking **Add parentheses to make the statement true.**

30. $5 \cdot 2 + 3 - 8 = 17$ $5 \cdot (2 + 3) - 8 = 17$

31. $12 \div 6 + 4 - 7 = 4$ $12 \div (6 + 4 - 7) = 4$

Extended Problem Solving **In Exercises 32–34, suppose Liz and Ty are making cookies for a school bake sale. Liz makes 5 batches of 36 cookies, and Ty makes 4 batches of 48 cookies.**

32. Translate Translate *5 batches of 36 cookies plus 4 batches of 48 cookies* into an expression. 5(36) + 4(48)

33. Evaluate Evaluate the expression. 372 cookies

34. Extend Liz and Ty decide to make packages of three cookies. Write and evaluate an expression to find the number of packages they can make. $372 \div 3 = 124$ packages

C **35. Number Sense** Complete the statement 12 _?_ 4 + 2 using each of the operations +, −, ×, and ÷. Which operation symbol gives the expression the greatest value? Find the greatest possible value if you add one set of parentheses to the four expressions. ×; $12 \times (4 + 2) = 72$

36. Challenge Your cousin is 14 years old. Your brother is 10 years less than twice your cousin's age. Write and evaluate an expression to find your brother's age. $2(14) - 10 = 18$ yr

Mixed Review

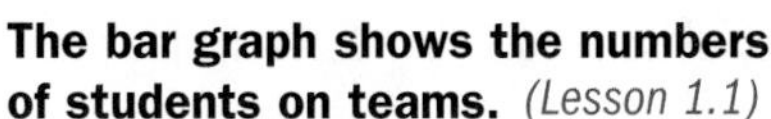

The bar graph shows the numbers of students on teams. *(Lesson 1.1)*

37. About how many students are on the basketball team? 32 students

38. Which team has the most students? soccer

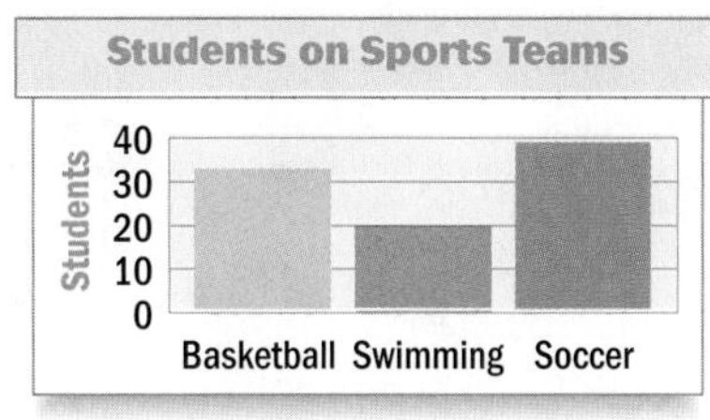

Basic Skills **Find the missing number.**

39. $11 - \underline{?} = 7$ 4

40. $\underline{?} \div 4 = 8$ 32

41. $9 \cdot \underline{?} = 54$ 6

Test-Taking Practice

INTERNET
State Test Practice
CLASSZONE.COM

42. Multiple Choice In what order should the operations be performed in the expression $2 \times 4 - 6 \div 3 + 1$? A

A. ×, ÷, −, + **B.** ×, −, ÷, + **C.** ×, ÷, +, − **D.** ×, +, −, ÷

43. Multiple Choice Which operation should be performed first when finding *the difference of twenty and the quotient of eighteen and six*? G

F. 20 − 18 **G.** 18 ÷ 6 **H.** 20 − 6 **I.** 20 ÷ 6

4 ASSESS

Assessment Resources

For more assessment resources, see:

- Assessment Book
- Test and Practice Generator

Mini-Quiz

Evaluate each expression.

1. $3 \times (17 - 5)$ **36**
2. $12 \times 5 - 15$ **45**
3. $10 \div (50 - 25)$ $\frac{2}{5}$, or 0.4
4. $8 + 9 \times 2 - 10$ **16**
5. $4(6 + 3) + 12 \div 2$ **42**
6. $100 \div [(8 + 2) \times 2]$ **5**
7. Tara orders pizza for herself and four friends. The pizza costs \$19 and delivery costs \$3. Write and evaluate an expression to find what each person should contribute. $\frac{19 + 3}{1 + 4} = \frac{22}{5} = \$4.40$

5 FOLLOW-UP

Reteaching/Remediation

- Study Guide in Chapter 1 Resource Book, pp. 21–22
- eTutorial Plus Online
- Extra Practice, p. 727
- Lesson Practice in Chapter 1 Resource Book, pp. 18–20

Challenge/Enrichment

- Challenge Practice in Chapter 1 Resource Book, p. 23
- Teacher's Edition, p. 2F

English Learner Support

- Spanish Study Guide
- Multi-Language Glossary
- Chapter Audio Summaries CDs

PLAN

Learn the Method

- Students will use a calculator to evaluate numerical expressions with decimals.
- To bolster students' understanding of the order of operations, have them use calculators to do Exercises 24–29 on page 12.

Grouping

Students can work individually or in pairs. If students work in pairs, they can check each other's work by comparing calculator displays. If the final displays are different, at least one of the students has made an error.

TEACH

Tips for Success

Stress to students that calculators cannot be assumed to "know" the order of operations without the appropriate input. Students should enter parentheses any time they are unsure how a calculator will handle multiple operators.

EXTRA EXAMPLES

Example Evaluate $\frac{24.3 + 4.2}{3.5 - 1.5}$.

14.25

CLOSE

Assessment

Use a calculator to evaluate the expression.

1. $4.5 + 3.3 \div 1.5$ 6.7
2. $\frac{2.4 \times 3.1}{3.9 - 1.9}$ 3.72

1.2 Technology Activity

CALCULATOR

Using Order of Operations

GOAL Use a calculator to evaluate numerical expressions with decimals.

Example **You and three friends are ordering a pizza. The cost of the pizza is $15.90, but you have a coupon for $1.50 off. How much should each of you pay if you want to divide the total cost equally?**

Solution

Cost per person $= \frac{\text{Price of a pizza} - \text{Coupon}}{\text{Number of friends} + \text{Yourself}}$ **Write a verbal model.**

$= \frac{15.90 - 1.50}{3 + 1}$ **Substitute.**

To find the cost per person, use the order of operations.

Keystrokes	**Display**
(15.90 − 1.50) ÷ (3 + 1) =	3.6

ANSWER Each person should pay $3.60 for the pizza.

HELP with Technology

The keystrokes shown here may not be the same as on your calculator. See your calculator's instruction manual for the appropriate keystrokes.

Your turn now **Use a calculator to evaluate the expression.**

1. $62 + 7 \times 6.4$ 106.8
2. $8.32 - 9 \div 2$ 3.82
3. $6.8 \div 4 + 15.9 \div 3$ 7
4. $36.2 - 4.3 \cdot 5$ 14.7
5. $\frac{14 + 11}{4 + 1}$ 5
6. $\frac{20 - 3.5}{10.3 - 7}$ 5
7. $\frac{10}{3.8 + 1.2}$ 2
8. $\frac{17.7 - 13.7}{0.2 + 4.8}$ 0.8
9. **Snacks** You buy 3 bags of snack mix for $1.49 each, 2 boxes of raisins for $1.79 each, and lemonade for $2.39. Find the total cost using the expression $3 \cdot 1.49 + 2 \cdot 1.79 + 2.39$. $10.44
10. **Clothing** You buy 3 T-shirts at $9.99 each, a pair of sneakers for $44.89, a hat for $10.59, and a pair of socks at a cost of 4 pairs for $8.60. Find the total cost. $87.60
11. **Music** You pick out 2 CDs for $12.99 each, 3 CDs for $9.49 each, and a CD for $15.97. At the register you find out that when you buy 5 CDs you get the sixth CD for half off. Find the total cost if you get the most expensive CD for half off. Round to the nearest cent. $62.44

ILLINOIS Standards and ISAT:
6.B.3a, 6.C.3a, 8.A.3a, 8.D.3a

Variables and Expressions

BEFORE	Now	WHY?
You evaluated numerical expressions.	You'll write and evaluate variable expressions.	So you can find how far you travel on a bike, as in Exs. 23–24.

Word Watch

variable, p. 15
variable expression, p. 15

In the Real World

Hot Air Balloons You are riding in a hot air balloon. After traveling 5 miles, the balloon speed changes to 6 miles per hour. What is the total distance you travel if the balloon stays at this speed for 1 hour? for 2 hours? You will find the answer in Example 1.

Variable Expressions A **variable** is a symbol, usually a letter, that represents one or more numbers. A **variable expression** consists of numbers, variables, and operations. To evaluate a variable expression, substitute a number for each variable. Then find the value of the numerical expression.

You can write the product of a number and a variable by writing the number next to that variable. For example, you can write $5 \cdot n$ as $5n$.

EXAMPLE 1 Using a Variable Expression

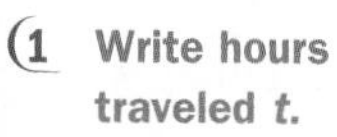

To answer the questions above about distance traveled, let t represent the time in hours that the balloon travels at 6 miles per hour. So, the total distance traveled is *original distance* + *speed* • *time*, which is $5 + 6t$.

(1) Write hours traveled t.	(2) Substitute for t in the expression $5 + 6t$.	(3) Evaluate to find total distance.
1	$5 + 6(1)$	11
2	$5 + 6(2)$	17

ANSWER If the balloon travels at 6 miles per hour for 1 hour, you travel a total of 11 miles. After 2 hours you travel a total of 17 miles.

Your turn now Use the information above about hot air balloons.

1. If you travel for 3 hours more, what is the total distance? 23 mi
2. If you travel for $\frac{1}{2}$ hour more, what is the total distance? 8 mi

ILLINOIS Standards and ISAT:
6.B.3a, 6.C.3a, 8.D.3a

1 PLAN

SKILL CHECK

1. $8 + 3(3) = \underline{?}$ 17
2. $2(3) + 3(6) = \underline{?}$ 24
3. $4(2) - 5(1) = \underline{?}$ 3
4. $6(3) \div [3(3)] = \underline{?}$ 2

LESSON OBJECTIVE

Write and evaluate variable expressions.

PACING

Suggested Number of Days
Basic Course: 2 days
Average Course: 2 days
Advanced Course: 2 days
Block: 0.5 block with 1.2
0.5 block with 1.4

TEACHING RESOURCES

For a complete list of Teaching Resources, see page 2B.

TRANSPARENCY

Warm-Up Exercises for this lesson are available on a transparency.

2 TEACH

MOTIVATING THE LESSON

Have students discuss how a pilot might control a hot air balloon's motion using different wind currents at different heights.

TIPS FOR NEW TEACHERS

Real-world formulas such as $d = rt$ or $A = lw$ may help students understand that using a letter for a quantity that can change is just a type of shorthand. See Tips for New Teachers in the *Chapter 1 Resource Book*.

EXTRA EXAMPLES

Example 1 The variable expression $10 + 15h$ describes the amount, in dollars, charged by a tutor for h hours. Find the amount charged for one hour and for two hours. **$25, $40**

Example 2 Evaluate the expression when $x = 4$ and $y = 7$.
a. $3y - 10$ **11**
b. $2x + 4y$ **36**

Example 3 Write the phrase as a variable expression using x.
a. 17 minus a number **$17 - x$**
b. a number divided by 2 **$x \div 2$**

VISUALIZE

Students can draw attention to variables by writing them using colored pens or pencils or by highlighting them, assigning one color to each variable.

COMMON ERROR

Watch for students who think that a variable represents a digit rather than a value. For example, if $x = 7$, some students might interpret $3x$ as 37 rather than 3(7), or 21.

Differentiating Instruction

Advanced Students Challenge advanced students by having them evaluate variable expressions involving three or more variables and a number of operations.

EXAMPLE 2 Evaluating Variable Expressions

Evaluate the expression when $x = 8$ and $y = 2$.

a. $7x + 15 = 7(8) + 15$ Substitute 8 for x.
$= 56 + 15$ Multiply.
$= 71$ Add.

b. $3x - 5y = 3(8) - 5(2)$ Substitute 8 for x and 2 for y.
$= 24 - 10$ Multiply.
$= 14$ Subtract.

Writing Expressions Many words and phrases suggest mathematical operations. The following common words and phrases indicate addition, subtraction, multiplication, and division.

Addition	Subtraction	Multiplication	Division
plus the sum of increased by total more than added to	minus the difference of decreased by fewer than less than subtracted from	times the product of multiplied by of	divided by the quotient of per

HELP with Reading

Order is important when translating verbal expressions that suggest subtraction and division.
The difference of a number and 6 means $n - 6$, not $6 - n$.
The quotient of a number and 10 means $n \div 10$, not $10 \div n$.

EXAMPLE 3 Translating Verbal Phrases

Verbal Phrase	Variable Expression
The sum of a number and 9	$n + 9$
The difference of a number and 21	$n - 21$
The product of 6 and a number	$6n$
The quotient of 48 and a number	$\frac{48}{n}$
One third of a number	$\frac{1}{3}n$

Your turn now **Evaluate the expression when $a = 12$ and $b = 3$.**

3. $9a$ 108 **4.** ab 36 **5.** $b(a - 6)$ 18 **6.** $\frac{6a}{a - b}$ 8

Write the phrase as a variable expression using x.

7. a number increased by 15 $x + 15$ **8.** 8 times a number $8x$

Heart Rate

To find a reasonable target heart rate during exercise, subtract your age from 220, then multiply that number by 0.7. What is your target heart rate?

EXAMPLE 4 **Writing and Evaluating an Expression**

Heart Rate To measure your heart rate in beats per minute, count the number of heartbeats n in 15 seconds. Then multiply by 4 to find your heart rate in beats per minute.

a. Use n to write an expression for heart rate in beats per minute.

b. You count 18 beats in 15 seconds. Find your heart rate.

Solution

a. The phrase *multiply by* suggests multiplication. So, the variable expression for heart rate in beats per minute is $4n$.

b. Substitute 18 for n in the expression $4n$ to find your heart rate.

$$4n = 4(18)$$
$$= 72$$

ANSWER Your heart rate is 72 beats per minute.

EXTRA EXAMPLES

Example 4 A copier can make c photocopies in one minute.

a. Use c to write an expression for the number of copies made in one hour. **$60c$**

b. If the copier makes 20 copies each minute, find the number of copies made each hour. **1200 copies**

CONCEPT CHECK

What do you need to do to evaluate a variable expression? **You need to substitute an appropriate number for each variable to form a numerical expression. Then simplify the numerical expression to find its value.**

DAILY PUZZLER

What value(s) of n make(s) the statement $n = n + n$ true? **$n = 0$**

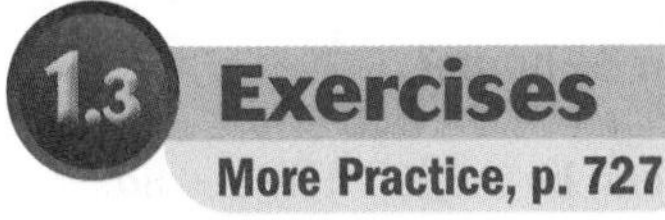

1.3 Exercises

More Practice, p. 727

What do you think? *Sample answer:* **For a 14-year-old, the target heart rate is $(220 - 14) \times 0.7 = 206 \times 0.7 = 144.2$, or about 144 beats per minute.**

Getting Ready to Practice

1. **Vocabulary** Copy and complete: $3t - 4$ is a(n) _?_ expression and $5 + 13$ is a(n) _?_ expression. **variable; numerical**

Match the phrase with the correct variable expression.

2. 8 times a number **B**
3. 8 fewer than a number **C**
4. a number increased by 8 **A**
5. the quotient of 8 and a number **D**

A. $n + 8$
B. $8n$
C. $n - 8$
D. $8 \div n$

Evaluate the expression when $p = 6$ and $s = 5$.

6. $11p$ **66**
7. $7s + 9$ **44**
8. $6s + 4p$ **54**
9. $\frac{50 - s}{p + 3}$ **5**

10. **Guided Problem Solving** You buy a hat for \$8 and rent 5 videos for \$2.50 each. How much do you spend?

(1) Write a variable expression for the cost to rent m videos. **$2.50m$**

(2) Add the cost of the hat to this expression. **$2.50m + 8$**

(3) Evaluate the expression for $m = 5$. **\$20.50**

APPLY

ASSIGNMENT GUIDE

Basic Course

Day 1: SRH p. 709 Exs. 1-4; pp. 18-19 Exs. 11-16, 23-25, 29-32, 41-43

Day 2: SRH p. 714 Exs. 1-5; pp. 18-19 Exs. 19-22, 26-28, 38, 39, 44-49

Average Course

Day 1: pp. 18-19 Exs. 13-18, 23-25, 31-34, 41-44

Day 2: pp. 18-19 Exs. 19-22, 26-28, 35-39, 45-49

Average Course

Day 1: pp. 18-19 Exs. 13-18, 23-25, 33-36, 47-49

Day 2: pp. 18-19 Exs. 19-22, 26-28, 37-43*

Block

pp. 18-19 Exs. 13-18, 23-25, 31-34, 41-44 (with 1.2)

pp. 18-19 Exs. 19-22, 26-28, 35-39, 45-49 (with 1.4)

EXTRA PRACTICE

- Student Edition, p. 727
- Chapter 1 Resource Book, pp. 28-30
- Test and Practice Generator

TRANSPARENCY

Even-numbered answers are available on transparencies.

HOMEWORK CHECK

When you review students' homework for this lesson, go over the following exercises to check understanding of key concepts.

Basic: 11, 19, 23, 26, 29

Average: 13, 20, 24, 26, 38

Advanced: 13, 22, 24, 27, 38

COMMON ERROR

In Exercise 20, watch for students who write $x - 10$.

Practice and Problem Solving

with Homework

Example	Exercises
1	23-24
2	11-18, 29-36
3	19-22
4	26-28

Online Resources
CLASSZONE.COM

- More Examples
- eTutorial Plus

Evaluate the expression for the given value(s) of the variable(s).

A
11. $4x - 5, x = 7$ 23
12. $10n + 115, n = 9$ 205
13. $11c + 34, c = 0.5$ 39.5
14. $2s - t, s = 8, t = 4$ 12
15. $p + 2q, p = 3, q = 1$ 5
16. $8a - 3b, a = 3, b = 8$ 0
17. $\frac{3}{4}x + y, x = 4, y = 3$ 6
18. $\frac{d + 10}{c - d}, c = 14, d = 8$ 3

Translate **Write the phrase as a variable expression. Let x represent the variable.**

19. two fifths of a number $\frac{2}{5}x$
20. a number subtracted from 10 $10 - x$
21. 12 increased by a number $12 + x$
22. the quotient of a number and 7 $\frac{x}{7}$

Bicycling **Evaluate the expression $9t$ to find how many miles you go if you ride your bike for t hours at 9 miles per hour.**

23. How far do you go if you ride your bike for 2 hours? 18 mi

24. How far do you go if you ride your bike for $3\frac{1}{2}$ hours? $31\frac{1}{2}$ mi

25. **Writing** Write a real world situation that can be modeled by $2 + 8d$.

25. *Sample answer:* Serena is saving to buy a gift for her sister. She starts with $2 and saves an additional $8 per week.

26. **Television** You watch x thirty-minute TV shows and y sixty-minute TV shows in one week. Write a variable expression representing the total number of minutes you spend watching television that week. $30x + 60y$

27. **CD Club** You are purchasing CDs from a music club. You pay $4 for shipping any number n of CDs, plus $17 for each CD. Write a variable expression for the cost of n CDs. Then find the cost of 6 CDs. $4 + 17n$; $106

28. **Estimation** A 17 inch vine grows 3 inches per week. Write a variable expression for the length of the vine after w weeks. Then estimate the vine's length after 19 weeks. $17 + 3w$; 74 in.

Evaluate the expression when $x = 2.4$ and $y = 8$.

B
29. $7x + 2y$ 32.8
30. $y - 2x$ 3.2
31. $5xy$ 96
32. $\frac{y}{x - 0.4}$ 4
33. $4x - y$ 1.6
34. $7.2y \div x$ 24
35. $\frac{3y}{x}$ 10
36. $1.6xy$ 30.72

37. **Writing** Write a variable expression that requires the use of the order of operations to evaluate correctly. Explain the correct order to use. See margin.

37. A good answer will include an expression that can only be evaluated correctly by using the order of operations. The explanation of the correct order to use will follow the rules for the order of operations.

38. **Nutrition** Rice has 13 grams of protein per serving, beans have 15 grams per serving, and an orange has 2 grams per serving. Write a variable expression for the total grams of protein in x servings of rice, y servings of beans, and z oranges. $13x + 15y + 2z$

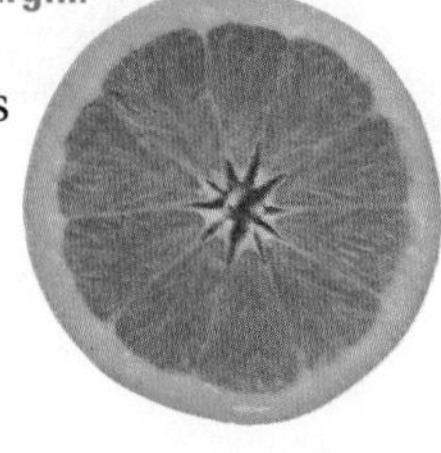

C 39. **Movies** At the movies, popcorn costs \$2.75 and drinks cost \$1.25. Write an expression to find the total cost of p popcorns and d drinks. Find the total cost for snacks if 3 people buy popcorn and 4 people buy drinks. **$2.75p + 1.25d$; \$13.25**

40. **Challenge** Evaluate the expression $\frac{5(3x + 2z + 0.5425)}{x + y + z}$ when $x = 1.05$, $y = 1.3$, and $z = 0.9$. **8.45**

Mixed Review 

Evaluate the expression. *(Lesson 1.2)*

41. $12 \cdot 3 + 14$ **50**
42. $93 - 74 \div 2$ **56**
43. $16 + 6 \cdot 3 \div 2 - 7$ **18**

Basic Skills **Find the product or quotient.**

44. $17 \cdot 52$ **884**
45. $91 \cdot 45$ **4095**
46. $123 \div 3$ **41**
47. $252 \div 6$ **42**

Test-Taking Practice

48. **Short Response** A personal CD player costs \$35 and CDs cost \$15 each. Write an expression to represent the total cost for the CD player and CDs. You buy a personal CD player and 4 CDs. Evaluate your expression to determine the total amount of money you spend. **$35 + 15c$; \$95**

49. **Multiple Choice** You are saving money to buy a bike that costs \$126. You want to buy the bike in 6 weeks by saving the same amount of money each day. How much money should you save each day? **C**

A. \$1 **B.** \$2 **C.** \$3 **D.** \$21

BRAIN GAME

Find the Key

A key will unlock a door if the variable expressions on the door have the same value when the number on the key is substituted for the variable.

Which key opens each door?
Key 1 unlocks door 1; key 4 unlocks door 2; key 2 unlocks door 3.

4 ASSESS

Assessment Resources

For more assessment resources, see:
- Assessment Book
- Test and Practice Generator

Mini-Quiz

Evaluate the expression for the given values of the variables.

1. $6x - 10, x = 5$ **20**
2. $33a - 20b, a = 3, b = 4$ **19**

Write the phrase as a variable expression. Let x represent the variable.

3. a number increased by 7 **$x + 7$**
4. twelve fewer than a number **$x - 12$**
5. An apartment complex rents x \$500 per month units and y \$800 per month units. Write a variable expression for the total monthly rental income. **$500x + 800y$**

5 FOLLOW-UP

Reteaching/Remediation

- Study Guide in Chapter 1 Resource Book, pp. 31-32
- Tutor Place, Algebra Cards 1, 4
- eTutorial Plus Online
- Extra Practice, p. 727
- Lesson Practice in Chapter 1 Resource Book, pp. 28-30

Challenge/Enrichment

- Challenge Practice in Chapter 1 Resource Book, p. 33
- Teacher's Edition, p. 2F

English Learner Support

- Spanish Study Guide
- Multi-Language Glossary
- Chapter Audio Summaries CDs

1 PLAN

SKILL CHECK

1. $4 \cdot 4 = ?$ 16
2. $2 \cdot 2 \cdot 2 = ?$ 8
3. $3 \cdot 3 \cdot 3 \cdot 3 = ?$ 81
4. $10 \cdot 10 \cdot 10 = ?$ 1000

LESSON OBJECTIVE

Evaluate expressions with powers.

PACING

Suggested Number of Days
Basic Course: 1 day
Average Course: 1 day
Advanced Course: 1 day
Block: 0.5 block with 1.3

TEACHING RESOURCES

For a complete list of Teaching Resources, see page 2B.

TRANSPARENCY

Warm-Up Exercises for this lesson are available on a transparency.

2 TEACH

MOTIVATING THE LESSON

Explain to students that objects fall due to gravity and that the number of feet they fall in t seconds is given by the expression $16t^2$.

TIPS FOR NEW TEACHERS

Have all students read aloud the word descriptions in Example 1. Write other powers on the board and have students read them aloud before continuing with the lesson. See Tips for New Teachers in the *Chapter 1 Resource Book*.

LESSON 1.4 Powers and Exponents

BEFORE	Now	WHY?
You evaluated numerical and variable expressions.	You'll evaluate expressions with powers.	So you can find the height of a cliff, as in Example 3.

Word Watch

power, p. 20
exponent, p. 20
base, p. 20

In the Real World

Waterfall A stone falls over the edge of a cliff next to a waterfall. The stone hits the water 5 seconds later. How tall is the cliff?

To find the height of the cliff, you will use an expression with a *power* in Example 3. A **power** is a product with a repeated factor. The **exponent** tells how many times the **base** is used as a factor.

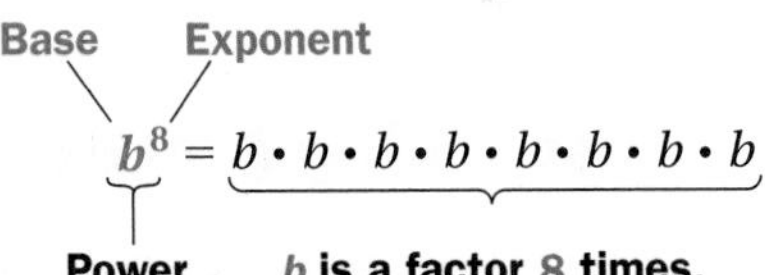

Taughannock Falls State Park, New York

EXAMPLE 1 Reading Powers

Power	Repeated Multiplication	Description in Words
4^2	$4 \cdot 4$	4 to the *second power*, or 4 *squared*
9^3	$9 \cdot 9 \cdot 9$	9 to the *third power*, or 9 *cubed*
y^5	$y \cdot y \cdot y \cdot y \cdot y$	y to the *fifth power*

EXAMPLE 2 Evaluating a Power

Evaluate five cubed.

$5^3 = 5 \cdot 5 \cdot 5$ Write 5 as a factor 3 times.

$= 125$ Multiply.

Your turn now Write the product as a power.

1. $7 \times 7 \times 7 \times 7 \times 7 \times 7$ 7^6
2. $10 \cdot 10 \cdot 10 \cdot 10$ 10^4
3. $w \cdot w$ w^2

Describe the power in words and then evaluate.

4. 6^3
5. 2^5 2 to the fifth power; 32
6. 13^2
7. 3^1 3 to the first power; 3

4. 6 to the third power, or 6 cubed; 216

6. 13 to the second power, or 13 squared; 169

ILLINOIS Standards and ISAT:
6.A.3, 8.A.3a, 8.D.3c; 8.D.3b

Order of Operations When you evaluate expressions with powers, evaluate any powers before multiplying or dividing.

Order of Operations

1. Evaluate expressions inside grouping symbols.
2. Evaluate powers.
3. Multiply and divide from left to right.
4. Add and subtract from left to right.

EXAMPLE 3 **Using a Power**

To find the height of the cliff from the previous page, use the expression $16t^2$. This expression gives the distance in feet that an object has fallen t seconds after it begins to fall.

$16t^2 = 16(5)^2$ Substitute 5 for t.

$= 16(25)$ Evaluate the power.

$= 400$ Multiply.

ANSWER The height of the cliff is 400 feet.

HELP with Notetaking

In your notes, you may want to label the different examples that you copy.

EXAMPLE 4 **Using the Order of Operations**

Evaluate the expression.

a. $(6-4)^3 + 5 - 3^2 = 2^3 + 5 - 3^2$ Evaluate inside grouping symbols.

$= 8 + 5 - 9$ Evaluate powers.

$= 4$ Add and subtract from left to right.

b. $2 \cdot (7+1)^2 \div 4^2 = 2 \cdot 8^2 \div 4^2$ Evaluate inside grouping symbols.

$= 2 \cdot 64 \div 16$ Evaluate powers.

$= 8$ Multiply and divide from left to right.

Your turn now **Evaluate the expression.**

8. $(5-2)^3 - 7 + 4^3$ 84 **9.** $12 + (4+2)^2 - 2^4$ 32 **10.** $7^3 + 24 \div (7-6)^4$ 367

11. Use the expression in Example 3 to find the height of a cliff if a stone hits the water 8 seconds after falling over the edge. 1024 ft

EXTRA EXAMPLES

Example 1 Write the power as a repeated multiplication and in words.

a. 3^2 **$3 \cdot 3$; 3 squared, or 3 to the second power**

b. k^4 **$k \cdot k \cdot k \cdot k$; k to the fourth power**

Example 2 Evaluate twelve squared. **144**

Example 3 Find the height of a radio tower using the expression $16t^2$, where t is the time in seconds it takes a stone to fall from the top of the tower, and $t = 7$. **784 ft**

Example 4 Evaluate the expression.

a. $2(2^3 + 7) - 17$ **13**

b. $20 \div (5-3)^2 + 3$ **8**

TEACHING TIP

Point out to students the alternate language that they may encounter regarding powers, such as "the fifth power of 3" or "the tenth power of z."

CONCEPT CHECK

Where does evaluating powers fit into the order of operations? **Powers should be evaluated after evaluating expressions inside grouping symbols and before multiplying or dividing.**

DAILY PUZZLER

What is 2^2? What is $(2^2)^2$? What is $((2^2)^2)^2$? **4; 16; 256**

3 APPLY

ASSIGNMENT GUIDE

Basic Course

Day 1: pp. 22-23 Exs. 12-23, 27-29, 32-37, 44-49

Average Course

Day 1: pp. 22-23 Exs. 12-17, 21-23, 27-42, 46-49

Average Course

Day 1: pp. 22-23 Exs. 12-17, 24-43*, 47-49

Block

pp. 22-23 Exs. 12-17, 21-23, 27-42, 46-49 (with 1.3)

EXTRA PRACTICE

- Student Edition, p. 727
- Chapter 1 Resource Book, pp. 37-39
- Test and Practice Generator

TRANSPARENCY

Even-numbered answers are available on transparencies.

HOMEWORK CHECK

When you review students' homework for this lesson, go over the following exercises to check understanding of key concepts.
Basic: 12, 15, 21, 27, 35
Average: 13, 16, 23, 29, 35
Advanced: 14, 17, 25, 29, 37

COMMON ERROR

In Exercises 32-34, watch for students who complete the statements with equals signs. These students may be reading the exercises so quickly that they do not notice that, for example, 3^2 is different from 2^3, or they may be confusing the fact that $3 \cdot 2 = 2 \cdot 3$. Students can avoid this problem by writing the powers as products to emphasize the difference.

1.4 Exercises

More Practice, p. 727

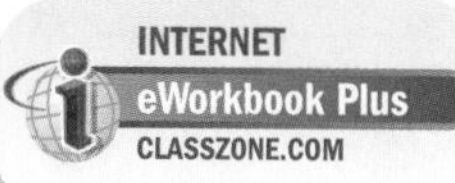

Getting Ready to Practice

1. **Vocabulary** Write a power and label the base and the exponent.
Sample answer: base → 3^2 ← exponent

Evaluate the power.

2. three squared 9
3. eleven cubed 1331
4. one to the ninth 1
5. 2^6 64
6. 5^5 3125
7. 0^7 0

Evaluate the expression.

8. $(2 + 1)^4 \div 9 - 4$ 5
9. $48 \div (9 - 7)^3$ 6
10. $(5 \times 3)^2 - 4$ 221
11. **Find the Error** Describe and correct the error in the solution.
7^2 means 7×7; $7^2 = 7 \times 7 = 49$.

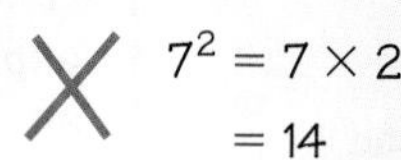

Practice and Problem Solving

HELP with Homework

Example	Exercises
1	12-14
2	15-20
3	27-29, 35-37
4	21-29

Online Resources
CLASSZONE.COM
· More Examples
· eTutorial Plus

Write the product as a power and describe the power in words.

A 12. $9 \cdot 9 \cdot 9 \cdot 9 \cdot 9$
9^5; 9 to the fifth power
13. $3 \cdot 3 \cdot 3$
3^3; 3 to the third power, or 3 cubed
14. $n \cdot n \cdot n \cdot n \cdot n \cdot n$
n^6; n to the sixth power

Evaluate the power.

15. 6^1 6
16. 11^2 121
17. 2^7 128
18. 10^3 1000
19. 1^8 1
20. 20^2 400

Evaluate the expression.

21. $(2 \times 5)^2 + 9$ 109
22. $500 \div (12 - 7)^1$ 100
23. $6 \times 18 \div 3^2$ 12
24. $(9 - 7)^5 + 17$ 49
25. $108 \div (5 + 1)^2$ 3
26. $9^2 - 3^3$ 54

Evaluate the expression when $g = 4$.

27. $g^4 \div 16$ 16
28. $(3 + g)^3$ 343
29. $(3g)^2 - 25$ 119
30. **Critical Thinking** If $x^2 = x^3$, give the two possible values for x. 0 or 1
31. **Football** The season attendance at your school's football games is 1000 people one year. The attendance doubles each year for the next 3 years. Write an expression with a power that shows the season attendance at the football games after 3 years. $1000 \cdot 2^3$

B **Copy and complete the statement using <, >, or =.**

32. 3^2 ? 2^3 > **33.** 5^4 ? 4^5 < **34.** 10^1 ? 1^{10} >

Evaluate the expression when $x = 4.2$, $y = 5.9$, and $z = 11.8$.

35. $y^2 - x^2$ 17.17 **36.** $10z^2 \div y$ 236 **37.** $(x + y)^3$ 1030.301

38. Writing Describe how to find the value of 3^9 using the fact that $3^8 = 6561$. Multiply 6561 by 3.

39. Cliff Diving At Kaunolo in Hawaii, divers jump from a platform on top of a cliff 82 feet above the water. At time t seconds, a diver has fallen $16t^2$ feet. Do the divers reach the surface of the water in 2 seconds? Explain your reasoning. No; $16 \cdot 2^2 = 64$, so the divers have fallen 64 feet after 2 seconds.

Evaluate the expression when $a = 3$, $b = 7$, and $c = 11$.

C **40.** a^3b^2 1323 **41.** $(c - a)^3 - 210$ 302 **42.** $2 \cdot (b + 2)^2 \div a$ 54

43. Challenge The personal computers of the early 1980s had 64 kilobytes of memory. Computers today often have more than one gigabyte of memory. Use the table to find how much memory personal computers of the early 1980s had in bytes. 65,536 bytes

Name	Bytes
Kilobyte	2^{10}
Megabyte	2^{20}
Gigabyte	2^{30}

Mixed Review

Evaluate the expression when $x = 3$ and $y = 9$. *(Lesson 1.3)*

44. $5x - 12$ 3 **45.** $6x - y$ 9 **46.** $\frac{y}{x} + 20$ 23

Choose a Strategy **Use a strategy from the list to solve the following problem. Explain your choice of strategy.**

Problem Solving Strategies
- Look for a Pattern
- Draw a Diagram
- Make a List

47. You have 3 shirts and 2 pairs of pants that you are packing for a trip. You can wear each shirt with each pair of pants. How many different outfits are possible? 6 outfits. *Sample answer:* I used Draw a Diagram because a tree diagram allowed me to find the total number of outfits in an organized way.

Test-Taking Practice

INTERNET
State Test Practice
CLASSZONE.COM

48. Multiple Choice What is the value of the expression $5^3 - 3^4$? C

A. 3 **B.** 19 **C.** 44 **D.** 128

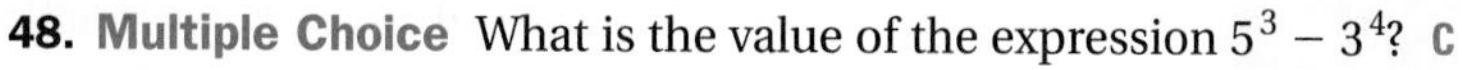

49. Multiple Choice The *volume* of a cube is s^3, where s is the length of one side of the cube. A cube has a side length of 14 centimeters. What is the volume of the cube in cubic centimeters? I

F. 42 **G.** 196 **H.** 1400 **I.** 2744

4 ASSESS

Assessment Resources

For more assessment resources, see:
- Assessment Book
- Test and Practice Generator

Mini-Quiz

Write the product as a power and describe the power in words.

1. $7 \cdot 7 \cdot 7 \cdot 7$ 7^4, seven to the fourth power

2. $2 \cdot 2 \cdot 2$ 2^3, two cubed, two to the third power

Evaluate the power.

3. 3^4 81

4. 6^3 216

Evaluate the expression.

5. $(3 + 7)^2$ 100

6. $100 - 2^4 \times 3$ 52

7. There are 2^5 students in James' class. How many students remain if 3 go outside? 29 students

5 FOLLOW-UP

Reteaching/Remediation
- Study Guide in Chapter 1 Resource Book, pp. 40-41
- Tutor Place, Algebra Cards 2, 3
- eTutorial Plus Online
- Extra Practice, p. 727
- Lesson Practice in Chapter 1 Resource Book, pp. 37-39

Challenge/Enrichment
- Challenge Practice in Chapter 1 Resource Book, p. 42
- Teacher's Edition, p. 2F

English Learner Support
- Spanish Study Guide
- Multi-Language Glossary
- Chapter Audio Summaries CDs

Additional Resources

The following resources are available to help review the materials in Lessons 1.1–1.4.

 ***Chapter 1 Resource Book***
- Lesson Practice
- Study Guide

 ***Assessment Book***
- Chapter 1 Quiz 1

 ***Technology***
- Test and Practice Generator
- eTutorial CD-ROM

 ***Internet***
- Classzone
- eWorkbook Plus Online
- eTutorial Plus Online

English Learner Support

- Spanish Study Guide
- Multi-Language Glossary
- Chapter Audio Summaries CDs

Notebook Review

Review the vocabulary definitions in your notebook.

Copy the review examples in your notebook. Then complete the exercises.

Check Your Definitions

bar graph, p. 5	numerical expression, p. 10	variable, p. 15
data, p. 5	evaluate, p. 10	variable expression, p. 15
frequency table, p. 6	order of operations, p. 10	power, p. 20
histogram, p. 6	verbal model, p. 11	exponent, base, p. 20

Use Your Vocabulary

1. What is the first step in the order of operations? **Evaluate expressions inside grouping symbols.**

1.1 Can you analyze data displays?

EXAMPLE The bar graph shows the average depths of the Great Lakes. Which of the lakes has the greatest average depth?

ANSWER Lake Superior has the longest bar, so it has the greatest average depth.

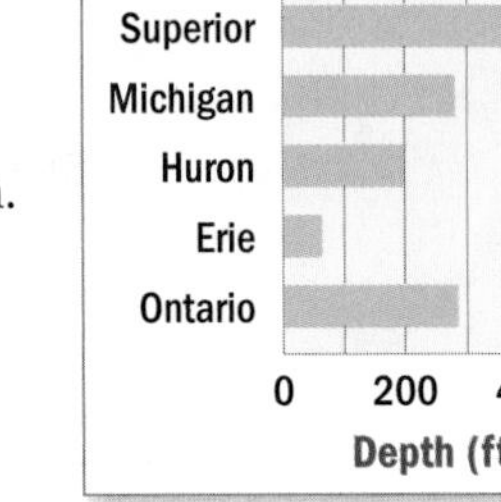

✓ **Use the bar graph above to answer the question or explain why you can't answer the question using the graph.**

2. Which of the Great Lakes is the largest in area? **The question cannot be answered using the bar graph because the depth does not determine the area of the lake.**

3. Which Great Lake is the shallowest on average? **Erie**

1.2–1.3 Can you evaluate variable expressions?

EXAMPLE Evaluate the expression $4x - y + 12$ when $x = 7$ and $y = 10$.

$4x - y + 12 = 4(7) - 10 + 12$ **Substitute 7 for *x* and 10 for *y*.**

$= 28 - 10 + 12$ **Multiply.**

$= 30$ **Add and subtract from left to right.**

 **Evaluate the expression when $x = 3$ and $y = 6$.**

4. $(x + 3) \cdot x$ **18** **5.** $\frac{3y - 9}{x}$ **3** **6.** $5 + y \div x$ **7**

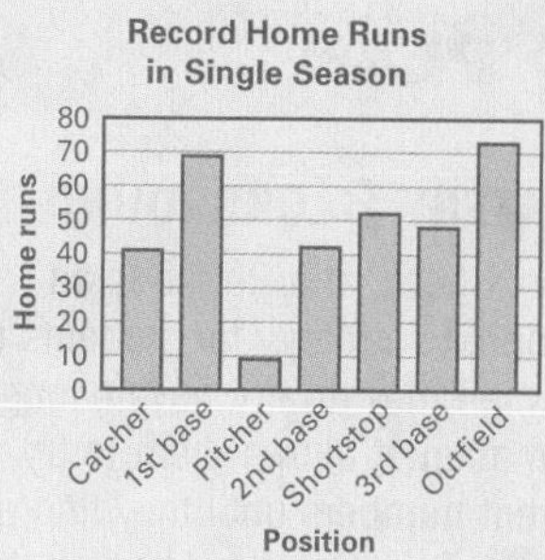

1.4 Can you evaluate expressions with powers?

EXAMPLE Evaluate the expression $4^3 \div (2 \times 2)^2$.

$4^3 \div (2 \times 2)^2 = 4^3 \div 4^2$ **Multiply inside parentheses.**

$= 64 \div 16$ **Evaluate powers.**

$= 4$ **Divide.**

☑ **Evaluate.**

7. $9 \times 2^3 - 15$ 57 **8.** $(2^5 + 8) \cdot 5^2$ 1000 **9.** $(18 \div 6)^3 + (11 - 4)^3$ 370

Stop and Think about Lessons 1.1–1.4

10. **Critical Thinking** The numbers 100 and 1000 can be written as 10^2 and 10^3. How does the number of zeros relate to the exponents of these powers of 10? The number of zeros is the same as the exponent.

Review Quiz 1

1. **Home Runs** The table shows the record number of home runs hit in a single season by position. Make a bar graph that displays the data. See margin.

2. How many more home runs is the record for outfield than for pitcher? 64 home runs

Position	Home Runs
Catcher	41
1st base	69
Pitcher	9
2nd base	42
Shortstop	52
3rd base	48
Outfield	73

Evaluate the expression.

3. $21 - 2 \cdot 7$ 7 **4.** $8 \times 10 - 40 + 25$ 65 **5.** $24 - (9 + 7) \div 4$ 20

6. $(3 + 1)^2 - 1^5$ 15 **7.** $10^4 \div 5^3$ 80 **8.** $3^4 + 7 \cdot 5$ 116

9. **Plants** A plant is 14 inches tall and grows 4 inches each year. Another plant is 8 inches tall and grows 6 inches each year. Write variable expressions for the plants' heights. Then evaluate the expressions to find the heights in 5 years. $14 + 4x$, $8 + 6x$; 34 in., 38 in.

Evaluate the expression for the given value of the variable.

10. $5a - 3 + 7$ when $a = 4$ 24 **11.** $8 + b + 4 \cdot 11$ when $b = 3$ 55

12. $2 \cdot z^4 \div 8$ when $z = 4$ 64 **13.** $(9 - x)^5 \cdot 3 - 16$ when $x = 7$ 80

PLAN

STRATEGY BACKGROUND

Guess, Check, and Revise is an appropriate strategy for students to use when they do not have enough information. It allows them to try different numbers until they find a solution. An advantage to using this strategy is that students will learn that guessing is a useful and acceptable technique in mathematics. They will learn to analyze their first result so that their next attempts are "educated" guesses.

TEACH

GUIDING STUDENTS' WORK

Point out to students that the first guess, 22, is not random, but is a reasonable estimate based on a thorough understanding of the problem. Guessing before understanding the problem is very inefficient. Also point out that the revisions are carefully chosen. The first guess leads to a result that is only a little too high, so the next guess is only revised downward slightly.

EXTRA EXAMPLES

Example Howard is twice the age of his sister Latesha, and four times the age of his brother Jared. The sum of their ages is 28. How old is each sibling? **Howard is 16, Latesha is 8, and Jared is 4.**

1.5 Problem Solving Strategies

- Look for a Pattern
- Draw a Diagram
- Act It Out
- Work Backward
- Guess, Check, and Revise
- Make a Table
- Solve a Simpler Problem

Guess, Check, and Revise

Problem Consecutive numbers are numbers that follow one after another. The numbers 1, 2, and 3 are consecutive numbers. The sum of three consecutive numbers is 66. What are these numbers?

1 Read and Understand

Read the problem carefully.

The problem asks for the three consecutive numbers that add up to 66.

2 Make a Plan

Decide on a strategy to use.

One way to solve the problem is to use the guess, check, and revise strategy. Guess the answer and check it to see if you are correct. If not, revise your guess and try again.

3 Solve the Problem

Reread the problem. Then make a guess, check the answer, and revise, if necessary.

Reasoning	Guess	Check
Because 22 is one third of 66, you might choose 22, 23, and 24 for the first guess.	22, 23, 24	$22 + 23 + 24 = 69$ ✗
Because the first guess was too high, revise your guess using smaller numbers.	20, 21, 22	$20 + 21 + 22 = 63$ ✗
Second guess is too low. Try again.	21, 22, 23	$21 + 22 + 23 = 66$ ✓

So, the consecutive numbers that add up to 66 are 21, 22, and 23.

4 Look Back

Check your answer by adding the numbers again to see if their sum is 66.

$$21 + 22 + 23 \stackrel{?}{=} 66$$
$$66 = 66 \checkmark$$

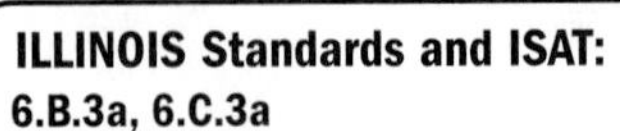

ILLINOIS Standards and ISAT:
6.B.3a, 6.C.3a

Practice the Strategy

Use the strategy *guess, check, and revise.*

1. **Consecutive Numbers** The sum of two consecutive numbers divided by 3 is 71. What are the numbers? **106, 107**
2. **Money** There are some nickels, dimes, and quarters in your pocket. You know you have exactly 15 coins, exactly 5 of them are nickels, and the total amount is $2.30. How many dimes do you have? How many quarters? **3 dimes; 7 quarters**
3. **Game** You are playing a game where you collect blue chips and green chips. For every blue chip you get one point. For every green chip you lose a point. If you have a total of 20 chips and a total of 14 points, how many blue chips do you have? How many green chips do you have? **17 blue chips; 3 green chips**
4. **Video Game** Damon has saved $33 to buy a new video game that costs $52. His mother offers to contribute $5. How much more does he need to save? **$14**
5. **Triangle** Copy the triangle below. Fill in the circles using each of the numbers 1, 2, 3, 4, 5, 6, and 7 exactly once so that the sum of each side and the sum of the middle column is 10.
   Sample:

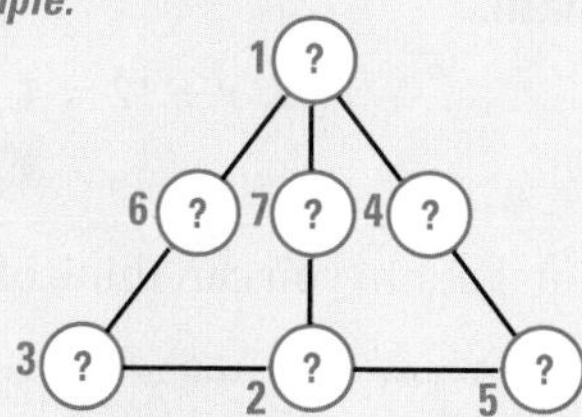

6. **Fundraising** You sell 14 items for a school fundraiser and make a total of $142. A T-shirt costs $11 and a hat costs $9. How many T-shirts did you sell? How many hats did you sell? **8 T-shirts; 6 hats**

Mixed Problem Solving

Use any strategy to solve the problem.

7. **Ice Cream** An ice cream shop offers week-long special deals when you purchase a large ice cream cake. They offer a free small ice cream cake every fifth week, a free pint of ice cream every sixth week, and a free ice cream cone every third week. How many times in one year will they offer all three deals in the same week if they offer all three the first week of the year? **twice**
8. **Flowers** Hannah is in charge of buying carnations to give away at a school dance. The flower shop sells carnations at a discount in groups of 12. Hannah needs 170 carnations for the dance. How many groups of 12 carnations should she buy? **15 groups**
9. **Height** Justin, Bob, Kelly, Michelle, and Tim are all different heights. Kelly is taller than Michelle and Justin. Tim is shorter than Justin but taller than Michelle. Bob is the tallest of the group. Put the students in order from tallest to shortest. **Bob, Kelly, Justin, Tim, Michelle**
10. **Talent Show** Your school talent show allows people to sign up for 3 or 5 minute acts. There is one minute between acts. The talent show has 15 acts and lasts for 79 minutes. How many 3 minute acts are there? **5**

3 APPLY

TRANSPARENCY

Even-numbered answers are available on transparencies.

TEACHING TIP

In Exercise 2, students may wish to make a sketch or model the problem in order to help them visualize it better before making their first guesses.

MATH REASONING

In Exercise 5, show students how reasoning quickly eliminates most options. Ask students how they can eliminate placing 7 in any corner circle (one side containing the corner would have to be 1, 2, 7 to make 10, but then the other side containing that corner would be greater than 10). Ask students how they can eliminate placing 6 in any corner circle (use the same reasoning as for 7). Similarly, students can deduce that 6 and 7 cannot go in the bottom center circle. Placing 6 and 7 in any two remaining circles quickly leads to a solution.

SUGGESTED STRATEGIES

You may wish to suggest the following strategies for the problems in the Mixed Problem Solving:

- Exercise 7: Draw a Diagram; Make a Table
- Exercise 8: Make a Table; Guess, Check, and Revise
- Exercise 9: Draw a Diagram; Make a Table
- Exercise 10: Guess, Check, and Revise; Make a Table

PLAN

SKILL CHECK

Evaluate the expression for the given values of the variables.

1. $43 - s, s = 18$ 25
2. $135 \div m, m = 15$ 9
3. $112 + r, r = 49$ 161

LESSON OBJECTIVE

Write and solve equations using mental math.

PACING

Suggested Number of Days
Basic Course: 1 day
Average Course: 1 day
Advanced Course: 1 day
Block: 0.5 block with 1.6

TEACHING RESOURCES

For a complete list of Teaching Resources, see page 2B.

TRANSPARENCY

Warm-Up Exercises for this lesson are available on a transparency. A support transparency is available for the Activity.

TEACH

MOTIVATING THE LESSON

Ask students who have used counters to model positive and negative integers to describe how the model helped their understanding.

ACTIVITY

Goal Use algebra tile models to solve equations.

Key Discovery You can solve equations with algebra tiles.

1–3. See Additional Answers beginning on page AA1.

28

Equations and Solutions

BEFORE

You wrote and evaluated variable expressions.

Now

You'll write and solve equations using mental math.

WHY?

So you can find the weight of a baby elephant, as in Ex. 29.

Word Watch

equation, p. 28
solution, p. 28
solving an equation, p. 28

Activity You can use algebra tiles to solve equations.

1–3. See margin for art.

In an *equation*, the quantities on each side of the equal sign have the same value. The algebra tile model below represents the equation $x + 2 = 6$.

(1) With how many 1-tiles should you replace the x-tile so that the quantities on both sides of the equal sign have the same value? Explain. 4; replacing the x-tile with 4 1-tiles will result in 6 1-tiles on each side of the equals sign.

(2) What value of x makes the equation $x + 2 = 6$ a true statement? 4

Make a model to represent the equation. Then tell what value of x makes the equation a true statement.

1. $x + 3 = 8$ 5
2. $x + 4 = 5$ 1
3. $6 + x = 10$ 4

An **equation** is a mathematical sentence formed by placing an equal sign (=) between two expressions.

A **solution** of a variable equation is a number that you can substitute for a variable to make the equation true. Finding all the solutions of an equation is called **solving an equation**.

EXAMPLE 1 Using Mental Math to Solve Equations

Solve the equation using mental math.

a. $15 - n = 4$ **b.** $8x = 32$ **c.** $r \div 12 = 4$

Solution

To solve simple equations using mental math, you can think of the equation as a question.

a. 15 minus what number equals 4? $15 - 11 = 4$, so $n = 11$.

b. 8 times what number equals 32? $8(4) = 32$, so $x = 4$.

c. What number divided by 12 equals 4? $48 \div 12 = 4$, so $r = 48$.

ILLINOIS Standards and ISAT:
8.A.3b, 8.D.3a

EXAMPLE 2 Checking Solutions of Equations

Tell whether the value of the variable is a solution of $n - 8 = 20$.

a. $n = 12$ **b.** $n = 28$

Solution

Substitute for n and then simplify.

a. $n - 8 = 20$
$12 - 8 \stackrel{?}{=} 20$
$4 \neq 20$

b. $n - 8 = 20$
$28 - 8 \stackrel{?}{=} 20$
$20 = 20$

ANSWER 12 is not a solution of $n - 8 = 20$, and 28 is a solution.

HELP with Reading

The $\stackrel{?}{=}$ symbol means *are these values equal?* The $\neq$ symbol means *is not equal to.*

Your turn now **Solve the equation using mental math.**

1. $5x = 45$ 9 **2.** $16 + n = 21$ 5 **3.** $t \div 6 = 9$ 54

Tell whether the value of the variable is a solution of the equation.

4. $a + 9 = 16$; $a = 7$ yes **5.** $88 \div y = 8$; $y = 8$ no **6.** $7n = 13$; $n = 2$ no

What do you think? New Year's

Times Square

The Times Square New Year's Eve Ball in New York City has a total of 696 lights. Of these, 168 are on the exterior and 432 are on the interior. The remaining lights are strobe lights. How many strobe lights are there? **96 strobe lights**

EXAMPLE 3 Writing an Equation

Times Square The Times Square New Year's Eve Ball drops a total of 77 feet in 60 seconds. After 54 seconds the ball has dropped 69 feet. How many more feet will the ball drop?

Solution

You can use a verbal model to write an equation. Let d represent the distance left to drop.

Total distance ball drops	=	Distance ball has dropped	+	Distance left to drop	**Write a verbal model.**
77	=	69	+	d	**Substitute.**
77	=	69	+	**8**	**Use mental math.**

ANSWER Because $d = 8$, the ball will drop 8 more feet.

✓ **Check** You can check your answer by finding the sum of 8 and 69.

$8 + 69 \stackrel{?}{=} 77$
$77 = 77$ ✓

TIPS FOR NEW TEACHERS

Be certain students understand the verbal model concept presented in Example 3. See Tips for New Teachers in the *Chapter 1 Resource Book*.

EXTRA EXAMPLES

Example 1 Solve the equation using mental math.
a. $23 + x = 30$ 7
b. $9x = 63$ 7
c. $x - 14 = 24$ 38

Example 2 Tell whether the value of the variable is a solution of $p \div 7 = 8$.
a. $p = 56$ yes
b. $p = 42$ no

Example 3 A bus has traveled 84 miles toward a city that is 126 miles away. How many more miles must the bus travel to reach the city? **42 mi**

COMMON ERROR

In Example 3, some students may try to incorporate the quantity 54 seconds into their models. Point out to them that part of understanding a problem is recognizing what information is necessary to solving the problem and what information is not.

CONCEPT CHECK

What is a solution of a variable equation? **a number you can substitute for the variable to make the equation true**

DAILY PUZZLER

Use all the digits 1, 2, 3, and 4 only once each to write three expressions that have a value of 5. ***Sample answer:*** **$(4 + 3 - 2) \times 1$, $12 - (4 + 3)$, $14 - 3^2$**

ASSIGNMENT GUIDE

Basic Course
Day 1: SRH p. 712 Exs. 1-3, p. 717 Exs. 1, 4; pp. 30-31 Exs. 11-22, 27, 29-31, 38-44

Average Course
Day 1: pp. 30-31 Exs. 11-22, 27-32, 37-40, 43-45

Average Course
Day 1: pp. 30-31 Exs. 11-16, 23-38*, 43-45

Block
pp. 30-31 Exs. 11-22, 27-32, 37-40, 43-45 (with 1.6)

EXTRA PRACTICE

- Student Edition, p. 727
- Chapter 1 Resource Book, pp. 46-48
- Test and Practice Generator

TRANSPARENCY

Even-numbered answers are available on transparencies.

HOMEWORK CHECK

When you review students' homework for this lesson, go over the following exercises to check understanding of key concepts.
Basic: 11, 15, 16, 19, 27
Average: 11, 15, 17, 20, 27
Advanced: 14, 15, 16, 25, 27

TEACHING TIP

If students have difficulty with division equations, as in Exercises 22 and 23, point out that every division problem has an equivalent multiplication problem. For example, $51 \div k = 3$ means that $3k = 51$, and $\frac{32}{n} = 16$ means that $16n = 32$. In general, dividend ÷ divisor = quotient implies quotient • divisor = dividend.

1.5 Exercises

More Practice, p. 727

Getting Ready to Practice

1. **Vocabulary** Give an example of an equation with a variable. Explain how to find the solution of the equation. *Sample answer:* $4 + x = 7$; use mental math and ask "4 plus what number is 7?" The answer is 3.

Solve the equation using mental math.

2. $9 + p = 21$ 12
3. $y - 10 = 34$ 44
4. $7x = 77$ 11
5. $56 \div k = 8$ 7

Tell whether the value of the variable is a solution of the equation.

6. $35 - x = 21; x = 16$ no
7. $75 \div x = 5; x = 15$ yes
8. $x + 29 = 42; x = 13$ yes
9. $7x = 84; x = 14$ no

10. **Fireworks** Your town's fireworks show cost \$1000 per minute. The total cost was \$25,000. Use a verbal model to write and solve an equation to find how many minutes the fireworks show lasted. Total cost = Cost per minute × Number of minutes; $25{,}000 = 1000m$; 25 min

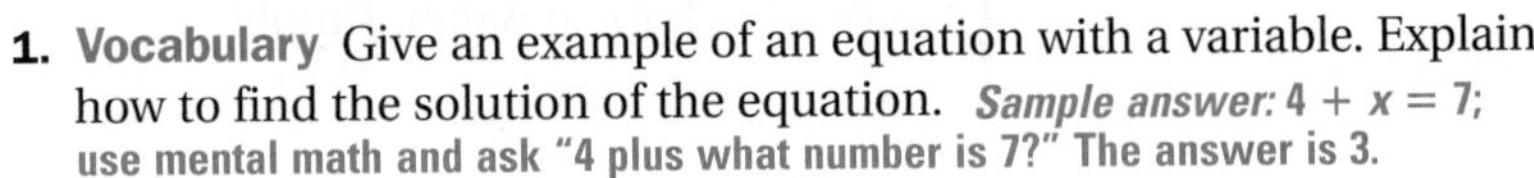

Practice and Problem Solving

Example	Exercises
1	11-14, 19-26
2	15-18
3	27

- More Examples
- eTutorial Plus

Match the equation with the corresponding question.

A 11. $24 \div t = 8$ B
12. $t + 8 = 24$ C
13. $24t = 8$ D
14. $\frac{t}{24} = 8$ A

A. What number divided by 24 equals 8?
B. 24 divided by what number equals 8?
C. What number plus 8 equals 24?
D. 24 times what number equals 8?

Tell whether the value of the variable is a solution of the equation.

15. $15 + b = 28; b = 13$ yes
16. $37 - d = 14; d = 21$ no
17. $6w = 72; w = 14$ no
18. $9c = 108; c = 12$ yes

Solve the equation using mental math.

19. $z + 8 = 19$ 11
20. $6m = 48$ 8
21. $c - 16 = 13$ 29
22. $51 \div k = 3$ 17
23. $\frac{32}{n} = 16$ 2
24. $26 - r = 17$ 9
25. $10y = 150$ 15
26. $7 + x = 31$ 24

27. **Rainfall** The highest recorded rainfall in the United States in a 24 hour period is 43 inches. Write an equation to find how much more rain needs to fall in the remaining time to equal the record, if 14 inches has already fallen in less than 24 hours. Then solve the equation. $14 + r = 43$; 29 in.

28. **Writing** Explain how you would tell whether 5 is a solution of the equation $4x = 20$. **Multiply 4 and 5 to see if the product is 20.**

B 29. **Elephants** A baby elephant at the Bronx Zoo would get on a scale only with its mother. The zoo weighed the mother as 5033 pounds. They weighed the mother and the baby together as 5396 pounds. Write and solve an equation to find the weight of the baby elephant. **$5033 + b = 5396$; 363 lb**

30. **Measurement** Describe how you could use mental math to find the number of feet in 3600 inches. **Ask what number times 12 equals 3600, and then find the number.**

31. **Invitations** You are writing invitations to a party. It takes you four minutes to complete each invitation. Write and solve an equation to find how many invitations you can complete in one hour. **$4p = 60$; 15 invitations**

32. **Guess, Check, and Revise** Find the value of x that makes the equation below true. **1**

$$[(x + 3) \cdot 4 - 7] \div 3 = 3$$

C **Challenge** **Tell which of the given values is a solution of the equation.**

33. $3x + 6 = x + 12$; $x = 1, 2, 3$ **3**

34. $2x - 7 = x + 1$; $x = 8, 9, 10$ **8**

35. $8 - 4x = 4x$; $x = 0, 1, 2$ **1**

36. $2x - 4.5 = x \div 2$; $x = 3, 4, 5$ **3**

37. **Marathon** To qualify for the Boston Marathon, Hillary has to run a qualifying time of 3 hours 40 minutes or less. Her best time so far is 4 hours 5 minutes. Write and solve an equation to find by how many minutes Hillary must improve her time to qualify. **$x + 220 = 245$; 25 min**

Mixed Review

Evaluate the expression when $y = 8$. *(Lesson 1.3)*

38. $7y + 17$ **73**

39. $(36 - 24) \cdot y$ **96**

40. $y \cdot 4 + 20 \cdot y$ **192**

Basic Skills **Estimate the sum or difference.** **41–43. Estimates may vary.**

41. $8748 - 3109$ **6000**

42. $876 + 622$ **1500**

43. $147 + 89 + 791$ **1000**

Test-Taking Practice

44. **Multiple Choice** Which of the following is a solution of $63 \div x = 9$? **B**

A. 6 **B.** 7 **C.** 9 **D.** 54

45. **Short Response** You and your friend volunteer at a zoo during the summer. One week you volunteer 12 hours. The sum of the hours you and your friend work that week is 23. Write an equation that can be used to determine how many hours your friend worked. Then solve the equation. **$12 + h = 23$; 11 h**

4 ASSESS

Assessment Resources

For more assessment resources, see:
- Assessment Book
- Test and Practice Generator

Mini-Quiz

Tell whether the value of the variable is a solution of the equation.

1. $5a = 40$; $a = 9$ **no**
2. $42 - b = 26$; $b = 16$ **yes**

Solve the equation using mental math.

3. $g + 4 = 31$ **27**
4. $b \div 3 = 22$ **66**
5. $72 \div h = 8$ **9**
6. The level of water in a pond rose 10 inches in one week. Over the first three days, the pond rose 7 inches. Write an equation to find how much the pond rose the last four days of the week. Then solve the equation. **$x + 7 = 10$; 3 in.**

5 FOLLOW-UP

Reteaching/Remediation

- Study Guide in Chapter 1 Resource Book, pp. 49–50
- Tutor Place, Algebra Card 7
- eTutorial Plus Online
- Extra Practice, p. 727
- Lesson Practice in Chapter 1 Resource Book, pp. 46–48

Challenge/Enrichment

- Challenge Practice in Chapter 1 Resource Book, p. 51
- Teacher's Edition, p. 2F

English Learner Support

- Spanish Study Guide
- Multi-Language Glossary
- Chapter Audio Summaries CDs

1 PLAN

EXPLORE THE CONCEPT

- Students will use tiles to develop formulas for finding the areas of rectangles and squares.
- This activity leads into the study of formulas in Lesson 1.6.

MATERIALS

Each student or group of students will need 32 square tiles. See also the Activity Support Master in the *Chapter 1 Resource Book*.

RECOMMENDED TIME

Work activity: 10 min
Discuss results: 5 min

GROUPING

Students can work individually or in pairs. In pairs, one can arrange tiles while the other completes the table.

TRANSPARENCY

A support transparency is available for this Activity.

2 TEACH

ALTERNATIVE STRATEGY

Students can use floor tiles and string to make rectangles.

3 CLOSE

KEY DISCOVERY

The area of a rectangle is its length times its width. The area of a square is the length of a side squared.

ASSESSMENT

1. Which has greater area, a square with side 5 or a rectangle with length 6 and width 4? **the square**
2. What kind of units are used to measure area? **square units**

1.6 Hands-on Activity

GOAL
Develop formulas for finding the areas of rectangles and squares.

MATERIALS
- square tiles

Modeling Area

You can use square tiles to find the *areas* of rectangles and squares.

Explore **Find the area of a 5 unit by 3 unit rectangle.**

1. Use square tiles to make a rectangle with side lengths of 5 units and 3 units.

2. The area of the rectangle is equal to the number of square unit tiles that cover it. Count the square tiles to find the area of the rectangle. **15 square units**

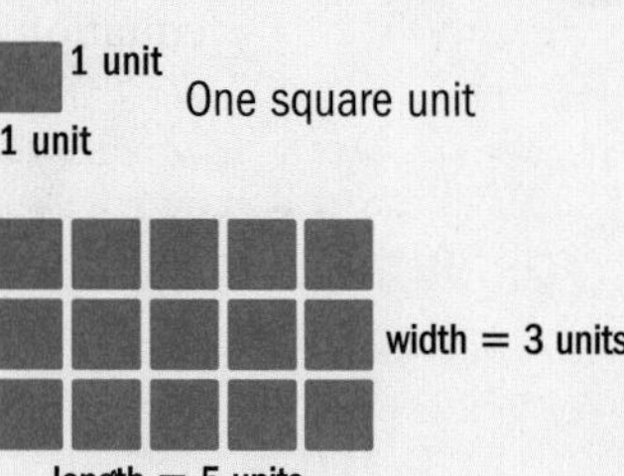

Your turn now

1. Use square tiles to make a rectangle that is the size given in the table. Copy and complete the table.

Dimensions	Length	Width	Number of square tiles	Area of rectangle	
3 by 4	? 3	? 4	? 12	?	12 square units
4 by 4	? 4	? 4	? 16	?	16 square units
5 by 6	? 5	? 6	? 30	?	30 square units
3 by 3	? 3	? 3	? 9	?	9 square units

2. Write a variable equation to find the area of a rectangle and explain what each variable represents. **$A = lw$, where A is the area, l is the length, and w is the width.**
3. Write a different equation to find the area of a square and explain what each variable represents. **$A = s^2$, where A is the area and s is the length of a side.**

Stop and Think

4. **Critical Thinking** Area is measured in square units. Perimeter is the distance around a shape. Is perimeter measured in square units? Why or why not? **No; it is a linear measurement, not a square measurement.**

ILLINOIS Standards and ISAT:
7.C.3b; 9.C.3a

Variables in Familiar Formulas

BEFORE	Now	WHY?
You evaluated variable expressions.	You'll use formulas to find unknown values.	So you can find the sizes of swimming pools, as in Ex. 22.

Word Watch

formula, p. 33
perimeter, p. 33
area, p. 33

A **formula** is an equation that relates two or more quantities such as *perimeter*, length, and width. The **perimeter** of a figure is the sum of the lengths of its sides. The **area** of a figure is the amount of surface the figure covers.

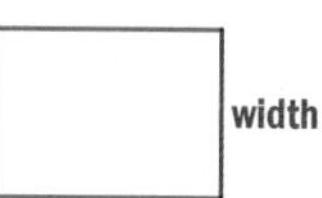

Perimeter is measured in linear units such as feet. Area is measured in square units such as square feet, or ft^2.

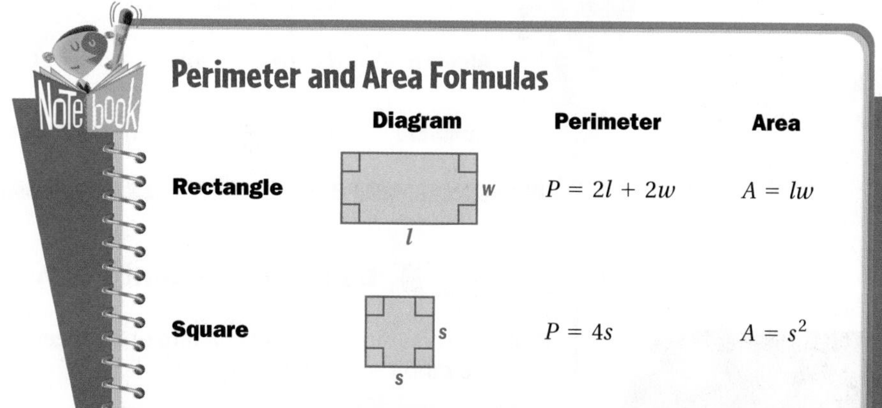

Perimeter and Area Formulas

	Diagram	Perimeter	Area
Rectangle		$P = 2l + 2w$	$A = lw$
Square		$P = 4s$	$A = s^2$

with Reading

The mark ⌐ tells you that an angle measures 90°.

EXAMPLE 1 Finding Perimeter and Area

Find the perimeter and area of the rectangle.

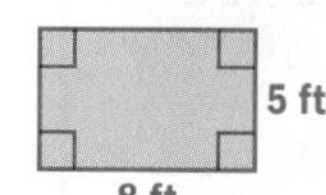

Solution

Find the perimeter.

$P = 2l + 2w$	**Write formula.**
$= 2(8) + 2(5)$	**Substitute.**
$= 26$	**Multiply, then add.**

Find the area.

$A = lw$	**Write formula.**
$= (8)(5)$	**Substitute.**
$= 40$	**Multiply.**

ANSWER The perimeter is 26 feet, and the area is 40 square feet.

ILLINOIS Standards and ISAT:
7.C.3b, 8.D.3b; 9.C.3a

1 PLAN

SKILL CHECK

Evaluate the expression for $x = 8$ and $y = 20$.

1. $x + y$ 28 **2.** y^2 400

3. xy 160 **4.** $\frac{y}{x}$ 2.5

LESSON OBJECTIVE

Use formulas to find unknown values.

PACING

Suggested Number of Days
Basic Course: 1 day
Average Course: 1 day
Advanced Course: 1 day
Block: 0.5 block with 1.5

TEACHING RESOURCES

For a complete list of Teaching Resources, see page 2B.

TRANSPARENCY

Warm-Up Exercises for this lesson are available on a transparency.

2 TEACH

MOTIVATING THE LESSON

Have students tile a desktop with 8 inch by 8 inch paper squares. Assign a side length of the square a name, such as a "dip." Have students estimate the area and perimeter of the desktop using these units, making sure they distinguish between "dips" and "square dips."

TIPS FOR NEW TEACHERS

Emphasize that proper units are part of a correct solution. See Tips for New Teachers in the *Chapter 1 Resource Book.*

EXTRA EXAMPLES

Example 1 Find the perimeter and the area of the rectangle.

24 cm, 27 cm²

Example 2 Find the side length of a square with an area of 121 square feet. **11 ft**

Example 3 A bicycle is moving at a rate of 10 feet per second. How far does the bicycle travel in 1 minute? **600 ft**

NOTETAKING

Encourage students to draw several rectangles and squares in their notebooks. Have them measure and record the lengths and widths of each, and show the work to find the perimeters and areas. Students should also record all formulas in a consistent, eye-catching way in their notebooks for easy reference.

MULTIPLE REPRESENTATIONS

The distance formula is shown in words and symbols on this page. To help students internalize the relationship of distance, rate, and time, have them walk across the classroom at different rates and ask them how changing the rate affects the time needed to walk across the room or the distance walked in a given time.

TEACHING TIP

Make sure students have made the connection between the terms *line* and *linear*. A linear unit is one you would use to measure the length of a line segment.

EXAMPLE 2 Finding Side Length

Find the side length of a square with an area of 81 square feet.

$A = s^2$	Write formula for area of a square.
$81 = s^2$	Substitute 81 for A.
$9 = s$	Use mental math: $9^2 = 81$.

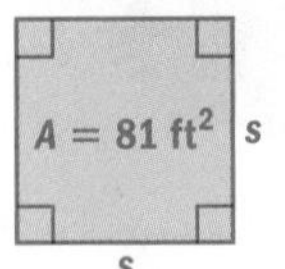

ANSWER The side length of the square is 9 feet.

Distance Formula Another useful formula is the distance formula. You can use the distance formula to find distance traveled.

Distance Formula

Words	The distance traveled d is the product of the rate r and the time t.		
Algebra	$d = r \cdot t$	or	$d = rt$
Numbers	$d = 45 \frac{\text{miles}}{\text{hour}} \cdot 3 \text{ hours} = 135 \text{ miles}$		

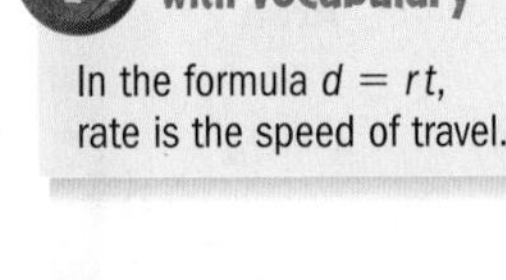

In the formula $d = rt$, rate is the speed of travel.

EXAMPLE 3 Using the Distance Formula

Rabbits A rabbit is running at a rate of 26.4 feet per second. How far does the rabbit travel in 5 seconds?

Solution

$d = r \cdot t$	Write distance formula.
$= 26.4 \cdot 5$	Substitute 26.4 for r and 5 for t.
$= 132$	Multiply.

ANSWER The rabbit travels 132 feet in 5 seconds.

Your turn now **Solve.**

1. Find the perimeter and area of a square with a 7 inch side length. **$P = 28$ in., $A = 49$ in.²**
2. Find the side length of a square that has an area of 100 square yards. **10 yd**
3. How far does a car travel in 2 hours at a rate of 40 miles per hour? **80 mi**

You can write the distance formula in different forms to find rate or time. Use $t = \frac{d}{r}$ to find the time and $r = \frac{d}{t}$ to find the rate.

EXAMPLE 4 Using the Distance Formula to Find Time

How long will it take a rabbit to travel 264 feet at a rate of 22 feet per second ?

Solution

$t = \frac{d}{r}$ **Write distance formula.**

$= \frac{264}{22}$ **Substitute 264 for *d* and 22 for *r*.**

$= 12$ **Divide.**

ANSWER It will take a rabbit 12 seconds to travel 264 feet.

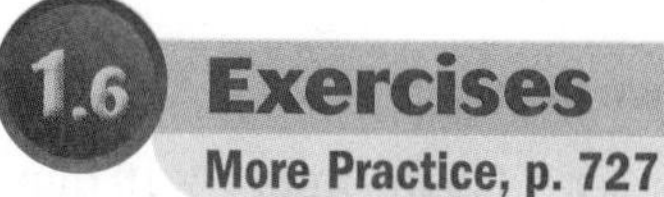

1.6 Exercises

More Practice, p. 727

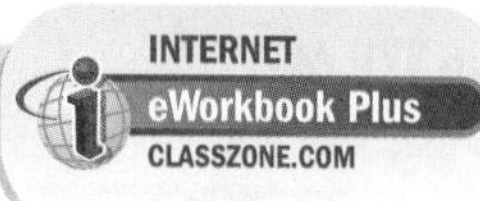

Getting Ready to Practice

1. **Vocabulary** Describe the difference between area and perimeter. **Area is the surface a figure covers, while perimeter is the distance around the figure.**

Find the perimeter and area of the rectangle or square.

2. 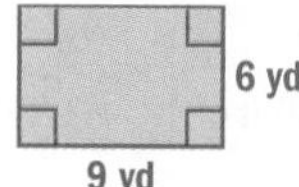

$P = 30$ yd, $A = 54$ yd^2

3. 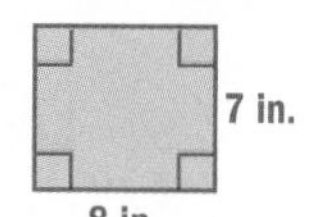

$P = 30$ in., $A = 56$ in.^{2}

4. 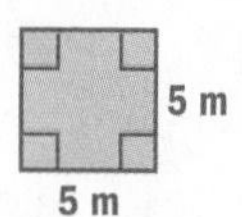

$P = 20$ m
$A = 25$ m^2

5. **Tiger Beetles** A tiger beetle runs at a rate of 53 centimeters per second for 3 seconds. How far does the beetle run? **159 cm**

6. **Find the Error** Describe and correct the error in the solution.

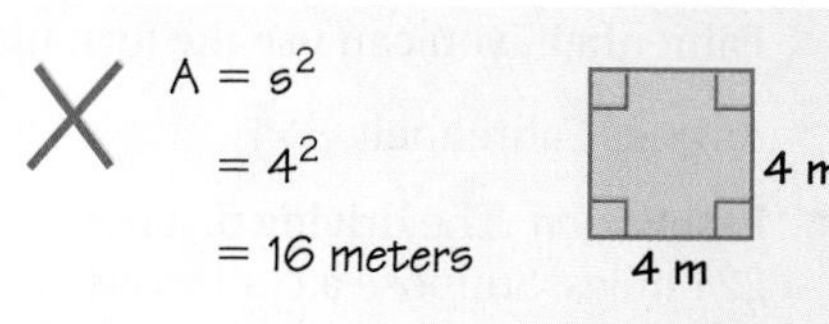

The units should be square meters; $A = s^2 = (4)^2 = 16$ square meters.

EXTRA EXAMPLES

Example 4 How long will it take a python to slither 20 feet at a rate of 6 in/sec? **40 sec**

Differentiating Instruction

Alternative Teaching Strategy
If you can clear a large area on the classroom floor, you can direct students to make rectangles from equal-length rulers or from yard- or meter-sticks. Some students may benefit from being able to walk around and inside their rectangles as they explore the concepts of area and perimeter.

CONCEPT CHECK

Is it correct to say that the area of a 3 inch by 4 inch rectangle is 12 inches? Explain. **No; area is measured in square units, so the area would be 12 square inches.**

DAILY PUZZLER

You are forming a rectangular landing outside your door using 3 inch by 6 inch bricks. The landing is to be 16 inches wide and 27 inches long. How many bricks would it take to fill the area? Can you fit the bricks into the rectangle without cutting any? If so, draw a diagram. **24 bricks; no**

3 APPLY

ASSIGNMENT GUIDE

Basic Course

Day 1: SRH p. 713 Exs. 1-5; pp. 36-37 Exs. 7-15, 17-24, 27-29, 33-39

Average Course

Day 1: pp. 36-37 Exs. 9-16, 19-29, 32-40

Average Course

Day 1: pp. 36-37 Exs. 9-11, 14-18, 21-34*, 38-40

Block

pp. 36-37 Exs. 9-16, 19-29, 32-40 (with 1.5)

EXTRA PRACTICE

- Student Edition, p. 727
- Chapter 1 Resource Book, pp. 55-57
- Test and Practice Generator

TRANSPARENCY

Even-numbered answers are available on transparencies.

HOMEWORK CHECK

When you review students' homework for this lesson, go over the following exercises to check understanding of key concepts.

Basic: 7, 14, 17, 21, 22
Average: 9, 14, 19, 21, 23
Advanced: 9, 14, 18, 21, 27

MATH REASONING

After students have worked Exercises 30 and 31, discuss the strategies they used to find the areas to emphasize that there are different ways to break each figure into smaller shapes.

HELP with Homework

Example	Exercises
1	7-13, 22
2	14-15, 22
3	17-21, 27
4	17-20, 23

- More Examples
- eTutorial Plus

What do you think? Travel

Arizona

U.S. Highway 66, often called Route 66, was commissioned in 1926. It connected Illinois to California traveling through eight states, including Arizona. Route 66 ceased to exist as an official highway in 1984. How many years was it an official highway? 58 yr

Practice and Problem Solving

A **Find the perimeter and area of the rectangle or square.**

7.

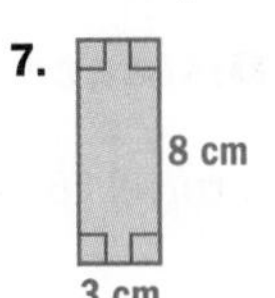

$P = 22$ cm, $A = 24$ cm^2

8.

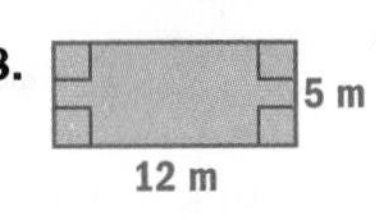

$P = 34$ m, $A = 60$ m^2

9.

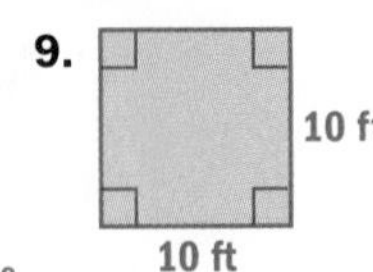

$P = 40$ ft, $A = 100$ ft^2

In Exercises 10–13, find the perimeter and area of the rectangle or square.

10. length = 17 m, width = 9 m $P = 52$ m, $A = 153$ m^2

11. side length = 18 in. $P = 72$ in., $A = 324$ in.^{2}

12. length = 11 ft, width = 2 ft $P = 26$ ft, $A = 22$ ft^2

13. length = 14 cm, width = 13 cm $P = 54$ cm, $A = 182$ cm^2

14. Find the side length of a square that has an area of 36 square yards. 6 yd

15. Find the side length of a square that has a perimeter of 24 meters. 6 m

16. **Mental Math** The area of a rectangle is 88 square inches. The width is 8 inches. Use mental math to find the length of the rectangle. 11 in.

Use the distance formula to find the unknown value.

17. $d = 36$ km, $r = ?$, $t = 4$ h 9 km/h

18. $d = ?$, $r = 0.5$ mi/min, $t = 10$ min 5 mi

19. $d = ?$, $r = 7$ mi/h, $t = 1.5$ h 10.5 mi

20. $d = 40$ ft, $r = 5$ ft/sec, $t = ?$ 8 sec

21. **Arizona** The speed limit on rural interstates in Arizona is 75 miles per hour. A car travels at this rate for 3 hours. How far does it travel? 225 mi

22. **Swimming Pools** The table shows information about two swimming pools. Copy and complete the table. Pool A: 1320 ft^2, 164 ft; Pool B: 60 ft, 180 ft

	Length	Width	Area	Perimeter
Pool A	60 ft	22 ft	?	?
Pool B	?	30 ft	1800 ft^2	?

B **23.** **Train** A train travels 226 miles from Washington, D.C., to New York City in about 2 hours 30 minutes. What is the average speed of the train in miles per hour? Round to the nearest mile per hour. 90 mi/h

24. **Temperature Formula** To convert from degrees Celsius to degrees Fahrenheit, you can use the formula $F = \frac{9}{5}C + 32$. Convert 20°C to degrees Fahrenheit. 68°F

25. **Estimation** The driving distance between Houston and Dallas is 224 miles. Suppose a car travels at an average rate of 52 miles per hour. Estimate how long the trip from Houston to Dallas takes. about 4 h

26. **Measurement** Write a formula for converting meters to centimeters. $c = 100m$

27. **Parachutist** A parachutist falls for 2 minutes at a speed of 13 feet per second. How far does the parachutist fall during this time? **1560 ft**

Yard Fencing In Exercises 28 and 29, your rectangular yard has a length of 50 feet and a width of 45 feet.

28. You want to fence in your yard. How much fencing do you need? **190 ft**

29. You want to fertilize your yard. Each bag of fertilizer covers 2000 square feet. How many bags should you buy? **2 bags**

C Challenge Find the perimeter and area of the figure.

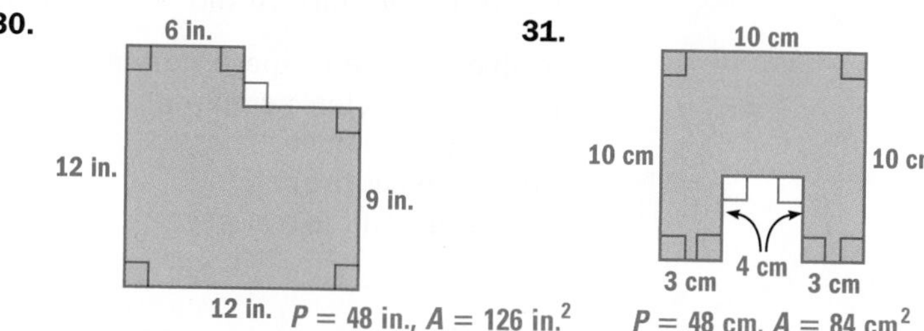

30. $P = 48$ in., $A = 126$ in.^{2} 31. $P = 48$ cm, $A = 84$ cm^2

32. **Critical Thinking** Find the perimeter and area of a rectangle with a length of 6 inches and a width of 5 inches. Then find the perimeter and area of a rectangle with a length of 12 inches and a width of 10 inches. How does the perimeter of a rectangle change if length and width are doubled? How does the area of a rectangle change if the length and width are doubled? **$P = 22$ in., $A = 30$ in.^{2}; $P = 44$ in., $A = 120$ in.^{2}; the perimeter is doubled; the area is multiplied by 4.**

Mixed Review 

Solve the equation using mental math. *(Lesson 1.5)*

33. $8x = 72$ **9**

34. $g - 19 = 37$ **56**

35. $\frac{y}{3} = 10$ **30**

Basic Skills Round the number to the place value of the red digit.

36. 7.528 **7.5**

37. 15.538 **15.54**

38. 13.974 **14.0**

Test-Taking Practice 

INTERNET
State Test Practice
CLASSZONE.COM

39. **Multiple Choice** You drive 50 miles per hour for 1 hour 30 minutes. Which expression can be used to find how many miles you travel? **C**

A. 50×130 **B.** 50×90 **C.** 50×1.5 **D.** $50 \div 90$

40. **Short Response** The area of a rectangle is 27 square meters. Explain how you can find the length of the rectangle if its width is 3 meters. What is the length of the rectangle? **Divide 27 by 3; 9 m.**

4 ASSESS

Assessment Resources

For more assessment resources, see:
- Assessment Book
- Test and Practice Generator

Mini-Quiz

1. Find the perimeter and area.

32 in., 48 in.^{2}

Use the distance formula to find the missing value.

2. $d = 20$ ft, $r = 2$ ft/sec, $t = \underline{?}$ **10 sec**

3. $d = \underline{?}$, $r = 0.25$ m/min, $t = 3$ min **0.75 m**

4. Satchi leaves at 10 A.M. on a 475 mile trip. She expects to arrive at 7:30 P.M. What must be her average rate of speed? **50 mi/h**

5 FOLLOW-UP

Reteaching/Remediation

- Study Guide in Chapter 1 Resource Book, pp. 58–59
- Tutor Place, Geometry and Measurement Cards 11, 12, 14, 28, Algebra Card 13
- eTutorial Plus Online
- Extra Practice, p. 727
- Lesson Practice in Chapter 1 Resource Book, pp. 55–57

Challenge/Enrichment

- Challenge Practice in Chapter 1 Resource Book, p. 61
- Teacher's Edition, p. 2F

English Learner Support

- Spanish Study Guide
- Multi-Language Glossary
- Chapter Audio Summaries CDs

1 PLAN

SKILL CHECK

Use the formula $d = rt$ to find the indicated value.

1. d, when $t = 4.5$ sec and $r = 60$ ft/sec **270 ft**
2. d, when $r = 0.5$ mi/h and $t = 10$ h **5 mi**
3. t, when $d = 248$ m and $r = 62$ m/sec **4 sec**
4. r, when $t = 7$ h and $d = 420$ mi **60 mi/h**

LESSON OBJECTIVE

Use a problem solving plan to solve problems.

PACING

Suggested Number of Days
Basic Course: 2 days
Average Course: 2 days
Advanced Course: 2 days
Block: 1 block

TEACHING RESOURCES

For a complete list of Teaching Resources, see page 2B.

TRANSPARENCY

Warm-Up Exercises for this lesson are available on a transparency.

2 TEACH

MOTIVATING THE LESSON

Ask students what they know about triathlons and biathlons. Some students may have competed in such events or volunteered to help run them.

A Problem Solving Plan

BEFORE	Now	WHY?
You used problem solving strategies to solve problems.	You'll use a problem solving plan to solve problems.	To find how much cheese you need for lasagna, as in Ex. 9.

Word Watch

Review Word
formula, p. 33

In the Real World

Triathlon You and a friend decide to compete in a triathlon. You both swim 200 meters, bike 10 kilometers, and then run 2 kilometers.

The table shows your speeds for swimming, in meters per minute, and biking, in kilometers per minute. Who has the better total time after these two stages?

	Swimming (m/min)	Biking (km/min)
You	76.9	0.43
Friend	82.6	0.41

EXAMPLE 1 Understanding and Planning

To solve the triathlon problem, you need to make sure you understand the problem. Then make a plan for solving the problem.

Read and Understand

What do you know?

The table tells you each of your speeds for each stage.

You both swim 200 meters and bike 10 kilometers.

What do you want to find out?

Who has the better total time for swimming and biking

Make a Plan

How can you relate what you know to what you want to find out?

Find each of your swimming and biking times.

Find each of your total times and then compare these times.

You will solve the problem in Example 2.

Your turn now **Use the information at the top of the page.**

1. Which formula would you use to find swimming and running times? Explain your reasoning. **B; you need to use the formula to find time.**

A. $distance = rate \cdot time$ **B.** $time = \frac{distance}{rate}$ **C.** $rate = \frac{distance}{time}$

ILLINOIS Standards and ISAT:
6.B.3a, 6.C.3a

EXAMPLE 2 Solving and Looking Back

To solve the triathlon problem from the previous page, you need to carry out the plan from Example 1 and then check the answer.

Solve the Problem

To find each of your times, use the formula $time = \frac{distance}{rate}$**.**

	You	Friend
Swimming	$t = \frac{d}{r}$ $= \frac{200}{76.9}$ $\approx$ **2.6 min**	$t = \frac{d}{r}$ $= \frac{200}{82.6}$ $\approx$ **2.4 min**
Biking	$t = \frac{d}{r}$ $= \frac{10}{0.43}$ $\approx$ **23.26 min**	$t = \frac{d}{r}$ $= \frac{10}{0.41}$ $\approx$ **24.39 min**

Add to find the total time for each of you.

You $2.6 + 23.26 = 25.86$ min
Friend $2.4 + 24.39 = 26.79$ min

ANSWER You have the better total time after the two stages.

Look Back

Does your answer make sense?

Notice that you swim at a slower rate than your friend, so it makes sense that your swimming time is greater. You bike at a faster rate than your friend, so it makes sense that your biking time is less. So the calculations appear reasonable.

HELP with Reading

The ≈ symbol means *is approximately equal to.*

Problem Solving Plan

1. **Read and Understand** Read the problem carefully. Identify the question and any important information.
2. **Make a Plan** Decide on a problem solving strategy.
3. **Solve the Problem** Use the problem solving strategy to answer the question.
4. **Look Back** Check that your answer is reasonable.

TIPS FOR NEW TEACHERS

Have pairs of students discuss Example 1. Students should practice defining what they know, what they need to know, and how to use what they know to find the unknown. Some students may find this skill more difficult than others. See Tips for New Teachers in the *Chapter 1 Resource Book*.

EXTRA EXAMPLES

Examples 1 and 2 Tara ran at 6 miles per hour for 45 minutes and then at 9 miles per hour for another 45 minutes. Jaime ran at 8 miles per hour for 1 hour and 30 minutes. Who ran at the faster overall rate, and by how much? How much farther did that person run?
Jaime; 0.5 mi/h; 0.75 mi

Differentiating Instruction

Less Proficient Students You may need to spend extra time with some students explaining the table in Example 2. Discuss each stage separately. Make sure students understand that a faster rate means less elapsed time. Also make sure students understand that the two activities are parts of one race, not two separate races.

EXTRA EXAMPLES

Example 3 Kiara bicycles at a rate of 14 feet per second for 20 minutes and then at 20 feet per second for 10 minutes. How many miles does she travel overall? (1 mi = 5280 ft) **about 5.45 mi**

CROSS-CURRICULUM

Physical Education Physical education and athletics frequently involve calculating and recording rates, times, and distances. "Distance" may be replaced by another quantity. For example, push-ups per minute (r) • number of minutes (t) = total push-ups, or pulse rate = number of heartbeats ÷ time of recording.

CONCEPT CHECK

What is the first step in solving a complicated problem? ***Sample answer:* Read and understand the problem thoroughly, identifying what you know and what you need to find out.**

DAILY PUZZLER

Alexis, Ben, Clay, and Deb are each buying one souvenir T-shirt. They buy an X-large, a large, a medium, and a small. Alexis' shirt is not an X-large or a medium. Ben bought either the large or the medium. Deb's shirt is smaller than Alexis' or Ben's. Who bought which size? **Alexis: large, Ben: medium, Clay: X-large, Deb: small**

Unit Analysis You can use *unit analysis* to evaluate expressions with units of measure and to check that your answer uses the correct units.

For example, when you find the product of rate and time using the units below, the units for distance will be miles.

$$\frac{\text{miles}}{\cancel{\text{hour}}} \cdot \cancel{\text{hour}} = \text{miles}$$

EXAMPLE 3 Using a Problem Solving Plan

New York City In parts of New York City, the blocks between avenues are called *long blocks*. There are 4 long blocks per mile. Blocks between streets are called *short blocks*. There are 20 short blocks per mile. You walk 40 short blocks and 6 long blocks. How many miles do you walk?

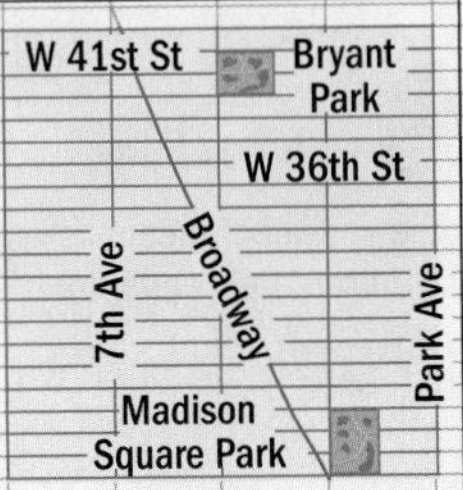

Solution

Read and Understand You walk 40 short blocks and 6 long blocks. There are 20 short blocks per mile and 4 long blocks per mile. You are asked to find how many miles you walk.

Make a Plan Convert short blocks to miles and long blocks to miles using unit analysis. Then add to find the total miles.

Solve the Problem

Because there are 20 short blocks in one mile, you can multiply the number of short blocks you walk by $\frac{1 \text{ mile}}{20 \text{ short blocks}}$ to convert short blocks to miles.

$$40 \cancel{\text{ short blocks}} \times \frac{1 \text{ mile}}{20 \cancel{\text{ short blocks}}} = 2 \text{ miles}$$

Multiply the number of long blocks you walk by $\frac{1 \text{ mile}}{4 \text{ long blocks}}$ to convert long blocks to miles.

$$6 \cancel{\text{ long blocks}} \times \frac{1 \text{ mile}}{4 \cancel{\text{ long blocks}}} = 1.5 \text{ miles}$$

ANSWER You walk a total of 2 + 1.5 = 3.5 miles.

Look Back Check your answer by drawing a diagram.

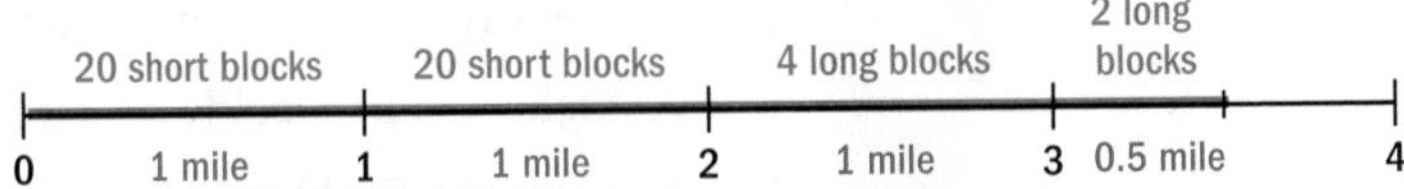

From the diagram you can see that 40 short blocks are 2 miles and 6 long blocks are 1.5 miles, which totals 3.5 miles. So, your answer checks. ✓

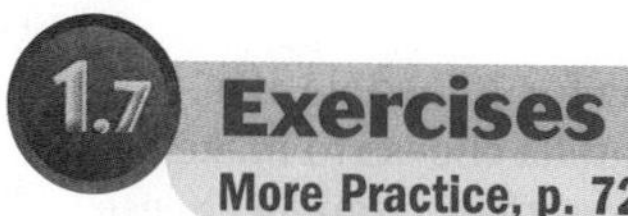

Exercises

More Practice, p. 727

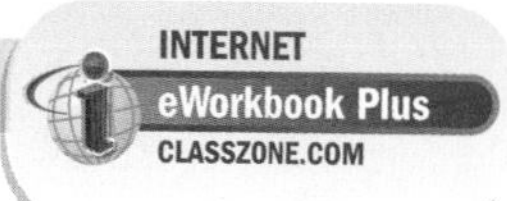

Getting Ready to Practice

1–3. See margin.

1. **Vocabulary** List the four steps of the problem solving plan.
2. **Tickets** You pay \$15 a ticket for 4 tickets and a service charge of \$2 for every ticket after the second one. You are charged \$64 for this order. Describe a way to check that this is the correct price.
3. **Guided Problem Solving** A monorail ride at an amusement park has 5 cars per trainload, and each car can hold 4 passengers. In one hour, 900 people can ride the monorail. How many trainloads run in one hour?
   (1 Write a verbal model of the problem.
   (2 Use the model to find the number of trainloads in one hour.
   (3 Check your answer.

1. Step 1. Read and Understand, Step 2. Make a Plan, Step 3. Solve the Problem, Step 4. Look Back
2. Multiply \$15 by 4 tickets and add \$2 times 2 tickets.
3. Step 1. Trains in one hour = people in one hour ÷ people per train, so trains in one hour = people in one hour ÷ (cars per train · passengers per car).
   Step 2. 45 trains
   Step 3. 45 • 20 = 900

with Homework

Example	Exercises
1	4-9
2	4-9
3	4-9

- More Examples
- eTutorial Plus

Practice and Problem Solving

A 4. **Find the Error** Daniel has enough film to take 96 pictures on a 5 day trip. He takes 45 pictures the first 2 days. He wants to take an equal number of pictures each day for the last 3 days. Describe and correct the error in the solution. See margin.

X $\frac{96}{3} = 32$

So, I can take 32 pictures each day.

4. Daniel has 96 − 45 = 51 pictures left to take the last 3 days, so 51 should be divided by 3. $\frac{51}{3} = 17$; So, I can take 17 pictures each day.

5. **Saving** Fran is saving money for a color printer that costs \$210. She makes \$6 an hour baby-sitting, and her parents will contribute \$120. Use the problem solving plan to find how many hours she needs to baby-sit to earn enough money for the printer. 15 h
6. **Look for a Pattern** Draw the next two shapes in the pattern below. See margin.

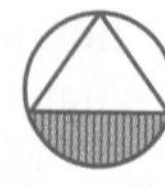  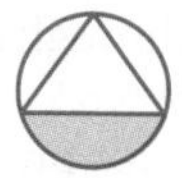 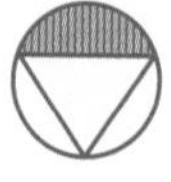 

7. **Music** You practice for 2 hours each weekday and for 3 hours on each weekend day. How many hours per week do you practice? 16 h
8. **Bicycle Race** A Tour de France bicycle race covered 3462 kilometers in 21 days. Riders traveled 3152 kilometers during the first 19 racing days and then traveled 160 kilometers the next day. How long was the ride on the last day? 150 km

3 APPLY

ASSIGNMENT GUIDE

Basic Course
Day 1: SRH p. 715 Exs. 1-5; pp. 41-43 Exs. 4-12 even, 15-18, 28-33
Day 2: pp. 41-43 Exs. 5-13 odd, 19-23, 34-38

Average Course
Day 1: pp. 41-43 Exs. 4-16 even, 17-21, 28-32
Day 2: pp. 41-43 Exs. 5-15 odd, 22-26, 33-38

Average Course
Day 1: pp. 41-43 Exs. 4-16 even, 19-23, 30-32
Day 2: pp. 41-43 Exs. 5-15 odd, 24-29*, 36-38

Block
pp. 41-43 Exs. 4-26, 28-38

EXTRA PRACTICE

- Student Edition, p. 727
- Chapter 1 Resource Book, pp. 64-66
- Test and Practice Generator

TRANSPARENCY

Even-numbered answers are available on transparencies.

HOMEWORK CHECK

When you review students' homework for this lesson, go over the following exercises to check understanding of key concepts.
Basic: 4, 6, 10, 11, 17
Average: 4, 6, 11, 15, 18
Advanced: 4, 6, 12, 16, 19

6. See Additional Answers beginning on page AA1.

COMMON ERROR

In Exercise 9, watch for students who read the problem too hastily, resulting in an incorrect answer that they do not substitute into the original problem to check for reasonableness. For example, students could give an answer of "4 oz," not noticing that 8 ounces of cheese serve 10 people, not 30, or they may give the answer as "12 oz," not noticing that the question asks not for the total amount of cheese needed, but for the additional amount needed.

9. Community Service You are making lasagna for 30 people at a homeless shelter. It takes 8 ounces of mozzarella cheese to make enough to serve 10 people. You have 12 ounces of mozzarella cheese. How much more do you need? 12 oz

Critical Thinking In Exercises 10–13, complete the pattern.

10. 2, 7, 12, ?, ? 17, 22

11. 9, 7, 5, ?, ? 3, 1

12. 3, 12, 48, ? 192

13. 21, 17, 13, ?, ? 9, 5

14. Writing Is there enough information to answer the following question? Explain how to solve the problem, or tell what information is needed.

Amanda has sold magazine subscriptions worth $330 for a school fundraiser. If she reaches a total of $500, she wins a gift certificate. How many more subscriptions does she need to sell to reach $500?
No; you need to know the cost of each subscription.

15. Sales During a 4 week period, a salesperson at a photography studio wants to sell photography packages worth a total of $16,000. Sales for the first 3 weeks are $1240, $3720, and $5980. What does the sales amount need to be in week 4 to reach the $16,000 goal? $5060

16. Number Sense The product of two numbers is 48. Their sum is 16. Find the two numbers. 4 and 12

B **Critical Thinking In Exercises 17–20, complete the pattern.**

17. $2x, 4x, 6x$, ?, ? $8x, 10x$

18. $65x, 52x, 39x$, ?, ? $26x, 13x$

19. $7x^2, 15x^2, 23x^2$, ?, ? $31x^2, 39x^2$

20. $81x, 78x^2, 75x^3, 72x^4$, ?, ? $69x^5, 66x^6$

21. Garden You have 28 feet of fencing and want to construct a rectangular garden with the largest possible area with whole number dimensions. Find the side lengths of the largest possible garden. What is its area? 7 ft; 49 ft^2

Guess, Check, and Revise In Exercises 22–25, find the solution of the equation.

22. $4x = 2x + 14$ 7

23. $6x = 9x - 15$ 5

24. $2x + 3 = 5x - 9$ 4

25. $9 - 3x = 2x - 11$ 4

C **26. Basketball** The table shows the numbers of people who attended Women's National Basketball Association (WNBA) games from 1997 through 2001. Describe how you could predict the attendance for WNBA games in 2002. What is your prediction? How can you check your prediction? *Sample answer:* Look for a pattern and complete it; 2,400,000; draw a graph.

Year	1997	1998	1999	2000	2001
Attendance	1,082,093	1,630,315	1,959,733	2,322,429	2,323,164

27. Challenge Bill's house is third in a row of 12 houses. There are 5 houses between Chris's house and Audrey's house, and 2 between Chris's house and Bill's house. How many houses are between Audrey's house and the first house? Explain how you got your answer. See margin.

27. 10. *Sample answer:* I drew a diagram to show the position of the houses.

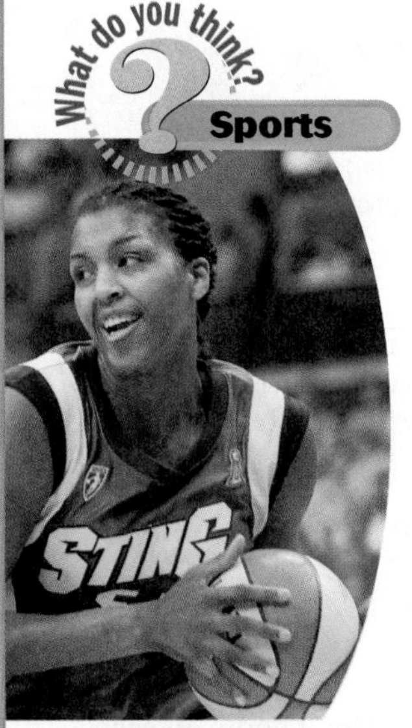

Basketball

In 1997, the WNBA had eight teams. Two teams were added in 1998. In 1999, two more teams were added. Four teams were added in 2000. How many teams were in the WNBA in 2000? 16 teams

Mixed Review 

Evaluate the expression. *(Lesson 1.2)*

28. $7 + 4 \times 3 - 6$ 13 **29.** $24 \div (2 \times 4) - 3$ 0 **30.** $70 \div [14 - 2 \times 2]$ 7

Find the perimeter and area of the figure. *(Lesson 1.6)*

31. a 16 in. by 3 in. rectangle
$P = 38$ in., $A = 48$ in.^{2}

32. a square with a 237 ft side
$P = 948$ ft, $A = 56{,}169$ ft^2

Basic Skills **Complete the statement using < or >.**

33. 23.2 _?_ 23 > **34.** 0.5 _?_ 5 < **35.** 0.1 _?_ 0.01 > **36.** 1.4 _?_ 4.1 <

Test-Taking Practice

37. Multiple Choice You are trying to earn 400 points in a game. In the first round you get 154 points. The next round you get 78 points. How many more points do you need? B

A. 76 **B.** 168 **C.** 176 **D.** 268

38. Multiple Choice Which picture represents the next arrow in the pattern? G

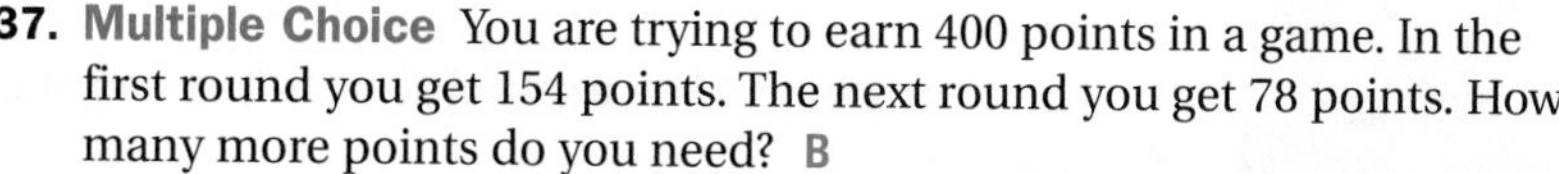

F. ↑ **G.** → **H.** ← **I.** ←

BrAIN GAME

What's Happening?

Scott, John, Annie, and Rebecca are each doing a different activity. Who is doing what?

- Scott and John are not at the debate.
- Scott can't go to the student council meeting.
- Annie is not going to student council or to art club.
- Rebecca is not a member of the student council.
- Annie and Rebecca do not tutor.

Scott is tutoring, John is going to the student council meeting, Annie is at the debate, and Rebecca is going to art club.

4 ASSESS

Assessment Resources

For more assessment resources, see:

- Assessment Book
- Test and Practice Generator

Mini-Quiz

1. Li offers tutoring at $30 an hour to earn money to buy a $900 computer. She has a $60 gift certificate she can use toward the computer purchase. How many hours must Li tutor to have enough money to buy the computer? **28 h**
2. On weekdays, Conrad feeds his ducks one cup of corn each day. On weekends, when children visit and feed the ducks bread, Conrad feeds his ducks one quarter of a cup each day. How much corn does Conrad feed his ducks in four weeks? **22 c**

5 FOLLOW-UP

Reteaching/Remediation

- Study Guide in Chapter 1 Resource Book, pp. 67–68
- Tutor Place, Algebra Card 13; Ratio, Proportion, and Percent Card 5
- eTutorial Plus Online
- Extra Practice, p. 727
- Lesson Practice in Chapter 1 Resource Book, pp. 64–66

Challenge/Enrichment

- Challenge Practice in Chapter 1 Resource Book, p. 69
- Teacher's Edition, p. 2F

English Learner Support

- Spanish Study Guide
- Multi-Language Glossary
- Chapter Audio Summaries CDs

Additional Resources

The following resources are available to help review the materials in Lessons 1.5–1.7.

Chapter 1 Resource Book
- Lesson Practice
- Study Guide

Assessment Book
- Chapter 1 Quiz 2

Technology
- Test and Practice Generator
- eTutorial CD-ROM

Internet
- Classzone
- eWorkbook Plus Online
- eTutorial Plus Online

English Learner Support

- Spanish Study Guide
- Multi-Language Glossary
- Chapter Audio Summaries CDs

Notebook Review

Review the vocabulary definitions in your notebook.

Copy the review examples in your notebook. Then complete the exercises.

Check Your Definitions

equation, p. 28	solving an equation, p. 28	perimeter, p. 33
solution, p. 28	formula, p. 33	area, p. 33

Use Your Vocabulary

1. What is the formula for the perimeter of a rectangle? $P = 2l + 2w$

1.5 Can you solve equations using mental math?

EXAMPLE Solve $32 \div n = 8$.

$32 \div n = 8$ — Write original equation.

$32 \div 4 = 8$, so $n = 4$. — Solve equation using mental math.

Use mental math to solve the equation.

2. $5 + m = 18$ 13 **3.** $t - 9 = 3$ 12 **4.** $7h = 21$ 3 **5.** $\frac{d}{3} = 6$ 18

1.6 Can you use formulas to find unknown values?

EXAMPLE In 1990, Arie Luyendyk set a record at the Indianapolis 500 race with an average speed of about 186 miles per hour. About how long did it take him to complete the 500 mile race?

Solution

$t = \frac{d}{r}$ — Write distance formula.

$= \frac{500}{186}$ — Substitute 500 for *d* and 186 for *r*.

≈ 2.69 — Divide. Round to the nearest hundredth.

ANSWER Arie Luyendyk completed the race in about 2.69 hours.

6. Find the perimeter and area of a rectangle with a length of 7 meters and a width of 4 meters. $P = 22$ m, $A = 28$ m^2

1.7 Can you use a problem solving plan?

EXAMPLE You are filling a 55 gallon aquarium with water using a pitcher from your kitchen. It takes 3 trips with the pitcher to fill a 5 gallon aquarium. How many trips with the pitcher will you need to fill the 55 gallon aquarium?

Read and Understand and Make a Plan Find how many times 5 gallons goes into 55 gallons. Multiply that number by 3, because it takes 3 pitchers to make 5 gallons.

Solve the Problem $\frac{55 \text{ gallons}}{5 \text{ gallons}} = 11$

$11 \cdot 3 \text{ trips} = 33 \text{ trips}$

ANSWER It will take 33 trips with the pitcher to fill the aquarium.

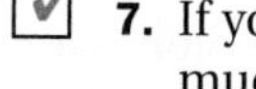

7. If you like 2 teaspoons of sugar in an 8 ounce glass of iced tea, how much sugar should you add to a 36 ounce thermos of iced tea? **9 teaspoons**

Stop and Think about Lessons 1.5–1.7

8. **Critical Thinking** Can you tell whether area or perimeter is being measured if you know only the unit of measurement? Explain.
Yes; perimeter is measured in linear units and area is measured in square units.

Review Quiz 2

Solve the equation using mental math.

1. $h + 12 = 21$ **9**
2. $22 - y = 8$ **14**
3. $54 = 6x$ **9**
4. $\frac{108}{r} = 9$ **12**
5. **Video Games** You have $24 to spend on video game rentals. Each rental costs $3. How many video games can you rent? **8 games**
6. **Geometry** Find the perimeter and area of a rectangle with a length of 14 feet and a width of 11 feet. $P = 50$ ft, $A = 154$ ft^2
7. **Driving** On the highway you drive at a speed of 55 miles per hour for 3 hours. How far do you drive? **165 mi**
8. **Exercise** You plan to exercise 200 minutes over 5 days. The first four days you exercise 45 minutes, 30 minutes, 20 minutes, and 1 hour. Use the problem solving plan to find the number of minutes you need to exercise on the fifth day to meet your goal. **45 min**

ADDITIONAL RESOURCES

The following resources are available to help review the materials in this chapter.

Chapter 1 Resource Book

- Chapter Review Games and Activities, p. 71
- Cumulative Practice, Ch. 1

English/Spanish Chapter Reviews and Tests

Chapter Audio Summaries CDs

eTutorial CD-ROM

eWorkbook Plus Online

eTutorial Plus Online

Chapter Review

Vocabulary

bar graph, p. 5
data, p. 5
frequency table, p. 6
histogram, p. 6
numerical expression, p. 10
evaluate, p. 10
order of operations, p. 10
verbal model, p. 11
variable, p. 15
variable expression, p. 15
power, p. 20
exponent, p. 20
base, p. 20
equation, p. 28
solution, p. 28
solving an equation, p. 28
formula, p. 33
perimeter, p. 33
area, p. 33

Vocabulary Review

Copy and complete the statement.

1. You can graph data organized in a frequency table using a(n) _?_. histogram

2. _?_ is the amount of surface covered by a figure. Area

3. To evaluate an expression that has more than one operation, use the _?_. order of operations

4. A(n) _?_ is a symbol, usually a letter, that represents one or more numbers. variable

5. A power has an exponent and a(n) _?_. base

Tell whether the statement is *true* or *false*.

6. A variable expression is a mathematical sentence that is formed by placing an equal sign between two expressions. false

7. A formula is an equation that has only one variable. false

8. The perimeter of a figure is the sum of the lengths of its sides. true

9. A solution of an equation is a number that, when substituted for a variable, makes the equation true. true

Review Questions

In Exercises 10 and 11, use the table at the right. It shows the numbers of volunteers at a local animal shelter. *(Lesson 1.1)*

Age group	Volunteers
15-24	24
25-34	30
35-44	31
45-54	30
55-64	27
65-74	12
75-84	11

10. Which age group has the most volunteers? Which age group has the fewest volunteers? 35–44; 75–84

11. Can you determine the number of volunteers who are teenagers? Explain. No; the age group that includes teenagers also includes other ages.

Evaluate the expression. *(Lesson 1.2)*

12. $16 + 5 \times 3 + 8$ 39

13. $40 \div [(14 + 6) \cdot 2)]$ 1

14. $10 + \frac{60}{31 - 26}$ 22

Review Questions

15. Clothes You are saving money to buy two sweaters that each cost \$28.50. You have already saved \$20. To find out how much more money you need to save, translate *2 times 28.5 minus 20* into an expression and then evaluate. *(Lesson 1.2)* **2 • 28.5 − 20; \$37**

Evaluate the expression when $x = 4$ and $y = 9$. *(Lesson 1.3)*

16. $\frac{xy}{3x}$ 3 **17.** $\frac{y + 19}{x + 3}$ 4 **18.** $5y - 6x$ 21 **19.** $3xy - xy$ 72

20. Dolphins After swimming 22 miles, a dolphin changes direction and swims at a rate of 18 miles per hour. Use the expression $22 + 18t$ to find the total distance traveled by the dolphin after 2 more hours. *(Lesson 1.3)* **58 mi**

Evaluate the power. *(Lesson 1.4)*

21. 15^2 225 **22.** 4^5 1024 **23.** 10^4 10,000 **24.** 9^3 729

Evaluate the expression. *(Lesson 1.4)*

25. $(5 + 4)^2 \div 3$ 27 **26.** $5 \cdot (6 - 3)^5 + 45$ 1260 **27.** $[10 + (4 \times 2)^3] \div 2$ 261

Solve the equation using mental math. *(Lesson 1.5)*

28. $7b = 56$ 8 **29.** $\frac{84}{x} = 12$ 7 **30.** $98 - t = 35$ 63

Find the perimeter and area of the rectangle or square. *(Lesson 1.6)*

31.

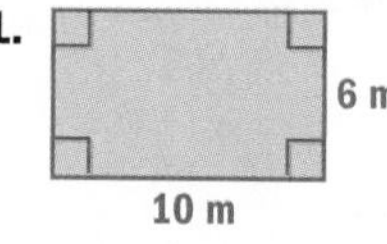

$P = 32$ m, $A = 60$ m^2

32.

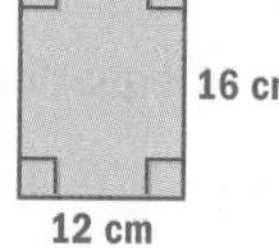

$P = 56$ cm, $A = 192$ cm^2

33.

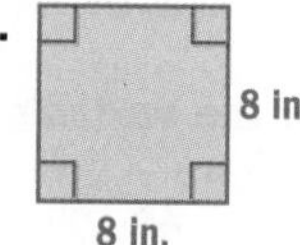

$P = 32$ in., $A = 64$ in.^{2}

34. Cars A car travels at an average rate of 50 miles per hour for 3 hours. How far does it travel? *(Lesson 1.6)* **150 mi**

35. Radio You are the disc jockey for a 15 minute radio show at your school. You must leave 3 minutes open for announcements, and you want to play 3 songs. Use the table at the right to determine the 3 songs you can play. *(Lesson 1.7)* **B, C, and D**

Song	A	B	C	D	E
Length (minutes)	6	4	3	5	6

ADDITIONAL RESOURCES

Assessment Book

- Chapter Test (3 levels), pp. 9–14
- Standardized Chapter Test, p. 15
- Alternative Assessment, pp. 16–17

Test and Practice Generator

1. 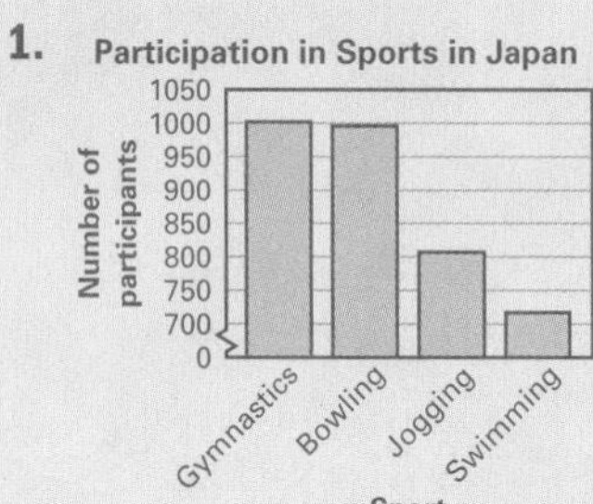

Chapter Test

Sports In a survey, 3000 people in Japan were asked about their participation in ten sports. The results for four sports are in the table.

Sport	Participants
Gymnastics	1002
Bowling	996
Jogging	807
Swimming	717

1. Make a bar graph of the data. See margin.

2. Is it possible to make a histogram of the data? Explain. No; there are no intervals.

Evaluate the expression.

3. $20 + 12 \div 4$ 23 **4.** $6 \times 5 - 20 \div 2$ 20 **5.** $(3 + 7) \div 5 + 10$ 12

6. Plumbing A plumber charges a flat rate of $25 plus an additional $55 for each hour of work. To find how much money the plumber makes in 5 hours at one location, evaluate the expression $25 + 55 \cdot 5$. $300

7. Fruit You are buying 3 apples and 4 oranges for a fruit salad. The cost of one apple is x dollars. The cost of one orange is y dollars. Write a variable expression to represent the cost of 3 apples and 4 oranges. If one apple costs $.75 and one orange costs $.50, what is the total cost? $3x + 4y$; $4.25

Evaluate the expression.

8. $(2 + 3)^4 \div 5$ 125 **9.** $10^2 - 3^4 + 22$ 41 **10.** $(11 - 5)^4 - 300 \div 12$ 1271

Solve the equation using mental math.

11. $17 - t = 5$ 12 **12.** $9n = 72$ 8 **13.** $49 \div b = 7$ 7 **14.** $21 + a = 27$ 6

Tell whether the value of the variable is a solution of the equation.

15. $z + 2 = 15$; $z = 13$ yes **16.** $65 \div y = 16$; $y = 4$ no **17.** $11x = 45$; $x = 4$ no

18. Court Area The lengths and widths of three different types of courts are listed in the table. Find the area of each court. Which court has the largest area? Which court has the smallest area? 672 ft^2, 2106 ft^2, 800 ft^2; tennis; squash

Court	Length	Width
Squash	32 feet	21 feet
Tennis	78 feet	27 feet
Racquetball	40 feet	20 feet

19. Horses A horse travels at a rate of 60 feet per second. How far does the horse travel in 4 seconds? 240 ft

20. Park A rectangular park that is 90 feet long and 60 feet wide needs to be planted with sod. A roll of sod covers 1 square yard. Use the problem solving plan to find how many rolls of sod are needed to cover the park. 600 rolls

Additional Resources

Assessment Book

- Standardized Chapter Test, p. 15

Test and Practice Generator

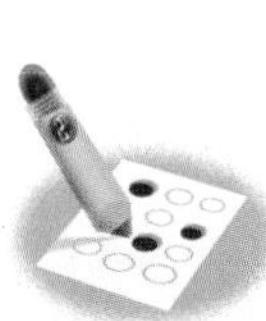

Chapter Standardized Test

Test-Taking Strategy **Most standardized tests are based on concepts and skills taught in school. The best way to prepare is to keep up with your daily studies.**

Multiple Choice

1. The histogram shows the times 25 people arrived at a party. How many people arrived between 9 and 10:59? B

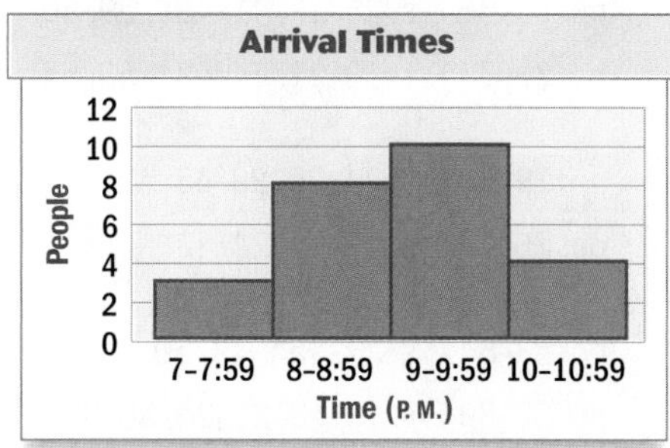

A. 4 **B.** 14 **C.** 21 **D.** 25

2. In what order should the operations be performed in the expression $3 + 7 \times 4 \div 2 - 6$? H

F. $\times, -, \div, +$ **G.** $+, \times, \div, -$

H. $\times, \div, +, -$ **I.** $+, -, \times, \div$

3. Which expression has a value of 20? B

A. $15 + 5 \times 4 \div 2 - 1$

B. $(15 + 5) \times (4 \div 2 - 1)$

C. $(15 + 5) \times 4 \div 2 - 1$

D. $(15 + 5) \times 4 \div (2 - 1)$

4. What is the correct value of the expression $(11 - 9)^4 + 6 \times 3$? G

F. 26 **G.** 34 **H.** 42 **I.** 66

5. Which statement is true? D

A. $2^6 < 6^2$ **B.** $4^7 < 7^4$

C. $1^9 > 9^1$ **D.** $3^5 > 5^3$

6. Which equation represents this statement: *The quotient of twenty and a number is five?* F

F. $20 \div r = 5$ **G.** $t \div 20 = 5$

H. $5 \div p = 20$ **I.** $20g = 5$

7. What is the solution of the equation in Exercise 6? C

A. $\frac{1}{4}$ **B.** 2 **C.** 4 **D.** 100

8. If $a = 4$ and $b = 9$, which equation is true? I

F. $a = 5 + b$ **G.** $ab = 13$

H. $b \div 3 = a$ **I.** $2a + b = 17$

Short Response

9. The area of the rectangle is 120 square centimeters. Write an equation you can use to find the width w. Then solve the equation for w. $120 = 15w$; 8 cm

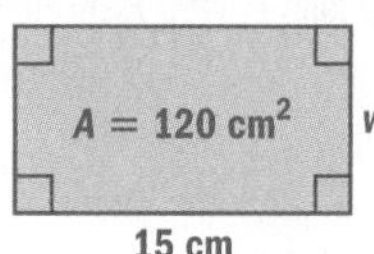

Extended Response

10. Your car's fuel gauge is broken. The car can go 22 miles on one gallon of gasoline. You start a trip with 13 gallons of gasoline. If you want to always have at least a gallon in the tank, what is the farthest you should drive before stopping for more gasoline? Explain.
264 mi; to leave one gallon in the tank, you can only use 12 gallons, on which you can travel $22 \times 12 = 264$ miles.

Pacing and Assignment Guide

REGULAR SCHEDULE

Lesson	Les. Day	BASIC	AVERAGE	ADVANCED
2.1	Day 1	pp. 55-56 Exs. 9-28, 40-45	pp. 55-56 Exs. 13-24, 27-36, 40-45	pp. 55-56 Exs. 13-18, 23-45*
2.2	Day 1	pp. 61-62 Exs. 13-32, 34-35, 51-57	pp. 61-62 Exs. 15-17, 22-43, 51-57	pp. 61-62 Exs. 16-17, 24-26, 31-57*
2.3	Day 1	SRH p. 712 Exs. 4-6; pp. 65-67 Exs. 12-20, 29-31, 49-54	pp. 65-67 Exs. 15-20, 29-34, 49-54	pp. 65-67 Exs. 18-20, 32-40, 49-54
	Day 2	pp. 65-67 Exs. 21-28, 55-60	pp. 65-67 Exs. 23-28, 35-41, 55-60	pp. 65-67 Exs. 23-28, 41-48*, 59, 60
2.4	Day 1	EP p. 727 Exs. 14-16; pp. 72-73 Exs. 10-21, 45-48	pp. 72-73 Exs. 14-21, 45-52	pp. 72-73 Exs. 18-21, 44-48*, 53, 54
	Day 2	pp. 72-73 Exs. 22-31, 49-54	pp. 72-73 Exs. 24-37, 53, 54	pp. 72-73 Exs. 24, 25, 29-43
2.5	Day 1	SRH p. 717 Exs. 2, 3; pp. 76-77 Exs. 11-25, 35-42	pp. 76-77 Exs. 15-30, 35-42	pp. 76-77 Exs. 16-21, 24-42*
2.6	Day 1	pp. 83-84 Exs. 14-29, 32-35, 44-50	pp. 83-84 Exs. 20-40, 44-50	pp. 83-84 Exs. 22-45*, 49, 50
2.7	Day 1	pp. 88-89 Exs. 9-29, 33, 46-52	pp. 88-89 Exs. 15-18, 21-37, 46-52	pp. 88-89 Exs. 16-18, 22-24, 30-52*
2.8	Day 1	pp. 93-95 Exs. 11-22, 32-40	pp. 93-95 Exs. 14-16, 19-29, 32-40	pp. 93-95 Exs. 15, 16, 19, 20, 23-37*, 39, 40
Review	Day 1	pp. 98-99 Exs. 1-52	pp. 98-99 Exs. 1-52	pp. 98-99 Exs. 1-52
Assess	Day 1	Chapter 2 Test	Chapter 2 Test	Chapter 2 Test

YEARLY PACING Chapter 2 Total – **12 days** Chapters 1-2 Total – **24 days** Remaining – **136 days**

*Challenge Exercises EP = Extra Practice SRH = Skills Review Handbook EC = Extra Challenge

BLOCK SCHEDULE

DAY 1	DAY 2	DAY 3	DAY 4	DAY 5	DAY 6
2.1 pp. 55-56 Exs. 13-24, 27-36, 40-45 **2.2** pp. 61-62 Exs. 15-17, 22-43, 51-57	**2.3** pp. 65-67 Exs. 15-20, 23-41, 49-60	**2.4** pp. 72-73 Exs. 14-21, 24-37, 45-54	**2.5** pp. 76-77 Exs. 15-30, 35-42 **2.6** pp. 83-84 Exs. 20-40, 44-50	**2.7** pp. 88-89 Exs. 15-18, 21-37, 46-52 **2.8** pp. 93-95 Exs. 14-16, 19-29, 32-40	**Review** pp. 98-99 Exs. 1-52 **Assess** Chapter 2 Test

YEARLY PACING Chapter 2 Total – **6 days** Chapters 1-2 Total – **12 days** Remaining – **68 days**

Support Materials

CHAPTER RESOURCE BOOK

CHAPTER SUPPORT								
Tips for New Teachers	p. 1			Parents as Partners			p. 3	

LESSON SUPPORT	2.1	2.2	2.3	2.4	2.5	2.6	2.7	2.8
Lesson Plans (regular and block)	p. 7	p. 16	p. 24	p. 34	p. 44	p. 54	p. 62	p. 70
Technology Activities & Keystrokes				p. 37	p. 46			p. 72
Activity Support Masters			p. 26					
Activity Masters				p. 36				
Practice (3 levels)	p. 9	p. 18	p. 27	p. 38	p. 47	p. 56	p. 64	p. 73
Study Guide	p. 12	p. 21	p. 30	p. 41	p. 50	p. 59	p. 67	p. 76
Real-World Problem Solving	p. 14				p. 52			
Challenge Practice	p. 15	p. 23	p. 32	p. 43	p. 53	p. 61	p. 69	p. 78

REVIEW			
Games Support Masters	pp. 5, 33, 79	Cooperative Project with Rubric	p. 83
Chapter Review Games and Activities	p. 80	Extra Credit Project with Rubric	p. 85
Real-Life Project with Rubric	p. 81	Cumulative Practice	p. 87
		Resource Book Answers	A1

ASSESSMENT

Quizzes	p. 18	Alternative Assessments with Rubrics	p. 27
Chapter Tests (3 levels)	p. 20	Unit Test	p. 40
Standardized Test	p. 26	Cumulative Test	p. 42

TRANSPARENCIES

	2.1	2.2	2.3	2.4	2.5	2.6	2.7	2.8
Warm-Up / Daily Homework Quiz	✔	✔	✔	✔	✔	✔	✔	✔
Notetaking Guide	✔	✔	✔	✔	✔	✔	✔	✔
Teacher Support	✔	✔	✔					✔
English/Spanish Problem Solving	✔	✔			✔			
Answer Transparencies	✔	✔	✔	✔	✔	✔	✔	✔

TECHNOLOGY

- EasyPlanner CD-ROM
- Test and Practice Generator
- Electronic Lesson Presentations
- eTutorial CD-ROM
- Chapter Audio Summaries CDs
- Classzone.com
- eEdition Plus Online
- eWorkbook Plus Online
- eTutorial Plus Online
- EasyPlanner Plus Online

ADDITIONAL RESOURCES

- Worked-Out Solution Key
- Notetaking Guide
- Practice Workbook
- Tutor Place
- Professional Development Book
- Special Activities Book
- Posters
- Spanish Study Guide
- Exercises in Spanish
- English/Spanish Ch. Reviews/Tests
- Multi-Language Visual Glossary

Math Background and Teaching Strategies

Lesson 2.1

MATH BACKGROUND

The set of whole numbers does not include the **opposites**, or *additive inverses*, of its members except in the case of 0, which is its own additive inverse. The set of **integers** consists of the whole numbers and their additive inverses. The **absolute value** of a number is its distance from 0 on the number line.

TEACHING STRATEGIES

Ask students, "About how many feet must I walk from where I am to reach the wall in front of me?" and have them respond. Then ask, "About how many feet must I walk from where I am to reach the wall behind me?" Point out that if you are just told, for example, to walk 15 feet to reach the wall, you do not know in which direction to walk. Then point out that an integer expresses both a distance from a given reference point, or its absolute value, and a direction from the reference point, either positive or negative.

Lesson 2.2

MATH BACKGROUND

INTEGER ADDITION As with whole numbers, you can model integer addition on a number line. The difference is that integer addition not only can be represented by a move to the right, but also by a move to the left. This shows how a sum of two or more integers can be negative. If two integers have the same sign, their sum is the sum of the absolute values, with the common sign applied. If the signs differ, the directions differ, so the absolute values are subtracted, and the sign of the sum matches that of the integer with greater absolute value.

TEACHING STRATEGIES

Help students see that the rule for adding integers with opposite signs makes intuitive sense. First point out that the reason the absolute values are *subtracted* instead of added is that the numbers are going in *different* (opposite) directions, which is represented by a *difference*. Also, a greater absolute value represents a larger move on the number line, so it is natural for the sum to carry the sign corresponding to the direction of the larger move.

Lesson 2.3

MATH BACKGROUND

INTEGER SUBTRACTION Subtraction can be represented on the number line by moving in the direction opposite that indicated by the number that is subtracted. So, it is logical that subtraction can be written as addition of the opposite. Because the opposite of a negative number is positive, subtracting a negative number is equivalent to adding the positive number with the same magnitude.

TEACHING STRATEGIES

Ask students for two numbers whose difference is 0. They should realize that the only possibility is for a number to be subtracted from itself, such as $7 - 7$ or $-7 - (-7)$. Next ask for two numbers whose difference is 5, for example, $9 - 4$, $2 - (-3)$, or $-2 - (-7)$. Students should notice that if they begin with a number greater than 5, they need to subtract a positive number, and if they begin with a number less than 5, they need to subtract a negative number (add a positive number). Finally, ask for two numbers whose difference is -5, for example, $3 - 8$, $-2 - 3$, or $-9 - (-4)$. Again, starting with a greater number requires subtracting a positive number, and starting with a lesser number requires subtracting a negative number.

Lesson 2.4

MATH BACKGROUND

INTEGER MULTIPLICATION Multiplication can be modeled as repeated addition, so it is natural that the product of positive numbers is positive. The product of a positive and a negative integer can always be expressed as adding a negative number a positive number of times, so it is also natural that the product of numbers with differing signs is negative. That the product of two negative numbers is positive is less transparent, but if it is accepted that -1 times a number gives its opposite, then it is logical. For example, $(-6)(-4) = (-1) \cdot 6(-4) = -1 \cdot (-24) = 24$.

TEACHING STRATEGIES

Have students write $3 \cdot 4$ as repeated addition: $3 \cdot 4 = 4 + 4 + 4 = 12$. Then have them write $3 \cdot (-4)$ as repeated addition: $3 \cdot (-4) = -4 + (-4) + (-4) = -12$. Point out that $-4 \cdot 3 = 3 \cdot (-4)$, so $-4 \cdot 3 = -12$. This illustrates that the product of numbers with differing signs is negative. To illustrate that the product of two negative numbers is positive, have students extend the pattern $-5 \cdot 2 = -10$, $-5 \cdot 1 = -5$, $-5 \cdot 0 = 0, \ldots$. Because the product increases by 5 with each step, the product of -5 and -1 must be 5.

Lesson 2.5

MATH BACKGROUND

Because $a \div b = c$ only if $c \cdot b = a$, the sign rules for dividing integers correspond to the sign rules for multiplication. The exception is that division by 0 is not permitted ($a \div 0 = c$ for $a \neq 0$ implies $c \cdot 0 = a$, and there is no such c).

TEACHING STRATEGIES

Students are familiar with using multiplication to check division. For example, they know that $24 \div 6 = 4$ because $4 \cdot 6 = 24$. Have students complete sentences such as those following and then summarize their results.

$15 \cdot (-4) = -60$, so $-60 \div 15 = \underline{?}$
$-9 \cdot (-7) = 63$, so $63 \div (-7) = \underline{?}$
$-5 \cdot 11 = -55$, so $-55 \div (-5) = \underline{?}$

Lesson 2.6

MATH BACKGROUND

The commutative properties of addition and multiplication state that changing the order of the addends in a sum or factors in a product does not change the sum or product. The associative properties of addition and multiplication state that changing the grouping of the addends in a sum or factors in a product does not change the sum or product.

TEACHING STRATEGIES

Emphasize the use of the commutative and associative properties to make solving problems easier, as in Examples 3 and 4 on pages 81 and 82. Here is another example.

$$(4 \cdot 37) \cdot (10 \cdot 25) = (4 \cdot 25) \cdot 10 \cdot 37 = (100 \cdot 10) \cdot 37 = 1000 \cdot 37 = 37{,}000$$

Lesson 2.7

MATH BACKGROUND

The distributive property makes it possible to write a product as a sum or difference and vice versa. It states that for any numbers a, b, and c, $a(b + c) = ab + ac$, and $a(b - c) = ab - ac$. You can use the distributive property to simplify the sum or difference of like terms in an expression as a single term by performing the indicated operation on the coefficients and using the common variable part.

TEACHING STRATEGIES

Students will need a lot of practice using the distributive property with subtraction and negative numbers. Have them use the distributive property to rewrite each expression below. Then have them choose a value for x, substitute it into each expression, and simplify the result.

$4(x + 9) - 4(x - 9)$ $\qquad$ $4(x - 9) - 4(-x + 9)$

Lesson 2.8

MATH BACKGROUND

TWO-DIMENSIONAL GRAPHS The **coordinate plane** extends the idea of a number line from one dimension to two dimensions by using two perpendicular number lines, the ***x*-axis** and ***y*-axis**, to locate points in a plane. By representing a point in the coordinate plane as an **ordered pair**, the coordinate plane allows geometric concepts, such as horizontal and vertical distance, to be expressed algebraically. Since the axes meet at the zero point of each, the **origin**, integers are used for the scales, with negative values to the left of the origin and below the origin.

TEACHING STRATEGIES

Point out that the coordinate plane combines the familiar number line, now called the x-axis, with a second number line, the y-axis. Because students often confuse which coordinate is first, point out that the x-coordinate is first because it corresponds to the original number line. This will also reinforce that the positive direction on the x-axis is to the right. Point out that the y-axis can be thought of as corresponding to height, so it is natural for up to be the positive direction. Emphasize with examples that a point on the x-axis has a y-coordinate of 0, and a point on the y-axis has an x-coordinate of 0, as students will often confuse this.

Differentiating Instruction

Strategies for Underachievers

ACT IT OUT

If there are significantly many underachievers in the classroom, you may wish to use the following activity, called "The Human Number Line," in conjunction with Lesson 2.1. Give each student a note card or slip of paper with an integer written on it. The integers need not be consecutive. Three or four at a time, have students come to the front of the room and order themselves according to the position of their integer on a number line. As students order themselves, they should display their numbers so that the next group can see them. When all students have positioned themselves, have them recite their numbers from least to greatest so other students can check their positions. When students are lined up, you can also ask them questions such as "Who has an integer between –7 and –2?" or "Who has an integer whose absolute value is its opposite?" and have them respond by holding up their numbers.

USE MANIPULATIVES AND MODELS

NUMBER LINES For Lessons 2.1–2.3, you may wish to provide prominent visual displays to students to reinforce their understanding of positive and negative integers on the number line. Products available for the classroom include a large number line that wraps around the walls of a room and individual number lines that adhere to the tops of student desks. Another option to provide students a hands-on way to represent, add, and subtract integers is to have them draw a number line on adding machine or cash register tape with length appropriate either for wall display or desktop use. Students can then use colored paper clips to represent integers or moves on the number line corresponding to addition or subtraction.

Beginning with Hands-on Activity 2.2, you might allow any student who desires to have access to a set of integer chips or unit algebra tiles until the student no longer feels the need to use them. Students should be shown how to manipulate chips or tiles and introduced to their use to represent opposites and zero pairs. Some students may be most comfortable using the chips or tiles if they place the tiles for each number in a single row, for example, three "+" chips across to represent the number 3 or five "–" chips across to represent the number 5. This makes the formation and removal of zero pairs very clear and convenient when adding integers. In addition to or instead of chips or tiles, some students will want to use a number line for adding and subtracting integers. These students should also be allowed to continue using this physical model for as long as necessary.

In Lesson 2.2, you may wish to introduce adding integers to underachievers by using real-world models like the exchange of money. For example, borrowing money or withdrawing money from an account would be represented by a negative number, and earning money or depositing money in an account would be represented by a positive number. Create scenarios that involve adding positive and negative numbers. For example, "You would like to attend a concert. A ticket costs $45.00. You have asked your parents to pay for the ticket with the promise that you will repay them as soon as possible. You have saved $11.50, and earn $8.00 babysitting on Mondays after school." You can continue or extend the scenario, asking students to keep a running total of their monetary standing.

The game of football also provides a model for the use of negative integers. A team must make at least 10 yards in 4 downs (plays) to earn a first down. A loss of yards on a play is represented by a negative integer. So, for example, if a team gains 7 yards on first down, loses 4 yards on second down, and makes 8 yards on third down, then the total gained on the three plays is $7 + (-4) + 8 = 11$ yards, and the team has earned a first down.

USE A CO-TEACHING MODEL

Problem Solving Strategies 2.4 requires much reading as well as employing the high-level skill of looking for a pattern. To help give all students access to the mathematics and logic of this lesson, you may need to remove any barriers related to language disabilities. You may wish to co-teach this lesson with a Reading Specialist who can give students strategies for gleaning the important information from each problem.

USE SCAFFOLDING

In Lesson 2.7, the distributive property can be difficult for underachievers to understand. You may wish to use an area model like the one below, which shows how the distributive property relates multiplication and addition.

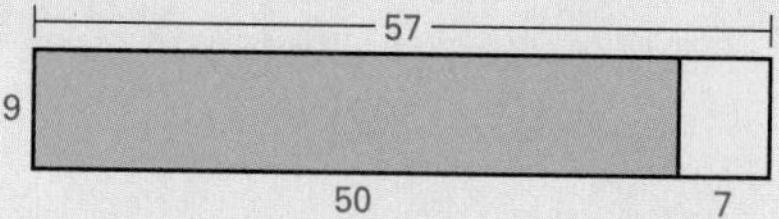

From the model, students should see that the total area can be represented as 9(57), which is equivalent to 9(50 + 7), or as the sum of two lesser areas: 9(50) + 9(7). So, 9(50 + 7) = 9(50) + 9(7). After students have seen several concrete examples, they may be able to generalize the distributive property: $a(b + c) = ab + ac$.

Strategies for English Learners

FOCUS ON THE BIG IDEAS

The concept of *opposite* is a key concept in mathematics and is an easy one to communicate to students learning English. The concept of *opposite* starts early with common words in the English language, progresses to mathematical terms, and then can be used to express a relationship between mathematical operations. For example, early in a student's study of English the student learns pairs of opposites such as *big* : *little*, *left* : *right*, *up* : *down*. As students progress, they learn mathematical terms that describe opposites such as *odd* : *even* and *positive* : *negative*. By the eighth grade, students should understand that certain mathematical operations can "undo" each other. For example, addition is the opposite of subtraction, and multiplication is the opposite of division. Understanding opposites is fundamental to algebra, where students will use their understanding of opposites to isolate a variable in an algebraic equation.

PRETEACH VOCABULARY

Vocabulary development in this chapter can focus on words that express opposites. Remind students of what the word *opposite* means with some simple examples such as *big* and *little*, *over* and *under*, *inside* and *outside*. Ask students to generate other common pairs of opposites. Call on volunteers and make a list. There are examples in the chapter you can point out, such as on page 54, where students are asked to find opposites on a number line, and then use this knowledge to understand *absolute value*. As homework, you might ask English learners to list all the pairs of opposites they can find on a page. Pick a page with word problems or description. In fact, you may want English learners to do this for the entire chapter and create an opposites list for their notebooks as well.

Strategies for Advanced Learners

INCREASE DEPTH AND COMPLEXITY

MATHEMATICAL REASONING Lesson 2.5 presents the concept that 0 divided by any integer is 0, for example, $0 \div (-5) = 0$. Have advanced students justify that division by 0 is not permitted. For example, they can show that $(-5) \div 0$ is undefined by restating $(-5) \div 0$ as a related multiplication problem. They should realize that there is no number q for which $(-5) \div 0 = q$ is true because there is no number q for which $q \cdot 0 = -5$.

After Lesson 2.6, encourage advanced students to review the commutative and associative properties and how each relates to the four integer operations. Have them use both positive and negative integers to show that addition and multiplication are commutative and associative, but subtraction and division are not. They should be able to demonstrate, however, that the non-commutativity and non-associativity of subtraction can be side-stepped by recasting subtraction problems as addition problems. If students are familiar with division as multiplication by the reciprocal, they may be able to make a similar demonstration for division.

USE CROSS-CURRICULAR CONNECTIONS

SCHOOL EVENTS In Example 4 of Lesson 2.2, on page 60, adding integers is related to the situation of a school fair. If your school organizes a fundraising event like a fair, car wash, bake sale, magazine drive, concert, or other event, encourage students to become involved. Have them represent costs as negative integers and incomes as positive integers. In a real situation such as this, students are likely to need to adapt their knowledge to more complicated situations than those in the text, and can learn about profit, loss, and break-even points.

2 Differentiating Instruction: Teaching Resources

Differentiating Assessment

McDougal Littell *Middle School Mathematics* offers a wide variety of assessment. This includes Level A, Level B, and Level C Chapter Tests, Standardized Tests, Cumulative Tests, and Quizzes from the *Assessment Book*, Daily Homework Quizzes from the *Warm-Up Transparencies*, and the *Test and Practice Generator*.

Assessment Book

The *Assessment Book* contains two quizzes, three levels of chapter tests, A (Basic), B (Average), and C (Advanced), and a standardized test for each chapter in the textbook. Also included are cumulative tests and unit tests.

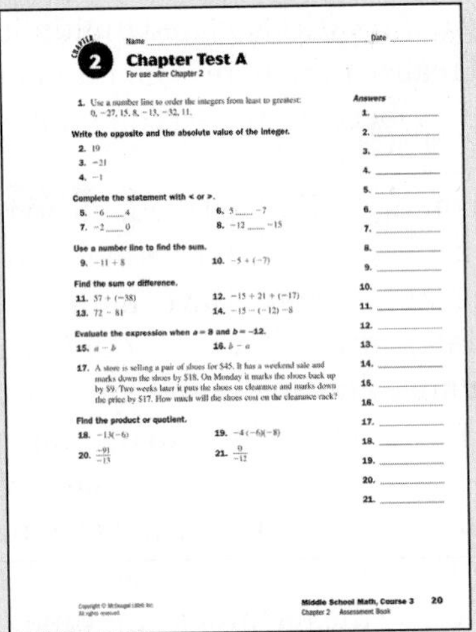

Chapter Test A
For use after Chapter 2

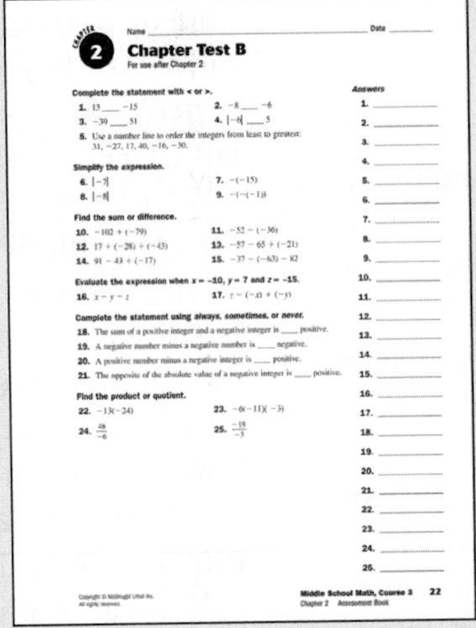

Chapter Test B
For use after Chapter 2

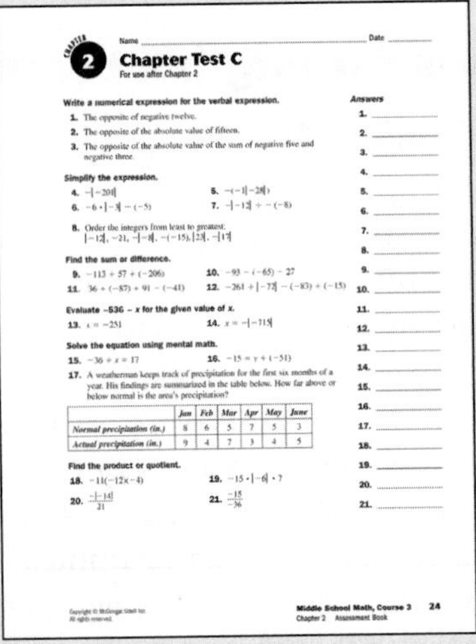

Chapter Test C
For use after Chapter 2

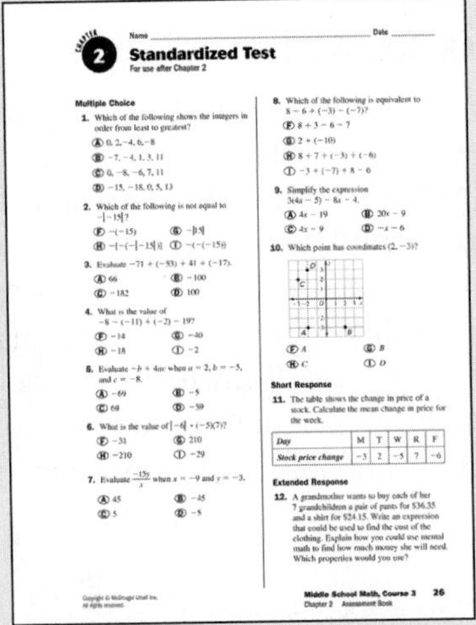

Standardized Test
For use after Chapter 2

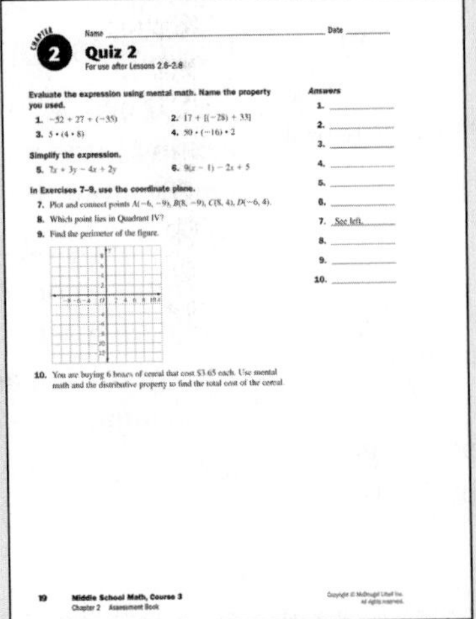

Quiz 2
For use after Lessons 2.6–2.8

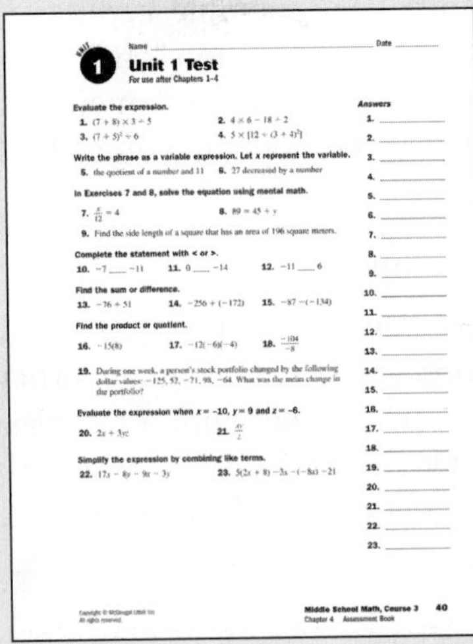

Unit 1 Test
For use after Chapters 1–4

WARM-UP TRANSPARENCIES WITH DAILY HOMEWORK QUIZ

The *Warm-Up Transparencies with Daily Homework Quiz* contains a daily homework quiz for each lesson in the textbook. Each quiz appears with a set of warm-up exercises.

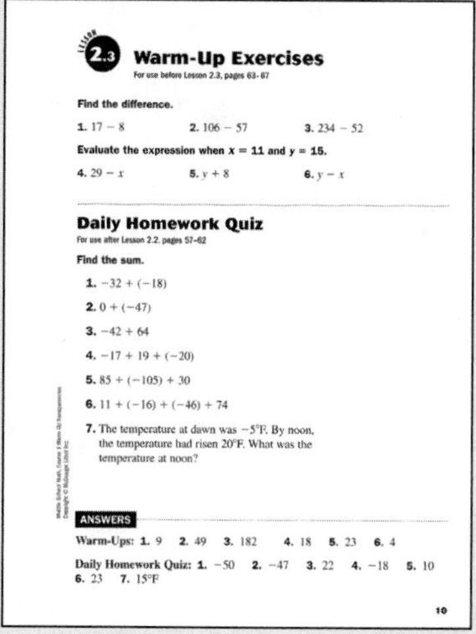

2.3 Warm-Up Exercises
For use before Lesson 2.3, pages 63–67

Find the difference.

1. $17 - 8$ 2. $106 - 57$ 3. $234 - 52$

Evaluate the expression when $x = 11$ and $y = 15$.

4. $29 - x$ 5. $y + 8$ 6. $y - x$

Daily Homework Quiz
For use after Lesson 2.2, pages 57–62

Find the sum.

1. $-32 + (-18)$
2. $0 + (-47)$
3. $-42 + 64$
4. $-17 + 19 + (-20)$
5. $85 + (-105) + 30$
6. $11 + (-16) + (-46) + 74$
7. The temperature at dawn was $-5°F$. By noon, the temperature had risen $20°F$. What was the temperature at noon?

ANSWERS
Warm-Ups: 1. 9 2. 49 3. 182 4. 18 5. 23 6. 4
Daily Homework Quiz: 1. −50 2. −47 3. 22 4. −18 5. 10 6. 23 7. 15°F

10

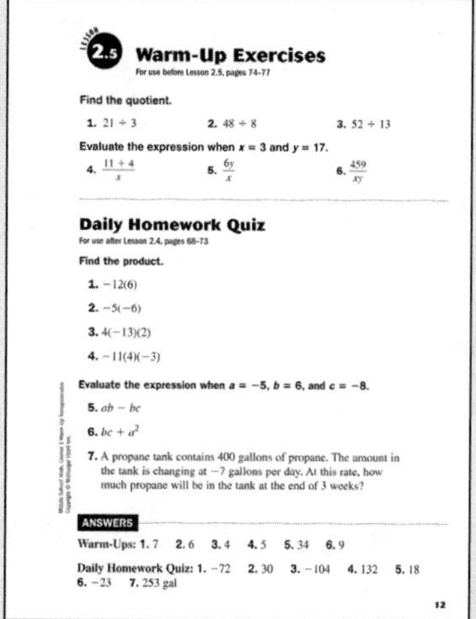

2.5 Warm-Up Exercises
For use before Lesson 2.5, pages 74–77

Find the quotient.

1. $21 \div 3$ 2. $48 \div 8$ 3. $52 \div 13$

Evaluate the expression when $x = 3$ and $y = 17$.

4. $\frac{11 + 4}{x}$ 5. $\frac{6y}{x}$ 6. $\frac{459}{xy}$

Daily Homework Quiz
For use after Lesson 2.4, pages 68–73

Find the product.

1. $-12(6)$
2. $-5(-6)$
3. $4(-13)(2)$
4. $-11(4)(-3)$

Evaluate the expression when $a = -5$, $b = 6$, and $c = -8$.

5. $ab - bc$
6. $bc + a^2$
7. A propane tank contains 400 gallons of propane. The amount in the tank is changing at −7 gallons per day. At this rate, how much propane will be in the tank at the end of 3 weeks?

ANSWERS
Warm-Ups: 1. 7 2. 6 3. 4 4. 5 5. 34 6. 9
Daily Homework Quiz: 1. −72 2. 30 3. −104 4. 132 5. 18 6. −23 7. 253 gal

12

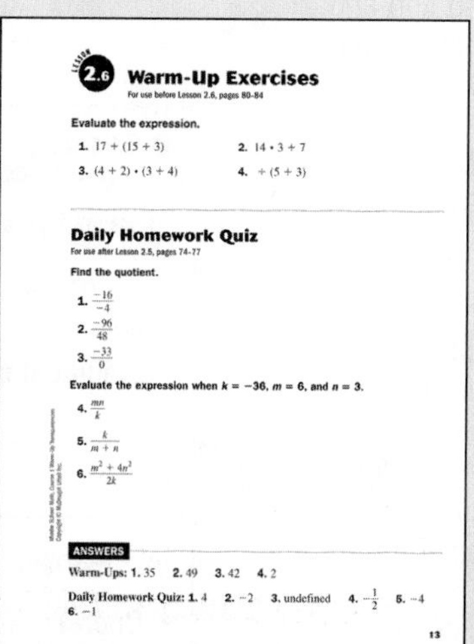

2.6 Warm-Up Exercises
For use before Lesson 2.6, pages 80–84

Evaluate the expression.

1. $17 + (15 + 3)$ 2. $14 \cdot 3 + 7$
3. $(4 + 2) \cdot (3 + 4)$ 4. $+ (5 + 3)$

Daily Homework Quiz
For use after Lesson 2.5, pages 74–77

Find the quotient.

1. $\frac{-16}{-4}$
2. $\frac{-96}{48}$
3. $\frac{-33}{0}$

Evaluate the expression when $k = -36$, $m = 6$, and $n = 3$.

4. $\frac{mn}{k}$
5. $\frac{k}{m + n}$
6. $\frac{m^2 + 4n^2}{2k}$

ANSWERS
Warm-Ups: 1. 35 2. 49 3. 42 4. 2
Daily Homework Quiz: 1. 4 2. −2 3. undefined 4. $-\frac{1}{2}$ 5. −4 6. −1

13

TEST AND PRACTICE GENERATOR CD-ROM

The *Test and Practice Generator* can be used to create numerous quizzes and tests for each lesson and for each chapter using both static and algorithmic exercises.

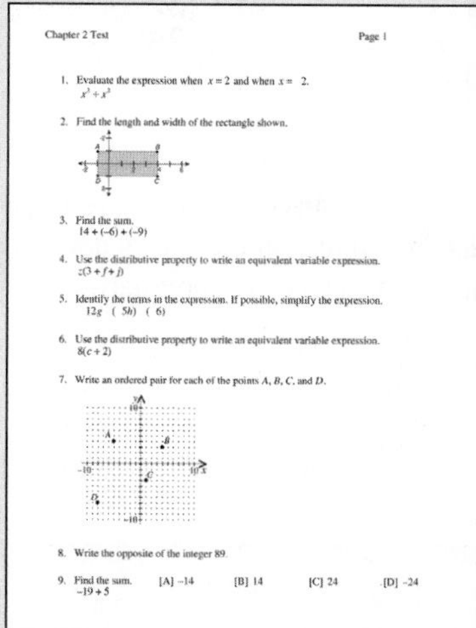

Chapter 2 Test Page 1

1. Evaluate the expression when $x = 2$ and when $x = 2$.
$x^3 + x^2$
2. Find the length and width of the rectangle shown.
3. Find the sum.
$14 + (-6) + (-9)$
4. Use the distributive property to write an equivalent variable expression.
$z(3 + f + j)$
5. Identify the terms in the expression. If possible, simplify the expression.
$12g \; (\; 5h) \; (\; 6)$
6. Use the distributive property to write an equivalent variable expression.
$8(c + 2)$
7. Write an ordered pair for each of the points A, B, C, and D.
8. Write the opposite of the integer 89.
9. Find the sum. [A] −14 [B] 14 [C] 24 [D] −24
$-19 + 5$

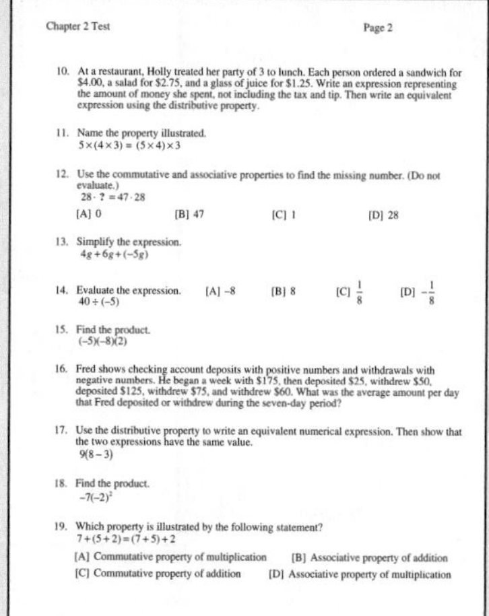

Chapter 2 Test Page 2

10. At a restaurant, Holly treated her party of 3 to lunch. Each person ordered a sandwich for $4.00, a salad for $2.75, and a glass of juice for $1.25. Write an expression representing the amount of money she spent, not including the tax and tip. Then write an equivalent expression using the distributive property.
11. Name the property illustrated.
$5 \times (4 \times 3) = (5 \times 4) \times 3$
12. Use the commutative and associative properties to find the missing number. (Do not evaluate.)
$28 \cdot ? = 47 \cdot 28$
[A] 0 [B] 47 [C] 1 [D] 28
13. Simplify the expression.
$4g + 6g + (-5g)$
14. Evaluate the expression. [A] −8 [B] 8 [C] $\frac{1}{8}$ [D] $-\frac{1}{8}$
$40 \div (-5)$
15. Find the product.
$(-5)(-8)(2)$
16. Fred shows checking account deposits with positive numbers and withdrawals with negative numbers. He began a week with $175, then deposited $25, withdrew $50, deposited $125, withdrew $75, and withdrew $60. What was the average amount per day that Fred deposited or withdrew during the seven-day period?
17. Use the distributive property to write an equivalent numerical expression. Then show that the two expressions have the same value.
$9(8 - 3)$
18. Find the product.
$-7(-2)^2$
19. Which property is illustrated by the following statement?
$7 + (5 + 2) = (7 + 5) + 2$
[A] Commutative property of multiplication [B] Associative property of addition
[C] Commutative property of addition [D] Associative property of multiplication

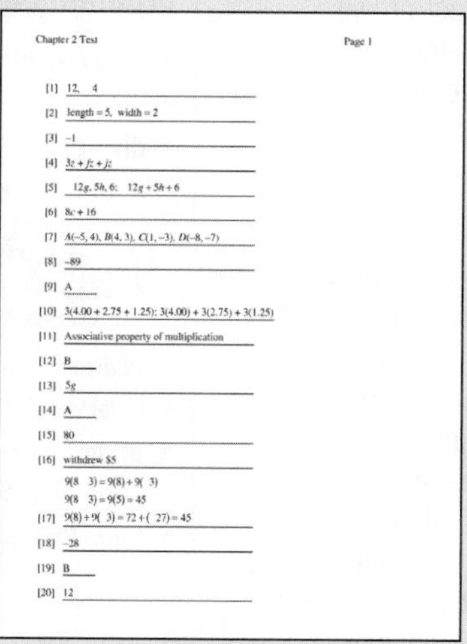

Chapter 2 Test Page 1

[1] 12, 4
[2] length = 5, width = 2
[3] −1
[4] $3z + fz + jz$
[5] $12g, 5h, 6;\; 12g + 5h + 6$
[6] $8c + 16$
[7] $A(-5, 4), B(4, 3), C(1, -3), D(-8, -7)$
[8] −89
[9] A
[10] 3(4.00 + 2.75 + 1.25); 3(4.00) + 3(2.75) + 3(1.25)
[11] Associative property of multiplication
[12] B
[13] $5g$
[14] A
[15] 80
[16] withdrew $5
$9(8 \; 3) = 9(8) + 9(\; 3)$
$9(8 \; 3) = 9(5) = 45$
[17] $9(8) + 9(\; 3) = 72 + (\; 27) = 45$
[18] −28
[19] B
[20] 12

OVERVIEW

Main Ideas

In this chapter, students use a number line to explore integers and absolute value, and they add, subtract, multiply, and divide integers. Students find the mean of a data set. Students use the commutative, associative, and distributive properties to evaluate expressions. Students also find and plot points in the coordinate plane.

Prerequisite Skills

The key skills reviewed in the games on these pages are:

- Multiplying whole numbers

Additional practice with prerequisite skills can be found in the Review What You Need to Know exercises on page 52. Additional resources for reviewing prerequisite skills are:

- Skills Review Handbook, pp. 704–726
- Tutor Place
- eTutorial Plus

Managing the Game

Tips for Success

Before playing *Four in a Row*, you may want to have each student in a pair make up and then solve a problem finding the product of two two-digit whole numbers. After solving their problems, the students in the pair can have the other student check the results.

Reflecting on the Game

Since each person creates her or his own answer card, more than one student can win at any given time. Point out to students that the order in which they write the numbers on their cards affects the chances of winning. You may want to allow students to create more than one card with the same numbers so they can play the cards simultaneously.

Integer Operations

BEFORE

In previous chapters you've...

- Performed operations on whole numbers
- Evaluated expressions

Now

In Chapter 2 you'll study...

- Operations on integers
- Using properties to evaluate expressions
- Identifying and plotting points in the coordinate plane

WHY?

So you can solve real-world problems about...

- space shuttles, p. 56
- dinosaurs, p. 66
- diving, p. 70
- murals, p. 89

Internet Preview
CLASSZONE.COM

- eEdition Plus Online
- eWorkbook Plus Online
- eTutorial Plus Online
- State Test Practice
- More Examples

Chapter Warm-Up Game

Review skills you need for this chapter in this quick game. Work with a partner.

Key Skill:
Multiplying whole numbers

FOUR IN A ROW

MATERIALS

- 2 Answer Cards
- 24 Expression Cards
- 24 Markers

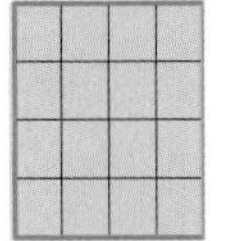

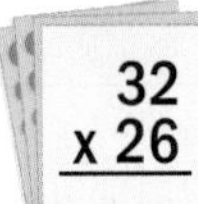

PREPARE Fill in your Answer Card with 16 of the 24 answers given below. Place the Expression Cards face down in a pile. On each turn follow the steps on the next page.

168	196	240	315	338	342
352	361	405	414	418	441
516	522	529	595	720	792
832	851	918	961	975	1020

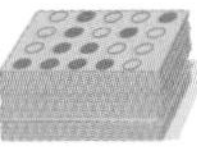

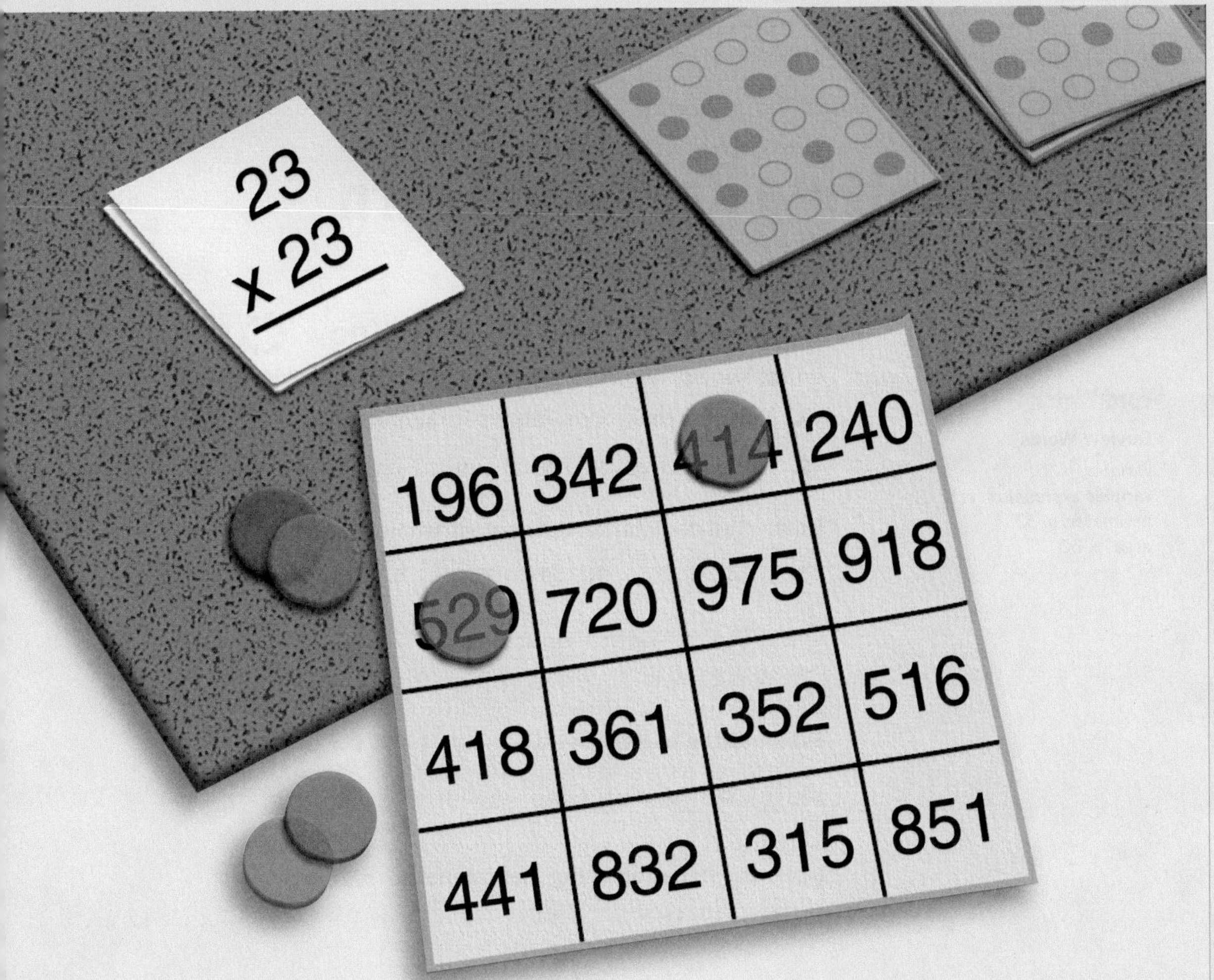

FLIP over an Expression Card. Both players solve the expression.

LOOK for the answer on your Answer Card. If you find it, place a marker over the answer.

HOW TO WIN Mark 4 answers in a row across, up and down, or diagonally.

Stop *and* Think

1. How many ways can you get 4 answers in a row on your card? **10 ways**
2. **Critical Thinking** How many squares can you mark without winning? **12 squares**

Chapter Resources

These resources are provided to help you prepare for the chapter and to customize review materials:

Chapter 2 Resource Book

- Tips for New Teachers, pp. 1–2
- Lesson Plan, pp. 7, 16, 24, 34, 44, 54, 62, 70
- Lesson Plan for Block Scheduling, pp. 8, 17, 25, 35, 45, 55, 63, 71

Technology

- EasyPlanner CD-ROM
- Test and Practice Generator
- Electronic Lesson Presentations CD-ROM
- eTutorial CD-ROM

Internet

- Classzone
- eEdition Plus Online
- eWorkbook Plus Online
- eTutorial Plus Online
- EasyPlanner Plus Online

English Learner Support

- Spanish Study Guide
- Multi-Language Glossary
- Chapter Audio Summaries CDs
- Teacher's Edition, pp. 50E–50F

PREPARE

Diagnosis/Remediation

Review What You Need to Know
The Review What You Need to Know exercises can help you diagnose whether students have the following skills needed in Chapter 2:

- Using vocabulary (Exs. 1-2)
- Rounding decimals to whole numbers (Exs. 3-6)
- Evaluating numerical and variable expressions (Exs. 7-12)
- Solving equations using mental math (Exs. 13-15)

Chapter 2 Resource Book

- Study Guide (Lessons 2.1-2.8)

Tutor Place

Notetaking Strategies

Stress to students that even if they think they will remember the definition of a new term, they should enter the term in their notebooks anyway, and highlight it in a way so that it stands out. Students will be exposed to many new terms, and it should be very easy for them to find all vocabulary terms to aid review. Further suggestions for keeping a notebook can be found on page 86.

For more support on notetaking, see:

- Notetaking Guide Workbook
- Notetaking Transparencies

Getting Ready to Learn

Word Watch

Review Words
variable, p. 15
variable expression, p. 15
perimeter, p. 33
area, p. 33

Review What You Need to Know

Using Vocabulary **Copy and complete using a review word.**

1. A symbol that represents one or more numbers is called a(n) _?_. variable
2. The surface covered by a figure is called the _?_. area

Round the decimal to the nearest whole number. *(p. 705)*

3. 10.61 11
4. 134.7 135
5. 0.25 0
6. 12.86 13

Evaluate the expression. *(p. 10)*

7. $32 - 27 + 14$ 19
8. $4 \cdot 12 \div 6$ 8
9. $6 + 34 \div 2$ 23

Evaluate the expression when $s = 4$ and $t = 16$. *(p. 15)*

10. $(t - 9) + s$ 11
11. $s(t - 5)$ 44
12. $\frac{1}{4}t - 4$ 0

Solve the equation using mental math. *(p. 28)*

13. $3x = 39$ 13
14. $x - 6 = 12$ 18
15. $x + 13 = 17$ 4

You should include material that appears on a notebook like this in your own notes.

Know How to Take Notes

Including Vocabulary Notes When you write down new vocabulary words, you should also write examples of how they are used. Label the examples with the new words.

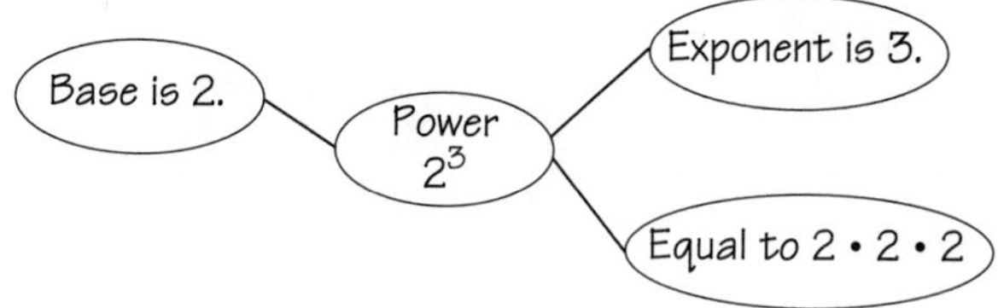

5^2 is read "five squared."

5^3 is read "five cubed."

5^4 is read "five to the fourth power."

As you work through Chapter 2, label examples of new vocabulary in your notes.

Integers and Absolute Value

BEFORE	Now	WHY?
You studied whole numbers.	You'll study integers.	So you can order lake elevations, as in Ex. 24.

In the Real World

Word Watch

integer, p. 53
negative integer, p. 53
positive integer, p. 53
absolute value, p. 54
opposite, p. 54

Geography The Global Positioning System (GPS) can be used to determine elevations. The table shows the minimum elevations of several countries. Which country in the table has the lowest elevation?

Minimum Elevations	
Country	**Elevation (m)**
United States	−86
Canada	0
China	−154
Bolivia	90
Czech Republic	115

Each number in the table is an *integer*. The following numbers are **integers**.

$$\ldots, -5, -4, -3, -2, -1, 0, 1, 2, 3, 4, 5, \ldots$$

Negative integers are less than 0. They lie *to the left* of 0 on a number line. **Positive integers** are greater than 0. They lie *to the right* of 0 on a number line. Zero is neither positive nor negative. When you use a number line to compare numbers, numbers increase as you move to the right.

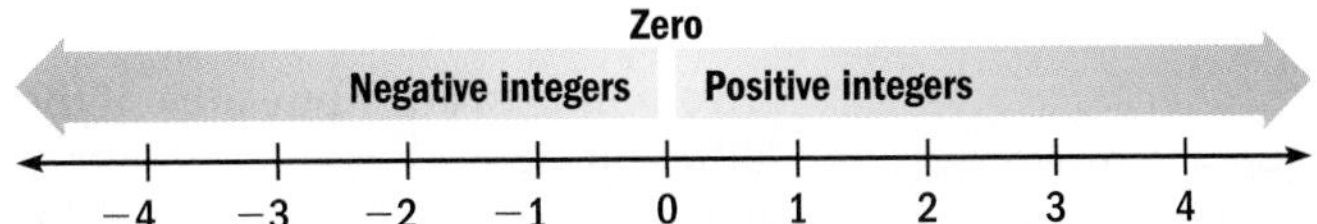

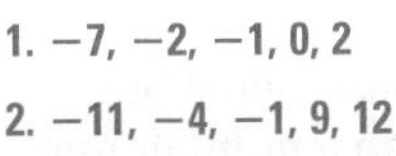

1. −7, −2, −1, 0, 2
2. −11, −4, −1, 9, 12
3. −99, −60, 0, 16, 44

EXAMPLE 1 Graphing and Ordering Integers

To find which country in the table above has the lowest elevation, graph each integer on a number line.

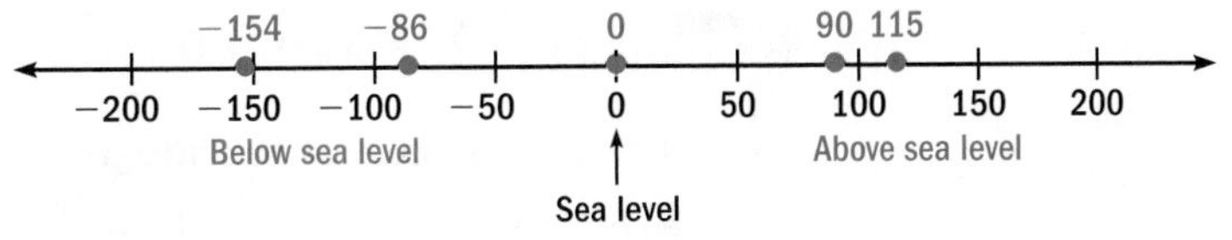

ANSWER China has the lowest elevation, at −154 meters.

Global Positioning System (GPS) satellite

Your turn now **Order the integers from least to greatest.** 1–3. See margin.

1. −7, 2, −1, 0, −2 **2.** 9, −4, 12, −11, −1 **3.** 0, −99, 44, −60, 16

ILLINOIS Standards and ISAT:
6.B.3a

1 PLAN

SKILL CHECK

Replace each ? with > or <.

1. 9 ? 14 <
2. 4 ? 24 <
3. 105 ? 103 >
4. 89 ? 98 <
5. 21 ? 12 >

LESSON OBJECTIVE

Study integers.

PACING

Suggested Number of Days
Basic Course: 1 day
Average Course: 1 day
Advanced Course: 1 day
Block: 0.5 block with 2.2

TEACHING RESOURCES

For a complete list of Teaching Resources, see page 50B.

TRANSPARENCY

Warm-Up Exercises for this lesson are available on a transparency. A support transparency is available for Examples 1 and 2.

2 TEACH

MOTIVATING THE LESSON

If possible, bring a GPS unit to class or ask an Earth Science teacher to talk about how GPS units work and what they can tell you about your latitude, longitude, and elevation.

TIPS FOR NEW TEACHERS
Make a large number line on the floor or on a wall with masking tape that students can walk on or touch as you refer to number lines throughout the chapter. Have different integers cut out that students can place on the number line. See Tips for New Teachers in the *Chapter 2 Resource Book*.

EXTRA EXAMPLES

Example 1 Graph each integer on a number line. Then order the integers from least to greatest.
2, −4, −2, 1, −3

−4, −3, −2, 1, 2

Example 2 In golf, a score of "even par" is represented by 0. Negative scores are better than even par, and positive scores are worse. Which of the scores +3, −6, −2, and +5 is farthest from even par? −6

Example 3 Write the opposite of the integer.
a. −17 **17**
b. 24 **−24**
c. $|6|$ **−6**

CONCEPT CHECK
Can an absolute value ever be negative? How do you know? **No; absolute value represents a distance, and distance is never negative.**

DAILY PUZZLER
Which of the numbers from −10 to 10 is the greatest distance on the number line from its absolute value? What is that distance? **−10; 20 units**

The **absolute value** of a number is the distance between the number and zero on a number line. The absolute value of a number n is written as $|n|$. The absolute value of 0 is 0.

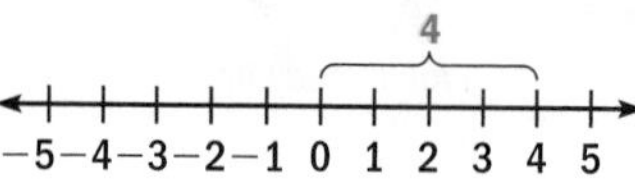
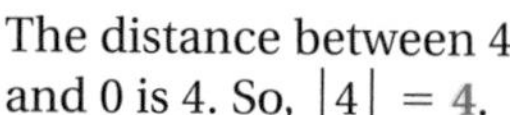

The distance between 4 and 0 is 4. So, $|4| = 4$.

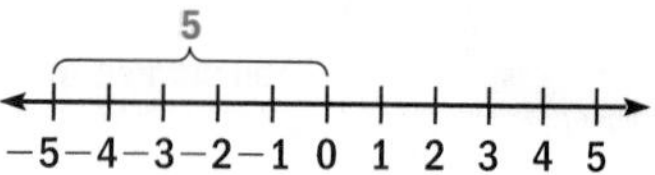

The distance between −5 and 0 is 5. So, $|-5| = 5$.

EXAMPLE 2 **Finding Absolute Value**

Eyeglasses An eyeglass prescription is given as a positive or negative number. A prescription of a person who is farsighted is positive. A prescription of a person who is nearsighted is negative. The greater the absolute value, the stronger the prescription. Which prescription is stronger, −3 or 2?

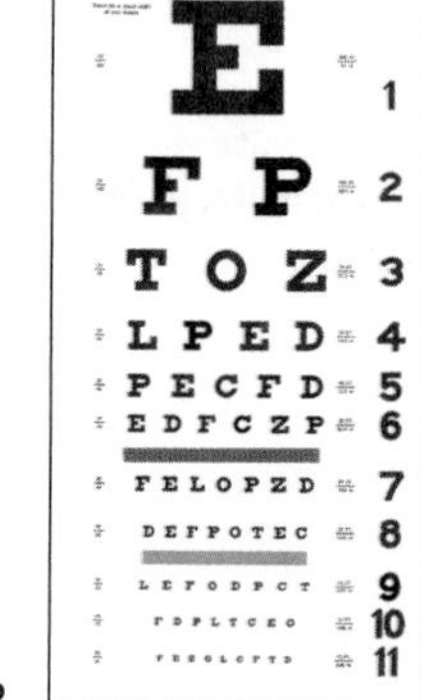

Solution
$|-3| = 3$ and $|2| = 2$.

ANSWER The prescription of −3 is stronger because 3 > 2.

with Reading
The integer "−2" can be read "negative 2" or "the opposite of 2."

Two numbers are **opposites** if they have the same absolute value but different signs. Opposites are the same distance from 0 on a number line and are on opposite sides of 0. The opposite of 0 is 0.

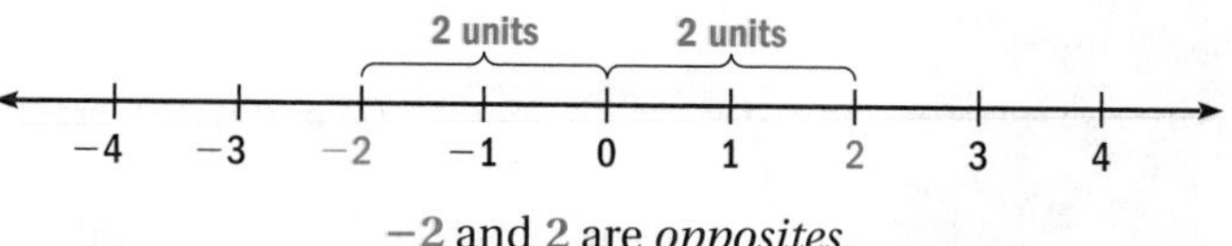

−2 and 2 are *opposites*.

EXAMPLE 3 **Finding Opposites**

Write the opposite of the integer.

a. 5 The opposite of 5 is −5.
b. −12 The opposite of −12 is 12.
c. $|-9|$ Because $|-9| = 9$, the opposite of $|-9|$ is −9.

Your turn now **Write the opposite and the absolute value of the integer.**

4. −16 16, 16 **5.** 140 −140, 140 **6.** 1 −1, 1 **7.** $|-55|$ −55, 55

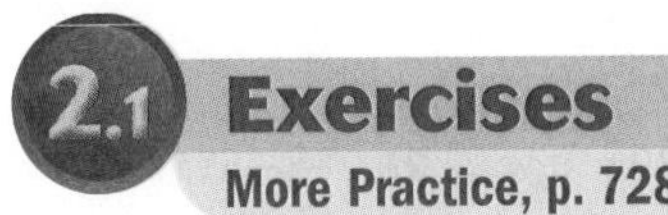

2.1 Exercises

More Practice, p. 728

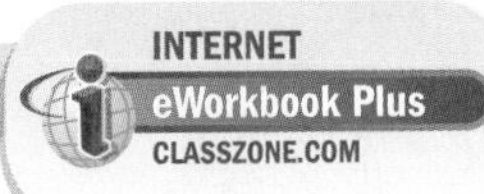

INTERNET eWorkbook Plus CLASSZONE.COM

Getting Ready to Practice

1. **Vocabulary** Copy and complete: Two integers are _?_ if they have the same absolute value but different signs. opposites

Use a number line to order the integers from least to greatest.

2. 5, −10, 15, 27, −20, 13 −20, −10, 5, 13, 15, 27
3. 120, 62, 0, −56, 74, −130 −130, −56, 0, 62, 74, 120

Write the opposite and the absolute value of the integer.

4. 19 −19, 19
5. −8 8, 8
6. −740 740, 740
7. 1327 −1327, 1327

8. **Find the Error** A student was asked to order the integers 3, 1, 0, −9, −2, and 5 from least to greatest. Describe and correct the error in the solution. The numbers are ordered from least to greatest absolute value; −9, −2, 0, 1, 3, 5

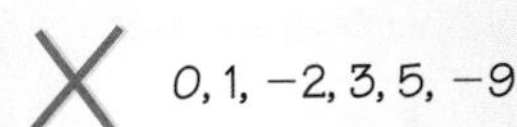

Practice and Problem Solving

HELP with Homework

Example	Exercises
1	9-18
2	19-22
3	19-22

Online Resources CLASSZONE.COM
- More Examples
- eTutorial Plus

Copy and complete the statement with < or >.

A 9. 4 _?_ −6 >
10. −12 _?_ 1 <
11. −9 _?_ −2 <
12. 0 _?_ −5 >
13. 5 _?_ −5 >
14. −17 _?_ 2 <
15. 34 _?_ −29 >
16. −20 _?_ −14 <

Use a number line to order the integers from least to greatest.

17. 64, −12, 18, 59, −20, 44 −20, −12, 18, 44, 59, 64
18. 278, 121, −301, 262, −155 −301, −155, 121, 262, 278

Match the integer expression with the verbal expression.

19. $-|7|$ B
20. $|-7|$ C
21. $-|-7|$ D
22. $-(-7)$ A

A. the opposite of negative seven
B. the opposite of the absolute value of seven
C. the absolute value of negative seven
D. the opposite of the absolute value of negative seven

In Exercises 23 and 24, use the table showing elevations of lakes.

Name	Elevation (ft)
Jones Lake	−30
Silver Lake	90
Gieselmann Lake	−162
Seneca Lake	445
Craigs Pond	0

23. **Compare** Which lake is at a lower elevation, Gieselmann Lake or Silver Lake? Gieselmann Lake
24. Arrange the lake elevations in order from least to greatest.

24. −162, −30, 0, 90, 445

3 APPLY

ASSIGNMENT GUIDE

Basic Course
Day 1: pp. 55-56 Exs. 9-28, 40-45

Average Course
Day 1: pp. 55-56 Exs. 13-24, 27-36, 40-45

Advanced Course
Day 1: pp. 55-56 Exs. 13-18, 23-45*

Block
pp. 55-56 Exs. 13-24, 27-36, 40-45 (with 2.2)

Extra Practice

- Student Edition, p. 728
- Chapter 2 Resource Book, pp. 9-11
- Test and Practice Generator

Transparency

Even-numbered answers are available on transparencies. A support transparency is available for Exercises 2, 3, 17, and 18.

Homework Check

When you review students' homework for this lesson, go over the following exercises to check understanding of key concepts.
Basic: 9, 14, 17, 19, 21
Average: 13, 16, 17, 20, 22
Advanced: 15, 16, 18, 21, 22

Common Error

In Exercises 11 and 16, watch for students who disregard the negative signs and compare only the digits.

Teaching Tip

In Exercises 19-22, have students work in pairs, reading each expression aloud to connect the sound of the words with the symbols.

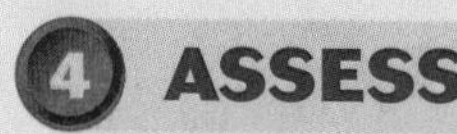

ASSESS

ASSESSMENT RESOURCES

For more assessment resources, see:

- Assessment Book
- Test and Practice Generator

MINI-QUIZ

Copy and complete the statement with < or >.

1. 8 ? −8 >

2. −17 ? −14 <

3. 1 ? −100 >

Simplify the expression.

4. $-|5|$ **−5**

5. $|-3|$ **3**

6. $-|-11|$ **−11**

7. $|-(-1)|$ **1**

8. The Caspian Sea has a surface elevation of −85 feet. The Dead Sea has a surface elevation of −1293 feet. Which sea is the farthest below sea level? **Dead Sea**

FOLLOW-UP

RETEACHING/REMEDIATION

- Study Guide in Chapter 2 Resource Book, pp. 12-13
- eTutorial Plus Online
- Extra Practice, p. 728
- Lesson Practice in Chapter 2 Resource Book, pp. 9-11

CHALLENGE/ENRICHMENT

- Challenge Practice in Chapter 2 Resource Book, p. 15
- Teacher's Edition, p. 50F

ENGLISH LEARNER SUPPORT

- Spanish Study Guide
- Multi-Language Glossary
- Chapter Audio Summaries CDs

HELP with Solving

The opposite of an opposite is the original number. For example, $-(-16) = 16$.

B **Simplify the expression.**

25. $|-32|$ 32 **26.** $-|9|$ −9 **27.** $-|29|$ −29 **28.** $-(-5)$ 5

29. $-(-81)$ 81 **30.** $-|-17|$ −17 **31.** $-|-3|$ −3 **32.** $-(-(-4))$ −4

Copy and complete the statement with <, >, or =.

33. $|4|$? $|-4|$ = **34.** $|-6|$? $-|6|$ > **35.** $-|-9|$? $-(-9)$ <

36. Critical Thinking What numbers have opposites that are the same as their absolute values? What numbers have opposites that are different from their absolute values? **negative numbers and zero; positive numbers**

C **37. Launch Countdown** Put the following activities for a shuttle launch in the order that they occur. "T−5 minutes" means 5 minutes before liftoff. **See margin.**

T−5 minutes	Pilot starts auxiliary power units.
T+7 seconds	Shuttle clears launch tower, and control switches to the Mission Control Center.
T−2 hours, 55 minutes	Flight crew departs for launch pad.
T−6 seconds	Main engine starts.
T−0	Liftoff.

37. Flight crew departs for launch pad. Pilot starts auxiliary power units. Main engine starts. Liftoff. Shuttle clears launch tower, and control switches to the Mission Control Center.

Challenge Order the numbers from least to greatest.

38. $-28, -(-73), |-65|, |95|, -|47|$ $-|47|, -28, |-65|, -(-73), |95|$

39. $|-19|, -74, -|12|, -(-56), -|-58|$ $-74, -|-58|, -|12|, |-19|, -(-56)$

Mixed Review

Evaluate the expression when $a = 8$ and $b = 2$. *(Lesson 1.3)*

40. $5ab$ 80 **41.** $\frac{a}{b} + 15$ 19 **42.** $4a - 3b$ 26

43. Patty needs to read a 238 page book in 6 days. By the end of the first day she has read 68 pages. How many pages does she need to read each day to finish the book on time? *(Lesson 1.7)* **34 pages**

Test-Taking Practice

INTERNET
State Test Practice
CLASSZONE.COM

44. Multiple Choice Which of the following shows the integers in order from least to greatest? **C**

A. −1, −6, −12, −34 **B.** −1, −12, −34, −6

C. −34, −12, −6, −1 **D.** −34, −6, −12, −1

45. Multiple Choice The Java Trench in the Indian Ocean lies 7258 meters below sea level. Which number represents this elevation in meters? **F**

F. −7258 **G.** $-(-7258)$ **H.** $|-7258|$ **I.** $|7258|$

2.2 Hands-on Activity

GOAL
Model integer addition on a number line.

MATERIALS
- pencil
- paper

Adding Integers

You can model addition of integers by using a number line.

Find the sum −15 + 11.

1. Draw a number line, place a pencil at 0, and move 15 units to the left to show −15.

2. Move 11 units to the right to show the addition of 11.

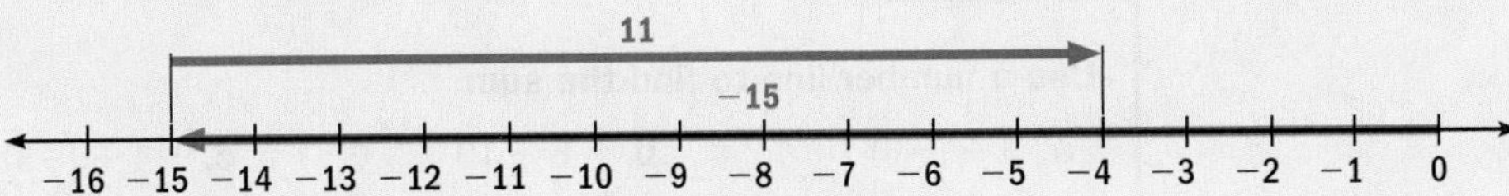

3. The final position is −4. So, −15 + 11 = −4.

Your turn now **Write an addition expression to represent the figure. Then evaluate the expression.**

1.

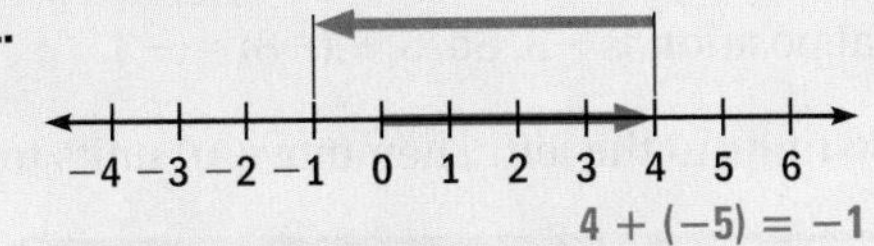

4 + (−5) = −1

2.

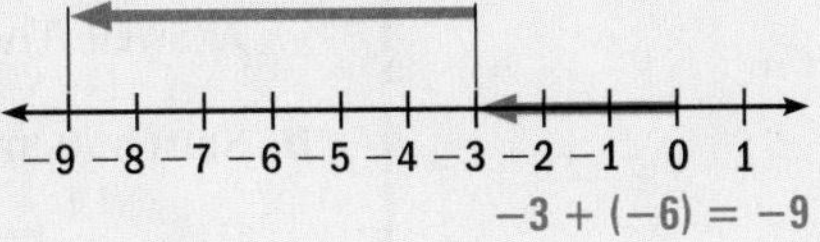

−3 + (−6) = −9

Use a number line to find the sum.

3. −7 + (−14) −21 **4.** 20 + (−50) −30 **5.** −10 + 65 55 **6.** −7 + (−33) −40

7. 41 + (−25) 16 **8.** −23 + 52 29 **9.** −18 + (−34) −52 **10.** 35 + (−37) −2

Stop and Think

11. The sum of two positive integers is always positive. What is the sign of the sum of two negative integers? Use a number line to explain. See margin.

12. Critical Thinking How can you predict the sign of the sum of a positive and a negative integer before you add the numbers? The sign will be the same as the integer with the greatest absolute value.

13. Writing Write the steps you use to evaluate 25 + (−13) + 5 + (−20). Then evaluate the expression. 25 + (−13) + 5 + (−20) = 12 + 5 + (−20) = 17 + (−20) = −3

ILLINOIS Standards and ISAT:
6.B.3a, 8.D.3a

1 PLAN

Explore the Concept

- Students will model integer addition on a number line.
- In Lesson 2.2, students will use number lines to model integer addition.

Materials

Students will need paper and pencil.

Recommended Time

Work activity: 10 min
Discuss results: 5 min

Grouping

Students should work individually.

Transparency

A support transparency is available for this Activity.

2 TEACH

Tips for Success

Make sure students count "one" *after* making their first move of one unit.

3 CLOSE

Key Discovery

The sum of two negative integers is negative. The sum of a positive integer and a negative integer can be positive, negative, or zero.

Assessment

1. A negative integer is farther from 0 on the number line than a positive integer. What is the sign of the sum of the integers? negative

11. See Additional Answers beginning on page AA1.

PLAN

SKILL CHECK

1. $8 + 7 = \underline{?}$ 15
2. $14 + 16 = \underline{?}$ 30
3. $6 + 11 + 5 = \underline{?}$ 22
4. $2 + 13 + 8 = \underline{?}$ 23

LESSON OBJECTIVE

Add integers.

PACING

Suggested Number of Days
Basic Course: 1 day
Average Course: 1 day
Advanced Course: 1 day
Block: 0.5 block with 2.1

TEACHING RESOURCES

For a complete list of Teaching Resources, see page 50B.

TRANSPARENCY

Warm-Up Exercises for this lesson are available on a transparency.

TEACH

MOTIVATING THE LESSON

Using a number line, have students practice moving left to add pairs of integers between -1 and -10 to see that the result is "more negative" than either integer.

TIPS FOR NEW TEACHERS

Using the floor or wall number line from the previous lesson, have students walk back and forth or trace with their fingers to model simple integer addition. See Tips for New Teachers in the *Chapter 2 Resource Book.*

Adding Integers

BEFORE
You added whole numbers.

Now
You'll add integers.

WHY?
So you can find a miniature golf score, as in Ex. 43.

Word Watch

Review Words
integer, p. 53
absolute value, p. 54
sum, p. 709

You can use a number line to add integers.

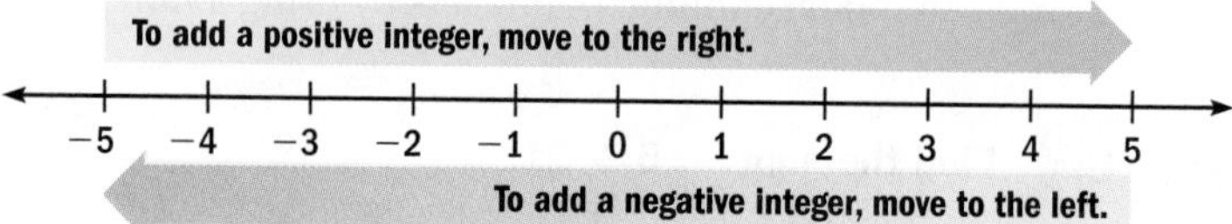

EXAMPLE 1 **Adding Integers Using a Number Line**

Use a number line to find the sum.

a. $5 + (-8)$ **b.** $-6 + 10$ **c.** $-4 + (-3)$

Solution

a. Start at 0, move 5 units to the right. Then move 8 units to the left.

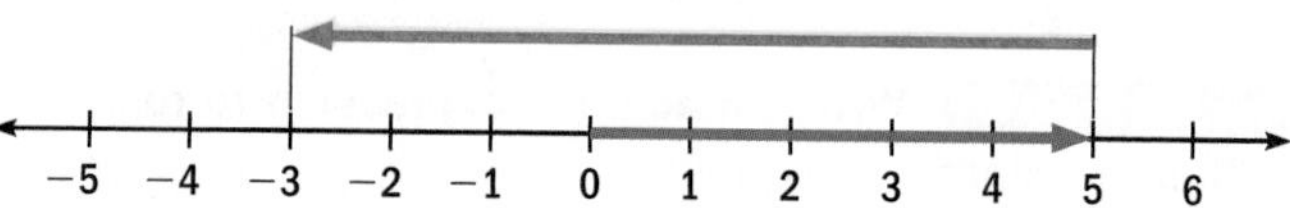

ANSWER The final position is -3. So, $5 + (-8) = -3$.

b. Start at 0, move 6 units to the left. Then move 10 units to the right.

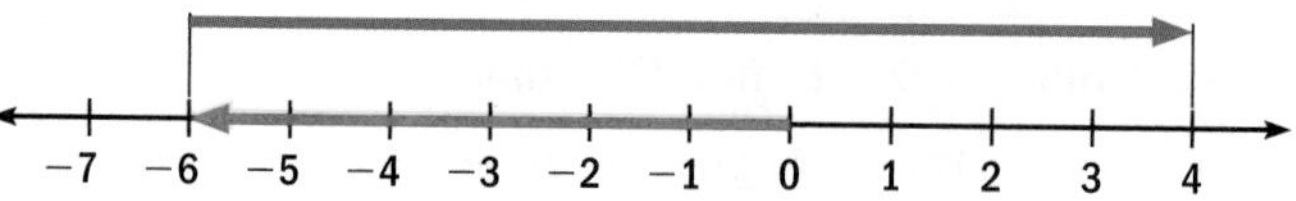

ANSWER The final position is 4. So, $-6 + 10 = 4$.

c. Start at 0, move 4 units to the left. Then move 3 units to the left.

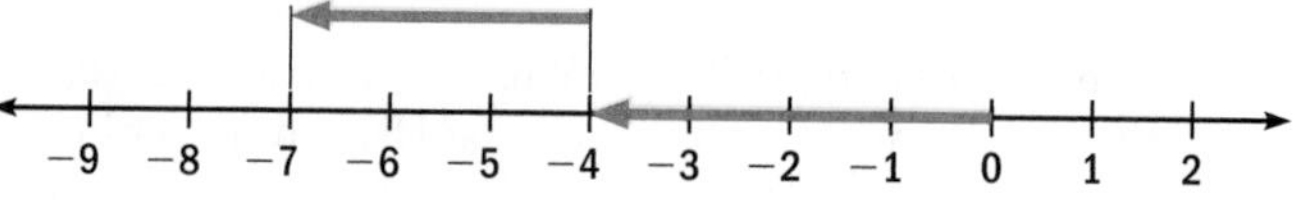

ANSWER The final position is -7. So, $-4 + (-3) = -7$.

Your turn now **Use a number line to find the sum.**

1. $12 + (-5)$ 7 **2.** $-8 + 4$ −4 **3.** $-1 + (-6)$ −7 **4.** $2 + (-2)$ 0

ILLINOIS Standards and ISAT:
6.B.3a, 8.D.3a; 8.A.3a

Using a Rule You can add integers without using a number line by following these rules.

Same sign Add the absolute values and use the common sign.

Different signs Subtract the lesser absolute value from the greater absolute value. Use the sign of the number with the greater absolute value.

EXAMPLE 2 Adding Integers

Find the sum −12 + 4.

$-12 + 4 = -8$ ← **Different signs, so subtract $|4|$ from $|-12|$.**

↑ **Use sign of number with greater absolute value.**

✓ **Check** Use a number line to find the sum.

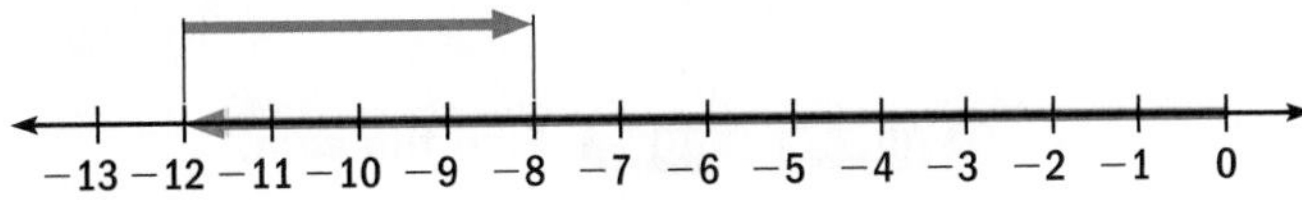

Additive Identity Property

Words The sum of an integer and zero is the integer.

Numbers $5 + 0 = 5$
$-3 + 0 = -3$

Algebra $a + 0 = a$

EXAMPLE 3 Adding More Than Two Integers

a. Use the left to right rule of order of operations to find the sum.

$-84 + 0 + (-124) = -84 + (-124)$ **Additive identity property**

$= -208$ **Same sign, so sum has common sign.**

b. Use the left to right rule of order of operations to find the sum.

$-46 + (-53) + 63 = -99 + 63$ **Same sign, so sum has common sign.**

$= -36$ **Use sign of number with greater absolute value.**

EXTRA EXAMPLES

Example 1 Use a number line to find the sum.
a. $6 + (-7)$ **−1**
b. $-4 + 9$ **5**
c. $-7 + (-2)$ **−9**

Example 2 Find the sum $-14 + 8$. **−6**

Example 3 Use the left to right rule of order of operations to find the sum.
a. $-32 + (-22) + (-4)$ **−58**
b. $-16 + (-20) + 52$ **16**

COMMON ERROR

In Example 3, remind students to always affix the sign of the sum after adding each pair of integers. Some students may forget to check the sign after subtracting absolute values.

Differentiating Instruction

Less Proficient Students Using colored counters or plastic coins, have students relate positive integers to money that they have and negative numbers to money that they owe. For example, $5 + (-8)$ might mean that a student who has 5 cents and owes 8 cents has a net result of owing 3 cents (−3).

TRANSPARENCY

A support transparency is available for Examples 1 and 2, and for Your turn now Exercises 1–4.

EXTRA EXAMPLES

Example 4 The table shows amounts of money that Shannon deposited and withdrew from her bank account. What is the overall amount of deposit or withdrawal?

Deposit	$400
Deposit	$125
Rent	−$300
Deposit	$50
Electricity bill	−$75

$200 deposit

 **CONCEPT CHECK**

If you add two integers with different signs, how do you find the sign of the sum? **You use the sign of the integer with the greater absolute value.**

 **DAILY PUZZLER**

Find two integers so that the absolute value of their sum is 6 and the sum of their absolute values is 20. **7 and −13 or −7 and 13**

EXAMPLE 4 **Adding More Than Two Integers**

School Fair Your class has a fair to raise money for a field trip. The table shows the incomes and expenses for the fair. How much money was raised?

Games	$750
Display tables	$625
Donations	$36
Advertising	−$16
Decorations	−$60
Game rentals	−$500

Solution

First, add the **positive integers**, and then add the **negative integers**.

$$750 + 625 + 36 + (-16) + (-60) + (-500) = 1411 + (-576)$$
$$= 835$$

ANSWER Your class raised $835.

Your turn now **Find the sum.**

5. $-20 + (-15)$ **−35**
6. $18 + 0 + (-54)$ **−36**
7. $300 + 111 + (-44) + (-256)$ **111**
8. $-230 + (-512) + 178 + 94$ **−470**

2.2 Exercises

More Practice, p. 728

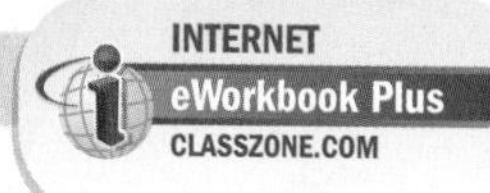

Getting Ready to Practice

1. Vocabulary Copy and complete: To add two integers with the same sign, add the _?_ and use the common sign. **absolute values**

Use a number line to find the sum.

2. $-6 + 8$ **2**
3. $-3 + (-9)$ **−12**
4. $5 + (-7)$ **−2**
5. $-4 + 4$ **0**

Find the sum.

6. $42 + (-23)$ **19**
7. $-32 + 0$ **−32**
8. $-51 + (-67)$ **−118**
9. $-19 + 19 + (-34)$ **−34**
10. $-12 + 9 + (-5)$ **−8**
11. $20 + (-15) + (-22)$ **−17**

12. Checking You record withdrawals and deposits in your checkbook. The starting balance is $125. The first withdrawal is $25. The second withdrawal is $13. The first deposit is $35. The second deposit is $50. The third withdrawal is $68. What is the final balance? **$104**

with Homework

Example	Exercises
1	13-16
2	17-26
3	18-26, 34-37
4	34-37

Online Resources
CLASSZONE.COM

- More Examples
- eTutorial Plus

17. Since the signs are different, the lesser absolute value should be subtracted from the greater absolute value and the sign of the number with the greater absolute value should be used; $-8 + 5 = -3$.

Practice and Problem Solving

A Use a number line to find the sum.

13. $-2 + (-1)$ -3 **14.** $-10 + (-9)$ -19 **15.** $-3 + 7$ 4 **16.** $7 + (-5)$ 2

17. Find the Error Describe and correct the error in the solution. See margin.

Find the sum of -8 and 5.
$-8 + 5 = -13$

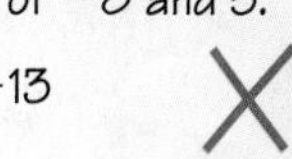

Find the sum.

18. $-63 + (-49)$ -112 **19.** $-93 + (-16)$ -109 **20.** $0 + (-25)$ -25

21. $-82 + 0$ -82 **22.** $98 + (-128)$ -30 **23.** $-57 + 31 + 27 + 11$ 12

24. $-42 + (-65) + 78$ -29 **25.** $-87 + 48 + 36$ -3 **26.** $-81 + (-75) + (-65)$ -221

Critical Thinking Copy and complete the statement using *always*, *sometimes*, or *never*.

27. The sum of two negative integers is _?_ negative. always

28. The sum of two positive integers is _?_ negative. never

29. The sum of a positive integer and a negative integer is _?_ negative. sometimes

30. The sum of an integer and zero is _?_ zero. sometimes

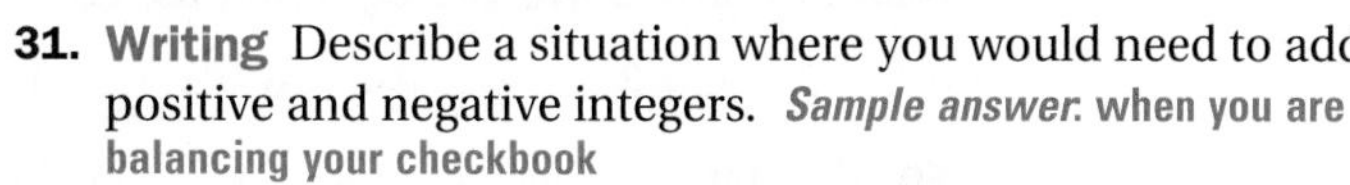

31. Writing Describe a situation where you would need to add positive and negative integers. *Sample answer:* when you are balancing your checkbook

In Exercises 32 and 33, use the information to write an expression. Then use a number line to find the sum.

32. Elevator You enter an elevator on the sixth floor. The elevator goes up 3 floors, then down 5 floors, where you exit. What floor is it? $6 + 3 + (-5) = 4$; fourth floor

33. Mexico The influential period of the *Olmec* culture in Mexico lasted approximately 800 years. It started about 1200 B.C. About what year did this period end? $-1200 + 800 = -400$; 400 B.C.

B Find the sum.

34. $42 + 36 + (-16) + 0 + (-84)$ -22 **35.** $(-17) + (-63) + 91 + 79$ 90

36. $174 + (-196) + 245 + (-210)$ 13 **37.** $-182 + 307 + 163 + (-142)$ 146

Algebra Evaluate $x + (-478)$ for the value of x.

38. $x = 806$ 328 **39.** $x = -729$ -1207 **40.** $x = |-349|$ -129 **41.** $x = -|-521|$ -999

42. Making Connections The sum of a number and its *additive inverse* is 0. For example, $5 + (-5) = 0$, so 5 and -5 are additive inverses. Give another example of additive inverses. What vocabulary word from this chapter is another name for additive inverses?
Sample answer: $10 + (-10) = 0$; opposites

Jade sculpture from the Olmec culture in Veracruz, Mexico

3 APPLY

ASSIGNMENT GUIDE

Basic Course
Day 1: pp. 61-62 Exs. 13-32, 34-35, 51-57

Average Course
Day 1: pp. 61-62 Exs. 15-17, 22-43, 51-57

Advanced Course
Day 1: pp. 61-62 Exs. 16-17, 24-26, 31-57*

Block
pp. 61-62 Exs. 15-17, 22-43, 51-57 (with 2.1)

Extra Practice

- Student Edition, p. 728
- Chapter 2 Resource Book, pp. 18-20
- Test and Practice Generator

Transparency

Even-numbered answers are available on transparencies. A support transparency is available for Exercises 2-5 and 13-16.

Homework Check

When you review students' homework for this lesson, go over the following exercises to check understanding of key concepts.
Basic: 13, 17, 18, 22, 34
Average: 15, 17, 22, 23, 35
Advanced: 16, 25, 26, 35, 36

Teaching Tip

In Exercises 34-37, point out to students that it may be easier for them to add all the positive integers, add all the negative integers, and then find the sum of the results.

ASSESS

ASSESSMENT RESOURCES

For more assessment resources, see:
- Assessment Book
- Test and Practice Generator

MINI-QUIZ

Find each sum.

1. $-32 + (-18)$ -50
2. $0 + (-47)$ -47
3. $-42 + 64$ 22
4. $-17 + 19 + (-20)$ -18
5. $85 + (-105) + 30$ 10
6. $11 + (-16) + (-46) + 74$ 23
7. The temperature at dawn was -5°F. By noon, the temperature had risen 20°F. What was the temperature at noon? 15°F

FOLLOW-UP

RETEACHING/REMEDIATION

- Study Guide in Chapter 2 Resource Book, pp. 21–22
- eTutorial Plus Online
- Extra Practice, p. 728
- Lesson Practice in Chapter 2 Resource Book, pp. 18–20

CHALLENGE/ENRICHMENT

- Challenge Practice in Chapter 2 Resource Book, p. 23
- Teacher's Edition, p. 50F

ENGLISH LEARNER SUPPORT

- Spanish Study Guide
- Multi-Language Glossary
- Chapter Audio Summaries CDs

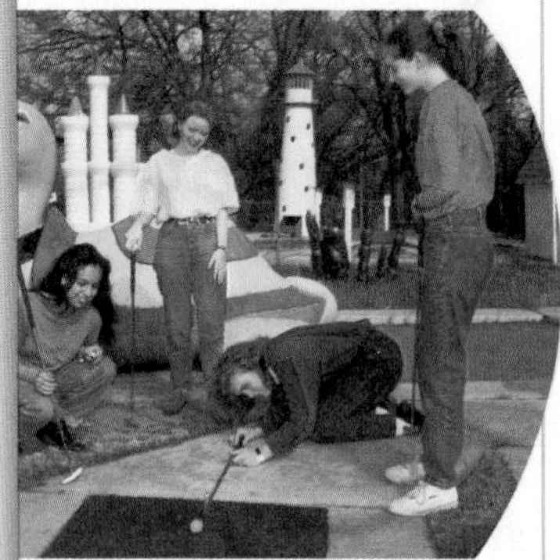

50. Yes; yes; no. *Sample answer*: If x and y are both positive, then $|x| = x$ and $|y| = y$. So $|x + y| = ||x| + |y|| = |x| + |y|$. If x and y are both negative, then $|x| = -x$ and $|y| = -y$. So $|x + y| = ||-x| + |-y|| = ||x| + |y|| = |x| + |y|$. If x is positive and y is negative, then their sum will be less than the sum of the absolute values. For example, $3 + (-5) = -2$ and $|3| + |-5| = 8$, so $3 + (-5) < |3| + |-5|$. Because $|3 + (-5)| = 2$, it is also true that $|3 + (-5)| < |3| + |-5|$, so they are not equal.

43. **Miniature Golf** In miniature golf, *par* is the number of strokes considered necessary to get a ball in the hole. The score for each hole is the number of strokes above or below par. Find the total score by adding the scores for each hole. Is Jill's score *above* par, *under* par, or *at* par? 0; at par

HOLE	1	2	3	4	5	6	7	8	9	OUT
PAR	4	5	3	3	5	4	3	5	3	35
Jill	0	+1	−2	−1	0	+1	+2	0	−1	

Chemistry In Exercises 44–46, use the information below. Find the sum of the charges. Tell whether the atom is an ion.

- A proton has a charge of $+1$.
- An electron has a charge of -1.
- An atom is an ion if it has a positive or negative charge.

44. Sodium: 11 protons, 10 electrons $+1$; yes
45. Chlorine: 17 protons, 17 electrons 0; no
46. Oxide: 8 protons, 10 electrons -2; yes

C **Mental Math Solve the equation using mental math.**

47. $-3 + k = 2$ 5
48. $-6 = x + (-9)$ 3
49. $-7 = 12 + j$ -19

50. **Challenge** Does $|x + y| = |x| + |y|$ if x and y are both positive? What if x and y are both negative? What if x is positive and y is negative? Explain.

Mixed Review

Evaluate the expression. *(Lesson 1.4)*

51. $5^3 + 21 \div 7 - 6$ 122
52. $6^2 \cdot (2 + 4) \div 18$ 12
53. $(12 - 4) \cdot (9 - 1)^2$ 512

Order the integers from least to greatest. *(Lesson 2.1)*

54. $-2479, 1802, 2479, -1802$ $-2479, -1802, 1802, 2479$
55. $-346, -125, -921, 724, 128$ $-921, -346, -125, 128, 724$

Test-Taking Practice

INTERNET
State Test Practice
CLASSZONE.COM

56. **Multiple Choice** Evaluate $-83 + 34$. B

 A. -117 **B.** -49 **C.** 49 **D.** 117

57. **Multiple Choice** Evaluate $-498 + (-512) + 573 + (-645)$. G

 F. -1232 **G.** -1082 **H.** 1082 **I.** 1232

Subtracting Integers

BEFORE You added integers.

Now You'll subtract integers.

WHY? So you can find the length of dinosaur periods, as in Ex. 41.

Word Watch

Review Words

integer, p. 53
opposite, p. 54
difference, p. 709

Activity You can use patterns and mental math to discover a rule for subtracting integers.

1. Copy the table. In the second column, write the answer to the subtraction problem. Use a pattern to find the differences involving negative integers.

2. In the third column, complete the addition problem so the sum is equal to the number in the difference column.

Subtraction problem	Difference	Addition problem
3 − 3	0	3 + −3
3 − 2	? 1	3 + ? −2
3 − 1	? 2	3 + ? −1
3 − 0	? 3	3 + ? 0
3 − (−1)	? 4	3 + ? 1
3 − (−2)	? 5	3 + ? 2
3 − (−3)	? 6	3 + ? 3

3. How is the second number in the addition problems related to the second number in the subtraction problems? It is the opposite.

4. Describe how to use addition to subtract integers. Add the opposite of the second integer.

In the activity above, you saw that when you subtract integers you can write the expression as an addition expression and then use the rules for adding integers.

Subtracting Integers

Words To subtract an integer, add its opposite.

Numbers $3 - 7 = 3 + (-7) = -4$
$2 - (-6) = 2 + 6 = 8$

Algebra $a - b = a + (-b)$
$a - (-b) = a + b$

ILLINOIS Standards and ISAT:
6.B.3a, 8.D.3a; 8.B.3

1 PLAN

SKILL CHECK

1. $124 - 35 = \underline{?}$ 89
2. $17 - 17 = \underline{?}$ 0
3. $18 + (-21) = \underline{?}$ −3
4. $-11 + (-9) = \underline{?}$ −20

Lesson Objective

Subtract integers.

Pacing

Suggested Number of Days
Basic Course: 2 days
Average Course: 2 days
Advanced Course: 2 days
Block: 1 block

Teaching Resources

For a complete list of Teaching Resources, see page 50B.

Transparency

Warm-Up Exercises for this lesson are available on a transparency.

2 TEACH

Motivating the Lesson

Ask students: You have $27. You buy CDs costing $22. How do you find the amount of money you have left? Now say you have $27 and want to buy CDs costing $33. How much more money do you need? Can you subtract 33 from 27? If so, what do you think the result should be?

Activity

Goal Use patterns to discover a rule for subtracting integers.

Key Discovery To subtract an integer, you add its opposite.

TIPS FOR NEW TEACHERS
Some students may need to practice finding the opposite of a negative number and expressing this concept in symbols before beginning the lesson. See Tips for New Teachers in the *Chapter 2 Resource Book*.

EXTRA EXAMPLES

Example 1 Find the difference.
a. $-41 - (-10)$ **−31**
b. $-52 - 23$ **−75**

Example 2 Evaluate $63 - c - d$ when $c = 18$ and $d = -45$. **90**

Example 3 Negative integers can be used to express the distance below the surface of a body of water. A turtle at −18 inches in a lake dives to −166 inches. How far did it dive? **148 in.**

NOTETAKING
Urge students to write several examples in their notebooks for each possible combination of using positive and negative integers in subtraction problems.

CONCEPT CHECK
Subtracting an integer is the same as what? **adding its opposite**

DAILY PUZZLER
$1 + 2 = \underline{?}$ **3**
$1 + 2 - 3 + 4 = \underline{?}$ **4**
$1 + 2 - 3 + 4 - 5 + 6 = \underline{?}$ **5**
$1 + 2 - 3 + 4 - \ldots - 49 + 50 = \underline{?}$ **27**

EXAMPLE 1 Subtracting Integers

a. $-56 - (-9) = -56 + 9$ **Add the opposite of −9.**
$= -47$ **Add.**

b. $-14 - 21 = -14 + (-21)$ **Add the opposite of 21.**
$= -35$ **Add.**

Your turn now **Find the difference.**

1. $15 - 41$ **−26** **2.** $-16 - 8$ **−24** **3.** $38 - (-27)$ **65** **4.** $-76 - (-109)$ **33**

EXAMPLE 2 Evaluating a Variable Expression

Evaluate $15 - a - b$ when $a = 24$ and $b = -36$.

Solution

$15 - a - b = 15 - 24 - (-36)$ **Substitute 24 for *a* and −36 for *b*.**
$= 15 + (-24) - (-36)$ **Add the opposite of 24.**
$= -9 - (-36)$ **Add 15 and −24.**
$= -9 + 36$ **Add the opposite of −36.**
$= 27$ **Add.**

What do you think? Science

SOFAR
Humpback whales use the SOFAR channel to communicate with other whales. The speed of sound in water at 68°F is 1482 meters per second. The speed of sound in air at 68°F is 344 meters per second. How much faster does sound travel in water? **1138 m/sec**

EXAMPLE 3 Using Integer Subtraction

SOFAR The SOFAR (*SO*und *F*ixing *A*nd *R*anging) channel is a layer of water in the oceans that allows sounds to travel extremely long distances. Use the diagram to find the vertical height of the SOFAR channel.

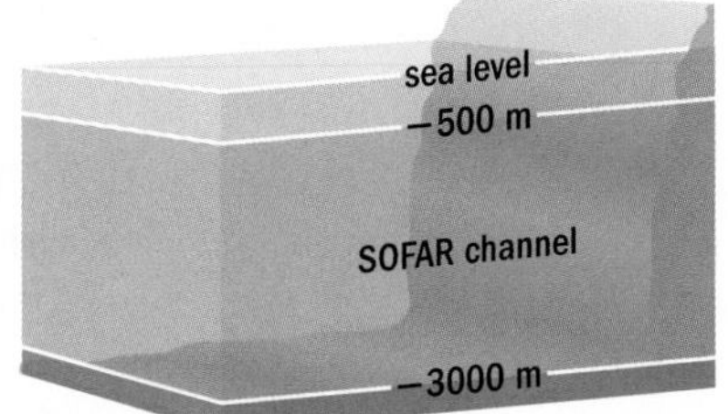

Solution

The vertical height is the difference of the upper and lower elevations.

Vertical height $= -500 - (-3000)$ **Write subtraction statement.**
$= -500 + 3000$ **Add the opposite of −3000.**
$= 2500$ **Add.**

ANSWER The vertical height of the SOFAR channel is 2500 meters.

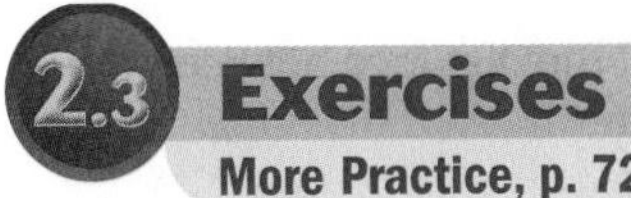

2.3 Exercises

More Practice, p. 728

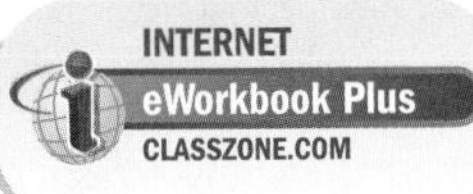

Getting Ready to Practice

Vocabulary **Translate the verbal phrase into a numerical expression.**

1. The difference of negative two and six $-2 - 6$

2. The difference of the opposite of five and the opposite of three $-5 - (-3)$

Find the difference.

3. $5 - 12$ -7 **4.** $6 - (-16)$ 22 **5.** $-11 - (-7)$ -4 **6.** $-9 - 10$ -19

Evaluate the expression when $x = 15$ and $y = -8$.

7. $5 - x$ -10 **8.** $-9 - y$ -1 **9.** $y - x$ -23 **10.** $x - y$ 23

11. Guided Problem Solving Use the diagram to find the distances between the bird and the boat, the boat and the reef, and the bird and the reef.

Step 1: 55 ft, 0 ft, −35 ft;
Step 2: $55 - 0 = 55$ ft, $0 - (-35) = 35$ ft, $55 - (-35) = 90$ ft

(1) Identify which elevation is greater for each situation.

(2) Subtract the lower elevation from the greater elevation.

(3) Answer the original question by completing each statement.

The bird is _?_ feet above the boat. 55

The boat is _?_ feet above the reef. 35

The bird is _?_ feet above the reef. 90

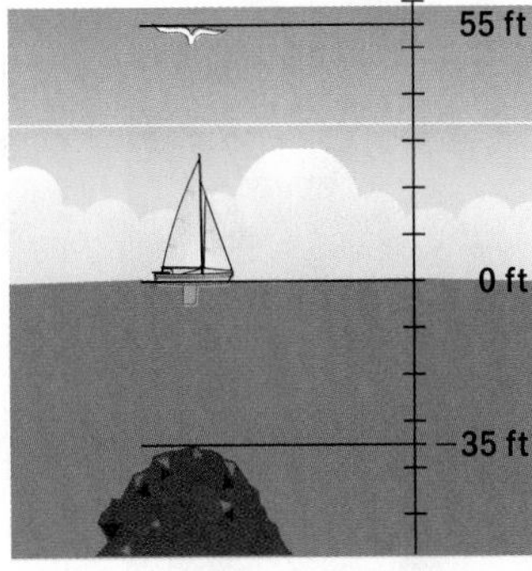

Practice and Problem Solving

Example	Exercises
1	12-20
2	22-24
3	21, 26-28

· More Examples
· eTutorial Plus

A Find the difference.

12. $-13 - 12$ -25 **13.** $-14 - (-14)$ 0 **14.** $11 - (-6)$ 17

15. $9 - 17$ -8 **16.** $-18 - (-12)$ -6 **17.** $-20 - 7$ -27

18. $32 - 40$ -8 **19.** $28 - (-16)$ 44 **20.** $-39 - (-13)$ -26

21. Game Show A game show contestant has -400 points. He answers a question incorrectly and loses 600 points. What is his total score? −1000 points

Evaluate the expression when $c = -5$ and $d = 10$.

22. $c - 6 - d$ -21 **23.** $10 - c - d$ 5 **24.** $c - d - 8 - 4$ -27

3 APPLY

ASSIGNMENT GUIDE

Basic Course
Day 1: SRH p. 712 Exs. 4-6; pp. 65-67 Exs. 12-20, 29-31, 49-54
Day 2: pp. 65-67 Exs. 21-28, 55-60

Average Course
Day 1: pp. 65-67 Exs. 15-20, 29-34, 49-54
Day 2: pp. 65-67 Exs. 23-28, 35-41, 55-60

Advanced Course
Day 1: pp. 65-67 Exs. 18-20, 32-40, 49-54
Day 2: pp. 65-67 Exs. 23-28, 41-48*, 59, 60

Block
pp. 65-67 Exs. 15-20, 23-41, 49-60

EXTRA PRACTICE

- Student Edition, p. 728
- Chapter 2 Resource Book, pp. 27-29
- Test and Practice Generator

TRANSPARENCY

Even-numbered answers are available on transparencies.

HOMEWORK CHECK

When you review students' homework for this lesson, go over the following exercises to check understanding of key concepts.
Basic: 12, 15, 16, 21, 22
Average: 16, 17, 18, 23, 26
Advanced: 18, 19, 20, 24, 27

Common Error

In Exercise 43, students may be tempted to write 14 − 9 − 18 after substituting. It is easy for many students to "lose" the negative sign when substituting a negative integer for a variable after a subtraction sign. Using parentheses when substituting may help students with this.

Transparency

A support transparency is available for Exercise 25.

25. **Critical Thinking** Explain how you can find the distance between the points on the number line using subtraction. Subtract −137 from 123.

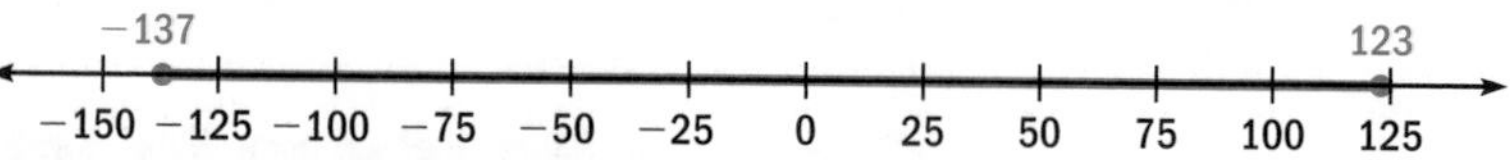

Temperatures **In Exercises 26–28, use the table. It shows the coldest temperatures ever recorded for four states.**

Coldest Recorded Temperatures

State	Temperature
Alaska	−80°F
Colorado	−61°F
Kentucky	−37°F
Mississippi	−19°F

26. How much colder is Alaska's coldest temperature than Kentucky's? 43°F

27. How much colder is Colorado's coldest temperature than Mississippi's? 42°F

28. Which two states have the greatest difference of coldest temperatures? Which two states have the least difference of coldest temperatures? Alaska and Mississippi; Kentucky and Mississippi

B **Evaluate the expression.**

29. 41 − 300 −259 **30.** 144 − 612 −468 **31.** −309 − (−2111) 1802

32. −5 − (−5) − (−5) 5 **33.** 8 − 2 − 6 − 10 −10 **34.** −4 − 7 + (−9) − 1 −21

35. −1 + (−8) − 9 −18 **36.** 6 − (−4) −10 0 **37.** 3 − (−7) − (−2) 12

38. 15 + (−29) − (−72) 58 **39.** −52 − (−18) − 37 −71 **40.** 91 + (−40) − 34 17

41. **Dinosaurs** The table shows the ranges of three dinosaur periods during the Mesozoic Era. Calculate how long each of the periods lasted. Triassic Period: 43 million yr; Jurassic Period: 64 million yr; Cretaceous Period: 79 million yr

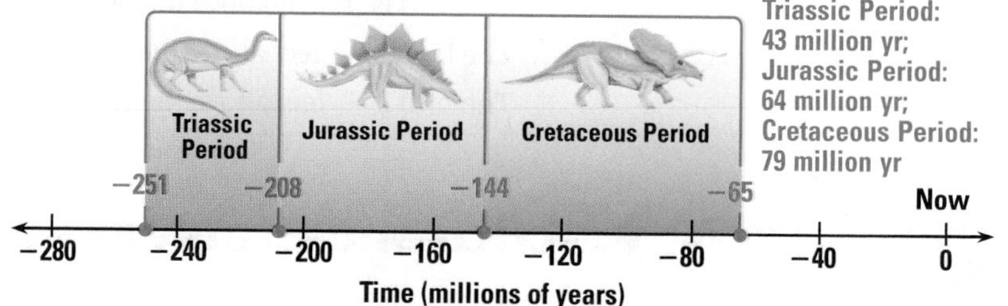

Evaluate the expression when *a* = −9, *b* = 18, and *c* = −4.

42. $a + c - 10$ −23 **43.** $14 - a - b$ 5 **44.** $a - b - c$ −23 **45.** $c + a - b$ −31

C **Challenge** **Copy and complete the statement using *always*, *sometimes*, or *never*.**

46. A negative number minus a positive number is _?_ negative. always

47. A positive number minus a negative number is _?_ negative. never

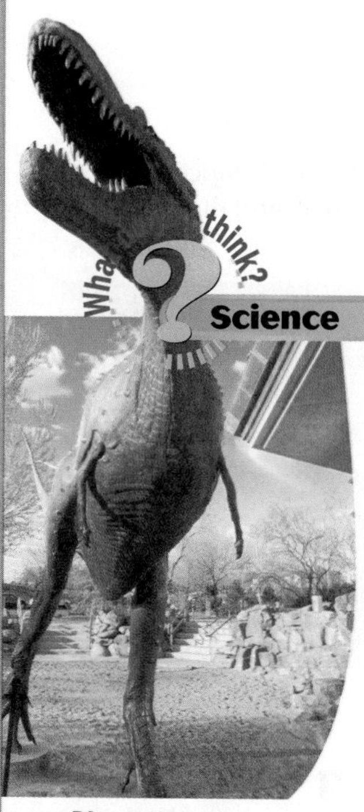

Dinosaurs

Scientists believe that if a Tyrannosaurus Rex was able to run more than 25 miles per hour it would have to have had more than 80% of its body mass in its legs. If a Tyrannosaurus Rex weighed 13,000 pounds, this would mean the legs weighed 10,400 pounds. How much would the rest of its body have weighed? 2600 lb

48. **Weather** To collect data on winter storms developing in the north Pacific Ocean, a cylinder that measures wind speed, humidity, and temperature at different elevations is dropped from a plane. If the plane is 40,000 feet above sea level and the cylinder drops to the bottom of the Pacific Ocean, 13,000 feet below sea level, how far does the cylinder fall? 53,000 ft

Mixed Review

Solve the equation using mental math. *(Lesson 1.5)*

49. $v + 5 = 13$ 8
50. $7w = 42$ 6
51. $12 - x = 9$ 3

Find the sum. *(Lesson 2.2)*

52. $-8 + 17$ 9
53. $11 + (-9)$ 2
54. $-22 + (-6)$ −28

Basic Skills **Find the difference.**

55. $257 - 89$ 168
56. $500 - 166$ 334
57. $6641 - 992$ 5649
58. $8250 - 98$ 8152

Test-Taking Practice

INTERNET
State Test Practice
CLASSZONE.COM

59. **Multiple Choice** What is the value of $-5 - (-7) - (-1) - 10$? C

A. -23 **B.** -13 **C.** -7 **D.** 13

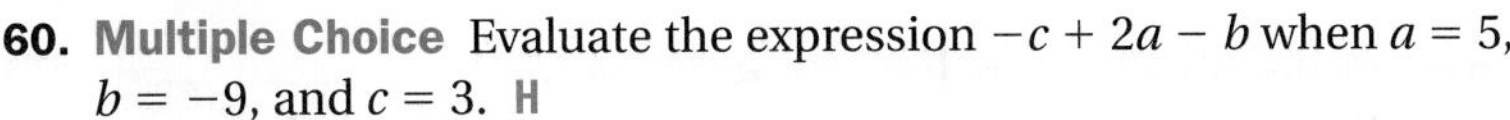

60. **Multiple Choice** Evaluate the expression $-c + 2a - b$ when $a = 5$, $b = -9$, and $c = 3$. H

F. -2 **G.** 4 **H.** 16 **I.** 22

Argyle Arithmetic

Each number in a purple diamond is the sum of the two numbers below it. Each number in a green diamond is the difference of the two numbers above it. Copy and complete the argyle arithmetic.

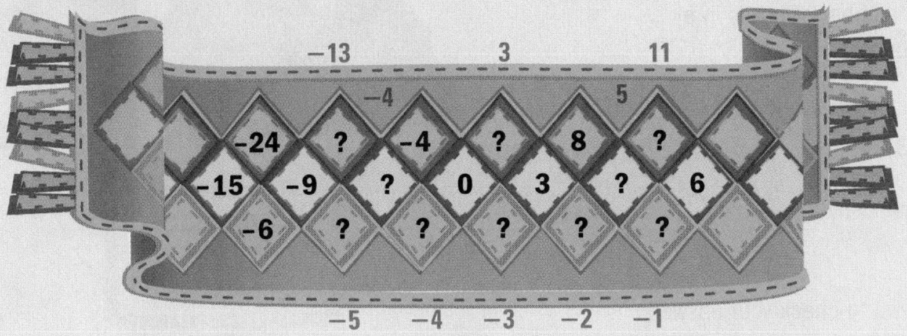

4 ASSESS

Assessment Resources

For more assessment resources, see:

- Assessment Book
- Test and Practice Generator

Mini-Quiz

Find the difference.

1. $-20 - 15$ −35
2. $11 - 0$ 11
3. $42 - 60$ −18
4. $-29 - (-14)$ −15

Evaluate the expression when $z = 5$ and $w = -6$.

5. $z - 13 - w$ −2
6. $w + z - 14 + 30$ 15
7. Sam has a score of −50 points in a game and then loses 20 more points. What is Sam's final score? −70 points

5 FOLLOW-UP

Reteaching/Remediation

- Study Guide in Chapter 2 Resource Book, pp. 30–31
- Tutor Place, Algebra Card 4
- eTutorial Plus Online
- Extra Practice, p. 728
- Lesson Practice in Chapter 2 Resource Book, pp. 27–29

Challenge/Enrichment

- Challenge Practice in Chapter 2 Resource Book, p. 32
- Teacher's Edition, p. 50F

English Learner Support

- Spanish Study Guide
- Multi-Language Glossary
- Chapter Audio Summaries CDs

1 PLAN

Strategy Background

The strategy Look for a Pattern involves three steps: (1) Identify data in the problem that may be useful; (2) Find what the data have in common; and (3) Use the common element as a pattern to continue that pattern beyond the given data. Students often find the third step to be the easiest because after identifying useful data and finding a pattern, they understand how to continue the pattern.

2 TEACH

Guiding Students' Work

In Step 3, the key to understanding the pattern is to recognize that each level of boxes has a square shape. Remind students that the area of a square is the square of a side. This should help students realize that the number of boxes in level n is n squared, or n^2.

EXTRA EXAMPLES

Example Enrique raises ducks. In 2001, he bought 4 ducks. By the end of 2002, he had 12 ducks. In 2003, he had 36 ducks, and in 2004, there were 108. If this pattern continues, how many ducks can Enrique expect to have in 2005? **324 ducks**

2.4 Problem Solving Strategies

- Guess, Check, and Revise
- Draw a Diagram
- Act It Out
- Work Backward
- Look for a Pattern
- Make a Table
- Solve a Simpler Problem

Look for a Pattern

Problem Greg is setting up for a craft fair and is stacking gift boxes for a display. He knows a pyramid with a height of 2 boxes contains 5 boxes, a pyramid with a height of 3 boxes contains 14 boxes, and a pyramid with a height of 4 boxes contains 30 boxes. How many boxes will he need to make a pyramid with a height of 6 boxes?

1 Read and Understand

Read the problem carefully.

You need to find how many boxes Greg needs to make a pyramid with a height of 6 boxes.

2 Make a Plan

Decide on a strategy to use.

Sketch or model a pyramid with 5 boxes and a pyramid with 14 boxes. Look for a pattern. You can follow the pattern to determine how many boxes Greg will need.

3 Solve the Problem

Reread the problem and look for a pattern.

Sketch or model several rectangular pyramids and count how many boxes are at each level. Make a table that shows the number of boxes in each level.

1 box
4 boxes

1 box
4 boxes
9 boxes

Level n	Boxes in level n	Boxes in n-level pyramid
1	1^2	$1^2 = 1$
2	2^2	$1^2 + 2^2 = 5$
3	3^2	$1^2 + 2^2 + 3^2 = 14$

The number of boxes in each level is the square of the number of the level. The number of boxes in a pyramid is the sum of the squares.

ANSWER To make a rectangular pyramid with a height of 6 boxes, Greg will need $1^2 + 2^2 + 3^2 + 4^2 + 5^2 + 6^2 = 91$ boxes.

Homemade Candy
$2.00 a box

4 Look Back

Sketch a top view of each level to check your answer.

ILLINOIS Standards and ISAT:
6.C.3a

Practice the Strategy

Use the strategy *look for a pattern.*

1. **Geometry** Make a table showing the number of dots in each triangle. Determine the number of dots in the ninth triangle in this sequence. **See margin for table; 55 dots.**

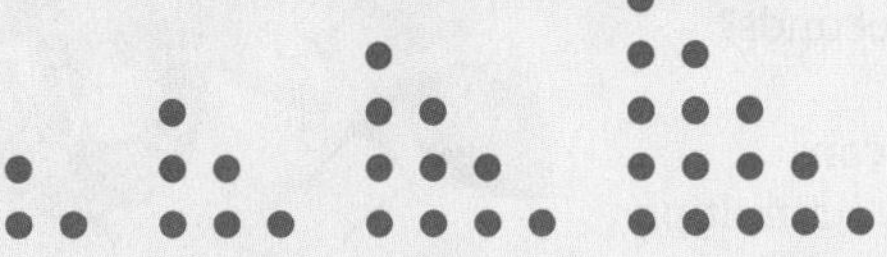

2. **Track** Your track coach tells you to do a running drill in which you run 16 feet and run back. Then you run 32 feet and run back. Next you run 48 feet and run back. How far would you expect to run next? **64 ft**

3. **Tiling** Jason and Emily are laying tiles in the kitchen of a restaurant that measures 36 feet by 24 feet. Each tile measures 1 foot by 1 foot. If they follow the pattern shown below, how many blue tiles will they need to fill the entire kitchen with this pattern? **144 blue tiles**

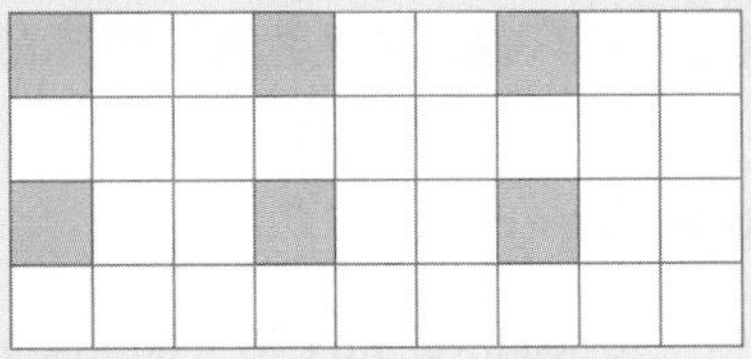

4. **Number Sense** Copy and complete the table below. Look for a pattern so you can evaluate 11 • 97 using mental math. **11 • 97 = 1067**

11 • 12	132	12 + 120	
11 • 13	143	13 + ?	130
11 • 14	154	14 + ?	140
11 • 15	165	15 + ?	150
11 • 16	176	16 + ?	160

Mixed Problem Solving

Use any strategy to solve the problem.

5. **Who's Oldest?** Scott is two years older than Anne, and Kelly is three years younger than Scott. Ben is nine years less than twice Scott's age, and Anne is 10 years old. Determine the ages of Scott, Ben, and Kelly. **Scott: 12 yr old, Ben: 15 yr old, Kelly: 9 yr old**

6. **Baking** You have a recipe that makes 24 cookies. The ingredients include 2 eggs, 1 cup of sugar, 1.5 cups of flour, 1 teaspoon of vanilla, and 1 teaspoon of baking soda. What is the greatest number of cookies you can make if you have 12 eggs, 4 cups of sugar, and 9 cups of flour? **96 cookies**

7. **Stock Prices** A newspaper reports these changes in the price of a stock during a 5-day period: −1, −8, +2, −4, and +6. The stock price ended at $35 on the fifth day. How much was the price of a stock before the 5-day period started? **$40**

8. **Cereal** You are stacking boxes of cereal for a display. You use a total of 78 boxes, and each row has one fewer box than the row below it. How many rows make up the display if the top row has one box? **12 rows**

9. **Basketball** In a basketball game, there are 1 point free throws, 2 point field goals and 3 point field goals. How many ways can you score 12 points? **19 ways**

3 APPLY

TRANSPARENCY

Even-numbered answers are available on transparencies.

COMMON ERROR

In Exercise 2, stress that the problem asks how many feet students run next before running back, not how many feet they run there and back or how many total feet they have run.

TEACHING TIP

In Exercise 3, it will help many students to use grid paper to model the floor. Students must understand that the pattern is in the individual tiles–it is not formed by repeating the 4 by 9 block of tiles shown.

SUGGESTED STRATEGIES

You may wish to suggest the following strategies for the problems in the Mixed Problem Solving:

- Exercise 5: Work Backward
- Exercise 6: Make a Table
- Exercise 7: Work Backward
- Exercise 8: Act It Out; Guess, Check, and Revise; Look for a Pattern
- Exercise 9: Make a Table; Draw a Diagram

1.

Triangle	Number of dots
1	3
2	3 + 3 = 6
3	6 + 4 = 10
4	10 + 5 = 15
5	15 + 6 = 21
6	21 + 7 = 28
7	28 + 8 = 36
8	36 + 9 = 45
9	45 + 10 = 55

PLAN

SKILL CHECK

1. 6(11) = ? 66
2. 13(8) = ? 104
3. 5(21)(2) = ? 210
4. 23(42)(0) = ? 0

LESSON OBJECTIVE

Multiply integers.

PACING

Suggested Number of Days
Basic Course: 2 days
Average Course: 2 days
Advanced Course: 2 days
Block: 1 block

TEACHING RESOURCES

For a complete list of Teaching Resources, see page 50B.

TRANSPARENCY

Warm-Up Exercises for this lesson are available on a transparency.

TEACH

MOTIVATING THE LESSON

Ask any students who have been scuba diving to describe their experiences, including how quickly they could move up and down under water.

TIPS FOR NEW TEACHERS

Encourage students to think up mnemonics to remember the signs of the product of integers with like or opposite signs (e.g., "like lifts; not like lowers"). See Tips for New Teachers in the *Chapter 2 Resource Book.*

LESSON 2.4

Multiplying Integers

BEFORE
You added and subtracted integers.

Now
You'll multiply integers.

WHY?
So you can find the worth of a coin in a game, as in Ex. 32.

Word Watch

Review Words
integer, p 53
product, p. 713

In the Real World

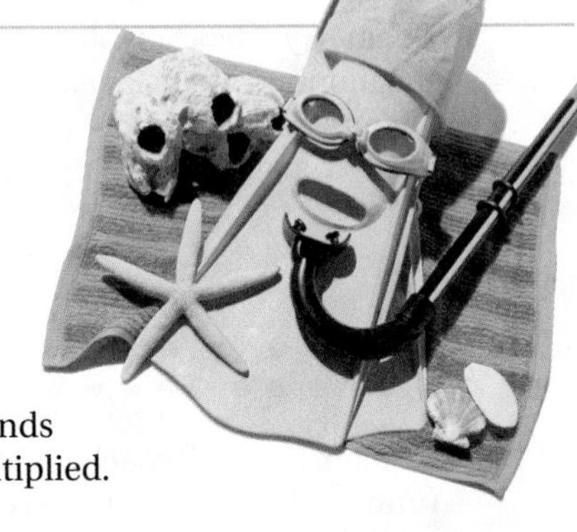

Diving A diver is exploring a coral reef. The diver's depth is changing by −6 feet per second. If the diver started at sea level, what is the diver's position after 10 seconds?

To find the position, you can multiply integers. When you multiply integers, the sign of the product depends on the signs of the integers being multiplied.

Notebook

Multiplying Integers

Words	Numbers
The product of two integers with the same sign is positive.	$4 \cdot 2 = 8$ $-3 \cdot (-7) = 21$
The product of two integers with different signs is negative.	$4 \cdot (-2) = -8$ $-3 \cdot 7 = -21$

EXAMPLE 1 **Multiplying Integers**

To find the diver's position relative to sea level after 10 seconds, use the distance formula $d = rt$.

$d = rt$	Write the distance formula.
$d = -6(10)$	Substitute −6 for r and 10 for t.
$d = -60$	Different signs, so product is negative.

ANSWER The diver's position relative to sea level is −60 feet.

Your turn now **Use the information above.**

1. Find the diver's position relative to sea level after 13 seconds. −78 ft

ILLINOIS Standards and ISAT:
6.B.3a, 8.D.3a

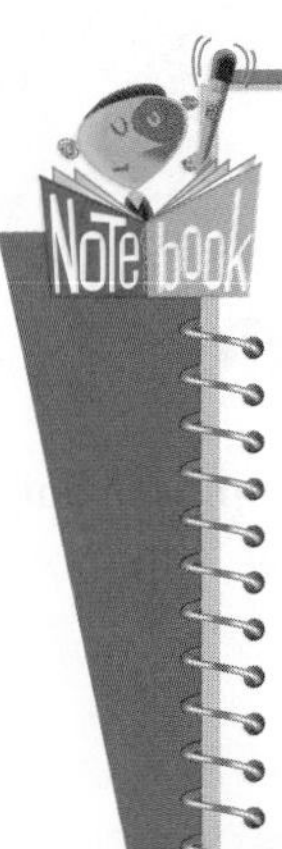

Multiplication Properties

Multiplication Property of Zero

Words The product of an integer and 0 is 0.

Numbers $-4 \cdot 0 = 0$ **Algebra** For any value of a, $a \cdot 0 = 0$.

Identity Property of Multiplication

Words The product of an integer and 1 is the integer.

Numbers $4(1) = 4$ **Algebra** For any value of a, $a(1) = a$.

When you multiply a number by -1, the product is the *opposite* of the original number.

with Solving

When you multiply more than two positive or negative integers:

- If there is an *even* number of negative factors then the product is *positive*.
- If there is an *odd* number of negative factors then the product is *negative*.

EXAMPLE 2 Multiplying Two or More Integers

a. $-1(6) = -6$ — Different signs, so product is negative.

b. $-8(-2) = 16$ — Same sign, so product is positive.

c. $-15(0) = 0$ — Product of an integer and 0 is 0.

d. $4(-10)(-12) = -40(-12)$ — Multiply from left to right.

$= 480$ — Multiply.

EXAMPLE 3 Evaluating an Expression with Integers

Evaluate $a^2 + 3b$ when $a = -5$ and $b = -11$.

$a^2 + 3b = (-5)^2 + 3(-11)$ — Substitute -5 for a and -11 for b.

$= 25 + 3(-11)$ — Evaluate the power.

$= 25 + (-33)$ — Multiply.

$= -8$ — Add.

Your turn now **Find the product.**

2. $-1(4)$ -4 **3.** $7(0)$ 0 **4.** $-6(-11)$ 66 **5.** $-1(-12)(-9)$ -108

Evaluate the expression when $a = 3$, $b = -4$ and $c = -8$.

6. $ac - b$ -20 **7.** $ac + b$ -28 **8.** $a^2 + bc$ 41 **9.** $ab - c^2$ -76

EXTRA EXAMPLES

Example 1 A hiker begins a descent from a mountain peak. The hiker's elevation with respect to the top of the peak is changing at a rate of -800 feet every half hour. What is the hiker's elevation with respect to the top of the peak after 3 hours? **-4800 ft**

Example 2 Multiply.

a. $-2(12)$ **-24**

b. $-6(-7)$ **42**

c. $0(-17)$ **0**

d. $3(-8)(-4)$ **96**

Example 3 Evaluate $c^2 + 5d$ when $c = -7$ and $d = -14$. **-21**

CONCEPT CHECK

When multiplying two or more integers, how can you tell if the product is positive, negative, or zero? **If the number of negative integers is even, the product is positive. If the number of negative integers is odd, the product is negative. If any of the integers is zero, the product is zero.**

DAILY PUZZLER

Find the value of x if $5 \cdot (-2) \cdot x \cdot (-3) = 0$. **0**

ASSIGNMENT GUIDE

Basic Course

Day 1: SRH p. 727 Exs. 14-16; pp. 72-73 Exs. 10-21, 45-48

Day 2: pp. 72-73 Exs. 22-31, 49-54

Average Course

Day 1: pp. 72-73 Exs. 14-21, 45-52

Day 2: pp. 72-73 Exs. 24-37, 53, 54

Advanced Course

Day 1: pp. 72-73 Exs. 18-21, 44-48*, 53, 54

Day 2: pp. 72-73 Exs. 24, 25, 29-43

Block

pp. 72-73 Exs. 14-21, 24-37, 45-54

EXTRA PRACTICE

- Student Edition, p. 728
- Chapter 2 Resource Book, pp. 38-40
- Test and Practice Generator

TRANSPARENCY

Even-numbered answers are available on transparencies.

HOMEWORK CHECK

When you review students' homework for this lesson, go over the following exercises to check understanding of key concepts.

Basic: 10, 12, 13, 18, 22

Average: 14, 16, 20, 21, 23

Advanced: 18, 20, 21, 24, 25

2.4 Exercises

More Practice, p. 728

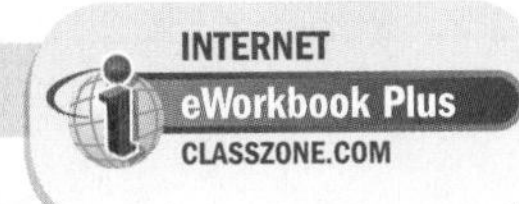

Getting Ready to Practice

1. **Vocabulary** Copy and complete: The product of a positive integer and a negative integer is a _?_ integer. **negative**

Find the product.

2. $-4(-7)$ **28**
3. $0(-9)$ **0**
4. $-3(6)$ **−18**
5. $-1(-2)(-3)$ **−6**
6. $2(-4)(5)$ **−40**
7. $10(-9)(-3)$ **270**
8. **Banking** You have \$500 in a savings account. Over a 2 month period, you make 9 withdrawals of \$30 each. What is your new balance? **\$230**
9. **Find the Error** Describe and correct the error in the solution. **The product of two negative integers is positive; $-8(-12) = 96$.**

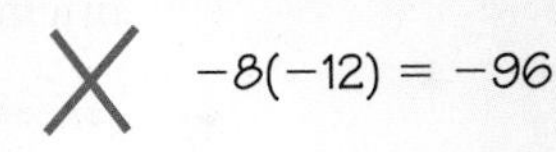

Practice and Problem Solving

HELP with Homework

Example	Exercises
1	10-21
2	10-21
3	22-25

Online Resources CLASSZONE.COM
- More Examples
- eTutorial Plus

A Find the product.

10. $-6(7)$ **−42**
11. $-1(-17)$ **17**
12. $0(-13)$ **0**
13. $-4(-11)$ **44**
14. $9(-2)$ **−18**
15. $3(-5)$ **−15**
16. $-15(-12)$ **180**
17. $-1(-32)$ **32**
18. $-2(5)(-6)$ **60**
19. $6(-4)(12)$ **−288**
20. $-8(-7)(-5)$ **−280**
21. $12(0)(-45)$ **0**

Evaluate the expression when $x = -9$, $y = -7$, and $z = -4$.

22. $xy + z$ **59**
23. $xy - y$ **70**
24. $2xyz$ **−504**
25. $-3xy + 2yz$ **−133**

B Find the product.

26. $|-2| \cdot 5$ **10**
27. $-12 \cdot |11|$ **−132**
28. $-7(-8) \cdot |-4|$ **224**

Mental Math Use mental math to solve the equation.

29. $2x = -8$ **−4**
30. $-21y = 63$ **−3**
31. $-5(-4)z = -80$ **−4**
32. **Video Game** David is playing a video game. If he falls into a pit, he loses 125 points. If he collects coins, he will gain points. He has 400 points before he falls into 3 pits. After he collects a coin in each pit, his score is 175 points. How many points is each coin worth? **50 points**
33. **Look for a Pattern** Evaluate $(-10)^1$, $(-10)^2$, $(-10)^3$, $(-10)^4$, and $(-10)^5$. How is the exponent related to the sign of the power? **The power is positive when the exponent is even and negative when the exponent is odd.**

34. **Critical Thinking** Does $(-3)^2$ equal -3^2? Explain your reasoning. No; $(-3)^2 = (-3)(-3) = 9$ and $-3^2 = -(3 \cdot 3) = -9$.

Evaluate the expression when $a = -8$ and $b = -11$.

35. $-a(-a)$ 64
36. $a(-b^2)b$ −10,648
37. $[a + (-a)b]^2$ 9216

38. **Check for Reasonableness** A coconut falls 100 feet from a palm tree. The equation $h = -16t^2 + 100$ gives the height h, in feet, of the coconut after falling for t seconds. Evaluate the equation when t equals 2, 2.5, and 3 seconds. When does the coconut hit the ground? What is the actual height of the coconut after 3 seconds? 36 ft, 0 ft, −44 ft; at 2.5 sec; 0 ft

39. **Stock Market** Your uncle owns 25 shares of stock A, 45 shares of stock B, and 60 shares of stock C. In one day, the price per share changed by +\$.56 for stock A, −\$1.46 for stock B, and −\$.50 for stock C. Find the total change in value of your uncle's stock. −\$81.70

C **Evaluate the expression when $w = -31$, $y = 52$, and $z = -63$.**

40. wyz 101,556
41. $yz - wyz$ −104,832
42. $3yz - wy$ −8216
43. $-2wy - 2wz$ −682

44. **Challenge** The product of a number and its *multiplicative inverse* is 1. For example, $4 \cdot \frac{1}{4} = 1$, so 4 and $\frac{1}{4}$ are multiplicative inverses. Give an example of a negative number and its multiplicative inverse. *Sample answer:* −4 and $-\frac{1}{4}$

Mixed Review

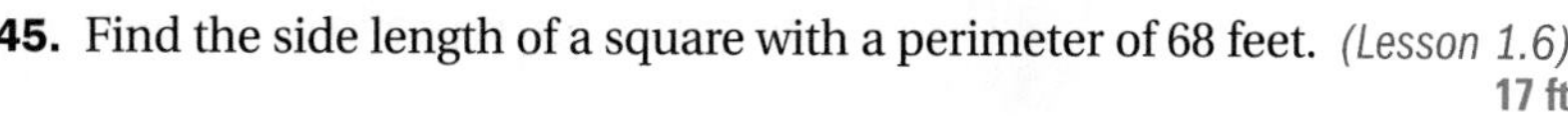

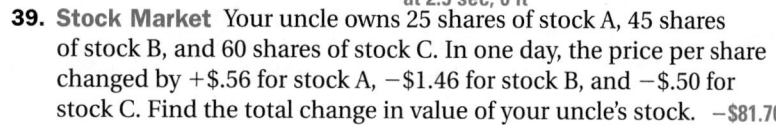

45. Find the side length of a square with a perimeter of 68 feet. *(Lesson 1.6)* 17 ft

Find the difference. *(Lesson 2.3)*

46. $5 - 7$ −2
47. $-9 - 14$ −23
48. $-23 - (-12)$ −11

Basic Skills **Find the quotient.**

49. $75 \div 5$ 15
50. $0 \div 12$ 0
51. $34 \div 17$ 2
52. $63 \div 7$ 9

Test-Taking Practice

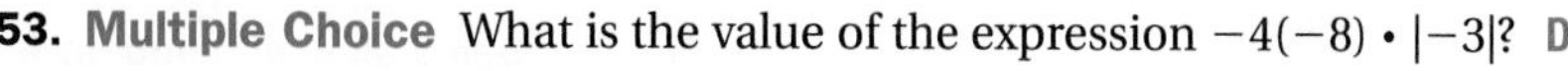

INTERNET
State Test Practice
CLASSZONE.COM

53. **Multiple Choice** What is the value of the expression $-4(-8) \cdot |-3|$? D

A. −96 **B.** −36 **C.** 12 **D.** 96

54. **Multiple Choice** When you multiply an integer less than 1 and an integer less than −1, the product is which of the following? I

F. less than zero **G.** greater than zero

H. less than or equal to zero **I.** greater than or equal to zero

4 ASSESS

Assessment Resources

For more assessment resources, see:
- Assessment Book
- Test and Practice Generator

Mini-Quiz

Find the product.

1. $-12(6)$ **−72**
2. $-5(-6)$ **30**
3. $4(-13)(2)$ **−104**
4. $-11(4)(-3)$ **132**

Evaluate the expression when $a = -5$, $b = 6$, and $c = -8$.

5. $ab - bc$ **18**
6. $bc + a^2$ **−23**
7. A propane tank contains 400 gallons of propane. The amount in the tank is changing at −7 gallons per day. At this rate, how much propane will be in the tank at the end of 3 weeks? **253 gal**

5 FOLLOW-UP

Reteaching/Remediation

- Study Guide in Chapter 2 Resource Book, pp. 41–42
- Tutor Place, Algebra Card 4
- eTutorial Plus Online
- Extra Practice, p. 728
- Lesson Practice in Chapter 2 Resource Book, pp. 38–40

Challenge/Enrichment

- Challenge Practice in Chapter 2 Resource Book, p. 43
- Teacher's Edition, p. 50F

English Learner Support

- Spanish Study Guide
- Multi-Language Glossary
- Chapter Audio Summaries CDs

PLAN

SKILL CHECK

Find the quotient.

1. $\frac{48}{8}$ 6
2. $\frac{108}{6}$ 18
3. $\frac{5(14)}{7}$ 10
4. $\frac{-23 + 53}{5}$ 6

LESSON OBJECTIVE

Divide integers.

PACING

Suggested Number of Days

Basic Course: 1 day

Average Course: 1 day

Advanced Course: 1 day

Block: 0.5 block with 2.6

TEACHING RESOURCES

For a complete list of Teaching Resources, see page 50B.

TRANSPARENCY

Warm-Up Exercises for this lesson are available on a transparency.

TEACH

MOTIVATING THE LESSON

Have students find other cities near the Arctic Circle on a map. Then have them find the winter average high temperatures for those cities.

Dividing Integers

BEFORE	Now	WHY?
You added, subtracted, and multiplied integers.	You'll divide integers.	So you can convert temperatures, as in Ex. 31.

Word Watch

mean, p. 75

In the Real World

Temperatures One of the coldest places on Earth is the Russian town of Verkhoyansk, located near the Arctic Circle. The table shows the average high temperatures in Verkhoyansk. What is the average of these temperatures?

Winter Temperatures

Month	Average High
December	−44°F
January	−48°F
February	−38°F
March	−7°F

You will use the rules for dividing integers to find an average temperature in Example 2. These rules are similar to the rules for multiplying integers.

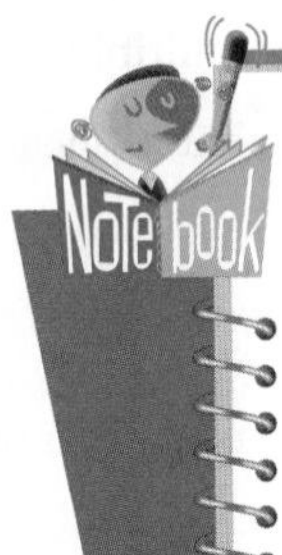

Dividing Integers

Words	Numbers	
The quotient of two integers with the same sign is positive.	$\frac{12}{6} = 2$	$\frac{-12}{-6} = 2$
The quotient of two integers with different signs is negative.	$\frac{12}{-6} = -2$	$\frac{-12}{6} = -2$
The quotient of zero and any nonzero integer is 0.	$\frac{0}{12} = 0$	$\frac{0}{-12} = 0$

Watch Out!

You cannot divide a number by 0. Any number divided by 0 is *undefined*.

EXAMPLE 1 Dividing Integers

a. $\frac{-40}{-8} = 5$ Same sign, so quotient is positive.

b. $\frac{-14}{2} = -7$ Different signs, so quotient is negative.

c. $\frac{36}{-9} = -4$ Different signs, so quotient is negative.

ILLINOIS Standards and ISAT:
6.B.3a, 8.D.3a, 8.D.3b

■ **Temperatures**

One of the lowest temperatures on Earth, -90°F, was recorded in Verkhoyansk, Russia, on February 7, 1892. How much colder is this than today's temperature where you live? **Check work.**

The **mean** of a data set is the sum of the values divided by the number of values.

$$\text{mean} = \frac{\text{sum of values}}{\text{number of values}}$$

EXAMPLE 2 Finding a Mean

Temperatures To find the mean of the monthly average high temperatures in Verkhoyansk, Russia, given on page 74, first find the sum of the temperatures.

$-44 + (-48) + (-38) + (-7) = -137$

Then, divide the sum by the number of temperatures.

$\frac{-137}{4} = -34.25$

ANSWER The mean of the temperatures is about -34°F.

Your turn now **Find the quotient.**

1. $\frac{-33}{11}$ **−3**
2. $\frac{-25}{-5}$ **5**
3. $\frac{0}{-4}$ **0**
4. $\frac{72}{-9}$ **−8**

Find the mean of the data.

5. −16, 17, 8, −23, −31 **−9**
6. 0, −4, −10, 4, 11 −9, −13 **−3**
7. −9, 26, −78, −40, −34 **−27**
8. −7, −2, −12, 15, −8, −25, −17 **−8**

EXAMPLE 3 Evaluating Expressions

Evaluate the expression when $a = -24$, $b = 8$, and $c = -4$.

a. $\frac{a}{b}$

b. $\frac{ab}{c}$

Solution

a. $\frac{a}{b} = \frac{-24}{8}$ **Substitute values.**

$= -3$ **Different signs, so quotient is negative.**

b. $\frac{ab}{c} = \frac{-24 \cdot 8}{-4}$ **Substitute values.**

$= \frac{-192}{-4}$ **Multiply.**

$= 48$ **Same sign, so quotient is positive.**

TIPS FOR NEW TEACHERS

Stress that the sign rules for division are the same as the sign rules for multiplication. Reassure students that the only thing new in the lesson is the use of division. See Tips for New Teachers in the *Chapter 2 Resource Book.*

EXTRA EXAMPLES

Example 1 Divide.

a. $\frac{-50}{-10}$ **5**

b. $\frac{-72}{9}$ **−8**

c. $\frac{60}{-12}$ **−5**

Example 2 Panya played five rounds of a card game. Her scores were −50, 41, −50, 32, and 22. Find the mean of her scores. **−1**

Example 3 Evaluate the expression when $d = -16$, $e = 8$, and $f = -2$.

a. $\frac{d}{e}$ **−2**

b. $\frac{ef}{d}$ **1**

CONCEPT CHECK

What sign does the quotient of two integers with different signs have? **negative**

DAILY PUZZLER

What is $\frac{32}{16}$? What is $\frac{32}{\frac{16}{8}}$? What is $\frac{\frac{32}{\frac{16}{8}}}{4}$? **2; 16; 1**

ASSIGNMENT GUIDE

Basic Course
Day 1: SRH p. 717 Exs. 2, 3; pp. 76-77 Exs. 11-25, 35-42

Average Course
Day 1: pp. 76-77 Exs. 15-30, 35-42

Advanced Course
Day 1: pp. 76-77 Exs. 16-21, 24-42*

Block
pp. 76-77 Exs. 15-30, 35-42 (with 2.6)

EXTRA PRACTICE

- Student Edition, p. 728
- Chapter 2 Resource Book, pp. 47-49
- Test and Practice Generator

TRANSPARENCY

Even-numbered answers are available on transparencies.

HOMEWORK CHECK

When you review students' homework for this lesson, go over the following exercises to check understanding of key concepts.
Basic: 11, 13, 19, 22, 23
Average: 15, 17, 20, 23, 24
Advanced: 16, 18, 24, 25, 26

TEACHING TIP

In Exercises 32-34, remind students that the normal order of operations rules apply. Remind them that the fraction bar acts as a grouping symbol so that the numerator and denominator are each simplified as though they were enclosed in parentheses or brackets.

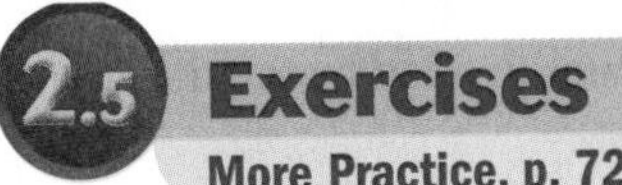

2.5 Exercises

More Practice, p. 728

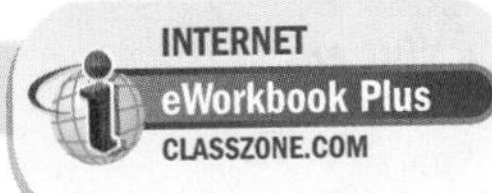

Getting Ready to Practice

1. **Vocabulary** Copy and complete: To find the _?_ of three numbers, add them and divide the sum by three. mean

Find the quotient.

2. $\frac{-44}{4}$ −11
3. $\frac{0}{-7}$ 0
4. $\frac{-81}{-9}$ 9
5. $\frac{50}{-10}$ −5

Evaluate the expression when $x = 18$, $y = -12$, and $z = -6$.

6. $\frac{y}{z}$ 2
7. $\frac{x}{z}$ −3
8. $\frac{xz}{y}$ 9
9. $\frac{z^2}{y}$ −3

10. **Guided Problem Solving** Will opened a used musical instrument shop. The table shows his profits for the first three months. Find his mean profit for these months.

Month	Profit
October	−\$172
November	−\$203
December	\$157

(1) Add the profits. −\$218
(2) Count the number of months given. 3 mo
(3) Divide the sum in Step 1 by the number in Step 2. Should you give an exact or approximate answer? −\$72.67; approximate

Practice and Problem Solving

A Find the quotient.

11. $\frac{-42}{-6}$ 7
12. $\frac{-28}{2}$ −14
13. $\frac{36}{-4}$ −9
14. $\frac{-19}{-1}$ 19
15. $\frac{-49}{-7}$ 7
16. $\frac{-66}{-11}$ 6
17. $\frac{0}{-18}$ 0
18. $\frac{-27}{0}$ undefined

Find the mean of the data.

19. −12, 5, −9, 10, 16, −8, −2, 8 1
20. 4, −3, −8, 7, −1, 4, −2, −9, −1 −1
21. **Writing** Is the mean of a set of negative numbers *always*, *sometimes*, or *never* negative? Give an example to support your reasoning.
Always. *Sample answer:* The mean of −3, −5, and −1 is $\frac{-9}{3} = -3$.

B Evaluate the expression when $m = 16$, $n = -8$, and $p = -32$.

22. $\frac{m}{n}$ −2
23. $\frac{p}{n}$ 4
24. $\frac{n^2}{m}$ 4
25. $\frac{p}{n+m}$ −4

HELP with Homework

Example	Exercises
1	11-18, 27-30
2	19-20, 26
3	22-25

Online Resources
CLASSZONE.COM
· More Examples
· eTutorial Plus

26. **Track and Field** In five trial runs of a 100 meter dash, a runner has times of 14.01, 15.27, 16.17, 14.42, and 15.01 seconds. The table shows the time differences between the team average, in seconds, and the runner's times. Find the mean of the differences between the team average and the runner's times. −0.544 sec

Trial	Difference
1	−1.51
2	−0.25
3	0.65
4	−1.1
5	−0.51

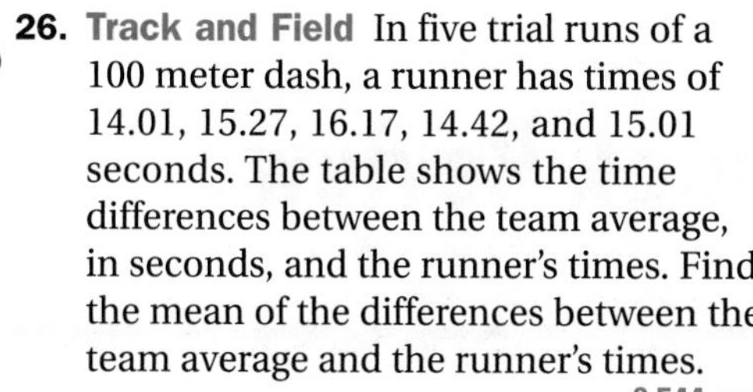

Find the quotient.

27. $\frac{-9}{6}$ −1.5 28. $\frac{15}{-12}$ −1.25 29. $\frac{-8}{-10}$ 0.8 30. $\frac{-6}{-30}$ 0.2

31. **Reindeer** The natural habitat of a reindeer is the Arctic tundra. The average temperature during the winter in the Arctic tundra is −34°C. You can convert degrees Celsius C to degrees Fahrenheit F by using the formula $F = \frac{9}{5}C + 32$. What is the average winter Arctic tundra temperature in degrees Fahrenheit? −29.2°F

C **Challenge** **Evaluate the expression when $a = -15$, $b = 50$, and $c = 20$.**

32. $\frac{b^2 + c}{c^2 a}$ −0.42 33. $\frac{-2(a^2 + c^2)}{b}$ −25 34. $\frac{(b + c)^2}{a}$ −326.7, or $-326\frac{2}{3}$

Mixed Review

Write the product as a power. *(Lesson 1.4)*

35. $5 \cdot 5 \cdot 5 \cdot 5 \cdot 5$ 5^5 36. $8 \cdot 8 \cdot 8 \cdot 8 \cdot 8 \cdot 8$ 8^6 37. $b \cdot b \cdot b \cdot b$ b^4

Find the product. *(Lesson 2.4)*

38. −11(−8) 88 39. 12(−6) −72 40. 6(−8)(−2) 96

Test-Taking Practice

INTERNET
State Test Practice
CLASSZONE.COM

41. **Multiple Choice** When you multiply the quotient of a negative integer and a positive integer by −1, what is the sign of the product? B

A. negative **B.** positive **C.** zero **D.** cannot be determined

42. **Short Response** The table shows the temperatures in Fairbanks, Alaska. Calculate the mean temperature. Show your work or explain in words how you determined the mean. Should you give an exact or approximate answer?

About −17°F. *Sample answer:* [−8 + (−1) + (−6) + (−21) + (−31) + (−34)] ÷ 6 = −16.83... ≈ −17; approximate.

Day	Temperature
Monday	−8°F
Tuesday	−1°F
Wednesday	−6°F
Thursday	−21°F
Friday	−31°F
Saturday	−34°F

4 ASSESS

Assessment Resources

For more assessment resources, see:
- Assessment Book
- Test and Practice Generator

Mini-Quiz

Find the quotient.

1. $\frac{-16}{-4}$ 4
2. $\frac{-96}{48}$ −2
3. $\frac{-33}{0}$ undefined

Evaluate the expression when $k = -36$, $m = 6$, and $n = 3$.

4. $\frac{mn}{k}$ $-\frac{1}{2}$
5. $\frac{k}{m + n}$ −4
6. $\frac{m^2 + 4n^2}{2k}$ −1

5 FOLLOW-UP

Reteaching/Remediation

- Study Guide in Chapter 2 Resource Book, pp. 50–51
- Tutor Place, Whole Numbers and Decimals Card 19, Algebra Card 4
- eTutorial Plus Online
- Extra Practice, p. 728
- Lesson Practice in Chapter 2 Resource Book, pp. 47–49

Challenge/Enrichment

- Challenge Practice in Chapter 2 Resource Book, p. 53
- Teacher's Edition, p. 50F

English Learner Support

- Spanish Study Guide
- Multi-Language Glossary
- Chapter Audio Summaries CDs

ADDITIONAL RESOURCES

The following resources are available to help review the materials in Lessons 2.1–2.5.

Chapter 2 Resource Book
- Lesson Practice
- Study Guide

Assessment Book
- Chapter 2 Quiz 1

Technology
- Test and Practice Generator
- eTutorial CD-ROM

Internet
- Classzone
- eWorkbook Plus Online
- eTutorial Plus Online

ENGLISH LEARNER SUPPORT

- Spanish Study Guide
- Multi-Language Glossary
- Chapter Audio Summaries CDs

1. 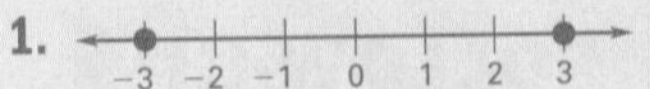

Notebook Review

Review the vocabulary definitions in your notebook.

Copy the review examples in your notebook. Then complete the exercises.

Check Your Definitions

integer, p. 53	positive integer, p. 53	opposite, p. 54
negative integer, p. 53	absolute value, p. 54	mean, p. 75

Use Your Vocabulary

1. Draw a number line. Label three positive integers and three negative integers. Graph the two integers that have an absolute value of 3. See margin.

2.1 Can you graph and order integers?

EXAMPLE Order the integers from least to greatest: 24, −6, −45, 0, 12, −20, −32.

In order from least to greatest: −45, −32, −20, −6, 0, 12, 24

Use a number line to order the integers from least to greatest.

2. −15, 16, 1, −5, 4, 8 **−15, −5, 1, 4, 8, 16**

3. 40, −60, 98, −85, −6, 42 **−85, −60, −6, 40, 42, 98**

2.2–2.3 Can you add and subtract integers?

EXAMPLE Find the sum or difference.

a. $-22 + (-18) = -40$ **Same sign, so sum has common sign.**

b. $19 - 34 = 19 + (-34)$ **Add the opposite of 34.**

$= -15$ **Add.**

Find the sum or difference.

4. $-26 + 64$ **38**
5. $37 + (-92)$ **−55**
6. $-41 + (-78)$ **−119**
7. $16 - 82$ **−66**
8. $-51 - 14$ **−65**
9. $-44 - (-29)$ **−15**

2.4–2.5 Can you multiply and divide integers?

EXAMPLE Find the product or quotient.

a. $-7 \cdot 6 = -42$ **Different signs, so product is negative.**

b. $\frac{-56}{-7} = 8$ **Same sign, so quotient is positive.**

Find the product or quotient.

10. $(-52)(-6)$ 312 **11.** $31(-2)$ −62 **12.** $\frac{-90}{15}$ −6 **13.** $\frac{-52}{-13}$ 4

Stop and Think about Lessons 2.1–2.5

14. Critical Thinking Is the opposite of the sum of two numbers equal to the sum of the opposites of the numbers? Explain.

14. Yes. *Sample answer:* The opposite of the sum can be written as $-1(a + b)$. Using the distributive property you get $-a + (-b)$, which is the sum of the opposites.

Review Quiz 1

Copy and complete the statement with < or >.

1. $-8 \underline{?} 8$ < **2.** $0 \underline{?} -14$ > **3.** $-20 \underline{?} -30$ > **4.** $-7 \underline{?} 5$ <

Evaluate the expression.

5. $-6 + 1$ −5 **6.** $-20 + (-10)$ −30 **7.** $-4 - (-3)$ −1

8. $-6(-8)$ 48 **9.** $-12(4)$ −48 **10.** $\frac{-48}{-8}$ 6

Find the mean of the data.

11. −9, −15, 16, 4, 2, −10, 8, 20 2 **12.** −10, 6, −11, −6, −7, 3, −4, 1, 1 −3

13. 8, −9, −13, 5, −4, −3, −5 −3 **14.** 5, −6, −10, −15, 7, 9, −1, −3, 4 $-1.\overline{1}$

Evaluate the expression when $a = -2$, $b = 10$, and $c = -3$.

15. $b - a$ 12 **16.** $a - c - b$ −9 **17.** abc 60 **18.** $\frac{b}{a}$ −5

19. 128 ft, 80 ft, 0 ft, −112 ft; at 3 sec

19. Gravity You drop a ball out of a window that is 144 feet above the ground. The equation $h = -16t^2 + 144$ gives the height h, in feet, of the ball after falling for t seconds. Find the height of the ball after 1, 2, 3, and 4 seconds. When does the ball hit the ground?

PLAN

SKILL CHECK

1. $12(5)(-3) = \underline{?}$ -180
2. $15 - 36 + (-4) = \underline{?}$ -25
3. $-4(16 - 18) = \underline{?}$ 8
4. $-47(1)(0) = \underline{?}$ 0

LESSON OBJECTIVE

Use properties to evaluate expressions.

PACING

Suggested Number of Days
Basic Course: 1 day
Average Course: 1 day
Advanced Course: 1 day
Block: 0.5 block with 2.5

TEACHING RESOURCES

For a complete list of Teaching Resources, see page 50B.

TRANSPARENCY

Warm-Up Exercises for this lesson are available on a transparency.

TEACH

MOTIVATING THE LESSON

Ask students the farthest distance that they have bicycled. You might point out that Lance Armstrong won the 2002 Tour de France, which covered about 2032 miles in 20 days, with a total riding time of about 82 hours at an average speed of about 24.75 miles per hour.

Number Properties

BEFORE	Now	WHY?
You evaluated expressions.	You'll use properties to evaluate expressions.	So you can find your weekly pay, as in Ex. 39.

Word Watch

Review Words

sum, p. 709
product, p. 713

In the Real World

Tour Biking You are going on a 400 mile bike trip. You plan to cycle at an average speed of 12 miles per hour for 7 hours a day. Can you complete the trip in 5 days?

The commutative properties of addition and multiplication can be used to make evaluating expressions using mental math easier.

Notebook: The Commutative Property

	Addition	Multiplication
Words	You can add numbers of a sum in any order.	You can multiply factors of a product in any order.
Numbers	$3 + (-8) = -8 + 3$	$5(-6) = -6(5)$
Algebra	$a + b = b + a$	$ab = ba$

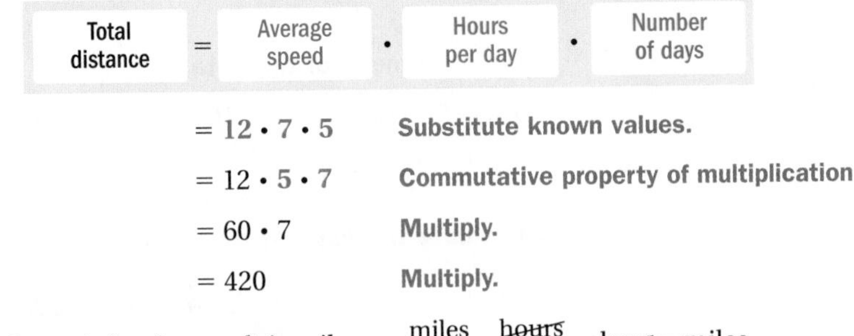

EXAMPLE 1 Using the Commutative Property

To find if you can complete the bike trip in 5 days, find the total distance you plan to cycle. Then compare that distance to the length of the trip.

Total distance = Average speed • Hours per day • Number of days

$= 12 \cdot 7 \cdot 5$ **Substitute known values.**

$= 12 \cdot 5 \cdot 7$ **Commutative property of multiplication**

$= 60 \cdot 7$ **Multiply.**

$= 420$ **Multiply.**

The unit for the result is miles. $\frac{\text{miles}}{\cancel{\text{hour}}} \cdot \frac{\cancel{\text{hours}}}{\cancel{\text{day}}} \cdot \cancel{\text{days}} = \text{miles}$

ANSWER Because 400 miles is less than the 420 miles you can travel in 5 days, you can complete the trip in 5 days.

ILLINOIS Standards and ISAT:
6.B.3a, 8.A.3a; 7.C.3b

with Solving

When deciding what numbers to add or multiply first, look for pairs whose sum or product ends in zero, because multiples of 10 are easier to work with.

Subtracting a number is the same as adding the opposite, so you can write expressions to use the commutative property of addition.

EXAMPLE 2 **Using the Commutative Property**

$-54 + 35 - 16 = -54 + 35 + (-16)$ — Change subtraction to addition

$= -54 + (-16) + 35$ — Commutative property of addition

$= -70 + 35$ — Add -54 and -16.

$= -35$ — Add -70 and -35.

Your turn now **Use the commutative property to evaluate.**

1. $2 \cdot (-9) \cdot 5$ -90 **2.** $47 + (-99) - (-53)$ 1 **3.** $94 - 56 - 44$ -6

The associative properties of addition and multiplication can also be used to make evaluating expressions using mental math easier.

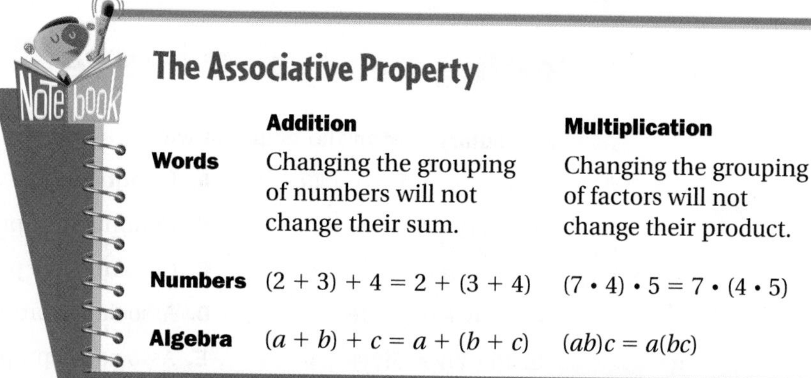

The Associative Property

	Addition	Multiplication
Words	Changing the grouping of numbers will not change their sum.	Changing the grouping of factors will not change their product.
Numbers	$(2 + 3) + 4 = 2 + (3 + 4)$	$(7 \cdot 4) \cdot 5 = 7 \cdot (4 \cdot 5)$
Algebra	$(a + b) + c = a + (b + c)$	$(ab)c = a(bc)$

EXAMPLE 3 **Using the Associative Property**

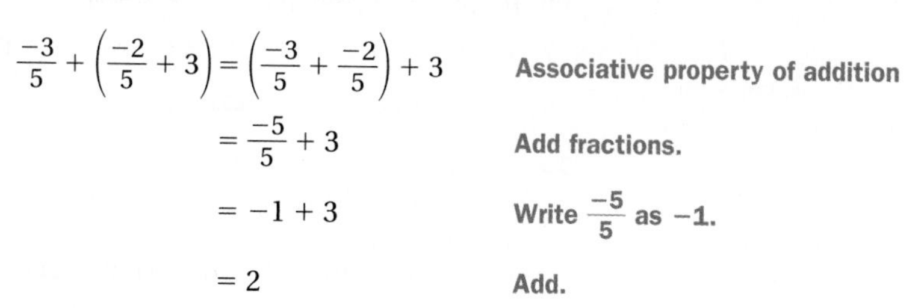

$\frac{-3}{5} + \left(\frac{-2}{5} + 3\right) = \left(\frac{-3}{5} + \frac{-2}{5}\right) + 3$ — Associative property of addition

$= \frac{-5}{5} + 3$ — Add fractions.

$= -1 + 3$ — Write $\frac{-5}{5}$ as -1.

$= 2$ — Add.

HELP with Review

Grouping fractions and adding them makes mental math easier. For help adding fractions with common denominators, see p. 710.

TIPS FOR NEW TEACHERS

Point out to students the relationship of "commutative" to "commute," as in "move," and of "associative" as in "associate," or "group" or "hang around with." See Tips for New Teachers in the *Chapter 2 Resource Book*.

EXTRA EXAMPLES

Example 1 If a trucker drove at an average speed of 50 miles per hour for 7 hours a day for 20 days, what is the total distance covered? **7000 mi**

Example 2 Evaluate.
$4 \cdot (-8) \cdot 5$ **-160**

Example 3 Evaluate.
$\frac{7}{8} + \left(-\frac{3}{8} + 6\right)$ **$6\frac{1}{2}$**

VISUALIZE

Write some numbers and operators on notecards and model expressions with them. Have students rearrange the cards to model the commutative and associative properties. Have them notice when it is beneficial to use these properties, for example, to rearrange $17 + 24 + 33 + 46$ so that pairs of addends have sums that are multiples of 10, or to rearrange $25(46)(4)$ so that the product of two factors is 100.

MULTIPLE REPRESENTATIONS

In the boxes for The Commutative Property and The Associative Property, point out that the words, numbers, and algebra are all describing the same property in different ways. Encourage each student to record the properties in the form that makes the most sense to her or him.

EXTRA EXAMPLES

Example 4 Evaluate $(4 \cdot 13) \cdot 5$ using mental math. **260**

Differentiating Instruction

Advanced Students For some students, the properties may seem so obvious that they have difficulty understanding why they deserve so much attention. Have these students examine why the properties do not apply to subtraction and division. Point out, for example, that $4 - 8 \neq 8 - 4$ because the first expression can be rewritten as $4 + (-8)$ and the second as $8 + (-4)$. So, the pairs of addends are not the same.

CONCEPT CHECK

Why are the commutative and associative properties useful? **They simplify addition and multiplication with multiple numbers or factors.**

DAILY PUZZLER

Using the commutative and associative properties, how can you find the sum 1 + 2 + 3 + ... + 100 without adding all the numbers? **(1 + 100) + (2 + 99) + (3 + 98) + ... + (50 + 51) = 101(50) = 5050**

with Vocabulary

Commute means change locations. You can use the *commutative properties* to change the order of numbers.
Associate means group together. You can use the *associative properties* to group numbers differently.

EXAMPLE 4 Using the Associative Property

$5 \cdot (11 \cdot 2) = 5 \cdot (2 \cdot 11)$	Commutative property of multiplication
$= (5 \cdot 2) \cdot 11$	Associative property of multiplication
$= 10 \cdot 11$	Multiply inside grouping symbols.
$= 110$	Multiply.

Your turn now Evaluate the expression using mental math.

4. $18 + (-34 + 12)$ **−4** **5.** $46 + (-63 - 46)$ **−63** **6.** $-2(46 \cdot 50)$ **−4600**

7. $4\left(\frac{1}{4} \cdot 23\right)$ **23** **8.** $\frac{3}{7} + \left(8 + \frac{4}{7}\right)$ **9** **9.** $[-21 \cdot (-29)] \cdot 0$ **0**

2.6 Exercises

More Practice, p. 728

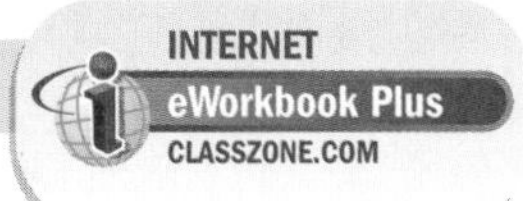

Getting Ready to Practice

Vocabulary **Match the equation with the property it illustrates.**

1. $(x + 9) + 1 = x + (9 + 1)$ **E**	**A.** Identity property of addition
2. $12(1) = 12$ **F**	**B.** Commutative property of multiplication
3. $8a = a \cdot 8$ **B**	**C.** Commutative property of addition
4. $-16 + 0 = -16$ **A**	**D.** Associative property of multiplication
5. $(5 \cdot 7)y = 5(7y)$ **D**	**E.** Associative property of addition
6. $-24 + a = a + (-24)$ **C**	**F.** Identity property of multiplication

Mental Math **Evaluate the expression using mental math. Name the property or properties you used.**

7. $17 + 15 + 13$ **8.** $43 + (-27) - 13$ **9.** $5 \cdot (-29) \cdot 2$

10. $-2(-9 \cdot 50)$ **11.** $-53 + (-27 + 44)$ **12.** $[-4 \cdot (-7)](-5)$

13. Juice Box You have a juice box that is 2.5 inches long, 1.5 inches wide, and 4 inches high. The formula for the *volume* of a box is $V = lwh$. How much juice is in the box, in cubic inches? **15 in.^{3}**

7. 45; commutative and associative properties of addition
8. 3; associative property of addition
9. −290; commutative and associative properties of multiplication
10. 900; commutative and associative properties of multiplication
11. −36; associative property of addition
12. −140; commutative and associative properties of multiplication

Practice and Problem Solving

Example **Exercises**

Example	Exercises
1	14-29, 32
2	14-26
3	14-26
4	14-26

Online Resources
CLASSZONE.COM
· More Examples
· eTutorial Plus

A **Use the properties of addition and multiplication to find the missing number. Name the property.** 14–17. See margin.

14. $28 + \underline{?} = 65 + 28$ **15.** $54 \cdot 16 = 16 \cdot \underline{?}$

16. $(7 \cdot 3)3 = \underline{?}\,(3 \cdot 3)$ **17.** $4 + (\underline{?} + 2) = (4 + 9) + 2$

Evaluate the expression. Justify each step. 18–26. Check justifications.

18. $-86 + 29 + (-34)$ -91 **19.** $45 - (-68) - 44$ 69 **20.** $-57 - 38 - (-57)$ -38

21. $12 + (-39 + 48)$ 21 **22.** $(-26 + 33) + (-4)$ 3 **23.** $[25 \cdot (-7)]4$ -700

24. $-40\left(\frac{1}{2} \cdot 45\right)$ -900 **25.** $(-20 \cdot 9) \cdot 5$ -900 **26.** $(3.2 \cdot 4.5)(10)$ 144

Algebra **Simplify the expression.**

27. $7 \cdot x \cdot 10$ $70x$ **28.** $-67 + [x + (-13)]$ $-80 + x$ **29.** $(52 + x) + 18$ $70 + x$

30. Writing You need to find the sum of 52, 99, 65, 38, and 11. Explain how the commutative and associative properties of addition can help you find the sum using mental math. See margin.

31. Critical Thinking Is division commutative? Justify your answer with an example. No. *Sample answer:* $20 \div 4 = 5$, but $4 \div 20 = 0.2$.

32. Super Bowl During Super Bowl XXXVI, six New England Patriots rushed the football for 92 yards, 22 yards, 15 yards, 5 yards, 3 yards, and -4 yards. What was the total number of their rushing yards? 133 yd

B **Evaluate the expression. Show each step.** 33–38. Check steps.

33. $3.6 + 5.7 + (-3.6)$ 5.7 **34.** $\frac{1}{2} \cdot 17 \cdot 20$ 170 **35.** $5(7 \cdot 4)(0.25)$ 35

36. $\left(-\frac{2}{7} + 5\right) + \frac{3}{7}$ $5\frac{1}{7}$ **37.** $12 \cdot (7 \cdot 1 \cdot 5)$ 420 **38.** $\left(\frac{2}{3} \cdot 7\right) \cdot 21$ 98

39. Paycheck The table shows the hours you worked during one week. Your hourly wage is \$6 per hour. Use the commutative property of multiplication to find the amount you earned for the week. \$60

Time Card

Day	Time in	Time out
Monday	4 P.M.	6 P.M.
Tuesday	4 P.M.	6 P.M.
Wednesday	—	—
Thursday	3 P.M.	5 P.M.
Friday	3 P.M.	5 P.M.
Saturday	11 A.M.	1 P.M.

40. Compare Is the expression $-15 + 34 - 44 - 19 + 51$ equivalent to the expression $34 - 19 + 15 - 44 + 51$? Explain your reasoning.
No; 15 is positive in the second expression but negative in the first.

14. 65; commutative property of addition

15. 54; commutative property of multiplication

16. 7; associative property of multiplication

17. 9; associative property of addition

3 APPLY

ASSIGNMENT GUIDE

Basic Course
Day 1: pp. 83-84 Exs. 14-29, 32-35, 44-50

Average Course
Day 1: pp. 83-84 Exs. 20-40, 44-50

Advanced Course
Day 1: pp. 83-84 Exs. 22-45*, 49, 50

Block
pp. 83-84 Exs. 20-40, 44-50 (with 2.5)

EXTRA PRACTICE

- Student Edition, p. 728
- Chapter 2 Resource Book, pp. 56-58
- Test and Practice Generator

TRANSPARENCY

Even-numbered answers are available on transparencies.

HOMEWORK CHECK

When you review students' homework for this lesson, go over the following exercises to check understanding of key concepts.
Basic: 14, 18, 21, 24, 27
Average: 20, 22, 24, 26, 28
Advanced: 24, 26, 28, 29, 32

TEACHING TIP

Some students may be uncomfortable with the mix of variables and numbers in Exercises 27-29. Remind them that a variable just takes the place of a number, and so is treated just like a number in an expression.

30. See Additional Answers beginning on page AA1.

4 ASSESS

ASSESSMENT RESOURCES

For more assessment resources, see:

- Assessment Book
- Test and Practice Generator

MINI-QUIZ

Use the properties of addition and multiplication to find the missing number. Name the property.

1. $37 + \underline{?} = 96 + 37$
   96; comm. prop. of add.
2. $\frac{1}{5} \cdot (5 \cdot 7) = \left(\frac{1}{5} \cdot \underline{?}\right) \cdot 7$
   5; assoc. prop. of mult.
3. Evaluate the expression. Justify each step.
   $-23 - 84 - (-23)$
   -84; $-23 + (-84) + 23$ (Change subtr. to add.); $-23 + 23 + (-84)$ (comm. prop. of add.); $0 + (-84)$ (Add -23 and 23.); -84 (add. identity)

5 FOLLOW-UP

RETEACHING/REMEDIATION

- Study Guide in Chapter 2 Resource Book, pp. 59–60
- Tutor Place, Algebra Card 5
- eTutorial Plus Online
- Extra Practice, p. 728
- Lesson Practice in Chapter 2 Resource Book, pp. 56–58

CHALLENGE/ENRICHMENT

- Challenge Practice in Chapter 2 Resource Book, p. 61
- Teacher's Edition, p. 50F

ENGLISH LEARNER SUPPORT

- Spanish Study Guide
- Multi-Language Glossary
- Chapter Audio Summaries CDs

C **41. Critical Thinking** Explain how the student used the commutative property of addition to go from the first expression to the second expression. Use the same method to find the sum of the numbers from 1 to 19. **See margin.**

$$1 + 2 + 3 + 4 + 5 + 6 + 7 + 8 + 9 = 10 + 10 + 10 + 10 + 5$$
$$= 45$$

42. Sale Price You are buying 8 yards of fabric that costs \$5.25 per yard. You have a coupon for half off the original price. What is the price of your purchase after the discount? **\$21**

43. Challenge Use the commutative properties of addition and multiplication to write three expressions equivalent to $4 \cdot 8 + 5$.
$8 \cdot 4 + 5$; $5 + 4 \cdot 8$; $5 + 8 \cdot 4$

41. The student grouped the first and last numbers, the second and next to last numbers, and so on, to make 10, and then all of the 10s and the 5 were added to find the sum; 190.

Mixed Review

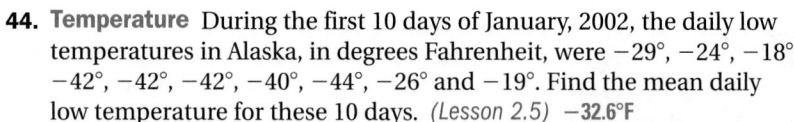

44. Temperature During the first 10 days of January, 2002, the daily low temperatures in Alaska, in degrees Fahrenheit, were $-29°$, $-24°$, $-18°$, $-42°$, $-42°$, $-42°$, $-40°$, $-44°$, $-26°$ and $-19°$. Find the mean daily low temperature for these 10 days. *(Lesson 2.5)* **-32.6°F**

Choose a Strategy **Use a strategy from the list to solve the following problem. Explain your choice of strategy.**

45. You have two stacking bookcases that are 60 inches tall when stacked on top of each other. If you place them side by side, the difference of their heights is 8 inches. How tall is each bookcase?

Problem Solving Strategies
- Guess, Check, and Revise
- Look for a Pattern
- Work Backward

45. 26 in. and 34 in. *Sample answer:* I used Guess, Check, and Revise because I decided to choose two numbers whose sum was 60 and then check to see if the difference was 8. I revised my guess until it was correct.

Basic Skills **Use a number line to compare the numbers.**

46. 1.2 and 0.8 **$1.2 > 0.8$** **47.** 1.35 and 1.53 **$1.35 < 1.53$** **48.** 0.24 and 0.25 **$0.24 < 0.25$**

Test-Taking Practice

INTERNET
State Test Practice
CLASSZONE.COM

49. Multiple Choice Which of the following is equivalent to $7 - 5 - (-4) + 6$? **D**

A. $7 - 6 - (-4) + 5$ **B.** $5 - 7 - (-4) + 6$

C. $7 - 5 + 2$ **D.** $7 + (-5) + 4 + 6$

50. Short Response You need to find the product of 25, 6, 4, and 7. Explain how the commutative and associative properties of multiplication can help you find the product using mental math.
Sample answer: **Reorder the numbers and group 25 with 4 and 6 with 7 because they are easy to multiply. Then multiply the products to find the final product. The result is $(25 \cdot 4)(6 \cdot 7) = 100 \cdot 42 = 4200$.**

The Distributive Property

BEFORE

You used addition and multiplication properties.

Now

You'll use the distributive property.

WHY?

So you can find the cost of souvenirs, as in Ex. 25.

Word Watch

distributive property, p. 85
terms, p. 86
like terms, p. 86
coefficient, p. 86
constant term, p. 86

In the Real World

Architecture A replica of the Parthenon, an ancient temple in Greece, was built in Nashville, Tennessee, in 1897. The diagram below shows the approximate dimensions of two adjacent rooms inside the replica. How can you find the total area of the two rooms?

EXAMPLE 1 Finding a Combined Area

Two methods can be used to find the total area of the two rooms.

Method 1 Find the area of each room, then find the total area.

Area $= 63(44) + 63(93)$

$= 2772 + 5859$

$= 8631$ square feet

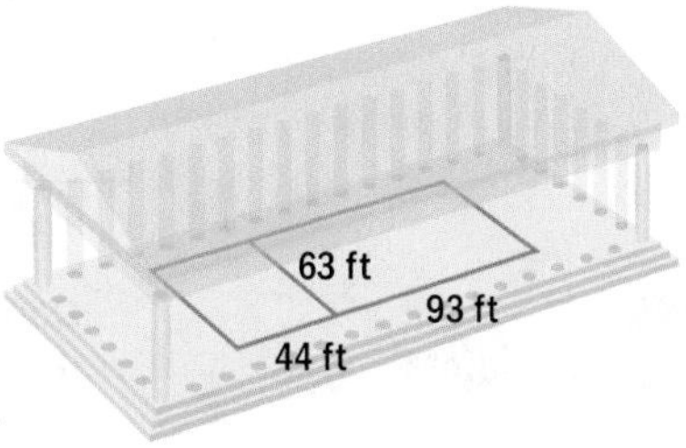

63 ft
93 ft
44 ft

Method 2 Find the total length, then multiply by the common width.

Area $= 63(44 + 93)$

$= 63(137)$

$= 8631$ square feet

ANSWER The total area of the two rooms is 8631 square feet.

Example 1 demonstrates the distributive property.

The Distributive Property

Algebra $a(b + c) = ab + ac$ **Numbers** $6(4 + 3) = 6(4) + 6(3)$

$a(b - c) = ab - ac$ $7(8 - 5) = 7(8) - 7(5)$

ILLINOIS Standards and ISAT:
8.A.3a, 8.D.3a; 9.A.3c

1 PLAN

SKILL CHECK

1. What is the area of a rectangle 2 feet long and 10 feet wide? **20 ft^2**
2. What is the area of a rectangle 3 meters long and 5 meters wide? **15 m^2**
3. $5(-4) + 6(-7) = \underline{?}$ **−62**
4. $-6(11) + (-6)(7) + (-6)(2) = \underline{?}$ **−120**

LESSON OBJECTIVE

Use the distributive property.

PACING

Suggested Number of Days
Basic Course: 1 day
Average Course: 1 day
Advanced Course: 1 day
Block: 0.5 block with 2.8

TEACHING RESOURCES

For a complete list of Teaching Resources, see page 50B.

TRANSPARENCY

Warm-Up Exercises for this lesson are available on a transparency.

2 TEACH

MOTIVATING THE LESSON

You may want to point out that the Parthenon was built in about 440 B.C., and that the exterior dimensions of the Parthenon are about 111 feet by 251 feet.

TIPS FOR NEW TEACHERS

The more numerical examples of the distributive property that students see before incorporating variables, the better. Caution students to be very methodical to avoid errors as they use the distributive property with subtraction. See Tips for New Teachers in the *Chapter 2 Resource Book*.

EXTRA EXAMPLES

Example 1 Find the combined area.

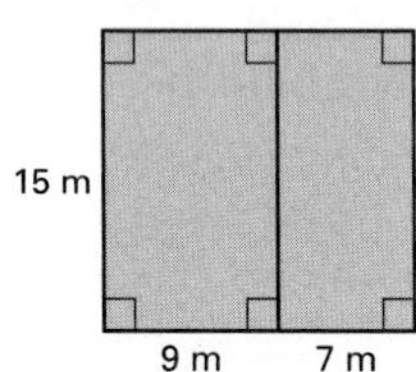

240 m^2

Example 2 Use the distributive property to simplify or evaluate the expression.

a. $-8(k + 4)$ **$-8k - 32$**

b. $5[-8 + (-3) + 10]$ **-5**

Example 3 Simplify the expression by combining like terms.

a. $12a + 3a$ **$15a$**

b. $-7b - 3b + 10$ **$-10b + 10$**

TEACHING TIP

To avoid any confusion with the slang word "like" as students approach Example 3, you may want to point out that the mathematical meaning of like terms is terms that are "alike" in the powers of their variable parts.

1. 10(12 + 22) and 10(12) + 10(22); 340 ft^2
2. 14(3 + 9) and 14(3) + 14(9); 168 ft^2

HELP with Notetaking

When you add new vocabulary words to your notebook be sure to include examples of how they are used.

The distributive property can be applied to expressions involving a sum or difference of two or more numbers or variable expressions.

EXAMPLE 2 Using the Distributive Property

a. $-5(x + 10) = -5x + (-5)(10)$ — Distributive property

$= -5x + (-50)$ — Multiply.

b. $3[1 - 20 + (-5)] = 3(1) - 3(20) + 3(-5)$ — Distributive property

$= 3 - 60 + (-15)$ — Multiply.

$= 3 + (-60) + (-15)$ — Add the opposite of 60.

$= -72$ — Add.

Your turn now **Write two expressions for the total area of the two rectangles. Find the total area.**

1. 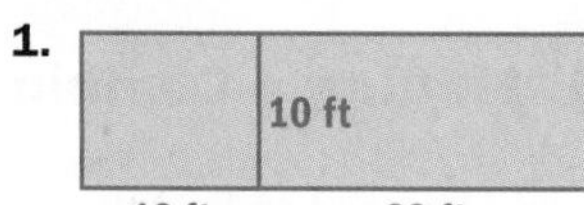

2. 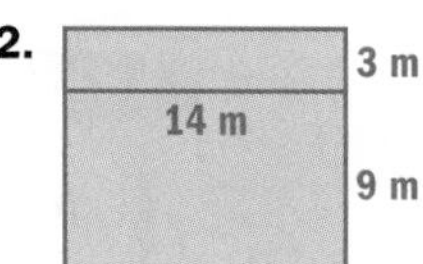

Use the distributive property to evaluate or simplify the expression.

3. $-2(5 + 12)$ -34 **4.** $-4(-7 - 10)$ 68 **5.** $2(w - 8)$ $2w - 16$ **6.** $-8(z + 25)$ $-8z - 200$

Combining Like Terms In a sum the parts that are added together are the **terms** of the expression. You can use the distributive property to combine *like terms.* **Like terms** have identical variable parts raised to the same power. In a term the number multiplied by the variable is the **coefficient** of the variable. A term that has no variable is a **constant term**.

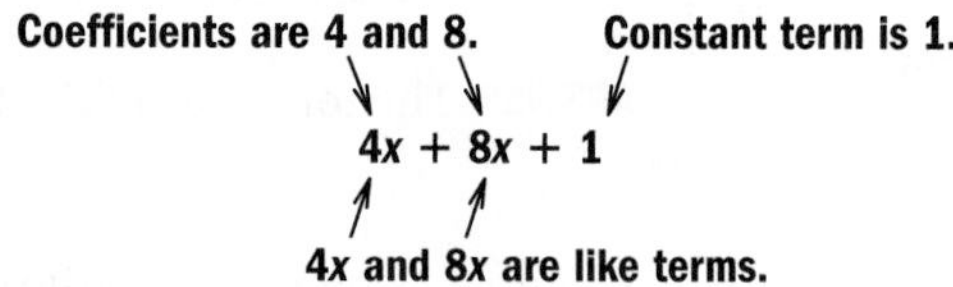

EXAMPLE 3 Combining Like Terms

a. $3x + 4x = (3 + 4)x$ — Distributive property

$= 7x$ — Add inside grouping symbols.

b. $-9y + 7y + 5z = (-9 + 7)y + 5z$ — Distributive property

$= -2y + 5z$ — Add inside grouping symbols.

EXTRA EXAMPLES

Example 4 Simplify $5(d + 3) - 2d$ by combining like terms. **$3d + 15$**

You may need to use the distributive property before you can combine like terms.

with Solving

Remember that $x = 1 \cdot x$, so x has a coefficient of 1.

EXAMPLE 4 Simplifying an Expression

a. $2(4 + x) + x = 8 + 2x + x$ — **Distributive property**

$= 8 + 3x$ — **Combine like terms.**

b. $-5(3x - 6) + 7x = -15x + 30 + 7x$ — **Distributive property**

$= -8x + 30$ — **Combine like terms.**

Your turn now **Simplify the expression by combining like terms.**

7. $4x - 7x$ $-3x$ **8.** $5y + 9z - 7 - 3y$ $2y + 9z - 7$ **9.** $5(x - 6) + 3x + 4$ $8x - 26$

2.7 Exercises

More Practice, p. 728

Getting Ready to Practice

1. Vocabulary Identify any *like terms* and *coefficients* in the expression $7x - 3y - 6y + x + 2$.
like terms: $7x$ and x, $-3y$ and $-6y$; coefficients: 7, −3, −6, 1

Use the distributive property to write an equivalent expression.

2. $4(7 + 8)$ $4(7) + 4(8)$ **3.** $-7(3 + 2)$ $-7(3) + (-7)(2)$ **4.** $3(5 + 6)$ $3(5) + 3(6)$

Simplify the expression by combining like terms.

5. $3y + 6y$ $9y$ **6.** $9a - 4b + a$ $10a - 4b$ **7.** $8m + n - 2m - 4b$ $6m + n - 4b$

8. Guided Problem Solving You are buying three pairs of flip-flops that cost \$12.90 each. Use mental math and the distributive property to find the total cost of the flip-flops.

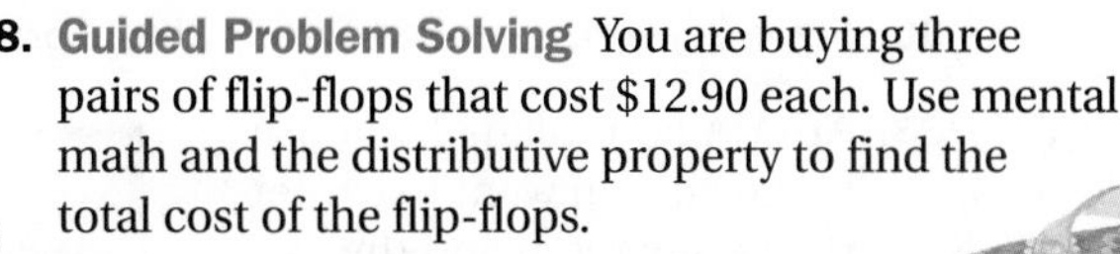

(1) Write 3(12.90) as 3(13 − 0.10).

(2) Find the products 3(13) and 3(0.10). 39, 0.30

(3) Find the difference of the products. \$38.70

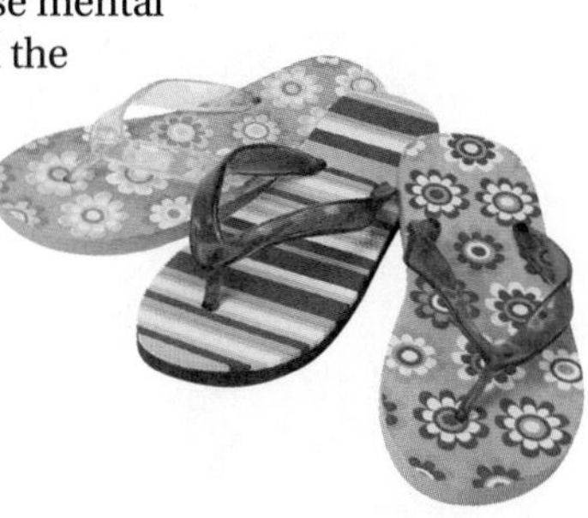

MATH REASONING

The distributive property gives students a chance to use their observation and reasoning skills to plan the simplest way to solve a problem before beginning. For example, evaluating $31(-33 - 67)$ is easiest by first simplifying inside parentheses, but evaluating $-16(10 + 100)$ is easiest by first applying the distributive property.

CONCEPT CHECK

What are like terms? **terms that have identical variable parts raised to the same power**

DAILY PUZZLER

If you know that a zip times a zap is a zowie, a zip times a zot is a zing, and half the difference of a zing and a zowie is a zoop, what is the product of a zip and the difference of a zot and a zap? **2 zoops**

ASSIGNMENT GUIDE

Basic Course
Day 1: pp. 88–89 Exs. 9–29, 33, 46–52

Average Course
Day 1: pp. 88–89 Exs. 15–18, 21–37, 46–52

Advanced Course
Day 1: pp. 88–89 Exs. 16–18, 22–24, 30–52*

Block
pp. 88–89 Exs. 15–18, 21–37, 46–52 (with 2.8)

EXTRA PRACTICE

- Student Edition, p. 728
- Chapter 2 Resource Book, pp. 64–66
- Test and Practice Generator

TRANSPARENCY

Even-numbered answers are available on transparencies.

HOMEWORK CHECK

When you review students' homework for this lesson, go over the following exercises to check understanding of key concepts.
Basic: 10, 14, 19, 21, 33
Average: 15, 18, 21, 23, 33
Advanced: 17, 18, 23, 24, 33

COMMON ERROR

Students may be especially prone to sign errors in Exercises 17 and 31. If they become confused, remind them that they can first rewrite the problems using only addition.

Practice and Problem Solving

HELP with Homework

Example	Exercises
1	33, 44
2	9–18, 27–32
3	19–24, 27–32
4	19–24, 27–32

Online Resources CLASSZONE.COM

- More Examples
- eTutorial Plus

A **Match the expression with its simplified expression.**

9. $3(x + 4)$ B **10.** $4(x + 3)$ D **11.** $2(2x - 6)$ A **12.** $x(4 + 9)$ C

A. $4x - 12$ **B.** $3x + 12$ **C.** $13x$ **D.** $4x + 12$

Use the distributive property to evaluate or simplify the expression.

13. $9(x - 3)$ $9x - 27$ **14.** $-12(4 + 5 + y)$ $-108 - 12y$ **15.** $8(5 + 2)$ 56

16. $19[7 + w + (-2)]$ $95 + 19w$ **17.** $-34(z - 21 - 5)$ $-34z + 884$ **18.** $-13(-12 + 9)$ 39

Simplify the expression by combining like terms.

19. $r + 2s + 3r$ $4r + 2s$ **20.** $11w + 9z + 3z + 5w$ $16w + 12z$

21. $7a - 2a + 8b - 2b$ $5a + 6b$ **22.** $3x + 2x + y + 2y - 3$ $5x + 3y - 3$

23. $-3x + 2x - 9y - 2x$ $-3x - 9y$ **24.** $r + 2s - (-3r) - s$ $4r + s$

25. Souvenirs You are on vacation in Massachusetts and want to buy souvenirs for 6 friends at home. You decide to buy a trading pin that costs \$2.35 and a pen that costs \$.65 for each friend. Explain how to use mental math to find how much money you will need. See margin.

26. Find the Error Describe and correct the error in the solution.

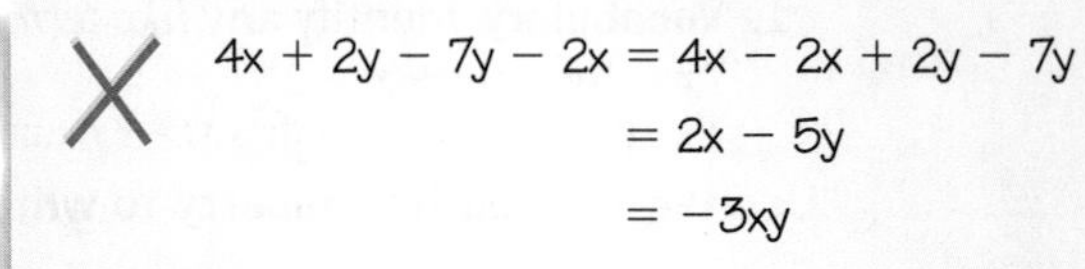

Because $2x$ and $-5y$ are not like terms, they cannot be added. $2x - 5y$ is in simplest form.

25. Add \$2.35 and \$.65 to get \$3.00. Multiply \$3.00 by 6 to find the total, \$18.

B **Simplify the expression.**

27. $7(y - 2)$ $7y - 14$ **28.** $9x(4 - 2 + 6)$ $72x$ **29.** $3x + 2 - 5x + 4x$ $2x + 2$

30. $5(z + 2z) - 4z$ $11z$ **31.** $8d - 2(3d - 5d)$ $12d$ **32.** $4(3c - 4) + 2 - 4c$ $8c - 14$

33. Area A floor plan of a house is shown. You want to carpet the family room and the living room. The carpeting you want to use in these two rooms sells for \$3.12 per square foot. How much will the carpet cost? \$786.24

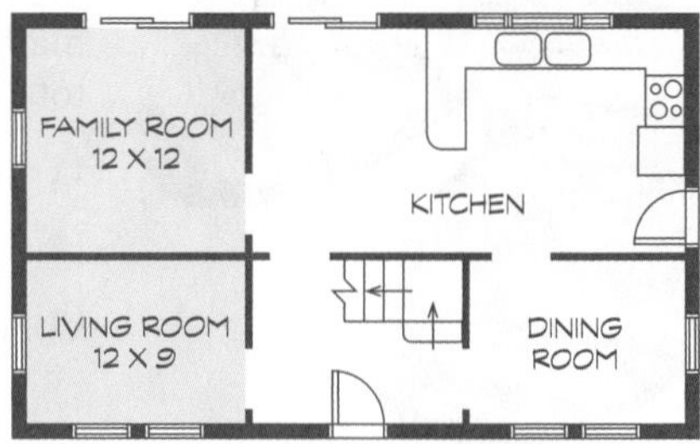

Simplify the expression by combining like terms.

34. $3a + 4b - 5 - a + 7b + 3 - b$ **$2a + 10b - 2$**

35. $5(x + 2) - 5(y + 3) - 2x + 5y$ **$3x - 5$**

36. $3.2(2z - 3x) + 4(1.1y + x) - 2z$ **$4.4z - 5.6x + 4.4y$**

37. $7(y - 1.3) + 2.4 - 5.3y$ **$1.7y - 6.7$**

38. You should consider whether it is easier to multiply 8 and 998 or to subtract 16 from 8000. *Sample answer:* 4(100 − 8), 4(112 − 12)

38. Writing Explain what you should consider when deciding which expression is easier to evaluate, $8(1000 - 2)$ or $8 \cdot 1000 - 8 \cdot 2$. Give an example of a problem you think is easier to solve using the distributive property and an example you think is not easier to solve using the distributive property.

Mental Math Use mental math to find the product using a method like the one in Exercise 8 on page 87. Explain your reasoning. 39–42. See margin.

39. 4(34) **40.** 9(19) **41.** 24(12) **42.** 65(24)

43. Critical Thinking Are $3xy$ and $4yx$ like terms? Explain your reasoning. See margin.

C **44. Mural** Some students have been given permission to paint murals on 5 walls at your school. The walls are all 8 feet tall. The mural widths are 21.5 feet, 35 feet, 27.5 feet, 33.5 feet, and 22.5 feet. Write two expressions to find the total area of the murals. Then find the total area.
$8(21.5 + 35 + 27.5 + 33.5 + 22.5) = 8(21.5) + 8(35) + 8(27.5) + 8(33.5) + 8(22.5) = 1120 \text{ ft}^2$

45. Challenge You are ordering T-shirts with your school logo. Each T-shirt costs $7.25. There is a $25 setup fee for silk-screening, and a screening charge of $1.85 per shirt. Write an expression to find the total cost for x T-shirts. What is the total cost for 75 T-shirts? for 170 T-shirts?
$7.25x + 25 + 1.85x$, or $9.1x + 25$; \$707.50; \$1572

39–42. Sample answers are given.

39. $4(30 + 4) = 120 + 16 = 136$; mental math can be used to multiply and then add.

40. $9(10 + 9) = 90 + 81 = 171$; mental math can be used to multiply and then add.

41. $24(10 + 2) = 240 + 48 = 288$; mental math can be used to multiply and then add.

42. $65(20 + 4) = 1300 + 260 = 1560$; mental math can be used to multiply and then add.

Mixed Review

Order the integers from least to greatest. *(Lesson 2.1)*

46. −90, 35, 19, −35, 80 **−90, −35, 19, 35, 80**

47. 70, −20, −90, 0, −100 **−100, −90, −20, 0, 70**

Evaluate the expression. *(Lesson 2.6)*

48. $-5(4 \cdot 17)$ **−340**

49. $(-23 + 14) - 12$ **−21**

50. $17 + (3 - 12) + 24(0)$ **8**

51. $(-4 \cdot 7) \cdot 25$ **−700**

Test-Taking Practice

INTERNET
State Test Practice
CLASSZONE.COM

52. Extended Response The perimeter of the entire stage is 200 feet. Find the value of x. Show your work. Explain two different ways to find the area of the stage. Use either method to find the area. See margin.

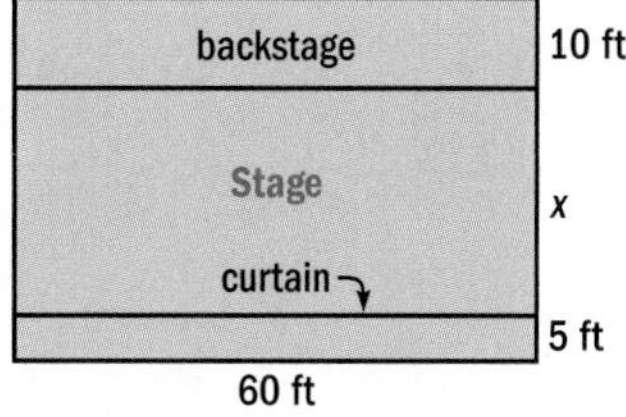

43. Yes; by the commutative property of multiplication, $xy = yx$.

4 ASSESS

Assessment Resources

For more assessment resources, see:
- Assessment Book
- Test and Practice Generator

Mini-Quiz

Evaluate.

1. $14(2 - d)$ **$28 - 14d$**
2. $-8(f + 2 + 3)$ **$-8f - 40$**

Combine like terms.

3. $m - p + 2m - 4p$ **$3m - 5p$**
4. $b + 3c - b + (-4b)$ **$3c - 4b$**
5. Simplify $5 - 4(2j - 4j)$. **$5 + 8j$**
6. Three adjacent offices, which together form a rectangle, are each 9 feet wide. The lengths of the offices are 12 feet, 11 feet, and 10 feet. What is the total area of the offices? **297 ft^2**

5 FOLLOW-UP

Reteaching/Remediation
- Study Guide in Chapter 2 Resource Book, pp. 67–68
- Tutor Place, Algebra Card 6
- eTutorial Plus Online
- Extra Practice, p. 728
- Lesson Practice in Chapter 2 Resource Book, pp. 64–66

Challenge/Enrichment
- Challenge Practice in Chapter 2 Resource Book, p. 69
- Teacher's Edition, p. 50F

English Learner Support
- Spanish Study Guide
- Multi-Language Glossary
- Chapter Audio Summaries CDs

52. See Additional Answers beginning on page AA1.

Learn the Method

- Students will evaluate expressions using a calculator.
- Students can use calculators to verify Example 2 part b on page 86, and to check their work on the first two problems following Example 2.

Tips for Success

Draw students' attention to the Watch Out feature in the margin. You may need to walk students step by step through one example so that they grasp when to use the negative and subtraction keys.

EXTRA EXAMPLES

Example Use a calculator to evaluate $\frac{-765}{-17 \cdot 15}$. 3

3 CLOSE

Assessment

1. Use a calculator to evaluate $-280(-55 - 25) - 100$. **22,300**
2. How many times would you use the subtraction key and how many times would you use the negative key to evaluate $-23 \cdot [-(-5 - 11)] - [-17[14 - (-32)]]$ on a calculator? **subtraction: 3; negative: 5**

CALCULATOR

2.7 Technology Activity

Using Integer Operations

GOAL Use a calculator to evaluate expressions.

Example **Use a calculator to evaluate the expression.**

a. $-900{,}018 + (-805{,}560)$ **b.** $\frac{-278 \cdot (-640)}{-139}$

Solution

Use the following keystrokes to find your answer.

	Keystrokes	Display
a.	(−) 900018 + (−) 805560 =	−1705578

ANSWER $-900{,}018 + (-805{,}560) = -1{,}705{,}578$

	Keystrokes	Display
b.	(−) 278 × (−) 640 ÷ (−) 139 =	−1280

ANSWER $\frac{-278 \cdot (-640)}{-139} = -1280$

Watch Out!

The − button performs subtraction. Use the (−) button to enter a negative number.

Your turn now **Use a calculator to evaluate the expression.**

1. $18{,}432 + (-46{,}978)$ **−28,546**
2. $-50{,}215 + 1315$ **−48,900**
3. $7010 - (-3999)$ **11,009**
4. $-14{,}300 - (-500)$ **−13,800**
5. $-751 \cdot 2804$ **−2,105,804**
6. $-1940 \cdot (-689)$ **1,336,660**
7. $3336(-198 \cdot 398)$ **−262,890,144**
8. $\frac{-105{,}638}{-221}$ **478**
9. $\frac{-67{,}771}{671}$ **−101**
10. **Moon** The distance of the moon's orbit around Earth is about 2,415,000 kilometers. The moon travels at an average speed of 3700 kilometers per hour. How long will it take the moon to complete one orbit? **about 653 h**
11. **Earth** The diameter of Earth is about 4 times the diameter of the moon. The diameter of the moon is 3476 kilometers. What is the diameter of Earth? Find the difference of the diameter of Earth and the diameter of the moon. **about 13,904 km; about 10,428 km**

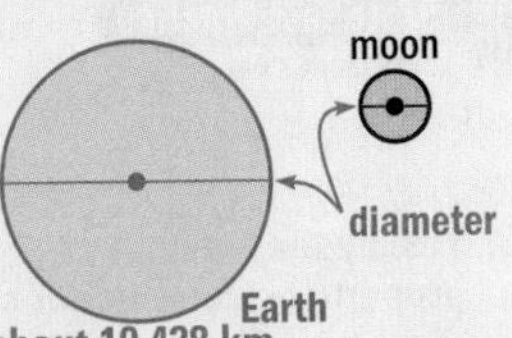

ILLINOIS Standards and ISAT:
6.B.3a; 6.C.3a

The Coordinate Plane

BEFORE	Now	WHY?
You used number lines.	You'll identify and plot points in a coordinate plane.	So you can predict the price of a phone call, as in Ex. 29.

Word Watch

coordinate plane, p. 91
x-axis, y-axis, p. 91
origin, p. 91
quadrant, p. 91
ordered pair, p. 91
x-coordinate, p. 91
y-coordinate, p. 91

A **coordinate plane** is formed by the intersection of a horizontal number line called the ***x*-axis** and a vertical number line called the ***y*-axis**. The axes meet at a point called the **origin** and divide the coordinate plane into four **quadrants**.

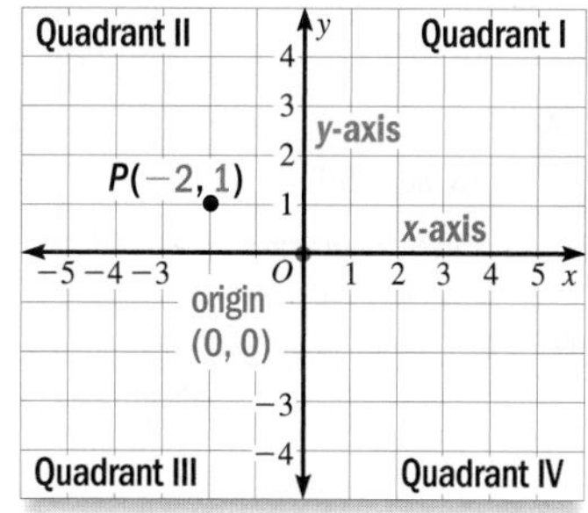

Points in a coordinate plane are represented by **ordered pairs**. The first number is the ***x*-coordinate**. The second number is the ***y*-coordinate**. Point *P* above is represented by the ordered pair (−2, 1).

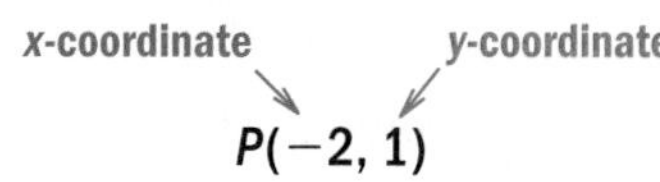

EXAMPLE 1 Naming Points in a Coordinate Plane

Give the coordinates of the point.

a. *A* **b.** *B* **c.** *C*

Solution

a. Point *A* is 3 units to the right of the origin and 1 unit up. So, the *x*-coordinate is 3 and the *y*-coordinate is 1. The coordinates of *A* are (3, 1).

b. Point *B* is 3 units to the left of the origin and 2 units down. So, the *x*-coordinate is −3 and the *y*-coordinate is −2. The coordinates of *B* are(−3, −2).

c. Point *C* is 2 units up from the origin. So, the *x*-coordinate is 0 and the *y*-coordinate is 2. The coordinates of *C* are (0, 2).

Your turn now **Give the coordinates of the point.**

1. *D* (3, −4) **2.** *E* (−2, 2) **3.** *F* (−3, 0)

ILLINOIS Standards and ISAT:
7.C.3b, 9.A.3a; 9.A.3b

1 PLAN

SKILL CHECK

1. $|-15| = \underline{?}$ 15
2. $|14 - 22| = \underline{?}$ 8
3. $|7 - (-3)| = \underline{?}$ 10

LESSON OBJECTIVE

Identify and plot points in a coordinate plane.

PACING

Suggested Number of Days
Basic Course: 1 day
Average Course: 1 day
Advanced Course: 1 day
Block: 0.5 block with 2.7

TEACHING RESOURCES

For a complete list of Teaching Resources, see page 50B.

TRANSPARENCY

Warm-Up Exercises for this lesson are available on a transparency. Support transparencies are available for Example 1.

2 TEACH

MOTIVATING THE LESSON

Bring a road map to class and have students find locations using the letter and number coordinates.

TIPS FOR NEW TEACHERS

To help students generalize the signs of the *x*- and *y*-coordinates in each quadrant, remind them that right and up represent positive moves, while left and down represent negative moves. See Tips for New Teachers in the *Chapter 2 Resource Book*.

EXTRA EXAMPLES

Example 1 Give the coordinates of the point.

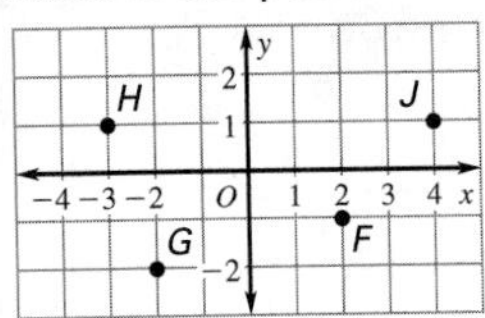

a. F (2, −1) **b.** G (−2, −2)
c. H (−3, 1) **d.** J (4, 1)

Example 2 Describe the location of the point.

a. $K(2, -3)$ **b.** $L(0, 2)$
c. $M(-1, 3)$

a. **Begin at the origin, move 2 units right, then 3 units down; Quadrant IV.**
b. **Begin at the origin, move 2 units up; *y*-axis.**
c. **Begin at the origin, move 1 unit left, then 3 units up; Quadrant II.**

Example 3 Identify the figure and find its perimeter.

A(−40, 20) B(20, 20) D(−40, −40) C(20, −40)

square; 240 units

TRANSPARENCY

Support transparencies are available for Examples 2 and 3, and Your turn now Exercises 4-8.

CONCEPT CHECK

How are points on a coordinate plane represented? **by ordered pairs**

DAILY PUZZLER

Find the *y*-coordinate of any point with *x*-coordinate −4 that is the same distance from both axes. **4 or −4**

4–8. See Additional Answers beginning on page AA1.

EXAMPLE 2 Graphing Points in a Coordinate Plane

Plot the point and describe its location.

a. $A(4, -2)$ **b.** $B(-1, 2)$ **c.** $C(0, -3)$

Solution

a. Begin at the origin, move 4 units to the right, then 2 units down. Point A lies in Quadrant IV.

b. Begin at the origin, move 1 unit to the left, then 2 units up. Point B lies in Quadrant II.

c. Begin at the origin, move 3 units down. Point C lies on the y-axis.

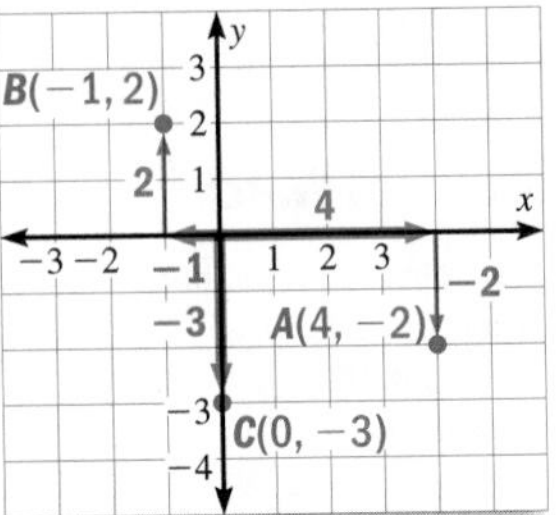

HELP with Solving

Points on the *x*-axis or *y*-axis do not lie in any quadrant.

EXAMPLE 3 Finding Perimeter

Identify the figure and find its perimeter.

Solution

Points A, B, C, and D form a rectangle.

To find the length l, find the *horizontal* distance from A to B.

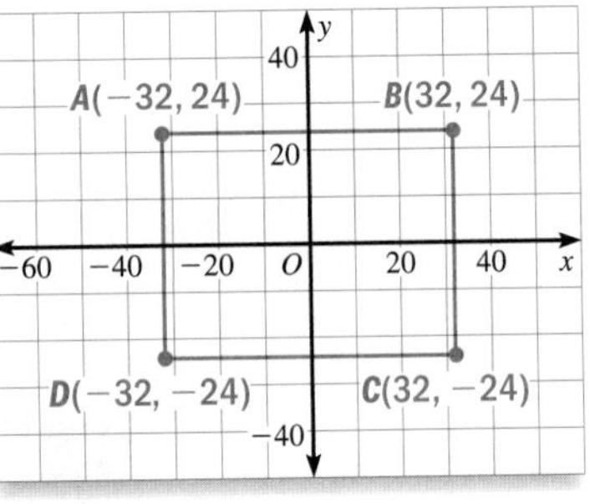

$$l = |x\text{-coordinate of } A - x\text{-coordinate of } B|$$
$$= |-32 - 32| = |-64| = 64$$

To find the width w, find the *vertical* distance from A to D.

$$w = |y\text{-coordinate of } A - y\text{-coordinate of } D|$$
$$= |24 - (-24)| = |48| = 48$$

$$\text{Perimeter} = 2l + 2w = 2(64) + 2(48) = 224$$

ANSWER The rectangle has a perimeter of 224 units.

HELP with Solving

You need to use absolute value signs because length and width are always positive.

Your turn now Plot the point and describe its location. **4–7. See margin for art.**

4. $R(-3, 4)$ **Quadrant II** **5.** $S(1, 2)$ **Quadrant I** **6.** $T(0, 3)$ ***y*-axis** **7.** $U(-4, 0)$ ***x*-axis**

8. Plot and connect points $A(-20, 25)$, $B(25, 25)$, $C(25, -20)$, and $D(-20, -20)$. Identify the resulting figure and find its perimeter. **See margin for art; square; 180 units.**

Exercises

More Practice, p. 728

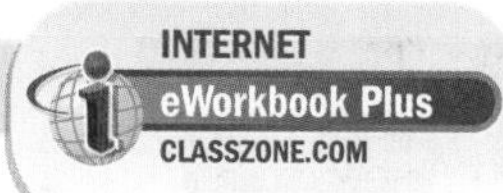

Getting Ready to Practice

1. Vocabulary Draw a coordinate plane and label the x-axis, y-axis, each quadrant, and the origin. See margin.

Give the coordinates of the point.

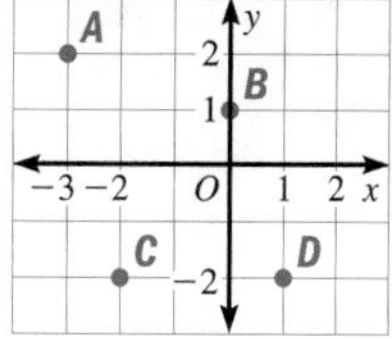

2. A (−3, 2) **3.** B (0, 1)

4. C (−2, −2) **5.** D (1, −2)

Plot the point in a coordinate plane. 6–9. See margin.

6. (4, 1) **7.** (2, −3) **8.** (−3, 0) **9.** (−2, −1)

10. City Park The rectangle with corners A, B, C, and D represents a city park. Find the distance around the city park if the length and width of each small square on the coordinate grid represents 100 feet. 2000 feet

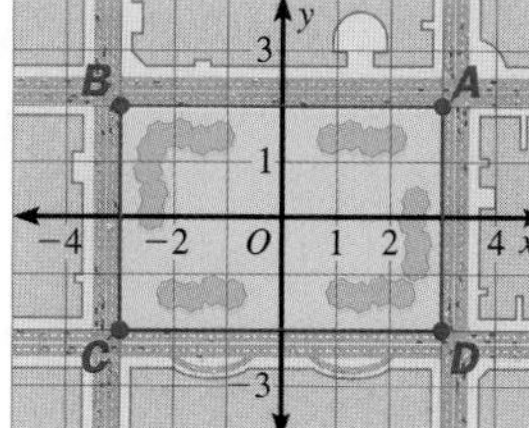

Practice and Problem Solving

Example	Exercises
1	11-16
2	17-20
3	21-22, 24-26

- More Examples
- eTutorial Plus

A **Give the coordinates of the point.**

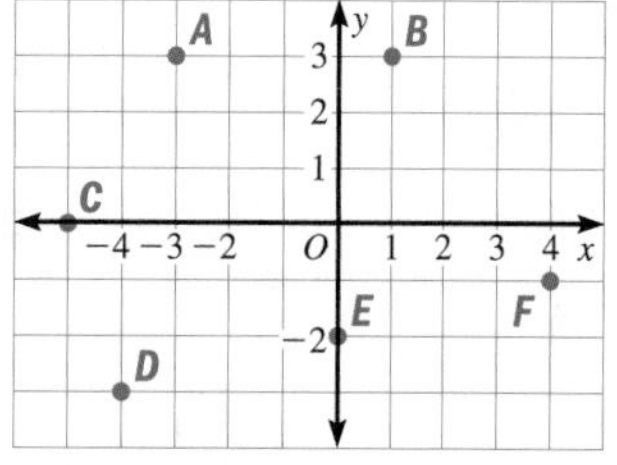

11. A (−3, 3) **12.** B (1, 3)

13. C (−5, 0) **14.** D (−4, −3)

15. E (0, −2) **16.** F (4, −1)

Plot the point in a coordinate plane and describe its location. 17–20. See margin for art.

17. (−2, 3) Quadrant II **18.** (3, −1) Quadrant IV **19.** (0, −5) y-axis **20.** (−3, −4) Quadrant III

B **Plot and connect the given points. Then identify the resulting figure and find its perimeter.** 21–22. See margin for art.

21. $A(-2, 6)$, $B(2, 6)$, $C(2, -6)$, $D(-2, -6)$ rectangle; 32 units

22. $J(5, 4)$, $K(5, -2)$, $L(-1, -2)$, $M(-1, 4)$ square; 24 units

3 APPLY

ASSIGNMENT GUIDE

Basic Course

Day 1: pp. 93-95 Exs. 11-22, 32-40

Average Course

Day 1: pp. 93-95 Exs. 14-16, 19-29, 32-40

Advanced Course

Day 1: pp. 93-95 Exs. 15, 16, 19, 20, 23-37*, 39, 40

Block

pp. 93-95 Exs. 14-16, 19-29, 32-40 (with 2.7)

EXTRA PRACTICE

- Student Edition, p. 728
- Chapter 2 Resource Book, pp. 73-75
- Test and Practice Generator

TRANSPARENCY

Even-numbered answers are available on transparencies. Support transparencies are available for Exercises 1, 6-9, 17-26, and 28-31.

HOMEWORK CHECK

When you review students' homework for this lesson, go over the following exercises to check understanding of key concepts.

Basic: 11, 14, 17, 19, 21
Average: 14, 19, 20, 22, 24
Advanced: 16, 19, 20, 24, 25

TEACHING TIP

In Exercises 8 and 19, make sure students realize that a point with an x-coordinate of 0 lies on the y-axis, while a point with a y-coordinate of 0 lies on the x-axis.

1, 6-9, 17-22. See Additional Answers beginning on page AA1.

23. 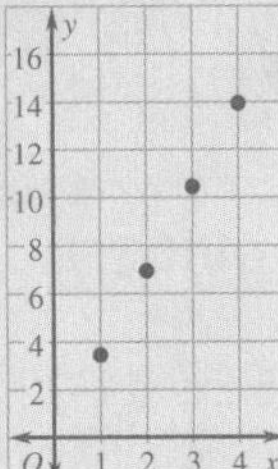

24. 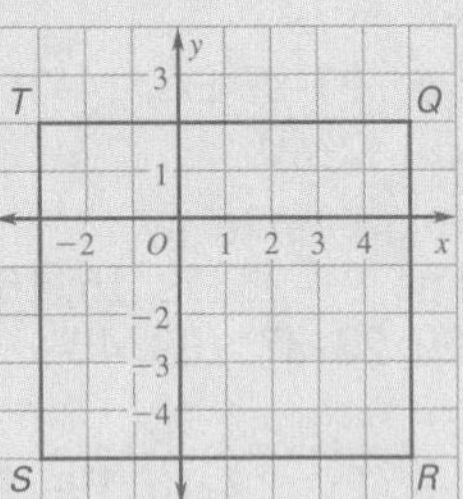

25. 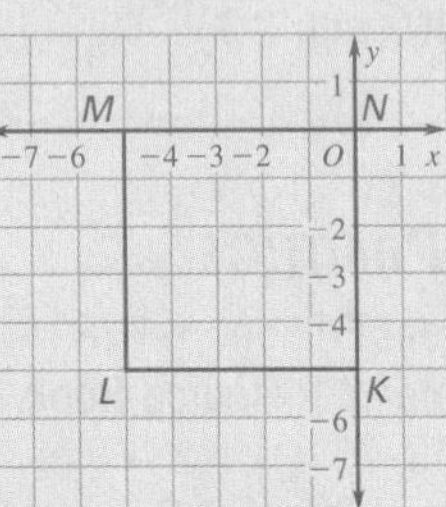

26. 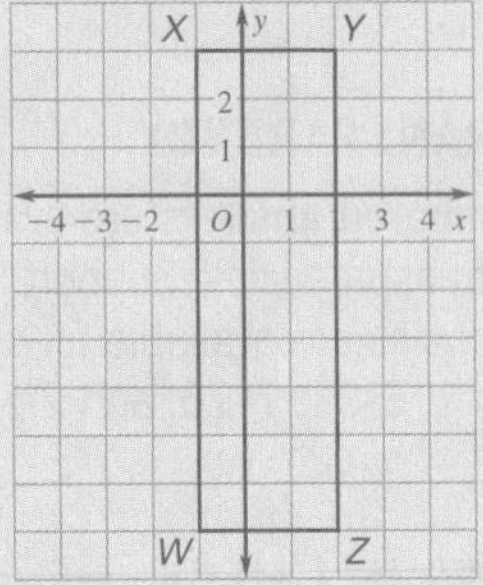

28–29. 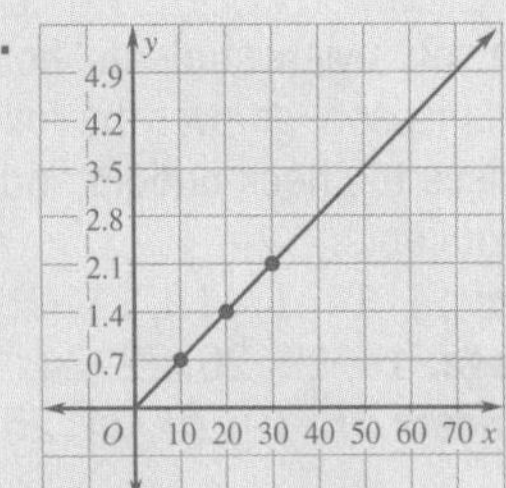

31. 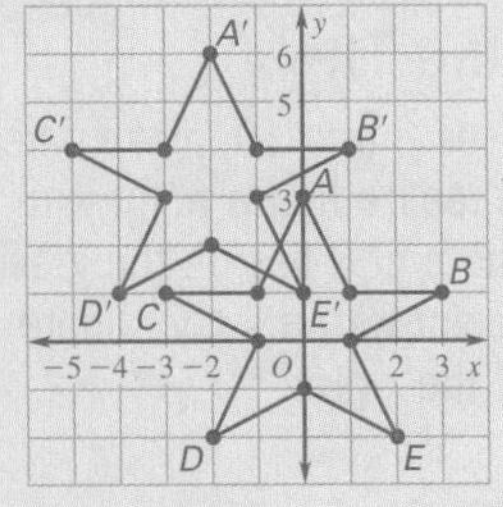

23. Fruit The following ordered pairs represent the cost of buying several weights of pineapple from a fruit stand. The x-coordinate represents the number of pounds and the y-coordinate represents the cost.

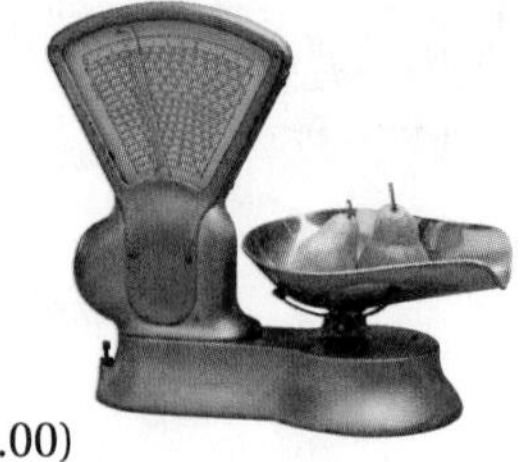

(1, \$3.50), (2, \$7.00), (3, \$10.50), (4, \$14.00)

Plot the points in a coordinate plane. Identify the pattern. Use the pattern to estimate the cost of $2\frac{1}{2}$ pounds of pineapple. **See margin for art; the points lie along a line; \$8.75.**

Plot and connect the points. Find the perimeter and area of the rectangle formed. **24–26. See margin for art.**

24. $Q(5, 2)$, $R(5, -5)$, $S(-3, -5)$, $T(-3, 2)$ **30 units; 56 square units**

25. $K(0, -5)$, $L(-5, -5)$, $M(-5, 0)$, $N(0, 0)$ **20 units; 25 square units**

26. $W(-1, -7)$, $X(-1, 3)$, $Y(2, 3)$, $Z(2, -7)$ **26 units; 30 square units**

Extended Problem Solving In Exercises 27–29, suppose your phone card charges 7 cents per minute for a phone call.

27. Calculate Find the cost of a 10 minute call, a 20 minute call, and a 30 minute call. **\$.70, \$1.40, \$2.10**

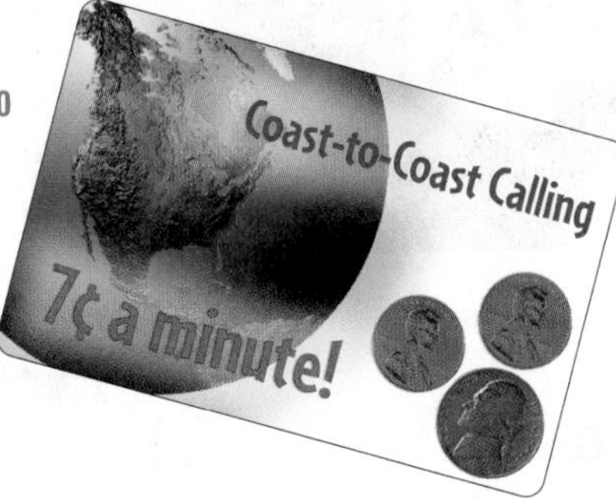

28. Graph Plot the costs you found in Exercise 27 in a coordinate plane, where the x-coordinate represents the length (in minutes) of the call and the y-coordinate represents the total cost of the call, in dollars. **28–29. See margin for art.**

29. Estimate Draw a line through the points. Use the line to estimate the cost of an hour-long call. **\$4.20**

C **30. Challenge** Draw a rectangle that has points in all four quadrants. Multiply each coordinate by 2 and draw this rectangle. Compare this rectangle with the original one and compare their perimeters. What do you find?

30. *Sample answer:* **It is larger than the original; the perimeter of the second rectangle is twice the perimeter of the original rectangle.**

31. Slide Copy the figure. Move the figure 2 units to the left and 3 units up. Give the new coordinates of A, B, C, D, and E. **See margin for art; $A(-2, 6)$, $B(1, 4)$, $C(-5, 4)$, $D(-4, 1)$, $E(0, 1)$.**

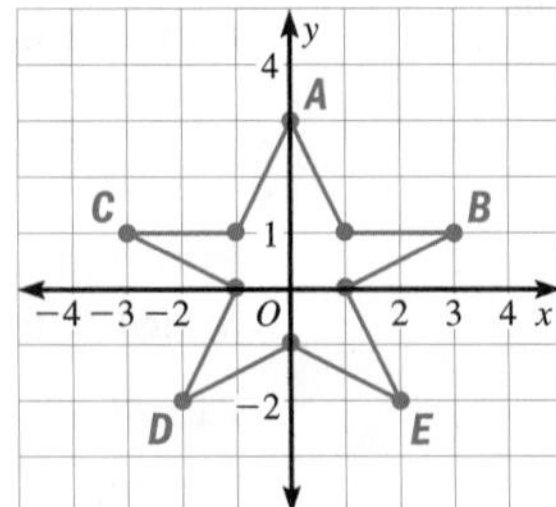

Mixed Review 

Find the sum. *(Lesson 2.2)*

32. $24 + (-9) + (-12)$ 3 **33.** $-14 + 30 + (-17)$ −1 **34.** $-40 + 8 + 12$ −20

Simplify the expression. *(Lesson 2.7)*

35. $4(x + 9)$ $4x + 36$ **36.** $6y(8 - 6)$ $12y$ **37.** $-9(z - 2)$ $-9z + 18$

38. Basic Skills You are selling T-shirts as a fundraiser for your school's soccer team. You need to sell 35 shirts to reach your goal, and you have sold 18 shirts. How many more T-shirts do you need to sell? 17 T-shirts

Test-Taking Practice 

39. Short Response On a coordinate plane, plot the points $A(2, 3)$, $B(2, 7)$, $C(6, 7)$, and $D(6, 3)$. Connect the points to form a square. Imagine that this square moves 4 units up. Write the new coordinates for points A, B, C, and D. See margin for art; $A(2, 7)$, $B(2, 11)$, $C(6, 11)$, $D(6, 7)$.

40. Multiple Choice Which labeled point shown has an x-coordinate of 2? B

A. M **B.** N

C. P **D.** R

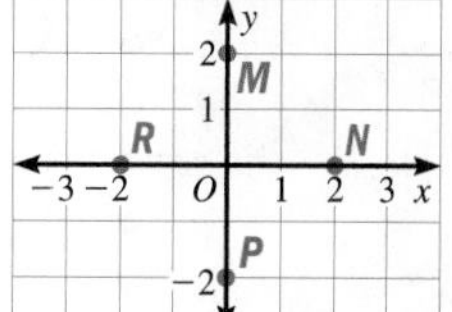

BRAIN GAME

Spatial Delivery

Jack delivers balloons in a city. Below is a grid of Jack's city and a list of the deliveries he made today. Copy the diagram on graph paper and plot each stop. How many blocks did Jack travel? 23 blocks

Delivery Stops

Began at Main and State Street

1. E 3rd St. and Main
2. E 3rd St. and N 2nd Ave.
3. E 1st St. and N 2nd Ave.
4. E 1st St. and S 2nd Ave.
5. W 2nd St. and S 3rd Ave.
6. W 3rd St. and S 1st Ave
7. W 3rd St. and N 2nd Ave.
8. W 1st St. and N 2nd Ave.

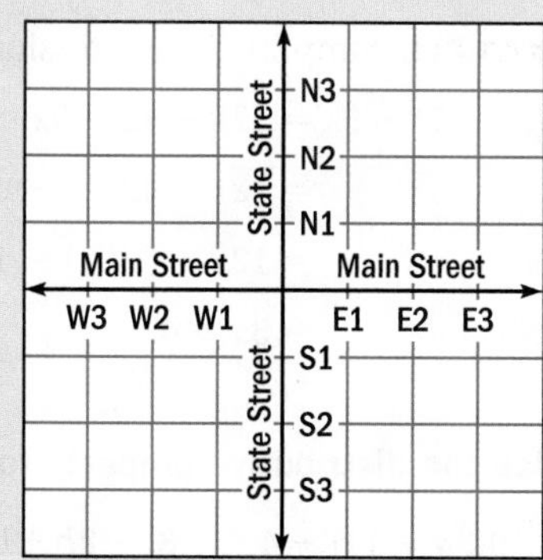

4 ASSESS

Assessment Resources

For more assessment resources, see:

- Assessment Book
- Test and Practice Generator

Mini-Quiz

Give the coordinates of the point.

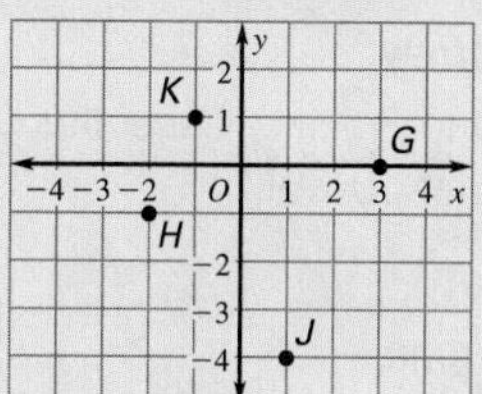

1. G (3, 0) **2.** H (−2, −1)

3. J (1, −4) **4.** K (−1, 1)

Describe the location of the point.

4. $N(0, 4)$ Begin at the origin, move 4 units up. Point N lies on the y-axis.

5. $P(-2, -3)$ Begin at the origin, move 2 units left, then 3 units down. Point P lies in Quadrant III.

5 FOLLOW-UP

Reteaching/Remediation

- Study Guide in Chapter 2 Resource Book, pp. 76–77
- Tutor Place, Algebra Cards 17, 18
- eTutorial Plus Online
- Extra Practice, p. 728
- Lesson Practice in Chapter 2 Resource Book, pp. 73–75

Challenge/Enrichment

- Challenge Practice in Chapter 2 Resource Book, p. 78
- Teacher's Edition, p. 50F

English Learner Support

- Spanish Study Guide
- Multi-Language Glossary
- Chapter Audio Summaries CDs

39. See Additional Answers beginning on page AA1.

ADDITIONAL RESOURCES

The following resources are available to help review the materials in Lessons 2.6–2.8.

Chapter 2 Resource Book
- Lesson Practice
- Study Guide

Assessment Book
- Chapter 2 Quiz 2

Technology
- Test and Practice Generator
- eTutorial CD-ROM

Internet
- Classzone
- eWorkbook Plus Online
- eTutorial Plus Online

ENGLISH LEARNER SUPPORT

- Spanish Study Guide
- Multi-Language Glossary
- Chapter Audio Summaries CDs

Notebook Review

Review the vocabulary definitions in your notebook.

Copy the review examples in your notebook. Then complete the exercises.

Check Your Definitions

distributive property, p. 85	constant term, p. 86	quadrant, p. 91
terms, like terms, p. 86	coordinate plane, p. 91	ordered pair, p. 91
coefficient, p. 86	x-axis, y-axis, p. 91	x-coordinate, p. 91
	origin, p. 91	y-coordinate, p. 91

Use Your Vocabulary

1. What is the y-coordinate of the point $(5, -5)$? -5

2.6 Can you use commutative and associative properties?

EXAMPLE Evaluate the expression.

$(-3 + 5) - 7 = (-3 + 5) + (-7)$	**Change subtraction to addition.**
$= [5 + (-3)] + (-7)$	**Commutative property of addition**
$= 5 + [-3 + (-7)]$	**Associative property of addition**
$= 5 + (-10)$	**Add inside grouping symbols.**
$= -5$	**Add.**

Use mental math to evaluate the expression. Justify.

2. $-5(19 \cdot 2)$ -190 **3.** $-25 \cdot 13 \cdot 4$ -1300 **4.** $-42 + (-18 - 23)$ -83

2.7 Can you use the distributive property?

EXAMPLE Simplify the expression.

$6(2x + 7) - 9x = 12x + 42 - 9x$	**Distributive property**
$= 12x + 42 + (-9x)$	**Change subtraction to addition.**
$= 12x + (-9x) + 42$	**Commutative property of addition**
$= 3x + 42$	**Combine like terms.**

Use the distributive property to simplify the expression.

5. $9(3a + 11) - 4$ $27a + 95$ **6.** $-8b + 12(7b + 3)$ $76b + 36$ **7.** $2c - 8(9c - 5)$ $-70c + 40$

Notebook Review

8–11.

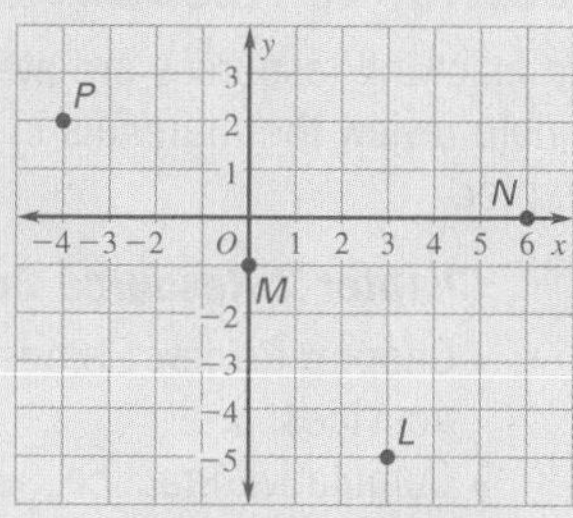

2.8 Can you identify and plot points?

EXAMPLE Plot the point and describe its location.

a. $A(-1, 1)$ **b.** $B(4, -3)$

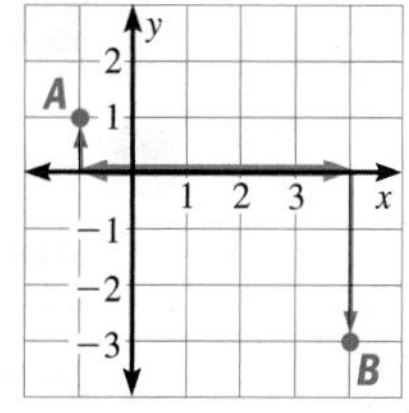

Solution

a. Begin at the origin, move 1 unit to the left and 1 unit up. Point A lies in Quadrant II.

b. Begin at the origin, move 4 units to the right and 3 units down. Point B lies in Quadrant IV.

Plot the point and describe its location. 8–11. See margin for art.

8. $L(3, -5)$ Quadrant IV **9.** $M(0, -1)$ y-axis **10.** $N(6, 0)$ x-axis **11.** $P(-4, 2)$ Quadrant II

Stop *and* Think about Lessons 2.6–2.8

12. Writing Explain how you can use the distributive property and mental math to evaluate the expression $4 \cdot 6.11$. Use $4(6 + 0.11) = 4(6) + 4(0.11) = 24 + 0.44 = 24.44$.

Review Quiz 2

Evaluate the expression. Justify each step. 1–3. Check justifications.

1. $(19 + 33) + 11$ 63 **2.** $15(23)(-4)$ -1380 **3.** $3(-4 \cdot 9)$ -108

Simplify the expression.

4. $9x + 22x$ $31x$ **5.** $3a - 2b + 6 - a$ $2a - 2b + 6$ **6.** $8(y + 2) - 4y$ $4y + 16$

In Exercises 7–9, use the coordinate plane.

7. Write the coordinates of points $A, B, C, D,$ and E. $A(-3, 1)$, $B(0, 3)$, $C(3, 4)$, $D(2, -3)$, $E(-2, -1)$

8. Which point lies on the y-axis? B

9. Which point lies in Quadrant II? A

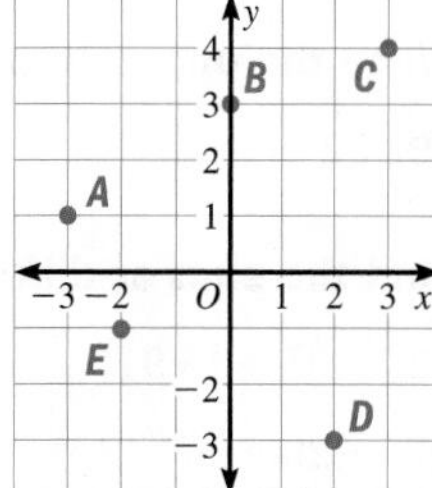

10. Basketball In a basketball game Joe scored 13 points in the first quarter, 6 points in the second quarter, 7 points in the third quarter, and 14 points in the fourth quarter. How many points did Joe score? 40 points

Additional Resources

The following resources are available to help review the materials in this chapter.

Chapter 2 Resource Book
- Chapter Review Games and Activities, p. 80
- Cumulative Practice, Chs. 1-2

English/Spanish Chapter Reviews and Tests

Chapter Audio Summaries CDs

eTutorial CD-ROM

eWorkbook Plus Online

eTutorial Plus Online

2. like terms: $-6y$ and $-21y$, $-7x$ and $17x$; coefficients: -6, -7, 17, -21

3.

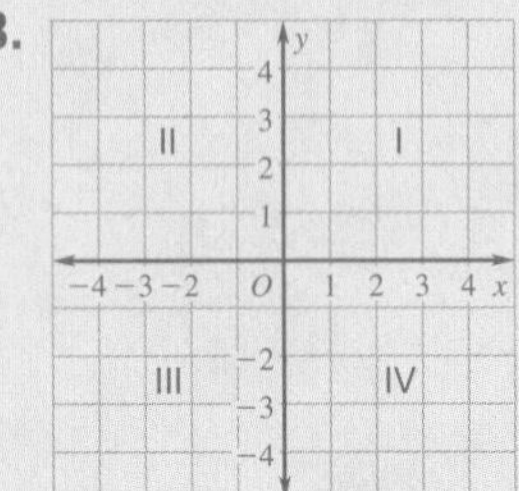

Chapter Review

Vocabulary

integer, p. 53	distributive property, p. 85	x-axis, p. 91
negative integer, p. 53	terms, p. 86	y-axis, p. 91
positive integer, p. 53	like terms, p. 86	origin, p. 91
absolute value, p. 54	coefficient, p. 86	quadrant, p. 91
opposite, p. 54	constant term, p. 86	ordered pair, p. 91
mean, p. 75	coordinate plane, p. 91	x-coordinate, p. 91
		y-coordinate, p. 91

Vocabulary Review

1. How many numbers have an absolute value of 15? List them. **2; 15, −15**
2. Copy the expression. List any like terms and coefficients.

$$-6y + 8 - 7x + 17x - 21y$$ **See margin.**

3. How many quadrants are in a coordinate plane? Draw a coordinate plane and label each quadrant. **4; see margin for art.**

Copy and complete the statement.

4. A point in a coordinate plane is represented by a(n) _?_. **ordered pair**
5. A(n) _?_ is formed by the intersection of a horizontal number line and a vertical number line. **coordinate plane**
6. The _?_ is the sum of the values divided by the number of values. **mean**

Review Questions

Order the integers from least to greatest. *(Lesson 2.1)*

7. −42, 53, 8, −31, −5, 11 **−42, −31, −5, 8, 11, 53**
8. −56, −102, 98, −58, 114 **−102, −58, −56, 98, 114**

Write the opposite and the absolute value of the integer. *(Lesson 2.1)*

9. 22 **−22, 22**
10. −13 **13, 13**
11. −512 **512, 512**
12. 102 **−102, 102**

Find the sum or difference. *(Lessons 2.2, 2.3)*

13. $-81 + (-91)$ **−172**
14. $32 + (-79)$ **−47**
15. $-324 + 500$ **176**
16. $-468 + (-196)$ **−664**
17. $-29 - 57$ **−86**
18. $62 - (-58)$ **120**
19. $-43 - (-122)$ **79**
20. $31 - 108$ **−77**

Find the product. *(Lesson 2.4)*

21. $-6(9)$ **−54**
22. $31(-4)$ **−124**
23. $-9(-23)(0)$ **0**
24. $-2(-3)(6)(-12)$ **−432**

Review Questions

Evaluate the expression when $x = -6$, $y = -4$, and $z = -8$. *(Lesson 2.4)*

25. xyz −192 **26.** $9z - 2x$ −60 **27.** $11y - 2xz$ −140 **28.** $2x + 3yz$ 84

29. **Hot Air Balloon** A hot air balloon at a height of 110 feet rises for 6 minutes at a rate of 18 feet per minute, then drops 22 feet per minute for 3 minutes. What is the height of the balloon? *(Lesson 2.4)* 152 ft

Find the quotient. *(Lesson 2.5)*

30. $\frac{-26}{2}$ −13 **31.** $\frac{-98}{-7}$ 14 **32.** $\frac{-120}{-15}$ 8 **33.** $\frac{63}{-7}$ −9

Find the mean of the data. *(Lesson 2.5)*

34. 5, 7, −9, −2, −6, 8, −9, 6 0 **35.** 15, −9, 6, −14, −18, 12, 7, 5, −2, 8 1

Evaluate the expression using mental math. Name the property or properties used. *(Lesson 2.6)* 36–41. See margin.

36. $19 - (-58 - 81)$ **37.** $(-45 + 97) - (-45)$ **38.** $(-28 - 95 + 85) + (-62)$

39. $4(19 \cdot 25)$ **40.** $(-15 \cdot 5) \cdot (-20)$ **41.** $[-54 \cdot (-56)] \cdot 0 \cdot (-17)$

Use the distributive property to simplify the expression. *(Lesson 2.7)*

42. $5(12x - 20)$ $60x - 100$ **43.** $7(9 + 11y)$ $63 + 77y$ **44.** $4(25z - 30)$ $100z - 120$

Simplify the expression by combining like terms. *(Lesson 2.7)*

45. $14x - 3y - 7x + y$ $7x - 2y$ **46.** $4x - 11y + 2(1 - x)$ $2x - 11y + 2$

47. **Baseball Caps** Use mental math and the distributive property to find the total price of 3 baseball caps that cost $12.90 each. *(Lesson 2.7)* $38.70

Give the coordinates of the point. *(Lesson 2.8)*

48. A (3, −1) **49.** B (−4, 3)

50. C (0, −4) **51.** D (−2, −3)

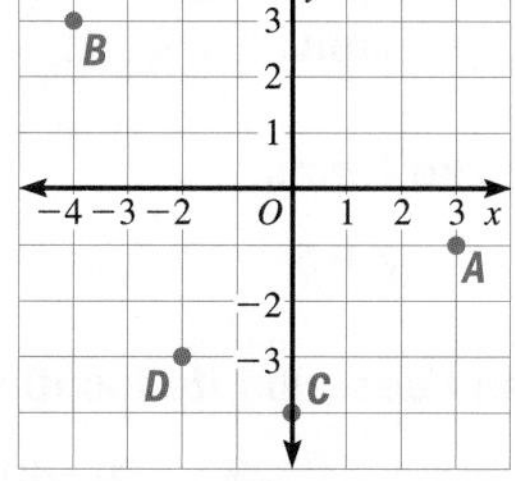

52. **Geometry** Plot, label, and connect in order the following points in a coordinate plane. Find the perimeter of the figure. *(Lesson 2.8)*

$A(0, 7)$, $B(4, 7)$, $C(4, 4)$, $D(8, 4)$, $E(8, 0)$, $F(0, 0)$
See margin for art; 30 units.

36. 158; commutative and associative properties of addition

37. 97; commutative and associative properties of addition, inverse property of addition

38. −100; commutative and associative properties of addition

39. 1900; commutative and associative properties of multiplication

40. 1500; associative property of multiplication

41. 0; multiplication property of zero

52.

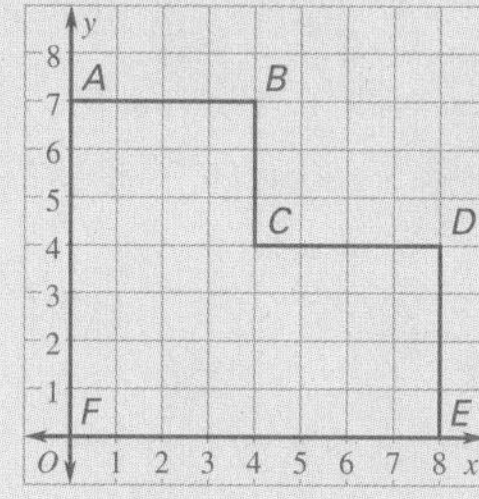

Additional Resources

Assessment Book

- Chapter Test (3 levels), pp. 20–25
- Standardized Chapter Test, p. 26
- Alternative Assessment, pp. 27–28

Test and Practice Generator

26–29.

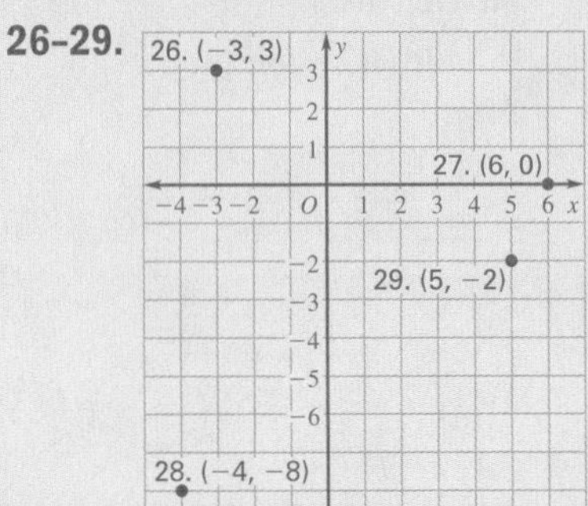

30.

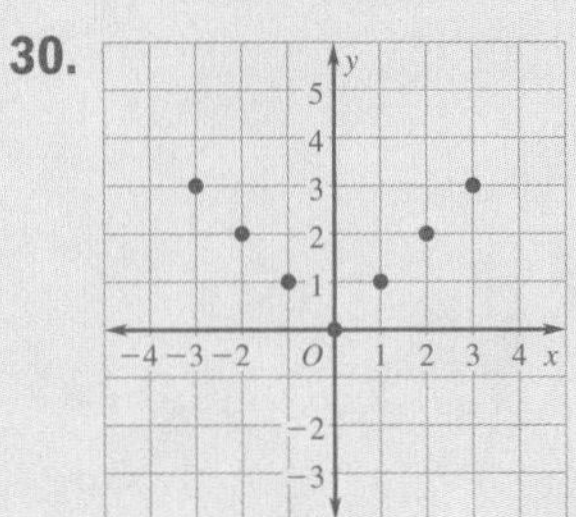

Chapter Test

Order the integers from least to greatest.

1. $-9, 8, 14, -11, 0, -1$ $-11, -9, -1, 0, 8, 14$
2. $123, 87, -59, -12, -111, 22$ $-111, -59, -12, 22, 87, 123$

Find the number.

3. Find $|x|$ when x is 2 and when x is -4. 2, 4
4. Find $-(-x)$ when x is -1 and when x is 7. $-1, 7$

Find the sum or difference.

5. $17 + (-9)$ 8
6. $-8 + (-14)$ -22
7. $-2 + (-21)$ -23
8. $-33 + 26$ -7
9. $1 - 19$ -18
10. $-4 - 17$ -21
11. $10 - (-15)$ 25
12. $-7 - (-18)$ 11

Find the product or the quotient.

13. $-5(14)$ -70
14. $-12(-20)$ 240
15. $\frac{-152}{-19}$ 8
16. $\frac{-132}{6}$ -22
17. **Temperature** The following temperatures were taken during a week in December in Nome, Alaska. What is the mean temperature to the nearest degree?
   −5°F, −8°F, −13°F, −16°F, −8°F, 11°F, 0°F −6°F

Evaluate the expression when $a = 3$, $b = -15$, and $c = 15$.

18. $\frac{c}{-a}$ -5
19. $\frac{6b}{2c}$ -3
20. $\frac{c}{-5a}$ -1
21. $\frac{b^2}{a^2}$ 25
22. **Groceries** You are purchasing a loaf of bread for \$2.16, a box of cereal for \$3.25, and 2 cans of soup for \$.42 each. Write an expression to find the total cost. Then evaluate your expression. $2.16 + 3.25 + 2(0.42)$; \$6.25

Simplify the expression by combining like terms.

23. $3x + 4 - x + 1$ $2x + 5$
24. $2x - 3y + 5x - (-9y)$ $7x + 6y$
25. $2(9x - 22y) + 4x$ $22x - 44y$

Plot the point in a coordinate plane and describe its location. 26–29. See margin for art.

26. $(-3, 3)$ Quadrant II
27. $(6, 0)$ x-axis
28. $(-4, -8)$ Quadrant III
29. $(5, -2)$ Quadrant IV
30. **Critical Thinking** Fill in the table for the equation $y = |x|$. Then plot the points on a coordinate plane. Describe the shape of the graph. See margin for art; V-shaped.

x	−3	−2	−1	0	1	2	3
y	?	?	?	?	?	?	?
	3	2	1	0	1	2	3

Assessment Book
- Standardized Chapter Test, p. 26

Test and Practice Generator

Chapter Standardized Test

Test-Taking Strategy **If you are unsure of an answer, try to eliminate answers that you know are wrong.**

1. Which of the following shows the integers in order from least to greatest? **C**

A. $-7, 11, 5, -6, 0$ **B.** $0, -7, -6, 5, 11$
C. $-7, -6, 0, 5, 11$ **D.** $0, -6, 5, -7, 11$

2. Which of the following is equal to -10? **F**

F. $-|-10|$ **G.** $-(-10)$
H. $|10|$ **I.** $|-10|$

3. Which numerical expression represents the verbal expression "the absolute value of the opposite of negative 6"? **C**

A. $-(-|6|)$ **B.** $-(-6)$
C. $|-(-6)|$ **D.** $-|-6|$

4. What is the value of $-21 + (-15) - 32$? **F**

F. -68 **G.** -24
H. -4 **I.** 39

5. If the temperature is $-6°$ Fahrenheit and it changes by $-12°$ Fahrenheit, what is the new temperature? **A**

A. $-18°$F **B.** $-6°$F
C. $6°$F **D.** $18°$F

6. What is the value of $20 - x - (-y)$ when $x = 9$ and $y = -6$? **G**

F. -23 **G.** 5
H. 17 **I.** 35

7. Which product is *not* equal to -336? **A**

A. $7(-8)(2)(-3)$ **B.** $56(-2)(3)$
C. $3(-7)(8)(2)$ **D.** $-8(-7)(-3)(2)$

8. Evaluate $-4ac + bc - 2a$ when $a = 6$, $b = -2$, and $c = -3$. **H**

F. -66 **G.** -54
H. 66 **I.** 90

9. What is the mean of the following set of data? **B**

$-7, 6, -1, 11, -8, -9, 0, -8$

A. -4 **B.** -2
C. 2 **D.** 6

10. Which ordered pair represents point S in the coordinate plane? **H**

F. $(3, -4)$
G. $(-3, 4)$
H. $(-4, -3)$
I. $(4, -3)$

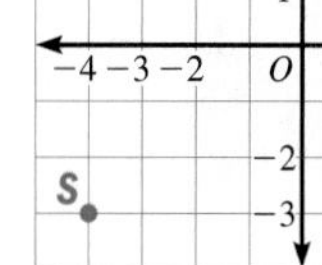

Short Response

11. Explain how the commutative and associative properties of addition can help you find the sum using mental math. **See margin.**

$$(57 + 24) + (36 + 83)$$

Extended Response

12. You are planning a field trip to a museum. The bus ride will cost \$250. Admission is \$8 and lunch is \$5 for each person. Write two expressions to find the total cost for x students. What would the cost be if 20 students went on the trip? 25 students? Did you use the distributive property to find your answer? Explain why or why not. **See margin.**

11. Use the commutative property to change the order to $57 + 83 + 24 + 36$. Then use the associative property to group 57 with 83 and 24 with 36. The result is $140 + 60 = 200$.

12. $250 + x(8 + 5)$ or $250 + 8x + 5x$; \$510; \$575. *Sample answer:* Yes, it made it easier to use mental math to find the answers.

1 PLAN

Explore the Concept

- Students apply their knowledge of adding, subtracting, and dividing integers.
- Addition, subtraction, and division of integers were studied in Chapter 2.
- The body temperature of a hibernating animal drops significantly, and may approach the surrounding temperature.

Science Background

During the winter when little or no food is available and it would require much extra energy to stay warm, some animals survive by hibernating. Their bodies use only stored energy and drastically reduce energy use.

Grouping

Students should work individually.

2 TEACH

Tips for Success

Students should be able to answer Critical Thinking Exercises 4 and 7, but these exercises should also be discussed as a class.

Guiding Students' Work

To help with Exercise 2, students may want to insert tick marks along the horizontal scale so they can better observe the time intervals over which the graph changes. When finding the temperature differences in Exercises 6 and 7, it may help students to use a straightedge or a ruler to make sure they are comparing corresponding parts of the graphs.

4. See Additional Answers beginning on page AA1.

EXPLORING MATH IN SCIENCE

Supercool Squirrels

Hibernating in the Arctic

Animals living in very cold climates may hibernate to survive during winter. Hibernating animals have a decreased heart rate and decreased respiratory rate. The body temperature of a hibernating animal also drops significantly, often to just a few degrees higher than the surrounding temperature.

The arctic ground squirrel's body temperature drops below 0°C during hibernation. The graph below shows the body temperature of an arctic ground squirrel during the last few months of its hibernation.

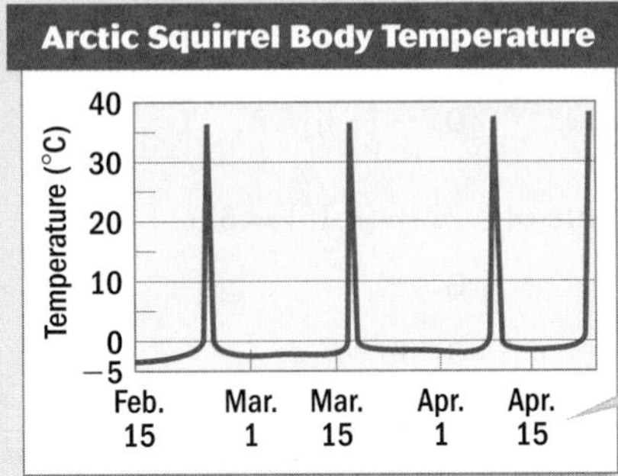

The squirrel hibernates from early September until late April.

The peaks in the graph represent short periods of time during which the squirrel wakes up from hibernation and warms itself up.

1. Estimate the difference of the squirrel's highest and lowest body temperatures for the period shown on the graph. **about 40°C**
2. Which is the best estimate for the longest period during which the squirrel's body temperature was above zero? below zero? **B; D**

   A. 1 hour **B.** 1 day **C.** 5 days **D.** 20 days
3. A squirrel's approximate body temperatures for several days in March were –3°C, –1°C, 36°C, 6°C, –2°C, and –3°C. What is the mean of the temperatures? **5.5°C**
4. **Critical Thinking** Do you think your answer from Exercise 3 is a good representation of the squirrel's usual body temperature during the period of time shown by the graph? Explain your reasoning. **See margin.**

Soil Temperature

The graph below displays the squirrel body temperature data for March and April. It has a smaller temperature range, so waking periods are not fully displayed in the graph.

It also shows the soil temperature at 1 meter below ground, the depth at which the squirrel usually digs its burrow.

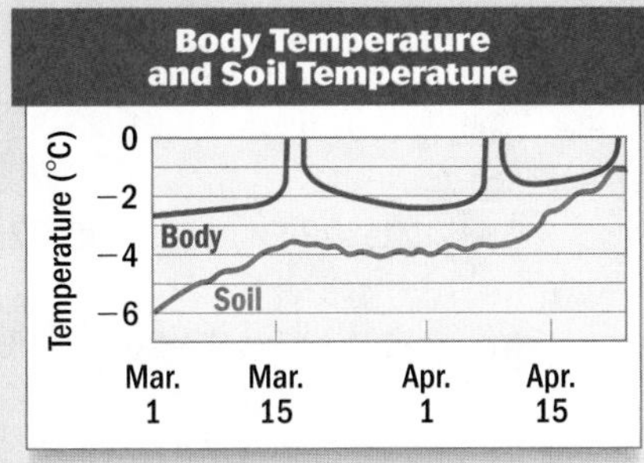

5. What is the difference of body temperature and soil temperature on March 1? What is the difference of these two temperatures on April 15th? **about 3°C; about 1°C**

6. Critical Thinking A scientist claims that a hibernating animal's body temperature is always within 1 or 2 degrees of the surrounding temperature. Discuss whether this claim seems reasonable for the arctic ground squirrel, based on the data given.
Answers may vary. *Sample answer:* No. The difference on March 1 is about 3.5°, and the difference is even greater than this during periods when the squirrel wakes up and its body temperature rises.

Project IDEAS

- **Report** Find out more about the arctic ground squirrel. In what areas does it live? What foods does it eat? What are its predators? Present your findings to the class.
- **Research** Some reptiles and amphibians, such as the Asiatic salamander and the wood frog, can survive subzero temperatures. Find out more about one of these animals. How low can its body temperature go? What mechanisms does it use to avoid freezing? Present your findings to the class.
- **Career** Find out more about the work that biologists do. What are some topics or areas in which a biologist might specialize? Present your findings to the class.

INTERNET
Project Support
CLASSZONE.COM

APPLY

Reflecting on the Activity

Except for brief periods, the body temperature of an arctic ground squirrel drops below the freezing point for the winter, with the difference between its body temperature and the temperature of the surrounding soil no more than a few degrees Celsius.

Project Ideas

For additional information on the Project Ideas and for suggestions for more projects, go to classzone.com

ASSESS

The rubric below can be used to assess the projects on the pupil page. For more information on rubrics, see the Professional Development Book.

4 The student fully achieves the mathematical and project goals. Students justify their reasoning with appropriate data. All work is complete and accurate.

3 The student substantially achieves the mathematical and project goals. The explanations, predictions, and discussion are mostly reasonable, but are not well-supported. There may be some minor misunderstanding of content or errors in computation.

2 The student partially achieves the mathematical and project goals. The student appears to know how to find a mean, but makes mistakes. Explanations, predictions, and discussion are inadequate or unreasonable. Some of the work may be incomplete, misdirected, or unclear.

1 The student makes little progress toward accomplishing the goals of the project because of a lack of understanding or lack of effort.

Pacing and Assignment Guide

REGULAR SCHEDULE

Lesson	Les. Day	BASIC	AVERAGE	ADVANCED
3.1	Day 1	SRH p. 709 Exs. 5-8; pp. 111-112 Exs. 6-16, 27-29, 39-43	pp. 111-112 Exs. 8-16, 25-29, 39-43	pp. 111-112 Exs. 8-14, 25-29, 40-43
	Day 2	SRH p. 710 Exs. 1-5; pp. 111-112 Exs. 17-24, 30-35, 44-49	pp. 111-112 Exs. 17-24, 30-36, 45-49	pp. 111-112 Exs. 19-24, 33-39*, 46-49
3.2	Day 1	SRH p. 713 Exs. 6-10; pp. 115-116 Exs. 5-13, 17-27, 38-46	pp. 115-116 Exs. 11-21, 25-35, 40-47	pp. 115-116 Exs. 11-21, 28-39*, 44-47
3.3	Day 1	EP p. 728 Exs. 29-32; pp. 121-123 Exs. 10-18, 30-32, 40, 48-53	pp. 121-123 Exs. 13-18, 30-36, 40-42, 48-52	pp. 121-123 Exs. 16-18, 30-32, 39-45*, 49-52
	Day 2	pp. 121-123 Exs. 19-29, 33-36, 54-58	pp. 121-123 Exs. 19-29, 37-39, 45-47, 55-58	pp. 121-123 Exs. 19-26, 36-38, 46-48, 56-58
3.4	Day 1	EP p. 727 Exs. 17-20; pp. 126-128 Exs. 7-10, 15-17, 27-29	pp. 126-128 Exs. 7-10, 15-19, 27-30	pp. 126-128 Exs. 7-10, 15-17, 21, 22, 27-29
	Day 2	pp. 126-128 Exs. 12-14, 18-20, 30-33	pp. 126-128 Exs. 11-14, 20-22, 31-34	pp. 126-128 Exs. 11-14, 18-20, 23-26*, 32-34
3.5	Day 1	pp. 137-139 Exs. 6-14, 17-25, 35-50	pp. 137-139 Exs. 8-18, 21-25, 29-33, 38-50	pp. 137-139 Exs. 8-16, 19-34*, 40-44, 48-50
3.6	Day 1	SRH p. 704 Exs. 1-6; pp. 143-145 Exs. 10-31, 37-40, 42-44, 53-59	pp. 143-145 Exs. 12-24, 31-36, 40-49, 55-60	pp. 143-145 Exs. 12-24, 31-33, 39-52*, 55-60
3.7	Day 1	EP p. 728 Exs. 37-40; pp. 148-149 Exs. 9-20, 26-33, 42-50	pp. 148-149 Exs. 11-16, 21-29, 33-37, 42-50	pp. 148-149 Exs. 11-16, 21-29, 33-45*, 50
Review	Day 1	pp. 152-153 Exs. 1-42	pp. 152-153 Exs. 1-42	pp. 152-153 Exs. 1-42
Assess	Day 1	Chapter 3 Test	Chapter 3 Test	Chapter 3 Test

YEARLY PACING Chapter 3 Total – **12 days** Chapters 1-3 Total – **36 days** Remaining – **124 days**

*Challenge Exercises EP = Extra Practice SRH = Skills Review Handbook EC = Extra Challenge

BLOCK SCHEDULE

DAY 1	DAY 2	DAY 3	DAY 4	DAY 5	DAY 6
3.1 pp. 111-112 Exs. 8-36, 39-43, 45-49	**3.2** pp. 115-116 Exs. 11-21, 25-35, 40-47 **3.3** pp. 121-123 Exs. 13-18, 30-36, 40-42, 48-52	**3.3 (cont.)** pp. 121-123 Exs. 19-29, 37-39, 45-47, 55-58 **3.4** pp. 126-128 Exs. 7-10, 15-19, 27-30	**3.4 (cont.)** pp. 126-128 Exs. 11-14, 20-22, 31-34 **3.5** pp. 137-139 Exs. 8-18, 21-25, 29-33, 38-50	**3.6** pp. 143-145 Exs. 12-24, 31-36, 40-49, 55-60 **3.7** pp. 148-149 Exs. 11-16, 21-29, 33-37, 42-50	**Review** pp. 152-153 Exs. 1-42 **Assess** Chapter 3 Test

YEARLY PACING Chapter 3 Total – **6 days** Chapters 1-3 Total – **18 days** Remaining – **62 days**

Support Materials

CHAPTER RESOURCE BOOK

CHAPTER SUPPORT							
Tips for New Teachers	p. 1		Parents as Partners			p. 3	

LESSON SUPPORT	3.1	3.2	3.3	3.4	3.5	3.6	3.7
Lesson Plans (regular and block)	p. 7	p. 16	p. 25	p. 36	p. 45	p. 54	p. 63
Technology Activities & Keystrokes		p. 18	p. 28				
Activity Support Masters	p. 9		p. 27				
Activity Masters						p. 56	
Practice (3 levels)	p. 10	p. 19	p. 30	p. 38	p. 47	p. 57	p. 65
Study Guide	p. 13	p. 22	p. 33	p. 41	p. 50	p. 60	p. 68
Real-World Problem Solving				p. 43	p. 52		
Challenge Practice	p. 15	p. 24	p. 35	p. 44	p. 53	p. 62	p. 70

REVIEW			
Games Support Masters	p. 5	Cooperative Project with Rubric	p. 74
Chapter Review Games and Activities	p. 71	Extra Credit Project with Rubric	p. 76
Real-Life Project with Rubric	p. 72	Cumulative Practice	p. 78
		Resource Book Answers	A1

ASSESSMENT

Quizzes	p. 29	Alternative Assessments with Rubrics	p. 38
Chapter Tests (3 levels)	p. 31	Unit Test	p. 40
Standardized Test	p. 37	Cumulative Test	p. 42

TRANSPARENCIES

	3.1	3.2	3.3	3.4	3.5	3.6	3.7
Warm-Up / Daily Homework Quiz	✔	✔	✔	✔	✔	✔	✔
Notetaking Guide	✔	✔	✔	✔	✔	✔	✔
Teacher Support	✔				✔	✔	✔
English/Spanish Problem Solving		✔				✔	✔
Answer Transparencies	✔	✔	✔	✔	✔	✔	✔

TECHNOLOGY

- EasyPlanner CD-ROM
- Test and Practice Generator
- Electronic Lesson Presentations
- eTutorial CD-ROM
- Chapter Audio Summaries CDs
- Classzone.com
- eEdition Plus Online
- eWorkbook Plus Online
- eTutorial Plus Online
- EasyPlanner Plus Online

ADDITIONAL RESOURCES

- Worked-Out Solution Key
- Notetaking Guide
- Practice Workbook
- Tutor Place
- Professional Development Book
- Special Activities Book
- Posters
- Spanish Study Guide
- Exercises in Spanish
- English/Spanish Ch. Reviews/Tests
- Multi-Language Visual Glossary

Math Background and Teaching Strategies

Lesson 3.1

MATH BACKGROUND

SOLVING EQUATIONS The key to solving an equation is to perform operations that produce successively simpler **equivalent equations**, with the goal of isolating the variable on one side of the equation. For a simple equation involving only addition or subtraction, this means applying the same **inverse operation** to each side: subtraction to undo addition, or addition to undo subtraction. The subtraction and addition properties of equality ensure that the result is an equivalent equation.

TEACHING STRATEGIES

Stress the following keys to solving an equation:

(1) You must perform the same operation on each side of an equation to keep it in "balance."
(2) Choose operations that undo what is done to the variable.
(3) The goal is to get the variable alone on one side of the equation.

For the simple equations of this lesson, students should be able to verbalize the operation to be undone and how to undo it. For example, "In the equation $x + 8 = 11$, 8 is added to the variable, so to get the variable alone I must subtract 8 from each side of the equation."

Lesson 3.2

MATH BACKGROUND

MULTIPLICATION/DIVISION EQUATIONS Solving a simple equation involving only multiplication or division is similar to solving an equation involving only addition or subtraction. Again, this involves performing the inverse operation on each side of the equation that undoes the given operation: multiplication to undo division, and division to undo multiplication. The multiplication and division properties of equality ensure that the result is an equivalent equation. Multiplying or dividing both sides of an equation by zero is not permitted, since doing so does not produce an equivalent equation.

TEACHING STRATEGIES

Point out that the three keys given in the Teaching Strategies for Lesson 3.1 also apply to solving equations involving multiplication or division. Encourage students again to verbalize the operation to be undone and how to undo it. For example, "In the equation $4x = -52$, the variable is multiplied by 4, so to get the variable alone I must divide each side of the equation by 4."

Lesson 3.3

MATH BACKGROUND

TWO-STEP EQUATIONS Solving equations involving both an addition or subtraction operation and a multiplication or division operation forms the next step in the sequence that will lead to solving equations that require simplification of one or both sides as the first step, and solving equations that have variable terms on both sides of the equation. The key at this step is the successive application of two different properties of equality to isolate the variable.

TEACHING STRATEGIES

Point out to students that there are no new principles or properties to learn in this lesson. The three keys mentioned before still guide solving the equations. The only new skill is applying two properties in order. It may help to encourage the use of algebra tiles, as in Hands-on Activity 3.3, as this not only stresses the importance of performing the same operation on each side of an equation, but also helps students learn to perform addition or subtraction before multiplication or division since it may be difficult or impossible to first divide the tiles into identical groups.

Lesson 3.4

MATH BACKGROUND

For teachers and students alike, the four-step process of understanding a problem, planning a strategy, solving using the plan, and looking back is helpful when solving real-world problems. A general understanding of the problem should first be gained, avoiding any quick assumptions as to the type of problem. Then the aim of the problem can be specified, a verbal model can be written, and the verbal model can be translated into an equation.

TEACHING STRATEGIES

Refer students back to the four-step problem solving plan from Lesson 1.7. Also remind them of the three keys for solving an equation from the Teaching Strategies for Lesson 3.1. Then have them write and solve a two-step equation for the following problem after first writing a verbal model.
"Isaiah plans to deposit $10 in his savings account every week until the balance is $200. He already has $150 in his account. How many weeks will it take him to reach his goal?"

After reading the problem thoroughly, students should ask themselves the following questions:
"What information am I given?"
"What information is sought?"
"What is the relationship between the information given and the information sought?"

Lesson 3.5

MATH BACKGROUND

GEOMETRIC FORMULAS The area formula for a triangle states that a triangle's area is one half the product of its base and its height. As with other formulas, you may need to find a value for a variable that is not the defined quantity, such as finding the base of a triangle given its area and height. To do this, substitute known values into the formula and solve the resulting equation for the unknown quantity.

TEACHING STRATEGIES

Students should be given plenty of experience finding the area of triangles, but because the real focus is solving equations, have them practice by substituting and solving to find the width of a rectangle with a perimeter of 72 inches and various lengths, such as 30 inches, 24 inches, and 20 inches. Having students repeat the process of solving will not only enhance their skills, but hint that there is a general solution for the unknown variable in terms of the other variables.

Lesson 3.6

MATH BACKGROUND

SOLVING INEQUALITIES Whereas an equation *equates* two expressions, an **inequality** expresses an order relation between two quantities that may ($\leq, \geq$) or may not ($<, >$) include equality. The solution to a simple linear equation is a single value (unless it is an identity or a contradiction like $x = x + 1$), but a simple linear inequality has infinitely many solutions that are indicated by shading along a number line. The subtraction and addition properties of inequality ensure that adding the same number to or subtracting the same number from each side of an inequality produces an equivalent inequality, just as the subtraction and addition properties of equality did for equations.

TEACHING STRATEGIES

The balance metaphor is not appropriate for solving inequalities, but students should realize that the addition and subtraction properties of inequality are true because order is preserved when adding to or subtracting from each side of an inequality. As an example, have students plot two points on a number line, for example -2 and 3, and write an order relation for them, in this case, $-2 < 3$. Adding the same value to each number shifts both points the same distance to the left or right, so their relative, or ordered, positions do not change.

Lesson 3.7

MATH BACKGROUND

The multiplication and division properties of inequality parallel the multiplication and division properties of equality with one important exception: multiplying or dividing both sides of an inequality by a negative number reverses the direction of the inequality symbol. One way to understand this intuitively is using opposites. For example, if a number is positive, then its opposite is negative. Thus, multiplying each side of the inequality $x > 0$ by -1 gives $-x < 0$.

TEACHING STRATEGIES

Multiplying or dividing each side of an inequality by a negative number is difficult for students. Encourage them to perform the operation in two steps. For example, to solve $-6x < 42$, students can first multiply each side by -1. They can understand this as just changing the signs and reversing the inequality symbol. Then they can divide each side of the resulting inequality, $6x > -42$, by 6 to obtain $x > -7$.

Differentiating Instruction

Strategies for Underachievers

USE MODELS

MANIPULATIVES Hands-on Activity 3.1 and Hands-on Activity 3.3, which use algebra tiles to solve equations, will be of special benefit to underachievers. Provide each student her or his own set of algebra tiles to manipulate. Students should have access to algebra tiles for as long as the tiles are helpful to them.

USE CALCULATORS

PROPERTIES OF EQUALITY When learning how to use the properties of equality to solve equations in Lessons 3.1–3.3, some students may benefit from the use of calculators. These students should still be required to show each step used in the equation solving process. This process should be the focus of the lesson, with the calculator used only to keep the focus on solving equations and away from computation.

USE REPETITION

After completing the Activity at the beginning of Lesson 3.5, some students may have the feeling that the result is some kind of "magic." Have them repeat this activity with several different triangles so that they become comfortable with the result. Students should also be allowed to view the work of other students for even more reinforcement.

SIMPLIFY

OPPOSITES/RECIPROCALS In Lesson 3.3, the Help with Solving tip in the left margin on page 120 suggests that students *add the opposite* to undo either addition or subtraction and *multiply by the reciprocal* to undo either division or multiplication. This tip may help some underachievers by reducing the number of inverse operations they have to choose from when solving an equation. Before suggesting this to a student, however, make sure that the student is comfortable with the concepts of opposites and reciprocals.

USE SCAFFOLDING

In Lesson 3.1, the equations involve only addition or subtraction. You may suggest to students that after they identify such an equation, they can use the method shown below as a template to guide them and help them show the steps of their work. First, the equation is written, in this case $x + 33 = 87$. Next, lines are drawn under each side of the equation, leaving space above the lines to add the same number to each side or subtract the same number from each side. Then an equal sign is placed in the next line, aligned with the original equal sign, to prompt students to write the result of the addition or subtraction.

$$\begin{array}{rcl} x + 33 & = & 87 \\ \hline & = & \end{array}$$

Notice in Example 1 of Lesson 3.3 on page 119 that a vertical addition or subtraction format can also be used as a template for the first step in a two-step equation, but in this case additional lines are required for the steps involving multiplication or division. Some students may benefit from using grid paper to keep their equation-solving work organized and aligned both horizontally and vertically.

In Lesson 3.3, you may wish to provide underachievers with additional scaffolded examples in the style of Exercise 9 on page 121.

IDENTIFY KEY TERMS

WRITING EQUATIONS In Lessons 3.1–3.3, and especially in Lesson 3.4, students will be writing equations to model situations that are presented verbally, that is, they will be solving "word problems." Underachievers may benefit from reviewing the vocabulary cards created for the Strategies for Underachievers from Chapter 1. As they encounter new words or phrases that model mathematical operations, have them create new vocabulary cards, or have them create a poster identifying key terms and language, updating it as necessary.

USE A CO-TEACHING MODEL

Lesson 3.4 requires extensive reading and the ability to analyze sentences carefully. You may wish to work with a Reading Specialist who can help underachievers with reading strategies and with strategies for locating the important information in each problem. It is especially helpful for these students to be taught simultaneously by both a language expert and a math content expert.

You may also wish to involve a Reading Specialist for Problem Solving Strategies 3.5.

Strategies for English Learners

VOCABULARY AND SYMBOLS

Since this chapter has students working with inequalities, have students review the symbols used and their meanings. You can use shapes or simple equations to get the point across.

is equal to	$=$
is not equal to	$\neq$
is approximately equal to	$\approx$
is less than	$<$
is greater than	$>$
is less than or equal to	$\leq$
is greater than or equal to	$\geq$

You can use antonyms such as: *equal : unequal*
same : different
approximate : exact
equivalent : unequivalent
(or *not equivalent*)

Students can also review in terms of synonyms: *equal, same, congruent, equivalent, identical.* You may wish to have students begin a symbols list in their notebooks and then add to it as the year progresses.

Strategies for Advanced Learners

INCREASE DEPTH AND COMPLEXITY

MEASUREMENT EQUIVALENCIES In Lesson 3.3, you may wish to challenge advanced students further in conjunction with Exercise 22 on page 121. Have these students research U.S. Customary measurements and their equivalents. You might interest students with less common units such as the *rod*, the *fathom*, the *dram*, and the *pennyweight*. They can then create examples of conversions between measurements by writing expressions such as the one they wrote to convert 81 feet 8 inches to 980 inches in Exercise 22.

In Lesson 3.7, you may wish to extend Challenge Exercises 38–40 on page 149 by having your advanced learners try to solve compound inequalities that require two or more steps, such as those shown below.

$$-3 < 5x - 9 < 12$$
$$-16 < 4(2x - 5) < -8$$

USE CROSS-CURRICULAR CONNECTIONS

Technology Activity 3.4 is based upon planning a field trip. If your class or grade is planning a field trip during the term, involve students as much as possible in the planning process. Facets of the planning that have mathematical aspects could include, but are not limited to, transportation costs, food and destination costs, collecting money, distance and rate of travel, and timing and scheduling. Have students write and solve equations based on their planning research.

In Lesson 3.6, you can build on the "What do you think?" margin feature on page 136 by having students do research on various animals and how fast these animals walk, run, hop, slither, climb, or swim. Students can use their data to create problem situations that they can model with equations and solve. For example, they might want to find out how much longer it would take a rabbit to run 100 yards than it would take a kangaroo.

Differentiating Instruction: Teaching Resources

Differentiating Alternative Assessment

McDougal Littell *Middle School Mathematics* offers teachers a wide variety of alternative assessment for all levels of students. Pictured here are facsimiles of the alternative assessment pages from the *Assessment Book*, and the various types of chapter projects available in the *Chapter 3 Resource Book*.

Assessment Book

The *Assessment Book* contains two pages of alternative assessment for each chapter in the textbook.

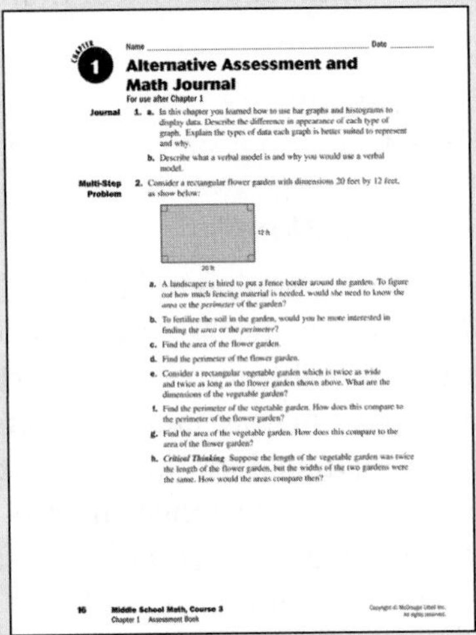

CHAPTER 1 Name ______ Date ______

Alternative Assessment and Math Journal

For use after Chapter 1

Journal

1. a. In this chapter you learned how to use bar graphs and histograms to display data. Describe the difference in appearance of each type of graph. Explain the types of data each graph is better suited to represent and why.
   b. Describe what a verbal model is and why you would use a verbal model.

Multi-Step Problem

2. Consider a rectangular flower garden with dimensions 20 feet by 12 feet, as show below:

   a. A landscaper is hired to put a fence border around the garden. To figure out how much fencing material is needed, would she need to know the *area* or the *perimeter* of the garden?
   b. To fertilize the soil in the garden, would you be more interested in finding the *area* or the *perimeter*?
   c. Find the area of the flower garden.
   d. Find the perimeter of the flower garden.
   e. Consider a rectangular vegetable garden which is twice as wide and twice as long as the flower garden shown above. What are the dimensions of the vegetable garden?
   f. Find the perimeter of the vegetable garden. How does this compare to the perimeter of the flower garden?
   g. Find the area of the vegetable garden. How does this compare to the area of the flower garden?
   h. *Critical Thinking* Suppose the length of the vegetable garden was twice the length of the flower garden, but the widths of the two gardens were the same. How would the areas compare then?

16 **Middle School Math, Course 3** Chapter 1 Assessment Book

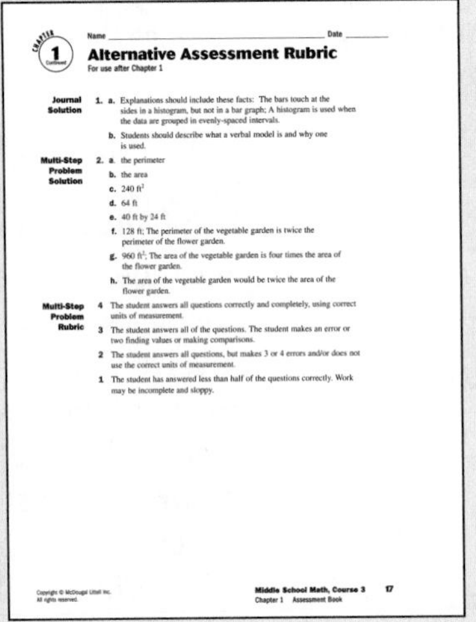

CHAPTER 1 Continued Name ______ Date ______

Alternative Assessment Rubric

For use after Chapter 1

Journal Solution

1. a. Explanations should include these facts: The bars touch at the sides in a histogram, but not in a bar graph; A histogram is used when the data are grouped in evenly-spaced intervals.
   b. Students should describe what a verbal model is and why one is used.

Multi-Step Problem Solution

2. a. the perimeter
   b. the area
   c. 240 ft^2
   d. 64 ft
   e. 40 ft by 24 ft
   f. 128 ft; The perimeter of the vegetable garden is twice the perimeter of the flower garden.
   g. 960 ft^2; The area of the vegetable garden is four times the area of the flower garden.
   h. The area of the vegetable garden would be twice the area of the flower garden.

Multi-Step Problem Rubric

4 The student answers all questions correctly and completely, using correct units of measurement.

3 The student answers all of the questions. The student makes an error or two finding values or making comparisons.

2 The student answers all questions, but makes 3 or 4 errors and/or does not use the correct units of measurement.

1 The student has answered less than half of the questions correctly. Work may be incomplete and sloppy.

Middle School Math, Course 3 Chapter 1 Assessment Book 17

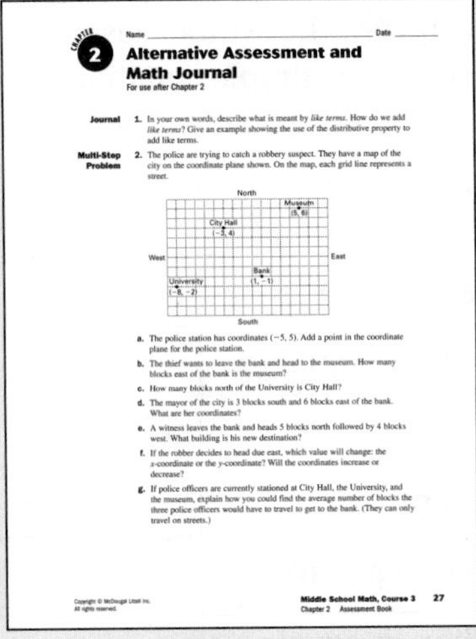

CHAPTER 2 Name ______ Date ______

Alternative Assessment and Math Journal

For use after Chapter 2

Journal

1. In your own words, describe what is meant by *like terms*. How do we add *like terms*? Give an example showing the use of the distributive property to add like terms.

Multi-Step Problem

2. The police are trying to catch a robbery suspect. They have a map of the city on the coordinate plane shown. On the map, each grid line represents a street.

   a. The police station has coordinates (−5, 5). Add a point in the coordinate plane for the police station.
   b. The thief wants to leave the bank and head to the museum. How many blocks east of the bank is the museum?
   c. How many blocks north of the University is City Hall?
   d. The mayor of the city is 3 blocks south and 6 blocks east of the bank. What are her coordinates?
   e. A witness leaves the bank and heads 5 blocks north followed by 4 blocks west. What building is his new destination?
   f. If the robber decides to head due east, which value will change: the *x*-coordinate or the *y*-coordinate? Will the coordinates increase or decrease?
   g. If police officers are currently stationed at City Hall, the University, and the museum, explain how you could find the average number of blocks the three police officers would have to travel to get to the bank. (They can only travel on streets.)

Middle School Math, Course 3 Chapter 2 Assessment Book 27

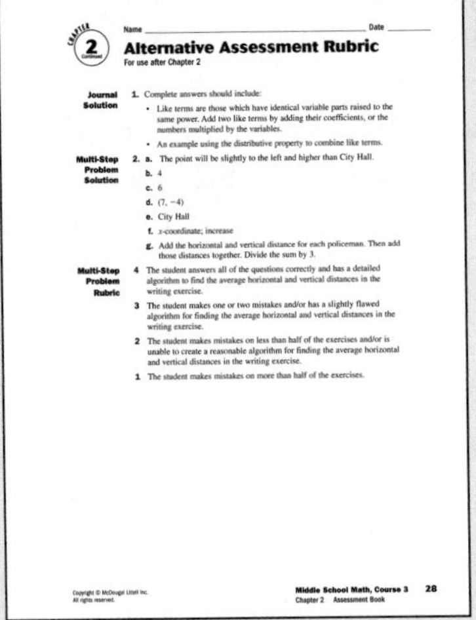

CHAPTER 2 Continued Name ______ Date ______

Alternative Assessment Rubric

For use after Chapter 2

Journal Solution

1. Complete answers should include:
   - Like terms are those which have identical variable parts raised to the same power. Add two like terms by adding their coefficients, or the numbers multiplied by the variables.
   - An example using the distributive property to combine like terms.

Multi-Step Problem Solution

2. a. The point will be slightly to the left and higher than City Hall.
   b. 4
   c. 6
   d. (7, −4)
   e. City Hall
   f. *x*-coordinate; increase
   g. Add the horizontal and vertical distance for each policeman. Then add those distances together. Divide the sum by 3.

Multi-Step Problem Rubric

4 The student answers all of the questions correctly and has a detailed algorithm to find the average horizontal and vertical distances in the writing exercise.

3 The student makes one or two mistakes and/or has a slightly flawed algorithm for finding the average horizontal and vertical distances in the writing exercise.

2 The student makes mistakes on less than half of the exercises and/or is unable to create a reasonable algorithm for finding the average horizontal and vertical distances in the writing exercise.

1 The student makes mistakes on more than half of the exercises.

Middle School Math, Course 3 Chapter 2 Assessment Book 28

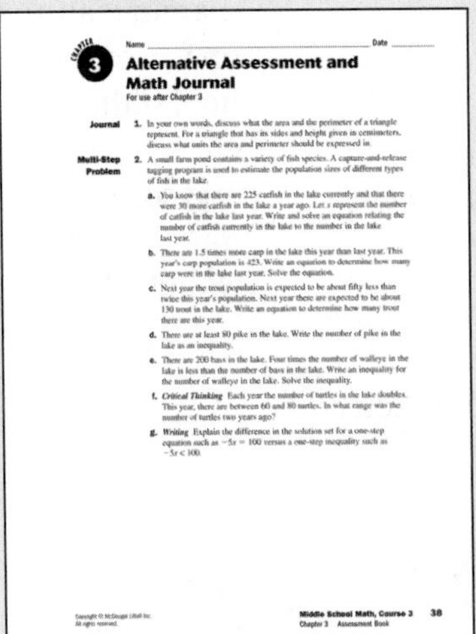

CHAPTER 3 Name ______ Date ______

Alternative Assessment and Math Journal

For use after Chapter 3

Journal

1. In your own words, discuss what the area and the perimeter of a triangle represent. For a triangle that has its sides and height given in centimeters, discuss what units the area and perimeter should be expressed in.

Multi-Step Problem

2. A small farm pond contains a variety of fish species. A capture-and-release tagging program is used to estimate the population sizes of different types of fish in the lake.
   a. You know that there are 225 catfish in the lake currently and that there were 30 more catfish in the lake a year ago. Let *x* represent the number of catfish in the lake last year. Write and solve an equation relating the number of catfish currently in the lake to the number in the lake last year.
   b. There are 1.5 times more carp in the lake this year than last year. This year's carp population is 423. Write an equation to determine how many carp were in the lake last year. Solve the equation.
   c. Next year the trout population is expected to be about fifty less than twice this year's population. Next year there are expected to be about 130 trout in the lake. Write an equation to determine how many trout there are this year.
   d. There are at least 80 pike in the lake. Write the number of pike in the lake as an inequality.
   e. There are 200 bass in the lake. Four times the number of walleye in the lake is less than the number of bass in the lake. Write an inequality for the number of walleye in the lake. Solve the inequality.
   f. *Critical Thinking* Each year the number of turtles in the lake doubles. This year, there are between 60 and 80 turtles. In what range was the number of turtles two years ago?
   g. *Writing* Explain the difference in the solution set for a one-step equation such as $-5x = 100$ versus a one-step inequality such as $-5x < 100$.

Middle School Math, Course 3 Chapter 3 Assessment Book 38

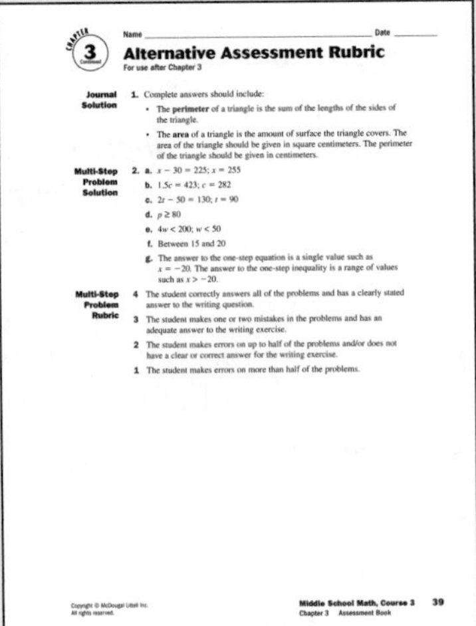

CHAPTER 3 Continued Name ______ Date ______

Alternative Assessment Rubric

For use after Chapter 3

Journal Solution

1. Complete answers should include:
   - The **perimeter** of a triangle is the sum of the lengths of the sides of the triangle.
   - The **area** of a triangle is the amount of surface the triangle covers. The area of the triangle should be given in square centimeters. The perimeter of the triangle should be given in centimeters.

Multi-Step Problem Solution

2. a. $x - 30 = 225$; $x = 255$
   b. $1.5c = 423$; $c = 282$
   c. $2t - 50 = 130$; $t = 90$
   d. $p \geq 80$
   e. $4w < 200$; $w < 50$
   f. Between 15 and 20
   g. The answer to the one-step equation is a single value such as $x = -20$. The answer to the one-step inequality is a range of values such as $x > -20$.

Multi-Step Problem Rubric

4 The student correctly answers all of the problems and has a clearly stated answer to the writing question.

3 The student makes one or two mistakes in the problems and has an adequate answer to the writing exercise.

2 The student makes errors on up to half of the problems and/or does not have a clear or correct answer for the writing exercise.

1 The student makes errors on more than half of the problems.

Middle School Math, Course 3 Chapter 3 Assessment Book 39

Resource Book

The *Chapter Resource Books* contain three different projects for each chapter: Real Life, Cooperative, and Independent Extra Credit. Each project is accompanied by a scoring rubric. Shown below are the three projects for Chapter 3 with their rubrics. A complete discussion of rubrics is available in the *Professional Development Book*.

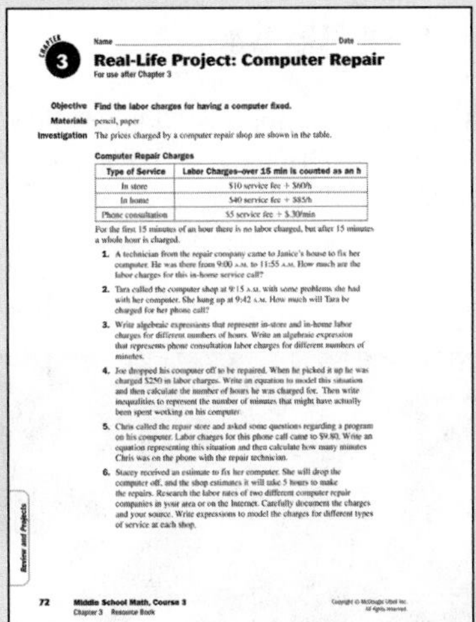

Chapter 3

Name ______ Date ______

Real-Life Project: Computer Repair

For use after Chapter 3

Objective **Find the labor charges for having a computer fixed.**

Materials pencil, paper

Investigation The prices charged by a computer repair shop are shown in the table.

Computer Repair Charges

Type of Service	Labor Charges–over 15 min is counted as an h
In store	\$10 service fee + \$60/h
In home	\$40 service fee + \$85/h
Phone consultation	\$5 service fee + \$.30/min

For the first 15 minutes of an hour there is no labor charged, but after 15 minutes a whole hour is charged.

1. A technician from the repair company came to Janice's house to fix her computer. He was there from 9:00 A.M. to 11:55 A.M. How much are the labor charges for this in-home service call?
2. Tara called the computer shop at 9:15 A.M. with some problems she had with her computer. She hung up at 9:42 A.M. How much will Tara be charged for her phone call?
3. Write algebraic expressions that represent in-store and in-home labor charges for different numbers of hours. Write an algebraic expression that represents phone consultation labor charges for different numbers of minutes.
4. Joe dropped his computer off to be repaired. When he picked it up he was charged \$250 in labor charges. Write an equation to model this situation and then calculate the number of hours he was charged for. Then write inequalities to represent the number of minutes that might have actually been spent working on his computer.
5. Chris called the repair store and asked some questions regarding a program on his computer. Labor charges for this phone call came to \$9.80. Write an equation representing this situation and then calculate how many minutes Chris was on the phone with the repair technician.
6. Stacey received an estimate to fix her computer. She will drop the computer off, and the shop estimates it will take 5 hours to make the repairs. Research the labor rates of two different computer repair companies in your area or on the Internet. Carefully document the charges and your source. Write expressions to model the charges for different types of service at each shop.

Review and Projects

72 **Middle School Math, Course 3** Chapter 3 Resource Book

Copyright © McDougal Littell Inc. All rights reserved.

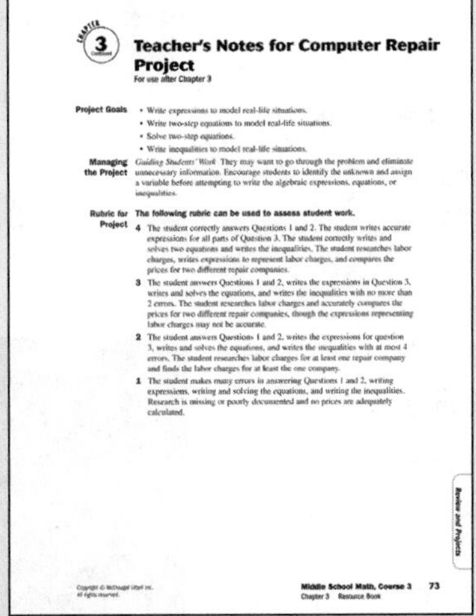

Chapter 3 Continued

Teacher's Notes for Computer Repair Project

For use after Chapter 3

Project Goals
- Write expressions to model real-life situations.
- Write two-step equations to model real-life situations.
- Solve two-step equations.
- Write inequalities to model real-life situations.

Managing the Project *Guiding Students' Work* They may want to go through the problem and eliminate unnecessary information. Encourage students to identify the unknown and assign a variable before attempting to write the algebraic expressions, equations, or inequalities.

Rubric for Project **The following rubric can be used to assess student work.**

4 The student correctly answers Questions 1 and 2. The student writes accurate expressions for all parts of Question 3. The student correctly writes and solves two equations and writes the inequalities. The student researches labor charges, writes expressions to represent labor charges, and compares the prices for two different repair companies.

3 The student answers Questions 1 and 2, writes the expressions in Question 3, writes and solves the equations, and writes the inequalities with no more than 2 errors. The student researches labor charges and accurately compares the prices for two different repair companies, though the expressions representing labor charges may not be accurate.

2 The student answers Questions 1 and 2, writes the expressions for question 3, writes and solves the equations, and writes the inequalities with at most 4 errors. The student researches labor charges for at least one repair company and finds the labor charges for at least the one company.

1 The student makes many errors in answering Questions 1 and 2, writing expressions, writing and solving the equations, and writing the inequalities. Research is missing or poorly documented and no prices are adequately calculated.

Review and Projects

Copyright © McDougal Littell Inc. All rights reserved.

Middle School Math, Course 3 Chapter 3 Resource Book 73

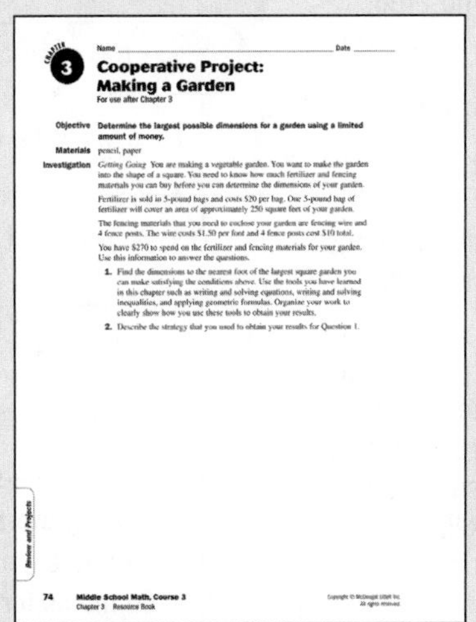

Chapter 3

Name ______ Date ______

Cooperative Project: Making a Garden

For use after Chapter 3

Objective **Determine the largest possible dimensions for a garden using a limited amount of money.**

Materials pencil, paper

Investigation *Getting Going* You are making a vegetable garden. You want to make the garden into the shape of a square. You need to know how much fertilizer and fencing materials you can buy before you can determine the dimensions of your garden.

Fertilizer is sold in 5-pound bags and costs \$20 per bag. One 5-pound bag of fertilizer will cover an area of approximately 250 square feet of your garden.

The fencing materials that you need to enclose your garden are fencing wire and 4 fence posts. The wire costs \$1.50 per foot and 4 fence posts cost \$10 total.

You have \$270 to spend on the fertilizer and fencing materials for your garden. Use this information to answer the questions.

1. Find the dimensions to the nearest foot of the largest square garden you can make satisfying the conditions above. Use the tools you have learned in this chapter such as writing and solving equations, writing and solving inequalities, and applying geometric formulas. Organize your work to clearly show how you use these tools to obtain your results.
2. Describe the strategy that you used to obtain your results for Question 1.

Review and Projects

74 **Middle School Math, Course 3** Chapter 3 Resource Book

Copyright © McDougal Littell Inc. All rights reserved.

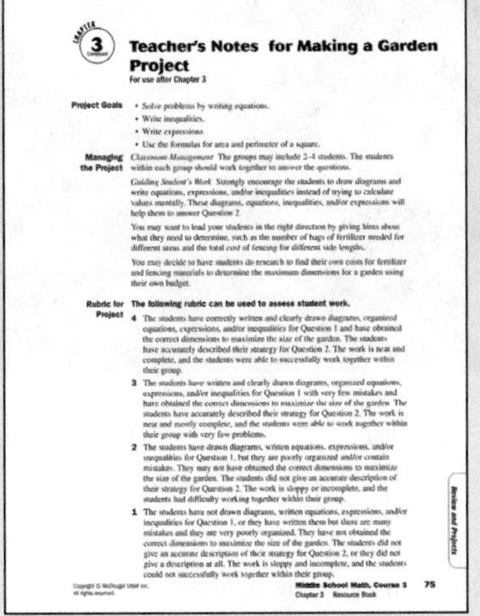

Chapter 3 Continued

Teacher's Notes for Making a Garden Project

For use after Chapter 3

Project Goals
- Solve problems by writing equations.
- Write inequalities.
- Write expressions.
- Use the formulas for area and perimeter of a square.

Managing the Project *Classroom Management* The groups may include 2–4 students. The students within each group should work together to answer the questions.

Guiding Student's Work Strongly encourage the students to draw diagrams and write equations, expressions, and/or inequalities instead of trying to calculate values mentally. These diagrams, equations, inequalities, and/or expressions will help them to answer Question 2.

You may want to lead your students in the right direction by giving hints about what they need to determine, such as the number of bags of fertilizer needed for different areas and the total cost of fencing for different side lengths.

You may decide to have students do research to find their own costs for fertilizer and fencing materials to determine the maximum dimensions for a garden using their own budget.

Rubric for Project **The following rubric can be used to assess student work.**

4 The students have correctly written and clearly drawn diagrams, organized equations, expressions, and/or inequalities for Question 1 and have obtained the correct dimensions to maximize the size of the garden. The students have accurately described their strategy for Question 2. The work is neat and complete, and the students were able to successfully work together within their group.

3 The students have written and clearly drawn diagrams, organized equations, expressions, and/or inequalities for Question 1 with very few mistakes and have obtained the correct dimensions to maximize the size of the garden. The students have accurately described their strategy for Question 2. The work is neat and mostly complete, and the students were able to work together within their group with very few problems.

2 The students have drawn diagrams, written equations, expressions, and/or inequalities for Question 1, but they are poorly organized and/or contain mistakes. They may not have obtained the correct dimensions to maximize the size of the garden. The students did not give an accurate description of their strategy for Question 2. The work is sloppy or incomplete, and the students had difficulty working together within their group.

1 The students have not drawn diagrams, written equations, expressions, and/or inequalities for Question 1, or they have written them but there are many mistakes and they are very poorly organized. They have not obtained the correct dimensions to maximize the size of the garden. The students did not give an accurate description of their strategy for Question 2, or they did not give a description at all. The work is sloppy and incomplete, and the students could not successfully work together within their group.

Review and Projects

Copyright © McDougal Littell Inc. All rights reserved.

Middle School Math, Course 3 Chapter 3 Resource Book 75

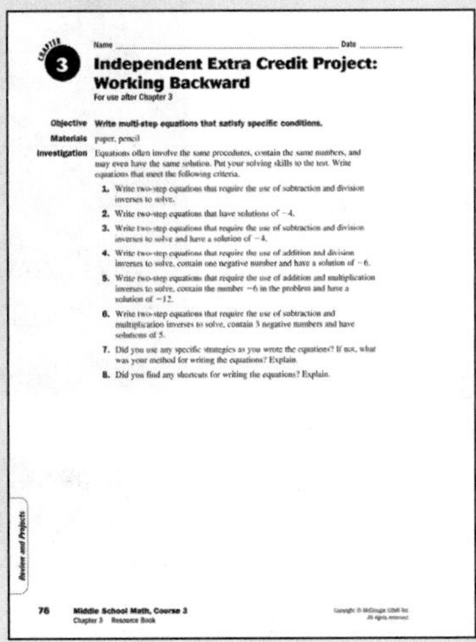

Chapter 3

Name ______ Date ______

Independent Extra Credit Project: Working Backward

For use after Chapter 3

Objective **Write multi-step equations that satisfy specific conditions.**

Materials paper, pencil

Investigation Equations often involve the same procedures, contain the same numbers, and may even have the same solution. Put your solving skills to the test. Write equations that meet the following criteria.

1. Write two-step equations that require the use of subtraction and division inverses to solve.
2. Write two-step equations that have solutions of -4.
3. Write two-step equations that require the use of subtraction and division inverses to solve and have a solution of -4.
4. Write two-step equations that require the use of addition and division inverses to solve, contain one negative number and have a solution of -6.
5. Write two-step equations that require the use of addition and multiplication inverses to solve, contain the number -6 in the problem and have a solution of -12.
6. Write two-step equations that require the use of subtraction and multiplication inverses to solve, contain 3 negative numbers and have solutions of 5.
7. Did you use any specific strategies as you wrote the equations? If not, what was your method for writing the equations? Explain.
8. Did you find any shortcuts for writing the equations? Explain.

Review and Projects

76 **Middle School Math, Course 3** Chapter 3 Resource Book

Copyright © McDougal Littell Inc. All rights reserved.

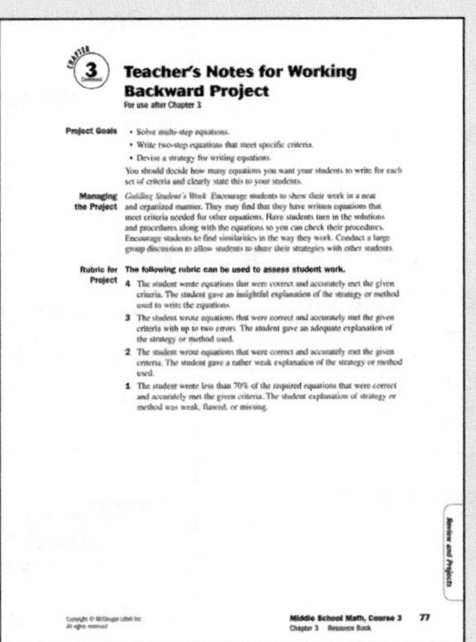

Chapter 3 Continued

Teacher's Notes for Working Backward Project

For use after Chapter 3

Project Goals
- Solve multi-step equations.
- Write two-step equations that meet specific criteria.
- Devise a strategy for writing equations.

You should decide how many equations you want your students to write for each set of criteria and clearly state this to your students.

Managing the Project *Guiding Student's Work* Encourage students to show their work in a neat and organized manner. They may find that they have written equations that meet criteria needed for other equations. Have students turn in the solutions and procedures along with the equations so you can check their procedures. Encourage students to find similarities in the way they work. Conduct a large group discussion to allow students to share their strategies with other students.

Rubric for Project **The following rubric can be used to assess student work.**

4 The student wrote equations that were correct and accurately met the given criteria. The student gave an insightful explanation of the strategy or method used to write the equations.

3 The student wrote equations that were correct and accurately met the given criteria with up to two errors. The student gave an adequate explanation of the strategy or method used.

2 The student wrote equations that were correct and accurately met the given criteria. The student gave a rather weak explanation of the strategy or method used.

1 The student wrote less than 70% of the required equations that were correct and accurately met the given criteria. The student explanation of strategy or method was weak, flawed, or missing.

Review and Projects

Copyright © McDougal Littell Inc. All rights reserved.

Middle School Math, Course 3 Chapter 3 Resource Book 77

OVERVIEW

Main Ideas

In this chapter, students use both algebra tiles and algebraic methods to solve linear equations and inequalities. Students use these methods to solve one- and two-step equations and inequalities. Students write and solve each type of equation and inequality to solve real-world problems. Students solve equations and find dimensions using formulas for perimeter and area.

Prerequisite Skills

The key skills reviewed in the games on these pages are:

- Solving mental math equations
- Performing operations with integers

Additional practice with prerequisite skills can be found in the Review What You Need to Know exercises on page 106. Additional resources for reviewing prerequisite skills are:

- Skills Review Handbook, pp. 704–726
- Tutor Place
- eTutorial Plus

Managing the Games

Tips for Success

In *Name that Planet*, suggest to students that they recast each equation in sentence form before trying to solve it. For example, the first equation can be restated as "3 times what number is 48?" This should help clarify what is being sought in each equation.

Solving Equations and Inequalities

BEFORE

In previous chapters you've...

- Evaluated expressions
- Solved word problems

Now

In Chapter 3 you'll study...

- Solving one-step equations
- Solving two-step equations
- Writing equations
- Formulas for area and perimeter
- Writing and solving inequalities
- Real life modeling

WHY?

So you can solve real-world problems about...

- sea lions, p. 112
- cartoonists, p. 121
- biplane rides, p. 143
- DJs, p. 149

Internet Preview
CLASSZONE.COM

- eEdition Plus Online
- eWorkbook Plus Online
- eTutorial Plus Online
- State Test Practice
- More Examples

Chapter Warm-Up Games

Review Skills you need for this chapter in these quick games. Work with a partner.

Key Skill:
Solving mental math equations

- Use mental math to find the missing number.
  16; 20; 21; 10; 5; 18; 9
- Match each answer with the corresponding letter of the alphabet. (1 = A, 2 = B, etc.)
- Rearrange the letters to find the name of a planet.
  Ans: Jupiter

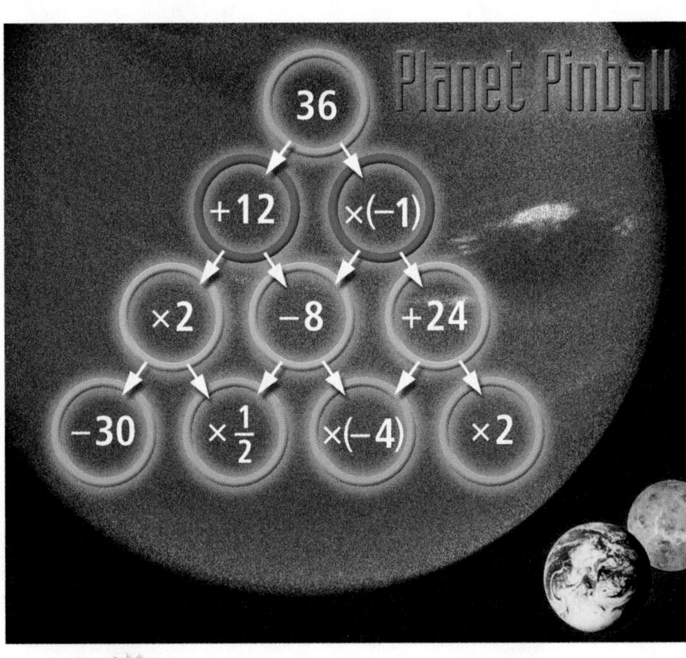

Key Skill: Operations with integers

Materials: penny

- Both players start at the top planet with 36 points.
- On your turn, toss a coin. If you get heads, go to the planet on the left. If you get tails, go to the planet on the right.
- Perform the operation written on the planet. The result is your current score.
- Take turns moving until both players reach the bottom row.
- The player with the higher score wins.

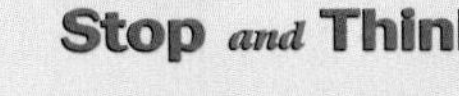

1. **Writing** Without tossing the coin, work with your partner to find the route through the planets in the *Planet Pinball* that gives the highest score. Explain how you know you have found the best route.
2. **Extension** Choose another planet name. Write a puzzle like *Name that Planet!* with that name as the solution. **See margin.**

1. $[[36 \times (-1)] - 8] \times (-4) = 176$. ***Sample answer:*** **I solved all the paths and this was the highest score.**

Reflecting on the Games

To help with Stop & Think Question 1, suggest students write the operations and results of those operations along each path. Help them realize that you can go one of two ways at each planet, so there are $2 \cdot 2 \cdot 2 = 8$ possible paths in all. You may want to challenge students to create their own *Planet Pinball* game using different numbers and operations.

CHAPTER RESOURCES

These resources are provided to help you prepare for the chapter and to customize review materials:

Chapter 3 Resource Book
- Tips for New Teachers, pp. 1–2
- Lesson Plan, pp. 7, 16, 25, 36, 45, 54, 63
- Lesson Plan for Block Scheduling, pp. 8, 17, 26, 37, 46, 55, 64

Technology
- EasyPlanner CD-ROM
- Test and Practice Generator
- Electronic Lesson Presentations CD-ROM
- eTutorial CD-ROM

Internet
- Classzone
- eEdition Plus Online
- eWorkbook Plus Online
- eTutorial Plus Online
- EasyPlanner Plus Online

ENGLISH LEARNER SUPPORT

- Spanish Study Guide
- Multi-Language Glossary
- Chapter Audio Summaries CDs
- Teacher's Edition, pp. 104E–104F

2. ***Sample answer:***

$5 \times \underline{?} = 95$	$(19 \rightarrow S)$
$16 \times \underline{?} = 16$	$(1 \rightarrow A)$
$\frac{180}{?} = 10$	$(18 \rightarrow R)$
$50 - \underline{?} = 37$	$(13 \rightarrow M)$

Answer: MARS

PREPARE

Diagnosis/Remediation

Review What You Need to Know
The Review What You Need to Know exercises can help you diagnose whether students have the following skills needed in Chapter 3:

- Use vocabulary correctly (Exs. 1-3)
- Solve equations using mental math (Exs. 4-11)
- Evaluate numerical expressions (Exs. 12-15)
- Write and solve an equation (Ex. 16)

Chapter 3 Resource Book

- Study Guide (Lessons 3.1-3.7)

Tutor Place

Notetaking Strategies

Besides being a problem solving strategy, making a table can help students organize information in a pictorial way in their notebooks. Make sure students are able to read the table on this page correctly using the rows and columns, for example, "positive times negative is negative." Further suggestions for keeping a notebook can be found on page 146.

For more support on notetaking, see:

- Notetaking Guide Workbook
- Notetaking Transparencies

Getting Ready to Learn

Word Watch

Review Words
variable, p. 15
equation, p. 28
solution, p. 28
opposite, p. 54
like terms, p. 86
coefficient, p. 86

Review What You Need to Know

Using Vocabulary **Copy and complete using a review word.**

1. 5 is the _?_ of -5. opposite
2. 6 is the _?_ in the expression $6x$. coefficient
3. A(n) _?_ shows that two expressions are equal. equation

Solve the equation using mental math. *(p. 28)*

4. $x - 1 = 5$ 6 **5.** $x - 2 = 9$ 11 **6.** $4 + x = 12$ 8 **7.** $10 = x + 3$ 7

8. $5 - x = 2$ 3 **9.** $x - 3 = 1$ 4 **10.** $x + 3 = 4$ 1 **11.** $8 + x = 8$ 0

In Exercises 12–15, evaluate the expression. *(pp. 58, 63, 70)*

12. $-3 - 2 + 8$ 3 **13.** $3 - 7 + 2 - 1$ -3 **14.** $-2(3 + 1) + 2$ -6 **15.** $8(1 - 4) - 9$ -33

16. A tsunami wave caused by an underwater earthquake travels across the ocean at 500 miles per hour. Write and solve an equation to find how far it travels in 15 minutes. *(p. 33)* $d = 500 \cdot 0.25 = 125$ mi

You should include material that appears on a notebook like this in your own notes.

Know How to Take Notes

Organizing Information Sometimes you can organize complicated information in a table to make it easier to understand.

Multiplying Integers

x	Positive	Negative
Positive	+	−
Negative	−	+

In Lesson 3.7, you may want to make a table to help you organize information about solving inequalities.

106

3.1 Hands-on Activity

GOAL
Solve addition and subtraction equations using algebra tiles.

MATERIALS
- algebra tiles

Modeling One-Step Equations

You can use algebra tiles to model and solve one-step addition equations and one-step subtraction equations.

Represents the variable x	Represents a positive unit, or 1	Represents a negative unit, or -1
+	+	−
x-tile	1-tile	-1-tile

When you combine a 1-tile and a -1-tile, the result is zero. This pair of tiles is called a *zero pair* and may be removed from the model.

Explore 1 **Model and solve $x + 3 = 8$.**

1. Model $x + 3 = 8$ using algebra tiles.

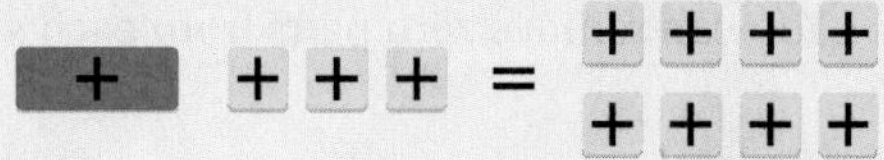

2. Remove three 1-tiles from each side so the x-tile is by itself.

3. The solution of the equation is 5.

Your turn now

1. Use algebra tiles to model each step below. Draw a picture of each step.

(1) Model the equation $x + 5 = 7$. **Steps 1–2. See margin.**

(2) Remove five 1-tiles from each side.

(3) Find the solution. 2

Use algebra tiles to model and solve the equation.

2. $x + 4 = 9$ 5 **3.** $5 + x = 7$ 2 **4.** $6 = x + 2$ 4 **5.** $7 + x = 9$ 2

ILLINOIS Standards and ISAT:
8.A.3b, 8.D.3a

1 PLAN

EXPLORE THE CONCEPT

- Solve addition and subtraction equations using algebra tiles.
- This activity leads into solving linear equations algebraically, which begins in Lesson 3.1.

MATERIALS

Each student or pair of students will need algebra tiles. See also the Activity Support Master in the *Chapter 3 Resource Book*.

RECOMMENDED TIME

Work activity: 10 min
Discuss results: 10 min

GROUPING

Students can work individually or in pairs. If students work in pairs, one can read aloud the instructions while the partner arranges the tiles.

TRANSPARENCY

A support transparency is available for this Activity.

3 APPLY

ALTERNATIVE STRATEGY

Write ×, +, and − on sheets of paper. Then have students, each holding a sheet of paper, group themselves to act out the tile arrangements.

1. Steps 1–2:

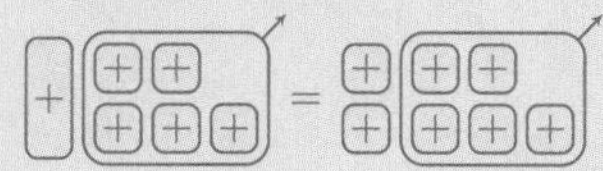

Discussion

As students work through the second Explore, have them discuss why it is necessary to form and remove zero pairs in this equation, but not in the equation in the first Explore. Point out that if the first equation had been $x + 8 = 3$ instead of $x + 3 = 8$, then zero pairs would have had to be created and then removed. Emphasize that the same number of 1- or -1-tiles are added to each side of an equation.

3 CLOSE

Key Discovery

You can solve equations that contain a variable and an addition or subtraction by performing the same operation on both sides of the equation.

Assessment

1. What tiles make up a zero pair? **one 1-tile and one -1-tile**
2. Why is a zero pair called by this name? **When you combine the tiles of a zero pair, their net value is $1 + (-1) = 0$.**

Hands-on Activity Continued

Explore 2 **Model and solve $x - 5 = -3$. Write the equation at each step.**

	Tile Model	Algebra
1	 To get the x-tile by itself, you can add the same number of 1-tiles to each side to create zero pairs. So, add five 1-tiles to each side.	$x - 5 = -3$
2	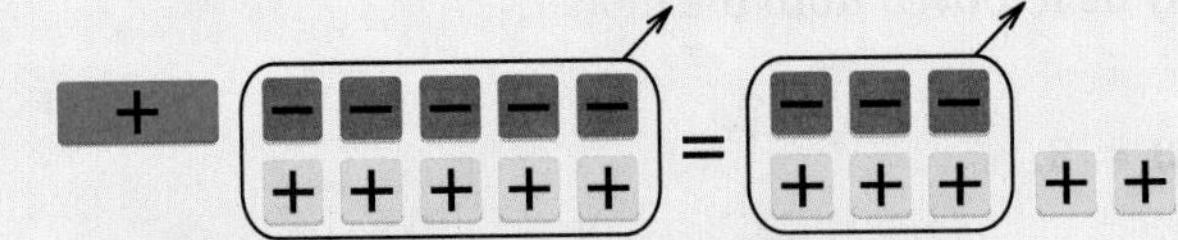 You can remove zero pairs from each side.	$x - 5 + 5 = -3 + 5$
3	 =  The solution is 2.	$x = 2$

Your turn now **Use algebra tiles to model and solve the equation. Write the equation at each step.**

6. $x - 3 = 6$
7. $x - 5 = 5$
8. $x + 6 = 2$
9. $8 + x = 1$
10. $x - 4 = -2$
11. $x - 7 = -3$
12. $x + 8 = 4$
13. $x - 3 = -6$

6. $x - 3 + 3 = 6 + 3$; $x = 9$
7. $x - 5 + 5 = 5 + 5$; $x = 10$
8. $x + 6 - 6 = 2 - 6$; $x = -4$
9. $8 - 8 + x = 1 - 8$; $x = -7$
10. $x - 4 + 4 = -2 + 4$; $x = 2$
11. $x - 7 + 7 = -3 + 7$; $x = 4$
12. $x + 8 - 8 = 4 - 8$; $x = -4$
13. $x - 3 + 3 = -6 + 3$; $x = -3$

Stop and Think

14. **Writing** Give an example of an equation that requires you to make zero pairs to solve. How do you know that zero pairs are required? ***Sample answer:*** **$x - 4 = -1$; there are not enough -1-tiles on the right to take away four -1-tiles.**
15. **Critical Thinking** Can you model the equation $x + \frac{3}{2} = 5$ using x-tiles and 1-tiles? Explain. **No; you cannot show half a tile.**

Solving Equations Using Addition or Subtraction

BEFORE	Now	WHY?
You solved equations using mental math.	You'll solve equations using addition or subtraction.	So you can find the amount that a sea lion grows, as in Ex. 36.

equivalent equations, p. 109
inverse operation, p. 109

You can model and solve an equation by using a scale as shown.

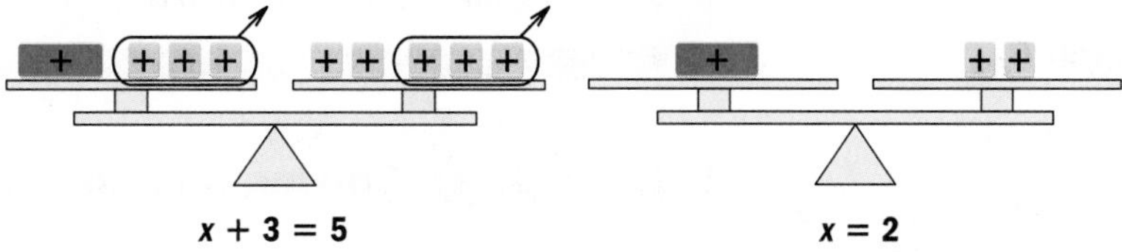

$x + 3 = 5$ $\qquad$ $x = 2$

In the model above, removing three 1-tiles from each side of the scale keeps the scale in balance.

When you perform the same operation on each side of an equation, the result is a new equation that has the same solution. Equations that have the same solution(s) are **equivalent equations**.

You can solve an equation by using *inverse operations* to write equivalent equations. An **inverse operation** is an operation that "undoes" another operation. Addition and subtraction are inverse operations.

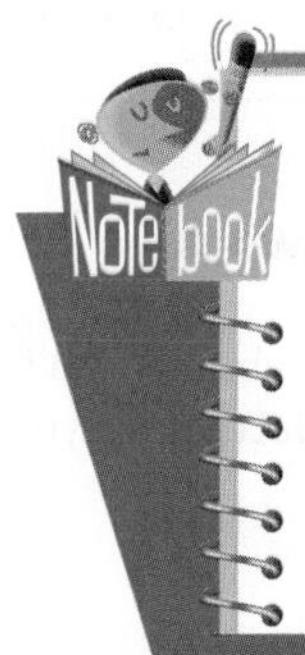

Subtraction Property of Equality

Words Subtracting the same number from each side of an equation makes an equivalent equation.

Numbers If $x + 5 = 7$, then $x + 5 - 5 = 7 - 5$.

Algebra If $a = b$, then $a - c = b - c$.

EXAMPLE 1 Solving an Equation Using Subtraction

$x + 8 = -15$	**Original equation**
$\underline{-8 \quad -8}$	**Subtract 8 from each side to undo addition.**
$x = -23$	**Simplify. *x* is by itself.**

ANSWER The solution is -23.

ILLINOIS Standards and ISAT:
8.A.3b, 8.D.3a

1 PLAN

SKILL CHECK
1. $-15 - 8 = \underline{?}$ $\quad -23$
2. $-4.5 + 4.5 = \underline{?}$ $\quad 0$
3. $-15 + 14 = \underline{?}$ $\quad -1$

LESSON OBJECTIVE
Solve equations using addition or subtraction.

PACING
Suggested Number of Days
Basic Course: 2 days
Average Course: 2 days
Advanced Course: 2 days
Block: 1 block

TEACHING RESOURCES
For a complete list of Teaching Resources, see page 104B.

TRANSPARENCY
Warm-Up Exercises for this lesson are available on a transparency. A support transparency is available for the beginning of the lesson.

2 TEACH

MOTIVATING THE LESSON
Use a scale to show how adding or removing the same number of identical items to or from both sides of a balanced scale maintains its balance.

TIPS FOR NEW TEACHERS
Emphasize that the goal is to have the weight representing the variable alone on one side of the scale balanced by its equivalent weight on the other side. See Tips for New Teachers in the *Chapter 3 Resource Book*.

EXTRA EXAMPLES

Example 1 Solve the equation $24 + z = -14$. **−38**

Example 2 Solve the equation $-6.4 + y = 3.4$. **9.8**

Example 3 José hikes 3.4 kilometers of a 10 kilometer trail before taking a break. How much farther does he have to hike to complete the trail? **6.6 km**

VISUALIZE

Demonstrate the addition and subtraction properties of equality using common classroom objects. For example, adding or subtracting the same number of identical textbooks to or from two equal-sized groups of textbooks does not change the fact that the groups contain the same number of books. Model this demonstration also using a "variable," such as a dictionary, that represents different numbers of textbooks.

CONCEPT CHECK

How can you use an inverse operation to solve an equation? ***Sample answer:*** **On both sides of an equation, perform the operation that "undoes" the operation with the variable. For example, if 5 is added to the variable, subtract 5 from both sides of the equation.**

DAILY PUZZLER

Luba needs to measure 4 ounces of chocolate for a recipe but can find only 5 and 9 ounce weights for her balance scale. How can she measure the chocolate? **Put the 9 ounce weight on one side, the 5 ounce weight on the other, and add chocolate to the side with the 5 ounce weight until the scale balances.**

You can also use the addition property of equality to solve an equation.

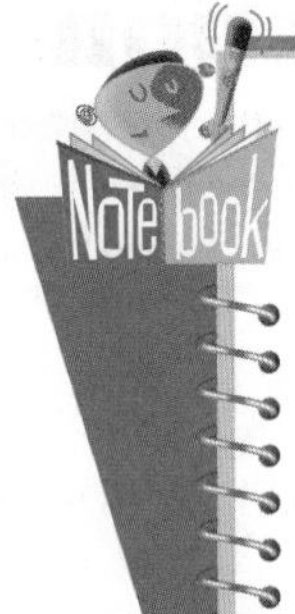

Addition Property of Equality

Words Adding the same number to each side of an equation makes an equivalent equation.

Numbers If $x - 2 = 6$, then $x - 2 + 2 = 6 + 2$.

Algebra If $a = b$, then $a + c = b + c$.

Watch Out! You can add or subtract horizontally or vertically to solve equations, but remember that when solving, you must perform the same operation on *each* side.

EXAMPLE 2 Solving an Equation Using Addition

$c - 4.5 = 13$	Original equation
$c - 4.5 + 4.5 = 13 + 4.5$	Add 4.5 to each side to undo subtraction.
$c = 17.5$	Simplify. c is by itself.
✓**Check** $17.5 - 4.5 \stackrel{?}{=} 13$	Substitute 17.5 for c in original equation.
$13 = 13$ ✓	

Your turn now **Solve the equation. Check your solution.**

1. $x + 9 = 20$ **11**
2. $-10 = 3 + y$ **−13**
3. $m - 14 = -15$ **−1**
4. $2 = z - 6.4$ **8.4**

EXAMPLE 3 Using a Verbal Model

Rock Climbing A cliff has a height of about 1500 feet. If you have already climbed 675 feet, how much farther do you have to climb to reach the top?

Solution

Write a verbal model. Let x represent the distance left to climb.

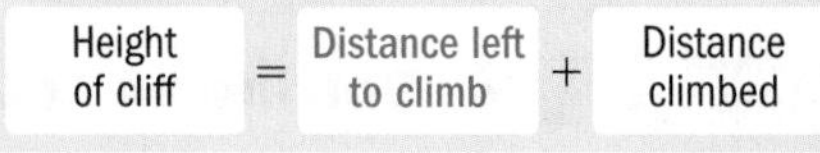

$1500 = x + 675$	Write an algebraic model.
$1500 - 675 = x + 675 - 675$	Subtract 675 from each side.
$825 = x$	Simplify. x is by itself.

ANSWER You have about 825 feet left to climb.

Exercises

More Practice, p. 729

INTERNET
eWorkbook Plus
CLASSZONE.COM

Getting Ready to Practice

1. **Vocabulary** Copy and complete: Addition and subtraction are _?_ operations. inverse

Solve the equation. Check your solution.

2. $x + 10 = 16$ 6
3. $12 = x - 8$ 20
4. $x + 1.3 = 2.5$ 1.2
5. **Guided Problem Solving** You buy new school supplies. The price of the items is \$54.99, but after sales tax is added, they cost \$58.29. How much is the sales tax?

(1) Copy and complete the verbal model. Sales tax

Price + _?_ = Total cost

(2) Substitute numbers and variables in the verbal model to write an algebraic model. $54.99 + x = 58.29$

(3) Solve the algebraic model. Check your solution. \$3.30

Practice and Problem Solving

HELP with Homework

Example	Exercises
1	9-20
2	9-20
3	21-24

Online Resources
CLASSZONE.COM
· More Examples
· eTutorial Plus

A **Describe an inverse operation that will undo the given operation.**

6. Adding 4 subtracting 4
7. Adding 4.5 subtracting 4.5
8. Subtracting 35 adding 35

Solve the equation.

9. $r + 2 = 7$ 5
10. $t - 5 = 2$ 7
11. $9 = p - 4$ 13
12. $6 + x = 8$ 2
13. $z + 9 = 11$ 2
14. $23 = 6 + s$ 17
15. $y - 15 = 9$ 24
16. $13 = d - 27$ 40
17. $24 = 52 + n$ −28
18. $204 = m - 41$ 245
19. $43 = a - 21$ 64
20. $11 = c + 48$ −37

Tell whether the equation correctly represents the real-life problem. If not, correct the equation.

21. At 62 inches tall, you are 5 inches taller than your sister. How tall is your sister? Equation: $62 = s + 5$. yes
22. There are 540 freshmen this year. This is 29 more than last year. How many freshmen were there last year? Equation: $f - 29 = 540$. no; $540 = f + 29$
23. The mean temperature for February 4 in Chicago is 3°F below the mean temperature of 29°F for all of February in Chicago. What is the mean temperature for February 4? Equation: $t - 3 = 29$. no; $t = 29 - 3$
24. An item that usually costs \$2.29 will cost \$1.79 with a coupon. How much is the coupon worth? Equation: $2.29 - c = 1.79$. yes

3 APPLY

ASSIGNMENT GUIDE

Basic Course

Day 1: SRH p. 709 Exs. 5-8; pp. 111-112 Exs. 6-16, 27-29, 39-43

Day 2: SRH p. 710 Exs. 1-5; pp. 111-112 Exs. 17-24, 30-35, 44-49

Average Course

Day 1: pp. 111-112 Exs. 8-16, 25-29, 39-43

Day 2: pp. 111-112 Exs. 17-24, 30-36, 45-49

Advanced Course

Day 1: pp. 111-112 Exs. 8-14, 25-29, 40-43

Day 2: pp. 111-112 Exs. 19-24, 33-39*, 46-49

Block

pp. 111-112 Exs. 8-36, 39-43, 45-49

Extra Practice

- Student Edition, p. 729
- Chapter 3 Resource Book, pp. 10-12
- Test and Practice Generator

Transparency

Even-numbered answers are available on transparencies.

Homework Check

When you review students' homework for this lesson, go over the following exercises to check understanding of key concepts.

Basic: 9, 15, 21, 27, 31
Average: 9, 16, 22, 28, 32
Advanced: 10, 14, 23, 28, 33

4 ASSESS

ASSESSMENT RESOURCES

For more assessment resources, see:
- Assessment Book
- Test and Practice Generator

MINI-QUIZ

Solve the equation.

1. $a + 4 = 11$ 7
2. $b - 6 = -18$ −12
3. $-2 = c + (-8)$ 6
4. $4.6 = x - (-3.2)$ 1.4
5. Shane spent $127 on masking tape and paint. The tape cost $12. How much did Shane spend on paint? $115
6. From noon to midnight, the temperature dropped 33°F to −7°F. What was the temperature at noon? 26°F

5 FOLLOW-UP

RETEACHING/REMEDIATION

- Study Guide in Chapter 3 Resource Book, pp. 13–14
- Tutor Place, Algebra Cards 8, 9, 12
- eTutorial Plus Online
- Extra Practice, p. 729
- Lesson Practice in Chapter 3 Resource Book, pp. 10–12

CHALLENGE/ENRICHMENT

- Challenge Practice in Chapter 3 Resource Book, p. 15
- Teacher's Edition, p. 104F

ENGLISH LEARNER SUPPORT

- Spanish Study Guide
- Multi-Language Glossary
- Chapter Audio Summaries CDs

40–43. See Additional Answers beginning on page AA1.

25. *Sample answer:* There are 55 cats at the shelter. There are 13 more cats than dogs. How many dogs are at the shelter?

Sea lions

B

25. **Writing** Write a word problem that can be represented by the equation $s + 13 = 55$.

26. **Critical Thinking** What inverse operation undoes adding −5 to a number? subtracting −5, which is equivalent to adding 5

Solve the equation.

27. $x + \frac{1}{2} = \frac{1}{2}$ 0
28. $\frac{2}{3} = d + \frac{1}{3}$ $\frac{1}{3}$
29. $y - \frac{3}{4} = \frac{1}{4}$ 1
30. $s + 3.4 = 4.4$ 1
31. $1.76 = a - 2.94$ 4.7
32. $3.777 + c = 3.977$ 0.2
33. $m + (-20) = -12$ 8
34. $-2 = b + (-4)$ 2
35. $r - (-36) = 5$ −31

36. **Sea Lions** The length of a Steller sea lion at birth is about 45 inches. The average adult female Steller sea lion is 104 inches long. About how many inches do female sea lions grow between birth and adulthood? Write a verbal model. Then write and solve an algebraic model for the problem. 59 in.; length at birth + inches grown = length of adult; $45 + I = 104$

C **Challenge** **Solve the equation.**

37. $3x - 2x + 8 - 10 = 7$ 9
38. $0.2x + 3.4 + 0.8x - 2.1 = 4.2$ 2.9

39. **Cost** You spent a total of $11.09 at the store. You bought two bottles of water for $1.29 each, a magazine for $3.50, trail mix for $1.49, and some markers. How much did the markers cost? (Assume there is no sales tax.) $3.52

Mixed Review

Plot the point in a coordinate plane and describe its location. *(Lesson 2.8)* 40–43. See margin for art.

40. (−2, 5) Quadrant II
41. (5, −2) Quadrant IV
42. (−2, −5) Quadrant III
43. (5, 5) Quadrant I

Basic Skills **Find a low and high estimate for the product.** 44–47. Estimates may vary.

44. 15×19 190, 300
45. 11×13 130, 220
46. 42×7 280, 350
47. 42×71 2800, 4000

Test-Taking Practice

48. **Multiple Choice** Five less than the total number of students is twenty-four. Which equation represents this sentence? D

A. $5 - x = 24$ **B.** $24 - 5 = x$ **C.** $x + 24 = 5$ **D.** $x - 5 = 24$

49. **Multiple Choice** Solve $-4 + x = 8$. I

F. −12 **G.** −4 **H.** 4 **I.** 12

Solving Equations Using Multiplication or Division

BEFORE

You solved equations using addition or subtraction.

Now

You'll solve equations using multiplication or division.

WHY?

So you can find how much a whole pizza costs, as in Ex. 17.

Word Watch

Review Words

equivalent equations, p. 109
inverse operation, p. 109

Activity You can use multiplication to solve equations.

$\frac{x}{2} = 5$ → Multiply each side by 2. → $\frac{x}{2} \cdot 2 = 5 \cdot 2$ → Simplify. → $x = 10$

Solve the equations.

1. $\frac{y}{5} = 4$ 20 **2.** $\frac{h}{6} = 9$ 54 **3.** $\frac{m}{6} = -3$ −18

4. What operation did you use to solve each division equation? How did you use that operation? Write a rule for solving division equations.

4. Multiplication; I multiplied each side by the same number; to solve a division equation, multiply each side of the equation by the divisor of the variable.

In the activity, you used multiplication to solve equations involving division. Multiplication and division are inverse operations.

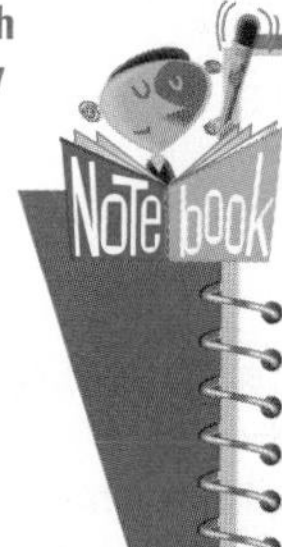

Multiplication Property of Equality

Words Multiplying each side of an equation by the same nonzero number makes an equivalent equation.

Numbers If $\frac{x}{3} = 4$, then $\frac{x}{3} \cdot 3 = 4 \cdot 3$.

Algebra If $a = b$ and $c \neq 0$, then $ac = bc$.

EXAMPLE 1 Solving an Equation Using Multiplication

	$\frac{y}{3} = 5$	**Original equation**
	$\frac{y}{3} \cdot 3 = 5 \cdot 3$	**Multiply each side by 3 to undo division.**
	$y = 15$	**Simplify. *y* is by itself.**
✓**Check**	$\frac{15}{3} = 5$ ✓	**Substitute 15 for *y* in original equation.**

with Solving

Remember to check your answer by substituting it in the original equation.

ILLINOIS Standards and ISAT:
8.A.3b, 8.D.3a

1 PLAN

SKILL CHECK

1. $\frac{1}{2} \cdot 26 = \underline{?}$ **13**
2. $360 \div 24 = \underline{?}$ **15**
3. $17 \div 4 = \underline{?}$ $4\frac{1}{4}$

Lesson Objective

Solve equations using multiplication or division.

Pacing

Suggested Number of Days
Basic Course: 1 day
Average Course: 1 day
Advanced Course: 1 day
Block: 0.5 block with 3.3

Teaching Resources

For a complete list of Teaching Resources, see page 104B.

Transparency

Warm-Up Exercises for this lesson are available on a transparency.

2 TEACH

Motivating the Lesson

Extend the balance metaphor to multiplying both sides of an equation by the same number. Ask students if they think this will give an equivalent equation.

Activity

Goal Explore solving a division equation by multiplying each side of the equation by the same number.

Key Discovery You can use multiplication to "undo," and thus solve, division equations.

TIPS FOR NEW TEACHERS

Students must understand that the multiplication and division properties of equality apply only to nonzero numbers. For example, $2x = 6$ and $0(2x) = 0(6)$ are not equivalent because the first is true only when $x = 3$, and the second simplifies to $0 = 0$, which is always true. See Tips for New Teachers in the *Chapter 3 Resource Book*.

EXTRA EXAMPLES

Example 1 Solve the equation $\frac{a}{8} = 6$. **48**

Example 2 Solve the equation $-12y = 132$. **−11**

Example 3 A city bus can carry 40 commuters. There are 240 commuters waiting at a bus terminal. Write and solve an equation to find the number of buses needed for the commuters.
$40x = 240$; 6 buses

MULTIPLE REPRESENTATIONS

Point out that in the Notebook boxes for the division and multiplication properties of equality, the words, numbers, and algebra describe the same property. Show how the representations using numbers are examples of the algebraic representations for specific values of *a*, *b*, and *c*.

CONCEPT CHECK

What would you do first to solve $\frac{x}{6} = 1.5$? **Multiply each side by 6.**

DAILY PUZZLER

Find x if $\frac{\frac{x}{2}}{3} = 4$. **24**

You can use division to solve equations involving multiplication.

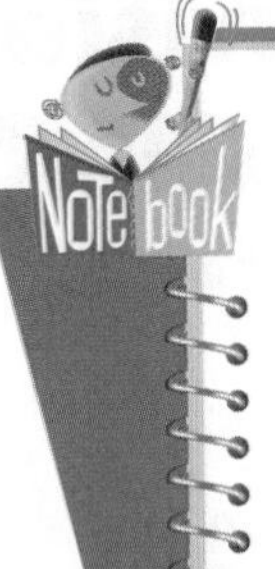

Division Property of Equality

Words Dividing each side of an equation by the same nonzero number makes an equivalent equation.

Numbers If $2x = 24$, then $\frac{2x}{2} = \frac{24}{2}$.

Algebra If $a = b$ and $c \neq 0$, then $\frac{a}{c} = \frac{b}{c}$.

Watch Out! When solving an equation, remember to perform the same operation on each side.

EXAMPLE 2 Solving an Equation Using Division

$-2.5x = 20$ **Original equation**

$\frac{-2.5x}{-2.5} = \frac{20}{-2.5}$ **Divide each side by −2.5 to undo multiplication.**

$x = -8$ **Simplify. *x* is by itself.**

Your turn now **Solve the equation. Check your solution.**

1. $21 = \frac{x}{9}$ 189 **2.** $\frac{x}{3.5} = 14$ 49 **3.** $9x = 54$ 6 **4.** $45 = -9x$ −5

EXAMPLE 3 Writing and Solving an Equation

Sports Fifty-four people show up for a basketball tournament. Write and solve an equation to find how many 3 person teams can be formed.

Solution

Let *t* be the number of 3 person teams that can be formed.

Total number of people = Number per team · Number of teams

$54 = 3t$ **Write an algebraic model.**

$\frac{54}{3} = \frac{3t}{3}$ **Divide each side by 3.**

$18 = t$ **Simplify.**

ANSWER Eighteen 3 person teams can be formed.

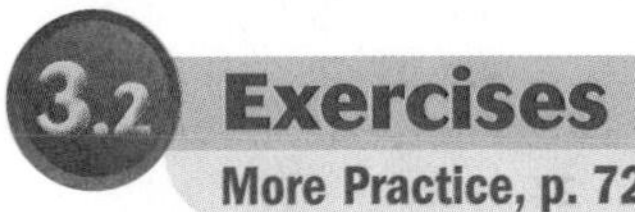

3.2 Exercises

More Practice, p. 729

INTERNET eWorkbook Plus CLASSZONE.COM

Getting Ready to Practice

1. **Vocabulary** Copy and complete: To solve $6x = 36$, __?__ each side of the equation by 6. divide

Copy and complete the solution. Justify each step. 2–3. See margin.

2. $6x = 72$

$\frac{6x}{?} = \frac{72}{?}$

$x = ?$

3. $\frac{y}{9} = -3$

$\frac{y}{9} \cdot ? = -3 \cdot ?$

$y = ?$

4. **Concert** You are at a sold-out concert. There are 1950 people at the concert, and the arena has 30 seats in each row.

People at concert	=	Seats per row	·	Number of rows

Write and solve an equation to find how many rows of seats there are. $1950 = 30n$; 65 rows

2. $\frac{6x}{6} = \frac{72}{6}$

$x = 12$

3. $\frac{y}{9} \cdot 9 = -3 \cdot 9$

$y = -27$

Practice and Problem Solving

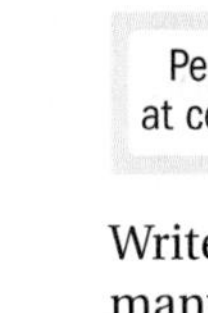

with Homework

Example	Exercises
1	5-16
2	5-16
3	17-18

Online Resources CLASSZONE.COM
- More Examples
- eTutorial Plus

A **Solve the equation. Check your solution.**

5. $\frac{p}{2} = 9$ 18
6. $\frac{t}{8} = 6$ 48
7. $14 = \frac{x}{5}$ 70
8. $4x = 32$ 8
9. $18 = 6g$ 3
10. $3b = 39$ 13
11. $7 = \frac{k}{15}$ 105
12. $25 = \frac{h}{14}$ 350
13. $\frac{r}{18} = 12$ 216
14. $17y = 51$ 3
15. $14h = 35$ 2.5
16. $48 = 96z$ 0.5

17. **Pizza** A pizza shop cuts a pizza into 8 slices. One slice costs \$1.10. Which equation can you use to find the cost of the whole pizza? C

A. $1.10x = 8$ **B.** $8x = 1.10$ **C.** $\frac{x}{8} = 1.10$ **D.** $x = \frac{1.10}{8}$

18. **Mowing Lawns** You charged your neighbors \$56 for mowing their lawn 7 times. How much do you charge for mowing the lawn once? \$8

Describe an inverse operation that will undo the given operation.

19. Multiplying by 5 — dividing by 5
20. Dividing by -9 — multiplying by -9
21. Adding -6 — subtracting -6, or adding 6

3 APPLY

ASSIGNMENT GUIDE

Basic Course

Day 1: SRH p. 713 Exs. 6-10; pp. 115-116 Exs. 5-13, 17-27, 38-46

Average Course

Day 1: pp. 115-116 Exs. 11-21, 25-35, 40-47

Advanced Course

Day 1: pp. 115-116 Exs. 11-21, 28-39*, 44-47

Block

pp. 115-116 Exs. 11-21, 25-35, 40-47 (with 3.3)

EXTRA PRACTICE
- Student Edition, p. 729
- Chapter 3 Resource Book, pp. 19-21
- Test and Practice Generator

TRANSPARENCY

Even-numbered answers are available on transparencies.

HOMEWORK CHECK

When you review students' homework for this lesson, go over the following exercises to check understanding of key concepts.

Basic: 5, 8, 17, 22, 23
Average: 11, 14, 17, 25, 26
Advanced: 12, 15, 17, 28, 30

COMMON ERROR

In Exercise 20, watch for students who think that because the division is by a negative number, the inverse operation is multiplying by $+9$ instead of multiplying by -9.

4 ASSESS

ASSESSMENT RESOURCES

For more assessment resources, see:
- Assessment Book
- Test and Practice Generator

MINI-QUIZ

Solve the equation.

1. $\frac{a}{7} = 4$ 28
2. $\frac{b}{15} = 6$ 90
3. $88 = 22c$ 4
4. $12d = 156$ 13
5. $-10.5 = 1.5x$ -7
6. $5.5 = -\frac{w}{2.2}$ -12.1
7. The average change in value of a company's high-resolution graphics printer is $-\$150$ per month. How many months later is its value relative to the original cost $-\$1200$? 8 mo

5 FOLLOW-UP

RETEACHING/REMEDIATION

- Study Guide in Chapter 3 Resource Book, pp. 22–23
- Tutor Place, Algebra Cards 10–12
- eTutorial Plus Online
- Extra Practice, p. 729
- Lesson Practice in Chapter 3 Resource Book, pp. 19–21

CHALLENGE/ENRICHMENT

- Challenge Practice in Chapter 3 Resource Book, p. 24
- Teacher's Edition, p. 104F

ENGLISH LEARNER SUPPORT

- Spanish Study Guide
- Multi-Language Glossary
- Chapter Audio Summaries CDs

B **Solve the equation. Check your solution.**

22. $12 = -2z$ -6 **23.** $\frac{h}{6} = -36$ -216 **24.** $-3x = -57$ 19

25. $44 = 4.4p$ 10 **26.** $\frac{z}{1.8} = 5$ 9 **27.** $13 = \frac{w}{2.3}$ 29.9

28. $-2.4k = 48$ -20 **29.** $-21 = -0.7p$ 30 **30.** $\frac{y}{-1.5} = 21$ -31.5

31. $1368 = 456x$ 3 **32.** $8 = \frac{-b}{5.5}$ -44 **33.** $12m = -25.2$ -2.1

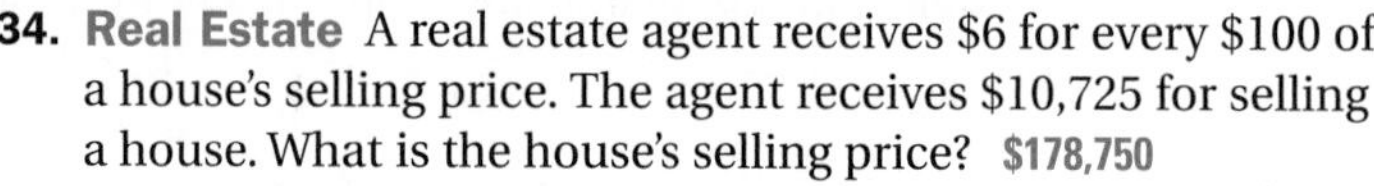

C **34. Real Estate** A real estate agent receives \$6 for every \$100 of a house's selling price. The agent receives \$10,725 for selling a house. What is the house's selling price? \$178,750

35. Critical Thinking Write a multiplication equation and a division equation that have the same solution. *Sample answer:* $3x = 18$, $\frac{x}{2} = 3$

36. Challenge Solve the equation.

$3(6n) + 5(3n) - 2^2n = 261$ 9

37. Hens About 240 million laying hens produce about 50 billion eggs each year in the United States. About how many eggs does each hen lay in a month? in a week? about 17 eggs; about 4 eggs

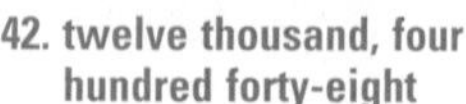

42. twelve thousand, four hundred forty-eight
43. sixteen and two hundredths
44. five and one hundred seven thousandths
45. seven million, five hundred forty thousand, six hundred eighty-eight

Mixed Review

Copy and complete the statement with < or >. *(Lesson 2.1)*

38. 3 _?_ -6 > **39.** -21 _?_ -17 < **40.** -12 _?_ -5 < **41.** 0 _?_ -3 >

Basic Skills Write the number in words.

42. 12,448 **43.** 16.02 **44.** 5.107 **45.** 7,540,688

INTERNET
State Test Practice
CLASSZONE.COM

Test-Taking Practice

46. Multiple Choice Which operation should you perform to solve the equation represented by the verbal sentence? B

The quotient of a number and four is the opposite of two.

A. Divide each side by 4. **B.** Multiply each side by 4.

C. Divide each side by -4. **D.** Multiply each side by -4.

47. Short Response Joanne drove for three hours traveling at a constant speed throughout her trip. She traveled a total of 204 miles. Write an equation that represents the situation. Let r represent Joanne's speed. Solve the equation to find her speed. Show all the steps you used to solve the equation. $204 = 3r$; $\frac{204}{3} = \frac{3r}{3}$; $r = 68$ mi/h

3.3 Hands-on Activity

GOAL
Use algebra tiles to solve two-step equations.

MATERIALS
• algebra tiles

Modeling Two-Step Equations

A *two-step equation* is an equation you solve using two operations. You can use algebra tiles to model and solve two-step equations.

Explore 1 **Model and solve $2x + 3 = 7$.**

1 Model the equation $2x + 3 = 7$.

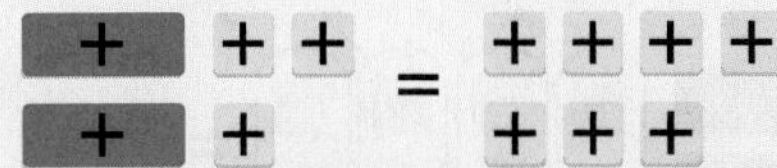

2 Remove three 1-tiles from each side.

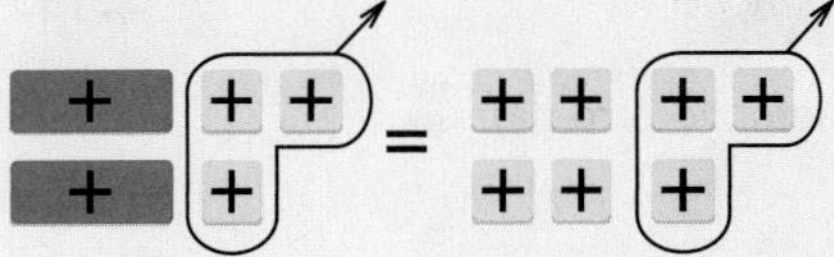

3 The coefficient of x is 2, so divide the remaining tiles on each side into 2 identical groups.

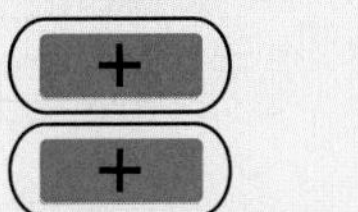
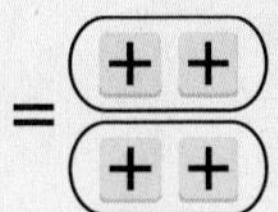

4 Keep one of these groups. One x-tile is equal to two 1-tiles. So, the solution is 2.

Your turn now **Use algebra tiles to model and solve the equation.**

1. Model each step described below. Draw a picture of each step.

(1) Use algebra tiles to model the equation $3x + 1 = 10$. **Steps 1–4. See margin.**

(2) Remove one 1-tile from each side.

(3) Divide the remaining tiles into three identical groups.

(4) Solve the equation. Then check your solution by substituting in the original equation.

ILLINOIS Standards and ISAT:
8.A.3b, 8.D.3a

1 PLAN

Explore the Concept

- Use algebra tiles to solve two-step equations.
- This activity introduces students to the techniques for solving two-step equations, which will be addressed formally in Lesson 3.3.

Materials

Each student or group of students will need algebra tiles. See also the Activity Support Master in the *Chapter 3 Resource Book*.

Recommended Time

Work activity: 10 min
Discuss results: 10 min

Grouping

Students can work individually or in pairs. If students work in pairs, one student can guide the other as he or she positions the tiles.

Transparency

A support transparency is available for this Activity.

2 TEACH

Tips for Success

Remind students that the goal is to get one x-tile alone on one side of the equation. After solving an equation using algebra tiles, students can verify their work by reproducing the original equation and substituting the appropriate number of 1- or −1-tiles for the x-tiles.

1. See Additional Answers beginning on page AA1.

Discussion

Students have been introduced to zero pairs, but it can be a difficult concept for them. As students begin the first step in the second Explore, ask them why it is necessary and why it is permissible to add 1-tiles to form and then remove zero pairs. (It is necessary because there are no negative tiles to remove from the right side of the equation to mirror removing them from the left side. It is permissible because they are adding the same tiles to both sides. The pairs can be removed because each zero pair is the same as adding zero to the left side.)

3 CLOSE

Key Discovery

To solve a two-step equation, first apply the methods for solving an addition or subtraction equation and then apply the methods for solving a multiplication or division equation.

Assessment

1. If you had an algebra tile equation with two x-tiles on one side and three 1-tiles on the other, would you be able to solve it using the tiles? Explain. **No. *Sample answer:* There is an odd number of 1-tiles, so you could not divide them into two equal groups to correspond to the two x-tiles.**
2. Describe the steps of solving the equation $3x - 4 = 5$ using algebra tiles. **Add four 1-tiles to each side. Remove the four zero pairs that are formed on the left side. There are three x-tiles on the left and nine 1-tiles on the right. Divide the tiles on each side into three equal groups. The solution is $x = 3$ because three 1-tiles are grouped with each x-tile.**

Hands-on Activity continued

Explore 2 **Model and solve $3x - 4 = 5$. Write the equation at each step.**

	Tile Model	Algebra
1	+ + + − − − − = + + + + +	$3x - 4 = 5$
2	 Remove zero pairs.	$3x - 4 + 4 = 5 + 4$
3	+ + + = +++ +++ +++	$\frac{3x}{3} = \frac{9}{3}$
4	+ = + + +	$x = 3$

2. $3x + 1 - 1 = 7 - 1$; $3x = 6$; $\frac{3x}{3} = \frac{6}{3}$; $x = 2$ 3. $2x - 3 + 3 = 7 + 3$; $2x = 10$; $\frac{2x}{2} = \frac{10}{2}$; $x = 5$

Your turn now **Use algebra tiles to model and solve the equation. Write the equation at each step.**

2. $3x + 1 = 7$ **3.** $2x - 3 = 7$ **4.** $4x + 2 = -10$ **5.** $2x - 5 = -9$

4. $4x + 2 - 2 = -10 - 2$; $4x = -12$; $\frac{4x}{4} = \frac{-12}{4}$; $x = -3$

5. $2x - 5 + 5 = -9 + 5$; $2x = -4$; $\frac{2x}{2} = \frac{-4}{2}$; $x = -2$

Stop and Think

6. Writing Explain what kinds of equations are difficult or impossible to solve using algebra tiles. Give an example. ***Sample answer:* equations that contain decimals or fractions; $x - 2.5 = 3.5$**

7. Work Backward Use algebra tiles to write a two-step equation whose solution is 1. ***Sample answer:* $2x + 3 = 5$**

LESSON 3.3

Solving Two-Step Equations

BEFORE	Now	WHY?
You solved one-step equations.	You'll solve two-step equations.	So you can make a plan to earn money, as in Ex. 36.

1 PLAN

SKILL CHECK

Solve the equation.

1. $-4 = -2x$ 2

2. $y - 14 = -8$ 6

LESSON OBJECTIVE

Solve two-step equations.

PACING

Suggested Number of Days
Basic Course: 2 days
Average Course: 2 days
Advanced Course: 2 days
Block: 0.5 block with 3.2
0.5 block with 3.4

TEACHING RESOURCES

For a complete list of Teaching Resources, see page 104B.

TRANSPARENCY

Warm-Up Exercises for this lesson are available on a transparency.

Word Watch

Review Words
equation, p. 28
solution, p. 28

In the Real World

Music Club You pay \$7 to join an Internet music club. You pay \$2 for each song that you download. Your cost for joining and downloading some songs is \$23. How many songs did you download?

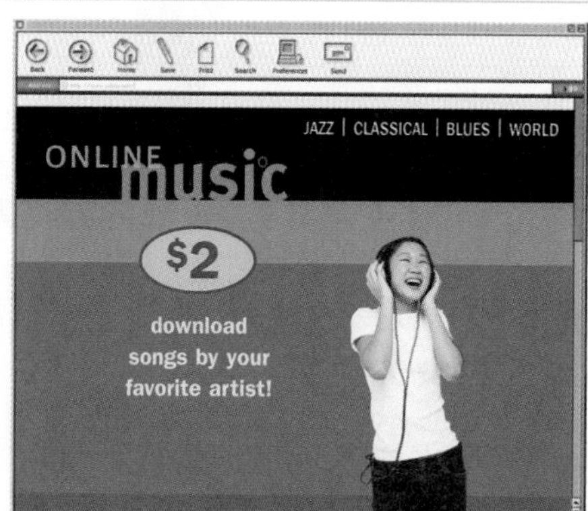

JAZZ | CLASSICAL | BLUES | WORLD
ONLINE music
$2
download songs by your favorite artist!

In Example 1, you will answer this question by solving the two-step equation $7 + 2x = 23$. The value of x is the number of songs you downloaded.

EXAMPLE 1 Solving a Real-World Problem

Cost to join + Cost per song • Number of songs = Total Cost

$7 + 2x = 23$	Write an algebraic model.
$-7 \qquad -7$	Subtract 7 from each side to undo addition.
$2x = 16$	Simplify.
$\frac{2x}{2} = \frac{16}{2}$	Divide each side by 2 to undo multiplication.
$x = 8$	Simplify. x is by itself.

ANSWER You downloaded 8 songs.

Your turn now **Use the equation in Example 1.**

1. Substitute 8 for x in the original equation in Example 1 to check the solution. $7 + 2(8) = 23; 23 = 23$
2. What is the cost to join the club and download 5 songs? \$17
3. Suppose the cost to join and download songs is \$27. How does this change the equation you solve to find the number of songs? The 23 would change to 27.

2 TEACH

MOTIVATING THE LESSON

Ask students if they are familiar with music clubs, health clubs, phone services, or any other services where you pay a set fee plus a charge per use or time interval.

TIPS FOR NEW TEACHERS

Make sure students add or subtract as a first step. Though not incorrect to multiply or divide first, it often results in difficult computations involving fractions. See Tips for New Teachers in the *Chapter 3 Resource Book*.

ILLINOIS Standards and ISAT:
8.A.3b, 8.D.3a; 6.C.3b

EXTRA EXAMPLES

Example 1 A long-distance phone company that charges \$3 per hour for calls and has a monthly fee of \$6 has a total monthly cost of $3t + 6$, where t is the number of hours of long distance. How many hours of long distance did you use in a month if your bill was \$45? **13 h**

Example 2 Solve the equation $\frac{y}{4} + 12 = 20$. **32**

Example 3 Solve the equation $40 = 55 - 3x$. **5**

Differentiating Instruction

- **Less Proficient Students** Emphasize that solving a two-step equation is like solving two one-step equations. For example, solving $-6 = 4 - 5x$ is like solving $-6 = 4 + x$ and then $-10 = -5x$.
- **Advanced Students** Students may enjoy pairing up to create multi-step equations for each other to solve. Point out that they already have the skills to solve equations involving the extra step(s) of simplifying one or both sides of an equation before obtaining a two-step equation. (See Exercises 38–44.)

CONCEPT CHECK

What is the first step in solving the equation $14 = -1 - 3x$? **Add 1 to each side of the equation.**

DAILY PUZZLER

If 3 pistachios and 1 walnut weigh the same as 10 peanuts, and 1 pistachio and 6 peanuts weigh the same as 1 walnut, how many peanuts weigh the same as 1 walnut? **7 peanuts**

Solving a Two-Step Equation

Some equations require two inverse operations to solve.

$2x + 1 = 5$	**Original equation**
$2x + 1 - 1 = 5 - 1$	**Undo addition or subtraction.**
$2x = 4$	**Simplify.**
$\frac{2x}{2} = \frac{4}{2}$	**Undo multiplication or division.**
$x = 2$	**Simplify.**

with Solving

Another way to undo operations is to add the opposite to undo addition or subtraction. Then multiply by the reciprocal to undo multiplication or division.

EXAMPLE 2 Solving with a Variable in the Numerator

$\frac{x}{2} - 14 = 8$	**Original equation**
$+14 \quad + 14$	**Add 14 to each side to undo subtraction.**
$\frac{x}{2} = 22$	**Simplify.**
$\frac{x}{2} \cdot 2 = 22 \cdot 2$	**Multiply each side by 2 to undo division.**
$x = 44$	**Simplify.**

✓**Check** $\frac{44}{2} - 14 \stackrel{?}{=} 8$ **Substitute 44 for x in original equation.**

$22 - 14 = 8$ ✓

with Review

Remember that you can solve an equation vertically or horizontally. See p. 110.

EXAMPLE 3 Solving with a Negative Coefficient

$8 = 12 - 2x$	**Original equation**
$8 - 12 = 12 - 2x - 12$	**Subtract 12 from each side to undo addition.**
$-4 = -2x$	**Simplify.**
$\frac{-4}{-2} = \frac{-2x}{-2}$	**Divide each side by −2 to undo multiplication.**
$2 = x$	**Simplify.**

Your turn now **Solve the equation. Check your answer.**

4. $13 = 11 + \frac{y}{3}$ **6** **5.** $\frac{z}{5} - 3 = 4$ **35** **6.** $-6x + 5 = 23$ **−3** **7.** $6 = 16 - a$ **10**

3.3 Exercises

More Practice, p. 729

9. Step 1. The main idea is your payment for drawing illustrations. You know that you charge $50 per illustration and $12 an hour to make changes and that you made $198 for 3 illustrations and changes. You need to find the number of hours you spent making changes.

9. Step 2. *Sample answer:* You already know the number of illustrations and your payment for them. The coefficient of n is 12, the charge per hour for making changes, so $12n$ describes your payment for n hours of making changes.

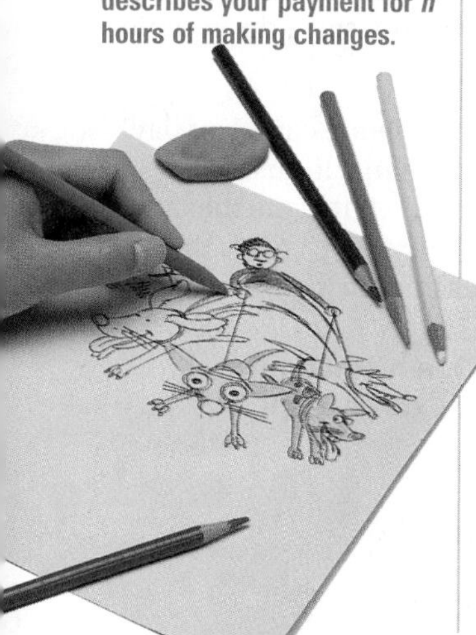

Getting Ready to Practice

1. Write the two operations, in order, that you would use to solve the equation $3w - 2 = 7$. Then solve the equation. addition, division; 3

2. Find the Error Describe and correct the error in the solution. 9 was subtracted from the right side when it should have been added; $3x - 9 = 18$, $3x = 27$, $x = 9$.

> X
> $3x - 9 = 18$
> $3x = 9$
> $x = 3$

Solve the equation. Check your answer.

3. $2x + 1 = 7$ 3 **4.** $3y - 4 = 2$ 2 **5.** $10 - 7z = 3$ 1

6. $15 = 4p + 7$ 2 **7.** $1 = 2k + 9$ −4 **8.** $11 = \frac{h}{6} + 8$ 18

9. Guided Problem Solving You draw illustrations. You charge $50 per illustration and $12 per hour to make changes. You get a check for $198 to pay for 3 illustrations and changes. How many hours did you spend making changes to the illustrations?

(1) Read the problem. What is the main idea? What do you know and what do you need to find? Steps 1–2. See margin.

(2) You can use the equation $3(50) + 12n = 198$ to find the number of hours you spent making changes to the illustrations. Why is the value of n the number of hours you spent making changes?

(3) Solve the equation and check your answer. 4 h

Practice and Problem Solving

with Homework

Example	Exercises
1	10-23
2	24-35
3	10-21, 24-35

- More Examples
- eTutorial Plus

Solve the equation. Check your answer.

A **10.** $4z + 8 = 12$ 1 **11.** $18 = 4h + 2$ 4 **12.** $29 = 5a + 4$ 5

13. $40 = 8p - 16$ 7 **14.** $100 - 7r = 44$ 8 **15.** $8q - 9 = -7$ $\frac{1}{4}$, or 0.25

16. $6 + 2c = 15$ $4\frac{1}{2}$, or 4.5 **17.** $3g + 4 = 13$ 3 **18.** $-9 + 2k = -25$ −8

19. $-36 = 18 - 6x$ 9 **20.** $7 + 5b = -23$ −6 **21.** $10 = 2d + 11$ $-\frac{1}{2}$, or −0.5

22. Measurement To find the number of inches in 5 feet 4 inches, you can evaluate the expression $5(12) + 4$. The diameter of the largest cookie ever made was 81 feet 8 inches. Write and evaluate an expression that will give the diameter of the cookie in inches. $81(12) + 8 = 972 + 8 = 980$ in.

3 APPLY

ASSIGNMENT GUIDE

Basic Course

Day 1: EP p. 728 Exs. 29-32; pp. 121-123 Exs. 10-18, 30-32, 40, 48-53

Day 2: pp. 121-123 Exs. 19-29, 33-36, 54-58

Average Course

Day 1: pp. 121-123 Exs. 13-18, 30-36, 40-42, 48-52

Day 2: pp. 121-123 Exs. 19-29, 37-39, 45-47, 55-58

Advanced Course

Day 1: pp. 121-123 Exs. 16-18, 30-32, 39-45*, 49-52

Day 2: pp. 121-123 Exs. 19-26, 36-38, 46-48, 56-58

Block

pp. 121-123 Exs. 13-18, 30-36, 40-42, 48-52 (with 3.2)

pp. 121-123 Exs. 19-29, 37-39, 45-47, 55-58 (with 3.4)

EXTRA PRACTICE

- Student Edition, p. 729
- Chapter 3 Resource Book, pp. 30-32
- Test and Practice Generator

TRANSPARENCY

Even-numbered answers are available on transparencies.

HOMEWORK CHECK

When you review students' homework for this lesson, go over the following exercises to check understanding of key concepts.

Basic: 10, 14, 16, 24, 27
Average: 13, 15, 17, 24, 27
Advanced: 16, 19, 22, 30, 32

TEACHING TIP

The concept of rate is introduced indirectly in Exercise 23, and may be difficult for some students. You may want to point out that the equation $x + 3 = 11$, where x is the number of miles remaining to be cleaned, expresses the situation in this exercise. So, $3h$ must also represent the number of miles to be cleaned. To clean $3h$ miles when you can clean 3 miles per hour must then take h hours (rate of cleaning • time cleaning = amount cleaned).

23. $2\frac{2}{3}$; because 3 miles is an estimate, $3h$ is an estimate for the number of miles of trail cleaned per hour, so the number of hours will also be an estimate.

23. Hiking Trails Students are cleaning up 11 miles of trails in a local park. After an hour, they have cleaned about 3 miles of trails. Solve the two-step equation $3h + 3 = 11$. Explain why the value of h is an estimate of the number of hours it will take to finish.

Solve the equation. Check your answer.

24. $3 = 12 - 3x$ 3 **25.** $-7 = 7 - 2r$ 7 **26.** $20 - 6w = 14$ 1

27. $9p + 8 = -7$ $-1\frac{2}{3}$ **28.** $\frac{x}{9} - 4 = 5$ 81 **29.** $-7 + \frac{z}{4} = 3$ 40

30. $8 = 5 + \frac{m}{2}$ 6 **31.** $3 + \frac{t}{5} = 14$ 55 **32.** $32 = 17 + \frac{d}{2}$ 30

33. $2 - z = 9$ -7 **34.** $11 - b = 34$ -23 **35.** $\frac{c}{3} - 7 = 1$ 24

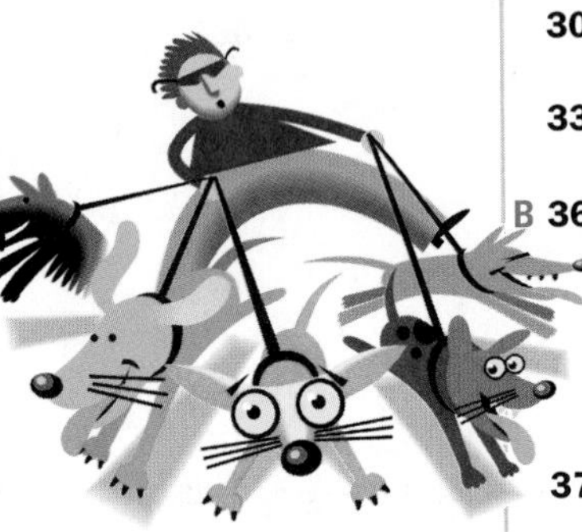

B **36. Walking Dogs** You earn money by walking dogs in your neighborhood. One neighbor pays you \$20 each week, and other neighbors pay you \$5 per walk. If your goal is to earn \$50 per week, how many walks do you need to do at \$5 each? To answer this question, solve the equation $20 + 5w = 50$. 6 walks

37. Phone Card You have \$2.10 remaining on your phone card. You pay 7 cents for each minute of a call and a 75 cent charge for using a pay phone. If you make a call from a pay phone, what is the maximum whole number of minutes that you can talk? (*Hint:* The cost is the sum of the pay phone charge and 7 cents per minute for your call.) 19 min

Compare and Contrast In Exercises 38 and 39, a method for solving the equation $2(m + 3) = 18$ is shown. Explain each step of the solution.

38. Use the distributive property; subtract 6 from each side; simplify; divide each side by 2; simplify.

39. Divide each side by 2; simplify; subtract 3 from each side; simplify.

38.

$$2(m + 3) = 18$$
$$2m + 6 = 18$$
$$2m + 6 - 6 = 18 - 6$$
$$2m = 12$$
$$\frac{2m}{2} = \frac{12}{2}$$
$$m = 6$$

39.

$$2(m + 3) = 18$$
$$\frac{2(m + 3)}{2} = \frac{18}{2}$$
$$m + 3 = 9$$
$$m + 3 - 3 = 9 - 3$$
$$m = 6$$

Choose a Method In Exercises 40–42, use one of the methods in Exercises 38 and 39 to solve the equation.

40. $3(r + 1) = 9$ 2 **41.** $4 = -1(z + 11)$ -15 **42.** $6\left(\frac{1}{3} + h\right) = 20$ 3

C **Challenge Solve the equation.**

43. $2(10 + x) + 4(12 - x) = 34$ 17 **44.** $-5(3 - z) + 1(z - 9) = 0$ 4

Extended Problem Solving **In Exercises 45–47, use the given information about the cost of using the city pool.**

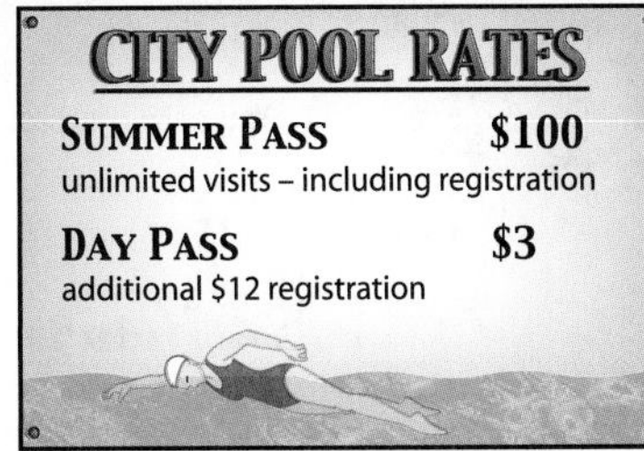

CITY POOL RATES
SUMMER PASS $100
unlimited visits – including registration
DAY PASS $3
additional $12 registration

45. Evaluate and Explain Evaluate the expression $3(40) + 12$. What does the answer tell you about the payment plans?

45–46. See margin.

46. Interpret Solve the two-step equation $3x + 12 = 100$. What does the answer tell you about the payment plans?

47. Compare and Contrast For each payment plan, give one reason why you might choose it. *Sample answer:* Choose the summer pass if you go to the pool more than 29 days because it is cheaper. Choose the day pass if you go to the pool 29 days or less because it is cheaper.

Mixed Review

Solve the equation. Check your answer. *(Lessons 3.1, 3.2)*

48. $p + 9 = 19$ 10 **49.** $13 = n - 6$ 19 **50.** $-20 = 4x$ −5 **51.** $\frac{1}{2}y = 24$ 48

Choose a Strategy **Use a strategy from the list to solve the following problem. Explain your choice of strategy.**

52. A running club has six members. The instructor wants each member to race one-on-one against every other member. How many times will each member race? How many races will there be altogether?

Problem Solving Strategies
- Guess, Check, and Revise
- Draw a Diagram
- Look for a Pattern

Basic Skills **Write the number as a percent.**

53. $\frac{1}{2}$ 50% **54.** 0.75 75% **55.** $\frac{20}{100}$ 20% **56.** 0.35 35%

Test-Taking Practice

57. Multiple Choice Solve the equation $21 = 3x + 9$. B

A. −2 **B.** 4 **C.** 10 **D.** 16

58. Short Response Jamie is a certified youth soccer referee. After completing a course that cost \$24, she earned \$16 per game. Her profit in the first season was \$280. Which equation should you use to find g, the number of games Jamie refereed? Explain.

A. $16g + 24 = 280$ **B.** $16g - 24 = 280$

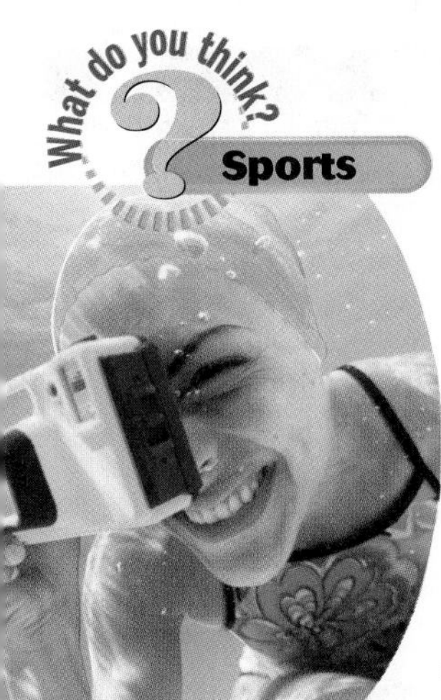

Swimming

About 8% of adults in the United States say that swimming is one of their three favorite leisure activities. About how many students would be 8% of your class? of your school? Check answers.

45. 132; the summer pass would be cheaper than paying for 40 day passes.

46. $29\frac{1}{3}$; if you plan to go to the pool for more than 29 days, it is cheaper to buy a summer pass than to buy day passes.

52. 5; 15. *Sample answer:* I used Draw a Diagram to show who would be in each race and then I counted to find the answers.

58. B; she earned \$16 per game for g games, for a total of \$16g. She spent \$24 on the course. Because profit is the difference between income and expenses, her total profit was $16g - 24$, which equals 280.

4 ASSESS

Assessment Resources

For more assessment resources, see:
- Assessment Book
- Test and Practice Generator

Mini-Quiz

Solve the equation.

1. $5a + 7 = 37$ 6
2. $-15 = 6b - 3$ −2
3. $7 - 4c = 15$ −2
4. $\frac{d}{2} + 1 = 4$ 6
5. $9 = 13 - \frac{j}{3}$ 12
6. $-16 + \frac{k}{5} = -19$ −15
7. Sahej ordered a pizza that cost \$8 plus 50 cents for each extra topping. The total cost of the pizza was \$10. How many extra toppings did Sahej order? To answer this question, solve the equation $8 + \frac{t}{2} = 10$. 4 toppings

5 FOLLOW-UP

Reteaching/Remediation

- Study Guide in Chapter 3 Resource Book, pp. 33–34
- eTutorial Plus Online
- Extra Practice, p. 729
- Lesson Practice in Chapter 3 Resource Book, pp. 30–32

Challenge/Enrichment

- Challenge Practice in Chapter 3 Resource Book, p. 35
- Teacher's Edition, p. 104F

English Learner Support

- Spanish Study Guide
- Multi-Language Glossary
- Chapter Audio Summaries CDs

PLAN

SKILL CHECK

Solve the equation.

1. $5x - 3 = 7$ 2
2. $147 = 36 - z$ −111
3. $11 + \frac{m}{3} = 8$ −9

Lesson Objective

Solve problems by writing two-step equations.

Pacing

Suggested Number of Days

Basic Course: 2 days

Average Course: 2 days

Advanced Course: 2 days

Block: 0.5 block with 3.3
0.5 block with 3.5

Teaching Resources

For a complete list of Teaching Resources, see page 104B.

Transparency

Warm-Up Exercises for this lesson are available on a transparency.

TEACH

Motivating the Lesson

Have students who have pets estimate what it costs to feed their pets in a year.

TIPS FOR NEW TEACHERS

Encourage students to read word problems several times, paying special attention to what is given and what is sought. See Tips for New Teachers in the *Chapter 3 Resource Book*.

LESSON 3.4

Writing Two-Step Equations

BEFORE	Now	WHY?
You solved two-step equations.	You'll solve problems by writing two-step equations.	So you can calculate sandwich sales, as in Ex. 9.

In the Real World

American Flamingos This year, a zoo spent \$1580 to feed its American flamingos. Next year, its budget for feeding the flamingos is \$2370. Next year it will cost \$395 to feed each additional flamingo. How many additional flamingos can the zoo buy? You can use a verbal model to help you write a two-step equation.

Word Watch

Review Words

equation, p. 28
solution, p. 28

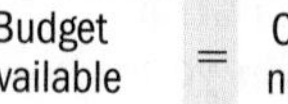

EXAMPLE 1 Writing and Solving a Two-Step Equation

You can write and solve a two-step equation to find how many additional flamingos the zoo can buy. Write a verbal model. Let n be the number of additional flamingos.

Budget available = Cost of each new flamingo · Number of new flamingos + Cost of existing flamingos

$2370 = 395n + 1580$ **Write an algebraic model.**

$2370 - 1580 = 395n + 1580 - 1580$ **Subtract 1580 from each side.**

$790 = 395n$ **Simplify.**

$\frac{790}{395} = \frac{395n}{395}$ **Divide each side by 395.**

$2 = n$ **Simplify.**

ANSWER The zoo can buy 2 additional flamingos next year.

✓ **Check** $2370 \stackrel{?}{=} 395(2) + 1580$ **Substitute 2 for n in original equation.**

$2370 \stackrel{?}{=} 790 + 1580$

$2370 = 2370$ ✓

Your turn now **Write a two-step equation to solve the problem.**

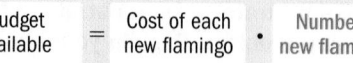

1. It costs a zoo \$1150 per year to feed its Aldabra tortoises. Each additional tortoise will cost \$575 per year to feed. The zoo's budget for the tortoises' food next year is \$2875. Write and solve an equation to find how many new tortoises the zoo can buy next year. $1150 + 575t = 2875$; 3 new tortoises

ILLINOIS Standards and ISAT:
8.A.3b, 8.D.3a

EXAMPLE 2 Writing and Solving a Two-Step Equation

The sum of 4 times a number and -6 is 14. What is the number?

Solution

4 times **a number** and -6 is 14.	**Write a verbal model.**
$4 \cdot n + (-6) = 14$	**Translate.**
$4n - 6 = 14$	**Write equation.**
$4n - 6 + 6 = 14 + 6$	**Add 6 to each side.**
$4n = 20$	**Simplify.**
$\frac{4n}{4} = \frac{20}{4}$	**Divide each side by 4.**
$n = 5$	**Simplify.**

HELP with Solving

Remember that adding -6 is the same as subtracting 6.

Your turn now **Write a two-step equation to find the number.**

2. The difference of six times a number and 9 is -3. What is the number? **$6n - 9 = -3$; 1**

3. The sum of a number divided by 6 and -5 is -2. What is the number? **See margin.**

3. $\frac{n}{6} + (-5) = -2$; 18

EXAMPLE 3 Writing and Solving a Two-Step Equation

Reading You have to read several books for a class. You want to find how many pages you need to read per week in order to finish by the time the term is over. There are a total of 1244 pages. You have already read 500 pages. If there are six weeks left in the term, how many pages do you have to read per week?

Solution

Let p be the number of pages to read per week.

Total pages	=	Weeks left	•	Pages per week	+	Pages I've read

$1244 = 6p + 500$	**Write an algebraic model.**
$1244 - 500 = 6p + 500 - 500$	**Subtract 500 from each side.**
$744 = 6p$	**Simplify.**
$\frac{744}{6} = \frac{6p}{6}$	**Divide each side by 6.**
$124 = p$	**Simplify.**

ANSWER You have to read 124 pages per week.

EXTRA EXAMPLES

Example 1 It costs \$825 a month for a city to buy fuel for its 11 official cars. Fuel for each additional car costs \$75 per month. The monthly budget for fuel for city cars has been increased to \$1050. Write and solve an equation to find for how many additional cars the city can afford to buy fuel each month. **$1050 = 825 + 75n$; 3 cars**

Example 2 The sum of 7 times a number and -8 is 69. Write and solve an equation to find the number. **$7n + (-8) = 69$; 11**

Example 3 Three people on vacation are sharing driving duty. They have driven 140 of 800 miles so far. They want to divide the remaining distance equally among themselves. Write and solve an equation to find how many miles each person should drive. **$800 = 3p + 140$; 220 mi**

CONCEPT CHECK

How does writing a verbal model help you in writing an equation to represent a real-world situation? ***Sample answer:*** **A verbal model helps you to identify the relationship between the information that is given and the quantity that is sought so that this relationship can be expressed using mathematical symbols.**

DAILY PUZZLER

Li-Shyung has a pocket full of coins, with quarters the largest denomination, but she cannot give you correct change for a dollar. What is the greatest possible value of the coins in her pocket? **\$1.19 (3 quarters, 4 dimes, 4 pennies)**

ASSIGNMENT GUIDE

Basic Course

Day 1: EP p. 727 Exs. 17-20; pp. 126-128 Exs. 7-10, 15-17, 27-29

Day 2: pp. 126-128 Exs. 12-14, 18-20, 30-33

Average Course

Day 1: pp. 126-128 Exs. 7-10, 15-19, 27-30

Day 2: pp. 126-128 Exs. 11-14, 20-22, 31-34

Advanced Course

Day 1: pp. 126-128 Exs. 7-10, 15-17, 21, 22, 27-29

Day 2: pp. 126-128 Exs. 11-14, 18-20, 23-26*, 32-34

Block

pp. 126-128 Exs. 7-10, 15-19, 27-30 (with 3.3)

pp. 126-128 Exs. 11-14, 20-22, 31-34 (with 3.5)

EXTRA PRACTICE

- Student Edition, p. 729
- Chapter 3 Resource Book, pp. 38-40
- Test and Practice Generator

Even-numbered answers are available on transparencies.

HOMEWORK CHECK

When you review students' homework for this lesson, go over the following exercises to check understanding of key concepts.

Basic: 7, 8, 9, 10, 12
Average: 7, 8, 9, 12, 13
Advanced: 7, 8, 9, 12, 14

3.4 Exercises

More Practice, p. 729

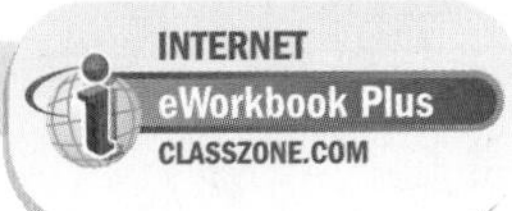

Getting Ready to Practice

Match the statement with the correct equation.

1. The sum of 3 and a number is 16. D
2. The product of 3 and a number is 16. C
3. The difference of three times a number and 2 is 16. A
4. The product of 3 and twice a number is 16. B

A. $3n - 2 = 16$
B. $3(2n) = 16$
C. $3n = 16$
D. $3 + n = 16$

5. **Bicycle Rental** A bicycle rental shop charges \$5 per hour plus a fee of \$10 each time you rent a bicycle. Which equation can you use to find the number of hours you can rent a bicycle if you have \$45? A

   A. $5h + 10 = 45$ **B.** $10h + 5 = 45$ **C.** $5 + h + 10 = 45$

6. **Guided Problem Solving** You and your friends decide to have a car wash as a fundraiser. You spend \$15 on supplies and charge \$6 per car. At the end of the day your profit is \$93. How many cars did you and your friends wash?

   (1) Write a verbal model. Cost per car • Number of cars − Amount spent on supplies = Profit
   (2) Translate your verbal model into an algebraic model. $6c - 15 = 93$
   (3) Solve the equation. 18 cars
   (4) Check that your answer is reasonable.

Practice and Problem Solving

Example	Exercises
1	9-13
2	7-8
3	9-13

Online Resources CLASSZONE.COM
- More Examples
- eTutorial Plus

8. $\frac{18}{n} - 7 = 2$; 2

A **In Exercises 7 and 8, translate the statement into an equation. Then solve the equation.**

7. The sum of 5 times a number and 4 is 9. $4 + 5n = 9$; 1
8. Seven subtracted from the quotient of 18 and a number is 2. See margin.
9. **Restaurant** At a restaurant one day, 60 sandwiches are sold in total, some on rye bread and some on white bread. The number of sandwiches sold on rye bread is twice the number sold the day before. The number of sandwiches on white bread is 28. How many sandwiches on rye bread were sold yesterday? 16 sandwiches on rye bread
10. **Hourly Wage** You had \$20 at the beginning of the week. You worked 10 hours during the week and ended the week having \$70. How much do you earn each hour? \$5

11. *Sample answer:* You buy 5 boxes of your favorite cereal at the store. With the store's double-coupon policy, you save \$6 with your coupons. You pay \$9 for the cereal. What was the original price of each box?

11. **Writing** Write a word problem that can be modeled by the equation $5x - 6 = 9$.

12. **Party Supplies** You need 124 plastic forks for a party. At one store you buy 5 boxes that contain 8 forks each. At another store you find boxes that contain 12 forks each. How many of these boxes do you need to buy? 7 boxes

13. **Magazine Subscription** You subscribe to a magazine that costs \$26 yearly. You make an initial payment of \$5 and then make three equal payments. How much is each payment? \$7

B 14. **Critical Thinking** Write a one-step equation and a two-step equation that both have 8 as a solution. *Sample answer:* $x - 3 = 5$; $2x + 2 = 18$

In Exercises 15–18, translate the statement into an equation. Then solve the equation.

15. The sum of 2 times a number and 5 is 12. $2x + 5 = 12$; 3.5

16. The difference of the product of 3 and a number and $-\frac{1}{2}$ is $-\frac{5}{2}$. $3n - \left(-\frac{1}{2}\right) = -\frac{5}{2}$; -1

17. The sum of -2 times a number and 3.5 is 7.5. $-2n + 3.5 = 7.5$; -2

18. Three less than the quotient of a number and 2 is 8. $\frac{n}{2} - 3 = 8$; 22

19. **School Fair** The senior class at your school made a \$300 profit at the school fair by having a dunk tank. The dunk tank cost \$125 to rent, and the senior class charged \$5 for each person to play. How many people played? 85 people

20. **Taxicab** A taxicab charges a \$2 fee plus an additional \$1.50 for every mile driven. Your cab ride cost \$17. How many miles did you travel? 10 mi

Critical Thinking **Exercises 21 and 22 are missing information. Tell what information is needed in order to solve the problem.**

21. You have a job in which you make \$6 per hour plus tips. You made a total of \$34 yesterday. How much did you make in tips? the number of hours worked

C 22. To train for a race, you jog for 5 minutes and then you run for 20 minutes. For each week after, you jog for 5 minutes, but increase the time that you run. After how many weeks will you be training for a total of 85 minutes? by how much your running time increases each week

Challenge **Translate the statement into an equation. Then solve the equation.**

23. The product of a number divided by 5 and 2 is 1. $\frac{n}{5} \cdot 2 = 1$; 2.5

24. The sum of 2 and 3, plus 3 times a number, is -4.

25. The quotient of -36 and 9, subtracted from 4 times a number, is -8.

26. The product of 8 squared divided by 16 and a number is 24.

24. $2 + 3 + 3n = -4$; -3

25. $4n - \left(\frac{-36}{9}\right) = -8$; -3

26. $\frac{8^2}{16} \cdot n = 24$; 6

COMMON ERROR

The difference stated in Exercise 16 will be hard for many students to identify. Because the statement begins "The difference of," students should look for the word "and" to identify the quantity subtracted. Because "and" occurs twice, there are two possibilities. The first makes no sense because "the product of 3" does not by itself describe a quantity. So, $-\frac{1}{2}$ must be the quantity subtracted, and "the product of 3 and a number," or $3n$, must be the quantity from which it is subtracted.

ASSESS

ASSESSMENT RESOURCES

For more assessment resources, see:

- Assessment Book
- Test and Practice Generator

MINI-QUIZ

Translate the statement into an equation. Then solve the equation.

1. The sum of 17 and twice a number is 25. $17 + 2x = 25$; 4
2. Four less than the quotient of a number and 16 is -3. $\frac{x}{16} - 4 = -3$; 16
3. Fourteen more than the product of 7 and a number is 56. $7x + 14 = 56$; 6
4. Lynn operated a backhoe for 16 hours this week and earned \$264. Of the \$264, \$40 was a bonus and the rest was calculated using an hourly rate. What was Lynn's hourly pay? \$14/h

5 FOLLOW-UP

RETEACHING/REMEDIATION

- Study Guide in Chapter 3 Resource Book, pp. 41-42
- Tutor Place, Algebra Cards 1, 7
- eTutorial Plus Online
- Extra Practice, p. 729
- Lesson Practice in Chapter 3 Resource Book, pp. 38-40

CHALLENGE/ENRICHMENT

- Challenge Practice in Chapter 3 Resource Book, p. 44
- Teacher's Edition, p. 104F

ENGLISH LEARNER SUPPORT

- Spanish Study Guide
- Multi-Language Glossary
- Chapter Audio Summaries CDs

Mixed Review 

Find the perimeter and area of the rectangle or square. *(Lesson 1.6)*

27. 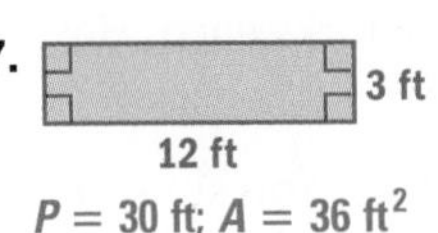

$P = 30$ ft; $A = 36$ ft^2

28. 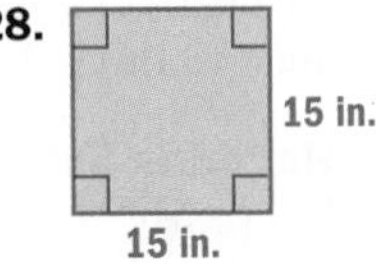

$P = 60$ in.; $A = 225$ in.^{2}

29. 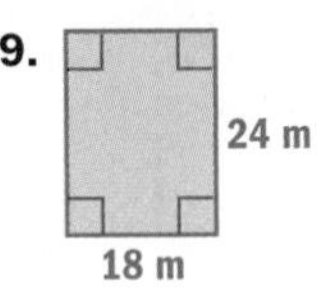

$P = 84$ m; $A = 432$ m^2

Solve the equation. *(Lessons 2.7, 3.3)*

30. $2(x + 5) = 30$ 10 **31.** $2x + 8(-2) = 54$ 35 **32.** $3(t - 6) = 9$ 9

Test-Taking Practice 

INTERNET
State Test Practice
CLASSZONE.COM

33. Multiple Choice Which equation has the solution -2? D

A. $2x + 7 = 11$ **B.** $2x - 7 = -3$ **C.** $2x + 7 = 8$ **D.** $2x - 7 = -11$

34. Extended Response Mr. Andreas has a video rental business. The table shows how much he charges to rent videos. Write an equation that could be used to find the cost of renting x videos. Explain how you found your equation. Use your equation to find the cost of renting 10 videos. $y = 2x + 2$; Use the Problem Solving Strategy: Guess, Check and Revise to find the pattern in the table; \$22

Videos	Price
1	\$4.00
2	\$6.00
3	\$8.00
4	\$10.00
5	\$12.00
6	\$14.00

Behind the Magic

- Choose any number.
- Multiply the number by 2.
- Add 14. Divide by 2.
- Subtract the number you started with.
- Multiply by 3. Your answer is 21.

To figure out why the answer is always 21, let x be the number you choose and write an algebraic expression that shows all of the steps. Then simplify the expression. What is your answer?

$3\left(\frac{2x + 14}{2} - x\right) = 3(x + 7 - x) = 3(7) = 21$

3.4 Technology Activity

INTERNET

Searching for Information

GOAL Use the Internet to search for information necessary to write an equation.

Example **A class is planning a trip to the Naismith Memorial Basketball Hall of Fame in Springfield, Massachusetts. The class has $190 to spend on admission. There are 35 students in the class. How many adults can they afford to bring?**

Solution

Follow these steps to perform a search on the Internet:

1. Pick a search engine.
2. Type keywords that cover the topic you would like to search. Then select Search.
3. Of the results the search engine finds, pick a site that is likely to have the information you need.

Use the steps described above to find the prices for students and adults. (*Hint:* There are over 35 people going, so the group rates would apply.)

Amount to spend	=	Number of students	•	Price per student	+	Number of adults	•	Price per adult

Your turn now **Use the results of your search.**

1. Write and solve an equation to solve the problem in the example. ***Sample answer:*** **$35(4) + 10x = 190$; 5 adults**
2. Your class is planning a trip to a museum. Use the Internet to research prices for student and adult tickets at a nearby museum. If your class has $200 to spend on admission, how many adults can you afford to bring?

2. **A good answer will include good research and an answer that is based on the results of the research, and should include an equation of the form Number of adult tickets • Cost per adult ticket + Number of student tickets • Cost per student ticket = $200.**

ILLINOIS Standards and ISAT:
8.A.3b, 8.D.3a

1 PLAN

Learn the Method

- Students will use the Internet to search for information necessary to write an equation.
- In Example 1 of Lesson 3.4, students were given costs to feed flamingos, but they can also research costs of caring for animals using the Internet.

Grouping

Group students if there are too few computers with Internet access for each to have one. Give each student a turn performing a search.

2 TEACH

Tips for Success

Have students examine the rules that a given search engine uses to locate information. For example, quotation marks might be used to find an exact phrase.

EXTRA EXAMPLES

Example Elsa earns $5 an hour. She has $10 now, and wants to adopt a cat from a shelter. Write and solve an equation to find how many hours Elsa must work to pay the adoption fee from an animal shelter near you. ***Sample answer:*** **$10 + 5x = 50$; 8 h**

3 CLOSE

Assessment

1. Have students write and solve a two-step equation using information from the Internet about vehicle fuel economy. **Check work.**

Additional Resources

The following resources are available to help review the materials in Lessons 3.1–3.4.

Chapter 3 Resource Book
- Lesson Practice
- Study Guide

Assessment Book
- Chapter 3 Quiz 1

Technology
- Test and Practice Generator
- eTutorial CD-ROM

Internet
- Classzone
- eWorkbook Plus Online
- eTutorial Plus Online

English Learner Support

- Spanish Study Guide
- Multi-Language Glossary
- Chapter Audio Summaries CDs

Notebook Review

Review the vocabulary definitions in your notebook.

Copy the review examples in your notebook. Then complete the exercises.

Check Your Definitions

equivalent equations, p. 109 — inverse operation, p. 109

Use Your Vocabulary

1. Name two pairs of inverse operations. addition and subtraction; multiplication and division

3.1 Can you solve addition and subtraction equations?

EXAMPLE Solve the equation.

$x - 23 = 9$	**Original equation**	$y + 17.3 = 68.8$	**Original equation**
$+23 \quad +23$	**Add 23 to each side.**	$-17.3 \quad -17.3$	**Subtract 17.3 from each side.**
$x = 32$	**Simplify.**	$y = 51.5$	**Simplify.**

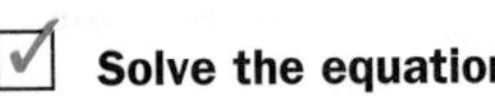

Solve the equation.

2. $c + 14 = 3$ −11
3. $y - 31 = 11$ 42
4. $7.7 = s - 4.3$ 12
5. $2 = r - 45$ 47
6. $29 = 40 + p$ −11
7. $b + 3.09 = -5.91$ −9

3.2 Can you solve multiplication and division equations?

EXAMPLE Solve the equation.

$\frac{y}{4} = -8$	**Original equation**	$-7x = -56$	**Original equation**
$\frac{y}{4} \cdot 4 = -8 \cdot 4$	**Multiply each side by 4.**	$\frac{-7x}{-7} = \frac{-56}{-7}$	**Divide each side by −7.**
$y = -32$	**Simplify.**	$x = 8$	**Simplify.**

Solve the equation.

8. $\frac{m}{3} = 9$ 27
9. $\frac{h}{5} = -8$ −40
10. $-5 = \frac{w}{-11}$ 55
11. $-15n = 60$ −4
12. $-25x = 0$ 0
13. $7 = 3.5t$ 2

3.3–3.4 Can you write and solve two-step equations?

EXAMPLE A catering company charges \$100 for setup plus \$15 per guest. How many guests can be served within a \$1000 budget?

Solution

Setup	+	Cost per guest	•	Number of guests	=	Budget

$100 + 15n = 1000$ **Write an algebraic model.**

$15n = 900$ **Subtract 100 from each side.**

$n = 60$ **Divide each side by 15.**

ANSWER Sixty guests can be served within a \$1000 budget.

☑ **14.** You are stuffing 560 envelopes for a school event. By 1:00 P.M., you have stuffed 140 envelopes. How many envelopes an hour do you need to stuff to finish by 5:00 P.M.? **105 envelopes per hour**

Stop and Think about Lessons 3.1–3.4

15. Critical Thinking How is the order of the steps you use to solve a two-step equation related to the order of operations for evaluating expressions? **It uses inverse operations in reverse order to their corresponding operations.**

Review Quiz 1

Solve the equation.

1. $x - 16 = 8$ **24** **2.** $-330 = -10x$ **33** **3.** $42 = \frac{1}{6}x$ **252** **4.** $5x - 12 = 23$ **7**

5. Field Trip Your class is going to a museum. Your teacher buys 32 tickets that are all the same price. The total charge for all the tickets is \$256. Write and solve an equation to find the price of one museum ticket. **$32t = 256$; \$8**

Translate the statement into an equation. Then solve.

6. The sum of 10 times a number and 5 is -15. **$10n + 5 = -15$; -2**

7. The difference of 4 times a number and -7 is 39. **$4n - (-7) = 39$; 8**

8. $\frac{280}{2} + 20n = 280$; 7 weeks

8. Bicycle Mary wants to buy a bicycle that costs \$280. Her parents agree to pay half. Mary will save \$20 a week. Write and solve an equation to find how long it will take her to save enough money.

1 PLAN

Strategy Background

Drawing a Diagram is appropriate when the words in the problem suggest a visual representation. Measurement and geometry problems are obvious applications of this strategy, but it is also useful for problems in logic, number theory, and probability. The strategy allows you to overview the problem with one glance, and this may lead to other strategies that you may not have considered.

TEACH

Guiding Students' Work

In Step 3, some students may worry that the location of the 10 by 10 space will affect the answer. Point out that as long as it is completely inside the classroom space, the calculations and results are exactly the same. Other students may note that there is a second method of solution. The remaining classroom area can also be thought of as the sum of the areas of two squares, one 20 feet on a side and one 10 feet on a side, with the missing side lengths found by subtracting dimensions of the demonstration space from dimensions of the classroom space.

EXTRA EXAMPLES

Example A rectangular counter in Talia's kitchen is 3 feet wide and 6 feet long. She places a microwave on the counter that is 2 feet wide and 2 feet long. How much counter space remains available? **14 ft^2**

3.5 Problem Solving Strategies

- Guess, Check, and Revise
- Look for a Pattern
- Act It Out
- Work Backward
- Draw a Diagram
- Solve a Simpler Problem
- Draw a Graph

Draw a Diagram

Problem Your class is hosting a science fair. Your classroom is 30 feet by 20 feet. You need to keep a 10 foot by 10 foot space empty for a demonstration. How much space do you have left for exhibits?

1 Read and Understand

Read the problem carefully.

- You need to find the area of the room after the demonstration space is identified.

2 Make a Plan

Decide on a strategy to use.

One way to see the situation is to draw a diagram. To solve this problem, you can draw a diagram of the classroom.

3 Solve the Problem

Reread the problem and draw a diagram.

First, draw and label a diagram of the classroom.

Next, draw a space to save for the demonstration. The problem doesn't specify where the space needs to be, so you might choose to put it in one corner.

30 ft
20 ft
10 ft
10 ft

The space available for exhibits is the total area of the classroom minus the area kept for the demonstration.

Total Area $= 30 \times 20$ Demonstration Area $= 10 \times 10$

Area for Exhibits = Total Area − Demonstration Area

$= 30 \times 20 - 10 \times 10$ **Write an algebraic model.**

$= 600 - 100$ **Multiply.**

$= 500$ **Subtract.**

Area is measured in square units, so the area for exhibits is 500 square feet.

4 Look Back

When the question involves measurements, check to be sure your answer includes the appropriate units.

ILLINOIS Standards and ISAT:
7.C.3b

Practice the Strategy

Use the strategy *draw a diagram.*

1. **Restaurant Space** Your favorite pizza place has a new addition. The original building was 30 feet by 16 feet. The addition is 12 feet by 16 feet. What is the total area of the building with the addition? **672 ft^2**

2. **Cafeteria** Mark, Kristine, Todd, and Alia are in line for lunch at the cafeteria in that order. Kristine lets Alia cut in front of her. Mark lets Todd cut in back of him. Todd then lets Kristine cut in front of him. In what order are they now? **Mark, Kristine, Todd, Alia**

3. **Mall Stores** Stores rent space in a mall. If the cost to rent Store 58 is $35 per square foot, what is the total rent for the store? **$118,125**

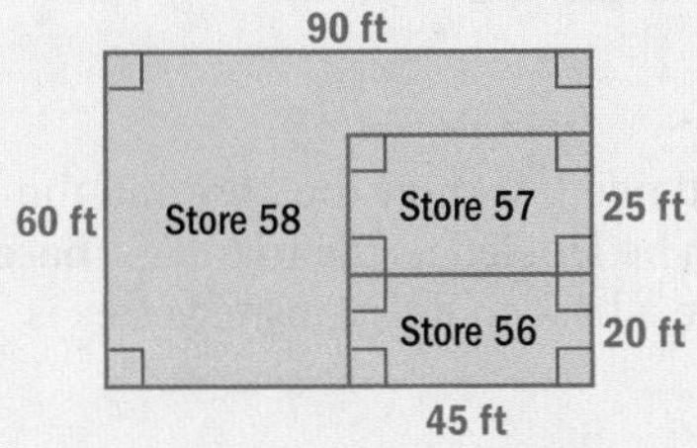

4. **School Gym** A gym is 100 feet by 70 feet. Bleachers are along both 100 foot sides of the gym. The bleachers are 4 feet deep when closed. When open, they are 9 feet deep. Compare the available area in the gym when the bleachers are closed to when they are open. **See margin.**

5. **Classrooms** Two classrooms are the same size. Each has seating for 28 students. In one room, each student has a desk and chair that take up 9 square feet. In the other room, each group of 4 students shares a table and chairs that take up 35 square feet. Each room also has one large table that takes up 15 square feet. Which room has more walking space? **the room where students share tables**

Mixed Problem Solving

Use any strategy to solve the problem.

6. **Internet Sales** In May 2001, spending on online auctions was $556 million, about $\frac{2}{3}$ of which was through one auction site. What was the total spending on auctions at that site in May 2001? **about $371 million**

7. **Survey** A group of 1238 students in grades 7–12 were asked to name the reasons for community involvement. How do you know that some students gave more than one answer? Graph the data. **The total number of students is greater than 1238. See margin for art.**

Reason	Number
Makes me feel good	842
Fun to do	829
Right thing to do	805

8. **Video Games** In a video game, when you reach 50 points, you reach Level 2. You need 70 more points to reach Level 3, and then you need 90 more points to reach Level 4. How many points do you need to reach Level 7 without skipping any levels? **600 points**

9. **Creating a Maze** You are painting a 10 foot by 10 foot maze at your school. Inside the maze will be a 2 foot by 2 foot area that is the goal. What is the longest path you can create if the path, including lines, is one foot wide? Draw one solution. Explain how you know you have found the longest path. **96 ft; See margin for art. *Sample answer:* I subtracted the number of squares in the goal from the total number of squares in the maze and got 96 ft.**

3 APPLY

Transparency

Even-numbered answers are available on transparencies.

Common Error

In Exercise 1, students who read too quickly may assume that the problem is of the same style as the one presented to introduce the strategy of drawing a diagram, and so may subtract. Encourage them to read slowly and draw their diagrams carefully to help them understand the problem completely.

Teaching Tip

In Exercise 2, encourage students to mark clearly the direction of the front of the line in their diagrams. Also, they should leave considerable space between the names or initials in their original drawing to allow room to "move" the students in the line.

Math Reasoning

There are several ways to calculate the area in Exercise 3. Challenge students to brainstorm and suggest all the ways they can think of to find the area.

Suggested Strategies

You may wish to suggest the following strategies for the problems in the Mixed Problem Solving:

- Exercise 6: Guess, Check, and Revise; Solve a Simpler Problem
- Exercise 7: Work Backward; Draw a Graph
- Exercise 8: Look for a Pattern
- Exercise 9: Draw a Diagram; Act It Out

4, 7, 9. See Additional Answers beginning on page AA1.

PLAN

SKILL CHECK

Find the area and perimeter.

1. a square with side 4 meters **$16\ m^2$, 16 m**
2. a rectangle with length 2 feet and width 3 feet **$6\ ft^2$, 10 ft**

LESSON OBJECTIVE

Use formulas for perimeter and area.

PACING

Suggested Number of Days
Basic Course: 1 day
Average Course: 1 day
Advanced Course: 1 day
Block: 0.5 block with 3.4

TEACHING RESOURCES

For a complete list of Teaching Resources, see page 104B.

TRANSPARENCY

Warm-Up Exercises for this lesson are available on a transparency. A support transparency is available for the Activity.

TEACH

MOTIVATING THE LESSON

Have students cut a rectangular piece of paper along a diagonal to form two congruent triangles. Ask how the area of each triangle compares to the area of the rectangle.

ACTIVITY

Goal Use graph paper to discover a formula for the area of a triangle.

Key Discovery The area of a triangle is half its base times its height.

Step 3. See Additional Answers beginning on page AA1.

Applying Geometric Formulas

BEFORE	Now	WHY?
You measured rectangles.	You'll use formulas for perimeter and area.	So you can evaluate advertising claims, as in Ex. 26.

Word Watch

base, p. 134
height, p. 134

Activity You can use a model to find the area of a triangle.

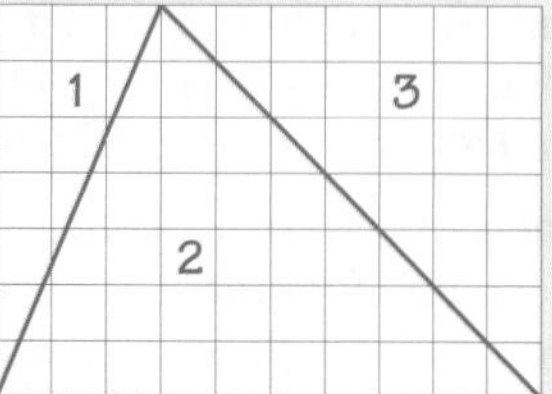

1. Copy the diagram on graph paper. **Check work.**
2. Cut out the three pieces. **Check work.**
3. Arrange the pieces to make two equal-sized triangles. **See margin.**
4. Compare the height of triangle 2 to the height of the original rectangle. What is the area of the rectangle? of triangle 2? **They are the same; 70 square units; 35 square units.**
5. Draw your own triangle on graph paper so that its longest side is a side of the rectangle and the vertex touches the opposite side. Find its area by following the steps above. **Check drawings.**
6. Write a formula for the area of a triangle. **$A = \frac{1}{2}bh$**

To find the area of a triangle, you need to know the *base* and the *height*. Any side of a triangle can be labeled as the triangle's **base**. The perpendicular distance from a base to its opposite vertex is the **height** of a triangle.

Notebook

Area and Perimeter of a Triangle

Words The *area* of a triangle is one half the product of its base b and height h.

The *perimeter* of a triangle is the sum of the lengths of all three sides a, b, and c.

Algebra $A = \frac{1}{2}bh$ $\qquad P = a + b + c$

Diagram

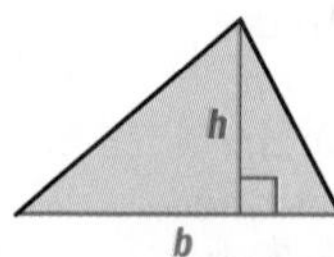

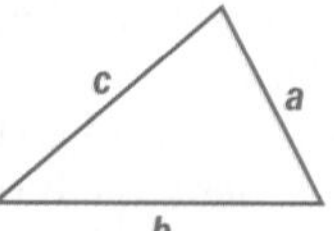

ILLINOIS Standards and ISAT:
7.C.3b, 8.D.3b; 9.C.3a

EXAMPLE 1 Finding Area and Perimeter of a Triangle

Find the area and perimeter of the triangle.

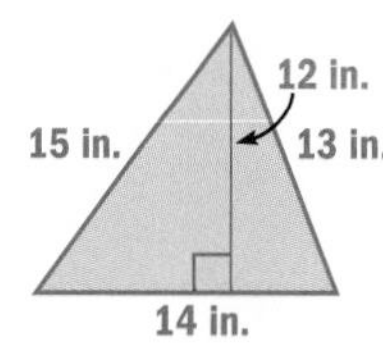

$A = \frac{1}{2}bh$ $\quad P = a + b + c$

$= \frac{1}{2}(14)(12)$ $\quad = 13 + 14 + 15$

$= 84 \text{ in.}^2$ $\quad = 42 \text{ in.}$

EXAMPLE 2 Finding the Area of a Triangle

Sailboats Find the area of the sail.

Solution

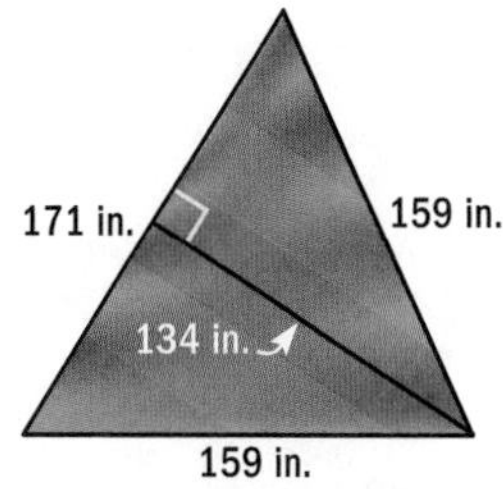

$A = \frac{1}{2}bh$ Write area formula.

$= \frac{1}{2}(171)(134)$ Substitute values.

$= 11{,}457$ Multiply.

ANSWER The area of the sail is 11,457 square inches.

Your turn now Use the given information about the triangle.

1. Its height is 9 inches and its base is 10 inches. Find its area. 45 in.^{2}
2. Its side lengths are 4 feet, 6 feet, and 2.5 feet. Find its perimeter. 12.5 ft

Now that you can solve equations, you can use area and perimeter formulas to find missing dimensions of geometric shapes.

EXAMPLE 3 Finding a Missing Width

Find the width of the rectangle shown if the area is 63 square feet.

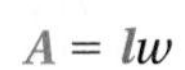
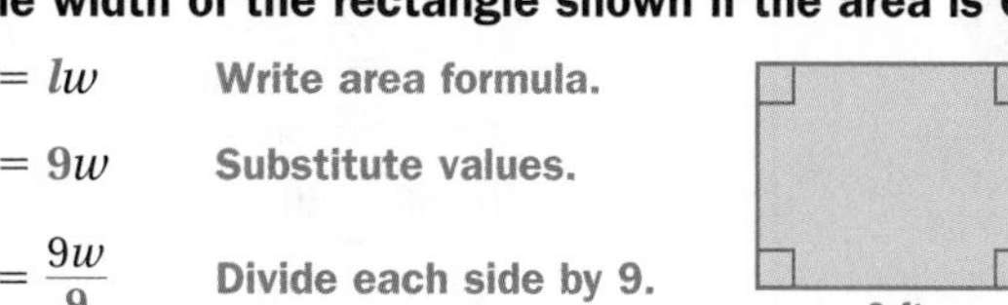

$A = lw$ Write area formula.

$63 = 9w$ Substitute values.

$\frac{63}{9} = \frac{9w}{9}$ Divide each side by 9.

$7 = w$ Simplify.

ANSWER The width of the rectangle is 7 feet.

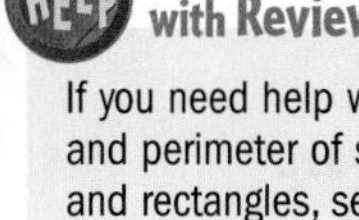

HELP with Review

If you need help with area and perimeter of squares and rectangles, see p. 33.

TIPS FOR NEW TEACHERS

To show that the area formula for a triangle is independent of orientation, tape a large paper triangle to a wall. Have students measure its base and height. Rotate the triangle so that a different side forms the base. Have students measure again. Repeat for the third side to show that the results agree. See Tips for New Teachers in the *Chapter 3 Resource Book*.

EXTRA EXAMPLES

Example 1 Find the area and perimeter of the triangle.

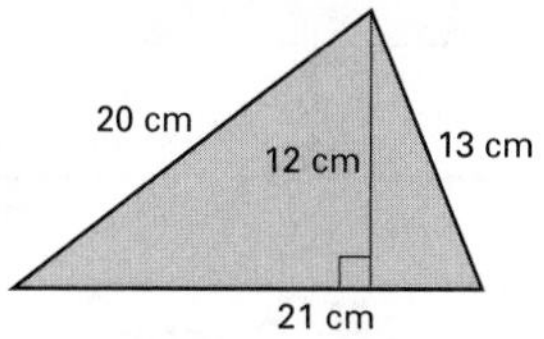

126 cm^2; 54 cm

Example 2 Find the area of the poster board. **780 in.^{2}**

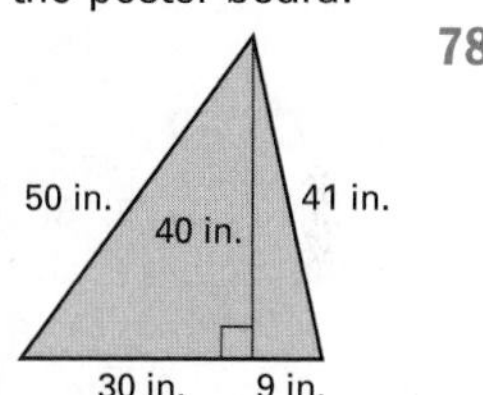

Example 3 Find the length of the rectangle shown if the area is 110 square inches. **11 in.**

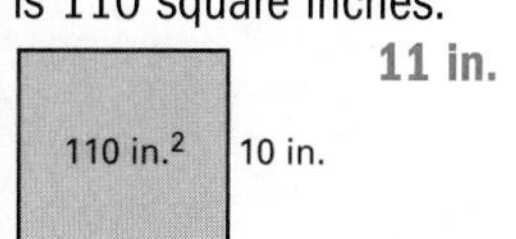

NOTETAKING

Have students sketch in their notes triangles in different orientations, labeling each triangle's base and height. Students should realize that any side can be the base.

EXTRA EXAMPLES

Example 4 The rectangle has a perimeter of 38 inches. Find the rectangle's length.

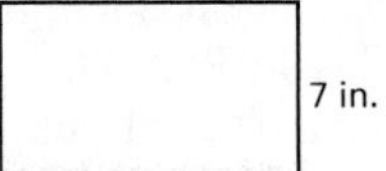

12 in.

Example 5 A patio has a planter on it as shown. Find the remaining area of the patio.

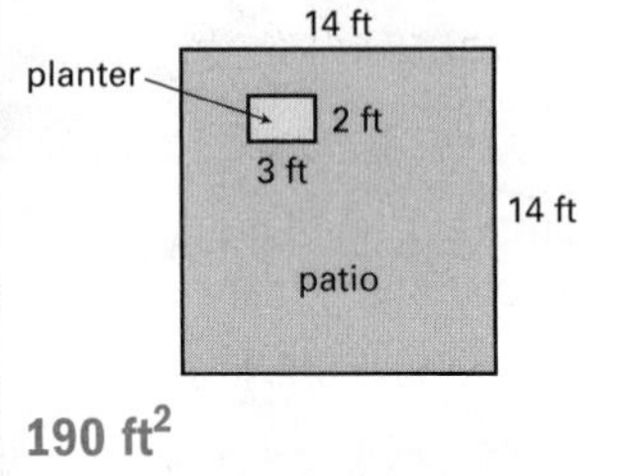

190 ft^2

CONCEPT CHECK

Describe how to find the area of a triangle. **Find half the product of the base and the height.**

DAILY PUZZLER

A square is 10 inches on a side. Lines are drawn connecting each pair of opposite corners of the square, dividing the square into 4 triangles. What is the height of each triangle? **5 in. or $5\sqrt{2}$ in.**

EXAMPLE 4 Finding a Missing Length

The rectangle has a perimeter of 20 inches. Find the length of the rectangle.

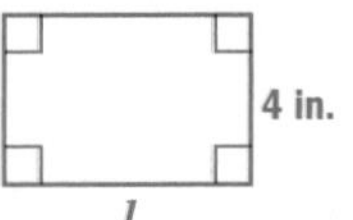

$P = 2l + 2w$	Write perimeter formula.
$20 = 2l + 2(4)$	Substitute 20 for *P* and 4 for *w*.
$20 = 2l + 8$	Multiply.
$20 - 8 = 2l + 8 - 8$	Subtract 8 from each side.
$12 = 2l$	Simplify.
$\frac{12}{2} = \frac{2l}{2}$	Divide each side by 2.
$6 = l$	Simplify.

ANSWER The length of the rectangle is 6 inches.

Your turn now **Find the unknown dimension.**

3. Perimeter = 36 ft

4. Area = 32 mm^2

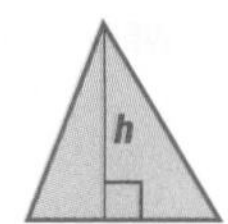

5. Area = 6 in.^{2}

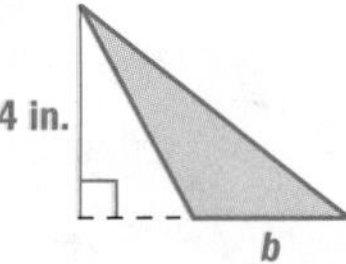

Polar Bears

Polar bears can swim up to 6.2 mi/h. About how far can a polar bear swim in 6 minutes? **up to 0.62 mi**

EXAMPLE 5 Using an Area Formula

Zoo A polar bear exhibit includes a pool and a region with rocks for climbing. Find the area of the region with rocks.

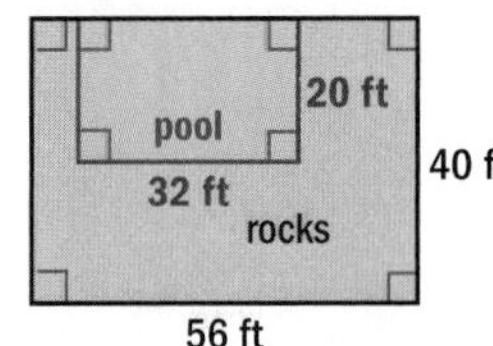

Solution

Let *r* be the area of the region with rocks.

Total area	=	Area of pool	+	Area of rock region

$40 \cdot 56 = 20 \cdot 32 + r$	
$2240 = 640 + r$	Write an algebraic model.
$2240 - 640 = 640 - 640 + r$	Subtract 640 from each side.
$1600 = r$	Simplify.

ANSWER The area of the region with rocks is 1600 square feet.

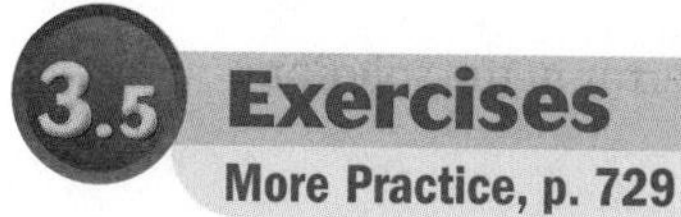

3.5 Exercises

More Practice, p. 729

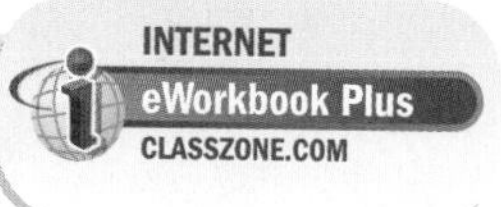

Getting Ready to Practice

1. Vocabulary Copy and complete: In order to find the area of a triangle, you need to know the length of a(n) _?_ and the _?_. base, height

Find the area and perimeter of the figure.

2.

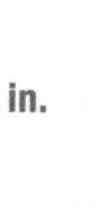

$A = 24$ in.^{2}; $P = 20$ in.

3.

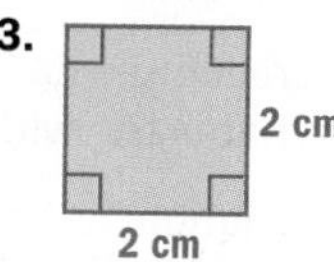

$A = 4$ cm^2; $P = 8$ cm

4.

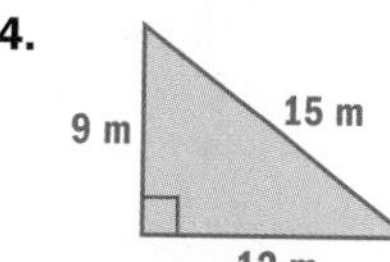

$A = 54$ m^2; $P = 36$ m

5. Guided Problem Solving Find the area of the patio shown at the right.

(1) Find the area of the rectangle. 42 yd^2

(2) Find the area of the square. 9 yd^2

(3) Add the two areas. 51 yd^2

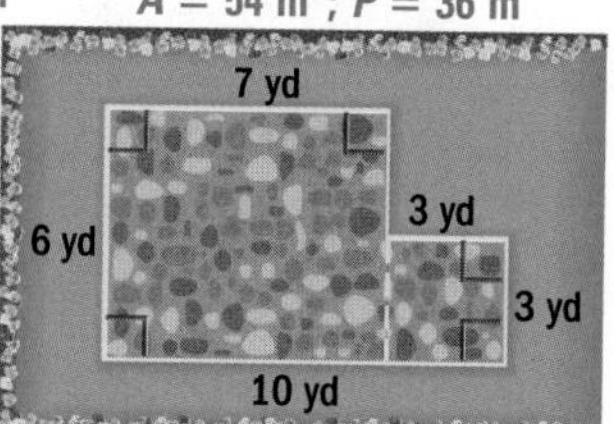

Practice and Problem Solving

A Find the area and perimeter of the triangle.

6.

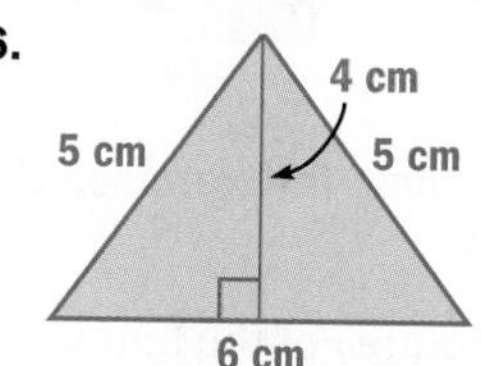

$A = 12$ cm^2; $P = 16$ cm

7.

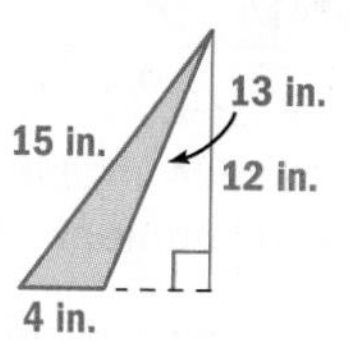

$A = 24$ in.^{2}; $P = 32$ in.

8.

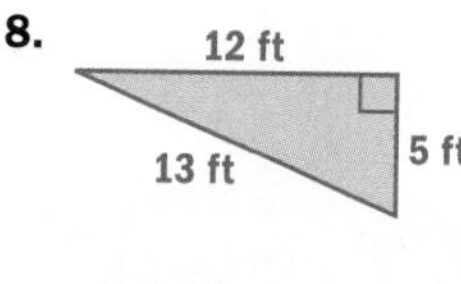

$A = 30$ ft^2; $P = 30$ ft

Find the unknown dimension.

9. $A = 18$ ft^2

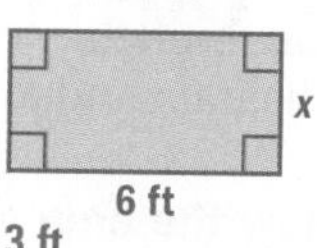

3 ft

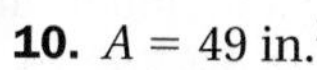

10. $A = 49$ in.^{2}

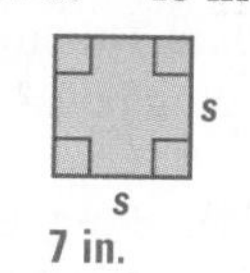

7 in.

11. $A = 12$ cm^2

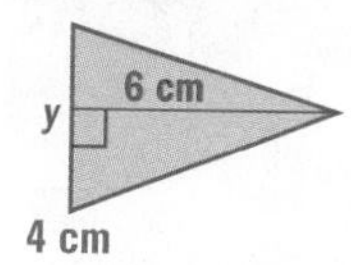

4 cm

Find the unknown dimension.

12. $P = 44$ in.

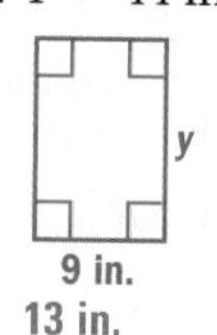

13 in.

13. $P = 60$ m

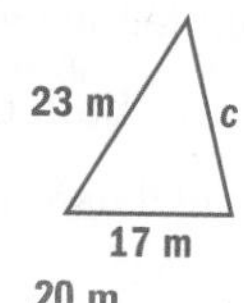

20 m

14. $P = 24$ ft

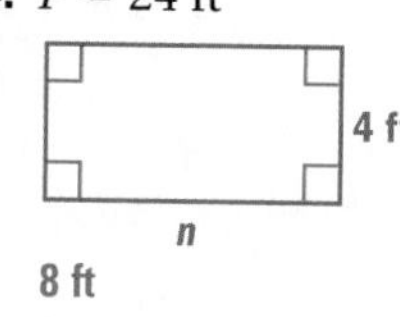

8 ft

HELP with Homework

Example	Exercises
1	6-8
2	6-8
3	9-11
4	12-14, 17
5	21-23

· More Examples
· eTutorial Plus

3 APPLY

ASSIGNMENT GUIDE

Basic Course

Day 1: pp. 137-139 Exs. 6-14, 17-25, 35-50

Average Course

Day 1: pp. 137-139 Exs. 8-18, 21-25, 29-33, 38-50

Advanced Course

Day 1: pp. 137-139 Exs. 8-16, 19-34*, 40-44, 48-50

Block

pp. 137-139 Exs. 8-18, 21-25, 29-33, 38-50 (with 3.4)

EXTRA PRACTICE

- Student Edition, p. 729
- Chapter 3 Resource Book, pp. 47-49
- Test and Practice Generator

TRANSPARENCY

Even-numbered answers are available on transparencies.

HOMEWORK CHECK

When you review students' homework for this lesson, go over the following exercises to check understanding of key concepts.
Basic: 6, 7, 9, 12, 21
Average: 8, 10, 12, 13, 22
Advanced: 8, 10, 12, 14, 23

TEACHING TIP

Cases such as the one in Exercise 7, where the height of the triangle is found by drawing a segment outside the triangle, may seem strange to some students. Have them draw several triangles with an obtuse angle adjoining the base to help accustom them to this case.

TEACHING TIP

Exercises 19 and 20 may be difficult for students, as these exercises indirectly introduce literal equations. Emphasize that in Exercise 19 they are solving for h, not x, and in Exercise 20 they are solving for l, not w. Point out that they can treat x and w respectively just as they would treat a number, so in Exercise 19 they can divide both sides by x, and in Exercise 20 they can divide both sides by $3.5w$ (if it is easier for them, they may want to divide both sides by 3.5, simplify, and then divide both sides by w).

26. Yes; they can fit as shown in the diagram below.

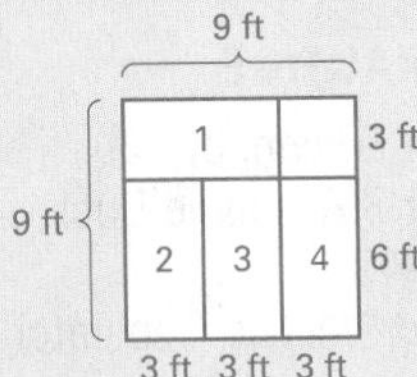

16. The perimeter of a rectangle is $P = 2l + 2w$. A square of side length s is a rectangle with length s and width s, so $P = 2s + 2s$, or $P = 4s$. The area of a rectangle is $A = lw$. For a square then, $A = s \cdot s$, or $A = s^2$.

15. Find the Error Describe and correct the error in the solution.

✗
$A = \frac{1}{2}(5 \text{ in.})(4 \text{ in.})$
$A = \frac{1}{2}(20 \text{ in.})$
$A = 10$ in.

Area is given in square units; $A = 10 \text{ in.}^2$

16. Critical Thinking Explain how the formulas for the perimeter and area of a rectangle can be used to find the perimeter and area of a square.

Find the dimension.

17. A rectangle has a perimeter of 146 inches and a length of 49 inches. What is the width of the rectangle? 24 in.

18. A triangle has an area of 36 square meters and a height of 8 meters. What is the length of its base? 9 m

19. A triangle has an area of 5 square meters and a base of $2x$. What is the height of the triangle in terms of x? $\frac{5}{x}$ m

20. A rectangle has an area of 70 square inches and a width of $3.5w$. What is the length of the rectangle in terms of w? $\frac{20}{w}$ in.

B Find the area of the shaded region in the figure.

21.

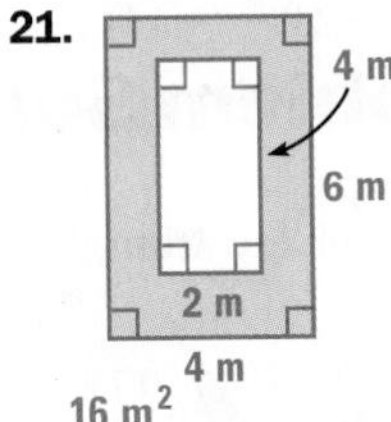

16 m^2

22.

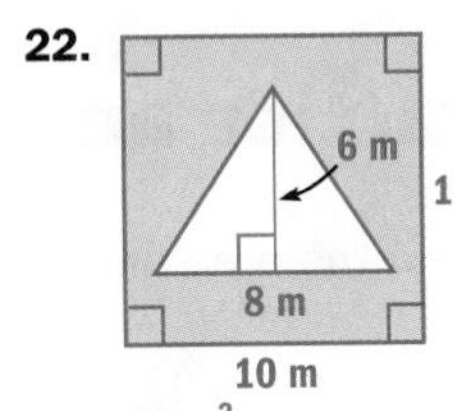

76 m^2

23.

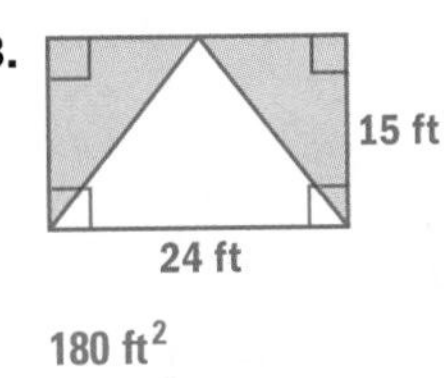

180 ft^2

Extended Problem Solving In Exercises 24–26, use the tent advertisement shown.

EXTREME

Measures 9 feet by 9 feet with 5 foot 10 inch peak height

COMFORTABLY FITS FOUR

24. Calculate Find the area of the tent floor. 81 ft^2

25. Estimate Estimate the dimensions of a rectangular sleeping bag and find its area. *Sample answer:* about 3 ft by 6 ft; 18 ft^2

26. Critical Thinking Do you think this tent will comfortably fit four sleeping bags? Draw a diagram and explain your answer. See margin.

Critical Thinking Explain how the area of a triangle changes if you change the triangle as described.

27. Double the height. Doubles the area.

28. Double the base. Doubles the area.

29. Double both the height and the base. Quadruples the area.

30. Change its shape, but not its base or height. Area stays the same.

31. **Sharing Space** Michelle and her sister Kate share a bedroom that is 18 feet by 14 feet. They want to divide the room so that each sister has half the area. Kate marks out her space. It is a square with sides 11 feet long in the center of the room. Does Kate have half the area of the room? Explain. **No; Kate has 121 square feet and the room has an area of 252 square feet, so Kate has less than half the area of the room.**

C **Find the area of the figure.**

32.

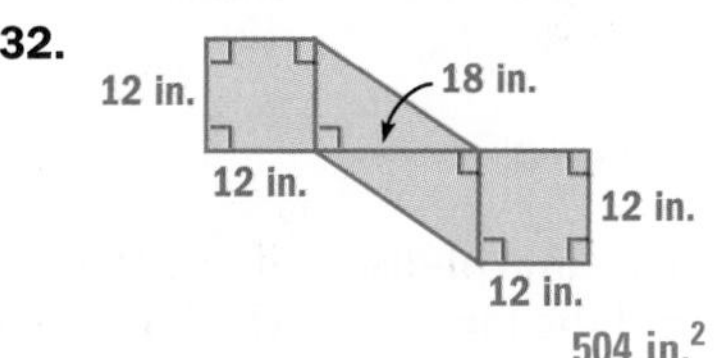

504 in.^{2}

33.

3 m, 5 m, 5 m, 5 m, 5 m, 5 m

37.5 m^2

34. **Challenge** A roll of weather stripping for windows is about 6 feet long. How many rolls are needed to go around three square windows that measure 3 feet on each side, and one rectangular window that measures 3 feet by 5 feet? **9 rolls**

Mixed Review

Find the sum or difference. *(Lessons 2.2, 2.3)*

35. $-18 - 42$ **−60**　　36. $-21 - (-14)$ **−7**　　37. $8 - (-10) - (-3)$ **21**

38. $15 + (-10)$ **5**　　39. $-20 + (-12)$ **−32**　　40. $11 + (-5) + (-8)$ **−2**

In Exercises 41–43, evaluate the expression when $a = 2$, $b = -5$, and $c = -7$. *(Lessons 2.3, 2.4)*

41. $a - b$ **7**　　42. $c + b^2$ **18**　　43. $abc - bc$ **35**

44. You have \$80 today. If you save \$40 a week, how many weeks will it take to save enough to buy a camera that costs \$320? How many weeks will it take if you save \$35 a week? *(Lesson 3.4)* **6 wk; about 7 wk**

Basic Skills **Copy and complete the statement with <, >, or =.**

45. $3 \underline{?} -3$ **>**　　46. $-5 \underline{?} -6$ **>**　　47. $-17 \underline{?} -13$ **<**　　48. $13 \underline{?} |13|$ **=**

Test-Taking Practice

INTERNET
State Test Practice
CLASSZONE.COM

49. **Multiple Choice** A rectangular garden has an area of 64 square feet. Its length is 16 feet. Which equation can you use to find the width? **D**

A. $64 - x = 16$　　**B.** $x + 16 = 32$　　**C.** $64x = 16$　　**D.** $16x = 64$

50. **Multiple Choice** What is the length of a rectangular room that is 22 feet wide with a perimeter of 114 feet? **I**

F. 20 feet　　**G.** 25 feet　　**H.** 30 feet　　**I.** 35 feet

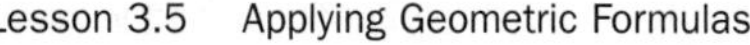

4 ASSESS

Assessment Resources

For more assessment resources, see:

- Assessment Book
- Test and Practice Generator

Mini-Quiz

Find the area and perimeter of the triangle.

1. Find the area and perimeter of the triangle.

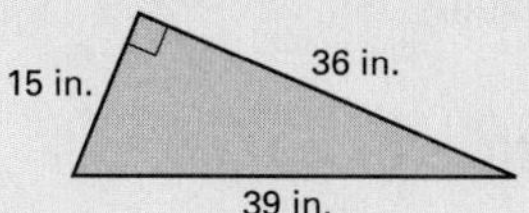

270 in.^{2}, 90 in.

2. Find the value of the variable if $P = 44$ m.

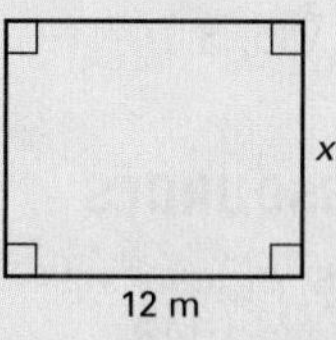

10 m

5 FOLLOW-UP

Reteaching/Remediation

- Study Guide in Chapter 3 Resource Book, pp. 50-51
- Tutor Place, Geometry and Measurement Cards 11–14
- eTutorial Plus Online
- Extra Practice, p. 729
- Lesson Practice in Chapter 3 Resource Book, pp. 47–49

Challenge/Enrichment

- Challenge Practice in Chapter 3 Resource Book, p. 53
- Teacher's Edition, p. 104F

English Learner Support

- Spanish Study Guide
- Multi-Language Glossary
- Chapter Audio Summaries CDs

1 PLAN

SKILL CHECK

Solve the equation.

1. $37 + x = -24$ — **−61**
2. $-4 = m - 11$ — **7**
3. $k - 4.7 = -3.2$ — **1.5**

LESSON OBJECTIVE

Solve inequalities using addition or subtraction.

PACING

Suggested Number of Days
Basic Course: 1 day
Average Course: 1 day
Advanced Course: 1 day
Block: 0.5 block with 3.7

TEACHING RESOURCES

For a complete list of Teaching Resources, see page 104B.

TRANSPARENCY

Warm-Up Exercises for this lesson are available on a transparency.

2 TEACH

MOTIVATING THE LESSON

Ask students who have played disc golf to explain the rules and how the target shown in the text works.

TIPS FOR NEW TEACHERS

Urge students to draw large clear open or closed dots when they graph inequalities. See Tips for New Teachers in the *Chapter 3 Resource Book*.

1–4. See Additional Answers beginning on page AA1.

LESSON 3.6

Solving Inequalities Using Addition or Subtraction

BEFORE	Now	WHY?
You solved equations using addition or subtraction.	You'll solve inequalities using addition or subtraction.	So you can find how much to improve your distance, as in Ex. 40.

Word Watch

inequality, p. 140
solution of an inequality, p. 140
equivalent inequalities, p. 141

In the Real World

Disc Golf In a game of disc golf, the target is beyond a pond the far end of which is 300 feet away. Your first throw travels 134 feet. How far does your second throw have to go in order to clear the pond? You will use an inequality to answer this question in Example 3.

Inequalities An **inequality** is a statement formed by placing an inequality symbol between two expressions, such as $x \le 6$. The **solution of an inequality** is the set of numbers that you can substitute for the variable to make the inequality true.

You can graph the solution of an inequality using a number line. When graphing inequalities with > or <, use an open circle. When graphing inequalities with ≥ or ≤, use a closed circle.

EXAMPLE 1 Graphing Inequalities

Inequality	Graph	Verbal Phrase
a. $y < 7$	2 3 4 5 6 7 8	All numbers less than 7
b. $q \le 3$	−2 −1 0 1 2 3 4	All numbers less than or equal to 3
c. $x > -5$	−6 −4 −2 0	All numbers greater than −5
d. $h \ge 2\frac{1}{2}$	0 1 2 3	All numbers greater than or equal to $2\frac{1}{2}$

Your turn now **Graph the inequality.** 1–4. See margin.

1. $z \ge -1$ **2.** $4 > p$ **3.** $k \le -3.5$ **4.** $m > \frac{1}{2}$

ILLINOIS Standards and ISAT:
8.A.3b, 8.D.3a

When you solve an inequality, you find all solutions of the inequality. Inequalities that have the same solutions are **equivalent inequalities**.

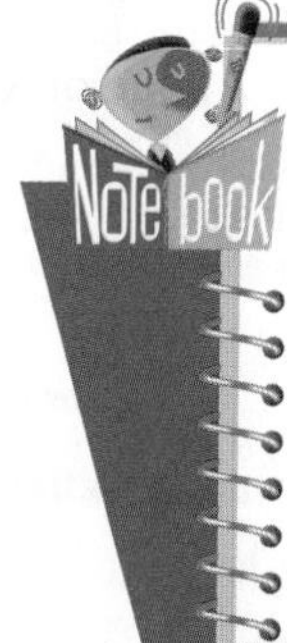

Addition and Subtraction Properties of Inequality

Words Adding or subtracting the same number on each side of an inequality produces an equivalent inequality.

Algebra If $a > b$, then $a + c > b + c$.

If $a > b$, then $a - c > b - c$.

with Solving

Remember that the inequality symbols can be read as follows.

$>$ "greater than"
$<$ "less than"
$\geq$ "greater than or equal to"
$\leq$ "less than or equal to"

EXAMPLE 2 Solving Inequalities

Solve the inequality. Then graph its solution.

a. $x - 5 < 8$ **Original inequality**

$x - 5 + 5 < 8 + 5$ **Add 5 to each side.**

$x < 13$ **Simplify.**

b. $y - 7 \geq -10$ **Original inequality**

$y - 7 + 7 \geq -10 + 7$ **Add 7 to each side.**

$y \geq -3$ **Simplify.**

c. $8 + m > 15$ **Original inequality**

$8 - 8 + m > 15 - 8$ **Subtract 8 from each side.**

$m > 7$ **Simplify.**

Your turn now **Solve the inequality. Then graph its solution.**

5–7. See margin for art.

5. $x - 3 > -2$ $x > 1$

6. $6 > t - 1$ $t < 7$

7. $12 \geq p + 14$ $p \leq -2$

Example 1 Graph the inequality.

a. $x < 8$

b. $y \geq -1\frac{1}{2}$

c. $k > -10$

d. $m \leq -4$

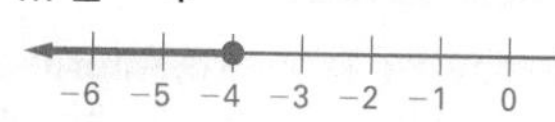

Example 2 Solve the inequality. Then graph its solution.

a. $k - 9 < 20$
$k < 29$

b. $m - 4 \geq -5$
$m \geq -1$

c. $18 + p > 4$
$p > -14$

TRANSPARENCY

A support transparency is available for Examples 1-2 and Your turn now Exercises 1-7.

EXTRA EXAMPLES

Example 3 Today Julia read the first 14 pages of her book. She wants to read at least 80 pages by the end of the week. Write and solve an inequality to find how many more pages Julia must read.
$p + 14 \geq 80$; $p \geq 66$ pages

Differentiating Instruction

Alternative Teaching Approach
Using tiles or marks on the floor, have students stand in a line at points representing different values. Call out inequalities and have students raise their hands if their position matches the inequality.

CONCEPT CHECK

When you graph an inequality with "greater than or equal to," do you use an open circle or a closed circle? **closed circle**

DAILY PUZZLER

Six equilateral triangles (triangles with all sides the same length) are placed together to form a hexagon (six-sided figure). Each triangle has a perimeter of 24 centimeters. What is the perimeter of the hexagon? **48 cm**

6.

7.

8.

9. Step 3:

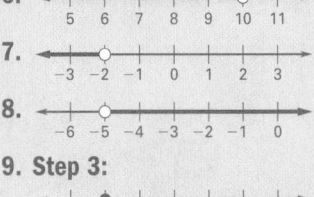

EXAMPLE 3 Writing and Solving an Inequality

Disc Golf Using an inequality, you can find the distance needed to clear the pond described on page 140.

Let d be the distance needed to clear the pond on your second throw.

Distance of 2nd throw	+	Distance of 1st throw	>	Distance to far end of pond

$d + 134 > 300$	**Write an algebraic model.**
$d + 134 - 134 > 300 - 134$	**Subtract 134 from each side.**
$d > 166$	**Simplify.**

ANSWER Your second throw needs to travel more than 166 feet.

3.6 Exercises

More Practice, p. 729

INTERNET
eWorkbook Plus
CLASSZONE.COM

Getting Ready to Practice

1. **Vocabulary** Copy and complete: $-4 + x < -6$ and $x < -2$ are ? . **equivalent inequalities**

Matching **Match the inequality with its graph.**

2. $x < -1$ **C**
3. $x \leq 1$ **A**
4. $x \geq 1$ **B**
5. $x > -1$ **D**

A.

B.

C.
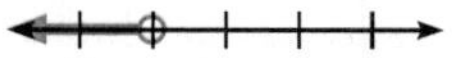

D.

Solve the inequality. Then graph its solution. **6–8. See margin for art.**

6. $x - 5 < 5$ **$x < 10$**
7. $8 > t + 10$ **$t < -2$**
8. $12 + p > 7$ **$p > -5$**

9. **Guided Problem Solving** On four tests you scored 90, 85, 98, and 87. To earn a B in math class, you need at least 425 points on 5 tests. Write and solve an inequality that represents the possible test scores you could get on your fifth test and still get at least a B in the class.
   (1) Add your current scores. **360**
   (2) Let x represent the fifth score. Write and solve the inequality. **$360 + x \geq 425$, $x \geq 65$**
   (3) Graph the possible test scores. **See margin.**

with Homework

Example	Exercises
1	10-21
2	22-30
3	31, 33

- More Examples
- eTutorial Plus

18. *z* is less than or equal to 8.
19. *j* is greater than −4.
20. *w* is greater than or equal to −15.
21. *n* is less than 0.

Practice and Problem Solving

Write the inequality represented by the graph.

A **10.** 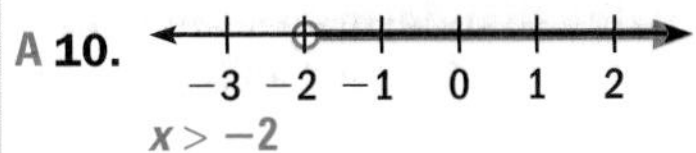 −3 −2 −1 0 1 2 $x > -2$

11. −10 −5 0 5 10 15 $x \geq -5$

12. −2 −1 0 1 2 3 $x \leq 2$

13. 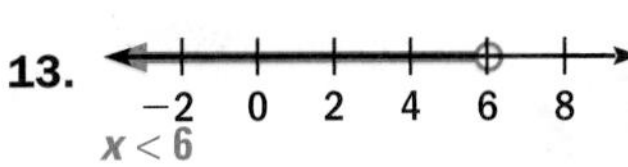 −2 0 2 4 6 8 $x < 6$

In Exercises 14–17, tell whether the number is a solution of the inequality graphed below.

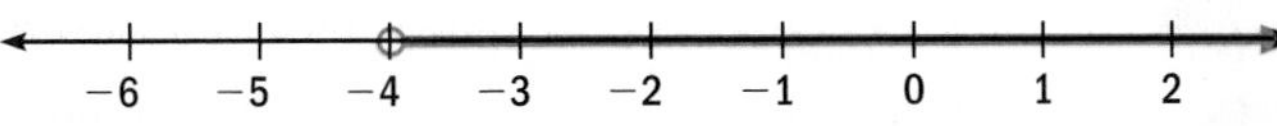

−6 −5 −4 −3 −2 −1 0 1 2

14. -4.5 no **15.** -4 no **16.** $2\frac{1}{2}$ yes **17.** 0 yes

Write a verbal phrase to describe the inequality.

18. $z \leq 8$ **19.** $j > -4$ **20.** $w \geq -15$ **21.** $n < 0$

Solve the inequality. Then graph its solution. 22–30. See margin for art.

22. $k + 4 \leq 11$ $k \leq 7$ **23.** $5 < 8 + t$ $t > -3$ **24.** $n - 6 > 3$ $n > 9$

25. $17 + r \geq 25$ $r \geq 8$ **26.** $m + 6 \geq -10$ $m \geq -16$ **27.** $p - 12 > -5$ $p > 7$

28. $-9 < d - 21$ $d > 12$ **29.** $-8 \geq m - 19$ $m \leq 11$ **30.** $-42 + x > -59$ $x > -17$

B **31.** **Banking** You have \$33.96 in a savings account. At your bank, you must have a minimum balance of \$50 in your account to avoid a fee. Write and solve an inequality to represent the amount of money you must deposit in order to reach or exceed the minimum balance. $33.96 + x \geq 50$; $x \geq \$16.04$

32. **Critical Thinking** Write an equivalent inequality that you would use addition to solve and whose solution is $p < 6$. *Sample answer:* $p - 3 < 3$

33. **Biplane Ride** Your family bought your grandmother a biplane ride for her 80th birthday. The flight can last up to one hour and 15 minutes. If she does 10 minutes of corkscrew rolls, 15 minutes of hammerheads, and 30 minutes of over-water flying, how much time can she use for scenic low-altitude flying without going over the time limit? 20 min

Solve the inequality. Then graph its solution. 34–39. See margin for art.

34. $5.45 + b < -3.55$ $b < -9$ **35.** $r - 3.1 < 4.4$ $r < 7.5$ **36.** $-3.5 < w - 9$ $w > 5.5$

37. $\frac{2}{3} \leq p - 2\frac{1}{3}$ $p \geq 3$ **38.** $-\frac{1}{2} \leq k + 2$ $k \geq -2\frac{1}{2}$ **39.** $t + \frac{1}{4} > 5$ $t > 4\frac{3}{4}$

3 APPLY

ASSIGNMENT GUIDE

Basic Course

Day 1: SRH p. 704 Exs. 1-6; pp. 143-145 Exs. 10-31, 37-40, 42-44, 53-59

Average Course

Day 1: pp. 143-145 Exs. 12-24, 31-36, 40-49, 55-60

Advanced Course

Day 1: pp. 143-145 Exs. 12-24, 31-33, 39-52*, 55-60

Block

pp. 143-145 Exs. 12-24, 31-36, 40-49, 55-60 (with 3.7)

EXTRA PRACTICE

- Student Edition, p. 729
- Chapter 3 Resource Book, pp. 57-59
- Test and Practice Generator

TRANSPARENCY

Even-numbered answers are available on transparencies. A support transparency is available for Exercises 6-9, 22-30, and 34-39.

HOMEWORK CHECK

When you review students' homework for this lesson, go over the following exercises to check understanding of key concepts.

Basic: 10, 12, 22, 24, 31
Average: 12, 14, 23, 24, 31
Advanced: 12, 14, 23, 24, 33

22-30, 34-39. See Additional Answers beginning on page AA1.

TEACHING TIP

Exercise 9 can be used to introduce the concept of compound inequalities. Ask students if every whole number greater than or equal to 65 is a reasonable solution. They should come to realize that in this case there is an upper limit to the inequality, usually 100. In this case the score must be at least 65, but cannot be more than 100. This concept occurs again in Exercises 45–50 and 52.

COMMON ERROR

In Exercise 44, watch for students who substitute incorrectly, since x is subtracted in this case. Also, students may notice that though they could answer Exercises 42 and 43 almost as easily by solving the inequalities as by substitution, they may likely be confused if they try to solve Exercise 44 directly, foreshadowing solving inequalities using multiplication and division in the next lesson.

40. Ski Jumping In a ski jumping competition, the top four jumpers perform as shown. How much farther does the fourth place jumper need to jump in order to place first? Write and solve an inequality that describes the situation. $233.6 + x > 250.2$; $x > 16.6$ m

Name	Distance
Cara	238.2 m
Jason	233.6 m
Marisa	250.2 m
Mitchell	236.3 m

41. Writing Explain why $x - 3 \geq 10$ and $x \geq 13$ are equivalent inequalities. $x \geq 13$ is the solution to $x - 3 \geq 10$.

Vocal Range

In an octave, the frequency doubles from the lowest to the highest note. Aretha Franklin's voice can range over about 3 octaves, but she is an exception. A typical person's singing voice can range over about 2 octaves. If your vocal range is 2 octaves and begins at 220 hertz, predict your full vocal range. 220 hertz to 880 hertz

Tell whether −6 is a solution of the inequality.

42. $8 + x \geq -2$ yes **43.** $x - 15 > -20$ no **44.** $-10 - x \leq -4$ yes

45. Vocal Range The frequency range of the human singing voice is between about 81 hertz and about 1100 hertz. Write two inequalities that describe this range. $x > 81$ hertz and $x < 1100$ hertz

46. Careers You are investigating a job that pays a maximum of \$34,000 and a minimum of \$25,000. Write two inequalities that describe this range. $x \geq \$25{,}000$ and $x \leq \$34{,}000$

EXAMPLE

Write a compound inequality that represents the set of all numbers greater than or equal to 0 and less than 4.

The set can be represented by two inequalities.

$0 \leq x$ and $x < 4$

The two inequalities can then be combined in a single inequality:

$0 \leq x < 4$

The compound inequality may be read in these two ways:

x is greater than or equal to 0 and x is less than 4.

x is greater than or equal to 0 and less than 4.

In Exercises 47–49, refer to the above example. Write a verbal sentence that describes the *compound inequality*.

C **47.** $-2 < y < 1$ **48.** $7 \leq t < 9$ **49.** $4 \leq m \leq 11$

50. Tigers Until 1900, the tiger population in India was approximately 40,000. Beginning in 1960, the population dropped dramatically until 1972, when the population fell below 2000. Now the tiger population is rising again. The current population can be described by the inequality $2000 \leq x \leq 4556$. Explain what this says about the current population. It has risen so it is at least 2000 and at most 4556.

51. Challenge Find the values of x that will make the following statement true: $4x - 10 < 8x + 4 - 3x$. $x > -14$

47. y is greater than −2 and y is less than 1.

48. t is greater than or equal to 7 and t is less than 9.

49. m is greater than or equal to 4 and m is less than or equal to 11.

52. Advertising During the first Super Bowl in 1967, a 30 second television commercial cost about $42,000. In 2001, advertisers paid about $2.4 million for a 30 second commercial. Assuming those were the least and greatest costs during that period, write an inequality that describes the cost c of 30 seconds of commercial time during the Super Bowl from 1967 through 2001.
$\$42,000 \le x \le \$2,400,000$

Mixed Review

Evaluate the expression. *(Lessons 2.2–2.5)*

53. $(-24) \div 3 + 5 \times (-9)$ -53

54. $(-12) \div (-33 + 45) - 19$ -20

55. $(-13 - 44) + 100 \div 2$ -7

56. $(-3) \times (15 - 7) \div 2 + 4$ -8

Basic Skills **Write the number in standard form.**

57. Nine and fifty-three thousandths 9.053

58. Sixty-four and seven tenths 64.7

Test-Taking Practice 

59. Multiple Choice What value of x makes $x - 3 \ge 20$ true? D

A. 17 **B.** 20 **C.** 22 **D.** 24

60. Short Response Lauren can spend at most $60 at the mall. She buys a birthday gift that costs $35. She also wants to buy a backpack for herself. Let x represent the cost of a backpack. Write and solve an inequality to find how much Lauren can spend on the backpack. Explain what the solution of the inequality means. $x + 35 \le 60$; $x \le 25$; the most Lauren can spend on the backpack is $25.

BRAIN GAME

Prized Positions

The student council is holding a raffle to raise money. The officers must decide how many prizes to award, but each officer has a different opinion.

- The president thinks there should be more than 1 prize.
- The vice president wants to give no more than 10 prizes.
- The treasurer believes at least 4 prizes should be awarded.
- The secretary says there should be fewer than 5.

How many prizes should the student council award? Find a number that will make everyone happy. 4 prizes

4 ASSESS

Assessment Resources

For more assessment resources, see:

- Assessment Book
- Test and Practice Generator

Mini-Quiz

1. Write the inequality represented by the graph.

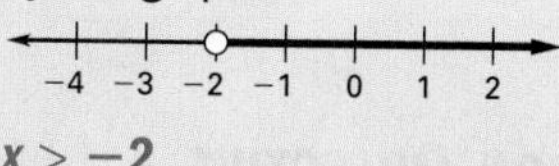

$x > -2$

Solve the inequality. Then graph its solution.

2. $-4 > y - 9$ $y < 5$

3. $d + 7 \le 26$ $d \le 19$

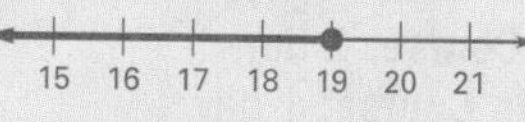

4. $f - 11 \ge -15$ $f \ge -4$

5 FOLLOW-UP

Reteaching/Remediation

- Study Guide in Chapter 3 Resource Book, pp. 60-61
- Tutor Place, Algebra Cards 14-16
- eTutorial Plus Online
- Extra Practice, p. 729
- Lesson Practice in Chapter 3 Resource Book, pp. 57-59

Challenge/Enrichment

- Challenge Practice in Chapter 3 Resource Book, p. 62
- Teacher's Edition, p. 104F

English Learner Support

- Spanish Study Guide
- Multi-Language Glossary
- Chapter Audio Summaries CDs

PLAN

SKILL CHECK

Solve the equation.

1. $\frac{x}{8} = 2$ 16
2. $6 = -\frac{n}{6}$ −36
3. $-4j = 56$ −14
4. $-91 = -13k$ 7

LESSON OBJECTIVE

Solve inequalities using multiplication or division.

PACING

Suggested Number of Days
Basic Course: 1 day
Average Course: 1 day
Advanced Course: 1 day
Block: 0.5 block with 3.6

TEACHING RESOURCES

For a complete list of Teaching Resources, see page 104B.

TRANSPARENCY

Warm-Up Exercises for this lesson are available on a transparency.

TEACH

MOTIVATING THE LESSON

Ask students what they know about bats. You may point out that in Austin, Texas, a colony of up to one and one-half million Mexican free-tail bats lives under the Congress Avenue bridge, and that the colony will eat from 10,000 to 30,000 pounds of insects in a single night.

LESSON 3.7

Solving Inequalities Using Multiplication or Division

BEFORE	Now	WHY?
You solved equations using multiplication or division.	You'll solve inequalities using multiplication or division.	So you can find how many students must attend a dance, as in Ex. 26.

Word Watch

Review Words

inequality, p. 140
solution of an inequality, p. 140
equivalent inequalities, p. 141

In the Real World

Bats About 15,000 fruit-eating bats live on Panama's Barro Colorado Island. Every year they consume up to 61,440,000 grams of fruit. About how many grams of fruit does each bat consume in a year? You will use an inequality to solve this in Example 3.

There is one important difference between solving inequalities and solving equations. When multiplying or dividing each side of an inequality by a negative number, you must *reverse the direction of the inequality symbol.*

HELP with Notetaking

You might want to use a table to organize this information about reversing the inequality symbol.

Multiplication Property of Inequality

Words	Algebra
Multiplying each side of an inequality by a *positive* number makes an equivalent inequality.	If $4x < 10$, then $\left(\frac{1}{4}\right)(4x) < \left(\frac{1}{4}\right)(10)$.
Multiplying each side of an inequality by a *negative* number and *reversing the direction of the inequality symbol* makes an equivalent inequality.	If $-5x < 10$, then $\left(-\frac{1}{5}\right)(-5x) > \left(-\frac{1}{5}\right)(10)$.

EXAMPLE 1 **Solving an Inequality Using Multiplication**

$-\frac{1}{8}n \geq 2$ Original inequality

$-8 \cdot \left(-\frac{1}{8}\right)n \leq -8 \cdot 2$ Multiply each side by −8. Reverse inequality symbol.

$n \leq -16$ Simplify.

ILLINOIS Standards and ISAT:
8.A.3b, 8.D.3a

Division Property of Inequality

Words	Algebra
Dividing each side of an inequality by a *positive* number makes an equivalent inequality.	If $2x < 10$, then $\frac{2x}{2} < \frac{10}{2}$.
Dividing each side of an inequality by a *negative* number and *reversing the direction of the inequality symbol* makes an equivalent inequality.	If $-5x < 15$, then $\frac{-5x}{-5} > \frac{15}{-5}$.

EXAMPLE 2 Solving an Inequality Using Division

$15 > -3m$	**Original inequality**
$\frac{15}{-3} < \frac{-3m}{-3}$	**Divide each side by −3. Reverse inequality symbol.**
$-5 < m$	**Simplify.**

Your turn now **Solve the inequality.**

1. $\frac{t}{6} > 4$ $t > 24$ **2.** $-\frac{1}{2}x \le 10$ $x \ge -20$ **3.** $27 > -3t$ $t > -9$ **4.** $9n < 63$ $n < 7$

EXAMPLE 3 Using the Division Property of Inequality

Bats You can find how much each fruit-eating bat eats annually as described on the previous page as follows.

Solution

Write a verbal model. Let g represent the number of grams one bat eats in a year.

Number of bats • Grams each bat eats ≤ Maximum amount eaten annually

$15{,}000g \le 61{,}440{,}000$	**Write an algebraic model.**
$\frac{15{,}000g}{15{,}000} \le \frac{61{,}440{,}000}{15{,}000}$	**Divide each side by 15,000.**
$g \le 4096$	**Simplify.**

ANSWER Each bat eats as much as 4096 grams of fruit in a year.

What do you think? Bats

Fruit Bats

Fruit bats help forests regrow by spreading the seeds from the figs that they eat each night. One kind of fruit bat is about 25 grams and can eat 2.5 times its body mass in figs in one night. How many grams of figs can one of these bats eat? 62.5 g

TIPS FOR NEW TEACHERS

To illustrate why an inequality is reversed when multiplying or dividing by a negative number, use the inequality $-x < 0$, or "the opposite of a number is less than zero." For this to be true, the original number must be greater than zero. See Tips for New Teachers in the *Chapter 3 Resource Book*.

EXTRA EXAMPLES

Example 1 Solve $-\frac{2}{3}k \ge 8$.
$k \le -12$

Example 2 Solve $60 > -5a$.
$a > -12$

Example 3 Each lunchtime in a school, students consume up to 3000 ounces of milk. If there are 250 students, write and solve an inequality to find the average amount of milk per student consumed each lunchtime.
$250m \le 3000$; $m \le 12$ oz

MATH REASONING

Because the graph of 3 is to the right of the graph of 2, $3 > 2$. Multiplying both numbers by -1 gives -3 and -2. Because the graph of -3 is to the left of the graph of -2, $-3 < -2$, that is, the inequality is reversed.

CONCEPT CHECK

When is it necessary to reverse the direction of the inequality symbol when solving an inequality? **when you multiply or divide each side of an inequality by a negative number**

DAILY PUZZLER

The perimeter of a square is x meters and the area of the square is x square meters. What is x? 16

ASSIGNMENT GUIDE

Basic Course
Day 1: EP p. 728 Exs. 37-40; pp. 148-149 Exs. 9-20, 26-33, 42-50

Average Course
Day 1: pp. 148-149 Exs. 11-16, 21-29, 33-37, 42-50

Advanced Course
Day 1: pp. 148-149 Exs. 11-16, 21-29, 33-45*, 50

Block
pp. 148-149 Exs. 11-16, 21-29, 33-37, 42-50

EXTRA PRACTICE

- Student Edition, p. 729
- Chapter 3 Resource Book, pp. 65-67
- Test and Practice Generator

TRANSPARENCY

Even-numbered answers are available on transparencies. A support transparency is available for Exercises 4-7, 13-24, and 27-32.

HOMEWORK CHECK

When you review students' homework for this lesson, go over the following exercises to check understanding of key concepts.
Basic: 9, 13, 15, 18, 26
Average: 11, 13, 15, 21, 26
Advanced: 11, 14, 16, 22, 26

TEACHING TIP

In Exercises 14, 15, 19, and 22-24, where an inequality is to be reversed, it may help students to take an extra step. For example, in Exercise 14, students can multiply both sides by 7 to obtain $-t \geq 21$, then multiply by -1 and reverse the inequality.

4-7, 13-24. See Additional Answers beginning on page AA1.

3.7 Exercises

More Practice, p. 729

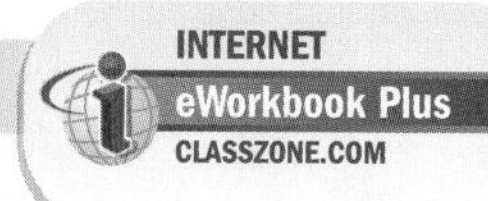

INTERNET eWorkbook Plus CLASSZONE.COM

Getting Ready to Practice

1. Vocabulary Copy and complete: When you multiply both sides of an inequality by a negative number, you need to _?_ the inequality symbol. reverse

Decide whether the solution strategy will require reversing the inequality symbol.

2. $\frac{1}{3}x < 18$ Multiply each side by 3. no

3. $-6x \geq 24$ Divide each side by -6. yes

Solve the inequality. Then graph its solution. 4–7. See margin for art.

4. $\frac{1}{2}x < 4$ $x < 8$ **5.** $\frac{m}{-7} \geq 6$ $m \leq -42$ **6.** $9 \leq -3z$ $z \leq -3$ **7.** $30 > -6p$ $p > -5$

8. Fundraising The diving club is selling lessons to raise money. The profit is \$15 per lesson. The diving club wants to raise at least \$300. How many lessons must be sold? at least 20 lessons

Practice and Problem Solving

Solve the inequality. Match the inequality with the graph of its solution.

A **9.** $\frac{1}{4}x \leq 8$ D **10.** $-4x \geq 8$ C **11.** $4x \geq -8$ A **12.** $-\frac{1}{4}x \leq 8$ B

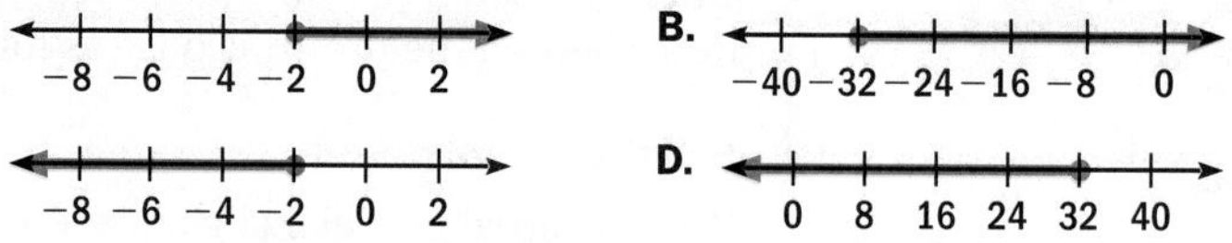

A. number line: −8 −6 −4 −2 0 2
B. number line: −40 −32 −24 −16 −8 0
C. number line: −8 −6 −4 −2 0 2
D. number line: 0 8 16 24 32 40

HELP with Homework

Example	Exercises
1	9-24
2	9-24
3	26

Online Resources CLASSZONE.COM
- More Examples
- eTutorial Plus

Solve the inequality. Then graph its solution. 13–24. See margin for art.

13. $\frac{1}{4}x > 1$ $x > 4$ **14.** $-\frac{1}{7}t \geq 3$ $t \leq -21$ **15.** $-\frac{1}{5}b \geq 72$ $b \leq -360$ **16.** $\frac{1}{3}d < -33$ $d < -99$

17. $4g < 24$ $g < 6$ **18.** $12 \geq -3s$ $s \geq -4$ **19.** $-9c \leq 54$ $c \geq -6$ **20.** $5z < -15$ $z < -3$

21. $7 > -\frac{1}{8}r$ $r > -56$ **22.** $-6t \geq 36$ $t \leq -6$ **23.** $-39 \leq -13k$ $k \leq 3$ **24.** $-\frac{1}{7}a < 54$ $a > -378$

25. Critical Thinking Is it possible to list every number in the solution set of an inequality? Explain your answer. No; there are infinitely many solutions.

26. Dance The student council must pay a DJ \$275 to work at a dance. A ticket to the dance costs \$5.50. The amount of money received from ticket sales must at least cover the cost of the DJ. Write and solve an inequality that gives the number of students that must attend the dance in order to pay the \$275 for the DJ. $5.5s \geq 275$; $s \geq 50$ students

Solve the inequality. Then graph its solution. 27–32. See margin for art.

B **27.** $12 > 6 - 2x$ $x > -3$ **28.** $3y - 4 < 2y + 5$ $y < 9$ **29.** $4p - 9 \geq -1$ $p \geq 2$

30. $5(1 - t) \leq 4(3 - t)$ $t \geq -7$ **31.** $4d < -2(33 + d)$ $d < -11$ **32.** $7z + 3 \leq 5z - 1$ $z \leq -2$

33. Writing How is solving an inequality like solving an equation? How is solving an inequality different from solving an equation? See margin.

34. Borrowing Money You borrow \$200 from your aunt to buy a new surfboard. If you pay her back at a rate of \$12 per week, when will you owe her less than \$60? in 12 wk

33. You undo the operations in the same way. If you multiply or divide by a negative number in an inequality, you must reverse the direction of the inequality.

Solve the inequality.

C **35.** $5(x - 20) \geq 3x + 60$ $x \geq 80$ **36.** $4(12 - 5x) \geq -4$ $x \leq 2.6$ **37.** $2(3 - x) \leq 10x$ $x \geq \frac{1}{2}$

Challenge Solve the compound inequality.

38. $-6 < 2x < 10$ $-3 < x < 5$ **39.** $-35 \leq 7x \leq -14$ $-5 \leq x \leq -2$ **40.** $10 < 5x < 100$ $2 < x < 20$

41. Monitor The height of a rectangular computer screen is 20 centimeters less than twice the width. The perimeter is at least 53 centimeters. Find the minimum dimensions of the screen if each dimension is an integer. 12 cm by 16 cm

Mixed Review 

Use mental math to solve the equation. *(Lessons 2.2, 2.4)*

42. $-4x = 0$ 0 **43.** $11a = 11$ 1 **44.** $z + (-12) = -12$ 0

Solve the inequality. Then graph its solution. *(Lesson 3.6)* 45–47. See margin for art.

45. $c + 7 \leq 11$ $c \leq 4$ **46.** $3 < 12 + s$ $s > -9$ **47.** $x - 12 > 17$ $x > 29$

Basic Skills Find the missing number.

48. 7 hours = _?_ minutes 420 **49.** 3 days = _?_ hours 72

Test-Taking Practice 

INTERNET
State Test Practice
CLASSZONE.COM

50. Short Response An elevator can hold a maximum of 2000 pounds. Using 150 pounds as the average weight per person, write an inequality that models the situation. What does the variable represent? If you solve the inequality, what does the answer tell you in terms of the number of people who can ride in the elevator? $150p \leq 2000$; the number of people; the maximum number of people the elevator can hold is 13.

4 ASSESS

Assessment Resources

For more assessment resources, see:

- Assessment Book
- Test and Practice Generator

Mini-Quiz

Solve the inequality. Then graph its solution.

1. $\frac{1}{7}d > 2$
   $d > 14$

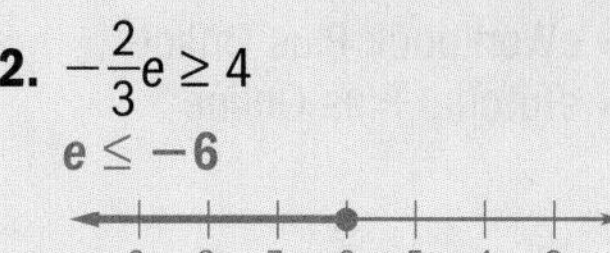

2. $-\frac{2}{3}e \geq 4$
   $e \leq -6$

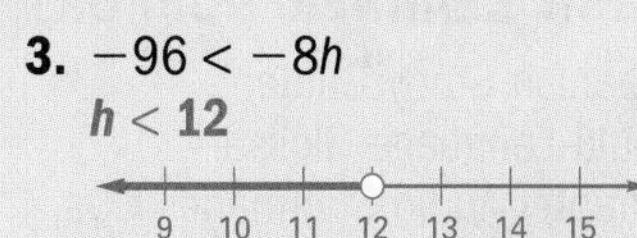

3. $-96 < -8h$
   $h < 12$

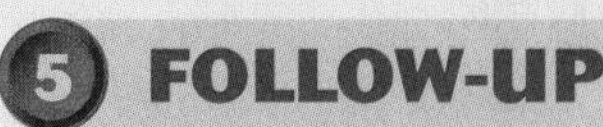

5 FOLLOW-UP

Reteaching/Remediation

- Study Guide in Chapter 3 Resource Book, pp. 68–69
- Tutor Place, Algebra Cards 15, 16
- eTutorial Plus Online
- Extra Practice, p. 729
- Lesson Practice in Chapter 3 Resource Book, pp. 65–67

Challenge/Enrichment

- Challenge Practice in Chapter 3 Resource Book, p. 70
- Teacher's Edition, p. 104F

English Learner Support

- Spanish Study Guide
- Multi-Language Glossary
- Chapter Audio Summaries CDs

27–32, 45–47. See Additional Answers beginning on page AA1.

ADDITIONAL RESOURCES

The following resources are available to help review the materials in Lessons 3.5–3.7.

Chapter 3 Resource Book
- Lesson Practice
- Study Guide

Assessment Book
- Chapter 3 Quiz 2

Technology
- Test and Practice Generator
- eTutorial CD-ROM

Internet
- Classzone
- eWorkbook Plus Online
- eTutorial Plus Online

ENGLISH LEARNER SUPPORT

- Spanish Study Guide
- Multi-Language Glossary
- Chapter Audio Summaries CDs

1. *Sample:*

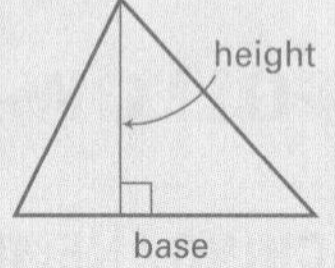

4.
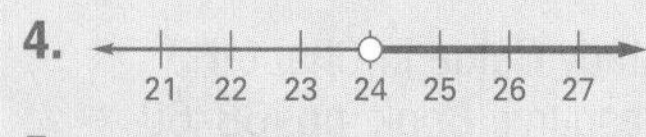

5.
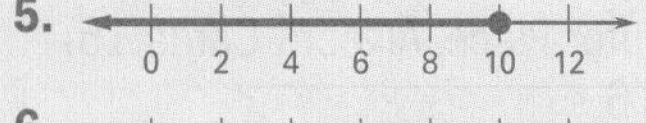

6.

7. −10 −8 −6 −4 −2 0 2

Notebook Review

Review the vocabulary definitions in your notebook.

Copy the review examples in your notebook. Then complete the exercises.

Check Your Definitions

base, p. 134
height, p. 134
inequality, p. 140
solution of an inequality, p. 140
equivalent inequalities, p. 141

Use Your Vocabulary

1. Draw a triangle. Label the base and the height. See margin.

3.5 Can you use formulas for perimeter and area?

EXAMPLE Find the height of the triangle. Its area is 21 square inches.

$A = \frac{1}{2}bh$	Write area formula.
$21 = \frac{1}{2}(6)(h)$	Substitute known values.
$21 = 3h$	Multiply.
$7 = h$	Divide each side by 3.

h
6 in.

ANSWER The height of the triangle is 7 inches.

Find the unknown dimension of the triangle.

2. $A = 50\text{ cm}^2$, $b = 10$ cm, $h = \underline{?}$ 10 cm **3.** $A = 45\text{ ft}^2$, $h = 10$ ft, $b = \underline{?}$ 9 ft

3.6 Can you solve addition or subtraction inequalities?

EXAMPLE Solve $x - 9 < -4$.

$x - 9 < -4$	Write original inequality.
$x - 9 + 9 < -4 + 9$	Add 9 to each side.
$x < 5$	Simplify.

Solve the inequality. Then graph its solution. 4–7. See margin for art.

4. $h - 12 > 12$ $h > 24$ **5.** $-4 + k \le 6$ $k \le 10$ **6.** $7 < 15 + p$ $p > -8$ **7.** $d + 11 \ge 5$ $d \ge -6$

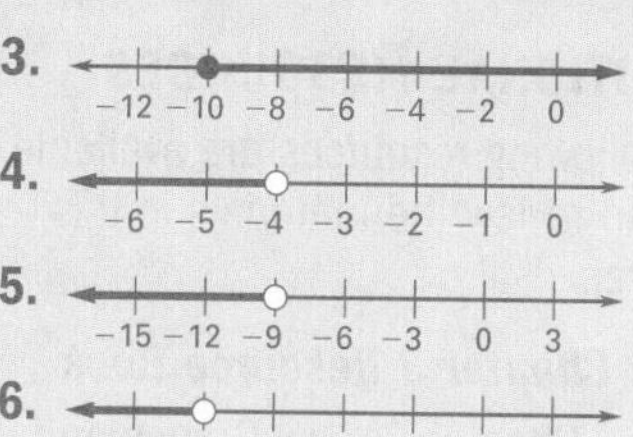

3.
4.
5.
6.

3.7 Can you solve multiplication or division inequalities?

EXAMPLE

$\frac{t}{7} > 2$	**Original inequality**	$-12k \le 60$	**Original inequality**
$7 \cdot \frac{t}{7} > 7 \cdot 2$	**Multiply each side by 7.**	$\frac{-12k}{-12} \ge \frac{60}{-12}$	**Divide each side by −12. Reverse inequality symbol.**
$t > 14$	**Simplify.**	$k \ge -5$	**Simplify.**

Solve the inequality.

8. $\frac{d}{6} \le 34$ $d \le 204$ **9.** $-\frac{1}{5}x \ge 20$ $x \le -100$ **10.** $5c > 25$ $c > 5$ **11.** $-15b < 60$ $b > -4$

Stop and Think about Lessons 3.5–3.7

12. Writing Mary claims that she has at least 50 CDs at home and she just got 4 more for her birthday. Write an inequality for the number of CDs she has now. $c \ge 54$

13. Critical Thinking What is the greatest integer solution of $-7x > -56$? Justify your answer. 7; the solution to the inequality is $x < 8$ and the greatest integer that is less than 8 is 7.

Review Quiz 2

Find the length of each side.

1. A rectangle has a perimeter of 30 millimeters and a width of 6 millimeters. Find the length. 9 mm

2. A triangle has an area of 26 square yards and a height of 4 yards. Find the base. 13 yd

Solve the inequality. Then graph its solution. 3–6. See margin for art.

3. $a + 9 \ge -1$ $a \ge -10$ **4.** $-16 > y - 12$ $y < -4$ **5.** $\frac{x}{3} < -3$ $x < -9$ **6.** $-x > 5$ $x < -5$

7. Apples An empty basket weighs 2 pounds. When filled with apples, the basket weighs more than 13 pounds. Write and solve an inequality that represents this situation. What does the variable stand for? $2 + a > 13$; $a > 11$; the weight of the apples

8. Calling Card You have \$9.50 with which to recharge your phone card. Write and solve an inequality to find how many minutes you can add to your phone card if each minute costs \$.10. $0.1m \le 9.50$; at most 95 min

Additional Resources

The following resources are available to help review the materials in this chapter.

Chapter 3 Resource Book
- Chapter Review Games and Activities, p. 71
- Cumulative Practice, Chs. 78–79

English/Spanish Chapter Reviews and Tests

Chapter Audio Summaries CDs

eTutorial CD-ROM

eWorkbook Plus Online

eTutorial Plus Online

1. **Addition and subtraction, multiplication and division; one operation undoes the other.**

Chapter Review

Vocabulary

equivalent equations, p. 109
inverse operations, p. 109
base, height, p. 134
inequality, p. 140
solution of an inequality, p. 140
equivalent inequalities, p. 141

Vocabulary Review

1. List 2 pairs of inverse operations. Explain why these are called inverse operations. **See margin.**
2. How can two inequalities be equivalent? Give an example of equivalent inequalities. **They are equivalent if they have exactly the same solutions. *Sample answer:* $x - 4 > 6$ and $x > 10$.**

Copy and complete the statement.

3. Two equations that have the same solution are __?__. **equivalent equations**
4. A(n) __?__ is a statement formed by placing an inequality symbol between two expressions. **inequality**

Review Questions

Solve the equation. *(Lessons 3.1, 3.2)*

5. $r - 11 = 21$ **32**
6. $v + 13 = 29$ **16**
7. $34 = g + 19$ **15**
8. $12p = 108$ **9**
9. $\frac{h}{5} = 8$ **40**
10. $\frac{z}{-7} = 23$ **−161**
11. $-46 = \frac{w}{-28}$ **1288**
12. $t - \frac{3}{7} = \frac{1}{7}$ **$\frac{4}{7}$**
13. $x + (-5) = -8$ **−3**
14. $3.9 + y = 10.9$ **7**
15. $-9.5m = -22.8$ **2.4**
16. $-72 = -6n$ **12**
17. **ATVs** You rent an all-terrain vehicle that has $\frac{5}{8}$ of a tank of fuel. When you are done riding, there is $\frac{3}{8}$ of a tank left. Write a verbal model to represent the fraction of a tank of fuel you used. Then write and solve an algebraic model. *(Lesson 3.1)* **Fuel in tank − Fuel used = Fuel left; $\frac{5}{8} - x = \frac{3}{8}$; $x = \frac{2}{8} = \frac{1}{4}$**
18. **Intramurals** A college brochure states that 215 students participate in intramural sports. This is one third of the students. How many students attend the college? *(Lesson 3.2)* **645 students**

Solve the equation. *(Lesson 3.3)*

19. $2p - 5 = 13$ **9**
20. $19 + 8v = 43$ **3**
21. $9g + 16 = -29$ **−5**
22. $-10c + 6 = 46$ **−4**
23. $-82 = 53 - 5t$ **27**
24. $-33 = -15t - 12$ **1.4**

37.  −72 −36 0 36 72 108 144

38. 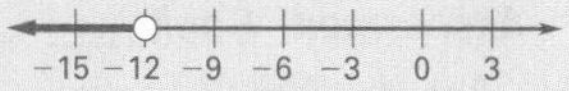 −15 −12 −9 −6 −3 0 3

39.  −5 −4 −3 −2 −1 0 1

40. 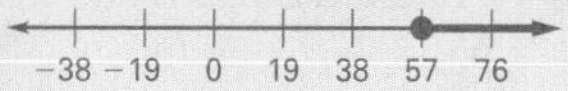 −38 −19 0 19 38 57 76

Review Questions

Solve the equation. *(Lesson 3.3)*

25. $\frac{d}{5} + 13 = -10$ **−115** **26.** $17 = \frac{x}{12} - 31$ **576** **27.** $-21 - \frac{t}{3} = -6$ **−45** **28.** $-57 = -9 + \frac{w}{-7}$ **336**

29. Fruit Baskets Your class is making fruit baskets and selling them to raise money for a charity. The supplies cost $26 and the baskets sell for $7 each. Your class makes a profit of $100. How many baskets did your class sell? *(Lesson 3.4)* **18 baskets**

Find the unknown dimension. *(Lesson 3.5)*

30. Perimeter = 11 in. **4 in.**

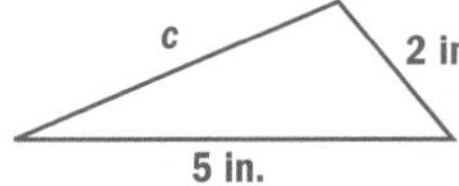

31. Perimeter = 28 m **8 m**

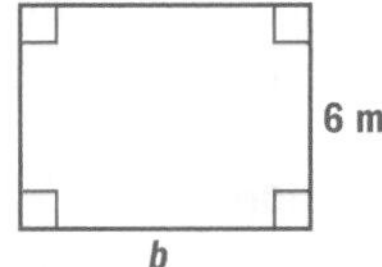

32. Perimeter = 26 cm **6.5 cm**

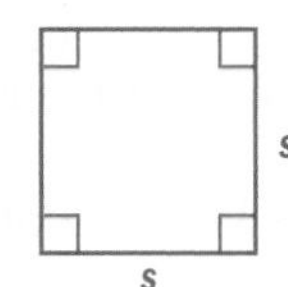

Find the area of the triangle. *(Lesson 3.5)*

33. **20 in.^{2}**

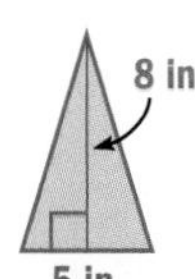

34. **27 cm^2**

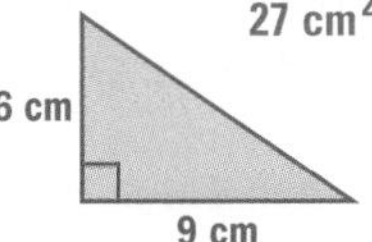

35. **60 yd^2**

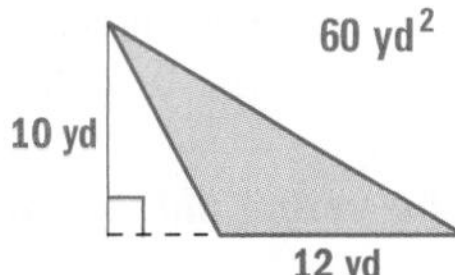

36. Ticket Line You are standing in line for concert tickets. The ticket window is at street level at the middle of one side of a building that is 30 feet long and 20 feet wide. The line extends from the ticket window, around the corner of the building, and all the way to the next corner of the building. How long is the line? Explain why there are two possible answers. *(Lesson 3.5)* **35 ft or 40 ft; the ticket window can be on either a 30 foot side or a 20 foot side of the building.**

Solve and graph the inequality. *(Lessons 3.6, 3.7)* **37–40. See margin for art.**

37. $96 \geq -12 + c$ $c \leq 108$ **38.** $-\frac{1}{3}x > 4$ $x < -12$ **39.** $-96 < 24h$ $h > -4$ **40.** $78 - k \leq 21$ $k \geq 57$

Find the Error Describe and correct the error in the solution.
(Lessons 3.6, 3.7)

41.

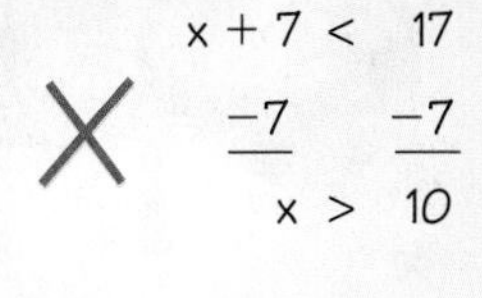

The inequality sign should not be reversed when subtracting; $x < 10$.

42.

$-6c < 18$

$\frac{-6c}{-6} < \frac{18}{-6}$

$c < -3$

Both sides were divided by a negative number, so the inequality sign should be reversed; $c > -3$.

Additional Resources

Assessment Book

- Chapter Test (3 levels), pp. 31–36
- Standardized Chapter Test, p. 37
- Alternative Assessment, pp. 38–39

Test and Practice Generator

Chapter Test

Solve the equation.

1. $s - 6 = 39$ 45
2. $x + 12 = -2$ −14
3. $14.6 = \frac{k}{2.5}$ 36.5
4. $24v = 288$ 12
5. $\frac{1}{9} = t + \frac{1}{9}$ 0
6. $-9.8 = \frac{y}{-4.7}$ 46.06
7. $5b - 7 = 120$ 25.4
8. $-236 = 29 - 5g$ 53
9. **Hiking** You go on a 20 mile hike. In the morning you hike 8.2 miles, and by 2:00 P.M., you have covered 7.5 more miles. Write and solve an equation to find how many miles you have left to go. $8.2 + 7.5 + x = 20$; 4.3 mi

In Exercises 10 and 11, write and solve an equation.

10. A bookstore offers three books in a set for $21.75. Each book costs the same amount. How much does each book cost? $3b = 21.75$; $7.25
11. A calf weighs 90 pounds. The calf gains 65 pounds a month. In how many months will the calf weigh 1000 pounds? $90 + 65w = 1000$; 14 mo

Translate the verbal phrase into an equation. Then solve the equation.

12. A number times 3 subtracted from 20 is −4. $20 - 3n = -4$; 8
13. The sum of 5 times a number and 14 is 9. $5n + 14 = 9$; −1

In Exercises 14 and 15, use the formula $P = 2l + 2w$. Solve the equation to find the unknown measure of the rectangle.

14. $P = 28$ in., $l = 13$ in. Find the width. 1 in.
15. $P = 62$ cm, $w = 10$ cm. Find the length. 21 cm
16. Find the height of a triangle with a base of 25 centimeters and an area of 200 square centimeters. 16 cm

Solve the inequality.

17. $y + 78 < -124$ $y < -202$
18. $-8.56 + k \geq 5.32$ $k \geq 13.88$
19. $-8x < 64$ $x > -8$

20. **Lunch** You and a friend are having lunch together. You can spend no more than $30 on both meals. The total cost of your friend's meal is $14.78. Write and solve an inequality to determine how much you can spend on your meal. $14.78 + x \leq 30$; $x \leq \$15.22$
21. **Figure Skating** You are taking figure skating lessons. You can rent skates for $5 per lesson. You can buy skates for $75. What inequality expresses the number of lessons for which it is cheaper to buy skates? more than 15 lessons

Chapter Standardized Test

Test-Taking Strategy **Start to work as soon as the testing time begins. Keep working and stay focused on the test.**

Multiple Choice

1. Which is an inverse operation for the operation of adding -7? A

A. Subtracting -7 **B.** Adding -7

C. Subtracting 7 **D.** Dividing by 7

2. Which equation does *not* have a solution of 8? I

F. $x - 4 = 4$ **G.** $7 + x = 15$

H. $x - 4.4 = 3.6$ **I.** $x + 6.2 = 1.8$

3. Which equations are equivalent? A

I. $\frac{3}{5}x = 3$ **II.** $\frac{x}{5} = 3$

III. $3x = 15$ **IV.** $-x = 15$

A. I and III **B.** II and IV

C. I, II, and IV **D.** I, III, and IV

4. The bill for the repair of a car is \$560. The cost of parts is \$440. The cost of labor is \$40 per hour. Which equation can you use to find the number of hours of labor? G

F. $40 + 440x = 560$

G. $40x + 440 = 560$

H. $40(x + 440) = 560$

I. $40 + x + 440 = 560$

5. A rectangle has a perimeter of 54 inches and a width of 8 inches. What is the length of the rectangle? A

A. 19 inches **B.** 26 inches

C. 38 inches **D.** 46 inches

6. A triangle has an area of 8 square feet. Which measurements *cannot* be the base length b and height h of the triangle? F

F. $h = 4$ ft, $b = 8$ ft

G. $h = 8$ ft, $b = 2$ ft

H. $h = 1$ ft, $b = 16$ ft

I. $h = 4$ ft, $b = 4$ ft

7. Which statement about the inequality $x - 8 \geq -5$ is true? D

A. The arrow on the graph of its solution set points to the left.

B. -5 is a solution.

C. 3 is not a solution.

D. The circle on the graph of the solution set is closed.

Short Response

8. Write and solve an equation for this sentence: The quotient of a number and -14 is 7. $\frac{n}{-14} = 7$; -98

Extended Response

9. The Uniform Building Code requires at least 20 square feet of space for each person in a classroom. A classroom is 28 feet long and 18 feet wide. Write and solve an inequality that models the number of people that can be in the classroom legally. Explain how to use the solution to find the maximum number of people allowed in the classroom.

See margin.

Additional Resources

Assessment Book
- Standardized Chapter Test, p. 37

Test and Practice Generator

9. $20p \leq 28(18)$; $p \leq 25.2$; 25 or fewer people; Since people must be counted using whole numbers, 25.2 must be rounded to down to 25 people.

Test-Taking Tip

Encourage students to quickly examine the answer choices for a multiple-choice question after reading the question. Suggest that this is a good time to eliminate choices that can be readily identified as incorrect, and also to notice answers that are very similar which could lead to inadvertently choosing the wrong one. For example, two answers might differ only in the location of their decimal points, as in 15.63 and 1.563, or they might differ only by the units used, as in 72 in. and 72 ft. Caution students to double-check their answer choice when a mistaken selection could easily be made.

Common Error

Students will often encounter some questions on a long multiple-choice test that they cannot answer quickly. If students bypass these questions, they may forget to return to some or all of them later after reaching the end of the test. Stress that if students use this test-taking strategy, they must have some method to remind themselves to return to each bypassed question, including where each of them is located.

BUILDING **Test-Taking Skills**

Strategies for Answering

Multiple Choice Questions

You can use the problem solving plan on page 39 to solve any problem. The strategies below can help you answer a multiple choice question. You can also use these strategies to check whether your answer to a multiple choice question is reasonable.

Strategy: Estimate the Answer

Problem 1

You will use powers and exponents to solve this problem.

The table shows how many pennies you save each day. If the pattern continues, what is the first day you will save more than ten dollars worth of pennies?

Day	1	2	3
Pennies	$2^1 = 2$	$2^2 = 4$	$2^3 = 8$

A. Day 8

B. Day 9

C. Day 10

D. Day 11

Estimate: 2^8 is a little more than 250, so $2^9 > 500$ and $2^{10} > 1000$. The correct answer is C.

Strategy: Use Visual Clues

Problem 2

The garden's area is 900 square feet. Use the Guess, Check, and Revise strategy to find the length of one side of the garden. Each side of the garden is 30 feet long.

How many feet of fencing do you need to enclose the square garden shown?

900 ft^2

F. 30 ft

G. 60 ft

H. 90 ft

I. 120 ft

Multiply the side length by 4 to find the total amount of fencing needed. To enclose the garden, you need 120 feet of fencing. The correct answer is I.

Strategy: Use Number Sense

Problem 3

The problem involves integers, not fractions or decimals.

When multiplying a positive integer by a negative integer, the product is ? .

A. greater than the positive integer

B. greater than the negative integer

C. less than or equal to the negative integer

D. less than the negative integer

The sign is negative and the absolute value of the product is greater than or equal to either factor. C is the correct answer.

Eliminating Unreasonable Choices The strategies used to find the correct answers for Problems 1–3 are the same strategies you can use to eliminate answer choices that are unreasonable or obviously incorrect.

Problem 4

Read the problem carefully. Degrees Fahrenheit are 32° more than almost twice the temperature in degrees Celsius.

The average body temperature of a polar bear is 37°C. Use the formula $F = 1.8C + 32$ to find the temperature in degrees Fahrenheit.

F. 34°F — *Not* correct. A temperature of about 1°C is 34°F.

G. 69°F

H. 74.95°F

I. 98.6°F — 1.8(37) + 32 = 98.6, so the correct answer is I.

Watch Out!

Some answers that appear correct at first glance may be incorrect. Be aware of common errors.

1. 2 times 7, plus 7, does not give a negative result.

Your turn now

Explain why the selected answer choice is unreasonable.

1. Two times a number plus 7 is −21. What is the number? See margin.

   A. −14 B. −7 ~~C. 7~~ D. 14

2. Your school earns $1.50 for every T-shirt sold. Find the minimum number of T-shirts you must sell in order to raise $500. $1.50 times 750 would be greater than $500.

   F. 333 G. 334 H. 500 ~~I. 750~~

GO ON

PRACTICING Test-Taking Skills

Multiple Choice

1. Ryan rode his bike 15 miles in 2 hours 30 minutes. What is his average speed in miles per hour? A

   A. 6 **B.** 6.5 **C.** 34.5 **D.** 37.5

2. Bob's exam of 21 questions takes 50 minutes. He needs at least 10 minutes for the extended response question. He uses an equal amount of time on all of the 20 multiple choice problems. What is the greatest number of minutes Bob can spend on one multiple choice problem? G

   F. 1 **G.** 2 **H.** 3 **I.** 4

3. The graph shows the inches of rainfall in Topeka, Kansas. What is the best estimate of rainfall in April? C

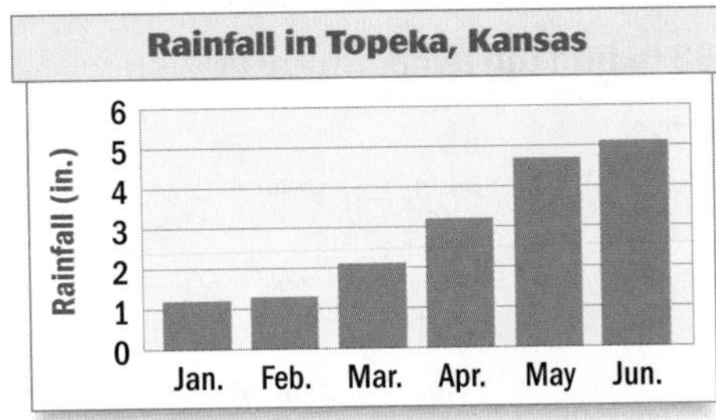

   A. 2.5 in. **B.** 3.0 in. **C.** 3.2 in. **D.** 3.5 in.

4. The height of a triangle is 12 inches, and its base is 5 inches long. What is its area? G

   F. 17 in. **G.** 30 in.^{2} **H.** 60 in. **I.** 60 in.^{2}

5. The student council made $130 at a school dance. Now they have $50. How much money did they spend? B

   A. $70 **B.** $80 **C.** $180 **D.** $190

6. A bank statement for the month of January is shown below. What is the sum of the transactions in this month? F

January 5	+$25
January 6	−$15
January 15	−$30

   F. −$20 **G.** $20 **H.** $40 **I.** $70

7. Meg is scuba diving. She ascends to the surface at a rate of 30 feet per minute. After 2 minutes, her elevation is −15 feet. What was Meg's elevation when she began her ascent? A

   A. −75 ft **B.** −45 ft **C.** 45 ft **D.** 75 ft

8. A lacrosse field is 110 yards long and 60 yards wide. Which of the following is true about a lacrosse field? I

   F. Its length is more than twice its width.

   G. Its perimeter is 170 yards.

   H. Its perimeter is 6600 yards.

   I. Its area is 6600 square yards.

9. Sara leaves at 8:30 A.M. and drives at an average speed of 55 miles per hour. She reaches her destination at 11:30 A.M. How many miles does Sara travel? C

   A. 18.3 **B.** 160 **C.** 165 **D.** 260

10. Each week Annie makes $40 babysitting, spends $25 at the mall, and spends $8 at the movies. Annie saves the rest of her money. Which expression tells how much money Annie saves after 5 weeks? I

    F. $40 - 25 - 8 + 5$ **G.** $40 - (25 + 8) \cdot 5$

    H. $5 \cdot (40 - 25 + 8)$ **I.** $(40 - 25 - 8) \cdot 5$

Short Response

11. A package of 8 erasers costs \$.64, and a package of 12 costs \$.88. Ms. Maddox needs at least 44 erasers for her class. How many of each kind of package should she buy in order to pay the least amount of money? Explain your answer. See margin.

12. The perimeter of a rectangular field is 500 feet. The field is 100 feet wide. How long is the field? Draw a diagram and explain how you found your answer. See margin.

13. A person must be at least 16 years old to have a driver's license in North Carolina. Tracy got her license 6 years ago. Write an inequality that expresses Tracy's age. Graph the solution of the inequality on a number line. Explain your inequality and your graph. $a - 6 \geq 16$; see margin for art; Tracy's age now minus 6 must be greater than or equal to 16 years old. The solution of the inequality is $a \geq 22$, so Tracy's age now is at least 22 and that is what is shown on the graph.

14. Caleb and Peter hiked for 2 hours, took a break, then hiked some more. They traveled 10.5 miles at an average speed of 3 miles per hour. For how many hours did Caleb and Peter hike after their break? Write and solve an equation to find your answer. Explain your steps. See margin.

15. Rachel has \$60 in savings. If she saves \$5 each week, in how many weeks will she have \$100 in savings? Write and solve an equation to find your answer. 8 wk; $100 = 60 + 5w$; $40 = 5w$; $8 = w$

16. Rob and Angela shared a roll of tickets at an amusement park. Angela took half of the tickets and used 15 of them. Now she has 30 tickets. How many tickets were on the original roll? Explain how you found your answer. 90 tickets; Angela has 30 tickets now, so she had 30 + 15, or 45 tickets before that. Since she shared half of the roll with Rob, there were 2(45), or 90 tickets on the original roll.

Extended Response

17. Alice bought carpet for two rooms in her house. The floor plan of the rooms is shown here. Find the area of the room with red carpet and the area of the room with blue carpet. 18 yd^2; 16 yd^2

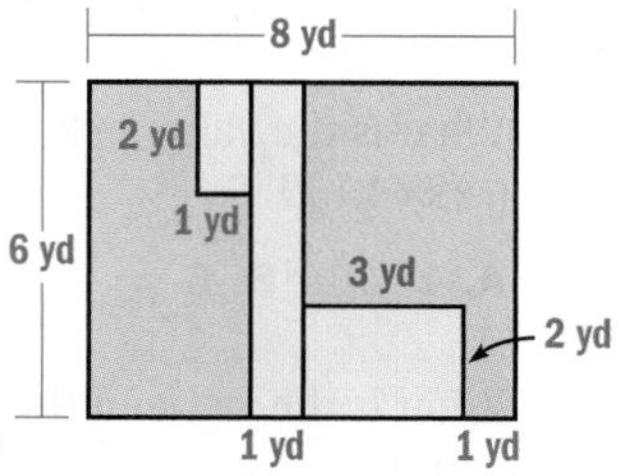

Alice spent \$444 total on carpet. The red carpet cost \$14 per square yard. Find the cost of the blue carpet per square yard. \$12 per square yard.

How much would it cost for Alice to carpet both rooms in blue? Explain how you found your answer. \$408; add the areas of the two rooms together and multiply by \$12.00.

18. The results of a poll are shown at the right. Use the data to make a frequency table using the following 4 intervals: *0–1 day, 2–3 days, 4–5 days,* and *6–7 days.*

Use your frequency table to create a histogram of the data.

How many people polled use a computer more than once a week? Which data display is more helpful when answering that question? Explain. See margin.

How many days a week do you use a computer at home?

6	4	2	1	7	3
5	3	0	1	2	2
5	7	6	4	2	3
1	3	2	3	2	

GO ON

11. 3 packages of 12 erasers and 1 package of 8 erasers; a package of 12 erasers is cheaper per eraser than a package of 8 erasers, so buying as many packages of 12 erasers as possible will keep the cost the lowest. Since $44 \div 12 = 3\frac{2}{3}$, at most 3 packages of 12 erasers can be purchased, leaving 1 package of 8 erasers to be purchased.

12. 150 ft;

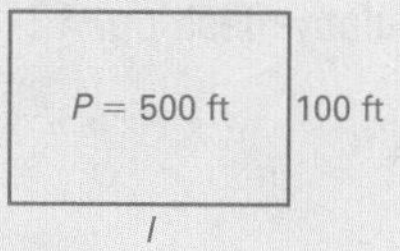

$500 = 2(100) + 2l$, and $l = 150$

13.

14. 1.5 h;

$10.5 = 3(t + 2)$

$10.5 = 3t + 6$ Distributive Property

$4.5 = 3t$ Subtract 6 from both sides.

$1.5 = t$ Divide both sides by 3.

18.

Days per week	Tally	Frequency
0–1	||||	4
2–3	~~||||~~ ~~||||~~ |	11
4–5	||||	4
6–7	||||	4

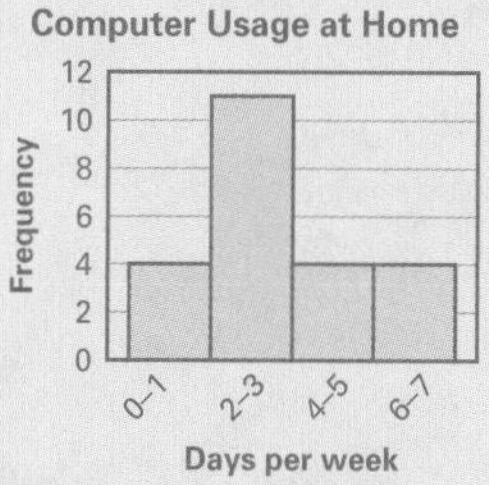

19 people; the frequency table; it is easy to see the exact numbers and then add them to find the answer.

ADDITIONAL RESOURCES

The following resources are available to help review the materials in this unit:

Chapter Resource Books

- Chapter 1 CRB, Cumulative Practice, pp. 78–79
- Chapter 2 CRB, Cumulative Practice, pp. 87–88
- Chapter 3 CRB, Cumulative Practice, pp. 78–79

Assessment Book

- Unit Test, pp. 40–41
- Cumulative Test, pp. 42–45

UNIT 1 Chapters 1–3

PRACTICING **Test-Taking Skills**

Cumulative Practice for Chapters 1–3

Chapter 1

Multiple Choice In Exercises 1–8, choose the letter of the correct answer.

1. How many more mums than tulips are in the garden? Refer to the graph. *(Lesson 1.1)* B

A. 10 **B.** 20 **C.** 30 **D.** 40

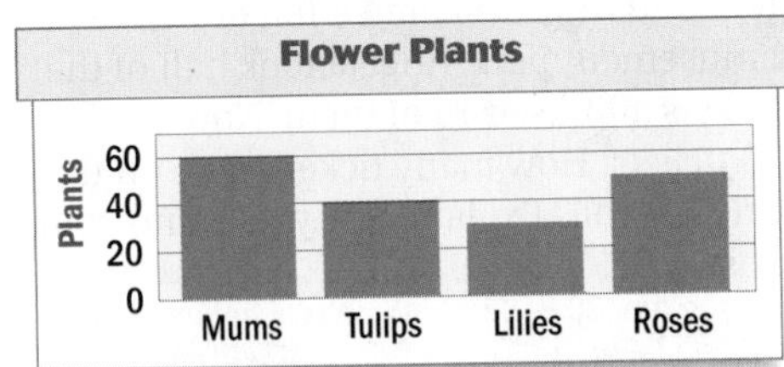

2. Which operation is performed first when evaluating the expression $9 + 3(4 - 2) \cdot 6 \div 3$? *(Lesson 1.2)* G

F. $+$ **G.** $-$ **H.** $\cdot$ **I.** $\div$

3. What is the value of $2 \cdot 6 - 10 \div 2$? *(Lesson 1.2)* C

A. 1 **B.** 6 **C.** 7 **D.** 17

4. What is the value of the expression $8x - 4y$ when $x = 4$ and $y = 6$? *(Lesson 1.3)* F

F. 8 **G.** 16 **H.** 32 **I.** 38

5. What is the value of the expression $(6 - 2)^2 - 8 + 3^3$? *(Lesson 1.4)* D

A. 9 **B.** 17 **C.** 27 **D.** 35

6. What is the value of w in the equation $w + 18 = 36$? *(Lesson 1.5)* H

F. $\frac{1}{2}$ **G.** 2 **H.** 18 **I.** 54

7. Nicki is driving at a rate of 50 miles per hour. How many hours will it take her to travel 275 miles? *(Lesson 1.6)* B

A. 5 **B.** 5.5 **C.** 22 **D.** 22.5

8. A package of 8 computer disks costs $10, and a package of 15 disks costs $16.50. How much money will you save per disk if you buy a package of 15 instead of a package of 8? *(Lesson 1.7)* F

F. $.15 **G.** $1.25 **H.** $1.50 **I.** $6.50

9. Short Response A store has 10 pairs of black shoes and three times as many pairs of brown shoes as black. There are 10 more pairs of sandals than black shoes. What is the total number of sandals and shoes? *(Lesson 1.7)* **60 pairs**

10. Extended Response You are planting a rectangular garden and want to separate the garden area from the rest of your yard with a wooden border. You have 32 pieces of wood that are each one foot long. You want to build the border without cutting any of the wood. *(Lesson 1.6)* **1 ft by 15 ft; 2 ft by 14 ft; 3 ft by 13 ft; 4 ft by 12 ft; 5 ft by 11 ft; 6 ft by 10 ft; 7 ft by 9 ft; 8 ft by 8 ft**

a. List all the possible dimensions (length and width) of the garden border that you can build with your 32 pieces of wood.

b. Find the area of each of the rectangles in your list. **15 ft²; 28 ft²; 39 ft²; 48 ft²; 55 ft²; 60 ft²; 63 ft²; 64 ft²**

c. Which of the dimensions in your list would give the garden the largest area? **8 ft by 8 ft**

d. Describe the difference in appearance between the rectangles with the largest area and the smallest area. **The rectangle with the largest area is a square, and the rectangle with the smallest area is a long, skinny rectangle.**

21. about 3.4 m; Salinas Chicas, Argentina; Lake Eyre, Australia; Baltic Sea; Laguna Salada, Mexico; Caspian Sea; Death Valley, United States

Chapter 2

Multiple Choice **In Exercises 11–20, choose the letter of the correct answer.**

11. Which set of integers is listed in order from least to greatest? *(Lesson 2.1)* **D**

A. $-3, -10, -5, -1, 0$

B. $0, -1, -3, -5, -10$

C. $0, -3, -1, -5, -10$

D. $-10, -5, -3, -1, 0$

12. What is the value of the expression $-39 + (-61) + 74 + (-24)$? *(Lesson 2.2)* **F**

F. -50 **G.** 28 **H.** 50 **I.** 150

13. A seal dove 120 meters beneath the surface of the sea, then ascended 90 meters. What is the elevation of the seal? *(Lesson 2.3)* **B**

A. -210 m **B.** -30 m

C. 30 m **D.** 210 m

14. Find the value of the expression $3c + 3a - b$ when $a = -4$, $b = 8$, and $c = -6$. *(Lesson 2.4)* **F**

F. -38 **G.** -32 **H.** -22 **I.** 18

15. What is the value of $\frac{147}{-7}$? *(Lesson 2.5)* **B**

A. -140 **B.** -21 **C.** 21 **D.** 140

16. Which expression is equivalent to $-3 + 5 - (-2) - 7$? *(Lesson 2.6)* **F**

F. $-3 - (-2) - 7 + 5$

G. $-3 + (-2) - 7 + 5$

H. $-3 - 7 - 2 + 5$

I. $-3 - (-2) + 7 - 5$

17. Which expression is equivalent to $5 - 3x + 4 - 2y - x$? *(Lesson 2.7)* **B**

A. $2x + 2y - x$ **B.** $9 - 4x - 2y$

C. $2x + y$ **D.** $9 - 2x - 2y$

18. Which expression is equivalent to $-3(2x + 4)$? *(Lesson 2.7)* **H**

F. $-6x + 4$ **G.** $-6x + 12$

H. $-6x - 12$ **I.** $-6x - 3$

19. Which points have a y-coordinate of -2 in the coordinate plane? *(Lesson 2.8)* **D**

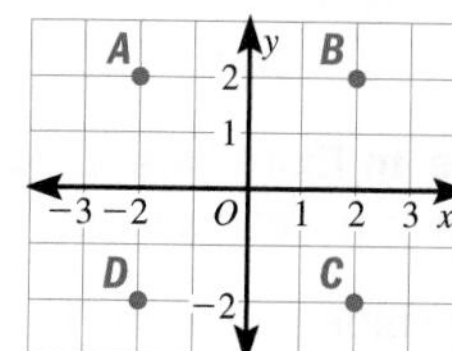

A. A and B **B.** B and C

C. A and D **D.** C and D

20. The point $(-3, 6)$ is in which quadrant? *(Lesson 2.8)* **G**

F. I **G.** II **H.** III **I.** IV

21. **Short Response** Find the mean elevation of the locations listed in the table below.

Location	Elevation
Salinas Chicas, Argentina	−40 m
Lake Eyre, Australia	−15 m
Baltic Sea	0 m
Laguna Salada, Mexico	−10 m
Caspian Sea	−20 m
Lake Maggiore, Switzerland	195 m
Death Valley, United States	−86 m

Which locations have an elevation below the mean? *(Lesson 2.5)* **See margin.**

GO ON

22. 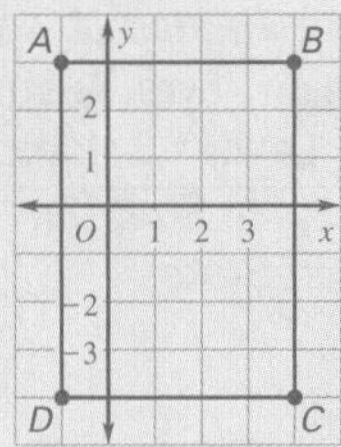

b. *Sample:*

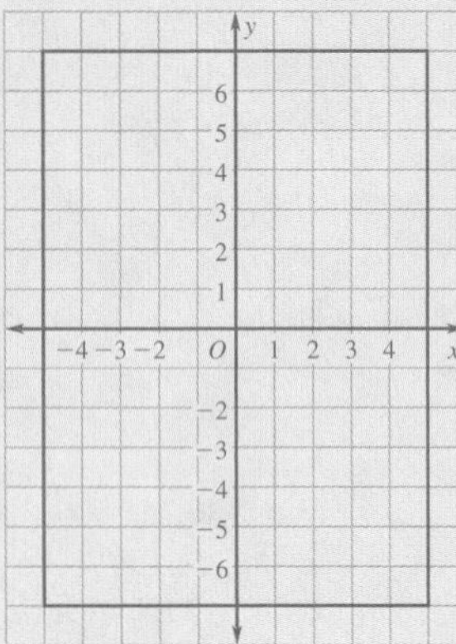

UNIT 1 Chapters 1–3

PRACTICING Test-Taking Skills

Cumulative Practice continued

22. **Extended Response** In a coordinate plane, plot the points $A(-1, 3)$, $B(4, 3)$, $C(4, -4)$, and $D(-1, -4)$. Connect the points to form a rectangle. *(Lesson 2.8)* **See margin.**

   a. Find the length, width, and area of the rectangle. **5 units, 7 units, 35 square units**

   b. Draw a new rectangle that has twice the length and twice the width of the original rectangle. Find the area of the new rectangle. **See margin for art; 140 square units.**

   c. Does the new rectangle have twice the area of the original rectangle? Explain. **No, it has 4 times the area because each dimension is doubled, so $A = 2l \cdot 2w = 4lw$.**

Chapter 3

Multiple Choice In Exercises 23–29, choose the letter of the correct answer.

23. What is the value of n in the equation $n - 34 = -17$? *(Lesson 3.1)* **C**

   A. -51 **B.** -17 **C.** 17 **D.** 51

24. Laura ran at a rate of 3.6 miles per hour. She ran 3 miles total. Which equation could you use to find how many hours Laura ran? *(Lesson 3.2)* **F**

   F. $3.6x = 3$ **G.** $x \div 3.6 = 3$

   H. $3x = 3.6$ **I.** $3.6 - 3 = x$

25. What is the value of x in the equation $20 = 3x + 2$? *(Lesson 3.3)* **A**

   A. 6 **B.** 7 **C.** 8.5 **D.** 16

26. On each weekday that she worked in July, Kate worked 6 hours. She also worked 9 hours on one Saturday. Kate worked 117 hours total in July. How many weekdays did Kate work in July? *(Lesson 3.4)* **I**

   F. 7 **G.** 9 **H.** 12 **I.** 18

27. What is the area of the triangle? *(Lesson 3.5)* **B**

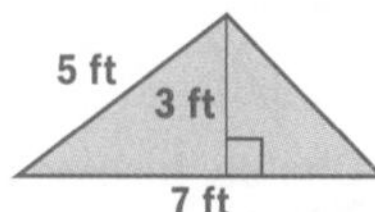

   A. $7.5\ ft^2$ **B.** $10.5\ ft^2$ **C.** $17.5\ ft^2$ **D.** $21\ ft^2$

28. Which inequality is represented by the graph? *(Lesson 3.6)* **H**

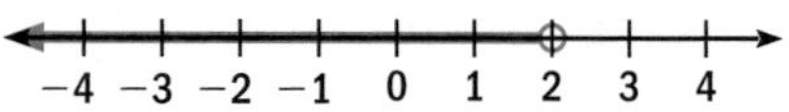

   F. $x \le 2$ **G.** $x > 2$ **H.** $x < 2$ **I.** $x \ge 2$

29. Solve the inequality $x - 4 \le -12$. *(Lesson 3.6)* **C**

   A. $x \le -16$ **B.** $x \ge -16$

   C. $x \le -8$ **D.** $x \ge -8$

30. **Short Response** Kaila traveled from her house to the city library by bus. She took one bus 2 miles. Then she changed buses. The second bus traveled at an average speed of 55 miles per hour. Kaila's entire trip covered 18 miles. How much time did she spend on the second bus? Write and solve an equation to answer the question. *(Lesson 3.4)* **$\frac{16}{55}$ h; $55t = 18 - 2$; $55t = 16$; $t = \frac{16}{55}$**

31. **Extended Response** Gabe, Frank, and Sam are playing a game. The player with the most points at the end is the winner. Gabe has four more than twice as many points as Frank. Frank has three less than half as many points as Sam. Sam has 60 points. *(Lessons 3.4, 3.6)*

   a. Write equations that you can use to find each player's total number of points. **$s = 60$, $f = \frac{1}{2}s - 3$, $g = 4 + 2f$**

   b. Which player is in first place? second place? third place? **Sam, Gabe, Frank**

   c. Write and solve an inequality to show how many more points Frank needs to win. **$27 + p > 60$; $p > 33$**

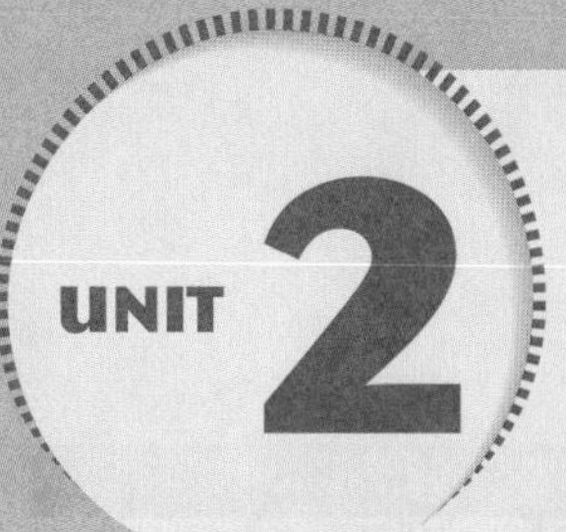

UNIT 2 Algebra and Rational Numbers

Chapter 4 Factors, Fractions, and Exponents

- Find greatest common factors and least common multiples.
- Identify equivalent fractions and write fractions in simplest form.
- Use rules of exponents and scientific notation.

Chapter 5 Rational Number Operations

- Perform operations with fractions, mixed numbers, and decimals.
- Compare and convert between fractions, mixed numbers, and decimals.
- Find the mean, median, and mode(s) of a data set.

Chapter 6 Multi-Step Equations and Inequalities

- Write and solve multi-step equations and inequalities.
- Find circumferences of circles.

Chapter 7 Ratio, Proportion, and Percent

- Write and identify ratios and rates.
- Write and solve proportions.
- Use proportions and the percent equation to solve percent problems.

From Chapter 5, p. 223
Which fruit juice blend do the most students prefer?

UNIT RESOURCES

These resources are provided to help you prepare for the unit and to customize review materials:

Chapter Resource Books
- Chapter 4
- Chapter 5
- Chapter 6
- Chapter 7

Assessment Book
- Chapters 4–7, pp. 46–95

Technology
- EasyPlanner CD-ROM
- Test and Practice Generator
- Electronic Lesson Presentations CD-ROM
- eTutorial CD-ROM

Internet
- Classzone
- eEdition Plus Online
- eWorkbook Plus Online
- eTutorial Plus Online
- EasyPlanner Plus Online

ENGLISH LEARNER SUPPORT

- Spanish Study Guide
- Multi-Language Glossary
- Chapter Audio Summaries CDs
- Teacher's Edition
  Chapter 4, pp. 164E–164F
  Chapter 5, pp. 216E–216F
  Chapter 6, pp. 268E–268F
  Chapter 7, pp. 314E–314F

Pacing and Assignment Guide

REGULAR SCHEDULE

Lesson	Les. Day	BASIC	AVERAGE	ADVANCED
4.1	Day 1	SRH p. 706 Exs. 1-5; pp. 171-172 Exs. 11-38, 52-62	pp. 171-172 Exs. 14-18, 21-49, 52-62	pp. 171-172 Exs. 17, 18, 21, 22, 25-57*, 62
4.2	Day 1	pp. 176-177 Exs. 8-20, 36-39	pp. 176-177 Exs. 8-11, 16-20, 28-31, 36-39	pp. 176-177 Exs. 10, 11, 16-20, 28-31, 36-39
	Day 2	pp. 176-177 Exs. 21-25, 40-45	pp. 176-177 Exs. 21, 25-27, 32, 33, 40-45	pp. 176-177 Exs. 25-27, 32-35*, 44, 45
4.3	Day 1	pp. 182-183 Exs. 13-38, 57-65	pp. 182-183 Exs. 17-20, 23, 24, 31-52, 57-65	pp. 182-183 Exs. 19, 20, 23, 24, 27, 28, 31-60*, 64, 65
4.4	Day 1	pp. 188-189 Exs. 8-23, 25-30, 42-49	pp. 188-189 Exs. 10, 11, 16-38, 42-49	pp. 188-189 Exs. 17-44*, 48, 49
4.5	Day 1	SRH p. 707 Exs. 1-9; pp. 194-195 Exs. 11-20, 22, 30-34	pp. 194-195 Exs. 14-26, 28, 30-34	pp. 194-195 Exs. 14-16, 20-31*, 33, 34
4.6	Day 1	pp. 199-200 Exs. 16-41, 55-62	pp. 199-200 Exs. 18-21, 26-49, 55-62	pp. 199-200 Exs. 30-35, 38-62*
4.7	Day 1	EP p. 728 Exs. 13-16; pp. 203-204 Exs. 9-12, 21, 35-45	pp. 203-204 Exs. 9-12, 21, 35-45	pp. 203-204 Exs. 11, 12, 27-31, 35-42
	Day 2	pp. 203-204 Exs. 13-20, 22-25, 46, 47	pp. 203-204 Exs. 17-20, 22-30, 46, 47	pp. 203-204 Exs. 17-20, 22-26, 32-34*, 46, 47
4.8	Day 1	pp. 207-208 Exs. 11-28, 30-31, 43-48	pp. 207-208 Exs. 14-16, 20-39, 43-48	pp. 207-208 Exs. 15, 16, 21, 22, 25-45*, 47, 48
Review	Day 1	pp. 212-213 Exs. 1-51	pp. 212-213 Exs. 1-51	pp. 212-213 Exs. 1-51
Assess	Day 1	Chapter 4 Test	Chapter 4 Test	Chapter 4 Test

YEARLY PACING Chapter 4 Total – **12 days** Chapters 1-4 Total – **48 days** Remaining – **112 days**

*Challenge Exercises EP = Extra Practice SRH = Skills Review Handbook EC = Extra Challenge

BLOCK SCHEDULE

DAY 1	DAY 2	DAY 3	DAY 4	DAY 5	DAY 6
4.1 pp. 171-172 Exs. 14-18, 21-49, 52-62 **4.2** pp. 176-177 Exs. 8-11, 16-20, 28-31, 36-39	**4.2 (cont.)** pp. 176-177 Exs. 21, 25-27, 32, 33, 40-45 **4.3** pp. 182-183 Exs. 17-20, 23, 24, 31-52, 57-65	**4.4** pp. 188-189 Exs. 10, 11, 16-38, 42-49 **4.5** pp. 194-195 Exs. 14-26, 28, 30-34	**4.6** pp. 199-200 Exs. 18-21, 26-49, 55-62 **4.7** pp. 203-204 Exs. 9-12, 21, 35-45	**4.7 (cont.)** pp. 203-204 Exs. 17-20, 22-30, 46, 47 **4.8** pp. 207-208 Exs. 14-16, 20-39, 43-48	**Review** pp. 212-213 Exs. 1-51 **Assess** Chapter 4 Test

YEARLY PACING Chapter 4 Total – **6 days** Chapters 1-4 Total – **24 days** Remaining – **56 days**

Support Materials

CHAPTER RESOURCE BOOK

CHAPTER SUPPORT								
Tips for New Teachers	p. 1			Parents as Partners			p. 3	

LESSON SUPPORT	4.1	4.2	4.3	4.4	4.5	4.6	4.7	4.8
Lesson Plans (regular and block)	p. 5	p. 14	p. 22	p. 31	p. 39	p. 50	p. 59	p. 67
Technology Activities & Keystrokes					p. 42			p. 69
Activity Support Masters	p. 7							
Activity Masters					p. 41			
Practice (3 levels)	p. 8	p. 16	p. 24	p. 33	p. 44	p. 52	p. 61	p. 70
Study Guide	p. 11	p. 19	p. 27	p. 36	p. 47	p. 55	p. 64	p. 73
Real-World Problem Solving			p. 29					p. 75
Challenge Practice	p. 13	p. 21	p. 30	p. 38	p. 49	p. 57	p. 66	p. 76

REVIEW			
Games Support Masters	p. 58	Cooperative Project with Rubric	p. 80
Chapter Review Games and Activities	p. 77	Extra Credit Project with Rubric	p. 82
Real-Life Project with Rubric	p. 78	Cumulative Practice	p. 84
		Resource Book Answers	A1

ASSESSMENT

Quizzes	p. 46	Alternative Assessments with Rubrics	p. 55
Chapter Tests (3 levels)	p. 48	Unit Test	p. 90
Standardized Test	p. 54	Cumulative Test	p. 92

TRANSPARENCIES

	4.1	4.2	4.3	4.4	4.5	4.6	4.7	4.8
Warm-Up / Daily Homework Quiz	✔	✔	✔	✔	✔	✔	✔	✔
Notetaking Guide	✔	✔	✔	✔	✔	✔	✔	✔
Teacher Support								
English/Spanish Problem Solving	✔			✔				✔
Answer Transparencies	✔	✔	✔	✔	✔	✔	✔	✔

TECHNOLOGY

- EasyPlanner CD-ROM
- Test and Practice Generator
- Electronic Lesson Presentations
- eTutorial CD-ROM
- Chapter Audio Summaries CDs
- Classzone.com
- eEdition Plus Online
- eWorkbook Plus Online
- eTutorial Plus Online
- EasyPlanner Plus Online

ADDITIONAL RESOURCES

- Worked-Out Solution Key
- Notetaking Guide
- Practice Workbook
- Tutor Place
- Professional Development Book
- Special Activities Book
- Posters
- Spanish Study Guide
- Exercises in Spanish
- English/Spanish Ch. Reviews/Tests
- Multi-Language Visual Glossary

Math Background and Teaching Strategies

Lesson 4.1

MATH BACKGROUND

FINDING FACTORS AND WRITING A FACTORIZATION

A **prime number** is a counting number greater than 1 whose only factors are itself and 1. A counting number with additional factors is **composite**. The **prime factorization** of a number expresses the number as the product of its prime factors. You can find the prime factors of a number by using a **factor tree**, in which you successively divide a number by its factors. There can be many factor trees for a composite number, but by the Fundamental Theorem of Arithmetic, each has a unique prime factorization.

TEACHING STRATEGIES

Show students the factor tree for 240 given below.

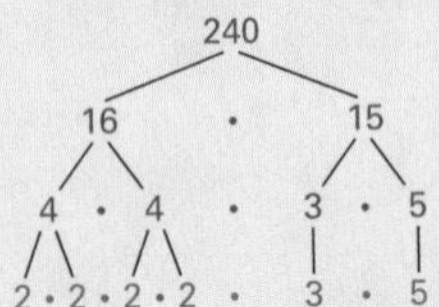

Ask students to produce alternative factor trees. Have them describe the strategy they used. Some strategies include dividing by the smallest factor possible or looking for factors that are close together in size, as shown for 240 above. Emphasize that though there are many factor trees, the resulting prime factorization of 240 remains the same: $240 = 2^4 \cdot 3 \cdot 5$.

Lesson 4.2

MATH BACKGROUND

The greatest whole number that is a factor of two or more nonzero whole numbers is their **greatest common factor**, or GCF. Two or more numbers with a GCF of 1 are **relatively prime**. The GCF is very useful in simplifying fractions and algebraic expressions. To find the GCF of two numbers, find the product of the prime factors that are common to both, using the smaller power of each common prime factor. You can find the greatest common factor of two monomials by factoring the monomials.

TEACHING STRATEGIES

To help students identify common factors, encourage them to align factors as shown for $4x^3$, $12x^2$, and $8x$ below.

$$\begin{aligned} 4x^3 &= 2 \cdot 2 \cdot \ x \cdot x \cdot x \\ 12x^2 &= 2 \cdot 2 \cdot \ 3 \cdot x \cdot x \\ 8x &= 2 \cdot 2 \cdot 2 \cdot \ x \end{aligned}$$

This makes it easy for students to identify and circle common factors to find the GCF. Then students can progress to finding GCFs from prime factorizations that use exponents, such as $2^2 \cdot 3^2 \cdot x^3$ for $36x^3$.

Lesson 4.3

MATH BACKGROUND

Equivalent fractions have the same **simplest form**, that is, they are the same when any common factors in the numerator and denominator of each have been divided out. To find the simplest form of a fraction or rational expression, divide its numerator and denominator by their GCF.

TEACHING STRATEGIES

Present students with the fraction $\frac{84}{504}$. Have them divide out 2 from the numerator and denominator to obtain $\frac{42}{252}$, and then repeat to obtain $\frac{21}{126}$. Then have them divide out 3 to obtain $\frac{7}{42}$. Ask if any common factors remain. Some students will recognize 7 as a common factor. Have them divide out 7 to obtain $\frac{1}{6}$. Point out that all of these fractions are equivalent, because the simplest form of each is $\frac{1}{6}$.

Lesson 4.4

MATH BACKGROUND

The smallest number that is a multiple of two or more numbers is their **least common multiple**, or LCM. If the numbers have no common factors other than 1, then their least common multiple is their product. To find the LCM of two numbers, find the product of the highest power of each prime number in the prime factorizations of the numbers.

TEACHING STRATEGIES

Point out that any of the following methods can be used to find the LCM of two numbers.

1. List consecutive multiples of each number beginning with the number. The first multiple that appears in the list for both numbers is their LCM.
2. List consecutive multiples of the greater number, beginning with the number. Divide the multiples by the lesser number until you obtain a whole number quotient.
3. Write the prime factorization of each number. Find the product of the highest power of each prime number in the factorizations of the numbers.

Lesson 4.5

MATH BACKGROUND

COMPARING FRACTIONS The least common multiple of the denominators of two or more fractions is their **least common denominator**. By writing fractions with different denominators as equivalent fractions using their least common denominator, it is easy to compare them. To compare mixed numbers, you can first rewrite them as improper fractions.

TEACHING STRATEGIES

You can break down the process of comparing fractions for students using the steps below.

1. Find the LCD of the fractions.
2. Rewrite the fractions as equivalent fractions in terms of the LCD.
3. Compare the numerators of the fractions.

Lesson 4.6

MATH BACKGROUND

RULES OF EXPONENTS The *product of powers property* states that to multiply two powers with the same base, add their exponents and use the original base. The *quotient of powers property* states that to divide two powers with the same base, subtract the exponent in the denominator from the exponent in the numerator, and use the original base. You cannot simplify the sum of different powers with the same base.

TEACHING STRATEGIES

Because students often confuse the properties of powers, urge them to have a simple example in mind that they can use if they get confused. For example, it is easy to use 2^2 and 2^3. Because $2^2 = 4$ and $2^3 = 8$, $2^2 \bullet 2^3 = 4 \bullet 8 = 32$, which is 2^5, not 2^6. Also, $2^2 + 2^3 = 4 + 8 = 12 \neq 2^5$.

Lesson 4.7

MATH BACKGROUND

NEGATIVE AND ZERO EXPONENTS For any nonzero number a, $a^0 = 1$. This makes sense because $\frac{a^b}{a^b} = 1$ for any natural number b, and the quotient of powers property states that $\frac{a^b}{a^b} = a^{b-b} = a^0$. The quotient of powers property also suggests that we define a^{-n} as $\frac{1}{a^n}$ for any integer n.

TEACHING STRATEGIES

Have students simplify $\frac{2^3}{2^3}$ in three ways: by dividing out common factors, by evaluating each power and then dividing, and using the quotient of powers property. This illustrates that it is logical that $2^0 = 1$. Use other examples to illustrate that $a^0 = 1$ for any nonzero number a. Also use numerical examples with the quotient of powers property to demonstrate the logic of the definition of negative exponents.

Lesson 4.8

MATH BACKGROUND

When a number is written in **scientific notation**, it is written as the product of a number between 1 and 10 (exclusive of 10) and a nonzero power of 10. Scientific notation provides a compact way of writing very large and very small numbers, and also makes calculations involving such numbers much less cumbersome and error-prone.

TEACHING STRATEGIES

You may wish to suggest that students use grid paper to write numbers of each place value from, say, billions to billionths, in descending order so that the numbers are aligned by place value. Then have students write the scientific notation form of each number to its right. This will give students a visual image of the relationship between the exponent in scientific notation and the standard form of a number.

Differentiating Instruction

Strategies for Underachievers

FOCUS ON VOCABULARY

Some students may be overwhelmed by all of the new vocabulary in this chapter. Help them increase their mathematical vocabulary a step at a time by building their understanding of new vocabulary upon previously learned terms. For example, students must first understand *multiple* before progressing to *common multiple* and then to *least common multiple*. Likewise, students must understand *factor* before progressing to *common factor* and then to *greatest common factor*. You might suggest that students use note cards to assimilate new vocabulary. You may want to suggest that they color code note cards of related vocabulary, such as all the vocabulary expressions containing the term *factor*.

REVIEW KEY CONCEPTS

Before underachieving students address finding a GCF in Lesson 4.2, you may want to review identifying factors of numbers with them, including how to identify quickly when a number is divisible by 2, 3, 4, 5, 9, or 10.

Before students find an LCM in Lesson 4.4, you may wish to point out how the concept of a multiple is related to simple multiplication tables. From thinking in terms of multiplication tables, students will realize instances when numbers have multiples that are the same.

CREATE AND USE MANIPULATIVES

USE FLASH CARDS Corresponding to Lessons 4.2 and 4.4, you may want to create or have students create flash cards that each have a pair of numbers on the front. On the back of the cards should be written the GCF and the LCM of the numbers. In addition, the backs of the cards could contain the prime factorization of each number written with and without exponents, lists of the factors of each number, and lists of the multiples of each number. You can have a large class set of cards, or students may have individual sets with which they can practice by themselves or with others. The multiple representations on the backs of the cards will help students connect the different ways for finding GCFs and LCMs. Make sure to include pairs of numbers that are relatively prime as well as pairs in which one number is a multiple of the other. As students gain mastery, they can add cards for monomials.

USE CONCRETE MODELING

MAKE TABLES For Lessons 4.6 and 4.7, you can have students make tables that concretely model the concepts of the lessons while providing logical support for the concepts. In Lesson 4.6, you can have students complete more tables in the style of the one in the Activity at the top of page 196 by including new expressions such as $2^2 \cdot 2^3$, $3^2 \cdot 3^4$, $2^5 \cdot 2^3$, and $4^4 \cdot 4^3$. You can have students create similar tables to illustrate the quotient of powers property.

In Lesson 4.7, it may be useful to explore zero and negative exponents with a table that presents the powers of 10, as shown below. Ask students to compare the left-hand and right-hand sides of the table. Then ask them how they might complete and extend the table.

10^6	1,000,000
10^5	100,000
10^4	10,000
10^3	1,000
10^2	100
10^1	10
10^0	?
10^{-1}	0.1
10^{-2}	?
10^{-3}	?
10^{-4}	?

Students should observe how the decimals shown in the table can be written as fractions. For example:

$$10^{-2} = 0.01 = \frac{1}{100} = \frac{1}{10^2}$$

This will help reinforce how exponents that are opposites are related to each other.

Strategies for English Learners

DISSECT WORD PROBLEMS

The last sentence of a word problem usually contains a verb that issues a command. It orders the reader to do something. Almost always it is followed by an additional description of what the person is to do, as in "Solve the following equation," with *solve* being the command, and *the following equation* identifying what is to be solved. These command verbs are signals to the student that explain what the student is to do in the word problem. Comprehending these verbs is essential to solving word problems.

COMMAND VERBS The following command verbs were compiled from sample standardized test problems, word problems found in mathematics textbooks, and state standards:

> Apply, approximate, assume, calculate, check, choose, circle, classify, compute, convert, create, decide, demonstrate, describe, design, determine, draw, establish, estimate, explain, examine, extend, find, fit, identify, interpret, investigate, list, make, mark, model, name, order, organize, perform, predict, prove, recognize, read, represent, round, select, show, sketch, solve, state, transform, translate, use, verify, visualize

Ask students to group the words into categories, such as words that tell you to pick from a list, words that tell you to calculate something, and so on. Allow students to make up their own categories. It is important here to let students express and discuss what they think these terms mean. Many of the words would fit into more than one category depending on the context. For example, the term *draw* can be used in the following ways: Draw a picture; Draw a conclusion. These are very different requests, and students need to know both meanings. Through discussion, students can expose the different meanings of words and expand their concepts of what words mean. Some of these words include *scale, model, square, cube,* and *degree.* Watch for the tendency of students to confuse words that sound or look similar, for example *make* and *mark*. Encourage students to write new words in their journals, accompanied by a picture or an explanation in their primary language. Use a dictionary and thesaurus to provide additional meanings of words, as well as synonyms and antonyms.

Strategies for Advanced Learners

INCORPORATE TECHNOLOGY

USE A CALCULATOR With Lesson 4.8, you may want to have advanced learners examine how numbers in scientific notation are entered and displayed using a calculator. Suggest also that these students examine the manual of their calculator to see when it will automatically display a number in scientific notation even if the numbers involved in an operation or operations are not in scientific notation. For example, if you enter and multiply the decimals 0.0065 and 0.0009 on a calculator, the result, which in decimal form is 0.00000585, will likely be displayed in scientific notation.

USE CO-CURRICULAR ACTIVITIES

RESEARCH PROJECTS In conjunction with Lesson 4.8, you may want to work with a science teacher to develop a project that involves research into an area of science that involves very large and/or very small numbers written in scientific notation. Possible areas of investigation include astronomy, the study of atomic particles, and the study of biological quantities like cells or DNA. You may also wish to have students work with a social studies teacher to find an area of research that involves very large or very small numbers. Some possibilities include the national budget and the deficit, the gross national product, the value of trade, resource and energy production and consumption, and population studies.

The following problem can be used with **Lesson 4.4**:

- **Challenge** Different instrument sections in a school symphonic group have different practice schedules. The brass section meets every third day to practice, the percussion section meets every fourth day, the woodwinds section meets every sixth day, and the strings section meets every other day. If all of the sections of the symphonic group practice together on September 1, when are the next two dates they all practice together? September 13 and September 25

You may also wish to have students create their own scheduling problems involving applying the least common multiple. Encourage students to relate their problems to their own interests or schedules. Students can then work with a partner, swapping and solving each other's problems.

Differentiating Instruction: Teaching Resources

Differentiating Review, Reteaching, and Remediation

McDougal Littell *Middle School Mathematics* offers teachers a wide variety of reteaching and remediation resources. Pictured here are facsimiles of various pages from the *Notetaking Guide*, the Study Guide pages from the *Chapter 4 Resource Book*, and remediation cards from *Tutor Place.*

NOTETAKING GUIDE

The *Notetaking Guide* easily allows students to take notes on and review each lesson in the textbook by using guided examples and Your Turn Now exercises. The *Notetaking Guide* is available on transparencies also.

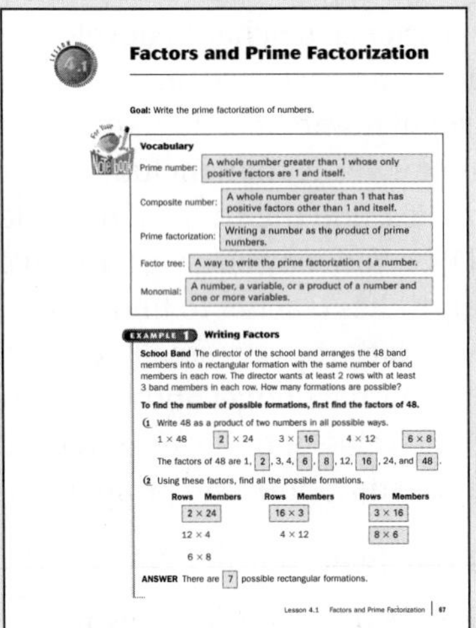

4.1 Factors and Prime Factorization

Goal: Write the prime factorization of numbers.

Vocabulary

Prime number: A whole number greater than 1 whose only positive factors are 1 and itself.

Composite number: A whole number greater than 1 that has positive factors other than 1 and itself.

Prime factorization: Writing a number as the product of prime numbers.

Factor tree: A way to write the prime factorization of a number.

Monomial: A number, a variable, or a product of a number and one or more variables.

EXAMPLE 1 Writing Factors

School Band The director of the school band arranges the 48 band members into a rectangular formation with the same number of band members in each row. The director wants at least 2 rows with at least 3 band members in each row. How many formations are possible?

To find the number of possible formations, first find the factors of 48.

1. Write 48 as a product of two numbers in all possible ways.

1 × 48 2 × 24 3 × 16 4 × 12 6 × 8

The factors of 48 are 1, 2, 3, 4, 6, 8, 12, 16, 24, and 48.

2. Using these factors, find all the possible formations.

Rows × Members	Rows × Members	Rows × Members
2 × 24	16 × 3	3 × 16
12 × 4	4 × 12	8 × 6
6 × 8		

ANSWER There are 7 possible rectangular formations.

Lesson 4.1 Factors and Prime Factorization 67

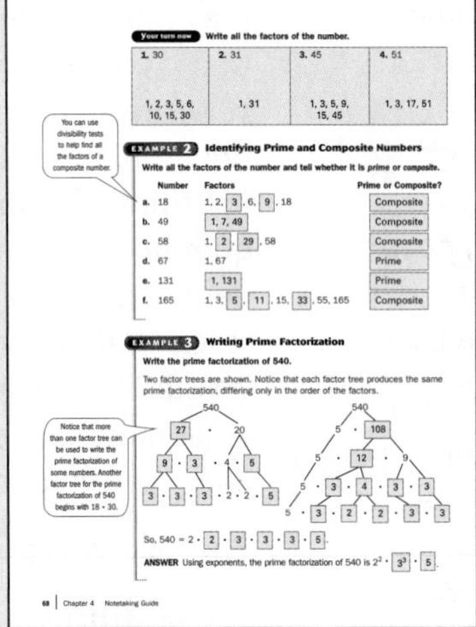

Your turn now Write all the factors of the number.

1. 30	2. 31	3. 45	4. 51
1, 2, 3, 5, 6, 10, 15, 30	1, 31	1, 3, 5, 9, 15, 45	1, 3, 17, 51

You can use divisibility tests to help find all the factors of a composite number.

EXAMPLE 2 Identifying Prime and Composite Numbers

Write all the factors of the number and tell whether it is *prime* or *composite*.

	Number	Factors	Prime or Composite?
a.	18	1, 2, 3, 6, 9, 18	Composite
b.	49	1, 7, 49	Composite
c.	58	1, 2, 29, 58	Composite
d.	67	1, 67	Prime
e.	131	1, 131	Prime
f.	165	1, 3, 5, 11, 15, 33, 55, 165	Composite

EXAMPLE 3 Writing Prime Factorization

Write the prime factorization of 540.

Two factor trees are shown. Notice that each factor tree produces the same prime factorization, differing only in the order of the factors.

Notice that more than one factor tree can be used to write the prime factorization of some numbers. Another factor tree for the prime factorization of 540 begins with 18 · 30.

So, 540 = 2 · 2 · 3 · 3 · 3 · 5

ANSWER Using exponents, the prime factorization of 540 is $2^2 \cdot 3^3 \cdot 5$.

68 Chapter 4 Notetaking Guide

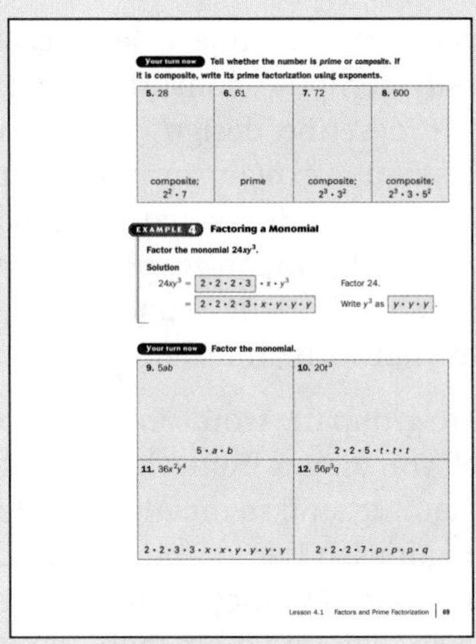

Your turn now Tell whether the number is *prime* or *composite*. If it is composite, write its prime factorization using exponents.

5. 28	6. 61	7. 72	8. 600
composite; $2^2 \cdot 7$	prime	composite; $2^3 \cdot 3^2$	composite; $2^3 \cdot 3 \cdot 5^2$

EXAMPLE 4 Factoring a Monomial

Factor the monomial $24xy^3$.

Solution

$24xy^3 = 2 \cdot 2 \cdot 2 \cdot 3 \cdot x \cdot y^3$ Factor 24.

$= 2 \cdot 2 \cdot 2 \cdot 3 \cdot x \cdot y \cdot y \cdot y$ Write y^3 as $y \cdot y \cdot y$.

Your turn now Factor the monomial.

9. 5ab	10. $20t^3$
$5 \cdot a \cdot b$	$2 \cdot 2 \cdot 5 \cdot t \cdot t \cdot t$
11. $36x^2y^4$	12. $56p^3q$
$2 \cdot 2 \cdot 3 \cdot 3 \cdot x \cdot x \cdot y \cdot y \cdot y \cdot y$	$2 \cdot 2 \cdot 2 \cdot 7 \cdot p \cdot p \cdot p \cdot q$

Lesson 4.1 Factors and Prime Factorization 69

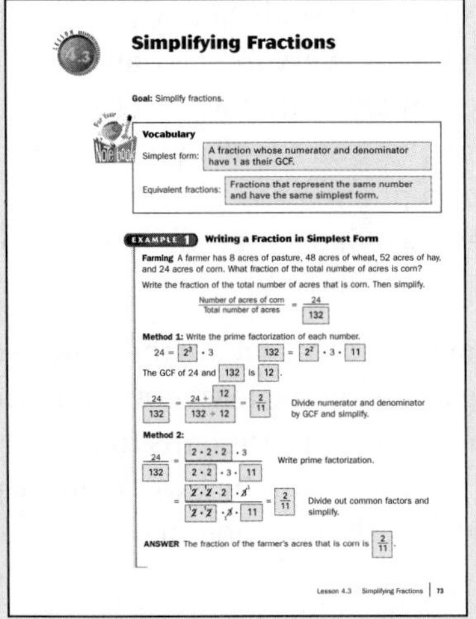

4.3 Simplifying Fractions

Goal: Simplify fractions.

Vocabulary

Simplest form: A fraction whose numerator and denominator have 1 as their GCF.

Equivalent fractions: Fractions that represent the same number and have the same simplest form.

EXAMPLE 1 Writing a Fraction in Simplest Form

Farming A farmer has 8 acres of pasture, 48 acres of wheat, 52 acres of hay, and 24 acres of corn. What fraction of the total number of acres is corn?

Write the fraction of the total number of acres that is corn. Then simplify.

$\frac{\text{Number of acres of corn}}{\text{Total number of acres}} = \frac{24}{132}$

Method 1: Write the prime factorization of each number.

$24 = 2^3 \cdot 3$ $132 = 2^2 \cdot 3 \cdot 11$

The GCF of 24 and 132 is 12.

$\frac{24}{132} = \frac{24 \div 12}{132 \div 12} = \frac{2}{11}$ Divide numerator and denominator by GCF and simplify.

Method 2:

$\frac{24}{132} = \frac{2 \cdot 2 \cdot 2 \cdot 3}{2 \cdot 2 \cdot 3 \cdot 11}$ Write prime factorization.

$= \frac{2}{11}$ Divide out common factors and simplify.

ANSWER The fraction of the farmer's acres that is corn is $\frac{2}{11}$.

Lesson 4.3 Simplifying Fractions 73

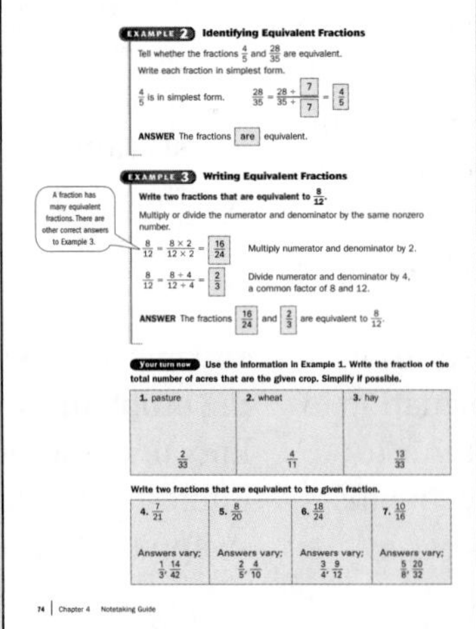

EXAMPLE 2 Identifying Equivalent Fractions

Tell whether the fractions $\frac{4}{5}$ and $\frac{28}{35}$ are equivalent.

Write each fraction in simplest form.

$\frac{4}{5}$ is in simplest form. $\frac{28}{35} = \frac{28 \div 7}{35 \div 7} = \frac{4}{5}$

ANSWER The fractions are equivalent.

EXAMPLE 3 Writing Equivalent Fractions

Write two fractions that are equivalent to $\frac{8}{12}$.

Multiply or divide the numerator and denominator by the same nonzero number.

A fraction has many equivalent fractions. There are other correct answers to Example 3.

$\frac{8}{12} = \frac{8 \times 2}{12 \times 2} = \frac{16}{24}$ Multiply numerator and denominator by 2.

$\frac{8}{12} = \frac{8 \div 4}{12 \div 4} = \frac{2}{3}$ Divide numerator and denominator by 4, a common factor of 8 and 12.

ANSWER The fractions $\frac{16}{24}$ and $\frac{2}{3}$ are equivalent to $\frac{8}{12}$.

Your turn now Use the information in Example 1. Write the fraction of the total number of acres that are the given crop. Simplify if possible.

1. pasture	2. wheat	3. hay
$\frac{2}{33}$	$\frac{4}{11}$	$\frac{13}{33}$

Write two fractions that are equivalent to the given fraction.

4. $\frac{7}{21}$	5. $\frac{8}{20}$	6. $\frac{18}{24}$	7. $\frac{10}{16}$
Answers vary: $\frac{1}{3}, \frac{14}{42}$	Answers vary: $\frac{2}{5}, \frac{4}{10}$	Answers vary: $\frac{3}{4}, \frac{9}{12}$	Answers vary: $\frac{5}{8}, \frac{20}{32}$

74 Chapter 4 Notetaking Guide

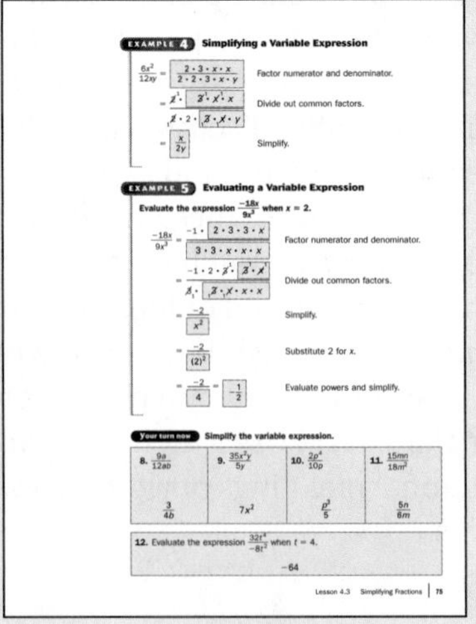

EXAMPLE 4 Simplifying a Variable Expression

$\frac{6x^2}{12xy} = \frac{2 \cdot 3 \cdot x \cdot x}{2 \cdot 2 \cdot 3 \cdot x \cdot y}$ Factor numerator and denominator.

Divide out common factors.

$= \frac{x}{2y}$ Simplify.

EXAMPLE 5 Evaluating a Variable Expression

Evaluate the expression $\frac{-18x}{9x^3}$ when $x = 2$.

$\frac{-18x}{9x^3} = \frac{-1 \cdot 2 \cdot 3 \cdot 3 \cdot x}{3 \cdot 3 \cdot x \cdot x \cdot x}$ Factor numerator and denominator.

Divide out common factors.

$= \frac{-2}{x^2}$ Simplify.

$= \frac{-2}{(2)^2}$ Substitute 2 for x.

$= \frac{-2}{4} = -\frac{1}{2}$ Evaluate powers and simplify.

Your turn now Simplify the variable expression.

8. $\frac{9a}{12ab}$	9. $\frac{35x^3y}{5y}$	10. $\frac{2p^4}{10p}$	11. $\frac{15mn}{18n^2}$
$\frac{3}{4b}$	$7x^3$	$\frac{p^3}{5}$	$\frac{5m}{6n}$

12. Evaluate the expression $\frac{32t^3}{-8t}$ when $t = 4$.

−64

Lesson 4.3 Simplifying Fractions 75

RESOURCE BOOK

The *Chapter Resource Books* contain Study Guide pages with reteaching examples and exercises for each lesson in the textbook. Pictured below are Study Guide pages from the *Chapter 4 Resource Book.* (The Study Guide pages are also available in Spanish in the *Spanish Study Guide.*)

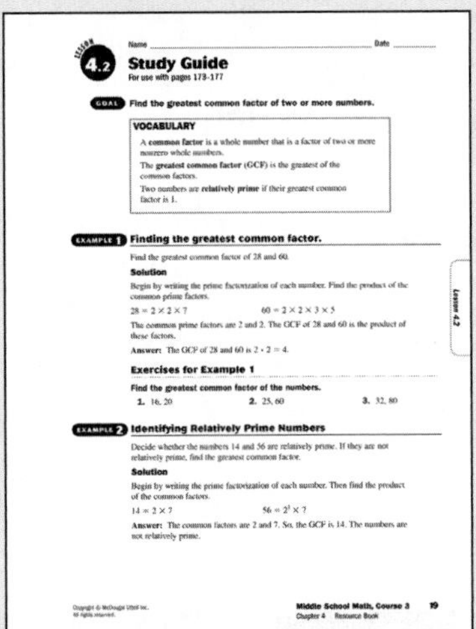

LESSON 4.2 Name ______ Date ______

Study Guide
For use with pages 173–177

GOAL **Find the greatest common factor of two or more numbers.**

VOCABULARY
A **common factor** is a whole number that is a factor of two or more nonzero whole numbers.
The **greatest common factor** (GCF) is the greatest of the common factors.
Two numbers are **relatively prime** if their greatest common factor is 1.

EXAMPLE 1 **Finding the greatest common factor.**

Find the greatest common factor of 28 and 60.

Solution

Begin by writing the prime factorization of each number. Find the product of the common prime factors.

$28 = 2 \times 2 \times 7$ $\quad 60 = 2 \times 2 \times 3 \times 5$

The common prime factors are 2 and 2. The GCF of 28 and 60 is the product of these factors.

Answer: The GCF of 28 and 60 is $2 \cdot 2 = 4$.

Exercises for Example 1

Find the greatest common factor of the numbers.

1. 16, 20 2. 25, 60 3. 32, 80

EXAMPLE 2 **Identifying Relatively Prime Numbers**

Decide whether the numbers 14 and 56 are relatively prime. If they are not relatively prime, find the greatest common factor.

Solution

Begin by writing the prime factorization of each number. Then find the product of the common factors.

$14 = 2 \times 7$ $\quad 56 = 2^3 \times 7$

Answer: The common factors are 2 and 7. So, the GCF is 14. The numbers are not relatively prime.

Lesson 4.2

Copyright © McDougal Littell Inc. All rights reserved.

Middle School Math, Course 3 19
Chapter 4 Resource Book

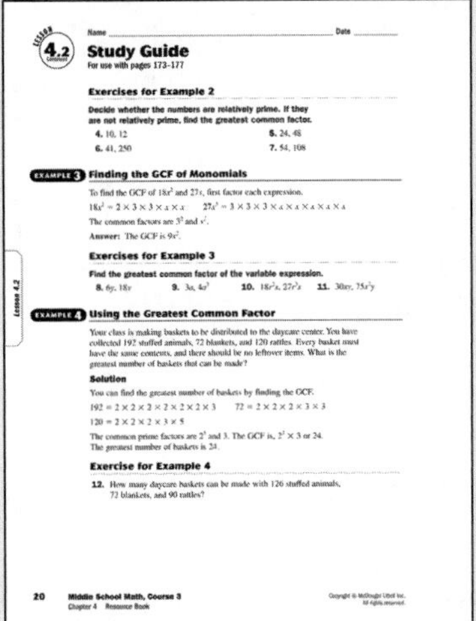

LESSON 4.2 Name ______ Date ______

Study Guide
For use with pages 173–177

Exercises for Example 2

Decide whether the numbers are relatively prime. If they are not relatively prime, find the greatest common factor.

4. 10, 12 5. 24, 48
6. 41, 250 7. 54, 108

EXAMPLE 3 **Finding the GCF of Monomials**

To find the GCF of $18x^2$ and $27x^5$, first factor each expression.

$18x^2 = 2 \times 3 \times 3 \times x \times x$ $\quad 27x^5 = 3 \times 3 \times 3 \times x \times x \times x \times x \times x$

The common factors are 3^2 and x^2.

Answer: The GCF is $9x^2$.

Exercises for Example 3

Find the greatest common factor of the variable expression.

8. $6y, 18y$ 9. $3x, 4x^3$ 10. $18r^2s, 27r^2s$ 11. $30xy, 75x^2y$

EXAMPLE 4 **Using the Greatest Common Factor**

Your class is making baskets to be distributed to the daycare center. You have collected 192 stuffed animals, 72 blankets, and 120 rattles. Every basket must have the same contents, and there should be no leftover items. What is the greatest number of baskets that can be made?

Solution

You can find the greatest number of baskets by finding the GCF.

$192 = 2 \times 2 \times 2 \times 2 \times 2 \times 2 \times 3$ $\quad 72 = 2 \times 2 \times 2 \times 3 \times 3$

$120 = 2 \times 2 \times 2 \times 3 \times 5$

The common prime factors are 2^3 and 3. The GCF is, $2^3 \times 3$ or 24.
The greatest number of baskets is 24.

Exercise for Example 4

12. How many daycare baskets can be made with 126 stuffed animals, 72 blankets, and 90 rattles?

Lesson 4.2

20 Middle School Math, Course 3
Chapter 4 Resource Book

Copyright © McDougal Littell Inc. All rights reserved.

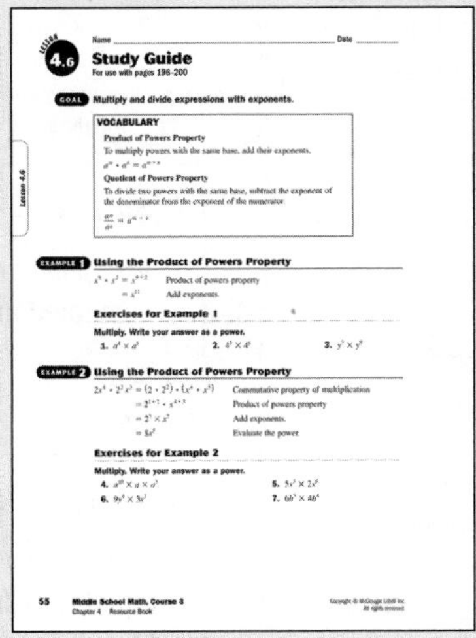

LESSON 4.6 Name ______ Date ______

Study Guide
For use with pages 196–200

GOAL **Multiply and divide expressions with exponents.**

VOCABULARY
Product of Powers Property
To multiply powers with the same base, add their exponents.
$a^m \cdot a^n = a^{m+n}$
Quotient of Powers Property
To divide two powers with the same base, subtract the exponent of the denominator from the exponent of the numerator.
$\frac{a^m}{a^n} = a^{m-n}$

Lesson 4.6

EXAMPLE 1 **Using the Product of Powers Property**

$x^9 \cdot x^2 = x^{9+2}$ Product of powers property
$= x^{11}$ Add exponents.

Exercises for Example 1

Multiply. Write your answer as a power.

1. $a^4 \times a^3$ 2. $4^3 \times 4^5$ 3. $y^5 \times y^9$

EXAMPLE 2 **Using the Product of Powers Property**

$2x^4 \cdot 2^2x^3 = (2 \cdot 2^2) \cdot (x^4 \cdot x^3)$ Commutative property of multiplication
$= 2^{1+2} \cdot x^{4+3}$ Product of powers property
$= 2^3 \times x^7$ Add exponents.
$= 8x^7$ Evaluate the power.

Exercises for Example 2

Multiply. Write your answer as a power.

4. $a^{10} \times a \times a^3$ 5. $5x^3 \times 2x^5$
6. $9y^4 \times 3y^2$ 7. $6b^3 \times 4b^4$

55 Middle School Math, Course 3
Chapter 4 Resource Book

Copyright © McDougal Littell Inc. All rights reserved.

TUTOR PLACE

Tutor Place helps students practice and master essential topics. Instruction is provided by 104 cards containing examples and two sets of practice exercises. Answers are provided in a handy answer key.

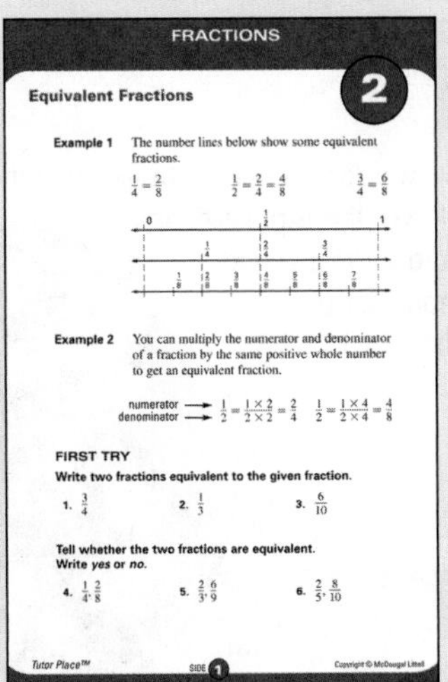

FRACTIONS

Equivalent Fractions 2

Example 1 The number lines below show some equivalent fractions.

$\frac{1}{4} = \frac{2}{8}$ $\quad \frac{1}{2} = \frac{2}{4} = \frac{4}{8}$ $\quad \frac{3}{4} = \frac{6}{8}$

Example 2 You can multiply the numerator and denominator of a fraction by the same positive whole number to get an equivalent fraction.

numerator →
denominator → $\frac{1}{2} = \frac{1 \times 2}{2 \times 2} = \frac{2}{4}$ $\quad \frac{1}{2} = \frac{1 \times 4}{2 \times 4} = \frac{4}{8}$

FIRST TRY

Write two fractions equivalent to the given fraction.

1. $\frac{3}{4}$ 2. $\frac{1}{3}$ 3. $\frac{6}{10}$

Tell whether the two fractions are equivalent. Write *yes* or *no*.

4. $\frac{1}{4}, \frac{2}{8}$ 5. $\frac{2}{3}, \frac{6}{9}$ 6. $\frac{2}{5}, \frac{8}{10}$

Tutor Place™ SIDE 1 Copyright © McDougal Littell

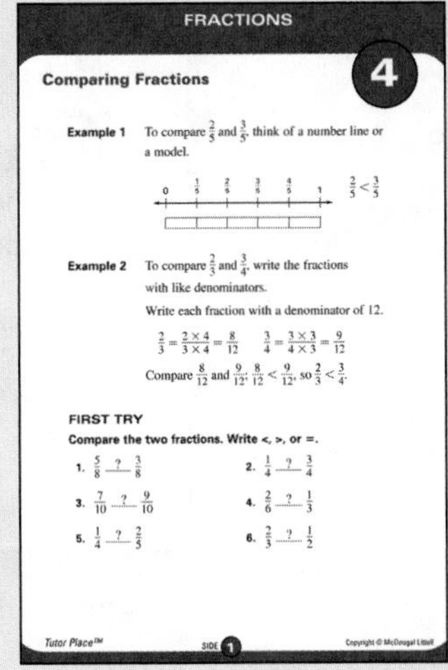

FRACTIONS

Comparing Fractions 4

Example 1 To compare $\frac{2}{5}$ and $\frac{3}{5}$, think of a number line or a model.

$\frac{2}{5} < \frac{3}{5}$

Example 2 To compare $\frac{2}{3}$ and $\frac{3}{4}$, write the fractions with like denominators.

Write each fraction with a denominator of 12.

$\frac{2}{3} = \frac{2 \times 4}{3 \times 4} = \frac{8}{12}$ $\quad \frac{3}{4} = \frac{3 \times 3}{4 \times 3} = \frac{9}{12}$

Compare $\frac{8}{12}$ and $\frac{9}{12}$. $\frac{8}{12} < \frac{9}{12}$, so $\frac{2}{3} < \frac{3}{4}$.

FIRST TRY

Compare the two fractions. Write <, >, or =.

1. $\frac{5}{8}$? $\frac{3}{8}$ 2. $\frac{1}{4}$? $\frac{3}{4}$
3. $\frac{7}{10}$? $\frac{9}{10}$ 4. $\frac{2}{6}$? $\frac{1}{3}$
5. $\frac{1}{4}$? $\frac{2}{5}$ 6. $\frac{2}{3}$? $\frac{1}{2}$

Tutor Place™ SIDE 1 Copyright © McDougal Littell

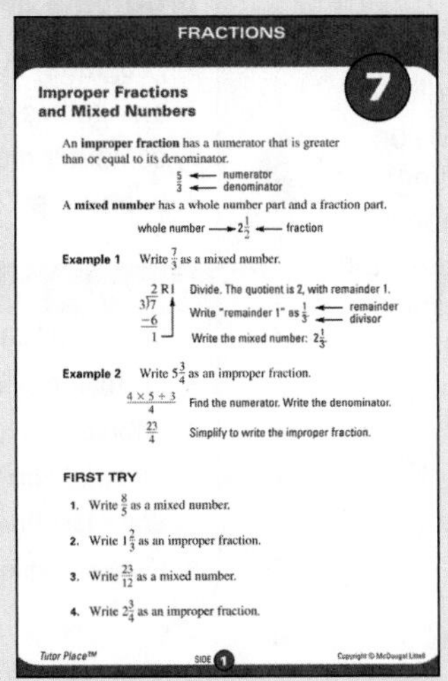

FRACTIONS

Improper Fractions and Mixed Numbers 7

An **improper fraction** has a numerator that is greater than or equal to its denominator.

$\frac{5}{3}$ ← numerator ← denominator

A **mixed number** has a whole number part and a fraction part.

whole number → $2\frac{1}{2}$ ← fraction

Example 1 Write $\frac{7}{3}$ as a mixed number.

$3\overline{)7}$ = 2 R1, -6, 1
Divide. The quotient is 2, with remainder 1.
Write "remainder 1" as $\frac{1}{3}$ ← remainder ← divisor
Write the mixed number: $2\frac{1}{3}$

Example 2 Write $5\frac{3}{4}$ as an improper fraction.

$\frac{4 \times 5 + 3}{4}$ Find the numerator. Write the denominator.
$\frac{23}{4}$ Simplify to write the improper fraction.

FIRST TRY

1. Write $\frac{8}{5}$ as a mixed number.
2. Write $1\frac{2}{3}$ as an improper fraction.
3. Write $\frac{23}{12}$ as a mixed number.
4. Write $2\frac{3}{4}$ as an improper fraction.

Tutor Place™ SIDE 1 Copyright © McDougal Littell

OVERVIEW

Main Ideas

In this chapter, students use factorization trees to write the prime factorization of numbers and also factor monomials. Students find the greatest common factor and least common multiple of numbers and monomials and use these quantities to simplify, compare, and order fractions and mixed numbers. Students multiply and divide expressions with exponents and simplify expressions with negative exponents. Students also read and write numbers in scientific notation and use scientific notation in real-world problems.

Prerequisite Skills

The key skills reviewed in the games on these pages are:

- Whole number division

Additional practice with prerequisite skills can be found in the Review What You Need to Know exercises on page 166. Additional resources for reviewing prerequisite skills are:

- Skills Review Handbook, pp. 704–726
- Tutor Place
- eTutorial Plus

Managing the Game

Tips for Success

Have students review how to divide whole numbers using long division and its abbreviated form (writing each remainder in small numbers beside the corresponding digit of the dividend) before playing this game. Remind students that a number divides another number evenly if there is no remainder.

Factors, Fractions, and Exponents

BEFORE

In previous chapters you've...

- Multiplied and divided numbers
- Compared and ordered integers

Now

In Chapter 4 you'll study...

- Factoring numbers
- Simplifying fractions
- Multiplying and dividing expressions with exponents
- Reading and writing numbers using scientific notation

WHY?

So you can solve real-world problems about...

- geography, p. 182
- orangutans, p. 193
- computer memory, p. 199
- bubbles, p. 205

Internet Preview
CLASSZONE.COM

- eEdition Plus Online
- eWorkbook Plus Online
- eTutorial Plus Online
- State Test Practice
- More Examples

Chapter Warm-Up Game

Review skills you need for this chapter in this quick game.

Key Skill:
Whole number division

BICYCLE MATH

HOW TO PLAY

1 PICK the number with each letter that divides evenly into the bold number in the matching fact.

A. 4, 8, 42 4
B. 7, 13, 23 13
C. 15, 17, 21 21

2 USE the answer for each letter to evaluate the expression below. The value of the expression is the world record bicycle speed in miles per hour, set by Fred Rompelberg in 1995.

A (B + C) + 30.9

166.9 miles per hour

A. In **1884**, the "safety bicycle," a bicycle resembling the ones we use today, was invented.

B. In 2001, **39,000,000** people in the United States rode a bicycle more than once.

C. In 2002, **189** cyclists competed in the Tour de France.

Stop and Think

1. **Writing** A student thinks that 42 divides evenly into 1884 because 42 divides evenly into 84. Explain what is wrong with the student's reasoning. See margin.
2. **Critical Thinking** What number will divide evenly into any even number? Explain.
The number 2 will divide evenly into any even number. You can think of the even numbers as the multiples of 2. Thus, all even numbers are divisible by 2.

Reflecting on the Game

After Stop & Think Question 1, have students list any divisibility rules they know. For example, 4 divides a number if it divides the last two digits of the number, 5 divides a number if the number ends in 0 or 5, and 9 divides a number if the sum of the digits is divisible by 9.

CHAPTER RESOURCES

These resources are provided to help you prepare for the chapter and to customize review materials:

Chapter 4 Resource Book
- Tips for New Teachers, pp. 1–2
- Lesson Plan, pp. 5, 14, 22, 31, 39, 50, 59, 67
- Lesson Plan for Block Scheduling, pp. 6, 15, 23, 32, 40, 51, 60, 68

Technology
- EasyPlanner CD-ROM
- Test and Practice Generator
- Electronic Lesson Presentations CD-ROM
- eTutorial CD-ROM

Internet
- Classzone
- eEdition Plus Online
- eWorkbook Plus Online
- eTutorial Plus Online
- EasyPlanner Plus Online

ENGLISH LEARNER SUPPORT

- Spanish Study Guide
- Multi-Language Glossary
- Chapter Audio Summaries CDs
- Teacher's Edition, pp. 164E–164F

1. When checking whether a number is divisible by another, you cannot look at just part of a number. You need to consider the entire number.

PREPARE

DIAGNOSIS/REMEDIATION

Review What You Need to Know
The Review What You Need to Know exercises can help you diagnose whether students have the following skills needed in Chapter 4:

- Using vocabulary (Exs. 1-3)
- Evaluating expressions (Exs. 4-11)
- Simplifying expressions (Exs. 12-15)
- Solving equations (Exs. 16-18)

 ***Chapter 4 Resource Book***

- Study Guide (Lessons 4.1-4.8)

 ***Tutor Place***

NOTETAKING STRATEGIES

Students' notes should include methods for finding equivalent fractions, writing fractions in simplest form, and comparing fractions, along with examples. Further suggestions for keeping a notebook can be found on page 181.

For more support on notetaking, see:

- Notetaking Guide Workbook
- Notetaking Transparencies

Getting Ready to Learn

Word Watch

Review Words
power, p. 20
base, p. 20
exponent, p. 20
fraction, p. 707

Review What You Need to Know

Using Vocabulary Copy and complete using a review word.

1. In the expression 2^6, 2 is called the ?. base
2. The expression 3^7 is a(n) ? of 3. power
3. In the expression 5^4, 4 is called the ?. exponent

Evaluate the expression. *(p. 20)*

4. $3^2 \cdot 3$ 27
5. $(2 + 3)^2$ 25
6. $4^2 \div 4^2$ 1
7. $(6 - 5)^7$ 1
8. $3^2 + 4 \cdot 5$ 29
9. $12 - 8 \div 2^2$ 10
10. $7^2 - 3^3$ 22
11. $6^2 \div 2^2$ 9

Simplify the expression by combining like terms. *(p. 85)*

12. $7x + 4 - 3x$ $4x + 4$
13. $-2x + 5x - x$ $2x$
14. $x + 4 - 12x$ $-11x + 4$
15. $6x - 5 + x$ $7x - 5$

Solve the equation. Check your answer. *(p. 119)*

16. $2a + 6 = 14$ 4
17. $8 - 4m = 20$ −3
18. $-7 + 5c = -32$ −5

You should include material that appears on a notebook like this in your own notes.

Know How to Take Notes

Preview the Chapter Skim the content of the chapter you are about to study. If you already know something about the topic, outline what you know in your notes.

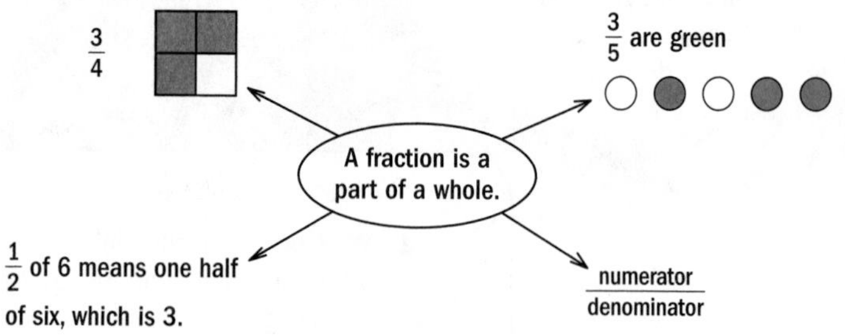

In Chapter 4, you will learn more things about fractions that you can add to your outline.

4.1 Hands-on Activity

GOAL
Introduce prime and composite numbers.

MATERIALS
- paper
- colored pencils

Investigating Factors

A *prime* number is a whole number that has exactly two factors: 1 and itself. A *composite* number has more than two factors. In this activity, you will look at a number pattern attributed to Eratosthenes, a mathematician who lived in Alexandria, Egypt, around 230 B.C.

Explore

Create the Sieve of Eratosthenes with the integers 1 to 60.

1 Write the whole numbers 1 to 60 in a rectangular array as shown at the right.

1	2	3	4	5	6	7	8	9	10
11	12	13	14	15	16	17	18	19	20
21	22	23	24	25	26	27	28	29	30
31	32	33	34	35	36	37	38	39	40
41	42	43	44	45	46	47	48	49	50
51	52	53	54	55	56	57	58	59	60

2 Start with the number 2. Circle it and cross out every multiple of 2 after 2.

3 Move to the next number that is not crossed out, 3. Circle it and cross out every multiple of 3 after 3.

1	(2)	(3)	~~4~~	5	~~6~~	7	~~8~~	~~9~~	~~10~~
11	~~12~~	13	~~14~~	~~15~~	~~16~~	17	~~18~~	19	~~20~~
~~21~~	~~22~~	23	~~24~~	25	~~26~~	~~27~~	~~28~~	29	~~30~~
31	~~32~~	~~33~~	~~34~~	35	~~36~~	37	~~38~~	~~39~~	~~40~~
41	~~42~~	43	~~44~~	~~45~~	~~46~~	47	~~48~~	49	~~50~~
~~51~~	~~52~~	53	~~54~~	55	~~56~~	~~57~~	~~58~~	59	~~60~~

Skip the numbers that have already been crossed out.

4 Move to the next number that is not crossed out. Circle it and cross out all other multiples of that number. **Steps 4–5. See margin.**

5 Repeat Step 4 until every number except 1 is either crossed out or circled.

Your turn now

1. What type of numbers are circled in your array? **prime**

2. What type of numbers are crossed out in your array? **composite**

Stop *and* Think

3. Writing If you continued this process with the numbers 61 to 100, what type of numbers would you expect to be circled? Why? **See margin.**

ILLINOIS Standards and ISAT:
6.B.3b

1 PLAN

Explore the Concept

- Students will investigate prime and composite numbers.
- This activity leads into the study of prime factorization in Lesson 4.1.

Materials

Each student or pair of students will need paper and colored pencils. See also the Activity Support Master in the *Chapter 4 Resource Book.*

Recommended Time

Work activity: 10 min
Discuss results: 10 min

Grouping

Students can work individually or in pairs. If in pairs, they can cross out numbers together and discuss the results.

2 TEACH

Alternative Strategy

Have students arrange note cards numbered 1 to 100 in an open area and turn face down cards that are multiples of 2, 3, 5, and so on.

3 CLOSE

Key Discovery

Some numbers are divisible only by themselves and 1.

Assessment

1. Find a prime number between 60 and 70. **61 or 67**

Steps 4–5, 3. See Additional Answers beginning on page AA1.

SKILL CHECK

1. $39 \div 3 = \underline{?}$ 13
2. $76 \div 19 = \underline{?}$ 4
3. $2^3 \cdot 5^2 = \underline{?}$ 200

LESSON OBJECTIVE

Write the prime factorization of numbers.

PACING

Suggested Number of Days
Basic Course: 1 day
Average Course: 1 day
Advanced Course: 1 day
Block: 0.5 block with 4.2

TEACHING RESOURCES

For a complete list of Teaching Resources, see page 164B.

Warm-Up Exercises for this lesson are available on a transparency.

MOTIVATING THE LESSON

Have students set up rectangular displays on the opening paragraphs of the lesson. Students can then compare their displays.

TIPS FOR NEW TEACHERS

Be sure students understand that there is more than one way to find the prime factorization of a number, but there is just one prime factorization. See Tips for New Teachers in the *Chapter 4 Resource Book.*

Factors and Prime Factorization

BEFORE	Now	WHY?
You multiplied and divided numbers.	You'll write the prime factorization of numbers.	So you can design a quilt with square patches, as in Ex. 10.

prime number, p. 169
composite number, p. 169
prime factorization, p. 169
factor tree, p. 169
monomial, p. 170

In the Real World

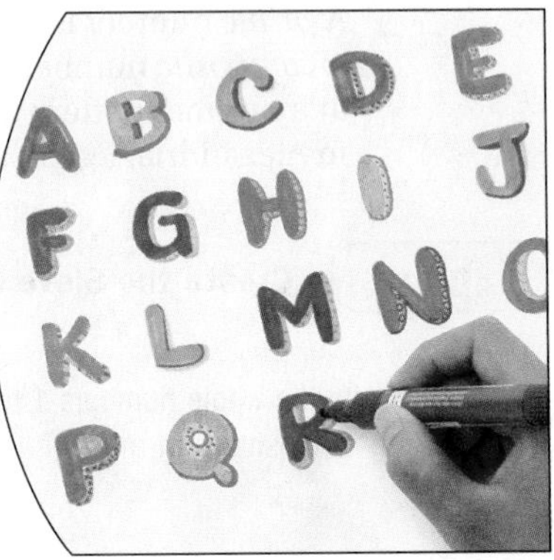

Lettering Members of the art club are designing their own lettering style, as part of their school arts program. Their first project is to make posters to display their new lettering style. Each poster will display the alphabet and the digits 0 through 9.

They want each row on the poster to have the same number of letters or digits. How many ways can they arrange the rectangular display?

You can use factors to determine how many arrangements are possible.

EXAMPLE 1 Writing Factors

Each arrangement will contain a total of 36 letters and digits (26 letters and the digits 0 through 9). To find the number of possible rectangular arrangements, first find the factors of 36.

(1) Write 36 as a product of two numbers in all possible ways.

1×36 2×18 3×12 4×9 6×6

The factors of 36 are 1, 2, 3, 4, 6, 9, 12, 18, and 36.

(2) Using these factors, find all the possible rectangular arrangements.

1×36 2×18 3×12 4×9 6×6

36×1 18×2 12×3 9×4

ANSWER There are nine possible rectangular arrangements.

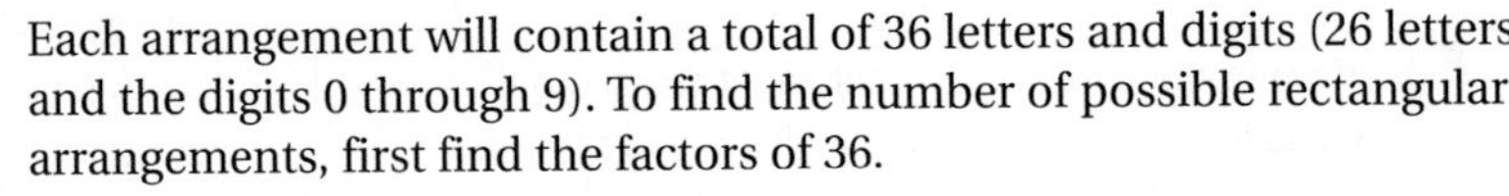

Your turn now **Write all the factors of the number.**

1. 20 1, 2, 4, 5, 10, 20
2. 29 1, 29
3. 42 1, 2, 3, 6, 7, 14, 21, 42
4. 57 1, 3, 19, 57

ILLINOIS Standards and ISAT:
6.B.3b

A **prime number** is a whole number greater than 1 whose only positive factors are 1 and itself. A **composite number** is a whole number greater than 1 that has positive factors other than 1 and itself.

HELP with Review

You can use divisibility tests to help find all the factors of a composite number. For help with divisibility tests, see p. 706.

EXAMPLE 2 Identifying Prime and Composite Numbers

Write all the factors of the number and tell whether it is *prime* or *composite*.

Number	Factors	Prime or Composite?
a. 32	1, 2, 4, 8, 16, 32	Composite
b. 39	1, 3, 13, 39	Composite
c. 43	1, 43	Prime
d. 76	1, 2, 4, 19, 38, 76	Composite
e. 149	1, 149	Prime
f. 189	1, 3, 7, 9, 21, 27, 63, 189	Composite

Prime Factorization When you write a number as the product of prime numbers, you are writing its **prime factorization**. One way to write the prime factorization of a number is to use a **factor tree**.

EXAMPLE 3 Writing Prime Factorization

Write the prime factorization of 450.

Three factor trees are shown. Notice that each factor tree produces the same prime factorization, differing only in the order of the factors.

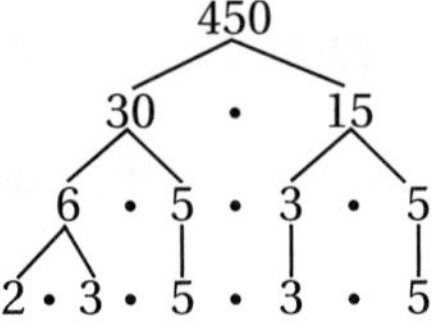

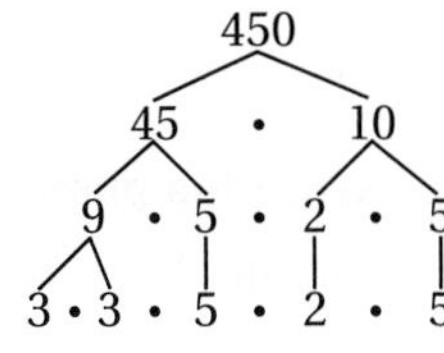

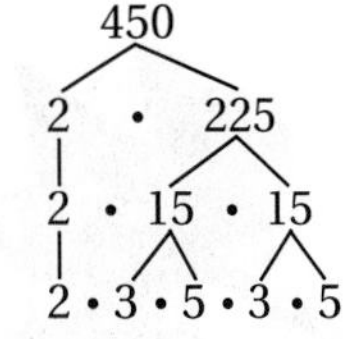

So, $450 = 2 \cdot 3 \cdot 3 \cdot 5 \cdot 5$.

ANSWER Using exponents, the prime factorization of 450 is $2 \cdot 3^2 \cdot 5^2$.

Your turn now **Tell whether the number is *prime* or *composite*. If it is composite, write its prime factorization using exponents.**

5. 24 composite; $2^3 \cdot 3$ **6.** 51 composite; $3 \cdot 17$ **7.** 73 prime **8.** 560 composite; $2^4 \cdot 5 \cdot 7$

EXTRA EXAMPLES

Example 1 Write all the factors of 64. **1, 2, 4, 8, 16, 32, 64**

Example 2 Tell whether the number is *prime* or *composite*.
a. 16 **composite**
b. 40 **composite**
c. 53 **prime**
d. 24 **composite**
e. 42 **composite**
f. 61 **prime**

Example 3 Write the prime factorization of 640. $2^7 \cdot 5$

COMMON ERROR

When writing a factor tree, students often make errors if they use too large a factor. Although it may take longer, suggest that students use small factors, such as 2, 3, 5, and so on, to create their factor trees.

Differentiating Instruction

Alternative Teaching Strategy
Show students how to write factors by working from the outside in. For example, to write all the factors of 100, write 1 on the left side of the page and 100 on the right side. Inside these two numbers, write 2 and 50 so the line becomes 1, 2, ______, 50, 100. Next fill in 4 and 25. The line now reads 1, 2, 4, ______, 25, 50, 100. Show students how the left and right values are approaching each other. Once students have written 1, 2, 4, 5, 10, 20, 25, 50, 100, they should recognize that they have listed all the factors.

Example 4 Factor the monomial $8xy^3$.
$2 \cdot 2 \cdot 2 \cdot x \cdot y \cdot y \cdot y$

CONCEPT CHECK

What is a prime number? a whole number whose only factors are 1 and itself

DAILY PUZZLER

What is the least odd number that is not prime? 1

10. Step 1: 1, 2, 3, 4, 5, 6, 8, 10, 12, 15, 20, 24, 30, 40, 60, 120; Step 2: 1 and 120, 2 and 60, 3 and 40, 4 and 30, 5 and 24, 6 and 20, 8 and 15, 10 and 12; Step 3: 8 and 15, 10 and 12. *Sample answer:* The other arrangements would make an unreasonably long and narrow quilt.

Factoring Monomials A **monomial** is a number, a variable, or a product of a number and one or more variables. To factor a monomial means to write the monomial as a product of its factors.

EXAMPLE 4 Factoring a Monomial

Factor the monomial $12x^2y$.

Solution

$12x^2y = 2 \cdot 2 \cdot 3 \cdot x^2 \cdot y$ Factor 12.

$= 2 \cdot 2 \cdot 3 \cdot x \cdot x \cdot y$ Write x^2 as $x \cdot x$.

Your turn now **Factor the monomial.**

9. $3mn$ 10. $18t^2$ 11. $14x^2y^3$ 12. $54w^3z^4$

9. $3 \cdot m \cdot n$
10. $2 \cdot 3 \cdot 3 \cdot t \cdot t$
11. $2 \cdot 7 \cdot x \cdot x \cdot y \cdot y \cdot y$
12. $2 \cdot 3 \cdot 3 \cdot 3 \cdot w \cdot w \cdot w \cdot z \cdot z \cdot z \cdot z$

4.1 Exercises

More Practice, p. 730

Getting Ready to Practice

1. **Vocabulary** Copy and complete: The only positive factors of a _?_ number are the number itself and one. prime

Write all the factors of the number.

2. 18 1, 2, 3, 6, 9, 18
3. 27 1, 3, 9, 27
4. 41 1, 41
5. 66 1, 2, 3, 6, 11, 22, 33, 66

Write the prime factorization of the number.

6. 28 $2^2 \cdot 7$
7. 55 $5 \cdot 11$
8. 82 $2 \cdot 41$
9. 96 $2^5 \cdot 3$

10. **Guided Problem Solving** You are making a quilt out of 120 square patches. What are the two most reasonable rectangular arrangements of the patches for the quilt?
    (1) List all of the factors of 120. Steps 1–3. See margin.
    (2) List all the pairs of factors from Step 1 that have a product of 120. These are the possible arrangements of the patches.
    (3) List the two most reasonable arrangements of the patches. Then explain why the other arrangements are not reasonable.

Practice and Problem Solving

with Homework

Example	Exercises
1	11-14, 31-38
2	15-18
3	19-25
4	27-30

Online Resources
CLASSZONE.COM
· More Examples
· eTutorial Plus

13. 1, 2, 3, 4, 6, 9, 12, 18, 27, 36, 54, 108

29. $3 \cdot 3 \cdot a \cdot a \cdot b \cdot b \cdot b \cdot b$

30. $2 \cdot 2 \cdot 2 \cdot 2 \cdot 3 \cdot n \cdot n \cdot n \cdot m \cdot m \cdot m$

32. 4 stars by 7 stars (or 2 stars by 14 stars)

33. 5 stars by 6 stars (or 3 stars by 10 stars, or 2 stars by 15 stars)

A **Write all the factors of the number.**

11. 34 1, 2, 17, 34
12. 64 1, 2, 4, 8, 16, 32, 64
13. 108 See margin.
14. 175 1, 5, 7, 25, 35, 175

Tell whether the number is *prime* or *composite*.

15. 21 composite
16. 45 composite
17. 59 prime
18. 91 composite

Write the prime factorization of the number.

19. 56 $2^3 \cdot 7$
20. 97 prime
21. 102 $2 \cdot 3 \cdot 17$
22. 135 $3^3 \cdot 5$

Copy and complete the factor tree. Then write the prime factorization of the number.

23.

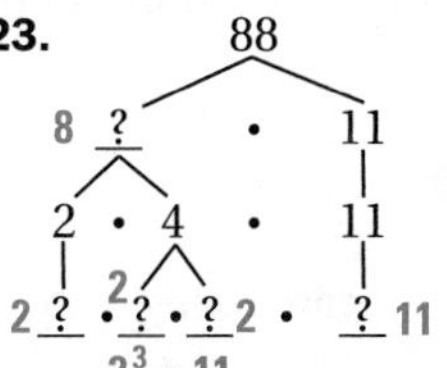

$2^3 \cdot 11$

24.

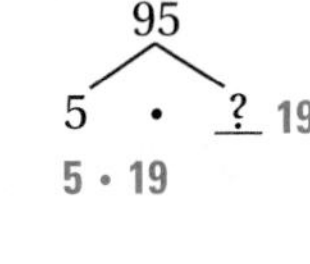

$5 \cdot 19$

25.

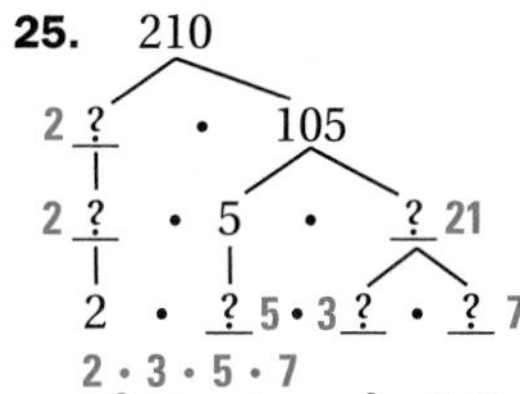

$2 \cdot 3 \cdot 5 \cdot 7$

26. Writing Explain how you can create two different factor trees for 540. Do both factor trees result in the same prime factorization?
Sample answer: Start with $10 \cdot 54$ or $5 \cdot 108$; yes.

Algebra **Factor the monomial.**

27. $15cd$ $3 \cdot 5 \cdot c \cdot d$
28. $40pq$ $2 \cdot 2 \cdot 2 \cdot 5 \cdot p \cdot q$
29. $9a^2b^4$ 29–30. See margin.
30. $48n^3m^3$

Flags of the United States **Each star on the U.S. flag represents a state. Some U.S. flags had a number of stars that could have been arranged in rows and columns evenly. Describe how to do this for the number of stars indicated.**

31. 15 3 stars by 5 stars
32. 28 32–33. See margin.
33. 30
34. 49 7 stars by 7 stars

B **Write all the factors of the number.** 35–38. See margin.

35. 299
36. 336
37. 400
38. 512

Write the prime factorization of the number using exponents.

39. 280 $2^3 \cdot 5 \cdot 7$
40. 396 $2^2 \cdot 3^2 \cdot 11$
41. 1125 $3^2 \cdot 5^3$
42. 2000 $2^4 \cdot 5^3$

Critical Thinking **Many even numbers can be expressed as the sum of two primes. For example, 8 can be expressed as 3 + 5. Write the number as the sum of two primes.** 43–46. Sample answers are given.

43. 10 $3 + 7$
44. 16 $5 + 11$
45. 28 $11 + 17$
46. 30 $13 + 17$

What do you think? History

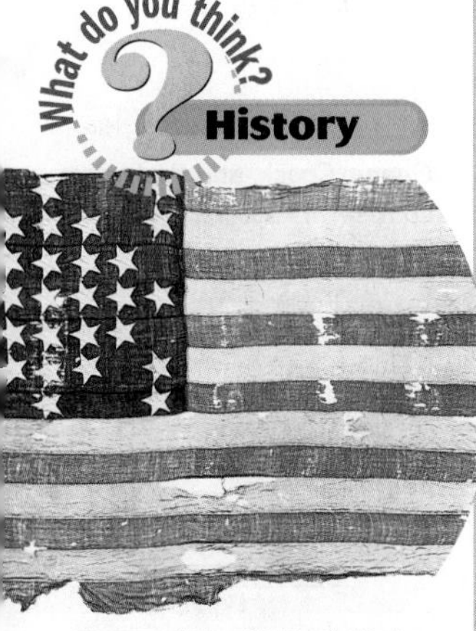

Flags of the United States

The flag shown above was displayed over Fort Sumter in 1861. The flag has 33 stars. What rectangular arrangement could have been used to display the stars?
3 stars by 11 stars

ASSIGNMENT GUIDE

Basic Course
Day 1: SRH p. 706 Exs. 1-5; pp. 171-172 Exs. 11-38, 52-62

Average Course
Day 1: pp. 171-172 Exs. 14-18, 21-49, 52-62

Advanced Course
Day 1: pp. 171-172 Exs. 17, 18, 21-22, 25-57*, 62

Block
pp. 171-172 Exs. 14-18, 21-49, 52-62 (with 4.2)

EXTRA PRACTICE

- Student Edition, p. 730
- Chapter 4 Resource Book, pp. 8-10
- Test and Practice Generator

TRANSPARENCY

Even-numbered answers are available on transparencies.

HOMEWORK CHECK

When you review students' homework for this lesson, go over the following exercises to check understanding of key concepts.
Basic: 11, 15, 19, 23, 28
Average: 17, 21, 24, 29, 31
Advanced: 14, 22, 25, 30, 32

35. 1, 13, 23, 299

36. 1, 2, 3, 4, 6, 7, 8, 12, 14, 16, 21, 24, 28, 42, 48, 56, 84, 112, 168, 336

37. 1, 2, 4, 5, 8, 10, 16, 20, 25, 40, 50, 80, 100, 200, 400

38. 1, 2, 4, 8, 16, 32, 64, 128, 256, 512

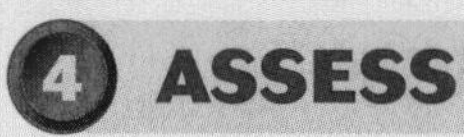

4 ASSESS

Assessment Resources

For more assessment resources, see:

- Assessment Book
- Test and Practice Generator

Mini-Quiz

Write all the factors of the number.

1. 105 **1, 3, 5, 21, 35, 105**

2. 200 **1, 2, 4, 5, 8, 10, 20, 25, 40, 50, 100, 200**

Tell whether the number is *prime* or *composite*.

3. 37 **prime**

4. 55 **composite**

5. Write the prime factorization of 100. $2^2 \cdot 5^2$

6. Factor $18x^3y^2$. $2 \cdot 3 \cdot 3 \cdot x \cdot x \cdot x \cdot y \cdot y$

5 FOLLOW-UP

Reteaching/Remediation

- Study Guide in Chapter 4 Resource Book, pp. 11–12
- Tutor Place, Whole Numbers and Decimals Card 14
- eTutorial Plus Online
- Extra Practice, p. 730
- Lesson Practice in Chapter 4 Resource Book, pp. 8–10

Challenge/Enrichment

- Challenge Practice in Chapter 4 Resource Book, p. 13
- Teacher's Edition, p. 164F

English Learner Support

- Spanish Study Guide
- Multi-Language Glossary
- Chapter Audio Summaries CDs

47. Ring Toss Game You are in charge of a ring toss game at a school fair. In this game, players try to throw a small ring over a bottle that is in a rectangular display. You have 140 bottles, and you want to arrange them in equal rows. Can you have 40 equal rows? Explain. **No; 40 is not a factor of 140.**

48. Field Day There are 180 students participating in field day activities. The students must be divided into teams of equal size. How many students will be on each team? List all the possibilities. **2, 3, 4, 5, 6, 9, 10, 12, 15, 18, 20, 30, 36, 45, 60, 90**

C **49. Critical Thinking** Name two prime numbers that have a difference of 1. **2 and 3**

50. Challenge Twin primes are prime numbers that have a difference of 2. For example, 5 and 7 are twin primes. List five pairs of twin primes other than 5 and 7. ***Sample answer:*** **11 and 13, 17 and 19, 29 and 31, 41 and 43, 59 and 61**

51. Volume The volume of a box can be found by using the formula *Volume = length × width × height.* A box has a volume of 200 cubic inches. Find all possible whole number dimensions of the box.

51. 1 in. by 1 in. by 200 in.; 1 in. by 2 in. by 100 in.; 1 in. by 4 in. by 50 in.; 1 in. by 5 in. by 40 in.; 1 in. by 8 in. by 25 in.; 1 in. by 10 in. by 20 in.; 2 in. by 2 in. by 50 in.; 2 in. by 4 in. by 25 in.; 2 in. by 5 in. by 20 in.; 4 in. by 5 in. by 10 in.; 5 in. by 5 in. by 8 in.

Mixed Review

Simplify the expression by combining like terms. *(Lesson 2.7)*

52. $4x - 5y + 3x - 4 + y$ $7x - 4y - 4$

53. $a - 2b - 5a + 2 + 6b$ $-4a + 4b + 2$

Solve the inequality. *(Lesson 3.7)*

54. $5x \leq -20$ $x \leq -4$

55. $\frac{1}{8}y \geq 5$ $y \geq 40$

56. $-9z > 108$ $z < -12$

Choose a Strategy Use a strategy from the list to solve the following problem. Explain your choice of strategy.

> Problem Solving Strategies
> - Guess, Check, and Revise
> - Look for a Pattern
> - Draw a Diagram

57. The bookstore at your favorite mall is expanding to include the space adjacent to it. The original store was 20 feet by 25 feet. The space adjacent to it is 14 feet by 25 feet. What is the total area of the store with the additional space? 850 ft^2. ***Sample answer:*** **I used Draw a Diagram to draw the spaces and find the area.**

Basic Skills Find low and high estimates for the product or quotient. **58–61. Estimates may vary.**

58. 37×21 **600; 1000**

59. 143×58 **7000; 9000**

60. $700 \div 14$ **35; 70**

61. $1330 \div 87$ **13; 20**

Test-Taking Practice 

INTERNET State Test Practice CLASSZONE.COM

62. Extended Response The area of a rectangle is 24 square inches. Its length and width are measured in whole inches. Find all possible dimensions of the rectangle. Show your work and explain how you found all of the possibilities. **1 in. by 24 in., 2 in. by 12 in., 3 in. by 8 in., 4 in. by 6 in.** ***Sample answer:*** **The possibilities are all of the pairs of whole-number factors of 24.**

Greatest Common Factor

BEFORE

You found the factors of a number.

Now

You'll find the greatest common factor of two or more numbers.

WHY?

So you can decide how many food baskets you can make, as in Ex. 21.

Word Watch

common factor, p. 173
greatest common factor (GCF), p. 173
relatively prime, p. 174

Activity The lists below show the factors of the given numbers.

Number	Factors
36	1, 2, 3, 4, 6, 9, 12, 18, 36
24	1, 2, 3, 4, 6, 8, 12, 24
20	1, 2, 4, 5, 10, 20

1. Which number(s) are factors of 20 and 36? 1, 2, 4
2. Which number(s) are factors of 24 and 36? 1, 2, 3, 4, 6, 12
3. Which number(s) are factors of 20, 24, and 36? 1, 2, 4
4. What is the greatest factor that is in all three lists? 4

HELP with Vocabulary

The GCF is sometimes called the greatest common divisor (GCD) because it is the largest common factor that can be divided evenly into the given numbers.

A **common factor** is a whole number that is a factor of two or more nonzero whole numbers. The greatest of the common factors is the **greatest common factor (GCF)**.

One method for finding the GCF of two or more numbers is to use the prime factorization of each number. The GCF is the product of all the factors that the numbers have in common.

EXAMPLE 1 Finding the Greatest Common Factor

Find the greatest common factor of 42 and 70.

Begin by writing the prime factorization of each number. Find the product of the common prime factors.

$42 = 2 \times 3 \times 7 \qquad 70 = 2 \times 5 \times 7$

The common prime factors are 2 and 7. The GCF of 42 and 70 is the product of these factors.

ANSWER The GCF of 42 and 70 is $2 \cdot 7$, or 14.

ILLINOIS Standards and ISAT:
6.B.3b; 9.C.3a

1 PLAN

SKILL CHECK

Write the prime factorization of the number.

1. 42 — $2 \cdot 3 \cdot 7$
2. 45 — $3^2 \cdot 5$
3. Factor the monomial $12a^3$. — $2 \cdot 2 \cdot 3 \cdot a \cdot a \cdot a$

Lesson Objective

Find the greatest common factor of two or more numbers.

Pacing

Suggested Number of Days
Basic Course: 2 days
Average Course: 2 days
Advanced Course: 2 days
Block: 0.5 block with 4.1
0.5 block with 4.3

Teaching Resources

For a complete list of Teaching Resources, see page 164B.

Transparency

Warm-Up Exercises for this lesson are available on a transparency.

2 TEACH

Motivating the Lesson

Discuss the meaning of *common* in the term *common factor*. Ask students what it means for two people to have something in *common*.

Activity

Goal Compare and find common factors.

Key Discovery Numbers with common factors have a greatest common factor.

TIPS FOR NEW TEACHERS
Be sure students understand that the GCF of two numbers will be less than either number unless one number is a factor of the other. See Tips for New Teachers in the *Chapter 4 Resource Book*.

EXTRA EXAMPLES

Example 1 Find the greatest common factor of 22 and 38. 2

Example 2 Decide whether the numbers 9 and 20 are relatively prime. If they are not relatively prime, find the greatest common factor. yes

Example 3 Find the GCF of $15x^2y$ and $18xy^2$. $3xy$

NOTETAKING
Once students are confident they understand how to find the GCF, have them write out directions in their notebooks and show a fully worked example.

COMMON ERROR
Watch for students who confuse prime and relatively prime. Explain that numbers need not be prime in order to be relatively prime.

Differentiating Instruction

Less Proficient Students Some students may have difficulty factoring because their knowledge of multiplication facts is weak. Provide these students with times tables so that they can refer to them when necessary.

Two numbers are **relatively prime** if their greatest common factor is 1. For example, 8 and 15 are relatively prime.

EXAMPLE 2 Identifying Relatively Prime Numbers

Decide whether the numbers 112 and 45 are relatively prime. If they are not relatively prime, find the greatest common factor.

Begin by writing the prime factorization of each number. Then find the product of the common prime factors.

$112 = 2^4 \cdot 7$ $\qquad 45 = 3^2 \cdot 5$

There are no common prime factors. However, two numbers always have 1 as a common factor. So, the GCF is 1.

ANSWER The numbers 112 and 45 are relatively prime.

Your turn now **Find the greatest common factor of the numbers.**

1. 12, 18 6
2. 24, 60 12
3. 36, 90 18
4. 96, 120 24

Decide whether the numbers are relatively prime. If they are not relatively prime, find the GCF.

5. 48, 72 no; 24
6. 124, 128 no; 4
7. 39, 44 yes
8. 200, 63 yes

You can find the greatest common factor of two monomials by factoring the monomials.

EXAMPLE 3 Finding the GCF of Monomials

Find the greatest common factor of $12a^3$ and $9a^2$.

First factor each expression.

$12a^3 = 2 \cdot 2 \cdot 3 \cdot a \cdot a \cdot a$ $\qquad 9a^2 = 3 \cdot 3 \cdot a \cdot a$

The common factors are 3 and a^2. The GCF is the product of the common factors.

ANSWER The GCF is $3a^2$.

Your turn now **Find the greatest common factor of the monomials.**

9. $6x$, $18x$ $6x$
10. $6xy$, $4xy^2$ $2xy$
11. $15y$, $9x^2y^2$ $3y$
12. $5xy^3$, $10x^2y^2$ $5xy^2$

EXAMPLE 4 Using the Greatest Common Factor

Pep Rally Packs Students at your school are planning to hand out pep rally packs to support your school's athletic program. The students have 240 bumper stickers, 360 pennants, and 720 pencils. Every pack must have the same contents, and there should be no leftover items. What is the greatest number of pep rally packs that can be made?

Solution

You can find the greatest number of pep rally packs by finding the GCF.

$240 = 2^4 \cdot 3 \cdot 5 \qquad 360 = 2^3 \cdot 3^2 \cdot 5 \qquad 720 = 2^4 \cdot 3^2 \cdot 5$

The common prime factors are 2^3, 3, and 5. The GCF is $2^3 \cdot 3 \cdot 5$, or 120.

ANSWER The greatest number of pep rally packs is 120. Each pack will contain 2 bumper stickers, 3 pennants, and 6 pencils.

EXTRA EXAMPLES

Example 4 Elisha and David are putting together snack packs for a large group of hikers. They have 160 apples, 320 carrot sticks, and 400 celery sticks. Each snack pack has the same contents and there are no left-over items. What is the greatest number of snack packs that can be made and what is in each pack? **80 snack packs containing 2 apples, 4 carrot sticks, and 5 celery sticks**

CONCEPT CHECK

What is a common factor? What is the GCF? **a whole number that is a factor of two or more nonzero whole numbers; the greatest number that is a common factor of two or more nonzero whole numbers**

DAILY PUZZLER

If a number p is prime, write an expression with p that describes the sum of all the factors of p. $p + 1$

4.2 Exercises

More Practice, p. 730

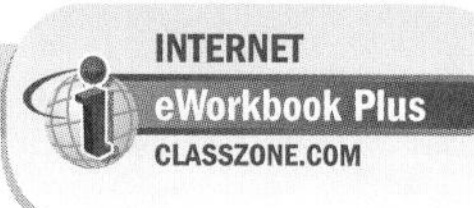

Getting Ready to Practice

1. **Vocabulary** Copy and complete: Six is the _?_ of 12 and 18. **greatest common factor, or GCF**

Matching **Match the pair of numbers with its GCF.**

2. 6, 9 B	**3.** 4, 10 D	**4.** 5, 15 A	**5.** 14, 21 C
A. 5	**B.** 3	**C.** 7	**D.** 2

6. **Find the Error** Describe and correct the error in the solution. **The two common factors are 3 and 5. The GCF is $3 \cdot 5 = 15$.**

$210 = 2 \cdot 3 \cdot 5 \cdot 7$
$495 = 3 \cdot 3 \cdot 5 \cdot 11$
The GCF is 5.

7. **Guided Problem Solving** There are 56 girls and 68 boys in a youth sports league. Each student will be placed on a team. Each team will have an equal number of players and will have the same number of girls. What is the greatest number of teams that can be formed?
   (1) Write the prime factorizations of the numbers 56 and 68. $56 = 2 \cdot 2 \cdot 2 \cdot 7$, $68 = 2 \cdot 2 \cdot 17$
   (2) What are the common prime factors of the two numbers? **2 and 2**
   (3) Multiply the common prime factors to get the GCF. What meaning does the GCF have in the situation? **4; the greatest number of teams that can be formed is 4, where each has 14 girls and 17 boys.**

3 APPLY

ASSIGNMENT GUIDE

Basic Course

Day 1: pp. 176–177 Exs. 8–20, 36–39

Day 2: pp. 176–177 Exs. 21–25, 40–45

Average Course

Day 1: pp. 176–177 Exs. 8–11, 16–20, 28–31, 36–39

Day 2: pp. 176–177 Exs. 21, 25–27, 32, 33, 40–45

Advanced Course

Day 1: pp. 176–177 Exs. 10, 11, 16–20, 28–31, 36–39

Day 2: pp. 176–177 Exs. 25–27, 32–35*, 44, 45

Block

pp. 176–177 Exs. 8–11, 16–20, 28–31, 36–39 (with 4.1)

pp. 176–177 Exs. 21, 25–27, 32–33, 40–45 (with 4.3)

EXTRA PRACTICE

- Student Edition, p. 730
- Chapter 4 Resource Book, pp. 16–18
- Test and Practice Generator

TRANSPARENCY

Even-numbered answers are available on transparencies.

HOMEWORK CHECK

When you review students' homework for this lesson, go over the following exercises to check understanding of key concepts.

Basic: 8, 12, 15, 21, 22

Average: 10, 16, 18, 21, 24

Advanced: 11, 17, 19, 25, 33

MATH REASONING

Exercises 20 and 28–31 should provide insight into students' understanding of GCF and relatively prime.

Practice and Problem Solving

HELP with Homework

Example	Exercises
1	8-11
2	12-20
3	22-27
4	21, 33

Online Resources CLASSZONE.COM

- More Examples
- eTutorial Plus

A Find the greatest common factor of the numbers.

8. 3, 9, 27 3 **9.** 21, 28, 56 7 **10.** 17, 18, 20 1 **11.** 24, 36, 180 12

Decide whether the numbers are relatively prime. If not, find the greatest common factor.

12. 5, 18 yes **13.** 10, 25 no; 5 **14.** 28, 42 no; 14 **15.** 55, 72 yes

16. 21, 66 no; 3 **17.** 18, 216 no; 18 **18.** 212, 312 no; 4 **19.** 268, 515 yes

20. Writing Can two even numbers be relatively prime? Explain why or why not. No; even numbers all have 2 as a common factor.

21. Food Baskets Your class is making Thanksgiving baskets to be distributed by a food bank. You have collected 60 cans of cranberry sauce, 120 cans of canned fruit, 90 cans of corn, and 60 boxes of muffin mixes. You want every basket to be the same with no leftover items. What is the greatest number of baskets you can assemble? What will each basket contain? 30 baskets; 2 cans of cranberry sauce, 4 cans of fruit, 3 cans of corn, 2 boxes of muffin mix

B Algebra Find the GCF of the monomials.

22. $3x^2, 9x$ $3x$ **23.** $4z^3, 2z^2$ $2z^2$ **24.** $5t^4, 15t^5$ $5t^4$

25. $12x^2y^2, 16xy^3$ $4xy^2$ **26.** $18rs^2, 30st^2$ $6s$ **27.** $15bc^3, 75b^3c$ $15bc$

Critical Thinking Copy and complete the statement using *always, sometimes,* or *never.*

28. The greatest common factor of two numbers is _?_ equal to one of the two numbers. sometimes

29. The number 1 is _?_ the greatest common factor of relatively prime numbers. always

30. The greatest common factor of two numbers is _?_ greater than both of the numbers. never

31. Critical Thinking Name two composite numbers that are relatively prime. *Sample answer:* 6 and 25

32. Carpentry You must cut four pieces of wood that measure 36 inches, 45 inches, 108 inches, and 81 inches, into smaller, equally sized pieces. What is the longest each piece can be so that each piece is the same length? 9 in.

33. Bouquets A florist must make a batch of identical bouquets. The florist has 360 tulips, 270 roses, and 180 lilies. There cannot be any flowers left over. What is the greatest number of bouquets that the florist can make? 90 bouquets

Jacob sheep can have two, four, and occasionally six horns.

34. *Sample answer:* The only factors of any prime number are 1 and the number itself. So the only common factor any two prime numbers have is 1. For example, $5 = 1 \cdot 5$ and $7 = 1 \cdot 7$ have only 1 as a common factor, as do $43 = 1 \cdot 43$ and $79 = 1 \cdot 79$.

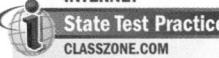

C **34. Challenge** Explain why any two prime numbers are always relatively prime. Give examples to justify your reasoning. See margin.

35. Sheep A farmer needs to build two adjacent rectangular pens for his sheep. He wants one pen to have an area of 204 square feet, and the other to have an area of 144 square feet. Fence lengths are available in one-foot increments. What is the greatest length the farmer can make the fence that is shared by the two pens? 12 ft

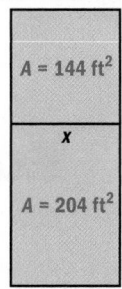

$A = 144\text{ ft}^2$

x

$A = 204\text{ ft}^2$

Mixed Review

In Exercises 36–38, solve the equation. *(Lesson 3.1)*

36. $-6 + n = 4$ 10 **37.** $n + 13 = 5$ -8 **38.** $n + 2.7 = 5.7$ 3

39. Write the prime factorization of 84. *(Lesson 4.1)* $2^2 \cdot 3 \cdot 7$

Basic Skills Use a metric ruler to draw a segment with the given length. 40–43. Check drawings.

40. 7 cm **41.** 15 cm **42.** 145 mm **43.** 84 mm

Test-Taking Practice

44. Multiple Choice What is the greatest common factor of $4x^2$ and $6x$? B

A. x **B.** $2x$ **C.** $4x$ **D.** $2x^2$

45. Multiple Choice What is the greatest common factor of 144, 300, and 240? H

F. 4 **G.** 6 **H.** 12 **I.** 60

Brain Game

Marble Mystery

You have a bucket full of marbles. If the marbles in the bucket are counted by twos, threes, fives, and sevens, there is exactly one left over each time. What is the fewest number of marbles that could be in the bucket? 211 marbles

4 ASSESS

Assessment Resources

For more assessment resources, see:
- Assessment Book
- Test and Practice Generator

Mini-Quiz

1. What is the GCF of 15, 18, and 27? 3
2. Are 27 and 36 relatively prime? If not, find the GCF. no; 9
3. Sara is making ribbon prizes from 70 red, 105 blue, and 140 orange ribbons. Each prize is made from the same number of ribbons and there are no ribbons left over. What is the greatest number of prizes Sara can make and what combination of colors are they made of? 35 prizes made of 2 red, 3 blue, and 4 orange ribbons

5 FOLLOW-UP

Reteaching/Remediation

- Study Guide in Chapter 4 Resource Book, pp. 19–20
- Tutor Place, Fractions Card 3
- eTutorial Plus Online
- Extra Practice, p. 730
- Lesson Practice in Chapter 4 Resource Book, pp. 16–18

Challenge/Enrichment

- Challenge Practice in Chapter 4 Resource Book, p. 21
- Teacher's Edition, p. 164F

English Learner Support

- Spanish Study Guide
- Multi-Language Glossary
- Chapter Audio Summaries CDs

EXPLORE THE CONCEPT

- Students will use area models to find equivalent fractions.
- This activity leads into the study of simplifying fractions in Lesson 4.3.

MATERIALS

Each student or pair of students will need paper and colored pencils.

RECOMMENDED TIME

Work activity: 10 min
Discuss results: 10 min

GROUPING

Students can work individually or in pairs. If students work in pairs, have them brainstorm ways to divide the model into equal parts.

TIPS FOR SUCCESS

Point out that by making smaller and smaller divisions of the rectangle, you can always find more equivalent fractions.

KEY DISCOVERY

There are many ways to represent equivalent fractions.

ASSESSMENT

1. Find two fractions equivalent to $\frac{14}{16}$. *Sample answer:* $\frac{7}{8}, \frac{21}{24}$

1–4. See Additional Answers beginning on page AA1.

4.3 Hands-on Activity

GOAL
Use area models to find equivalent fractions.

MATERIALS
- graph paper
- colored pencils

Equivalent Fractions

You can use area models to find equivalent fractions.

Explore **Find two fractions equivalent to $\frac{6}{8}$.**

1. Draw a rectangle on a piece of graph paper. Divide the rectangle into 8 equal parts and shade 6 of the parts.

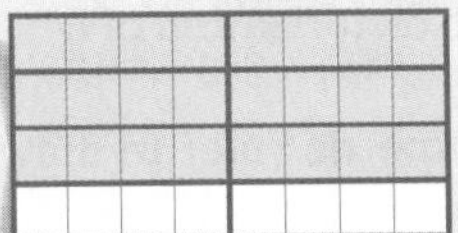

2. Look for other ways of dividing the rectangle into equal parts.

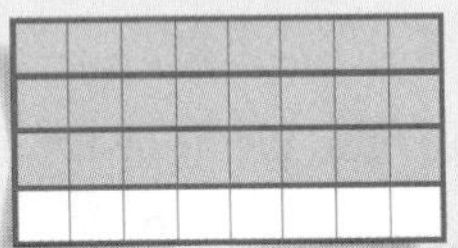

There are 4 parts and 3 are shaded.

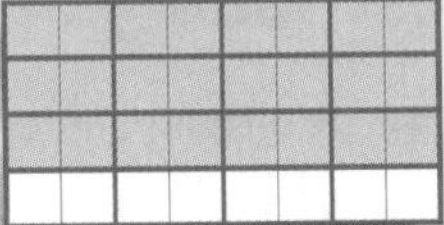

There are 16 parts and 12 are shaded.

3. Write the equivalent fractions.

The fractions $\frac{3}{4}$ and $\frac{12}{16}$ are equivalent to $\frac{6}{8}$.

Your turn now **Draw a model of the given fraction. Then find two equivalent fractions.** 1–4. See margin for art. Sample answers are given.

1. $\frac{4}{6}$ $\frac{2}{3}, \frac{8}{12}$ **2.** $\frac{10}{12}$ $\frac{5}{6}, \frac{20}{24}$ **3.** $\frac{4}{16}$ $\frac{1}{4}, \frac{8}{32}$ **4.** $\frac{10}{16}$ $\frac{5}{8}, \frac{20}{32}$

Stop and Think

5. Writing How can factoring both the numerator and denominator of a fraction help to write an equivalent fraction? ***Sample answer:*** **You can find and cancel the GCF or any other common factor.**

ILLINOIS Standards and ISAT:
6.A.3, 6.B.3b, 7.C.3b

Simplifying Fractions

BEFORE	Now	WHY?
You evaluated numerical expressions.	You'll simplify fractions.	So you can find the fractions of threatened species, as in Ex. 39.

Word Watch

simplest form, p. 179
equivalent fractions, p. 179

In the Real World

History One of the Czech Republic's royal coronation jewels is the St. Wenceslas crown. It was made around 1345 and is decorated with 44 spinels, 30 emeralds, 22 pearls, 19 sapphires, and 1 ruby. What fraction of jewels in the crown are emeralds? You will see how to solve this problem in Example 1.

Fractions A *fraction* is a number of the form $\frac{a}{b}$ $(b \neq 0)$ where a is called the numerator and b is called the denominator. A fraction is in **simplest form** if its numerator and denominator have 1 as their GCF. **Equivalent fractions** represent the same number. They have the same simplest form.

EXAMPLE 1 Writing a Fraction in Simplest Form

Write the fraction of jewels in the crown that are emeralds. Then simplify.

$$\frac{\text{Number of emeralds}}{\text{Total number of jewels in the crown}} = \frac{30}{116}$$

Method 1: Write the prime factorization of each number.

$30 = 2 \cdot 3 \cdot 5 \qquad 116 = 2^2 \cdot 29$

The GCF of 30 and 116 is 2.

$\frac{30}{116} = \frac{30 \div 2}{116 \div 2}$ **Divide numerator and denominator by GCF.**

$= \frac{15}{58}$ **Simplify.**

Method 2:

$\frac{30}{116} = \frac{2 \cdot 3 \cdot 5}{2 \cdot 2 \cdot 29}$ **Write prime factorizations.**

$= \frac{\not{2}^1 \cdot 3 \cdot 5}{\not{2}_1 \cdot 2 \cdot 29}$ **Divide out common factor.**

$= \frac{15}{58}$ **Simplify.**

ANSWER The fraction of jewels that are emeralds is $\frac{15}{58}$.

Emerald

Ruby

Sapphire

Pearl

ILLINOIS Standards and ISAT:
6.A.3, 6.B.3b, 8.D.3a

1 PLAN

SKILL CHECK

1. $48 \div 8 = \underline{?}$ 6
2. $18 \div 6 = \underline{?}$ 3
3. $x^2 \div x = \underline{?}$ x
4. $-4 \div 2 = \underline{?}$ -2

LESSON OBJECTIVE

Simplify fractions.

PACING

Suggested Number of Days
Basic Course: 1 day
Average Course: 1 day
Advanced Course: 1 day
Block: 0.5 block with 4.2

TEACHING RESOURCES

For a complete list of Teaching Resources, see page 164B.

TRANSPARENCY

Warm-Up Exercises for this lesson are available on a transparency.

2 TEACH

MOTIVATING THE LESSON

Ask students to state half of 2, 4, 6, and 8, respectively. Then ask if $\frac{1}{2}$, $\frac{2}{4}$, $\frac{3}{6}$, and $\frac{4}{8}$ represent the same quantity.

TIPS FOR NEW TEACHERS

Emphasize that numerator and denominator must be divided by the same factors when writing an equivalent fraction in simplest form. See Tips for New Teachers in the *Chapter 4 Resource Book*.

EXTRA EXAMPLES

Example 1 Twelve students in a group of 30 are boys. What fraction of the group are boys? $\frac{2}{5}$

Example 2 Tell whether the fractions $\frac{5}{7}$ and $\frac{40}{56}$ are equivalent. **yes**

Example 3 Write two fractions that are equivalent to $\frac{5}{8}$. ***Sample answer:*** $\frac{10}{16}, \frac{15}{24}$

Example 4 Simplify $\frac{18cd}{27d}$. $\frac{2c}{3}$

TEACHING TIP

Lead students to recognize that there are infinitely many fractions equivalent to a given fraction.

CROSS-CURRICULUM

Social Studies Students will find references to fractions in analyzing population trends. For example, students will use and simplify fractions describing subsets of a population.

EXAMPLE 2 Identifying Equivalent Fractions

Tell whether the fractions $\frac{3}{8}$ and $\frac{18}{48}$ are equivalent.

Write each fraction in simplest form.

$\frac{3}{8}$ is in simplest form. $\qquad \frac{18}{48} = \frac{18 \div 6}{48 \div 6} = \frac{3}{8}$

ANSWER The fractions are equivalent.

EXAMPLE 3 Writing Equivalent Fractions

Write two fractions that are equivalent to $\frac{4}{10}$.

Multiply or divide the numerator and denominator by the same nonzero number.

$\frac{4}{10} = \frac{4 \times 3}{10 \times 3} = \frac{12}{30}$ **Multiply numerator and denominator by 3.**

$\frac{4}{10} = \frac{4 \div 2}{10 \div 2} = \frac{2}{5}$ **Divide numerator and denominator by 2, a common factor of 4 and 10.**

ANSWER The fractions $\frac{12}{30}$ and $\frac{2}{5}$ are equivalent to $\frac{4}{10}$.

HELP with Solving

A fraction has many equivalent fractions. There are other correct answers to Example 3.

Spinel

Sapphire

Your turn now **Use the information on page 179. Write the fraction of jewels in the crown that are the given jewel. Simplify if possible.**

4–7. Sample answers are given.

1. pearls $\frac{22}{116} = \frac{11}{58}$ **2.** sapphires $\frac{19}{116}$ **3.** spinels $\frac{44}{116} = \frac{11}{29}$

Write two fractions that are equivalent to the given fraction.

4. $\frac{8}{16}$ $\frac{1}{2}, \frac{2}{4}$ **5.** $\frac{9}{15}$ $\frac{3}{5}, \frac{6}{10}$ **6.** $\frac{10}{12}$ $\frac{5}{6}, \frac{15}{18}$ **7.** $\frac{21}{24}$ $\frac{7}{8}, \frac{14}{16}$

You can use Method 2 of Example 1 to simplify fractions that contain variable expressions.

EXAMPLE 4 Simplifying a Variable Expression

$\frac{14x}{7xy} = \frac{2 \cdot 7 \cdot x}{7 \cdot x \cdot y}$ **Factor numerator and denominator.**

$= \frac{2 \cdot \cancel{7}^{1} \cdot \cancel{x}^{1}}{\cancel{7}_{1} \cdot \cancel{x}_{1} \cdot y}$ **Divide out common factors.**

$= \frac{2}{y}$ **Simplify.**

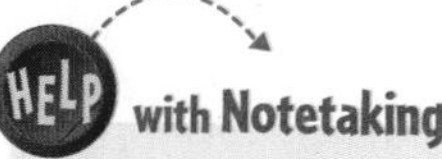

with Notetaking

You may want to add information on simplifying fractions with variable expressions to the outline that you started on p. 166.

EXAMPLE 5 Evaluating a Variable Expression

Evaluate the expression $\frac{-4x^3}{2x}$ when $x = 5$.

$\frac{-4x^3}{2x} = \frac{-1 \cdot 2 \cdot 2 \cdot x \cdot x \cdot x}{2 \cdot x}$ — **Factor numerator and denominator.**

$= \frac{-1 \cdot 2 \cdot \overset{1}{\cancel{2}} \cdot \overset{1}{\cancel{x}} \cdot x \cdot x}{\underset{1}{\cancel{2}} \cdot \underset{1}{\cancel{x}}}$ — **Divide out common factors.**

$= -2x^2$ — **Simplify.**

$= -2(5)^2$ — **Substitute 5 for x.**

$= -50$ — **Evaluate powers and simplify.**

Your turn now **Simplify the variable expression.**

8. $\frac{4xy}{6x}$ $\frac{2y}{3}$ **9.** $\frac{32a}{8ab}$ $\frac{4}{b}$ **10.** $\frac{2m^3}{6m}$ $\frac{m^2}{3}$ **11.** $\frac{5r^2s}{10rs}$ $\frac{r}{2}$

12. Evaluate the expression $\frac{35a^4}{-5a^2}$ when $a = 3$. -63

EXTRA EXAMPLES

Example 5 Evaluate the expression $\frac{3b^3}{9b^2}$ when $b = -4$. $-\frac{4}{3}$

CONCEPT CHECK

When is a fraction in simplest form? **when the numerator and denominator have 1 as their GCF**

DAILY PUZZLER

The word form for the integer x has x letters. What is x? 4

4.3 Exercises

More Practice, p. 730

INTERNET eWorkbook Plus CLASSZONE.COM

Getting Ready to Practice

Vocabulary **Tell whether the fractions are equivalent.**

1. $\frac{2}{3}, \frac{4}{6}$ yes **2.** $\frac{15}{25}, \frac{3}{4}$ no **3.** $\frac{15}{18}, \frac{5}{6}$ yes **4.** $\frac{21}{49}, \frac{3}{7}$ yes

Write the fraction in simplest form.

5. $\frac{10}{15}$ $\frac{2}{3}$ **6.** $\frac{16}{20}$ $\frac{4}{5}$ **7.** $\frac{25}{40}$ $\frac{5}{8}$ **8.** $\frac{36}{72}$ $\frac{1}{2}$

9. Write two fractions that are equivalent to $\frac{1}{5}$. *Sample answer:* $\frac{2}{10}, \frac{3}{15}$

10. Write two fractions that are equivalent to $\frac{12}{15}$. *Sample answer:* $\frac{4}{5}, \frac{8}{10}$

11. Evaluate the expression $\frac{8x^3}{2x}$ when $x = 4$. 64

12. Eggs In a carton of one dozen eggs, 2 eggs are broken. What fraction of the eggs are broken? What fraction of the eggs are unbroken? Write your answers in simplest form. $\frac{1}{6}, \frac{5}{6}$

3 APPLY

ASSIGNMENT GUIDE

Basic Course

Day 1: pp. 182–183 Exs. 13–38, 57–65

Average Course

Day 1: pp. 182–183 Exs. 17–20, 23, 24, 31–52, 57–65

Advanced Course

Day 1: pp. 182–183 Exs. 19, 20, 23, 24, 27–28, 31–60*, 64, 65

Block

pp. 182–183 Exs. 17–20, 23, 24, 31–52, 57–65 (with 4.2)

EXTRA PRACTICE

- Student Edition, p. 730
- Chapter 4 Resource Book, pp. 24–26
- Test and Practice Generator

TRANSPARENCY

Even-numbered answers are available on transparencies.

HOMEWORK CHECK

When you review students' homework for this lesson, go over the following exercises to check understanding of key concepts.
Basic: 14, 18, 21, 26, 29
Average: 19, 23, 27, 30, 33
Advanced: 20, 24, 28, 32, 37

TEACHING TIP

In Exercises 29–32, point out that you can substitute the values for x and y before simplifying the fraction; however, substituting before simplifying may make the evaluation more difficult.

HELP with Homework

Example	Exercises
1	13–16, 33–39
2	21–24
3	25–28
4	17–20
5	29–32

Online Resources
CLASSZONE.COM
- More Examples
- eTutorial Plus

39. For birds, about $\frac{60}{1500} = \frac{1}{25}$ are threatened; a greater fraction of mammals is threatened than birds; $\frac{1}{40}$ (reptiles), $\frac{64}{1541}$ (birds), $\frac{1}{10}$ (mammals).

Yellow-faced Parrot

Practice and Problem Solving

A Write the fraction in simplest form.

13. $\frac{39}{52}$ $\frac{3}{4}$
14. $\frac{18}{27}$ $\frac{2}{3}$
15. $\frac{-9}{72}$ $\frac{-1}{8}$, or $-\frac{1}{8}$
16. $\frac{-49}{56}$ $\frac{-7}{8}$, or $-\frac{7}{8}$
17. $\frac{4ab}{8a}$ $\frac{b}{2}$
18. $\frac{6c}{18cd}$ $\frac{1}{3d}$
19. $\frac{-9rst}{30rs}$ $\frac{-3t}{10}$, or $-\frac{3t}{10}$
20. $\frac{25xy}{35xyz}$ $\frac{5}{7z}$

Tell whether the fractions are equivalent.

21. $\frac{4}{5}, \frac{20}{25}$ yes
22. $\frac{21}{28}, \frac{1}{3}$ no
23. $\frac{7}{35}, \frac{2}{10}$ yes
24. $\frac{32}{72}, \frac{4}{9}$ yes

Write two fractions that are equivalent to the given fraction.

25–28. Sample answers are given.

25. $\frac{45}{90}$ $\frac{1}{2}, \frac{2}{4}$
26. $\frac{36}{81}$ $\frac{4}{9}, \frac{8}{18}$
27. $\frac{24}{60}$ $\frac{2}{5}, \frac{4}{10}$
28. $\frac{48}{140}$ $\frac{12}{35}, \frac{24}{70}$

Evaluate the expression when $x = 3$ and $y = 5$.

29. $\frac{3x}{x^3}$ $\frac{1}{3}$
30. $\frac{2y^2}{-5y}$ -2
31. $\frac{5y}{y^2}$ 1
32. $\frac{4x^4}{24x^3}$ $\frac{1}{2}$

Geography **Write the number of states in the region as a fraction of all of the states. Write your answer in simplest form.**

33. Northeast: 9 $\frac{9}{50}$
34. Midwest: 12 $\frac{6}{25}$
35. South: 16 $\frac{8}{25}$
36. West: 13 $\frac{13}{50}$

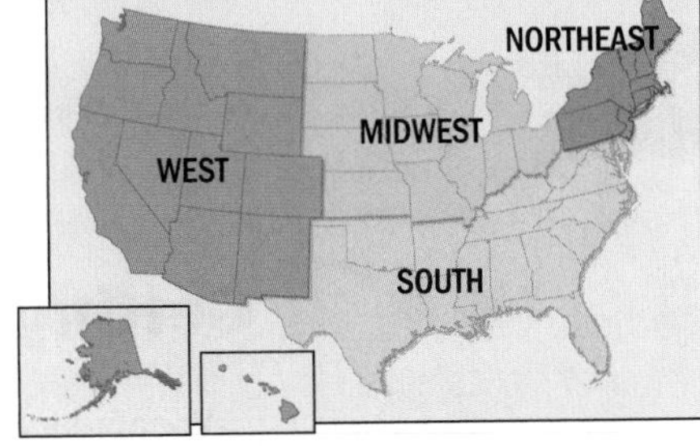

The U.S. Census Bureau divides the 50 states into 4 regions.

Extended Problem Solving **In Exercises 37–39, use the table. It gives information about animals in Peru. Write your answer in simplest form.**

37. What fraction of mammal species are threatened? $\frac{1}{10}$
38. What fraction of reptile species are threatened? $\frac{1}{40}$
39. **Number Sense** Use rounding to compare the fractions of threatened mammal and bird species. Then write the fractions of threatened species in each group (mammals, birds, and reptiles) in order from least to greatest. See margin.

Peruvian Animal Species

	Known	Threatened
Mammals	460	46
Birds	1541	64
Reptiles	360	9

B Write the fractions in simplest form. Tell whether they are equivalent.

40. $\frac{30}{60}, \frac{27}{54}$ $\frac{1}{2}, \frac{1}{2}$; yes **41.** $\frac{24}{40}, \frac{30}{50}$ $\frac{3}{5}, \frac{3}{5}$; yes **42.** $\frac{15}{18}, \frac{36}{48}$ $\frac{5}{6}, \frac{3}{4}$; no **43.** $\frac{24}{32}, \frac{15}{24}$ $\frac{3}{4}, \frac{5}{8}$; no

44. $\frac{30}{75}, \frac{75}{105}$ $\frac{2}{5}, \frac{5}{7}$; no **45.** $\frac{45}{54}, \frac{90}{108}$ $\frac{5}{6}, \frac{5}{6}$; yes **46.** $\frac{54}{96}, \frac{144}{256}$ $\frac{9}{16}, \frac{9}{16}$; yes **47.** $\frac{84}{112}, \frac{168}{192}$ $\frac{3}{4}, \frac{7}{8}$; no

Write the fraction in simplest form.

48. $\frac{-2x^3y}{xy}$ $-2x^2$ **49.** $\frac{5xy^2z}{5xz}$ y^2 **50.** $\frac{2x^3y}{-3xyz}$ $-\frac{2x^2}{3z}$ **51.** $\frac{-8^2z^2}{16x^2yz}$

52. Critical Thinking If you divide the numerator and denominator of a fraction by a common factor, will the resulting fraction always be in simplest form? Give an example to justify your answer.
No. *Sample answer:* $\frac{12}{20} = \frac{12 \div 2}{20 \div 2} = \frac{6}{10}$, which is not in simplest form.

C Tell whether the fractions are equivalent.

53. $\frac{4abc}{5ab}, \frac{4c}{5a}$ no **54.** $\frac{3a}{5}, \frac{6a^2}{10a}$ yes **55.** $\frac{2a}{3b}, \frac{10a^2b}{15ab^2}$ yes

56. Challenge Jason believes that if the numerator or the denominator of a fraction is prime, then the fraction is in simplest form. Explain why this is not always true. See margin.

Mixed Review 

In Exercises 57–59, evaluate the expression. Justify each step. *(Lesson 2.6)* 57–59. See margin.

57. $-12 + 46 - 18$ **58.** $10 \cdot (-25) \cdot 0$ **59.** $\frac{1}{3} \cdot (20 \cdot 15)$

60. Find the greatest common factor of $3x^3y$ and $6x^2y^2$. *(Lesson 4.2)* $3x^2y$

Basic Skills **Use a protractor to draw an angle with the given measure.** 61–63. See margin.

61. 53° **62.** 97° **63.** 145°

Test-Taking Practice 

64. Multiple Choice Mr. Wilkens has attended 18 of his son's 24 basketball games. What fraction of the games has he attended? C

A. $\frac{3}{8}$ **B.** $\frac{2}{3}$ **C.** $\frac{3}{4}$ **D.** $\frac{4}{3}$

65. Multiple Choice Which pair of fractions are equivalent? H

F. $\frac{6}{10}, \frac{9}{25}$ **G.** $\frac{3}{8}, \frac{15}{35}$ **H.** $\frac{14}{21}, \frac{24}{36}$ **I.** $\frac{2}{5}, \frac{5}{20}$

INTERNET
State Test Practice
CLASSZONE.COM

51. $\frac{-4z}{x^2y}$, or $-\frac{4z}{x^2y}$

56. *Sample answer:* The prime number can be a factor of the other number, as in $\frac{7}{49}$, which is not in simplest form.

57. $-12 + 46 - 18$
$= -12 + (-18) + 46$ (Comm. Prop. of Add.)
$= [-12 + (-18)] + 46$ (Assoc. Prop. of Add.)
$= -30 + 46$ (Simplify.)
$= 16$ (Simplify.)

58. $10 \cdot (-25) \cdot 0$
$= 10 \cdot [(-25) \cdot 0]$ (Assoc. Prop. of Mult.)
$= 10 \cdot 0$ (Mult. Prop. of Zero)
$= 0$ (Mult. Prop. of Zero)

59. $\frac{1}{3} \cdot (20 \cdot 15)$
$= \frac{1}{3} \cdot (15 \cdot 20)$ (Comm. Prop. of Mult.)
$= \left(\frac{1}{3} \cdot 15\right) \cdot 20$ (Assoc. Prop. of Mult.)
$= 5 \cdot 20$ (Simplify.)
$= 100$ (Simplify.)

4 ASSESS

Assessment Resources

For more assessment resources, see:
- Assessment Book
- Test and Practice Generator

Mini-Quiz

Simplify.

1. $\frac{17}{34}$ $\frac{1}{2}$
2. $\frac{15}{20}$ $\frac{3}{4}$
3. $\frac{3cd}{9d}$ $\frac{c}{3}$
4. Jan notices that it has rained 4 days in the last 2 weeks. In simplest form, what fraction of the days in the last two weeks have seen rain? $\frac{2}{7}$

5 FOLLOW-UP

Reteaching/Remediation

- Study Guide in Chapter 4 Resource Book, pp. 27-28
- Tutor Place, Fractions Cards 2, 3
- eTutorial Plus Online
- Extra Practice, p. 730
- Lesson Practice in Chapter 4 Resource Book, pp. 24-26

Challenge/Enrichment

- Challenge Practice in Chapter 4 Resource Book, p. 30
- Teacher's Edition, p. 164F

English Learner Support

- Spanish Study Guide
- Multi-Language Glossary
- Chapter Audio Summaries CDs

61-63. See Additional Answers beginning on page AA1.

1 PLAN

STRATEGY BACKGROUND

The strategy Make a List provides two useful kinds of information. Students can use the list to find the total number of possibilities for a problem, and they can also use the list to identify patterns or properties of the entries in the list. Before making a list, students should always take time to think about the heading or headings for the list.

2 TEACH

GUIDING STUDENTS' WORK

In Step 3, point out that each row of numbers is written in order from least to greatest. This is one way of organizing all the entries.

EXTRA EXAMPLES

Example Jana has forgotten the 4-digit PIN for her debit card. She remembers that the first digit is 6, the second digit is 8, and that the last two digits are odd numbers. How many possible PIN codes does Jana have to choose from? **25 PIN codes**

4.4 Problem Solving Strategies

- Guess, Check, and Revise
- Look for a Pattern
- Draw a Diagram
- Act It Out
- **Make a List**
- Work Backward
- Solve a Simpler Problem

Make a List

Problem Mia is trying to remember Jasmine's phone number. She knows the first three digits are 889, but she is confused about the last four numbers. Mia knows the last four digits are a 3, 4, 5, and 6, but she cannot recall their correct order. How many possibilities are there for Jasmine's phone number?

1 Read and Understand

Read the problem carefully.

You know the last four digits of a phone number, but not their order. You need to find how many ways these numbers can be arranged.

2 Make a Plan

Decide on a strategy to use.

One way to solve the problem is to make a list of all the possible four-digit numbers. Then you can use the list to count the number of possibilities for a phone number.

3 Solve the Problem

Reread the problem and make a list.

First, list all of the four-digit numbers that begin with the number **3**.

3456 3465 3546 3564 3645 3654

Similarly, list all of the four-digit numbers that begin with the numbers **4**, **5**, and **6**.

4356 4365 4536 4563 4635 4653

5346 5364 5436 5463 5634 5643

6345 6354 6435 6453 6534 6543

Now count all of the four-digit numbers in the list.

ANSWER There are 24 possibilities for Jasmine's phone number.

4 Look Back

Double-check your list to make sure you didn't repeat any numbers or forget a number.

ILLINOIS Standards and ISAT:
6.B.3a, 6.C.3a

Practice the Strategy

Use the strategy *make a list.*

1. **Baseball** The first team to win 3 out of 5 possible games will be the winner of a baseball tournament. In how many ways can a team win 3 out of 5 games? **10 ways**
2. **Telephone Prefixes** A certain town can use the digits 0, 1, 2, 6, 7, and 8 for its telephone prefixes. How many three-digit telephone prefixes are possible for this town if each digit can be used only once in a prefix and the first digit cannot be a 1 or a 0? **80 prefixes**
3. **Number Cube** Derek rolled 2 number cubes and added the two numbers on the top of each cube. List all the possible sums. In how many different ways can he roll a sum of 7? **See margin.**
4. **Tennis** Three boys and three girls sign up for a mixed doubles tennis tournament. In mixed doubles a team consists of one boy and one girl. How many mixed doubles teams can be made? **9 teams**
5. **Checkbook Covers** A bank has checkbook covers that are either pocket or desk size. The covers can be white, black, red, or tan. The customer's name will be stamped on the cover in gold or silver. How many different choices are available for checkbook covers? **16 choices**
6. **Summer Job** A student was hired by a city's maintenance department to paint parking space numbers in a city parking lot. Each digit had to be painted separately, and the student earned 20 cents per digit. The student painted parking space numbers from 1 to 225. How much did the student earn? **$113.40**

Mixed Problem Solving

Use any strategy to solve the problem.

7. **Car Show** The manager of a mall is asked to rope off a rectangular section of the parking lot for a car show. The area roped off is 250 feet by 300 feet. Posts are to be placed every 25 feet around the lot. How many posts are needed? **44 posts**
8. **Consultant Fees** Two consultants were hired by a company. The total consultant fees were $12,500. If one consultant had earned $500 less, each consultant would have been paid the same. How much did each consultant earn? **$6000 and $6500**
9. **Gardening** Joyce has planted a kudzu vine in her yard. The kudzu vine is a fast growing Japanese plant that was brought to the United States in 1876. Use the information in the table below to predict how long Joyce's vine will be after 2 weeks. **168 in., or 14 ft**

Days	1	2	3	4
Length of kudzu vine (inches)	12	24	36	48

10. **Video Games** Chris buys a video game and two T-shirts for $44 at the mall. One week later he buys two more video games and a T-shirt for $52. Each video game has the same price, and each T-shirt has the same price. How much does one video game cost? **$20**

3 APPLY

TRANSPARENCY

Even-numbered answers are available on transparencies.

MATH REASONING

As students work Exercise 6, invite them to suggest strategies for solving the problem without having to list and then count the total digits from 1 to 225. Be sure to praise students who suggest effective shortcuts. Students may discover the strategy of solving a simpler problem.

SUGGESTED STRATEGIES

You may wish to suggest the following strategies for the problems in the Mixed Problem Solving:

- Exercise 7: Draw a Diagram; Make a Model
- Exercise 8: Guess, Check and Revise; Work Backward
- Exercise 9: Look for a Pattern; Make a List
- Exercise 10: Guess, Check, and Revise; Act It Out

3. $1+1=2, 1+2=3, 1+3=4, 1+4=5, 1+5=6, 1+6=7, 2+1=3, 2+2=4, 2+3=5, 2+4=6, 2+5=7, 2+6=8, 3+1=4, 3+2=5, 3+3=6, 3+4=7, 3+5=8, 3+6=9, 4+1=5, 4+2=6, 4+3=7, 4+4=8, 4+5=9, 4+6=10, 5+1=6, 5+2=7, 5+3=8, 5+4=9, 5+5=10, 5+6=11, 6+1=7, 6+2=8, 6+3=9, 6+4=10, 6+5=11, 6+6=12$; 6 ways

PLAN

SKILL CHECK

Write the prime factorization.

1. 32 2^5 **2.** 96 $2^5 \cdot 3$

LESSON OBJECTIVE

Find the least common multiple of two numbers.

PACING

Suggested Number of Days
Basic Course: 1 day
Average Course: 1 day
Advanced Course: 1 day
Block: 0.5 block with 4.5

TEACHING RESOURCES

For a complete list of Teaching Resources, see page 164B.

TRANSPARENCY

Warm-Up Exercises for this lesson are available on a transparency.

TEACH

MOTIVATING THE LESSON

Tell students to imagine that they get an email from a cousin on a Wednesday and that they get an email from the cousin every other day after that. Ask when the cousin's email will again come on Wednesday.

TIPS FOR NEW TEACHERS

After Example 1, students may conclude that the LCM is just the product of the two numbers. Use an example to show that this is not always the case. See Tips for New Teachers in the *Chapter 4 Resource Book*.

Least Common Multiple

BEFORE	Now	WHY?
You found the greatest common factor of two numbers.	You'll find the least common multiple of two numbers.	So you can plan your weekly schedule, as in Ex. 26.

Word Watch

multiple, p. 186
common multiple, p. 186
least common multiple (LCM), p. 186

In the Real World

Animal Clinic A veterinarian at an animal clinic is on call every four days. Today is Saturday, and the vet is on call. In how many more days will the vet be on call on a Saturday again? You will see how to solve this problem in Example 1.

S	M	T	W	T	F	S
						1
2	3	4	5	6	7	8
9	10	11	12	13	14	15
16	17	18	19	20	21	22
23	24	25	26	27	28	29
30						

JUNE

A **multiple** of a number is the product of the number and any nonzero whole number. A multiple that is shared by two or more numbers is a **common multiple**. The least of the common multiples of two or more whole numbers is the **least common multiple (LCM)**.

EXAMPLE 1 Finding the Least Common Multiple

The veterinarian described above is on call every 4 days. A Saturday occurs every 7 days. To determine the next Saturday the vet will be on call, find the least common multiple of 4 and 7.

Method 1: Make a list.

List the multiples of each number.

Multiples of 4: 4, 8, 12, 16, 20, 24, 28, 32, 36, 40, 44, ...

Multiples of 7: 7, 14, 21, 28, 35, 42, 49, 56, ...

The LCM of 4 and 7 is 28.

Method 2: Use prime factorization.

Write the prime factorization of each number.

$4 = 2^2$ $7 = 7$

Write the product of the highest power of each prime number in the prime factorizations.

$2^2 \cdot 7 = 28$

The LCM of 4 and 7 is 28.

ANSWER In 28 days, the veterinarian will be on call on a Saturday.

ILLINOIS Standards and ISAT:
6.B.3b

EXAMPLE 2 Finding the Least Common Multiple

Find the LCM of 32, 96, and 120 using prime factorization.

Solution

Write the prime factorization of each number.

$32 = 2^5$ $\quad$ $96 = 2^5 \cdot 3$ $\quad$ $120 = 2^3 \cdot 3 \cdot 5$

Write the product of the highest power of each prime number in the prime factorizations.

$2^5 \cdot 3 \cdot 5 = 480$

ANSWER The LCM of 32, 96, and 120 is 480.

Your turn now **Find the least common multiple of the numbers.**

1. 6, 15 30 **2.** 4, 20 20 **3.** 12, 28 84 **4.** 24, 36, and 72 72

Method 2 of Example 1 is also useful for finding the least common multiples of monomials.

EXAMPLE 3 Finding the LCM of Monomials

Find the LCM of $6x^2y$ and $9x^4z$.

Solution

Factor each expression using exponents.

$6x^2y = 2 \cdot 3 \cdot x^2 \cdot y$

$9x^4z = 3^2 \cdot x^4 \cdot z$

Find the product of the highest power of each factor, including the variables.

$2 \cdot 3^2 \cdot x^4 \cdot y \cdot z = 18x^4yz$

ANSWER The LCM of $6x^2y$ and $9x^4z$ is $18x^4yz$.

Your turn now **Find the least common multiple of the monomials.**

5. $8x^3, 20x^7$ $40x^7$ **6.** $12y^4, 36y^8$ $36y^8$

7. $4ab^2, 10a^2b$ $20a^2b^2$ **8.** $6m^3np^2, 8mp^3$ $24m^3np^3$

EXTRA EXAMPLES

Example 1 Refer to Example 1 in the student text. An additional veterinarian is hired and is on call every 5 days, beginning with Monday. How long will it be before the on-call day is again Monday? **35 days**

Example 2 Find the LCM of 16, 20, and 28. **560**

Example 3 Find the LCM of $4a^3b^2$ and $12ab^4$. $12a^3b^4$

VISUALIZE

After Example 1, have students study a calendar to see why it takes so long for Saturday to be the on-call day.

CONCEPT CHECK

What is a common multiple? What is the LCM? **a multiple that is shared by two or more nonzero whole numbers; the least number that is a common multiple of two or more nonzero whole numbers.**

DAILY PUZZLER

The LCM of three consecutive single digit positive integers is 168. What are the integers? **6, 7, 8**

APPLY

ASSIGNMENT GUIDE

Basic Course

Day 1: pp. 188–189 Exs. 8-23, 25-30, 42-49

Average Course

Day 1: pp. 188–189 Exs. 10, 11, 16-38, 42-49

Advanced Course

Day 1: pp. 188–189 Exs. 17-44*, 48, 49

Block

pp. 188–189 Exs. 10, 11, 16-38, 42-49 (with 4.5)

EXTRA PRACTICE

- Student Edition, p. 730
- Chapter 4 Resource Book, pp. 33-35
- Test and Practice Generator

TRANSPARENCY

Even-numbered answers are available on transparencies.

HOMEWORK CHECK

When you review students' homework for this lesson, go over the following exercises to check understanding of key concepts.

Basic: 8, 10, 12, 15, 20

Average: 11, 14, 17, 22, 25

Advanced: 16, 19, 23, 25, 26

COMMON ERROR

In Exercise 33, watch for students who think the LCM is 120 instead of 60. Explain that 60 is a multiple of 60 because $60 \times 1 = 60$.

8-11. See Additional Answers beginning on page AA1.

4.4 Exercises

More Practice, p. 730

INTERNET eWorkbook Plus CLASSZONE.COM

12. $36 = 2^2 \cdot 3^2$, $90 = 2 \cdot 3^2 \cdot 5$; 180
13. $17 = 17$, $57 = 3 \cdot 19$; 969
14. $90 = 2 \cdot 3^2 \cdot 5$, $108 = 2^2 \cdot 3^3$; 540
15. $125 = 5^3$, $500 = 2^2 \cdot 5^3$; 500
16. $6 = 2 \cdot 3$, $8 = 2^3$, $12 = 2^2 \cdot 3$; 24
17. $8 = 2^3$, $16 = 2^4$, $32 = 2^5$; 32
18. $6 = 2 \cdot 3$, $15 = 3 \cdot 5$, $45 = 3^2 \cdot 5$; 90
19. $20 = 2^2 \cdot 5$, $24 = 2^3 \cdot 3$, $60 = 2^2 \cdot 3 \cdot 5$; 120

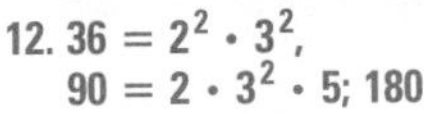

Getting Ready to Practice

Vocabulary Copy and complete the statement.

1. A(n) _?_ of 6 and 9 is 54. common multiple

2. The _?_ of 6 and 9 is 18. least common multiple or LCM

Matching Match the pair of numbers with its LCM.

3. 36, 18 B   **4.** 45, 75 D   **5.** 6, 18 A   **6.** 42, 105 C

A. 18   **B.** 36   **C.** 210   **D.** 225

7. Find the Error Describe and correct the error in the solution. 4 is the GCF of 12 and 24. The LCM is $2 \cdot 2 \cdot 2 \cdot 3$, or 24.

Find the LCM of 12 and 24.

$12 = 2 \cdot 2 \cdot 3 \quad 24 = 2 \cdot 2 \cdot 2 \cdot 3$

The LCM is $2 \cdot 2$, or 4.

Practice and Problem Solving

HELP with Homework

Example	Exercises
1	8-11, 25, 26
2	12-19
3	20-23

Online Resources CLASSZONE.COM
- More Examples
- eTutorial Plus

A **List the first few multiples of each number. Then use the lists to find the LCM of the numbers.** 8–11. See margin.

8. 4, 6   **9.** 6, 21   **10.** 8, 10   **11.** 10, 15

Write the prime factorization of the numbers. Then find their LCM. 12–19. See margin.

12. 36, 90   **13.** 17, 57   **14.** 90, 108   **15.** 125, 500

16. 6, 8, 12   **17.** 8, 16, 32   **18.** 6, 15, 45   **19.** 20, 24, 60

Find the LCM of the monomials.

20. $5ab, 7ab^2$ $35ab^2$ **21.** $7s^3t, 49st^2$ $49s^3t^2$

22. $4x^3y^3, 18xy^5$ $36x^3y^5$ **23.** $24c^2d^3, 60c^2d^6$ $120c^2d^6$

24. Writing Could you find the *greatest* common multiple of two numbers? Explain your reasoning. No; there are infinitely many multiples of each number.

25. Traffic Lights One traffic light turns red every 45 seconds. Another traffic light turns red every 60 seconds. Both traffic lights just turned red. In how many seconds will they turn red at the same time again? 180 sec

26. Schedule Your class schedule changes on a three-day rotation. Every three days you have math class during the last class period of the day. This week, you have math class the last period on Friday. In how many more school days will you have math class the last period on Friday? 15 days

B **Find the LCM of the numbers using prime factorization.**

27. 160, 432 4320 **28.** 144, 576 576 **29.** 21, 36, 57 4788 **30.** 18, 54, 84 756

31. 30, 75, 100 300 **32.** 36, 54, 72 216 **33.** 10, 12, 30, 60 60 **34.** 21, 42, 63, 105 630

Find the LCM of the monomials.

35. $24x^4y, 30y^7$ $120x^4y^7$ **36.** $17m^3n^3, 9m^2n^6$ $153m^3n^6$ **37.** $45gh^5k^3, 33g^4hk^3$ $495g^4h^5k^3$

38. Lasagna Zoe is making lasagna for a family reunion. Her recipe calls for twelve noodles for each batch of lasagna. One box of lasagna noodles contains 14 noodles. What is the least number of batches of lasagna that Zoe can make without having any noodles left over? 7 batches

C **39. Swimming** Will swims one lap in 160 seconds, while Martin swims one lap in 180 seconds. The boys start their laps at the same time from the same side of the pool and maintain their pace. When will they both be at their starting place at the same time again? Write your answer in minutes and seconds. 24 min

40. Writing You are asked to find the LCM of two numbers. One of the numbers is a factor of the other number. Is there a shortcut to finding their LCM? Explain. Yes; the greatest number is the LCM.

41. Challenge Could the GCF of two different numbers also be the LCM of those numbers? Explain. No. *Sample answer:* The GCF of two different numbers cannot be more than the smaller number, so it is less than the larger number. The LCM is at least as large as the larger number, so the GCF and the LCM cannot be the same.

Mixed Review

42. Rebecca ran on her treadmill at 5.6 miles per hour for one half hour. How many miles did Rebecca run? *(Lesson 1.6)* 2.8 mi

43. Simplify the expression $7x + 9 + 12x + 11 + 2y$ by combining like terms. *(Lesson 2.7)* $19x + 20 + 2y$

44. Find the greatest common factor of 121 and 187. *(Lesson 4.2)* 11

Basic Skills **Find the sum.**

45. 24.63 + 49.07 73.7 **46.** 14.125 + 16.8 30.925 **47.** 33.87 + 100.9 134.77

Test-Taking Practice

48. Multiple Choice What is the prime factorization of 72? C

A. $2^2 \cdot 3 \cdot 6$ **B.** $2 \cdot 6^2$ **C.** $2^3 \cdot 3^2$ **D.** $2^2 \cdot 3^2 \cdot 6$

49. Short Response A teacher can arrange a class into groups of 2, 5, or 6 students with no one left out. What is the least number of students that the teacher can have in class to do this? Explain how you found your answer. 30 students. *Sample answer:* I found the LCM of 2, 5, and 6.

4 ASSESS

Assessment Resources

For more assessment resources, see:
- Assessment Book
- Test and Practice Generator

Mini-Quiz

Write the prime factorization of the numbers. Then find their LCM.

1. 18, 40 $2 \cdot 3^2, 2^3 \cdot 5$; 360
2. 9, 12 $3^2, 2^2 \cdot 3$; 36
3. Find the LCM of $6g^2h$ and $10gh^3$. $30g^2h^3$
4. Amber gives every 7th shopper a flier about a new store. Bryan gives every 12th shopper a dollar-off coupon. Which shopper first receives both a flier and a coupon? 84th shopper

5 FOLLOW-UP

Reteaching/Remediation

- Study Guide in Chapter 4 Resource Book, pp. 36–37
- Tutor Place, Fractions Card 10
- eTutorial Plus Online
- Extra Practice, p. 730
- Lesson Practice in Chapter 4 Resource Book, pp. 33–35

Challenge/Enrichment

- Challenge Practice in Chapter 4 Resource Book, p. 38
- Teacher's Edition, p. 164F

English Learner Support

- Spanish Study Guide
- Multi-Language Glossary
- Chapter Audio Summaries CDs

ADDITIONAL RESOURCES

The following resources are available to help review the materials in Lessons 4.1–4.4.

Chapter 4 Resource Book
- Lesson Practice
- Study Guide

Assessment Book
- Chapter 4 Quiz 1

Technology
- Test and Practice Generator
- eTutorial CD-ROM

Internet
- Classzone
- eWorkbook Plus Online
- eTutorial Plus Online

ENGLISH LEARNER SUPPORT

- Spanish Study Guide
- Multi-Language Glossary
- Chapter Audio Summaries CDs

Notebook Review

Review the vocabulary definitions in your notebook.

Copy the review examples in your notebook. Then complete the exercises.

Check Your Definitions

prime number, p. 169
composite number, p. 169
prime factorization, p. 169
factor tree, p. 169
monomial, p. 170
common factor, p. 173
greatest common factor (GCF), p. 173
relatively prime, p. 174
simplest form, p. 179
equivalent fractions, p. 179
multiple, p. 186
common multiple, p. 186
least common multiple (LCM), p. 186

Use Your Vocabulary

1. Copy and complete: A factor tree can be used to find the _?_ of a number. prime factorization

4.1 Can you write a prime factorization?

EXAMPLE Write the prime factorization of 504.

$504 = 2 \cdot 2 \cdot 2 \cdot 3 \cdot 3 \cdot 7$, or $2^3 \cdot 3^2 \cdot 7$

ANSWER The prime factorization of 504 is $2^3 \cdot 3^2 \cdot 7$.

☑ **Write the prime factorization of the number.**

2. 40 $2^3 \cdot 5$ **3.** 7 7 **4.** 85 $5 \cdot 17$ **5.** 120 $2^3 \cdot 3 \cdot 5$

4.2 Can you find the GCF of two numbers?

EXAMPLE Find the GCF of 36 and 60.

$36 = 2^2 \cdot 3^2$ $60 = 2^2 \cdot 3 \cdot 5$

The common factors are 2^2 and 3. So, the GCF is $2^2 \cdot 3$, or 12.

ANSWER The GCF of 36 and 60 is 12.

☑ **Find the GCF of the numbers or monomials.**

6. 48, 80 16 **7.** 60, 100 20 **8.** $14a^3, 21a$ $7a$ **9.** $20y^4, 60y^5$ $20y^4$

4.3 Can you write a fraction in simplest form?

EXAMPLE Write $\frac{48}{72}$ in simplest form.

$$\frac{48}{72} = \frac{48 \div 24}{72 \div 24} = \frac{2}{3}$$

Write the fraction in simplest form.

10. $\frac{15}{45}$ $\frac{1}{3}$ **11.** $\frac{12}{80}$ $\frac{3}{20}$ **12.** $\frac{9ab}{27a}$ $\frac{b}{3}$ **13.** $\frac{18n^3}{54n}$ $\frac{n^2}{3}$

4.4 Can you find the LCM of two numbers?

EXAMPLE Find the LCM of 20 and 48.

$20 = 2^2 \cdot 5$ $48 = 2^4 \cdot 3$

ANSWER The LCM of 20 and 48 is $2^4 \cdot 3 \cdot 5$, or 240.

Find the LCM of the numbers or monomials.

14. 28, 42 84 **15.** 54, 90 270 **16.** $10cd, 25c^2$ $50c^2d$ **17.** $9n^3, 12n^2$ $36n^3$

Stop *and* Think about Lessons 4.1–4.4

18. Writing Explain the difference between listing the factors of a number and finding the prime factorization of a number.

18. *Sample answer:* When you list the factors of a number, you list all numbers by which the number is divisible, including one, composite numbers, and the number itself. When you find the prime factorization of a number, you write the number as a product only of its prime factors.

Review Quiz 1

Find the GCF of the numbers or monomials.

1. 24, 90 6 **2.** 36, 72, 108 36 **3.** $20c^3, 48c^2$ $4c^2$ **4.** $64m^2, 80m^5$ $16m^2$

Find the LCM of the numbers or monomials.

5. 88, 99 792 **6.** 36, 96 288 **7.** $7xy, 21y^3$ $21xy^3$ **8.** $6ab^2, 30ab$ $30ab^2$

Tell whether the fractions are equivalent.

9. $\frac{9}{27}, \frac{60}{180}$ yes **10.** $\frac{39}{91}, \frac{42}{56}$ no **11.** $\frac{40}{48}, \frac{70}{84}$ yes **12.** $\frac{108}{120}, \frac{189}{210}$ yes

13. Supermarket A supermarket gives every tenth customer a coupon and every twenty-fifth customer a gift. Which of the first 200 customers receive both a coupon and a gift?
50th, 100th, 150th, and 200th customers

1 PLAN

SKILL CHECK

Complete with < or >.

1. $\frac{5}{6}$? $\frac{4}{6}$ >
2. $\frac{2}{3}$? $\frac{4}{3}$ <
3. $\frac{15}{19}$? $\frac{16}{19}$ <

LESSON OBJECTIVE

Compare and order fractions and mixed numbers.

PACING

Suggested Number of Days
Basic Course: 1 day
Average Course: 1 day
Advanced Course: 1 day
Block: 0.5 block with 4.4

TEACHING RESOURCES

For a complete list of Teaching Resources, see page 164B.

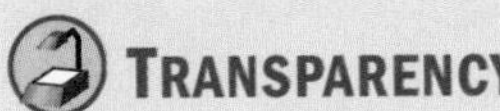

TRANSPARENCY

Warm-Up Exercises for this lesson are available on a transparency.

2 TEACH

MOTIVATING THE LESSON

Expand upon the lesson opening by having students compare other fractions using models.

TIPS FOR NEW TEACHERS

Lead students in a discussion of other ways to compare $\frac{2}{3}$ and $\frac{3}{4}$. See Tips for New Teachers in the *Chapter 4 Resource Book*.

LESSON 4.5

Comparing Fractions and Mixed Numbers

BEFORE	Now	WHY?
You compared and ordered integers.	You'll compare and order fractions and mixed numbers.	So you can determine the greater fraction of games won, as in Ex. 28.

Word Watch

least common denominator (LCD), p. 192

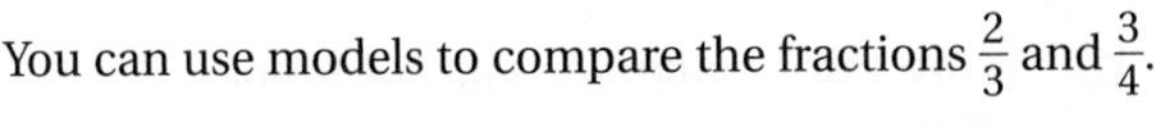

You can use models to compare the fractions $\frac{2}{3}$ and $\frac{3}{4}$.

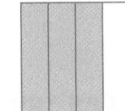

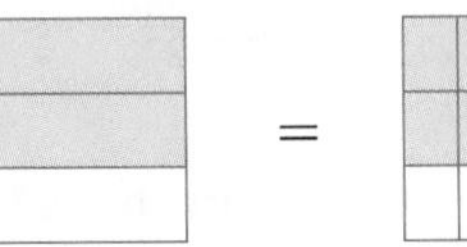

$\frac{2}{3} = \frac{2 \cdot 4}{3 \cdot 4} = \frac{8}{12}$

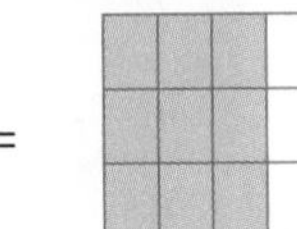

$\frac{3}{4} = \frac{3 \cdot 3}{4 \cdot 3} = \frac{9}{12}$

In the diagram above, $\frac{8}{12} < \frac{9}{12}$, so $\frac{2}{3} < \frac{3}{4}$.

The **least common denominator (LCD)** of two or more fractions is the least common multiple of the denominators. You can compare fractions by using the least common denominator to write equivalent fractions.

EXAMPLE 1 Comparing Fractions Using the LCD

Compare $\frac{3}{8}$ and $\frac{5}{12}$.

(1) Find the least common denominator of the fractions.
The LCM of 8 and 12 is 24, so the least common denominator is 24.

(2) Use the least common denominator to write equivalent fractions.

$\frac{3}{8} = \frac{3 \cdot 3}{8 \cdot 3} = \frac{9}{24}$ $\qquad$ $\frac{5}{12} = \frac{5 \cdot 2}{12 \cdot 2} = \frac{10}{24}$

(3) Compare the numerators: 9 < 10, so $\frac{9}{24} < \frac{10}{24}$.

ANSWER Because $\frac{9}{24} < \frac{10}{24}$, you can write $\frac{3}{8} < \frac{5}{12}$.

HELP with Solving

You can write equivalent fractions by multiplying or dividing the numerator and denominator by the same nonzero number.

Your turn now **Copy and complete the statement with <, >, or =.**

1. $\frac{2}{3}$? $\frac{5}{8}$ > 2. $\frac{2}{4}$? $\frac{15}{20}$ < 3. $\frac{3}{10}$? $\frac{2}{4}$ < 4. $\frac{9}{16}$? $\frac{11}{18}$ <

ILLINOIS Standards and ISAT:
6.A.3, 6.B.3b

To compare or order improper fractions and mixed numbers, first write any mixed numbers as improper fractions.

with Review

For help with writing mixed numbers as improper fractions, see p.707.

EXAMPLE 2 Ordering Fractions and Mixed Numbers

Order the numbers $4\frac{7}{16}$, $\frac{19}{4}$, and $\frac{35}{8}$ from least to greatest.

(1 Find the least common denominator of the fractions.

The LCM of 16, 4, and 8 is 16, so the LCD is 16.

(2 Use the least common denominator to write equivalent fractions.

$4\frac{7}{16} = \frac{4 \cdot 16 + 7}{16} = \frac{71}{16}$ $\frac{19}{4} = \frac{19 \cdot 4}{4 \cdot 4} = \frac{76}{16}$ $\frac{35}{8} = \frac{35 \cdot 2}{8 \cdot 2} = \frac{70}{16}$

(3 Compare the numerators: $70 < 71$, and $71 < 76$, so $\frac{70}{16} < \frac{71}{16}$ and $\frac{71}{16} < \frac{76}{16}$.

ANSWER From least to greatest, the numbers are $\frac{35}{8}$, $4\frac{7}{16}$, and $\frac{19}{4}$.

EXAMPLE 3 Comparing Mixed Numbers

Orangutans A female orangutan is about $3\frac{1}{2}$ feet tall. A male orangutan is about $3\frac{2}{5}$ feet tall. Which of the two orangutans is taller?

Solution

The LCM of 2 and 5 is 10, so the least common denominator is 10.

Use the least common denominator to write equivalent fractions.

$3\frac{1}{2} = \frac{3 \cdot 2 + 1}{2} = \frac{7}{2}$ $3\frac{2}{5} = \frac{3 \cdot 5 + 2}{5} = \frac{17}{5}$

$\frac{7}{2} = \frac{7 \cdot 5}{2 \cdot 5} = \frac{35}{10}$ $\frac{17}{5} = \frac{17 \cdot 2}{5 \cdot 2} = \frac{34}{10}$

Because $35 > 34$, you can write $\frac{35}{10} > \frac{34}{10}$.

ANSWER The female orangutan is taller.

What do you think? **Zoology**

Orangutans

An orangutan's arms are about two thirds as long as its height. How long would the arms of a 3 foot orangutan be? **about 2 ft**

Your turn now **Copy and complete the statement with <, >, or =.**

5. $\frac{16}{5}$? $3\frac{1}{3}$ < **6.** $1\frac{4}{5}$? $\frac{21}{12}$ > **7.** $-2\frac{2}{3}$? $-4\frac{5}{6}$ >

8. Order the numbers $2\frac{7}{9}$, $2\frac{5}{12}$, and $\frac{11}{4}$ from least to greatest. $2\frac{5}{12}$, $\frac{11}{4}$, $2\frac{7}{9}$

EXTRA EXAMPLES

Example 1 Compare $\frac{7}{10}$ and $\frac{5}{6}$. $\frac{7}{10} < \frac{5}{6}$

Example 2 Order $3\frac{1}{3}$, $\frac{10}{2}$, and $\frac{14}{5}$ from least to greatest. $\frac{14}{5}$, $3\frac{1}{3}$, $\frac{10}{2}$

Example 3 Janelle's puppy weighs $4\frac{2}{3}$ pounds and Erika's puppy weighs $4\frac{7}{8}$ pounds. Whose puppy weighs more? **Erika's puppy**

MULTIPLE REPRESENTATIONS

Before discussing Example 1, make sure students recognize that the models shown at the top of page 192 correspond to the fractions shown underneath. You can also encourage students to draw other models that represent those fractions.

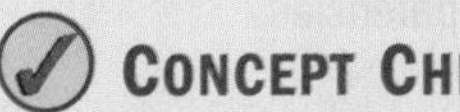

CONCEPT CHECK

How can you use the least common denominator to order fractions? **You can use the least common denominator to rewrite the fractions as equivalent fractions over the same denominator and then order them by comparing the numerators.**

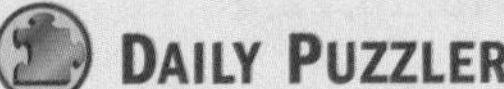

DAILY PUZZLER

If $a < b$ and $a \geq 2$, which is greater: $a\frac{b}{a}$ or $b\frac{a}{b}$? $b\frac{a}{b}$

3 APPLY

ASSIGNMENT GUIDE

Basic Course

Day 1: SRH p. 707 Exs. 1-9; pp. 194-195 Exs. 11-20, 22, 30-34

Average Course

Day 1: pp. 194-195 Exs. 14-26, 28, 30-34

Advanced Course

Day 1: pp. 194-195 Exs. 14-16, 20-31*, 33, 34

Block

pp. 194-195 Exs. 14-26, 28, 30-34 (with 4.4)

EXTRA PRACTICE

- Student Edition, p. 730
- Chapter 4 Resource Book, pp. 44-46
- Test and Practice Generator

TRANSPARENCY

Even-numbered answers are available on transparencies.

HOMEWORK CHECK

When you review students' homework for this lesson, go over the following exercises to check understanding of key concepts.

Basic: 11, 14, 17, 20, 22

Average: 14, 15, 18, 20, 23

Advanced: 15, 16, 22, 23, 28

TEACHING TIP

In Exercise 11, point out to students that they can complete the statement without rewriting the numbers, since $\frac{13}{12}$ is just a little over 1 and must be less than $3\frac{1}{4}$.

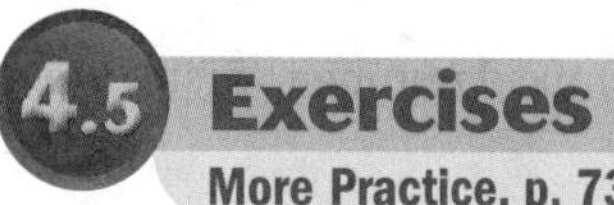

4.5 Exercises

More Practice, p. 730

Getting Ready to Practice

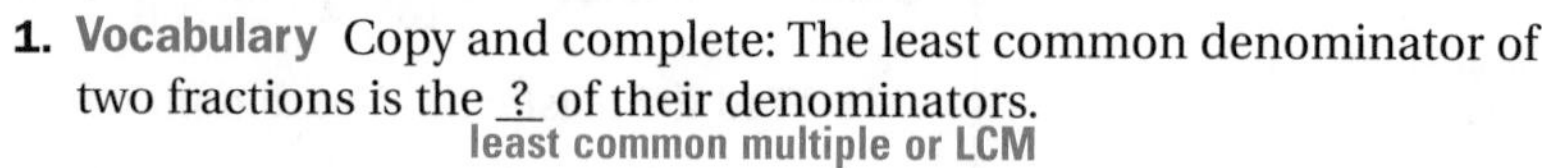

1. **Vocabulary** Copy and complete: The least common denominator of two fractions is the _?_ of their denominators. least common multiple or LCM

Find the least common denominator of the fractions.

2. $\frac{1}{2}, \frac{2}{3}$ 6
3. $\frac{3}{4}, \frac{7}{20}$ 20
4. $\frac{11}{24}, \frac{5}{6}$ 24
5. $\frac{5}{12}, \frac{7}{18}$ 36

Copy and complete the statement with <, >, or =.

6. $\frac{3}{5}$ _?_ $\frac{7}{10}$ <
7. $\frac{7}{18}$ _?_ $\frac{5}{9}$ <
8. $\frac{24}{32}$ _?_ $\frac{3}{4}$ =
9. $\frac{5}{8}$ _?_ $\frac{7}{12}$ >

10. **Guided Problem Solving** Sarah walks two thirds of a mile to school every day. Amy walks five eighths of a mile to school. Whose walk to school is longer?

   (1) Find the least common denominator. 24

   (2) Rewrite both fractions using the LCD. $\frac{16}{24}, \frac{15}{24}$

   (3) Use your answer to find whose walk is longer. Sarah's walk is longer.

Practice and Problem Solving

A **Copy and complete the statement with <, >, or =.**

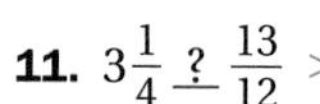

11. $3\frac{1}{4}$ _?_ $\frac{13}{12}$ >
12. $\frac{31}{6}$ _?_ $5\frac{1}{6}$ =
13. $\frac{5}{11}$ _?_ $\frac{42}{55}$ <
14. $2\frac{4}{5}$ _?_ $\frac{7}{3}$ >
15. $\frac{165}{36}$ _?_ $4\frac{5}{12}$ >
16. $\frac{11}{18}$ _?_ $\frac{9}{14}$ <

Order the numbers from least to greatest.

17. $\frac{1}{2}, \frac{1}{8}, \frac{3}{4}, \frac{5}{16}$ $\frac{1}{8}, \frac{5}{16}, \frac{1}{2}, \frac{3}{4}$
18. $1\frac{1}{2}, \frac{5}{4}, \frac{11}{6}$ $\frac{5}{4}, 1\frac{1}{2}, \frac{11}{6}$
19. $\frac{5}{3}, \frac{35}{15}, 2\frac{2}{5}, \frac{15}{16}$

20. **Commercials** During a 30 minute TV show, there are 8 minutes of commercials. During a 2 hour movie, there are 31 minutes of commercials. Write each commercial time as a fraction of the total time. Which TV program has a greater fraction of commercial time?

21. **Writing** Explain how comparing fractions with like denominators differs from comparing fractions with unlike denominators.
Sample answer: To compare fractions with like denominators, you simply compare the numerators. To compare fractions with unlike denominators, you must first write the fractions with a common denominator and then compare the numerators.

with Homework

Example	Exercises
1	11-16
2	17-19, 22, 23
3	11-16, 20

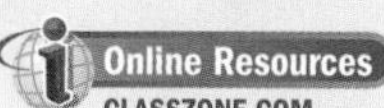

- More Examples
- eTutorial Plus

19. $\frac{15}{16}, \frac{5}{3}, \frac{35}{15}, 2\frac{2}{5}$

20. $\frac{8}{30} = \frac{4}{15}, \frac{31}{120}$; 30 min show

with Solving

A negative fraction can be written in various ways. For example, $-\frac{a}{b} = \frac{a}{-b} = \frac{-a}{b}$.

B **Write the numbers in order from least to greatest.**

22. $7\frac{1}{4}, \frac{31}{4}, \frac{63}{8}, \frac{47}{6}, 7\frac{19}{24}$ $7\frac{1}{4}, \frac{31}{4}, 7\frac{19}{24}, \frac{47}{6}, \frac{63}{8}$

23. $\frac{-34}{3}, -11\frac{7}{12}, -11\frac{17}{48}, \frac{-23}{2}, \frac{-47}{4}$ $\frac{-47}{4}, -11\frac{7}{12}, \frac{-23}{2}, -11\frac{17}{48}, \frac{-34}{3}$

Copy and complete the statement with <, >, or = by first comparing each fraction to $\frac{1}{2}$.

24. $\frac{25}{50} \underline{?} \frac{37}{74}$ =

25. $\frac{17}{30} \underline{?} \frac{10}{33}$ >

26. $\frac{23}{100} \underline{?} \frac{19}{36}$ <

27. Critical Thinking In Exercises 24–26, does it help to compare each number to $\frac{1}{2}$ first? Will this step always work? If not, could you use another fraction to help make comparisons? See margin.

28. Little League Teams from California have played in the Little League World Series 19 times and won the championship 5 times. Texas teams have appeared in 7 Little League World Series and won twice. Which state has won a greater fraction of their World Series games? Texas

C **29. Challenge** Consider the fractions $\frac{1}{2x}$ and $\frac{1}{x}$. What is their LCD? Write each fraction using the LCD. $2x$; $\frac{1}{2x}$ and $\frac{2}{2x}$

Mixed Review

30. Find the area of the figure at the right. *(Lesson 3.5)* 48 ft^2

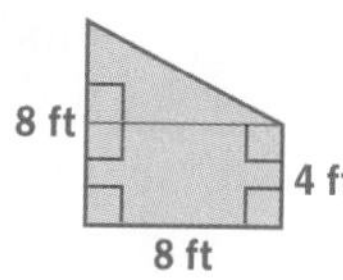

31. Write the prime factorization of 336. *(Lesson 4.1)* $2^4 \cdot 3 \cdot 7$

32. Basic Skills Find the quotient of 1998 and 42. Round your answer to the nearest thousandth. 47.571

27. Yes; no, it will not work if both fractions are less than $\frac{1}{2}$ or greater than $\frac{1}{2}$; yes, but it needs to be an easily recognized fraction such as $-\frac{1}{4}$ or $\frac{2}{3}$, and will depend on the fractions given.

Test-Taking Practice

INTERNET
State Test Practice
CLASSZONE.COM

33. Multiple Choice Which list of fractions is written correctly in order from least to greatest? B

A. $\frac{12}{18}, \frac{13}{30}, \frac{8}{15}$ **B.** $\frac{4}{18}, \frac{9}{15}, \frac{18}{27}$ **C.** $\frac{6}{10}, \frac{4}{18}, \frac{16}{24}$ **D.** $\frac{7}{11}, \frac{7}{8}, \frac{15}{25}$

34. Multiple Choice In a class of 32 people, 28 were at school, so $\frac{28}{32}$ of the class was present. What is another way to express this number? H

F. $\frac{4}{8}$ **G.** $\frac{24}{28}$ **H.** $\frac{7}{8}$ **I.** $\frac{15}{16}$

4 ASSESS

Assessment Resources

For more assessment resources, see:
- Assessment Book
- Test and Practice Generator

Mini-Quiz

Copy and complete the statement with <, >, or =.

1. $2\frac{2}{3} \underline{?} \frac{16}{6}$ =

2. $\frac{12}{17} \underline{?} \frac{30}{51}$ >

Order the numbers from least to greatest.

3. $\frac{8}{7}, \frac{7}{10}, \frac{2}{7}, \frac{6}{14}$ $\frac{2}{7}, \frac{6}{14}, \frac{7}{10}, \frac{8}{7}$

4. $\frac{21}{10}, \frac{19}{18}, 3\frac{1}{2}, \frac{30}{9}$ $\frac{19}{18}, \frac{21}{10}, \frac{30}{9}, 3\frac{1}{2}$

5 FOLLOW-UP

Reteaching/Remediation

- Study Guide in Chapter 4 Resource Book, pp. 47–48
- Tutor Place, Fractions Cards 4, 7, 10
- eTutorial Plus Online
- Extra Practice, p. 730
- Lesson Practice in Chapter 4 Resource Book, pp. 44–46

Challenge/Enrichment

- Challenge Practice in Chapter 4 Resource Book, p. 49
- Teacher's Edition, p. 164F

English Learner Support

- Spanish Study Guide
- Multi-Language Glossary
- Chapter Audio Summaries CDs

PLAN

SKILL CHECK

1. $12 - 7 = \underline{?}$ 5
2. $4 + 7 = \underline{?}$ 11
3. $3^2 = \underline{?}$ 9
4. $3^3 = \underline{?}$ 27

LESSON OBJECTIVE

Multiply and divide expressions with exponents.

PACING

Suggested Number of Days
Basic Course: 1 day
Average Course: 1 day
Advanced Course: 1 day
Block: 0.5 block with 4.7

TEACHING RESOURCES

For a complete list of Teaching Resources, see page 164B.

TRANSPARENCY

Warm-Up Exercises for this lesson are available on a transparency.

TEACH

MOTIVATING THE LESSON

Expand the Activity by setting up a quotient table and asking students to redo the activity using division.

ACTIVITY

Goal Discover rules for multiplying powers.

Key Discovery To multiply powers with the same base, add their exponents.

Rules of Exponents

BEFORE	Now	WHY?
You multiplied and divided numerical expressions.	You'll multiply and divide expressions with exponents.	So you can compare the memory in two computers, as in Exs. 49–50.

Word Watch

Review Words
exponent, p. 20
power, p. 20

Activity Using patterns to discover rules for multiplying powers.

(1 Copy and complete the table.

Expression	Expanded Expression	Number of Factors	Product as a Power
$2^2 \cdot 2^4$	$(2 \cdot 2) \cdot (2 \cdot 2 \cdot 2 \cdot 2)$	6	2^6
$3^3 \cdot 3^1$	$(3 \cdot 3 \cdot 3) \cdot 3$	? 4	$3^?$ 4
$7^2 \cdot 7^3$	? $(7 \cdot 7) \cdot (7 \cdot 7 \cdot 7)$	? 5	? 7^5

(2 How are the exponents in the first and last columns related?
The exponent in the last column is the sum of the exponents in the first column.

(3 Write the product $6^5 \cdot 6^{11}$ as a single power. 6^{16}

As you saw in the activity, you can expand expressions to find their product. The following equation suggests a rule for multiplying powers with the same base when the exponents are integers.

$$a^4 \cdot a^2 = \underbrace{(\overbrace{a \cdot a \cdot a \cdot a}^{4\text{ factors}}) \cdot (\overbrace{a \cdot a}^{2\text{ factors}})}_{6\text{ factors}} = a^{4+2} = a^6$$

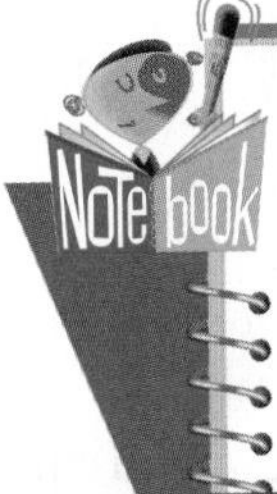

Product of Powers Property

Words To multiply powers with the same base, add their exponents.

Algebra $a^m \cdot a^n = a^{m+n}$ **Numbers** $5^6 \cdot 5^3 = 5^{6+3} = 5^9$

EXAMPLE 1 **Using the Product of Powers Property**

$x^4 \cdot x^7 = x^{4+7}$ Product of powers property

$= x^{11}$ Add exponents.

ILLINOIS Standards and ISAT:
6.A.3, 6.B.3c; 7.A.3b

Watch Out!

Remember that numbers raised to the first power are usually written without an exponent. For example, $3 = 3^1$.

EXAMPLE 2 Using the Product of Powers Property

$3^2x^2 \cdot 3x^3 = (3^2 \cdot 3) \cdot (x^2 \cdot x^3)$ — Commutative property of multiplication

$= 3^{2+1} \cdot x^{2+3}$ — Product of powers property

$= 3^3x^5$ — Add exponents.

$= 27x^5$ — Evaluate the power.

The following equation suggests a rule for dividing powers with the same base when the exponents are integers.

$$\frac{a^5}{a^3} = \frac{\overbrace{a \cdot a \cdot a \cdot a \cdot a}^{\text{5 factors}}}{\underbrace{a \cdot a \cdot a}_{\text{3 factors}}} = \frac{a \cdot a \cdot \cancel{a}^{1} \cdot \cancel{a}^{1} \cdot \cancel{a}^{1}}{\cancel{a}_{1} \cdot \cancel{a}_{1} \cdot \cancel{a}_{1}} = \overbrace{a \cdot a}^{\text{2 factors}} = a^{5-3} = a^2$$

Quotient of Powers Property

Words To divide two powers with the same nonzero base, subtract the exponent of the denominator from the exponent of the numerator.

Algebra $\frac{a^m}{a^n} = a^{m-n}$ **Numbers** $\frac{4^7}{4^4} = 4^{7-4} = 4^3$

EXAMPLE 3 Using the Quotient of Powers Property

Simplify the expression. Write your answer as a power.

a. $\frac{x^{12}}{x^7} = x^{12-7}$ — Quotient of powers property

$= x^5$ — Subtract exponents.

b. $\frac{9^7}{9^3} = 9^{7-3}$ — Quotient of powers property

$= 9^4$ — Subtract exponents.

Your turn now **Simplify the expression. Write your answer as a power.**

1. $a^6 \cdot a^4$ a^{10} **2.** $2^3 \cdot 2^4$ 2^7 **3.** $\frac{a^6}{a^4}$ a^2 **4.** $\frac{10^9}{10^6}$ 10^3

TIPS FOR NEW TEACHERS

Some students will err when one exponent is a factor of another exponent. For example, students might divide exponents when simplifying $\frac{4^{12}}{4^4}$. When possible, give students examples of exponent combinations such as these so students learn to avoid the temptation to divide exponents. See Tips for New Teachers in the *Chapter 4 Resource Book*.

EXTRA EXAMPLES

Example 1 Simplify $a^5 \cdot a^8$. a^{13}

Example 2 Simplify $5^3b^2 \cdot 5^2b^4$. $3125b^6$

Example 3 Simplify the expression. Write your answer as a power.

a. $\frac{a^{13}}{a^3}$ a^{10} **b.** $\frac{7^8}{7^6}$ 7^2

COMMON ERROR

In Example 2, watch for students who evaluate 3^3 as 9 instead of 27.

Differentiating Instruction

Advanced Students Explain that a kilobyte is 1024 bytes, not 1000, because computers are based on a binary system. Challenge interested students to research binary and hexadecimal number systems and how they relate to computers.

EXTRA EXAMPLES

Example 4 Simplify the expression. Write your answer as a power.

a. $\frac{5^4 \cdot 5^3}{5^5}$ 5^2

b. $\frac{f^3g^4}{fg^2}$ f^2g^2

CONCEPT CHECK

How do you multiply powers with the same base? How do you divide powers with the same base? **Add their exponents; subtract their exponents.**

DAILY PUZZLER

What is $(2^3)^4$? **2^{12}, or 4096**

Watch Out!

The bases of the powers must be the same to use the product or quotient property. In part (b) of Example 4, you cannot simplify the numerator any further because the bases, x and y, are different.

EXAMPLE 4 **Simplifying Fractions with Powers**

a. $\frac{y^4 \cdot y}{y^3} = \frac{y^5}{y^3}$ — Simplify numerator using product of powers property.

$= y^{5-3}$ — Quotient of powers property

$= y^2$ — Subtract exponents.

b. $\frac{xy^4}{y^3} = xy^{4-3}$ — Quotient of powers property

$= xy$ — Subtract exponents.

Your turn now **Simplify the expression. Write your answer as a power.**

5. $\frac{q^3 \cdot q^5}{q^4}$ q^4
6. $\frac{4^3 \cdot 4^{12}}{4^5}$ 4^{10}
7. $\frac{a^2b^8}{b^2}$ a^2b^6
8. $\frac{x^5y^{11}}{y^5}$ x^5y^6

4.6 Exercises

More Practice, p. 730

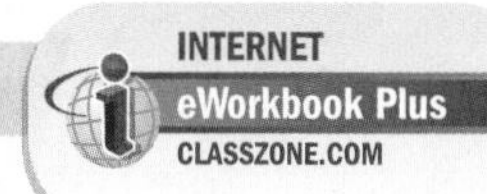

Getting Ready to Practice

Vocabulary **Copy and complete the statement.**

1. Three is the _?_ of the expression 3^4. **base**
2. Seven is the _?_ of the expression 4^7. **exponent**

Tell whether the product of powers property can be used to simplify the expression.

3. $9^3 \cdot 9^4$ yes
4. $7^2 \cdot 2^7$ no
5. $r^6 \cdot s^6$ no
6. $n^5 \cdot n^8$ yes

Simplify the expression. Write your answer as a power.

7. $4^2 \cdot 4^4$ 4^6
8. $8 \cdot 8^3$ 8^4
9. $a^5 \cdot a^7$ a^{12}
10. $b^9 \cdot b^9$ b^{18}
11. $\frac{c^6}{c^5}$ c
12. $\frac{5^8}{5^4}$ 5^4
13. $\frac{8^7}{8^2}$ 8^5
14. $\frac{d^8}{d}$ d^7

15. **Find the Error** Describe and correct the error in the solution. **The bases should not be multiplied; $2^2 \cdot 2^4 = 2^{2+4} = 2^6$.**

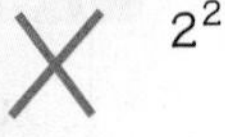

$2^2 \cdot 2^4 = (2 \cdot 2)^{2+4}$
$= 4^6$

with Homework

Example	Exercises
1	16–19, 24–27, 32, 33
2	36–39
3	20–23, 28–31, 34, 35
4	40–43

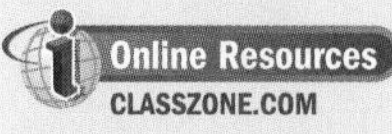

Online Resources
CLASSZONE.COM
- More Examples
- eTutorial Plus

Practice and Problem Solving

Simplify the expression.

A **16.** $u^7 \cdot u^8$ u^{15} **17.** $v^2 \cdot v^{10}$ v^{12} **18.** $b^9 \cdot b^6$ b^{15} **19.** $m^{11} \cdot m^8$ m^{19}

20. $\frac{a^4}{a}$ a^3 **21.** $\frac{x^{10}}{x^6}$ x^4 **22.** $\frac{w^{15}}{w^9}$ w^6 **23.** $\frac{y^{20}}{y^{18}}$ y^2

Simplify the expression. Write your answer as a power.

24. $3^2 \cdot 3^4$ 3^6 **25.** $(-4)^2 \cdot (-4)^3$ $(-4)^5$ **26.** $5^4 \cdot 5$ 5^5 **27.** $7^2 \cdot 7^2$ 7^4

28. $\frac{(-7)^7}{(-7)^4}$ $(-7)^3$ **29.** $\frac{2^{13}}{2^3}$ 2^{10} **30.** $\frac{6^{11}}{6^8}$ 6^3 **31.** $\frac{9^8}{9^4}$ 9^4

Determine the number that correctly completes the equation.

32. $2^3 \cdot 2^? = 2^{11}$ 8 **33.** $5^4 \cdot ?^5 = 5^9$ 5 **34.** $\frac{8^7}{8^?} = 8^3$ 4 **35.** $\frac{12^?}{12^5} = 12^4$ 9

B **Simplify the expression.**

36. $3a^3 \cdot 3a^2$ $9a^5$ **37.** $2y^3 \cdot 2y^2$ $4y^5$ **38.** $3^2x^5 \cdot 3^3x^4$ $243x^9$ **39.** $4a^3b^4 \cdot 4^2a^4b^6$ $64a^7b^{10}$

40. $\frac{p^5q^9}{pq^5}$ p^4q^4 **41.** $\frac{z^6 \cdot z^3}{z^4}$ z^5 **42.** $\frac{3^3m^9}{3^2m^5}$ $3m^4$ **43.** $\frac{5^5n^{15}}{5^3n^{12}}$ $25n^3$

44. Critical Thinking Write a quotient that simplifies to x^4y^4. *Sample answer:* $\frac{x^5y^6}{xy^2}$

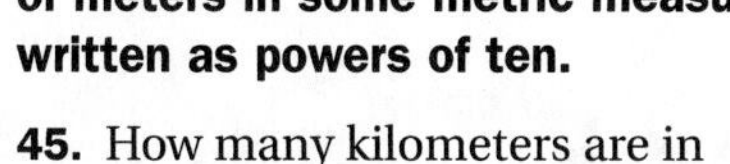

Measurement In Exercises 45–48, use the table. It shows the number of meters in some metric measures written as powers of ten.

45. How many kilometers are in a petameter? 10^{12}

46. How many gigameters are in a zettameter? 10^{12}

47. How many terameters are in a yottameter? 10^{12}

48. How many megameters are in an exameter? 10^{12}

Metric Units

Unit	Meters
Yottameter	10^{24}
Zettameter	10^{21}
Exameter	10^{18}
Petameter	10^{15}
Terameter	10^{12}
Gigameter	10^9
Megameter	10^6
Kilometer	10^3
Decameter	10^1

Computers In the 1970s and early 1980s, computer random access memory was measured in kilobytes (KB) and could be added only in quantities equal to a power of 2. In Exercises 49 and 50, how many times more memory did the newer computer have?

49. 1979: 2^3 KB; 1980: 2^5 KB 2^2 **50.** 1982: 2^6 KB; 1987: 2^9 KB 2^3

What do you think? **Astronomy**

Measurement

The distance to the Andromeda Galaxy is 21 quintillion kilometers, which is 21 followed by 18 zeros. How many exameters are in 21 quintillion kilometers? **21 exameters**

3 APPLY

ASSIGNMENT GUIDE

Basic Course
Day 1: pp. 199–200 Exs. 16–41, 55–62

Average Course
Day 1: pp. 199–200 Exs. 18–21, 26–49, 55–62

Advanced Course
Day 1: pp. 199–200 Exs. 30–35, 38–62*

Block
pp. 199–200 Exs. 18–21, 26–49, 55–62 (with 4.7)

EXTRA PRACTICE
- Student Edition, p. 730
- Chapter 4 Resource Book, pp. 52–54
- Test and Practice Generator

TRANSPARENCY

Even-numbered answers are available on transparencies.

HOMEWORK CHECK

When you review students' homework for this lesson, go over the following exercises to check understanding of key concepts.
Basic: 16, 20, 24, 36, 40
Average: 18, 26, 28, 37, 41
Advanced: 30, 32, 34, 36, 42

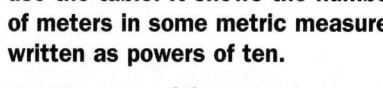

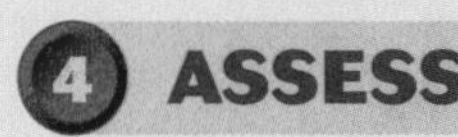

ASSESS

ASSESSMENT RESOURCES

For more assessment resources, see:

- Assessment Book
- Test and Practice Generator

MINI-QUIZ

Simplify the expression. Write your answer as a power.

1. $p^4 \cdot p^3$ p^7

2. $\frac{x^{17}}{x^{14}}$ x^3

Multiply or divide. Write your answer as a power.

3. $2^3 \cdot 2^2$ 2^5

4. $\frac{8^{19}}{8^{17}}$ 8^2

FOLLOW-UP

RETEACHING/REMEDIATION

- Study Guide in Chapter 4 Resource Book, pp. 55-56
- Tutor Place, Algebra Card 2
- eTutorial Plus Online
- Extra Practice, p. 730
- Lesson Practice in Chapter 4 Resource Book, pp. 52-54

CHALLENGE/ENRICHMENT

- Challenge Practice in Chapter 4 Resource Book, p. 57
- Teacher's Edition, p. 164F

ENGLISH LEARNER SUPPORT

- Spanish Study Guide
- Multi-Language Glossary
- Chapter Audio Summaries CDs

C **Challenge** **Evaluate the expression.**

51. $(3^2 \cdot 3)^2$ 729 **52.** $(2^0 \cdot 2^2)^3$ 64 **53.** $\left(\frac{4^7}{4^5}\right)^2$ 256 **54.** $\left(\frac{5^8}{5^7}\right)^4$ 625

Mixed Review

Evaluate the expression. *(Lesson 1.4)*

55. $(4 \times 3)^2 + 13$ 157 **56.** $405 \div (14 - 11)^4$ 5 **57.** $96 \div 2^5 \times 6$ 18

Copy and complete the statement with <, >, or =. *(Lesson 4.5)*

58. $\frac{5}{2}$? $\frac{15}{6}$ = **59.** $\frac{9}{24}$? $\frac{5}{16}$ > **60.** $\frac{5}{8}$? $\frac{7}{11}$ <

Test-Taking Practice

61. Multiple Choice What is the value of $3^2 \cdot 3^2 - 4^3$? C

A. -46 **B.** -17 **C.** 17 **D.** 46

62. Multiple Choice What is another expression for $\frac{a^9 \cdot a^4}{a^5}$? H

F. a^4 **G.** a^5 **H.** a^8 **I.** a^{13}

BRAIN GAME

Mix and Match

Materials: cards marked from 1 to 6

Number of Players: 2 or 3 players

Winning Strategy: Make the largest number possible in each round.

Mix the cards and place them face down on a flat surface. Each player takes two cards. Then using only the two cards, make the largest number possible. For example, if you picked the cards 2 and 6, you could make the following numbers:

26 62 2^6 6^2

The largest number you can make is 2^6, or 64. So, you would score 64 points for that round. After each round, reshuffle the cards to play another round.

The player with the highest score after three rounds wins.

Check work.

Negative and Zero Exponents

BEFORE

You simplified expressions with positive exponents.

Now

You'll simplify expressions with negative exponents.

WHY?

So you can describe very small objects, as in Ex. 31.

In the Real World

Review Words

exponent, p. 20

common factor, p. 173

Strobes The picture at the right was taken using a strobe light. The flash of the strobe light lasted about 1 microsecond. How can you write this time in seconds as a power of ten? You will see how to solve this problem in Example 1.

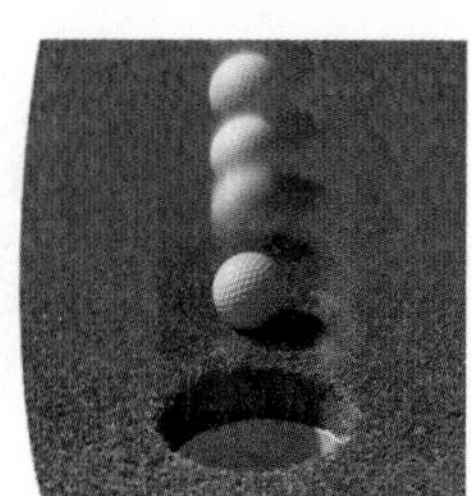

You have seen two methods for evaluating expressions involving division of powers.

Divide out common factors.

$$\frac{x^5}{x^7} = \frac{\cancel{x}^1 \cdot \cancel{x}^1 \cdot \cancel{x}^1 \cdot \cancel{x}^1 \cdot \cancel{x}^1}{\cancel{x}_1 \cdot \cancel{x}_1 \cdot \cancel{x}_1 \cdot \cancel{x}_1 \cdot \cancel{x}_1 \cdot x \cdot x} = \frac{1}{x^2}$$

Quotient of powers property

$$\frac{x^5}{x^7} = x^{5-7} = x^{-2}$$

So $\frac{1}{x^2} = x^{-2}$, which suggests the definition for negative exponents.

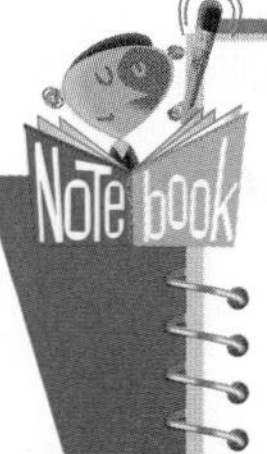

Negative Exponents

Words For any integer n and any number $a \neq 0$, a^{-n} is equal to $\frac{1}{a^n}$.

Algebra $a^{-n} = \frac{1}{a^n}$ **Numbers** $2^{-3} = \frac{1}{2^3}$

EXAMPLE 1 Using a Negative Exponent

The flash above lasts 1 microsecond, or $\frac{1}{1{,}000{,}000}$ second.

$\frac{1}{1{,}000{,}000} = \frac{1}{10^6}$ **Write 1,000,000 as 10^6.**

$= 10^{-6}$ **Definition of negative exponent**

ANSWER One flash of a strobe light lasts about 10^{-6} second.

ILLINOIS Standards and ISAT:
6.A.3, 6.B.3c; 7.A.3b

1 PLAN

SKILL CHECK

1. $2 + (-5) = \underline{?}$ -3
2. $1 + (-3) = \underline{?}$ -2
3. $-5 - 7 = \underline{?}$ -12
4. $-4 + 2 = \underline{?}$ -2

LESSON OBJECTIVE

Simplify expressions with negative exponents.

PACING

Suggested Number of Days
Basic Course: 2 days
Average Course: 2 days
Advanced Course: 2 days
Block: 0.5 block with 4.6
0.5 block with 4.8

TEACHING RESOURCES

For a complete list of Teaching Resources, see page 164B.

TRANSPARENCY

Warm-Up Exercises for this lesson are available on a transparency.

2 TEACH

MOTIVATING THE LESSON

Show students the pattern $10^2 = 100$, $10^1 = 10$, $10^0 = 1$. Then ask what the value of 10^{-1} might be.

TIPS FOR NEW TEACHERS

Encourage students to rewrite expressions with negative exponents as expressions with positive exponents in the denominator. See Tips for New Teachers in the *Chapter 4 Resource Book*.

EXTRA EXAMPLES

Example 1 A camera shutter is open for 1 one-thousandth of a second. Rewrite $\frac{1}{1000}$ with a negative exponent. **10^{-3}**

Example 2 Evaluate $3^7 \cdot 3^{-10}$. **3^{-3} or $\frac{1}{27}$**

Example 3 Simplify.

a. $\frac{5x^0}{3}$ **$\frac{5}{3}$**

b. $2y^{-3}$ **$\frac{2}{y^3}$**

c. $\frac{6x^{-4}}{x^{-2}}$ **$\frac{6}{x^2}$**

Differentiating Instruction

Alternative Teaching Strategy
For division exercises involving quotients, some students may find it easier to eliminate negative exponents as a first step in simplifying. For instance, Example 3c can be done by first writing $\frac{8x^{-3}}{x}$ as $\frac{8}{x \cdot x^3}$, which easily simplifies to $\frac{8}{x^4}$.

CONCEPT CHECK

What is the value of a nonzero number with a zero exponent? **1**

DAILY PUZZLER

Imagine taking a sheet of paper and folding it in half. This step is called F1. Fold the sheet in half again. This step is F2. After step F7, how many layers of paper will you have? **2^7, or 128 layers**

EXAMPLE 2 Evaluating a Numerical Expression

$5^2 \cdot 5^{-5} = 5^{2+(-5)}$	Product of powers property
$= 5^{-3}$	Simplify.
$= \frac{1}{5^3} = \frac{1}{125}$	Use definition of negative exponent and evaluate power.

Zero Exponents

Algebra If a is a nonzero number, then $a^0 = 1$.

Numbers $2^0 = 1$

Watch Out!

In an expression such as $-2n^0$ and $4n^{-5}$, the exponent is applied only to the variable, not to the coefficient.

EXAMPLE 3 Simplifying Variable Expressions

Simplify. Write the expression using only positive exponents.

a. $-2n^0 = -2 \cdot n^0$	Zero exponent applies only to n.
$= -2 \cdot 1$	Definition of zero exponent
$= -2$	Multiply.
b. $4n^{-5} = 4 \cdot n^{-5}$	Exponent applies only to n.
$= 4 \cdot \frac{1}{n^5}$	Definition of negative exponent
$= \frac{4}{n^5}$	Multiply.
c. $\frac{8x^{-3}}{x} = \frac{8 \cdot x^{-3}}{x^1}$	Exponent applies only to x.
$= 8 \cdot x^{-3-1}$	Quotient of powers property
$= 8 \cdot x^{-4}$	Simplify.
$= \frac{8}{x^4}$	Definition of negative exponent

Your turn now Evaluate the expression.

1. 7^{-2} **$\frac{1}{49}$** **2.** $(-2)^{-5}$ **$-\frac{1}{32}$** **3.** $6 \cdot 6^{-3}$ **$\frac{1}{36}$** **4.** $10^{-5} \cdot 10^7$ **100**

Simplify. Write the expression using only positive exponents.

5. $-6m^{-1}$ **$\frac{-6}{m}$, or $-\frac{6}{m}$** **6.** $b^2 \cdot b^{-2}$ **1** **7.** $\frac{5x^4}{x^7}$ **$\frac{5}{x^3}$** **8.** $\frac{10a^{-3}}{a^4}$ **$\frac{10}{a^7}$**

4.7 Exercises

More Practice, p. 730

Getting Ready to Practice

Vocabulary Determine whether the statement is *true* or *false*.

1. The base of the expression 2^{-5} is 2. true
2. The exponent of the expression 2^{-5} is 5. false

Evaluate the expression.

3. 3^{-4} $\frac{1}{81}$ 4. $(-4)^{-3}$ $\frac{-1}{64}$ 5. $2^{-10} \cdot 2^{6}$ $\frac{1}{16}$ 6. 12^{0} 1

7. **Find the Error** Describe and correct the error in the solution.

$5^{-3} = (-5)(-5)(-5)$
$= -125$ ✗

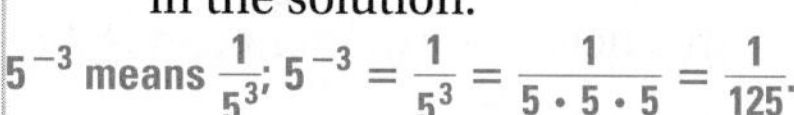

5^{-3} means $\frac{1}{5^3}$; $5^{-3} = \frac{1}{5^3} = \frac{1}{5 \cdot 5 \cdot 5} = \frac{1}{125}$.

8. **Biology** Plankton is made up of tiny plants (called phytoplankton) and tiny animals (called zooplankton). One type of phytoplankton may be as small as 0.2 micrometer. A micrometer is 10^{-6} meter. What part of a meter is this phytoplankton? Use a positive exponent to write your answer. $\frac{2}{10^7}$

Single-celled alga

Practice and Problem Solving

A Evaluate the expression.

9. $(-6)^{-2}$ $\frac{1}{36}$ 10. $2 \cdot 2^{-6}$ $\frac{1}{32}$ 11. $5^4 \cdot 5^{-8}$ $\frac{1}{625}$ 12. 9^0 1

Simplify. Write the expression using only positive exponents.

13. $m^{-9} \cdot m^5$ $\frac{1}{m^4}$ 14. $x^5 \cdot x^{-5}$ 1 15. $9n^{-3}$ $\frac{9}{n^3}$ 16. $c^{-1} \cdot c^{-2} \cdot c^{-4}$ $\frac{1}{c^7}$

17. $b^3 \cdot b^{-4} \cdot b^{-5}$ $\frac{1}{b^6}$ 18. $\frac{4z^{-2}}{z^4}$ $\frac{4}{z^6}$ 19. $\frac{a^{-5}}{a^8}$ $\frac{1}{a^{13}}$ 20. $\frac{18r^{-6}}{3r^3}$ $\frac{6}{r^9}$

21. **Physics** Pressure is measured in units called *pascals*. This unit can be expressed as $kg \cdot m^{-1} \cdot s^{-2}$. Write the unit without negative exponents. $\frac{kg}{m \cdot s^2}$

B Find the missing exponent.

22. $(4x^5)^? = 1$ 0 23. $15a^? = \frac{15}{a^8}$ −8 24. $y^? \cdot y^4 = \frac{1}{y}$ −5 25. $\frac{x^{-3}}{x^?} = \frac{1}{x^{13}}$ 10

26. **Writing** Your friend missed today's class. Write a note to show your friend how to simplify the expression $\frac{6a^{-3}}{a^3}$.

Example	Exercises
1	21, 31
2	9-12
3	13-20

· More Examples
· eTutorial Plus

26. *Sample answer*: To simplify $\frac{6a^{-3}}{a^3}$, first use the quotient of powers property to rewrite it as $6a^{-3-3}$ which simplifies to $6a^{-6}$. Then use the definition of a negative exponent to rewrite the expression as $\frac{6}{a^6}$.

3 APPLY

ASSIGNMENT GUIDE

Basic Course

Day 1: EP p. 728 Exs. 13-16; pp. 203-204 Exs. 9-12, 21, 35-45

Day 2: pp. 203-204 Exs. 13-20, 22-25, 46, 47

Average Course

Day 1: pp. 203-204 Exs. 9-12, 21, 35-45

Day 2: pp. 203-204 Exs. 17-20, 22-30, 46, 47

Advanced Course

Day 1: pp. 203-204 Exs. 11, 12, 27-31, 35-42

Day 2: pp. 203-204 Exs. 17-20, 22-26, 32-34*, 46, 47

Block

pp. 203-204 Exs. 9-12, 21, 35-45 (with 4.6)

pp. 203-204 Exs. 17-20, 22-30, 46, 47 (with 4.8)

EXTRA PRACTICE

- Student Edition, p. 730
- Chapter 4 Resource Book, pp. 61-63
- Test and Practice Generator

TRANSPARENCY

Even-numbered answers are available on transparencies.

HOMEWORK CHECK

When you review students' homework for this lesson, go over the following exercises to check understanding of key concepts.

Basic: 9, 10, 13, 16, 21
Average: 10, 11, 16, 18, 21
Advanced: 11, 12, 18, 20, 31

COMMON ERROR

In Exercise 4, watch for students who do something inappropriate with the two negative signs, such as trying to multiply them together to get 4^3.

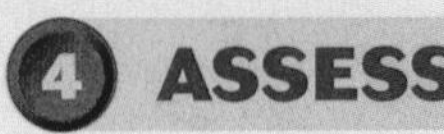

4 ASSESS

Assessment Resources

For more assessment resources, see:
- Assessment Book
- Test and Practice Generator

Mini-Quiz

Evaluate the expression.

1. $(-9)^0$ 1
2. $4^4 \cdot 4^{-2}$ 16

Write the expression using only positive exponents.

3. $y^{-7} \cdot y^5$ $\frac{1}{y^2}$
4. $\frac{24a^{-3}}{8a^{-4}}$ $3a$

5 FOLLOW-UP

Reteaching/Remediation

- Study Guide in Chapter 4 Resource Book, pp. 64–65
- eTutorial Plus Online
- Extra Practice, p. 730
- Lesson Practice in Chapter 4 Resource Book, pp. 61–63

Challenge/Enrichment

- Challenge Practice in Chapter 4 Resource Book, p. 66
- Teacher's Edition, p. 164F

English Learner Support

- Spanish Study Guide
- Multi-Language Glossary
- Chapter Audio Summaries CDs

Measurement **In Exercises 27–30, use the table. It shows the number of meters in some metric measures written as powers of ten.**

Metric Units	
Unit	Meter
Decimeter	10^{-1}
Centimeter	10^{-2}
Millimeter	10^{-3}
Micrometer	10^{-6}
Nanometer	10^{-9}
Picometer	10^{-12}
Attometer	10^{-18}
Yoctometer	10^{-24}

27. How many picometers are in a decimeter? 10^{11}
28. How many yoctometers are in a micrometer? 10^{18}
29. How many nanometers are in a decimeter? 10^8
30. How many attometers are in a centimeter? 10^{16}

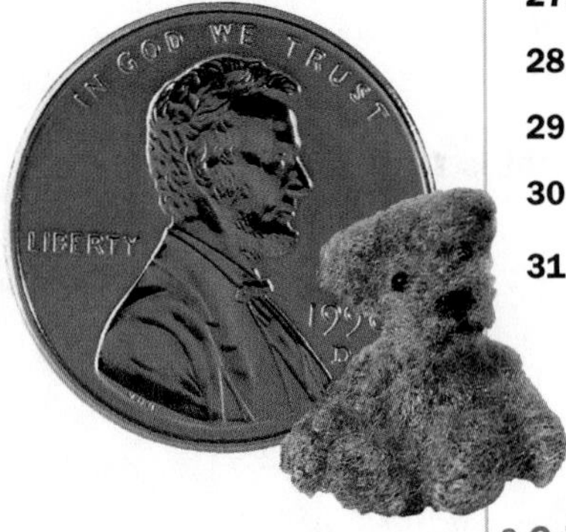

31. **Teddy Bear** In 1997, German teddy bear specialist Hanne Schramm made the smallest teddy bear in the world. It measures 0.47 inch or about 10 millimeters. How many nanometers are in 10 millimeters? 10^7

C **Critical Thinking** **In Exercises 32–33, copy and complete the statement using *always*, *sometimes*, or *never*.**

32. A power with a negative exponent can _?_ be written as a fraction. always
33. A power with a positive base and a negative exponent is _?_ negative. never
34. **Challenge** Use the product of powers property to explain why $a^0 = 1$, where a is a nonzero number, makes sense.
Sample answer: $a^0 = a^{-1+1} = a^{-1} \cdot a^1 = \frac{1}{a} \cdot a = \frac{a}{a} = 1$

Mixed Review

Simplify the expression. *(Lessons 2.2–2.5)*

35. $-18 + (-7)$ -25 36. $-46 + 0$ -46 37. $34 - (-18)$ 52 38. $16 - 30$ -14

39. $-6 \cdot (-15)$ 90 40. $0(-8)$ 0 41. $51 \div (-3)$ -17 42. $-18 \div (-9)$ 2

Basic Skills **Find the unknown number.**

43. _?_ $+ 8 = 7$ -1 44. $9 \times$ _?_ $= 108$ 12 45. _?_ $\div 12 = 6$ 72

Test-Taking Practice

INTERNET
State Test Practice
CLASSZONE.COM

46. **Multiple Choice** Simplify the expression $\left(\frac{8^{-2}}{8}\right)^0$. C

A. $\frac{1}{512}$ B. $\frac{1}{8}$ C. 1 D. 8

47. **Multiple Choice** Simplify the expression $\frac{-3x^{-4}}{x^2}$. F

F. $\frac{-3}{x^6}$ G. $-3x^6$ H. $\frac{-3}{x^{-6}}$ I. $\frac{-3x}{x^6}$

Scientific Notation

BEFORE	Now	WHY?
You multiplied numbers by powers of 10.	You'll read and write numbers using scientific notation.	So you can find the number of new \$1 bills printed, as in Ex. 39.

scientific notation, p. 205

In the Real World

Bubbles The brilliant colors observed in soap bubbles occur as a result of light reflecting from the inner and outer surfaces of the bubble. The thickness of a soap bubble is about 0.000004 meter. How can you use the powers of 10 to write 0.000004? You will see how to solve this problem in Example 1, part (a).

One way to write very small or very large numbers is to use *scientific notation.*

Using Scientific Notation

A number is written in **scientific notation** if it has the form $c \times 10^n$ where $1 \leq c < 10$ and n is an integer.

Standard form	Product form	Scientific notation
325,000	$3.25 \times 100{,}000$	3.25×10^5
0.0005	5×0.0001	5×10^{-4}

Powers of ten

$10^5 = 100{,}000$
$10^4 = 10{,}000$
$10^3 = 1000$
$10^2 = 100$
$10^1 = 10$
$10^0 = 1$
$10^{-1} = 0.1$
$10^{-2} = 0.01$
$10^{-3} = 0.001$
$10^{-4} = 0.0001$
$10^{-5} = 0.00001$

EXAMPLE 1 Writing Numbers in Scientific Notation

a. The thickness of a soap bubble is about 0.0000004 meter.

Standard form	Product form	Scientific notation
0.000004	4×0.000001	4×10^{-6}
Move decimal point 6 places to the right.		Exponent is −6.

b. There are over 300,000,000,000 stars in the Andromeda Galaxy.

Standard form	Product form	Scientific notation
300,000,000,000	$3 \times 100{,}000{,}000{,}000$	3×10^{11}
Move decimal point 11 places to the left.		Exponent is 11.

ILLINOIS Standards and ISAT:
6.A.3

SKILL CHECK

1. $100 \times 10 = \underline{?}$ 1000
2. $10{,}000 \div 1000 = \underline{?}$ 10
3. $100 \div 1000 = \underline{?}$ $\frac{1}{10}$

LESSON OBJECTIVE

Read and write numbers using scientific notation.

PACING

Suggested Number of Days
Basic Course: 1 day
Average Course: 1 day
Advanced Course: 1 day
Block: 0.5 block with 4.7

TEACHING RESOURCES

For a complete list of Teaching Resources, see page 164B.

TRANSPARENCY

Warm-Up Exercises for this lesson are available on a transparency.

2 TEACH

MOTIVATING THE LESSON

Ask students how to write 1,000,000 and 0.000001 as powers of 10.

TIPS FOR NEW TEACHERS

Students may have problems moving decimal points correctly when there are more than 3 or 4 zeros. Encourage students to count decimal places slowly and carefully. See Tips for New Teachers in the *Chapter 4 Resource Book*.

EXTRA EXAMPLES

Example 1 Write the numbers in scientific notation.

a. A molecule has a diameter of about 0.000000004 cm. 4×10^{-9}

b. A cubic meter of aluminum has a mass of 2700 kg. 2.7×10^{3}

Example 2 Write the number in standard form.

a. 4.1×10^5 410,000

b. 2.15×10^{-3} 0.00215

Example 3 Write the product $(2.7 \times 10^4) \times (6.1 \times 10^2)$ in scientific notation. 1.647×10^7

CONCEPT CHECK

Is 12.43×10^3 written in scientific notation? Explain. **No; by definition the value of c in the form $c \times 10^n$ must be greater than or equal to 1 and less than 10 for the number to be in scientific notation.**

DAILY PUZZLER

What number do you multiply 6×10^{-6} by to get 6×10^6? 1×10^{12}

EXAMPLE 2 Writing Numbers in Standard Form

	Scientific notation	Product form	Standard form
a.	7.2×10^5	$7.2 \times 100{,}000$	720,000
	Exponent is 5.		Move decimal point 5 places to the right.
b.	4.65×10^{-7}	4.65×0.0000001	0.000000465
	Exponent is -7.		Move decimal point 7 places to the left.

Your turn now Write the number in scientific notation.

1. 4000 4×10^3
2. 7,300,000 7.3×10^6
3. 63,000,000,000 6.3×10^{10}
4. 0.00475 4.75×10^{-3}
5. 0.00000526 5.26×10^{-6}
6. 0.0000000082 8.2×10^{-9}

Write the number in standard form.

7. 3.5×10^3 3500
8. 2.48×10^6 2,480,000
9. 6×10^{11} 600,000,000,000
10. 5.1×10^{-4} 0.00051
11. 9.16×10^{-2} 0.0916
12. 1.02×10^{-8} 0.0000000102

You can use the product of powers property to multiply two numbers written in scientific notation.

Watch Out!

When a number is in scientific notation, the factor c must be greater than or equal to 1 and less than 10. The number 28.35×10^{10} is not written in scientific notation because $28.35 > 10$.

EXAMPLE 3 Multiplying Numbers in Scientific Notation

Find the product $(4.5 \times 10^3) \times (6.3 \times 10^7)$.

Solution

$(4.5 \times 10^3) \times (6.3 \times 10^7)$

$= 4.5 \times 6.3 \times 10^3 \times 10^7$ — Commutative property of multiplication

$= (4.5 \times 6.3) \times (10^3 \times 10^7)$ — Associative property of multiplication

$= 28.35 \times 10^{10}$ — Product of powers property

$= 2.835 \times 10^1 \times 10^{10}$ — Write 28.35 in scientific notation.

$= 2.835 \times 10^{11}$ — Product of powers property

Your turn now Write the product in scientific notation.

13. $(1.25 \times 10^6) \times (7.6 \times 10^{12})$ 9.5×10^{18}
14. $(8 \times 10^5) \times (5.65 \times 10^4)$ 4.52×10^{10}

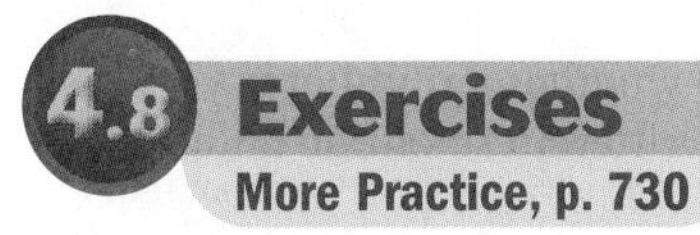

4.8 Exercises

More Practice, p. 730

Getting Ready to Practice

Vocabulary **Tell whether the number is expressed in scientific notation.**

1. 9.32×10^5 yes **2.** 56.8×10^2 no **3.** 7×10^{-4} yes

Write the number in scientific notation.

4. 89,200,000,000 8.92×10^{10} **5.** 0.468 4.68×10^{-1} **6.** 0.0000671 6.71×10^{-5}

Write the number in standard form.

7. 4.35×10^6 4,350,000 **8.** 5.72×10^{-3} 0.00572 **9.** 9.62×10^7 96,200,000

10. Guided Problem Solving The mass of Earth is about 1.3×10^{25} pounds. The mass of Jupiter is about 4.2×10^{27} pounds. About how many times greater is Jupiter's mass than Earth's mass?

(1) Write the quotient of 4.2 and 1.3 as a decimal. about 3.2

(2) Write the quotient of the powers of 10. 10^2

(3) Write the product of the quotients in scientific notation. 3.2×10^2

Practice and Problem Solving

with Homework

Example	Exercises
1	11-16, 27
2	17-22, 28
3	23-26

Online Resources
CLASSZONE.COM
- More Examples
- eTutorial Plus

A **Write the number in scientific notation.**

11. 7900 7.9×10^3 **12.** 8,100,000,000 8.1×10^9 **13.** 2,130,000 2.13×10^6

14. 0.0312 3.12×10^{-2} **15.** 0.000000415 4.15×10^{-7} **16.** 0.0000000342 3.42×10^{-8}

Write the number in standard form.

17. 8.71×10^{-2} 0.0871 **18.** 6.35×10^{-6} 0.00000635 **19.** 1.76×10^{-9} 0.00000000176

20. 4.13×10^9 4,130,000,000 **21.** 2.83×10^{12} 2,830,000,000,000 **22.** 3.61×10^7 36,100,000

Write the product in scientific notation.

23. $(3 \times 10^3) \times (2 \times 10^5)$ 6×10^8 **24.** $(8 \times 10^6) \times (7 \times 10^4)$ 5.6×10^{11}

25. $(7.8 \times 10^6) \times (8.4 \times 10^7)$ 6.552×10^{14} **26.** $(3.6 \times 10^8) \times (5.2 \times 10^5)$ 1.872×10^{14}

27. Well Water In the United States, 15,000,000 households use private wells for their water supply. Write this number in scientific notation. 1.5×10^7

28. State Parks The United States has a total of 1.2916×10^7 acres of land reserved for state parks. Write this number in standard form. 12,916,000

3 APPLY

ASSIGNMENT GUIDE

Basic Course

Day 1: pp. 207-208 Exs. 11-28, 30-31, 43-48

Average Course

Day 1: pp. 207-208 Exs. 14-16, 20-39, 43-48

Advanced Course

Day 1: pp. 207-208 Exs. 15, 16, 21, 22, 25-45*, 47, 48

Block

pp. 207-208 Exs. 14-16, 20-39, 43-48 (with 4.7)

EXTRA PRACTICE

- Student Edition, p. 730
- Chapter 4 Resource Book, pp. 70-72
- Test and Practice Generator

TRANSPARENCY

Even-numbered answers are available on transparencies.

HOMEWORK CHECK

When you review students' homework for this lesson, go over the following exercises to check understanding of key concepts.
Basic: 11, 13, 17, 19, 23
Average: 14, 15, 20, 21, 24
Advanced: 15, 20, 25, 27, 28

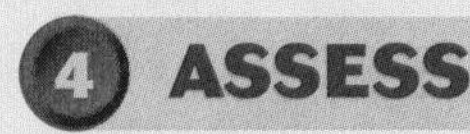

ASSESSMENT RESOURCES

For more assessment resources, see:

- Assessment Book
- Test and Practice Generator

MINI-QUIZ

Write the number in scientific notation.

1. 78,000 7.8×10^4

2. 0.000025 2.5×10^{-5}

Write the number in standard form.

3. 4.5×10^6 4,500,000

4. 1.7×10^{-8} 0.000000017

5. Write the product $(4 \times 10^{-3}) \times (5 \times 10^5)$ in scientific notation. 2×10^3

FOLLOW-UP

RETEACHING/REMEDIATION

- Study Guide in Chapter 4 Resource Book, pp. 73–74
- eTutorial Plus Online
- Extra Practice, p. 730
- Lesson Practice in Chapter 4 Resource Book, pp. 70–72

CHALLENGE/ENRICHMENT

- Challenge Practice in Chapter 4 Resource Book, p. 76
- Teacher's Edition, p. 164F

ENGLISH LEARNER SUPPORT

- Spanish Study Guide
- Multi-Language Glossary
- Chapter Audio Summaries CDs

29. Number Sense Explain how you can tell whether a number is very small or very large when the number is written in scientific notation. See margin.

B **Copy and complete the statement with <, >, or =.**

30. 6.92×10^{11} _?_ 6.92×10^{12} <

31. 3.67×10^{-3} _?_ 3.76×10^{-4} >

Find the product or quotient. Write your answer in scientific notation.

32. $(6.8 \times 10^{-2}) \times (3.9 \times 10^{-5})$ 2.652×10^{-6}

33. $(2.6 \times 10^7) \times (4.1 \times 10^{-3})$ 1.066×10^5

34. $(7.6 \times 10^{-8}) \times (4.8 \times 10^{-6})$ 3.648×10^{-13}

35. $(5.4 \times 10^{-5}) \times (3.6 \times 10^{-9})$ 1.944×10^{-13}

36. $\frac{4.08 \times 10^6}{3.4 \times 10^2}$ 1.2×10^4

37. $\frac{2.765 \times 10^{21}}{7.9 \times 10^9}$ 3.5×10^{11}

38. $\frac{5.46 \times 10^{28}}{6.5 \times 10^{24}}$ 8.4×10^3

U.S. Currency

The United States Bureau of Engraving and Printing prints about 4,440,000 new $5 bills each day. What is the dollar value of these bills? $22,200,000

39. U.S. Currency The United States Bureau of Engraving and Printing prints about 17 million new $1 bills each day. About how many bills are printed in one week? in one year? Write your answers in scientific notation. 1.19×10^8; 6.205×10^9

40. Critical Thinking Order the numbers from least to greatest.

3.75×10^8 37,500,000 3.57×10^9 5.37×10^7 37,500,000; 5.37×10^7; 3.75×10^8; 3.57×10^9

C **41. Science** The radius of a proton is about 1.2 Fermis. One Fermi is equal to 10^{-15} meter. How many centimeters is the radius of a proton? Write your answer in scientific notation. 1.2×10^{-13} cm

42. Challenge Light travels 1.86×10^5 miles in 1 second. How far does light travel in one year? about 5.87×10^{12} mi

29. *Sample answer:* Very large numbers have positive powers of 10. The larger the exponent, the larger the number. Very small numbers have negative powers of 10. The larger the absolute value of the exponent, the smaller the number.

Mixed Review

In Exercises 43–44, evaluate the expression. *(Lessons 2.2, 2.3)*

43. $-8 + 12 + (-16) + 18$ 6

44. $34 - (-43) - (3 - 6)$ 80

45. Simplify $\frac{6n}{9mn}$. *(Lesson 4.3)* $\frac{2}{3m}$

46. Basic Skills Find the amount of time that has elapsed from 10:46 A.M. to 3:13 P.M. 4 h 27 min

Test-Taking Practice

INTERNET State Test Practice CLASSZONE.COM

47. Multiple Choice In 2000, there were approximately 281,000,000 people in the United States. Which of the following is *not* another way of expressing the number 281,000,000? A

A. 28.1 million **B.** 0.281 billion **C.** 28.1×10^7 **D.** 2.81×10^8

48. Short Response A space probe travels about 1.5×10^6 miles per day to its destination 21 million miles away. It has already traveled 9 million miles. About how many days of travel does it have left? 8 days

4.8 Technology Activity

CALCULATOR

Using Scientific Notation

GOAL Use a calculator to perform operations on numbers written in scientific notation.

Example **The Sun is about 1.5×10^8 kilometers from Earth, and Proxima Centauri is about 2.5×10^5 times farther from Earth than the Sun. How far is Proxima Centauri from Earth?**

Solution

To find how far Proxima Centauri is from Earth, multiply the distance between the Sun and Earth by 2.5×10^5.

Keystrokes	Display
1.5 EE 8 × 2.5 EE 5 =	3.75 x10 13

ANSWER Proxima Centauri is approximately 3.75×10^{13} kilometers from Earth.

HELP with Technology

The EE key on a calculator means "times 10 raised to the power of."

Your turn now **Use a calculator to evaluate the expression. Write your answer in scientific notation.**

1. $(3.19 \times 10^7) \times (8.5 \times 10^6)$ 2.7115×10^{14}
2. $(6.7 \times 10^{-3}) \times (1.12 \times 10^{15})$ 7.504×10^{12}
3. $(3.3 \times 10^{-3}) \times (4.8 \times 10^{-9})$ 1.584×10^{-11}
4. $(7.1 \times 10^{-9}) \times (2.05 \times 10^6)$ 1.4555×10^{-2}
5. $\frac{8.1 \times 10^{10}}{3.02 \times 10^3}$ 2.682119205×10^7
6. $\frac{1.44 \times 10^{-15}}{1.6 \times 10}$ 9×10^{-17}
7. $\frac{2.8 \times 10^{-11}}{2.05 \times 10^{-4}}$ $1.365853659 \times 10^{-7}$
8. **Water** About 110 billion gallons of water flow through Lake Erie each day. How many gallons of water flow through Lake Erie in a week? in a year? about 7.7×10^{11} gal; about 4.015×10^{13} gal
9. **Biology** The nucleus of a human cell is about 7×10^{-6} meter in diameter. A ribosome, another part of a cell, is about 3×10^{-8} meter in diameter. How many times larger is a nucleus than a ribosome? about 2.3×10^2

ILLINOIS Standards and ISAT:
6.A.3

1 PLAN

LEARN THE METHOD

- Students will use a calculator to perform operations on numbers written in scientific notation.
- Students can redo Exercises 23-26 and 32-38 of Lesson 4.8 for more practice in using their calculators to perform operations in scientific notation.

2 TEACH

TIPS FOR SUCCESS

Show students how to estimate the exponent of the product before keying in their data so they can check the reasonableness of their answers.

EXTRA EXAMPLES

Example Evaluate $(3.6 \times 10^{-12}) \times (9.8 \times 10^{20})$. Write your answer in scientific notation. 3.528×10^9

3 CLOSE

ASSESSMENT

1. What does 4.7 EE 22 represent? 4.7×10^{22}
2. How would you multiply 3.2×10^{12} by 4.1×10^{-3}? Enter the keystrokes 3.2 EE 12 × 4.1 EE (−) 3.

Additional Resources

The following resources are available to help review the materials in Lessons 4.5–4.8.

Chapter 4 Resource Book
- Lesson Practice
- Study Guide

Assessment Book
- Chapter 4 Quiz 2

Technology
- Test and Practice Generator
- eTutorial CD-ROM

Internet
- Classzone
- eWorkbook Plus Online
- eTutorial Plus Online

English Learner Support

- Spanish Study Guide
- Multi-Language Glossary
- Chapter Audio Summaries CDs

Notebook Review

Review the vocabulary definitions in your notebook.

Copy the review examples in your notebook. Then complete the exercises.

Check Your Definitions

least common denominator (LCD), p. 192 scientific notation, p. 205

Use Your Vocabulary

1. Copy and complete: A number is written in _?_ if it has the form $c \times 10^n$ where $1 \le c < 10$ and n is an integer. scientific notation

4.5 Can you compare and order fractions?

EXAMPLE Compare $\frac{11}{18}$ and $\frac{3}{4}$.

The LCM of 18 and 4 is 36, so the least common denominator is 36.

$\frac{11}{18} = \frac{11 \cdot 2}{18 \cdot 2} = \frac{22}{36}$ $\frac{3}{4} = \frac{3 \cdot 9}{4 \cdot 9} = \frac{27}{36}$

ANSWER Because $\frac{22}{36} < \frac{27}{36}$, you can write $\frac{11}{18} < \frac{3}{4}$.

Copy and complete the statement with <, >, or =.

2. $\frac{2}{3}\ \underline{?}\ \frac{5}{9}$ > **3.** $\frac{5}{12}\ \underline{?}\ \frac{1}{3}$ > **4.** $\frac{4}{5}\ \underline{?}\ \frac{6}{7}$ < **5.** $\frac{16}{24}\ \underline{?}\ \frac{20}{30}$ =

4.6 Can you use the rules of exponents?

EXAMPLE Multiply or divide. Write your answer as a power.

a. $x^7 \cdot x^8 = x^{7+8}$
$= x^{15}$

b. $\frac{a^6}{a^3} = a^{6-3}$
$= a^3$

Simplify. Write your answer as a power.

6. $n^4 \cdot n^9$ n^{13} **7.** $y^6 \cdot y^{10}$ y^{16} **8.** $\frac{x^7}{x^5}$ x^2 **9.** $\frac{c^{12}}{c^8}$ c^4

4.7 Can you use negative exponents?

EXAMPLE Write $x^{-4} \cdot x^{-3}$ using only positive exponents.

$$x^{-4} \cdot x^{-3} = x^{-4+(-3)} = x^{-7} = \frac{1}{x^7}$$

Simplify. Write the expression using only positive exponents.

10. $12a^{-5}$ $\frac{12}{a^5}$ **11.** $n^7 \cdot n^{-10}$ $\frac{1}{n^3}$ **12.** $\frac{m^{-6}}{m^5}$ $\frac{1}{m^{11}}$ **13.** $\frac{c^{-9}}{c^4}$ $\frac{1}{c^{13}}$

4.8 Can you write a number in scientific notation?

EXAMPLE Write the number in scientific notation.

a. $980{,}000{,}000 = 9.8 \times 10^8$ **b.** $0.000012 = 1.2 \times 10^{-5}$

Write the number in scientific notation.

14. 34,600,000,000 3.46×10^{10} **15.** 0.0000009 9×10^{-7} **16.** 0.000000000502 5.02×10^{-10}

Stop and Think about Lessons 4.5–4.8

17. Writing Explain how to find the product $(5 \times 10^9) \times (4 \times 10^{15})$ without using a calculator.

17. *Sample answer:* Use the commutative and associative properties to rewrite the product as $(5 \times 4) \times (10^9 \times 10^{15})$. Use multiplication and the product of powers property to simplify this to 20×10^{24}. Move the decimal point to write the product in scientific notation as 2.0×10^{25}.

Review Quiz 2

Copy and complete the statement with <, >, or =.

1. $\frac{2}{5} \underline{?} \frac{6}{15}$ = **2.** $\frac{5}{6} \underline{?} \frac{4}{9}$ > **3.** $\frac{9}{15} \underline{?} \frac{5}{9}$ > **4.** $\frac{35}{40} \underline{?} \frac{21}{24}$ =

Order the numbers from least to greatest.

5. $\frac{2}{3}, \frac{5}{6}, \frac{1}{2}, \frac{5}{12}$ $\frac{5}{12}, \frac{1}{2}, \frac{2}{3}, \frac{5}{6}$

6. $1\frac{4}{7}, 1\frac{5}{14}, \frac{5}{4}, 1\frac{5}{8}$ $\frac{5}{4}, 1\frac{5}{14}, 1\frac{4}{7}, 1\frac{5}{8}$

Multiple or divide. Write your answer as a power using only positive exponents.

7. $b^2 \cdot b^4$ b^6 **8.** $c^5 \cdot c^{-2}$ c^3 **9.** $\frac{a^7}{a^2}$ a^5 **10.** $\frac{n^{-2}}{n^3}$ $\frac{1}{n^5}$

11. Popcorn People in the United States eat 1,120,000,000 pounds of popcorn a year. Write this number in scientific notation. 1.12×10^9 lb

ADDITIONAL RESOURCES

The following resources are available to help review the materials in this chapter.

Chapter 4 Resource Book

- Chapter Review Games and Activities, p. 77
- Cumulative Practice, Chs. 84–85

English/Spanish Chapter Reviews and Tests

Chapter Audio Summaries CDs

eTutorial CD-ROM

eWorkbook Plus Online

eTutorial Plus Online

1. The greatest common factor is the greatest number that is a factor of both numbers. The least common multiple is the smallest number that is a multiple of both numbers.

Chapter Review

Vocabulary

prime number, p. 169
composite number, p. 169
prime factorization, p. 169
factor tree, p. 169
monomial, p. 170
common factor, p. 173
greatest common factor (GCF), p. 173
relatively prime, p. 174
simplest form, p. 179
equivalent fractions, p. 179
multiple, p. 186
common multiple, p. 186
least common multiple (LCM), p. 186
least common denominator (LCD), p. 192
scientific notation, p. 205

Vocabulary Review

1. Describe the difference between the *greatest common factor* and the *least common multiple* of two numbers. See margin.
2. Give three examples of prime numbers greater than 20. *Sample answer:* 23, 31, 37
3. Give three examples of monomials. *Sample answer:* $3x$, $4s^2$, $7ab^3$
4. Describe what it means for two numbers to be relatively prime. Their only common factor is 1.

Copy and complete the statement.

5. A fraction is in _?_ if its numerator and denominator have 1 as their GCF. simplest form
6. A(n) _?_ is a whole number that has positive factors other than 1 and itself. composite number
7. When you write a number as the product of prime numbers, you are writing its _?_. prime factorization
8. Two fractions are _?_ if they represent the same number. equivalent

Review Questions

Write the prime factorization of the number. *(Lesson 4.1)*

9. 54 $2 \cdot 3^3$
10. 70 $2 \cdot 5 \cdot 7$
11. 150 $2 \cdot 3 \cdot 5^2$
12. 184 $2^3 \cdot 23$

Factor the monomial. *(Lesson 4.1)*

13. $19a^2b$ $19 \cdot a \cdot a \cdot b$
14. $28xy^3$ $2 \cdot 2 \cdot 7 \cdot x \cdot y \cdot y \cdot y$
15. $56u^2v^2$ $2 \cdot 2 \cdot 2 \cdot 7 \cdot u \cdot u \cdot v \cdot v$
16. $80p^4q^3$ $2 \cdot 2 \cdot 2 \cdot 2 \cdot 5 \cdot p \cdot p \cdot p \cdot p \cdot q \cdot q \cdot q$

Find the greatest common factor of the numbers or monomials. *(Lesson 4.2)*

17. 20, 40, 90 10
18. 56, 84, 196 28
19. 48, 60, 165 3
20. $2x, x^2, x^3$ x
21. $18xy^2, 81xy$ $9xy$
22. $54s^4t^4, 164st^3$ $2st^3$

Review Questions

Write the fraction in simplest form. *(Lesson 4.3)*

23. $\frac{16}{48}$ $\frac{1}{3}$ **24.** $-\frac{38}{95}$ $-\frac{2}{5}$ **25.** $-\frac{32}{102}$ $-\frac{16}{51}$ **26.** $\frac{104}{39}$ $\frac{8}{3}$

27. $\frac{3bc}{9b}$ $\frac{c}{3}$ **28.** $-\frac{9abc}{12a}$ $-\frac{3bc}{4}$ **29.** $\frac{20m}{5mn}$ $\frac{4}{n}$ **30.** $\frac{21bcd}{7bc}$ $3d$

Find the least common multiple of the numbers or monomials. *(Lesson 4.4)*

31. 15, 35 **105** **32.** 180, 240 **720** **33.** $5m^2n^4, 25mn^3$ $25m^2n^4$ **34.** $6p^2q^3r^4, 14pq^2r^3$ $42p^2q^3r^4$

35. Fountain A fountain in an amusement park has special-effect devices called *shooters*. They shoot columns of water at different time intervals. One shooter goes off every 8 seconds while another goes off every 12 seconds. How long after the fountain is turned on will both shooters go off at the same time? *(Lesson 4.4)* **24 sec**

Copy and complete the statement with <, >, or =. *(Lesson 4.5)*

36. $\frac{79}{16} \ \underline{?} \ \frac{35}{8}$ $>$ **37.** $6\frac{2}{3} \ \underline{?} \ \frac{81}{12}$ $<$ **38.** $\frac{161}{9} \ \underline{?} \ 17\frac{8}{9}$ $=$ **39.** $\frac{223}{15} \ \underline{?} \ 14\frac{4}{5}$ $>$

40. Calories One serving of rice pilaf has 220 calories, including 35 calories from fat. One serving of soup has 70 calories, including 15 calories from fat. Write the calories from fat as a fraction of the total calories for each food. Which food has a greater fraction of calories from fat? *(Lesson 4.5)* **rice pilaf: $\frac{35}{220} = \frac{7}{44}$, soup: $\frac{15}{70} = \frac{3}{14}$; soup**

Simplify the expression. Write your answer as a power. *(Lesson 4.6)*

41. $8 \cdot 8^3$ 8^4 **42.** $2^2 \cdot 2^5$ 2^7 **43.** $7^9 \div 7^7$ 7^2 **44.** $\frac{5^{10}}{5^7}$ 5^3

Simplify. Write the expression using only positive exponents. *(Lesson 4.7)*

45. $7x^{-4}$ $\frac{7}{x^4}$ **46.** $a^{-6} \cdot a^4$ $\frac{1}{a^2}$ **47.** $\frac{8w^{-6}}{24w^2}$ $\frac{1}{3w^8}$ **48.** $\frac{16r^{-2}}{4r^3}$ $\frac{4}{r^5}$

49. Write 6.58×10^{-4} in standard form. *(Lesson 4.8)* **0.000658**

50. Write 78,900,000,000 in scientific notation. *(Lesson 4.8)* **7.89×10^{10}**

51. Niagara Falls In tourist season, the water at Niagara Falls flows at 100,000 cubic feet per second during the day. How fast does it flow per minute? per hour? Write your answers in scientific notation. *(Lesson 4.8)* **6×10^6 ft^3/min; 3.6×10^8 ft^3/h**

Additional Resources

Assessment Book

- Chapter Test (3 levels), pp. 48–53
- Standardized Chapter Test, p. 54
- Alternative Assessment, pp. 55–56

Test and Practice Generator

16. Yellow; chocolate. *Sample answer:* Writing the fractions with a common denominator gives $\frac{1}{8} = \frac{6}{48}$, $\frac{3}{16} = \frac{9}{48}$, and $\frac{1}{6} = \frac{8}{48}$. Comparing numerators, 6 (yellow) < 8 (carrot) < 9 (chocolate).

Chapter Test

Write the prime factorization of the number.

1. 49 7^2 **2.** 68 $2^2 \cdot 17$ **3.** 95 $5 \cdot 19$ **4.** 112 $2^4 \cdot 7$

Find the greatest common factor of the monomials.

5. $3pq$, $12pq$ $3pq$ **6.** $12a^2$, $18ab$ $6a$ **7.** $2z^3$, $3z^2$ z^2 **8.** $14r^2$, $42r$ $14r$

Find the least common multiple of the numbers or monomials.

9. 4, 16, 32 32 **10.** 18, 24, 36 72 **11.** $5x^2y$, $21xy^3$ $105x^2y^3$ **12.** $54pq^2$, $63p^3q^3$ $378p^3q^3$

Copy and complete the statement with <, >, or =.

13. $\frac{11}{12} \underline{?} \frac{41}{48}$ > **14.** $4\frac{3}{6} \underline{?} \frac{9}{2}$ = **15.** $8\frac{7}{16} \underline{?} \frac{17}{2}$ <

16. Cake Three equal-sized round layer cakes were served at a party. Each cake was cut into a different number of equal-sized slices. After the guests left, $\frac{1}{8}$ of the yellow cake, $\frac{3}{16}$ of the chocolate cake, and $\frac{1}{6}$ of the carrot cake remained. Which type of cake had the least amount left over? Which had the most? Explain your reasoning. See margin.

Simplify the expression. Write your answer as a power.

17. $m^8 \cdot m^3$ m^{11} **18.** $6^2 \cdot 6^6$ 6^8 **19.** $\frac{n^{16}}{n^{10}}$ n^6

Simplify. Write the expression using only positive exponents.

20. $5x^{-3}$ $\frac{5}{x^3}$ **21.** $c^{-1} \cdot c^{-7}$ $\frac{1}{c^8}$ **22.** $\frac{-4u^{-9}}{u^3}$ $\frac{-4}{u^{12}}$, or $-\frac{4}{u^{12}}$ **23.** $\frac{16a^2b^5}{8a^4b}$ $\frac{2b^4}{a^2}$

24. Science Scientists have created a microfabric using molded plastic. Its narrowest links are $\frac{1}{1,000,000}$ meter. Write this fraction as a power of ten. 1×10^{-6}

Write the product in scientific notation.

25. $(6 \times 10^5) \times (5 \times 10^7)$ 3×10^{13} **26.** $(8.1 \times 10^4) \times (9.2 \times 10^8)$ 7.452×10^{13} **27.** $(4.2 \times 10^{-5}) \times (6 \times 10^{-2})$ 2.52×10^{-6}

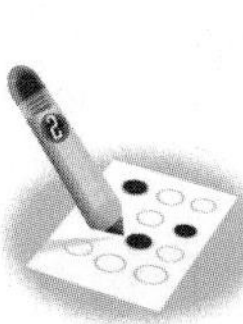

Chapter Standardized Test

Test-Taking Strategy **Be careful about choosing an answer that seems obvious. Carefully read the problem and all the choices before answering.**

Multiple Choice

1. Which number is a prime number? B

A. 51 **B.** 67 **C.** 82 **D.** 93

2. What is the greatest common factor of 420 and 385? H

F. 5 **G.** 15 **H.** 35 **I.** 4620

3. Which fraction is written in simplest form? A

A. $\frac{3}{16}$ **B.** $\frac{4}{10}$ **C.** $\frac{9}{21}$ **D.** $\frac{15}{33}$

4. Two toy cars begin at the starting line of a circular track at the same time. Car A goes around the track every 20 seconds. Car B goes around the track every 8 seconds. In how many seconds will the two cars reach the starting line at the same time? H

F. 4 seconds **G.** 24 seconds

H. 40 seconds **I.** 60 seconds

5. Which list is *not* in order from least to greatest? C

A. $\frac{1}{4}, \frac{3}{8}, \frac{7}{12}, \frac{2}{3}$

B. $\frac{1}{2}, \frac{3}{4}, \frac{13}{16}, \frac{7}{8}$

C. $1\frac{5}{18}, 1\frac{7}{9}, \frac{17}{12}, \frac{11}{6}$

D. $2\frac{4}{21}, 2\frac{5}{14}, \frac{18}{7}, \frac{17}{6}$

6. Which expression is *not* equal to 5^4? I

F. $5^3 \cdot 5$ **G.** $5^2 \cdot 5^2$

H. $\frac{5^8}{5^4}$ **I.** $\frac{5^8}{5^2}$

7. Which number is equal to $\frac{2^9}{2^3}$? B

A. 8 **B.** 64 **C.** 520 **D.** 4096

8. Write $\frac{-5x^{-6}}{x^3}$ using only positive exponents. F

F. $\frac{-5}{x^9}$ **G.** $\frac{1}{5x^9}$ **H.** $-5x^6$ **I.** $30x^3$

9. Simplify $(5 \times 10^{-7}) \times (3.6 \times 10^4)$. C

A. 1.8×10^{-4} **B.** 1.8×10^{-3}

C. 1.8×10^{-2} **D.** 18×10^{-4}

Short Response

10. **Planting Trees** A conservation group wants to plant 48 trees in a rectangular arrangement so that each row has the same number of trees. How many trees can be planted in each row? List all possibilities. Of the possible arrangements, which one is closest to having a length three times its width? See margin.

Extended Response

11. **History** The Orb of 1661 is a gold sphere set with 365 diamonds, 363 pearls, 18 rubies, 9 emeralds, 9 sapphires, and 1 amethyst. What is the total number of jewels? What fraction of jewels are rubies? What fraction are emeralds? Write each fraction in simplest form. Jane estimates that about half of the jewels in the Orb are diamonds. Do you agree with this estimate? Explain. 765 jewels; $\frac{2}{85}$; $\frac{1}{85}$; yes; 365 is close to half of 765.

Additional Resources

Assessment Book
- Standardized Chapter Test, p. 54

Test and Practice Generator

10. 2, 3, 4, 6, 8, 12, 16, or 24 trees (excluding the trivial cases of 1 row or 48 rows); 4 rows of 12 trees

Pacing and Assignment Guide

REGULAR SCHEDULE

Lesson	Les. Day	BASIC	AVERAGE	ADVANCED
5.1	Day 1	SRH p. 710 Exs. 6-10; pp. 222-223 Exs. 12-28, 31-36, 41, 47-63	pp. 222-223 Exs. 16-30, 34-44, 49-64	pp. 222-223 Exs. 20-30, 37-58*, 62-64
5.2	Day 1	pp. 226-227 Exs. 7-19, 21-28, 30, 34-42	pp. 226-227 Exs. 9-20, 23-32, 34-43	pp. 226-227 Exs. 11-20, 23-37*, 40-43
5.3	Day 1	SRH p. 707 Exs. 10-14; pp. 232-233 Exs. 7-18, 20-24, 26-29, 37-45	pp. 232-233 Exs. 12-21, 24-34, 37-46	pp. 232-233 Exs. 15-21, 24-36*, 39-46
5.4	Day 1	EP p. 728 Exs. 21-24; pp. 237-238 Exs. 12-15, 20-23, 29-34, 36-39, 47-56	pp. 237-238 Exs. 14-19, 24-28, 31-35, 38-43, 47-56	pp. 237-238 Exs. 18-21, 28-36, 40-50*, 53-55
5.5	Day 1	pp. 245-246 Exs. 14-21, 42-44, 53-59	pp. 245-246 Exs. 16-25, 42-46, 52-57	pp. 245-246 Exs. 18-25, 43-50, 60-62
	Day 2	pp. 245-246 Exs. 26-37, 46-48, 60-62	pp. 245-246 Exs. 28-41, 47-50, 60-62	pp. 245-246 Exs. 30-41, 51-56*
5.6	Day 1	SRH p. 709 Exs. 9-12; pp. 249-250 Exs. 13-24, 29-31, 35-37, 39-42, 48-56	pp. 249-250 Exs. 17-28, 32-43, 48-57	pp. 249-250 Exs. 21-28, 32-47*, 50-57
5.7	Day 1	SRH p. 714 Exs. 6-10; pp. 253-254 Exs. 7-14, 24, 27-29, 37-41	pp. 253-254 Exs. 7-14, 23-28, 37-42	pp. 253-254 Exs. 7-14, 23-28, 37-41
	Day 2	SRH p. 715 Exs. 6-10; pp. 253-254 Exs. 15-22, 26, 30-32, 42-46	pp. 253-254 Exs. 15-22, 29-35, 43-47	pp. 253-254 Exs. 15-22, 29-36*, 45-47
5.8	Day 1	pp. 259-261 Exs. 8-15, 17-19, 24-34	pp. 259-261 Exs. 10-22, 24-34	pp. 259-261 Exs. 10-25*, 28-34
Review	Day 1	pp. 264-265 Exs. 1-50	pp. 264-265 Exs. 1-50	pp. 264-265 Exs. 1-50
Assess	Day 1	Chapter 5 Test	Chapter 5 Test	Chapter 5 Test

YEARLY PACING Chapter 5 Total – **12 days** Chapters 1–5 Total – **60 days** Remaining – **100 days**

*Challenge Exercises EP = Extra Practice SRH = Skills Review Handbook EC = Extra Challenge

BLOCK SCHEDULE

DAY 1	DAY 2	DAY 3	DAY 4	DAY 5	DAY 6
5.1 pp. 222-223 Exs. 16-30, 34-44, 49-64 **5.2** pp. 226-227 Exs. 9-20, 23-32, 34-43	**5.3** pp. 232-233 Exs. 12-21, 24-34, 37-46 **5.4** pp. 237-238 Exs. 14-19, 24-28, 31-35, 38-43, 47-56	**5.5** pp. 245-246 Exs. 16-25, 28-50, 52-57, 60-62	**5.6** pp. 249-250 Exs. 17-28, 32-43, 48-57 **5.7** pp. 253-254 Exs. 7-14, 23-28, 37-42	**5.7 (cont.)** pp. 253-254 Exs. 15-22, 29-35, 43-47 **5.8** pp. 259-261 Exs. 10-22, 24-34	**Review** pp. 264-265 Exs. 1-50 **Assess** Chapter 5 Test

YEARLY PACING Chapter 5 Total – **6 days** Chapters 1–5 Total – **30 days** Remaining – **50 days**

Support Materials

CHAPTER RESOURCE BOOK

CHAPTER SUPPORT								
Tips for New Teachers	p. 1			Parents as Partners			p. 3	

LESSON SUPPORT	5.1	5.2	5.3	5.4	5.5	5.6	5.7	5.8
Lesson Plans (regular and block)	p. 5	p. 13	p. 22	p. 31	p. 40	p. 48	p. 57	p. 65
Technology Activities & Keystrokes				p. 33				p. 67
Activity Support Masters								
Activity Masters			p. 24					
Practice (3 levels)	p. 7	p. 15	p. 25	p. 34	p. 42	p. 50	p. 59	p. 69
Study Guide	p. 10	p. 18	p. 28	p. 37	p. 45	p. 53	p. 62	p. 72
Real-World Problem Solving		p. 20				p. 55		
Challenge Practice	p. 12	p. 21	p. 30	p. 39	p. 47	p. 56	p. 64	p. 74

REVIEW			
Chapter Review Games and Activities	p. 75	Extra Credit Project with Rubric	p. 80
Real-Life Project with Rubric	p. 76	Cumulative Practice	p. 82
Cooperative Project with Rubric	p. 78	Resource Book Answers	A1

ASSESSMENT

Quizzes	p. 57	Alternative Assessments with Rubrics	p. 66
Chapter Tests (3 levels)	p. 59	Unit Test	p. 90
Standardized Test	p. 65	Cumulative Test	p. 92

TRANSPARENCIES

	5.1	5.2	5.3	5.4	5.5	5.6	5.7	5.8
Warm-Up / Daily Homework Quiz	✔	✔	✔	✔	✔	✔	✔	✔
Notetaking Guide	✔	✔	✔	✔	✔	✔	✔	✔
Teacher Support					✔			
English/Spanish Problem Solving		✔		✔	✔			✔
Answer Transparencies	✔	✔	✔	✔	✔	✔	✔	✔

TECHNOLOGY

- EasyPlanner CD-ROM
- Test and Practice Generator
- Electronic Lesson Presentations
- eTutorial CD-ROM
- Chapter Audio Summaries CDs
- Classzone.com
- eEdition Plus Online
- eWorkbook Plus Online
- eTutorial Plus Online
- EasyPlanner Plus Online

ADDITIONAL RESOURCES

- Worked-Out Solution Key
- Notetaking Guide
- Practice Workbook
- Tutor Place
- Professional Development Book
- Special Activities Book
- Posters
- Spanish Study Guide
- Exercises in Spanish
- English/Spanish Ch. Reviews/Tests
- Multi-Language Visual Glossary

Math Background and Teaching Strategies

Lesson 5.1

MATH BACKGROUND

LIKE DENOMINATORS Adding and subtracting fractions with common denominators is similar to adding and subtracting like terms, with the denominator playing the role of the common variable part. Once the numerators are added or subtracted, however, it is often possible to simplify the result further by dividing out common factors.

TEACHING STRATEGIES

Students will likely feel comfortable adding and subtracting fractions that have a common denominator, but may not when the numerators and/or denominators are variable expressions. Point out that they can already add and subtract like terms, and that a common denominator that is a variable expression works just like one that is a number, that is, it is used as the denominator of the result without performing any operations with it.

Lesson 5.2

MATH BACKGROUND

UNLIKE DENOMINATORS To add or subtract fractions with unlike denominators, first write them as equivalent fractions with the same denominator, preferably the least common denominator. When operating with mixed numbers, work with the integer parts and fractional parts separately.

TEACHING STRATEGIES

A common ruler can provide students a model for adding and subtracting fractions with unlike denominators, and stress the need for a common denominator. For example, ask students to use a ruler to add $\frac{1}{2}$ and $\frac{3}{16}$. They can see that the result will need to be expressed in sixteenths, because the distance on the ruler represented by the sum is indicated by a tick mark for sixteenths. They can also see by the divisions on the ruler that $\frac{1}{2} = \frac{8}{16}$. Altogether, the sum requires $8 + 3 = 11$ of the sixteenths divisions on the ruler, so $\frac{1}{2} + \frac{3}{16} = \frac{8}{16} + \frac{3}{16} = \frac{8+3}{16} = \frac{11}{16}$.

Lesson 5.3

MATH BACKGROUND

Multiplication of fractions is often expressed using the word *of*. For example, $\frac{2}{3} \cdot \frac{3}{4}$ can be expressed as "two thirds of three quarters." When multiplying fractions that are less than 1, this makes it reasonable that the result is smaller than either fraction, since it is a "part of a part." When multiplying fractions, dividing out common factors before evaluating the product of the numerators and the product of the denominators makes simplification easier.

TEACHING STRATEGIES

Make sure students understand that when fractions are multiplied, their denominators are multiplied, but when fractions are added, their denominators are not added. Also, students who are used to thinking in terms of "multiplication makes bigger" may need extra practice estimating products involving fractions and evaluating them for reasonableness.

Lesson 5.4

MATH BACKGROUND

Multiplicative inverses, or **reciprocals**, are two numbers whose product is 1. To find the reciprocal of a fraction, simply invert it. Dividing a number by a fraction is equivalent to multiplying the number by the reciprocal of the fraction. To solve a multiplication equation such as $\frac{2}{3}z = 15$, multiply each side by the reciprocal of the coefficient of the variable, since this results in a coefficient of 1.

TEACHING STRATEGIES

Work extra examples of dividing mixed numbers, which requires a broad range of skills. Also work extra examples of division by fractions less than 1, as students are often uncomfortable with a quotient being larger than the dividend. For example, ask students to divide 5 by $\frac{1}{6}$. Point out that this is asking how many sixths there are in 5. There are 6 sixths in 1, and 5 1s in 5, so there are $6 \cdot 5 = 30$ sixths in 5.

Lesson 5.5

MATH BACKGROUND

Any **rational number** can be written in the form $\frac{a}{b}$, where a and b are integers and $b \neq 0$. By carrying out the division, you can write any rational number in decimal form. If there is a zero remainder, the decimal form *terminates.* If there is a nonzero remainder, the decimal form has a *repeating* sequence of digits that is expressed by placing a bar over the sequence. Writing a repeating decimal as a fraction requires multiplying it by a power of 10 and then subtracting the original decimal or its product with a lesser power of 10.

TEACHING STRATEGIES

Point out that the decimal form of a fraction repeats when the denominator of the fraction in simplest form will not divide evenly into a power of 10. Because 6 does not divide evenly into any power of 10, $\frac{1}{6}$ and $\frac{5}{6}$ have decimal forms that repeat. Because $10 = 2 \cdot 5$, fractions in simplest form that have terminating decimal forms can be expressed as powers of 2 and/or 5, such as $8 = 2^3$, $40 = 2^3 \cdot 5$, and $625 = 5^4$.

Lesson 5.6

MATH BACKGROUND

Adding and subtracting decimals is the same as adding and subtracting whole numbers except that the place values include those that are less than one. To use **front-end estimation** to estimate the sum of a sequence of positive numbers that have an integer part and a decimal part, add the integer parts to get a lower bound, then estimate the sum of the decimal parts and adjust your original result.

TEACHING STRATEGIES

Most students will have had considerable experience adding and subtracting decimals, but may still be somewhat uncomfortable with it. You may want to point out that the vertical format is just a more efficient way to write down the process. For example, when you add 23.45 and 7.24, you are really finding the sum of $(2 \cdot 10) + (3 \cdot 1) + (4 \cdot 0.1) + (5 \cdot 0.01)$ and $(7 \cdot 1) + (2 \cdot 0.1) + (4 \cdot 0.01)$. The vertical format allows you to apply the distributive property for each place value without having to write it out.

Lesson 5.7

MATH BACKGROUND

MULTIPLYING AND DIVIDING DECIMALS The number of decimal places in a product is the total number of decimal places in the factors. When dividing by a decimal, it is easiest to keep track of the decimal place by multiplying the divisor and dividend by the power of 10 that makes the divisor an integer, for example, recasting the quotient $54.621 \div 4.82$ as $5462.1 \div 482$ by multiplying 54.621 and 4.82 by 100.

TEACHING STRATEGIES

Students may need help avoiding pitfalls when multiplying and dividing decimals. For one, make sure that students do not drop trailing zeros when multiplying. For example, if students find the product $2.25 \cdot 4.12$ in vertical format, the last line will be 92700 before the decimal point is placed. Students need to include the zeros in the four decimal places that are counted. Also, make sure that students are comfortable rewriting a division problem so that the divisor is an integer, and that they are able to use zeros correctly as placeholders in the dividend or quotient of a long-division problem.

Lesson 5.8

MATH BACKGROUND

STATISTICS The **mean**, **median**, and **mode** are *measures of central tendency*, or *averages*. That is, each gives a single number designed to represent some kind of "middle" or "typical" value in a data set. For different data sets and different purposes, which measure is taken to be most representative may vary. The **range** of a data set, the difference between its extreme values, is the simplest *measure of dispersion* of a data set, or measure of how the data are spread out.

TEACHING STRATEGIES

Students may be confused by having three different "averages." Have them examine everyday uses of the word to point out that the word "average" does not always mean the same thing. For example, students are used to an average as the mean in a situation such as a class average on a test, but what is an "average" student or an "average" springtime day, or an "average" eye color? Examine with students possible mathematical interpretations of these and other uses of the word "average" in everyday life.

Differentiating Instruction

Strategies for Underachievers

USE MANIPULATIVES

In Lesson 5.1 and beyond, it may be very helpful for some underachieving and concrete learners if you model operations involving fractions using fraction bars or similar manipulatives. You may wish to allow some students access to these tools for as long as they desire, including on assessments.

ACT IT OUT For the exercises in Problem Solving Strategies 5.3, you may want to have available for students objects that they can physically use to act out these problems, such as coins, beads, and ribbon. For Exercise 5, you can allow students actually to line up to model the problem situation.

In Lessons 5.6 and 5.7, it may help students to have access to grid paper to keep their work aligned and organized when performing operations with decimals.

DECREASE DEPTH AND COMPLEXITY

In Lesson 5.2, it may help some students first to use fractions that will involve only manipulating natural numbers before including fractions that will involve or result in manipulating negative integers. This will allow them to focus solely on learning the operations with fractions before including the complexities caused by negative numbers. Alternately, you may wish to allow these students to use a fraction-compatible calculator to simplify expressions involving negative fractions as detailed in Technology Activity 5.4 on page 239.

In Lesson 5.5, the algorithm for writing repeating decimals as fractions in Example 4 on page 244 may prove confusing for some students. For these students, you may wish to focus instead on a few basic patterns that they can explore using their calculators. Some examples are the pattern illustrated by $0.\overline{1} = \frac{1}{9}$ and $0.\overline{2} = \frac{2}{9}$, or by $0.\overline{19} = \frac{19}{99}$ and $0.\overline{61} = \frac{61}{99}$. Alternatively, it may help students to approach these problems by having them multiply the original decimal by the power of 10 that has the same number of zeros as the number of repeating places in the decimal and then subtract the original decimal. In this case, however, repeating decimals like $0.8\overline{3}$ and $0.2\overline{07}$ should be avoided, since they do not fit this pattern.

USE SCAFFOLDING

TEMPLATES Beginning in Lesson 5.1, some underachievers may have difficulty completing all of the steps involved in subtracting mixed numbers when borrowing is required. You may wish to provide these students with additional detailed examples that illustrate this process step-by-step for them to follow when working on their own. You may also want to provide them with templates that require them to fill in missing values with each step.

In Lesson 5.7, you can lessen the time required in having underachieving students do too many long division problems yet still teach about place value by providing them with decimal division problems where the digits are already written but the decimal points and place-holding zeros are missing. Have students place the decimal points and place-holding zeros correctly to reinforce their understanding of place value.

FOCUS ON VOCABULARY

In Lesson 5.4, help students build mastery of vocabulary related to division before they begin performing division with fractions. Students should be comfortable with terms that should be familiar, such as *dividend*, *divisor*, and *quotient*, before they concentrate on terms like *reciprocal* and *multiplicative inverse*. Students can make flash cards or use other methods to master these terms.

Strategies for English Learners

DISSECT WORD PROBLEMS

With your students, examine the following word problem:

TICKET PRICE You buy six tickets for a concert that you and your friends want to attend. The total charge for all of the tickets is $72. Write and solve an equation to find the price of one concert ticket.

Point out the features shown in the following chart:

Heading (optional)	
TICKET PRICE	A word or short phrase at the beginning gives you a clue about something in the problem. In this case it gives you a context for the problem but is not needed to solve the problem. In other cases the title may give you a clue as to the type of problem (for example, Multiple Choice, see page 223, Exercise 63) or the concept or skill you will use (for example, Algebra, see page 227, starting with Exercise 30).

First sentence	
You buy six tickets for a concert that you and your friends want to attend.	Sometimes the first sentence is a background sentence that provides more context, but usually it provides the first fact or number you will need to work with, in this case *six*. Usually that refers to a number of something that is named in the sentence, often immediately following, in this case *tickets*.
Second sentence *The total charge for all of the tickets is $72.*	The second sentence usually gives you the second fact or number you will be working with, in this case $72. You need to see what 72 refers to somewhere in the sentence, in this case the total charge.
Third sentence *Write and solve an equation to find the price of one concert ticket.*	The last sentence or two sentences often contain one of the following words or phrases: *who, what, when, where, why, which, how many, how much, how long.* These signal words are usually followed closely by a description of what you are supposed to provide in your answer, in this case the price of one concert ticket.

Strategies for Advanced Learners

INCREASE DEPTH AND COMPLEXITY

In Lesson 5.3, in the Notebook section on page 230, you may wish to have advanced learners write an explanation about the notation "$b, d \neq 0$" that follows the algebraic description of multiplying fractions. Similar notation that students should be able to explain appears in the Notebook section about dividing fractions in Lesson 5.4 on page 234.

In Lesson 5.3, in conjunction with Exercise 32 on page 233, you may wish to have advanced learners investigate and report on the speeds of various models and generations of computers. Students should be encouraged to organize their data visually using bar graphs, time lines, and so on, as well as to incorporate scientific notation.

In Lesson 5.4, in conjunction with Exercise 11 on page 236, you may wish to organize an activity in which students plan a meal or food for a party that would feed the class. You may wish to ask students to bring in their favorite recipes and then have them work together to adapt these recipes for the entire class.

In Lesson 5.5, you can encourage advanced students to do research that will enable them to extend the Venn diagram on page 242 to incorporate and give examples of natural numbers, irrational numbers (students should be familiar with square roots and π), and real numbers. Also with this lesson, you may wish to have some students produce a presentation that shows which divisors produce repeating decimals and which do not. In all cases, students can show patterns related to dividing successive whole numbers by a particular divisor.

Students can expand Hands-on Activity 5.8 by collecting other data that they can analyze using measures of central tendency, using anything from the number of heads that appear in tosses of several coins to data, such as height, about students in the class.

USE CROSS-CURRICULAR ACTIVITIES

In Lesson 5.3, in conjunction with Exercise 19 on page 232, you may wish to work with a science teacher to develop an activity in which students make their own craters in sand and/or other materials, and then make conclusions about their measurements and observations. Students can supplement this project by researching other impact craters on the moon or on Earth, including how and when they were formed as well as their dimensions.

Differentiating Instruction: Teaching Resources

Differentiating Technology

McDougal Littell *Middle School Mathematics* offers teachers a wide variety of technology, ranging from calculator activities in the *Chapter Resource Books* to the *Test and Practice Generator CD-ROM* to interactive, online resources and products accessed at Classzone.com.

CLASSZONE.COM

Classzone.com provides helpful online resources for students and teachers, including More Examples, Vocabulary Support, and State Test Practice. Classzone.com is also the access point for the following online products: *eEdition Plus Online,* an interactive, online version of the textbook; *eWorkbook Plus Online,* an interactive practice workbook correlated to the textbook; *eTutorial Plus Online,* an Internet tutorial that makes it easier than ever to help students master skills and concepts; and *EasyPlanner Plus Online,* an online resource with teacher tools and a lesson planner.

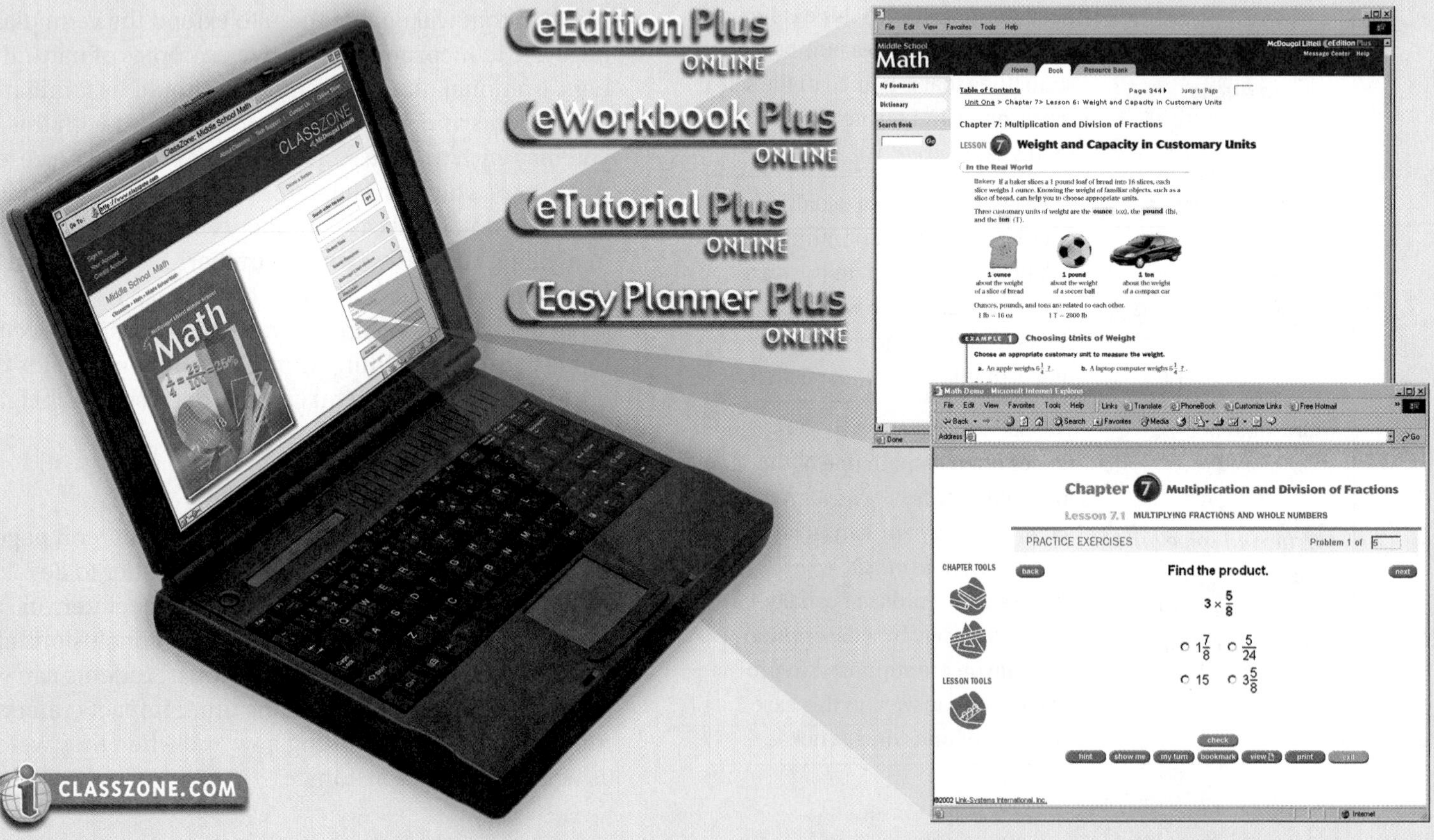

eEdition Plus ONLINE
eWorkbook Plus ONLINE
eTutorial Plus ONLINE
Easy Planner Plus ONLINE

CLASSZONE.COM

Test and Practice Generator CD-ROM

The *Test and Practice Generator* can be used to create numerous practice sheets and quizzes for each lesson and tests for each chapter using both static and algorithmic exercises. Information about creating and editing questions is provided.

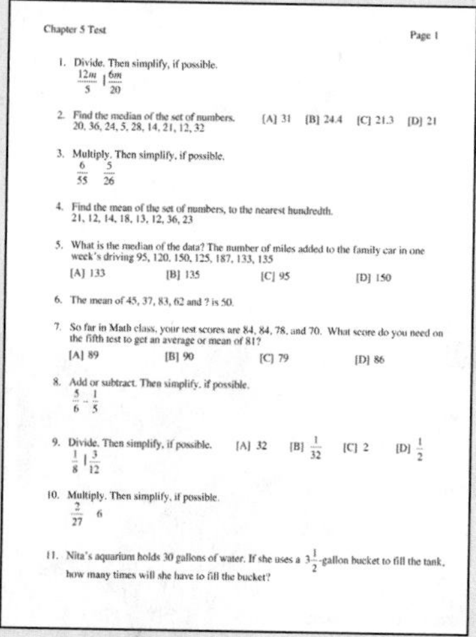
Chapter 5 Test Page 1

1. Divide. Then simplify, if possible. $\frac{12m}{5} \div \frac{6m}{20}$
2. Find the median of the set of numbers. 20, 36, 24, 5, 28, 14, 21, 12, 32 [A] 31 [B] 24.4 [C] 21.3 [D] 21
3. Multiply. Then simplify, if possible. $\frac{6}{55} \cdot \frac{5}{26}$
4. Find the mean of the set of numbers, to the nearest hundredth. 21, 12, 14, 18, 13, 12, 36, 23
5. What is the median of the data? The number of miles added to the family car in one week's driving 95, 120, 150, 125, 187, 133, 135 [A] 133 [B] 135 [C] 95 [D] 150
6. The mean of 45, 37, 83, 62 and ? is 50.
7. So far in Math class, your test scores are 84, 84, 78, and 70. What score do you need on the fifth test to get an average or mean of 81? [A] 89 [B] 90 [C] 79 [D] 86
8. Add or subtract. Then simplify, if possible. $\frac{5}{6} - \frac{1}{5}$
9. Divide. Then simplify, if possible. $\frac{1}{8} \div \frac{3}{12}$ [A] 32 [B] $\frac{1}{32}$ [C] 2 [D] $\frac{1}{2}$
10. Multiply. Then simplify, if possible. $\frac{2}{27} \cdot 6$
11. Nita's aquarium holds 30 gallons of water. If she uses a $3\frac{1}{2}$-gallon bucket to fill the tank, how many times will she have to fill the bucket?

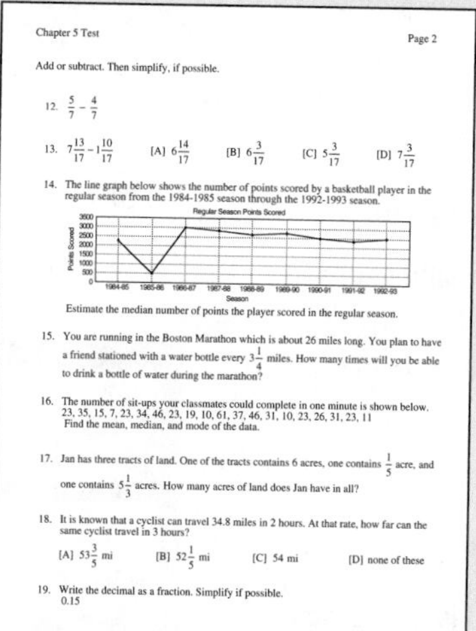
Chapter 5 Test Page 2

Add or subtract. Then simplify, if possible.

12. $\frac{5}{7} - \frac{4}{7}$
13. $7\frac{13}{17} - 1\frac{10}{17}$ [A] $6\frac{14}{17}$ [B] $6\frac{3}{17}$ [C] $5\frac{3}{17}$ [D] $7\frac{3}{17}$
14. The line graph below shows the number of points scored by a basketball player in the regular season from the 1984-1985 season through the 1992-1993 season.

Estimate the median number of points the player scored in the regular season.

15. You are running in the Boston Marathon which is about 26 miles long. You plan to have a friend stationed with a water bottle every $3\frac{1}{4}$ miles. How many times will you be able to drink a bottle of water during the marathon?
16. The number of sit-ups your classmates could complete in one minute is shown below. 23, 35, 15, 7, 23, 34, 46, 23, 19, 10, 61, 37, 46, 31, 10, 23, 26, 31, 23, 11 Find the mean, median, and mode of the data.
17. Jan has three tracts of land. One of the tracts contains 6 acres, one contains $\frac{1}{5}$ acre, and one contains $5\frac{1}{3}$ acres. How many acres of land does Jan have in all?
18. It is known that a cyclist can travel 34.8 miles in 2 hours. At that rate, how far can the same cyclist travel in 3 hours? [A] $53\frac{3}{5}$ mi [B] $52\frac{1}{5}$ mi [C] 54 mi [D] none of these
19. Write the decimal as a fraction. Simplify if possible. 0.15

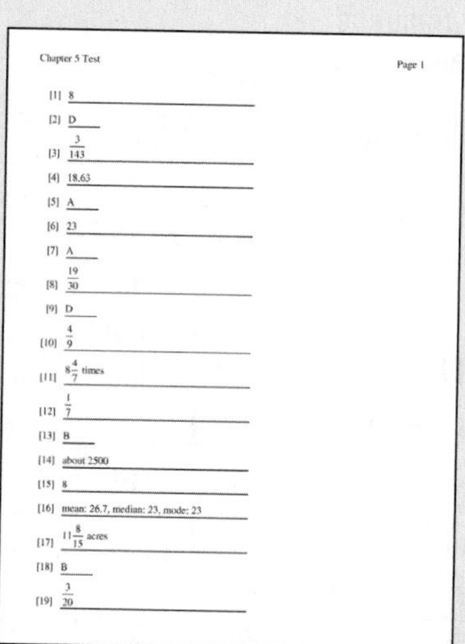
Chapter 5 Test Page 1

[1] 8
[2] D
[3] $\frac{3}{143}$
[4] 18.63
[5] A
[6] 23
[7] A
[8] $\frac{19}{30}$
[9] D
[10] $\frac{4}{9}$
[11] $8\frac{4}{7}$ times
[12] $\frac{1}{7}$
[13] B
[14] about 2500
[15] 8
[16] mean: 26.7, median: 23, mode: 23
[17] $11\frac{8}{15}$ acres
[18] B
[19] $\frac{3}{20}$

Resource Book

The *Chapter Resource Books* contain technology activities that are different from the activities given in the textbook. Also included, where appropriate, are calculator keystrokes that can be used to do the technology activities and exercises that appear in the textbook and in the *Chapter Resource Books*.

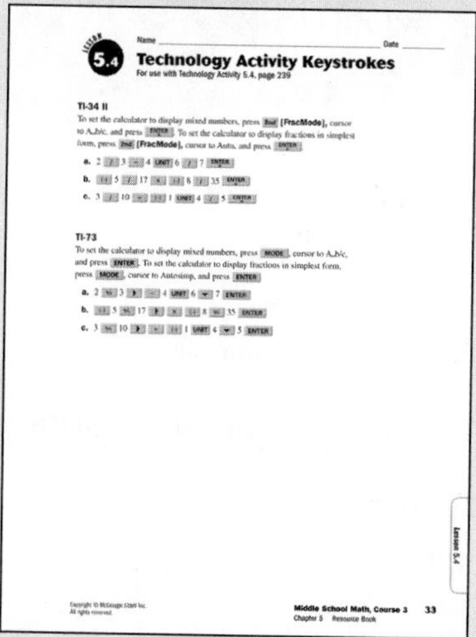
5.4 Technology Activity Keystrokes

For use with Technology Activity 5.4, page 239

Middle School Math, Course 3 33

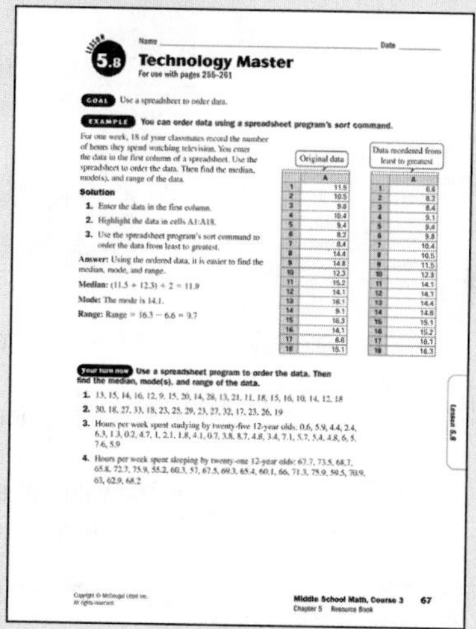
5.8 Technology Master

For use with pages 255–261

Middle School Math, Course 3 67

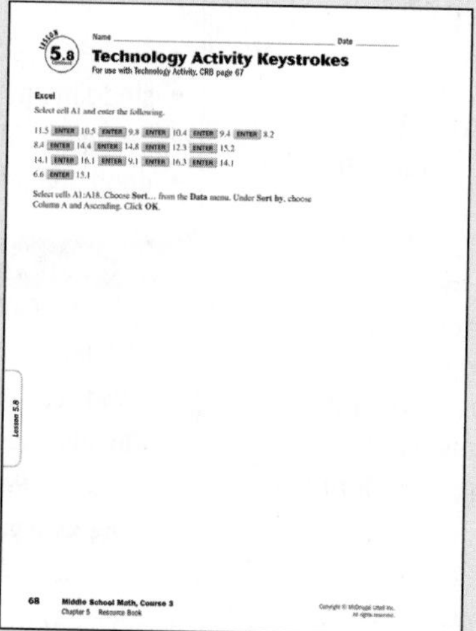
5.8 Technology Activity Keystrokes

For use with Technology Activity, CRB page 67

68 Middle School Math, Course 3

OVERVIEW

Main Ideas

In this chapter, students add and subtract fractions and mixed numbers with like and unlike denominators, and multiply and divide fractions and mixed numbers. Students write fractions and mixed numbers as decimals, and vice versa. Students add and subtract decimals, including using front-end estimation, and multiply and divide decimals. Students use operations with fractions and decimals to solve real-world problems. Students also find the mean, median, mode, and range of a data set.

Prerequisite Skills

The key skills reviewed in the games on these pages are:

- Comparing fractions
- Identifying equivalent fractions

Additional practice with prerequisite skills can be found in the Review What You Need to Know exercises on page 218. Additional resources for reviewing prerequisite skills are:

- Skills Review Handbook, pp. 704–726
- Tutor Place
- eTutorial Plus

Managing the Games

Tips for Success

If time is short, you may want to allow students to use calculators to compare the decimal forms of the fractions in *Scale the Cliff*. They can then verify the results by rewriting pairs of corresponding fractions as they ascend with the same denominator. In *Tangled Fractions*, one strategy is first to have students write each fraction shown in simplest form.

Rational Number Operations

BEFORE

In previous chapters you've...

- Added, subtracted, multiplied, and divided integers
- Interpreted tables and graphs

Now

In Chapter 5 you'll study...

- Performing operations on fractions, mixed numbers, and decimals
- Rewriting fractions and decimals
- Describing data sets using mean, median, mode, and range

WHY?

So you can solve real-world problems about...

- snakes, p. 220
- sledding, p. 226
- rafting, p. 251
- deep sea jellies, p. 257

Internet Preview
CLASSZONE.COM

- eEdition Plus Online
- eWorkbook Plus Online
- eTutorial Plus Online
- State Test Practice
- More Examples

Chapter Warm-Up Games

Review skills you need for this chapter in these quick games.

Scale the Cliff

$\frac{7}{32}$	$\frac{1}{3}$	$\frac{2}{7}$	$\frac{3}{11}$
$\frac{7}{17}$	$\frac{4}{9}$	$\frac{4}{15}$	$\frac{11}{25}$
$\frac{6}{11}$	$\frac{13}{21}$	$\frac{4}{7}$	$\frac{3}{8}$
$\frac{1}{2}$	$\frac{5}{8}$	$\frac{7}{11}$	$\frac{9}{14}$
$\frac{3}{4}$	$\frac{5}{6}$	$\frac{3}{5}$	$\frac{5}{7}$
	$\frac{2}{3}$		

Key Skill:
Comparing fractions

Find the handholds you can use to scale the cliff.

- Start at $\frac{2}{3}$ and move up, selecting a handhold in each row.
- The value of each handhold must be less than the value of the handhold below it. $\frac{2}{3} \to \frac{3}{5} \to \frac{1}{2} \to \frac{3}{8} \to \frac{4}{15} \to \frac{7}{32}$

BRAIN GAME **Key Skill:**
Identifying equivalent fractions

Susan is going rock climbing. Help her figure out what equipment she is missing.

- In each column, find a fraction equivalent to the top one to decode the name of the equipment Susan is missing. shoes

Stop *and* Think

1. **Critical Thinking** A student thinks that a fraction cannot be smaller than another fraction if the first fraction's denominator is greater than the second fraction's denominator. Explain why the student is wrong.
2. **Writing** Explain how to tell whether fractions with different denominators are equivalent. ***Sample answer:*** **First you have to find a common denominator. Next, rewrite each fraction using the common denominator. Then, compare the numerators. If the numerators are equal, the fractions are equivalent.**

1. *Sample answer:* Fractions are numbers that represent parts of a whole. You cannot compare different fractions by just looking at their denominators. You must rewrite the fractions as equivalent fractions with the same denominator first and then compare the numerators.

Reflecting on the Games

Students need to have a firm understanding of comparing fractions by writing them with a common denominator, but you may want to introduce cross multiplication as a quick way to check that two fractions are equivalent. As an additional exercise to follow up *Tangled Fractions*, you may want to have students write an additional equivalent fraction for each pair of equivalent fractions identified.

Chapter Resources

These resources are provided to help you prepare for the chapter and to customize review materials:

 ***Chapter 5 Resource Book***

- Tips for New Teachers, pp. 1–2
- Lesson Plan, pp. 5, 13, 22, 31, 40, 48, 57, 65
- Lesson Plan for Block Scheduling, pp. 6, 14, 23, 32, 41, 49, 58, 66

 ***Technology***

- EasyPlanner CD-ROM
- Test and Practice Generator
- Electronic Lesson Presentations CD-ROM
- eTutorial CD-ROM

 ***Internet***

- Classzone
- eEdition Plus Online
- eWorkbook Plus Online
- eTutorial Plus Online
- EasyPlanner Plus Online

English Learner Support

- Spanish Study Guide
- Multi-Language Glossary
- Chapter Audio Summaries CDs
- Teacher's Edition, pp. 216E–216F

PREPARE

DIAGNOSIS/REMEDIATION

Review What You Need to Know

The Review What You Need to Know exercises can help you diagnose whether students have the following skills needed in Chapter 5:

- Using vocabulary (Exs. 1-2)
- Multiplying and dividing integers (Exs. 3-6)
- Simplifying fractions (Exs. 7-11)
- Adding decimals (Ex. 12)

 ***Chapter 5 Resource Book***

- Study Guide (Lessons 5.1-5.8)

 ***Tutor Place***

NOTETAKING STRATEGIES

Explain to students that math techniques that seem obvious in class will seem less obvious in a few days or weeks when new skills have been learned. For this reason, students should take careful notes, even when they feel that they have mastered the skills. Further suggestions for keeping a notebook can be found on pages 219 and 244.

For more support on notetaking, see:

- Notetaking Guide Workbook
- Notetaking Transparencies

Getting Ready to Learn

Word Watch

Review Words

simplest form, p. 179
least common denominator (LCD), p. 192
improper fraction, p. 707
mixed number, p. 707

Review What You Need to Know

Using Vocabulary **Copy and complete using a review word.**

1. If 1 is the greatest common factor of the numerator and the denominator, then the fraction is in _?_. **simplest form**

2. A number like $3\frac{4}{7}$, whose value is the sum of a whole number part and a fraction part, is called a(n) _?_. **mixed number**

In Exercises 3–6, find the product or quotient. *(pp. 70, 74)*

3. $-125 \cdot 2$ **−250** **4.** $-4 \cdot (-23)$ **92** **5.** $-39 \div 3$ **−13** **6.** $-136 \div (-17)$ **8**

Write the fraction in simplest form. *(p. 179)*

7. $\frac{4}{12}$ $\frac{1}{3}$ **8.** $\frac{35}{50}$ $\frac{7}{10}$ **9.** $\frac{12}{32}$ $\frac{3}{8}$ **10.** $\frac{24}{52}$ $\frac{6}{13}$ **11.** $\frac{14}{49}$ $\frac{2}{7}$

12. You bought a sweater for \$15.65 and a pair of jeans for \$23.95. What was the total cost of your purchase? *(p. 709)* **\$39.60**

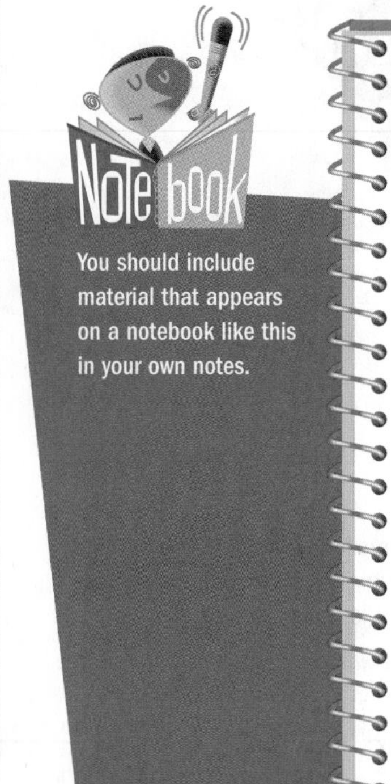

You should include material that appears on a notebook like this in your own notes.

Know How to Take Notes

Writing Helpful Hints In your notebook, write down any helpful hints your teacher or your textbook gives you for solving problems.

Equivalent Fractions

Write equivalent fractions by multiplying by a fraction that is equal to one.

$\frac{3}{5} \times \frac{4}{4} = \frac{12}{20}$ $\frac{3}{5} \times \frac{9}{9} = \frac{27}{45}$ $\frac{3}{5} \times \frac{100}{100} = \frac{300}{500}$ ← **A fraction has many equivalent forms.**

You can rename a mixed number as an equivalent improper fraction.

$$3\frac{5}{6} = \frac{6 \cdot 3 + 5}{6} = \frac{23}{6}$$

In Lesson 5.1, you should write down helpful hints about subtracting with mixed numbers.

Fractions with Common Denominators

BEFORE	Now	WHY?
You added and subtracted whole numbers and integers.	You'll add and subtract fractions with common denominators.	So you can compare coin sizes, as in Ex. 28.

Word Watch

Review words

order of operations, p. 10
numerator, p. 707
denominator, p. 707

One way to add or subtract fractions with common denominators is to use a model.

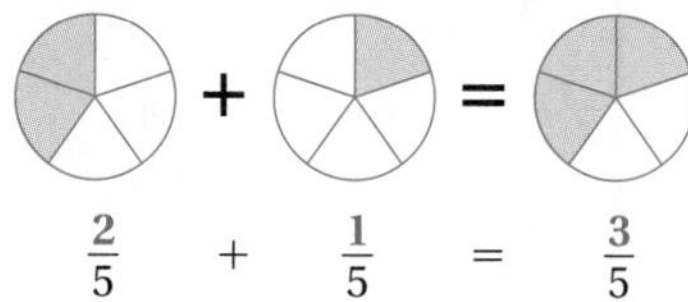

$$\frac{2}{5} + \frac{1}{5} = \frac{3}{5}$$

The model suggests the following rule.

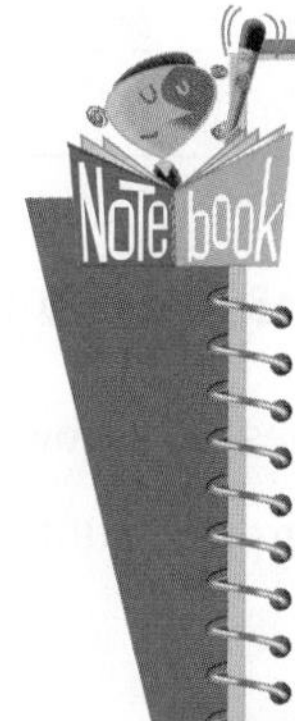

Adding and Subtracting Fractions

Words To add fractions or subtract fractions with a common denominator, write the sum or difference of the numerators over the denominator.

Numbers $\frac{3}{9} + \frac{5}{9} = \frac{8}{9}$ **Algebra** $\frac{a}{c} + \frac{b}{c} = \frac{a+b}{c}$ $(c \neq 0)$

$\frac{3}{5} - \frac{2}{5} = \frac{1}{5}$ $\frac{a}{c} - \frac{b}{c} = \frac{a-b}{c}$ $(c \neq 0)$

To add or subtract mixed numbers, find the sum or difference of the whole numbers and the sum or difference of the fractions. Then combine these quantities.

EXAMPLE 1 **Fractions and Mixed Numbers**

a. $-\frac{11}{13} + \frac{8}{13} = \frac{-11+8}{13}$

$= -\frac{3}{13}$

b. $-5\frac{6}{7} + 3\frac{2}{7} = -5 - \frac{6}{7} + 3 + \frac{2}{7}$

$= -5 + 3 - \frac{6}{7} + \frac{2}{7}$

$= -2\frac{4}{7}$

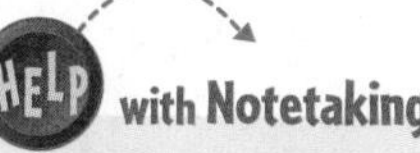

with Notetaking

Part (b) of Example 1 shows how to operate with negative mixed numbers. You may wish to copy this into your notebook.

ILLINOIS Standards and ISAT:
6.A.3, 6.B.3b, 8.A.3a

1 PLAN

SKILL CHECK

1. $-17 + 9 = \underline{?}$ **−8**
2. $5 - 16 = \underline{?}$ **−11**
3. $3a + (-7a) = \underline{?}$ **$-4a$**
4. $15x - 5x = \underline{?}$ **$10x$**

Lesson Objective

Add and subtract fractions with common denominators.

Pacing

Suggested Number of Days
Basic Course: 1 day
Average Course: 1 day
Advanced Course: 1 day
Block: 0.5 block with 5.2

Teaching Resources

For a complete list of Teaching Resources, see page 216B.

Transparency

Warm-Up Exercises for this lesson are available on a transparency.

2 TEACH

Motivating the Lesson

Discuss the examples $2 + 5 = 7$, $\frac{2}{10} + \frac{5}{10} = \frac{7}{10}$, and $2 + (-5) = -3$ with students. Then ask what $\frac{2}{10} + \left(-\frac{5}{10}\right)$ would be.

TIPS FOR NEW TEACHERS
Be sure students understand that in the algebraic form of the rules on page 219, *c* represents the common denominator. See Tips for New Teachers in the *Chapter 5 Resource Book*.

EXTRA EXAMPLES

Example 1 Find the sum or difference.

a. $-\frac{4}{7}+\frac{2}{7}$ $-\frac{2}{7}$

b. $9\frac{1}{3}-6\frac{2}{3}$ $2\frac{2}{3}$

Example 2 Find the sum or difference.

a. $-\frac{2b}{5}+\frac{12b}{5}$ $2b$

b. $\frac{7c}{12d}-\frac{10c}{12d}$ $-\frac{c}{4d}$

Example 3 Monday morning, the pile of entries for a radio contest was $7\frac{3}{4}$ inches high. Tuesday morning, the pile was $11\frac{1}{4}$ inches high. By how many inches did the pile grow? $3\frac{1}{2}$ in.

NOTETAKING
After Example 1, have students record in their notebooks how to rename a mixed number and why and when to rename it.

Differentiating Instruction

Alternative Approach Show students how to add and subtract mixed numbers by rewriting them as improper fractions. For instance, Example 3 becomes $\frac{109}{4}-\frac{59}{4}=\frac{109-59}{4}=\frac{50}{4}=\frac{25}{2}=12\frac{1}{2}$.

HELP with Solving
Remember that the following fractions are equivalent.
$\frac{-a}{b}=\frac{a}{-b}=-\frac{a}{b}$

EXAMPLE 2 Simplifying Fractions with Variables

a. $-\frac{a}{9}+\frac{7a}{9}=\frac{-a+7a}{9}$ Write sum over common denominator.

$=\frac{6a}{9}$ Combine like terms.

$=\frac{\overset{2}{\cancel{6}}a}{\cancel{9}_{3}}$ Divide out common factor.

$=\frac{2a}{3}$ Simplify.

b. $\frac{6x}{11y}-\frac{10x}{11y}=\frac{6x-10x}{11y}$ Write difference over common denominator.

$=\frac{-4x}{11y}$, or $-\frac{4x}{11y}$ Combine like terms.

Your turn now **Find the sum or difference. Then simplify if possible.**

1. $\frac{1}{12}+\frac{5}{12}$ $\frac{1}{2}$
2. $\frac{3}{8}-2\frac{1}{8}$ $-1\frac{3}{4}$
3. $-\frac{t}{3}-\frac{2t}{3}$ $-t$
4. $\frac{y}{8a}+\frac{-5y}{8a}$ $-\frac{y}{2a}$

EXAMPLE 3 Solving an Equation with Mixed Numbers

Biology A corn snake that is $14\frac{3}{4}$ inches long grows g inches to a length of $27\frac{1}{4}$ inches. To find the amount of growth, subtract the original length from the current length.

$g=27\frac{1}{4}-14\frac{3}{4}$ $\frac{1}{4}<\frac{3}{4}$, so rename $27\frac{1}{4}$ so its fraction part is greater than $\frac{3}{4}$.

$=26\frac{5}{4}-14\frac{3}{4}$

$=\left(26+\frac{5}{4}\right)-\left(14+\frac{3}{4}\right)$

$=26+\frac{5}{4}-14-\frac{3}{4}$ ← Remember to distribute the subtraction.

$=(26-14)+\left(\frac{5}{4}-\frac{3}{4}\right)$

$=12+\frac{2}{4}$

$=12\frac{1}{2}$ ← $\frac{2}{4}=\frac{1}{2}$

ANSWER The snake grows $12\frac{1}{2}$ inches.

Order of Operations The rules for adding and subtracting fractions can be applied to longer expressions. Remember to use the order of operations.

EXAMPLE 4 Evaluating Longer Expressions

a. $\frac{2}{11} - \frac{5}{11} + \frac{9}{11} = \frac{2 - 5 + 9}{11}$ **Write 2 − 5 + 9 over common denominator.**

$= \frac{6}{11}$ **Evaluate numerator from left to right.**

b. $3\frac{6}{7} - 2\frac{3}{7} + 4\frac{5}{7} = (3 - 2 + 4) + \left(\frac{6}{7} - \frac{3}{7} + \frac{5}{7}\right)$ **Group whole numbers and fractions.**

$= 5\frac{8}{7}$ **Evaluate inside parentheses.**

$= 6\frac{1}{7}$ **Rename.**

Your turn now **Evaluate. Then simplify if possible.**

5. $\frac{3}{4} + \frac{7}{4} + \frac{5}{4}$ $3\frac{3}{4}$ **6.** $\frac{15}{8} - \frac{7}{8} + \frac{3}{8}$ $1\frac{3}{8}$ **7.** $2\frac{1}{3} - \frac{2}{3} + 3\frac{2}{3}$ $5\frac{1}{3}$

5.1 Exercises

More Practice, p. 731

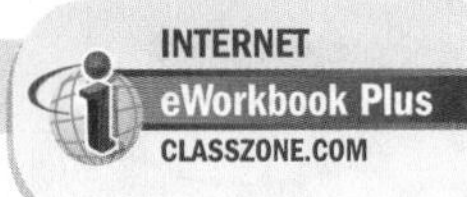

Getting Ready to Practice

1. Vocabulary Copy and complete: In the fraction $\frac{4}{9}$, 9 is the _?_ and 4 is the _?_. **denominator, numerator**

2. Find the Error Describe and correct the error. **See margin.**

✗ $\frac{3}{4} + \frac{3}{4} = \frac{3 + 3}{4 + 4} = \frac{6}{8}$

Find the sum or difference. Then simplify if possible.

3. $\frac{5}{18} + \frac{7}{18}$ $\frac{2}{3}$ **4.** $\frac{3}{10} - \frac{7}{10}$ $-\frac{2}{5}$ **5.** $\frac{4}{15} - \frac{1}{15}$ $\frac{1}{5}$ **6.** $1\frac{5}{9} + \frac{2}{9}$ $1\frac{7}{9}$

7. $3\frac{1}{7} - 1\frac{5}{7}$ $1\frac{3}{7}$ **8.** $2\frac{7}{9} + \frac{8}{9}$ $3\frac{2}{3}$ **9.** $\frac{c}{6} + \frac{5c}{6}$ c **10.** $\frac{3d}{5} - \frac{2d}{5}$ $\frac{d}{5}$

11. Knitting When the scarf you are knitting is $21\frac{3}{8}$ inches long, you find a mistake and have to pull out $2\frac{5}{8}$ inches. How much scarf is left? $18\frac{3}{4}$ **in.**

EXTRA EXAMPLES

Example 4 Evaluate. Then simplify if possible.

a. $\frac{4}{15} + \frac{8}{15} - \frac{2}{15}$ $\frac{2}{3}$

b. $4\frac{3}{4} - 1\frac{1}{4} + 2\frac{3}{4}$ $6\frac{1}{4}$

CONCEPT CHECK

How do you add or subtract fractions with common denominators? **Write the sum or difference of the numerators over the common denominator. Then simplify if necessary.**

DAILY PUZZLER

On Monday, Phil ate half a pizza. On Tuesday, he ate half the remainder. On Wednesday, he ate half the remainder. On Thursday, he ate half the remainder. After eating Thursday, what fraction of the original pizza did Phil have left? $\frac{1}{16}$

2. The denominators were added; $\frac{3}{4} + \frac{3}{4} = \frac{3 + 3}{4} = \frac{6}{4} = 1\frac{1}{2}$.

APPLY

ASSIGNMENT GUIDE

Basic Course

Day 1: SRH p. 710 Exs. 6-10; pp. 222-223 Exs. 12-28, 31-36, 41, 47-63

Average Course

Day 1: pp. 222-223 Exs. 16-30, 34-44, 49-64

Advanced Course

Day 1: pp. 222-223 Exs. 20-30, 37-58*, 62-64

Block

pp. 222-223 Exs. 16-30, 34-44, 49-64 (with 5.2)

EXTRA PRACTICE

- Student Edition, p. 731
- Chapter 5 Resource Book, pp. 7-9
- Test and Practice Generator

TRANSPARENCY

Even-numbered answers are available on transparencies.

HOMEWORK CHECK

When you review students' homework for this lesson, go over the following exercises to check understanding of key concepts.

Basic: 12, 17, 24, 28, 31

Average: 20, 21, 25, 28, 34

Advanced: 20, 21, 26, 29, 37

TEACHING TIP

Students may wish to use the method presented in the Differentiating Instruction note on page 220 for Exercises 20-23 and 34-39.

with Homework

Example	Exercises
1	12-23
2	24-27
3	28-30, 40
4	31-39

Online Resources

CLASSZONE.COM

- More Examples
- eTutorial Plus

What do you think? Sports

spoiler

Auto Racing

Decreasing the height of a race car's spoiler reduces *drag*, increasing speed. What do you think happens when the spoiler's height is increased? **Drag is increased and speed is decreased.**

Practice and Problem Solving

Find the sum or difference.

A **12.** $\frac{4}{17} + \frac{8}{17}$ $\frac{12}{17}$ **13.** $\frac{7}{18} - \frac{5}{18}$ $\frac{1}{9}$ **14.** $\frac{9}{14} - \frac{5}{14}$ $\frac{2}{7}$ **15.** $\frac{-13}{24} + \frac{-9}{24}$ $-\frac{11}{12}$

16. $\frac{5}{21} + \frac{2}{21}$ $\frac{1}{3}$ **17.** $\frac{12}{25} + \frac{-7}{25}$ $\frac{1}{5}$ **18.** $\frac{1}{6} - \frac{11}{6}$ $-1\frac{2}{3}$ **19.** $-\frac{3}{4} - \left(-\frac{1}{4}\right)$ $-\frac{1}{2}$

20. $-2\frac{5}{12} + 1\frac{11}{12}$ $-\frac{1}{2}$ **21.** $1\frac{4}{15} + \left(-\frac{11}{15}\right)$ $\frac{8}{15}$ **22.** $-4\frac{2}{7} - 4\frac{2}{7}$ $-8\frac{4}{7}$ **23.** $-7\frac{3}{5} - \frac{4}{5}$ $-8\frac{2}{5}$

Algebra Simplify the expression.

24. $\frac{h}{13} + \frac{6h}{13}$ $\frac{7h}{13}$ **25.** $-\frac{8n}{21} + \frac{5n}{21}$ $-\frac{n}{7}$ **26.** $\frac{9a}{20b} - \frac{7a}{20b}$ $\frac{a}{10b}$ **27.** $-\frac{5q}{18p} - \frac{13q}{18p}$ $-\frac{q}{p}$

28. Euros A 2-euro coin is $25\frac{3}{4}$ millimeters at its widest. A 1-euro coin is $23\frac{1}{4}$ millimeters at its widest. How much wider is a 2-euro coin? $2\frac{1}{2}$ mm

29. Volunteering You did volunteer work for $6\frac{1}{6}$ hours last week and $8\frac{5}{6}$ hours this week. For how many total hours have you volunteered? How many more hours did you volunteer this week than last week? 15 h; $2\frac{2}{3}$ h

30. Auto Racing Some cars in a recent race were allowed to reduce the height of their rear spoilers by one fourth inch. After the change, one car's spoiler was $6\frac{1}{4}$ inches tall. How tall was the spoiler before the change in height? $6\frac{1}{2}$ in.

Evaluate.

B **31.** $\frac{13}{18} + \frac{5}{18} + \frac{11}{18}$ $1\frac{11}{18}$ **32.** $-\frac{4}{5} - \frac{1}{5} - \frac{2}{5}$ $-1\frac{2}{5}$ **33.** $-\frac{4}{25} + \frac{3}{25} + \frac{9}{25}$ $\frac{8}{25}$

34. $\frac{5}{7} - 1\frac{3}{7} + \frac{4}{7}$ $-\frac{1}{7}$ **35.** $-\frac{3}{16} + 2\frac{1}{16} - \frac{15}{16}$ $\frac{15}{16}$ **36.** $1\frac{3}{8} + \frac{5}{8} - 1\frac{7}{8}$ $\frac{1}{8}$

37. $-5\frac{4}{15} - 3\frac{7}{15} + \frac{8}{15}$ $-8\frac{1}{5}$ **38.** $-\frac{9}{20} + \frac{19}{20} - 1\frac{1}{20}$ $-\frac{11}{20}$ **39.** $4\frac{5}{12} - \left(1\frac{11}{12} - \frac{7}{12}\right)$ $3\frac{1}{12}$

40. Long Jump You want to match your school's long jump record of 17 feet $8\frac{1}{4}$ inches. Your best long jump so far is 15 feet $11\frac{3}{4}$ inches. How much farther do you need to jump to match the school record? 1 ft $8\frac{1}{2}$ in.

Algebra Solve the equation.

41. $x + \frac{5}{8} = \frac{7}{8}$ $\frac{1}{4}$ **42.** $\frac{10}{11} - y = \frac{2}{11}$ $\frac{8}{11}$ **43.** $z - \frac{9}{15} = \frac{11}{15}$ $1\frac{1}{3}$

C **44. Writing** One hundred students try three new fruit juice blends, and each picks a favorite, as shown at the right.

Your friend says that if you make each number the numerator in a fraction with a denominator of 100, the sum of these fractions must be 1. Is your friend right? Explain. See margin.

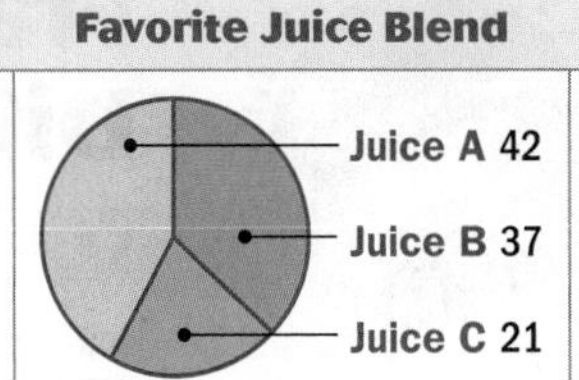

Challenge **Find the value that makes the equation true.**

45. $\frac{5}{11}+\frac{9}{11}-\underline{?}=-\frac{2}{11}$ $1\frac{5}{11}$

46. $\frac{7}{16}+\frac{9}{16}-\underline{?}=\frac{5}{16}$ $\frac{11}{16}$

Mixed Review 

Find the sum or difference. *(Lessons 2.2, 2.3)*

47. $22+(-17)$ 5 **48.** $-14-9$ -23 **49.** $-7+(-35)$ -42 **50.** $16-(-13)$ 29

Find the least common multiple of the numbers. *(Lesson 4.4)*

51. 15, 35 105 **52.** 19, 76 76 **53.** 37, 50 1850 **54.** 27, 81 81

Find the least common denominator of the fractions. *(Lesson 4.5)*

55. $\frac{2}{3}, \frac{4}{9}$ 9 **56.** $\frac{1}{5}, \frac{9}{20}$ 20 **57.** $\frac{3}{8}, \frac{7}{12}$ 24 **58.** $\frac{1}{6}, \frac{4}{15}$ 30

Basic Skills **Find the quotient.**

59. $32 \div 2$ 16 **60.** $60 \div 5$ 12 **61.** $10 \div 8$ 1.25 **62.** $50 \div 4$ 12.5

Test-Taking Practice

63. Multiple Choice You have $\frac{7}{8}$ of a box of pasta. If you serve $\frac{3}{8}$ of the box for dinner, how much of the box do you have left? B

A. $\frac{1}{4}$ **B.** $\frac{1}{2}$ **C.** $\frac{5}{8}$ **D.** $\frac{3}{4}$

64. Multiple Choice You are fencing a rectangular plot of land. The plot and its dimensions are shown. How many feet of fencing do you need? I

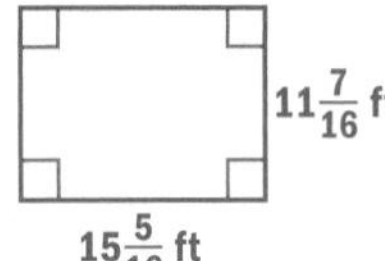

F. $26\frac{3}{4}$ feet **G.** $52\frac{1}{2}$ feet

H. $53\frac{1}{4}$ feet **I.** $53\frac{1}{2}$ feet

44. Yes. *Sample answer:* The total of the numerators will be the total number of students, 100. Since you add the fractions by adding the numerators and keeping the same denominator, the total will be $\frac{100}{100}$, or 1.

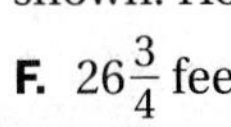

4 ASSESS

ASSESSMENT RESOURCES

For more assessment resources, see:

- Assessment Book
- Test and Practice Generator

MINI-QUIZ

Find the sum or difference.

1. $\frac{9}{14}-\frac{7}{14}$ $\frac{1}{7}$
2. $-2\frac{3}{10}+1\frac{7}{10}$ $-\frac{3}{5}$

Simplify the expression.

3. $\frac{2g}{3}+\frac{4g}{3}$ $2g$
4. $\frac{5h}{7k}-\frac{4h}{7k}$ $\frac{h}{7k}$
5. Before lunch, Tara hiked $3\frac{5}{8}$ miles. After lunch, she hiked another $2\frac{7}{8}$ miles. How far did she hike altogether? $6\frac{1}{2}$ mi

5 FOLLOW-UP

RETEACHING/REMEDIATION

- Study Guide in Chapter 5 Resource Book, pp. 10–11
- Tutor Place, Fractions Cards 8, 9, 13, 14, Algebra Cards 8, 9, 12
- eTutorial Plus Online
- Extra Practice, p. 731
- Lesson Practice in Chapter 5 Resource Book, pp. 7–9

CHALLENGE/ENRICHMENT

- Challenge Practice in Chapter 5 Resource Book, p. 12
- Teacher's Edition, p. 216F

ENGLISH LEARNER SUPPORT

- Spanish Study Guide
- Multi-Language Glossary
- Chapter Audio Summaries CDs

1 PLAN

SKILL CHECK

1. $\frac{10}{25} = \frac{?}{5}$ 2
2. $\frac{7}{10} = \frac{?}{30}$ 21
3. $\frac{5}{8} = \frac{?}{16}$ 10

LESSON OBJECTIVE

Add and subtract fractions with different denominators.

PACING

Suggested Number of Days
Basic Course: 1 day
Average Course: 1 day
Advanced Course: 1 day
Block: 0.5 block with 5.1

TEACHING RESOURCES

For a complete list of Teaching Resources, see page 216B.

TRANSPARENCY

Warm-Up Exercises for this lesson are available on a transparency.

2 TEACH

MOTIVATING THE LESSON

Develop with students a list of hobbies and activities that would involve measuring and computing with fractions.

TIPS FOR NEW TEACHERS

Walk students through the steps for finding the LCD and rewriting fractions using the LCD. See Tips for New Teachers in the *Chapter 5 Resource Book*.

LESSON 5.2

Fractions with Different Denominators

BEFORE
You added and subtracted with common denominators.

Now
You'll add and subtract with different denominators.

WHY?
So you can find a sled length, as in Ex. 20.

Word Watch

Review Words
least common denominator (LCD), p. 192

In the Real World

Carpentry A board is $36\frac{5}{8}$ inches long. You cut off a piece $12\frac{3}{4}$ inches long. The saw blade destroys an additional $\frac{1}{16}$ inch of wood. You will find the length of the remaining piece of wood in Example 3 on page 225.

Rewriting Fractions To add or subtract fractions with different denominators, first rewrite the fractions so the denominators are the same.

HELP with Review

For help with rewriting fractions with common denominators, see p. 192.

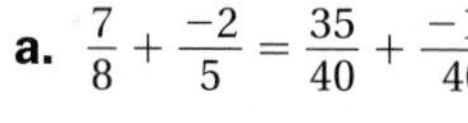

EXAMPLE 1 Adding and Subtracting Fractions

a. $\frac{7}{8} + \frac{-2}{5} = \frac{35}{40} + \frac{-16}{40}$ Rewrite fractions using LCD of 40.

$= \frac{35 + (-16)}{40}$ Write sum over LCD.

$= \frac{19}{40}$ Evaluate numerator.

b. $\frac{3}{10} - \frac{5}{6} = \frac{9}{30} - \frac{25}{30}$ Rewrite fractions using LCD of 30.

$= \frac{9 - 25}{30}$ Write difference over LCD.

$= \frac{-16}{30}$ Evaluate numerator.

$= -\frac{8}{15}$ Simplify.

Your turn now Find the sum or difference. Then simplify if possible.

1. $\frac{1}{3} + \frac{3}{8}$ $\frac{17}{24}$
2. $\frac{3}{4} - \frac{9}{10}$ $-\frac{3}{20}$
3. $\frac{5}{12} + \frac{-7}{9}$ $-\frac{13}{36}$
4. $\frac{1}{6} - \frac{11}{15}$ $-\frac{17}{30}$

ILLINOIS Standards and ISAT:
6.A.3, 6.B.3b, 6.C.3a, 8.D.3a

EXAMPLE 2 Simplifying Variable Expressions

Algebra **Simplify the expression.**

a. $\frac{2x}{5} - \frac{x}{6} = \frac{12x}{30} - \frac{5x}{30}$ **Rewrite fractions using LCD of 30.**

$= \frac{12x - 5x}{30}$ **Write difference over LCD.**

$= \frac{7x}{30}$ **Combine like terms.**

b. $\frac{5}{y} + \frac{7}{8} = \left(\frac{5}{y} \cdot \frac{8}{8}\right) + \left(\frac{7}{8} \cdot \frac{y}{y}\right)$ **Multiply $\frac{5}{y}$ by $\frac{8}{8}$ and $\frac{7}{8}$ by $\frac{y}{y}$ for LCD of $8y$.**

$= \frac{40}{8y} + \frac{7y}{8y}$ **Multiply inside parentheses.**

$= \frac{40 + 7y}{8y}$ **Write sum over LCD.**

Watch Out!

In part (b) of Example 2, notice that

$\frac{40 + 7y}{8y} \neq \frac{47y}{8y}$

because 40 and $7y$ are not like terms. The expression is already in simplest form.

EXAMPLE 3 Modeling with Mixed Numbers

Carpentry To find the length of the remaining piece of wood from the problem at the top of page 224, write a verbal model.

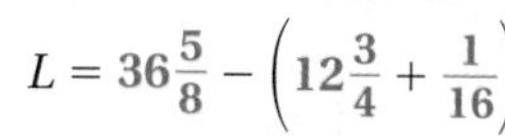

Remaining length L = Original length − (Length cut off + Blade width)

$L = 36\frac{5}{8} - \left(12\frac{3}{4} + \frac{1}{16}\right)$ **Write an algebraic model.**

$= 36\frac{10}{16} - \left(12\frac{12}{16} + \frac{1}{16}\right)$ **Rewrite fractions using LCD of 16.**

$= 36\frac{10}{16} - 12\frac{13}{16}$ **Add inside parentheses.**

$= 35\frac{26}{16} - 12\frac{13}{16}$ **Rename $36\frac{10}{16}$ as $35\frac{26}{16}$.**

$= (35 - 12) + \left(\frac{26}{16} - \frac{13}{16}\right)$ **Group whole numbers and fractions.**

$= 23\frac{13}{16}$ **Subtract whole numbers and fractions.**

ANSWER The remaining piece of wood is $23\frac{13}{16}$ inches long.

Your turn now **Find the sum or difference. Then simplify if possible.**

5. $\frac{w}{3} + \frac{w}{12}$ $\frac{5w}{12}$ **6.** $\frac{2}{5} - \frac{2}{z}$ $\frac{2z - 10}{5z}$ **7.** $5\frac{3}{4} + 2\frac{3}{5}$ $8\frac{7}{20}$ **8.** $7\frac{5}{6} - 3\frac{8}{9}$ $3\frac{17}{18}$

EXTRA EXAMPLES

Example 1 Find the sum or difference. Then simplify if possible.

a. $\frac{4}{7} - \frac{1}{2}$ $\frac{1}{14}$

b. $\frac{1}{6} - \frac{3}{8}$ $-\frac{5}{24}$

Example 2 Simplify the expression.

a. $\frac{5d}{8} - \frac{2d}{5}$ $\frac{9d}{40}$

b. $\frac{10}{x} + \frac{3}{4}$ $\frac{40 + 3x}{4x}$

Example 3 On Monday, the new leaf on Teofolo's banana plant was $2\frac{3}{4}$ inches long. By Friday, the leaf was $8\frac{1}{8}$ inches long. How much did the new leaf grow? $5\frac{3}{8}$ **in.**

Differentiating Instruction

Alternative Approach The method of rewriting mixed numbers as improper fractions presented in the note on page 220 can be used in this lesson as well. The only extra step is finding the LCD.

CONCEPT CHECK

When you add or subtract fractions with different denominators, what do you do first? **Rewrite the fractions so the denominators are the same.**

DAILY PUZZLER

Replace each variable in the expression $\frac{a}{b} + \frac{c}{d} + \frac{e}{f} + \frac{g}{h}$ with a digit from 1 to 8, using each digit once, so that the expression has the smallest possible value. $\frac{1}{5} + \frac{2}{6} + \frac{3}{7} + \frac{4}{8}$

APPLY

ASSIGNMENT GUIDE

Basic Course

Day 1: pp. 226–227 Exs. 7–19, 21–28, 30, 34–42

Average Course

Day 1: pp. 226–227 Exs. 9–20, 23–32, 34–43

Advanced Course

Day 1: pp. 226–227 Exs. 11–20, 23–37*, 40–43

Block

pp. 226–227 Exs. 9–20, 23–32, 34–43 (with 5.1)

EXTRA PRACTICE

- Student Edition, p. 731
- Chapter 5 Resource Book, pp. 15–17
- Test and Practice Generator

TRANSPARENCY

Even-numbered answers are available on transparencies.

HOMEWORK CHECK

When you review students' homework for this lesson, go over the following exercises to check understanding of key concepts.

Basic: 7, 12, 14, 21, 24

Average: 11, 12, 14, 23, 24

Advanced: 11, 12, 15, 23, 25

5.2 Exercises

More Practice, p. 731

Getting Ready to Practice

1. **Vocabulary** Copy and complete: To add two fractions with different denominators, rewrite the fractions using the _?_ of the fractions. least common denominator or LCD

Find the sum or difference. Then simplify if possible.

2. $\frac{1}{2} + \frac{1}{3}$ $\frac{5}{6}$
3. $4\frac{5}{8} - 2\frac{2}{3}$ $1\frac{23}{24}$
4. $\frac{2x}{7} - \frac{x}{2}$ $-\frac{3x}{14}$
5. $\frac{4}{x} + \frac{1}{9}$ $\frac{36 + x}{9x}$

6. **Guided Problem Solving** You are building a stone wall 13 feet long. You build $4\frac{1}{3}$ feet of wall on Monday and $5\frac{3}{4}$ feet on Tuesday. How much wall do you have left to build?

   (1) Write a verbal model to describe the problem.

   (2) Substitute the given values into the model. $L = 13 - \left(4\frac{1}{3} + 5\frac{3}{4}\right)$

   (3) Solve the equation to find the length left to build. $2\frac{11}{12}$ ft

Step 1. Length left to build = Length of wall − (Length built on Monday + Length built on Tuesday)

Practice and Problem Solving

with Homework

Example	Exercises
1	7–13, 21–22
2	24–27
3	14–20, 23

- More Examples
- eTutorial Plus

Find the sum or difference.

A

7. $\frac{7}{8} - \frac{1}{4}$ $\frac{5}{8}$
8. $\frac{3}{7} + \frac{9}{14}$ $1\frac{1}{14}$
9. $\frac{5}{9} + \frac{1}{6}$ $\frac{13}{18}$
10. $\frac{2}{3} - \frac{3}{10}$ $\frac{11}{30}$
11. $\frac{1}{8} - \frac{5}{32}$ $-\frac{1}{32}$
12. $-\frac{7}{12} + \frac{4}{15}$ $-\frac{19}{60}$
13. $\frac{-3}{8} + \frac{-9}{20}$ $-\frac{33}{40}$
14. $5\frac{1}{2} - \frac{7}{10}$ $4\frac{4}{5}$
15. $12\frac{5}{18} - \frac{3}{4}$ $11\frac{19}{36}$
16. $-7\frac{3}{11} - (-8)$ $\frac{8}{11}$
17. $7\frac{4}{5} + 5\frac{3}{7}$ $13\frac{8}{35}$
18. $12\frac{2}{9} - 16\frac{3}{7}$ $-4\frac{13}{63}$

19. **Tree Removal** A dead tree $25\frac{1}{2}$ feet tall is being cut down. On the first cut, $9\frac{1}{3}$ feet are cut off. On the next cut, $7\frac{5}{6}$ feet are cut off. How much of the tree remains to be cut down? $8\frac{1}{3}$ ft

20. **Olympic Sledding** Olympic skeleton sleds range from $31\frac{1}{2}$ inches to $47\frac{1}{4}$ inches long. What is the difference in length of the longest and shortest sleds? $15\frac{3}{4}$ in.

Tell whether the statement is *true* or *false*.

B

21. $\frac{1}{4} - \frac{6}{7} + \frac{3}{14} = -\frac{11}{28}$ true
22. $\frac{4}{5} + \frac{5}{8} - \frac{7}{10} = \frac{57}{80}$ false
23. $1\frac{1}{3} - \frac{2}{9} - \frac{5}{6} = \frac{7}{18}$ false

26. $\frac{54 + 11a}{21a}$

29. West; traveling east is $\frac{27}{50}$ of the way around the equator, while traveling west is $1 - \frac{27}{50} = \frac{23}{50}$ of the way. Since $\frac{23}{50} < \frac{27}{50}$, traveling west is shorter.

30. $4\frac{1}{24}$

31. $1\frac{11}{72}$

32. $3\frac{23}{70}$

33. Yes. *Sample answer:* The original fractions and the rewritten fractions with common denominators are equivalent, it is does not matter at what stage the fractions are rewritten.

INTERNET
State Test Practice
CLASSZONE.COM

Algebra Simplify the expression.

24. $\frac{6t}{13} - \frac{6t}{7}$ $-\frac{36t}{91}$ **25.** $\frac{9s}{4} - \frac{7s}{5}$ $\frac{17s}{20}$ **26.** $\frac{18}{7a} + \frac{11}{21}$ **27.** $\frac{16}{25n} + \frac{9}{10n}$ $\frac{77}{50n}$

Equator In Exercises 28 and 29, use the following information.

Traveling east from the Galapagos Islands to Nairobi, Kenya, you go about $\frac{9}{25}$ of the way around Earth's equator. It is then about $\frac{9}{50}$ of the way around the equator from Nairobi traveling east to Singapore.

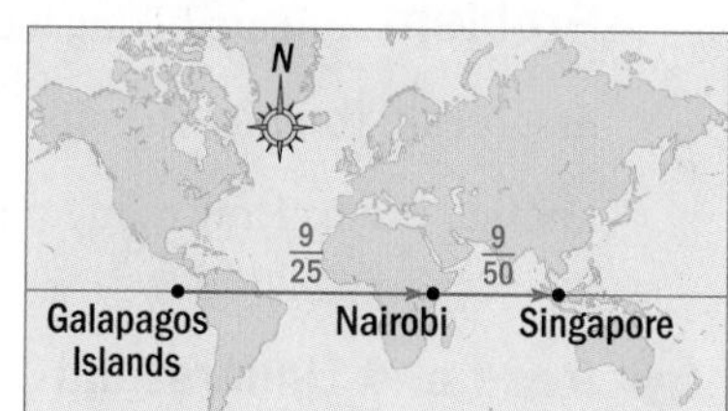

28. What fraction of the equator do you cover if you travel east from the Galapagos Islands to Singapore? $\frac{27}{50}$

29. Writing Is traveling from the Galapagos Islands to Singapore a shorter trip if you travel *east* or *west*? Explain. See margin.

Algebra Solve the equation. 30–32. See margin.

C **30.** $6\frac{3}{8} + 2\frac{5}{12} - x = 4\frac{3}{4}$ **31.** $7\frac{7}{8} - 6\frac{5}{9} - y = \frac{1}{6}$ **32.** $z + 3\frac{4}{7} - 5\frac{2}{5} = 1\frac{1}{2}$

33. Challenge To evaluate $3\frac{1}{4} + 5\frac{3}{8}$, Cal groups the whole numbers and the fractions, and then rewrites the fractions with a common denominator. May rewrites the fractions with a common denominator first, and then groups the whole numbers and the fractions. Do Cal and May get the same sum? Explain. See margin.

Mixed Review 

Find the product. *(Lesson 2.4)*

34. $-9(7)$ -63 **35.** $0(-5)$ 0 **36.** $7(-3)(13)$ -273 **37.** $-9(-7)(-2)$ -126

Copy and complete the statement with <, >, or =. *(Lesson 4.5)*

38. $\frac{1}{7} \underline{?} \frac{1}{8}$ $>$ **39.** $\frac{3}{8} \underline{?} \frac{4}{9}$ $<$ **40.** $\frac{5}{12} \underline{?} \frac{7}{16}$ $<$ **41.** $\frac{7}{10} \underline{?} \frac{18}{25}$ $<$

Test-Taking Practice 

42. Multiple Choice What is the value of $\frac{5}{6} + \frac{1}{9} - \frac{2}{3}$? C

A. $\frac{1}{6}$ **B.** $\frac{2}{9}$ **C.** $\frac{5}{18}$ **D.** $\frac{1}{3}$

43. Short Response You are getting ready for a backpacking trip. You pack $4\frac{2}{3}$ pounds of food and $5\frac{1}{8}$ pounds of equipment into a $2\frac{1}{4}$ pound backpack. What is the total weight you will carry? $12\frac{1}{24}$ lb

4 ASSESS

Assessment Resources

For more assessment resources, see:
- Assessment Book
- Test and Practice Generator

Mini-Quiz

Find the sum or difference.

1. $\frac{5}{6} - \frac{1}{3}$ $\frac{1}{2}$
2. $\frac{7}{8} + \frac{1}{16}$ $\frac{15}{16}$
3. $10\frac{1}{2} - 6\frac{7}{8}$ $3\frac{5}{8}$
4. $-5\frac{3}{4} + 7\frac{7}{12}$ $1\frac{5}{6}$
5. In 1990, Louise the python was $7\frac{1}{4}$ feet long. In 2000, Louise was $10\frac{7}{8}$ feet long. How much did Louise grow from 1990 to 2000? $3\frac{5}{8}$ ft

5 FOLLOW-UP

Reteaching/Remediation

- Study Guide in Chapter 5 Resource Book, pp. 18–19
- Tutor Place, Fractions Cards 11–14
- eTutorial Plus Online
- Extra Practice, p. 731
- Lesson Practice in Chapter 5 Resource Book, pp. 15–17

Challenge/Enrichment

- Challenge Practice in Chapter 5 Resource Book, p. 21
- Teacher's Edition, p. 216F

English Learner Support

- Spanish Study Guide
- Multi-Language Glossary
- Chapter Audio Summaries CDs

1 PLAN

STRATEGY BACKGROUND

The strategy Act It Out helps students visualize the problem they need to solve. When it is appropriate, this strategy allows students to simulate the conditions of the problem so that they can understand it better.

2 TEACH

GUIDING STUDENTS' WORK

If the classroom floor does not have tiles, a yardstick and chalk can be used to create the path by marking off 30 feet in the classroom or in a hallway. Let each foot represent $\frac{1}{4}$ of a mile.

EXTRA EXAMPLES

Example Five friends meet for lunch. Each person shakes hands with the other 4 people. How many handshakes are there? **10 handshakes**

5.3 Problem Solving Strategies

- Guess, Check, and Revise
- Look for a Pattern
- Draw a Diagram
- Make a Model
- Act It Out
- Make a Table
- Solve a Simpler Problem

Act It Out

Problem You are hiking a trail that is $7\frac{1}{2}$ miles long. Before your first break, you hike $2\frac{3}{4}$ miles. Then you hike $2\frac{1}{2}$ miles and take another break. How many miles do you have left to hike?

1 Read and Understand

Read the problem carefully.

- You know that you are hiking a total distance of $7\frac{1}{2}$ miles, and that you have already hiked $2\frac{3}{4}$ miles and $2\frac{1}{2}$ miles.
- You want to find the remaining distance that you have left to hike.

2 Make a Plan

Decide on a strategy to use.

One way to solve this problem is to use the act it out strategy. You can act out the hike by using a common item like floor tiles to represent distance traveled.

3 Solve the Problem

Reread the problem and act it out.

The fractions have an LCD of 4, so let each floor tile represent $\frac{1}{4}$ of a mile. Use masking tape to mark off 30 tiles for $7\frac{1}{2}$ miles. Walk across 11 tiles to represent $2\frac{3}{4}$ miles hiked and 10 more tiles to represent $2\frac{1}{2}$ miles hiked. Notice that 9 tiles remain, which represent $2\frac{1}{4}$ miles left to hike.

ANSWER You have $2\frac{1}{4}$ miles left to hike.

4 Look Back

Add your answer to the first two distances.

$2\frac{3}{4} + 2\frac{1}{2} + 2\frac{1}{4} = 7\frac{1}{2}$ ✓

ILLINOIS Standards and ISAT:
6.B.3a, 6.C.3a

Practice the Strategy

Use the strategy *act it out*. Tell how you acted out the problem to get your answer. **1–5. See margin.**

1. **Pets** There are 18 students in your class. Eight students have a cat and five students have a dog. Two students in your class have both a cat and a dog. How many students have neither a cat nor a dog?

2. **Money** You have 8 quarters, 10 dimes, and 7 nickels. You give half of your dimes and 2 nickels to a friend. Then you spend one fourth of your quarters and one nickel. How much money do you have left?

3. **Gifts** You buy a roll of ribbon 20 yards long. The amounts of ribbon you use to decorate a gift and to make a bow are shown below.

You decorate 5 gifts. How many bows can you make with the ribbon you have left?

4. **Beads** There are 24 beads in a bowl. Anna takes $\frac{1}{6}$ of the beads. Then John takes two beads. Lena takes $\frac{1}{9}$ of what Anna and John left. Dawn takes $\frac{1}{4}$ of what Lena left, and then Jamal takes five beads. How many beads are left in the bowl?

5. **Lunch Line** You are in a lunch line with 4 students in front of you and 6 students behind you. You let a friend into the line in front of you, who then lets 2 students get in line behind her. Finally, 2 students join the end of the lunch line. How many students are in the lunch line? What is your new position in the lunch line?

Mixed Problem Solving

Use any strategy to solve the problem.

6. **Vacation** On each day of your three day vacation, you can choose one activity. The table below shows your choices. How many different groups of activities can you choose? **18 groups**

Day	Activities
Friday	museum, picnic, bus tour
Saturday	baseball game, bicycling
Sunday	hike, shopping, water park

7. **Fundraising** To raise money for a class trip, you are selling sweatshirts for \$19 and T-shirts for \$11. You have sold 17 items worth a total of \$227. How many of each item have you sold? **5 sweatshirts and 12 T-shirts**

8. **Floors** You are choosing a floor covering for the room shown below. It costs \$3 per square foot for carpeting. It costs \$8 per square foot for a wood floor. **\$549 for carpet, \$1,464 for a wood floor**

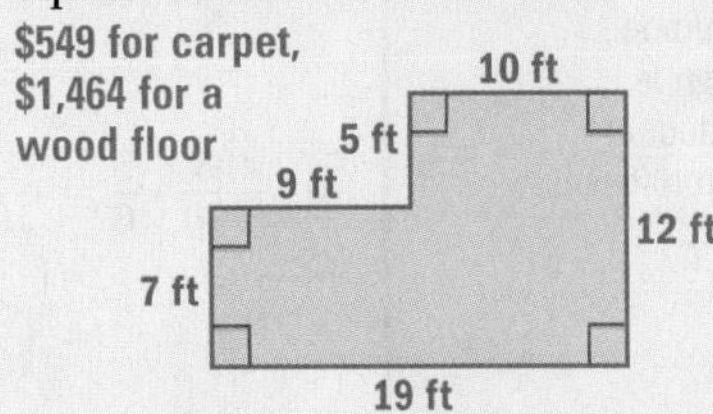

What is the cost to cover the floor with each type of flooring?

APPLY

TRANSPARENCY

Even-numbered answers are available on transparencies.

TEACHING TIP

In Exercise 3, clarify that making a bow is a different activity from decorating a gift.

SUGGESTED STRATEGIES

You may wish to suggest the following strategies for the problems in the Mixed Problem Solving:

- Exercise 6: Make a List; Solve a Simpler Problem
- Exercise 7: Guess, Check, and Revise; Make a List
- Exercise 8: Draw a Diagram; Solve a Simpler Problem

1. 7 students. *Sample answer:* Choose 18 classmates. Let 2 classmates represent the students that have both a dog and a cat. Six more classmates are needed to represent the students that have a dog and 3 more to represent those that have a cat. There are 7 classmates left over.

2. \$2.20. *Sample answer:* Count out 8 quarters, 10 dimes, and 7 nickels. Take away 5 of the dimes, 2 of the nickels, and 2 of the quarters. Take away one more nickel. There are 6 quarters, 5 dimes, and 4 nickels left, for a total of 6(.25) + 5(.10) + 4(.05) = \$2.20.

3–5. See Additional Answers beginning on page AA1.

PLAN

SKILL CHECK

1. $(-7)(-16) = \underline{?}$ 112
2. Find the area of a rectangle if $l = 15$ inches and $w = 11$ inches. 165 in.^{2}
3. Find x^2 if $x = 8$. 64

LESSON OBJECTIVE

Multiply fractions and mixed numbers.

PACING

Suggested Number of Days
Basic Course: 1 day
Average Course: 1 day
Advanced Course: 1 day
Block: 0.5 block with 5.4

TEACHING RESOURCES

For a complete list of Teaching Resources, see page 216B.

TRANSPARENCY

Warm-Up Exercises for this lesson are available on a transparency.

TEACH

MOTIVATING THE LESSON

Ask students for suggestions as to how they might multiply $5\frac{1}{2}$ by $3\frac{3}{4}$.

TIPS FOR NEW TEACHERS

Students may be tempted to multiply mixed numbers by multiplying whole number parts and fraction parts separately. Give examples to demonstrate why this does not produce the correct answer. See Tips for New Teachers in the *Chapter 5 Resource Book*.

Multiplying Fractions

BEFORE You added and subtracted fractions and mixed numbers.

Now You'll multiply fractions and mixed numbers.

WHY? So you can find a moon crater's depth, as in Ex. 19.

Word Watch

Review Words
numerator, p. 707
denominator, p. 707

In the Real World

Postcards A postcard is $5\frac{1}{2}$ inches long and $3\frac{3}{4}$ inches wide. What is the area of this postcard? In Example 2 on page 231, you will multiply mixed numbers to find the postcard's area.

Multiplication To multiply fractions, you can use the rule below.

Note book

Multiplying Fractions

Words The product of two or more fractions is equal to the product of the numerators divided by the product of the denominators.

Numbers $\frac{3}{4} \cdot \frac{5}{8} = \frac{3 \cdot 5}{4 \cdot 8} = \frac{15}{32}$

Algebra $\frac{a}{b} \cdot \frac{c}{d} = \frac{a \cdot c}{b \cdot d}$ $(b, d \neq 0)$

with Review

Remember that the product of two numbers with the same sign is positive. The product of two numbers with different signs is negative.

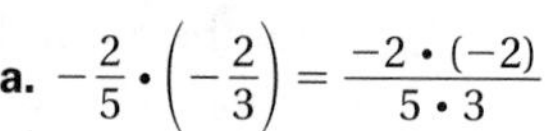

EXAMPLE 1 Multiplying Fractions

a. $-\frac{2}{5} \cdot \left(-\frac{2}{3}\right) = \frac{-2 \cdot (-2)}{5 \cdot 3}$ Use rule for multiplying fractions.

$= \frac{4}{15}$ Evaluate numerator and denominator.

b. $-\frac{3}{10} \cdot \frac{5}{6} = \frac{-3 \cdot 5}{10 \cdot 6}$ Use rule for multiplying fractions.

$= \frac{\overset{-1}{\cancel{-3}} \cdot \overset{1}{\cancel{5}}}{\underset{2}{\cancel{10}} \cdot \underset{2}{\cancel{6}}}$ Divide out common factors.

$= -\frac{1}{4}$ Multiply.

ILLINOIS Standards and ISAT:
6.B.3a, 6.C.3a, 8.D.3a; 7.C.3b

Mixed Numbers To multiply mixed numbers, first write them as improper fractions.

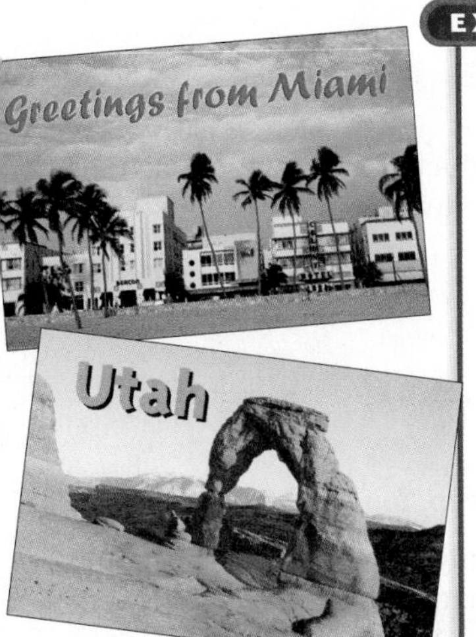

EXAMPLE 2 Multiplying Mixed Numbers

To find the area of the postcard on page 230, use an area formula.

Area = length • width	**Write formula for area of a rectangle.**
$= 5\frac{1}{2} \cdot 3\frac{3}{4}$	**Substitute values.**
$= \frac{11}{2} \cdot \frac{15}{4}$	**Write as improper fractions.**
$= \frac{11 \cdot 15}{2 \cdot 4}$	**Use rule for multiplying fractions.**
$= \frac{165}{8}$, or $20\frac{5}{8}$	**Multiply.**

ANSWER The area of the postcard is $20\frac{5}{8}$ square inches.

Watch Out!

Be careful when you write a negative mixed number as an improper fraction.

$$-4\frac{5}{6} = \frac{-4 \cdot 6 + (-5)}{6}$$

$$-4\frac{5}{6} \neq \frac{-4 \cdot 6 + 5}{6}$$

Your turn now **Find the product. Simplify if possible.**

1. $\frac{5}{12} \cdot 15$ $6\frac{1}{4}$ **2.** $-\frac{5}{12} \cdot \frac{9}{10}$ $-\frac{3}{8}$ **3.** $1\frac{2}{5} \cdot 3\frac{1}{2}$ $4\frac{9}{10}$ **4.** $-2\frac{1}{3} \cdot \left(-\frac{3}{4}\right)$ $1\frac{3}{4}$

EXAMPLE 3 Evaluating a Variable Expression

Algebra **Evaluate x^2y when $x = -\frac{4}{5}$ and $y = \frac{2}{3}$.**

$x^2y = \left(-\frac{4}{5}\right)^2 \cdot \frac{2}{3}$	**Substitute $-\frac{4}{5}$ for x and $\frac{2}{3}$ for y.**
$= \left(-\frac{4}{5}\right) \cdot \left(-\frac{4}{5}\right) \cdot \frac{2}{3}$	**Write $-\frac{4}{5}$ as a factor 2 times.**
$= \frac{-4 \cdot (-4) \cdot 2}{5 \cdot 5 \cdot 3}$	**Use rule for multiplying fractions.**
$= \frac{32}{75}$	**Multiply.**

Your turn now **Evaluate the expression when $x = -\frac{3}{4}$ and $y = \frac{5}{6}$. Simplify if possible.**

5. $\frac{1}{2}x$ $-\frac{3}{8}$ **6.** $2y$ $1\frac{2}{3}$ **7.** xy $-\frac{5}{8}$ **8.** xy^2 $-\frac{25}{48}$

EXTRA EXAMPLES

Example 1 Find the product. Simplify if possible.

a. $-\frac{3}{4} \cdot \left(-\frac{7}{9}\right)$ $\frac{7}{12}$

b. $\frac{9}{10} \cdot \left(-\frac{5}{6}\right)$ $-\frac{3}{4}$

Example 2 The heating pad for a dog's crate is $2\frac{1}{8}$ feet wide and $5\frac{1}{3}$ feet long. What is the area of the heating pad? **$11\frac{1}{3}$ ft^2**

Example 3 Evaluate a^2b when $a = \frac{5}{6}$ and $b = -\frac{9}{10}$. $-\frac{5}{8}$

Concept Check

What do you do first when multiplying mixed numbers? **Rewrite the mixed numbers as improper fractions.**

Daily Puzzler

A man has lived one fourth of his life in Topeka, one fifth in Sacramento, one third in Houston, and for the last 13 years in Hartford. He has lived in no other cities. How old is the man? **60 yr**

ASSIGNMENT GUIDE

Basic Course

Day 1: SRH p. 707 Exs. 10-14; pp. 232-233 Exs. 7-18, 20-24, 26-29, 37-45

Average Course

Day 1: pp. 232-233 Exs. 12-21, 24-34, 37-46

Advanced Course

Day 1: pp. 232-233 Exs. 15-21, 24-36*, 39-46

Block

pp. 232-233 Exs. 12-21, 24-34, 37-46 (with 5.4)

EXTRA PRACTICE

- Student Edition, p. 731
- Chapter 5 Resource Book, pp. 25-27
- Test and Practice Generator

TRANSPARENCY

Even-numbered answers are available on transparencies.

HOMEWORK CHECK

When you review students' homework for this lesson, go over the following exercises to check understanding of key concepts.
Basic: 7, 12, 15, 20, 24
Average: 15, 19, 20, 25, 27
Advanced: 15, 19, 21, 25, 27

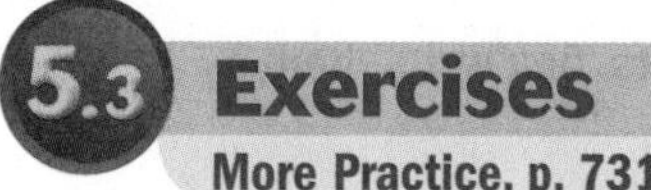

5.3 Exercises

More Practice, p. 731

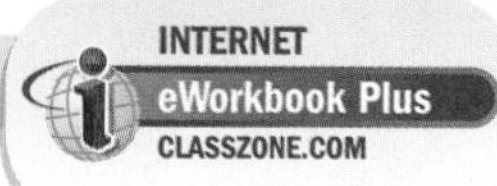

INTERNET eWorkbook Plus CLASSZONE.COM

Getting Ready to Practice

1. **Vocabulary** Copy and complete: The product of two or more fractions is equal to the product of the fractions' _?_ divided by the product of the fractions' _?_. numerators, denominators

Find the product. Simplify if possible.

2. $\frac{5}{8} \cdot \frac{7}{16}$ $\frac{35}{128}$
3. $-\frac{9}{4} \cdot \frac{5}{6}$ $-1\frac{7}{8}$
4. $-4 \cdot \frac{3}{5}$ $-2\frac{2}{5}$
5. $5\frac{3}{4} \cdot \frac{1}{8}$ $\frac{23}{32}$

6. **Snack Mix** A serving of a snack mix is $\frac{7}{8}$ cup. You need to take 15 servings to your friend's party. How many cups of snack mix should you bring? Explain how you can use estimation to check your answer. $13\frac{1}{8}$ c. *Sample answer:* Round $\frac{7}{8}$ cup to 1 cup and multiply by 15.

25. 35 ft. *Sample answer:* Let one floor tile represent $\frac{1}{4}$ of a foot. Mark off 7 tiles to represent $1\frac{3}{4}$ feet. Mark off 7 tiles 19 more times to get 140 total tiles. Since 140 tiles times $\frac{1}{4}$ foot per tile equals 35, the answer is 35 feet.

Practice and Problem Solving

with Homework

Example	Exercises
1	7-13, 19
2	14-18
3	20-23

Online Resources CLASSZONE.COM

- More Examples
- eTutorial Plus

Find the product.

A 7. $\frac{7}{11} \cdot \frac{1}{6}$ $\frac{7}{66}$
8. $\frac{4}{5} \cdot \frac{3}{10}$ $\frac{6}{25}$
9. $-\frac{3}{4} \cdot \left(-\frac{2}{9}\right)$ $\frac{1}{6}$
10. $-\frac{5}{6} \cdot \frac{5}{12}$ $-\frac{25}{72}$
11. $12 \cdot \frac{3}{8}$ $4\frac{1}{2}$
12. $-9 \cdot \frac{1}{9}$ -1
13. $-5 \cdot \left(-\frac{7}{4}\right)$ $8\frac{3}{4}$
14. $-4 \cdot 2\frac{9}{16}$ $-10\frac{1}{4}$
15. $6\frac{2}{3} \cdot 4\frac{1}{12}$ $27\frac{2}{9}$
16. $-3\frac{3}{8} \cdot 7\frac{1}{5}$ $-24\frac{3}{10}$
17. $-8 \cdot \left(-1\frac{4}{5}\right)$ $14\frac{2}{5}$
18. $6\frac{3}{16} \cdot \left(-3\frac{1}{5}\right)$ $-19\frac{4}{5}$

19. **Moon Craters** Simple impact craters on the moon are about $\frac{1}{5}$ as deep as they are wide. Moltke Crater is a simple impact crater on the moon that is 7 kilometers wide. About how deep is Moltke Crater? $1\frac{2}{5}$ km

Algebra Evaluate the expression when $a = \frac{5}{8}$ and $b = -\frac{7}{6}$.

20. $-\frac{1}{4}a$ $-\frac{5}{32}$
21. $1\frac{1}{2} \cdot b$ $-1\frac{3}{4}$
22. $-8a$ -5
23. ab $-\frac{35}{48}$

B 24. **Critical Thinking** A banana bread recipe uses 3 bananas and $\frac{1}{4}$ cup of butter. You need to make a smaller recipe because you have only 2 bananas. How much butter will you need? Explain. $\frac{1}{6}$ c. *Sample answer:* You will make $\frac{2}{3}$ of the recipe, and $\frac{2}{3} \times \frac{1}{4} = \frac{1}{6}$.

25. **Act It Out** A section of the town beach is shrinking by $1\frac{3}{4}$ feet per year. Use the *act it out* strategy to find how much the beach will erode in 20 years. Explain how you used the strategy. See margin.

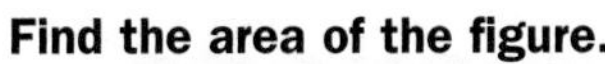

Find the area of the figure.

26. 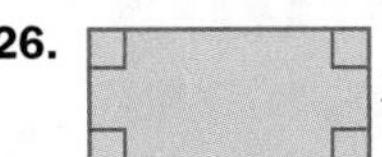

$1\frac{7}{8}$ in.^{2}

27. 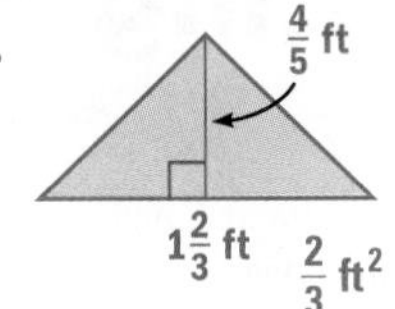

$\frac{2}{3}$ ft^2

28. 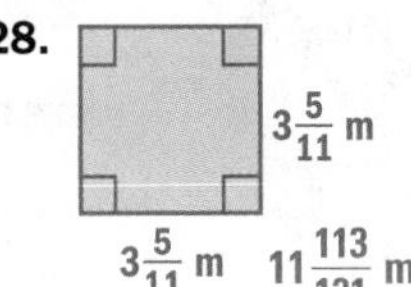

$11\frac{113}{121}$ m^2

Find the product.

29. $\frac{1}{4} \cdot \left(-\frac{2}{5}\right) \cdot \frac{9}{10}$ $-\frac{9}{100}$ **30.** $\frac{2}{5} \cdot 1\frac{1}{5} \cdot \left(-4\frac{7}{12}\right)$ $-2\frac{1}{5}$ **31.** $-9\frac{2}{7} \cdot 1\frac{2}{5} \cdot \frac{3}{4}$ $-9\frac{3}{4}$

32. Computers One of the first computers, the ENIAC, performed one operation in $\frac{1}{5000}$ second. How long would it take the ENIAC to perform 11,000 operations? $2\frac{1}{5}$ sec

Evaluate the expression.

C **33.** $-\frac{7}{8} + 5\frac{1}{2} \cdot \frac{11}{15}$ $3\frac{19}{120}$ **34.** $\frac{5}{2} \cdot \left(\frac{8}{9} - \frac{5}{12}\right)$ $1\frac{13}{72}$ **35.** $5 - \left(\frac{1}{3} + \frac{1}{6}\right)^2$ $4\frac{3}{4}$

36. Challenge Mosaic tiles sometimes measure $\frac{2}{5}$ inch by $\frac{2}{5}$ inch. What area would 500 tiles cover? 80 in.^{2}

Mosaic tiling

Mixed Review

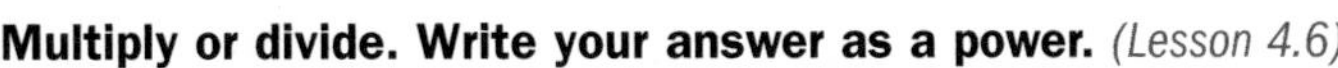

Multiply or divide. Write your answer as a power. *(Lesson 4.6)*

37. $7^3 \cdot 7^2$ 7^5 **38.** $3^5 \cdot 3$ 3^6 **39.** $\frac{8^6}{8^4}$ 8^2 **40.** $\frac{5^{10}}{5^5}$ 5^5

Find the sum or difference. *(Lesson 5.2)*

41. $\frac{4}{5} + \frac{7}{10}$ $1\frac{1}{2}$ **42.** $-2\frac{4}{9} + \frac{5}{21}$ $-2\frac{13}{63}$ **43.** $\frac{13}{20} - \frac{1}{6}$ $\frac{29}{60}$ **44.** $-\frac{15}{22} - \frac{9}{16}$ $-1\frac{43}{176}$

Test-Taking Practice

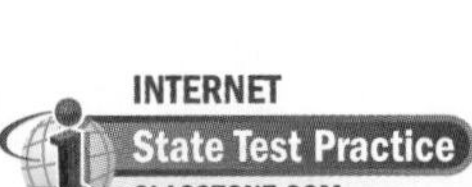

45. Multiple Choice You have a poster that measures $8\frac{1}{2}$ inches by 11 inches. You want to multiply each dimension by $1\frac{1}{2}$. What is the area of the new poster? C

A. $93\frac{1}{2}$ in.^{2} **B.** $140\frac{1}{4}$ in.^{2} **C.** $210\frac{3}{8}$ in.^{2} **D.** $280\frac{1}{2}$ in.^{2}

46. Short Response You run 1 mile in 8 minutes at a constant speed. How far do you run in 1 minute? Write an equation to represent how far you can run in m minutes. How far can you run in 11 minutes? See margin.

46. $\frac{1}{8}$ mi; $d = \frac{m}{8}$; $1\frac{3}{8}$ mi

4 ASSESS

Assessment Resources

For more assessment resources, see:

- Assessment Book
- Test and Practice Generator

Mini-Quiz

Find the product.

1. $\frac{7}{8} \cdot \frac{4}{5}$ $\frac{7}{10}$
2. $-\frac{3}{10} \cdot \frac{15}{16}$ $-\frac{9}{32}$
3. Evaluate the expression $2ab$ when $a = \frac{1}{3}$ and $b = -\frac{3}{4}$. $-\frac{1}{2}$
4. Find the area of the figure.

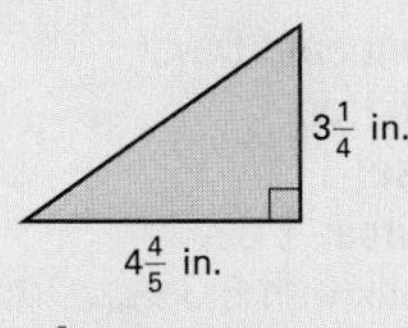

$7\frac{4}{5}$ in.^{2}

5 FOLLOW-UP

Reteaching/Remediation

- Study Guide in Chapter 5 Resource Book, pp. 28–29
- Tutor Place, Fractions Cards 15, 18, Algebra Card 4
- eTutorial Plus Online
- Extra Practice, p. 731
- Lesson Practice in Chapter 5 Resource Book, pp. 25–27

Challenge/Enrichment

- Challenge Practice in Chapter 5 Resource Book, p. 30
- Teacher's Edition, p. 216F

English Learner Support

- Spanish Study Guide
- Multi-Language Glossary
- Chapter Audio Summaries CDs

PLAN

SKILL CHECK

1. $\frac{5}{6} \cdot \frac{21}{10} = \underline{?}$ $\frac{7}{4}$
2. Simplify $\frac{16}{24}$. $\frac{2}{3}$

Write as improper fractions.

3. $6\frac{1}{3}$ $\frac{19}{3}$ 4. $2\frac{5}{6}$ $\frac{17}{6}$

LESSON OBJECTIVE

Divide fractions.

PACING

Suggested Number of Days
Basic Course: 1 day
Average Course: 1 day
Advanced Course: 1 day
Block: 0.5 block with 5.3

TEACHING RESOURCES

For a complete list of Teaching Resources, see page 216B.

TRANSPARENCY

Warm-Up Exercises for this lesson are available on a transparency.

TEACH

MOTIVATING THE LESSON

Sketch $\frac{7}{8}$ of a pizza on the board. Ask students how they would divide the remaining pizza into four equal pieces. After students have shared their methods, explain that $\frac{7}{8} \div 4$ models this situation.

Step 3. See Additional Answers beginning on page AA1.

Dividing Fractions

BEFORE
You added, subtracted, and multiplied fractions.

Now
You'll divide fractions.

WHY?
So you can find how long your batteries will last, as in Ex. 34.

Word Watch

reciprocal, p. 234
multiplicative inverse, p. 234

Activity You can use models to divide fractions.

(1) The model shows that $\frac{3}{4}$ is a part of 6 eight times, so $6 \div \frac{3}{4} = 8$.

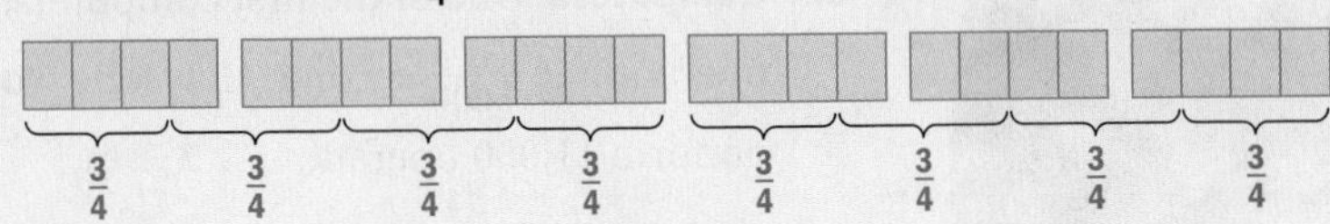

(2) Calculate $6 \cdot \frac{4}{3}$. Compare the values of $6 \div \frac{3}{4}$ and $6 \cdot \frac{4}{3}$. 8; they are the same.

(3) Use the model below to evaluate $4 \div \frac{2}{5}$. See margin for art; 10.

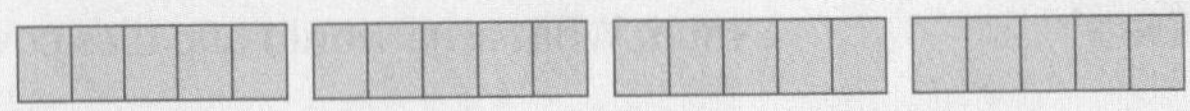

(4) Calculate $4 \cdot \frac{5}{2}$. Compare the values of $4 \div \frac{2}{5}$ and $4 \cdot \frac{5}{2}$. 10; they are the same.

(5) What fraction can you multiply by 5 to find the value of $5 \div \frac{2}{3}$? $\frac{3}{2}$

Reciprocals As the activity suggests, dividing a number by a fraction and multiplying the number by the fraction's *reciprocal* give the same result. Two nonzero numbers are **reciprocals** if their product is 1. Reciprocals, like $\frac{3}{7}$ and $\frac{7}{3}$, are also called **multiplicative inverses**.

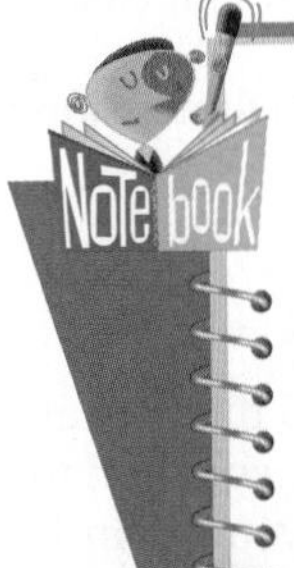

Dividing Fractions

Words To divide by a fraction, multiply by its reciprocal.

Numbers $\frac{3}{10} \div \frac{4}{7} = \frac{3}{10} \cdot \frac{7}{4} = \frac{21}{40}$

Algebra $\frac{a}{b} \div \frac{c}{d} = \frac{a}{b} \cdot \frac{d}{c}$ $(b, c, d \neq 0)$

ILLINOIS Standards and ISAT:
6.B.3a, 6.C.3a, 8.D.3a

with Solving

Notice in part (b) of Example 1 that the reciprocal of a negative number is also a negative number.

EXAMPLE 1 Dividing a Fraction by a Fraction

a. $\frac{5}{6} \div \frac{10}{21} = \frac{5}{6} \cdot \frac{21}{10}$

$= \frac{\overset{1}{\cancel{5}} \cdot \overset{7}{\cancel{21}}}{\underset{2}{\cancel{6}} \cdot \underset{2}{\cancel{10}}}$

$= \frac{7}{4}$, or $1\frac{3}{4}$

b. $\frac{9}{14} \div \frac{-2}{7} = \frac{9}{14} \cdot \frac{7}{-2}$

$= \frac{9 \cdot \overset{1}{\cancel{7}}}{\underset{2}{\cancel{14}} \cdot (-2)}$

$= \frac{9}{-4}$, or $-2\frac{1}{4}$

EXAMPLE 2 Dividing a Fraction by a Whole Number

$\frac{6}{13} \div 3 = \frac{6}{13} \cdot \frac{1}{3}$ **$3 \cdot \frac{1}{3} = 1$, so the reciprocal of 3 is $\frac{1}{3}$.**

$= \frac{\overset{2}{\cancel{6}} \cdot 1}{13 \cdot \underset{1}{\cancel{3}}}$ **Multiply fractions. Divide out common factor.**

$= \frac{2}{13}$ **Multiply.**

Your turn now **Find the quotient. Simplify if possible.**

1. $\frac{5}{8} \div \left(-\frac{7}{10}\right)$ $-\frac{25}{28}$ **2.** $\frac{2}{15} \div \frac{8}{9}$ $\frac{3}{20}$ **3.** $-\frac{3}{4} \div \frac{-7}{12}$ $1\frac{2}{7}$ **4.** $\frac{6}{7} \div 2$ $\frac{3}{7}$

EXAMPLE 3 Dividing Mixed Numbers

$6\frac{1}{3} \div \left(-2\frac{5}{6}\right) = \frac{19}{3} \div \left(-\frac{17}{6}\right)$ **Write $6\frac{1}{3}$ and $-2\frac{5}{6}$ as improper fractions.**

$= \frac{19}{3} \cdot \left(-\frac{6}{17}\right)$ **Multiply by $-\frac{6}{17}$, the reciprocal of $-\frac{17}{6}$.**

$= \frac{19 \cdot \overset{-2}{\cancel{(-6)}}}{\underset{1}{\cancel{3}} \cdot 17}$ **Multiply. Divide out common factor.**

$= -\frac{38}{17}$, or $-2\frac{4}{17}$ **Multiply.**

✓**Check** Use estimation to check your answer. Because $6 \div (-3)$ is equal to -2, you know that $-2\frac{4}{17}$ is a reasonable answer.

Your turn now **Find the quotient. Simplify if possible.**

5. $6\frac{2}{7} \div 4$ $1\frac{4}{7}$ **6.** $-12\frac{1}{4} \div 7$ $-1\frac{3}{4}$ **7.** $7\frac{1}{3} \div 1\frac{4}{7}$ $4\frac{2}{3}$ **8.** $15\frac{3}{4} \div \left(-2\frac{5}{8}\right)$ -6

ACTIVITY

Goal Students use models to divide fractions.

Key Discovery You can use multiplication to solve problems that involve division by a fraction.

TIPS FOR NEW TEACHERS

Students are more likely to forget to find reciprocals when they see pairs of numbers with common factors, such as $\frac{2}{3} \div \frac{9}{4}$. Give students pairs of fractions such as these so they practice avoiding the temptation to divide common factors before finding the reciprocal. See Tips for New Teachers in the *Chapter 5 Resource Book*.

MULTIPLE REPRESENTATIONS

After you have discussed the Notebook box at the bottom of page 234, refer back to the Activity model in Step 1. Write the division modeled in numbers and in algebra so students can see how the different representations relate to the model.

EXTRA EXAMPLES

Example 1 Find the quotient. Simplify if possible.

a. $\frac{7}{9} \div \frac{2}{3}$ $1\frac{1}{6}$

b. $-\frac{11}{12} \div \frac{5}{6}$ $-1\frac{1}{10}$

Example 2 Divide $\frac{10}{27}$ by 5. $\frac{2}{27}$

Example 3 Divide $-8\frac{1}{4}$ by $2\frac{5}{8}$. $-3\frac{1}{7}$

EXTRA EXAMPLES

Example 4 An elephant ear plant grows a new leaf every $1\frac{2}{7}$ weeks. The growing season lasts 27 weeks. How many new leaves will the elephant ear grow? **21 leaves**

CONCEPT CHECK

How do you divide by a fraction? **Multiply by its reciprocal.**

DAILY PUZZLER

Alek and Patrice hiked up a mountain trail at a rate of 1.5 miles per hour and descended back down the same trail at a rate of 4 miles per hour. Their hike took 6 hours. How long was the trail to the top of the mountain? **$6\frac{6}{11}$ mi**

EXAMPLE 4 Solving an Equation with a Fraction

Photography You use 16 of the 24 pictures of a roll of film on your first day of vacation. At this rate, how long will 4 rolls of film last?

Solution

Write a verbal model to describe the problem. Let d = the number of days.

Number of rolls of film	=	Fraction of roll of film used each day	•	Number of days

$4 = \frac{16}{24}d$ **Write an algebraic model.**

$4 \cdot \frac{24}{16} = \frac{24}{16} \cdot \frac{16}{24}d$ **The multiplicative inverse of $\frac{16}{24}$ is $\frac{24}{16}$.**

$\frac{\cancel{4}^{1}}{1} \cdot \frac{24}{\cancel{16}_{4}} = d$ **Divide out common factor.**

$6 = d$ **Divide.**

ANSWER Four rolls will last six days.

5.4 Exercises

More Practice, p. 731

INTERNET eWorkbook Plus CLASSZONE.COM

Getting Ready to Practice

1. **Vocabulary** What is the multiplicative inverse of a number? **1. The multiplicative inverse, or reciprocal, of a number is the number that when multiplied by the original number equals 1.**
2. Write the reciprocal of each of the numbers: $\frac{1}{2}, \frac{4}{7}, -8, 1\frac{1}{2}$. **$2, \frac{7}{4}, -\frac{1}{8}, \frac{2}{3}$**

Find the quotient. Simplify if possible.

3. $\frac{3}{4} \div \frac{1}{8}$ **6**
4. $\frac{5}{6} \div \left(-\frac{1}{3}\right)$ **$-2\frac{1}{2}$**
5. $\frac{11}{12} \div \frac{11}{16}$ **$1\frac{1}{3}$**
6. $-\frac{5}{6} \div (-2)$ **$\frac{5}{12}$**
7. $\frac{2}{3} \div 3$ **$\frac{2}{9}$**
8. $2\frac{1}{2} \div \frac{-9}{14}$ **$-3\frac{8}{9}$**
9. $2\frac{2}{3} \div \left(-1\frac{3}{5}\right)$ **$-1\frac{2}{3}$**
10. $4\frac{1}{8} \div 1\frac{5}{6}$ **$2\frac{1}{4}$**

11. **Guided Problem Solving** How many hamburgers can you make from 5 pounds of hamburger if you use $\frac{1}{4}$ pound of meat per hamburger?
    (1 Write a verbal model. **Number of pounds of hamburger = Pounds per hamburger • Number of hamburgers**
    (2 Substitute the given values into the model. **$5 = \frac{1}{4}h$**
    (3 Solve the equation. **20 hamburgers**

with Homework

Example	Exercises
1	12-15, 32
2	16-19, 28-31
3	20-27
4	33-34

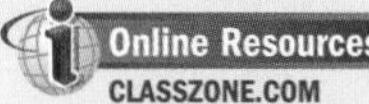

Online Resources
CLASSZONE.COM

- More Examples
- eTutorial Plus

20. $2\frac{1}{4}$ 21. $-3\frac{1}{2}$
22. $2\frac{4}{49}$ 23. $-7\frac{1}{12}$
24. $1\frac{1}{5}$ 25. $-\frac{2}{7}$
26. $1\frac{3}{13}$ 27. $2\frac{11}{35}$

35. Yes. *Sample answer:* When the two fractions are written with the same denominator *c*, then they can be represented as $\frac{a}{c}$ and $\frac{b}{c}$. Then $\frac{a}{c} \div \frac{b}{c} = \frac{a}{c} \cdot \frac{c}{b} = \frac{a}{b}$, so Juan's method works.

36. 20
37. 40
38. $-5\frac{2}{3}$
39. $1\frac{1}{5}$

Practice and Problem Solving

Find the quotient.

A **12.** $\frac{4}{9} \div \frac{4}{7}$ $\frac{7}{9}$ **13.** $-\frac{3}{8} \div \frac{7}{12}$ $-\frac{9}{14}$ **14.** $\frac{9}{14} \div \left(-\frac{3}{26}\right)$ $-5\frac{4}{7}$ **15.** $-\frac{21}{22} \div \frac{-7}{11}$ $1\frac{1}{2}$

16. $\frac{8}{11} \div 4$ $\frac{2}{11}$ **17.** $\frac{9}{10} \div (-12)$ $-\frac{3}{40}$ **18.** $-\frac{5}{12} \div 10$ $-\frac{1}{24}$ **19.** $\frac{63}{8} \div (-9)$ $-\frac{7}{8}$

Find the quotient. 20–27. See margin.

20. $5\frac{1}{4} \div 2\frac{1}{3}$ **21.** $7\frac{7}{8} \div \left(-2\frac{1}{4}\right)$ **22.** $12\frac{1}{7} \div 5\frac{5}{6}$ **23.** $-22\frac{2}{3} \div 3\frac{1}{5}$

24. $-9\frac{3}{5} \div (-8)$ **25.** $1\frac{5}{7} \div (-6)$ **26.** $8\frac{4}{13} \div 6\frac{3}{4}$ **27.** $9\frac{9}{14} \div 4\frac{1}{6}$

28. Writing Are the numbers $\frac{1}{9}$ and -9 reciprocals? Explain. No; their product is -1, not 1.

Use mental math to find the quotient.

29. $\frac{1}{2} \div 3$ $\frac{1}{6}$ **30.** $4 \div \frac{1}{2}$ 8 **31.** $1 \div \frac{4}{7}$ $1\frac{3}{4}$ **32.** $\frac{2}{3} \div \frac{3}{2}$ $\frac{4}{9}$

33. Dog Food Your dog Bodie eats about $\frac{3}{5}$ of a pound of dog food per day. How long will a five pound bag of dog food last? about $8\frac{1}{3}$ days

34. CD Player Your CD player runs for about $6\frac{1}{2}$ hours on new batteries. If the average length of the CDs in your collection is about $\frac{5}{6}$ hour, how many CDs can you expect to listen to using one new set of batteries? about $7\frac{4}{5}$ CDs

35. Critical Thinking Juan says, "To divide a fraction by another fraction, rewrite the fractions with common denominators. Then use the formula $\frac{a}{c} \div \frac{b}{c} = \frac{a}{b}$." Does Juan's method work? Explain. See margin.

Algebra Solve the equation. 36–39. See margin.

B **36.** $\frac{3}{4}a = 15$ **37.** $\frac{7}{10}b = 28$ **38.** $-\frac{9}{17}r = 3$ **39.** $-11 = -9\frac{1}{6}h$

40. Wages Haley earns $180 working three days a week. On each of those days she works $7\frac{1}{2}$ hours. How much does Haley earn per hour? $8

41. Survey Two of every five people surveyed, or 350 people, said they prefer spring to fall. How many people were surveyed? Explain how you got your answer. 875 people. *Sample answer:* I solved the equation $\frac{2}{5}p = 350$.

Algebra Evaluate the expression when $a = 4$ and $b = 9$.

C **42.** $\frac{a}{5} \div \frac{8}{150}$ 15 **43.** $\frac{3}{4}a \div \frac{5b}{6}$ $\frac{2}{5}$ **44.** $-\frac{18}{a} \div \frac{b}{16}$ -8 **45.** $\frac{-4}{21} \div \frac{2a}{-b}$ $\frac{3}{14}$

3 APPLY

ASSIGNMENT GUIDE

Basic Course
Day 1: EP p. 728 Exs. 21-24; pp. 237-238 Exs. 12-15, 20-23, 29-34, 36-39, 47-56

Average Course
Day 1: pp. 237-238 Exs. 14-19, 24-28, 31-35, 38-43, 47-56

Advanced Course
Day 1: pp. 237-238 Exs. 18-21, 28-36, 40-50*, 53-55

Block
pp. 237-238 Exs. 14-19, 24-28, 31-35, 38-43, 47-56 (with 5.3)

Extra Practice

- Student Edition, p. 731
- Chapter 5 Resource Book, pp. 34-36
- Test and Practice Generator

Transparency

Even-numbered answers are available on transparencies.

Homework Check

When you review students' homework for this lesson, go over the following exercises to check understanding of key concepts.
Basic: 12, 14, 20, 29, 33
Average: 16, 18, 24, 32, 33
Advanced: 18, 21, 28, 32, 33

Teaching Tip

In Exercise 2, remind students that the reciprocal of a negative number is a negative number. The *opposite* of a negative number is a positive number.

4 ASSESS

Assessment Resources

For more assessment resources, see:
- Assessment Book
- Test and Practice Generator

Mini-Quiz

Find the quotient.

1. $\frac{3}{11} \div \left(-\frac{3}{7}\right)$ $-\frac{7}{11}$
2. $\frac{6}{13} \div 36$ $\frac{1}{78}$
3. $10\frac{3}{4} \div 2\frac{3}{8}$ $4\frac{10}{19}$
4. $7\frac{5}{6} \div 1\frac{9}{10}$ $4\frac{7}{57}$
5. Howard uses $2\frac{1}{3}$ teaspoons of yeast for each loaf of bread he bakes. How many loaves of bread can he bake with 40 teaspoons of yeast? **17 loaves**

5 FOLLOW-UP

Reteaching/Remediation

- Study Guide in Chapter 5 Resource Book, pp. 37–38
- Tutor Place, Fractions Cards 16–18, Algebra Card 10
- eTutorial Plus Online
- Extra Practice, p. 731
- Lesson Practice in Chapter 5 Resource Book, pp. 34–36

Challenge/Enrichment

- Challenge Practice in Chapter 5 Resource Book, p. 39
- Teacher's Edition, p. 216F

English Learner Support

- Spanish Study Guide
- Multi-Language Glossary
- Chapter Audio Summaries CDs

46. Challenge You are creating a board game. You want to cut square game pieces that measure $1\frac{1}{4}$ inches on each side from a piece of paper that measures $8\frac{1}{2}$ inches by 11 inches. How many game pieces can you cut from the paper? Explain.

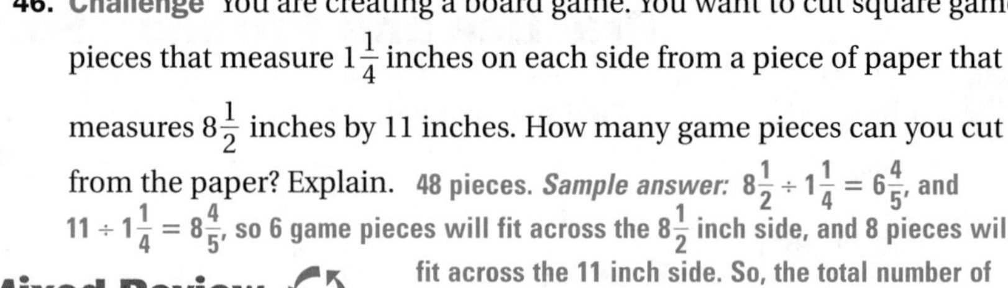

48 pieces. ***Sample answer:*** $8\frac{1}{2} \div 1\frac{1}{4} = 6\frac{4}{5}$, and $11 \div 1\frac{1}{4} = 8\frac{4}{5}$, so 6 game pieces will fit across the $8\frac{1}{2}$ inch side, and 8 pieces will fit across the 11 inch side. So, the total number of game pieces that can be cut is $6 \cdot 8 = 48$.

Mixed Review

Simplify the variable expression. *(Lesson 4.3)*

47. $\frac{9x^2}{27x}$ $\frac{x}{3}$
48. $\frac{24y^4}{15y^2}$ $\frac{8y^2}{5}$
49. $\frac{14x^3y}{18xy^3}$ $\frac{7x^2}{9y^2}$
50. $\frac{54yz^2}{81xz^2}$ $\frac{2y}{3x}$

Basic Skills **Write the improper fraction as a mixed number.**

51. $\frac{17}{9}$ $1\frac{8}{9}$
52. $\frac{16}{5}$ $3\frac{1}{5}$
53. $\frac{28}{3}$ $9\frac{1}{3}$
54. $\frac{120}{7}$ $17\frac{1}{7}$

Test-Taking Practice

INTERNET
State Test Practice
CLASSZONE.COM

55. Multiple Choice Solve $\frac{5}{6}a = -15$. **A**

A. -18 **B.** $-\frac{25}{2}$ **C.** $\frac{25}{2}$ **D.** 18

56. Multiple Choice Use the formula $C = (F - 32) \div \frac{9}{5}$ to convert 77°F to °C, where C is degrees Celsius and F is degrees Fahrenheit. **G**

F. 20°C **G.** 25°C **H.** 30°C **I.** 45°C

Brain Game

Who's in First?

The number that makes each equation true represents the place in which the runner finished the race. Find the order in which the runners finished. **Cornell was first, Maya second, Martin third, and Harriet fourth.**

Martin $1\frac{2}{?} \div \frac{1}{6} = 10$ Harriet $? \div \frac{2}{11} = 22$

Maya $\frac{5}{7} \div \frac{?}{3} = \frac{15}{14}$ Cornell $\frac{?}{5} \div \frac{7}{9} = \frac{9}{35}$

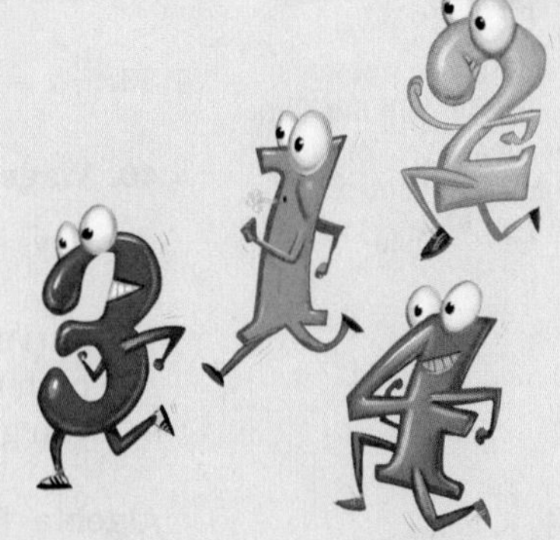

5.4 Technology Activity

CALCULATOR

Operations with Fractions

GOAL Use a fraction calculator to evaluate expressions with fractions.

You can use a calculator to evaluate expressions with fractions. First, set your calculator to display the answers as fractions or mixed numbers in simplest form.

Press [2nd] [FracMode]. Select *A⌴b/c* and press [=] to set the calculator to mixed number mode.

Press [2nd] [FracMode]. Select *Auto* and press [=] to set the calculator to automatically simplify fractions.

Example **Use a calculator to evaluate the expression.**

	Keystrokes	Display	Answer
a. $\frac{2}{3} - 4\frac{6}{7}$	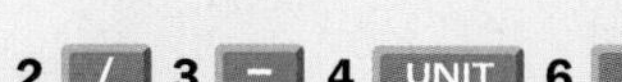 2 [/] 3 [−] 4 [UNIT] 6 [/] 7 [=]	−4⌴4/21	$-4\frac{4}{21}$
b. $-\frac{5}{17} \cdot \left(-\frac{8}{35}\right)$	 [(−)] 5 [/] 17 [×]  [(−)] 8 [/] 35 [=]	8/119	$\frac{8}{119}$
c. $\frac{3}{10} \div \left(-1\frac{4}{5}\right)$	3 [/] 10  [÷] [(−)] 1 [UNIT] 4 [/] 5 [=]	−1/6	$-\frac{1}{6}$

Your turn now **Use a calculator to evaluate the expression.**

1. $\frac{5}{11} + \frac{2}{5}$ $\frac{47}{55}$ **2.** $3\frac{1}{4} + \left(-\frac{6}{7}\right)$ $2\frac{11}{28}$ **3.** $7\frac{1}{2} - 6\frac{5}{6}$ $\frac{2}{3}$ **4.** $\frac{2}{5} - \frac{2}{3}$ $-\frac{4}{15}$

5. $\frac{7}{9} \cdot 1\frac{1}{3}$ $1\frac{1}{27}$ **6.** $\frac{2}{5} \cdot \left(-\frac{3}{4}\right)$ $-\frac{3}{10}$ **7.** $9\frac{4}{5} \div \frac{7}{8}$ $11\frac{1}{5}$ **8.** $-10\frac{2}{13} \div \left(-3\frac{1}{3}\right)$ $3\frac{3}{65}$

9. Car Care Rosa's car needs $4\frac{1}{4}$ quarts of oil to run properly. She notices her car has only three fourths of the amount of oil that it needs. How much oil should she add for her car to run properly? $1\frac{1}{16}$ qt

ILLINOIS Standards and ISAT:
6.B.3a, 6.C.3a

1 PLAN

Learn the Method

- Students will use a fraction calculator to evaluate expressions with fractions.
- Students can use the Examples from Lessons 5.3 and 5.4 to check that they are entering the fractions into the calculator correctly.

2 TEACH

Tips for Success

Urge students to key in the expressions carefully. Unless they verify their answer with an estimate, they will not be able to detect an error caused by an incorrect keystroke.

EXTRA EXAMPLES

Example Use a calculator to evaluate $\frac{3}{8} \div 1\frac{2}{3}$. $\frac{9}{40}$

3 CLOSE

Assessment

1. What is the difference between the [/] key and the [÷] key? **The slash is used to enter a fraction bar. The divide symbol indicates the operation of division.**

2. How do you know whether to enter the subtract key or the minus key? **The subtract key is used for the operation of subtraction. The minus is used to enter negative numbers.**

Additional Resources

The following resources are available to help review the materials in Lessons 5.1–5.4.

Chapter 5 Resource Book

- Lesson Practice
- Study Guide

Assessment Book

- Chapter 5 Quiz 1

Technology

- Test and Practice Generator
- eTutorial CD-ROM

Internet

- Classzone
- eWorkbook Plus Online
- eTutorial Plus Online

English Learner Support

- Spanish Study Guide
- Multi-Language Glossary
- Chapter Audio Summaries CDs

Notebook Review

Review the vocabulary definitions in your notebook.

Copy the review examples in your notebook. Then complete the exercises.

Check Your Definitions

reciprocal, p. 234 — multiplicative inverse, p. 234

Use Your Vocabulary

1. What is the product of a number and its reciprocal? 1

5.1–5.2 Can you add and subtract fractions?

EXAMPLES

a. $\frac{2}{9} + 3\frac{4}{9} = 3 + \left(\frac{2}{9} + \frac{4}{9}\right)$

$= 3\frac{6}{9}$

$= 3\frac{2}{3}$

b. $\frac{9}{14} - \frac{6}{7} = \frac{9}{14} - \frac{12}{14}$

$= \frac{9-12}{14}$

$= -\frac{3}{14}$

Find the sum or difference.

2. $-\frac{5}{12} + \frac{11}{12}$ $\frac{1}{2}$ **3.** $\frac{15}{16} - 2\frac{1}{16}$ $-1\frac{1}{8}$ **4.** $6\frac{1}{4} - 4\frac{3}{8}$ $1\frac{7}{8}$ **5.** $\frac{2x}{3} + \frac{4x}{5}$ $\frac{22x}{15}$

5.3 Can you multiply fractions and mixed numbers?

EXAMPLES

a. $-\frac{5}{8} \cdot \frac{3}{10} = -\frac{5 \cdot 3}{8 \cdot 10}$

$= -\frac{\overset{1}{\cancel{5}} \cdot 3}{8 \cdot \underset{2}{\cancel{10}}}$

$= -\frac{3}{16}$

b. $3\frac{2}{3} \cdot \frac{4}{9} = \frac{11}{3} \cdot \frac{4}{9}$

$= \frac{11 \cdot 4}{3 \cdot 9}$

$= \frac{44}{27}$, or $1\frac{17}{27}$

Find the product.

6. $-\frac{6}{7} \cdot \left(-\frac{5}{12}\right)$ $\frac{5}{14}$ **7.** $2\frac{1}{2} \cdot \frac{4}{5}$ 2 **8.** $-3 \cdot 2\frac{5}{6}$ $-8\frac{1}{2}$ **9.** $-3\frac{1}{3} \cdot \left(-3\frac{1}{4}\right)$ $10\frac{5}{6}$

5.4 Can you divide fractions and mixed numbers?

EXAMPLES

a. $\frac{1}{3} \div \frac{5}{6} = \frac{1}{3} \cdot \frac{6}{5}$

$= \frac{1 \cdot \cancel{6}^{2}}{{}_{1}\cancel{3} \cdot 5}$

$= \frac{2}{5}$

b. $2\frac{1}{5} \div 2\frac{3}{4} = \frac{11}{5} \div \frac{11}{4}$

$= \frac{11}{5} \cdot \frac{4}{11}$

$= \frac{{}^{1}\cancel{11} \cdot 4}{5 \cdot \cancel{11}_{1}} = \frac{4}{5}$

☑ **Divide.** **10.** $\frac{3}{4} \div \frac{1}{12}$ 9 **11.** $-\frac{5}{9} \div \frac{7}{18}$ $-1\frac{3}{7}$ **12.** $-2\frac{1}{4} \div \left(-1\frac{2}{7}\right)$ $1\frac{3}{4}$

Stop and Think about Lessons 5.1–5.4 **13–14. See margin.**

13. Writing How can you check your answer to a division problem involving fractions? Use an example to explain.

14. Critical Thinking You divide a positive number by a fraction greater than 0 and less than 1. Will the result be *less than, equal to,* or *greater than* the original number? Explain.

Notebook Review:

13. Multiply the answer by the divisor. The answer should be the dividend.

Sample answer:

$\frac{2}{5} \div \frac{5}{6} = \frac{12}{25}$ and $\frac{12}{25} \cdot \frac{5}{6} = \frac{2}{5}$

14. Greater than. ***Sample answer:*** **Since dividing by a number is the same as multiplying by its reciprocal, and the reciprocal of a fraction between 0 and 1 will be greater than 1, the quotient will be greater than the original number.**

Review Quiz 1

Find the sum or difference.

1. $1\frac{5}{8} - \frac{7}{8}$ $\frac{3}{4}$ **2.** $\frac{4}{9} + 3\frac{5}{9}$ 4 **3.** $\frac{x}{12} + \frac{5x}{12}$ $\frac{x}{2}$ **4.** $\frac{4}{9} - \frac{8}{9} + \frac{5}{9}$ $\frac{1}{9}$

5. $\frac{2}{3} + \frac{9}{6}$ $2\frac{1}{6}$ **6.** $5\frac{3}{4} - 2\frac{1}{3}$ $3\frac{5}{12}$ **7.** $\frac{5}{6} + 2\frac{1}{8}$ $2\frac{23}{24}$ **8.** $\frac{3}{10} + 4\frac{2}{5} - 1\frac{1}{2}$ $3\frac{1}{5}$

9. Recipe A recipe uses $4\frac{2}{3}$ cups of flour. Another recipe uses $4\frac{1}{4}$ cups. If you have 9 cups of flour, can you make both recipes? Explain. **Yes; you need a total of $4\frac{2}{3} + 4\frac{1}{4}$, or $8\frac{11}{12}$ cups of flour, which is less than 9 cups.**

Find the product or quotient.

10. $\frac{7}{12} \cdot \frac{8}{21}$ $\frac{2}{9}$ **11.** $-\frac{11}{12} \cdot \left(-\frac{3}{10}\right)$ $\frac{11}{40}$ **12.** $-\frac{14}{5} \cdot 2\frac{6}{7}$ -8 **13.** $1\frac{1}{8} \cdot (-3)$ $-3\frac{3}{8}$

14. $\frac{1}{2} \div \frac{5}{6}$ $\frac{3}{5}$ **15.** $\frac{4}{9} \div 8$ $\frac{1}{18}$ **16.** $-\frac{4}{5} \div \frac{3}{2}$ $-\frac{8}{15}$ **17.** $-1\frac{3}{4} \div \left(-\frac{7}{12}\right)$ 3

18. Hair Growth An average human hair grows about $\frac{1}{2}$ inch per month. How much does a human hair grow in $3\frac{1}{2}$ months? $1\frac{3}{4}$ **in.**

1 PLAN

SKILL CHECK

Order from least to greatest.

1. 5, −5, −17 **−17, −5, 5**
2. $\frac{1}{2}, \frac{1}{4}, \frac{1}{3}$ $\frac{1}{4}, \frac{1}{3}, \frac{1}{2}$
3. $\frac{9}{20}, \frac{3}{20}, \frac{7}{20}$ $\frac{3}{20}, \frac{7}{20}, \frac{9}{20}$

LESSON OBJECTIVE

Write fractions as decimals and decimals as fractions.

PACING

Suggested Number of Days
Basic Course: 2 days
Average Course: 2 days
Advanced Course: 2 days
Block: 1 block

TEACHING RESOURCES

For a complete list of Teaching Resources, see page 216B.

TRANSPARENCY

Warm-Up Exercises for this lesson are available on a transparency.

2 TEACH

MOTIVATING THE LESSON

Have students name all the different groups of numbers they have studied so far.

TIPS FOR NEW TEACHERS

Be sure students understand that *every* rational number can be written as a decimal, either terminating or repeating. See Tips for New Teachers in the *Chapter 5 Resource Book*.

LESSON 5.5

Fractions and Decimals

BEFORE	Now	WHY?
You divided whole numbers.	You'll write fractions as decimals and decimals as fractions.	So you can analyze breakfast food popularity, as in Exs. 46–48.

Word Watch

rational number, p. 242
terminating decimal, p. 242
repeating decimal, p. 242

A **rational number** is a number that can be written as a quotient $\frac{a}{b}$, where a and b are integers and $b \neq 0$. The diagram shows how rational numbers, integers, and whole numbers are related.

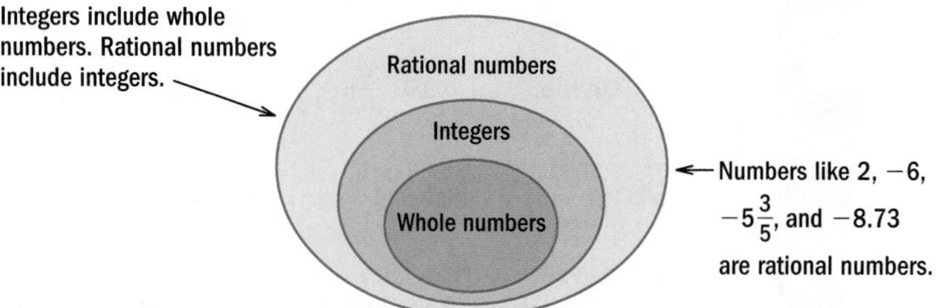
Integers include whole numbers. Rational numbers include integers.
Rational numbers
Integers
Whole numbers
Numbers like 2, −6, $-5\frac{3}{5}$, and −8.73 are rational numbers.

To write any rational number $\frac{a}{b}$ as a decimal, divide a by b. If the quotient has a remainder of zero, the result is a **terminating decimal**. If the quotient has a digit or group of digits that repeats without end, the result is a **repeating decimal**.

EXAMPLE 1 Writing Fractions as Decimals

To write a fraction as a decimal, divide the numerator by the denominator.

a. $\frac{5}{11} = 11\overline{)5.0000\ldots}$ with quotient 0.4545 . . .

```
      0.4545 . . .
11)5.0000 . . .
   44
    60
    55
     50
     44
      60
      55
```

ANSWER The quotient 0.4545. . . is a repeating decimal. To indicate this, place a bar over the repeating digits: $\frac{5}{11} = 0.\overline{45}$.

b. $\frac{7}{20} = 20\overline{)7.00}$ with quotient 0.35

```
     0.35
20)7.00
   60
   100
   100
     0
```

ANSWER The remainder is zero, so $\frac{7}{20} = 0.35$, a terminating decimal.

ILLINOIS Standards and ISAT:
6.A.3

Indigo bunting

EXAMPLE 2 Ordering Rational Numbers

Biology The table lists the lengths of five finches. Order the finches from shortest to longest.

Finch Species	Length (inches)
House finch	$5\frac{5}{8}$
Painted bunting	5.25
Lazuli bunting	$5\frac{7}{16}$
Purple finch	$5\frac{3}{4}$
Indigo bunting	5.5

Solution

Write mixed numbers as decimals.

$5\frac{5}{8} = 5.625$ $5\frac{7}{16} = 5.4375$

$5\frac{3}{4} = 5.75$

Then graph all the finches' lengths on a number line.

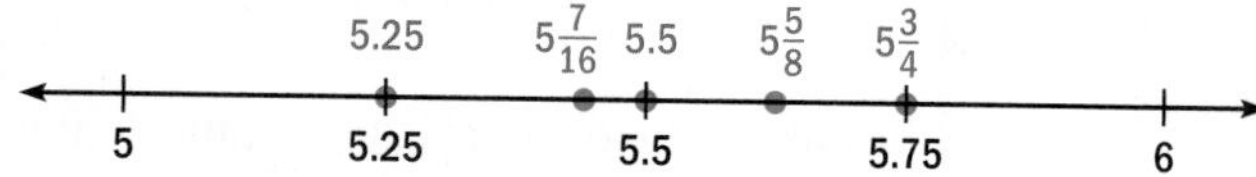

ANSWER From shortest to longest: painted bunting, lazuli bunting, indigo bunting, house finch, purple finch.

Your turn now **Order the numbers from least to greatest.**

1. $0.51, \frac{3}{5}, \frac{11}{20}, \frac{2}{3}, 0.62$

2. $-1\frac{1}{8}, -1\frac{3}{7}, -1.1, -1.43, -1\frac{4}{15}$

1. $0.51, \frac{11}{20}, \frac{3}{5}, 0.62, \frac{2}{3}$

2. $-1.43, -1\frac{3}{7}, -1\frac{4}{15}, -1\frac{1}{8}, -1.1$

Terminating Decimals To write a terminating decimal as a fraction or mixed number, use the place value of the decimal's last digit to determine the denominator. For example, you can write 0.37 as $\frac{37}{100}$, or thirty-seven hundredths, because 7 is in the hundredths' place.

EXAMPLE 3 Writing Terminating Decimals as Fractions

Write the decimal as a fraction or mixed number.

a. 0.4

b. −1.905

Solution

a. $0.4 = \frac{4}{10}$ 4 is in the tenths' place.

$= \frac{2}{5}$

b. $-1.905 = -1\frac{905}{1000}$ 5 is in the thousandths' place.

$= -1\frac{\cancel{905}^{181}}{\cancel{1000}_{200}}$

$= -1\frac{181}{200}$

EXTRA EXAMPLES

Example 1 Write the fraction as a decimal.

a. $\frac{8}{9}$ $0.\overline{8}$

b. $\frac{3}{8}$ **0.375**

Example 2 A school nurse measures the heights of five students. Order the students from shortest to tallest.

Student	Height (feet)
Amber	$5\frac{1}{4}$
Kenny	$6\frac{1}{6}$
Teshawna	5.5
Shiangtai	$5\frac{2}{3}$
Fran	5.1

Fran, Amber, Teshawna, Shiangtai, Kenny

Example 3 Write the decimal as a fraction or mixed number.

a. −1.7 $-1\frac{7}{10}$

b. 0.65 $\frac{13}{20}$

NOTETAKING

Encourage students to make a list of some common fractions and their decimal equivalents.

Differentiating Instruction

Advanced Students Challenge students to formulate and then write a generalization about which fractions can be represented by terminating decimals.

TRANSPARENCY

A support transparency is available for Example 2 and Your turn now Exercises. 1–2.

EXTRA EXAMPLES

Example 4 Write $0.\overline{36}$ as a decimal. $\frac{4}{11}$

 **CONCEPT CHECK**

When you write a terminating decimal as a fraction or mixed number, how do you determine the denominator? **Use the place value of the decimal's last digit.**

 **DAILY PUZZLER**

Celia, Darryl, and Emilie ate an entire pie. Darryl ate twice as much as Celia and Emilie ate three times as much as Celia. What fraction of the pie did Celia eat? $\frac{1}{6}$

1. **rational number, integer, whole number**
2. **rational number**
3. **rational number, integer**
4. **rational number**

13. **1.8 in., $1\frac{7}{8}$ in., 2.1 in., $2\frac{1}{9}$ in.**

Repeating Decimals To write a repeating decimal as a fraction or mixed number, form two equivalent equations by multiplying by a power of 10. Then subtract the equations.

 **with Notetaking**

You may wish to copy examples into your notebook that show writing repeating decimals as fractions. Include examples with one, two, and three repeating digits.

EXAMPLE 4 Writing Repeating Decimals as Fractions

To write $0.\overline{48}$ as a fraction, let $x = 0.\overline{48}$, or $0.484848\ldots.$

(1) The number has 2 repeating digits, so multiply by 100. Let $100x = 48.\overline{48}$, or $48.484848\ldots.$

(2) Then subtract x from $100x$.

$$\begin{aligned} 100x &= 48.484848\ldots \\ -\quad x &= 0.484848\ldots \\ \hline 99x &= 48.000000\ldots \end{aligned}$$

(3) Solve for x. Simplify. $x = \frac{48}{99}$, or $\frac{16}{33}$

ANSWER The decimal $0.\overline{48}$ is equivalent to the fraction $\frac{16}{33}$.

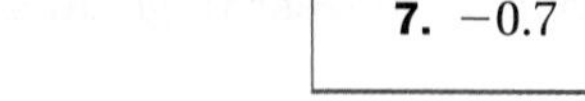

Your turn now **Write the decimal as a fraction or mixed number.**

3. 0.3 $\frac{3}{10}$
4. 0.62 $\frac{31}{50}$
5. −2.45 $-2\frac{9}{20}$
6. −1.24 $-1\frac{6}{25}$
7. $-0.\overline{7}$ $-\frac{7}{9}$
8. $-10.\overline{1}$ $-10\frac{1}{9}$
9. $0.\overline{24}$ $\frac{8}{33}$
10. $0.8\overline{3}$ $\frac{5}{6}$

5.5 Exercises

More Practice, p. 731

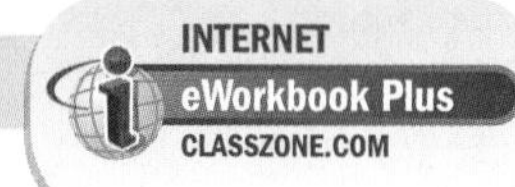

Getting Ready to Practice

Vocabulary **Tell whether the number is included in each of the following number groups: *rational number, integer, whole number.*** 1–4. See margin.

1. 0
2. 0.55
3. −14
4. 0.3

Write the fraction or mixed number as a decimal.

5. $\frac{4}{5}$ 0.8
6. $2\frac{1}{4}$ 2.25
7. $\frac{1}{3}$ $0.\overline{3}$
8. $1\frac{5}{8}$ 1.625

Write the decimal as a fraction or mixed number.

9. 0.6 $\frac{3}{5}$
10. −1.02 $-1\frac{1}{50}$
11. $0.\overline{8}$ $\frac{8}{9}$
12. $0.\overline{53}$ $\frac{53}{99}$
13. **Caterpillars** Write the following lengths of caterpillars in order from least to greatest: $1\frac{7}{8}$ inches, 1.8 inches, $2\frac{1}{9}$ inches, 2.1 inches. See margin.

Practice and Problem Solving

with Homework

Example	Exercises
1	14-25, 44-45
2	42, 43, 46
3	26-33
4	34-41

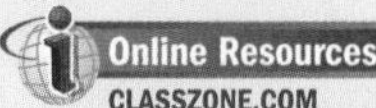

Online Resources
CLASSZONE.COM
· More Examples
· eTutorial Plus

Write the fraction or mixed number as a decimal.

A **14.** $\frac{3}{4}$ 0.75 **15.** $-\frac{1}{9}$ $-0.\overline{1}$ **16.** $-\frac{12}{25}$ -0.48 **17.** $\frac{7}{12}$ $0.58\overline{3}$

18. $-\frac{4}{25}$ -0.16 **19.** $\frac{27}{50}$ 0.54 **20.** $3\frac{11}{16}$ 3.6875 **21.** $-\frac{33}{80}$ -0.4125

22. $\frac{8}{15}$ $0.5\overline{3}$ **23.** $-14\frac{7}{11}$ $-14.\overline{63}$ **24.** $-\frac{14}{33}$ $-0.\overline{42}$ **25.** $\frac{27}{44}$ $0.61\overline{36}$

Write the decimal as a fraction or mixed number.

26. -0.48 $-\frac{12}{25}$ **27.** -0.56 $-\frac{14}{25}$ **28.** 1.31 $1\frac{31}{100}$ **29.** 2.79 $2\frac{79}{100}$

30. 0.365 $\frac{73}{200}$ **31.** 7.253 $7\frac{253}{1000}$ **32.** -0.0012 $-\frac{3}{2500}$ **33.** -5.0032 $-5\frac{2}{625}$

34. $0.\overline{2}$ $\frac{2}{9}$ **35.** $0.\overline{8}$ $\frac{8}{9}$ **36.** $-0.1\overline{5}$ $-\frac{7}{45}$ **37.** $0.\overline{15}$ $\frac{5}{33}$

38. $0.\overline{63}$ $\frac{7}{11}$ **39.** $0.\overline{042}$ $\frac{14}{333}$ **40.** $-0.\overline{243}$ $-\frac{9}{37}$ **41.** $20.2\overline{07}$ $20\frac{41}{198}$

Order the numbers from least to greatest.

42. $-\frac{4}{5}, -0.4, -\frac{3}{8}, -\frac{3}{10}, -0.2$

42. $-\frac{4}{5}, -\frac{3}{10}, -\frac{3}{8}, -0.2, -0.4$ **43.** $9\frac{3}{4}, 9.74, 9\frac{5}{7}, 9.72, 9\frac{9}{13}$ $9\frac{9}{13}, 9\frac{5}{7}, 9.72, 9.74, 9\frac{3}{4}$

44. Stock Listings The New York Stock Exchange once used fractions to list the values of its stocks. It switched to decimals in 2001. Write the following stock prices as decimals rounded to the nearest cent. \$5.25, \$44.50, \$53.38, \$17.44

$\$5\frac{1}{4}, \$44\frac{1}{2}, \$53\frac{3}{8}, \$17\frac{7}{16}$

46. $\frac{1}{8} = 0.125$, $\frac{1}{12} = 0.08\overline{3}$, $\frac{3}{16} = 0.1875$, $\frac{1}{4} = 0.25$, $\frac{3}{25} = 0.12$; cereal, eggs, bagels, pancakes, bacon

B **45. Look for a Pattern** Write the fractions $\frac{1}{11}$, $\frac{2}{11}$, and $\frac{3}{11}$ as decimals.

Use your results to predict the decimal forms of $\frac{4}{11}$ and $\frac{5}{11}$.
$0.\overline{09}, 0.\overline{18}, 0.\overline{27}; 0.\overline{36}, 0.\overline{45}$

Extended Problem Solving In Exercises 46–48, use the table below. It tells the fraction of students in a survey that named each breakfast food as their favorite.

Breakfast food	Bagels	Bacon	Eggs	Cereal	Pancakes
Fraction of students	$\frac{1}{8}$	$\frac{1}{12}$	$\frac{3}{16}$	$\frac{1}{4}$	$\frac{3}{25}$

46. Order Write each fraction as a decimal and order the foods from most popular to least popular. See margin.

47. Compare How many more students picked the most popular food than the least popular food if 1200 students responded to the survey? 200 students

48. Analyze How many of the 1200 students did not choose any of the foods shown? 281 students

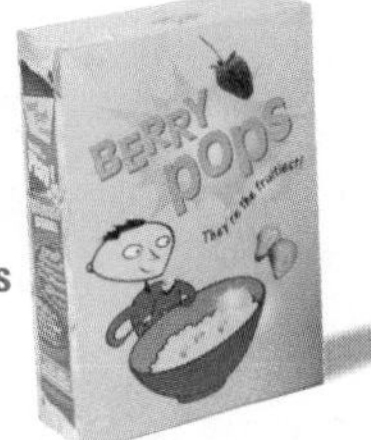

3 APPLY

ASSIGNMENT GUIDE

Basic Course

Day 1: pp. 245-246 Exs. 14-21, 42-44, 53-59

Day 2: pp. 245-246 Exs. 26-37, 46-48, 60-62

Average Course

Day 1: pp. 245-246 Exs. 16-25, 42-46, 52-57

Day 2: pp. 245-246 Exs. 28-41, 47-50, 60-62

Advanced Course

Day 1: pp. 245-246 Exs. 18-25, 43-50, 60-62

Day 2: pp. 245-246 Exs. 30-41, 51-56*

Block

pp. 245-246 Exs. 16-25, 28-50, 52-57, 60-62

EXTRA PRACTICE

- Student Edition, p. 731
- Chapter 5 Resource Book, pp. 42-44
- Test and Practice Generator

TRANSPARENCY

Even-numbered answers are available on transparencies. A support transparency is available for Exercises 13, 42, 43, and 46.

HOMEWORK CHECK

When you review students' homework for this lesson, go over the following exercises to check understanding of key concepts.
Basic: 14, 20, 26, 34, 42
Average: 18, 24, 30, 38, 42
Advanced: 18, 24, 31, 39, 43

TEACHING TIP

In Exercises 36 and 37, draw students' attention to the difference between the two values. Students may not have noticed that the bar over the repeating digits differs.

ASSESSMENT RESOURCES

For more assessment resources, see:

- Assessment Book
- Test and Practice Generator

MINI-QUIZ

Write the fraction or mixed number as a decimal.

1. $\frac{5}{8}$ **0.625**

2. $-\frac{5}{16}$ **−0.3125**

Write the decimal as a fraction or mixed number.

3. −6.25 $-6\frac{1}{4}$

4. $5.\overline{2}$ $5\frac{2}{9}$

5. Order the numbers from least to greatest: 6.7, $6\frac{1}{7}$, 6.2, $6\frac{2}{9}$, 6.35

$6\frac{1}{7}$, 6.2, $6\frac{2}{9}$, 6.35, 6.7

RETEACHING/REMEDIATION

- Study Guide in Chapter 5 Resource Book, pp. 45–46
- Tutor Place, Fractions Cards 5, 6, Whole Numbers and Decimals Card 4
- eTutorial Plus Online
- Extra Practice, p. 731
- Lesson Practice in Chapter 5 Resource Book, pp. 42–44

CHALLENGE/ENRICHMENT

- Challenge Practice in Chapter 5 Resource Book, p. 47
- Teacher's Edition, p. 216F

ENGLISH LEARNER SUPPORT

- Spanish Study Guide
- Multi-Language Glossary
- Chapter Audio Summaries CDs

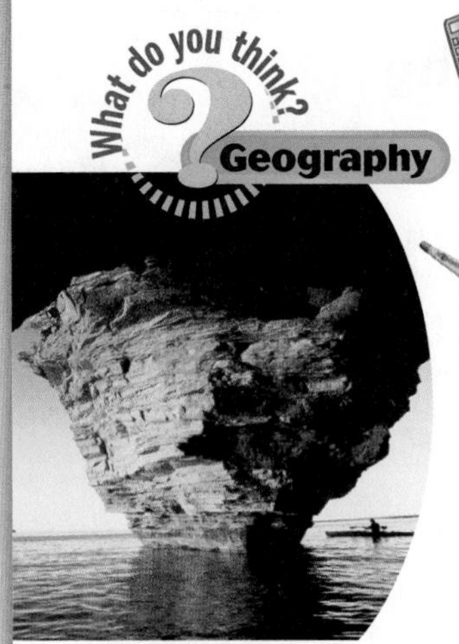

Lake Superior

Lake Superior has a surface area of about 32,000 square miles. About what fraction of the 182,000 square miles of U.S. water surface area is this? Write this fraction as a decimal. $\frac{16}{91}$; $0.\overline{175824}$

50. Yes. *Sample answer:* **The improper fraction is equivalent to the mixed number, and the mixed number is the whole number plus the fraction, which is the same as the whole number plus the fraction's equivalent decimal.**

49. Area The total area of the United States is about 3,718,000 square miles. The portion of this area that is covered by water is $\frac{182,000}{3,718,000}$. Express this fraction as a decimal rounded to three places. About what fraction of the area of the United States is covered by water? **0.049; $\frac{1}{20}$**

50. Writing Jim says, "Write a mixed number as a decimal by writing it as an improper fraction, and then dividing." Estela says, "Just convert the fraction part of a mixed number to a decimal, and then you can add that to the whole number part." Do both methods work? Explain why or why not. **See margin.**

C **51. Challenge** In the following expressions, $x > 0$. Order the expressions from least to greatest: $x, \frac{x}{5}, \frac{x}{3}, \frac{x}{7}, \frac{x}{8}, \frac{x}{6}, \frac{x}{2}, \frac{x}{4}$. $\frac{x}{8}, \frac{x}{7}, \frac{x}{6}, \frac{x}{5}, \frac{x}{4}, \frac{x}{3}, \frac{x}{2}, x$

52. Critical Thinking Find a rational number between $\frac{1}{6}$ and $\frac{2}{9}$. Explain your reasoning. ***Sample answer:*** **$\frac{1}{5}$; $\frac{1}{5}$ is greater than $\frac{1}{6}$, and its decimal form, 0.2, is less than the decimal form for $\frac{2}{9}$, $0.\overline{2}$.**

Mixed Review

Solve the equation using mental math. *(Lesson 1.5)*

53. $s - 7 = 10$ **17** **54.** $4d = 24$ **6** **55.** $5 + t = 18$ **13**

Choose a Strategy Use a strategy from the list to solve the following problem. Explain your choice of strategy.

Problem Solving Strategies
- Guess, Check, and Revise
- Make a List
- Draw a Diagram

56. You are racing with Al, Sue, and Kim. In how many orders can you and your friends finish the race? **24. *Sample answer:* I used Make a List to list all of the possible combinations.**

Basic Skills Estimate the sum or difference. **57–60. Estimates may vary.**

57. 129 + 42 **170** **58.** 457 + 301 **760** **59.** 91 − 28 **60** **60.** 217 − 188 **30**

Test-Taking Practice 

INTERNET
State Test Practice
CLASSZONE.COM

61. Multiple Choice Which list is in order from least to greatest? **C**

A. $\frac{1}{7}$, 0.125, 0.45, $\frac{4}{9}$ **B.** $\frac{1}{7}$, 0.125, $\frac{4}{9}$, 0.45

C. 0.125, $\frac{1}{7}$, $\frac{4}{9}$, 0.45 **D.** 0.125, $\frac{1}{7}$, 0.45, $\frac{4}{9}$

62. Multiple Choice In a class, $\frac{22}{25}$ of the students are right-handed. What is another way to express this number? **I**

F. 0.22 **G.** 0.25 **H.** 0.47 **I.** 0.88

Lesson 5.6 Adding and Subtracting Decimals

BEFORE	Now	WHY?
You added and subtracted fractions.	You'll add and subtract decimals.	So you can compare snowfall amounts, as in Ex. 34.

Word Watch

front-end estimation, p. 248

In the Real World

Dancing The table shows the amounts of money (in billions of dollars) that people in the United States spent on dance studios, schools, and halls. How much was spent in 1995 and 1996? How much more was spent in 1998 than in 1997?

Money Spent on Dancing

Year	Dollars (billions)
1994	0.906
1995	0.947
1996	1.046
1997	1.08
1998	1.138

You can use a vertical format to add or subtract decimals. Begin by lining up the decimal points. Then add or subtract as with whole numbers. Be sure to include the decimal point in your answer.

EXAMPLE 1 Adding and Subtracting Decimals

a. To find how many billions of dollars were spent in 1995 and 1996, add the values from the table for 1995 and 1996.

$$\begin{array}{r} 0.947 \\ +\ 1.046 \\ \hline 1.993 \end{array}$$

ANSWER In 1995 and 1996, 1.993 billion dollars was spent.

b. To find how much more was spent in 1998 than in 1997, subtract the value for 1997 from the value for 1998.

$$\begin{array}{r} 1.138 \\ -\ 1.080 \\ \hline 0.058 \end{array}$$

Use a zero as a placeholder.

ANSWER In 1998, 0.058 billion dollars more was spent than in 1997.

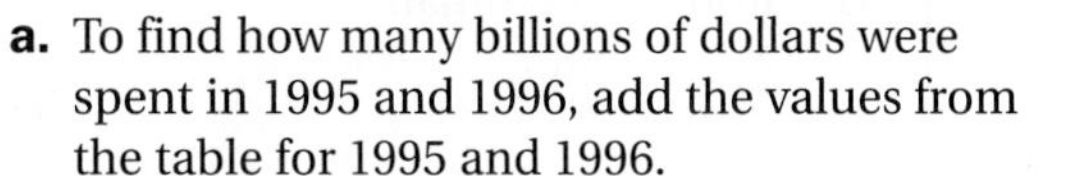

Your turn now Find the sum or difference.

1. $-12.5 + (-4.55)$ -17.05
2. $8.93 + 0.367$ 9.297
3. $7.624 + (-0.05)$ 7.574
4. $8.91 - 2.745$ 6.165
5. $-5.3 - 11.49$ -16.79
6. $5.376 - (-0.8)$ 6.176

ILLINOIS Standards and ISAT:
6.B.3a, 6.C.3a, 6.C.3b

1 PLAN

SKILL CHECK

1. $-12 + (-5) = \underline{?}$ -17
2. Find y if $y - 2 = 7$. 9
3. Find x if $x + (-2) = 4$. 6
4. Find a if $-a + 1 = -3$. 4

LESSON OBJECTIVE

Add and subtract decimals.

PACING

Suggested Number of Days
Basic Course: 1 day
Average Course: 1 day
Advanced Course: 1 day
Block: 0.5 block with 5.7

TEACHING RESOURCES

For a complete list of Teaching Resources, see page 216B.

TRANSPARENCY

Warm-Up Exercises for this lesson are available on a transparency.

2 TEACH

MOTIVATING THE LESSON

Ask students to rewrite the numbers in the table as whole numbers (e.g., 0.906 billion = 906,000,000). Then have them answer the questions in the opening paragraph.

TIPS FOR NEW TEACHERS

Use examples in vertical format to show that adding decimals is like adding integers. In both cases, place value is used to line up the digits. See Tips for New Teachers in the *Chapter 5 Resource Book*.

EXTRA EXAMPLES

Example 1 Refer to the table on page 247.

a. Find how much was spent for 1994 and 1995 combined. **$1.853 billion**

b. Find the difference in spending between 1994 and 1998. **$0.232 billion**

Example 2 Solve the equation.

a. $k - 3.24 = 7.9$ **11.14**

b. $m + (-10.8) = -1.04$ **9.76**

Example 3 Ruth bought 2 gallons of milk at $3.09 each, a sack of potatoes costing $3.59, and a sack of dog food costing $15.99. Use front-end estimation to find her total before tax. **$26**

CONCEPT CHECK

How is adding decimals different from adding whole numbers? ***Sample answer:* You must line up the decimal points; you can use zeros as placeholders.**

DAILY PUZZLER

Travis cashed a check but did not notice that the cashier gave him dollars for cents and cents for dollars. Pocketing his cash, Travis dropped a nickel. When he got home, Travis counted his money and found he had exactly twice the amount of the check. What was the amount of the check? **$31.63**

EXAMPLE 2 Solving Equations with Decimals

a.

$y - 1.537 = 6.48$	**Original equation**
$y - 1.537 + 1.537 = 6.48 + 1.537$	**Add 1.537 to each side.**
$y = 8.017$	**Simplify.**

b.

$x + (-0.34) = 4.27$	**Original equation**
$x + (-0.34) + 0.34 = 4.27 + 0.34$	**Add 0.34 to each side to undo adding −0.34.**
$x = 4.61$	**Simplify.**

Estimating You can estimate sums using **front-end estimation**. Add the front-end digits to get a low estimate. Then use the remaining digits to adjust the sum to a closer estimate.

EXAMPLE 3 Using Front-End Estimation

Theater You want to estimate the cost of supplies for a play. Is the cost of the items shown (excluding tax) more or less than your $50 budget?

Theater Supplies	
cowboy hat	$18.97
cotton fabric	$9.49
rope	$3.49
safety pins	$2.19
picnic basket	$16.77

Solution

Use front-end estimation.

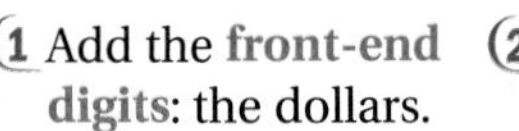

(1) Add the **front-end digits**: the dollars.

(2) Estimate the sum of the **remaining digits**: the cents.

(3) Add your results.

(1)	(2)	(3)
$18.97	$18.97 — $1	
$9.49	$9.49 and $3.49 → $1	
$3.49		
$2.19	$2.19 and $16.77 → $1	$48
$16.77		+ $3
$48	$3	$51

ANSWER The cost of the items is more than your $50 budget.

Your turn now **Solve the equation.**

7. $x + 1.38 = 2.55$ **1.17** **8.** $z - 5.3 = 16.29$ **21.59** **9.** $y - (-0.83) = 0.48$ **−0.35**

10. Use front-end estimation to estimate the sum $1.95 + $7.49 + $3.50. **about $13**

5.6 Exercises

More Practice, p. 731

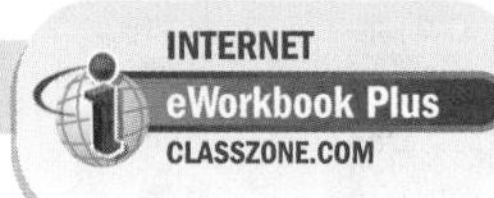

INTERNET eWorkbook Plus CLASSZONE.COM

Getting Ready to Practice

1. **Vocabulary** Copy and complete: You can get a low estimate of 13.56 + 11.42 + 25.94 by adding the front-end digits _?_, _?_, and _?_. 13, 11, 25

2. **Find the Error** Describe and correct the error in the solution. The decimal points are not lined up; 10.43 + 7.521 = 17.951.

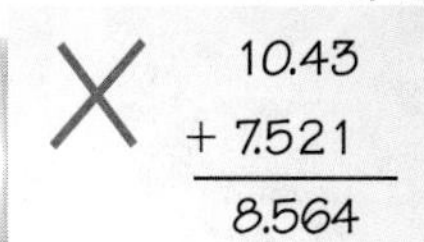

Find the sum or difference.

3. 1.35 + 6.02 7.37
4. 14.1 − 3.662 10.438

Solve the equation.

5. $x + 2.9 = 5.3$ 2.4
6. $y - 4.15 = -4.26$ −0.11
7. $z - (-7.7) = 13.31$ 5.61

Use front-end estimation to estimate the sum.

8. 2.32 + 6.69 + 8.50 + 4.46 22
9. 10.23 + 6.98 + 9.05 + 5.80 32

10. **Sales Tax** Your purchase costs $9.87 plus sales tax of $.49. What is the total amount you pay? $10.36

Practice and Problem Solving

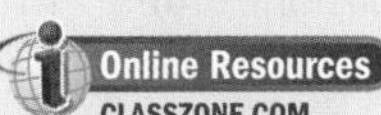

HELP with Homework

Example	Exercises
1	11-25, 34, 36
2	26-31
3	32-33, 35

Online Resources CLASSZONE.COM
· More Examples
· eTutorial Plus

Find the sum or difference.

A 11. 30.193 + 7.91 38.103
12. 2.507 + 0.586 3.093
13. −6.08 + 2.661 −3.419
14. −0.37 + (−1.8) −2.17
15. 6.8 + (−1.812) 4.988
16. −12.09 + 1.20 −10.89
17. 3.28 + (−4.91) −1.63
18. 1.46 + (−1.564) −0.104
19. 1.57 − 9.28 −7.71
20. 68.79 − 9.18 59.61
21. 15.7 − (−6.4) 22.1
22. −0.99 − 0.304 −1.294
23. 25.885 − 6.9 18.985
24. 29.1 − (−3.05) 32.15
25. −4.22 − 0.807 −5.027

Algebra **Solve the equation.**

26. $y + 1.5 = 37$ 35.5
27. $-2.8 + x = 4.51$ 7.31
28. $10.4 = 12.46 + z$ −2.06
29. $7.81 = 7.98 + y$ −0.17
30. $z + (-3.19) = 5.83$ 9.02
31. $x - 0.013 = -6.36$ −6.347

Use front-end estimation to estimate the sum.

32. 5.62 + 4.89 + 3.44 + 9.98 24
33. 23.70 + 16.12 + 5.96 + 14.18 60

34. **Snowfall** Chicago's average snowfall in December is 11.2 inches. In 2001, only 1.6 inches fell in December. In inches, how much below average was this? 9.6 in.

3 APPLY

ASSIGNMENT GUIDE

Basic Course

Day 1: SRH p. 709 Exs. 9-12; pp. 249-250 Exs. 13-24, 29-31, 35-37, 39-42, 48-56

Average Course

Day 1: pp. 249-250 Exs. 17-28, 32-43, 48-57

Advanced Course

Day 1: pp. 249-250 Exs. 21-28, 32-47*, 50-57

Block

pp. 249-250 Exs. 17-28, 32-43, 48-57 (with 5.7)

Extra Practice

- Student Edition, p. 731
- Chapter 5 Resource Book, pp. 50-52
- Test and Practice Generator

Transparency

Even-numbered answers are available on transparencies.

Homework Check

When you review students' homework for this lesson, go over the following exercises to check understanding of key concepts.
Basic: 13, 21, 29, 31, 35
Average: 17, 23, 32, 34, 36
Advanced: 21, 23, 33, 35, 38

Teaching Tip

Have students use estimation to check their answers for Exercises 11-25.

4 ASSESS

ASSESSMENT RESOURCES

For more assessment resources, see:
- Assessment Book
- Test and Practice Generator

MINI-QUIZ

Find the sum or difference.

1. 6.2 + 0.07 6.27
2. 38 − 52.61 −14.61
3. Solve 12.9 − *m* = 0.45. 12.45
4. Use front-end estimation to estimate the sum: 15.2 + 6.6 + 18.8 + 11.3. 52
5. Find the perimeter of the figure. 14 in.

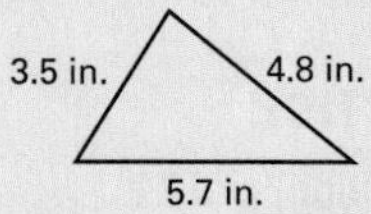

5 FOLLOW-UP

RETEACHING/REMEDIATION

- Study Guide in Chapter 5 Resource Book, pp. 53–54
- Tutor Place, Whole Numbers and Decimals Card 6, Algebra Cards 8, 9
- eTutorial Plus Online
- Extra Practice, p. 731
- Lesson Practice in Chapter 5 Resource Book, pp. 50–52

CHALLENGE/ENRICHMENT

- Challenge Practice in Chapter 5 Resource Book, p. 56
- Teacher's Edition, p. 216F

ENGLISH LEARNER SUPPORT

- Spanish Study Guide
- Multi-Language Glossary
- Chapter Audio Summaries CDs

54. See Additional Answers beginning on page AA1.

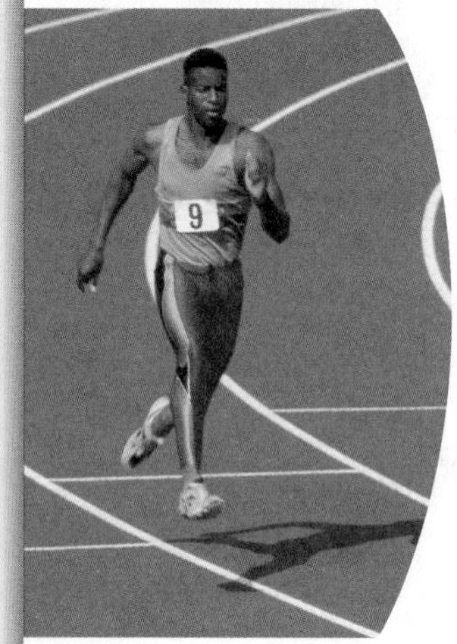

B **35. Critical Thinking** The number 29.32 can be written as the sum 20 + 9 + 0.3 + 0.02. Write 345.692 as a sum in this form. 300 + 40 + 5 + 0.6 + 0.09 + 0.002

36. Track You run 400 meters in 58.01 seconds. What is the difference of your time and the school record of 55.49 seconds? 2.52 sec

Geometry Find the perimeter of the figure.

37.

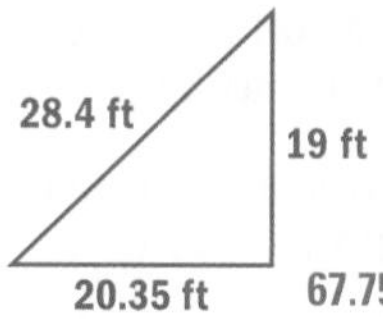

67.75 ft

38.

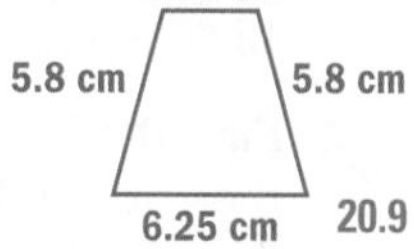

20.9 cm

39.

26.42 m

40. Banking Use the bank record for the month of January. The beginning balance was $83.47. Estimate the balance at the end of the month. Then find the exact balance.
Sample answer: $125; $122.92

Date	Transaction	Deposit	Withdrawal
1/02	deposit	$50	
1/10	groceries		$75.35
1/16	bookstore		$12.95
1/22	deposit	$112.81	
1/29	video rentals		$13.08
1/31	computer game		$21.98

Challenge Find the sum or difference. Write your answer in decimal form.

C **41.** $6.28 + \frac{5}{2}$ 8.78 **42.** $\frac{3}{8} + 4.6$ 4.975 **43.** $12.853 - \frac{3}{4}$ 12.103 **44.** $\frac{9}{20} - 0.35$ 0.1

Mixed Review

Simplify the expression using only positive exponents. *(Lesson 4.7)*

45. -12^0 −1 **46.** $3^{-2} \cdot 3^5$ 3^3 **47.** $\frac{b^{-4}}{b^{10}}$ $\frac{1}{b^{14}}$ **48.** $\frac{32m^{-8}}{8m^2}$ $\frac{4}{m^{10}}$

Find the product or quotient. Simplify if possible. *(Lessons 5.3, 5.4)*

49. $-\frac{8}{9} \cdot \left(\frac{-5}{7}\right)$ $\frac{40}{63}$ **50.** $5\frac{3}{7} \cdot \frac{21}{22}$ $5\frac{2}{11}$ **51.** $-5 \div \left(\frac{-2}{3}\right)$ $7\frac{1}{2}$ **52.** $6\frac{5}{12} \div 2\frac{3}{4}$ $2\frac{1}{3}$

Test-Taking Practice

INTERNET
State Test Practice
CLASSZONE.COM

53. Multiple Choice When adding two positive decimals that are less than 1, the sum is always __?__. D

A. less than 1 **B.** negative **C.** more than 1 **D.** positive

54. Short Response Plot the following points in a coordinate plane. Then connect the points to form a rectangle and find its perimeter.
A(1.25, 3.5), *B*(4.25, 3.5), *C*(4.25, 6.75), *D*(1.25, 6.75) See margin.

Multiplying and Dividing Decimals

BEFORE
You multiplied and divided integers and fractions.

Now
You'll multiply and divide decimals.

WHY?
So you can find how many balloons you can buy, as in Ex. 24.

In the Real World

Word Watch

leading digit, p. 251

Rafting You travel downstream in a raft at a rate of about 4.3 miles per hour. How far will you travel in 2.5 hours?

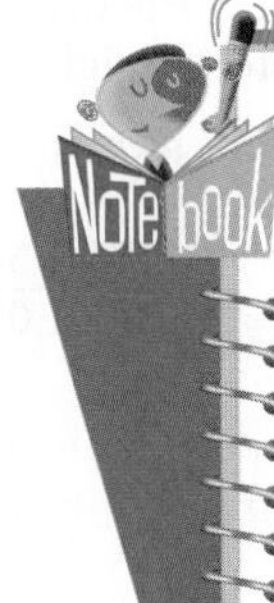

Multiplying Decimals

Words Multiply decimals as you do whole numbers. Then place the decimal point. The number of decimal places in the product is the total number of decimal places in the factors.

Numbers 2.25 (2 places) × 8.9 (1 place) = 20.025 (3 places)

EXAMPLE 1 Multiplying Decimals

To find how far you travel in the problem above about rafting, substitute the given values into the distance formula. Distance = rate • time, so distance = 4.3 • 2.5.

```
   4.3    1 decimal place
 × 2.5   +1 decimal place
   215
   86
 10.75    2 decimal places
```

ANSWER You will travel about 10.75 miles.

A number's **leading digit** is its leftmost nonzero digit. To check that a product is reasonable, round each factor to its leading digit and multiply.

4.3 • 2.5 → Round factors to leading digit. → 4 • 3 = 12 ✓

Your turn now **Multiply. Show that your answer is reasonable.**

1. −7.39 • 2.1
2. 19.62 • 5.07
3. 1.13 • 0.04
4. −0.85 • (−8)

1. −15.519; −7 • 2 = −14
2. 99.4734; 20 • 5 = 100
3. 0.0452; 1 • 0.04 = 0.04
4. 6.8; −1 • (−8) = 8

ILLINOIS Standards and ISAT:
6.B.3a, 6.C.3a; 9.C.3a

1 PLAN

SKILL CHECK

1. 43 × 22 = ? 946
2. 603 ÷ 3 = ? 201
3. 60 ÷ 12 = ? 5
4. 126 ÷ 18 = ? 7

LESSON OBJECTIVE

Multiply and divide decimals.

PACING

Suggested Number of Days
Basic Course: 2 days
Average Course: 2 days
Advanced Course: 2 days
Block: 0.5 block with 5.6
0.5 block with 5.8

TEACHING RESOURCES

For a complete list of Teaching Resources, see page 216B.

TRANSPARENCY

Warm-Up Exercises for this lesson are available on a transparency.

2 TEACH

MOTIVATING THE LESSON

Tell students that multiplying and dividing decimals is almost the same as multiplying and dividing whole numbers. The only thing extra they have to worry about is where to place the decimal point.

TIPS FOR NEW TEACHERS

Show students how to verify that they have placed the decimal point in the product or quotient correctly by estimating the answer. See Tips for New Teachers in the *Chapter 5 Resource Book*.

EXTRA EXAMPLES

Example 1 A goose walks at a rate of 1.5 feet per second. How far will this goose walk in 6 seconds? **9 ft**

Example 2 Find the quotient 56.95 ÷ 6.7. **8.5**

Example 3 Find the quotient 0.055 ÷ 2.5. **0.022**

CONCEPT CHECK

When multiplying decimals, how do you determine the number of decimal places in the product? **You find the sum of the number of decimal places in the factors.**

DAILY PUZZLER

Rosita spent half her cash buying furniture at a yard sale. She noticed that the number of cents in the amount she had left after the purchase equaled the number of dollars she had before the purchase, and the number of dollars she had after the purchase equaled half the number of cents in the amount she had before the purchase. How much cash did Rosita take to the yard sale? **$99.98**

Dividing Decimals

Words When you divide by a decimal, multiply both the divisor and the dividend by the power of ten that will make the divisor an integer. Then divide.

Numbers $2.75\overline{)15.125}$ **Multiply by 100.** $275\overline{)1512.5}$ (quotient 5.5)

EXAMPLE 2 Dividing Decimals

To find the quotient 60.102 ÷ 6.3, multiply the divisor and dividend by 10. Move the decimal points 1 place to the right.

$6.3\overline{)60.102}$ **Move decimal points.** $63\overline{)601.02}$

Then divide. $63\overline{)601.02}$ (quotient 9.54)

✓**Check** To check that the quotient is reasonable, round the quotient and the divisor to the leading digit. Then multiply. The result should be close in value to the dividend.

$9.54 \cdot 6.3$ **Round.** $10 \cdot 6 = 60$ ✓

EXAMPLE 3 Using Zeros as Placeholders

To find some quotients, you may need to use zeros as placeholders.

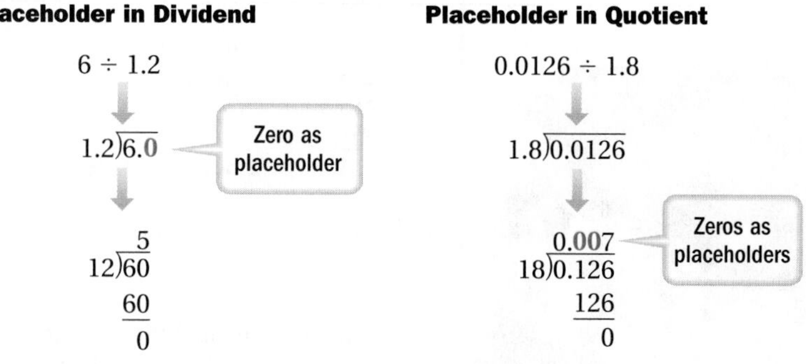

Placeholder in Dividend

6 ÷ 1.2

$1.2\overline{)6.0}$ Zero as placeholder

$12\overline{)60}$ = 5; 60; 0

Placeholder in Quotient

0.0126 ÷ 1.8

$1.8\overline{)0.0126}$

$18\overline{)0.126}$ = 0.007; 126; 0

Your turn now **Find the quotient.**

5. 1.6 ÷ 0.04 **40** **6.** 0.632 ÷ 0.79 **0.8** **7.** −13 ÷ (−0.65) **20**

8. −4.365 ÷ (−4.5) **0.97** **9.** 0.3744 ÷ 1.56 **0.24** **10.** −0.0108 ÷ 2.7 **−0.004**

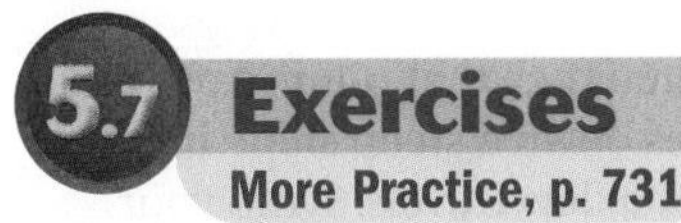

5.7 Exercises

More Practice, p. 731

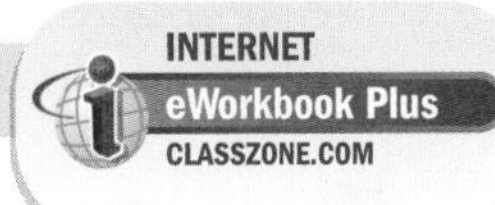

INTERNET eWorkbook Plus CLASSZONE.COM

Getting Ready to Practice

1. **Vocabulary** Copy the division problem. Use the words *quotient, dividend,* and *divisor* to label each number.

0.8 ← ?
? → 9)7.2 ← ?

0.8 ← quotient
divisor → 9)7.2 ← dividend

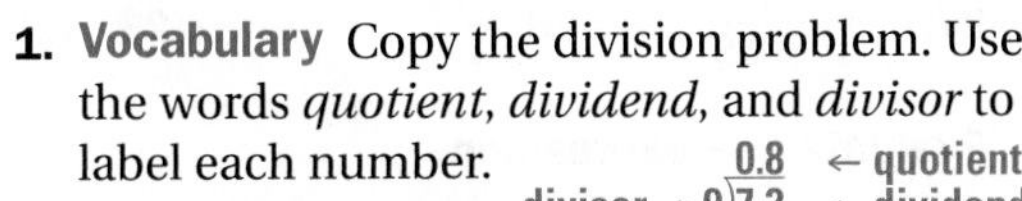

Multiply or divide. Show that your answer is reasonable.

2. 7.8 • 2.6 — 20.28; 8 • 3 = 24
3. 3.75 • 0.4 — 1.5; 4 • 0.4 = 1.6
4. 13.2 ÷ 1.1 — 12; 13 ÷ 1 = 13
5. 0.5 ÷ 1.25 — 0.4; 0.5 ÷ 1 = 0.5

6. **Guided Problem Solving** A mother rhinoceros weighs 3600 pounds. Her baby weighs 0.38 of her weight. How much does the baby weigh? Explain why your answer is reasonable.

(1) Write a verbal model to describe the problem. Baby's weight = Mother's weight • 0.38

(2) Substitute the given values and solve. b = 3600 • 0.38; 1368 lb

(3) Check to see that your answer is reasonable. 4000 • 0.4 = 1600

Practice and Problem Solving

HELP with Homework

Example	Exercises
1	7-22, 23, 25
2	7-22, 24, 26
3	7-22

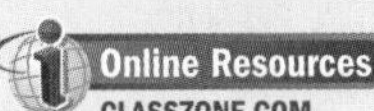

Online Resources CLASSZONE.COM

- More Examples
- eTutorial Plus

Find the product or quotient.

A

7. 25 • 0.2 5
8. 2.4 • 0.3 0.72
9. −8.2 • 0.7 −5.74
10. 13.65 • 1.1 15.015
11. 4.8 ÷ 1.2 4
12. 4.9 ÷ 0.07 70
13. 5 ÷ (−0.1) −50
14. −8 ÷ (−3.2) 2.5
15. 5.41 • 0.35 1.8935
16. −0.57 ÷ 0.38 −1.5
17. 4.844 ÷ 0.56 8.65
18. −2.687 • (−9) 24.183
19. 37.41 ÷ 4.3 8.7
20. 0.098 • 0.55 0.0539
21. 6.025 • 48.2 290.405
22. 1.11 ÷ 0.925 1.2

23. **Find the Error** Describe and correct the error in the solution. The answer should have 2 + 1 = 3 decimal places; 33.252.

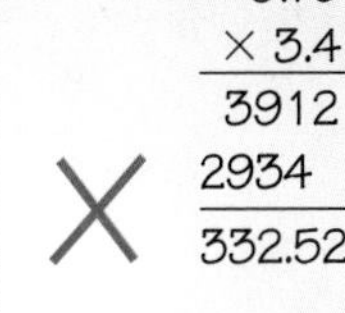

9.78
× 3.4
3912
2934
332.52

24. **Balloons** You are buying balloons that cost \$.89 per package to decorate for a school dance. You have \$14.75 to spend. How many packages of balloons can you buy? 16 packages

25. **Look for a Pattern** Copy and complete the table by multiplying each number in the leftmost column by the number at the top of each other column. Describe the pattern.

×	1	0.1	0.01	0.001	0.0001
87	87	8.7	?	?	?
356	356	?	?	?	?
1200	?	?	?	?	?

25. First row: 0.87, 0.087, 0.0087; second row: 35.6, 3.56, 0.356, 0.0356; third row: 1200, 120, 12, 1.2, 0.12; the decimal point moves one place to the left in the product each time it does in the factor.

3 APPLY

ASSIGNMENT GUIDE

Basic Course

Day 1: SRH p. 714 Exs. 6-10; pp. 253-254 Exs. 7-14, 24, 27-29, 37-41

Day 2: SRH p. 715 Exs. 6-10; pp. 253-254 Exs. 15-22, 26, 30-32, 42-46

Average Course

Day 1: pp. 253-254 Exs. 7-14, 23-28, 37-42

Day 2: pp. 253-254 Exs. 15-22, 29-35, 43-47

Advanced Course

Day 1: pp. 253-254 Exs. 7-14, 23-28, 37-41

Day 2: pp. 253-254 Exs. 15-22, 29-36*, 45-47

Block

pp. 253-254 Exs. 7-14, 23-28, 37-42 (with 5.6)

pp. 253-254 Exs. 15-22, 29-35, 43-47 (with 5.8)

EXTRA PRACTICE

- Student Edition, p. 731
- Chapter 5 Resource Book, pp. 59-61
- Test and Practice Generator

TRANSPARENCY

Even-numbered answers are available on transparencies.

HOMEWORK CHECK

When you review students' homework for this lesson, go over the following exercises to check understanding of key concepts.

Basic: 7, 12, 15, 22, 24
Average: 7, 13, 15, 23, 24
Advanced: 9, 13, 18, 24, 25

ASSESSMENT RESOURCES

For more assessment resources, see:

- Assessment Book
- Test and Practice Generator

MINI-QUIZ

Find the product or quotient.

1. 17×0.4 **6.8**
2. -250×0.01 **−2.5**
3. $3.252 \div 1.2$ **2.71**
4. $-42.6 \div (-0.8)$ **53.25**
5. Juwan makes 150 photocopies that each cost $.055. What is his total before tax? **$8.25**

RETEACHING/REMEDIATION

- Study Guide in Chapter 5 Resource Book, pp. 62–63
- Tutor Place, Whole Numbers and Decimals Cards 8, 9, 12, 13
- eTutorial Plus Online
- Extra Practice, p. 731
- Lesson Practice in Chapter 5 Resource Book, pp. 59–61

CHALLENGE/ENRICHMENT

- Challenge Practice in Chapter 5 Resource Book, p. 64
- Teacher's Edition, p. 216F

ENGLISH LEARNER SUPPORT

- Spanish Study Guide
- Multi-Language Glossary
- Chapter Audio Summaries CDs

Kilauea Volcano, Hawaii

33. If you multiply both 4.6 and 0.23 by 100, you get 460 and 23; yes; because you have multiplied $\frac{4.6}{0.23}$ by $\frac{100}{100} = 1$ to get $\frac{460}{23}$.

35. One; two; three; seven. *Sample answer:* The exponent tells you how many factors to multiply. If each factor has one decimal place, then the exponent tells you the number of decimal places.

26. Lava Flows A lava flow is a stream of molten rock that pours from an erupting vent. A lava flow travels 15.5 miles down a steep slope in 2.5 hours. Find the average rate at which the flow travels. Write your answer in miles per hour. Explain why your answer is reasonable.
6.2 mi/h; rounding to leading digits gives $20 \div 3 = 6.\overline{6}$ which is close to 6.2.

Algebra Solve the equation.

B **27.** $9 = \frac{a}{-0.9}$ −8.1 **28.** $\frac{c}{4.5} = 0.16$ 0.72 **29.** $1.2x = 0.321$ 0.2675 **30.** $-8.25y = -3.3$ 0.4

Evaluate the expression.

31. $3.4^3 + 5.1 \div 1.7 - 4.89$ 37.414 **32.** $6.2 \cdot (18.77 - 6.27) + 9.1^2$ 160.31

33. Writing Explain how 4.6 divided by 0.23 is related to 460 divided by 23. Are the quotients the same? Why? See margin.

34. Postal Rates The table shows rates to mail a first class letter. How much does it cost to mail a first class letter that weighs 3.5 ounces? $1.06

First ounce or fraction of ounce	$.37
Each additional ounce or fraction	$.23

C **35. Critical Thinking** How many decimal places does 1.3^1 have? 1.3^2? 1.3^3? 1.3^7? Explain your reasoning. See margin.

36. Challenge One micron is equal to 0.001 millimeter. If a bacteria is 4 microns wide, how many times would you have to magnify it for the bacteria to appear 1 millimeter wide? 250 times

Mixed Review 

Write the number in standard form. *(Lesson 4.8)*

37. 6.89×10^9 6,890,000,000 **38.** 1.3×10^{-12} 0.0000000000013 **39.** 7.405×10^{-6} 0.000007405

Order the numbers from least to greatest. *(Lesson 5.5)*

40. $2.32, \frac{9}{4}, 2.5, 2\frac{3}{10}, 2, \frac{11}{5}$
$2, \frac{11}{5}, \frac{9}{4}, 2\frac{3}{10}, 2.32, 2.5$

41. $-\frac{9}{20}, -0.46, -\frac{3}{8}, -\frac{5}{12}, -0.4$
$-0.46, -\frac{9}{20}, -\frac{5}{12}, -0.4, -\frac{3}{8}$

Basic Skills Find the quotient.

42. $55 \div 6$ 9 R1 **43.** $127 \div 5$ 25 R2 **44.** $307 \div 29$ 10 R17 **45.** $8607 \div 42$ 204 R39

Test-Taking Practice 

46. Multiple Choice The quotient $-0.57 \div 0.38$ is _?_. B

A. an integer **B.** negative **C.** more than 1 **D.** positive

47. Short Response You have $75 to spend on party decorations that cost $4.89 per bag, including tax. Find how many bags you can buy. Estimate to check that your answer is reasonable. Show your work.

47. 15 bags; $75 ÷ $4.89 ≈ 15.337, or about 15; 75 ÷ 5 = 15.

5.8 Hands-on Activity

GOAL

Collect and analyze data.

MATERIALS

- number cubes

Collecting and Analyzing Data

You can collect data and find a number that represents the data. The *median* is the middle value when the values are written in order. The *mode* is the value that occurs most often.

Explore 1 **Collect data by rolling two number cubes to explore how often each sum occurs.**

1. Roll a pair of number cubes eleven times and record the results.

$3+2=5 \quad 4+4=8 \quad 6+6=12 \quad 1+2=3 \quad 1+6=7 \quad 2+1=3$

$5+3=8 \quad 4+1=5 \quad 1+5=6 \quad 2+6=8 \quad 2+2=4$

2. Add the sums together. Divide by the number of rolls to find the mean.

$$\frac{5+8+12+3+7+3+8+5+6+8+4}{11} = \frac{69}{11} \approx 6.3$$

3. Order the sums. Find the median and the mode.

3, 3, 4, 5, 5, 6, 7, 8, 8, 8, 12

middle number (6) — most frequent number (8, 8, 8)

4. Which sum do you think occurs most often? Compare your results with other groups.

Your turn now **Find the mean, median, and mode of the data set.**

1. 4.2, 6.1, 3.8, 4.1, 10.2, 9.6, 6.1, 7.3, 2.1, 2.4, 9.8
   mean ≈ 5.97, median = 6.1, mode = 6.1
2. 105, 121, 42, 78, 77, 63, 108, 32, 33, 121, 64
   mean ≈ 76.7, median = 77, mode = 121
3. $2\frac{1}{2}, 7\frac{3}{4}, 9\frac{1}{4}, 7\frac{1}{2}, 4\frac{3}{8}, 7\frac{3}{4}, 3\frac{7}{8}$ mean $\approx 6\frac{1}{7}$, median $= 7\frac{1}{2}$, mode $= 7\frac{3}{4}$

ILLINOIS Standards and ISAT:
10.A.3b

1 PLAN

EXPLORE THE CONCEPT

- Students will collect data to analyze its content.
- In Lesson 5.8, students will be introduced to the concepts of mean, median, mode, and range, and will make judgments about which average best represents a set of data.

MATERIALS

Each student will need number cubes.

RECOMMENDED TIME

Work activity: 10 min
Discuss results: 10 min

GROUPING

Students can work individually on Explore 1. You may want to begin Explore 2 by having students one by one call out the number of letters in their last names while you record the data on the board. Students can then work individually with the data.

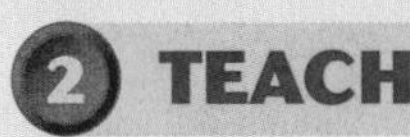

2 TEACH

TIPS FOR SUCCESS

Point out that the number cube results in Explore 1 are an example. Students should expect their results to be different. Stress that the data are the sums for the two cubes.

CLOSE

KEY DISCOVERY

There are three numbers that can be used to summarize a set of data: the mean, the middle number, and the most frequent number.

ASSESSMENT

1. If you wanted to change the most frequent number for the lengths of names in your class, which students should you transfer to another class? **Answers will vary depending on class data.**
2. If you wanted to change the mean for the lengths of names in your class, which student in your school should you transfer into your class? **Students should name a student with a very short or very long last name.**

Hands-on Activity *Continued*

Explore 2 **Collect data about the number of letters in the last name of each student in your class.**

1. Find the shortest and longest names so you can make a frequency table.
2. Count the number of letters in each name. Make a tally mark for each name.
3. Find the most frequent name length. This is the mode.

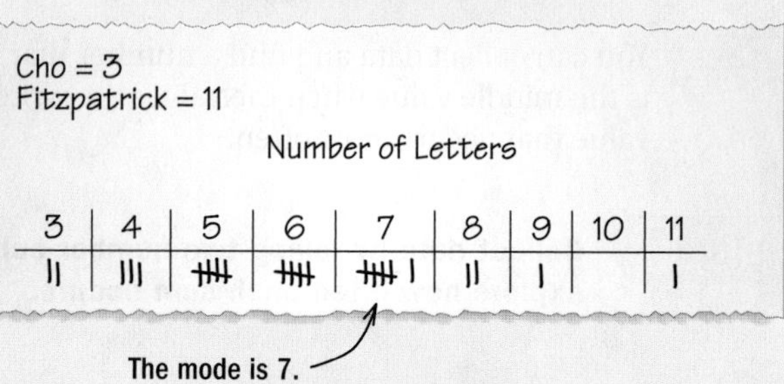

Cho = 3
Fitzpatrick = 11

Number of Letters

3	4	5	6	7	8	9	10	11
II	III	𝍸	𝍸	𝍸 I	II	I		I

The mode is 7.

4. Find the mean number of letters in the last names.
5. Can you use the mean to describe the average length of a last name in your class? Can you use the mode? Explain. ***Sample answer:*** **In the example shown, both the mean and the mode are reasonable descriptions of average name length.**

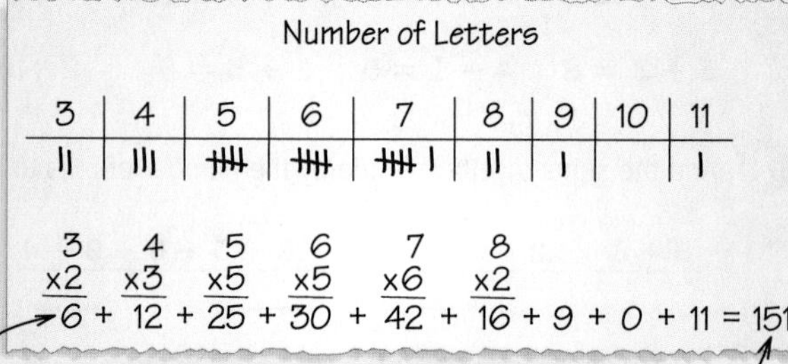

Number of Letters

3	4	5	6	7	8	9	10	11
II	III	𝍸	𝍸	𝍸 I	II	I		I

$3 \times 2 = 6$, $4 \times 3 = 12$, $5 \times 5 = 25$, $6 \times 5 = 30$, $7 \times 6 = 42$, $8 \times 2 = 16$

$6 + 12 + 25 + 30 + 42 + 16 + 9 + 0 + 11 = 151$

You can multiply to count the number of letters for each column. Then add the column totals.

Divide by the number of students. The mean is $151 \div 25 \approx 6$.

Your turn now

4. A new student whose last name has 16 letters joins your class. If you add "16" to your data, how does this affect the mean and the mode? Explain. ***Sample answer:*** **It will increase the mean because it will greatly increase the sum used to find the mean. It is unlikely to affect the mode.**

Stop *and* Think

5. **Writing** You are designing a form to collect data. Students will write their last names in a row of small boxes, one letter per box. How many boxes do you think the form should provide? Explain. **Answers should include reasoning based on expected name lengths.**

Mean, Median, and Mode

BEFORE	Now	WHY?
You used tables and graphs to analyze data sets.	You'll describe data sets using mean, median, mode, and range.	So you can describe World Series attendance, as in Ex. 14.

Word Watch

mean, p. 257
median, p. 257
mode, p. 257
range, p. 258

In the Real World

Biology A marine biologist records the locations of deep sea jellies in relation to the ocean surface. Jellies are found at −2278 feet, −1875 feet, −3210 feet, −2755 feet, −2407 feet, and −2901 feet. What is the average location of a deep sea jelly?

Three types of averages can be used to describe a data set.

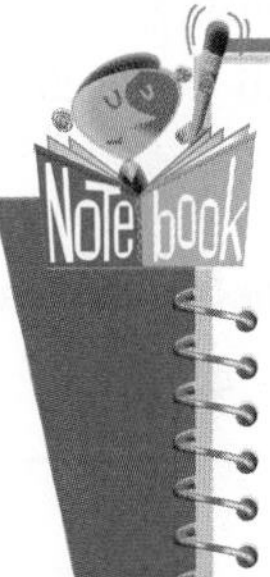

Averages

The **mean** of a data set is the sum of the values divided by the number of values.

The **median** of a data set is the middle value when the values are written in numerical order. If a data set has an even number of values, the median is the mean of the two middle values.

The **mode** of a data set is the value that occurs most often. A data set can have no mode, one mode, or more than one mode.

EXAMPLE 1 Finding a Mean

To find the mean of the 6 locations of the deep sea jellies in the problem above, divide the sum of the locations by 6.

$$\text{Mean} = \frac{-2278 + (-1875) + (-3210) + (-2755) + (-2407) + (-2901)}{6}$$

$$= \frac{-15{,}426}{6}$$

$$= -2571$$

ANSWER The mean location in relation to the ocean surface is −2571 ft.

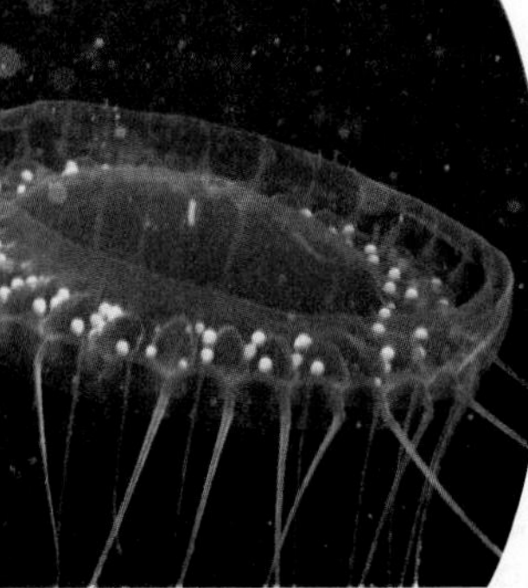

Deep sea jelly

Your turn now Find the mean of the data.

1. −3°C, 44°C, −11°C, 9°C, −21°C 3.6°C
2. $12\frac{1}{2}$ in., $14\frac{3}{4}$ in., $20\frac{1}{2}$ in., $16\frac{3}{4}$ in. $16\frac{1}{8}$ in.

ILLINOIS Standards and ISAT:
10.A.3b

1 PLAN

SKILL CHECK

1. $\frac{16 + 18}{2} = \underline{?}$ 17
2. $29.3 - 7.2 = \underline{?}$ 22.1
3. $-3200 - 2400 = \underline{?}$ −5600
4. $45 \div 10 = \underline{?}$ 4.5

LESSON OBJECTIVE

Describe data sets using mean, median, mode, and range.

PACING

Suggested Number of Days
Basic Course: 1 day
Average Course: 1 day
Advanced Course: 1 day
Block: 0.5 block with 5.7

TEACHING RESOURCES

For a complete list of Teaching Resources, see page 216B.

TRANSPARENCY

Warm-Up Exercises for this lesson are available on a transparency.

2 TEACH

MOTIVATING THE LESSON

Ask students to explain their understanding of an average.

TIPS FOR NEW TEACHERS

Be sure students understand that a data set with an even number of values has two middle numbers that must be averaged to find the median. See Tips for New Teachers in the *Chapter 5 Resource Book*.

EXTRA EXAMPLES

Example 1 Charlene opened a part-time business. In the first four months, the business earned \$585, \$1250, \$973, and \$907. Find the mean of her income in the first four months. **\$928.75**

Example 2 Alma finds the mass of her six ducklings. Find the median, mode(s), and range of the masses:
0.8 kg, 1.2 kg, 0.75 kg, 1.05 kg, 0.6 kg, 0.9 kg
median 0.85; no mode; range 0.6

Example 3 Groups A and B try a new Internet service and rate it on a scale of 1 to 10 as shown. Which average best represents each group?
Group A: 2, 4, 6, 6, 6, 7, 8, 8, 9, 10
Group B: 1, 2, 2, 9, 9, 9, 9, 10, 10, 10
Group A: The mean (6.6), median (6.5), and mode (6) are very close. So each average is a fair representation of the group.
Group B: The mean (7.1) is much lower than the median (9) and mode (9). So the median or mode best represents the group.

CONCEPT CHECK

Name the mean, median, and mode of 3, 5, 6, 7, 7. **5.6, 6, 7**

DAILY PUZZLER

Name a set of five numbers that have the same mean, median, mode, and range. ***Sample answer:* 2, 4, 4, 4, 6**

Range The **range** of a data set is the difference of the greatest value and the least value.

EXAMPLE 2 Finding Median, Mode, and Range

Movies Find the median, mode(s), and range of the movie prices below.

\$7.20, \$13.25, \$14.94, \$16.56, \$18.74, \$19.99, \$19.99, \$29.49

Median: The data set has an even number of prices, so the median is the mean of the two middle values, \$16.56 and \$18.74.

$$\text{Median} = \frac{\$16.56 + \$18.74}{2} = \frac{\$35.30}{2} = \$17.65$$

Mode: The price that occurs most often is \$19.99. This is the mode.

Range: Find the difference of the greatest and the least values.

$$\text{Range} = \$29.49 - \$7.20 = \$22.29$$

Watch Out! If the data are not ordered, you need to order the data so you can find the median.

Your turn now **Find the median, mode(s), and range of the data.**

3. 14, 13, 20, 24, 15, 10, 22, 17, 18 **17; no mode; 14**

4. 9, 7, 4, 9, 4, 10, 5, 14, 9, 4 **8; 4 and 9; 10**

EXAMPLE 3 Choosing a Representative Average

Ice Cream Groups A and B try a new ice cream flavor and rate it on a scale of 1 to 10 as shown. Which average best represents each group?

Group A Ratings	Group B Ratings
1, 2, 3, 3, 5, 5, 5, 7, 8, 10	1, 1, 1, 2, 3, 4, 4, 9, 10, 10

Solution

Group A

$\text{Mean} = \frac{49}{10} = 4.9$

$\text{Median} = \frac{5+5}{2} = \frac{10}{2} = 5$

Mode: 5

ANSWER The mean, median, and mode are very close. So each average is a fair representation of the ratings as a group.

Group B

$\text{Mean} = \frac{45}{10} = 4.5$

$\text{Median} = \frac{3+4}{2} = \frac{7}{2} = 3.5$

Mode: 1

ANSWER The mean is higher than all but 3 ratings. The mode is equal to the lowest rating. So, mean and mode are not good choices. The median best represents the ratings.

5.8 Exercises

More Practice, p. 731

INTERNET eWorkbook Plus CLASSZONE.COM

Getting Ready to Practice

Vocabulary In Exercises 1–3, use the data set 6, 12, 4, 15, 10, 6, 2, 9. Complete the statement using *mean, median, mode, or range.*

1. The _?_ is 8. mean
2. The _?_ is 6. mode
3. The _?_ is 13. range

Find the mean, median, mode(s), and range of the data.

4. 8.98, 3.67, 11.13, 8.98, 11.24 8.8; 8.98; 8.98; 7.57
5. −71, −56, −62, −44, −56, −47 −56; −56; −56; 27
6. **Find the Error** Describe and correct the error in the solution. The data set has two modes, 5 and 8.

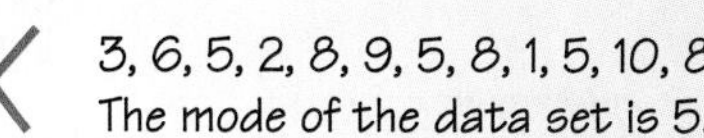

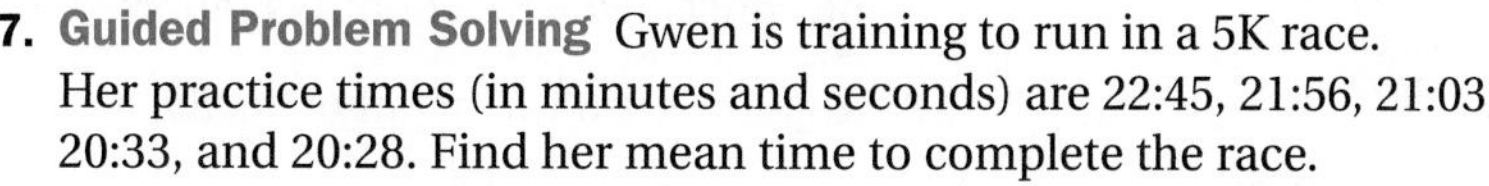

X 3, 6, 5, 2, 8, 9, 5, 8, 1, 5, 10, 8
The mode of the data set is 5.

7. **Guided Problem Solving** Gwen is training to run in a 5K race. Her practice times (in minutes and seconds) are 22:45, 21:56, 21:03, 20:33, and 20:28. Find her mean time to complete the race.
   (1) Change Gwen's practice times to seconds. 1365 sec, 1316 sec, 1263 sec, 1233 sec, 1228 sec
   (2) Find the sum of the practice times. Divide by the number of times. 6405 sec; 1281 sec
   (3) Convert your answer to minutes and seconds. 21:21

Practice and Problem Solving

14. 52,327; 49,707; 49,646. *Sample answer:* I think the mean better represents the data because it reflects overall ticket sales.

Find the mean, median, mode(s), and range of the data.

A 8. Distances: 16 km, 23 km, 11 km, 6 km, 15 km, 23 km, 17 km, 16 km 15.875 km; 16 km; 16 km and 23 km; 17 km
9. Weekly hits at a Web site: 115, 157, 289, 185, 164, 225, 185, 208 191; 185; 185; 174
10. Golf scores: −2, 0, 3, 1, 0, −1, 2, −2, −3, 0, 4, 1 0.25; 0; 0; 7
11. Elevations: 127 ft, −8 ft, 436 ft, 508 ft, −23 ft, 47 ft $181.1\overline{6}$ ft; 87 ft; none; 531 ft
12. Daily calories: 2000, 1872, 2112, 2255, 2080, 1795, 1977 2013; 2000; none; 460
13. Shoe lengths: $10\frac{3}{4}$ in., $9\frac{1}{2}$ in., $8\frac{7}{8}$ in., $10\frac{1}{2}$ in., $8\frac{3}{8}$ in., $10\frac{1}{2}$ in. $9\frac{3}{4}$ in.; 10 in.; $10\frac{1}{2}$ in.; $2\frac{3}{8}$ in.
14. **Baseball** The attendance for the 2001 World Series is shown in the table. Find the mean, median, and mode(s) of the data. Which average do you think best represents the attendance data? Explain. See margin.

Game	1	2	3	4	5	6	7
Attendance	49,646	49,646	55,820	55,863	56,018	49,707	49,589

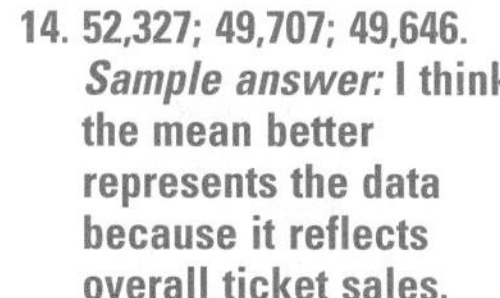

HELP with Homework

Example	Exercises
1	8-13, 14-16
2	8-13, 14, 16
3	14, 17

Online Resources CLASSZONE.COM

- More Examples
- eTutorial Plus

3 APPLY

ASSIGNMENT GUIDE

Basic Course

Day 1: pp. 259-261 Exs. 8-15, 17-19, 24-34

Average Course

Day 1: pp. 259-261 Exs. 10-22, 24-34

Advanced Course

Day 1: pp. 259-261 Exs. 10-25*, 28-34

Block

pp. 259-261 Exs. 10-22, 24-34

EXTRA PRACTICE

- Student Edition, p. 731
- Chapter 5 Resource Book, pp. 69-71
- Test and Practice Generator

TRANSPARENCY

Even-numbered answers are available on transparencies.

HOMEWORK CHECK

When you review students' homework for this lesson, go over the following exercises to check understanding of key concepts.
Basic: 8, 10, 12, 13, 14
Average: 10, 12, 14, 16, 17
Advanced: 10, 13, 14, 16, 17

TEACHING TIP

In Exercise 7, students can simplify the math by subtracting 20 minutes from every time, converting to seconds, finding the mean time, and adding 20 minutes to the result.

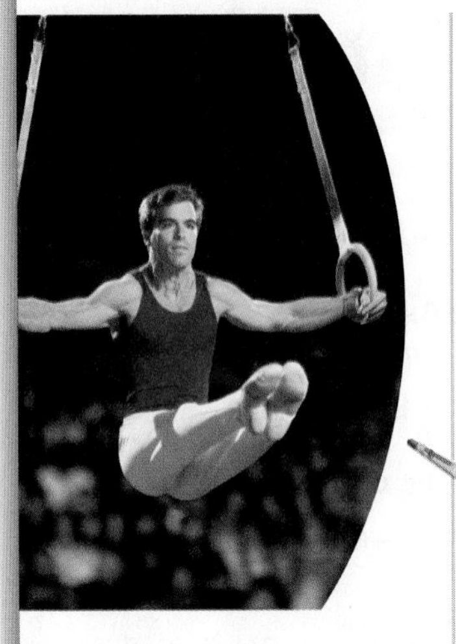

B **15. Gymnastics** A gymnast's performance is rated by six judges. The highest and lowest scores are dropped, and the mean of the remaining four scores is the final score awarded. Find the final score of each gymnast based on the judge's ratings given. Whose final score is the highest? **Isaac: 9.375, Carl: 9.6, Kurt: 9.425; Carl's**

	Judge 1	Judge 2	Judge 3	Judge 4	Judge 5	Judge 6
Isaac	9.5	9.1	9.3	9.3	9.6	9.4
Carl	9.8	9.7	9.3	9.7	9.6	9.4
Kurt	9.4	9.3	9.3	9.5	9.5	9.6

16. Writing Why does it make sense to find the median of a data set with an even number of values by finding the mean of the middle values? **See margin.**

17. Salary You are researching the average salaries for several different careers. Would you rather know the mean, median, or mode(s) of the salaries for each career? Explain your reasoning. **See margin.**

18. Lakes The average depth of a local lake is reported to be 2 feet. You want to know if you can wade across the lake. What information might be concealed when depth is reported as an average? **See margin.**

19. Algebra Find the mean of $3b$, $5b$, b, $6b$, $-6b$, and $-2b$. $\frac{7b}{6}$

20. Bowling You are bowling three games. In the first two games, you score 125 and 113 points. How many points do you need in the third game to have a mean score of 126 points? **140 points**

21. Compare and Contrast Jerry and Roberta find the mean of $-2a$, a, $3a$, $6a$, and $9a$ when $a = 2.5$, as shown below. Do both methods work? If so, which method do you prefer? Explain.

Jerry

$-2a = -5 \quad a = 2.5 \quad 3a = 7.5$

$6a = 15 \quad 9a = 22.5$

$$\frac{-5 + 2.5 + 7.5 + 15 + 22.5}{5} = \frac{42.5}{5}$$

$$= 8.5$$

Roberta

$$\frac{-2a + a + 3a + 6a + 9a}{5} = \frac{17a}{5}$$

$$= \frac{17 \cdot 2.5}{5}$$

$$= 8.5$$

C **22. Number Sense** Make two different lists of numbers that have a mean of 8 and a median and mode of 10. ***Sample answer:* first list: 4, 10, 10; second list: 1, 10, 10, 11**

23. Challenge The table shows the numbers of points you scored during your first 14 basketball games of the 15-game season. By halftime of your final game, you have scored 7 points. How many points do you need to score in the second half to have a mean of 10 points per game? **8 points**

Game	1	2	3	4	5	6	7	8	9	10	11	12	13	14
Points	15	8	7	10	12	4	20	13	7	7	5	3	10	14

16. *Sample answer:* If the number of data values is even, there is no single middle value, so the mean of the two middle values is used.

17. *Sample answer:* The median; there are equally many salaries above and below it, so it should reflect the most likely salary for me in each career.

18. *Sample answer:* Even if the lake is shallow overall, there could still be deep holes in it.

21. Yes. *Sample answer:* I prefer Roberta's method because it is shorter and can be used for any value of *a*.

Mixed Review

Find the quotient. *(Lesson 2.5)*

24. $\frac{-39}{13}$ −3 **25.** $\frac{200}{-40}$ −5 **26.** $\frac{-44}{-11}$ 4 **27.** $\frac{0}{-197}$ 0

Solve the equation. *(Lessons 3.1–3.3)*

28. $x - 15 = -10$ 5 **29.** $-8 + x = -24$ −16 **30.** $-7x = 84$ −12

31. $-\frac{1}{6}x = -11$ 66 **32.** $3x - 28 = -37$ −3 **33.** $-\frac{x}{4} + 12 = 16$ −16

Test-Taking Practice 

34. Extended Response The table shows attendance at school dances for a year.

Make a bar graph of the data. Find the mean and median attendance. The student council wants to find the total amount of money collected from students for admission to the dances. Would they find the bar graph, the mean, or the median most useful? Explain.

Dance	Number of Students
Fall	97
Winter Ball	88
Valentine's Day	133
Spring Fling	210
End of Year	198

What other information is also needed to find how much money was collected?

145.2; 133; *Sample answer:* The bar graph because it shows the total number of students at each dance; the other information needed is the cost of admission to each dance.

The Prize is Right!

You are a contestant on a television game show. To win a trip you must find the prices of the five items in a shopping cart.

The game show host gives you four hints about the prices.

- The mean of the prices is $1.68.
- The mode of the prices is $1.50.
- The median of the prices is $1.65.
- One item costs $.10 more than the median.

List the prices of the items in the cart in order from least to greatest. $1.50, $1.50, $1.65, $1.75, $2.00

4 ASSESS

Assessment Resources

For more assessment resources, see:
- Assessment Book
- Test and Practice Generator

Mini-Quiz

Find the mean, median, mode(s), and range of the data.

1. Weekly income from part-time job designing web pages: $120, $84, $95, $120, $75, $200, $130 **$117.71, $120, $120, $125**
2. Dogs boarded each week at Sunshine Kennels: 22, 28, 21, 21, 35, 32 **26.5, 25, 21, 14**

Reteaching/Remediation

- Study Guide in Chapter 5 Resource Book, pp. 72–73
- Tutor Place, Whole Numbers and Decimals Card 19
- eTutorial Plus Online
- Extra Practice, p. 731
- Lesson Practice in Chapter 5 Resource Book, pp. 69–71

Challenge/Enrichment

- Challenge Practice in Chapter 5 Resource Book, p. 74
- Teacher's Edition, p. 216F

English Learner Support

- Spanish Study Guide
- Multi-Language Glossary
- Chapter Audio Summaries CDs

34. See Additional Answers beginning on page AA1.

ADDITIONAL RESOURCES

The following resources are available to help review the materials in Lessons 5.5–5.8.

Chapter 5 Resource Book
- Lesson Practice
- Study Guide

Assessment Book
- Chapter 5 Quiz 2

Technology
- Test and Practice Generator
- eTutorial CD-ROM

Internet
- Classzone
- eWorkbook Plus Online
- eTutorial Plus Online

ENGLISH LEARNER SUPPORT

- Spanish Study Guide
- Multi-Language Glossary
- Chapter Audio Summaries CDs

Notebook Review

Review the vocabulary definitions in your notebook.

Copy the review examples in your notebook. Then complete the exercises.

Check Your Definitions

rational number, p. 242
terminating decimal, p. 242
repeating decimal, p. 242
front-end estimation, p. 248
leading digit, p. 251
mean, p. 257
median, p. 257
mode, p. 257
range, p. 258

Use Your Vocabulary

1. Name three averages you can use to represent a data set.
mean, median, mode

5.5 Can you order rational numbers?

EXAMPLE Order the numbers 3.7, $3\frac{5}{8}$, 3.6, and $3\frac{2}{3}$ from least to greatest.

$3\frac{5}{8} = 3.625$ $\quad$ $3\frac{2}{3} = 3.\overline{6}$ $\quad$ So, the order is 3.6, $3\frac{5}{8}$, $3\frac{2}{3}$, 3.7.

☑ **2.** Order the numbers 6.4, $6\frac{4}{9}$, $6\frac{3}{8}$, and $6\frac{5}{12}$ from least to greatest.
$6\frac{3}{8}$, 6.4, $6\frac{5}{12}$, $6\frac{4}{9}$

5.6–5.7 Can you perform operations with decimals?

a. $\begin{array}{r} 14.02 \\ +\ 9.80 \\ \hline 23.82 \end{array}$

b. $\begin{array}{r} 20.500 \\ -\ 3.764 \\ \hline 16.736 \end{array}$

c. $\begin{array}{r} 14.75 \\ \times\ 1.3 \\ \hline 4425 \\ 1475 \\ \hline 19.175 \end{array}$ $\quad$ **2 decimal places** / **+1 decimal place** / **3 decimal places**

d. $4.26\overline{)21.726} \rightarrow 426\overline{)2172.6}$, quotient 5.1

☑ **Find the sum, difference, product, or quotient.**

3. 1.2 + 0.67 **1.87**
4. 33.2 + 9.398 **42.598**
5. 3.16 − 1.845 **1.315**
6. 90.3 − (−7.81) **98.11**
7. 6.24 • 0.375 **2.34**
8. 3.348 • 0.9 **3.0132**
9. 66.96 ÷ (−2.7) **−24.8**
10. 18.91 ÷ 9.455 **2**

5.8 Can you find mean, median, mode, and range?

EXAMPLE Find the mean, median, mode(s), and range of the data set: 4, 5, 6, 6, 7, 9, 11, and 12.

$$\text{Mean} = \frac{4 + 5 + 6 + 6 + 7 + 9 + 11 + 12}{8} = \frac{60}{8} = 7.5$$

$$\text{Median} = \frac{6 + 7}{2} = \frac{13}{2} = 6.5$$

Mode = 6   Range = 12 − 4 = 8

Find the mean, median, mode(s), and range of the data set.

11. 25, 20, 30, 22, 24, 23, 24 **24; 24; 24; 10**

12. 7.2, 7.3, 7.5, 7.7, 7.9, 7.2, 7.7, 7.1 **7.45; 7.4; 7.2 and 7.7; 0.8**

Stop *and* Think about Lessons 5.5–5.8

13. Critical Thinking Write an example of a data set whose mode is greater than its mean. ***Sample answer:*** **3, 4, 12, 12**

14. Writing Explain why terminating decimals and repeating decimals are rational numbers. Use examples. **See margin.**

Notebook Review

14. They both can be written as ratios. *Sample answer:* $0.2 = \frac{1}{5}$ **and** $0.\overline{2} = \frac{2}{9}$.

Review Quiz 2

Write the fraction as a decimal or the decimal as a fraction.

1. $\frac{1}{25}$ **0.04**   **2.** $\frac{4}{9}$ $0.\overline{4}$ **3.** 0.58 $\frac{29}{50}$ **4.** $0.\overline{2}$ $\frac{2}{9}$

Find the sum or difference.

5. −2.301 + 8.4 **6.099**   **6.** 15.25 + 9.636 **24.886**   **7.** 14.65 − 3.608 **11.042**   **8.** 3.2 − (−0.225) **3.425**

Find the product or quotient.

9. −15.3 • 0.48 **−7.344**   **10.** 3.88 • 0.9 **3.492**   **11.** 0.162 ÷ 2.7 **0.06**   **12.** 2.07 ÷ 0.225 **9.2**

13. Racing Camel A racing camel can travel at a speed of 11.75 miles per hour. How far does it travel in 0.02 hour at this speed? **0.235 mi**

14. Tornadoes The table shows the numbers of tornadoes in the United States from 1995–2001. Find the mean, median, mode(s), and range. **1171; 1173; no mode; 619**

Year	1995	1996	1997	1998	1999	2000	2001
Tornadoes	1234	1173	1148	1424	1342	1071	805

Additional Resources

The following resources are available to help review the materials in this chapter.

Chapter 5 Resource Book

- Chapter Review Games and Activities, p. 75
- Cumulative Practice, Chs. 82–83

English/Spanish Chapter Reviews and Tests

Chapter Audio Summaries CDs

eTutorial CD-ROM

eWorkbook Plus Online

eTutorial Plus Online

Chapter Review

Vocabulary

reciprocal, p. 234
multiplicative inverse, p. 234
rational number, p. 242
terminating decimal, p. 242
repeating decimal, p. 242
front-end estimation, p. 248
leading digit, p. 251
mean, p. 257
median, p. 257
mode, p. 257
range, p. 258

Vocabulary Review

Copy and complete the statement.

1. The fractions $\frac{3}{5}$ and $\frac{5}{3}$ are _?_ because their product is 1. **reciprocals**
2. If the remainder of the quotient $\frac{a}{b}$ is 0, then the decimal form of $\frac{a}{b}$ is a _?_ decimal. **terminating**
3. You can use _?_ when you do not need to find an exact sum of a set of numbers. **front-end estimation**
4. A value that occurs most often in a data set is a _?_. **mode**
5. For a data set, the sum of the values divided by the number of values is the _?_. **mean**
6. The difference of the greatest value and the least value of a data set is the _?_. **range**

Review Questions

Find the sum or difference. *(Lessons 5.1, 5.2)*

7. $\frac{8}{9}+\frac{4}{9}$ $1\frac{1}{3}$
8. $-3\frac{5}{8}+\frac{7}{8}$ $-2\frac{3}{4}$
9. $-\frac{19}{25}-\frac{11}{25}$ $-1\frac{1}{5}$
10. $\frac{3}{10}-\frac{7}{10}-\frac{9}{10}$ $-1\frac{3}{10}$
11. $\frac{3}{5}+\frac{1}{4}$ $\frac{17}{20}$
12. $\frac{3}{5}-\frac{2}{3}$ $-\frac{1}{15}$
13. $6\frac{2}{7}+\left(-7\frac{1}{8}\right)$ $-\frac{47}{56}$
14. $-9\frac{3}{4}-4\frac{2}{3}$ $-14\frac{5}{12}$
15. $-\frac{7n}{9}-\frac{5n}{9}$ $-\frac{4n}{3}$
16. $-\frac{m}{4}+\left(-\frac{m}{4}\right)$ $-\frac{m}{2}$
17. $\frac{3}{c}-\frac{7}{2c}$ $-\frac{1}{2c}$
18. $\frac{5v}{3}+\frac{4v}{5}$ $\frac{37v}{15}$
19. **Coins** A quarter's width is about $\frac{15}{16}$ inch. A dime's width is about $\frac{11}{16}$ inch. How much wider is a quarter? *(Lesson 5.1)* $\frac{1}{4}$ **in.**
20. **Robots** It took Central High's robot team $107\frac{1}{3}$ hours of labor to build their robot. East High built their robot in $111\frac{5}{6}$ hours. How much longer did East High School take to build their robot? *(Lesson 5.2)* $4\frac{1}{2}$ **h**

49. $3\frac{1}{10}$ in.; $3\frac{1}{8}$ in.; no mode; $\frac{3}{4}$ in.

Review Questions

Find the product or quotient. *(Lessons 5.3, 5.4)*

21. $-\frac{5}{8} \cdot \frac{2}{5}$ $-\frac{1}{4}$

22. $-\frac{9}{5} \cdot \left(-\frac{11}{15}\right)$ $1\frac{8}{25}$

23. $-6\frac{3}{7} \cdot 2\frac{1}{2}$ $-16\frac{1}{14}$

24. $4 \cdot \left(-3\frac{5}{12}\right)$ $-13\frac{2}{3}$

25. $\frac{9}{21} \div 5$ $\frac{3}{35}$

26. $\frac{13}{18} \div \frac{5}{6}$ $\frac{13}{15}$

27. $5\frac{8}{11} \div \left(-\frac{3}{4}\right)$ $-7\frac{7}{11}$

28. $12\frac{1}{2} \div 4\frac{1}{6}$ 3

Solve the equation. *(Lesson 5.4)*

29. $\frac{5}{6}x = 25$ 30

30. $\frac{2}{3}b = \frac{8}{9}$ $1\frac{1}{3}$

31. $-\frac{9}{10}y = 6\frac{3}{7}$ $-7\frac{1}{7}$

32. $\frac{4}{9}a + 4\frac{1}{3} = 5\frac{2}{3}$ 3

Order the numbers from least to greatest. *(Lesson 5.5)*

33. $2\frac{3}{10}, \frac{11}{5}, 2.32, \frac{5}{2}, 2.25, 2$
$2, \frac{11}{5}, 2.25, 2\frac{3}{10}, 2.32, \frac{5}{2}$

34. $-0.45, -\frac{3}{8}, -\frac{5}{12}, -0.4, -0.46$
$-0.46, -0.45, -\frac{5}{12}, -0.4, -\frac{3}{8}$

Find the sum, difference, product, or quotient. *(Lessons 5.6, 5.7)*

35. $5.2 + 20.68$ 25.88

36. $0.103 + 0.7$ 0.803

37. $9.6 - 3.555$ 6.045

38. $-4.23 - 8.093$ -12.323

39. $16.7 \cdot (-3.2)$ -53.44

40. $43.4 \cdot 0.13$ 5.642

41. $3.434 \div 8.08$ 0.425

42. $-13 \div (-0.52)$ 25

Newborn Animals In Exercises 43 and 44, use the table. It shows approximate weights, in pounds, of several newborn animals. *(Lesson 5.6)*

Newborn Animal	Birth Weight (lb)
Hippopotamus	93
Grizzly bear	1
Giant panda	0.29
Giraffe	150
Polar bear	2.09
Gentoo penguin	0.21

43. How much more does the hippopotamus weigh than the gentoo penguin? 92.79 lb

44. How much more does the polar bear weigh than the giant panda? 1.8 lb

45. **Icebergs** When an iceberg broke free from Antarctica in May of 2002, it was about 34.5 miles long and 6.9 miles wide. About how much area did the iceberg cover? *(Lesson 5.7)* 238.05 mi^2

46. **Cats** A tiger at a zoo has a mass of 144.9 kilograms. This is 40.25 times the mass of a house cat. What is the mass of the house cat? *(Lesson 5.7)* 3.6 kg

Find the mean, median, mode(s), and range of the data set. *(Lesson 5.8)*

47. Temperatures (°C): $-7, -1, 0, 8, 4, 2, -7, 2$
0.125°C; 1°C; -7°C and 2°C; 15°C

48. Jumps (meters): 14.6, 19.2, 11, 16.5, 12, 11, 10.9
13.6 m; 12 m; 11 m; 8.3 m

49. Hand widths (in.): $3\frac{1}{2}, 2\frac{7}{8}, 3\frac{1}{8}, 3\frac{1}{4}, 2\frac{3}{4}$
See margin.

50. Bike trails (km): 7, 8.3, 17.1, 4.8, 3.9, 7, 4.8, 13.1
8.25 km; 7 km; 4.8 km and 7 km; 13.2 km

ADDITIONAL RESOURCES

Assessment Book

- Chapter Test (3 levels), pp. 59–61
- Standardized Chapter Test, p. 65
- Alternative Assessment, pp. 66–67

Test and Practice Generator

Chapter Test

Find the sum or difference.

1. $4\frac{5}{11} - 2\frac{6}{11}$ $1\frac{10}{11}$ **2.** $\frac{9}{16} - \left(-\frac{11}{16}\right)$ $1\frac{1}{4}$ **3.** $-\frac{5}{6} + \frac{1}{8}$ $-\frac{17}{24}$ **4.** $\frac{3}{7} + \left(-\frac{8}{21}\right) + \frac{2}{3}$ $\frac{5}{7}$

5. Roller Coaster Yesterday you had to wait in line for $1\frac{3}{4}$ hours to ride a roller coaster. Today you waited $1\frac{1}{4}$ hours. How much longer did you wait yesterday? $\frac{1}{2}$ h

Find the product or quotient.

6. $\frac{2}{9} \cdot (-4)$ $-\frac{8}{9}$ **7.** $\frac{5}{2} \cdot \frac{4}{15}$ $\frac{2}{3}$ **8.** $3\frac{1}{2} \div 2$ $1\frac{3}{4}$ **9.** $7\frac{3}{4} \div 2\frac{7}{12}$ 3

10. Balloons You are inflating balloons for a party. If you can inflate one balloon in $\frac{5}{6}$ minute, how many balloons can you inflate in $\frac{1}{2}$ hour? 36 balloons

Write the fraction as a decimal or the decimal as a fraction.

11. $\frac{7}{20}$ 0.35 **12.** $\frac{3}{40}$ 0.075 **13.** 0.0082 $\frac{41}{5000}$ **14.** $0.\overline{4}$ $\frac{4}{9}$

Find the sum, difference, product, or quotient.

15. 6.2 − 5.984 0.216 **16.** 2.608 + 12.93 15.538 **17.** 0.7992 ÷ 0.333 2.4 **18.** −34.69 • 12.7 −440.563

Bagels In Exercises 19 and 20, use the table. It shows the approximate supermarket sales of three types of bagels (in billions of dollars) in the year 2000 in the United States.

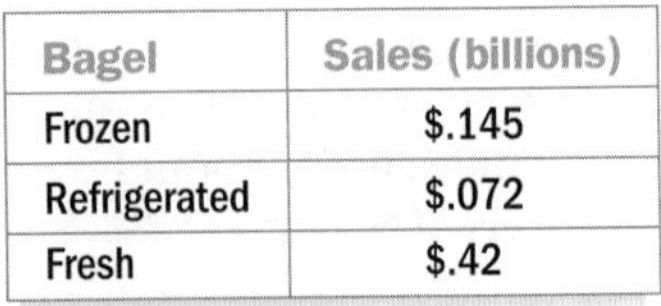

Bagel	Sales (billions)
Frozen	$.145
Refrigerated	$.072
Fresh	$.42

19. How much greater were the sales for frozen bagels than the sales for refrigerated bagels? $0.073 billion

20. What is the total amount of supermarket sales of all three types of bagels? $0.637 billion

21. Algebra Evaluate $0.2x$ and $\frac{x}{0.2}$ when $x = -4.1$, 0.06, and 1.8.
$0.2x$: −0.82, 0.012, 0.36; $\frac{x}{0.2}$: −20.5, 0.3, 9

22. Energy Bill A gas supplier charges 64.5 cents per therm of gas used. How much does it cost for 116 therms of gas? $74.82

23. Studying Twelve students spent 2, 5, 3, 7, 10, 9, 8, 7, 6, 7, 6, and 2 hours studying. Find the mean, median, mode(s), and range of the data. 6 h; 6.5 h; 7 h; 8 h

Additional Resources

Assessment Book

- Standardized Chapter Test, p. 65

Test and Practice Generator

Chapter Standardized Test

Test-Taking Strategy **Mark unanswered questions in your test booklet so you can find them quickly when you go back.**

Multiple Choice

1. What is the sum of $11\frac{5}{9}$ and $-14\frac{11}{12}$? A

A. $-3\frac{13}{36}$ **B.** $-3\frac{1}{3}$ **C.** $-2\frac{13}{36}$ **D.** $-2\frac{33}{108}$

2. You have hiked $2\frac{1}{10}$ miles of a 5 mile trail. How much farther must you hike? G

F. $1\frac{9}{20}$ miles **G.** $2\frac{9}{10}$ miles

H. $3\frac{1}{10}$ miles **I.** $7\frac{1}{10}$ miles

3. You need $4\frac{1}{3}$ yards of fabric to make a costume for your dance team. How much fabric do you need to make 7 costumes? D

A. $11\frac{1}{3}$ yards **B.** $18\frac{2}{3}$ yards

C. $28\frac{1}{3}$ yards **D.** $30\frac{1}{3}$ yards

4. What is the quotient of $-\frac{3}{4}$ and $\frac{5}{2}$? H

F. $-1\frac{3}{20}$ **G.** $-\frac{7}{20}$ **H.** $-\frac{3}{10}$ **I.** $-\frac{3}{20}$

5. You order pants for \$25.60, two shirts for \$15.99 each, and socks for \$6.35. Estimate your cost. D

A. about \$46 **B.** about \$48

C. about \$54 **D.** about \$64

6. By what number can you divide $\frac{5}{6}$ to get the quotient $\frac{5}{9}$? H

F. $\frac{1}{3}$ **G.** $\frac{2}{3}$ **H.** $\frac{3}{2}$ **I.** 2

7. What is the value of x when $\frac{3}{4}x = \frac{9}{16}$? B

A. $\frac{3}{16}$ **B.** $\frac{3}{4}$ **C.** 3 **D.** 4

8. Solve $1.312 + x = 15.6$. H

F. 2.48 **G.** 11.56

H. 14.288 **I.** 15.4688

9. You use 0.75 meter of wire to hold together bunches of flowers. How many bunches can you make with 15 meters of wire? B

A. 2 **B.** 20 **C.** 200 **D.** 2000

10. Which fraction is greater than 0.34? I

F. $\frac{5}{16}$ **G.** $\frac{1}{3}$ **H.** $\frac{55}{162}$ **I.** $\frac{8}{23}$

11. What is the median of the data set −2, 0.4, 1, −2.6, 4.5, −3.7, 1, 3? B

A. 0.2 **B.** 0.7 **C.** 1 **D.** 2.275

Short Response

12. Your rectangular garden is 3.4 meters by 2.6 meters. Your friend's square garden has sides of 2.9 meters. Whose garden has a greater area? your garden

Extended Response

13. Your most recent phone calls lasted 1, 2, 5, 46, 2, 8, 5, 3, 7, and 2 minutes. Find the mean, median, and mode(s) of the phone call lengths. Use your understanding of mean, median, and mode to explain which of these averages is most representative of the phone calls. See margin.

13. 8.1 min; 4 min; 2 min. *Sample answer:* The median is most representative because the mean is higher than all but one call length and there is only one time lower than the mode.

Pacing and Assignment Guide

REGULAR SCHEDULE

Lesson	Les. Day	BASIC	AVERAGE	ADVANCED
6.1	Day 1	EP p. 728 Exs. 41-43; pp. 274-275 Exs. 11, 14-17, 24-28, 39, 41-44	pp. 274-275 Exs. 11, 15-17, 25-32, 41-45	pp. 274-275 Exs. 11, 15-17, 24-30, 41-43
	Day 2	EP p. 729 Exs. 9-12; pp. 274-275 Exs. 12, 13, 18-23, 33-36, 45-47	pp. 274-275 Exs. 13, 18-23, 33-39, 46-48	pp. 274-275 Exs. 13, 21-23, 34-40*, 46-48
6.2	Day 1	EP p. 729 Exs. 13-16; pp. 280-281 Exs. 7-12, 16-22, 26-28, 36-49	pp. 280-281 Exs. 10-19, 23-27, 30-34, 38-49	pp. 280-281 Exs. 10-19, 23-39*, 45-49
6.3	Day 1	pp. 284-285 Exs. 9-12, 17, 24, 27-34	pp. 284-285 Exs. 10-12, 17, 25, 27-34	pp. 284-285 Exs. 10-12, 17, 25-30*, 36-38
	Day 2	pp. 284-285 Exs. 13-16, 18-23, 35-38	pp. 284-285 Exs. 14-16, 18-24, 35-38	pp. 284-285 Exs. 14-16, 18-24, 31-33
6.4	Day 1	SRH p. 705 Exs. 1-5; pp. 293-294 Exs. 9-20, 23-25, 28, 33-44	pp. 293-294 Exs. 11-17, 21-29, 33-44	pp. 293-294 Exs. 11-17, 23-37*, 41-44
6.5	Day 1	EP p. 729 Exs. 25-28; pp. 297-299 Exs. 9-18, 21-23, 25-29, 41-48	pp. 297-299 Exs. 15-24, 27-33, 38-48	pp. 297-299 Exs. 15-24, 29-42*, 46-48
6.6	Day 1	EP p. 729 Exs. 29-32; pp. 304-305 Exs. 6-13, 16-19, 24-30	pp. 304-305 Exs. 8-11, 14-21, 24-31	pp. 304-305 Exs. 8-11, 14-26, 29-31, EC: TE p. 268D*
Review	Day 1	pp. 308-309 Exs. 1-34	pp. 308-309 Exs. 1-34	pp. 308-309 Exs. 1-34
Assess	Day 1	Chapter 6 Test	Chapter 6 Test	Chapter 6 Test

YEARLY PACING Chapter 6 Total – **10 days** Chapters 1-6 Total – **70 days** Remaining – **90 days**

*Challenge Exercises EP = Extra Practice SRH = Skills Review Handbook EC = Extra Challenge

BLOCK SCHEDULE

DAY 1	DAY 2	DAY 3	DAY 4	DAY 5
6.1 pp. 274-275 Exs. 11, 13, 15-23, 25-39, 41-48	**6.2** pp. 280-281 Exs. 10-19, 23-27, 30-34, 38-49 **6.3** pp. 284-285 Exs. 10-12, 17, 25, 27-34	**6.3 (cont.)** pp. 284-285 Exs. 14-16, 18-24, 35-38 **6.4** pp. 293-294 Exs. 11-17, 21-29, 33-44	**6.5** pp. 297-299 Exs. 15-24, 27-33, 38-48 **6.6** pp. 304-305 Exs. 8-11, 14-21, 24-31	**Review** pp. 308-309 Exs. 1-34 **Assess** Chapter 6 Test

YEARLY PACING Chapter 6 Total – **5 days** Chapters 1-6 Total – **35 days** Remaining – **45 days**

Support Materials

CHAPTER RESOURCE BOOK

CHAPTER SUPPORT						
Tips for New Teachers	p. 1		Parents as Partners			p. 3

LESSON SUPPORT	6.1	6.2	6.3	6.4	6.5	6.6
Lesson Plans (regular and block)	p. 7	p. 16	p. 26	p. 35	p. 43	p. 52
Technology Activities & Keystrokes		p. 18			p. 45	
Activity Support Masters						
Activity Masters			p. 28			
Practice (3 levels)	p. 9	p. 20	p. 29	p. 37	p. 46	p. 54
Study Guide	p. 12	p. 23	p. 32	p. 40	p. 49	p. 57
Real-World Problem Solving	p. 14					p. 59
Challenge Practice	p. 15	p. 25	p. 34	p. 42	p. 51	p. 60

REVIEW			
Games Support Masters	p. 5	Cooperative Project with Rubric	p. 64
Chapter Review Games and Activities	p. 61	Extra Credit Project with Rubric	p. 66
Real-Life Project with Rubric	p. 62	Cumulative Practice	p. 68
		Resource Book Answers	A1

ASSESSMENT

Quizzes	p. 68	Alternative Assessments with Rubrics	p. 77
Chapter Tests (3 levels)	p. 70	Unit Test	p. 90
Standardized Test	p. 76	Cumulative Test	p. 92

TRANSPARENCIES

	6.1	6.2	6.3	6.4	6.5	6.6
Warm-Up / Daily Homework Quiz	✔	✔	✔	✔	✔	✔
Notetaking Guide	✔	✔	✔	✔	✔	✔
Teacher Support		✔			✔	
English/Spanish Problem Solving	✔	✔				
Answer Transparencies	✔	✔	✔	✔	✔	✔

TECHNOLOGY

- EasyPlanner CD-ROM
- Test and Practice Generator
- Electronic Lesson Presentations
- eTutorial CD-ROM
- Chapter Audio Summaries CDs
- Classzone.com
- eEdition Plus Online
- eWorkbook Plus Online
- eTutorial Plus Online
- EasyPlanner Plus Online

ADDITIONAL RESOURCES

- Worked-Out Solution Key
- Notetaking Guide
- Practice Workbook
- Tutor Place
- Professional Development Book
- Special Activities Book
- Posters
- Spanish Study Guide
- Exercises in Spanish
- English/Spanish Ch. Reviews/Tests
- Multi-Language Visual Glossary

Math Background and Teaching Strategies

Lesson 6.1

MATH BACKGROUND

MULTI-STEP EQUATIONS After solving linear two-step equations that involve an addition or subtraction operation and a multiplication or division operation, the next step in increasing complexity is a linear equation that needs simplification on one side to become a two-step equation. This often involves combining like terms, using the distributive property first when necessary, and following the order of operations. If the variable expression is in the form of a fraction, you can multiply each side of the equation by the denominator of the fraction to create an equivalent equation without fractions.

TEACHING STRATEGIES

Emphasize to students that this lesson does not require new skills, just combining previously-learned skills. Students can view the process of solving the multi-step equations in this lesson just as two basic steps. First, simplify the side of the equation involving the variable just as you would simplify any expression by applying the distributive property if necessary and combining like terms. Second, solve the two-step equation that results using the same methods as before. If the variable expression is the numerator of a fraction, first remove the fraction by using the multiplication property of equality to multiply each side of the equation by the denominator of the fraction.

Lesson 6.2

MATH BACKGROUND

EQUATIONS WITH VARIABLES ON BOTH SIDES Because the addition property of equality applies both to numerical and variable expressions, you can simplify an equation that has variable terms on both sides by adding the additive inverse of one of the variable terms to each side of the equation. The resulting equation can then be solved as before.

TEACHING STRATEGIES

Point out to students that, again, they need no new skills to solve equations with a variable on each side, they just need to apply one more previously-learned skill. Solving each new type of equation presented is just like taking a small step up the stairs. Remind students that the goal in solving an equation has been to get the variable by itself on one side of the equation. So, if there are variable expressions on both sides of the equation, one of them needs to be removed. Just as they did to remove a constant term from one side of an equation, they can use the addition property of equality to remove a variable term. For students who are in the practice of always keeping the variable term on the left side of the equation, you may want to point out that if they are flexible about which side of the equation a variable is on, they can often avoid having to multiply or divide by a negative number. For example, $4x + 19 = 7x - 2$ can be simplified either to $-3x = -21$ or $21 = 3x$.

Lesson 6.3

MATH BACKGROUND

EQUATIONS WITH FRACTIONS AND DECIMALS To avoid the complications involved when an equation involves fractions or decimals, you can multiply each side of the equation by the LCD of all the fractions or decimals in the equation, making sure to multiply each term of each side by this number. For an equation involving decimals, the LCD is just the denominator of the fractional form of the decimal in the equation that contains the most decimal places.

TEACHING STRATEGIES

Because the only new step in the equations of this lesson is clearing decimals or fractions, you may want to create or have students create extra problems for which the only step they are to carry out is to use the multiplication property of equality to write an equivalent equation that has no decimals or fractions. Remind students that the LCD used in clearing fractions is the LCD of *all* denominators in the equation, not just of the denominators on one side or the other of the equation. Also, make sure they understand that to clear decimals, they should multiply each side of the equation by the power of 10 that has the same number of zeros as the greatest number of decimal places in any of the terms.

Lesson 6.4

MATH BACKGROUND

EQUATIONS AND CIRCLES The ratio of the **circumference**, or distance around, any circle to the circle's **diameter**, or width across the circle through its center, is given by the *incommensurable* (impossible completely to measure) number π, which is about 3.1415926536…, and is often estimated as 3.14 or $\frac{22}{7}$ $\left(\text{as shown in antiquity, } \pi \text{ actually lies between } \frac{22}{7} \text{ and } \frac{223}{71}\right)$. So, the formula for the circumference, C, of a circle with diameter d is given by $C = \pi d$ or $C = 2\pi r$, where r is the **radius** of the circle, or the distance from the circle to its center. Whether the estimate 3.14 or $\frac{22}{7}$ is used usually depends on conveience, since 3.14 is about the same amount less than π as $\frac{22}{7}$ is greater than π. For example, it is convenient to estimate the circumference of a circle with radius 56 using $\pi \approx \frac{22}{7}$, since 56 is a multiple of 7.

TEACHING STRATEGIES

Finding the circumference of a circle from its radius or diameter is a simple act of substitution, and solving for the circumference of a circle given its radius or diameter results in a simple multiplication equation, but using the estimates 3.14 or $\frac{22}{7}$ for π means that the equation will involve decimals or fractions. You may want to have students develop explicit rules for when to use the estimate $\frac{22}{7}$. When finding circumference, this will usually be when the radius or denominator is divisible by 7, and when finding radius or diameter, this will usually be when the circumference is divisible by 22.

Lesson 6.5

MATH BACKGROUND

MULTI-STEP INEQUALITIES Solving a multi-step linear inequality is similar to solving a multi-step linear equation, except that the addition and multiplication properties of *inequality* apply instead of the corresponding properties of equality. As with the addition property of equality and equations, the addition property of inequalities can be used to remove a variable term from one side of an inequality when there are variable terms on both sides of the inequality.

TEACHING STRATEGIES

Students may feel that solving inequalities is more difficult than solving equations because of the complication when multiplying and dividing by a negative number. Emphasize that this (and the nature of the solution set) is the only real difference, and that everything else remains the same. Multiplying to clear fractions or decimals is the same because it is always by a positive number, simplifying by combining like terms and using the distributive property is the same, and the use of adding or subtracting the same quantity from each side is the same. Students do not have to worry about the inequality sign until the last step. And, for an inequality with a variable term on both sides, using the strategy mentioned in the Teaching Strategies for Lesson 6.2 can avoid division by a negative number.

Lesson 6.6

MATH BACKGROUND

APPLICATIONS OF INEQUALITIES The process of writing and solving inequalities to solve real-world problems is just the same as that for equations, but is predicated upon being able to recognize language that indicates that an inequality model should be used, such as *at least* for $\geq$, *no more than* for $\leq$, *exceeds* for $>$, and *is fewer than* for $<$.

TEACHING STRATEGIES

Writing inequalities to describe problem situations requires much practice. Here is an additional example that you can work with students:

Kalima gets two job offers. Sound Studio offers her \$400 per week plus \$.05 on each dollar of merchandise she sells. Maximum Music offers her \$300 per week plus \$.07 on each dollar of merchandise she sells. Write and solve an inequality that describes the value of weekly sales for which Kalima will earn more at Maximum Music than at Sound Studio.
$300 + 0.07s > 400 + 0.05s$; $s > \$5{,}000$

Differentiating Instruction

Strategies for Underachievers

FOCUS ON VOCABULARY

As students work through this chapter, they will continually be exposed to words and expressions related to solving equations in the directions for problems and explanations of examples. Some students may need to review the meanings of these words and expressions to avoid confusion. These include *expression, equation, simplify, solve, evaluate, verbal model, verbal sentence, algebraic model, distribute, terms, coefficient, constant terms, like terms, combine like terms*, and *represent*.

DEVELOP PROBLEM SOLVING MODELS

BUILDING ON A FOUNDATION Learning to solve linear equations and inequalitiesproceeds in discrete steps, from one-step equations to two-step equations to multi-step equations to solving equations with variables on both sides, and so on. Encourage students to create posters or notebook entries that detail each step in increasing complexity, beginning with solving one-step equations from Chapter 5. For each step, students should give examples and give the order of the steps that they need to carry out. Doing so should help students see how the same basic strategy applies at each level even though steps are added.

USE MANIPULATIVES

For Lessons 6.1 and 6.2, you may wish to provide algebra tiles to students so they can physically practice the steps in solving equations. You may need to guide students' work with the tiles so that the equations that they attempt to solve with the tiles are equations that can be easily modeled using algebra tiles.

In Hands-on Activity 6.4, you may wish to provide students with easily-measured circular objects that have labeled centers. Students would also benefit from a cloth or plastic tape measure.

USE SCAFFOLDING

In Lessons 6.1 and 6.3, it may help some students first to underline the variable terms and circle the constant terms before combining like terms. Remind students also to underline or circle the sign preceding each term so that they correctly identify each term's coefficient as positive or negative.

Lessons 6.1–6.3 and 6.5 present problems with many steps, which are often intimidating for students. You may wish to help students use scaffolding to break down problems such as these into manageable steps. One way to do this is to provide students with templates for problems for which they can fill in the blanks as they work through the steps. Another way is to provide students with several model problems for which you have shown all the necessary steps. Students can then use these models to guide them when working problems on their own.

USE A CO-TEACHING MODEL

WORKING BACKWARD In Problem Solving Strategies 6.2, you may wish to enlist the help of a Reading Specialist to assist students with potential reading difficulties associated with these problems. Because the strategy involved is working backward, these problem situations can be es pecially difficult for some students to comprehend. Many underachieving students need the encouragement to realize that they possess the ability to think through and solve mathematical problems. Addressing their language disabilities or deficits in an understanding way with a co-worker with specialized skills can provide a great benefit to students in approaching problems and in building their mathematical confidence.

REDUCE COMPLEXITY

In Lessons 6.5 and 6.6, you may wish to have underachievers work extra examples with inequalities that do not require multiplication or division by a negative number before they attempt problems for which this is needed.

Strategies for English Learners

ELIMINATE UNNECESSARY INFORMATION

This chapter has more word problems and fewer strictly numerical problems than other chapters, so it may be more difficult for English learners to read. You can minimize the amount of reading required and focus on the mathematics by making sure that students know key phrases and by presenting problems in a predictable format. For example, the following phrase occurs in many of the problems in Lessons 5 and 6 in this chapter:

Write and solve an inequality . . .

In several places in this chapter, the questions are organized so that the basic sentence structure remains consistent, and the student must come up with the same type of answer each time even though the particular facts of the problem change.

For example, on page 298, Exercises 23 and 33 use the same format: "Use the verbal model to write and solve an inequality . . ." Presenting questions to students in this way helps them focus on the mathematics because the English only has to be understood once. You can use this technique of repetitive English with any type of mathematics problem.

Furthermore, it would be helpful for English learners to cross out all but the most essential words (think telegram), as a way of demonstrating that it's not always necessary to know every word. For example, English learners don't need to spend a lot of time decoding a proper noun that appears to be someone's name, but instead can substitute a familiar name with the same result.

Also, make sure that English learners are attending to the beginning and end of sentences (not all languages use punctuation and capitals). This would be preliminary to identifying the predictable format of word problems. (How many sentences? Look at first sentence. Where is the question mark? and so on.)

Strategies for Advanced Learners

INCREASE DEPTH AND COMPLEXITY

The following may be a fun and challenging activity in conjunction with Lesson 6.5 for some advanced learners. Have these students create several of their own "Find the Error" problems like the one in Exercise 8 on page 297. These students can share their creations with each other to see if they can identify and correct each other's intentional errors. In both the incorrect examples and in the corrections, students should be required to show neat and complete work.

Also in Lesson 6.5, many students will enjoy challenging each other by creating difficult equations such as those in Exercises 34–37 on page 298. Point out that students must first solve their own equations, neatly showing their work and checking their solutions, before administering their equations to others. Students may also enjoy challenging you, the teacher. To ensure that students' created equations are not ridiculous, remind them that very large numbers do not really increase the complexity of an equation and are more annoying than challenging.

USE CROSS-CURRICULAR ACTIVITIES

PHYSICAL EDUCATION Lesson 6.4 can provide many opportunities for students to do mathematical work in conjunction with their physical education classes. For example, students can work with a physical education teacher to find the diameter and circumference of the basketballs and the hoop used by professional women's and men's basketball teams. Students can research why there is a difference in the size of the basketballs used by women's teams and men's teams. Students can also explore the differing sizes of baseballs and softballs, and offer conjectures about why a softball is larger than a baseball. Students can extend their research into the sizes and properties of balls in other sports and the requirements for the balls to be "official," including any differences that are allowed (for example, not all official golf balls are the same).

VALUE COMPARISON In conjunction with Lesson 6.6, if students have any classes that involve consumer education or technology, you can have them use the content and resources of these classes to investigate the best deals on services or products. For example, there are many cell phone plans available. Students can investigate the plans and their pros and cons. Students can use inequalities to compare the values of different plans under different types and times of use.

The following problem, which involves a compound inequality but can be solved by breaking into two separate problems, can be used with **Lesson 6.6**:

- **Challenge** The sum of Flavia's age and her son Gonzalvo's age is 43. If Gonzalvo is more than one third his mother's age but less than one half his mother's age, how old are they now? Gonzalvo can be anywhere from 11 to 14 years old, which means that his mother is from 32 to 29 years old.

Differentiating Instruction: Teaching Resources

Differentiating Enrichment and Activities

McDougal Littell *Middle School Mathematics* offers teachers enrichment for all levels of students. Pictured on these pages are facsimiles of the Real-World Problem Solving pages, Chapter Review Games, and Chapter Projects from the *Chapter 6 Resource Book* and a number of activities from the *Special Activities Book*. Also available is the *Poster Package* containing large, full-color posters, one for each unit.

RESOURCE BOOK

The *Chapter Resource Books* contain Real-World Problem Solving activities for various lessons in the textbook, Chapter Review Games for a motivating review of each chapter, and Chapter Projects with rubrics that apply the mathematics of the chapter.

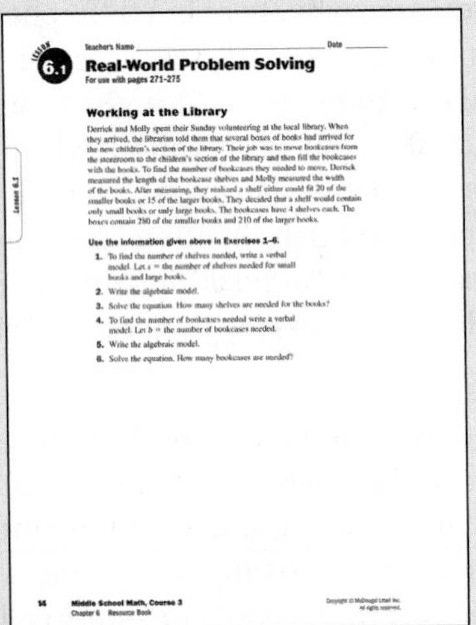

Lesson 6.1 — Teacher's Name ______ Date ______

Real-World Problem Solving

For use with pages 271–275

Working at the Library

Derrick and Molly spent their Sunday volunteering at the local library. When they arrived, the librarian told them that several boxes of books had arrived for the new children's section of the library. Their job was to move bookcases from the storeroom to the children's section of the library and then fill the bookcases with the books. To find the number of bookcases they needed to move, Derrick measured the length of the bookcase shelves and Molly measured the width of the books. After measuring, they realized a shelf either could fit 20 of the smaller books or 15 of the larger books. They decided that a shelf would contain only small books or only large books. The bookcases have 4 shelves each. The boxes contain 280 of the smaller books and 210 of the larger books.

Use the information given above in Exercises 1–6.

1. To find the number of shelves needed, write a verbal model. Let s = the number of shelves needed for small books and large books.
2. Write the algebraic model.
3. Solve the equation. How many shelves are needed for the books?
4. To find the number of bookcases needed write a verbal model. Let b = the number of bookcases needed.
5. Write the algebraic model.
6. Solve the equation. How many bookcases are needed?

14 Middle School Math, Course 3 Chapter 6 Resource Book — Copyright © McDougal Littell Inc. All rights reserved.

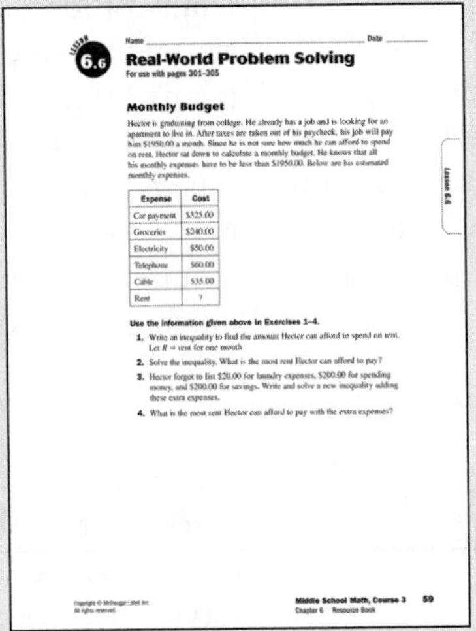

Lesson 6.6 — Name ______ Date ______

Real-World Problem Solving

For use with pages 301–305

Monthly Budget

Hector is graduating from college. He already has a job and is looking for an apartment to live in. After taxes are taken out of his paycheck, his job will pay him \$1950.00 a month. Since he is not sure how much he can afford to spend on rent, Hector sat down to calculate a monthly budget. He knows that all his monthly expenses have to be less than \$1950.00. Below are his estimated monthly expenses.

Expense	Cost
Car payment	\$325.00
Groceries	\$240.00
Electricity	\$50.00
Telephone	\$60.00
Cable	\$35.00
Rent	?

Use the information given above in Exercises 1–4.

1. Write an inequality to find the amount Hector can afford to spend on rent. Let R = rent for one month.
2. Solve the inequality. What is the most rent Hector can afford to pay?
3. Hector forgot to list \$20.00 for laundry expenses, \$200.00 for spending money, and \$200.00 for savings. Write and solve a new inequality adding these extra expenses.
4. What is the most rent Hector can afford to pay with the extra expenses?

Copyright © McDougal Littell Inc. All rights reserved. — Middle School Math, Course 3 Chapter 6 Resource Book 59

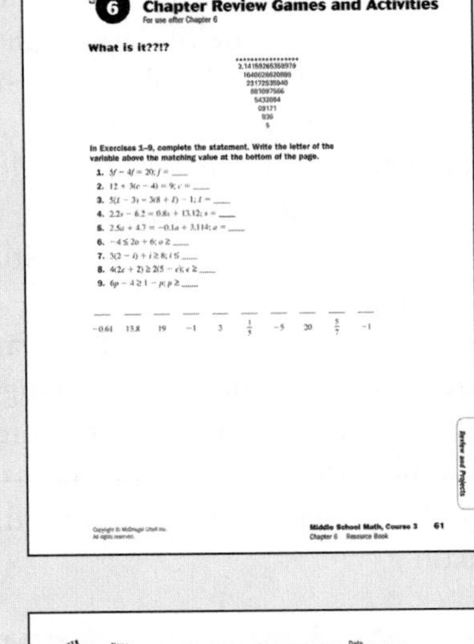

Chapter 6 — Name ______ Date ______

Chapter Review Games and Activities

For use after Chapter 6

What is it??!?

In Exercises 1–9, complete the statement. Write the letter of the variable above the matching value at the bottom of the page.

1. $5f - 4f = 20; f =$ ___
2. $12 + 3(c - 4) = 9; c =$ ___
3. $5(t - 3) = 3(8 + t) - 1; t =$ ___
4. $2.2s - 6.2 = 0.8s + 13.12; s =$ ___
5. $2.5a + 4.7 = -0.1a + 3.114; a =$ ___
6. $-4 \le 2o + 6; o \ge$ ___
7. $3(2 - i) + i \ge 8; i \le$ ___
8. $4(2e + 2) \ge 2(5 - e); e \ge$ ___
9. $6p - 4 \ge 1 - p; p \ge$ ___

−0.61 13.8 19 −1 3 $\frac{1}{5}$ −5 20 $\frac{5}{7}$ −1

Copyright © McDougal Littell Inc. All rights reserved. — Middle School Math, Course 3 Chapter 6 Resource Book 61

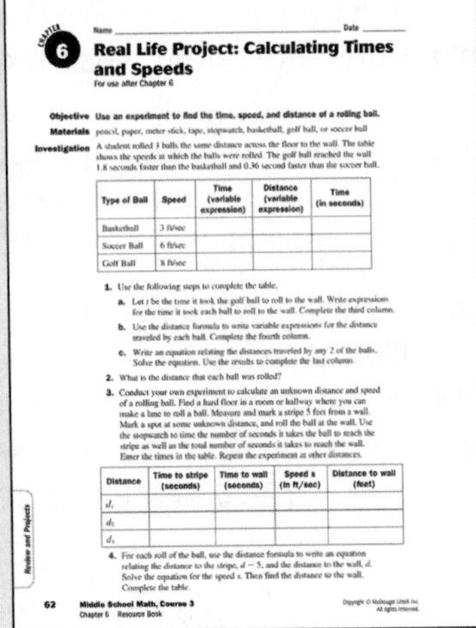

Chapter 6 — Name ______ Date ______

Real Life Project: Calculating Times and Speeds

For use after Chapter 6

Objective Use an experiment to find the time, speed, and distance of a rolling ball.

Materials pencil, paper, meter stick, tape, stopwatch, basketball, golf ball, or soccer ball

Investigation A student rolled 3 balls the same distance across the floor to the wall. The table shows the speeds at which the balls were rolled. The golf ball reached the wall 1.8 seconds faster than the basketball and 0.36 second faster than the soccer ball.

Type of Ball	Speed	Time (variable expression)	Distance (variable expression)	Time (in seconds)
Basketball	3 ft/sec			
Soccer Ball	6 ft/sec			
Golf Ball	8 ft/sec			

1. Use the following steps to complete the table.
   a. Let t be the time it took the golf ball to roll to the wall. Write expressions for the time it took each ball to roll to the wall. Complete the third column.
   b. Use the distance formula to write variable expressions for the distance traveled by each ball. Complete the fourth column.
   c. Write an equation relating the distances traveled by any 2 of the balls. Solve the equation. Use the results to complete the last column.
2. What is the distance that each ball was rolled?
3. Conduct your own experiment to calculate an unknown distance and speed of a rolling ball. Find a hard floor in a room or hallway where you can make a lane to roll a ball. Measure and mark a stripe 5 feet from a wall. Mark a spot at some unknown distance, and roll the ball at the wall. Use the stopwatch to time the number of seconds it takes the ball to reach the stripe as well as the total number of seconds it takes to reach the wall. Enter the times in the table. Repeat the experiment at other distances.

Distance	Time to stripe (seconds)	Time to wall (seconds)	Speed s (in ft/sec)	Distance to wall (feet)
d_1				
d_2				
d_3				

4. For each roll of the ball, use the distance formula to write an equation relating the distance to the stripe, $d - 5$, and the distance to the wall, d. Solve the equation for the speed s. Then find the distance to the wall. Complete the table.

62 Middle School Math, Course 3 Chapter 6 Resource Book — Copyright © McDougal Littell Inc. All rights reserved.

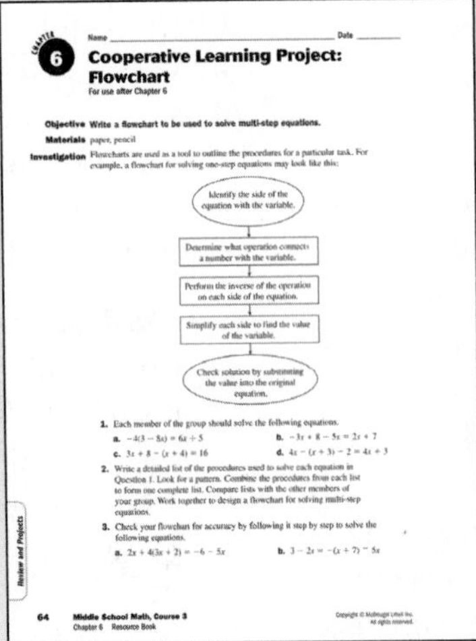

Chapter 6 — Name ______ Date ______

Cooperative Learning Project: Flowchart

For use after Chapter 6

Objective Write a flowchart to be used to solve multi-step equations.

Materials paper, pencil

Investigation Flowcharts are used as a tool to outline the procedures for a particular task. For example, a flowchart for solving one-step equations may look like this:

1. Each member of the group should solve the following equations.
   a. $-4(3 - 8x) = 6x + 5$ b. $-3x + 8 - 5x = 2x + 7$
   c. $3x + 8 - (x + 4) = 16$ d. $4x - (x + 3) - 2 = 4x + 3$
2. Write a detailed list of the procedures used to solve each equation in Question 1. Look for a pattern. Combine the procedures from each list to form one complete list. Compare lists with the other members of your group. Work together to design a flowchart for solving multi-step equations.
3. Check your flowchart for accuracy by following it step by step to solve the following equations.
   a. $2x + 4(3x + 2) = -6 - 5x$ b. $3 - 2x = -(x + 7) - 5x$

64 Middle School Math, Course 3 Chapter 6 Resource Book — Copyright © McDougal Littell Inc. All rights reserved.

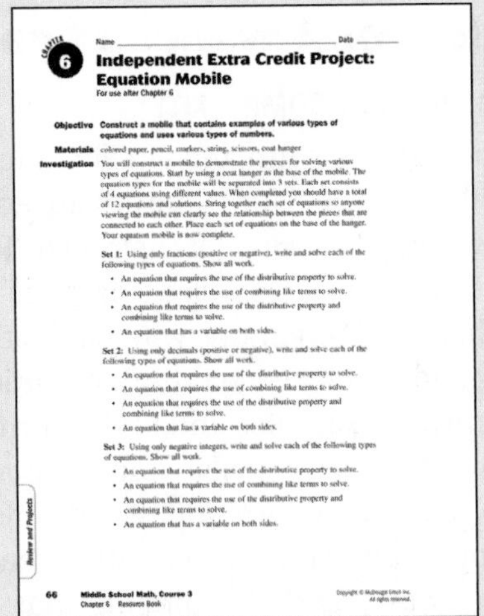

Chapter 6 — Name ______ Date ______

Independent Extra Credit Project: Equation Mobile

For use after Chapter 6

Objective Construct a mobile that contains examples of various types of equations and uses various types of numbers.

Materials colored paper, pencil, markers, string, scissors, coat hanger

Investigation You will construct a mobile to demonstrate the process for solving various types of equations. Start by using a coat hanger as the base of the mobile. The equation types for the mobile will be separated into 3 sets. Each set consists of 4 equations using different values. When completed you should have a total of 12 equations and solutions. String together each set of equations so anyone viewing the mobile can clearly see the relationship between the pieces that are connected to each other. Place each set of equations on the base of the hanger. Your equation mobile is now complete.

Set 1: Using only fractions (positive or negative), write and solve each of the following types of equations. Show all work.

- An equation that requires the use of the distributive property to solve.
- An equation that requires the use of combining like terms to solve.
- An equation that requires the use of the distributive property and combining like terms to solve.
- An equation that has a variable on both sides.

Set 2: Using only decimals (positive or negative), write and solve each of the following types of equations. Show all work.

- An equation that requires the use of the distributive property to solve.
- An equation that requires the use of combining like terms to solve.
- An equation that requires the use of the distributive property and combining like terms to solve.
- An equation that has a variable on both sides.

Set 3: Using only negative integers, write and solve each of the following types of equations. Show all work.

- An equation that requires the use of the distributive property to solve.
- An equation that requires the use of combining like terms to solve.
- An equation that requires the use of the distributive property and combining like terms to solve.
- An equation that has a variable on both sides.

66 Middle School Math, Course 3 Chapter 6 Resource Book — Copyright © McDougal Littell Inc. All rights reserved.

SPECIAL ACTIVITIES BOOK

The *Special Activities Book* contains numerous activities including activities for the start of school, activities for substitute teachers, activities for use before holiday breaks, and short change-of-pace activities.

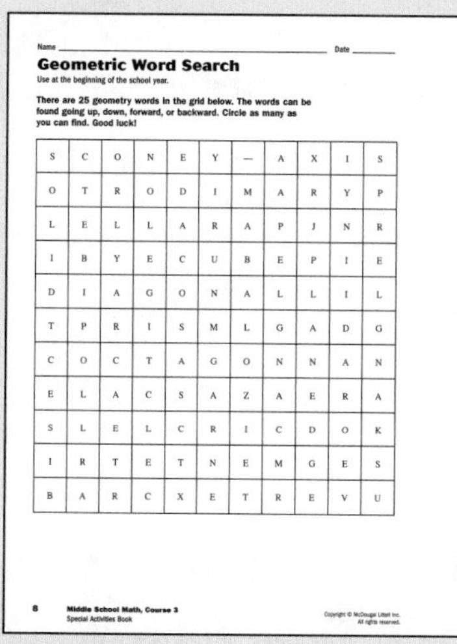

Name ____________________ Date ________

Geometric Word Search

Use at the beginning of the school year.

There are 25 geometry words in the grid below. The words can be found going up, down, forward, or backward. Circle as many as you can find. Good luck!

S	C	O	N	E	Y	—	A	X	I	S
O	T	R	O	D	I	M	A	R	Y	P
L	E	L	L	A	R	A	P	J	N	R
I	B	Y	E	C	U	B	E	P	I	E
D	I	A	G	O	N	A	L	L	I	L
T	P	R	I	S	M	L	G	A	D	G
C	O	C	T	A	G	O	N	N	A	N
E	L	A	C	S	A	Z	A	E	R	A
S	L	E	L	C	R	I	C	D	O	K
I	R	T	E	T	N	E	M	G	E	S
B	A	R	C	X	E	T	R	E	V	U

8 **Middle School Math, Course 3** Special Activities Book

Copyright © McDougal Littell Inc. All rights reserved.

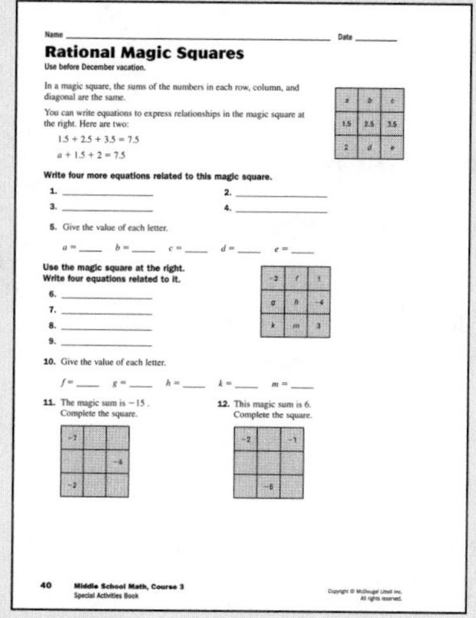

Name ____________________ Date ________

Rational Magic Squares

Use before December vacation.

In a magic square, the sums of the numbers in each row, column, and diagonal are the same.

You can write equations to express relationships in the magic square at the right. Here are two:

$1.5 + 2.5 + 3.5 = 7.5$

$a + 1.5 + 2 = 7.5$

a	b	c
1.5	2.5	3.5
2	d	e

Write four more equations related to this magic square.

1. __________ 2. __________

3. __________ 4. __________

5. Give the value of each letter.

$a =$ ____ $b =$ ____ $c =$ ____ $d =$ ____ $e =$ ____

Use the magic square at the right. Write four equations related to it.

−3	f	1
g	h	−4
k	m	3

6. __________
7. __________
8. __________
9. __________

10. Give the value of each letter.

$f =$ ____ $g =$ ____ $h =$ ____ $k =$ ____ $m =$ ____

11. The magic sum is −15. Complete the square.

−7		
		−4
−2		

12. This magic sum is 6. Complete the square.

−2		−1
	−6	

40 **Middle School Math, Course 3** Special Activities Book

Copyright © McDougal Littell Inc. All rights reserved.

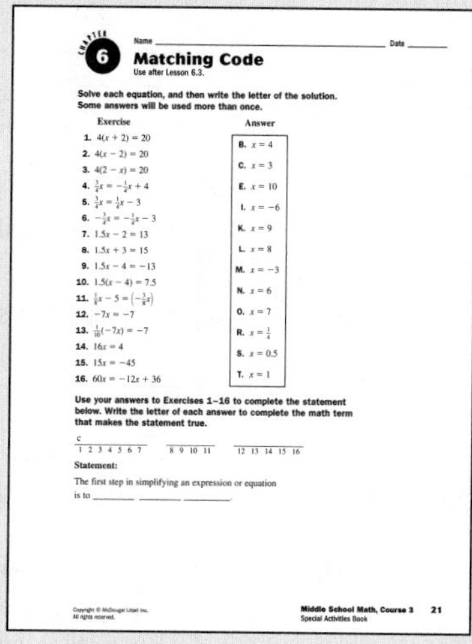

CHAPTER 6 Name ____________________ Date ________

Matching Code

Use after Lesson 6.3.

Solve each equation, and then write the letter of the solution. Some answers will be used more than once.

Exercise	Answer
1. $4(x + 2) = 20$	B. $x = 4$
2. $4(x - 2) = 20$	C. $x = 3$
3. $4(2 - x) = 20$	E. $x = 10$
4. $\frac{3}{4}x = -\frac{1}{4}x + 4$	I. $x = -6$
5. $\frac{3}{4}x = \frac{1}{4}x - 3$	K. $x = 9$
6. $-\frac{3}{4}x = -\frac{1}{4}x - 3$	L. $x = 8$
7. $1.5x - 2 = 13$	M. $x = -3$
8. $1.5x + 3 = 15$	N. $x = 6$
9. $1.5x - 4 = -13$	O. $x = 7$
10. $1.5(x - 4) = 7.5$	R. $x = \frac{1}{4}$
11. $\frac{1}{8}x - 5 = \left(-\frac{3}{8}x\right)$	S. $x = 0.5$
12. $-7x = -7$	T. $x = 1$
13. $\frac{1}{10}(-7x) = -7$	
14. $16x = 4$	
15. $15x = -45$	
16. $60x = -12x + 36$	

Use your answers to Exercises 1–16 to complete the statement below. Write the letter of each answer to complete the math term that makes the statement true.

C
1 2 3 4 5 6 7 8 9 10 11 12 13 14 15 16

Statement:

The first step in simplifying an expression or equation is to ______ ______ ______.

Copyright © McDougal Littell Inc. All rights reserved.

Middle School Math, Course 3 Special Activities Book 21

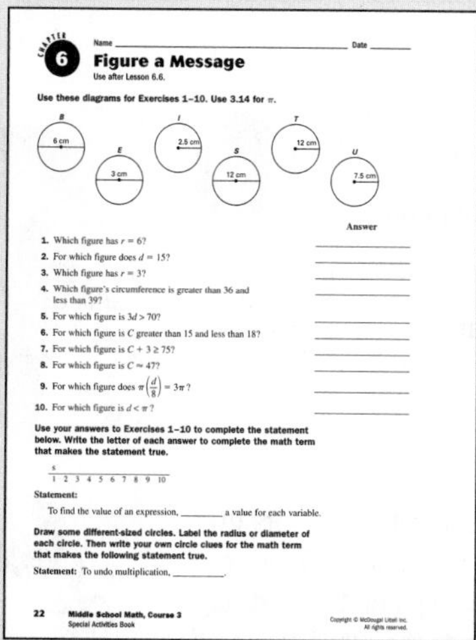

CHAPTER 6 Name ____________________ Date ________

Figure a Message

Use after Lesson 6.6.

Use these diagrams for Exercises 1–10. Use 3.14 for π.

Answer

1. Which figure has $r = 6$? ______
2. For which figure does $d = 15$? ______
3. Which figure has $r = 3$? ______
4. Which figure's circumference is greater than 36 and less than 39? ______
5. For which figure is $3d > 70$? ______
6. For which figure is C greater than 15 and less than 18? ______
7. For which figure is $C + 3 \geq 75$? ______
8. For which figure is $C \approx 47$? ______
9. For which figure does $\pi\left(\frac{d}{8}\right) = 3\pi$? ______
10. For which figure is $d < \pi$? ______

Use your answers to Exercises 1–10 to complete the statement below. Write the letter of each answer to complete the math term that makes the statement true.

S
1 2 3 4 5 6 7 8 9 10

Statement:

To find the value of an expression, ________ a value for each variable.

Draw some different-sized circles. Label the radius or diameter of each circle. Then write your own circle clues for the math term that makes the following statement true.

Statement: To undo multiplication, ________.

22 **Middle School Math, Course 3** Special Activities Book

Copyright © McDougal Littell Inc. All rights reserved.

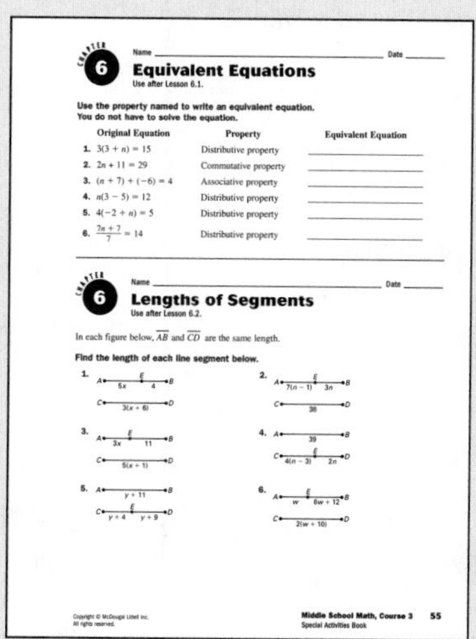

CHAPTER 6 Name ____________________ Date ________

Equivalent Equations

Use after Lesson 6.1.

Use the property named to write an equivalent equation. You do not have to solve the equation.

Original Equation	Property	Equivalent Equation
1. $3(3 + n) = 15$	Distributive property	______
2. $2n + 11 = 29$	Commutative property	______
3. $(n + 7) + (-6) = 4$	Associative property	______
4. $n(3 - 5) = 12$	Distributive property	______
5. $4(-2 + n) = 5$	Distributive property	______
6. $\frac{7n + 7}{7} = 14$	Distributive property	______

CHAPTER 6 Name ____________________ Date ________

Lengths of Segments

Use after Lesson 6.2.

In each figure below, $\overline{AB}$ and $\overline{CD}$ are the same length.

Find the length of each line segment below.

Copyright © McDougal Littell Inc. All rights reserved.

Middle School Math, Course 3 Special Activities Book 55

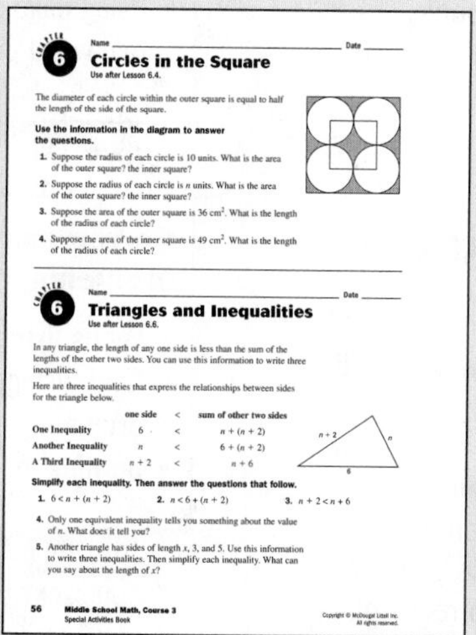

CHAPTER 6 Name ____________________ Date ________

Circles in the Square

Use after Lesson 6.4.

The diameter of each circle within the outer square is equal to half the length of the side of the square.

Use the information in the diagram to answer the questions.

1. Suppose the radius of each circle is 10 units. What is the area of the outer square? the inner square?
2. Suppose the radius of each circle is n units. What is the area of the outer square? the inner square?
3. Suppose the area of the outer square is 36 cm^2. What is the length of the radius of each circle?
4. Suppose the area of the inner square is 49 cm^2. What is the length of the radius of each circle?

CHAPTER 6 Name ____________________ Date ________

Triangles and Inequalities

Use after Lesson 6.6.

In any triangle, the length of any one side is less than the sum of the lengths of the other two sides. You can use this information to write three inequalities.

Here are three inequalities that express the relationships between sides for the triangle below.

	one side	<	sum of other two sides
One Inequality	6	<	$n + (n + 2)$
Another Inequality	n	<	$6 + (n + 2)$
A Third Inequality	$n + 2$	<	$n + 6$

Simplify each inequality. Then answer the questions that follow.

1. $6 < n + (n + 2)$ 2. $n < 6 + (n + 2)$ 3. $n + 2 < n + 6$

4. Only one equivalent inequality tells you something about the value of n. What does it tell you?

5. Another triangle has sides of length x, 3, and 5. Use this information to write three inequalities. Then simplify each inequality. What can you say about the length of x?

56 **Middle School Math, Course 3** Special Activities Book

Copyright © McDougal Littell Inc. All rights reserved.

OVERVIEW

Main Ideas

In this chapter, students solve multi-step equations by combining like terms and using the distributive property. Students use algebra tiles and algebraic methods to solve equations with variables on both sides. Students extend these methods to solve equations involving fractions and decimals, and apply them to solve equations involving the circumference of a circle and other real-world problems. Students also solve multi-step inequalities and use them to solve real-world problems.

Prerequisite Skills

The key skills reviewed in the games on these pages are:

- Solving one and two-step equations

Additional practice with prerequisite skills can be found in the Review What You Need to Know exercises on page 270. Additional resources for reviewing prerequisite skills are:

- Skills Review Handbook, pp. 704–726
- Tutor Place
- eTutorial Plus

Managing the Game

Tips for Success

Review the multiplication and addition properties of equality before students play this game. Make sure each player verifies that the other places markers only when appropriate. You may want to add a penalty of a loss of turn for incorrectly placing a marker to give students an incentive to pay close attention and be accurate.

Multi-Step Equations and Inequalities

BEFORE

In previous chapters you've...

- Solved equations that required using one or two steps
- Solved one-step inequalities

Now

In Chapter 6 you'll study...

- Solving multi-step equations
- Solving equations that have variables on both sides
- Using multi-step inequalities to solve real-world problems

WHY?

So you can solve real-world problems about...

- Venus flytraps, p. 271
- fundraising, p. 274
- drumming, p. 278
- bowling, p. 296

Internet Preview
CLASSZONE.COM

- eEdition Plus Online
- eWorkbook Plus Online
- eTutorial Plus Online
- State Test Practice
- More Examples

Chapter Warm-Up Game

Review skills you need for this chapter in this quick game. Work with a partner.

Key Skill:
Solving one- and two-step equations

TREASURE HUNT

MATERIALS

- 1 number cube
- 1 Treasure Hunt board
- 20 red markers
- 20 yellow markers

PREPARE Each player gets 20 markers of the same color. On your turn, follow the steps on the next page. You can challenge the other player when you believe they have covered an incorrect space.

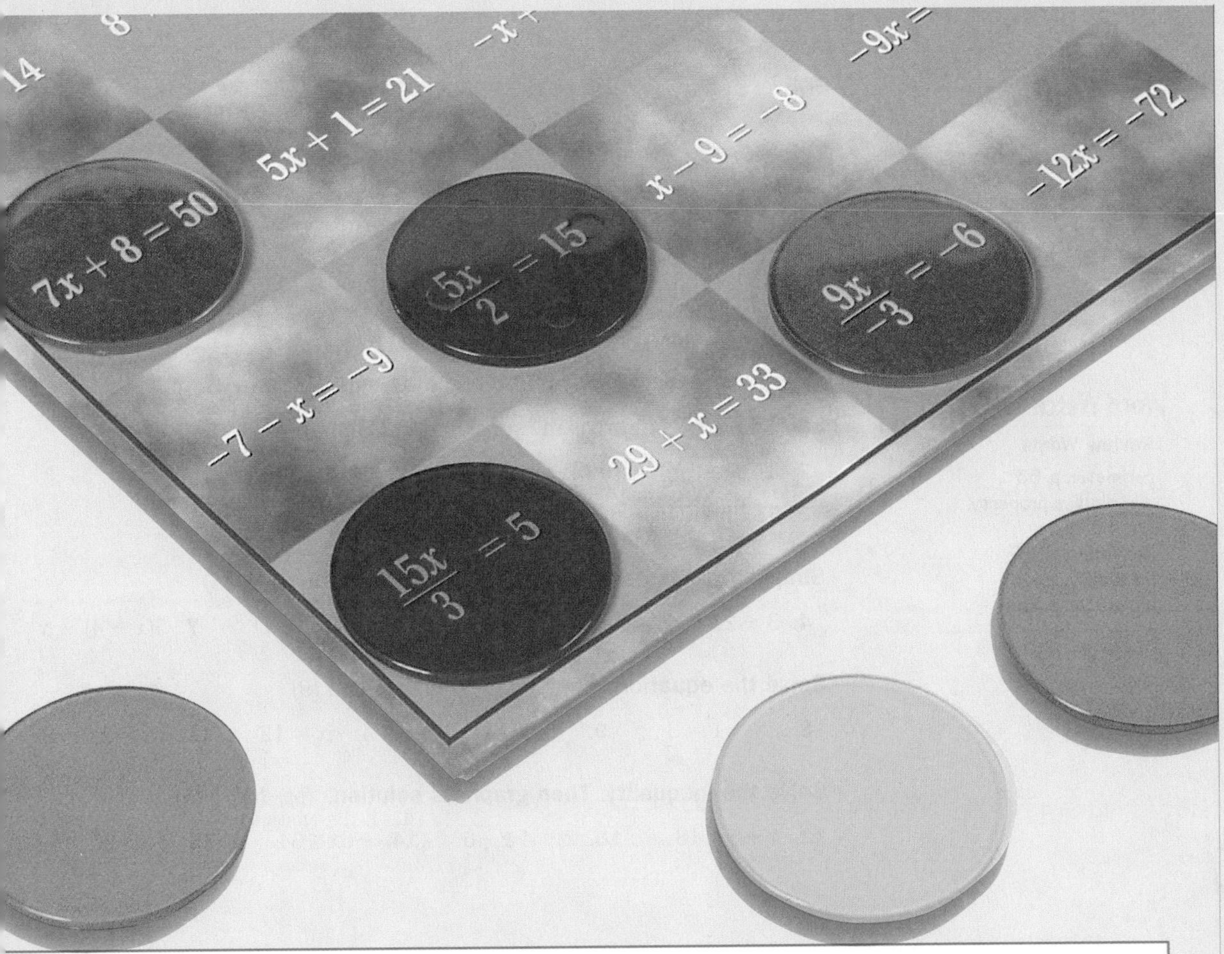

14 8 $-x+$ $-9x=$

$5x+1=21$ $x-9=-8$ $-12x=-72$

$7x+8=50$ $\frac{5x}{2}=15$ $\frac{9x}{-3}=-6$

$-7-x=-9$ $29+x=33$

$\frac{15x}{3}=5$

1 ROLL a number cube. This is your solution.

2 COVER an equation that has your solution with a marker. If there are no equations that have your solution, you cannot place a marker and it is the next player's turn. Each space you cover is a piece of treasure.

3 CHECK that you cover a correct space for your roll. If you cover an incorrect space, then you must remove your marker and it is the next player's turn.

HOW TO WIN Be the player with the most spaces covered (the most treasure collected) when all spaces on the board are covered.

1. The best number to roll is 4 because 4 is the solution of two of the equations ($5x + 1 = 21$ and $11 - 2x = 3$). The second best number to roll is 2 because 2 is the solution of $-7 - x = -9$.

Stop and Think

1. **Writing** If the only spaces left on the board are $5x + 1 = 21$, $-7 - x = -9$, and $11 - 2x = 3$, what is the best number to roll? What is the second best number to roll? Explain.
2. **Critical Thinking** How many spaces on the board have a solution of 5? Explain how you found your answer. **4; I solved each equation and counted the spaces that have 5 as a solution.**

Reflecting on the Game

After playing the game and answering the Stop & Think questions, students are likely to realize that there are two different approaches to deciding when to place a marker: solving the equations or using substitution. Ask students for the advantages of each method. Ask if the number of times they might expect to play the game might make a difference, so that they may come to see that a general solution is desirable.

Chapter Resources

These resources are provided to help you prepare for the chapter and to customize review materials:

Chapter 6 Resource Book

- Tips for New Teachers, pp. 1–2
- Lesson Plan, pp. 7, 16, 26, 35, 43, 52
- Lesson Plan for Block Scheduling, pp. 8, 17, 27, 36, 44, 53

Technology

- EasyPlanner CD-ROM
- Test and Practice Generator
- Electronic Lesson Presentations CD-ROM
- eTutorial CD-ROM

Internet

- Classzone
- eEdition Plus Online
- eWorkbook Plus Online
- eTutorial Plus Online
- EasyPlanner Plus Online

English Learner Support

- Spanish Study Guide
- Multi-Language Glossary
- Chapter Audio Summaries CDs
- Teacher's Edition, pp. 268E–268F

PREPARE

DIAGNOSIS/REMEDIATION

Review What You Need to Know
The Review What You Need to Know exercises can help you diagnose whether students have the following skills needed in Chapter 6:

- Using vocabulary (Exs. 1-3)
- Simplifying expressions (Exs. 4-7)
- Solving equations (Exs. 8-11)
- Solving and graphing inequalities (Exs. 12-15)

Chapter 6 Resource Book

- Study Guide (Lessons 6.1-6.6)

Tutor Place

NOTETAKING STRATEGIES

Stress that the process of solving an equation or inequality usually involves getting the variable alone on one side and the solution alone on the other side. Students should record many stepped-out examples for each lesson in this chapter in their notebooks. This will give them a sufficient number of worked-out examples for each type of equation and inequality when they review their notes prior to the chapter assessment. Further suggestions for keeping a notebook can be found on page 282.

For more support on notetaking, see:

- Notetaking Guide Workbook
- Notetaking Transparencies

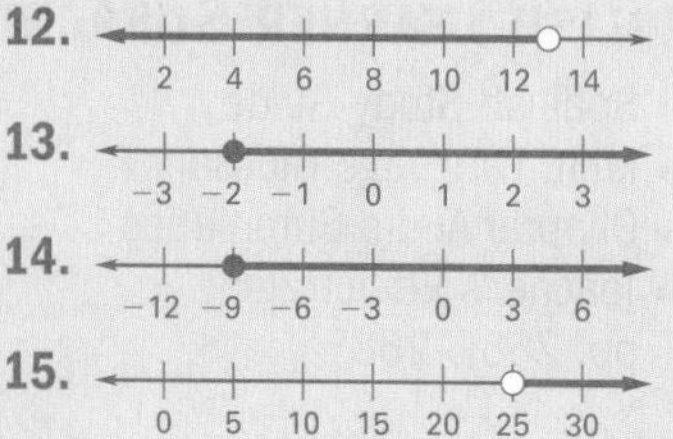

Getting Ready to Learn

Word Watch

Review Words

perimeter, p. 33
distributive property, p. 85
like terms, p. 86
inequality, p. 140
reciprocal, p. 234

Review What You Need to Know 

Using Vocabulary **Copy and complete using a review word.**

1. The _?_ of a figure is the sum of its side lengths. **perimeter**
2. The four _?_ symbols are <, >, ≤, and ≥. **inequality**
3. To divide by a fraction, you multiply by its _?_. **reciprocal**

Simplify the expression by combining like terms. *(p. 85)*

4. $3 - 2x + 4$ **$-2x + 7$** **5.** $4x + 5 + x - 1$ **$5x + 4$** **6.** $-2(3x + 1)$ **$-6x - 2$** **7.** $5(x - 4) - x$ **$4x - 20$**

Solve the equation. Check your answer. *(p. 119)*

8. $2x - 1 = 3$ **2** **9.** $-3x - 2 = 7$ **−3** **10.** $4 - x = 12$ **−8** **11.** $13 = 2x + 3$ **5**

Solve the inequality. Then graph its solution. *(pp. 140, 146)*
12–15. See margin for art.

12. $x + 5 < 18$ **$x < 13$** **13.** $x - 4 \geq -6$ **$x \geq -2$** **14.** $-6x \leq 54$ **$x \geq -9$** **15.** $\frac{4}{5}x > 20$ **$x > 25$**

You should include material that appears on a notebook like this in your own notes.

Know How to Take Notes

Recording the Process Copy examples your teacher explains during class. Be sure to record each step of the solution to help you remember the process.

Solving Two-Step Equations

$-2x - 3 = 11$	Original equation
$-2x - 3 + 3 = 11 + 3$	Add 3 to each side.
$-2x = 14$	Simplify.
$\frac{-2x}{-2} = \frac{14}{-2}$	Divide each side by −2.
$x = -7$	Simplify.

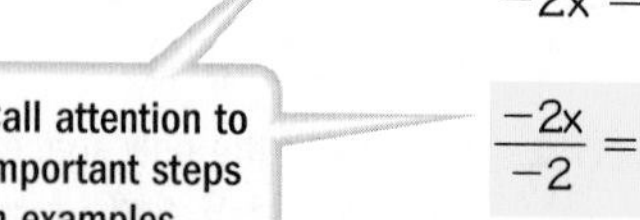

In Lesson 6.3, recording each step of the solution may help you remember the process for solving equations involving fractions and decimals.

Solving Multi-Step Equations

BEFORE

You solved equations that required using one or two steps.

Now

You'll solve equations that require using two or more steps.

WHY?

So you know how long to save to buy a mountain bike, as in Ex. 26.

Word Watch

Review Words

distributive property, p. 85
like terms, p. 86

In the Real World

Science For a science fair, you perform an experiment to see how the number of Venus flytrap seeds planted in a cup affects plant growth. In each cup, you plant either 5 seeds or 10 seeds. You want to use an equal number of cups for each seed amount. You have 75 seeds. How many cups do you need?

Before using inverse operations to solve an equation, check to see if you can simplify one or both sides of the equation by combining like terms.

EXAMPLE 1 Writing and Solving a Multi-Step Equation

To find the number of cups for each seed amount, first write a verbal model. Let c = the number of cups for each seed amount.

5 seeds			10 seeds			Total
Seeds per cup · Number of cups		+	Seeds per cup · Number of cups		=	Number of seeds

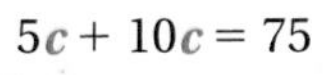
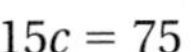

$5c + 10c = 75$ **Write algebraic model.**

$15c = 75$ **Combine like terms.**

$\frac{15c}{15} = \frac{75}{15}$ **Divide each side by 15.**

$c = 5$ **Simplify.**

ANSWER You can plant five cups with 5 seeds and five cups with 10 seeds.

✓ **Check** Substitute 5 for c in original equation.

$5(5) + 10(5) \stackrel{?}{=} 75$

$25 + 50 \stackrel{?}{=} 75$

$75 = 75$ ✓

ILLINOIS Standards and ISAT:
8.A.3b, 8.D.3a; 7.B.3, 7.C.3b, 8.A.3a

1 PLAN

SKILL CHECK

Solve.

1. $5x = 75$ 15
2. $3x = 18$ 6
3. $-x = 4$ −4
4. $-4x = -28$ 7

LESSON OBJECTIVE

Solve equations that require using two or more steps.

PACING

Suggested Number of Days
Basic Course: 2 days
Average Course: 2 days
Advanced Course: 2 days
Block: 1 block

TEACHING RESOURCES

For a complete list of Teaching Resources, see page 268B.

TRANSPARENCY

Warm-Up Exercises for this lesson are available on a transparency.

2 TEACH

MOTIVATING THE LESSON

Ask students who have grown plants to describe what they did and how they kept track of growth.

TIPS FOR NEW TEACHERS

Stress the step of combining like terms shown in Examples 1-3. Be sure students see that this step precedes the steps of using inverse operations. See Tips for New Teachers in the *Chapter 6 Resource Book*.

EXTRA EXAMPLES

Example 1 As a reward for winning a math competition, 120 students visit a theme park. On one ride, students can form only groups of 4 or 6 riders. The students form an equal number of groups of 4 and 6 riders. How many groups did they form? Let g = the number of groups for each number of riders.
12 groups

Example 2 Solve $7f + 15 - 10f = 21$. **-2**

Example 3 Solve $5(7 - x) - 3x = 43$. **-1**

VISUALIZE

Encourage students to highlight like terms in an equation using different colors in order to help them see which terms can be combined.

NOTETAKING

As students work the Examples and exercises, encourage them to record in their notebooks the exercises they found difficult or that they initially worked incorrectly.

EXAMPLE 2 Combining Like Terms

$3x + 12 - 4x = 20$	**Original equation**
$-x + 12 = 20$	**Combine like terms: $3x - 4x = -x$.**
$-x + 12 - 12 = 20 - 12$	**Subtract 12 from each side.**
$-x = 8$	**Simplify.**
$\frac{-x}{-1} = \frac{8}{-1}$	**Divide each side by -1.**
$x = -8$	**Simplify.**

Your turn now **Solve the equation. Then check the solution.**

1. $-6 = 11w - 5w$ -1
2. $4p + 10 + p = 25$ 3
3. $-8r - 2 + 7r = -9$ 7

Before you combine like terms in an equation, you may have to use the distributive property.

HELP with Review

When distributing a negative number, remember to distribute the negative sign to *each* term inside the parentheses. For help with the distributive property, see p. 85.

EXAMPLE 3 Using the Distributive Property

$6n - 2(n + 1) = 26$	**Original equation**
$6n - 2n - 2 = 26$	**Distributive property**
$4n - 2 = 26$	**Combine like terms.**
$4n - 2 + 2 = 26 + 2$	**Add 2 to each side.**
$4n = 28$	**Simplify.**
$\frac{4n}{4} = \frac{28}{4}$	**Divide each side by 4.**
$n = 7$	**Simplify.**

✓**Check** Substitute 7 for n in the original equation.

$$6(7) - 2(7 + 1) \stackrel{?}{=} 26$$
$$6(7) - 2(8) \stackrel{?}{=} 26$$
$$42 - 16 \stackrel{?}{=} 26$$
$$26 = 26 \checkmark$$

Your turn now **Solve the equation. Then check the solution.**

4. $3(x - 9) = -39$ -4
5. $z + 4(6 - z) = 21$ 1
6. $8 = -7(y + 1) + 2y$ -3

Clearing Fractions In equations involving a fraction, you may want to multiply each side by a number to change the equation into an equivalent equation that does not have fractions.

EXAMPLE 4 Solving an Equation with a Fraction

$\frac{3x + 10}{4} = 7$	Original equation
$\frac{3x + 10}{4} \cdot 4 = 7 \cdot 4$	Multiply each side by 4.
$3x + 10 = 28$	Simplify.
$3x + 10 - 10 = 28 - 10$	Subtract 10 from each side.
$3x = 18$	Simplify.
$\frac{3x}{3} = \frac{18}{3}$	Divide each side by 3.
$x = 6$	Simplify.

6.1 Exercises

More Practice, p. 732

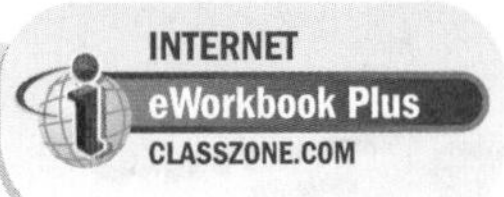

Getting Ready to Practice

Vocabulary **Identify the like terms in the expression.**

1. $5x + 6 - 2 - 9x$ **5x and −9x, 6 and −2**
2. $8y + 3x - 1 + 6y$ **8y and 6y**
3. $-t - 15 + 1 - 20$ **−15, 1, and −20**

Solve the equation. Then check the solution.

4. $8b + 2b - 4 = 6$ **1**
5. $-n - 9 + 8n = 26$ **5**
6. $5(w - 7) = -15$ **4**
7. $m + 3(m - 4) = 16$ **7**
8. $\frac{k - 6}{2} = -10$ **−14**
9. $\frac{z + 2}{7} = 12$ **82**

10. **Guided Problem Solving** Tickets to the county fair cost $8 each. Seventy people purchased their tickets in advance and the rest bought them at the gate. The revenue from ticket sales is $2560. How many people bought their tickets at the gate?

(1) Use the verbal model to write an equation to find the number of tickets sold at the gate. **8(70 + t) = 2560**

Price per ticket	·	(Tickets sold in advance	+	Tickets sold at gate)	=	Total revenue

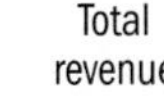

(2) Solve the equation. Then check the solution. **250 tickets**

EXTRA EXAMPLES

Example 4 Solve $\frac{7x + 5}{5} = 15$. **10**

CONCEPT CHECK

If a variable appears more than once in an equation, what do you do first to solve the equation? **Combine like terms.**

DAILY PUZZLER

Carlos is two thirds of Jose's age. Eight years ago, Carlos was half Jose's age. How old is Jose now? **24 years old**

APPLY

ASSIGNMENT GUIDE

Basic Course

Day 1: EP p. 728 Exs. 41-43; pp. 274-275 Exs. 11, 14-17, 24-28, 39, 41-44

Day 2: EP p. 729 Exs. 9-12; pp. 274-275 Exs. 12, 13, 18-23, 33-36, 45-47

Average Course

Day 1: pp. 274-275 Exs. 11, 15-17, 25-32, 41-45

Day 2: pp. 274-275 Exs. 13, 18-23, 33-39, 46-48

Advanced Course

Day 1: pp. 274-275 Exs. 11, 15-17, 24-30, 41-43

Day 2: pp. 274-275 Exs. 13, 21-23, 34-40*, 46-48

Block

pp. 274-275 Exs. 11, 13, 15-23, 25-39, 41-48

EXTRA PRACTICE

- Student Edition, p. 732
- Chapter 6 Resource Book, pp. 9-11
- Test and Practice Generator

TRANSPARENCY

Even-numbered answers are available on transparencies.

HOMEWORK CHECK

When you review students' homework for this lesson, go over the following exercises to check understanding of key concepts.

Basic: 11, 13, 18, 22, 24
Average: 11, 13, 19, 22, 26
Advanced: 11, 13, 17, 23, 26

HELP with Homework

Example	Exercises
1	24, 26
2	11-23
3	11-23
4	11-23

Online Resources CLASSZONE.COM

- More Examples
- eTutorial Plus

26. Money already saved + Babysitting money per week • Weeks + Grocery store money per week • Weeks = Price of mountain bike; $25 + 15w + 25w = 225$; 5 wk

Practice and Problem Solving

Decide whether the given value is a solution of the equation. If not, find the solution.

A **11.** $7x - 3x - 8 = -32; x = 6$ no; −6

12. $2y - 5(y + 1) = 25; y = -10$ yes

13. $\frac{4m - 3}{3} = 3; m = 2$ no; 3

14. $2 - 8a + 3a = 17; a = -3$ yes

Solve the equation. Then check the solution.

15. $4x - 7 - 7x = -1$ −2

16. $-2z + 6z - 9 = 15$ 6

17. $-22 + 3k + 6 = -28$ −4

18. $-2(m + 7) = -22$ 4

19. $5(3 - 2n) = 65$ −5

20. $-4 = -1 - 3(2p + 3)$ −1

21. $\frac{5a - 2}{3} = -9$ −5

22. $\frac{2b + 8}{5} = -12$ −34

23. $\frac{c - 5}{8} = 4$ 37

24. Fundraiser You are collecting money during a student council T-shirt sale. Today you collected money from Maria for 13 shirts, money from Kevin for 9 shirts, and money from Emma for 10 shirts. You collected a total of $352. How much did each T-shirt cost? $11

B **25. Measurement** The perimeter of the rectangle is $3(x - 8)$ millimeters. Use a ruler to measure the rectangle and find the perimeter. Then find the value of x. length: 40 mm, width: 17 mm, perimeter: 114 mm; 46

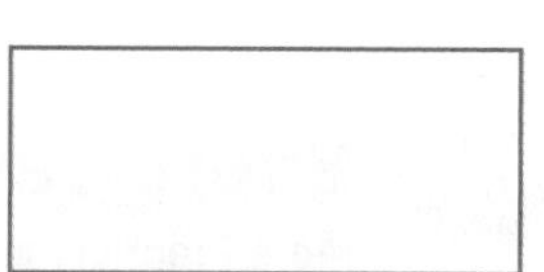

26. After-school Job You are saving to buy a mountain bike that costs $225. You already have $25. Each week, you make $15 babysitting and $25 working at a grocery store. Write a verbal model for the money you have using *Money already saved, Weeks, Babysitting money per week, Grocery store money per week,* and *Price of mountain bike*. Use the verbal model to write an equation. In how many weeks will you have enough money? See margin.

Solve the equation. Then check the solution.

27. $5y - 2y + 9y = -16$ $-1\frac{1}{3}$

28. $8k - 4 - 3k - 17 = -21$ 0

29. $7t - 3(1 + t) = -19$ −4

30. $2z - 4(9 - 3z) = 62$ 7

31. $-10 = 6n - (3n + 12)$ $\frac{2}{3}$

32. $\frac{m - 14}{9} = -27$ −229

33. $-11 = \frac{24 - b}{13}$ 167

34. $-34 = \frac{3d + 8}{3}$ $-36\frac{2}{3}$

Geometry **Write an equation for the area of the triangle. Then solve for x.**

35. The lengths are in inches. The area is 228 square inches.

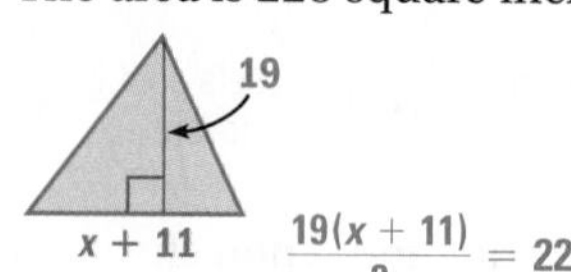

$\frac{19(x + 11)}{2} = 228$; 13 in.

36. The lengths are in meters. The area is 918 square meters.

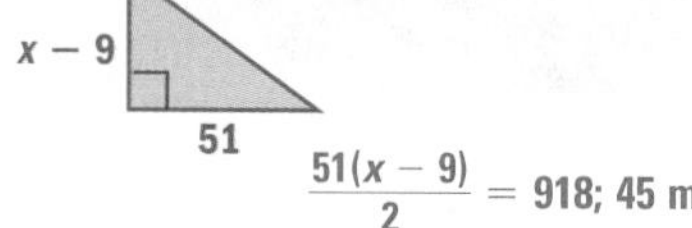

$\frac{51(x - 9)}{2} = 918$; 45 m

37. **Critical Thinking** Suppose you want to solve an equation that involves parentheses, such as $3(x + 2) = 9$. You might use the distributive property to rewrite the left side. Would the result be the same if instead you first divide each side by 3? Explain. See margin.

38. **Number Sense** Sara has $20 to spend at a yard sale. She decides to buy a teapot and as many sets of teacups and saucers as she can afford. The teacups are $2 each and the saucers are $1 each. She figures that she can buy 8 teacups and 8 saucers. How can you tell that she's made an error without knowing the cost of the teapot? See margin.

C 39. **Geometry** Find the values of x and y so that the rectangle and the triangle have the same perimeter. What is the perimeter? $x = 5$, $y = 8$; 34

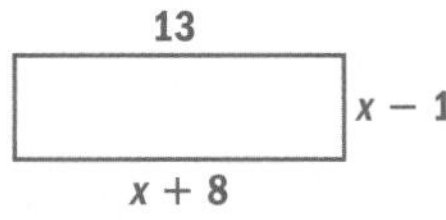

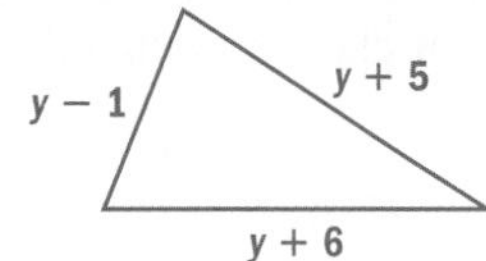

40. **Challenge** You have $12 to spend on earrings. You can calculate the sales tax by multiplying the price by 0.05. What is the most that the earrings can cost before the sales tax is added on? $11.42

37. Yes. *Sample answer:* If you divide each side by 3, you get $x + 2 = 3$, so $x = 1$. This is the same answer you get using the distributive property.

38. *Sample answer:* The cost of 8 teacups and 8 saucers is $8(\$2) + 8(\$1) = \$24$, which is more than the $20 she has to spend.

Mixed Review

Copy and complete the statement with <, >, or =. *(Lesson 4.8)*

41. 1.54×10^{-5} ? 1.54×10^{-6} >

42. 0.57×10^{4} ? 5.7×10^{4} <

Find the mean, median, mode(s), and range of the data. *(Lesson 5.8)*

43. 35, 32, 31, 32, 35, 32, 37, 38, 34 — 34, 34, 32, 7

44. 101, 100, 101, 105, 112, 105 — 104, 103, 101 and 105, 12

Basic Skills **Find the unknown number.**

45. 8 hours = ? seconds 28,800

46. 3 days = ? minutes 4320

Test-Taking Practice

47. **Multiple Choice** What is the value of v in the equation $3 + 8v - 9v = 21$? B

A. −24 **B.** −18 **C.** 18 **D.** 24

48. **Short Response** Your summer job is to paint and hang wallpaper in people's homes. You charge x dollars per hour for painting and $(x + 5)$ dollars per hour for hanging wallpaper. In one week, you paint for 12 hours and wallpaper for 15 hours. Your expenses for the week are $430. Your profit for the week is $590. How much do you charge per hour for painting and hanging wallpaper? Write a verbal model and an algebraic equation. Then solve the algebraic equation.

INTERNET
State Test Practice
CLASSZONE.COM

48. $35, $40. *Sample answer:* Hours painting • Hourly charge for painting + Hours hanging wallpaper • Hourly charge for hanging wallpaper − Expenses = Profit; $12x + 15(x + 5) - 430 = 590$; 35

4 ASSESS

Assessment Resources

For more assessment resources, see:
- Assessment Book
- Test and Practice Generator

Mini-Quiz

Solve the equation.

1. $9x - 10 - 7x = -4$ 3
2. $-3(2b - 3) = -15$ 4
3. $\frac{4y + 7}{3} = 13$ 8
4. $-6 = 2n - (4n + 10)$ −2
5. Write an equation for the area of the triangle. The area is 80 square inches. The lengths are in inches. Then solve for x.

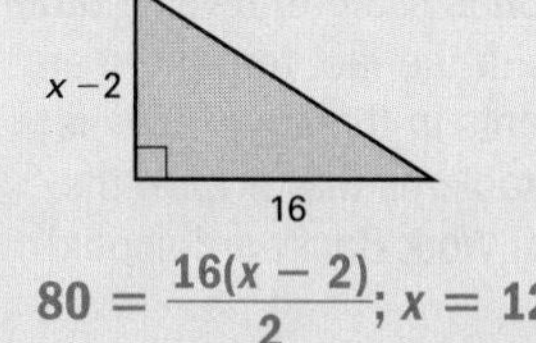

$80 = \frac{16(x - 2)}{2}$; $x = 12$

5 FOLLOW-UP

Reteaching/Remediation

- Study Guide in Chapter 6 Resource Book, pp. 12–13
- Tutor Place, Algebra Card 6
- eTutorial Plus Online
- Extra Practice, p. 732
- Lesson Practice in Chapter 6 Resource Book, pp. 9–11

Challenge/Enrichment

- Challenge Practice in Chapter 6 Resource Book, p. 15
- Teacher's Edition, p. 268F

English Learner Support

- Spanish Study Guide
- Multi-Language Glossary
- Chapter Audio Summaries CDs

1 PLAN

STRATEGY BACKGROUND

Work Backward is an appropriate strategy for students to use when they need information that will lead to a known result. Students are told the result and asked to determine what led to the result. To use this strategy, students start with the result and retrace steps backward. An advantage of this strategy is that it makes sense to students.

2 TEACH

GUIDING STUDENTS' WORK

Point out to students that the given information is listed in reverse order, starting with the fact that there are four students in the group. This is how all problems that involve the strategy of Work Backward should be done.

EXTRA EXAMPLES

Example In April, Jan bought some ducks for her pond. In May, two ducks flew away. A week later, an animal shelter gave Jan six ducks they had rescued. In June, another duck flew away. Jan had 27 ducks at the end of June. How many did she buy in April? **24 ducks**

6.2 Problem Solving Strategies

- Guess, Check, and Revise
- Look for a Pattern
- Draw a Diagram
- Write an Equation
- **Work Backward**
- Act It Out
- Solve a Simpler Problem

Work Backward

Problem At the beginning of the year your class divides into seven equal study groups. Then your group joins another group, and two students leave your group when they change classes. Now there are four students in your group. How many students were in your class at the beginning of the year?

1 Read and Understand

Read the problem carefully.

- You know how the class divided and how your group changed.
- You need to find the number of students in the class at the beginning of the year.

2 Make a Plan

Decide on a strategy to use.

One way to solve the problem is to work backward. Start with the final number of students in your group and undo each change that your group went through.

3 Solve the Problem

Reread the problem. Work backward from the final number of students.

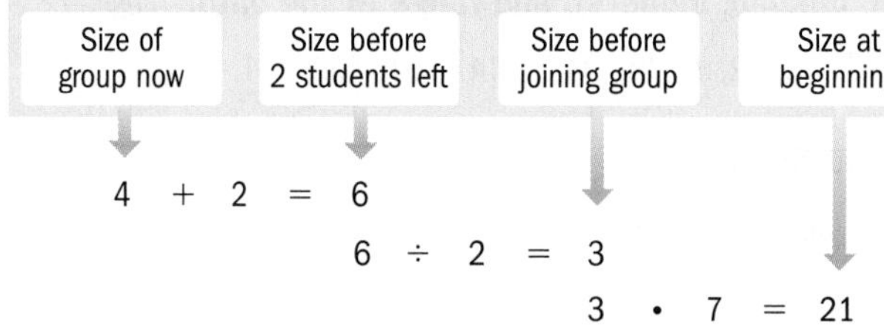

$4 + 2 = 6$

$6 \div 2 = 3$

$3 \cdot 7 = 21$

ANSWER There were 21 students at the beginning of the year.

4 Look Back

Check your answer. Start with your solution and reread the problem, calculating as you read.

At the beginning of the year your class	21
divides into seven equal study groups.	$21 \div 7 = 3$
Then **your group joins another** group,	$3 \cdot 2 = 6$
and **two students leave** your group.	$6 - 2 = 4$
Now there are **four students** in your group.	4 ✓

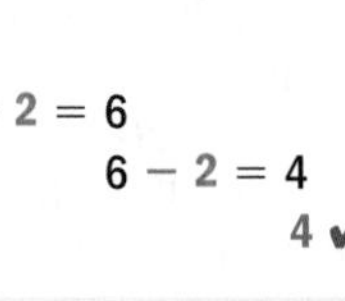

ILLINOIS Standards and ISAT:
6.B.3a, 6.C.3a

Practice the Strategy

Use the strategy *work backward.*

1. **Road Trip** In the last 3 days you've driven 720 miles, 650 miles, and 800 miles. Your car's odometer reads 20,490 miles. What did the odometer read three days ago? **18,320 mi**
2. **Money** You put half of your money in the bank. The next day you receive your $10 allowance and buy jeans for $25. You have $17 left. Copy and complete the diagram to find out how much money you started with. **$64**

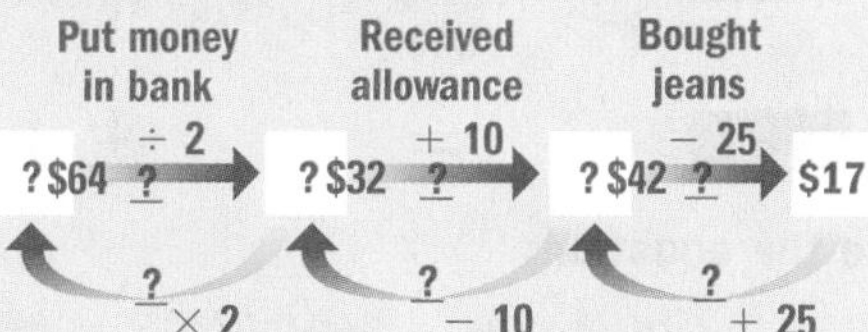

3. **Phone Card** Jill uses three fifths of the minutes on her phone card to call her brother, 15 minutes to call a friend, and 5 minutes to order a pizza. If she has 4 minutes left, how many minutes were on the card before she called her brother? **60 min**
4. **Studying** You spend one hour on math homework and 45 minutes studying for each of your 3 tests. If you finish studying at 6:30 P.M., what time did you start? **3:15 P.M.**
5. **Notebook** You use half of your notebook for your research paper and two thirds of the remaining paper for class notes. You have ten pages left for homework. How many pages are in your notebook? **60 pages**
6. **CD Burning** Some friends are recording songs on a CD. The first fifth of the CD has songs from Alex's favorite band. The next 12 minutes are songs Henrique chose. One third of the time remaining is filled with Brian's favorite songs. Sally chose songs for the next 32 minutes. How many minutes of music did they record? **75 min**

Mixed Problem Solving

Use any strategy to solve the problem.

7. **Consecutive Odd Numbers** The sum of three consecutive odd numbers is 501. What is the value of each number? **165, 167, 169**
8. **Traveling** The following directions describe the path Denzel takes to his friend's house from school.
   - First he travels 5 miles north and then 8 miles west.
   - Next he travels 2 miles north and then 3 miles east.
   - Finally he travels 1 mile south.

   Draw a map showing Denzel's path from school to his friend's house. **See margin.**
9. **Population** The table shows the population of a small town over 15 years. If the population continues to grow in this manner, in what year will the population reach 160,000? **2012**

Year	Population
1987	5,000
1992	10,000
1997	20,000
2002	40,000

10. **Getting Ready** Each morning, Angie needs half an hour to shower and dress, 15 minutes to eat, and 5 minutes to brush her teeth. It takes her 15 minutes to walk to school. What is the latest Angie can get up and still arrive at school by 8:10 A.M.? **7:05 A.M.**

3 APPLY

TRANSPARENCY

Even-numbered answers are available on transparencies.

TEACHING TIP

In Exercise 2, point out that students are trying to find the amount of money they started with, *not* the amount they put in the bank.

COMMON ERROR

In Exercise 4, stress the word *each* and make sure students understand that each of the three tests requires 45 minutes of studying, for a total of 135 minutes.

SUGGESTED STRATEGIES

You may wish to suggest the following strategies for the problems in the Mixed Problem Solving:

- Exercise 7: Guess, Check and Revise
- Exercise 8: Draw a Diagram
- Exercise 9: Look for a Pattern
- Exercise 10: Work Backward

8.

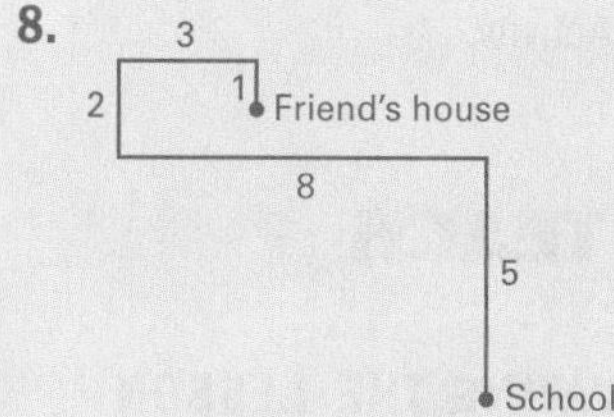

SKILL CHECK

Solve.

1. $24 = 4x$ — 6
2. $15x = 90$ — 6
3. $2x + 5 = 27$ — 11
4. $8x - 12x = 4$ — -1

Lesson Objective

Solve equations that have variables on both sides.

Pacing

Suggested Number of Days

Basic Course: 1 day

Average Course: 1 day

Advanced Course: 1 day

Block: 0.5 block with 6.3

Teaching Resources

For a complete list of Teaching Resources, see page 268B.

Transparency

Warm-Up Exercises for this lesson are available on a transparency. Support transparencies are available for the Activity.

Motivating the Lesson

Ask a volunteer to suggest a simple equation with the same variable on both sides. Have students discuss how they would solve the equation.

Activity

Goal Use algebra tiles to model and solve an equation.

Key Discovery To solve an equation with variables on both sides, remove the same number of x-tiles and unit tiles from each side.

Solving Equations with Variables on Both Sides

BEFORE You solved equations that had variables on one side.

Now You'll solve equations that have variables on both sides.

WHY? So you can determine the cost of party supplies, as in Ex. 27.

Word Watch

Review Words

perimeter, p. 33

distributive property, p. 85

like terms, p. 86

Activity Use algebra tiles to model and solve an equation.

(1) Represent the equation $2x + 3 = x + 5$ using algebra tiles.

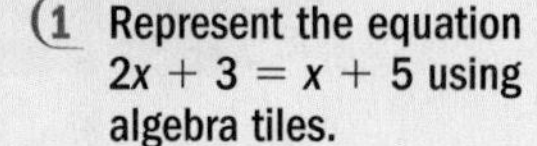
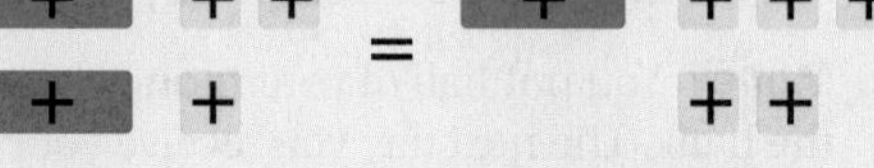

(2) Remove one x-tile and three 1-tiles from each side.

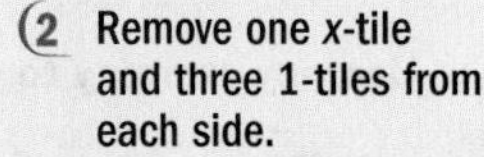
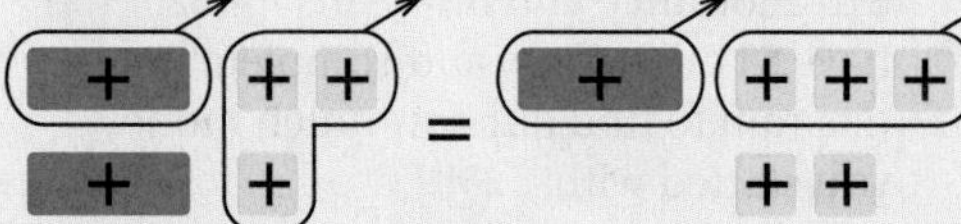

(3) The solution is 2.

Use algebra tiles to solve the equation.

1. $2x + 7 = 3x + 2$ 5
2. $5x - 2 = 3x + 6$ 4
3. $4x - 1 = x - 7$ -2

To solve equations with variables on both sides, collect like terms on the same side.

EXAMPLE 1 **Collecting Like Terms**

Drum lessons at the youth center cost $8 for members and $12 for nonmembers. Membership is $24. For what number of lessons is the cost the same for a member and a nonmember?

Solution

Cost for member						Cost for nonmember		
Member fee	+	Price for members	•	Number of lessons	=	Price for nonmembers	•	Number of lessons

$24 + 8n = 12n$ **Let n = the number of lessons.**

$24 = 4n$ **Subtract $8n$ from each side.**

$6 = n$ **Divide each side by 4.**

ANSWER Six lessons cost the same for members and nonmembers.

ILLINOIS Standards and ISAT:
7.C.3b, 8.A.3b, 8.D.3a; 8.A.3a

EXAMPLE 2 Finding the Perimeter of a Triangle

Each side of the triangle has the same length. What is the perimeter of the triangle?

$5x + 9$ $7x + 5$

Solution

$5x + 9 = 7x + 5$	**Write an equation.**
$5x + 9 - 5x = 7x + 5 - 5x$	**Subtract 5*x* from each side.**
$9 = 2x + 5$	**Simplify.**
$9 - 5 = 2x + 5 - 5$	**Subtract 5 from each side.**
$4 = 2x$	**Simplify.**
$\frac{4}{2} = \frac{2x}{2}$	**Divide each side by 2.**
$2 = x$	**Simplify.**

Because $5x + 9 = 5(2) + 9 = 19$, each side of the triangle is 19 units long.

The three sides of the triangle are the same length, so the perimeter is $3 \cdot 19$, or 57, units.

ANSWER The perimeter of the triangle is 57 units.

Watch Out! In Example 2, don't think that because $x = 2$, each side of the triangle has length 2 units. You must substitute 2 into the expressions for side length.

Sometimes you can use the distributive property to simplify one or both sides of an equation before you solve.

EXAMPLE 3 Using the Distributive Property

$21x = 3(2x + 30)$	**Original equation**
$21x = 6x + 90$	**Distributive property**
$21x - 6x = 6x + 90 - 6x$	**Subtract 6*x* from each side.**
$15x = 90$	**Simplify.**
$\frac{15x}{15} = \frac{90}{15}$	**Divide each side by 15.**
$x = 6$	**Simplify.**

Your turn now **Solve the equation.**

1. $4a + 5 = a + 11$ 2
2. $3n + 7 = 2n - 1$ -8
3. $-6c + 1 = -9c + 7$ 2
4. $28 - 3s = 5s - 12$ 5
5. $4(w - 9) = 7w + 18$ -18
6. $2(y + 4) = -3y - 7$ -3

TIPS FOR NEW TEACHERS

Give examples to help students understand that they can add or subtract a variable expression to or from each side of an equation just as they can add or subtract a number to or from each side. See Tips for New Teachers in the *Chapter 6 Resource Book*.

EXTRA EXAMPLES

Example 1 Books from a book club cost \$7 for members and \$10 for non-members. Membership is \$15. For what number of books is the cost the same for a member and a non-member? **5 books**

Example 2 Two sides of a square are shown. What is the perimeter of the square?

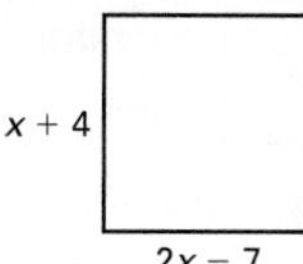

60 units

Example 3 Solve $2x - 6 = 4(5x + 12)$. **−3**

CONCEPT CHECK

To solve equations with variables on both sides, what do you do first? **Collect like terms on the same side.**

DAILY PUZZLER

Saraj has dogs, birds, and a snake. Altogether her 8 pets have 22 legs. How many of each animal does she have? **4 dogs, 3 birds, 1 snake**

ASSIGNMENT GUIDE

Basic Course

Day 1: EP p. 729 Exs. 13-16; pp. 280-281 Exs. 7-12, 16-22, 26-28, 36-49

Average Course

Day 1: pp. 280-281 Exs. 10-19, 23-27, 30-34, 38-49

Advanced Course

Day 1: pp. 280-281 Exs. 10-19, 23-39*, 45-49

Block

pp. 280-281 Exs. 10-19, 23-27, 30-34, 38-49 (with 6.3)

EXTRA PRACTICE

- Student Edition, p. 732
- Chapter 6 Resource Book, pp. 20-22
- Test and Practice Generator

Even-numbered answers are available on transparencies.

HOMEWORK CHECK

When you review students' homework for this lesson, go over the following exercises to check understanding of key concepts.

Basic: 7, 16, 19, 22, 26

Average: 10, 16, 19, 23, 26

Advanced: 10, 16, 19, 24, 27

6.2 Exercises

More Practice, p. 732

Getting Ready to Practice

1. **Vocabulary** What is the perimeter of a rectangle? **the sum of the lengths of the sides, or twice the length plus twice the width**
2. Is 5 a solution of the equation $4x - 2 = 3x + 12$? **no**

Solve the equation. Then check the solution.

3. $3x = 2x + 5$ **5**
4. $5x = 2(x + 5)$ $3\frac{1}{3}$
5. $x = 5(2x + 3)$ $-1\frac{2}{3}$
6. **Geometry** Each side of the triangle has the same length. What is the perimeter of the triangle? **15**

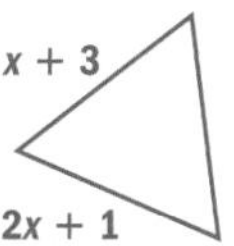

Practice and Problem Solving

Example	Exercises
1	7-15, 19-21, 26-27
2	16-18
3	16-18, 22-25

Online Resources CLASSZONE.COM
- More Examples
- eTutorial Plus

Solve the equation.

A 7. $7x = x + 18$ **3**

8. $7m = 4m + 21$ **7**

9. $30 - 2s = 4s$ **5**

10. $81 + 2k = 5k$ **27**

11. $13q - 48 = -3q$ **3**

12. $-11r = -4r + 56$ **−8**

13. $5z - 43 = 2z + 80$ **41**

14. $16y - 43 = 4y + 65$ **9**

15. $8f + 11 = -7f - 19$ **−2**

Geometry **Find the perimeter of the triangle or rectangle. The sides of each triangle are equal in length.**

16. 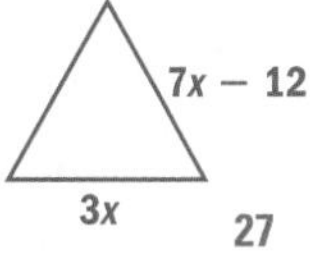

27

17. 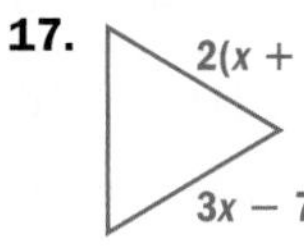

132

18. 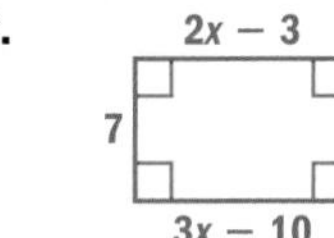

36

19. **Saving** David has $32 and is saving $8 each week. Emily has $56 and is saving $6 each week. When will David and Emily have the same amount of money? **12 wk**

Solve the equation.

B 20. $-1 + 11a = 6 - 3a$ $\frac{1}{2}$

21. $9b - 10 = -b - 18$ $-\frac{4}{5}$

22. $3(t - 7) = 6t$ **−7**

23. $-3h = 9(2 - 3h)$ $\frac{3}{4}$

24. $-n = 2(n - 33)$ **22**

25. $3d = 9(d - 1)$ $1\frac{1}{2}$

26. **Working Backward** Mark had $20 before he began earning the same amount each week at his new job. He used half of his first week's pay to pay back a loan. He spent $15 at the movies and $12 on a book, and got $25 for his birthday. After his second paycheck he had $20 less than two weeks' pay combined. How much is his paycheck? **$76**

27. **Party Supplies** You are decorating for a school picnic. Balloons cost \$8 for a dozen but cost more if bought individually. With the money you have, you can buy 7 dozen and 5 single balloons, or 75 single balloons. How much is one balloon? How much money do you have? \$.80; \$60

Solve the equation.

C 28. $5p + 4 = 11p - 2 - p$ $1\frac{1}{5}$	29. $-5g + 3 = -3g + 6g$ $\frac{3}{8}$
30. $3(j + 4) = -2j + j$ -3	31. $5(t + 7) = 2(2t + 7)$ -21
32. $2(c + 6) = 5(c + 12)$ -16	33. $6(s - 4) = 3(s + 9)$ 17

34. **Critical Thinking** How many different values of x will make the equation $2(x + 3) = 2x + 6$ true? Explain your answer. See margin.

35. **Challenge** In 1999, there were 3940 museums and some number of historical sites in the United States. The total number of these attractions was 376 more than five times the number of historical sites. How many historical sites were there in the United States in 1999? 891 sites

34. Infinitely many. *Sample answer:* When the left side of the equation is simplified, the expressions on both sides of the equation are exactly the same.

Mixed Review 

Find the least common denominator of the fractions. *(Lesson 4.5)*

36. $\frac{1}{2}, \frac{2}{3}, \frac{5}{6}$ 6	37. $\frac{2}{9}, \frac{3}{4}, \frac{11}{12}$ 36	38. $\frac{4}{5}, \frac{1}{2}, \frac{3}{70}$ 70

Find the sum or difference. *(Lesson 5.6)*

39. $7.31 + 2.248$ 9.558	40. $10.26 - 3.72$ 6.54	41. $16.508 + 4.53$ 21.038

Solve the equation. *(Lesson 6.1)*

42. $5c + 24 - 3c = 2$ -11	43. $3(2z - 3) = 75$ 14	44. $7x - 2(x - 11) = -23$ -9
45. $3b - 5b = -14$ 7	46. $4(x - 7) = 4$ 8	47. $\frac{y + 3}{5} = 10$ 47

Test-Taking Practice 

INTERNET
State Test Practice
CLASSZONE.COM

48. **Multiple Choice** One phone card charges \$.025 a minute with a \$.50 monthly fee. Another card charges \$.038 a minute with no monthly fee. You need a card for 3 months. Which equation could you use to find the number of minutes for which both cards cost the same? B

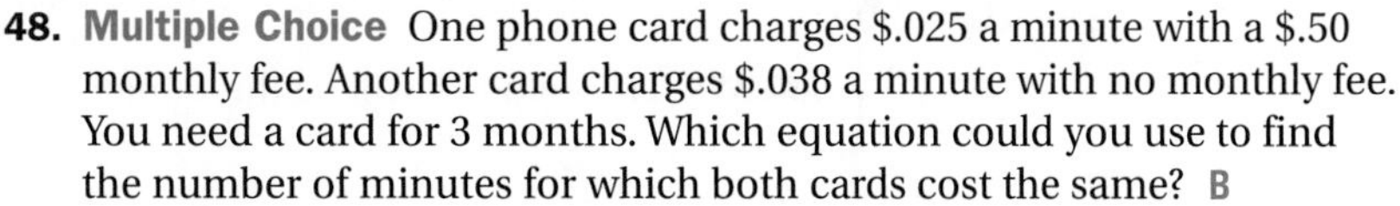

A. $0.025x = 0.038x + 3(0.50)$ **B.** $0.025x + 3(0.50) = 0.038x$

C. $0.025x = 0.038x$ **D.** $0.025x + 0.50 = 0.038x$

49. **Multiple Choice** What is the value of x in the equation $5x + 14 = 3x - 12$? G

F. -26 **G.** -13 **H.** -1 **I.** 1

4 ASSESS

Assessment Resources

For more assessment resources, see:
- Assessment Book
- Test and Practice Generator

Mini-Quiz

Solve the equation.

1. $17b = 2b - 45$ -3
2. $33 + 5k = 8k$ 11
3. $18d + 10 = -7d - 15$ -1
4. Find the perimeter of the triangle. The sides are equal in length.

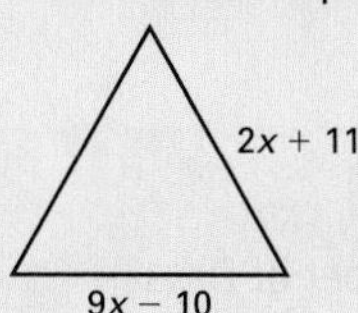

51 units

5 FOLLOW-UP

Reteaching/Remediation

- Study Guide in Chapter 6 Resource Book, pp. 23–24
- Tutor Place, Algebra Card 6
- eTutorial Plus Online
- Extra Practice, p. 732
- Lesson Practice in Chapter 6 Resource Book, pp. 20–22

Challenge/Enrichment

- Challenge Practice in Chapter 6 Resource Book, p. 25
- Teacher's Edition, p. 268F

English Learner Support

- Spanish Study Guide
- Multi-Language Glossary
- Chapter Audio Summaries CDs

PLAN

SKILL CHECK

1. $0.06 \div 0.016 = \underline{?}$ 3.75
2. $0.025 \times 1000 = \underline{?}$ 25
3. $0.11 \times 1000 = \underline{?}$ 110
4. $\frac{3}{10} \times 30 = \underline{?}$ 9

Lesson Objective

Solve equations with fractions and decimals.

Pacing

Suggested Number of Days
Basic Course: 2 days
Average Course: 2 days
Advanced Course: 2 days
Block: 0.5 block with 6.2
0.5 block with 6.4

Teaching Resources

For a complete list of Teaching Resources, see page 268B.

Transparency

Warm-Up Exercises for this lesson are available on a transparency.

TEACH

Motivating the Lesson

Write an equation such as $3x + 5 = x - 3$ on the board. Multiply both sides first by 10 and then by 0.1. In each case, ask students if they think the resulting equation has the same solution as the original equation.

Solving Equations Involving Fractions and Decimals

BEFORE	Now	WHY?
You solved equations involving whole numbers.	You'll solve equations with fractions and decimals.	So you can determine the size of a lawn, as in Ex. 18.

Word Watch

Review Words

least common denominator (LCD), p. 192

In the Real World

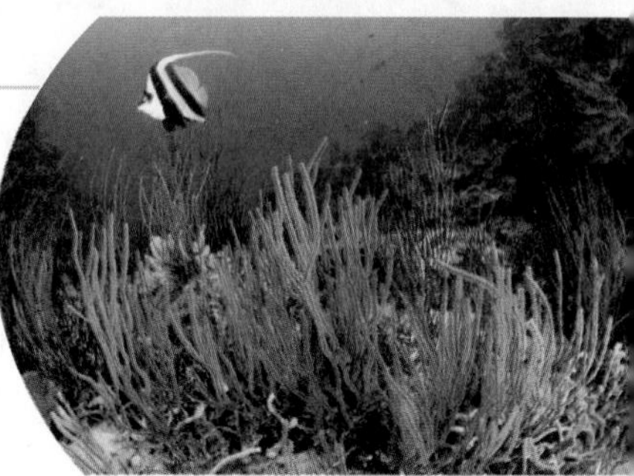

Environment A colony of coral is 0.17 meter high and is growing at a rate of 0.025 meter per year. Another colony is 0.11 meter high. It is growing at a rate of 0.041 meter per year. In how many years will the colonies be the same height?

EXAMPLE 1 Solving an Equation Involving Decimals

To solve the coral problem, you need to solve an equation involving decimals. First write a verbal model. Let n = the number of years.

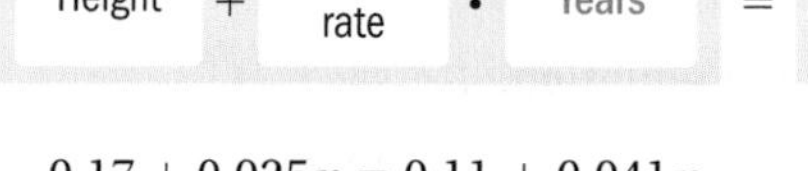

Colony 1						Colony 2				
Height	+	Growth rate	•	Years	=	Height	+	Growth rate	•	Years

$0.17 + 0.025n = 0.11 + 0.041n$ Write algebraic model.

$0.17 = 0.11 + 0.016n$ Subtract $0.025n$ from each side.

$0.06 = 0.016n$ Subtract 0.11 from each side.

$\frac{0.06}{0.016} = \frac{0.016n}{0.016}$ Divide each side by 0.016.

$3.75 = n$ Simplify.

ANSWER The colonies will be the same height in a little less than 4 years.

with Notetaking

In Example 1, some of the steps are not shown. You may want to identify these steps and include them in your notes.

Your turn now **Write a verbal model. Then solve.**

1. You and a friend are buying snowboarding gear. You buy a pair of goggles that costs \$39.95 and 4 tubes of wax. Your friend buys a helmet that costs \$54.95 and 2 tubes of wax. If you each spend the same amount, how much does each tube of wax cost?

1. *Sample answer:* Cost of goggles + Number of tubes of wax you buy • Cost per tube = Cost of helmet + Number of tubes of wax your friend buys • Cost per tube; \$7.50

ILLINOIS Standards and ISAT:
8.A.3b, 8.D.3a

Clearing Decimals The multiplication property of equality allows you to multiply each side of an equation by the same number, so you can clear decimals from an equation if you wish.

with Solving

To clear decimals, multiply each side of the equation by a power of ten that will make all the coefficients integers. In Example 2, multiply by 100.

EXAMPLE 2 Solving an Equation Involving Decimals

$1.4x - 1.8 + 2.35x = 0.21$	Original equation
$(1.4x - 1.8 + 2.35x)100 = (0.21)100$	Multiply each side by 100 to clear decimals.
$140x - 180 + 235x = 21$	Simplify.
$375x - 180 = 21$	Combine like terms.
$375x = 201$	Add 180 to each side.
$\frac{375x}{375} = \frac{201}{375}$	Divide each side by 375.
$x = 0.536$	Simplify.

Clearing Fractions When solving an equation with fractions, you can multiply each side by the LCD to clear the fractions.

EXAMPLE 3 Solving an Equation Involving Fractions

$\frac{3}{10}x = -\frac{1}{6}x + \frac{7}{10}$	Original equation
$\left(\frac{3}{10}x\right)30 = \left(-\frac{1}{6}x + \frac{7}{10}\right)30$	Multiply each side by the LCD, 30.
$\left(\frac{3}{10}x\right)30 = \left(-\frac{1}{6}x\right)30 + \left(\frac{7}{10}\right)30$	Distributive property
$\frac{3 \cdot \cancel{30}^{3}}{{}_{1}\cancel{10}}x = -\frac{1 \cdot \cancel{30}^{5}}{{}_{1}\cancel{6}}x + \frac{7 \cdot \cancel{30}^{3}}{{}_{1}\cancel{10}}$	Divide out common factors.
$9x = -5x + 21$	Simplify.
$14x = 21$	Add $5x$ to each side.
$x = \frac{21}{14} = \frac{3}{2}$, or $1\frac{1}{2}$	Divide each side by 14. Simplify.

Your turn now Solve the equation. Then check the solution.

2. $-1.7k + 6.7k = 13.1$ **2.62**
3. $1.2n - 0.24 = 0.7n$ **0.48**
4. $8.3 - 8y = 1.2y + 6$ **0.25**
5. $\frac{4}{5}x + 3 = -\frac{7}{10}$ **$-4\frac{5}{8}$**
6. $2s - 1\frac{1}{4}s = \frac{1}{3}$ **$\frac{4}{9}$**
7. $\frac{5}{6}v + \frac{5}{8} = \frac{3}{8}v$ **$-1\frac{4}{11}$**

TIPS FOR NEW TEACHERS

Before beginning Example 3, you may want to spend a few minutes reviewing how to find the LCD. See Tips for New Teachers in the *Chapter 6 Resource Book*.

EXTRA EXAMPLES

Example 1 One stalactite is 25 centimeters long and is growing at a rate of 1.2 centimeters per year. Another stalactite is 22 centimeters long and is growing at a rate of 1.8 centimeters per year. In how many years will the stalactites be the same length? **5 yr**

Example 2 Solve $0.62a - 0.64 + 1.78a = 0.36$. **$0.41\overline{6}$**

Example 3 Solve $\frac{1}{3}a = \frac{20}{21} - \frac{1}{7}a$. **2**

TEACHING TIP

In Example 2, be sure students understand why 100 is chosen as the multiplier rather than 10 or 1000.

CONCEPT CHECK

How do you solve an equation involving fractions? **Multiply each side by the LCD to eliminate the fractions.**

DAILY PUZZLER

If a hen and a half lays an egg and a half in a day and a half, how long will it take 3 hens to lay 12 eggs? **4 days**

3 APPLY

ASSIGNMENT GUIDE

Basic Course

Day 1: pp. 284–285 Exs. 9–12, 17, 24, 27–34

Day 2: pp. 284–285 Exs. 13–16, 18–23, 35–38

Average Course

Day 1: pp. 284–285 Exs. 10–12, 17, 25, 27–34

Day 2: pp. 284–285 Exs. 14–16, 18–24, 35–38

Advanced Course

Day 1: pp. 284–285 Exs. 10–12, 17, 25–30*, 36–38

Day 2: pp. 284–285 Exs. 14–16, 18–24, 31–33

Block

pp. 284–285 Exs. 10–12, 17, 25, 27–34 (with 6.2)

pp. 284–285 Exs. 14–16, 18–24, 35–38 (with 6.4)

EXTRA PRACTICE

- Student Edition, p. 732
- Chapter 6 Resource Book, pp. 29–31
- Test and Practice Generator

TRANSPARENCY

Even-numbered answers are available on transparencies.

HOMEWORK CHECK

When you review students' homework for this lesson, go over the following exercises to check understanding of key concepts.

Basic: 9, 13, 18, 19, 23

Average: 10, 14, 18, 19, 23

Advanced: 11, 15, 18, 20, 24

COMMON ERROR

In Exercise 18, watch for students who begin by finding $\frac{3}{5}$ of 2400.

6.3 Exercises

More Practice, p. 732

Getting Ready to Practice

1. **Vocabulary** Copy and complete: 24 is the _?_ of $\frac{1}{4}$, $\frac{5}{6}$, and $\frac{3}{8}$. **least common denominator or LCD**

Tell what number you would multiply each side of the equation by to eliminate the decimals or fractions. Then solve the equation.

2. $1.5a - 1.2 = 1.8a$ **10; −4**
3. $5.85b = 8.68 + 3.68b$ **100; 4**
4. $0.5c + 3.49 - 2c = 4$ **100; −0.34**
5. $\frac{3}{8}m + \frac{7}{8} = 2m$ **8; $\frac{7}{13}$**
6. $-\frac{4}{15}n + \frac{2}{3} = \frac{2}{5}n$ **15; 1**
7. $-\frac{1}{5}p + \frac{3}{4}p = 11$ **20; 20**
8. **Find the Error** Describe and correct the error in the solution.

$$1.5x + 0.25 = 1.6x$$
$$15x + 25 = 16x$$
$$25 = x$$

8. In the second step, the terms were not all multiplied by the same number. Each term on both sides of the equation should be multiplied by 100, which gives $150x + 25 = 160x$. This simplifies to $25 = 10x$, or $x = 2.5$.

with Homework

Example	Exercises
1	23-24
2	9-16, 19-22
3	9-16, 18-23

Online Resources CLASSZONE.COM
- More Examples
- eTutorial Plus

Practice and Problem Solving

Solve the equation. Then check the solution.

A 9. $r + 8.2 + 0.4r = -8.6$ **−12**

10. $1.5s - 1.2 - s = 0.5$ **3.4**

11. $5.3 + u = 3.2u - 2.7$ **$3.\overline{63}$**

12. $4.93 - 9.20v = 0.66v$ **0.5**

13. $p - \frac{4}{9}p = -\frac{7}{9}$ **$-1\frac{2}{5}$**

14. $\frac{3}{10} - w = \frac{4}{5} - \frac{3}{5}w$ **$-1\frac{1}{4}$**

15. $\frac{1}{6}x + \frac{2}{3}x = 1$ **$1\frac{1}{5}$**

16. $\frac{7}{4}z - \frac{1}{6} = \frac{17}{6} + \frac{3}{4}z$ **3**

17. **Estimation** Round each coefficient and constant in the equation $6.95x - 2.13 = 1.8x + 3.07$ to the nearest integer. Solve the new equation. What does your answer tell you about the answer to the original equation? Solve the original equation. Compare your answers. **$7x - 2 = 2x + 3$; 1; it is about 1; about 1.0097; the answers are very close.**

18. **Mowing the Lawn** You mow $\frac{1}{5}$ of the lawn and your sister mows $\frac{2}{5}$ of the lawn. The two of you mow a total of 2400 square feet. What is the area of the lawn? How much area is left to mow? **4000 ft^2; 1600 ft^2**

Solve the equation. Then check the solution.

B 19. $-2.67g - 8.4 = 6.072 + 0.03g$ **−5.36**

20. $0.25(66 + 42.4h) = 3.1652$ **−1.258**

21. $\frac{3}{8} + \frac{9}{20}m = \frac{23}{20} + \frac{7}{8}m$ **$-1\frac{14}{17}$**

22. $6\frac{4}{5}n - \frac{8}{9} = \frac{7}{15}n$ **$\frac{8}{57}$**

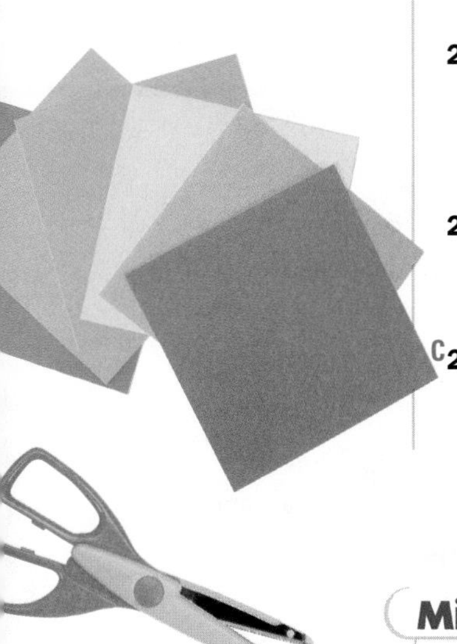

23. **Fabric** At a fabric store you buy a clothes pattern for \$7. You also buy $\frac{3}{4}$ yard of red fabric, $2\frac{1}{2}$ yards of purple fabric, and $\frac{7}{8}$ yard of blue fabric. The total cost is \$23.50. If all three fabrics are the same price per yard, how much do you spend on each fabric?
   \$3 on red, \$10 on purple, and \$3.50 on blue

24. **Art Supplies** Joyce buys scissors for \$6.20 and 7 packages of paper. Paul buys paints for \$9.94 and 5 packages of paper. They each spend the same amount, and each package of paper costs the same amount. How much does each package of paper cost? \$1.87

25. **Critical Thinking** If you multiply each side of an equation by a common multiple of the denominators that is not the LCD, should you still get the correct answer? Explain. See margin.

C 26. **Challenge** Your batting average was 0.245 for your first baseball game and 0.251 for your second. After your third game your *overall* batting average is 0.250. What was your batting average for your third game? 0.254

25. Yes. *Sample answer:* The extra factor(s) will divide out, so the simplified result will be the same.

Mixed Review

Evaluate the expression. *(Lessons 5.2, 5.3, 5.6, 5.7)*

27. $6.239 + 12.2$ 18.439
28. $5\frac{1}{2} - 2\frac{3}{8}$ $3\frac{1}{8}$
29. 4.1×8.235 33.7635
30. $\frac{4}{9} \times \frac{11}{13}$ $\frac{44}{117}$

Solve the equation. *(Lesson 6.2)*

31. $6n + 11 = 2n - 1$ −3
32. $16 - 3s = 2s - 14$ 6
33. $-3(w - 7) = 5w + 3$ 2.25

Basic Skills **Write an equivalent expression.**

34. $9(8 + x)$ $72 + 9x$
35. $-15(y - 4)$ $-15y + 60$
36. $-z(4 + 3 - 5)$ $-2z$

Test-Taking Practice

INTERNET
State Test Practice
CLASSZONE.COM

37. **Multiple Choice** At a basketball game, you buy 10 raffle tickets. Your friend buys a T-shirt for \$13.50 and 1 raffle ticket. If you each spend the same amount, which equation can you use to find how much each raffle ticket costs? D

   A. $11x = 13.5$ **B.** $13.5 = 10x + x$
   C. $10x + 13.5 = x$ **D.** $10x = 13.5 + x$

38. **Multiple Choice** At the deli, Swiss cheese costs \$3.95 per pound and turkey costs \$4.75 per pound. You buy the same amount of each and spend \$13.05. How much did you buy of each? H

   F. 0.15 pound **G.** 0.18 pound **H.** 1.5 pounds **I.** 1.8 pounds

4 ASSESS

Assessment Resources

For more assessment resources, see:
- Assessment Book
- Test and Practice Generator

Mini-Quiz

Solve the equation.

1. $f + 0.4 + 0.6f = -0.6$ -0.625
2. $0.9 + a = 6.4a - 0.7$ $0.\overline{296}$
3. $\frac{2}{5}g + \frac{7}{10}g = 22$ 20
4. $\frac{2}{3} - k = \frac{5}{6} - \frac{k}{3}$ $-\frac{1}{4}$
5. Cedric tiled $\frac{3}{8}$ of a hall and Danielle tiled $\frac{1}{4}$ of the hall. Together they tiled 18,750 square feet. What is the area of the hall? 30,000 ft^2

5 FOLLOW-UP

Reteaching/Remediation

- Study Guide in Chapter 6 Resource Book, pp. 32–33
- Tutor Place, Whole Numbers and Decimals Cards 6, 12, 13, Fractions Card 15
- eTutorial Plus Online
- Extra Practice, p. 732
- Lesson Practice in Chapter 6 Resource Book, pp. 29–31

Challenge/Enrichment

- Challenge Practice in Chapter 6 Resource Book, p. 34
- Teacher's Edition, p. 268F

English Learner Support

- Spanish Study Guide
- Multi-Language Glossary
- Chapter Audio Summaries CDs

ADDITIONAL RESOURCES

The following resources are available to help review the materials in Lessons 6.1–6.3.

Chapter 6 Resource Book
- Lesson Practice
- Study Guide

Assessment Book
- Chapter 6 Quiz 1

Technology
- Test and Practice Generator
- eTutorial CD-ROM

Internet
- Classzone
- eWorkbook Plus Online
- eTutorial Plus Online

ENGLISH LEARNER SUPPORT

- Spanish Study Guide
- Multi-Language Glossary
- Chapter Audio Summaries CDs

1. ***Sample answer:*** **To combine like terms, find the terms with the same variable part, including exponents, and add or subtract the coefficients. The result is the coefficient of the term with that same variable part. Constants are like terms.**

Notebook Review

Review the vocabulary definitions in your notebook.

Copy the review examples in your notebook. Then complete the exercises.

Check Your Definitions

perimeter, p. 33
distributive property, p. 85
like terms, p. 86
least common denominator (LCD), p. 192

Use Your Vocabulary

1. In your own words, explain how to combine like terms. **See margin.**

6.1–6.2 Can you solve multi-step equations?

EXAMPLE Solve $4(x - 8) = -x + 4 + 7x$.

$4(x - 8) = -x + 4 + 7x$	**Original equation**
$4x - 32 = 6x + 4$	**Use the distributive property and combine like terms.**
$-32 = 2x + 4$	**Subtract $4x$ from each side.**
$-36 = 2x$	**Subtract 4 from each side.**
$-18 = x$	**Divide each side by 2.**

Solve the equation.

2. $-2x + 8 + x = 12$ -4 **3.** $4z = 8(3 + z)$ -6 **4.** $-6 + 10a = 3 - 2a$ $\frac{3}{4}$

6.3 Can you solve equations involving fractions and decimals?

EXAMPLE Solve $\frac{3}{4}y = \frac{1}{6}y - 4$.

$\frac{3}{4}y = \frac{1}{6}y - 4$	**Original equation**
$9y = 2y - 48$	**Multiply each side by the LCD, 12.**
$9y - 2y = 2y - 48 - 2y$	**Subtract $2y$ from each side.**
$7y = -48$	**Simplify.**
$y = -\frac{48}{7}$, or $-6\frac{6}{7}$	**Divide each side by 7.**

☑ **Solve the equation.**

5. $-3.5a - 19.5 + 9.8a = 10.74$ 4.8
6. $3\frac{1}{4} - 6b = 1\frac{1}{2} + 2\frac{3}{4}b$ $\frac{1}{5}$

Stop and Think about Lessons 6.1–6.3

7. **Writing** Explain how you can clear the decimals from the equation $16.2 - 4.32x = 10.8 + 0.023x$ before solving for x. Multiply each side by 1000.

Review Quiz 1

Solve the equation.

1. $2(x + 16) = 46$ 7
2. $79 = 10x - 23 + 7x$ 6
3. $-108 = -16(x + 5) + 9x$ 4
4. $12n = 17 - 22n$ $\frac{1}{2}$
5. $27.2m + 15.7 = -85.94 + 0.8m$ −3.85
6. $\frac{1}{2}v + \frac{11}{12} - \frac{5}{4}v = -\frac{5}{12}$ $1\frac{7}{9}$
7. **Geometry** Find the perimeter of the rectangle. The lengths are measured in feet. 22 ft

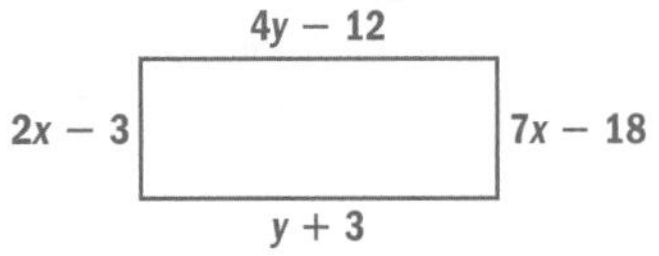

8. **Color Printer** You have \$445 to buy a printer. You find one that costs \$235. It uses a black ink cartridge that costs \$30 and a color ink cartridge that costs \$40. Write and solve an equation to determine how many pairs of ink cartridges you can buy for the printer.
$235 + (30 + 40)n = 445$; 3 pairs

Brain Game

Going Bananas

Solve each equation and use the value to move the monkey that number of spaces in the direction indicated. This will lead the monkey to his favorite set of bananas.
Favorite set is B.

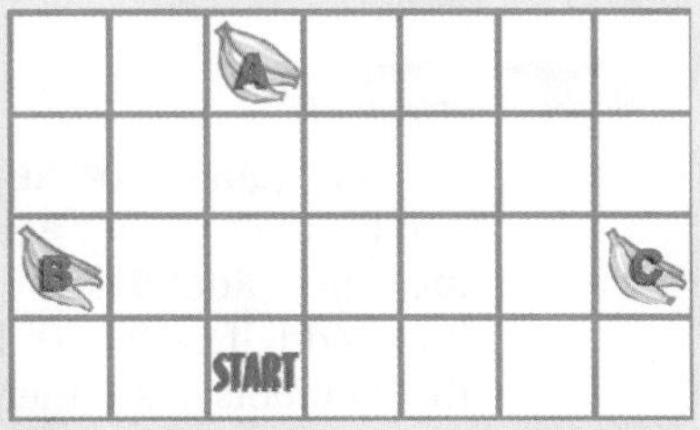

1. $x - 5 = 2x - 8$; right 3
2. $-4x = 2(x - 6)$; up 2
3. $\frac{1}{2}x = \frac{1}{3}x - \frac{1}{2} + \frac{4}{3}$; left 5
4. $5(3x + 6) = 9(6x - 1)$; down 1

PLAN

Explore the Concept

- Students will find the relationship between diameter and circumference.
- This activity leads into solving problems involving circumference and diameter in Lesson 6.4.

Materials

Each student or group of students will need a tape measure or ruler, string, paper, and pencil.

Recommended Time

Work activity: 15 min
Discuss results: 5 min

Grouping

Students can work individually or in groups of three. If students work in groups, two students can take measurements while the third records the results. The students can share their results in computing quotients and finding averages.

Transparency

A support transparency is available for this Activity.

TEACH

Tips for Success

When students find quotients, they should carry out the divisions to the thousandths place.

6.4 Hands-on Activity

GOAL
Find the relationship between diameter and circumference.

MATERIALS
- metric tape measure or ruler
- string
- paper and pencil

Diameter and Circumference

In this activity, you will investigate the relationship between the diameter and circumference of a circle.

The ***diameter*** is the distance across a circle through the center.

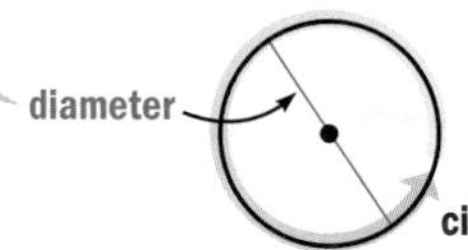

The ***circumference*** is the distance around a circle.

Explore 1 **Find the diameter and circumference of circular objects.**

Measure the diameter and circumference of several circular objects. If necessary, wrap a string around the object and measure the length of the string with a ruler. Record the measurements in a table like the one below.

Object	Diameter	Circumference	$\frac{\text{Circumference}}{\text{Diameter}}$
Water bottle	65 mm	206 mm	?
Tuna can	84 mm	264 mm	?
Clock	174 mm	549 mm	?
Quarter	24 mm	74 mm	?
Mug	82 mm	261 mm	?

Your turn now

1. Find the quotient of the circumference and the diameter for each object you measured. Round to the nearest hundredth if necessary. Record the quotients in another column of the table. **The quotients should all be about 3.14.**
2. What do you notice about the numbers in the new column of your table? **They are all about the same.**

ILLINOIS Standards and ISAT:
7.C.3b, 8.B.3, 8.D.3b, 9.C.3b

Explore 2 **Write a circumference formula.**

1. Find an average of the quotients $\frac{\text{circumference}}{\text{diameter}}$ in your table.

   How does your average compare to the averages found by the other students in your class?
   The average quotients should all be about 3.14. All of the averages should be about the same.

2. Find an average of the quotients $\frac{\text{circumference}}{\text{diameter}}$ collected by your whole class.
   The average quotient should be about 3.14.

3. Use the result in Step 2 to write a formula for the circumference of a circle in terms of the diameter.
   $C = 3.14d$

Your turn now **Use the formula you wrote in Step 3 above to calculate the circumference of the circle given its diameter *d*.**

3. $d = 64$ mm

200.96 mm

4. $d = 140$ mm

439.6 mm

5. $d = 36$ cm

113.04 cm

6. $d = 20$ cm

62.8 cm

7. $d = 4$ in.

12.56 in.

8. $d = 1.25$ in.

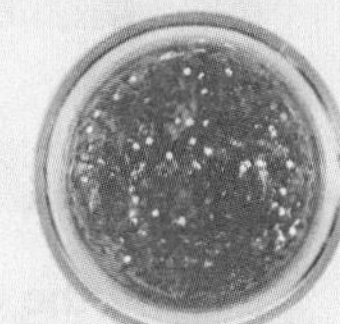

3.925 in.

Stop and Think

9. Writing Write a formula for the diameter of a circle in terms of the circumference. $d = \frac{C}{3.14}$

3 CLOSE

Key Discovery

Circumference is always a little more than 3 times the diameter, regardless of the length of the diameter.

Assessment

1. If two objects have the same circumference, what can you predict about their diameters? **Their diameters are the same.**
2. If you double the diameter of a circle, what will happen to the circumference? **It will double.**

PLAN

SKILL CHECK

1. $4.96 \div 2 = \underline{?}$ 2.48
2. $2.6 \times 3.14 = \underline{?}$ 8.164
3. $\frac{49}{2} \times \frac{22}{7} = \underline{?}$ 77

LESSON OBJECTIVE

Solve equations involving the circumference of a circle.

PACING

Suggested Number of Days
Basic Course: 1 day
Average Course: 1 day
Advanced Course: 1 day
Block: 0.5 block with 6.3

TEACHING RESOURCES

For a complete list of Teaching Resources, see page 268B.

TRANSPARENCY

Warm-Up Exercises for this lesson are available on a transparency.

TEACH

MOTIVATING THE LESSON

Point out that the distance around Earth at the equator is about 25,000 miles. Ask how to use this fact to find Earth's diameter at the equator.

TIPS FOR NEW TEACHERS

Ask students to notice whether they are working with radius or diameter. Remind them that a given radius must be doubled before finding circumference. See Tips for New Teachers in the *Chapter 6 Resource Book*.

Solving Equations Involving Circumference

BEFORE

You solved equations involving fractions and decimals.

Now

You'll solve equations involving the circumference of a circle.

WHY?

So you can find the diameter of a clock, as in Ex. 28.

Word Watch

circle, p. 290
center, p. 290
radius, p. 290
diameter, p. 290
circumference, p. 290
pi (π), p. 290

A **circle** is the set of all points in a plane that are the same distance from a fixed point called the **center**. The distance from the center to any point on the circle is the **radius**. The **diameter** is the distance across the circle through the center.

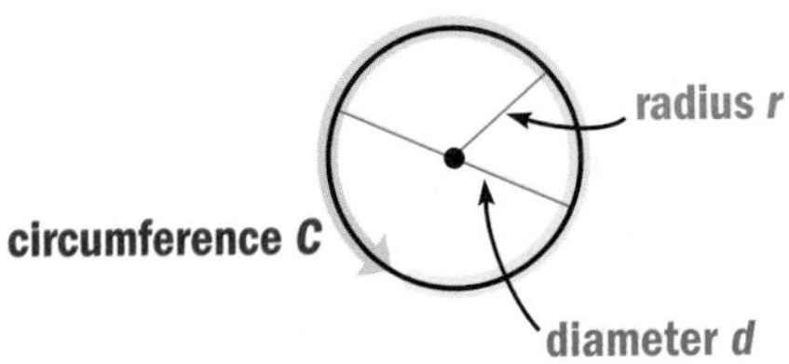

The **circumference** of a circle is the distance around the circle. For every circle, the quotient of its circumference and its diameter is the same: about 3.14159. This constant is represented by the Greek letter **pi**, π. You can approximate π using 3.14, $\frac{22}{7}$, or the π key on a calculator.

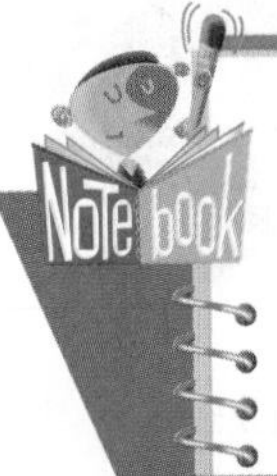

Circumference of a Circle

Words The circumference of a circle is the product of π and the diameter.

Algebra $C = \pi d$ or $C = 2\pi r$

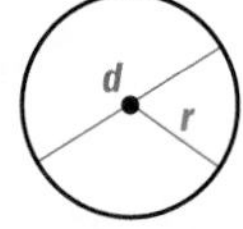

EXAMPLE 1 Using Radius to Find Circumference

Find the circumference of a circle with a radius of 11 meters.

Solution

$C = 2\pi r$	Circumference formula
$\approx 2(3.14)(11)$	Substitute 3.14 for π and 11 for r.
$= 69.08$	Multiply.

ANSWER The circumference is about 69.08 meters.

ILLINOIS Standards and ISAT:
7.C.3b, 8.D.3b; 7.B.3

with Solving

When deciding whether to use $\frac{22}{7}$ for π, look for numbers that are divisible by 22 or 7.

4. 100 in.; I used 3.14 because 32 is not divisible by 7.
5. 440 ft; I used $\frac{22}{7}$ because 140 is divisible by 7.
6. 9.42 km; I used 3.14 because 1.5 is not divisible by 7.

EXAMPLE 2 Using Diameter to Find Circumference

Find the circumference of the circle.

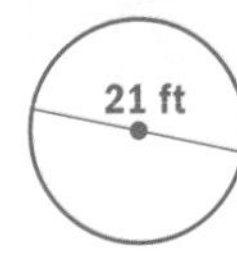

Solution

The measure shown is a diameter, so use the circumference formula that involves the diameter.

$C = \pi d$	**Circumference formula**
$\approx \frac{22}{\cancel{7}_1} \cdot \cancel{21}^3$	**Substitute. Use $\frac{22}{7}$ for π because 21 is divisible by 7.**
$= 66$	**Multiply.**

ANSWER The circumference is about 66 feet.

Your turn now **Find the circumference of the circle. Use 3.14 or $\frac{22}{7}$ for π. Explain your choice of value of π.**

1. 

176 mi; I used $\frac{22}{7}$ because 28 is divisible by 7.

2. 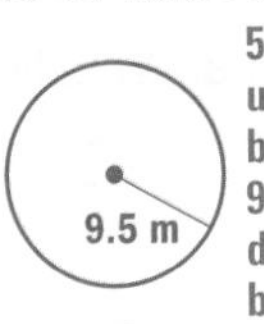

59.7 m; I used 3.14 because 9.5 is not divisible by 7.

3. 16 cm
50.2 cm; I used 3.14 because 16 is not divisible by 7.

4. diameter = 32 in.
5. diameter = 140 ft
6. radius = 1.5 km

4–6. See margin.

EXAMPLE 3 Finding Diameter in Real Life

Ferris Wheel **A ferris wheel has a circumference of about 423.9 feet. Find its diameter.**

Solution

You are asked to find the diameter, so use the circumference formula that involves diameter.

$C = \pi d$	**Circumference formula**
$423.9 \approx 3.14d$	**Substitute 423.9 for C and 3.14 for π.**
$\frac{423.9}{3.14} \approx \frac{3.14d}{3.14}$	**Divide each side by 3.14.**
$135 \approx d$	**Simplify.**

ANSWER The diameter is about 135 feet.

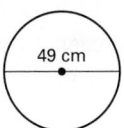

Ferris Wheels

This ride has 16 swinging cars and 8 stationary cars, and it can hold 144 people at a time. How many people can ride in each car?
6 people

EXTRA EXAMPLES

Example 1 Find the circumference of a circle with a radius of 15 feet. **about 94.2 ft**

Example 2 Find the circumference of the circle.

49 cm

about 154 cm

Example 3 A giant twine ball in Darwin, Minnesota, has a circumference of about 37.7 feet. Find its diameter. **about 12 ft**

CROSS-CURRICULUM

Art Ask students for examples of ways in which circles appear in pottery, sculpture, painting, and other forms of art.

EXTRA EXAMPLES

Example 4 A circle has a circumference of 220 centimeters. Find the radius. **about 35 cm**

CONCEPT CHECK

How do you find the circumference of a circle? **Multiply the diameter (or twice the radius) times an approximation of π.**

DAILY PUZZLER

In 2002, the London Eye was listed as the largest Ferris wheel in the world, with a diameter of 443 feet. If you were riding on this wheel, how many revolutions of the wheel would you travel to cover one mile (5280 feet)? **about 3.8 revolutions**

1.

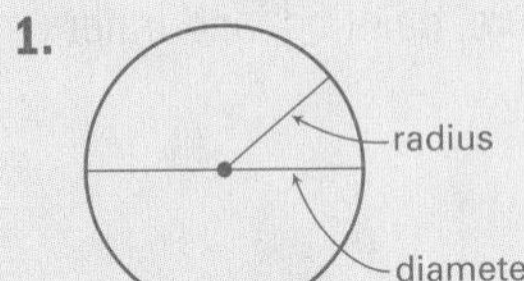

HELP with Review

For help with reciprocals, see p. 234.

EXAMPLE 4 Using Circumference to Find the Radius

A circle has a circumference of 88 inches. Find the radius.

Solution

$C = 2\pi r$	Circumference formula
$88 \approx 2\left(\frac{22}{7}\right)r$	Use $\frac{22}{7}$ for π.
$88 \approx \frac{44}{7}r$	Simplify.
$\overset{2}{\cancel{88}} \cdot \frac{7}{\cancel{44}_1} \approx \frac{44}{7}r \cdot \frac{7}{44}$	Multiply each side by $\frac{7}{44}$, the reciprocal of $\frac{44}{7}$.
$14 \approx r$	Simplify.

ANSWER The radius is about 14 inches.

Your turn now Use 3.14 or $\frac{22}{7}$ for π. Explain your choice of value of π.

7. A circle has a circumference of 20.41 inches. Find the diameter.
8. A circle has a circumference of 132 inches. Find the radius.

7. 6.5 in.; I used 3.14 because 20.41 is not divisible by 22.
8. 21 in.; I used $\frac{22}{7}$ because 132 is divisible by 22.

6.4 Exercises

More Practice, p. 732

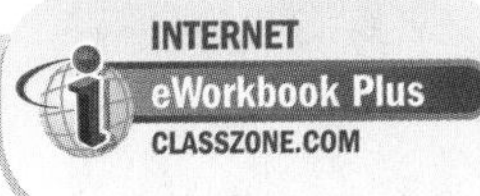

Getting Ready to Practice

1. **Vocabulary** Draw and label a circle with a radius and a diameter. **See margin.**

Find the indicated measurement, where r = radius, d = diameter, and C = circumference. Use 3.14 or $\frac{22}{7}$ for π. Explain your choice.

2. $d = 56$ m, $C = \underline{?}$
3. $C = 66$ in., $r = \underline{?}$
4. $r = 6\frac{1}{4}$ ft, $C = \underline{?}$
5. $d = 11$ cm, $C = \underline{?}$
6. $C = 3.14$ m, $r = \underline{?}$
7. $C = 330$ yd, $d = \underline{?}$
8. **Find the Error** Describe and correct the error in the solution.

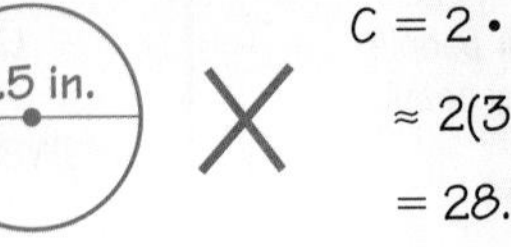

Sample answer: **The diameter is given, not the radius. The circumference formula that involves diameter should be used. This gives $C = \pi \cdot d \approx (3.14)(4.5) = 14.1$ inches.**

2. 176 m; I used $\frac{22}{7}$ because 56 is divisible by 7.
3. 10.5 in.; I used $\frac{22}{7}$ because 66 is divisible by 22.
4. 39.3 ft; I used 3.14 because $6\frac{1}{4}$ is not divisible by 7.
5. 34.5 cm; I used 3.14 because 11 is not divisible by 7.
6. 0.5 m; I used 3.14 because 3.14 is not divisible by 22.
7. 105 yd; I used $\frac{22}{7}$ because 330 is divisible by 22.

Example	Exercises
1	12-20
2	12-20, 23
3	28-29
4	12-20

· More Examples
· eTutorial Plus

Practice and Problem Solving

Measurement **Use a ruler to find the indicated measure. Then use the measure to find the circumference of the circle. Use 3.14 for π.**

A **9.**

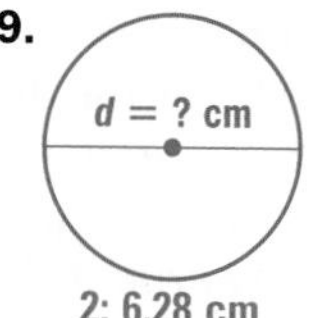

2; 6.28 cm

10.

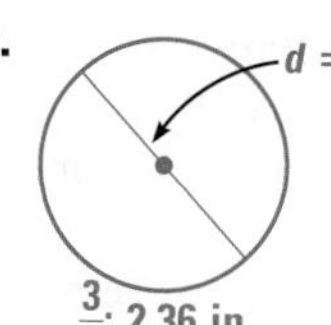

$\frac{3}{4}$; 2.36 in.

11.

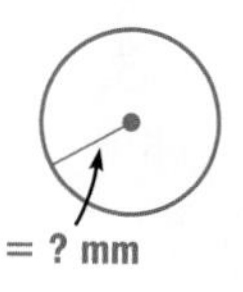

7; 44.0 mm

In Exercises 12–20, find the indicated measurement, where r = radius, d = diameter, and C = circumference. Use 3.14 or $\frac{22}{7}$ for π.

12. $C = 44$ m

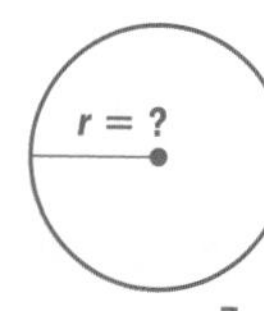

7 m

13. $C = 157$ yd

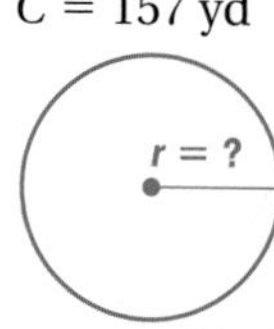

25 yd

14. $C = 235.5$ cm

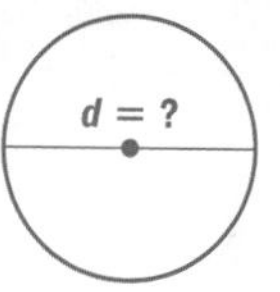

75 cm

15. $r = 10$ mm, $C = \underline{?}$ 62.8 mm
16. $r = 21$ ft, $C = \underline{?}$ 132 ft
17. $d = 14$ in., $C = \underline{?}$ 44 in.

18. $d = 15$ mi, $C = \underline{?}$ 47.1 mi
19. $C = 33$ km, $d = \underline{?}$ 10.5 km
20. $C = 628$ cm, $r = \underline{?}$ 100 cm

21. Estimation Use mental math to solve Exercises 9–11 again, using 3 for π. How can these estimates help you to check your answers?

21. 9. 6 cm; 10. 2.25 in.; 11. 42 mm; the actual answers should be close to these estimates.

22. Critical Thinking Find the circumferences of circles with the radii 1, 2, 4, 8, and 16 meters. Leave your answers in terms of π. Then compare the circumferences. What happens to the circumference of a circle as its radius doubles? 2π, 4π, 8π, 16π, 32π; the circumference doubles.

23. Dome The diameter of the U.S. Capitol Building's dome is 96 feet at its widest point. Find its circumference. Use 3.14 for π. about 301 ft

24. Writing Look up the word *circumnavigate* in the dictionary. How is the definition like the definition of *circumference*?

24. *Sample answer:* The word means to sail or fly around something, for example, an island; it involves going all the way around something.

Extended Problem Solving **Adventurer Mike Horn traveled around the world as close to the equator as possible without using any motorized transportation.**

B **25. Calculate** The radius of Earth is 3963 miles. Approximate its circumference. Use 3.14 for π. about 24,900 mi

26. Compare In order to avoid some dangerous areas, Mike Horn actually traveled 29,000 miles. About how much farther did Mike Horn travel than if he had followed the equator? about 4110 mi

27. Analyze To the nearest mile, find what the radius of Earth would be if its circumference was 29,000 miles. Use 3.14 for π. about 4620 mi

3 APPLY

ASSIGNMENT GUIDE

Basic Course

Day 1: SRH p. 705 Exs. 1-5; pp. 293-294 Exs. 9-20, 23-25, 28, 33-44

Average Course

Day 1: pp. 293-294 Exs. 11-17, 21-29, 33-44

Advanced Course

Day 1: pp. 293-294 Exs. 11-17, 23-37*, 41-44

Block

pp. 293-294 Exs. 11-17, 21-29, 33-44 (with 6.3)

EXTRA PRACTICE

- Student Edition, p. 732
- Chapter 6 Resource Book, pp. 37-39
- Test and Practice Generator

TRANSPARENCY

Even-numbered answers are available on transparencies.

HOMEWORK CHECK

When you review students' homework for this lesson, go over the following exercises to check understanding of key concepts.
Basic: 12, 15, 19, 23, 28
Average: 12, 16, 17, 23, 28
Advanced: 12, 16, 17, 23, 29

4 ASSESS

Assessment Resources

For more assessment resources, see:
- Assessment Book
- Test and Practice Generator

Mini-Quiz

Find the indicated measurement, where r = radius, d = diameter, and C = circumference. Use 3.14 or $\frac{22}{7}$ for π.

1. $r = 28$ mm, $C = \underline{?}$ 176 mm
2. $d = 10$ ft, $C = \underline{?}$ 31.4 ft
3. $C = 440$ cm, $r = \underline{?}$ 70 cm
4. Chloe has a banana plant in a planter with a diameter of 2.5 feet. What is the circumference of her planter? about 7.85 ft

5 FOLLOW-UP

Reteaching/Remediation

- Study Guide in Chapter 6 Resource Book, pp. 40-41
- Tutor Place, Geometry and Measurement Cards 15, 16, Algebra Cards 10, 11
- eTutorial Plus Online
- Extra Practice, p. 732
- Lesson Practice in Chapter 6 Resource Book, pp. 37-39

Challenge/Enrichment

- Challenge Practice in Chapter 6 Resource Book, p. 42
- Teacher's Edition, p. 268F

English Learner Support

- Spanish Study Guide
- Multi-Language Glossary
- Chapter Audio Summaries CDs

33–36. See Additional Answers beginning on page AA1.

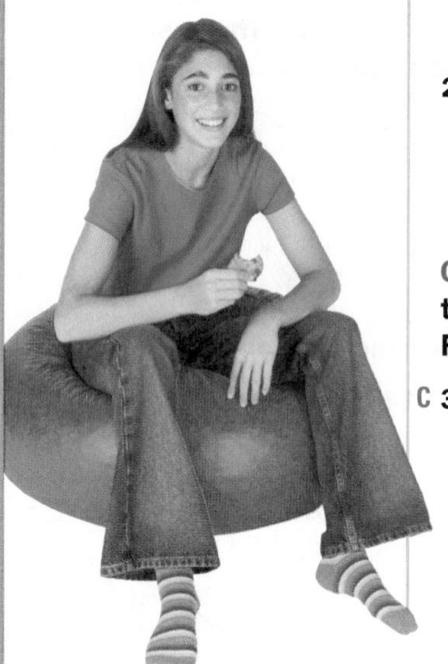

28. **Clock Face** The Great Clock of Westminster rings the bell known as "Big Ben" in London, England. The circumference of the clock face is about 72 feet 3 inches. What is the diameter of the clock face in feet? Use 3.14 for π. Round your answer to the nearest hundredth. 23.01 ft

29. **Fashion** To measure the leg opening of a pair of flared jeans, you flatten them out and measure the width. The width is 12 inches, which is half the circumference. What is the diameter of the leg opening? Use 3.14 for π. Round your answer to the nearest hundredth. 7.64 in.

Challenge **Two circles are *concentric* if they share a center, as in the diagrams below. The circumference of the outer circle is given. Find x. Use 3.14 for π. (All measures are in meters.)**

C 30. $C = 100.48$ m 7 m

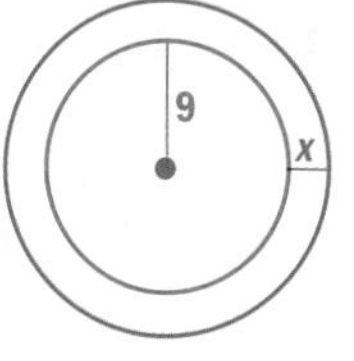

31. $C = 109.9$ m 9 m

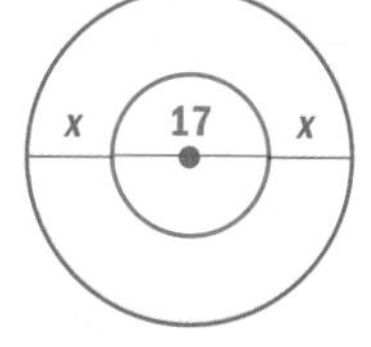

32. $C = 94.2$ m 10 m

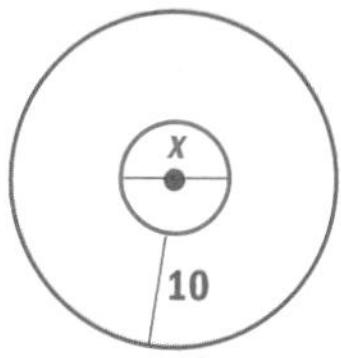

Mixed Review

Plot the point in a coordinate plane. *(Lesson 2.8)* 33–36. See margin.

33. $A(6, -10)$ 34. $B(-4, 4)$ 35. $C(-2, -6)$ 36. $D(-12, 0)$

Solve the inequality. *(Lessons 3.6, 3.7)*

37. $-15 + x \le 8$ $x \le 23$
38. $r + 11 > 6$ $r > -5$
39. $-4a \ge -8$ $a \le 2$
40. $3m < -63$ $m < -21$

Solve the equation. *(Lesson 6.1)*

41. $-4n - 9 + 5n = -6$ 3
42. $20 = 8c + 2 + c$ 2
43. $6 + 2(5 - z) = 7$ $4\frac{1}{2}$

Test-Taking Practice

44. **Extended Response** A basketball hoop has a circumference of about 56.5 inches. A basketball has a circumference of about 28.5 inches. What is the approximate difference between the diameter of the hoop and the diameter of the basketball? Use 3.14 for π. Round your answer to the nearest inch. Show how you found your answer. See margin.

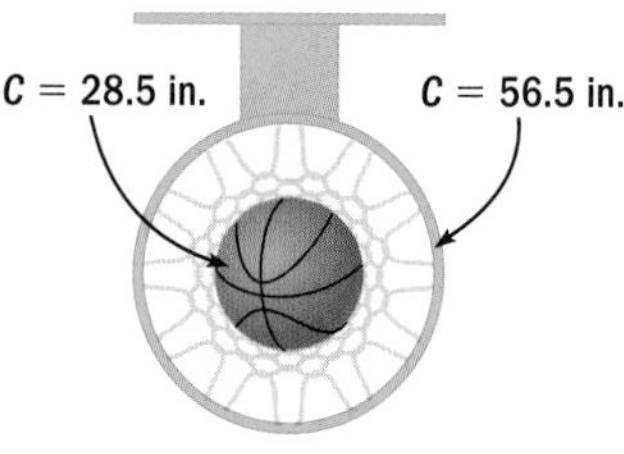

44. hoop: $C = \pi d$

$56.5 \approx 3.14d$

$\frac{56.5}{3.14} \approx \frac{3.14d}{3.14}$

$18 \text{ in.} \approx d$

basketball: $C = \pi d$

$28.5 \approx 3.14d$

$\frac{28.5}{3.14} \approx \frac{3.14d}{3.14}$

$9 \text{ in.} \approx d$

The approximate difference between the diameter of the hoop and the basketball is 18 − 9, or 9 inches.

INTERNET
State Test Practice
CLASSZONE.COM

Solving Multi-Step Inequalities

BEFORE	Now	WHY?
You solved multi-step equations and one-step inequalities.	You'll use two or more steps to solve inequalities.	So you can determine how much a salesperson must sell, as in Ex. 21.

Word Watch

Review Words

distributive property, p. 85
like terms, p. 86
inequality, p. 140

Activity Use a table to solve the inequality $x + 4 \geq 3x$.

(1) Copy and complete the table.

x	$x + 4$	$3x$	Is $x + 4 \geq 3x$?
−1	3	−3	Yes
0	? 4	? 0	? Yes
1	? 5	? 3	? Yes
2	? 6	? 6	? Yes
3	? 7	? 9	? No
4	? 8	? 12	? No

(2) For what values of x is the inequality true? What do you think is the solution of the inequality? Explain your reasoning.
−1, 0, 1, 2; $x \leq 2$; all numbers less than or equal to 2 make the inequality true.

(3) How is the solution of $4x + 3 > 9x - 7$ different from the solution in Part 2?
The solution of this inequality is $x < 2$, so 2 is not included in this solution.

(4) If you substitute a number less than −1 for x in the inequality above, will the inequality be true? Explain.
Yes; any number less than −1 is also less than 2, so it is a solution.

In Lessons 6.1 through 6.3, you solved multi-step equations algebraically. You can use many of the same steps to solve multi-step inequalities.

HELP with Review

For help with solving inequalities, see pp. 140 and 146.

EXAMPLE 1 Solving and Graphing a Two-Step Inequality

$10 + 4y < 18$	Original inequality
$10 + 4y - 10 < 18 - 10$	Subtract 10 from each side.
$4y < 8$	Simplify.
$\frac{4y}{4} < \frac{8}{4}$	Divide each side by 4.
$y < 2$	Simplify.
(number line 0 1 2 3 4 5)	Use an open circle and draw the arrow to the left.

ILLINOIS Standards and ISAT:
8.A.3b, 8.D.3a

1 PLAN

SKILL CHECK

Solve.

1. $4x < 12$ $x < 3$
2. $-16 < -8y$ $y < 2$
3. $5d \geq 100$ $d \geq 20$

Lesson Objective

Use two or more steps to solve inequalities.

Pacing

Suggested Number of Days
Basic Course: 1 day
Average Course: 1 day
Advanced Course: 1 day
Block: 0.5 block with 6.6

Teaching Resources

For a complete list of Teaching Resources, see page 268B.

Transparency

Warm-Up Exercises for this lesson are available on a transparency. A support transparency is available for Example 1.

2 TEACH

Motivating the Lesson

Ask students how solving inequalities is different from solving equations. Remind them that multiplying or dividing by a negative number reverses the inequality symbol.

Activity

Goal Use a table to solve an inequality.

Key Discovery Solutions of an inequality can be found by using replacements for the variable.

TIPS FOR NEW TEACHERS
In Example 2, some students may find the step of dividing by -4 confusing. On the board, show how multiplying each side by -1 first and then dividing by 4 achieves the same result in a way that may be clearer. See Tips for New Teachers in the *Chapter 6 Resource Book*.

EXTRA EXAMPLES

Example 1 Solve $22 + 5k < 52$. $k < 6$

Example 2 Solve $-7x + 10 > -9x - 16$. $x > -13$

Example 3 At a street fair, each meat pie sells for $5. The pie ingredients cost $2 per pie and the booth rental cost is $250. How many pies must the vendor sell to earn a profit of at least $500? **at least 250 pies**

CONCEPT CHECK
When do you reverse the inequality symbol? **when you multiply or divide each side of an inequality by a negative number**

DAILY PUZZLER
The largest bicycle in the world, Frankencycle, has a wheel diameter of 10 feet. If you pedaled one rotation of this wheel, how far along the ground would you travel? **about 31.4 ft**

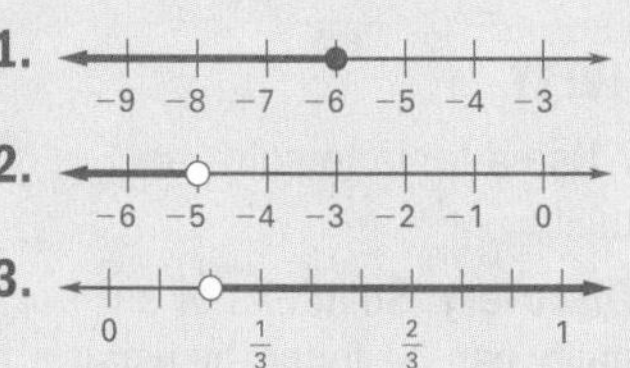

EXAMPLE 2 Combining Like Terms

$3x - 8 < -x + 4$	Original inequality
$3x - 8 - 3x < -x + 4 - 3x$	Subtract $3x$ from each side.
$-8 < -4x + 4$	Combine like terms.
$-8 - 4 < -4x + 4 - 4$	Subtract 4 from each side.
$-12 < -4x$	Simplify.
$\frac{-12}{-4} > \frac{-4x}{-4}$	Divide each side by -4 and reverse the inequality symbol.
$3 > x$	Simplify.

To check your solution, substitute different values for x in the original inequality. Choose a value less than 3, a value greater than 3, and 3.

Your turn now Solve the inequality. Then graph the solution.
1–3. See margin for art.

1. $-7z + 15 \geq 57$ $z \leq -6$
2. $11n + 36 < 3n - 4$ $n < -5$
3. $9(y - 2) > -16$ $y > \frac{2}{9}$

EXAMPLE 3 Writing and Solving a Multi-Step Inequality

Charity Bowling You are organizing a bowling night for charity. Each ticket costs $10 and includes shoe rental. Shoes cost you $5 per pair and door prizes cost you $50. How many people need to attend for you to raise at least $200?

Solution

To find the amount you can raise, subtract the total costs from the total ticket sales. Let x = the number of people.

Ticket Sales: Ticket price · Number of people − Costs: (Shoe price · Number of people + Cost of prizes) ≥ Profit: Amount raised

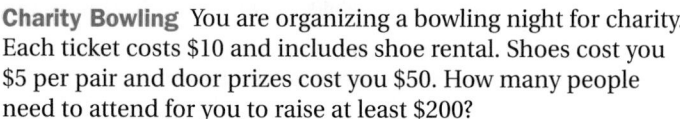

$10x - (5x + 50) \geq 200$	Write an inequality.
$10x - 5x - 50 \geq 200$	Distributive property
$5x - 50 \geq 200$	Combine like terms.
$5x \geq 250$	Add 50 to each side.
$x \geq 50$	Divide each side by 5.

ANSWER At least 50 people need to attend the bowling night.

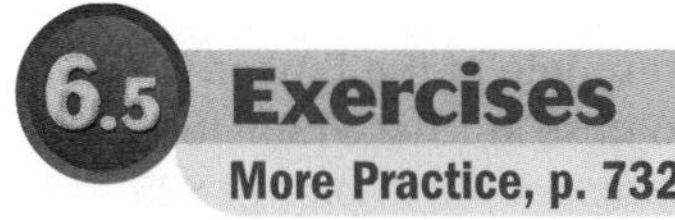

6.5 Exercises

More Practice, p. 732

INTERNET eWorkbook Plus CLASSZONE.COM

Getting Ready to Practice

1. **Vocabulary** Write the meanings of the symbols <, >, ≤, and ≥. less than; greater than; less than or equal to; greater than or equal to

Solve the inequality. Then graph the solution. 2–7. See margin for art.

2. $5x - 8 < 2$ $x < 2$
3. $2x + 1 \geq -7$ $x \geq -4$
4. $-3x + 4 \leq -11$ $x \geq 5$
5. $x - 13 - 2x > 2$ $x < -15$
6. $4x - 8 \geq 7x + 1$ $x \leq -3$
7. $1 < 3(x - 1)$ $x > 1\frac{1}{3}$
8. **Find the Error** Describe and correct the error in the solution.

$$9 - 2x \leq 3$$
$$-2x \leq -6$$
$$\frac{-2x}{-2} \leq \frac{-6}{-2}$$
$$x \leq 3$$

The inequality sign was not reversed when each side was divided by −2. The third step should be $\frac{-2x}{-2} \geq \frac{-6}{-2}$, which simplifies to $x \geq 3$.

Practice and Problem Solving

with Homework

Example	Exercises
1	9-20
2	9-20
3	21-23

Online Resources CLASSZONE.COM
- More Examples
- eTutorial Plus

Solve the inequality. Then graph the solution. 9–20. See margin for art.

A
9. $4a + 7 \geq 11$ $a \geq 1$
10. $16 < 3b + 22$ $b > -2$
11. $7 - 2p \geq -5$ $p \leq 6$
12. $-3y + 2 < -16$ $y > 6$
13. $-2w + 6 < 2$ $w > 2$
14. $23s - 30 \leq 39$ $s \leq 3$
15. $12c + 12 > 48c$ $c < \frac{1}{3}$
16. $5x - 14 \leq 2x + 7$ $x \leq 7$
17. $5 - 4z > 17 - z$ $z < -4$
18. $10 \geq 5(3 + t)$ $t \leq -1$
19. $2(5 + n) \leq 6$ $n \leq -2$
20. $-3(d + 2) < -3$ $d > -1$

21. **Sales** A salesperson in a clothing store earns $350 per week plus a 20% commission on the clothes she sells. She wants to know how much she has to sell in one week to earn at least $500 that week. Solve the inequality $350 + 0.2x \geq 500$. What does the solution mean in this situation? $x \geq 750$; the salesperson must sell at least $750 in clothes in that week to make at least $500 for the week.

22. $16{,}000 + 150d > 18{,}550$; $d > 17$; you must catch more than 17 discs to have the high score.

22. **Video Games** You are approaching the high score of 18,550 on a video game where you have to catch discs for 150 points each. Your current score is 16,000. You want to know how many more discs you need to catch to have a new high score. Use the verbal model to write an inequality. Then solve the inequality. What does the solution mean in this situation?

Current score + Points earned per disc • Discs caught > Current high score

3 APPLY

ASSIGNMENT GUIDE

Basic Course

Day 1: EP p. 729 Exs. 25-28; pp. 297-299 Exs. 9-18, 21-23, 25-29, 41-48

Average Course

Day 1: pp. 297-299 Exs. 15-24, 27-33, 38-48

Advanced Course

Day 1: pp. 297-299 Exs. 15-24, 29-42*, 46-48

Block

pp. 297-299 Exs. 15-24, 27-33, 38-48 (with 6.6)

EXTRA PRACTICE
- Student Edition, p. 732
- Chapter 6 Resource Book, pp. 46-48
- Test and Practice Generator

TRANSPARENCY

Even-numbered answers are available on transparencies. A support transparency is available for Exercises 2-7, 9-20, and 34-37.

HOMEWORK CHECK

When you review students' homework for this lesson, go over the following exercises to check understanding of key concepts.

Basic: 9, 15, 17, 18, 21
Average: 15, 16, 18, 19, 21
Advanced: 15, 16, 19, 20, 22

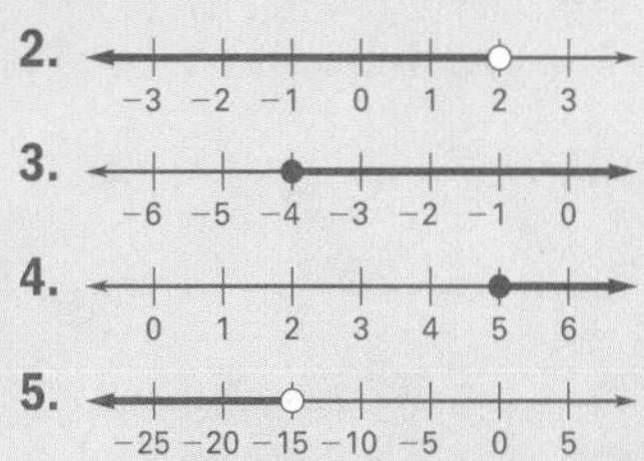

6, 7, 9-20. See Additional Answers beginning on page AA1.

Differentiating Instruction

Less Proficient Students Some students have trouble remembering to reverse the inequality sign when multiplying or dividing by a negative number. This can be avoided in multi-step inequalities with variables on both sides, such as Exercises 15–17, 25, and 28–31 by always adding or subtracting to keep the coefficient of the variable positive. For example, in Exercise 25 the steps would be as follows.

$$\frac{1}{6}k + \frac{1}{2}k - 6 \le -\frac{1}{6}k + \frac{1}{6}k$$

$$\frac{2}{3}k - 6 \le 0$$

$$\frac{2}{3}k \le 6$$

$$k \le 9$$

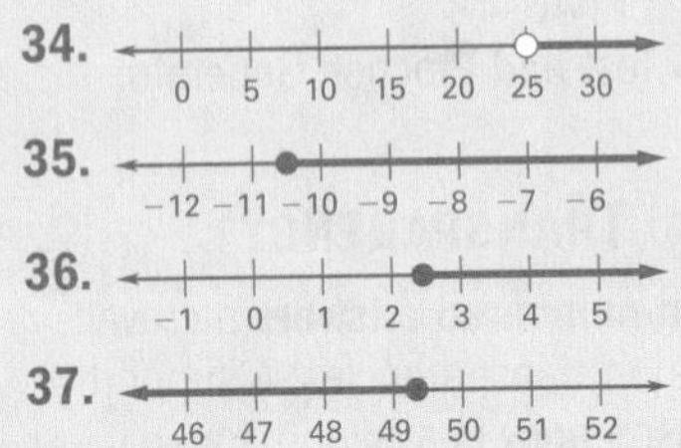

Boston Marathon

Edith Hunkeler of Switzerland won the women's wheelchair division of the Boston Marathon in 2002. She finished the 26.2 mile race in 1 hour, 45 minutes, and 57 seconds. What was her mean speed?

about 14.9 mi/h

24. *Sample answer:* It is the same in that what you do to one side of the equation or inequality, you must do to the other side. It is different in that, with an inequality, if you multiply or divide each side by a negative number, you must reverse the direction of the inequality sign.

38. You only have \$25 to spend, so it is impossible to buy up to 120 drinks.

39. You cannot buy a negative number of soft drinks.

40. The solution must be less than or equal to some number.

23. Boston Marathon You are planning to compete in the Boston Marathon. To officially enter, you have to raise at least \$1500 for charity. You've already raised \$925 by asking people to pledge \$25 each. How many more \$25 pledges do you need to enter?

Money already raised	+	Amount per pledge	•	Additional pledges	≥	Minimum required

Use the verbal model to write and solve an inequality to find the number p of additional pledges that will satisfy the donation requirements. at least 23 pledges; $925 + 25p \ge 1500$; $p \ge 23$

24. Writing Describe how solving an inequality is similar to solving an equation and how it is different from solving an equation. See margin.

Solve the inequality.

B **25.** $\frac{1}{2}k - 6 \le -\frac{1}{6}k$ $k \le 9$

26. $\frac{1}{3}m - \frac{1}{2}m > -4$ $m < 24$

27. $-\frac{1}{4}d - \frac{2}{5}d \le 13$ $d \ge -20$

28. $4.56h - 7.912 \ge 1.12h$ $h \ge 2.3$

29. $4.32 - 0.14x < 0.76x$ $x > 4.8$

30. $0.5w > 12.53 - 0.2w$ $w > 17.9$

31. $3.7z \le 33.32 - 3.1z$ $z \le 4.9$

32. $-0.6y - 3.79 + 5.2y < 19.67$ $y < 5.1$

33. Magazines It costs a magazine publisher \$1.20 to produce each magazine. Overhead costs, such as salaries and office space, are \$25,000 per month. The publisher sells the magazine for \$3.95. How many magazines does the publisher need to produce and sell each month to make a profit?

Price per magazine	•	Number of magazines	−	Cost per magazine	•	Number of magazines	≥	Overhead costs

Use the verbal model to write and solve an inequality. What does the solution mean in this situation? $3.95m - 1.2m \ge 25{,}000$; $m \ge 9090.\overline{90}$; the publisher must sell at least 9091 magazines each month to make a profit.

Challenge Solve the inequality. Then graph the solution. 34–37. See margin for art.

C **34.** $\frac{2}{3}x + \frac{4}{3} - \frac{3}{4}x < -\frac{3}{4}$ $x > 25$

35. $\frac{2}{3}x + 18 \ge 5 - \frac{4}{7}x$ $x \ge -10\frac{1}{2}$

36. $0.05a + 9.367 - 1.65a \le 5.44$ $a \ge 2.454375$

37. $2.3x - 52.46 \le -0.9(x - 117)$ $x \le 49.3$

Number Sense For Exercises 38–40, use the information below. Then tell what the solution represents in this situation and why it cannot be correct.

You and your sisters have \$25 to spend at a baseball game. You buy 3 ice creams for \$4 each, then use the rest for \$3 drinks. You write and solve an inequality to find the number of drinks you can afford.

38. $d < 120$ **39.** $d \le 0$ **40.** $d \ge 4$

Mixed Review

Choose a Strategy Use a strategy from the list to solve the following problem. Explain your choice of strategy.

Problem Solving Strategies
- Guess, Check, and Revise
- Make a List
- Draw a Diagram

41. You are making a sandwich. For bread, you can use either white or wheat. For meat, you can use turkey, ham, or roast beef. Finally, you can have mustard, mayonnaise, or neither. How many different kinds of sandwiches can you make? **18 sandwiches. *Sample answer:* I used Make a List to list all of the possibilities.**

Find the mean, median, and mode(s) of the data set. *(Lesson 5.8)*

42. 3.22, 4.45, 6.13, 6.27, 6.34 **5.282, 6.13, no mode**

43. 14, 22, 22, 23, 25, 28 **$22\frac{1}{3}$, 22.5, 22**

Solve the equation. *(Lesson 6.3)*

44. $3.3c - 2.1 = 7.8$ **3**

45. $4.8 - 2.3x = -3.02$ **3.4**

46. $23.06 + 4.3y = 6.72$ **−3.8**

Test-Taking Practice

47. Multiple Choice You are making some items to sell at a fair. The materials cost \$55. You decide to sell each item for \$2. You want to make a profit of at least \$100. Which inequality can you use to find the number of items you need to sell? **B**

A. $2x - 55 \le 100$ **B.** $2x - 55 \ge 100$

C. $2x + 55 \ge 100$ **D.** $2x + 55 \le 100$

48. Multiple Choice Solve the inequality $-3b + 9 - 11b < 65$. **G**

F. $b < -4$ **G.** $b > -4$ **H.** $b < 4$ **I.** $b > 4$

Brain Game

City Solutions

Fill in the blanks with variables so that each inequality on the right is the solution of an inequality on the left. When you are finished, the letters will spell out the name of a city found in 12 states.

1. $2a + 7 - 3a \ge 12$ **$a \le -5$**
2. $4p + 1 > 9p - 4$ **$p < 1$**
3. $s - 2(s + 1) > 3$ **$s < -5$**
4. $12 \le -3r - 13 + 8r$ **$r \ge 5$**
5. $-i + 4 + 7i > 10$ **$i > 1$**

p $\underline{?} < 1$
a $\underline{?} \le -5$
r $\underline{?} \ge 5$
i $\underline{?} > 1$
s $\underline{?} < -5$

4 ASSESS

Assessment Resources

For more assessment resources, see:
- Assessment Book
- Test and Practice Generator

Mini-Quiz

1. Solve $7 - 3a \ge 21 - a$. Graph the solution. **$a \le -7$**

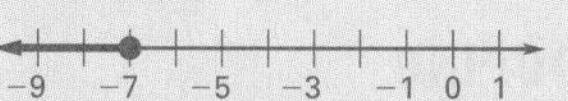

2. Rebecca has \$1250 in her savings account. She wants to buy a used car costing \$3000. She earns \$20 per hour tutoring math. At least how many hours must she tutor to earn enough to buy the car? **at least 87.5 h**

5 FOLLOW-UP

Reteaching/Remediation
- Study Guide in Chapter 6 Resource Book, pp. 49-50
- Tutor Place, Algebra Cards 15, 16
- eTutorial Plus Online
- Extra Practice, p. 732
- Lesson Practice in Chapter 6 Resource Book, pp. 46-48

Challenge/Enrichment
- Challenge Practice in Chapter 6 Resource Book, p. 51
- Teacher's Edition, p. 268F

English Learner Support
- Spanish Study Guide
- Multi-Language Glossary
- Chapter Audio Summaries CDs

LEARN THE METHOD

- Students will use spreadsheet software and truth functions to solve inequalities.
- Many of the examples and exercises in Lesson 6.5 can be checked using the technique learned in this activity.

GROUPING

Students can work individually or in pairs. If students work in pairs, one student can enter the data while the partner reads the formula and data to be keyed into the spreadsheet. Make sure students take turns.

ALTERNATIVE STRATEGY

If there are not enough computers available, demonstrate the activity on a computer to small groups of students, having them read aloud the material to be entered while you key in the values and formulas.

EXTRA EXAMPLES

Example Solve the inequality $6x + 8 > 3x + 14$. $x > 2$

ASSESSMENT

1. In the spreadsheet, what does *True* refer to? **The inequality is true for the value of x in that row.**
2. Cells B4 and C4 are equal. Why does cell D4 contain *False*? **To be true, B4 should be less than C4, not equal to C4.**

6.5 Technology Activity

SPREADSHEET

Solving Inequalities

GOAL Use a spreadsheet and truth functions to solve inequalities.

Example **Solve the inequality $3x + 2 < 2x - 6$.**

Solution

1. Enter the integers -10 to 10 in column A. Column A contains possible solutions of the inequality.
2. Type the formula "=3*A2 + 2" in cell B2. Use the fill down feature. Column B contains values of the left side of the inequality.

B2	=3*A2+2			
	A	B	C	D
1	x-values	3x + 2		
2	–10	–28		
3	–9	–25		
4	–8	–22		
5	–7	–19		

3. Type the formula "=2*A2 − 6" in cell C2. Use the fill down feature. Column C contains values of the right side of the inequality.
4. Type the truth function "=B2 < C2" in cell D2. Use the fill down feature. Column D tells whether the inequality is true or false for the x-value in that row.

C4	=2*A4–6			
	A	B	C	D
1	x-values	3x + 2	2x – 6	B < C?
2	–10	–28	–26	True
3	–9	–25	–24	True
4	–8	–22	–22	False
5	–7	–19	–20	False

HELP with Technology

A *truth function* compares values and returns *True* or *False*.

ANSWER The solution is all numbers less than -8.

Your turn now **Use spreadsheet software to solve the inequality.**

1. $13 - 3y > -2y$ $y < 13$
2. $7 - 2s < s - 2$ $s > 3$
3. $2n - 10 \geq 12n$ $n \leq -1$
4. $p + 16 \leq -3p$ $p \leq -4$
5. $-2t + 9 > -5t$ $t > -3$
6. $x - 3 < 5x + 1$ $x > -1$
7. **Shopping** Dani has \$10 to buy school supplies. A notebook costs \$1.50, a pencil costs \$.25, and a pen costs \$.95. She needs two notebooks, three pens, and a few pencils. How many pencils can she buy? **16 pencils**

ILLINOIS Standards and ISAT:
8.A.3b, 8.B.3

Lesson 6.6 Problem Solving and Inequalities

BEFORE
You solved multi-step inequalities.

Now
You'll use multi-step inequalities to solve real-world problems.

WHY?
So you can determine how many CDs you can buy, as in Ex. 16.

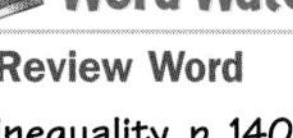

Word Watch

Review Word
inequality, p. 140

In the Real World

Season Tickets Individual tickets for a college hockey game cost \$8 each plus a one-time transaction fee of \$5. You can buy a season ticket for \$99. How many games would you have to attend so that buying a season ticket is a better value than buying individual tickets?

EXAMPLE 1 Writing and Solving an Inequality

To decide how many games you would have to attend so that buying a season ticket is a better value than buying individual game tickets, write and solve an inequality.

Price of single ticket • Number of games + Transaction fee > Price of season ticket

$8x + 5 > 99$	**Write an inequality.**
$8x > 94$	**Subtract 5 from each side.**
$x > 11.75$	**Divide each side by 8.**

ANSWER It doesn't make sense to attend 11.75 games. So you would have to attend 12 or more games to make buying a season ticket a better value than buying individual tickets.

1. $8 \cdot 12 + 5 = \$101$, which is more than \$99, so the season ticket is a better value.

Your turn now **Look back at Example 1.**

1. Check that the solution in Example 1 is reasonable. See margin.
2. Individual tickets for a college basketball game cost \$12 each plus a one-time transaction fee of \$8. A season ticket costs \$125. How many games would you have to attend so that buying a season ticket is a better value than buying individual tickets? 10 games

ILLINOIS Standards and ISAT:
8.A.3b, 8.C.3, 8.D.3a

1 PLAN

SKILL CHECK
Solve the inequality.
1. $2y - 3 \le -5$ $y \le -1$
2. $-3x + 7 > 4x + 21$ $x < -2$
3. $3w - 11 \ge 53 - w$ $w \ge 16$

LESSON OBJECTIVE
Use multi-step inequalities to solve real-world problems.

PACING
Suggested Number of Days
Basic Course: 1 day
Average Course: 1 day
Advanced Course: 1 day
Block: 0.5 block with 6.5

TEACHING RESOURCES
For a complete list of Teaching Resources, see page 268B.

TRANSPARENCY
Warm-Up Exercises for this lesson are available on a transparency.

2 TEACH

MOTIVATING THE LESSON
Ask students if they know anyone who has season tickets to any kind of sports or cultural event. Ask if they know how much was saved by buying season tickets.

TIPS FOR NEW TEACHERS

Before discussing Example 2, plan to spend extra time with students practicing the different ways of expressing inequalities. Have students substitute integers for a and b and say the phrases aloud. See Tips for New Teachers in the *Chapter 6 Resource Book*.

EXTRA EXAMPLES

Example 1 Membership in a dance group costs \$25 per year. Dances cost \$8 for members and \$10 for nonmembers. How many dances would you have to attend so that buying a membership is a better value than being a nonmember? **at least 13 dances**

Example 2 Write the sentence as an inequality.

a. 7 times the difference of a number and 10 is at least 30. $7(x - 10) \geq 30$

b. 10 less than 6 times a number is less than 2 times the number. $6x - 10 < 2x$

Writing Inequalities The following common sentences indicate the four types of inequalities.

$a < b$	$a > b$
a is less than b. a is fewer than b.	a is greater than b. a is more than b.
$a \leq b$	$a \geq b$
a is less than or equal to b. a is at most b. a is no more than b.	a is greater than or equal to b. a is at least b. a is no less than b.

HELP
with Reading

The phrase "a more than b" means $b + a$, while "a is more than b" means $a > b$.

EXAMPLE 2 **Translating Verbal Sentences**

Write the sentence as an inequality.

a. Six times the difference of a number and 3 is more than 24.

b. Nine more than 4 times a number is at least 30 plus 11 times the number.

Solution

First decide which inequality symbol to use. Then substitute numbers, variables, and operation symbols.

a. The phrase "is more than" means >.

6 times the difference of a number and 3 **is more than** 24.

$6 \cdot (x - 3) > 24$

ANSWER The inequality is $6(x - 3) > 24$.

b. The phrase "is at least" means ≥.

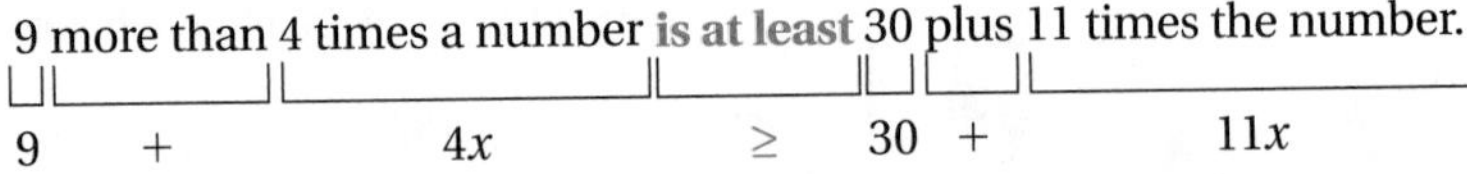
9 more than 4 times a number is at least 30 plus 11 times the number.

$9 + 4x \geq 30 + 11x$

ANSWER The inequality is $9 + 4x \geq 30 + 11x$.

Your turn now **Write the sentence as an inequality. Let x represent the unknown number.**

3. Six times the sum of a number and 8 is no more than 12 less than twice the number. $6(x + 8) \leq 2x - 12$

4. The difference of a number and 4 is less than 10 more than 3 times the number. $x - 4 < 3x + 10$

EXAMPLE 3 Writing and Solving an Inequality

Owning a Business You use the Internet to sell mousepads. You pay a wholesaler \$6 for each mousepad. You then sell the mousepads for \$10 each. You pay \$21 per month for Web page hosting. How many mousepads should you sell each month to earn a profit?

Solution

To earn a profit, your revenue must be greater than your expenses.

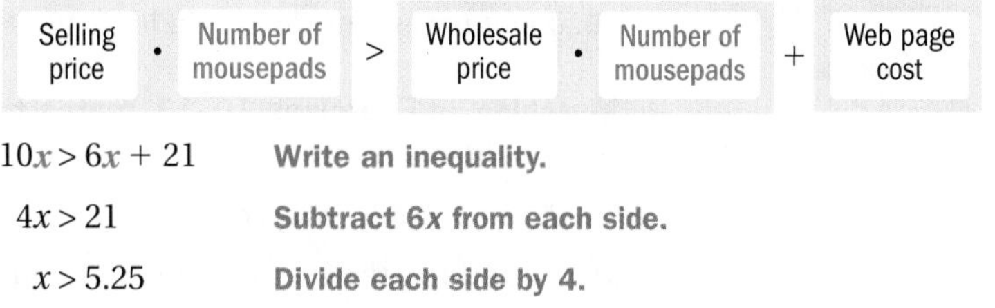

$10x > 6x + 21$	**Write an inequality.**
$4x > 21$	**Subtract 6*x* from each side.**
$x > 5.25$	**Divide each side by 4.**

ANSWER You cannot sell part of a mousepad. So, you should sell at least 6 mousepads per month to earn a profit.

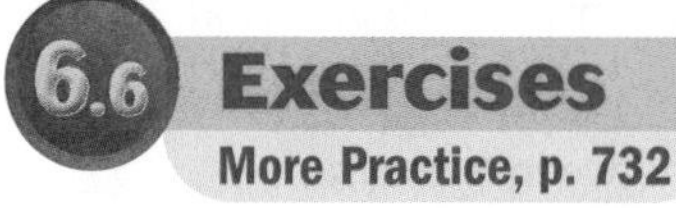

Exercises

More Practice, p. 732

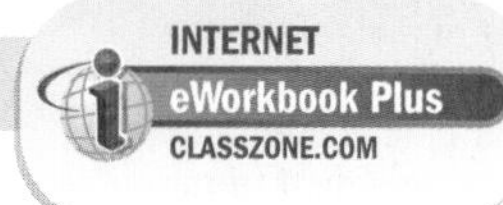

Getting Ready to Practice

Vocabulary Write the sentence as an inequality. Let *x* represent the unknown number.

1. A number is at least 5. $x \geq 5$
2. A number plus 5 is greater than 9. $x + 5 > 9$
3. Eight minus a number is at most 6. $8 - x \leq 6$
4. Four times a number is less than 28. $4x < 28$
5. **Guided Problem Solving** You have \$200 to spend on a health club membership. The initial fee to join is \$50. There is a monthly fee of \$32. For how many months can you be a member without spending more than \$200?

   (1 Write a variable expression for the total cost of a health club membership. $32m + 50$

   (2 Use the expression from Step 1 to write an inequality. $32m + 50 \leq 200$

   (3 Solve the inequality and check that the answer makes sense. Explain what the solution means in the situation. $m \leq 4.6875$; you can be a member up to 4 months without spending more than \$200.

EXTRA EXAMPLES

Example 3 You sell personalized bumper stickers. You buy blank stickers for \$.10 each and you spend \$1200 for software and a special printer. How much should you sell each printed bumper sticker for if you want to at least break even after selling 300 stickers? **at least \$4.10 each**

Differentiating Instruction

Advanced Students Give students the following inequalities and ask them what they can conclude about them.

$2x + 2 \geq 2x + 3$ (not true for any value of x)

$4x + 5 \leq 9x + 5 - 5x$ (true for all values of x)

CONCEPT CHECK

When writing a sentence as an inequality, how do you decide which inequality symbol to use? **Look for the common words and phrases listed in the table on page 302.**

DAILY PUZZLER

In 1994, a taxi drove passengers from London to Cape Town, South Africa and back. The distance was 21,691 miles and the fare was about \$64,650. What does the taxi ride cost per mile? **about \$3 per mile**

APPLY

ASSIGNMENT GUIDE

Basic Course
Day 1: EP p. 729 Exs. 29-32; pp. 304-305 Exs. 6-13, 16-19, 24-30

Average Course
Day 1: pp. 304-305 Exs. 8-11, 14-21, 24-31

Advanced Course
Day 1: pp. 304-305 Exs. 8-11, 14-26, 29-31, EC: TE p. 268D*

Block
pp. 304-305 Exs. 8-11, 14-21, 24-31 (with 6.5)

EXTRA PRACTICE

- Student Edition, p. 732
- Chapter 6 Resource Book, pp. 54-46
- Test and Practice Generator

TRANSPARENCY

Even-numbered answers are available on transparencies.

HOMEWORK CHECK

When you review students' homework for this lesson, go over the following exercises to check understanding of key concepts.
Basic: 6, 7, 10, 16, 17
Average: 8, 10, 16, 17, 18
Advanced: 9, 11, 16, 17, 18

COMMON ERROR

In Exercise 6, students can write either $x + 2$ or $2 + x$. However, in Exercise 8, students cannot interchange $7 - x$ and $x - 7$. Make sure students correctly write seven less than a number as $x - 7$.

with Homework

Example	Exercises
1	16-18
2	6-13
3	16-18

Online Resources
CLASSZONE.COM
- More Examples
- eTutorial Plus

14. *Sample answer:* You have at most \$31 to spend at a discount music store. You buy a cassette for \$5 and want to buy some \$8 CDs. What is the greatest number of CDs you can buy? Solution: $x \le 3.25$; you can buy at most 3 CDs.

15. "3 less than a number" is equivalent to the expression $n - 3$, while "3 is less than a number" is equivalent to the inequality $3 < n$.

19. $2 + 0.5n \ge 6$; 3 A.M.; no. *Sample answer:* If there are 6 inches of snow at 3 A.M., and it keeps snowing at the same rate, then there will be 7.5 inches of snow at 6 A.M.

Practice and Problem Solving

Write the sentence as an inequality. Let *x* represent the unknown number. Then solve the inequality.

A **6.** A number plus 2 is at most 6. $x + 2 \le 6$; $x \le 4$

7. Nine is less than a number plus 1. $9 < x + 1$; $x > 8$

8. Seven less than a number is more than 14. $x - 7 > 14$; $x > 21$

9. Eight times a number is at least 40. $8x \ge 40$; $x \ge 5$

Matching In Exercises 10–13, match the verbal sentence with the inequality.

A. $4(x + 2) \ge 18$ **B.** $4x + 2 < 18$ **C.** $2x - 4 > 18$ **D.** $2(x - 4) \le 18$

10. Four times the sum of a number and 2 is at least 18. A

11. The difference of 2 times a number and 4 is more than 18. C

12. Two times the difference of a number and 4 is no more than 18. D

13. The sum of 4 times a number and 2 is fewer than 18. B

B **14. Writing** Write a real-world problem that can be solved using the inequality $5 + 8x \le 31$. Solve the inequality and explain what the solution means in the situation.

15. Critical Thinking Explain the difference between *3 less than a number* and *3 is less than a number.*

16. Buying CDs Each CD you order online costs \$12. Shipping and handling charges are \$4. You have \$50 to spend. Use the verbal model to write and solve an inequality. How many CDs can you buy? $12c + 4 \le 50$, $c \le 3.8\overline{3}$; you can buy 3 CDs.

Cost of CD · Number of CDs + Shipping charges ? Money you have

17. Teen Club A teen club has weekly dances. You can become a member of the club for \$30 a year and pay only \$4 to attend each dance. Otherwise, each dance costs \$6. How many dances do you have to attend so that becoming a member will cost less than paying the nonmember rate? more than 15 dances

18. Signatures To get a question on a state ballot, you need at least 419,260 signatures on a petition. You've collected 209,260 signatures and have 30 days to collect the rest. Find the mean number of signatures you need to collect per day. at least 7000 signatures

19. Snowstorm School will be cancelled if there are at least 6 inches of snow at 6 A.M. There are 2 inches of snow at 7:00 P.M. the night before. The snow is predicted to continue falling at a rate of 0.5 inch per hour. Write an inequality to represent the situation. When will there be at least 6 inches of snow? Will there be school the next day? Explain. See margin.

20. $6x + 30 + 24 \le 108$, $x \le 9$; no more than 9 boxes

C **20. Express Mail** A package sent via Express Mail must be no more than 108 inches in total length and girth. You want to wrap as many boxes together as possible to send as one package. Each box is the same size. Write and solve an inequality to find how many boxes you could wrap as one package if they are arranged as shown.

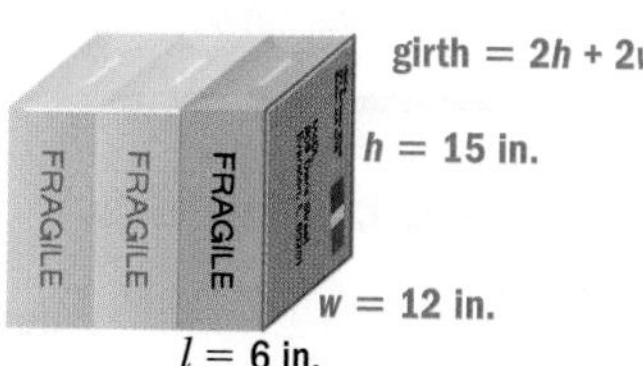

girth = $2h + 2w$
h = 15 in.
w = 12 in.
l = 6 in.

Extended Problem Solving Town Taxi charges $2.00 plus $.40 for every $\frac{1}{5}$ mile. City Cab charges $2.50 plus $.25 for every $\frac{1}{7}$ mile.

21. Interpret Write expressions for the total cost of a ride with Town Taxi and the total cost of a ride with City Cab. $2 + 0.4 \cdot 5 \cdot m$; $2.50 + 0.25 \cdot 7 \cdot m$

22. Compare For what distances does City Cab cost less than Town Taxi? Express your answer as an inequality. distances greater than 2 mi; $m > 2$ mi

23. Analyze Use the expressions from Exercise 21 to express the distances that Town Taxi costs less than City Cab. $m < 2$ mi

Mixed Review

Find the indicated measurement, where r = radius, d = diameter, and C = circumference. Use 3.14 for π. *(Lesson 6.4)*

24. $d = 27$ m, r = ? 13.5 m **25.** $r = 34$ in., C = ? 213.52 in. **26.** $C = 62.8$ ft, d = ? 20 ft

Basic Skills Evaluate the expression.

27. $9 + (10 - 8)^4 \times 5$ 89 **28.** $3 + 50 \div 5^2 - 8$ −3 **29.** $275 - 2(3 + 2)^3$ 25

Test-Taking Practice

INTERNET
State Test Practice
CLASSZONE.COM

30. Multiple Choice While at camp, you call your parents from a pay phone. The first minute costs you $.25 and each additional minute costs you $.10. You have $1.65 in change. Solve the inequality $0.25 + 0.10m \le 1.65$. How many additional minutes m can you talk? B

A. less than 14 **B.** no more than 14

C. at most 19 **D.** fewer than 19

31. $\frac{90 + 92 + 115 + x}{4} \ge 100$; $x \ge 103$

31. Short Response Your scores on the last 3 bowling games are 90, 92, and 115. What do you need to score in the next game to have a mean of at least 100? Write and solve an inequality.

4 ASSESS

Assessment Resources

For more assessment resources, see:
- Assessment Book
- Test and Practice Generator

Mini-Quiz

Write the sentence as an inequality. Let x represent the unknown number. Then solve the inequality.

1. 14 less than a number is more than 6. $x - 14 > 6$; $x > 20$
2. 9 times a number is at least four less than 12 times the number $9x \ge 12x - 4$; $x \le \frac{4}{3}$
3. The Carolina Songbird Club is hoping to see 100 different species of birds in 5 days. On the first day, they see 36 species. Find the mean number of bird species they need to see each remaining day to achieve their goal. at least 16 species

5 FOLLOW-UP

Reteaching/Remediation

- Study Guide in Chapter 6 Resource Book, pp. 49-50
- Tutor Place, Algebra Cards 14, 16
- eTutorial Plus Online
- Extra Practice, p. 732
- Lesson Practice in Chapter 6 Resource Book, pp. 54-56

Challenge/Enrichment

- Challenge Practice in Chapter 6 Resource Book, p. 51
- Teacher's Edition, p. 268F

English Learner Support

- Spanish Study Guide
- Multi-Language Glossary
- Chapter Audio Summaries CDs

The following resources are available to help review the materials in Lessons 6.4–6.6.

Chapter 6 Resource Book
- Lesson Practice
- Study Guide

Assessment Book
- Chapter 6 Quiz 2

Technology
- Test and Practice Generator
- eTutorial CD-ROM

Internet
- Classzone
- eWorkbook Plus Online
- eTutorial Plus Online

English Learner Support

- Spanish Study Guide
- Multi-Language Glossary
- Chapter Audio Summaries CDs

LESSONS 6.4 TO 6.6

Notebook Review

Review the vocabulary definitions in your notebook.

Copy the review examples in your notebook. Then complete the exercises.

Check Your Definitions

circle, p. 290 radius, p. 290 circumference, p. 290
center, p. 290 diameter, p. 290 pi (π), p. 290

Use Your Vocabulary

1. Copy and complete: Pi is the quotient of a circle's _?_ and its _?_. circumference; diameter

6.4 Can you solve equations involving circumference?

EXAMPLE Find the circumference of a circle with diameter 30.5 cm.

$C = \pi d$ — Circumference formula

$\approx (3.14)(30.5)$ — Substitute 3.14 for π and 30.5 for d.

$= 95.77$ cm — Multiply.

Find the indicated measurement, where r = radius, d = diameter, and C = circumference. Use 3.14 or $\frac{22}{7}$ for π.

2. $r = 7$; $C =$ _?_ 44
3. $C = 121$; $d =$ _?_ 38.5
4. $C = 314$; $r =$ _?_ 50

6.5 Can you solve multi-step inequalities?

EXAMPLE Solve $-5(x + 9) \geq 30$.

$-5(x + 9) \geq 30$ — Original inequality

$-5x - 45 \geq 30$ — Distributive property

$-5x \geq 75$ — Add 45 to each side.

$x \leq -15$ — Divide each side by -5 and reverse the inequality symbol.

Solve the inequality.

5. $2b - 32 < 52$ $b < 42$
6. $5j - 18 > 18 - j$ $j > 6$
7. $6y \leq 3(9 + y)$ $y \leq 9$

6.6 Can you write and solve an inequality?

EXAMPLE You and 3 friends plan to use a \$50 gift certificate to pay for dinner. You order an appetizer that costs \$6. What is the most each of you can spend so the total cost of the meal is no more than \$50?

Number of people	•	Cost per person	+	Price of appetizer	≤	Amount of gift certificate

$4x + 6 \le 50$ **Write an inequality.**

$4x \le 44$ **Subtract 6 from each side.**

$x \le 11$ **Divide each side by 4.**

ANSWER The most that each of you can spend is \$11.

8. You want to work out for at least 45 minutes. You jog for 20 minutes, then divide your time evenly among the stationary bike, stair machine, and rowing machine. How long should you use each machine? $8\frac{1}{3}$ min

Stop *and* Think about Lessons 6.4–6.6

9. Writing Describe how you know which inequality symbol to use when translating a sentence. See margin.

9. *Sample answer:* Use < if the expressions "is less than" or "is fewer than" are used. Use > if "is greater than" or "is more than" are used. Use ≤ if "is less than or equal to," "is at most," or "is not more than" are used. Use ≥ if "is greater than or equal to," "is at least," or "is not less than" are used.

Review Quiz 2

Find the indicated measurement, where r = radius, d = diameter, and C = circumference. Use 3.14 or $\frac{22}{7}$ for π.

1. $d = 28$ in., $C = \underline{?}$ 88

2. $C = 150$ cm, $r = \underline{?}$ 23.9

Solve the inequality.

3. $-8a - 10 > 14$ $a < -3$

4. $3z \le 35 - 2z$ $z \le 7$

5. $5b \ge 2(b + 2.25)$ $b \ge 1.5$

Write the sentence as an inequality. Then solve.

6. Two less than six times a number is at least forty. $6x - 2 \ge 40$; $x \ge 7$

7. Five times the sum of four and a number is greater than ten. $5(4 + x) > 10$; $x > -2$

8. Video Games Your current score in a video game is 33,600 points. At each level you earn 2500 points for catching objects and 1700 points for overcoming the obstacles. How many more levels must you go through to beat your high score of 54,000? at least 5 levels

ADDITIONAL RESOURCES

The following resources are available to help review the materials in this chapter.

Chapter 6 Resource Book

- Chapter Review Games and Activities, p. 61
- Cumulative Practice, Chs. 1-6

English/Spanish Chapter Reviews and Tests

Chapter Audio Summaries CDs

eTutorial CD-ROM

eWorkbook Plus Online

eTutorial Plus Online

15. In the last step, the values of x and y were substituted for the length and the width to find the perimeter. Instead, the values of x and y must first be substituted into the expressions for the length and width of the rectangle. The length is $4x + 2 = 4(3) + 2 = 14$. The width is $2y = 2(4) = 8$. So, $P = 2(14) + 2(8) = 44$.

Chapter Review

Vocabulary

circle, p. 290
center, p. 290
radius, p. 290
diameter, p. 290
circumference, p. 290
pi (π), p. 290

Vocabulary Review

Copy and complete the statement.

1. A ? is the set of all points in a plane that are the same distance from a fixed point called the center. circle
2. You can approximate ? with the decimal 3.14 or the fraction $\frac{22}{7}$. pi or π

Matching **Match the word with the correct definition.**

3. diameter B
4. circumference A
5. radius C

A. the distance around a circle
B. the distance across a circle through the center
C. the distance from the center to any point on the circle

Review Questions

Solve the equation. *(Lessons 6.1–6.3)*

6. $6a - 14a = 96$ -12
7. $18 + 4(p - 9) = 6$ 6
8. $4(12 + z) - z = -192$ -80
9. $7c - 10 = c + 44$ 9
10. $6(t - 5) = 2(t + 5)$ 10
11. $-7b + 10 = -11 - 4b$ 7
12. $\frac{11}{16}n - 3 + \frac{1}{4}n = \frac{7}{4}$ $5\frac{1}{15}$
13. $5s + 3\frac{1}{8} = \frac{5}{24} - 2s$ $-\frac{5}{12}$
14. $5(m - 9) = 13 - 4(10 + m)$ 2
15. **Find the Error** Describe and correct the error made in finding the perimeter of the rectangle. *(Lesson 6.2)* See margin.

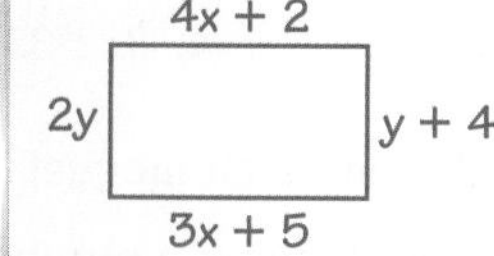

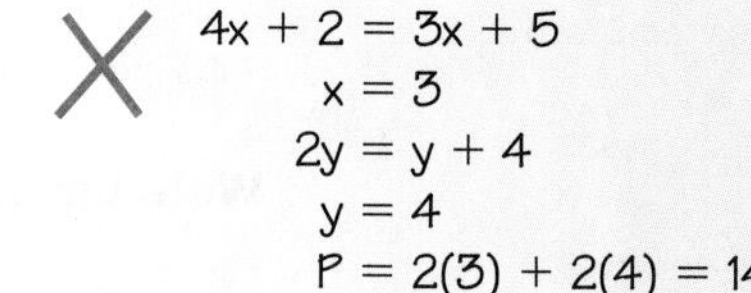

16. **Critical Thinking** What number would you multiply the equation $\frac{5}{9} + \frac{3}{4}x = \frac{2}{3}x - \frac{1}{6}$ by to clear the fractions? *(Lesson 6.3)* 36

25.
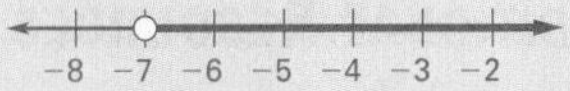

26.

27.
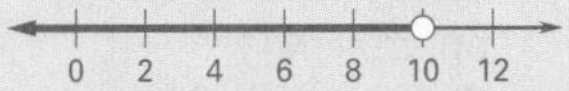

28.

29.
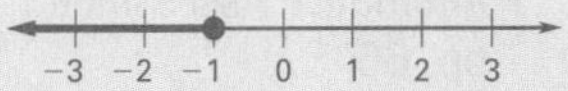

30.
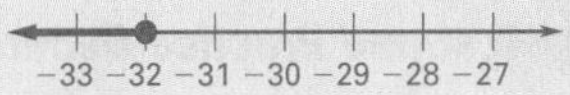

Review Questions

17. Rowing Teams Fifty more than twice the number of women's rowing teams is equal to eighty-seven less than three times the number of women's rowing teams. Write and solve an equation to find the number of women's rowing teams. *(Lesson 6.2)* **$2w + 50 = 3w - 87$; 137 teams**

18. Recycling Deposit When you buy a can of soda, you pay for the soda and you pay a \$.05 recycling deposit. You pay \$4.56 for a 12-pack of soda. How much did each soda cost before the deposit? *(Lesson 6.3)* **\$.33**

19. Race You and a friend are running in a race for a charity event. You have completed $\frac{3}{8}$ of the race. Your friend has completed $\frac{1}{4}$ of the race and is $\frac{3}{16}$ mile behind you. How long (in miles) is the race? *(Lesson 6.3)* **$1\frac{1}{2}$ mi**

Find the indicated measurement, where r = radius, d = diameter, and C = circumference. Use 3.14 or $\frac{22}{7}$ for π. *(Lesson 6.4)*

20. $C = \underline{?}$ **132 ft**

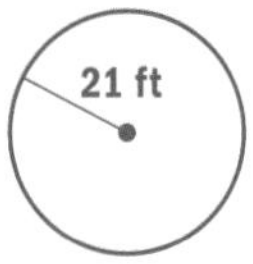

21. $C = \underline{?}$ **25.1 mm**

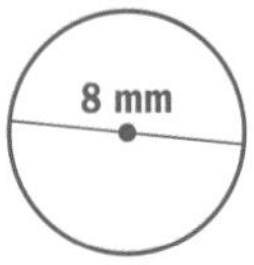

22. $C = 62.8$ mm **20 mm**

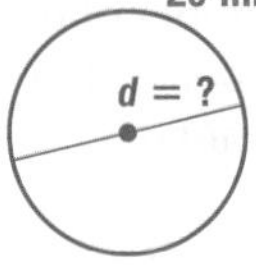

23. $C = 12$ in. **1.91 in.**

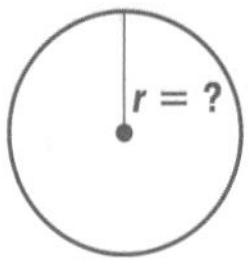

24. Dome The Minnesota State Capitol Building has one of the largest unsupported marble domes in the world, with a diameter of 89 feet at its widest point. Find its circumference using 3.14 for π. *(Lesson 6.4)* **279 ft**

Solve the inequality. Graph the solution. *(Lesson 6.5)* **25–30. See margin for art.**

25. $-5 < 3x + 16$ **$x > -7$**

26. $\frac{2}{3}h - 3 \geq 1$ **$h \geq 6$**

27. $6 - \frac{2}{5}a > 2$ **$a < 10$**

28. $m + 4(5 - m) > -7$ **$m < 9$**

29. $6 - (g - 7) \leq 6 - 8g$ **$g \leq -1$**

30. $2(3k + 1) \leq 5(k - 6)$ **$k \leq -32$**

Write the sentence as an inequality. Then solve the inequality. *(Lesson 6.6)*

31. Fourteen minus three times a number is at most eleven. **$14 - 3x \leq 11$; $x \geq 1$**

32. Nine plus four times a number is less than twenty-one. **$9 + 4x < 21$; $x < 3$**

33. Seven times the difference of fifteen and a number is at least fifty-six. **$7(15 - x) \geq 56$; $x \leq 7$**

34. School Fundraiser You are selling magazine subscriptions for a school fundraiser. If you sell at least 75 subscriptions in 2 weeks you win a prize. You sold 26 subscriptions in one week. What is the mean number of subscriptions you have to sell per day to sell at least 75 total? *(Lesson 6.6)* **at least 7 subscriptions**

ADDITIONAL RESOURCES

Assessment Book

- Chapter Test (3 levels), pp. 59-64
- Standardized Chapter Test, p. 65
- Alternative Assessment, pp. 66, 67

Test and Practice Generator

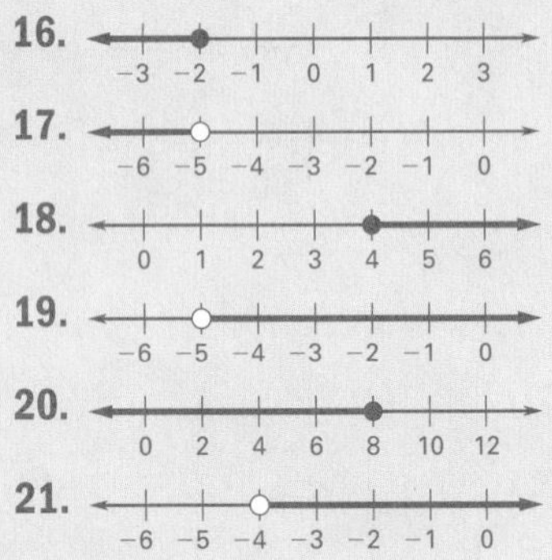

Chapter Test

Solve the equation.

1. $-3z + 17 + 12z = 11$ $-\frac{2}{3}$
2. $m - 6(m + 10) = 50$ -22
3. $7(12 - r) = -84$ 24
4. $3b + 4 = b - 4$ -4
5. $-25 - a = 2a + 20$ -15
6. $3(2x - 11) = 3(x + 10)$ 21
7. $\frac{3n - 5}{10} = 7$ 25
8. $\frac{-3r + 54}{5} = 2r + 3$ 3
9. $\frac{3}{5}w = 5w + \frac{22}{25}$ $-\frac{1}{5}$

10. Shopping You bought a new shirt for \$15.95 and 5 pairs of socks. Your friend bought 10 pairs of socks and spent \$4.20 less than you. How much did each pair of socks cost? **\$2.35**

11. Newspapers In 1999 there were 1647 daily and 7471 weekly newspapers published in the United States, as well as x other kinds of newspapers. The total number of newspapers was 700 greater than seven times the number x. How many newspapers were published in 1999 that were not daily or weekly? **at least 1403 newspapers**

Find the indicated measurement, where r = radius, d = diameter, and C = circumference. Use 3.14 or $\frac{22}{7}$ for π.

12. $d = 12.3$ mm, $C = \underline{?}$ **38.6 mm**
13. $C = 22$ in., $r = \underline{?}$ **3.5 in.**
14. $C = 9.42$ ft, $d = \underline{?}$ **3 ft**

15. Tetherball A tetherball pole is 12 feet high. The tetherball is attached to the top of the pole with a string so that the ball hangs 2 feet above the ground. How long is the string attached to the tetherball? What is the circumference of the largest path that the ball could make through the air around the pole? Use 3.14 for π. **10 ft; 62.8 ft**

Solve the inequality. Then graph the solution. 16–21. See margin for art.

16. $6n + 19 \le 7$ $n \le -2$
17. $10 - 3x > 25$ $x < -5$
18. $9c - 8 \ge 3c + 16$ $c \ge 4$
19. $3(k + 3) > k - 1$ $k > -5$
20. $8y + 3y + 36 \le 124$ $y \le 8$
21. $w - 4(w + 5) < -8$ $w > -4$

Write the sentence as an inequality. Then solve the inequality.

22. Nine added to the product of 11 and a number is at most 4. $11x + 9 \le 4$; $x \le -\frac{5}{11}$

23. A number times 2 minus 13 is less than the number plus 8. $2x - 13 < x + 8$; $x < 21$

24. Seven times the difference of 12 and a number is at least 14. $7(12 - x) \ge 14$; $x \le 10$

Chapter Standardized Test

Test-Taking Strategy **Work at a pace that is right for you. Do not worry about how fast others are working.**

Multiple Choice

1. What is the radius of a circle whose circumference is 110 inches? Use $\frac{22}{7}$ for π. A

A. $17\frac{1}{2}$ inches **B.** 35 inches

C. $172\frac{6}{7}$ inches **D.** $345\frac{5}{7}$ inches

2. Solve $9 + \frac{1}{4}x = -1\frac{1}{8} - \frac{1}{2}x$. F

F. $-13\frac{1}{2}$ **G.** $-10\frac{1}{2}$

H. $-7\frac{19}{32}$ **I.** 3

3. Solve $4x + 9 \geq -7$. C

A. $x \leq -4$ **B.** $x \leq \frac{1}{2}$

C. $x \geq -4$ **D.** $x \geq \frac{1}{2}$

4. All three sides of the triangle have equal length. What is the perimeter? F

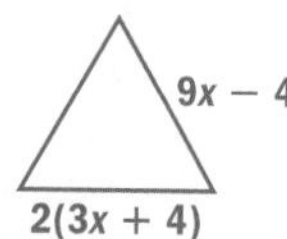

F. 96 units **G.** 32 units

H. 12 units **I.** 4 units

5. A dome has a diameter of 50 feet at its widest point. What is its circumference? Use 3.14 for π. B

A. 314 feet **B.** 157 feet

C. 78.5 feet **D.** 39.25 feet

6. Solve $4(x + 5) = x - 19$. F

F. -13 **G.** $\frac{1}{4}$ **H.** $\frac{1}{3}$ **I.** 19

7. The circumference of a checker is about 2.355 inches. What is its diameter? Use 3.14 for π. B

A. 0.375 inch **B.** 0.75 inch

C. 7.3947 inches **D.** 14.7894 inches

8. Which inequality represents the sentence *ten plus the product of four and a number is at most 9?* I

F. $10n + 4 \geq 9$ **G.** $10n + 4 \leq 9$

H. $10 + 4n \geq 9$ **I.** $10 + 4n \leq 9$

9. What is the value of x in the equation $6 - 9(x - 3) = -12$? D

A. -5 **B.** $-2\frac{1}{3}$ **C.** $2\frac{1}{3}$ **D.** 5

Short Response

10. You are buying 2.2 pounds of bubble gum that costs \$4.50 per pound and lollipops that cost \$1.70 per pound. You can't spend more than \$15. How many pounds of lollipops can you buy? Explain your reasoning. See margin.

Extended Response

11. Each ride on the subway costs \$1.25. If you buy a monthly pass for \$47, you can ride as often as you want. Write and solve an inequality that models the number of times you need to ride the subway so that buying a pass costs less than paying for each ride. Explain how to use the solution to find the minimum number of times you must ride the subway. See margin.

Additional Resources

Assessment Book
- Standardized Chapter Test, p. 65

Test and Practice Generator

10. 3 lb. *Sample answer:* The gum costs 2.2(\$4.50) = \$9.90. This leaves \$15 − \$9.90 = \$5.10 to buy lollipops. Then \$5.10 ÷ \$1.70 = 3, so you can buy 3 pounds of lollipops.

11. $1.25x > 47$; $x > 37.6$, you must ride at least 38 times. Since $x > 37.6$ subway rides, and each ride is represented by a whole number, round 37.6 up to 38.

1 PLAN

Explore the Concept

- Students apply formulas and equations.
- Using formulas was studied in Chapter 1. Solving equations was studied in Chapters 3 and 6.
- How high a ball bounces depends on the energy with which it hits the ground and how bouncy it is.

Science Background

The energy, E, of a falling object is given by $E = mgh$, where m is the mass, g is the acceleration due to gravity, and h is the height.

Grouping

Students should do this activity in pairs.

2 TEACH

Tips for Success

Encourage each student in a pair to answer the questions individually. Then the students can check each other's work and refine their answers. Both students in a pair should agree on their explanations so they can defend them in class.

Guiding Students' Work

Students can use a graphing calculator to complete the table of values of energy versus height.

Alternative Strategy

Have several types of balls available in the classroom. Students can measure the bounce height of each ball from a given drop height and use the results to calculate the bounciness of each ball.

5. See Additional Answers beginning on page AA1.

EXPLORING MATH IN SCIENCE

The Physics of Basketball

Dropping Basketballs

The energy with which a basketball hits the ground affects how high the ball will bounce. When a ball is dribbled, several factors affect this energy, including the energy transmitted to the ball by your hand.

When a ball is dropped, the energy with which it hits the ground depends *only* on the mass of the ball, gravity, and the height from which the ball is dropped. Use the equation below to calculate this energy.

Energy E (in Joules) = mass m (in kilograms) × acceleration due to gravity g × height h (in meters)

$$E = mgh$$

For objects on Earth, the acceleration due to gravity g is about 9.8 meters per second squared. You can rewrite the equation above as follows.

$$E = 9.8mh$$

1. Copy and complete the table below. The mass of a typical basketball is 0.6 kilogram. Find the energy with which the ball hits the ground when dropped from each height in the table.

Height (meters)	0.5	1	1.5	2	2.5
Energy (Joules)	?	?	?	?	?
	2.94	5.88	8.82	11.76	14.7

2. You drop a basketball with a mass of 0.6 kilogram. It hits the ground with 12 Joules of energy. From what height did you drop it? **about 2 m**

3. You drop a ball from 3 meters and it hits the ground with 15 Joules of energy. What is the mass of the ball? **about 0.51 kg**

4. Writing Explain how the energy with which a ball hits the ground changes as you increase the height from which you drop it. **It increases because 9.8m is multiplied times the height.**

5. Critical Thinking You drop two identical basketballs from two different heights. One height is twice as great as the other. How will the energies of the two balls as they hit the ground compare? Explain. **See margin.**

Bouncing Basketballs

How high a ball bounces is affected by how bouncy the ball is. For example, a fully inflated basketball bounces higher than a partially inflated one, if both balls hit the ground with the same energy. The fully inflated ball is more bouncy.

You can express the bounciness of a ball by finding the ratio of the bounce height to the drop height. Height is measured from the bottom of the ball to the ground. A standard basketball inflated for game play has a bounciness ratio of about 0.6.

$$\frac{\text{Bounce height (in meters)}}{\text{Drop height (in meters)}} \approx 0.6$$

A ball's bounce height is the height of the *first* bounce.

6. You drop a standard basketball 3 meters. About how high will it bounce on its first bounce? **about 1.8 m**
7. You drop a standard basketball. It bounces to a height of 2 meters on its first bounce. From about what height was it dropped? **about 3.3 m**
8. **Critical Thinking** A ball drops 1.5 meters. It bounces 0.6 meters. Is this ball more or less bouncy than a standard basketball? Explain. **less; $0.4 < 0.6$**
9. **Challenge** You drop a standard basketball 6 meters. Explain how to use the bounciness ratio to find how high the ball bounces on its second bounce. Then find the height of the second bounce. **The bounce height for the first bounce is the drop height for the second bounce; about 2.2 m.**

Project IDEAS

- **Experiment** Design and carry out an experiment to compare the bounciness of several types of ball. Describe your experiment and present your results.
- **Report** A given ball may be designed to perform well during the play of the game in which it is commonly used. Choose a sport and find information on the design of the balls and other equipment used in the sport. Present your findings to the class.
- **Research** The unit of energy called the Joule was named after the scientist James Prescott Joule. Find out more about James Prescott Joule and his work. Present your findings to the class.
- **Career** A variety of professionals do scientific research to study how athletes can improve performance and avoid injury. Investigate some of these careers and present your findings to the class.

INTERNET
Project Support
CLASSZONE.COM

3 APPLY

Reflecting on the Activity

The height to which a ball bounces depends upon the height from which it is dropped. Bounciness can be expressed as the ratio of bounce height to drop height.

Project Ideas

For additional information on the Project Ideas and for suggestions for more projects, go to classzone.com

4 ASSESS

The rubric below can be used to assess the projects on the pupil page. For more information on rubrics, see the Professional Development Book.

4 The student fully achieves the mathematical and project goals. Explanations indicate a solid understanding of the energy and bounciness formulas. All work is complete and accurate.

3 The student substantially achieves the mathematical and project goals. Explanations indicate that the student understands the energy and bounciness formulas. There may be some minor misunderstanding of content or errors in computation.

2 The student partially achieves the mathematical and project goals. Students are able to make attempts at solving most problems and providing explanations. Some of the work may be incomplete, misdirected, or unclear.

1 The student makes little progress toward accomplishing the goals of the project because of a lack of understanding or lack of effort. The student shows little understanding of how to use the energy and bounciness formulas.

Pacing and Assignment Guide

REGULAR SCHEDULE

Lesson	Les. Day	BASIC	AVERAGE	ADVANCED
7.1	Day 1	SRH p. 708 Exs. 1-3; pp. 319-320 Exs. 10-19, 23-32, 37-43	pp. 319-320 Exs. 14-24, 27-35, 37-44	pp. 319-320 Exs. 14-22, 25-38*, 41-44
7.2	Day 1	pp. 325-326 Exs. 8-23, 25-27, 29-31, 36-41	pp. 325-326 Exs. 10-17, 20-31, 35-41	pp. 325-326 Exs. 10-15, 20-36*, 39-41
7.3	Day 1	pp. 329-330 Exs. 7-18, 20-27, 29-32, 35-41	pp. 329-330 Exs. 9-20, 22-28, 30-32, 35-42	pp. 329-330 Exs. 9-20, 23-37*, 40-42
7.4	Day 1	EP p. 731 Exs. 17, 18, 23, 24; pp. 334-335 Exs. 12-23, 32-41, 45-51, 59-66	pp. 334-335 Exs. 20-35, 42-48, 52-56, 58-67	pp. 334-335 Exs. 20-35, 42-48, 52-61*, 65-67
7.5	Day 1	pp. 340-341 Exs. 7-18, 20-25, 32-41	pp. 340-341 Exs. 11-21, 24-29, 31-41	pp. 340-341 Exs. 11-16, 19-37*, 41
7.6	Day 1	pp. 345-346 Exs. 8-18, 20-22, 27-29, 33-41	pp. 345-346 Exs. 10-19, 23-30, 32-36, 39-42	pp. 345-346 Exs. 10-19, 23-36*, 40-42
7.7	Day 1	pp. 349-350 Exs. 7-18, 21-24, 28-35	pp. 349-350 Exs. 9-20, 22-26, 28-36	pp. 349-350 Exs. 9-20, 22-30*, 33-36
7.8	Day 1	EP p. 730 Exs. 17-20; pp. 356-357 Exs. 4-12, 15-22, 27-34	pp. 356-357 Exs. 6-16, 19-25, 27-34	pp. 356-357 Exs. 6-14, 17-28*, 31-34
Review	Day 1	pp. 360-361 Exs. 1-33	pp. 360-361 Exs. 1-33	pp. 360-361 Exs. 1-33
Assess	Day 1	Chapter 7 Test	Chapter 7 Test	Chapter 7 Test

YEARLY PACING Chapter 7 Total – **10 days** Chapters 1-7 Total – **80 days** Remaining – **80 days**

*Challenge Exercises EP = Extra Practice SRH = Skills Review Handbook EC = Extra Challenge

BLOCK SCHEDULE

DAY 1	DAY 2	DAY 3	DAY 4	DAY 5
7.1 pp. 319-320 Exs. 14-24, 27-35, 37-44 **7.2** pp. 325-326 Exs. 10-17, 20-31, 35-41	**7.3** pp. 329-330 Exs. 9-20, 22-28, 30-32, 35-42 **7.4** pp. 334-335 Exs. 20-35, 42-48, 52-56, 58-67	**7.5** pp. 340-341 Exs. 11-21, 24-29, 31-41 **7.6** pp. 345-346 Exs. 10-19, 23-30, 32-36, 39-42	**7.7** pp. 349-350 Exs. 9-20, 22-26, 28-36 **7.8** pp. 356-357 Exs. 6-16, 19-25, 27-34	**Review** pp. 360-361 Exs. 1-33 **Assess** Chapter 7 Test

YEARLY PACING Chapter 7 Total – **5 days** Chapters 1-7 Total – **40 days** Remaining – **40 days**

Support Materials

CHAPTER RESOURCE BOOK

CHAPTER SUPPORT

Tips for New Teachers	p. 1
Parents as Partners	p. 3

LESSON SUPPORT	7.1	7.2	7.3	7.4	7.5	7.6	7.7	7.8
Lesson Plans (regular and block)	p. 6	p. 14	p. 24	p. 32	p. 42	p. 52	p. 60	p. 68
Technology Activities & Keystrokes				p. 34				
Activity Support Masters								
Activity Masters					p. 44			
Practice (3 levels)	p. 8	p. 16	p. 26	p. 36	p. 45	p. 54	p. 62	p. 70
Study Guide	p. 11	p. 19	p. 29	p. 39	p. 48	p. 57	p. 65	p. 73
Real-World Problem Solving		p. 21			p. 50			
Challenge Practice	p. 13	p. 22	p. 31	p. 41	p. 51	p. 59	p. 67	p. 75

REVIEW

Games Support Masters	pp. 5, 23
Chapter Review Games and Activities	p. 76
Real-Life Project with Rubric	p. 77
Cooperative Project with Rubric	p. 79
Extra Credit Project with Rubric	p. 81
Cumulative Practice	p. 83
Resource Book Answers	A1

ASSESSMENT

Quizzes	p. 79
Chapter Tests (3 levels)	p. 81
Standardized Test	p. 87
Alternative Assessments with Rubrics	p. 88
Unit Test	p. 90
Cumulative Test	p. 92

TRANSPARENCIES

	7.1	7.2	7.3	7.4	7.5	7.6	7.7	7.8
Warm-Up / Daily Homework Quiz	✔	✔	✔	✔	✔	✔	✔	✔
Notetaking Guide	✔	✔	✔	✔	✔	✔	✔	✔
Teacher Support								
English/Spanish Problem Solving	✔	✔	✔	✔	✔		✔	
Answer Transparencies	✔	✔	✔	✔	✔	✔	✔	✔

TECHNOLOGY

- EasyPlanner CD-ROM
- Test and Practice Generator
- Electronic Lesson Presentations
- eTutorial CD-ROM
- Chapter Audio Summaries CDs
- Classzone.com
- eEdition Plus Online
- eWorkbook Plus Online
- eTutorial Plus Online
- EasyPlanner Plus Online

ADDITIONAL RESOURCES

- Worked-Out Solution Key
- Notetaking Guide
- Practice Workbook
- Tutor Place
- Professional Development Book
- Special Activities Book
- Posters
- Spanish Study Guide
- Exercises in Spanish
- English/Spanish Ch. Reviews/Tests
- Multi-Language Visual Glossary

Math Background and Teaching Strategies

Lesson 7.1

MATH BACKGROUND

Both *ratios* and *rates* use a fraction to compare two quantities. In a **ratio**, the quantities compared in the numerator and denominator have no units or the same units. In a **rate**, the quantities compared have different units. A **unit rate** has a denominator of 1 unit. Rates are often used as *conversion factors* to convert between measurements that are in different units using *dimensional analysis.*

TEACHING STRATEGIES

The biggest confusion for students regarding ratios and rates is often working with the units of measurement. Ratios are easiest since the units cancel. It will help students to see more problems in the style of Example 2 on page 318 to help them become comfortable with choosing appropriate conversion fractions and to decide which unit in the fraction goes in the numerator and which in the denominator.

Lesson 7.2

MATH BACKGROUND

A **proportion** is an equation that states the equivalence of two ratios. You can solve a proportion using a special result of the multiplication property of equality called the *cross products property,* in which the **cross products** of the proportion are equated. For the proportion $\frac{a}{b} = \frac{c}{d}$, the cross products are ad and bc. Proportions are used in problems involving **scale models** and drawings to compare dimensions of an actual object to dimensions of the model or drawing.

TEACHING STRATEGIES

Many students like the cross products property because it is easy to remember and apply. They may need guidance in identifying proportions to avoid misapplying this property. To show that the cross products property is not "magic," you can solve with students a simple proportion like $\frac{4}{5} = \frac{x}{8}$ by multiplying both sides by the LCD. This leads to $4 \cdot 8 = 5 \cdot x$, which matches the result of applying the cross products property. To help students set up proportions, work with them in using the language "… is to … as … is to …," for example, "the height of a model car is to its length as the height of the real car is to its length."

Lesson 7.3

MATH BACKGROUND

THE PERCENT PROPORTION One method of solving percent problems is using the basic percent proportion $\frac{a}{b} = \frac{p}{100}$, where a is part of the base b and p is the percent. This can be translated as "a is the same part of b as p is part of 100." In this proportion, b and 100 are equated because each represents the whole, while a and p represent parts of the whole.

TEACHING STRATEGIES

An advantage of using the percent proportion is that it allows students to set up the same basic proportion for any percent problem. The problem lies in deciding what to substitute where. It is not usually difficult for students to identify p, since the word or the symbol for percent will be present. To help students identify a and b, encourage them to ask themselves, "What is a part and what is a whole?" It may require them to do some mental rearranging of a problem. For example, in Example 3 on page 328, students must recognize that the wording means that "24 is a part of some number."

Lesson 7.4

MATH BACKGROUND

FRACTIONS, DECIMALS, AND PERCENTS To write a fraction as a percent, substitute the fraction for $\frac{a}{b}$ in the basic percent proportion and solve for p. To write a decimal as a percent, move the decimal right two places and add a percent sign. To write a percent as a fraction, write the percent as the numerator of a fraction whose denominator is 100 and simplify. To write a percent as a decimal, remove the percent sign and move the decimal point left two places.

TEACHING STRATEGIES

It is useful to have students make charts or posters that give relationships among specific fractions, decimals, and percents. These could include equivalents such as $\frac{1}{4} = 0.25 = 25\%$, $\frac{1}{3} = 0.\overline{3} = 33\frac{1}{3}\%$, $\frac{2}{5} = 0.4 = 40\%$, and $\frac{7}{8} = 0.875 = 87.5\%$. Students can also include equivalents for values less than 1%, such as $\frac{1}{1000} = 0.001 = 0.1\%$, and for counting numbers, such as $1 = 100\%$ and $10 = 1000\%$.

Lesson 7.5

MATH BACKGROUND

Sometimes, absolute quantities may mean less than relative changes in them. For example, the value of the gross domestic product is incomprehensibly large, but we can understand small percent changes in it because they are reflected in everyday life. A **percent of change** describes a change in relation to an original amount, and can be a **percent of increase** or a **percent of decrease**. To find the percent of change, divide the change from the original amount by the original amount and write the result as a percent.

TEACHING STRATEGIES

Point out to students that how they find the difference in a percent of change problem can be important in how they interpret the problem. If students always subtract the lesser quantity from the greater quantity, they need to return to the problem context to determine whether the change is a percent increase or a percent decrease. If they always subtract the original amount from the new amount to find the difference, a positive result will indicate a percent of increase and a negative result will indicate a percent of decrease.

Lesson 7.6

MATH BACKGROUND

PERCENT APPLICATIONS Percents of change are used extensively in buying and selling. The retail price a store charges is the wholesale price it pays plus the **markup**, a percent of increase in the wholesale price. When a retail item goes on sale, the price charged the customer is the original retail price minus the **discount**, a percent of decrease in the retail price. Sales taxes and tips are also percents of increase in the amount paid based on the original stated price.

TEACHING STRATEGIES

Have students write the verbal formula involved in a problem explicitly as a beginning point. For example, in Example 1, students can write out the formula for sale price. Then they can substitute the original price, which points out that they need to find the amount of the discount to find the sale price.

Lesson 7.7

MATH BACKGROUND

THE PERCENT EQUATION Lesson 7.3, percent problems were solved using the proportion $\frac{a}{b} = \frac{p}{100}$. You can also use the percent equation $a = p\% \cdot b$, which is the percent proportion solved for a. The equation can be read "a is p percent of b," where b is interpreted as the whole that a is a part of.

TEACHING STRATEGIES

In percent problems, students need to ask themselves what is the part and what is the whole, and whether one or both of these quantities are given. Also, you may need to observe students' work very carefully to ensure that they are working correctly when translating between percents expressed using a percent sign and percents expressed using a decimal.

Lesson 7.8

MATH BACKGROUND

A thought or actual experiment can have different results, or **outcomes**. The **probability** of an outcome or collection of outcomes (an **event**) is the ratio of the number of favorable outcomes either to the number of possible outcomes—this is **theoretical probability**, and relates to the thought experiment for equally likely outcomes—or to the number of times the experiment was performed—this is **experimental probability**, and relates to an actual experiment.

TEACHING STRATEGIES

This lesson contains difficult new vocabulary and concepts. It may be hard for students to distinguish between events and outcomes. Present many concrete examples to students in which they must distinguish between events and outcomes and identify favorable outcomes from among possible outcomes without having to calculate probabilities.

Differentiating Instruction

Strategies for Underachievers

USE MODELS AND MANIPULATIVES

TIPPING In Lesson 7.6, you may want to spend more time with students discussing tipping, and help them move this concept outside the classroom. Explain to students that some people carry a tip reference card with them when they dine out that is similar to a tax reference table that some small businesses use to calculate sales tax. The card gives sample dinner prices and then appropriate tips based on those prices. Point out that 15% is often considered a standard tip, though many people may leave 20% for very good service. Encourage students to make their own tip reference cards. You may also want to point out the mental model that many people use to decide on an appropriate tip when they are eating out. First, round off the restaurant bill for ease of calculation. For example, you can round a restaurant bill of \$45.83 to \$46.00. Now divide by 10, which means to move the decimal point one place to the left. In this case, this gives \$4.60. This is 10% of \$46.00. Now take half of the result of your previous division, which in this case gives \$2.30. This is 5% of \$46.00. Adding these two amounts gives the amount of a 15% tip, in this case, \$4.60 + \$2.30 = \$6.90. To calculate a 20% tip, just double the 10% amount that you found. In this case, the result is 2 • \$4.60 = \$9.20.

In Lesson 7.8, it will be helpful for some students to have physical models—buttons, marbles, number cubes, playing cards, coins, spinners, and so on—available to use when working with probability. Besides giving them the ability actually to determine experimental probabilities, it can be helpful for students to carry out an actual experiment (such as flipping one or more coins) to show that the results of a theoretical probability calculation are reasonable.

ISOLATE AND MODEL PROBLEM TYPES

In Lesson 7.3, you may wish to slow the pace for some underachievers. It can be very confusing for many students to study the three types of percent problems at once (finding an unknown percent, amount, or base). You may instead wish to focus on one type of percent problem at a time. As you work with each type of problem, students should work both straightforward examples such as those in Exercises 7–18 on page 329 as well as real-world application problems that follow the same model. After focusing individually on each problem type, you can decide when and how to expose these students to simultaneous presentation of problem types. You may wish to have students create reference note cards detailing the Summary of Percent Problems at the bottom of page 328. They can also make cards illustrating worked example problems for each type, both non-application and application problems. Allow students access to these cards at will.

USE SCAFFOLDING

MEASUREMENT CONVERSIONS In Lesson 7.1, problems such as Example 2 on page 318 that involve using rates to convert units of measurement can be very difficult for underachievers. You may first want to review multiplying and simplifying fractions with these students. You may also want to provide students with sample problems involving unit conversions that have fraction rules with correctly-placed units on them but are lacking numbers. Have students fill in these templates. Make sure that students observe how the fractions are chosen and oriented so that units cancel to leave only the desired units.

USE A CO-TEACHING MODEL

In Lessons 7.3 and 7.7, which can be difficult even for the best students, you may wish to consider co-teaching with a Reading Specialist who can help students with language-based disabilities or limitations recognize cues and develop strategies to help them differentiate among the three types of percent problems.

In Problem Solving Strategies 7.8, you may wish to co-teach with a Reading Specialist who can help students determine the most important information in the problems. Furthermore, the Specialist can help students with strategies for organization, which are necessary in successfully approaching problems requiring them to perform an experiment.

Strategies for English Learners

DISSECT WORD PROBLEMS

Word problems are a big challenge for English learners. For an English learner, a word problem can look something like the first two lines of Lewis Carroll's "Jabberwocky," where the only words you know are *and, the, did, in, all,* and *were.*

In some cases the teacher can turn the "word" problem into a "picture" problem:

Word problem: If a 10-ounce bottle of shampoo costs $3.45, how much will a 15-ounce bottle cost? This is a ratio problem that students can set up in the following way: $\frac{3.45}{10} = \frac{x}{15}$

Picture problem:

In many contexts, however, including standardized tests, students will need to be able to decipher word problems. Fortunately, most word problems follow a standard format and there are clues provided by "signal words," words of high frequency that signal what will follow or what came before. Most word problems also contain numbers, and usually you must do something with the numbers to solve the problems. Analyzing the units in a problem can provide a clue to the answer that is needed.

Strategies for Advanced Learners

INCREASE DEPTH AND COMPLEXITY

In Hands-on Activity 7.2, in the "Your turn now" exercises, students are led to discover that the ratio of the areas of a square and its enlargement is equal to the square of the ratio of their sides. You may wish to challenge some advanced learners into investigating three-dimensional scale models. Encourage them to investigate and draw conclusions about the ratio of the volumes of a cube and its enlargement to the ratio of their sides.

In Lesson 7.2, you may wish to have some students create scale drawings or models of objects in the classroom. Students should be able to express the scale that they are using correctly and explain how they applied it.

In conjunction with Lesson 7.6, you may wish to have students investigate sales taxes. Most U.S. states levy a sales tax, which is often combined with county and/or city sales taxes. Have students investigate sales tax rates in their cities and compare these to sales tax rates in other cities and states. Students may also want to see to what kinds of purchases these taxes apply. Suggest that students investigate how much revenue is brought to a state or city by sales taxes and how much a small increase in the sales tax rate, such as 0.1%, can bring in. Students may also want to extend their research on taxes to the mill rate assessment, which is based on thousandths of a dollar and is used in calculating property taxes, which often provide a significant portion of the revenues for schools.

USE CROSS-CURRICULAR CONNECTIONS

ART AND GRAPHICS In Hands-on Activity 7.2, you may wish to work with an art teacher to investigate scale drawings. The art teacher may be able to provide or give information about tools that are used to enlarge drawings manually.

Lesson 7.2 provides a good opportunity to collaborate with an English teacher to present to students the concept of an analogy, which is often presented using the "... is to ... as ... is to ...," language also used for setting up proportions.

Differentiating Instruction: Teaching Resources

Differentiating Teacher Materials

McDougal Littell *Middle School Mathematics* offers a wide variety of materials to help with professional development and teaching. These resources can be found in this *Teacher's Edition*, in the *Professional Development Book*, in the *Chapter Resource Books*, and in the multi-language resources.

PROFESSIONAL DEVELOPMENT BOOK

The *Professional Development Book* contains ideas for in-service workshops, professional articles, mathematical background notes, bulletin board ideas, teacher tips, and a reprint of the Parents as Partners pages from the Chapter Resource Books. (Parents as Partners is also available in Spanish in the *Spanish Study Guide*.)

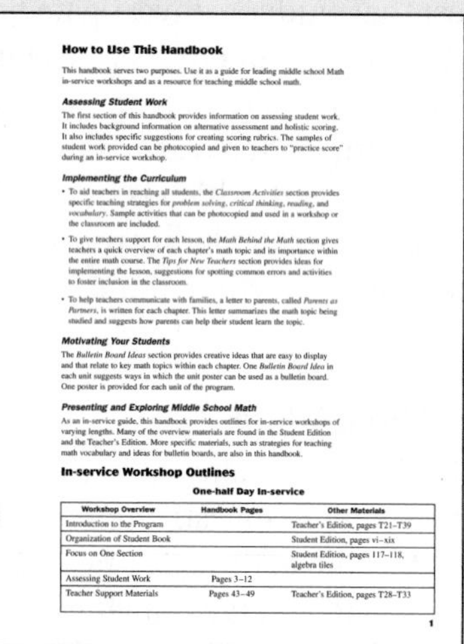

How to Use This Handbook

This handbook serves two purposes. Use it as a guide for leading middle school Math in-service workshops and as a resource for teaching middle school math.

Assessing Student Work

The first section of this handbook provides information on assessing student work. It includes background information on alternative assessment and holistic scoring. It also includes specific suggestions for creating scoring rubrics. The samples of student work provided can be photocopied and given to teachers to "practice score" during an in-service workshop.

Implementing the Curriculum

- To aid teachers in reaching all students, the *Classroom Activities* section provides specific teaching strategies for *problem solving*, *critical thinking*, *reading*, and *vocabulary*. Sample activities that can be photocopied and used in a workshop or the classroom are included.
- To give teachers support for each lesson, the *Math Behind the Math* section gives teachers a quick overview of each chapter's math topic and its importance within the entire math course. The *Tips for New Teachers* section provides ideas for implementing the lesson, suggestions for spotting common errors and activities to foster inclusion in the classroom.
- To help teachers communicate with families, a letter to parents, called *Parents as Partners*, is written for each chapter. This letter summarizes the math topic being studied and suggests how parents can help their student learn the topic.

Motivating Your Students

The *Bulletin Board Ideas* section provides creative ideas that are easy to display and that relate to key math topics within each chapter. One *Bulletin Board Idea* in each unit suggests ways in which the unit poster can be used as a bulletin board. One poster is provided for each unit of the program.

Presenting and Exploring Middle School Math

As an in-service guide, this handbook provides outlines for in-service workshops of varying lengths. Many of the overview materials are found in the Student Edition and the Teacher's Edition. More specific materials, such as strategies for teaching math vocabulary and ideas for bulletin boards, are also in this handbook.

In-service Workshop Outlines

One-half Day In-service

Workshop Overview	Handbook Pages	Other Materials
Introduction to the Program		Teacher's Edition, pages T21–T39
Organization of Student Book		Student Edition, pages vi–xix
Focus on One Section		Student Edition, pages 117–118, algebra tiles
Assessing Student Work	Pages 3–12	
Teacher Support Materials	Pages 43–49	Teacher's Edition, pages T28–T33

1

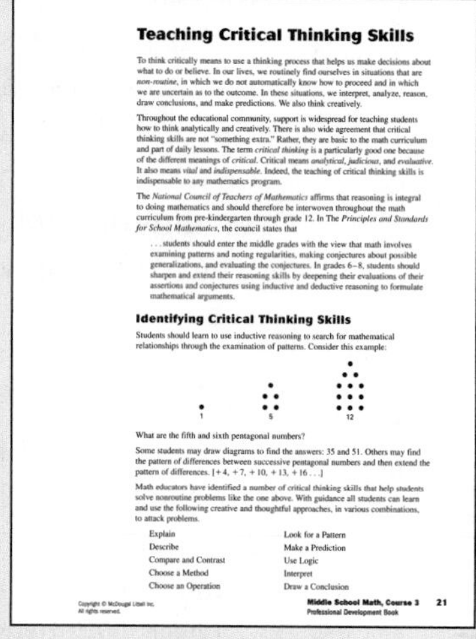

Teaching Critical Thinking Skills

To think critically means to use a thinking process that helps us make decisions about what to do or believe. In our lives, we routinely find ourselves in situations that are *non-routine*, in which we do not automatically know how to proceed and in which we are uncertain as to the outcome. In these situations, we interpret, analyze, reason, draw conclusions, and make predictions. We also think creatively.

Throughout the educational community, support is widespread for teaching students how to think analytically and creatively. There is also wide agreement that critical thinking skills are not "something extra." Rather, they are basic to the math curriculum and part of daily lessons. The term *critical thinking* is a particularly good one because of the different meanings of *critical*. Critical means *analytical*, *judicious*, and *evaluative*. It also means *vital* and *indispensable*. Indeed, the teaching of critical thinking skills is indispensable to any mathematics program.

The *National Council of Teachers of Mathematics* affirms that reasoning is integral to doing mathematics and should therefore be interwoven throughout the math curriculum from pre-kindergarten through grade 12. In The *Principles and Standards for School Mathematics*, the council states that

> . . . students should enter the middle grades with the view that math involves examining patterns and noting regularities, making conjectures about possible generalizations, and evaluating the conjectures. In grades 6–8, students should sharpen and extend their reasoning skills by deepening their evaluations of their assertions and conjectures using inductive and deductive reasoning to formulate mathematical arguments.

Identifying Critical Thinking Skills

Students should learn to use inductive reasoning to search for mathematical relationships through the examination of patterns. Consider this example:

1 5 12

What are the fifth and sixth pentagonal numbers?

Some students may draw diagrams to find the answers: 35 and 51. Others may find the pattern of differences between successive pentagonal numbers and then extend the pattern of differences. [+4, +7, +10, +13, +16 . . .]

Math educators have identified a number of critical thinking skills that help students solve nonroutine problems like the one above. With guidance all students can learn and use the following creative and thoughtful approaches, in various combinations, to attack problems.

Explain	Look for a Pattern
Describe	Make a Prediction
Compare and Contrast	Use Logic
Choose a Method	Interpret
Choose an Operation	Draw a Conclusion

Middle School Math, Course 3 21
Professional Development Book

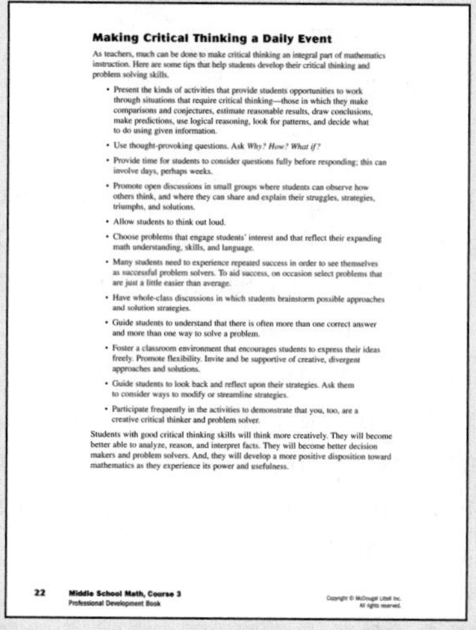

Making Critical Thinking a Daily Event

As teachers, much can be done to make critical thinking an integral part of mathematics instruction. Here are some tips that help students develop their critical thinking and problem solving skills.

- Present the kinds of activities that provide students opportunities to work through situations that require critical thinking—those in which they make comparisons and conjectures, estimate reasonable results, draw conclusions, make predictions, use logical reasoning, look for patterns, and decide what to do using given information.
- Use thought-provoking questions. Ask *Why? How? What if?*
- Provide time for students to consider questions fully before responding; this can involve days, perhaps weeks.
- Promote open discussions in small groups where students can observe how others think, and where they can share and explain their struggles, strategies, triumphs, and solutions.
- Allow students to think out loud.
- Choose problems that engage students' interest and that reflect their expanding math understanding, skills, and language.
- Many students need to experience repeated success in order to see themselves as successful problem solvers. To aid success, on occasion select problems that are just a little easier than average.
- Have whole-class discussions in which students brainstorm possible approaches and solution strategies.
- Guide students to understand that there is often more than one correct answer and more than one way to solve a problem.
- Foster a classroom environment that encourages students to express their ideas freely. Promote flexibility. Invite and be supportive of creative, divergent approaches and solutions.
- Guide students to look back and reflect upon their strategies. Ask them to consider ways to modify or streamline strategies.
- Participate frequently in the activities to demonstrate that you, too, are a creative critical thinker and problem solver.

Students with good critical thinking skills will think more creatively. They will become better able to analyze, reason, and interpret facts. They will become better decision makers and problem solvers. And, they will develop a more positive disposition toward mathematics as they experience its power and usefulness.

22 **Middle School Math, Course 3**
Professional Development Book

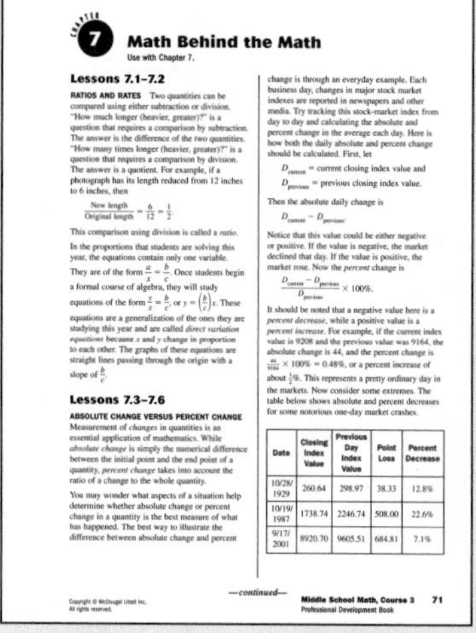

Math Behind the Math
Use with Chapter 7.

Lessons 7.1–7.2

RATIOS AND RATES Two quantities can be compared using either subtraction or division. "How much longer (heavier, greater)?" is a question that requires a comparison by subtraction. The answer is the difference of the two quantities. "How many times longer (heavier, greater)?" is a question that requires a comparison by division. The answer is a quotient. For example, if a photograph has its length reduced from 12 inches to 6 inches, then

$$\frac{\text{New length}}{\text{Original length}} = \frac{6}{12} = \frac{1}{2}.$$

This comparison using division is called a *ratio*.

In the proportions that students are solving this year, the equations contain only one variable. They are of the form $\frac{a}{x} = \frac{b}{c}$. Once students begin a formal course of algebra, they will study equations of the form $\frac{y}{x} = \frac{b}{c}$, or $y = \left(\frac{b}{c}\right)x$. These equations are a generalization of the ones they are studying this year and are called *direct variation equations* because x and y change in proportion to each other. The graphs of these equations are straight lines passing through the origin with a slope of $\frac{b}{c}$.

Lessons 7.3–7.6

ABSOLUTE CHANGE VERSUS PERCENT CHANGE Measurement of *changes* in quantities is an essential application of mathematics. While *absolute change* is simply the numerical difference between the initial point and the end point of a quantity, *percent change* takes into account the ratio of a change to the whole quantity.

You may wonder what aspects of a situation help determine whether absolute change or percent change in a quantity is the best measure of what has happened. The best way to illustrate the difference between absolute change and percent change is through an everyday example. Each business day, changes in major stock market indexes are reported in newspapers and other media. Try tracking this stock-market index from day to day and calculating the absolute and percent change in the average each day. Here is how both the daily absolute and percent change should be calculated. First, let

$D_{current}$ = current closing index value and
$D_{previous}$ = previous closing index value.

Then the absolute daily change is

$$D_{current} - D_{previous}.$$

Notice that this value could be either negative or positive. If the value is negative, the market declined that day. If the value is positive, the market rose. Now the *percent* change is

$$\frac{D_{current} - D_{previous}}{D_{previous}} \times 100\%.$$

It should be noted that a negative value here is a *percent decrease*, while a positive value is a *percent increase*. For example, if the current index value is 9208 and the previous value was 9164, the absolute change is 44, and the percent change is $\frac{44}{9164} \times 100\% = 0.48\%$, or a percent increase of about $\frac{1}{2}\%$. This represents a pretty ordinary day in the markets. Now consider some extremes. The table below shows absolute and percent decreases for some notorious one-day market crashes.

Date	Closing Index Value	Previous Day Index Value	Point Loss	Percent Decrease
10/28/1929	260.64	298.97	38.33	12.8%
10/19/1987	1738.74	2246.74	508.00	22.6%
9/17/2001	8920.70	9605.51	684.81	7.1%

—continued—

Middle School Math, Course 3 71
Professional Development Book

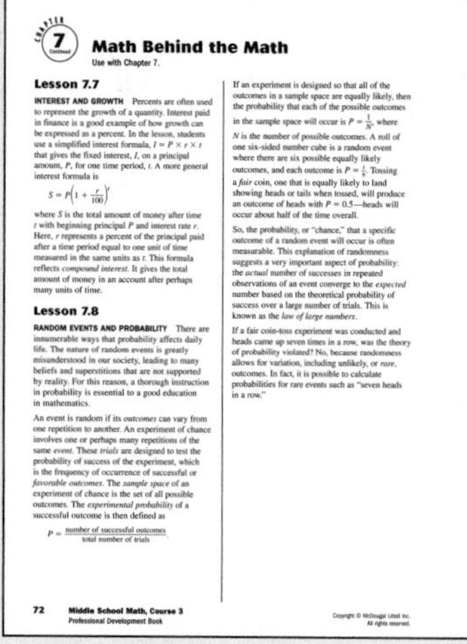

Math Behind the Math
Use with Chapter 7.

Lesson 7.7

INTEREST AND GROWTH Percents are often used to represent the growth of a quantity. Interest paid in finance is a good example of how growth can be expressed as a percent. In the lesson, students use a simplified interest formula, $I = P \times r \times t$ that gives the fixed interest, I, on a principal amount, P, for one time period, t. A more general interest formula is

$$S = P\left(1 + \frac{r}{100}\right)^t$$

where S is the total amount of money after time t with beginning principal P and interest rate r. Here, r represents a percent of the principal paid after a time period equal to one unit of time measured in the same units as t. This formula reflects *compound interest*. It gives the total amount of money in an account after perhaps many units of time.

Lesson 7.8

RANDOM EVENTS AND PROBABILITY There are innumerable ways that probability affects daily life. The nature of random events is greatly misunderstood in our society, leading to many beliefs and superstitions that are not supported by reality. For this reason, a thorough instruction in probability is essential to a good education in mathematics.

An event is random if its *outcomes* can vary from one repetition to another. An experiment of chance involves one or perhaps many repetitions of the same *event*. These *trials* are designed to test the probability of success of the experiment, which is the frequency of occurrence of successful or *favorable outcomes*. The *sample space* of an experiment of chance is the set of all possible outcomes. The *experimental probability* of a successful outcome is then defined as

$$P = \frac{\text{number of successful outcomes}}{\text{total number of trials}}.$$

If an experiment is designed so that all of the outcomes in a sample space are equally likely, then the probability that each of the possible outcomes in the sample space will occur is $P = \frac{1}{N}$, where N is the number of possible outcomes. A roll of one six-sided number cube is a random event where there are six possible equally likely outcomes, and each outcome is $P = \frac{1}{6}$. Tossing a *fair* coin, one that is equally likely to land showing heads or tails when tossed, will produce an outcome of heads with $P = 0.5$—heads will occur about half of the time overall.

So, the probability, or "chance," that a specific outcome of a random event will occur is often measurable. This explanation of randomness suggests a very important aspect of probability: the *actual* number of successes in repeated observations of an event converge to the *expected* number based on the theoretical probability of success over a large number of trials. This is known as the *law of large numbers*.

If a fair coin-toss experiment was conducted and heads came up seven times in a row, was the theory of probability violated? No, because randomness allows for variation, including unlikely, or *rare*, outcomes. In fact, it is possible to calculate probabilities for rare events such as "seven heads in a row."

72 **Middle School Math, Course 3**
Professional Development Book

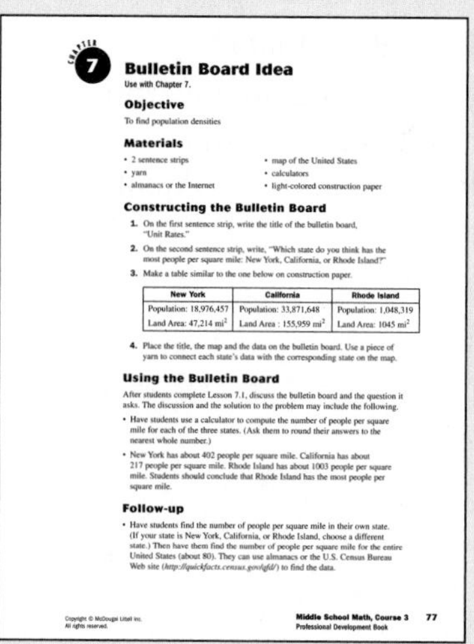

Bulletin Board Idea
Use with Chapter 7.

Objective

To find population densities

Materials

- 2 sentence strips
- yarn
- almanacs or the Internet
- map of the United States
- calculators
- light-colored construction paper

Constructing the Bulletin Board

1. On the first sentence strip, write the title of the bulletin board, "Unit Rates."
2. On the second sentence strip, write, "Which state do you think has the most people per square mile: New York, California, or Rhode Island?"
3. Make a table similar to the one below on construction paper.

New York	California	Rhode Island
Population: 18,976,457 Land Area: 47,214 mi²	Population: 33,871,648 Land Area : 155,959 mi²	Population: 1,048,319 Land Area: 1045 mi²

4. Place the title, the map and the data on the bulletin board. Use a piece of yarn to connect each state's data with the corresponding state on the map.

Using the Bulletin Board

After students complete Lesson 7.1, discuss the bulletin board and the question it asks. The discussion and the solution to the problem may include the following.

- Have students use a calculator to compute the number of people per square mile for each of the three states. (Ask them to round their answers to the nearest whole number.)
- New York has about 402 people per square mile. California has about 217 people per square mile. Rhode Island has about 1003 people per square mile. Students should conclude that Rhode Island has the most people per square mile.

Follow-up

- Have students find the number of people per square mile in their own state. (If your state is New York, California, or Rhode Island, choose a different state.) Then have them find the number of people per square mile for the entire United States (about 80). They can use almanacs or the U.S. Census Bureau Web site (*http://quickfacts.census.gov/qfd/*) to find the data.

Middle School Math, Course 3 77
Professional Development Book

Resource Book

Each *Chapter Resource Book* contains a section of tips for new teachers and a section on parental involvement. There is also a lesson plan page for both a regular schedule course and a block schedule course for each lesson in the textbook.

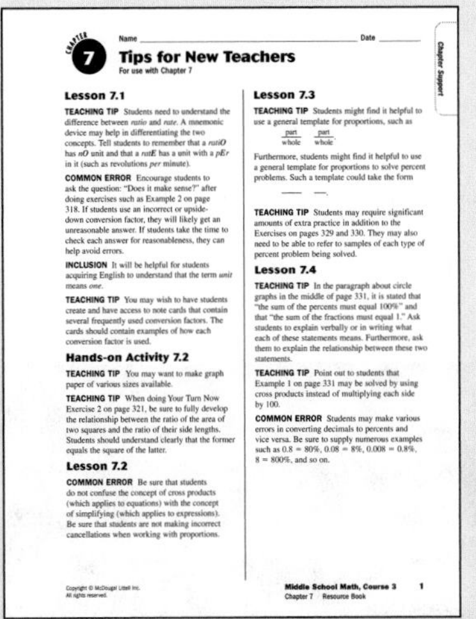

Chapter 7

Name ____________ Date ______

Tips for New Teachers

For use with Chapter 7

Chapter Support

Lesson 7.1

TEACHING TIP Students need to understand the difference between *ratio* and *rate*. A mnemonic device may help in differentiating the two concepts. Tell students to remember that a *ratiO* has *nO* unit and that a *ratE* has a unit with a *pEr* in it (such as revolutions *per* minute).

COMMON ERROR Encourage students to ask the question: "Does it make sense?" after doing exercises such as Example 2 on page 318. If students use an incorrect or upside-down conversion factor, they will likely get an unreasonable answer. If students take the time to check each answer for reasonableness, they can help avoid errors.

INCLUSION It will be helpful for students acquiring English to understand that the term *unit* means *one*.

TEACHING TIP You may wish to have students create and have access to note cards that contain several frequently used conversion factors. The cards should contain examples of how each conversion factor is used.

Hands-on Activity 7.2

TEACHING TIP You may want to make graph paper of various sizes available.

TEACHING TIP When doing Your Turn Now Exercise 2 on page 321, be sure to fully develop the relationship between the ratio of the area of two squares and the ratio of their side lengths. Students should understand clearly that the former equals the square of the latter.

Lesson 7.2

COMMON ERROR Be sure that students do not confuse the concept of cross products (which applies to equations) with the concept of simplifying (which applies to expressions). Be sure that students are not making incorrect cancellations when working with proportions.

Lesson 7.3

TEACHING TIP Students might find it helpful to use a general template for proportions, such as

$\frac{\text{part}}{\text{whole}} = \frac{\text{part}}{\text{whole}}$.

Furthermore, students might find it helpful to use a general template for proportions to solve percent problems. Such a template could take the form

$\frac{}{} = \frac{}{}$.

TEACHING TIP Students may require significant amounts of extra practice in addition to the Exercises on pages 329 and 330. They may also need to be able to refer to samples of each type of percent problem being solved.

Lesson 7.4

TEACHING TIP In the paragraph about circle graphs in the middle of page 331, it is stated that "the sum of the percents must equal 100%" and that "the sum of the fractions must equal 1." Ask students to explain verbally or in writing what each of these statements means. Furthermore, ask them to explain the relationship between these two statements.

TEACHING TIP Point out to students that Example 1 on page 331 may be solved by using cross products instead of multiplying each side by 100.

COMMON ERROR Students may make various errors in converting decimals to percents and vice versa. Be sure to supply numerous examples such as 0.8 = 80%, 0.08 = 8%, 0.008 = 0.8%, 8 = 800%, and so on.

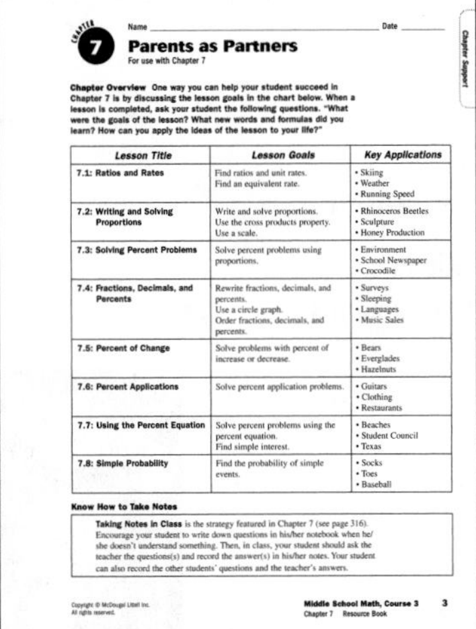

Chapter 7

Name ____________ Date ______

Parents as Partners

For use with Chapter 7

Chapter Support

Chapter Overview One way you can help your student succeed in Chapter 7 is by discussing the lesson goals in the chart below. When a lesson is completed, ask your student the following questions. "What were the goals of the lesson? What new words and formulas did you learn? How can you apply the ideas of the lesson to your life?"

Lesson Title	*Lesson Goals*	*Key Applications*
7.1: Ratios and Rates	Find ratios and unit rates. Find an equivalent rate.	• Skiing • Weather • Running Speed
7.2: Writing and Solving Proportions	Write and solve proportions. Use the cross products property. Use a scale.	• Rhinoceros Beetles • Sculpture • Honey Production
7.3: Solving Percent Problems	Solve percent problems using proportions.	• Environment • School Newspaper • Crocodile
7.4: Fractions, Decimals, and Percents	Rewrite fractions, decimals, and percents. Use a circle graph. Order fractions, decimals, and percents.	• Surveys • Sleeping • Languages • Music Sales
7.5: Percent of Change	Solve problems with percent of increase or decrease.	• Bears • Everglades • Hazelnuts
7.6: Percent Applications	Solve percent application problems.	• Guitars • Clothing • Restaurants
7.7: Using the Percent Equation	Solve percent problems using the percent equation. Find simple interest.	• Beaches • Student Council • Texas
7.8: Simple Probability	Find the probability of simple events.	• Socks • Toes • Baseball

Know How to Take Notes

Taking Notes in Class is the strategy featured in Chapter 7 (see page 316). Encourage your student to write down questions in his/her notebook when he/she doesn't understand something. Then, in class, your student should ask the teacher the questions(s) and record the answer(s) in his/her notes. Your student can also record the other students' questions and the teacher's answers.

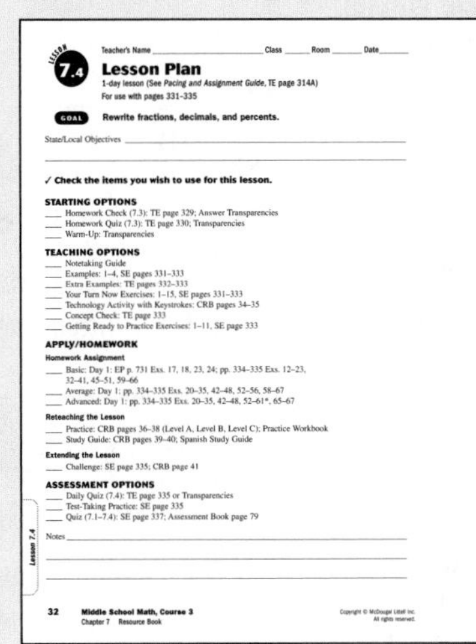

Lesson 7.4

Teacher's Name ____________ Class ____ Room ____ Date ____

Lesson Plan

1-day lesson (See *Pacing and Assignment Guide*, TE page 314A)

For use with pages 331-335

GOAL **Rewrite fractions, decimals, and percents.**

State/Local Objectives ____________

✓ **Check the items you wish to use for this lesson.**

STARTING OPTIONS

____ Homework Check (7.3): TE page 329; Answer Transparencies
____ Homework Quiz (7.3): TE page 330; Transparencies
____ Warm-Up: Transparencies

TEACHING OPTIONS

____ Notetaking Guide
____ Examples: 1–4, SE pages 331–333
____ Extra Examples: TE pages 332–333
____ Your Turn Now Exercises: 1–15, SE pages 331–333
____ Technology Activity with Keystrokes: CRB pages 34–35
____ Concept Check: TE page 333
____ Getting Ready to Practice Exercises: 1–11, SE page 333

APPLY/HOMEWORK

Homework Assignment

____ Basic: Day 1: EP p. 731 Exs. 17, 18, 23, 24; pp. 334–335 Exs. 12–23, 32–41, 45–51, 59–66
____ Average: Day 1: pp. 334–335 Exs. 20–35, 42–48, 52–56, 58–67
____ Advanced: Day 1: pp. 334–335 Exs. 20–35, 42–48, 52–61*, 65–67

Reteaching the Lesson

____ Practice: CRB pages 36–38 (Level A, Level B, Level C); Practice Workbook
____ Study Guide: CRB pages 39–40; Spanish Study Guide

Extending the Lesson

____ Challenge: SE page 335; CRB page 41

ASSESSMENT OPTIONS

____ Daily Quiz (7.4): TE page 335 or Transparencies
____ Test-Taking Practice: SE page 335
____ Quiz (7.1–7.4): SE page 337; Assessment Book page 79

Notes ____________

Lesson 7.4

Multi-Language Resources

A number of resources are available to help students acquiring English. These include a *Spanish Study Guide, Exercises in Spanish, English/Spanish Chapter Reviews and Tests, English-Spanish Problem Solving Transparencies, Chapter Audio Summaries,* and a *Multi-Language Visual Glossary.*

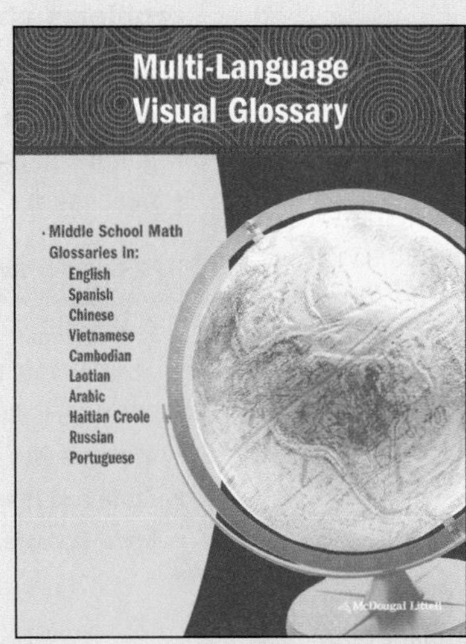

OVERVIEW

Main Ideas

In this chapter, students find ratios and unit rates, and write and then solve proportions, including by using cross products. Students solve percent problems both by writing proportions and by using the percent equation. Students translate among fractions, decimals, and percents, including in the use of circle graphs. Students apply percents to solving discount, markup, and other problems involving price. Students also find the probability of simple events.

Prerequisite Skills

The key skills reviewed in the games on these pages are:

- Solving equations
- Performing operations with decimals

Additional practice with prerequisite skills can be found in the Review What You Need to Know exercises on page 316. Additional resources for reviewing prerequisite skills are:

- Skills Review Handbook, pp. 704–726
- Tutor Place
- eTutorial Plus

Managing the Games

Tips for Success

In *Video Maze*, encourage students to draw all the paths they can find using different colors so they make sure they find all possible sums. Encourage them to use a systematic approach to finding all the paths. Encourage students to try *Find the Path* using mental math.

Reflecting on the Games

For two positive numbers with one decimal place each (neither equal to 0), ask students (1) when the sum is a whole number, (2) when the product has only one decimal place, and (3) when the product is smaller than either of the decimals.

Ratio, Proportion, and Percent

BEFORE

In previous chapters you've...

- Found equivalent fractions
- Rewritten fractions and decimals

Now

In Chapter 7 you'll study...

- Finding ratios and unit rates
- Writing and solving proportions
- Solving percent problems
- Rewriting fractions, decimals, and percents
- Finding probabilities of events

WHY?

So you can solve real-world problems about...

- lightning, p. 318
- crocodiles, p. 329
- guitars, p. 342
- beaches, p. 347

Internet Preview

CLASSZONE.COM

- eEdition Plus Online
- eWorkbook Plus Online
- eTutorial Plus Online
- State Test Practice
- More Examples

Chapter Warm-Up Games

Review skills you need for this chapter in these quick games.

Key Skill:
Solving equations

Find a path through the maze from start to finish.

- Then find the sum of all the solutions of the equations to find your total number of points.
- Which path has the least number of points? $72 \div x = 8 \rightarrow x + 7 = 11 \rightarrow x \div 4 = 3 \rightarrow x - 1 = 3 \rightarrow 7x = 7 \rightarrow 9 - x = 8 \rightarrow 64 \div x = 8 \rightarrow x + 8 = 19 \rightarrow 3x = 27 \rightarrow 10 - x = 6 \rightarrow 2x = 14 \rightarrow 14 - x = 8$

314

Key Skill:
Performing operations on decimals

Find your way from start to finish in the maze above.

- Evaluate each expression. Then move to the nearest expression that begins with the number that is the value of the previous expression. **See above for the correct path.**
- For example, if you start from 5.3 + 4.2 and your choices are 1.4 + 7.2 and 9.5 − 8, you would move to 9.5 − 8 because 5.3 + 4.2 = 9.5.

Stop *and* Think

1. **Writing** A student says that a decimal divided by a decimal is never a whole number. Explain the error in the student's reasoning. **See margin.**
2. **Critical Thinking** How many different paths are there through the *Video Maze* that do not cover the same ground more than once? **3**

Chapter Resources

These resources are provided to help you prepare for the chapter and to customize review materials:

 ***Chapter 7 Resource Book***

- Tips for New Teachers, pp. 1-2
- Lesson Plan, pp. 6, 14, 23, 32, 42, 52, 60, 68
- Lesson Plan for Block Scheduling, pp. 7, 15, 24, 33, 43, 53, 61, 69

 ***Technology***

- EasyPlanner CD-ROM
- Test and Practice Generator
- Electronic Lesson Presentations CD-ROM
- eTutorial CD-ROM

 ***Internet***

- Classzone
- eEdition Plus Online
- eWorkbook Plus Online
- eTutorial Plus Online
- EasyPlanner Plus Online

English Learner Support

- Spanish Study Guide
- Multi-Language Glossary
- Chapter Audio Summaries CDs
- Teacher's Edition, pp. 314E–314F

1. When dividing decimals, you move the decimal point in both the divisor and dividend the same number of places. Then divide. As with whole numbers, it is then possible to get a whole number or decimal answer. Therefore it is not true to say that when dividing decimals you can never get a whole number. For example, 4.75 ÷ 0.25 = 19.

PREPARE

Diagnosis/Remediation

Review What You Need to Know
The Review What You Need to Know exercises can help you diagnose whether students have the following skills needed in Chapter 7:

- Use vocabulary about fractions (Exs. 1–2)
- Solve linear equations by multiplication or division (Exs. 3–7)
- Order fractions and decimals (Exs. 8–9)

 ***Chapter 7 Resource Book***

- Study Guide (Lessons 7.1–7.8)

T ***Tutor Place***

Notetaking Strategies

In addition to recording examples, encourage students to make notes of steps or procedures they found confusing. Once they understand, encourage students to record what they initially were confused about and how their confusion was resolved. Further suggestions for keeping a notebook can be found on page 328.

For more support on notetaking, see:

- Notetaking Guide Workbook
- Notetaking Transparencies

Getting Ready to Learn

Word Watch

Review Words

data, p. 5
equation, p. 28
formula, p. 33
simplest form, p. 179
equivalent fractions, p. 179

Review What You Need to Know

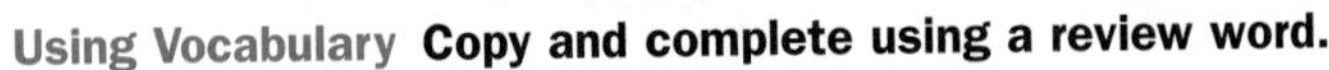

Using Vocabulary Copy and complete using a review word.

1. The fraction $\frac{1}{2}$ is in __?__, but $\frac{2}{4}$ is not. simplest form

2. The fractions $\frac{2}{3}$ and $\frac{4}{6}$ are __?__. equivalent fractions

Solve the equation. *(p. 113)*

3. $\frac{x}{7} = 3$ 21
4. $\frac{x}{-2} = 4$ −8
5. $-9x = 108$ −12
6. $8x = 56$ 7

7. You have 15 pairs of socks in your drawer, including exactly 6 pairs of black socks. What fraction of your socks are black? *(p. 179)* $\frac{2}{5}$

Order the numbers from least to greatest. *(p. 242)*

8. $0, -0.25, \frac{1}{3}, -1.11, \frac{9}{8}, \frac{12}{9}$
$-1.11, -0.25, 0, \frac{1}{3}, \frac{9}{8}, \frac{12}{9}$

9. $-\frac{7}{8}, 1.28, \frac{1}{12}, -0.02, 0.34, \frac{10}{3}$
$-\frac{7}{8}, -0.02, \frac{1}{12}, 0.34, 1.28, \frac{10}{3}$

You should include material that appears on a notebook like this in your own notes.

Know How to Take Notes

Taking Notes in Class When your teacher answers your question in class, include the answer in your notes.

Writing Decimals as Fractions

$0.007 = \frac{7}{1000}$ — 0.007 has 3 decimal places. 1000 has 3 zeros.

$0.13 = \frac{13}{100}$ — 0.13 has 2 decimal places. 100 has 2 zeros.

Number of decimal places equals number of zeros!

As you work on solving proportions in Chapter 7, be sure to ask questions about things you don't understand and write the answers in your notes.

Ratios and Rates

BEFORE	Now	WHY?
You found equivalent fractions.	You'll find ratios and unit rates.	So you can tell whether a TV has a wide screen, as in Ex. 22.

Word Watch

ratio, p. 317
equivalent ratios, p. 317
rate, p. 318
unit rate, p. 318

Activity You can compare side lengths and perimeters of squares.

1. Copy and complete the table using the squares shown. Write the relationship between the side length and the perimeter of each square as a fraction in simplest form.

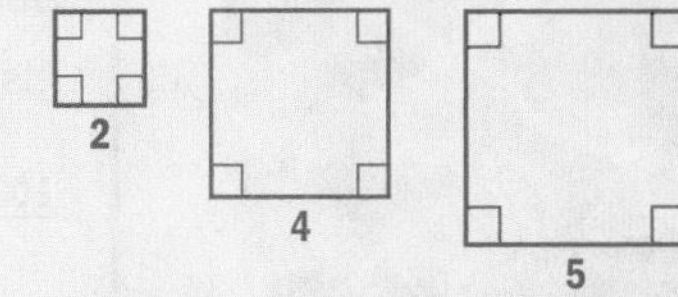

2. What do you notice about the fractions in the table? They are all the same.

3. Describe the relationship between the side length and the perimeter of a square with side length s. $P = 4s$

Side length	2	4	5
Perimeter	? 8	? 16	? 20
$\frac{\text{Side length}}{\text{Perimeter}}$	? $\frac{1}{4}$	? $\frac{1}{4}$	? $\frac{1}{4}$

In the activity, you used a *ratio* to reach a conclusion about the relationship between the side length and the perimeter of a square. A **ratio** uses division to compare two numbers. You can write the ratio of a to b ($b \neq 0$) in three ways.

$$\frac{a}{b} \qquad a:b \qquad a \text{ to } b$$

Ratios that have the same value are called **equivalent ratios**.

1. $\frac{15}{7}$, 15 : 7, 15 to 7

2. $\frac{11}{15}$, 11 : 15, 11 to 15

EXAMPLE 1 Writing a Ratio

Skiing A ski resort has 15 easy, 25 intermediate, 7 difficult, and 11 expert-only trails. Write the ratio intermediate trails : easy trails in three ways.

$$\frac{\text{intermediate trails}}{\text{easy trails}} = \frac{25}{15} = \frac{5}{3}$$ Write as a fraction and simplify.

ANSWER The ratio can be written as $\frac{5}{3}$, 5 : 3 , or 5 to 3.

Your turn now Use the information in Example 1 to write the ratio as a fraction in simplest form and two other ways. See margin.

1. easy trails to difficult trails
2. expert-only trails to easy trails

ILLINOIS Standards and ISAT:
6.D.3

1 PLAN

SKILL CHECK

Write in simplest form.

1. $\frac{25}{15}$ $\frac{5}{3}$
2. $\frac{8}{20}$ $\frac{2}{5}$
3. $\frac{6}{12}$ $\frac{1}{2}$
4. $\frac{18}{27}$ $\frac{2}{3}$

LESSON OBJECTIVE

Find ratios and unit rates.

PACING

Suggested Number of Days
Basic Course: 1 day
Average Course: 1 day
Advanced Course: 1 day
Block: 0.5 block with 7.1

TEACHING RESOURCES

For a complete list of Teaching Resources, see page 314B.

TRANSPARENCY

Warm-Up Exercises for this lesson are available on a transparency.

2 TEACH

MOTIVATING THE LESSON

Ask students to describe the properties of squares and what it means to find the perimeter of a figure.

ACTIVITY

Goal Use ratios to compare side lengths and perimeters of squares.

Key Discovery The ratio of the side length to the perimeter of a square is always the same, $\frac{1}{4}$.

TIPS FOR NEW TEACHERS

Stress that a ratio is just a different way of viewing a fraction, and a rate is basically a fraction with units. See Tips for New Teachers in the *Chapter 7 Resource Book*.

EXTRA EXAMPLES

Example 1 At Park Apartments, there are 3 maintenance workers for 150 apartments. Write the ratio maintenance workers : apartments in three ways. **$\frac{1}{50}$, 1 : 50, 1 to 50**

Example 2 Li types 75 words per minute. How many words can she type in an hour at this rate? **4500 words**

Example 3 Write 24 pages in 15 minutes as a unit rate. **$\frac{1.6 \text{ pages}}{1 \text{ min}}$**

Differentiating Instruction

Advanced Students Challenge students to find Earth's diameter and estimate how fast in miles per hour a person at the equator is moving around Earth's axis. **about 7900 mi; about 1030 mi/h**

CONCEPT CHECK

What are three ways you can write the ratio of two numbers x and y ($y \neq 0$)? **$\frac{x}{y}$, $x : y$, x to y**

DAILY PUZZLER

Jessie runs 6 laps in 10 minutes; Zhenia runs 6 laps in 12 minutes. What is the ratio of Jessie's running speed to Zhenia's speed? **6 to 5**

Rates A **rate** is a ratio of two quantities that have *different* units. Two rates are equivalent if they have the same value.

EXAMPLE 2 Finding an Equivalent Rate

Weather Lightning strikes about 100 times per second around the world. About how many times does lightning strike per minute around the world?

Solution

Use the fact that 60 sec = 1 min. So, $\frac{60 \text{ sec}}{1 \text{ min}}$ is equivalent to 1.

$\frac{100 \text{ times}}{1 \text{ sec}} = \frac{100 \text{ times}}{1 \text{ sec}} \cdot \frac{60 \text{ sec}}{1 \text{ min}}$ **Multiply by a fraction that is equivalent to 1.**

$= \frac{6000 \text{ times}}{1 \text{ min}}$ **Simplify.**

ANSWER Lightning strikes about 6000 times per minute around the world.

Unit Rates A **unit rate** is a rate that has a denominator of 1 unit. To write a unit rate, find an equivalent rate with a denominator of 1 unit.

with Review

For help with equivalent fractions, see p. 179.

EXAMPLE 3 Finding a Unit Rate

Write −24 feet per 5 seconds as a unit rate.

$\frac{-24 \text{ ft}}{5 \text{ sec}} = \frac{-24 \div 5}{5 \div 5}$ **Divide numerator and denominator by 5 to get a denominator of 1 unit.**

$= \frac{-4.8}{1}$ **Simplify.**

ANSWER The unit rate is −4.8 feet per second.

✓ **Check** Round −4.8 ft/sec to −5 ft/sec. The product $-5 \cdot 5 = -25$, which is about −24, so your answer is reasonable.

Your turn now Write your answer as a rate.

3. A water pump moves 2 gallons of water per second. How many gallons of water are pumped per minute? **120 gal/min**

Write the rate as a unit rate.

4. $\frac{114 \text{ points}}{6 \text{ games}}$ 5. $\frac{365 \text{ people}}{5 \text{ months}}$ 6. $\frac{329 \text{ miles}}{10 \text{ gallons}}$ 7. $\frac{-49 \text{ m}}{14 \text{ sec}}$

4. $\frac{19 \text{ points}}{1 \text{ game}}$
5. $\frac{73 \text{ people}}{1 \text{ mo}}$
6. $\frac{32.9 \text{ mi}}{1 \text{ gal}}$
7. $\frac{-3.5 \text{ m}}{1 \text{ sec}}$

7.1 Exercises

More Practice, p. 733

INTERNET eWorkbook Plus CLASSZONE.COM

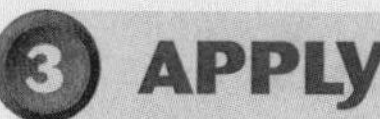

3 APPLY

ASSIGNMENT GUIDE

Basic Course

Day 1: SRH p. 708 Exs. 1-3; pp. 319-320 Exs. 10-19, 23-32, 37-43

Average Course

Day 1: pp. 319-320 Exs. 14-24, 27-35, 37-44

Advanced Course

Day 1: pp. 319-320 Exs. 14-22, 25-38*, 41-44

Block

pp. 319-320 Exs. 14-24, 27-35, 37-44 (with 7.2)

EXTRA PRACTICE

- Student Edition, p. 733
- Chapter 7 Resource Book, pp. 8-10
- Test and Practice Generator

TRANSPARENCY

Even-numbered answers are available on transparencies.

HOMEWORK CHECK

When you review students' homework for this lesson, go over the following exercises to check understanding of key concepts.

Basic: 10, 18, 19, 23, 27
Average: 14, 18, 20, 23, 27
Advanced: 14, 18, 21, 25, 28

TEACHING TIP

In Exercise 9, point out that the goal is to "cancel out" the intermediate units, leaving just the desired units. So, for example, if "days" is in the denominator of one rate, it must be in the numerator of the next rate for "days" to cancel.

HELP with Homework

Example	Exercises
1	10-17, 27-28
2	18-21
3	23-26

Online Resources CLASSZONE.COM

- More Examples
- eTutorial Plus

Getting Ready to Practice

1. **Vocabulary** Copy and complete: Three gallons to \$4.50 and five gallons to \$7.50 are equivalent _?_. rates

Write the ratio as a fraction in simplest form and two other ways.

2. $\frac{12}{36}$ $\frac{1}{3}$, 1 to 3, 1 : 3
3. $\frac{15}{10}$ $\frac{3}{2}$, 3 to 2, 3 : 2
4. $\frac{6}{4}$ $\frac{3}{2}$, 3 to 2, 3 : 2

Tell whether the ratios are equivalent.

5. $\frac{5}{2}$ and $\frac{20}{8}$ yes
6. 12 to 3 and 6 to 2 no
7. 6 : 18 and 10 : 30 yes

8. **Wages** You are paid \$47.25 for working 7 hours. How much are you paid per hour? \$6.75

9. **Find the Error** Describe and correct the error in the solution.

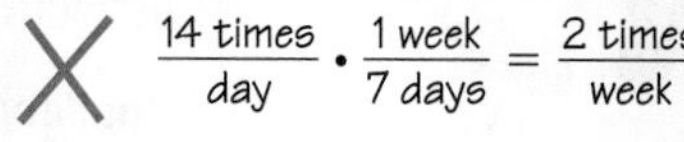

Find an equivalent rate of 14 times a day.

$$\times \quad \frac{14\text{ times}}{\text{day}} \cdot \frac{1\text{ week}}{7\text{ days}} = \frac{2\text{ times}}{\text{week}}$$

9. Multiply by $\frac{7\text{ days}}{1\text{ week}}$: $\frac{14\text{ times}}{1\text{ day}} \cdot \frac{7\text{ days}}{1\text{ week}} = \frac{98\text{ times}}{1\text{ week}}$.

Practice and Problem Solving

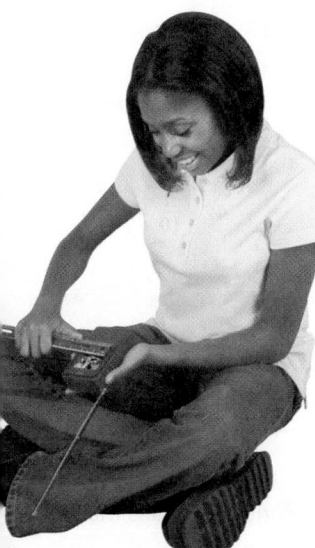

A Write the ratio as a fraction in simplest form and two other ways.

10. $\frac{33}{22}$ $\frac{3}{2}$, 3 to 2, 3 : 2
11. $\frac{20}{25}$ $\frac{4}{5}$, 4 to 5, 4 : 5
12. $-8:6$ $-\frac{4}{3}$, -4 to 3, $-4:3$
13. 35 to 49 $\frac{5}{7}$, 5 to 7, 5 : 7
14. 51 to 17 $\frac{3}{1}$, 3 to 1, 3 : 1
15. 26 : 39 $\frac{2}{3}$, 2 to 3, 2 : 3
16. $\frac{27}{42}$ $\frac{9}{14}$, 9 to 14, 9 : 14
17. $\frac{-12}{4}$ $\frac{-3}{1}$, -3 to 1, $-3:1$

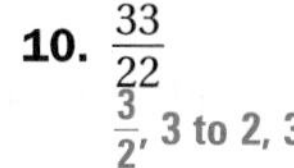

Measurement Write the equivalent rate.

18. $\frac{60\text{ miles}}{\text{hour}} = \frac{?\text{ miles}}{\text{minute}}$ 1
19. $\frac{32\text{ ounces}}{\text{serving}} = \frac{?\text{ pounds}}{\text{serving}}$ 2
20. $\frac{105\text{ min}}{\text{game}} = \frac{?\text{ h}}{\text{game}}$ 1.75
21. $\frac{\$1.44}{\text{ft}} = \frac{\$\,?}{\text{yd}}$ 4.32

22. **Television** The aspect ratio of a TV screen is the ratio of its length to its width. The aspect ratio of a *standard* TV screen is 4 : 3. The aspect ratio of a *wide screen* TV in the United States is 16 : 9. Describe how you would tell whether a TV has a standard or wide screen given the length and width of the screen.
Write the ratio of its length to its width, and simplify.

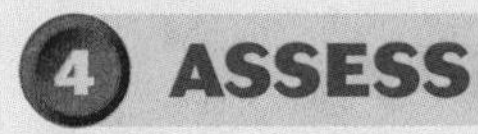

ASSESSMENT RESOURCES

For more assessment resources, see:
- Assessment Book
- Test and Practice Generator

MINI-QUIZ

Write the ratio as a fraction in simplest form and two other ways.

1. $\frac{16}{24}$ $\frac{2}{3}$, 2 to 3, 2 : 3
2. −15 to 5 $-\frac{3}{1}$, −3 to 1, −3 : 1

Write the equivalent rate.

3. $\frac{\$5.50}{\text{ounce}} = \frac{\$\,?}{\text{pound}}$ 88
4. $\frac{6 \text{ kilometers}}{\text{hour}} = \frac{?\text{ meters}}{\text{minute}}$ 100
5. What value of x makes the ratios $\frac{3}{4}$ and $\frac{42}{x}$ equivalent? 56

RETEACHING/REMEDIATION

- Study Guide in Chapter 7 Resource Book, pp. 11–12
- Tutor Place, Ratio, Proportion, and Percents Cards 1, 2
- eTutorial Plus Online
- Extra Practice, p. 733
- Lesson Practice in Chapter 7 Resource Book, pp. 8–10

CHALLENGE/ENRICHMENT

- Challenge Practice in Chapter 7 Resource Book, p. 13
- Teacher's Edition, p. 314F

ENGLISH LEARNER SUPPORT

- Spanish Study Guide
- Multi-Language Glossary
- Chapter Audio Summaries CDs

38. 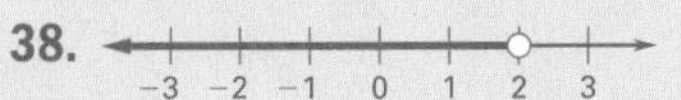

23. $\frac{4 \text{ adults}}{1 \text{ car}}$

24. $\frac{-4.25 \text{ m}}{1 \text{ sec}}$

25. $\frac{1.5 \text{ lb}}{1 \text{ dollar}}$

26. $\frac{122 \text{ rotations}}{1 \text{ min}}$

33. Check work; $\frac{1}{10}$ of the people in the class are left-handed, so divide the number of people by 10.

Write the rate as a unit rate.

23. $\frac{24 \text{ adults}}{6 \text{ cars}}$ **24.** $\frac{-34 \text{ meters}}{8 \text{ seconds}}$ **25.** $\frac{3 \text{ pounds}}{\$2}$ **26.** $\frac{610 \text{ rotations}}{5 \text{ minutes}}$

B **Write the ratio of shaded to unshaded squares.**

27. 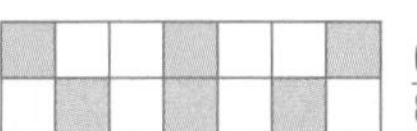 $\frac{5}{5} = \frac{1}{1}$ **28.** $\frac{6}{8} = \frac{3}{4}$

Find the value of the variable that makes the ratios equivalent.

29. $\frac{x}{8} = \frac{4}{16}$ 2 **30.** $\frac{9}{c} = \frac{27}{30}$ 10 **31.** $\frac{6}{10} = \frac{15}{n}$ 25 **32.** $\frac{2}{12} = \frac{z}{18}$ 3

33. Writing About one out of every ten people is left-handed. How many people in your math class would you predict to be left-handed? Explain. See margin.

34. Running Speed At top speed, a greyhound can run 330 feet in 5 seconds, a roadrunner can run 75 feet in 3 seconds, and a cheetah can run 198 feet in 2 seconds. Write each speed as a unit rate. Which animal is the fastest? Which animal is the slowest? 66 ft/sec, 25 ft/sec, 99 ft/sec; cheetah; roadrunner

C **35. Population Density** New Jersey's population in 2000 was about 8,414,000. New Jersey's area is 7417 square miles. What was the population per square mile, or *population density*, in New Jersey in 2000? Round to the nearest whole number. 1134 people/mi^2

36. Challenge You can buy your favorite crackers in a 10 ounce box or a 1 pound box. The 10 ounce box costs \$2.69 and the 1 pound box costs \$3.28. Which is the better buy? Explain. The 1 pound box. *Sample answer:* The 10 ounce box costs \$.269 per ounce and the 1 pound box costs \$.205 per ounce, so the 1 pound box costs less per ounce.

Mixed Review

37. Find the radius of a circle with a circumference of 39.25 feet. Use 3.14 for π. *(Lesson 6.4)* 6.25 ft

38. Solve the inequality $10y + 4 < 24$ and graph the solution. *(Lesson 6.5)* $y < 2$; see margin for art.

Basic Skills **Solve the equation.**

39. $3c = 18$ 6 **40.** $9x = -81$ −9 **41.** $\frac{v}{4} = -2$ −8 **42.** $\frac{n}{10} = 8$ 80

Test-Taking Practice 

INTERNET
State Test Practice
CLASSZONE.COM

43. Multiple Choice Which rate is equivalent to 232 miles per 4 hours? B

A. $\frac{58 \text{ mi}}{4 \text{ h}}$ **B.** $\frac{174 \text{ mi}}{3 \text{ h}}$ **C.** $\frac{232 \text{ mi}}{3 \text{ h}}$ **D.** $\frac{116 \text{ mi}}{1 \text{ h}}$

44. Short Response Emily runs 1600 meters in 5 minutes 30 seconds, and Megan runs 800 meters in 2 minutes 40 seconds. Who has the faster average speed? Explain your reasoning. See margin.

44. Megan; Emily runs about 4.8 meters per second and Megan runs 5 meters per second, and 4.8 < 5.

7.2 Hands-on Activity

GOAL

Make scale drawings.

MATERIALS

- ruler
- grid paper
- colored pencils
- magazine

Making a Scale Drawing

A *scale drawing* of an object preserves ratios of lengths but is either smaller or larger than the original object.

Explore **Make an enlarged drawing of the picture.**

1. Draw a grid on the original picture.

2. On your grid paper, draw a rectangle that is the same number of units long and wide as the picture you want to enlarge. These unit squares should be bigger than the grid squares on the original picture.

3. Starting in a corner, copy the image that appears in the corresponding corner of the original onto your grid paper. Continue copying the image one block at a time until you have drawn the entire picture.

4. The *scale* of the drawing is the ratio of corresponding measurements of the copy to the original. Measure the width of the copy and of the original. What is the scale of your drawing? **Answers may vary.**

Your turn now

1. Cut out a picture from a magazine and create an enlarged scale drawing of it. Measure the original picture and the enlarged drawing to determine the scale. **A good answer will include a clear scale drawing and accurate measurements.**

2. Is the ratio of the area of a unit square in the copy to the area of a unit square in the original the same as the ratio of their sides? Explain. **No. *Sample answer:* The ratio of the areas is the ratio of the sides of the unit squares multiplied by itself.**

Stop and Think

3. **Critical Thinking** What would happen if different scales were used in the same drawing? **The drawing would appear distorted by being stretched either horizontally or vertically.**

ILLINOIS Standards and ISAT:
7.C.3a

1 PLAN

Explore the Concept

- Students will make scale drawings.
- This activity leads into using ratios with scale models in Lesson 7.2.

Materials

Each student or group of students will need a ruler, grid paper, colored pencils, and a magazine.

Recommended Time

Work activity: 15 min
Discuss results: 5 min

Grouping

Students can work individually or in groups. If working in groups, each student can enlarge a portion of the picture. The drawings can be combined to see the enlargement.

2 TEACH

Tips for Success

To save time, stress that this is not "artwork." The proportion is the key.

3 CLOSE

Key Discovery

A scale drawing maintains the same ratio between all parts of the original object and the drawing.

Assessment

1. Why use the same scale for every square in the grid? **so the drawing is not distorted**

PLAN

SKILL CHECK

1. 88.8 ÷ 0.125 = ? 710.4
2. 11.4 × 20.5 = ? 233.7
3. 685.4 ÷ 9.2 = ? 74.5
4. Solve for x: $16x = \frac{4}{5}$ 0.05

Lesson Objective

Write and solve proportions.

Pacing

Suggested Number of Days
Basic Course: 1 day
Average Course: 1 day
Advanced Course: 1 day
Block: 0.5 block with 7.1

Teaching Resources

For a complete list of Teaching Resources, see page 314B.

Transparency

Warm-Up Exercises for this lesson are available on a transparency.

TEACH

Motivating the Lesson

Ask students what they think the ratio of the weight they could carry to their own weight is.

Writing and Solving Proportions

BEFORE	Now	WHY?
You wrote ratios.	You'll write and solve proportions.	So you can find the dimensions of a model car, as in Ex. 35.

Word Watch

proportion, p. 322
cross products, p. 323
scale model, p. 324
scale, p. 324

In the Real World

Rhinoceros Beetles An adult rhinoceros beetle weighs only 0.525 ounce but can carry about 446.25 ounces on its back. If a person were as strong as a rhinoceros beetle, how much weight could a 100 pound person carry?

A **proportion** is an equation that states that two ratios are equivalent.

$$\frac{a}{b} = \frac{c}{d}, b \neq 0, d \neq 0$$

The proportion above is read "a is to b as c is to d."

EXAMPLE 1 Writing and Solving a Proportion

To answer the question about strength above, write and solve a proportion.

	Beetle	Person
Carries	446.25	x
Weighs	0.525	100

Use a table to set up a proportion.

$\frac{446.25}{0.525} = \frac{x}{100}$ **Write a proportion.**

$\frac{446.25}{0.525} \cdot 100 = \frac{x}{100} \cdot 100$ **Multiply each side by 100.**

$85,000 = x$ **Simplify.**

ANSWER If human strength were proportional to that of a rhinoceros beetle, a 100 pound person could carry 85,000 pounds.

HELP with Solving

In Example 1, the ratios in the proportion use the following units: $\frac{\text{ounces}}{\text{ounces}}$ and $\frac{\text{pounds}}{\text{pounds}}$.

Your turn now **Solve the proportion.**

1. $\frac{n}{12} = \frac{3}{4}$ 9
2. $\frac{50}{20} = \frac{z}{16}$ 40
3. $\frac{250}{30} = \frac{t}{51}$ 425

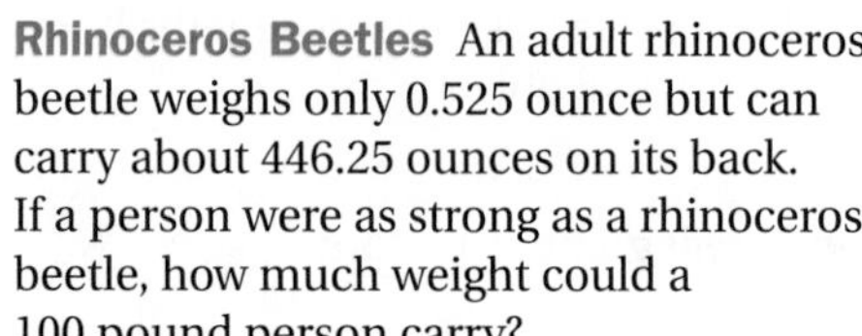

ILLINOIS Standards and ISAT:
6.D.3, 7.C.3a

Cross Products The proportion $\frac{a}{b} = \frac{c}{d}$ has **cross products** ad and bc.

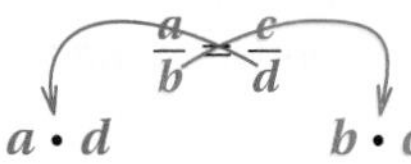

$a \cdot d$ $\qquad$ $b \cdot c$

You can use cross products to solve a proportion. You can also use cross products to check whether two ratios form a proportion.

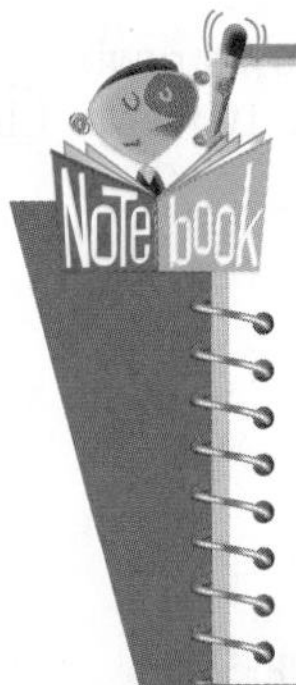

Cross Products Property

Words The cross products of a proportion are equal.

Algebra If $\frac{a}{b} = \frac{c}{d}$, where b and d are nonzero numbers, then $ad = bc$.

Numbers Because $\frac{3}{4} = \frac{9}{12}$, you know that $3 \cdot 12 = 4 \cdot 9$.

EXAMPLE 2 Using the Cross Products Property

$\frac{6.8}{15.4} = \frac{40.8}{m}$	Original proportion
$6.8 \cdot m = 15.4 \cdot 40.8$	Cross products property
$6.8m = 628.32$	Multiply.
$\frac{6.8m}{6.8} = \frac{628.32}{6.8}$	Divide each side by 6.8.
$m = 92.4$	Simplify.

✓ **Check** You can check your solution by finding the cross products of the proportion. If the cross products are equal, the solution is correct.

$\frac{6.8}{15.4} \stackrel{?}{=} \frac{40.8}{92.4}$ Substitute 92.4 for m in original proportion.

$6.8 \cdot 92.4 \stackrel{?}{=} 15.4 \cdot 40.8$

$628.32 = 628.32$ ✓

Your turn now **Solve the proportion. Then check your solution.**

4. $\frac{6}{c} = \frac{54}{99}$ 11 **5.** $\frac{n}{14} = \frac{63}{98}$ 9 **6.** $\frac{2.1}{0.9} = \frac{27.3}{y}$ 11.7

TIPS FOR NEW TEACHERS

As students write proportions for applications, you will likely need to remind them that the ratios must compare corresponding quantities. It may help to write a sentence. For Example 1, this could be "the weight a beetle can carry compares to its own weight as the weight a person can carry compares to the person's weight." See Tips for New Teachers in the *Chapter 7 Resource Book*.

EXTRA EXAMPLES

Example 1 Sondra's car can go about 380 miles on 12 gallons of gas. About how many gallons will her car use to travel 2000 miles? **about 63.2 gal**

Example 2 Solve the proportion $\frac{4.8}{7.2} = \frac{z}{16.2}$. **10.8**

NOTETAKING

Before students work Example 2, urge them to take careful notes about how to use cross products to solve proportions. Have them include descriptions of how the property works in their own words.

MATH REASONING

Point out that the Cross Products Property is just a result of the Multiplication Property of Equality. Multiplying each side of $\frac{a}{b} = \frac{c}{d}$ by bd, the LCD of the fractions, and then simplifying gives $ad = bc$.

EXTRA EXAMPLES

Example 3 An architect draws a blueprint for the front of a townhouse. On the blueprint, the townhouse is 50 centimeters wide. If the scale of the blueprint is 1 centimeter to 0.5 meter, how wide is the front of the townhouse? **25 m**

TEACHING TIP

When a scale is written as a ratio, it usually takes the form scale model : actual object.

CONCEPT CHECK

How can you use cross products to see whether two ratios form a proportion? **If the cross products are equal, the ratio is a proportion.**

DAILY PUZZLER

The average distances from the nine planets of our solar system to the sun vary from about 58,000,000 kilometers to 5,900,000,000 kilometers. What scale would you use to make a model of the solar system that would fit within the classroom? ***Sample answer:*** **1 m to 1,000,000,000 km**

Sculpture

How many inches tall is the giant strawberry? Write the scale of the strawberry sculpture without units.
180 in.; 120 : 1

Scale The dimensions of a **scale model** are proportional to the dimensions of the actual object. The **scale** gives the relationship between the model's dimensions and the actual object's dimensions. A scale can be written as a ratio with or without units. For example, the scale 1 in. : 3 ft can also be written as 1 : 36.

EXAMPLE 3 Using a Scale

Sculpture Strawberry Point, Iowa, has a strawberry sculpture that is 15 feet tall. If the scale of this model is 10 feet to 1 inch, how tall was the original strawberry?

Solution

$\text{Scale} = \dfrac{\text{Height of strawberry model}}{\text{Height of original strawberry}}$ **Write a verbal model.**

$\dfrac{10\text{ ft}}{1\text{ in.}} = \dfrac{15\text{ ft}}{h\text{ in.}}$ **Write a proportion.**

$10h = 15$ **Cross products property**

$h = 1.5$ **Divide each side by 10.**

ANSWER The height of the original strawberry was 1.5 inches.

7.2 Exercises

More Practice, p. 733

INTERNET
eWorkbook Plus
CLASSZONE.COM

Getting Ready to Practice

1. **Vocabulary** Describe how to use cross products to solve a proportion. **Find the cross products and solve the resulting equation to solve the proportion.**

Solve the proportion. Then check your solution.

2. $\frac{1}{2} = \frac{x}{6}$ **3**
3. $\frac{2}{3} = \frac{4}{z}$ **6**
4. $\frac{6}{a} = \frac{3}{1}$ **2**
5. $\frac{c}{10} = \frac{3}{5}$ **6**

6. **Find the Error** Describe and correct the error in solving the proportion.

$\frac{3}{9} = \frac{12}{m}$ ✗

$9m = 3 \cdot 12$

$9m = 36$

$m = 4$

6. **In the second step, the cross multiplication was done incorrectly. It should be $3m = 9 \cdot 12$, which gives $3m = 108$, or $m = 36$.**

7. **Cars** A car moving at a constant speed travels 88 feet in 2 seconds. Use a proportion to find how many feet it travels in one minute. **2640 ft**

Practice and Problem Solving

with Homework

Example	Exercises
1	12-19
2	8-19, 25-27
3	20-23

Online Resources
CLASSZONE.COM

· More Examples
· eTutorial Plus

A **Decide** **Tell whether the ratios form a proportion.**

8. $\frac{3}{4} \stackrel{?}{=} \frac{6}{8}$ yes **9.** $\frac{1}{2} \stackrel{?}{=} \frac{2}{5}$ no **10.** $\frac{14}{21} \stackrel{?}{=} \frac{21}{35}$ no **11.** $\frac{15}{45} \stackrel{?}{=} \frac{45}{135}$ yes

Solve the proportion.

12. $\frac{3}{8} = \frac{x}{32}$ 12 **13.** $\frac{4}{c} = \frac{20}{45}$ 9 **14.** $\frac{39}{13} = \frac{9}{d}$ 3 **15.** $\frac{68}{12} = \frac{51}{p}$ 9

16. $\frac{67.2}{g} = \frac{16.8}{3.3}$ 13.2 **17.** $\frac{t}{29.4} = \frac{5.5}{4.2}$ 38.5 **18.** $\frac{f}{5.4} = \frac{483}{18.9}$ 138 **19.** $\frac{712}{8.8} = \frac{x}{18.7}$ 1513

Scale Models **You use a scale of 1 inch to 20 feet to make scale models of buildings. A building's actual height is given. Find the model's height.**

20. $h = 100$ ft 5 in. **21.** $h = 240$ ft 12 in. **22.** $h = 316$ ft 15.8 in. **23.** $h = 545$ ft 27.25 in.

24. **Mental Math** Explain how you can use equivalent fractions and mental math to solve $\frac{5}{x} = \frac{10}{16}$. *Sample answer:* Since $5 = 10 \div 2$, divide 16 by 2 to find x; $x = 16 \div 2 = 8$.

25. **Earnings** You earn $54 mowing 3 lawns. You charge the same amount for each lawn. How much would you earn if you mowed 5 lawns? $90

B **Extended Problem Solving** **To produce one pound of honey, the bees from a hive fly over 55,000 miles and visit about 2 million flowers.**

26. About how many flowers are visited to make 10 ounces of honey? 1.25 million

27. About how many miles do the bees fly to make 10 ounces of honey? 34,375 mi

28. **Explain** What is the mean number of flowers visited per mile traveled? Explain your reasoning. About 36 flowers; divide 2 million flowers by 55,000 miles to find the number of flowers visited per mile.

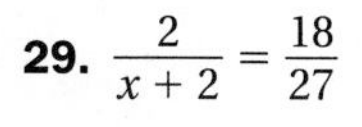

EXAMPLE **Finding the Value of x**

$\frac{30}{2+x} = \frac{6}{7}$	Original proportion
$7 \cdot 30 = 6(2 + x)$	Cross products property
$210 = 12 + 6x$	Multiply and use distributive property.
$33 = x$	Solve the two-step equation for x.

In Exercises 29–31, find the value of x.

29. $\frac{2}{x+2} = \frac{18}{27}$ 1 **30.** $\frac{x-2}{8} = \frac{30}{40}$ 8 **31.** $\frac{9}{5} = \frac{36}{x-3}$ 23

3 APPLY

ASSIGNMENT GUIDE

Basic Course

Day 1: pp. 325-326 Exs. 8-23, 25-27, 29-31, 36-41

Average Course

Day 1: pp. 325-326 Exs. 10-17, 20-31, 35-41

Advanced Course

Day 1: pp. 325-326 Exs. 10-15, 20-36*, 39-41

Block

pp. 325-326 Exs. 10-17, 20-31, 35-41 (with 7.1)

EXTRA PRACTICE

- Student Edition, p. 733
- Chapter 7 Resource Book, pp. 16-18
- Test and Practice Generator

TRANSPARENCY

Even-numbered answers are available on transparencies.

HOMEWORK CHECK

When you review students' homework for this lesson, go over the following exercises to check understanding of key concepts.
Basic: 8, 12, 15, 20, 25
Average: 10, 12, 16, 21, 25
Advanced: 10, 12, 15, 22, 26

COMMON ERROR

In Exercises 29-31, watch for students who fail to apply the distributive property properly when cross multiplying.

ASSESS

ASSESSMENT RESOURCES

For more assessment resources, see:
- Assessment Book
- Test and Practice Generator

MINI-QUIZ

Solve the proportion.

1. $\frac{10.5}{b} = \frac{2.8}{6.4}$ **24**
2. $\frac{62.5}{18.5} = \frac{52.5}{d}$ **15.54**

You use a scale of 1 inch to 50 feet to make models of buildings. Find the model's height for the given building height h.

3. $h = 550$ ft **11 in.**
4. $h = 800$ ft **16 in.**
5. If three bundles of shingles cover 75 square feet of a roof, how many bundles will it take to cover a roof that is 1800 square feet? **72 bundles**

FOLLOW-UP

RETEACHING/REMEDIATION

- Study Guide in Chapter 7 Resource Book, pp. 19–20
- Tutor Place, Ratio, Proportion, and Percent Cards 3–5
- eTutorial Plus Online
- Extra Practice, p. 733
- Lesson Practice in Chapter 7 Resource Book, pp. 16–18

CHALLENGE/ENRICHMENT

- Challenge Practice in Chapter 7 Resource Book, p. 22
- Teacher's Edition, p. 314F

ENGLISH LEARNER SUPPORT

- Spanish Study Guide
- Multi-Language Glossary
- Chapter Audio Summaries CDs

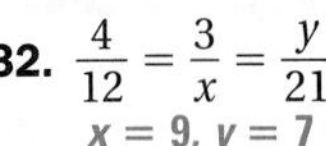

C Challenge **Find the value of each variable.**

32. $\frac{4}{12} = \frac{3}{x} = \frac{y}{21}$ $x = 9, y = 7$

33. $\frac{7}{12} = \frac{a}{72} = \frac{28}{b}$ $a = 42, b = 48$

34. $\frac{8}{5} = \frac{n}{7} = \frac{21}{p}$ $n = 11.2, p = 13.125$

35. Model Car A toy manufacturer plans to make a model version of a car using a scale of 1 inch to 43 inches. The actual vehicle is 215 inches long, 75.25 inches wide, and 53.75 inches high. Find the length, width, and height of the model car. **length: 5 in.; width: 1.75 in.; height: 1.25 in.**

Mixed Review

36. Write and solve an inequality for the sentence: *Four less than nine times a number is at most 95.* (Lesson 6.6) $9x - 4 \le 95;\ x \le 11$

Write the rate as a unit rate. (Lesson 7.1)

37. $\frac{\text{42 people}}{\text{14 taxis}}$

38. $\frac{\text{258 miles}}{\text{6 hours}}$

39. $\frac{\text{36 dogs}}{\text{18 households}}$

37. $\frac{\text{3 people}}{\text{1 taxi}}$

38. $\frac{\text{43 mi}}{\text{1 h}}$

39. $\frac{\text{2 dogs}}{\text{1 household}}$

Test-Taking Practice

INTERNET
State Test Practice
CLASSZONE.COM

40. Multiple Choice Solve $\frac{12}{15} = \frac{x}{25}$. **C**

A. 31 **B.** 21 **C.** 20 **D.** 4

41. Multiple Choice The scale on a map is $\frac{1}{4}$ inch : 20 miles. The distance from Montgomery, Alabama, to Atlanta, Georgia, is about 2 inches on the map. About how far is it from Montgomery to Atlanta? **H**

F. 20 miles **G.** 80 miles **H.** 160 miles **I.** 200 miles

BRAIN GAME

Balancing Act

The middle person below is holding the same weight on both trays. What shapes do you need to add to the other people's trays to balance the weights they are holding?

Sample answer: The girl on the right should add 2 blocks and 1 cone to the tray in her left hand. The boy on the left should add 11 blocks to the tray in his right hand (or 8 blocks and 2 cones, or 5 blocks and 4 cones, or 2 blocks and 6 cones).

Solving Percent Problems

BEFORE	Now	WHY?
You solved proportions.	You'll solve percent problems using proportions.	So you can find the length of a crocodile, as in Ex. 19.

Word Watch

percent, p. 327

In the Real World

Environment A service club is planting seedlings as part of an erosion prevention project. Out of 240 newly planted seedlings, 15 are laurel sumac. What *percent* of the seedlings are laurel sumac?

The word *percent* means "per hundred." A **percent** is a ratio whose denominator is 100. The symbol for percent is %.

Solving Percent Problems

To represent "*a* is *p* percent of *b*," use the proportion

$$\frac{a}{b} = \frac{p}{100}$$

where *a* is part of the base *b* and *p* is the percent.

EXAMPLE 1 Finding a Percent

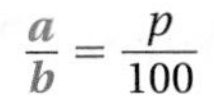

To find the percent of seedlings that are laurel sumac as described above, use a percent proportion.

$\frac{a}{b} = \frac{p}{100}$ — Write a percent proportion.

$\frac{15}{240} = \frac{p}{100}$ — Substitute 15 for *a* and 240 for *b*.

$\frac{15}{240} \cdot 100 = \frac{p}{100} \cdot 100$ — Multiply each side by 100.

$6.25 = p$ — Simplify.

ANSWER Of the seedlings, 6.25% are laurel sumac.

Your turn now Use a percent proportion.

1. 126 is what percent of 150? 84%
2. 84 is what percent of 70? 120%

ILLINOIS Standards and ISAT:
6.A.3, 6.C.3a, 6.D.3

1 PLAN

SKILL CHECK

Solve the proportion.

1. $\frac{45}{60} = \frac{x}{100}$ 75
2. $\frac{33}{12} = \frac{x}{100}$ 275
3. $\frac{x}{25} = \frac{76}{100}$ 19

Lesson Objective

Solve percent problems using proportions.

Pacing

Suggested Number of Days
Basic Course: 1 day
Average Course: 1 day
Advanced Course: 1 day
Block: 0.5 block with 7.4

Teaching Resources

For a complete list of Teaching Resources, see page 314B.

Transparency

Warm-Up Exercises for this lesson are available on a transparency.

2 TEACH

Motivating the Lesson

Ask students if they are familiar with any erosion control projects.

TIPS FOR NEW TEACHERS

You may want to encourage students to write down and solve several numerical examples of each type of percent problem in their notebooks. See Tips for New Teachers in the *Chapter 7 Resource Book*.

EXTRA EXAMPLES

Example 1 Of 80 dogs in an animal shelter, 15 were adopted this week. What percent of the dogs were adopted? **18.75%**

Example 2 The population of a city this year is 102% of last year's population, which was 125,000. What is this year's population? **127,500**

Example 3 15 is 3% of what number? **500**

Differentiating Instruction

Less Proficient Students Use very simple examples such as the ones following to help students become comfortable with the form of the questions in the summary of percent problems on page 328.
5 is what percent of 10?
What number is 50% of 20?
2 is 50% of what number?

TEACHING TIP

As students work the examples and study the summary of percent problems, they should come to realize that the base usually follows the word "of" in a percent problem. Example 3 could be confusing from this standpoint, but it can be rewritten as "24 is 0.8% of what number?"

CONCEPT CHECK

In the problem "380 people is what percent of 500 people," what is the base? **500 people**

DAILY PUZZLER

What is 50% of 50%? **25%**

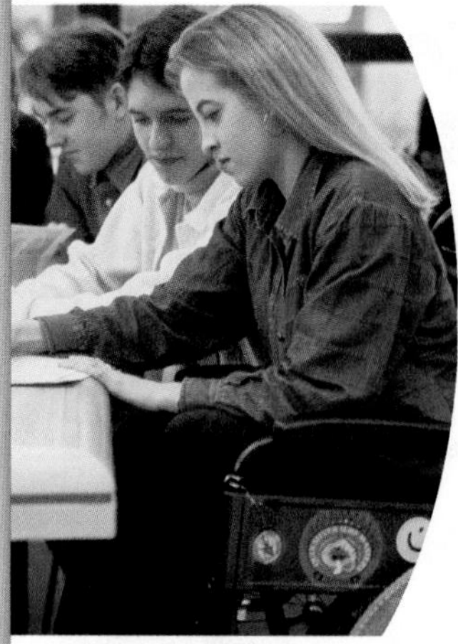

EXAMPLE 2 Finding Part of a Base

School Newspaper Your school newspaper's budget this year is 160% of last year's budget, which was \$2125. What is this year's budget?

Solution

$\frac{a}{b} = \frac{p}{100}$ **Write a percent proportion.**

$\frac{a}{2125} = \frac{160}{100}$ **Substitute 2125 for b and 160 for p.**

$\frac{a}{2125} \cdot 2125 = \frac{160}{100} \cdot 2125$ **Multiply each side by 2125.**

$a = 3400$ **Simplify.**

ANSWER This year's budget is \$3400.

The Eagle
September 2004 ❖ Beauford's Oldest Pap
Votes Still Being Counted in Student
Fall Dance Planned for October

HELP with Notetaking

In your notes, you may want to include each step of the process of solving a percent proportion.

EXAMPLE 3 Finding a Base

Find the number of which 24 is 0.8%.

$\frac{a}{b} = \frac{p}{100}$ **Write a percent proportion.**

$\frac{24}{b} = \frac{0.8}{100}$ **Substitute 24 for a and 0.8 for p.**

$24 \cdot 100 = b \cdot 0.8$ **Cross products property**

$3000 = b$ **Divide each side by 0.8 and simplify.**

ANSWER The number of which 24 is 0.8% is 3000.

Summary of Percent Problems

Question	Method	Proportion
a is what percent of b?	Solve for p.	$\frac{a}{b} = \frac{p}{100}$
What number is p% of b?	Solve for a.	$\frac{a}{b} = \frac{p}{100}$
a is p% of what number?	Solve for b.	$\frac{a}{b} = \frac{p}{100}$

Your turn now **Use a percent proportion.**

3. What number is 0.5% of 65? **0.325** **4.** 260 is 325% of what number? **80**

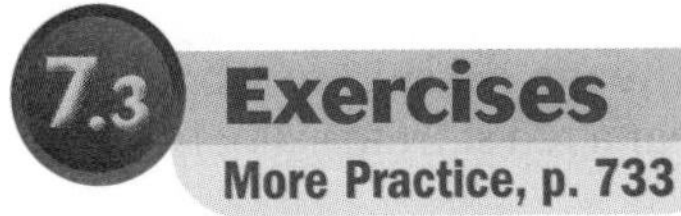

Exercises

More Practice, p. 733

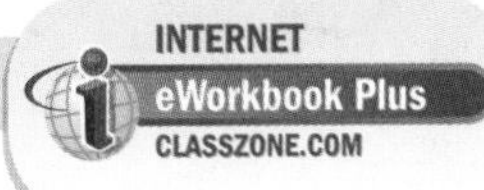

Getting Ready to Practice

1. **Vocabulary** Copy and complete: Another way to say 25 songs of 100 is to say 25 _?_ of the songs. percent

Use a percent proportion.

2. 6 is what percent of 75? 8%
3. 27 is what percent of 108? 25%
4. What number is 45% of 246? 110.7
5. 209 is 38% of what number? 550
6. **Guided Problem Solving** You ask 356 people if they enjoy drawing. Of these people, 89 say they do like to draw. What percent of the people surveyed like to draw?
   (1 Write a percent proportion. $\frac{a}{b} = \frac{p}{100}$
   (2 Substitute the known values for the variables. $\frac{89}{356} = \frac{p}{100}$
   (3 Solve the proportion. 25%

Practice and Problem Solving

A **In Exercises 7–18, use a percent proportion.**

7. 5 is what percent of 125? 4%
8. 39 is what percent of 50? 78%
9. 756 is what percent of 840? 90%
10. 111 is what percent of 740? 15%
11. What number is 45% of 245? 110.25
12. What number is 30% of 120? 36
13. What number is 76% of 775? 589
14. What number is 66% of 95? 62.7
15. 179.2 is 32% of what number? 560
16. 16.1 is 35% of what number? 46
17. 481 is 52% of what number? 925
18. 351 is 78% of what number? 450
19. **Reptiles** The largest crocodiles alive today are 24 feet in length. Recently, researchers discovered bones of an ancient crocodile. It was 167% as long as today's crocodiles. How long was the ancient crocodile? 40.08 ft
20. **Water** A child's body is approximately 75% water. About how many pounds of a 60 pound child's weight is water? 45 lb

B **In Exercises 21–26, use a percent proportion.**

21. 567 is what percent of 420? 135%
22. 1.26 is what percent of 42? 3%
23. What number is 520% of 550? 2860
24. What number is 0.36% of 675? 2.43
25. 918 is 170% of what number? 540
26. 79 is 0.01% of what number? 790,000

HELP with Homework

Example	Exercises
1	7-18, 21-26
2	7-26
3	7-18, 21-26

Online Resources
CLASSZONE.COM
- More Examples
- eTutorial Plus

3 APPLY

ASSIGNMENT GUIDE

Basic Course
Day 1: pp. 329-330 Exs. 7-18, 20-27, 29-32, 35-41

Average Course
Day 1: pp. 329-330 Exs. 9-20, 22-28, 30-32, 35-42

Advanced Course
Day 1: pp. 329-330 Exs. 9-20, 23-37*, 40-42

Block
pp. 329-330 Exs. 9-20, 22-28, 30-32, 35-42 (with 7.4)

EXTRA PRACTICE
- Student Edition, p. 733
- Chapter 7 Resource Book, pp. 26-28
- Test and Practice Generator

TRANSPARENCY

Even-numbered answers are available on transparencies.

HOMEWORK CHECK

When you review students' homework for this lesson, go over the following exercises to check understanding of key concepts.
Basic: 7, 14, 20, 21, 23
Average: 9, 13, 20, 22, 25
Advanced: 9, 15, 20, 23, 26

COMMON ERROR

In Exercises 24 and 26, watch for students who interpret 0.36% as 36% and 0.01% as 1%. Students often become confused when dealing with fractions of one percent.

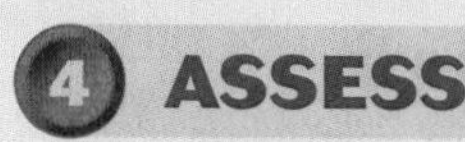

4 ASSESS

ASSESSMENT RESOURCES

For more assessment resources, see:

- Assessment Book
- Test and Practice Generator

MINI-QUIZ

Use a percent proportion.

1. 28 is what percent of 80? **35%**
2. 15 is 5% of what number? **300**
3. What is 35% of 300? **105**
4. What is 0.5% of 200? **1**
5. Salina's dog Ralph weighs 250% more than the 12 pounds he weighed last year. What does Ralph weigh now? **30 lb**
6. The Suarez family spends 30% of its monthly income on the house payment. If the house payment is $1200, what is the family's monthly income? **$4000**

5 FOLLOW-UP

RETEACHING/REMEDIATION

- Study Guide in Chapter 7 Resource Book, pp. 29–30
- Tutor Place, Ratio, Proportion, and Percent Cards 11–13, 15
- eTutorial Plus Online
- Extra Practice, p. 733
- Lesson Practice in Chapter 7 Resource Book, pp. 26–28

CHALLENGE/ENRICHMENT

- Challenge Practice in Chapter 7 Resource Book, p. 31
- Teacher's Edition, p. 314F

ENGLISH LEARNER SUPPORT

- Spanish Study Guide
- Multi-Language Glossary
- Chapter Audio Summaries CDs

27. Number Sense One day, 32 of 80 people wear a red shirt to school. What percent of the 80 people did *not* wear a red shirt to school? **60%**

28. Critical Thinking Explain how to find 10% of 400 without writing a proportion. **Since you are multiplying 400 by 0.1, move the decimal point in 400 one place to the left.**

Write and solve the percent problem in terms of *y*.

29. What number is 50% of $8y$? **$4y$** **30.** $3y$ is 60% of what number? **$5y$**

31. Weekends There are about 52 weeks in a year and two weekend days each week. About what percent of the year falls on a weekend? Round your answer to the nearest tenth of a percent. **28.6%**

32. Dilophosaurus You buy your little brother a scale model of a Dilophosaurus. The scale of the model is 1 inch to 3 feet 4 inches. Use the scale to find what percent the model's height is of the actual height. **C** **2.5%**

33. Challenge You use a photocopier to reduce an 8 inch by 10 inch photograph. When you press the reduction button, it reduces the length and width by the same percent. What is the new area if you reduce the photograph to 64% of its original size and then reduce the result to 78% of its size? What is the new area if you reduce to 78% first and then to 64%? Compare the two values. **About 19.9 in.^{2}; about 19.9 in.^{2}; the areas are the same.**

34. Marathon Of the 23,513 people who entered the Honolulu Marathon one year, 19,236 finished. What percent of the runners finished? Round your answer to the nearest tenth of a percent. **81.8%**

Mixed Review

Write the decimal as a fraction or mixed number. *(Lesson 5.5)*

35. 1.86 **$1\frac{43}{50}$** **36.** 8.714 **$8\frac{357}{500}$** **37.** 0.624 **$\frac{78}{125}$**

Find the product or quotient. *(Lesson 5.7)*

38. 0.023×8.45 **0.19435** **39.** 47.1×0.96 **45.216** **40.** $11.48 \div 8.2$ **1.4**

Test-Taking Practice

INTERNET
State Test Practice
CLASSZONE.COM

41. Multiple Choice You decide to save 20% of all the money that you earn. One month you earn $90. How much do you save? **A**

A. $18 **B.** $20 **C.** $22 **D.** $70

42. Short Response You read in your school newspaper that 560 of the students at your school belong to a school club, and 875 students attend your school. Write a proportion to determine the percent of students in your school who belong to a club. Solve the proportion. **$\frac{560}{875} = \frac{p}{100}$; $p = 64\%$**

Fractions, Decimals, and Percents

BEFORE

You wrote fractions as decimals and decimals as fractions.

Now

You'll rewrite fractions, decimals, and percents.

WHY?

So you can express circle graph sectors as percents, as in Ex. 46.

circle graph, p. 331

In the Real World

Survey The *circle graph* below shows the results of a survey of how 500 students prefer to spend time. What percent of students prefer to spend time with friends?

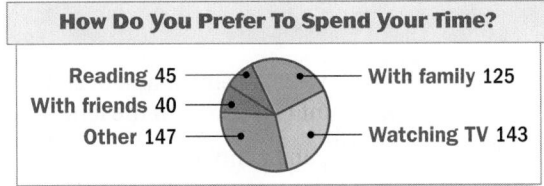

How Do You Prefer To Spend Your Time?

Reading 45
With friends 40
Other 147
With family 125
Watching TV 143

A **circle graph** represents data as parts of a circle. Each part is a percent of the data. The sum of the percents must equal 100% because the circle graph represents all of the data. Each part is also a fraction of the data. The sum of the fractions must equal 1.

EXAMPLE 1 Writing a Fraction as a Percent

The fraction of students who prefer to spend time with friends is $\frac{40}{500}$. To write this fraction as a percent, write a percent proportion and solve for p.

$\frac{40}{500} = \frac{p}{100}$ Write a percent proportion.

$\frac{40}{500} \cdot 100 = \frac{p}{100} \cdot 100$ Multiply each side by 100.

$8 = p$ Simplify.

ANSWER 8% of the students prefer to spend time with friends.

Your turn now Write the fraction as a percent.

1. $\frac{4}{5}$ 80%
2. $\frac{27}{50}$ 54%
3. $\frac{1}{20}$ 5%
4. $\frac{3}{8}$ 37.5%

ILLINOIS Standards and ISAT:
6.A.3, 6.C.3a; 10.A.3a

1 PLAN

SKILL CHECK

Write in decimal form.

1. $\frac{2}{5}$ 0.4
2. $\frac{1}{4}$ 0.25
3. $\frac{9}{10}$ 0.9
4. $2\frac{1}{8}$ 2.125

LESSON OBJECTIVE

Rewrite fractions, decimals, and percents.

PACING

Suggested Number of Days
Basic Course: 1 day
Average Course: 1 day
Advanced Course: 1 day
Block: 0.5 block with 7.3

TEACHING RESOURCES

For a complete list of Teaching Resources, see page 314B.

TRANSPARENCY

Warm-Up Exercises for this lesson are available on a transparency.

2 TEACH

MOTIVATING THE LESSON

Ask students how they prefer to spend their time, using the categories in the circle graph on page 331. Record the data on the board for use in making a class circle graph.

TIPS FOR NEW TEACHERS

Students may already have some understanding of percents. Have them discuss what they already know about percents. See Tips for New Teachers in the *Chapter 7 Resource Book*.

EXTRA EXAMPLES

Example 1 Refer to the circle graph on page 331. What percent of students prefer to spend time reading? **9%**

Example 2 Write the decimal as a percent.

a. 1.15 **115%**

b. 0.02 **2%**

Example 3 Write the percent as a decimal and as a fraction in simplest form.

a. 0.05% **0.0005, $\frac{1}{2000}$**

b. 220% **2.2, $2\frac{1}{5}$**

c. 8.5% **0.085, $\frac{17}{200}$**

TEACHING TIP

Examples 2 and 3 introduce percents greater than 100, which may confuse some students. Point out that a circle graph totals 100% because 100% = 1, or the whole. But just as a number like 2.5 can be expressed in hundredths even though it is greater than 100 hundredths, it can also be expressed as a percent even though it is greater than 100%.

To write a decimal as a percent, write the decimal as a fraction with a denominator of 100. The numerator is the percent. For example:

$$0.89 = \frac{89}{100} = 89\%$$

So, 0.89 = 89%. Notice that 0.89 can be written as a percent by moving the decimal point two places to the right and adding a percent sign.

HELP with Solving

Make sure you move the decimal point two places to the right. Add a zero on the right if necessary, as in part (b) of Example 2.

EXAMPLE 2 Writing Decimals as Percents

Write the decimal as a percent.

a. 0.63 = 0.63 = 63%

b. 2.7 = 2.70 = 270%

c. 0.007 = 0.007 = 0.7%

To write a percent as a decimal, remove the % sign and move the decimal point two places to the left. To write a percent as a fraction, write n% as $\frac{n}{100}$ and simplify.

EXAMPLE 3 Writing Percents as Decimals and Fractions

Write the percent as a decimal and as a fraction.

	As a decimal	As a fraction
a.	0.32% = 00.32% = 0.0032	$0.32\% = \frac{0.32}{100} = \frac{32}{10{,}000} = \frac{2}{625}$
b.	120% = 120% = 1.2	$120\% = \frac{120}{100} = \frac{6}{5} = 1\frac{1}{5}$
c.	2.5% = 02.5% = 0.025	$2.5\% = \frac{2.5}{100} = \frac{25}{1000} = \frac{1}{40}$

Your turn now **Write the decimal as a percent.**

5. 0.62 **62%** **6.** 0.9 **90%** **7.** 0.248 **24.8%** **8.** 5.09 **509%**

Write the percent as a decimal and as a fraction in simplest form.

9. 45% **0.45, $\frac{9}{20}$** **10.** 214% **2.14, $2\frac{7}{50}$** **11.** 77.5% **0.775, $\frac{31}{40}$** **12.** 0.5% **0.005, $\frac{1}{200}$**

EXAMPLE 4 Ordering Fractions, Decimals, and Percents

Order the numbers from least to greatest: 8.7%, $\frac{1}{8}$, and 0.1.

Write 8.7% as a decimal: 8.7% = 08.7 = 0.087

Write $\frac{1}{8}$ as a decimal: $\frac{1}{8}$ = 0.125

Use a number line to order the decimals.

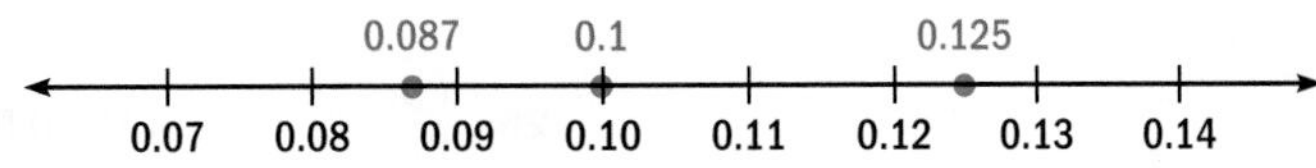

ANSWER The numbers ordered from least to greatest are 8.7%, 0.1, and $\frac{1}{8}$.

13. 0.389, 41%, $\frac{9}{20}$

14. 0.099, $\frac{9}{10}$, 95%

15. $\frac{7}{5}$, 145%, 1.5

Your turn now **Order the numbers from least to greatest.**

13. 41%, $\frac{9}{20}$, 0.389 **14.** $\frac{9}{10}$, 0.099, 95% **15.** 1.5, 145%, $\frac{7}{5}$

7.4 Exercises

More Practice, p. 733

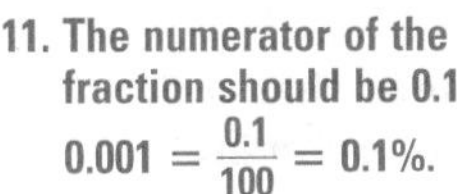

11. The numerator of the fraction should be 0.1; 0.001 = $\frac{0.1}{100}$ = 0.1%.

Getting Ready to Practice

1. Vocabulary In a circle graph, what is the sum of the percents? What is the sum of the fractions? **100%; 1**

Write the decimal or fraction as a percent.

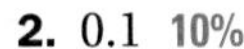

2. 0.1 **10%** **3.** 0.09 **9%** **4.** $\frac{5}{8}$ **62.5%** **5.** $\frac{3}{2}$ **150%**

Write the percent as a decimal and as a fraction in simplest form.

6. 80% **0.8, $\frac{4}{5}$** **7.** 12.5% **0.125, $\frac{1}{8}$** **8.** 7.5% **0.075, $\frac{3}{40}$** **9.** 110% **1.1, $1\frac{1}{10}$**

10. Sleeping You survey 48 people and find that 18 of them sleep eight hours a night. What percent sleep eight hours a night? **37.5%**

11. Find the Error Describe and correct the error in writing 0.001 as a percent. **See margin.**

✗ $0.001 = \frac{1}{100} = 1\%$

EXTRA EXAMPLES

Example 4 Order the numbers from least to greatest: 12%, $\frac{1}{12}$, and 1.2. **$\frac{1}{12}$, 12%, 1.2**

VISUALIZE

To familiarize students with circle graphs and to help them visualize how percents and fractions relate, draw a circle on the board and write 100% beside it. Lead students to recognize that half the circle represents 50%, one quarter of the circle represents 25%, and so on. Write the percents and the fractions on the board.

CONCEPT CHECK

How do you write a percent as a fraction? **Write the percent over a denominator of 100 and simplify.**

DAILY PUZZLER

Simplify $\frac{0.5}{\frac{1}{2} \cdot \frac{1}{2}\%}$. Write the result as a decimal. **200**

APPLY

ASSIGNMENT GUIDE

Basic Course

Day 1: EP p. 731 Exs. 17, 18, 23, 24; pp. 334–335 Exs. 12–23, 32–41, 45–51, 59–66

Average Course

Day 1: pp. 334–335 Exs. 20–35, 42–48, 52–56, 58–67

Advanced Course

Day 1: pp. 334–335 Exs. 20–35, 42–48, 52–61*, 65–67

Block

pp. 334–335 Exs. 20–35, 42–48, 52–56, 58–67 (with 7.3)

EXTRA PRACTICE

- Student Edition, p. 733
- Chapter 7 Resource Book, pp. 36–38
- Test and Practice Generator

TRANSPARENCY

Even-numbered answers are available on transparencies.

HOMEWORK CHECK

When you review students' homework for this lesson, go over the following exercises to check understanding of key concepts.

Basic: 12, 17, 32, 40, 45
Average: 20, 24, 28, 42, 46
Advanced: 20, 24, 33, 42, 47

TEACHING TIP

In Exercises 40–43, urge students not to attempt to use mental math, but to write out each number as a decimal and then order the numbers.

HELP with Homework

Example	Exercises
1	12–27, 45–48
2	12–27
3	28–39
4	40–43

Online Resources CLASSZONE.COM

- More Examples
- eTutorial Plus

Practice and Problem Solving

A Write the decimal or fraction as a percent.

12. 1.27 127% **13.** 0.057 5.7% **14.** 0.039 3.9% **15.** 0.004 0.4%

16. $\frac{1}{80}$ 1.25% **17.** $\frac{3}{20}$ 15% **18.** $\frac{31}{10}$ 310% **19.** $\frac{4}{800}$ 0.5%

20. 47.3 4730% **21.** 1.056 105.6% **22.** $\frac{1}{125}$ 0.8% **23.** $\frac{105}{200}$ 52.5%

24. $\frac{5}{9}$ $55\frac{5}{9}\%$ **25.** $\frac{128}{150}$ $85\frac{1}{3}\%$ **26.** 0.0028 0.28% **27.** 0.7 70%

Write the percent as a decimal and as a fraction.

28. 40% 0.4, $\frac{2}{5}$ **29.** 87% 0.87, $\frac{87}{100}$ **30.** 32.5% 0.325, $\frac{13}{40}$ **31.** 101% 1.01, $1\frac{1}{100}$

32. 1% 0.01, $\frac{1}{100}$ **33.** 4.2% 0.042, $\frac{21}{500}$ **34.** 200.2% 2.002, $2\frac{1}{500}$ **35.** 124% 1.24, $1\frac{6}{25}$

36. 187.09% 1.8709, $1\frac{8709}{10,000}$ **37.** 0.4% 0.004, $\frac{1}{250}$ **38.** 0.78% 0.0078, $\frac{39}{5000}$ **39.** 44.55% 0.4455, $\frac{891}{2000}$

Order the numbers from least to greatest.

40. 0.022, $\frac{9}{40}$, 22%, 0.228, $\frac{28}{125}$ 0.022, 22%, $\frac{28}{125}$, $\frac{9}{40}$, 0.228

41. 6.6%, $\frac{3}{50}$, 0.0606, 0.6%, 0.606 0.6%, $\frac{3}{50}$, 0.0606, 6.6%, 0.606

42. $\frac{4}{7}$, 0.058, 58, 58%, 0.58% 0.58%, 0.058, $\frac{4}{7}$, 58%, 58

43. 212%, 21.2, $\frac{21}{100}$, 0.212, $\frac{21}{10}$ $\frac{21}{100}$, 0.212, $\frac{21}{10}$, 212%, 21.2

44. Critical Thinking If a fraction is greater than 1, what do you know about the equivalent percent? It is greater than 100%.

Languages The circle graph shows the world languages that U.S. high school students studied in a recent year. Each fraction in the graph represents part of the total number of U.S. high school students who studied a world language.

45. Which language was the most popular? Spanish

46. What percent of the students studied German? 5%

47. What percent of the students studied French or German? 23%

48. What percent of the students did *not* study Spanish? 31%

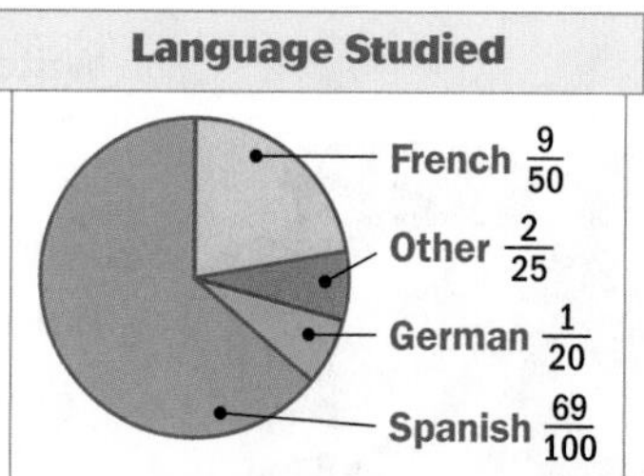

B Copy and complete the statement using <, >, or =.

49. $\frac{1}{4}$? 26% < **50.** 450% ? $\frac{9}{2}$ = **51.** $\frac{13}{25}$? 0.5 >

52. 0.0825 ? $\frac{17}{200}$ < **53.** 4.5% ? 0.045 = **54.** 101% ? 0.101 >

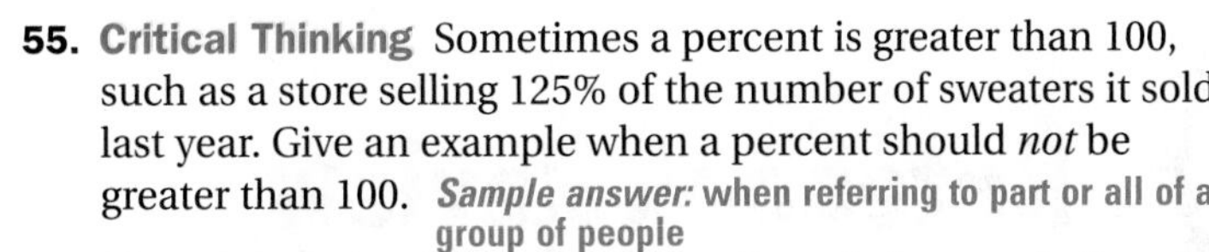

55. **Critical Thinking** Sometimes a percent is greater than 100, such as a store selling 125% of the number of sweaters it sold last year. Give an example when a percent should *not* be greater than 100. ***Sample answer:*** **when referring to part or all of a group of people**

56. **Measurement** A football field is 100 yards long excluding the end zones. What percent of a mile is a football field's length? **about 5.7%**

C 57. **Challenge** Use graph paper to illustrate 45% and 4.5%. **See margin.**

58. **Explain** The table shows the percents of people who buy various types of music. Explain why the data should not be represented in a circle graph. Then find an appropriate way to display the data. **The total of the percents is not 100%; a bar graph would be an appropriate way to display the data.**

Music	Percent
Rock	24.4%
Pop	12.1%
Rap	11.4%
R&B	10.6%
Country	10.5%

Mixed Review

Write the sentence as an inequality. Then solve. *(Lesson 6.6)*

59. The sum of 13 and 4 times a number is at most 9. **$13 + 4x \le 9$; $x \le -1$**

60. Eight less than the quotient of a number and 6 is greater than −7. **$\frac{x}{6} - 8 > -7$; $x > 6$**

Choose a Strategy **Use a strategy from the list to solve the following problem. Explain your choice of strategy.**

61. You work for 4 hours. You spend $5.75 of the money you earn on a movie ticket and $2 on popcorn. Then your sister gives you $3 she owes you. You now have $19.25. How much were you paid per hour?

Problem Solving Strategies
- *Guess, Check, and Revise*
- *Draw a Diagram*
- *Work Backward*
- *Solve a Simpler Problem*

61. $6. ***Sample answer:*** **I used Work Backward because it allowed me to start with the known final amount and then "undo" each of the steps one at a time.**

Basic Skills **Find the product or quotient.**

62. 9.2×13.4 **123.28**
63. $41.3 \div 11.8$ **3.5**
64. $9.9 \div 4.5$ **2.2**
65. 1.98×6 **11.88**

Test-Taking Practice

66. **Multiple Choice** Which numbers are in order from least to greatest? **B**

A. 0.25, 2.5%, $\frac{2}{7}$ **B.** 2.5%, 0.25, $\frac{2}{7}$ **C.** 0.25, $\frac{2}{7}$, 2.5% **D.** 2.5%, $\frac{2}{7}$, 0.25

67. **Multiple Choice** Which choice shows 53.72% written as a decimal? **I**

F. 5372 **G.** 53.72 **H.** 5.372 **I.** 0.5372

4 ASSESS

Assessment Resources

For more assessment resources, see:
- Assessment Book
- Test and Practice Generator

Mini-Quiz

Write the decimal or fraction as a percent.

1. 6.5 **650%** **2.** $\frac{27}{50}$ **54%**

Write the percent as a decimal and as a fraction in simplest form.

3. 32% **0.32, $\frac{8}{25}$**

4. 125% **1.25, $1\frac{1}{4}$**

5. Order the numbers from least to greatest: 0.8, 8%, 18%, $\frac{1}{8}$, $\frac{8}{18}$ **8%, $\frac{1}{8}$, 18%, $\frac{8}{18}$, 0.8**

5 FOLLOW-UP

Reteaching/Remediation

- Study Guide in Chapter 7 Resource Book, pp. 39–40
- Tutor Place, Ratio, Proportion, and Percent Cards 8, 9, 12
- eTutorial Plus Online
- Extra Practice, p. 733
- Lesson Practice in Chapter 7 Resource Book, pp. 36–38

Challenge/Enrichment

- Challenge Practice in Chapter 7 Resource Book, p. 41
- Teacher's Edition, p. 314F

English Learner Support

- Spanish Study Guide
- Multi-Language Glossary
- Chapter Audio Summaries CDs

57. See Additional Answers beginning on page AA1.

ADDITIONAL RESOURCES

The following resources are available to help review the materials in Lessons 7.1–7.4.

Chapter 7 Resource Book
- Lesson Practice
- Study Guide

Assessment Book
- Chapter 7 Quiz 1

Technology
- Test and Practice Generator
- eTutorial CD-ROM

Internet
- Classzone
- eWorkbook Plus Online
- eTutorial Plus Online

ENGLISH LEARNER SUPPORT

- Spanish Study Guide
- Multi-Language Glossary
- Chapter Audio Summaries CDs

Notebook Review

Review the vocabulary definitions in your notebook.

Copy the review examples in your notebook. Then complete the exercises.

Check Your Definitions

ratio, p. 317	proportion, p. 322	scale, p. 324
equivalent ratios, p. 317	cross products, p. 323	percent, p. 327
rate, unit rate, p. 318	scale model, p. 324	circle graph, p. 331

Use Your Vocabulary

1. Copy and complete: In a(n) _?_, the cross products are equal. **proportion**

7.1 Can you write a unit rate?

EXAMPLE Write 282 miles per 6 hours as a unit rate.

$\frac{282 \text{ miles}}{6 \text{ hours}} = \frac{282 \div 6}{6 \div 6}$ **Divide numerator and denominator by 6.**

$= \frac{47}{1}$ **Simplify.**

ANSWER The unit rate is 47 miles per hour.

 **Write the rate as a unit rate.**

2. 30 feet per 4 seconds $\frac{7.5 \text{ ft}}{1 \text{ sec}}$ **3.** \$3.36 per 2 gallons $\frac{\$1.68}{1 \text{ gal}}$

7.2–7.3 Can you solve percent problems?

EXAMPLE 36 is 15% of what number?

$\frac{a}{b} = \frac{p}{100}$ **Write a percent proportion.**

$\frac{36}{b} = \frac{15}{100}$ **Substitute 36 for *a* and 15 for *p*.**

$36 \cdot 100 = 15b$ **Cross products property**

$240 = b$ **Divide each side by 15.**

 **Use a percent proportion.**

4. 72 is what percent of 1200? **6%** **5.** What number is 95% of 26? **24.7**

7.4 Can you rewrite percents, decimals, and fractions?

EXAMPLE Write 28% as a decimal and as a fraction.

28% = 28% = 0.28 — Remove % sign and move decimal point two places to the left.

$28\% = \frac{28}{100} = \frac{7}{25}$ — Write as a fraction and simplify.

ANSWER 28% can be written as 0.28 or $\frac{7}{25}$.

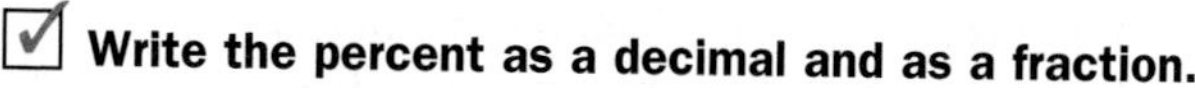

Write the percent as a decimal and as a fraction.

6. 74% 0.74, $\frac{37}{50}$ **7.** 3.8% 0.038, $\frac{19}{500}$ **8.** 16.8% 0.168, $\frac{21}{125}$ **9.** 130% 1.3, $1\frac{3}{10}$

Stop and Think about Lessons 7.1–7.4

10. Writing Explain how to use the cross products property to check if two ratios form a proportion.
If the cross products are equal, then the ratios form a proportion.

Review Quiz 1

A box of animal crackers contains 6 gorillas, 5 bears, 4 camels, 2 monkeys, 2 sheep, and 1 lion. Write the ratio in simplest form.

1. gorillas to sheep $\frac{3}{1}$ **2.** monkeys to camels $\frac{1}{2}$ **3.** bears to lions $\frac{5}{1}$

Find the value of the variable.

4. $\frac{a}{72} = \frac{5}{6}$ 60 **5.** $\frac{2}{3} = \frac{7}{x}$ 10.5 **6.** $\frac{18}{27} = \frac{y}{3}$ 2

7. $\frac{6}{8} = \frac{b}{28}$ 21 **8.** $\frac{12}{c} = \frac{23}{92}$ 48 **9.** $\frac{z+1}{8} = \frac{95}{19}$ 39

10. Clothing You save 40% when buying a shirt that originally cost \$29. How much do you save? \$11.60

Gardening **The circle graph shows the numbers of flowers that you planted in a flowerbed.**

11. How many flowers did you plant? 30 flowers

12. What percent of the flowerbed is roses? 30%

13. What two types of flowers combine to equal 70%? carnations and roses

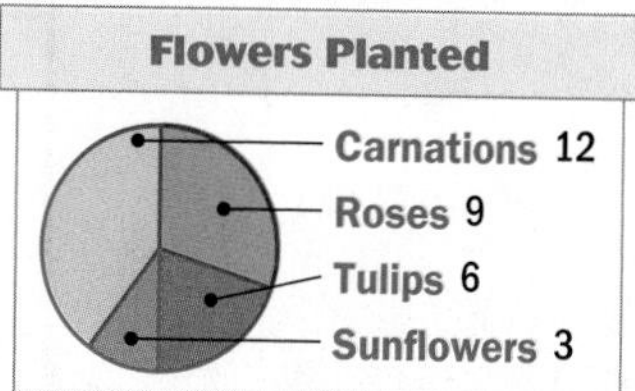

PLAN

SKILL CHECK

1. 130% of 450 = ? 585
2. 27.4% of 59,000 = ? 16,166
3. 0.8% of 50 = ? 0.4

LESSON OBJECTIVE

Solve problems with percent of increase or decrease.

PACING

Suggested Number of Days
Basic Course: 1 day
Average Course: 1 day
Advanced Course: 1 day
Block: 0.5 block with 7.6

TEACHING RESOURCES

For a complete list of Teaching Resources, see page 314B.

TRANSPARENCY

Warm-Up Exercises for this lesson are available on a transparency.

TEACH

MOTIVATING THE LESSON

Ask students what they know about hibernating animals.

TIPS FOR NEW TEACHERS

Stress that the comparison in a percent of change problem is always to the original amount. This means that the denominator is the original amount whether the change is an increase or a decrease. See Tips for New Teachers in the *Chapter 7 Resource Book*.

Percent of Change

BEFORE	Now	WHY?
You solved problems with percents.	You'll solve problems with percent of increase or decrease.	So you can find tons of hazelnuts produced, as in Ex. 19.

Word Watch

percent of change, p. 338
percent of increase, p. 338
percent of decrease, p. 338

In the Real World

Bears During the summer, a bear's heart rate is about 60 beats per minute, but it can drop to as low as 8 beats per minute during winter. What is the *percent of change* in a bear's heart rate from the summer rate to the winter low rate?

A **percent of change** shows how much a quantity has increased or decreased in relation to the original amount. When the new amount is greater than the original amount, the percent of change is called a **percent of increase**. When the new amount is less than the original amount, it is called a **percent of decrease**.

Notebook

Percent of Change

Use the following equation to find the percent of change p.

$$p = \frac{\text{Amount of increase or decrease}}{\text{Original amount}}$$

HELP with Review

For help with repeating decimals, see p. 242.

EXAMPLE 1 Finding a Percent of Decrease

To find the percent of decrease in a bear's heart rate as described above, use the percent of change equation.

$p = \frac{60 - 8}{60}$ — **Write amount of decrease and divide by original amount.**

$= \frac{52}{60}$ — **Subtract.**

$= 0.8\overline{6}6$ — **Write fraction as a decimal.**

ANSWER The percent of decrease is about 86.7%.

ILLINOIS Standards and ISAT:
6.C.3a, 8.D.3b

EXAMPLE 2 Finding a Percent of Increase

School A school had 825 students enrolled last year. This year, 870 students are enrolled. Find the percent of increase.

Solution

$p = \frac{870 - 825}{825}$ **Write amount of increase and divide by original amount.**

$= \frac{45}{825}$ **Subtract.**

$= 0.05\overline{45}$ **Write fraction as a decimal.**

ANSWER The percent of increase is about 5.5%.

Watch Out! Make sure you use the original amount, not the new amount, in the denominator when finding a percent of change.

Your turn now **Tell whether the change is an *increase* or *decrease*. Then find the percent of change.**

1. Original amount: 50
New amount: 36
decrease; 28%
2. Original amount: 10
New amount: 29.5
increase; 195%
3. Original amount: 90
New amount: 110
increase; 22.2%

Decimal Method A shortcut to finding a percent of a number is to write the percent as a decimal and then find the product of the decimal and the number. For example, 10% of 60 = 0.10(60) = 6.

EXAMPLE 3 Using Percent of Increase

Everglades From October to November one year, there was about a 27.4% increase in attendance at Everglades National Park. There were 59,084 visitors in October. About how many people visited in November?

Solution

(1) Find the increase.

Increase = 27.4% of 59,084

= 0.274(59,084) **Write 27.4% as a decimal.**

≈ 16,189 **Multiply.**

(2) Add the increase to the original amount.

New Amount ≈ 59,084 + 16,189

= 75,273

ANSWER About 75,273 people visited the park in November.

What do you think? Science

Everglades

During the wet season, water flows south through the Everglades at a rate of 100 feet per day. How many days does it take water to flow one mile? 52.8 days

EXTRA EXAMPLES

Example 1 Monday morning, Ken had 90 e-mails to answer. By noon, he had 65 e-mails to answer. Find the percent of decrease. **27.7%**

Example 2 Yesterday, a new leaf on Lauren's banana plant was 16 inches long. Today the leaf is 19 inches long. Find the percent of increase in length. **18.75%**

Example 3 Andre sold 32% more dog toys this year than last year. Last year he sold about 8500 dog toys. How many did he sell this year? **about 11,220 dog toys**

Differentiating Instruction

Alternative Teaching Approach
Have students brainstorm quantifiable changes in their lives such as changes in height, in allowance, in prices, in running times, or in class size. Use these examples to work percent of change problems as a class.

CONCEPT CHECK

How do you find the percent of change? **Find the amount of increase or decrease and then divide it by the original amount.**

DAILY PUZZLER

An 8-foot ladder with rungs 12 inches apart hangs over the side of a floating boat. At low tide, 35 percent of the ladder is submerged. The tide rises at a rate of 9 inches every 10 minutes for 40 minutes. What percent of the ladder will be submerged at high tide? Explain. **35%; the boat rises with the tide.**

3 APPLY

ASSIGNMENT GUIDE

Basic Course
Day 1: pp. 340-341 Exs. 7-18, 20-25, 32-41

Average Course
Day 1: pp. 340-341 Exs. 11-21, 24-29, 31-41

Advanced Course
Day 1: pp. 340-341 Exs. 11-16, 19-37*, 41

Block
pp. 340-341 Exs. 11-21, 24-29, 31-41 (with 7.6)

EXTRA PRACTICE

- Student Edition, p. 733
- Chapter 7 Resource Book, pp. 45-47
- Test and Practice Generator

TRANSPARENCY

Even-numbered answers are available on transparencies.

HOMEWORK CHECK

When you review students' homework for this lesson, go over the following exercises to check understanding of key concepts.
Basic: 7, 9, 11, 13, 14
Average: 11, 12, 13, 14, 19
Advanced: 11, 12, 15, 16, 19

TEACHING TIP

In Exercise 24, the first response of many students may be "false," since they see that the final result is three times the original amount and so assume a 300% increase. Emphasize the difference between "percent of" problems, which compare two numbers directly, and "percent of change" problems, which compare a change in a number to the original number.

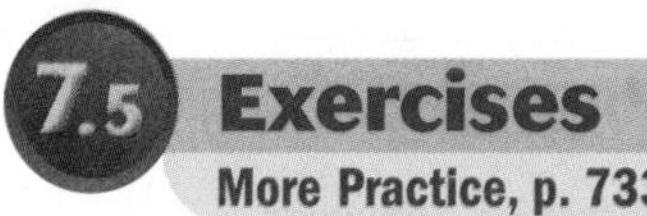

7.5 Exercises

More Practice, p. 733

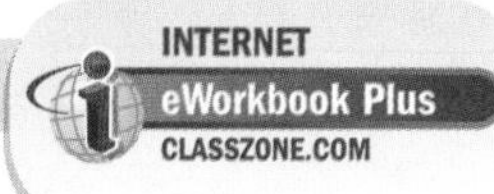

Getting Ready to Practice

1. **Vocabulary** Copy and complete: When the original amount is less than the new amount, the percent of change is called a(n) __?__. increase

Tell whether the change is an *increase* or *decrease*. Then find the percent of change.

2. Original amount: 10
New amount: 14 increase; 40%

3. Original amount: 20
New amount: 16 decrease; 20%

Find the new amount.

4. 78 is decreased by 22%. 60.84

5. 105 is decreased by 78%. 23.1

6. **Tennis** In 1975, there were 130,000 tennis courts in the United States. This number increased by 69% from 1975 to 1985. The number then increased by 9% from 1985 to 1995. How many tennis courts were there in the United States in 1985 and in 1995?
   (1 Find the number of tennis courts in 1985. about 219,700 courts
   (2 Find the amount of the second increase. about 19,800 courts
   (3 Find the number of tennis courts in 1995. about 239,500 courts

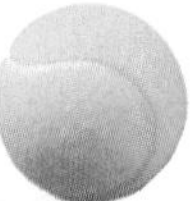

Practice and Problem Solving

A **Decide** **Tell whether the change is an *increase* or *decrease*. Then find the percent of change.**

7. 10 rabbits to 16 rabbits increase; 60%
8. 360 pounds to 352 pounds decrease; $2.\overline{2}$%
9. \$33,300 to \$31,080 decrease; $6.\overline{6}$%
10. 12,200 voters to 13,908 voters increase; 14%
11. 50 minutes to 45 minutes decrease; 10%
12. 350 meters to 420 meters increase; 20%

Find the new amount.

13. 1100 is increased by 4%. 1144
14. 24,700 is decreased by 13%. 21,489
15. 8 is increased by 60%. 12.8
16. 65 is decreased by 30%. 45.5
17. 88,450 is decreased by 12.5%. 77,393.75
18. 26,856 is increased by 14.6%. 30,776.976
19. **Hazelnuts** Oregon produces 98% of the hazelnuts grown in the United States. One year, Oregon produced 46,650 tons of hazelnuts. The crop decreased by 67% the following year. How many tons of hazelnuts were produced in Oregon the second year? about 15,390 tons

HELP with Homework

Example	Exercises
1	7-12
2	7-12
3	13-19

- More Examples
- eTutorial Plus

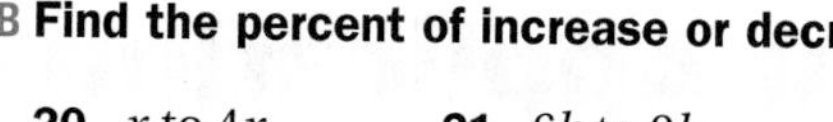

B **Find the percent of increase or decrease.**

20. x to $4x$ 300% increase
21. $6b$ to $9b$ 50% increase
22. y to $\frac{3}{8}y$ 62.5% decrease
23. $4.5a$ to $2.25a$ 50% decrease

In Exercises 24–27, tell whether the statement is *true* or *false*. Explain your reasoning.

24. An increase from 1 to 3 is a 200% increase. True; the increase is 2, and $\frac{2}{1} = 2$, or 200%.

25. Multiplying a number by 5 is a 500% increase. False; multiplying by 5 gives a 400% increase.

26. Multiplying a number by $\frac{1}{4}$ is a 25% decrease. False; multiplying by $\frac{1}{4}$ gives a 75% decrease.

27. Dividing a number by 5 is an 80% decrease. See margin.

28. Coins In 1996, a 1943 copper penny was sold for \$82,500. What was the percent of increase in the penny's value in 1943 to the value it was sold for in 1996? 824,999,900%

29. Population The population of the United States in 1992 was about 255,374,000. In 2002, it was about 280,562,000. Find the approximate percent of increase to the nearest tenth. 9.9%

C **30. Challenge** A number increases by 50%, then decreases by 50%. What is the percent of change from the original number to the final number? 25% decrease

31. Enlargements You have a photograph that is 6 inches by 4 inches. You want to enlarge it so that these dimensions are increased by 50%. What will the new dimensions be? What will be the percent of increase in the area of the new photograph? 9 in. by 6 in.; 125%

27. True; to find an 80% decrease, multiply by 80% and subtract. The final result is 20% of the original number, and finding 20% of a number is the same as dividing by 5.

Mixed Review

Find the product or quotient. *(Lesson 5.7)*

32. $4.412 \cdot 0.36$ 1.58832
33. $-6.7 \cdot 0.8$ -5.36
34. $-0.91 \div 0.35$ -2.6

Solve the equation. *(Lesson 6.3)*

35. $14.2 + 1.4x = -5.4$ -14
36. $0.2s - 1.3 = 0.3$ 8
37. $1.14y - 2 = y + 1.64$ 26

Basic Skills Solve the equation.

38. $7x = 63$ 9
39. $1.5c = 18$ 12
40. $2.5n = 80$ 32

41. *Sample answer*: 138 h; increasing 115 by 20% gives 138; 136.002 h; the estimate and prediction are almost the same.

Test-Taking Practice

INTERNET
State Test Practice
CLASSZONE.COM

41. Extended Response The average person in the United States was predicted to spend 114 hours playing video games in 2002. The prediction of the average time spent on video games increased by about 19.3% from 2002 to 2003. Estimate the predicted hours for 2003. Explain your method. Find the actual prediction for 2003 using the given information. Compare your estimate to the actual prediction. See margin.

4 ASSESS

Assessment Resources

For more assessment resources, see:
- Assessment Book
- Test and Practice Generator

Mini-Quiz

Use the percent of change equation to find the new amount.

1. a goose population of 25 increases 20% **30 geese**
2. a bank balance of \$500 decreases 60% **\$200**
3. a dieter's weight of 180 pounds decreases 5% **171 lb**
4. Find the percent of increase or decrease in $4z$ to $11z$. **175% increase**
5. The number of tenants in an apartment complex increases from 36 to 92 in six months. Find the percent of increase to the nearest tenth. **155.6%**

5 FOLLOW-UP

Reteaching/Remediation

- Study Guide in Chapter 7 Resource Book, pp. 48–49
- Tutor Place, Ratio, Proportion, and Percent Card 12
- eTutorial Plus Online
- Extra Practice, p. 733
- Lesson Practice in Chapter 7 Resource Book, pp. 45–47

Challenge/Enrichment

- Challenge Practice in Chapter 7 Resource Book, p. 51
- Teacher's Edition, p. 314F

English Learner Support

- Spanish Study Guide
- Multi-Language Glossary
- Chapter Audio Summaries CDs

1 PLAN

SKILL CHECK

Find the amount.

1. 4% of $25 $1
2. 30% of $78 = ? $23.40
3. 110% of $64 $70.40
4. 7.75% of $252 $19.53

LESSON OBJECTIVE

Solve percent application problems.

PACING

Suggested Number of Days
Basic Course: 1 day
Average Course: 1 day
Advanced Course: 1 day
Block: 0.5 block with 7.5

TEACHING RESOURCES

For a complete list of Teaching Resources, see page 314B.

TRANSPARENCY

Warm-Up Exercises for this lesson are available on a transparency.

TEACH

MOTIVATING THE LESSON

Ask students who have bought sale items that are marked down by a given percent from regular price if they were able to find the sale price before paying for the item, and if so, how.

Percent Applications

BEFORE	Now	WHY?
You solved problems with percent of increase or decrease.	You'll solve percent application problems.	So you can find the sale price of a pair of jeans, as in Ex. 18.

Word Watch

markup, p. 342
discount, p. 342

In the Real World

Guitars You are shopping for a guitar and find one with an original price of $160. The store is offering a 30% *discount* on all guitars. What is the sale price of the guitar?

Markup and Discount A retail store buys items from manufacturers at *wholesale prices*. The store then sells the items to customers at *retail prices*. The increase in the wholesale price of an item is a **markup**. A decrease in the price of an item is a **discount**. You can find the retail price or sale price of an item using the equations below.

Retail price = Wholesale price + Markup

Sale price = Original price − Discount

EXAMPLE 1 Finding a Sale Price

To find the sale price of the guitar above, use the sale price equation.

Solution

(1) Find the amount of the discount.

Discount = 30% of $160
= 0.3(160) **Write 30% as a decimal.**
= 48 **Multiply.**

(2) Subtract the discount from the original price.

160 − 48 = 112

ANSWER The sale price of the guitar is $112.

Your turn now **Find the sale price.**

1. Original price: $25
Percent discount: 10% $22.50
2. Original price: $85.50
Percent discount: 30% $59.85

ILLINOIS Standards and ISAT:
6.C.3a, 8.C.3, 8.D.3b

EXAMPLE 2 Finding a Retail Price

Clothing A shirt has a wholesale price of \$16. The percent markup is 120%. What is the retail price?

HELP with Solving
Remember that the markup must be added to the wholesale price to find the retail price.

Solution

1 Find the amount of the markup.

Markup = 120% of \$16

= 1.2(16) **Write 120% as a decimal.**

= 19.2 **Multiply.**

2 Add the markup to the wholesale price.

16 + 19.2 = 35.2

ANSWER The retail price of the shirt is \$35.20.

Sales Tax and Tips Sales tax and tips are amounts that are added to the price of some purchases. Sales tax and tips are usually calculated using a percent of the purchase price.

EXAMPLE 3 Finding Sales Tax

Compact Disc Player A portable CD player costs \$48 before tax. The sales tax is 4.5%. What is the total cost?

Solution

1 Find the amount of the sales tax.

4.5% of \$48 = 0.045(48)

= 2.16

2 Add the sales tax to the price of the portable CD player.

48 + 2.16 = 50.16

ANSWER The total cost of the CD player is \$50.16.

Your turn now **Find the retail price.**

3. Wholesale price: \$64
Percent markup: 85% **\$118.40**

4. Wholesale price: \$35
Percent markup: 110% **\$73.50**

Find the total cost.

5. Price: \$8.90
Sales tax: 5% **\$9.35**

6. Price: \$54.07
Sales tax: 7% **\$57.85**

TIPS FOR NEW TEACHERS

Point out to students that markup rates vary greatly according to the item. For example, groceries may have a markup of only a few percent, a car may have a markup of 8% or 10%, and a luxury item like jewelry may have a markup well over 100%. You may want to have students do Internet research to find typical markup rates. See Tips for New Teachers in the *Chapter 7 Resource Book*.

EXTRA EXAMPLES

Example 1 A boxed set of 5 CDs costing \$60 is marked 15% off. Find the sale price of the CDs. **\$51**

Example 2 A holiday decoration has a wholesale price of \$3. The percent markup is 150%. What is the retail price? **\$7.50**

Example 3 A printer costs \$115 before tax. The sales tax is 5%. What is the total cost? **\$120.75**

COMMON ERROR

In cases like Example 2, where the markup is over 100%, it may be easy for students to forget to add the markup to the wholesale price. Point out that a 100% markup means a doubling of the wholesale price, and a 200% markup means a tripling of the wholesale price.

TEACHING TIP

After working Example 2, ask students if an item can have a discount of 120%, and have them explain their reasoning. They should come to realize that because a discount is a part of a whole, it can never exceed 100%.

EXTRA EXAMPLES

Example 4 A haircut at a salon costs $16. The sales tax is 5%. You leave a 15% tip. What is the total cost of the haircut? **$19.20**

CONCEPT CHECK

How can you find the retail price of an item if you know its wholesale price and its percent markup? **Find the amount of the markup by multiplying the markup rate by the wholesale price, and then add the markup rate to the wholesale price.**

DAILY PUZZLER

Three friends share a $30 meal and split the bill evenly, paying $10 each. The waiter tells the friends he has overcharged them, as the meal cost only $25. He returns $5. The friends each pocket $1 and leave the $2 as a tip. Each friend thus paid $9, for a total of $27 plus the $2 tip, which makes $29. Where is the missing dollar? **This is a famous puzzle. There is no missing dollar. The $2 tip is included in the total of $27 that the friends spent. The trick lies in the misleading phrasing of the puzzle.**

EXAMPLE 4 Finding Sales Tax and Tip

Restaurants Your food bill at a restaurant is $24. You leave a 20% tip. The sales tax is 6%. What is the total cost of the meal?

Solution

1. Find the amount of the tip.

   20% of $24 = 0.20(24)

   = 4.8

2. Find the amount of the sales tax.

   6% of $24 = 0.06(24)

   = 1.44

3. Add the food bill, tip, and sales tax.

   24 + 4.8 + 1.44 = 30.24

ANSWER The total cost of the meal is $30.24.

Your turn now **Find the total cost.**

7. Your food bill at a restaurant is $35. The sales tax is 5%. You leave a 15% tip. What is the total cost of the meal? **$42**

7.6 Exercises

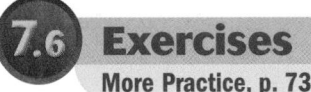

More Practice, p. 733

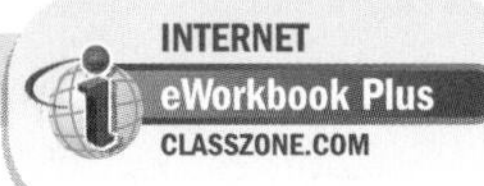

Getting Ready to Practice

1. **Vocabulary** Copy and complete: To find the retail price, add the _?_ to the wholesale price. **markup**

Find the sale price or retail price.

2. Original price: $60
   Percent discount: 15% **$51**
3. Original price: $28.50
   Percent discount: 60% **$11.40**
4. Wholesale price: $25
   Percent markup: 65% **$41.25**
5. Wholesale price: $14.50
   Percent markup: 140% **$34.80**
6. **Lamps** A lamp costs $25.75. The sales tax is 4%. What is the total cost? **$26.78**
7. **Restaurants** Your food bill at a restaurant is $30. You leave a 20% tip. The sales tax is 6%. What is the total cost of the meal? **$37.80**

3 APPLY

Practice and Problem Solving

with Homework

Example	Exercises
1	8-13, 20-25
2	8-13, 20-25
3	14-17
4	14-17

Online Resources
CLASSZONE.COM

- More Examples
- eTutorial Plus

A Find the sale price or retail price. Round to the nearest cent.

8. Original price: $42
Percent discount: 30% $29.40

9. Wholesale price: $19
Percent markup: 110% $39.90

10. Wholesale price: $16.49
Percent markup: 130% $37.93

11. Original price: $22.40
Percent discount: 25% $16.80

12. Original price: $54.75
Percent discount: 20% $43.80

13. Wholesale price: $65.40
Percent markup: 55% $101.37

Find the total cost. Round to the nearest cent.

14. Original price: $72
Sales tax: 6% $76.32

15. Original price: $58.40
Sales tax: 5.5% $61.61

16. Food bill: $25.80
Tip: 18%
Sales tax: 4.5% $31.61

17. Food bill: $18
Tip: 20%
Sales tax: 5% $22.50

18. **Jeans** The wholesale price of a pair of jeans is $15. A store marks up the price by 75%. When the jeans don't sell, the store offers a 20% discount. What is the sale price of the jeans? $21

19. **Critical Thinking** A store is having an end of season sale and offers a discount of 40% on all coats. One week later the store discounts the coats an additional 60%. Is the store giving away the coats for free? Explain your reasoning.

19. No. *Sample answer:* The discounts are applied successively, not added. For example, a coat that originally cost $100 costs $60 after the first discount. The 60% discount is then applied to the cost of $60 to give a final cost of $24.

B Tell whether the new price is a *discount* or *markup*. Then find the percent of discount or markup.

20. Old price: $32
New price: $24
discount; 25%

21. Old price: $45
New price: $40.50
discount; 10%

22. Old price: $19
New price: $33.25
markup; 75%

23. Old price: $55
New price: $121
markup; 120%

24. Old price: $12.50
New price: $22.50
markup; 80%

25. Old price: $199.99
New price: $119.99
discount; about 40%

26. **Writing** People often leave tips between 15% and 20% on restaurant bills. Find both the 15% and 20% tips of a food bill that totals $24.20. Explain why people often leave a tip between 15% and 20% rather than leaving exactly 15% or 20%. $3.63, $4.84. *Sample answer:* The wider range allows them to avoid leaving coins.

27. **Tipping** You order a pizza to be delivered. The bill comes to $12.60. You give the delivery person $15 and tell them to keep the change. What percent tip did you give? Round to the nearest percent. 19%

28. **DVDs** A DVD has a regular price of $26 and is on sale for $16.90. What is the percent discount? 35%

29. **Subscription** A magazine subscription has a regular price of $24.50. You pay $14.70 for your subscription. What is the percent discount? 40%

ASSIGNMENT GUIDE

Basic Course
Day 1: pp. 345-346 Exs. 8-18, 20-22, 27-29, 33-41

Average Course
Day 1: pp. 345-346 Exs. 10-19, 23-30, 32-36, 39-42

Advanced Course
Day 1: pp. 345-346 Exs. 10-19, 23-36*, 40-42

Block
pp. 345-346 Exs. 10-19, 23-30, 32-36, 39-42 (with 7.5)

EXTRA PRACTICE

- Student Edition, p. 733
- Chapter 7 Resource Book, pp. 54-56
- Test and Practice Generator

TRANSPARENCY

Even-numbered answers are available on transparencies.

HOMEWORK CHECK

When you review students' homework for this lesson, go over the following exercises to check understanding of key concepts.
Basic: 8, 10, 14, 16, 20
Average: 10, 12, 14, 16, 23
Advanced: 10, 12, 15, 17, 25

TEACHING TIP

Exercise 19 illustrates an important tactic–successive discounts–used by retailers to make their discounts seem bigger. Have students work a few more examples of applying one discount after another to show that the net discount rate is always smaller than the sum of the separate discount rates.

4 ASSESS

Assessment Resources

For more assessment resources, see:

- Assessment Book
- Test and Practice Generator

Mini-Quiz

Find the sale price or retail price.

1. Original price: \$60
   Discount: 20% **\$48**
2. Original price: \$38
   Markup: 150% **\$95**

Find the total cost.

3. Original price: \$120
   Sales tax: 4.5% **\$125.40**
4. Food bill: \$22.50
   Tip: 20%
   Sales tax: 4% **\$27.90**
5. A computer has an old price of \$1250 and a new price of \$1200. Is the new price a discount or markup? What is the percent of discount or markup? **discount; 4%**

5 FOLLOW-UP

Reteaching/Remediation

- Study Guide in Chapter 7 Resource Book, pp. 57–58
- Tutor Place, Ratio, Proportion, and Percent Cards 14, 15
- eTutorial Plus Online
- Extra Practice, p. 733
- Lesson Practice in Chapter 7 Resource Book, pp. 54–56

Challenge/Enrichment

- Challenge Practice in Chapter 7 Resource Book, p. 59
- Teacher's Edition, p. 314F

English Learner Support

- Spanish Study Guide
- Multi-Language Glossary
- Chapter Audio Summaries CDs

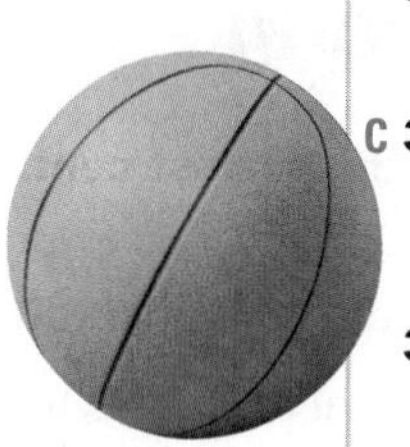

30. Estimation The original price of an item is \$42 and the percent of discount is 25%. Explain how to estimate the sale price. See margin.

C **31. Challenge** A total restaurant bill including sales tax and tip is \$33. The tax is 4% and the tip is 16% of the bill before tax. What was the food bill before tax and tip? **\$27.50**

32. Shopping A basketball has a wholesale price of \$12 and is marked up 115%. Later it is discounted 15%. The sales tax is 4.5%. Find the final cost of the basketball including tax. Round to the nearest cent. **\$22.92**

30. *Sample answer:* You can round \$42 down to \$40. Since $25\% = \frac{1}{4}$, find $\frac{1}{4}$ of 40, which is 10. Then subtract 10 from 40 to find the estimated sale price, about \$30.

Mixed Review

Solve the equation. *(Lesson 6.2)*

33. $4a = a + 9$ 3 **34.** $n - 2 = 2n - 9$ 7

Use a percent proportion. *(Lesson 7.3)*

35. What number is 35% of 80? 28 **36.** 308 is what percent of 440? 70%

Basic Skills Solve the equation.

37. $2.4b = 108$ 45 **38.** $8.5y = 51$ 6 **39.** $3.5x = 140$ 40 **40.** $1.6d = 38.4$ 24

Test-Taking Practice

INTERNET
State Test Practice
CLASSZONE.COM

41. Multiple Choice A book costs \$7.95 and is on sale for 15% off. The sales tax is 6%. What is the total cost of the book? B

A. \$5.64 **B.** \$7.16 **C.** \$7.74 **D.** \$8.27

42. Multiple Choice You and two friends eat at a restaurant and split the total bill evenly. The food bill is \$20.88. Sales tax is 5%. You leave a 20% tip. How much should each person pay? I

F. \$6.96 **G.** \$7.31 **H.** \$8.35 **I.** \$8.70

Shrink Ray

Ray invents two zappers that shrink and enlarge things. After shrinking almost everything in the house to 40% of its original size, Ray's mother demands that he return things to normal. What percent setting should he use to zap objects back to their original size?

If Ray had instead used the zapper to enlarge things by 60%, what percent setting would he use on the shrink zapper to get them back to their normal size? **250%; 62.5%**

Using the Percent Equation

BEFORE	Now	WHY?
You solved percent problems using proportions.	You'll solve percent problems using the percent equation.	So you can find the interest paid on a bank loan, as in Ex. 25.

Word Watch

interest, p. 348
principal, p. 348
annual interest rate, p. 348

In the Real World

Beaches In a survey of 2000 people, 26.7% said that they had visited a beach during the past year. Find the number of people who said they had visited a beach.

In Lesson 7.3, you solved percent problems with proportions. You can also use the decimal method from Lesson 7.5 to solve percent problems.

The Percent Equation

To represent the statement "a is p percent of b" use the equation:

$a = p\% \cdot b$ Part of the base = Percent • Base

EXAMPLE 1 Finding Part of a Base

To find the number of people who said they had visited a beach in the past year, use the percent equation.

$a = p\% \cdot b$	Write percent equation.
$= 26.7\% \cdot 2000$	Substitute 26.7 for p and 2000 for b.
$= 0.267 \cdot 2000$	Write percent as a decimal.
$= 534$	Multiply.

ANSWER The number of people who said they had visited a beach during the past year is 534.

Your turn now Use the percent equation.

1. Find 45% of 700. 315
2. Find 24.5% of 800. 196

ILLINOIS Standards and ISAT:
6.C.3a, 8.C.3, 8.D.3b

1 PLAN

SKILL CHECK
Solve.

1. $x = 0.2(2000)$ 400
2. $252 = 0.3d$ 840
3. $500 = 1000k$ 0.5

LESSON OBJECTIVE
Solve percent problems using the percent equation.

PACING
Suggested Number of Days
Basic Course: 1 day
Average Course: 1 day
Advanced Course: 1 day
Block: 0.5 block with 7.8

TEACHING RESOURCES
For a complete list of Teaching Resources, see page 314B.

TRANSPARENCY
Warm-Up Exercises for this lesson are available on a transparency.

2 TEACH

MOTIVATING THE LESSON
Survey the class to find what percent of the class has visited various destinations near your area.

TIPS FOR NEW TEACHERS
Before Example 3, point out that if you take out a loan or use a credit card, you pay interest to borrow the money. If you have an account at a bank, the bank pays you interest to use your money. See Tips for New Teachers in the *Chapter 7 Resource Book*.

EXTRA EXAMPLES

Example 1 Of 15,000 residents of a town, 15.4% said they had traveled overseas in the past 10 years. Find the number of people in the town who said they had traveled overseas. **2310 people**

Example 2 Market researchers found that 88, or 22%, of customers sampled preferred a new ice-cream flavor to a previously popular flavor. How many customers were sampled? **400 customers**

Example 3 You deposit \$200 in a savings account that pays a simple interest rate of 2.25% per year. How much interest will you earn after 5 years? **\$22.50**

MULTIPLE REPRESENTATIONS

Work some simple interest problems using play money or other models of money.

MATH REASONING

Ask whether it ever makes sense for a percent to be negative. Students should realize that it does not make sense in terms of relating two numbers or a part of a whole (for example, a number cannot be −40% of another number), but a negative sign with a percent can represent that a percent change is a decrease.

CONCEPT CHECK

How do you find simple interest? **Multiply the principal, the annual interest rate, and the time in years.**

DAILY PUZZLER

How many years would it take a bank account balance to double if the account is receiving 3% annual simple interest? **$33\frac{1}{3}$ yr**

EXAMPLE 2 Finding a Base

Student Council Marc received 273, or 35%, of the votes in the student council election. How many students voted in the election?

Solution

$a = p\% \cdot b$	Write percent equation.
$273 = 35\% \cdot b$	Substitute 273 for a and 35 for p.
$273 = 0.35 \cdot b$	Write 35% as a decimal.
$780 = b$	Divide each side by 0.35.

ANSWER In the election, 780 students voted.

Your turn now Solve using the percent equation.

3. 6.4 is 62.5% of what number? **10.24** **4.** 15 is what percent of 120? **12.5%**

HELP with Vocabulary

When you borrow money from a bank, you pay back interest as well as the amount you borrowed.

Simple Interest **Interest** is an amount paid for the use of money. **Principal** is the amount you borrow or deposit. When interest is paid only on the principal, it is called simple interest. The percent of the principal you pay or earn per year is the **annual interest rate**.

Simple Interest

Words To find simple interest I, find the product of the principal P, the annual interest rate r written as a decimal, and the time t in years.

Algebra $I = Prt$

EXAMPLE 3 Finding Simple Interest

You deposit \$500 in a savings account that pays a simple interest rate of 2.5% per year. How much interest will you earn after 18 months?

Solution

$I = Prt$	Write formula for simple interest.
$= (500)(0.025)(1.5)$	Substitute values. 18 months = 1.5 years
$= 18.75$	Multiply.

ANSWER You will earn \$18.75 in interest.

7.7 Exercises

More Practice, p. 733

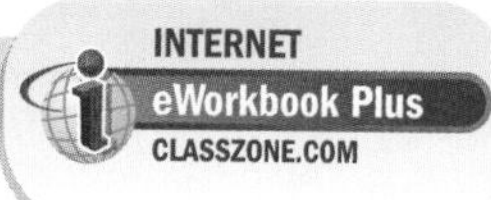

Getting Ready to Practice

1. **Vocabulary** Copy and complete: To find simple interest, multiply the annual rate written as a decimal, the time in years, and the _?_. principal

Solve using the percent equation.

2. What number is 46% of 900? 414
3. 205 is what percent of 250? 82%
4. 132 is 24% of what number? 550
5. What number is 95% of 420? 399
6. **Guided Problem Solving** A savings account pays a 3% annual interest rate. How much must you put in the savings account to earn $100 in interest in 6 months?
   1. Write the simple interest formula. $I = Prt$
   2. Substitute known values in the formula. $100 = P \cdot 0.03 \cdot 0.5$
   3. Solve the equation for P. Round to the nearest cent. $6666.67

Practice and Problem Solving

HELP with Homework

Example	Exercises
1	7-16
2	7-16
3	17-18

· More Examples
· eTutorial Plus

A Solve using the percent equation.

7. What number is 65% of 320? 208
8. What number is 6% of 450? 27
9. What number is 120% of 55? 66
10. What number is 0.4% of 150? 0.6
11. 115 is 46% of what number? 250
12. 26 is 130% of what number? 20
13. 62.4 is 80% of what number? 78
14. 289.25 is 89% of what number? 325
15. 3 is what percent of 600? 0.5%
16. 291.04 is what percent of 856? 34%

Find the amount of simple interest earned.

17. Principal: $250
    Annual rate: 2%
    Time: 3 years $15
18. Principal : $940
    Annual rate: 3.5%
    Time: 30 months $82.25
19. **Weather** In Charlotte, North Carolina, an average of 112 days of the year have precipitation of 0.01 inch or more. What percent of days in Charlotte have precipitation of 0.01 inch or more? Round your answer to the nearest percent. 31%
20. **Writing** Are the solutions of $\frac{12}{b} = \frac{3}{100}$ and $12 = 3\% \cdot b$ the same or different? Explain your reasoning.

20. The same. *Sample answer:* Because $\frac{3}{100} = 3\%$, you can rewrite the original equation as $\frac{12}{b} = 3\%$. Cross multiplying then gives $12 = 3\% \cdot b$.

ASSIGNMENT GUIDE

Basic Course
Day 1: pp. 349-350 Exs. 7-18, 21-24, 28-35

Average Course
Day 1: pp. 349-350 Exs. 9-20, 22-26, 28-36

Advanced Course
Day 1: pp. 349-350 Exs. 9-20, 22-30*, 33-36

Block
pp. 349-350 Exs. 9-20, 22-26, 28-36 (with 7.8)

Extra Practice

- Student Edition, p. 733
- Chapter 7 Resource Book, pp. 62-64
- Test and Practice Generator

Transparency

Even-numbered answers are available on transparencies.

Homework Check

When you review students' homework for this lesson, go over the following exercises to check understanding of key concepts.
Basic: 7, 8, 11, 15, 17
Average: 9, 11, 14, 15, 17
Advanced: 9, 12, 15, 17, 18

Teaching Tip

After students have worked Exercises 21 and 22, challenge an advanced student to explain why both statements are equal. If they need a hint, you may tell them to write each product of two numbers as a product of three numbers (one of them being 0.01).

ASSESSMENT RESOURCES

For more assessment resources, see:
- Assessment Book
- Test and Practice Generator

MINI-QUIZ

Solve using the percent equation.

1. What is 22% of 1200? 264
2. 52 is 5% of what number? 1040
3. 80 is what percent of 400? 20%
4. Find the amount of simple interest earned on a principal of \$850 at an annual rate of 3.5% for 2.5 years. \$74.38
5. If a circle is drawn inside a square so that the circle just touches the middle of each side of the square, the circle's area is about 78.5% of the square's. If such a circle is 80 square inches in area, what is the area of the square to the nearest square inch? 102 in.^{2}

RETEACHING/REMEDIATION

- Study Guide in Chapter 7 Resource Book, pp. 65–66
- Tutor Place, Ratio, Proportion, and Percent Cards 14, 15
- eTutorial Plus Online
- Extra Practice, p. 733
- Lesson Practice in Chapter 7 Resource Book, pp. 62–64

CHALLENGE/ENRICHMENT

- Challenge Practice in Chapter 7 Resource Book, p. 67
- Teacher's Edition, p. 314F

ENGLISH LEARNER SUPPORT

- Spanish Study Guide
- Multi-Language Glossary
- Chapter Audio Summaries CDs

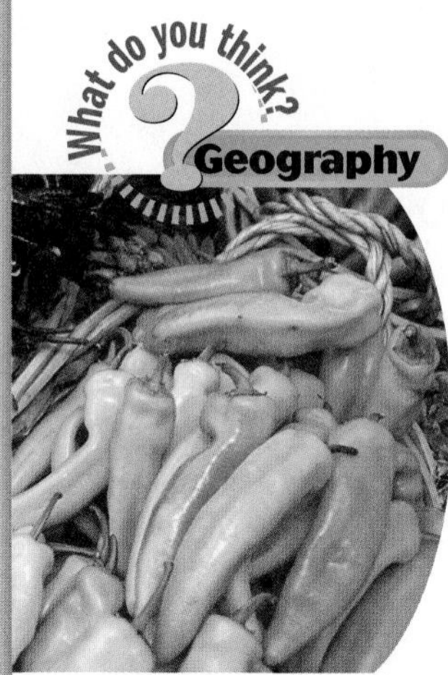

Texas

There are about 10,500 acres of cropland in Texas planted with peppers. What percent of cropland in Texas is planted with peppers? Round to the nearest hundredth of a percent. 0.04%

INTERNET
State Test Practice
CLASSZONE.COM

B **Copy and complete the statement with <, >, or =.**

21. 60% of 75 _?_ 75% of 60 =

22. 30% of 120 _?_ 120% of 30 =

23. Look for a Pattern Copy and complete the table by finding the percent of each number. Describe the relationship you see among the three percents in each row. For 22, the number increased by 1.1 each time; for 50, the number increased by 2.5 each time; for 76, the number increased by 3.8 each time.

	5%	10%	15%
22	? 1.1	2.2	? 3.3
50	? 2.5	? 5	? 7.5
76	? 3.8	? 7.6	? 11.4

24. Savings How much money must you deposit in a savings account that pays a 4% simple annual interest rate to earn \$50 in 2 years? \$625

25. Loan You borrow \$1200 from the bank. The bank charges an annual simple interest rate of 9.5%. It takes you 15 months to pay back the loan. How much interest do you pay on the loan? What is the total amount that you pay the bank? \$142.50; \$1342.50

C **26. Texas** The area of the state of Texas is 171.1 million acres. Of this, 26.9 million acres are cropland. What percent of Texas is cropland? Round your answer to the nearest hundredth of a percent. 15.72%

27. Challenge *Compound interest* on a savings account is earned on both the principal and on any interest that has already been earned. You deposit \$500 into an account that earns 4% compounded annually. How much will you have in your account after the third year? after the sixth year? Round your answers to the nearest cent. \$562.43; \$632.66

Mixed Review

Find the quotient. *(Lesson 5.4)*

28. $\frac{8}{3} \div \frac{32}{21}$ $1\frac{3}{4}$

29. $\frac{5}{9} \div \frac{2}{3}$ $\frac{5}{6}$

30. $\frac{11}{14} \div \frac{1}{2}$ $1\frac{4}{7}$

In Exercises 31–33, solve the equation or inequality. *(Lessons 6.3, 6.5)*

31. $5.4 - 4.6x = 19.2$ -3

32. $\frac{3}{8}u - \frac{1}{2} = \frac{7}{12}$ $2\frac{8}{9}$

33. $3n - 27 \le -5n + 64$ $n \le 11\frac{3}{8}$

34. Solve the proportion $\frac{8}{25} = \frac{7}{d}$. *(Lesson 7.2)* 21.875

Test-Taking Practice

35. Multiple Choice What percent of 75 is 30? B

A. 30% **B.** 40% **C.** 45% **D.** 75%

36. Short Response Vicki hears on the local news that 37.5% of the movie theaters in her city, or 6 theaters, offer discount tickets to students. Write an equation that could be used to determine the number of theaters in Vicki's city. Then solve the equation. $0.375b = 6$; 16 theaters

7.7 Technology Activity

CALCULATOR

Compound Interest

GOAL Use a calculator to compute compound interest.

Example **Mark deposits $2000 into an account that pays an interest rate of 3.5% compounded annually. He doesn't add or remove money from his account for 4 years. How much money will Mark have in 4 years?**

HELP with Vocabulary

Compound interest is interest earned on both the principal and on any interest that has already been earned.

Solution

The balance of an account after a year can be found by multiplying the principal balance by the quantity one plus the annual interest rate. Use the keystrokes below to find the amount of money in the account in 4 years.

Keystrokes	Display	
2000   1.035 =	2070	In 1 year
=	2142.45	In 2 years
=	2217.43575	In 3 years
=	2295.046001	In 4 years

ANSWER Mark will have $2295.05 in his account in 4 years.

Your turn now **Find the balance of the account earning compound interest.**

1. Principal: $7000
Annual rate: 2%
Time: 4 years
$7577.03

2. Principal: $7000
Annual rate: 4%
Time: 2 years
$7571.20

3. Principal: $1995
Annual rate: 6.5%
Time: 10 years
$3744.89

4. You deposit $1500 into an account that pays an interest rate of 4% compounded annually. Your friend deposits $1500 into an account that pays a simple annual interest rate of 4%. Compare the balances of the two accounts after 5 years.

4. **After 5 years, your balance is $1824.98 and your friend's balance is $1800. Your account with interest compounded annually earns $24.98 more than your friend's account.**

ILLINOIS Standards and ISAT:
8.D.3b

1 PLAN

LEARN THE METHOD

- Students will use a calculator to compute compound interest.
- In Example 3 of Lesson 7.7, students learned to calculate simple interest. In the real world, interest is usually calculated by compounding.

2 TEACH

ALTERNATIVE STRATEGY

Before students work the Example, have them calculate the simple interest for 1, 2, 3, and 4 years using the amount and rate from the Example to compare to the results of compounding the interest.

EXTRA EXAMPLES

Example Find the balance after 4 years on an account with a principal of $1000 earning 4.75% compound interest. **$1203.97**

3 CLOSE

ASSESSMENT

1. What is the total percent of increase on $10,000 earning 6% compound interest for 6 years? **about 41.9%**

2. Would you prefer receiving compound interest or simple interest on your savings account? Explain. **Compound interest; you make more money with compound interest because you earn interest on your interest.**

PLAN

STRATEGY BACKGROUND

When students use the strategy Perform an Experiment, they often construct and use an object or objects to generate data. The experiment usually results in a comparison of measurable quantities such as volume or time.

TEACH

GUIDING STUDENTS' WORK

Instead of recording the actual sums, students can also use a tally chart to record the number of odd or even rolls. Point out to students that though they might get three or even four odd or even rolls in a row, the more times that they roll the number cubes, the closer the overall results will be to a single number.

EXTRA EXAMPLES

Example Howard and Alma are playing a board game that involves rolling two number cubes. Howard can advance forward a square if he rolls 7 or less. Alma can advance forward a square if she rolls 7 or more. Perform an experiment to predict which player is more likely to win. **Student's results should reflect an equal chance of winning.**

7.8 Problem Solving Strategies

Guess, Check, and Revise
Look for a Pattern
Draw a Diagram
Act It Out
Perform an Experiment
Work Backward
Make a Table

Perform an Experiment

Problem You are playing a board game that involves rolling 2 cubes numbered from 1 to 6. If your cubes sum to an even number, you may advance your game piece forward. If your cubes sum to an odd number, you may not move your piece. Predict the number of times you will be able to move forward in 100 rolls.

1 Read and Understand

Read the problem carefully.

The problem asks you to predict the number of times you will roll two number cubes that sum to an even number in 100 rolls.

2 Make a Plan

Decide on a strategy to use.

Because it might take a while to roll number cubes 100 times, you can make a prediction by performing an experiment. Roll two number cubes 20 times and use the results to make a prediction.

3 Solve the Problem

Reread the problem and perform an experiment.

First, roll two number cubes 20 times and record the results as shown.

Results

5, 12, 7, 9, 4, 8, 7, 6, 6, 3, 8, 4, 7, 5, 6, 9, 2, 4, 10, 11

There are 11 even numbers and 9 odd numbers.

Then, use the results of the experiment to set up and solve a proportion.

$$\frac{\text{Number of even numbers in 20 rolls}}{\text{20 rolls}} = \frac{\text{Number of even numbers in 100 rolls}}{\text{100 rolls}}$$

$$\frac{11}{20} = \frac{x}{100}$$

$$\frac{11}{20} \cdot 100 = \frac{x}{100} \cdot 100$$

$$55 = x$$

You predict that you will get 55 even numbers in 100 rolls.

4 Look Back

To test the accuracy of your prediction, perform another experiment and compare the results.

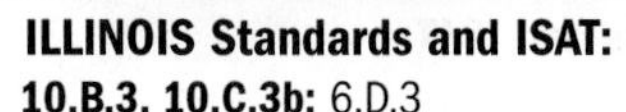

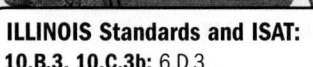

ILLINOIS Standards and ISAT:
10.B.3, 10.C.3b; 6.D.3

 APPLY

 TRANSPARENCY

Even-numbered answers are available on transparencies.

Practice the Strategy

Use the strategy *perform an experiment.*

1. **Marbles** You conduct an experiment by randomly drawing 10 marbles from a bag of 100 red and blue marbles, and recording how many of each color were drawn. The results of 5 of these experiments are shown below. Estimate how many marbles of each color are in the bag. Explain. See margin.

	1	2	3	4	5
Red	6	7	5	7	6
Blue	4	3	5	3	4

2. **Spinner** You are playing a board game that uses a spinner like the one below to determine how many spaces to move. The spinner seems to give the result "5" more often than it should. Describe an experiment you could use to test this assumption. What results would support the assumption? ***Sample answer:*** **Spin the spinner 60 times and record the results. If you spin a "5" considerably more than one sixth of the time, which is 10 times, your assumption is supported.**

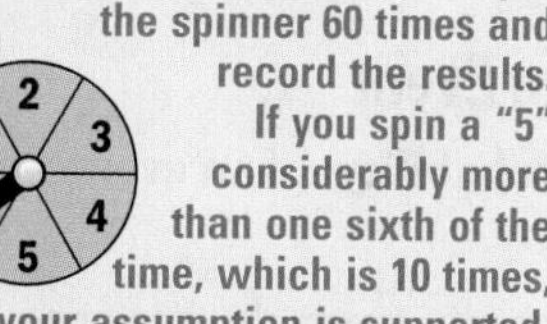

3. **Names** Write each of the letters of your name on a slip of paper. Place all the slips into a bag and then randomly draw one slip. Record what letter it is, replace it, and repeat the process. Design an experiment to help you predict the number of times you would draw a consonant in 60 draws. Describe your experiment. See margin.

4. **Socks** A drawer has exactly 20 white socks and 20 black socks. You randomly draw two socks 100 times and replace them after each draw. Describe an experiment you could use to predict how many times out of 100 you would draw matching socks. See margin.

Mixed Problem Solving

Use any strategy to solve the problem.

5. **Shopping** You pick out a sweater and a pair of pants. When you get to the cashier, you find that all sweaters are on sale for 40% off the original price and your bill is \$40.40. So, you decide to add two more sweaters to your purchase, bringing the bill to \$81.20. How much does one pair of pants cost? What is the original price of one sweater? **\$20; \$34**

6. **Groups** A class is divided into groups of four. Betty, Jamal, Fiona, and Juan are in one group. Each person's name is written on a separate slip of paper. The teacher draws a name each week (and then replaces it for the next week) to find the leader of the group for that week. How often do you predict Fiona's name will be picked in 36 weeks? **9 times**

7. **Triangles** How many triangles are shown in the figure? Be sure to count triangles of different sizes. **27 triangles**

MATH REASONING

After Exercise 1, ask students if it would be possible to draw out 10 marbles that are all blue. Lead a discussion about the difference between what is possible and what is likely.

TEACHING TIP

In Exercise 3, students may need a reminder about which letters are consonants.

SUGGESTED STRATEGIES

You may wish to suggest the following strategies for the problems in the Mixed Problem Solving:

- Exercise 5: Work Backward
- Exercise 6: Act It Out
- Exercise 7: Make a List; Draw a Diagram

1. **62 red, 38 blue. *Sample answer:* In the 5 trials, 31 red marbles were chosen and 19 blue marbles were chosen. So $\frac{31}{50} = \frac{x}{100}$, or $x = 62$, and $\frac{19}{50} = \frac{y}{100}$, or $y = 38$.**
3. ***Sample answer:*** **Draw and then replace a letter 20 times and record the results. Write a proportion comparing the ratio of the number of consonants drawn in the experiment to the ratio that would be drawn in 60 trials. Solve the proportion to find the predicted number of consonants drawn.**
4. **See Additional Answers beginning on page AA1.**

SKILL CHECK

Simplify.

1. $\frac{25}{50}$ $\frac{1}{2}$
2. $\frac{18}{141}$ $\frac{6}{47}$
3. $\frac{10}{18}$ $\frac{5}{9}$
4. $\frac{16}{72}$ $\frac{2}{9}$

LESSON OBJECTIVE

Find probabilities of events.

PACING

Suggested Number of Days
Basic Course: 1 day
Average Course: 1 day
Advanced Course: 1 day
Block: 0.5 block with 7.7

TEACHING RESOURCES

For a complete list of Teaching Resources, see page 314B.

TRANSPARENCY

Warm-Up Exercises for this lesson are available on a transparency.

MOTIVATING THE LESSON

Ask students whether it is more likely that a coin flipped four times will land H, T, H, T or T, T, T, T. They may be surprised that though it is more likely for the coin to land on heads twice than tails four times, each sequence is equally likely.

ACTIVITY

Goal Toss a coin to perform a simple probability experiment.

Key Discovery By repeating an experiment many times, you can predict the probability of a particular result.

Simple Probability

BEFORE	Now	WHY?
You found ratios.	You'll find probabilities of events.	So you can find the probability of a batter getting a hit, as in Ex. 24.

Word Watch

outcome, event, p. 354
favorable outcome, p. 354
probability of an event, p. 354
theoretical probability, p. 354
experimental probability, p. 355

Activity You can toss a coin to perform a probability experiment.

1. Copy and complete the table at the right by tossing a coin 20 times.
   Sample answer: 8, 12

Number of heads	?
Number of tails	?

2. Use the data to write each ratio below. Then compare the ratios.

   a. $\frac{\text{Number of heads}}{\text{Total number of coin tosses}}$ $\frac{8}{20}$ or $\frac{2}{5}$

   b. $\frac{\text{Number of tails}}{\text{Total number of coin tosses}}$ $\frac{12}{20}$ or $\frac{3}{5}$

3. **Comparing Results** Combine your results with those of the other students in your class. Compare the class ratios with your own ratios. The ratios should all be about $\frac{1}{2}$.

In the activity, you performed an experiment. The possible results of an experiment are **outcomes**. An **event** is a collection of outcomes. Once you specify an event, the outcomes for that event are called **favorable outcomes**. The **probability of an event** is the likelihood that the event will occur.

Probability of an Event

The **theoretical probability** of an event when all outcomes are equally likely is:

$$P(\text{event}) = \frac{\text{Number of favorable outcomes}}{\text{Number of possible outcomes}}$$

EXAMPLE 1 **Using Theoretical Probability**

Use theoretical probability to predict the number of times a coin will land heads up in 50 coin tosses. There are two equally likely outcomes when you toss the coin, heads or tails.

$$P(\text{heads}) = \frac{\text{Number of favorable outcomes}}{\text{Number of possible outcomes}} = \frac{1}{2}$$

ANSWER You can predict that $\frac{1}{2}$, or 25, of the tosses will land heads up.

ILLINOIS Standards and ISAT:
10.C.3a, 10.C.3b; 10.B.3

An **experimental probability** is based on the results of a sample or experiment. Experimental probability is the ratio of number of favorable outcomes to total number of times the experiment was performed.

HELP with Solving

A probability can be expressed as a fraction, as a decimal, or as a percent.

EXAMPLE 2 Finding Experimental Probability

You roll a number cube 100 times. Your results are shown. Find the experimental probability of rolling a 6.

Number	Rolls	Number	Rolls
1	17	4	16
2	15	5	14
3	20	6	18

Solution

$P(\text{rolling a 6}) = \frac{18}{100}$ ← Number of favorable outcomes / ← Total number of rolls

$= 0.18 = 18\%$

ANSWER The experimental probability of rolling a 6 is 18%.

EXAMPLE 3 Using Experimental Probability

You randomly draw a button from a bag of red, blue, green, and yellow buttons 18 times. Each time you record its color and place it back in the bag. There are 80 buttons in the bag. Predict how many are red.

Color	Tally
Red	
Blue	III
Green	III
Yellow	II

Solution

(1) Find the experimental probability of drawing a red button.

$P(\text{red}) = \frac{10}{18}$ ← Number of favorable outcomes / ← Total number of draws

$= \frac{5}{9}$ Simplify.

(2) Multiply the probability by the total number of buttons and round to the nearest whole number.

$\frac{5}{9} \times 80 \approx 44$

ANSWER You can predict that there are 44 red buttons in the bag.

Your turn now **Use the information in Example 3.**

1. There are 18 green buttons in the bag. What is the theoretical probability of drawing a green button at random? What is the experimental probability? $\frac{9}{40}, \frac{1}{6}$

TIPS FOR NEW TEACHERS

This lesson has many new vocabulary terms. Pay special attention to the difference between an outcome and an event, which can confuse students. See Tips for New Teachers in the *Chapter 7 Resource Book*.

EXTRA EXAMPLES

Example 1 Use theoretical probability to predict the number of times a fair four-sided pyramid with the numbers 1, 2, 3, and 4 on its faces will land on "4" in 80 tosses. **20 times**

Example 2 In 40 spins of a spinner with two sections labeled "Yes" and "No," the spinner lands on "No" 18 times. Find the experimental probability that the spinner lands on "Yes." **55%**

Example 3 You randomly draw a marble from a bag of yellow, black, and clear marbles 10 times. Each time you record its color and place it back in the bag. There are 50 marbles in the bag. Predict how many marbles are black. **20 marbles**

Color	Tally
Yellow	IIII
Black	IIII
Clear	II

CONCEPT CHECK

How can you find the theoretical probability of an event? **Divide the number of favorable outcomes by the number of possible outcomes.**

DAILY PUZZLER

When you roll two dice, what sum are you most likely to roll? **7**

3 APPLY

ASSIGNMENT GUIDE

Basic Course

Day 1: EP p. 730 Exs. 17–20; pp. 356–357 Exs. 4–12, 15–22, 27–34

Average Course

Day 1: pp. 356–357 Exs. 6–16, 19–25, 27–34

Advanced Course

Day 1: pp. 356–357 Exs. 6–14, 17–28*, 31–34

Block

pp. 356–357 Exs. 6–16, 19–25, 27–34 (with 7.7)

EXTRA PRACTICE

- Student Edition, p. 733
- Chapter 7 Resource Book, pp. 70–72
- Test and Practice Generator

TRANSPARENCY

Even-numbered answers are available on transparencies.

HOMEWORK CHECK

When you review students' homework for this lesson, go over the following exercises to check understanding of key concepts.

Basic: 4, 10, 12, 15, 20

Average: 6, 10, 13, 16, 21

Advanced: 6, 10, 17, 18, 22

7.8 Exercises

More Practice, p. 733

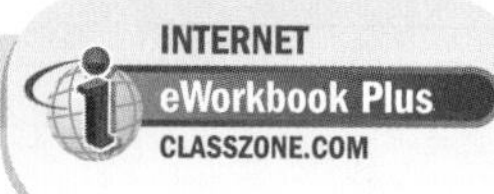

Getting Ready to Practice

1. **Vocabulary** Copy and complete: The favorable outcomes for rolling an even number on a number cube are _?_, _?_, and _?_. 2, 4, 6

2. **Socks** You have 4 white socks, 2 black socks, and 2 brown socks. What is the probability that you will choose a black sock at random from these socks? $\frac{1}{4}$

3. **Find the Error** A student spins a two-color spinner 20 times. The pointer lands on red 7 times and on blue 13 times. Describe and correct the error in the solution.

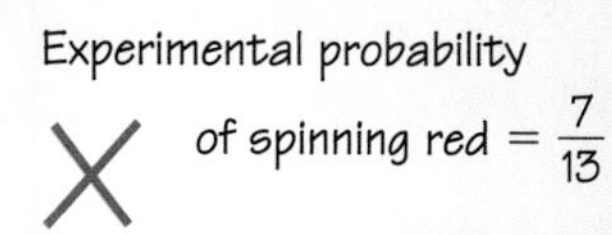

3. The experimental probability is the ratio of favorable outcomes to total outcomes, not to unfavorable outcomes as shown. The number of total outcomes is 20, so the experimental probability of spinning red is $\frac{7}{20}$.

Practice and Problem Solving

HELP with Homework

Example	Exercises
1	4–9, 20–22
2	10–14
3	15–18

Online Resources
CLASSZONE.COM
· More Examples
· eTutorial Plus

A **You randomly draw a tile from a bag that contains 10 A-tiles, 7 E-tiles, 6 I-tiles, 5 O-tiles, and 2 U-tiles. Find the probability of the event.**

4. You draw an A. $\frac{1}{3}$

5. You draw an I. $\frac{1}{5}$

6. You draw an I or an O. $\frac{11}{30}$

7. You draw an E or a U. $\frac{3}{10}$

8. You draw a Z. 0

9. You draw a vowel. 1

You roll a number cube 250 times. Your results are shown in the table. Find the experimental probability of the event.

Number	Outcomes	Number	Outcomes
1	40	4	50
2	42	5	35
3	48	6	35

10. You roll a 4. 20%

11. You roll a 2. 16.8%

12. You roll a number greater than 3. 48%

13. You roll an odd number. 49.2%

14. You roll a number divisible by 1. 1

You randomly draw a marble from a bag of 120 marbles. You record its color and replace it. Use the results to estimate the number of marbles in the bag that are the given color.

Red	Yellow	Green
7	3	5

15. Yellow 24

16. Green 40

17. Red 56

18. Blue 0

19. **Toes** In a survey of 896 people, 409 responded that their second toes are longer than their big toes. What is the probability that a randomly chosen person from the survey has a longer second toe? **about 46%**

B **Find the probability of the event.**

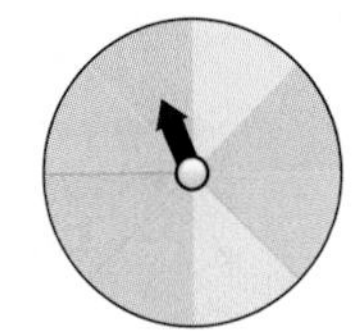

20. *Not* rolling a 2 on a number cube $\frac{5}{6}$

21. *Not* spinning blue on the spinner $\frac{3}{4}$

22. *Not* spinning blue, red, or yellow on the spinner $\frac{1}{8}$

23. **Writing** Describe the difference between experimental and theoretical probability. **See margin.**

24. **Softball** Sharon and Erica are both softball players. Out of 20 times at bat, Sharon got 7 hits. Out of 35 times at bat, Erica got 10 hits. Who do you think is more likely to get a hit her next time at bat? Explain. **See margin.**

C 25. **Number Cube** Rachel rolled a number cube 24 times and got a 6 once. She thinks that her chances of getting a 6 on her next roll are high. Explain why her chances are no different than on any other roll. **See margin.**

26. **Challenge** You have 15 coins in your pocket: 4 quarters, 3 pennies, 5 dimes, and 3 nickels. Why wouldn't theoretical probability be a good way to predict which coin you pull out of your pocket?
Sample answer: **The coins are different sizes, so it is easy to tell which coin you are choosing by its feel. Also, even if you try to choose the first coin you touch, it is more likely to be a larger coin.**

Mixed Review

27. Find the percent of increase from 140 to 154. *(Lesson 7.5)* **10%**

28. You deposit \$750 in an account with a simple annual interest rate of 2.75%. Find the interest you will earn after 30 months. Round to the nearest cent. *(Lesson 7.7)* **\$51.56**

Basic Skills **Find the sum.**

29. $-47 + 19$ **-28** 30. $20 + (-18)$ **2** 31. $-7 + (-25)$ **-32** 32. $-32 + (-56)$ **-88**

Test-Taking Practice

33. **Multiple Choice** What is the probability of getting a number divisible by 3 when rolling a number cube? **B**

A. $\frac{3}{10}$ **B.** $\frac{1}{3}$ **C.** $\frac{1}{2}$ **D.** $\frac{2}{3}$

34. **Multiple Choice** In a group of 40 people, 24 prefer dogs to cats. One person is selected at random from the larger group. What is the probability that the person will prefer dogs to cats? **I**

F. 0.16 **G.** 0.24 **H.** 0.4 **I.** 0.6

23. ***Sample answer:*** Theoretical probability is a ratio of the number of favorable outcomes to the number of possible outcomes for outcomes that are equally likely to occur. Experimental probability is a ratio of the number of favorable outcomes to the total number of outcomes, based on the results of actually performing an experiment.

24. Sharon. ***Sample answer:*** Sharon got a hit 35% of her times at bat, while Erica got a hit only about 29% of her times at bat.

INTERNET

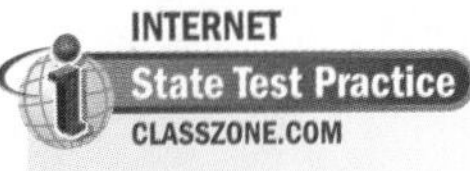

25. ***Sample answer:*** Each time she rolls the number cube has no effect on any other time she rolls the number cube.

4 ASSESS

Assessment Resources

For more assessment resources, see:
- Assessment Book
- Test and Practice Generator

Mini-Quiz

You roll a number cube that has the numbers 2, 3, 5, 7, 11, and 13 on its faces. Find the theoretical probability of each event.

1. You roll a 5. **$16.\overline{6}\%$**
2. You roll an even number. **$16.\overline{6}\%$**

You randomly draw a marble from a bag of yellow, blue, and green marbles 20 times. You record its color and replace it. You record yellow 8 times, blue 5 times, and green 7 times. Use the results to estimate the probability that the next marble will be the color given.

3. yellow **40%** 4. blue **25%**

5 FOLLOW-UP

Reteaching/Remediation

- Study Guide in Chapter 7 Resource Book, pp. 73–74
- Tutor Place, Fractions Card 19, Ratio, Proportion, and Percent Card 16
- eTutorial Plus Online
- Extra Practice, p. 733
- Lesson Practice in Chapter 7 Resource Book, pp. 70–72

Challenge/Enrichment

- Challenge Practice in Chapter 7 Resource Book, p. 75
- Teacher's Edition, p. 314F

English Learner Support

- Spanish Study Guide
- Multi-Language Glossary
- Chapter Audio Summaries CDs

ADDITIONAL RESOURCES

The following resources are available to help review the materials in Lessons 7.5–7.8.

Chapter 7 Resource Book
- Lesson Practice
- Study Guide

Assessment Book
- Chapter 7 Quiz 2

Technology
- Test and Practice Generator
- eTutorial CD-ROM

Internet
- Classzone
- eWorkbook Plus Online
- eTutorial Plus Online

ENGLISH LEARNER SUPPORT

- Spanish Study Guide
- Multi-Language Glossary
- Chapter Audio Summaries CDs

Notebook Review

Review the vocabulary definitions in your notebook.

Copy the review examples in your notebook. Then complete the exercises.

Check Your Definitions

percent of change, p. 338
percent of increase, p. 338
percent of decrease, p. 338
markup, discount, p. 342
interest, annual interest rate, p. 348
principal, p. 348
outcome, favorable outcome, p. 354
event, probability of an event, p. 354
theoretical probability, p. 354
experimental probability, p. 355

Use Your Vocabulary

1. Describe how to find theoretical probability. **Find the ratio of the number of favorable outcomes to the number of possible outcomes.**

7.5–7.6 Can you find a sale price?

EXAMPLE A pair of shoes has an original price of \$40. What is the sale price after a 15% discount?

$40 \times 0.15 = 6$ **Multiply to find discount.**

$40 - 6 = 34$ **Subtract discount from original price.**

ANSWER The sale price of the shoes is \$34.

☑ **Find the sale price or retail price.**

2. Wholesale price: \$30
Percent markup: 70% **\$51**

3. Original price: \$72
Percent discount: 18% **\$59.04**

7.7 Can you use the percent equation?

EXAMPLE What number is 26% of 300?

$a = p\% \cdot b$ **Write percent equation.**

$a = 26\% \cdot 300$ **Substitute 26 for *p* and 300 for *b*.**

$a = 78$ **Multiply.**

4. 72 is 75% of what number? **96** **5.** What number is 34% of 856? **291.04**

7.8 Can you find the probability of an event?

EXAMPLE Two scientists spin a Belgian euro coin 250 times and it lands heads up 140 times. Find the experimental probability of the coin landing heads up.

Use the results to find the experimental probability.

$P(\text{heads}) = \frac{140}{250}$ ← Number of favorable outcomes / ← Total number of spins

$= \frac{14}{25} = 0.56 = 56\%$

6. You randomly draw a marble out of a bag that contains 8 red, 5 yellow, and 4 blue marbles. Find the probability of drawing each color. red: $\frac{8}{17}$; yellow: $\frac{5}{17}$; blue: $\frac{4}{17}$

Stop *and* Think about Lessons 7.5–7.8

7. Critical Thinking You invest $300 at a simple annual interest rate of 3.5% for one year. How much would you need to invest at a 2% simple annual interest rate to earn the same amount of interest that year? $525

Review Quiz 2

Tell whether the change is an *increase* or *decrease*. Then find the percent of change.

1. Original amount: $120
New amount: $138
increase; 15%

2. Original amount: 260 miles
New amount: 169 miles
decrease; 35%

3. Retail A shirt has a $20 wholesale price and is marked up 50%. The sales tax is 5%. What is the total cost of the shirt? $31.50

Solve using the percent equation.

4. 75 is 125% of what number? 60

5. 552.5 is what percent of 85,000? 0.65%

6. Koalas Koalas absorb only about 25% of the fiber they eat. How much fiber is absorbed by a koala that eats 10.5 ounces of fiber per day? 2.625 oz

You spin the spinner below 40 times. Predict how many times the spinner lands on the specified color.

7. Red 15

8. Blue 20

9. Yellow 5

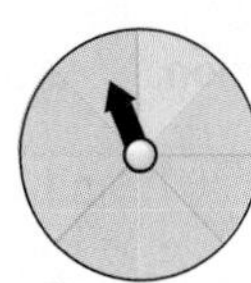

ADDITIONAL RESOURCES

The following resources are available to help review the materials in this chapter.

Chapter 7 Resource Book
- Chapter Review Games and Activities, p. 76
- Cumulative Practice, Chs. 1–7

English/Spanish Chapter Reviews and Tests

Chapter Audio Summaries CDs

eTutorial CD-ROM

eWorkbook Plus Online

eTutorial Plus Online

Chapter Review

Vocabulary

ratio, equivalent ratios, p. 317
rate, unit rate, p. 318
proportion, p. 322
cross products, p. 323
scale model, scale, p. 324
percent, p. 327
circle graph, p. 331
percent of change, p. 338
percent of increase, p. 338
percent of decrease, p. 338
markup, discount, p. 342
interest, p. 348
principal, p. 348
annual interest rate, p. 348
outcome, p. 354
event, p. 354
favorable outcome, p. 354
probability of an event, p. 354
theoretical probability, p. 354
experimental probability, p. 355

Vocabulary Review

Copy and complete the statement.

1. If you write $\frac{180 \text{ miles}}{3 \text{ hours}}$ as $\frac{60 \text{ miles}}{1 \text{ hour}}$, you have written the rate as a(n) _?_. **unit rate**
2. A(n) _?_ is a ratio whose denominator is 100. **percent**
3. The theoretical probability of an event is the ratio of the number of _?_ to the number of _?_. **favorable outcomes; possible outcomes**

Match the word with the correct definition.

4. annual interest rate **C**
5. interest **B**
6. principal **A**

A. the amount of money that you borrow or deposit

B. the amount paid for the use of money

C. the percent of the principal that you pay or earn each year

Review Questions

Write the equivalent rate. *(Lesson 7.1)*

7. $\frac{286.8 \text{ m}}{\text{min}} = \frac{? \text{ m}}{\text{sec}}$ **4.78**
8. $\frac{4.2 \text{ in.}}{\text{month}} = \frac{? \text{ in.}}{\text{year}}$ **50.4**
9. $\frac{6 \text{ times}}{\text{min}} = \frac{? \text{ times}}{\text{hour}}$ **360**

Solve the proportion. *(Lesson 7.2)*

10. $\frac{5}{13} = \frac{18}{c}$ **46.8**
11. $\frac{48}{36} = \frac{x}{6}$ **8**
12. $\frac{n}{12} = \frac{7}{8}$ **10.5**
13. $\frac{25}{b} = \frac{55}{22}$ **10**

Review Questions

Use a percent proportion. *(Lesson 7.3)*

14. What number is 500% of 16? 80

15. 200.2 is 65% of what number? 308

16. 44 is what percent of 80? 55%

17. 1.7 is what percent of 340? 0.5%

Write the decimal or fraction as a percent. *(Lesson 7.4)*

18. 0.43 43%

19. 0.003 0.3%

20. $\frac{3}{10}$ 30%

21. $\frac{29}{20}$ 145%

Final Project In Exercises 22–24, use the circle graph. It shows the results of a survey of 300 students who were asked what they would choose for a final project. *(Lesson 7.4)*

22. What percent of students chose an oral report? 12%

23. What fraction of students chose a visual project? Write the fraction in simplest form. $\frac{7}{20}$

24. Which final project was chosen by 21% of the students? taking a test

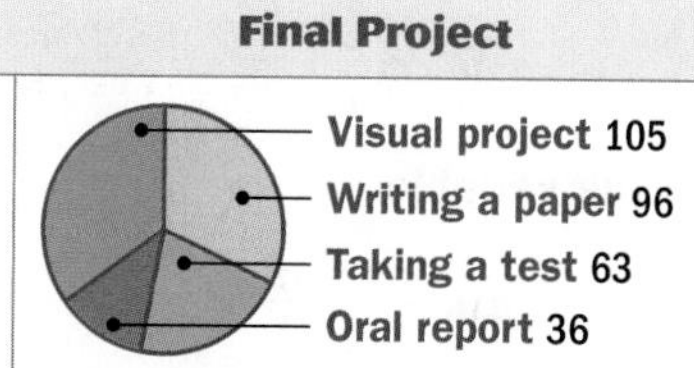

25. Moving A moving van's load changes from 800 to 984 pounds after picking up an appliance. Find the percent of increase. *(Lesson 7.5)* 23%

Find the sale price or retail price. *(Lesson 7.6)*

26. Wholesale price: $22.40 $35.84
Percent markup: 60%

27. Original price: $21.25 $14.45
Percent discount: 32%

Find the amount of simple interest earned in 3 years. *(Lesson 7.7)*

28. Principal: $460 $48.30
Annual rate: 3.5%

29. Principal: $1540 $127.05
Annual rate: 2.75%

30. Fundraiser At a school fundraiser, the science club made 58% of their money selling juice, 27% selling cookies, and 15% selling apples. The club made $87 selling juice. How much did the club make selling cookies? How much did they make selling apples? *(Lesson 7.7)* $40.50; $22.50

Find the probability of the event. *(Lesson 7.8)*

31. A random 5-digit ZIP code ends with a number less than 5. $\frac{1}{2}$

32. You roll a number cube and get a 7. 0

33. A number less than 4 is randomly drawn from the numbers 1, 2, 3, and 4. $\frac{3}{4}$

361

Additional Resources

Assessment Book

- Chapter Test (3 levels), pp. 81–86
- Standardized Chapter Test, p. 87
- Alternative Assessment, pp. 88–89

Test and Practice Generator

Chapter 7 Chapter Test

Write the ratio of shaded to unshaded squares.

1. 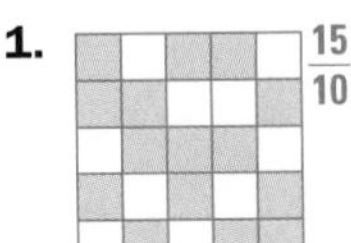 $\frac{15}{10}$, or $\frac{3}{2}$

2. 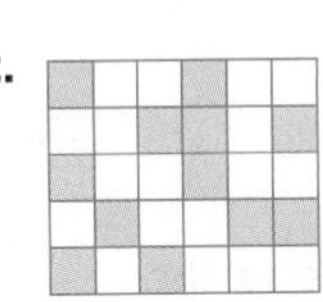 $\frac{12}{18}$, or $\frac{2}{3}$

3.  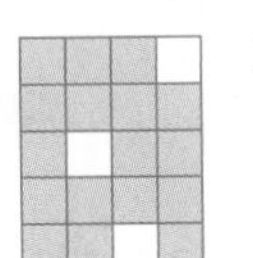 $\frac{17}{3}$

4. 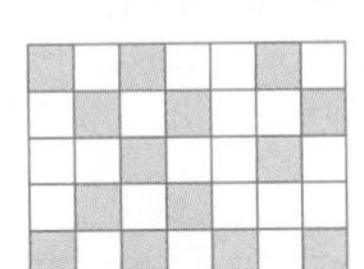 $\frac{14}{21}$, or $\frac{2}{3}$

Write the rate as a unit rate.

5. $\frac{156 \text{ miles}}{3 \text{ hours}}$ $\frac{52 \text{ mi}}{1 \text{ h}}$

6. $\frac{18 \text{ servings}}{6 \text{ people}}$ $\frac{3 \text{ servings}}{1 \text{ person}}$

7. $\frac{448 \text{ cycles}}{5 \text{ days}}$ $\frac{89.6 \text{ cycles}}{1 \text{ day}}$

8. $\frac{54 \text{ meters}}{21 \text{ seconds}}$ $\frac{2\frac{4}{7} \text{ m}}{1 \text{ sec}}$

Find the value of the variable

9. $\frac{12}{16} = \frac{18}{a}$ 24

10. $\frac{15}{6} = \frac{d}{4}$ 10

11. $\frac{9}{n} = \frac{21}{14}$ 6

12. $\frac{t-3}{12} = \frac{11}{6}$ 25

13. **Maps** The road distance from Miami, Florida, to Columbia, South Carolina, on a map is about 6.7 centimeters. The scale is 1 cm : 150 km. What is the actual distance from Miami to Columbia? 1005 km

14. **Survey** In a survey, 34%, or 102 people, said they enjoy in-line skating. How many people were surveyed? 300 people

Write the percent as a decimal and as a fraction.

15. 0.7% 0.007, $\frac{7}{1000}$

16. 419% 4.19, $4\frac{19}{100}$

17. 8% 0.08, $\frac{2}{25}$

18. 7.8% 0.078, $\frac{39}{500}$

Find the percent of increase or decrease.

19. Original amount: 40
New amount: 36 10% decrease

20. Original amount: 225
New amount: 324 44% increase

21. Original amount: 258
New amount: 6.45
97.5% decrease

22. **Food** Your food bill at a restaurant totals \$26. There is a 6.5% sales tax and you leave a 16% tip. What is the total cost of the meal? \$31.85

23. **Recycling** The average person in the United States generates about 4.5 pounds of waste per day. About 30% of this waste is recycled. About how many pounds of waste are recycled per person per day? 1.35 lb

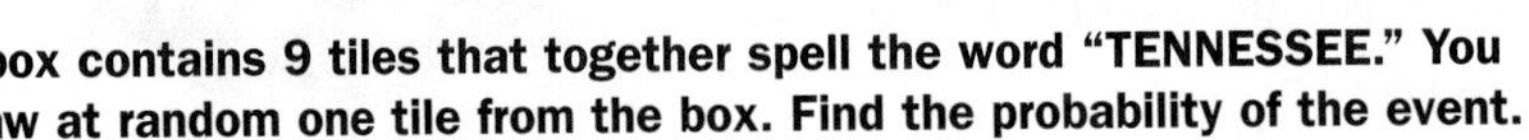

A box contains 9 tiles that together spell the word "TENNESSEE." You draw at random one tile from the box. Find the probability of the event.

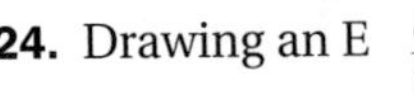

24. Drawing an E $\frac{4}{9}$

25. Drawing an S $\frac{2}{9}$

Chapter Standardized Test

Test-Taking Strategy **Avoid spending too much time on one question. Skip questions you have trouble with, and return to them after you have finished.**

Multiple Choice

1. Which ratio is *not* equivalent to $\frac{3}{7}$? D

A. $\frac{9}{21}$ **B.** $\frac{1.5}{3.5}$ **C.** $\frac{300}{700}$ **D.** $\frac{18}{39}$

2. Susan types at a speed of 54 words per minute. What is her typing speed in words per second? I

F. 5400 words per second

G. 3240 words per second

H. $1.\overline{1}$ words per second

I. 0.9 word per second

3. Which choice shows $\frac{10 \text{ feet}}{4 \text{ seconds}}$ correctly written as a unit rate? C

A. $\frac{5 \text{ ft}}{2 \text{ sec}}$ **B.** $\frac{5 \text{ ft}}{\text{sec}}$ **C.** $\frac{2.5 \text{ ft}}{\text{sec}}$ **D.** $\frac{2 \text{ ft}}{5 \text{ sec}}$

4. A scale model of a school building is 11 inches long and 3 inches high. The actual building is 231 feet long. How tall is the actual building? H

F. 21 ft **G.** 33 ft

H. 63 ft **I.** 99 ft

5. Which choice is equal to 0.48? C

A. 4.8% **B.** $\frac{2}{5}$

C. $\frac{12}{25}$ **D.** 480%

6. A crowd of 280 people grows to a crowd of 315 people. What is the percent of increase? G

F. $11.\overline{1}\%$ **G.** 12.5% **H.** 35% **I.** $88.\overline{8}\%$

7. An item with a wholesale price of $8.40 is marked up 60%. What is the retail price? C

A. $3.36 **B.** $5.04 **C.** $13.44 **D.** $14.40

8. You and your friend are leaving a tip after eating dinner. The cost of the dinner is $15.35. You want to leave *about* an 18% tip. How much should you leave as a tip? G

F. $1.25 **G.** $2.75 **H.** $8.50 **I.** $18.00

9. You randomly draw a marble from a bag of 3 red, 8 yellow, and 13 blue marbles. What is the probability that the marble is yellow? C

A. $\frac{13}{24}$ **B.** $\frac{1}{2}$ **C.** $\frac{1}{3}$ **D.** $\frac{1}{8}$

Short Response

10. You deposit $1350 into a savings account that pays a simple annual interest rate of 2.8%. How much interest will you earn in 15 months? Compare this to the interest you would earn for the same amount of time in an account with a simple annual interest rate of 4%. See margin.

Extended Response

11. You draw a marble at random from a bag of red, blue, green, and yellow marbles 24 times. Each time you record its color and place it back in the bag of 75 marbles. The results are shown in the table below. How many of each color marble do you predict are in the bag? Explain. See margin.

Red	Blue	Green	Yellow
7	3	5	9

ADDITIONAL RESOURCES

Assessment Book
- Standardized Chapter Test, p. 87

Test and Practice Generator

10. $47.25; you would earn $67.50 with a simple interest rate of 4%, which is more than for the other account.

11. Red: 22, blue: 9, green: 16, yellow: 28. *Sample answer:* For red, $\frac{7}{24} = \frac{x}{75}$, so $x = 21.875 \approx 22$. For blue, $\frac{3}{24} = \frac{y}{75}$, so $y = 9.375 \approx 9$. For green, $\frac{5}{24} = \frac{z}{75}$, so $z = 15.625 \approx 16$. For yellow, $\frac{9}{24} = \frac{w}{75}$, so $w = 28.125 \approx 28$.

Using Rubrics

The rubric given on the pupil page is a sample of a three-level rubric. Other rubrics may contain four, five, or six levels. For more information on rubrics, see the Professional Development Book.

Test-Taking Tip

Caution students, especially advanced students, to show all of the steps they perform when solving a short response question. Some students may do part of their calculations mentally and then neglect to write down enough information to receive full credit. Encourage students to "think like a reviewer" who is scoring their work, asking themselves if they have shown all of the important information.

 Common Error

Students can become so focused on doing all of the necessary computations and getting a solution for a short response question that they fail to answer the question posed. Remind students to quickly read the problem again after completing their computations. Stress that the result of their calculations is not always the answer to the question.

Visualize

While discussing the Problem on this page, suggest that students draw a graph showing the daily pay for both plans. The graph should show the days along the horizontal axis and the daily pay along the vertical axis. Have students use two different colors for plotting the points. The two series of dots on the graph can then be used to verify the given full credit solution.

UNIT 2 Chapters 4–7

BUILDING Test-Taking Skills

Scoring Rubric

Full credit
- answer is correct, *and*
- work and reasoning are included

Partial credit
- answer is correct, but reasoning is incorrect, *or*
- answer is incorrect, but reasoning is correct

No credit
- no answer is given *or*
- answer makes no sense

Strategies for Answering Short Response Questions

Problem

You work for your uncle this summer. He pays you $20 on your first day. Each day after that, you will get a raise. You can choose from 2 payment plans. With Plan A, you earn a $5 raise each day. With Plan B, you earn a 20% raise each day. Which plan is a better deal?

Full credit solution

Plan B is a better deal if you work more than 5 days.

Data is used to justify the solution.

Day	1	2	3	4	5	6
Plan A pay	20.00	25.00	30.00	35.00	40.00	45.00
Plan A total	20.00	45.00	75.00	110.00	150.00	195.00
Plan B pay	20.00	24.00	28.80	34.56	41.47	49.76
Plan B total	20.00	44.00	72.80	107.36	148.83	198.59

The question is answered clearly and in complete sentences.

Plan A is better if you work 5 days or less, but Plan B is better if you work more than 5 days. By day 6, the pay with a 20% increase is more than the pay with a $5 raise, so it will continue to be the better plan.

Partial credit solution

I think Plan B is better than Plan A.

The calculations are correct.

Day	1	2	3	4	5	6
Plan A	20.00	25.00	30.00	35.00	40.00	45.00
Plan B	20.00	24.00	28.80	34.56	41.47	49.76

The reasoning is faulty, because the total amount earned was not considered.

The first 4 days, Plan A is better. The next 2 days, Plan B is better. By day 5 Plan B pays you more money, so it is the better plan.

Partial credit solution

The data does not include information past Day 4. So, the answer is incorrect.

Plan A is better. The table shows that over the first four days, Plan A pays out $2.64 more than Plan B.

Day	1	2	3	4
Plan A	20.00	25.00	30.00	35.00
Plan B	20.00	24.00	28.80	34.56
Difference	0	1.00	1.20	0.44

The data is calculated correctly.

No credit solution

The answer is incorrect.

Plan A is better.

Day	1	2	3	4
Plan A	20.00	25.00	30.00	35.00
Plan B	20.00	24.00	26.00	28.00

The data is not calculated correctly.

Your turn now

Watch Out! Be sure to explain your reasoning clearly.

Score each solution to the short response question below as *full credit*, *partial credit*, or *no credit*. Explain your reasoning.

Problem The Spiff travels 226.8 miles on 14 gallons of gas. The Flyte travels 280 miles on 17.5 gallons of gas. Which car is more fuel efficient?

1. The Spiff is the more fuel efficient car because it gets 16.2 miles per gallon. The Flyte gets 16 miles per gallon.

2. The Flyte gets 16 miles per gallon, because $280 \div 17.5 = 16$. The Spiff gets 16.2 miles per gallon, because $226.8 \div 14 = 16.2$. The more fuel efficient car gets a greater number of miles per gallon. Because 16.2 is greater than 16, the Spiff is more fuel efficient.

1. **Partial credit; the answer is correct but no reasoning is included.**
2. **Full credit; the answer is correct and the work and reasoning are included.**

GO ON

3. The \$38.25 watch on sale for 20% off; the sale price of the \$35.95 watch is $35.95 - 0.10(35.95) \approx \$32.36$. The sale price of the \$38.25 watch is $38.25 - 0.20(38.25) = \$30.60$. With 8% sales tax, the first watch costs $32.36 + 32.36(0.08) \approx \$34.95$ and the second watch costs $30.60 + 30.60(0.08) \approx \$33.05$, which is less than the first watch.

5. $\frac{5}{7}$; there are $5 + 3 + 2 = 10$ marbles that are not green and 14 marbles in all. So the probability that a marble is not green is $\frac{10}{14}$, or $\frac{5}{7}$.

9. \$2.00; she will pay to park for 3 hours and 45 minutes, which will take 8 quarters, or \$2.00. The last 2 hours she parks will be free.

UNIT 2 Chapters 4–7 PRACTICING Test-Taking Skills

Short Response

1. Joanne is using a map to plan her trip. Measure the distance, in inches, between the two cities on the map. Then use the scale on the map to estimate the actual distance in miles. $1\frac{1}{8}$ in.; 22.5 miles

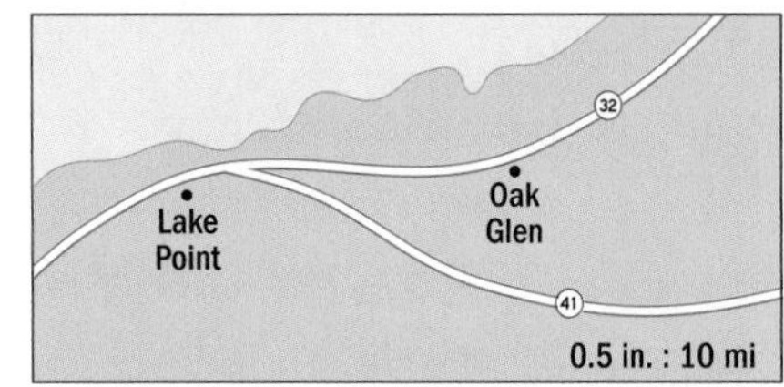

2. John has a pile of quarters. Justin has five more than twice as many quarters as John. Jason has three times as many quarters as John. Justin and Jason have the same number of quarters. How much money does John have? Write your answer in dollars and cents. \$1.25

3. Amber is shopping for a new watch. The first watch she finds is on sale for 10% off the original price of \$35.95. The second watch she finds is on sale for 20% off the original price of \$38.25. There is an 8% sales tax on both watches. Which watch costs less? Explain your answer. See margin.

4. Michelle needs at least \$75 for a school trip. She has \$22 already. Michelle makes \$5 per hour babysitting. How many hours does she need to babysit in order to have enough money for her trip? Write and solve an inequality to answer the question.
   10.6 h; $75 \le 22 + 5h$, $53 \le 5h$, $10.6 \le h$

5. A bowl contains 5 yellow marbles, 4 green marbles, 3 blue marbles, and 2 red marbles. Kim picks one marble at random. What is the probability that Kim's marble is *not* green? Explain your answer. See margin.

6. Vincent's math teacher gives a test every 14 school days, and his English teacher gives a test every 8 school days. Vincent had a math test and an English test today. When will Vincent have an English test and a math test on the same day again? Give the smallest number of school days possible.
   in 56 school days

7. Ryan, Nelson, and Mia worked together on a project. Ryan completed 35% of the project, and Nelson completed $\frac{2}{5}$ of the project. How much of the project did Mia complete? Give your answer as a fraction and as a percent. $\frac{1}{4}$ or 25% of the project.

8. A baseball coach counts the number of home runs that each player hits in a season. The table shows the current totals.

Player	Number of Home Runs
Carmine	5
Larry	2
Ray	4
Anthony	6
Michael	0
David	6
Paul	5
Mickey	4
Frank	3

What is the mean number of home runs hit by the team? How many players hit more home runs than this average?
   $3\frac{8}{9}$ home runs; 6 players

9. Trish parks in front of a parking meter at 2:15 P.M. After 6:00 P.M., she doesn't have to pay to park. The meter only takes quarters, and \$.25 pays for 30 minutes of parking. Trish plans to leave her car in the same place until 8:00 P.M. How much money should she put in the meter? Give your answer in dollars and cents. Explain.
   See margin.

Test-Taking Skills

Multiple Choice

10. A softball team keeps two kinds of bats in the equipment bag. There are 15 metal bats and 9 wooden bats. A player chooses her bat at random. What is the probability that the bat is made of wood? A

A. $\frac{3}{8}$ **B.** $\frac{8}{15}$ **C.** $\frac{3}{5}$ **D.** $\frac{5}{8}$

11. The circumference of a circular swimming pool is about 38 feet. What is the best estimate of the pool's diameter? H

F. 6 ft **G.** 6.3 ft **H.** 12.1 ft **I.** 12.6 ft

12. A long distance telephone call costs $.25 for the first minute, and each minute after the first costs $.15. How many minutes long is a call that costs $1.75? C

A. 9 minutes **B.** 10 minutes

C. 11 minutes **D.** 12 minutes

13. Lucia has 5 quarters for every 7 nickels in her purse. Lucia wants to know how many nickels she has if she has 35 quarters. Which proportion can Lucia use? I

F. $\frac{n}{35} = \frac{5}{7}$ **G.** $\frac{35}{n} = \frac{7}{5}$

H. $\frac{5}{n} = \frac{7}{35}$ **I.** $\frac{35}{n} = \frac{5}{7}$

14. What is the prime factorization of 80? A

A. $2^4 \cdot 5$ **B.** $2^2 \cdot 4 \cdot 5$

C. $2^3 \cdot 10$ **D.** $2^2 \cdot 20$

15. Three scout troops are each divided into small groups. Every small group has exactly 4 scouts in it, and every scout is in a small group. How many total scouts could be in each of the three troops? G

F. 12, 21, 27 **G.** 36, 40, 60

H. 6, 18, 24 **I.** 10, 40, 80

Extended Response

16. Mr. Fay has given his students 20 homework assignments. The table shows the number of homework assignments that each student has completed so far. Find the median number of assignments completed.

Amy	Bill	Dan	Dave	Erin	Jack	Kyle	Matt	Mike	Ron	Tara
17	16	19	20	17	18	17	15	16	19	20

Jillian was left off of Mr. Fay's list by mistake. What is the minimum number of assignments Jillian must complete in order for the median of the group to be 17.5? Explain your answer.

16. 17 assignments; 18 assignments; when Jillian is added to the list, there are 12 students and the median will be the mean of the sixth and seventh numbers, which must be 17 and 18 for the median to be 17.5.

17. Cindy wants to use a 20% discount coupon to buy a coat that originally cost $78. She also wants to use a 10% discount coupon to buy a sweater that originally cost $36. To find the total cost of the items after the discounts, Cindy found the sum of their original prices and subtracted 30% of the total. Explain the mistake that Cindy made. Then show how to find the correct total cost before sales tax.

17. Cindy found the sum of the percents. Instead, you must find the discounted price of each item and then add the prices; $(78 - 0.20 \cdot 78) + (36 - 0.10 \cdot 36) = \$94.80$.

GO ON

ADDITIONAL RESOURCES

The following resources are available to help review the materials in this unit:

Chapter Resource Books

- Chapter 4 CRB, Cumulative Practice, pp. 84-85
- Chapter 5 CRB, Cumulative Practice, pp. 82-83
- Chapter 6 CRB, Cumulative Practice, pp. 68-69
- Chapter 7 CRB, Cumulative Practice, pp. 83-84

Assessment Book

- Unit Test, pp. 90-91
- Cumulative Test, pp. 92-95

8. Every 120 min; the LCM of 12, 15, and 8 is 120.

UNIT 2 Chapters 4–7 PRACTICING **Test-Taking Skills**

Cumulative Practice for Chapters 4–7

Chapter 4

Multiple Choice In Exercises 1–7, choose the letter of the correct answer.

1. What is the prime factorization of 54? *(Lesson 4.1)* C

   A. $6 \cdot 9$ **B.** $6 \cdot 3^2$ **C.** $2 \cdot 3^3$ **D.** $2^2 \cdot 3^3$

2. What is the greatest common factor of 72 and 90? *(Lesson 4.2)* I

   F. 6 **G.** 9 **H.** 12 **I.** 18

3. Which fractions are equivalent? *(Lesson 4.3)* C

   A. $\frac{5}{8}, \frac{3}{16}$ **B.** $\frac{15}{30}, \frac{60}{80}$ **C.** $\frac{18}{72}, \frac{7}{28}$ **D.** $\frac{12}{24}, \frac{8}{24}$

4. Which set of fractions is ordered from least to greatest? *(Lesson 4.5)* F

   F. $\frac{3}{16}, \frac{1}{4}, \frac{3}{8}, \frac{1}{2}$ **G.** $\frac{3}{8}, \frac{1}{2}, \frac{3}{16}, \frac{1}{4}$

   H. $\frac{3}{8}, \frac{1}{4}, \frac{1}{2}, \frac{3}{16}$ **I.** $\frac{3}{8}, \frac{1}{2}, \frac{1}{4}, \frac{3}{16}$

5. What is the value of the expression $4^2 \cdot 4^3 - 5^3$? *(Lesson 4.6)* C

   A. -899 **B.** 81 **C.** 899 **D.** 10,800

6. What is the value of the expression $3 \cdot 3^{-5}$? *(Lesson 4.7)* F

   F. $\frac{1}{81}$ **G.** $\frac{1}{5}$ **H.** 45 **I.** 81

7. Which is *not* in scientific notation? *(Lesson 4.8)* D

   A. 1×10^6 **B.** 4.4×10^{-2}

   C. 8.03×10^4 **D.** 13.4×10^{-8}

8. **Short Response** Train A leaves the station every 12 minutes. Train B leaves every 15 minutes. A bus leaves every 8 minutes. How often do two trains and a bus depart at the same time? Explain. *(Lesson 4.4)* See margin.

9. **Extended Response** A hole at a miniature golf course has 3 doors that swing open on different schedules. You see the 3 doors open at the same time. After 4 seconds, the red door opens again. Two seconds after that, the blue door opens. The red door opens after 2 more seconds. One second later, the yellow door opens. *(Lesson 4.4)*

   a. How often does each door open?
   red: 4 seconds; blue: 6 seconds; yellow: 9 seconds

   b. How often do all 3 doors open at the same time? Explain your answer.
   Every 36 seconds; the LCM of 4, 6, and 9 is 36.

Chapter 5

Multiple Choice In Exercises 10–16, choose the letter of the correct answer.

10. You need $4\frac{1}{2}$ yards of fabric for drapes and $3\frac{1}{2}$ yards for a bedspread. How many yards of fabric should you purchase? *(Lesson 5.1)* C

    A. $1\frac{1}{2}$ **B.** $7\frac{1}{2}$ **C.** 8 **D.** $8\frac{1}{2}$

11. Find the difference $\frac{18}{21} - \frac{6}{14}$. *(Lesson 5.2)* F

F. $\frac{3}{7}$ **G.** $\frac{4}{7}$ **H.** $\frac{6}{7}$ **I.** $\frac{12}{7}$

12. Find the product $-1\frac{1}{2} \cdot \frac{9}{20}$. *(Lesson 5.3)* C

A. $-1\frac{9}{20}$ **B.** $-1\frac{1}{20}$ **C.** $-\frac{27}{40}$ **D.** $-\frac{3}{10}$

13. What is the value of a in the equation $\frac{2}{3}a = -12$? *(Lesson 5.4)* G

F. -27 **G.** -18 **H.** -12 **I.** -2

14. In your class, $\frac{21}{30}$ of the students ride the bus to school. What is another way to write this number? *(Lesson 5.5)* D

A. 0.24 **B.** 0.33 **C.** 0.66 **D.** 0.7

15. What is the value of the expression $-2.643 + (-9.9)$? *(Lesson 5.6)* F

F. -12.543 **G.** -11.643

H. 7.257 **I.** 12.543

16. What is the value of the expression $-2.84 \cdot 8.6$? *(Lesson 5.7)* A

A. -24.424 **B.** -11.44

C. 5.76 **D.** 24.424

17. **Short Response** Four friends shared a pizza. Each person ate only whole slices. Kerry ate $\frac{1}{6}$ of the pizza, and Amy ate 0.25 of the pizza. Brian ate 0.5 of the pizza. Jeff ate $\frac{1}{12}$ of the pizza. Who ate the most pizza? *(Lesson 5.5)* Brian

18. **Extended Response** Rebecca's long distance plan charges \$.10 per minute before 7:00 P.M. and \$.05 per minute after 7:00 P.M. Rebecca begins a long distance call at 6:39 P.M. and ends the call at 7:12 P.M. *(Lessons 5.6, 5.7)*

a. Find the cost of the phone call. \$2.70

b. At 7:15 P.M. Rebecca makes another long distance call. She talks for the same amount of time as she did on the previous call. Find the cost of the second phone call. \$1.65

c. What is the price difference of Rebecca's first call and her second call? \$1.05

Chapter 6

Multiple Choice In Exercises 19–23, choose the letter of the correct answer.

19. What is the value of n in the equation $3n + 9 + 4n = 2$? *(Lesson 6.1)* B

A. -2 **B.** -1 **C.** 1 **D.** 2

20. What is the value of x in the equation $22 + x = 37 + 6x$? *(Lesson 6.2)* F

F. -3 **G.** 3 **H.** 6 **I.** 12

21. Find the circumference of the circle. Use 3.14 for π. *(Lesson 6.4)* D

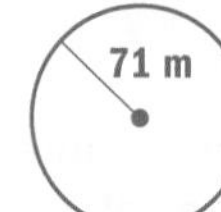

A. 45.22 m **B.** 111.47 m

C. 222.94 m **D.** 445.88 m

22. What is the solution to the inequality $2y - 5 < 7$? *(Lesson 6.5)* H

F. $y < -6$ **G.** $y > -6$

H. $y < 6$ **I.** $y > 6$

GO ON

24. 400 m; the perimeter is the sum of the two long sides plus the circumference of the two half circles, or (85 + 85) + (74 · 3.14) = 402.36, or about 400 meters.

32. $\frac{11}{20}$; there are 11 houses with a 4 in the address (34, 40, 41, 42, 43, 44, 45, 46, 47, 48, and 49) and there are a total of 20 houses, so the probability is $\frac{11}{20}$.

UNIT 2 Chapters 4–7 PRACTICING Test-Taking Skills

Cumulative Practice continued

23. Mark has $40 to spend on CDs that cost $11.95 each. What is the greatest number of CDs that Mark can buy? *(Lesson 6.6)* **B**

A. 2 **B.** 3 **C.** 4 **D.** 5

24. Short Response The diagram shows the approximate measures of a track. Find the perimeter. Explain your steps. Round your answer to the nearest 100. *(Lesson 6.4)* **See margin.**

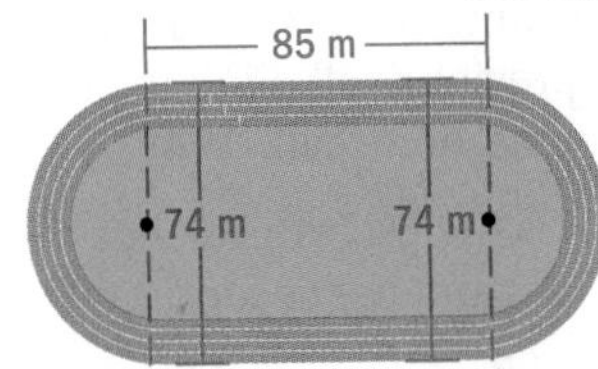

25. Extended Response Pat rode his bike at a speed of 9 mi/h. Rick rode at a speed of 8 mi/h. Pat rode 13.5 miles. *(Lesson 6.3)*

a. How many hours and minutes did Pat spend riding? **1 h 30 min**

b. Rick rode his bike for the same amount of time as Pat. How far did Rick ride? **12 miles**

c. Pat and Rick ride at the same speeds for another 45 minutes. Find the total distance traveled by each person. **Pat: 20.25 mi, Rick: 18 mi**

Chapter 7

Multiple Choice In Exercises 26–31, choose the letter of the correct answer.

26. Lauren types 1040 words in 20 minutes. What is Lauren's typing speed in words per minute? *(Lesson 7.1)* **A**

A. 52 **B.** 104 **C.** 208 **D.** 5700

27. Solve the proportion $\frac{7}{23} = \frac{49}{x}$. *(Lesson 7.2)* **H**

F. 7 **G.** 115 **H.** 161 **I.** 207

28. 18 is what percent of 45? *(Lesson 7.3)* **B**

A. 9% **B.** 40% **C.** 50% **D.** 60%

29. The cost of a concert ticket increased by 4%. The new cost is $31.20. What was the cost before the increase? *(Lesson 7.5)* **H**

F. $18.00 **G.** $29.50 **H.** $30.00 **I.** $31.80

30. What is the total cost of a television priced at $86.90 with 7% sales tax? *(Lesson 7.6)* **D**

A. $66.88 **B.** $80.82 **C.** $89.99 **D.** $92.98

31. Joan invested $100 in an account that pays 5% simple annual interest. What is the account balance after 5 years? *(Lesson 7.7)* **G**

F. $105 **G.** $125 **H.** $150 **I.** $525

32. Short Response Houses on your block are numbered 31 through 50. You choose a house at random. What is the probability that the house you choose has a 4 in its number? Explain your answer. *(Lesson 7.8)* **See margin.**

33. Extended Response The graph shows the results of a poll in which 504 people would choose to be a zookeeper. *(Lesson 7.4)*

a. How many people chose rodeo star? **312 people**

b. Find the total number of people who participated in the poll. **2400 people**

c. How many people chose either a veterinarian or a pet store owner? **1368 people**

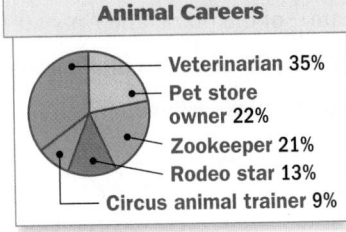

Animal Careers

Veterinarian 35%
Pet store owner 22%
Zookeeper 21%
Rodeo star 13%
Circus animal trainer 9%

Geometry and Measurement

Chapter 8 Polygons and Transformations

- Classify angles, triangles, and other polygons.
- Use properties of congruent and similar polygons to solve problems.
- Describe transformations and symmetry of geometric figures.

Chapter 9 Real Numbers and Right Triangles

- Use square roots and the Pythagorean theorem to solve problems.
- Identify rational and irrational numbers.
- Use special relationships in right triangles to solve problems.

Chapter 10 Measurement, Area, and Volume

- Find areas of parallelograms, trapezoids, and circles.
- Find surface areas and volumes of prisms, cylinders, pyramids, and cones.
- Classify and sketch solids.

From Chapter 9, p. 444
How high can you parasail?

Unit Resources

These resources are provided to help you prepare for the unit and to customize review materials:

 ***Chapter Resource Books***
- Chapter 8
- Chapter 9
- Chapter 10

 ***Assessment Book***
- Chapters 8–10, pp. 96–134

 ***Technology***
- EasyPlanner CD-ROM
- Test and Practice Generator
- Electronic Lesson Presentations CD-ROM
- eTutorial CD-ROM

 ***Internet***
- Classzone
- eEdition Plus Online
- eWorkbook Plus Online
- eTutorial Plus Online
- EasyPlanner Plus Online

English Learner Support

- Spanish Study Guide
- Multi-Language Glossary
- Chapter Audio Summaries CDs
- Teacher's Edition
  Chapter 8, pp. 372E–372F
  Chapter 9, pp. 428E–428F
  Chapter 10, pp. 478E–478F

Pacing and Assignment Guide

REGULAR SCHEDULE

Lesson	Les. Day	BASIC	AVERAGE	ADVANCED
8.1	Day 1	SRH p. 719 Exs. 1-6; pp. 378-379 Exs. 6-8, 13, 16, 19-22	pp. 378-379 Exs. 6-10, 16, 23-27	pp. 378-379 Exs. 6-10, 18-22
	Day 2	SRH p. 719 Exs. 7-10; pp. 378-379 Exs. 9-11, 14, 23-27	pp. 378-379 Exs. 11-14, 17-22	pp. 378-379 Exs. 11-17*, 25-27
8.2	Day 1	pp. 384-385 Exs. 6-15, 19-22, 25-30	pp. 384-385 Exs. 6-16, 19-23, 25-30	pp. 384-385 Exs. 8-13, 15-18, 20-30*
8.3	Day 1	pp. 388-389 Exs. 8-10, 18-20, 27-32	pp. 388-389 Exs. 8-10, 17-19, 27-32	pp. 388-389 Exs. 8-10, 17-19, 27-32
	Day 2	pp. 388-389 Exs. 11-16, 21-23, 33-35	pp. 388-389 Exs. 11-16, 22-25, 33-35	pp. 388-389 Exs. 11-16, 23-26*, 33-35
8.4	Day 1	EP p. 727 Exs. 4-9; pp. 392-393 Exs. 11-16, 18-23, 29-36	pp. 392-393 Exs. 13-17, 20-24, 26-36	pp. 392-393 Exs. 13-17, 20-30*, 33-36
8.5	Day 1	pp. 400-401 Exs. 8-15, 19, 22-32	pp. 400-401 Exs. 8-10, 13-20, 22-32	pp. 400-401 Exs. 8-10, 13-26*, 29-32
8.6	Day 1	EP p. 728 Exs. 44-47; pp. 407-408 Exs. 11-16, 18-20, 23-28	pp. 407-408 Exs. 11-15, 17-21, 23-29	pp. 407-408 Exs. 11-15, 17-23*, 25-29
8.7	Day 1	pp. 412-413 Exs. 5-10, 16-18, 28-32	pp. 412-413 Exs. 5-10, 16-18, 25, 28-32	pp. 412-413 Exs. 5-10, 16-18, 25-30*
	Day 2	pp. 412-413 Exs. 11-15, 19-24, 33-36	pp. 412-413 Exs. 11-15, 19-22, 27, 33-36	pp. 412-413 Exs. 11-15, 19-22, 31-36
8.8	Day 1	EP p. 733 Exs. 7-10; pp. 419-421 Exs. 6-8, 12, 13, 23, 26-30	pp. 419-421 Exs. 6-8, 12, 13, 22-24, 26-29	pp. 419-421 Exs. 6-8, 12, 13, 22-28*
	Day 2	pp. 419-421 Exs. 9-11, 14-21	pp. 419-421 Exs. 9-11, 14-21, 30	pp. 419-421 Exs. 9-11, 14-21, 30
Review	Day 1	pp. 424-425 Exs. 1-29	pp. 424-425 Exs. 1-29	pp. 424-425 Exs. 1-29
Assess	Day 1	Chapter 8 Test	Chapter 8 Test	Chapter 8 Test

YEARLY PACING Chapter 8 Total – **14 days** Chapters 1-8 Total – **94 days** Remaining – **66 days**

*Challenge Exercises EP = Extra Practice SRH = Skills Review Handbook EC = Extra Challenge

BLOCK SCHEDULE

DAY 1	DAY 2	DAY 3	DAY 4	DAY 5	DAY 6	DAY 7
8.1 pp. 378-379 Exs. 6-14, 16-27	**8.2** pp. 384-385 Exs. 6-16, 19-23, 25-30 **8.3** pp. 388-389 Exs. 8-10, 17-19, 27-32	**8.3 (cont.)** pp. 388-389 Exs. 11-16, 22-25, 33-35 **8.4** pp. 392-393 Exs. 13-17, 20-24, 26-36	**8.5** pp. 400-401 Exs. 8-10, 13-20, 22-32 **8.6** pp. 407-408 Exs. 11-15, 17-21, 23-29	**8.7** pp. 412-413 Exs. 5-22, 25, 27-36	**8.8** pp. 419-421 Exs. 6-24, 26-30	**Review** pp. 424-425 Exs. 1-29 **Assess** Chapter 8 Test

YEARLY PACING Chapter 8 Total – **7 days** Chapters 1-8 Total – **47 days** Remaining – **33 days**

Support Materials

CHAPTER RESOURCE BOOK

CHAPTER SUPPORT

Tips for New Teachers	p. 1	Parents as Partners	p. 3

LESSON SUPPORT	8.1	8.2	8.3	8.4	8.5	8.6	8.7	8.8
Lesson Plans (regular and block)	p. 6	p. 14	p. 25	p. 33	p. 43	p. 51	p. 61	p. 69
Technology Activities & Keystrokes		p. 17						
Activity Support Masters				p. 35		p. 53		
Activity Masters		p. 16						
Practice (3 levels)	p. 8	p. 19	p. 27	p. 36	p. 45	p. 54	p. 63	p. 71
Study Guide	p. 11	p. 22	p. 30	p. 39	p. 48	p. 57	p. 66	p. 74
Real-World Problem Solving				p. 41		p. 59		
Challenge Practice	p. 13	p. 24	p. 32	p. 42	p. 50	p. 60	p. 68	p. 76

REVIEW

Games Support Masters	p. 5	Cooperative Project with Rubric	p. 80
Chapter Review Games and Activities	p. 77	Extra Credit Project with Rubric	p. 82
Real-Life Project with Rubric	p. 78	Cumulative Practice	p. 84
		Resource Book Answers	A1

 ASSESSMENT

Quizzes	p. 96	Alternative Assessments with Rubrics	p. 105
Chapter Tests (3 levels)	p. 98	Unit Test	p. 129
Standardized Test	p. 104	Cumulative Test	p. 131

TRANSPARENCIES

TRANSPARENCIES	8.1	8.2	8.3	8.4	8.5	8.6	8.7	8.8
Warm-Up / Daily Homework Quiz	✔	✔	✔	✔	✔	✔	✔	✔
Notetaking Guide	✔	✔	✔	✔	✔	✔	✔	✔
Teacher Support						✔	✔	✔
English/Spanish Problem Solving		✔	✔		✔		✔	✔
Answer Transparencies	✔	✔	✔	✔	✔	✔	✔	✔

TECHNOLOGY

- EasyPlanner CD-ROM
- Test and Practice Generator
- Electronic Lesson Presentations
- eTutorial CD-ROM
- Chapter Audio Summaries CDs
- Classzone.com
- eEdition Plus Online
- eWorkbook Plus Online
- eTutorial Plus Online
- EasyPlanner Plus Online

ADDITIONAL RESOURCES

- Worked-Out Solution Key
- Notetaking Guide
- Practice Workbook
- Tutor Place
- Professional Development Book
- Special Activities Book
- Posters
- Spanish Study Guide
- Exercises in Spanish
- English/Spanish Ch. Reviews/Tests
- Multi-Language Visual Glossary

Math Background and Teaching Strategies

Lesson 8.1

MATH BACKGROUND

Two angles are **complementary** if their measures total 90°, and **supplementary** if their measures total 180°. **Vertical angles**, nonadjacent angles formed by two intersecting lines, are congruent. Parallel lines intersected by a line not parallel to them, a *transversal*, form several sets of congruent angles: **corresponding angles**, lying on the same side of the transversal and in the same relative position to the parallel lines; **alternate interior angles**, lying on opposite sides of the transversal and between the parallel lines; and **alternate exterior angles**, lying on opposite sides of the transversal and outside the parallel lines.

TEACHING STRATEGIES

Have students identify pairs of corresponding angles, alternate interior angles, and alternate exterior angles in the figure below, which consists of two pairs of parallel lines.

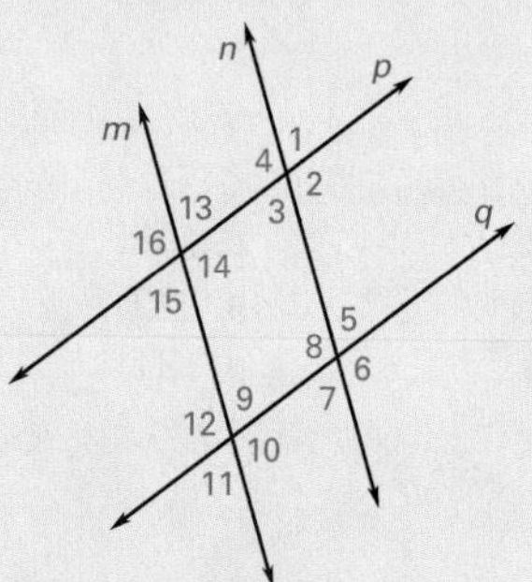

Lesson 8.2

MATH BACKGROUND

The sum of the angle measures in any triangle is 180°. Triangles can be classified by their angle measures as **acute**, **right**, or **obtuse**, and by their side lengths as **equilateral**, **isosceles**, or **scalene**. A categorization by angle may or may not exclude a categorization by side, and vice versa.

TEACHING STRATEGIES

Have students make a poster that gives definitions and examples, with angle measures and congruent sides indicated, for each class of triangle by angle and by side length. Each class by angle (side length) should include an example of each class by side length (angle) if possible, or an explanation if not possible. For example, the entry for an obtuse triangle should show an obtuse isosceles triangle and an obtuse scalene triangle, but explain that an obtuse equilateral triangle is not possible because each angle in an equilateral triangle measures 60°.

Lesson 8.3

MATH BACKGROUND

Quadrilaterals are classified as *trapezoids*, *parallelograms*, *rhombuses*, *rectangles*, or *squares* by whether and how many pairs of sides are parallel, by whether all sides are congruent, and by whether all angles are right angles. The category of trapezoids is exclusive of the category of parallelograms, of which the others are subcategories. Squares form a subcategory both of rhombuses and rectangles, which overlap only in the case of squares.

TEACHING STRATEGIES

Copy the design below on the board or overhead. Point out that line segments that appear to be parallel are parallel. Have students identify any special quadrilaterals they can find. Encourage students to come up with their own simple designs in which many special quadrilaterals can be identified.

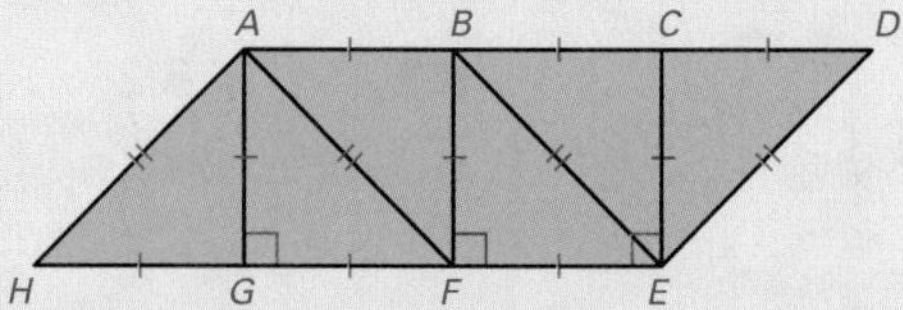

Lesson 8.4

MATH BACKGROUND

A **polygon** is a closed figure with sides formed by line segments that intersect only at their endpoints. Polygons include the *pentagon* (5 sides), *hexagon* (6 sides), *heptagon* (7 sides), and *octagon* (8 sides). A **regular** polygon has equal side lengths and equal angle measures. The sum of the angle measures in any n-sided polygon is $(n - 2) \cdot 180°$.

TEACHING STRATEGIES

Students may forget the formula for the sum of the angle measures in a polygon. Emphasize that they can always go back to the process in the Activity at the beginning of the lesson to help them remember. You may also want to have students perform the process of dividing a polygon into triangles for a concave polygon, such as the polygon shaped like a plus sign shown on page 390, so students can see that the formula applies to *any* polygon.

Lesson 8.5

MATH BACKGROUND

Two polygons are **congruent** if corresponding sides are the same length and corresponding angles have the same measure. Three ways to show triangles congruent are to show that the three sides of one triangle are congruent to the three sides of another (**SSS**), that two sides and the included angle of one triangle are congruent to two sides and the included angle of another (**SAS**), and that two angles and the included side of one triangle are congruent to two angles and the included side of another (**ASA**).

TEACHING STRATEGIES

Have students try to draw triangles that meet the criteria of SSS, SAS, or ASA that are not congruent. Then ask them to draw two non-congruent triangles that have a congruent angle and two congruent sides to show that SSA does not establish congruence.

Lesson 8.6

MATH BACKGROUND

A **reflection** of a figure in a line is a *transformation* that results in a mirror image of the original figure. Reflection in a line reverses the orientation of a figure. In the coordinate plane, the image of a point reflected in the x-axis has the same x-coordinate, but opposite y-coordinate; the image of a point reflected in the y-axis has the same y-coordinate, but opposite x-coordinate.

TEACHING STRATEGIES

Have students work in pairs to carry out the following activity. Fold a piece of tracing paper in half. Unfold the paper and label the halves I and II. On half I, draw triangle ABC. Refold the paper. On the back of half II, trace the triangle. Unfold the paper and trace this triangle onto the front of half II. Label the vertices of the new triangle A', B', and C' to correspond to the vertices of ABC. Compare the distances of A and A' from the fold. Do the same for the other vertices.

Lesson 8.7

MATH BACKGROUND

Translations, which "slide" a figure, and **rotations**, which turn a figure about a point, are both examples of transformations that do not change the orientation of a figure. In the coordinate plane, the image of a point with coordinates (x, y) after a translation a units horizontally and b units vertically is $(x + a, y + b)$, where $a > 0$ represents a move right, $a < 0$ a move left, $b > 0$ a move up, and $b < 0$ a move down. For rotations about the origin, the point $P(x, y)$ has image $P'(y, -x)$ after a 90° clockwise rotation, $P'(-y, x)$ after a 90° counterclockwise rotation, and $P'(-x, -y)$ after a 180° rotation.

TEACHING STRATEGIES

Help students model rotations physically. For example, by using tracing paper that has grids on it, students can draw axes and a figure, turn the paper the indicated amount and direction, and use the tracing paper to sketch the figure and its image. Also, if you have a large coordinate grid, you can use a dowel rod as an axis to which you can attach various figures.

Lesson 8.8

MATH BACKGROUND

For **similar polygons**, corresponding angles are congruent, and corresponding sides are proportional. In mathematics, a **dilation** represents an enlargement or a shrinking. The ratio of the corresponding side lengths of a polygon and its image after a dilation is the **scale factor** of the dilation. In the coordinate plane, the image of a point $P(x, y)$ in a figure after a dilation by a scale factor of k is $P'(kx, ky)$.

TEACHING STRATEGIES

If you have access to a copy machine that performs enlargements and reductions, you can make copies of a polygon with different scale factors for students to examine.

Differentiating Instruction

Strategies for Underachievers

FOCUS ON VOCABULARY

Every lesson in this chapter is full of new vocabulary for students. You might suggest that students create note cards or an organized glossary for learning and practicing this vocabulary. If students use note cards, you may want to suggest that they color code cards related to the same topic. For example, one color group might contain all the vocabulary terms related to angles, such as *acute angle*, *complementary angles*, *vertical angles*, and so on. Point out that some vocabulary terms may belong in more than one color group. If so, have students place a card for the term in each group. For example, if students have a "similarity" group and a "congruence" group, they could include a card for *corresponding parts* in each. Creating multiple note cards for some terms will help reinforce understanding.

Especially in Lesson 8.1, try to help students connect the mathematical vocabulary terms with the everyday use of words that they contain. For example, if students alternate hands when dribbling a basketball, it means that they change from one hand to the other. In the same way, alternate interior and exterior angles lie on "opposite hands" of the transversal.

USE MODELS AND MANIPULATIVES

LINGUINE MODELS In Lesson 8.1, it will prove very helpful to have models that students can manipulate to investigate angles. One way is to provide each student with several pieces of linguine (linguine won't roll off a desk as spaghetti might, and does not break as easily). Students can use two pieces of linguine to model vertical angles. By "opening" and "closing" the pieces of linguine as they would a pair of scissors, students can easily observe which angle pairs remain the same.

Using three pieces of linguine, students can model two parallel lines and a transversal. You may want to suggest using a piece of tape to secure the parallel "lines" so that students can manipulate the "transversal" without moving the other pieces of linguine. Again, have students study which pairs of angles appear to stay the same as they vary the angle of the transversal. You may want to suggest that students repeat this process with the two parallel lines in at least one other orientation so that students form a more general conception of which angles are corresponding, which alternate interior, and so on. After students seem comfortable identifying congruent angle pairs, you may want them to arrange the two pieces of linguine that represent the parallel lines so that they are no longer parallel. Then students can see that the relationships no longer hold.

Students can also use linguine for modeling the different classifications of triangles in Lesson 8.2. Students could break off pieces of linguine to model triangles with different side lengths, but as this would take a lot of linguine and possibly create a mess, you may want to instruct them to ignore any overlap in the pieces as they form different triangles. Encourage students to explore whether a triangle with a given angle (side) classification can have a given side (angle) classification. For example, students can form a right angle with two pieces of linguine and then experiment with the placement of the third piece to find that a right triangle can be isosceles or scalene, but not equilateral.

In Lesson 8.3, you may want to have students keep clear the relationships of the special quadrilaterals given by having them create a hierarchy chart such as the one below, or by having them create some other sort of chart or diagram, such as a Venn Diagram.

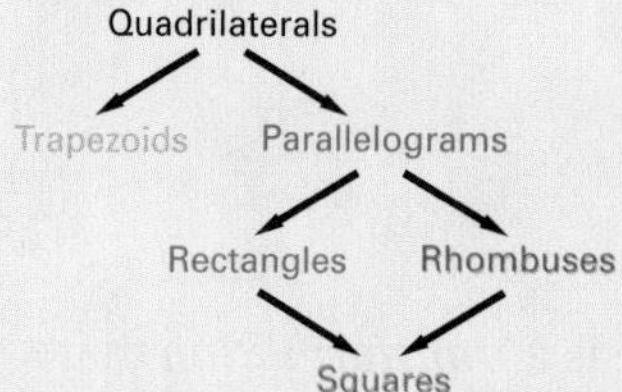

Students may want to add parenthetical notes to each type of quadrilateral, such as inserting "1 pair of parallel sides" beside "Trapezoids," to help them distinguish the features. Students should understand that as you descend the hierarchy, the features of the quadrilaterals become more specific. For example, every square is a rectangle but not every rectangle is a square.

In Lessons 8.6 and 8.7, it will be extremely helpful for underachieving students to be able to perform rotations manually. Some suggestions for doing this are given in the Teaching Strategies notes for Lessons 8.6 and 8.7.

Strategies for English Learners

VOCABULARY

Ask students to consider how prefixes contribute to these words: *similar* : *dissimilar*, *continuous* : *discontinuous*, *order* : *disorder*, *solve* : *dissolve*, *unite* : *disunite*, *biangular*, *bisect*, *commutative*, *congruent*, *coordinate*, *diagram*, *diameter*, *distance*, *distribute*, *isosceles*, *monomial*, *multiple*, *multiply*, *parabola*, *parallax*, *parallelogram*, *parallel*, *parameter*, *percent*, *polynomial*, *polygon*, *quadrilateral*, *quadrant*, *subtract*, and *triangle*. Students will be amazed to see how many words in English start from the prefixes *poly-* or *multi-*.

NUMBERS Latin and Greek numbers have also influenced English mathematical words. Put these Latin and Greek words for cardinal numbers on the board and ask students to think of words that use these:

English	Cardinal Numbers in Latin	Cardinal Numbers in Greek
one	unus, una, unum	heis, miam, hen
two	duo, duae	duo
three	tres, tria	treis, tria
four	quattor	tessares, tessara
five	quinque	pente
six	sex	hex
seven	septum	hepta
eight	octo	okto
nine	novem	ennea
ten	decem	deka

Students may think of words such as *uniform* or *unicorn*, *duo*, *duet*, *triangle*, *quad*, *quadrilateral*, *pentagon*, *sextuplet*, *hexagonal*, *octagon*, and *decathlon*. Spanish speakers may be amazed at the similarity between the names for numbers in Latin and in Spanish.

Strategies for Advanced Learners

INCREASE DEPTH AND COMPLEXITY

In Lesson 8.2, you may want to ask your advanced learners which classifications of triangle by side and by angle are mutually exclusive, and then to explain why. For example, an equilateral triangle cannot be obtuse because each angle measure in an equilateral triangle is $180° \div 3 = 60°$, which is an acute measure. You may also suggest to these students that they extend their investigation to compare the measures of the angles of a triangle with the lengths of the opposite sides to see if they make the connection that the longest side is always opposite the angle with the greatest measure and that the shortest side is always opposite the angle with the smallest measure. As corollaries, they should recognize that the base angles of an isosceles triangle have the same measure, and that in a triangle in which two angles have the same measure, the sides opposite them have the same length.

The hierarchy of quadrilaterals shown on the Strategies for Underachievers for Lesson 8.3 is not an exhaustive classification. You may want to have your advanced learners "flesh out" the hierarchy, including sample quadrilaterals. For example, they could add a category called "Other" at the level of trapezoids and parallelograms and include drawings of quadrilaterals that are neither, and add a second "Other" category at the level of rectangles and rhombuses that shows parallelograms that are neither of these. By doing some research, students may also be able to add named quadrilaterals such as isosceles trapezoids and kites to the hierarchy.

USE CROSS-CURRICULAR CONNECTIONS

TRANSFORMATIONS AND SYMMETRY In conjunction with Lessons 8.6 and 8.7, there are many opportunities for advanced learners to explore the topics of transformations and symmetry, including their applications in tessellations. Students may wish to describe symmetries or tessellating patterns in nature (such as in a honeycomb) or in man-made objects (such as in architecture). Encourage students to create their own symmetric designs or tessellations. They should be able to describe any transformations they use and any symmetries that are exhibited. Many students will enjoy investigating the complex tessellations created by M.C. Escher or those present in quilts, rugs, or tile designs.

Differentiating Instruction: Teaching Resources

Differentiating Practice

McDougal Littell *Middle School Mathematics* offers teachers a wide variety of practice for all levels of students. Pictured on these pages are facsimiles of the Level A, Level B, Level C, and Challenge Practice pages from the *Chapter 8 Resource Book*, pages from the *Practice Workbook*, and the *Test and Practice Generator*.

Resource Book

The *Chapter Resource Books* contain three levels of practice, A (Basic), B (Average), and C (Advanced), for each lesson in the textbook. Also, included is a page of Challenge practice for each lesson for your most advanced students.

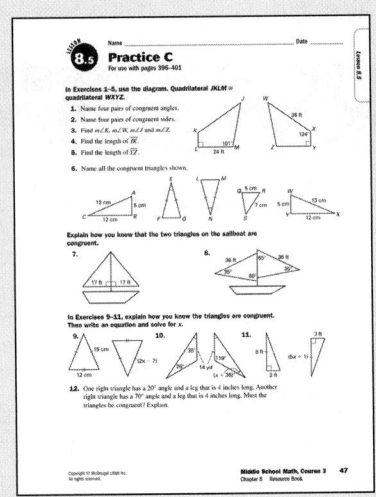

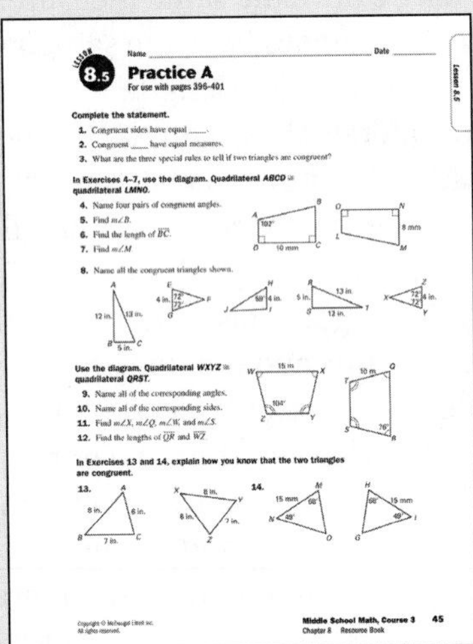
LESSON 8.5 Practice A
For use with pages 396–401

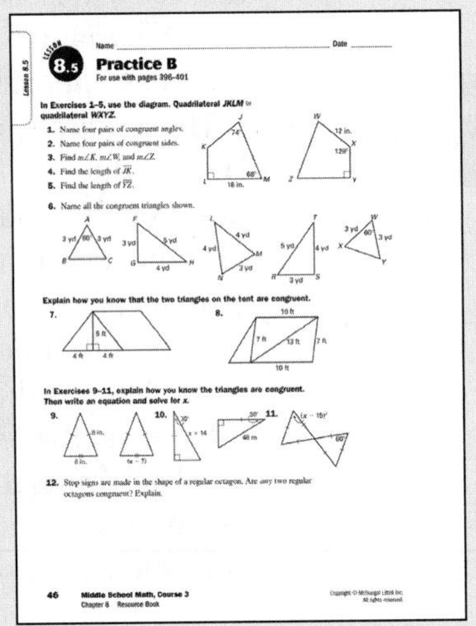
LESSON 8.5 Practice B
For use with pages 396–401

LESSON 8.5 Practice C
For use with pages 396–401

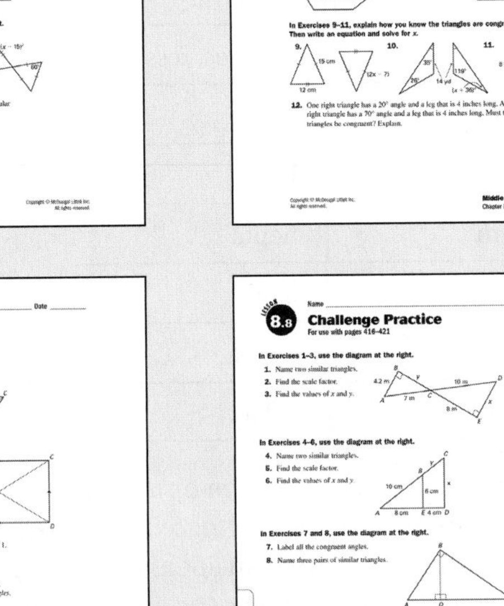

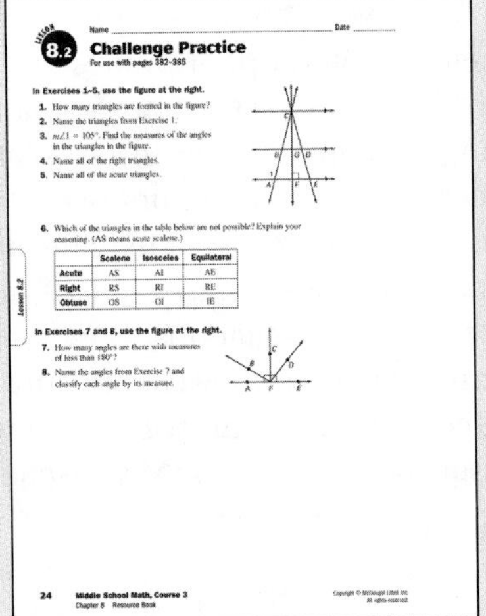
LESSON 8.2 Challenge Practice
For use with pages 382–385

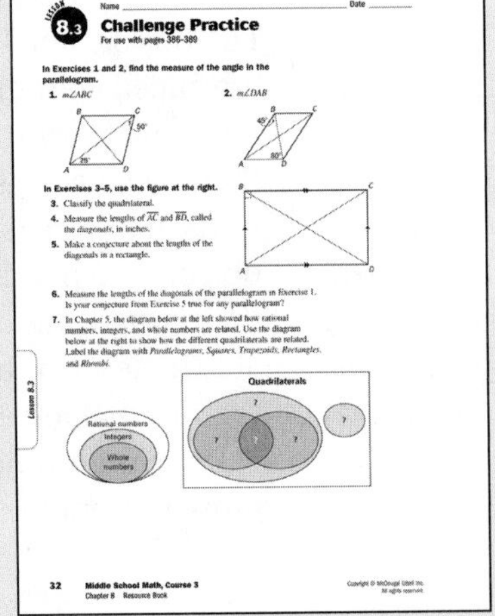
LESSON 8.3 Challenge Practice
For use with pages 386–389

LESSON 8.8 Challenge Practice
For use with pages 416–421

PRACTICE WORKBOOK

The *Practice Workbook* contains the average B-level practice for each lesson reformatted in workbook form to allow students to show their work for each exercise.

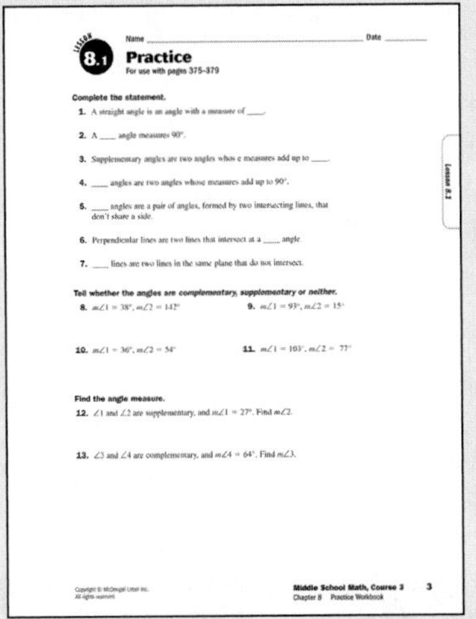
Name ___ Date ___

8.1 Practice
For use with pages 375–379

Complete the statement.

1. A straight angle is an angle with a measure of ___.
2. A ___ angle measures 90°.
3. Supplementary angles are two angles whose measures add up to ___.
4. ___ angles are two angles whose measures add up to 90°.
5. ___ angles are a pair of angles, formed by two intersecting lines, that don't share a side.
6. Perpendicular lines are two lines that intersect at a ___ angle.
7. ___ lines are two lines in the same plane that do not intersect.

Tell whether the angles are *complementary*, *supplementary* or *neither*.

8. $m\angle 1 = 38°, m\angle 2 = 142°$
9. $m\angle 1 = 85°, m\angle 2 = 15°$
10. $m\angle 1 = 36°, m\angle 2 = 54°$
11. $m\angle 1 = 103°, m\angle 2 = 77°$

Find the angle measure.

12. $\angle 1$ and $\angle 2$ are supplementary, and $m\angle 1 = 27°$. Find $m\angle 2$.
13. $\angle 3$ and $\angle 4$ are complementary, and $m\angle 4 = 64°$. Find $m\angle 3$.

Copyright © McDougal Littell Inc. All rights reserved.
Middle School Math, Course 3 Chapter 8 Practice Workbook 3

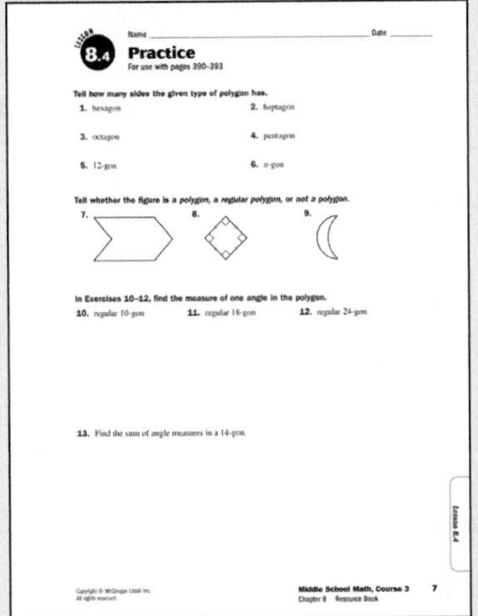
Name ___ Date ___

8.4 Practice
For use with pages 390–393

Tell how many sides the given type of polygon has.

1. hexagon
2. heptagon
3. octagon
4. pentagon
5. 12-gon
6. n-gon

Tell whether the figure is a *polygon*, a *regular polygon*, or *not a polygon*.

7. 8. 9.

In Exercises 10–12, find the measure of one angle in the polygon.

10. regular 10-gon
11. regular 16-gon
12. regular 24-gon

13. Find the sum of angle measures in a 14-gon.

Copyright © McDougal Littell Inc. All rights reserved.
Middle School Math, Course 3 Chapter 8 Resource Book 7

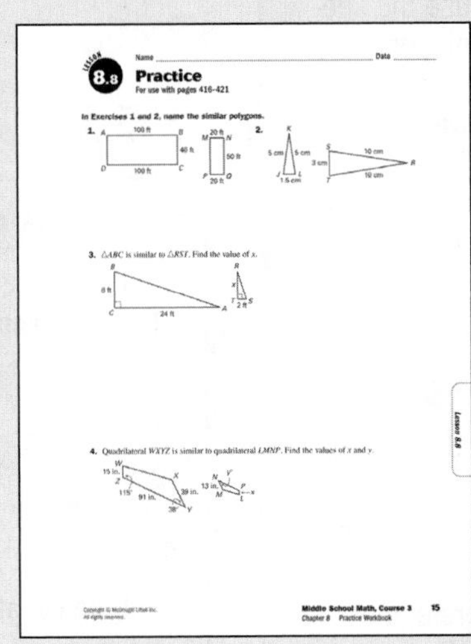
Name ___ Date ___

8.8 Practice
For use with pages 416–421

In Exercises 1 and 2, name the similar polygons.

1. 2.

3. $\triangle ABC$ is similar to $\triangle RST$. Find the value of x.

4. Quadrilateral $WXYZ$ is similar to quadrilateral $LMNP$. Find the values of x and y.

Copyright © McDougal Littell Inc. All rights reserved.
Middle School Math, Course 3 Chapter 8 Practice Workbook 15

TEST AND PRACTICE GENERATOR CD-ROM

The *Test and Practice Generator* allows you to create practice worksheets for each lesson using both static and algorithmic exercises.

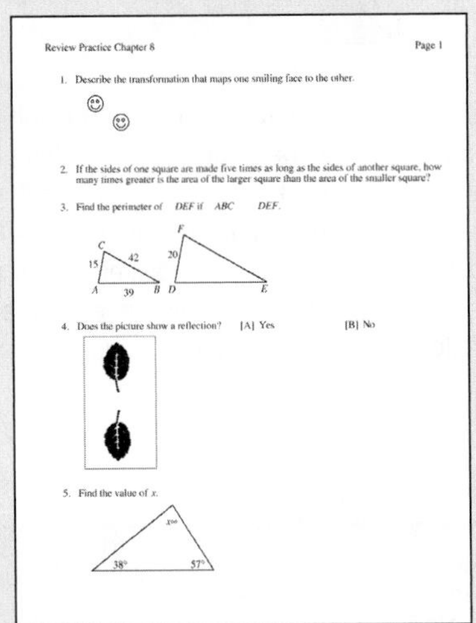
Review Practice Chapter 8 Page 1

1. Describe the transformation that maps one smiling face to the other.
2. If the sides of one square are made five times as long as the sides of another square, how many times greater is the area of the larger square than the area of the smaller square?
3. Find the perimeter of DEF if $ABC \sim DEF$.
4. Does the picture show a reflection? [A] Yes [B] No
5. Find the value of x.

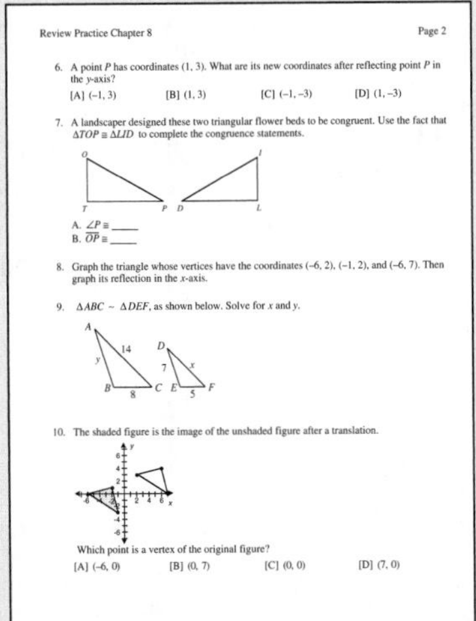
Review Practice Chapter 8 Page 2

6. A point P has coordinates (1, 3). What are its new coordinates after reflecting point P in the y-axis?
[A] (–1, 3) [B] (1, 3) [C] (–1, –3) [D] (1, –3)
7. A landscaper designed these two triangular flower beds to be congruent. Use the fact that $\Delta TOP \cong \Delta LID$ to complete the congruence statements.
A. $\angle P \cong$ ___
B. $\overline{OP} \cong$ ___
8. Graph the triangle whose vertices have the coordinates (–6, 2), (–1, 2), and (–6, 7). Then graph its reflection in the x-axis.
9. $\Delta ABC \sim \Delta DEF$, as shown below. Solve for x and y.
10. The shaded figure is the image of the unshaded figure after a translation.
Which point is a vertex of the original figure?
[A] (–6, 0) [B] (0, 7) [C] (0, 0) [D] (7, 0)

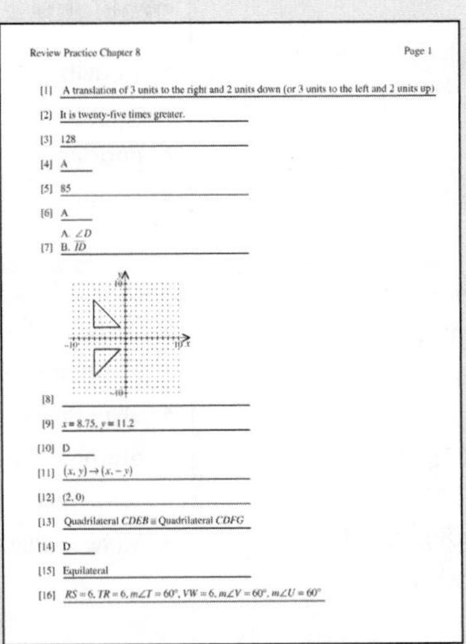
Review Practice Chapter 8 Page 1

[1] A translation of 3 units to the right and 2 units down (or 3 units to the left and 2 units up)
[2] It is twenty-five times greater.
[3] 128
[4] A
[5] 85
[6] A
[7] A. $\angle D$ B. $\overline{ID}$
[8]
[9] $x = 8.75, y = 11.2$
[10] D
[11] $(x, y) \rightarrow (x, -y)$
[12] (2, 0)
[13] Quadrilateral $CDEB \cong$ Quadrilateral $CDFG$
[14] D
[15] Equilateral
[16] $RS = 6, TR = 6, m\angle T = 60°, VW = 6, m\angle V = 60°, m\angle U = 60°$

OVERVIEW

MAIN IDEAS

In this chapter, students solve equations to find angle measures involving supplementary and complementary angles and angles formed by a line intersecting parallel lines. Students classify angles, triangles, and quadrilaterals, and find angle measures in polygons. Students identify and name congruent polygons, and use the special rules for identifying congruent triangles. Students identify reflected figures and their axes of symmetry and reflect, translate, and rotate figures in a coordinate plane. Students also use similar polygons to find missing measures.

PREREQUISITE SKILLS

The key skills reviewed in the games on these pages are:

- Plotting points on a coordinate plane

Additional practice with prerequisite skills can be found in the Review What You Need to Know exercises on page 374. Additional resources for reviewing prerequisite skills are:

- Skills Review Handbook, pp. 704–726
- Tutor Place
- eTutorial Plus

MANAGING THE GAME

Tips for Success

Before playing *Find the Flags*, review with students the order of the coordinates in an ordered pair and the signs of the x- and y-coordinates in each quadrant. Many students may be familiar with the strategies involved in this game from playing a popular game involving hiding and "sinking" ships. If so, they may want to share tips with the class before beginning.

Polygons and Transformations

BEFORE

In previous chapters you've...

- Solved equations
- Plotted points in a coordinate plane

Now

In Chapter 8 you'll study...

- Solving equations to find angle measures
- Classifying angles and triangles
- Reflecting, translating, and rotating figures in a coordinate plane

WHY?

So you can solve real-world problems about...

- weaving, p. 378
- referees, p. 384
- geodesic domes, p. 393
- origami, p. 412

Internet Preview
CLASSZONE.COM

- eEdition Plus Online
- eWorkbook Plus Online
- eTutorial Plus Online
- State Test Practice
- More Examples

Chapter Warm-Up Game

Review skills you need for this chapter in this quick game. Work with a partner.

Key Skill:
Plotting points on a coordinate plane

FIND THE FLAGS

MATERIALS

- 2 sheets of grid paper for each player
- Pencils

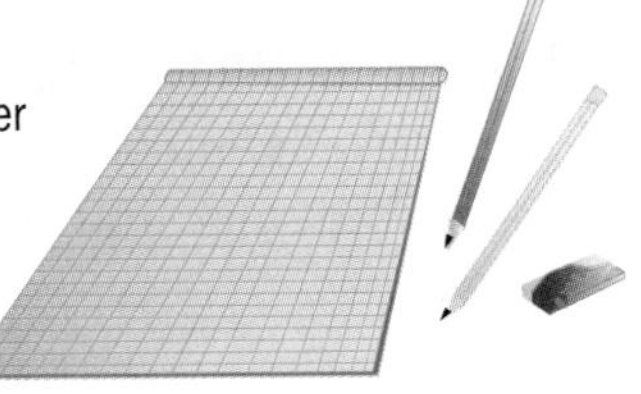

PREPARE Each player draws a coordinate graph on both sheets of grid paper. Each player draws squares along the grid lines passing through the points (7, 0), (0, −7), (−7, 0), and (0, 7). A player secretly marks 4 flags on one graph. A flag is three consecutive points with integer coordinates, either horizontally or vertically. Flags cannot touch the outside borders. On each turn, a player should follow the steps on the next page.

Find the Flags

1 **CALL** out a point. The other player lets you know if you hit or missed one of their flags.

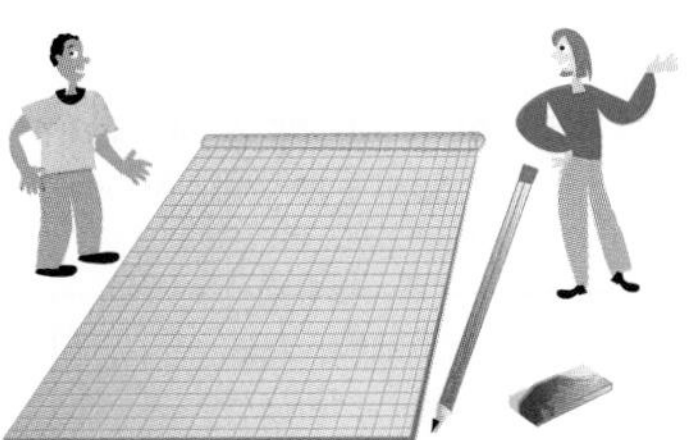

2 **MARK** a hit with an "X" and a miss with an "O" on your second graph where your flags are not marked. If you hit a flag, you get to go again.

HOW TO WIN Be the first player to hit all the points in the other player's flags.

Stop and Think

1. **Writing** How did you decide where to put your flags? Did it work? Explain. What strategy did you use when trying to find the other player's flags? Did it work? Explain. **Check work.**
2. **Critical Thinking** How many points are there (not including any on the border) in each graph? Explain how you got your answer. **See margin.**

373

Reflecting on the Game

When students offer their strategies after the game, have others evaluate how well the strategy used the fact that the three points of a flag are consecutive and aligned horizontally or vertically. Ask students to find the lowest number of points they can pick that will guarantee finding at least one flag, and to explain how they found this number.

CHAPTER RESOURCES

These resources are provided to help you prepare for the chapter and to customize review materials:

Chapter 8 Resource Book

- Tips for New Teachers, pp. 1-2
- Lesson Plan, pp. 6, 14, 25, 34, 43, 51, 61, 69
- Lesson Plan for Block Scheduling, pp. 7, 15, 26, 35, 44, 52, 62, 70

Technology

- EasyPlanner CD-ROM
- Test and Practice Generator
- Electronic Lesson Presentations CD-ROM
- eTutorial CD-ROM

Internet

- Classzone
- eEdition Plus Online
- eWorkbook Plus Online
- eTutorial Plus Online
- EasyPlanner Plus Online

ENGLISH LEARNER SUPPORT

- Spanish Study Guide
- Multi-Language Glossary
- Chapter Audio Summaries CDs
- Teacher's Edition, pp. 372E-372F

2. 169 points; I found this answer by multiplying the number of horizontal grid lines from −6 to 6 on the *y*-axis (13) by the number of vertical grid lines from −6 to 6 on the *x*-axis (13); 13 × 13 = 169.

PREPARE

Diagnosis/Remediation

Review What You Need to Know
The Review What You Need to Know exercises can help you diagnose whether students have the following skills needed in Chapter 8:

- Use vocabulary about geometry (Exs. 1–4)
- Use a protractor to measure angles (Exs. 5–10)
- Use scale models (Ex. 11)

Chapter 8 Resource Book

- Study Guide (Lessons 8.1–8.8)

Tutor Place

Notetaking Strategies

Along with concept maps, notetaking in this chapter can make great use of tables and diagrams, including using Venn diagrams and flow charts for classification. Whenever possible, students should be encouraged to include illustrations of figures in their notes. Further suggestions for keeping a notebook can be found on page 386.

For more support on notetaking, see:

- Notetaking Guide Workbook
- Notetaking Transparencies

Chapter 8 Getting Ready to Learn

Word Watch

Review Words

point, p. 718
line, p. 718
ray, p. 718
plane, p. 718
angle, p. 719
vertex, p. 719
degree, p. 721

Review What You Need to Know

Using Vocabulary **Identify the object with a review word.** *(p. 718)*

1. line **2.** point **3.** angle

4. Copy and complete with a review word: An angle is measured in _?_. degrees

Use a protractor to measure the angle. *(p. 721)*

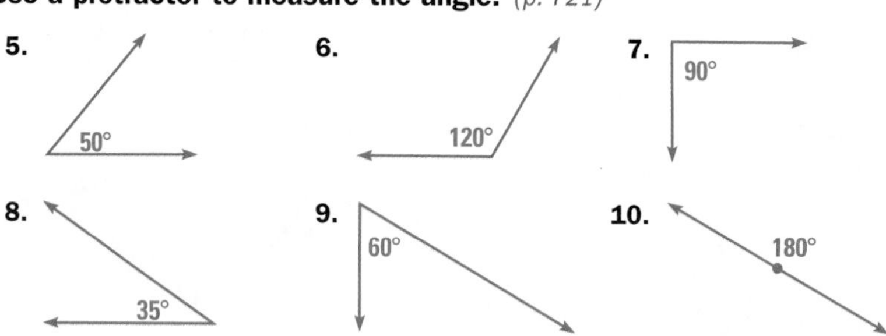

11. You have a giant crayon that is a scale model of a regular crayon. A regular crayon is about 0.25 inch wide and 3.5 inches long. The giant crayon is 6 inches wide. How long is it? *(p. 322)* **84 in.**

Notebook

You should include material that appears on a notebook like this in your own notes.

Know How to Take Notes

Making a Concept Map You will often learn new concepts that are related to each other. It is helpful to organize these concepts in your notes with a map or chart.

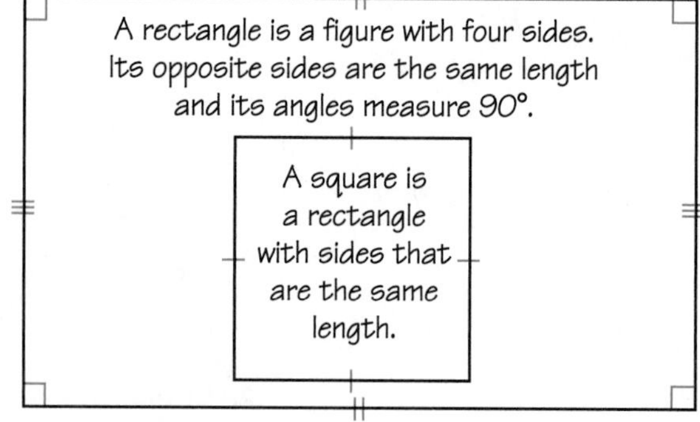

A rectangle is a figure with four sides.
Its opposite sides are the same length
and its angles measure 90°.
A square is
a rectangle
with sides that
are the same
length.

In Lesson 8.3, you can use a concept map to organize information about special four-sided shapes.

Angle Pairs

BEFORE	Now	WHY?
You solved equations to find the value of a variable.	You'll solve equations to find angle measures.	So you can design stationery, as in Ex. 13.

Word Watch

straight angle, right angle, p. 375
supplementary, complementary angles, p. 375
vertical angles, p. 376
perpendicular lines, p. 376
parallel lines, p. 377

A **straight angle** measures 180°. A **right angle** measures 90°. The mark ⌝ tells you that an angle measures 90°.

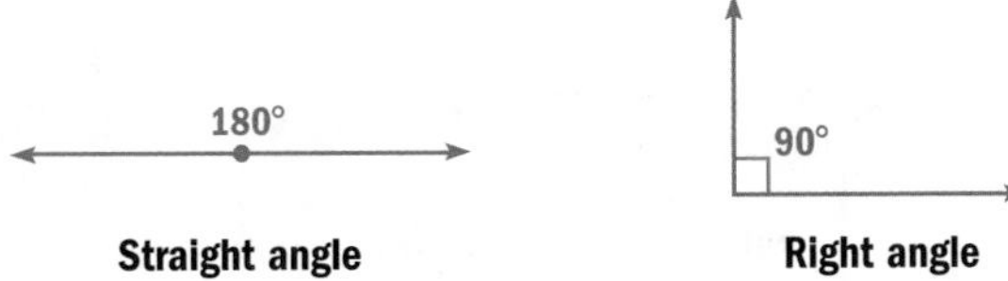

Straight angle   Right angle

Two angles are **supplementary** if the sum of their measures is 180°. Two angles are **complementary** if the sum of their measures is 90°. You can write "the measure of angle 1" as $m\angle 1$.

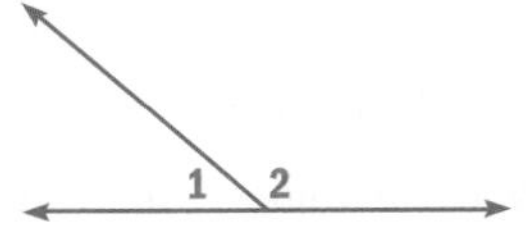

$\angle 1$ and $\angle 2$ are supplementary.
$m\angle 1 + m\angle 2 = 180°$

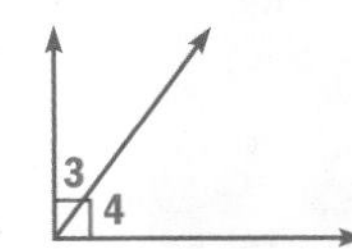

$\angle 3$ and $\angle 4$ are complementary.
$m\angle 3 + m\angle 4 = 90°$

EXAMPLE 1 Finding an Angle Measure

$\angle 1$ and $\angle 2$ are complementary, and $m\angle 2 = 32°$. Find $m\angle 1$.

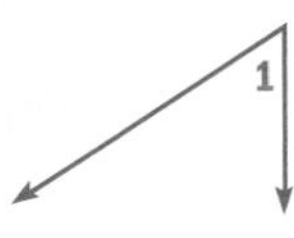

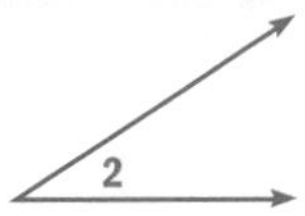

Solution

$m\angle 1 + m\angle 2 = 90°$	Definition of complementary angles
$m\angle 1 + 32° = 90°$	Substitute 32° for $m\angle 2$.
$m\angle 1 = 58°$	Subtract 32° from each side.

Your turn now Tell whether $\angle 1$ and $\angle 2$ are *complementary*, *supplementary*, or *neither*.

1. $m\angle 1 = 79°$, $m\angle 2 = 101°$ supplementary
2. $m\angle 1 = 64°$, $m\angle 2 = 36°$ neither
3. $m\angle 1 = 52°$, $m\angle 2 = 38°$ complementary
4. $m\angle 1 = 44°$, $m\angle 2 = 46°$ complementary
5. $m\angle 1 = 53°$, $m\angle 2 = 47°$ neither
6. $m\angle 1 = 95°$, $m\angle 2 = 85°$ supplementary

ILLINOIS Standards and ISAT:
7.A.3b; 8.A.3b

1 PLAN

SKILL CHECK

Solve.

1. $74 + x = 90$ **16**
2. $x + 21 = 90$ **69**
3. $89 + x = 180$ **91**
4. $x + 45 = 180$ **135**

Lesson Objective

Solve equations to find angle measures.

Pacing

Suggested Number of Days
Basic Course: 2 days
Average Course: 2 days
Advanced Course: 2 days
Block: 1 block

Teaching Resources

For a complete list of Teaching Resources, see page 372B.

Transparency

Warm-Up Exercises for this lesson are available on a transparency.

TEACH

Motivating the Lesson

Ask students what they know about angle measurement and angle relationships.

TIPS FOR NEW TEACHERS

Students often confuse *complementary* and *supplementary*. Have them suggest mnemonics to remember the terms, such as Complement is to Corner as Supplement is to Straight. See Tips for New Teachers in the *Chapter 8 Resource Book*.

EXTRA EXAMPLES

Example 1 $\angle 1$ and $\angle 2$ are complementary, and $m\angle 2 = 71°$. Find $m\angle 1$. **19°**

Example 2 Find $m\angle 2$, $m\angle 3$, and $m\angle 4$.

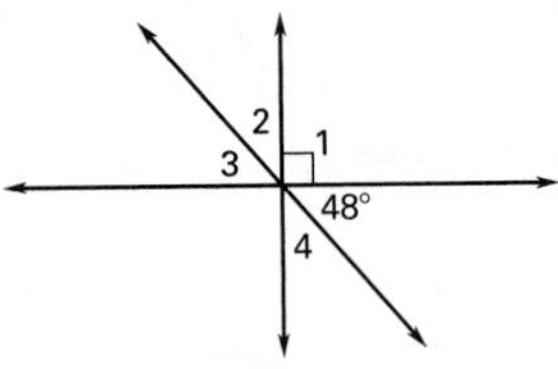

$m\angle 2 = 42°$, $m\angle 3 = 48°$, $m\angle 4 = 42°$

Example 3 Use the diagram to find $m\angle 8$. **35°**

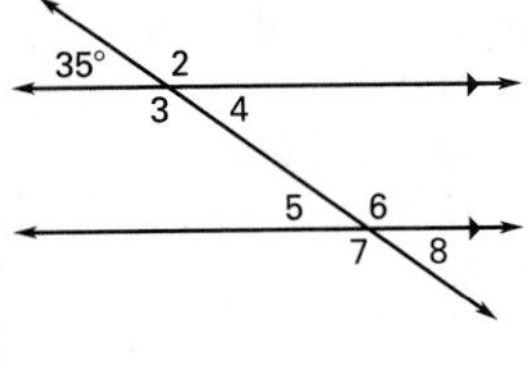

VISUALIZE

Have students find examples in the classroom of right angles, vertical angles, and parallel and perpendicular lines.

Vertical Angles When two lines intersect at a point, they form two pairs of angles that do not share a side. These pairs are called **vertical angles**, and they always have the same measure.

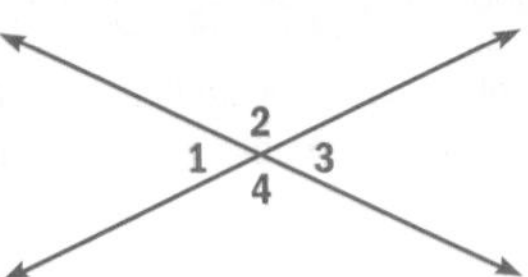

$\angle 1$ and $\angle 3$ are vertical angles. $m\angle 1 = m\angle 3$

$\angle 2$ and $\angle 4$ are vertical angles. $m\angle 2 = m\angle 4$

EXAMPLE 2 Using Vertical Angles

Find $m\angle 2$, $m\angle 3$, and $m\angle 4$.

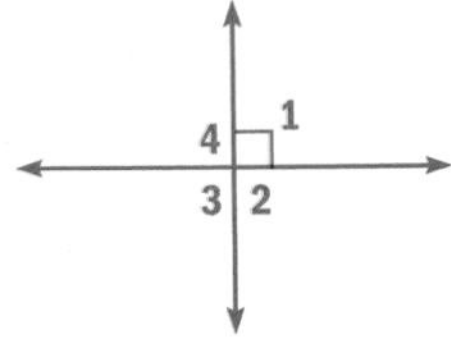

Solution

The diagram shows that $m\angle 1 = 90°$.

$\angle 1$ and $\angle 3$ are vertical angles. Their measures are equal, so $m\angle 3 = 90°$.

$\angle 1$ and $\angle 2$ are supplementary.

$m\angle 1 + m\angle 2 = 180°$	Definition of supplementary angles
$90° + m\angle 2 = 180°$	Substitute 90° for $m\angle 1$.
$m\angle 2 = 90°$	Subtract 90° from each side.

$\angle 2$ and $\angle 4$ are vertical angles. Their measures are equal, so $m\angle 4 = 90°$.

ANSWER $m\angle 2 = m\angle 3 = m\angle 4 = 90°$

Perpendicular Lines You saw in Example 2 that when two lines intersect to form one right angle, they form four right angles. Two lines that intersect at a right angle are called **perpendicular lines**.

Your turn now **Find the measures of the numbered angles.**

7.

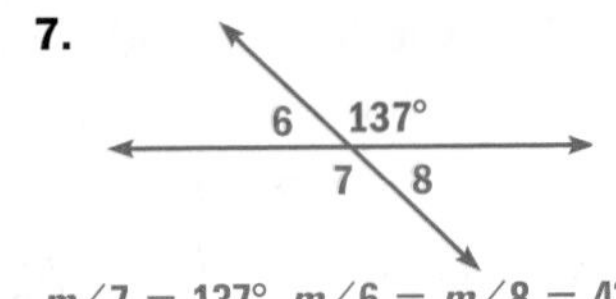

$m\angle 7 = 137°$, $m\angle 6 = m\angle 8 = 43°$

8.

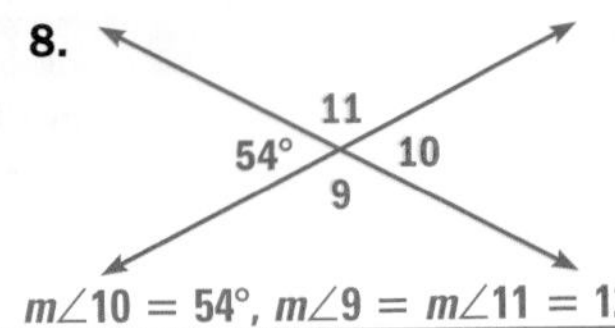

$m\angle 10 = 54°$, $m\angle 9 = m\angle 11 = 126°$

Parallel Lines Two lines in the same plane that do not intersect are called **parallel lines**. When a line intersects two parallel lines, several pairs of angles that are formed have equal measures.

Angles and Parallel Lines

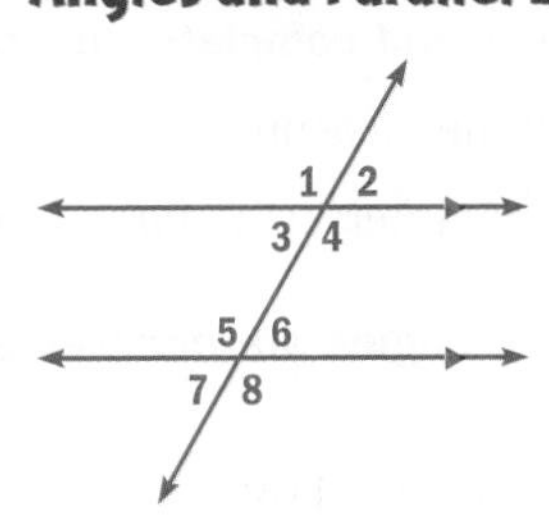

Corresponding Angles

$m\angle 1 = m\angle 5$ $m\angle 2 = m\angle 6$
$m\angle 3 = m\angle 7$ $m\angle 4 = m\angle 8$

Alternate Interior Angles

$m\angle 3 = m\angle 6$ $m\angle 4 = m\angle 5$

Alternate Exterior Angles

$m\angle 1 = m\angle 8$ $m\angle 2 = m\angle 7$

HELP with Solving

Triangles on lines indicate that lines are parallel.

EXAMPLE 3 Using Parallel Lines

Use the diagram to find $m\angle 1$.

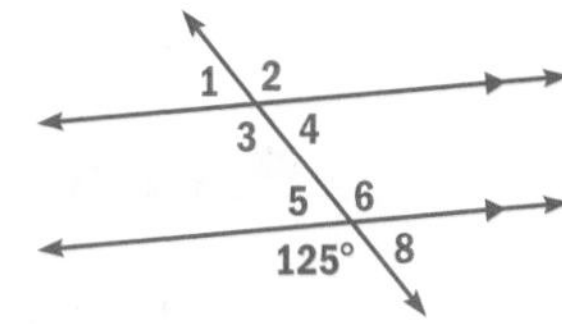

Solution

$\angle 1$ and $\angle 5$ are corresponding angles, so they have equal measures. Find $m\angle 5$.

The angle with measure 125° and $\angle 5$ are supplementary.

$m\angle 5 + 125° = 180°$ **Definition of supplementary angles**

$m\angle 5 = 55°$ **Subtract 125° from each side.**

$\angle 1$ and $\angle 5$ have equal measures.

ANSWER $m\angle 1 = 55°$

Your turn now **Find the angle measure.**

9. $m\angle 2$ 85° **10.** $m\angle 3$ 95°

11. $m\angle 4$ 85° **12.** $m\angle 6$ 85°

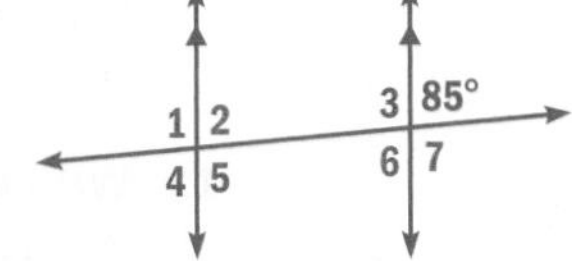

TEACHING TIP

In Example 3, point out that the same person can be a sister, a mother, and an aunt to different people. These terms describe relationships. In the same way, for example, the same angle can be a vertical angle, a corresponding angle, and an alternate interior angle to different angles.

Differentiating Instruction

Less Proficient Students Many students will need extra help to become comfortable with the angle terms before Example 3. Ask them the everyday meanings of "corresponding," "alternate," "interior," and "exterior." Identify answers that can be used to help explain the meanings of the terms.

CONCEPT CHECK

What are the similarities and differences between a pair of alternate interior angles and a pair of alternate exterior angles? **Each is a pair of congruent angles lying on opposite sides of a line that intersects two parallel lines. Alternate interior angles both lie inside the parallel lines, while alternate exterior angles both lie outside the parallel lines.**

DAILY PUZZLER

Two lines intersect to form four angles, each supplementary to the other three. What do you know about the lines? **They are perpendicular.**

3 APPLY

ASSIGNMENT GUIDE

Basic Course

Day 1: SRH p. 719 Exs. 1–6; pp. 378–379 Exs. 6–8, 13, 16, 19–22

Day 2: SRH p. 719 Exs. 7–10; pp. 378–379 Exs. 9–11, 14, 23–27

Average Course

Day 1: pp. 378–379 Exs. 6–10, 16, 23–27

Day 2: pp. 378–379 Exs. 11–14, 17–22

Advanced Course

Day 1: pp. 378–379 Exs. 6–10, 18–22

Day 2: pp. 378–379 Exs. 11–17*, 25–27

Block

pp. 378–379 Exs. 6–14, 16–27

EXTRA PRACTICE

- Student Edition, p. 734
- Chapter 8 Resource Book, pp. 8–10
- Test and Practice Generator

TRANSPARENCY

Even-numbered answers are available on transparencies.

HOMEWORK CHECK

When you review students' homework for this lesson, go over the following exercises to check understanding of key concepts.

Basic: 6, 7, 8, 10, 14

Average: 6, 7, 8, 11, 14

Advanced: 6, 8, 10, 13, 14

11.

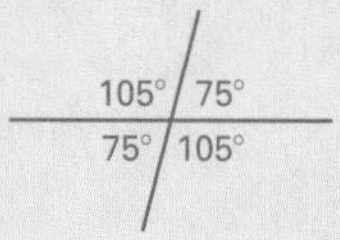

8.1 Exercises

More Practice, p. 734

INTERNET eWorkbook Plus CLASSZONE.COM

Getting Ready to Practice

Vocabulary **Copy and complete the statement.**

1. The sum of the measures of two __?__ angles is 180°. supplementary
2. Two lines that intersect to form a right angle are called __?__. perpendicular

Tell whether the angles are *complementary, supplementary,* or *neither.*

3. $m\angle 1 = 62°$, $m\angle 2 = 118°$ supplementary
4. $m\angle 1 = 51°$, $m\angle 2 = 39°$ complementary
5. **Find the Error** Describe and correct the error in the solution. Vertical angles have the same measure, so $m\angle 2 = 112°$.

X $m\angle 2 = 68°$, because vertical angles add up to 180°.

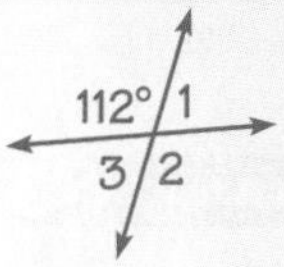

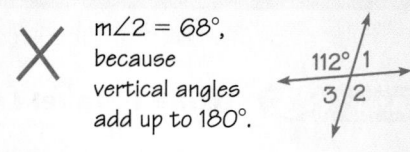

Practice and Problem Solving

HELP with Homework

Example	Exercises
1	6-7, 13
2	8-11
3	14

Online Resources CLASSZONE.COM
- More Examples
- eTutorial Plus

A **Find the angle measure.**

6. $\angle 1$ and $\angle 2$ are complementary, and $m\angle 1 = 56°$. Find $m\angle 2$. 34°
7. $\angle 3$ and $\angle 4$ are supplementary, and $m\angle 4 = 71°$. Find $m\angle 3$. 109°

Find the measures of the numbered angles.

8.

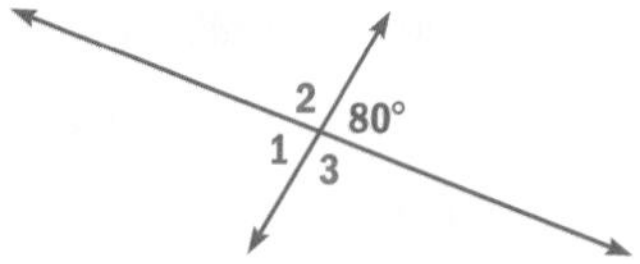

$m\angle 1 = 80°$, $m\angle 2 = m\angle 3 = 100°$

9.

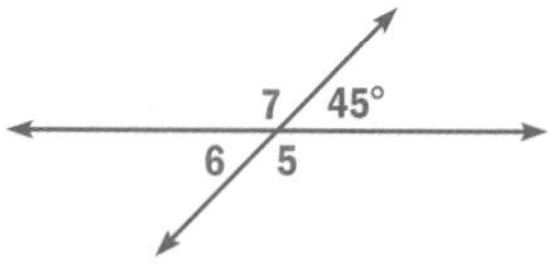

$m\angle 6 = 45°$, $m\angle 5 = m\angle 7 = 135°$

10. **Weaving** Find the angle measures in the weaving if $m\angle 1 = 122°$.
$m\angle 2 = 58°$, $m\angle 3 = 122°$, $m\angle 4 = 58°$

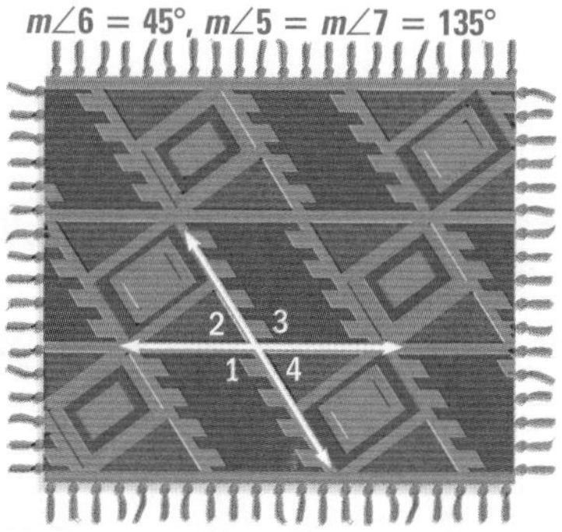

B 11. **Intersecting Streets** Two streets intersect to form a 75° angle. Sketch the intersection and find the measure of each angle formed. See margin.

12. **Writing** Can parallel lines form vertical angles? Explain.
No; parallel lines never intersect.

13. Stationery A student designed the stationery border shown here. Explain how to find $m\angle 2$ if $m\angle 1 = 135°$.
Sample answer: Together, the angles form a straight angle, so the sum of their measures is 180°. So, $135° + m\angle 2 = 180°$ and $m\angle 2 = 180° - 135° = 45°$.

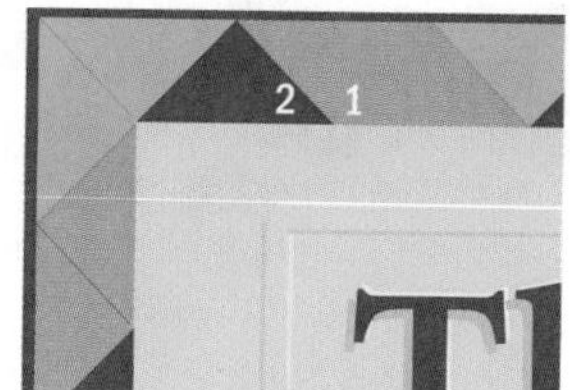

14. In the diagram, $m\angle 4 = 44°$. Find the measure of each angle.
$m\angle 1 = m\angle 3 = m\angle 6 = m\angle 8 = 136°$; $m\angle 2 = m\angle 5 = m\angle 7 = 44°$

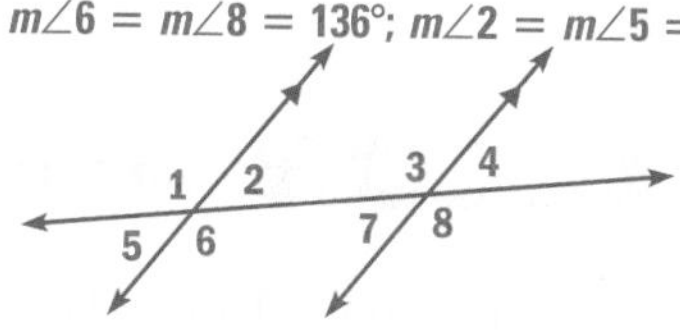

C **15. Challenge** Find the measure of each angle if $m\angle 9 = 106°$.

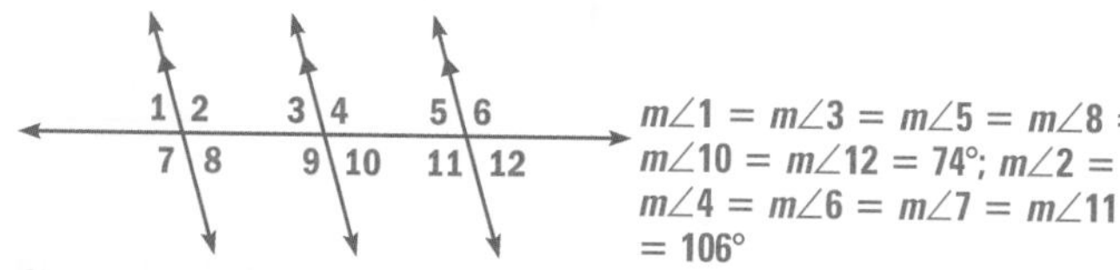

$m\angle 1 = m\angle 3 = m\angle 5 = m\angle 8 = m\angle 10 = m\angle 12 = 74°$; $m\angle 2 = m\angle 4 = m\angle 6 = m\angle 7 = m\angle 11 = 106°$

Algebra Find the value of the variable and the angle measures.

16. $m\angle 1 = (5x + 15)°$ and $m\angle 2 = 28x°$
$x = 5$; $m\angle 1 = 40°$, $m\angle 2 = 140°$

17. $m\angle 6 = (100 - 10y)°$ and $m\angle 3 = 45y°$
See margin.

18. $m\angle 4 = (7n + 39)°$ and $m\angle 5 = (11n - 13)°$
$n = 13$; $m\angle 4 = 130°$, $m\angle 5 = 130°$

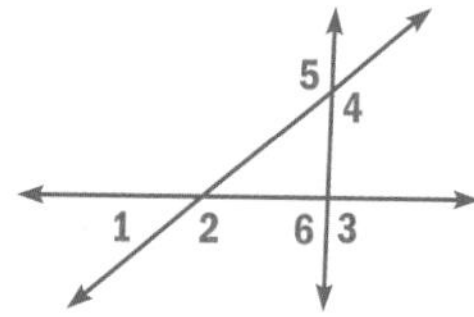

17. $y = 2\frac{2}{7}$; $m\angle 6 = 77\frac{1}{7}°$; $m\angle 3 = 102\frac{6}{7}°$

Mixed Review

Write the percent as a fraction in simplest form. *(Lesson 7.4)*

19. 22.6% $\frac{113}{500}$ **20.** 6.5% $\frac{13}{200}$ **21.** 0.45% $\frac{9}{2000}$ **22.** 602% $6\frac{1}{50}$

Basic Skills Find the area of a triangle with the given base and height.

23. $b = 3$ in., $h = 2$ in. 3 in.^2 **24.** $b = 9$ cm, $h = 4$ cm 18 cm^2 **25.** $b = 13$ ft, $h = 5$ ft 32.5 ft^2

Test-Taking Practice

26. Multiple Choice Which angles are complementary? B

A. $\angle 1$ and $\angle 2$ **B.** $\angle 2$ and $\angle 3$

C. $\angle 3$ and $\angle 4$ **D.** $\angle 4$ and $\angle 1$

27. Short Response In the diagram, $m\angle 3 = 43°$. Explain how to find $m\angle 2$.

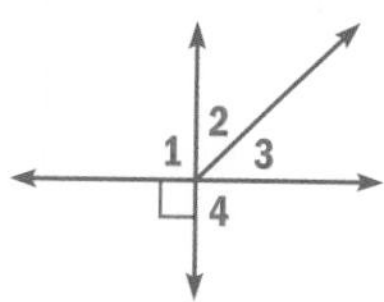

27. Since $\angle 2$ and $\angle 3$ are complementary, subtract 43° from 90° to find $m\angle 2$.

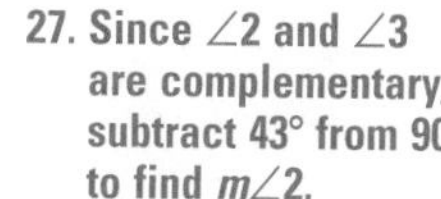

4 ASSESS

Assessment Resources

For more assessment resources, see:
- Assessment Book
- Test and Practice Generator

Mini-Quiz

1. $\angle 1$ and $\angle 2$ are complementary, and $m\angle 1 = 31°$. Find $m\angle 2$. 59°
2. $\angle 3$ and $\angle 4$ are supplementary, and $m\angle 3 = 71°$. Find $m\angle 4$. 109°
3. In the diagram, $m\angle 4 = 38°$. Find the measure of each angle.

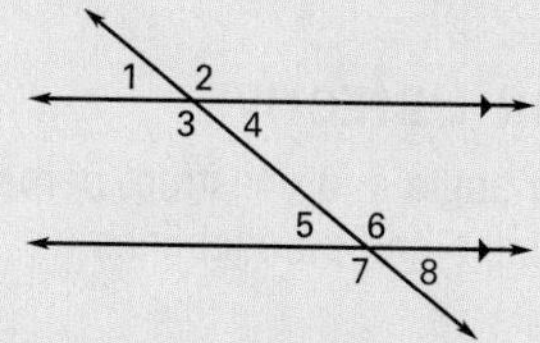

$m\angle 1 = m\angle 5 = m\angle 8 = 38°$, $m\angle 2 = m\angle 3 = m\angle 6 = m\angle 7 = 142°$

5 FOLLOW-UP

Reteaching/Remediation

- Study Guide in Chapter 8 Resource Book, pp. 11–12
- Tutor Place, Geometry and Measurement Cards 3, 4
- eTutorial Plus Online
- Extra Practice, p. 734
- Lesson Practice in Chapter 8 Resource Book, pp. 8–10

Challenge/Enrichment

- Challenge Practice in Chapter 8 Resource Book, p. 13
- Teacher's Edition, p. 372F

English Learner Support

- Spanish Study Guide
- Multi-Language Glossary
- Chapter Audio Summaries CDs

1 PLAN

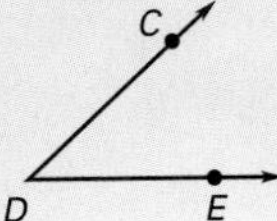

SKILL CHECK

Use the figure for Questions 1 and 2.

1. Name the vertex of the angle. **D**
2. Name the rays that form the angle. $\overrightarrow{DC}$ **and** $\overrightarrow{DE}$
3. What is the measure of a right angle? **90°**

LESSON OBJECTIVE

Copy an angle and construct perpendicular lines and parallel lines.

2 TEACH

EXTRA EXAMPLES

Example 1 Draw an angle whose measure is greater than 90° but less than 180°. Then copy the angle.

Sample:

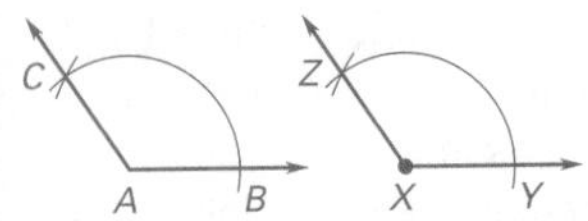

TEACHING TIP

In Example 1, encourage students to draw their own acute angles and not to try to copy the one in the text.

TRANSPARENCY

A support transparency is available for this Special Topic.

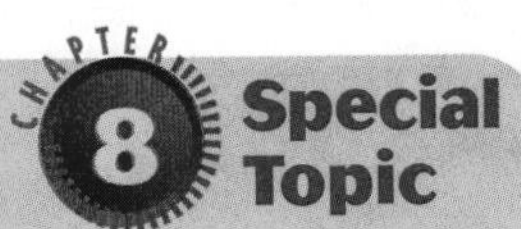

Constructions

GOAL Copy an angle and construct perpendicular lines and parallel lines.

You can *construct* geometric figures using special tools. A *compass* is used to draw parts of circles called *arcs*. A *straightedge* is used to draw a straight line.

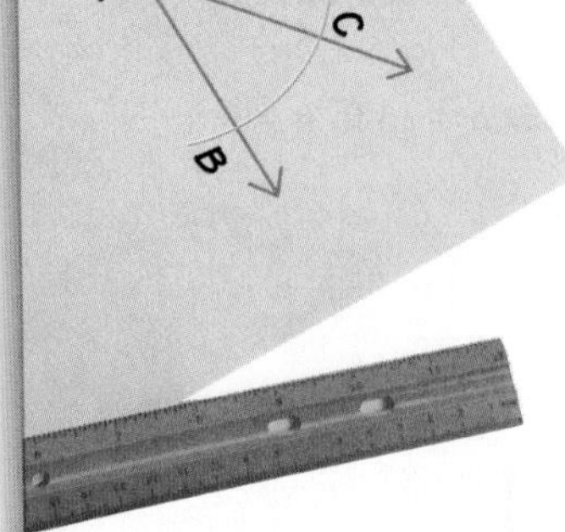

EXAMPLE 1 Copying an Angle

1 Draw an angle. Label its vertex A. Then draw a ray with endpoint X.

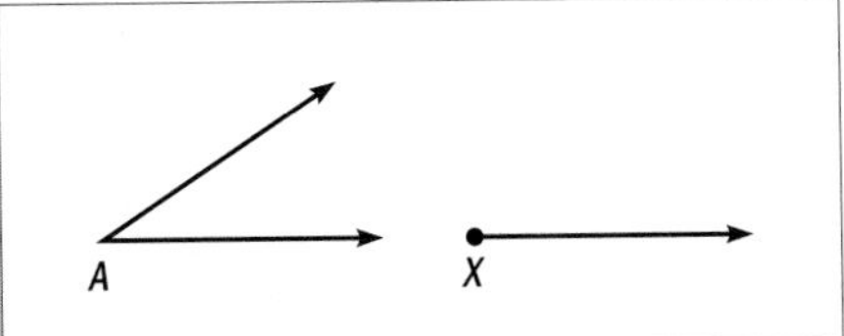

2 Draw an arc with center A. Label B and C on $\angle A$. Use the same compass setting to draw an arc with center X. Label point Y.

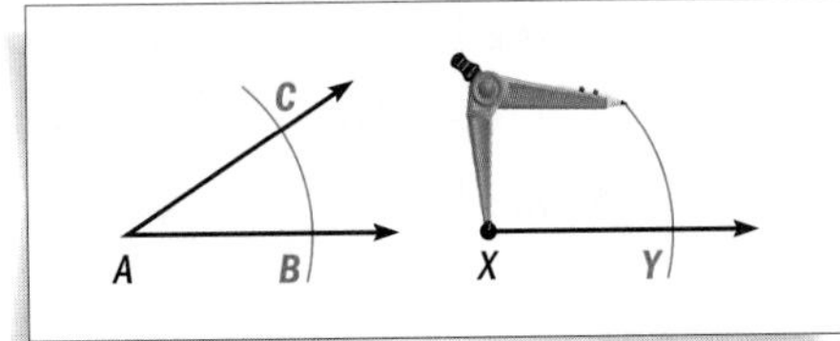

3 Draw an arc with center B that passes through C. Use the same compass setting to draw an arc with center Y. Label point Z.

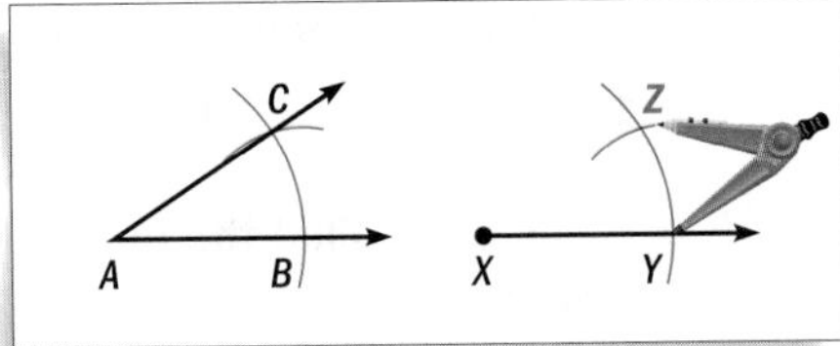

4 Use a straightedge to draw a ray with endpoint X through Z.

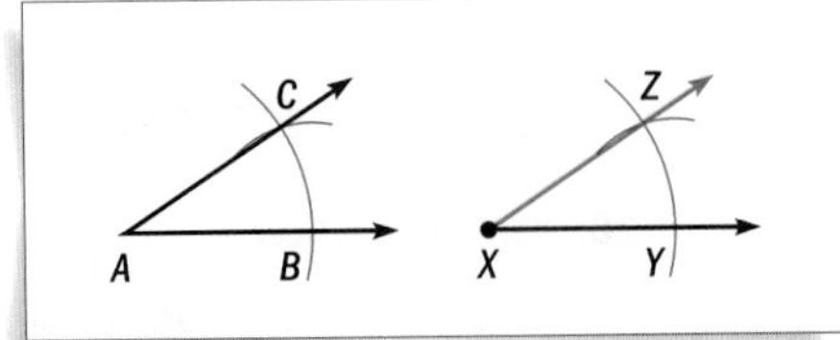

✓**CHECK** Use a protractor to check that $m\angle A = m\angle X$.

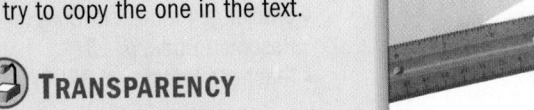

ILLINOIS Standards and ISAT:
9.A.3a

EXAMPLE 2 Constructing a Perpendicular Line

1 Draw a line and a point *P* not on the line. Draw an arc with center *P* that intersects the line twice. Label *A* and *B*. Using the same compass setting, draw arcs with centers *A* and *B*.

2 Where the last two arcs intersect label point *Q*. Draw a line through *P* and *Q*. The two lines are perpendicular.

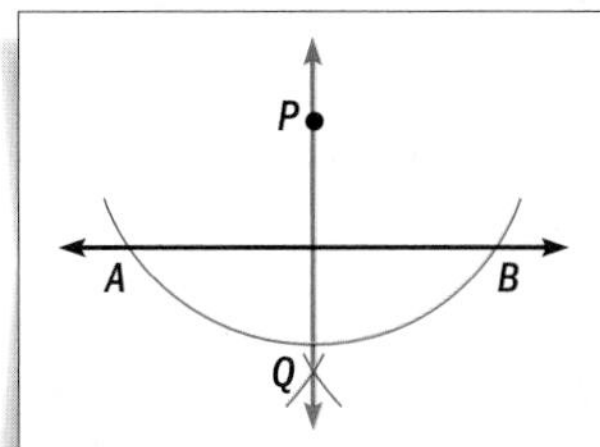

HELP with Solving

The method of construction shown in Example 2 can also work when *P* is on the line through points *A* and *B*. For the last two arcs, use a compass setting greater than half the distance from *A* to *B*.

EXAMPLE 3 Constructing a Parallel Line

1 Follow the steps in Example 2 to construct perpendicular lines. Label ∠1.

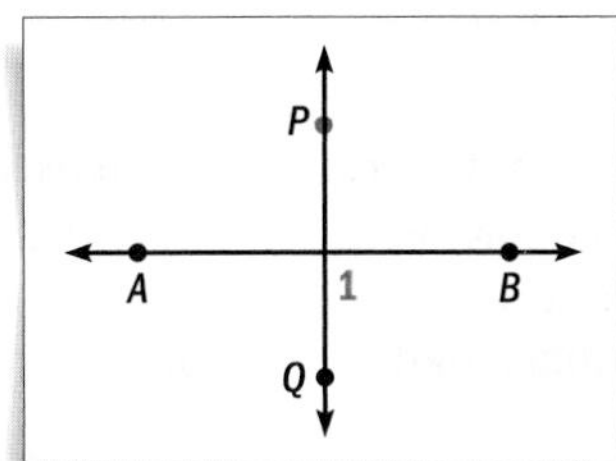

2 Follow the steps in Example 1 to copy ∠1 at point *P* as shown.

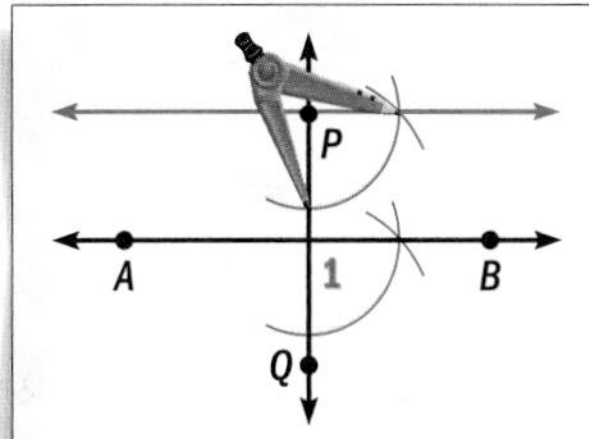

Exercises

Use a protractor to draw an angle with the given measure. Then use a compass and straightedge to copy the angle. 1–4. See margin.

1. 45° **2.** 120° **3.** 135° **4.** 60°

5. Use a compass and a straightedge to construct three parallel lines. See margin.

6. Use a compass and straightedge to construct one right triangle. See margin.

7. Use a compass and straightedge to construct a rectangle. See margin.

EXTRA EXAMPLES

Example 2 Draw a line and a point *P* on the line. Draw an arc with center *P* that intersects the line twice. Label the intersection points *A* and *B*. Using the same compass setting, draw arcs with centers *A* and *B*. Where the last two arcs intersect label point *Q*. Draw a line through *P* and *Q*. The two lines are perpendicular.

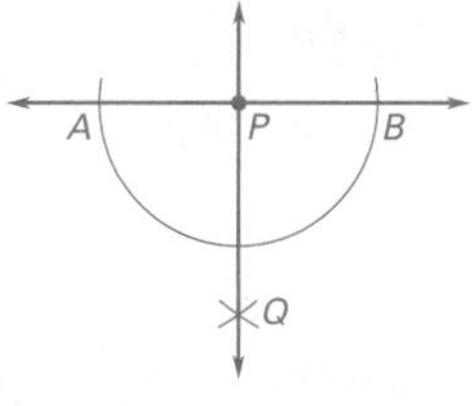

COMMON ERROR

In Example 2, watch for students who try to copy the figures without carefully reading the directions. Students may label arbitrary points on the line *A* and *B* and begin by placing the compass on *B*. Urge students to read the directions carefully before beginning.

3 APPLY

TRANSPARENCY

Even-numbered answers are available on transparencies.

TEACHING TIP

Point out that there may be more than one way to construct a figure. For example, in Exercise 5, students can construct two parallel lines above $\overleftrightarrow{AB}$, two parallel lines below $\overleftrightarrow{AB}$, or one parallel line above and one parallel line below $\overleftrightarrow{AB}$. In Exercise 7, they can construct three perpendicular lines or two perpendicular lines and one parallel line.

1–7. See Additional Answers beginning on page AA1.

PLAN

SKILL CHECK

Solve.

1. $x + 90 + 30 = 180$ **60**
2. $x + 11 + 21 = 180$ **148**
3. $44 + 35 + x = 180$ **101**

LESSON OBJECTIVE

Classify angles and triangles.

PACING

Suggested Number of Days
Basic Course: 1 day
Average Course: 1 day
Advanced Course: 1 day
Block: 0.5 block with 8.3

TEACHING RESOURCES

For a complete list of Teaching Resources, see page 372B.

TRANSPARENCY

Warm-Up Exercises for this lesson are available on a transparency.

TEACH

MOTIVATING THE LESSON

As you describe acute, right, obtuse, and straight angles, have students model each type using their arms.

TIPS FOR NEW TEACHERS

Make cards with each class of triangle by angle and by side. Have students take turns picking an angle card and a side card without looking and then draw a triangle that fits both cards or tell why no triangle fits both cards. See Tips for New Teachers in the *Chapter 8 Resource Book*.

Angles and Triangles

BEFORE	Now	WHY?
You identified pairs of angles.	You'll classify angles and triangles.	So you can classify referee signals, as in Exs. 6–8.

Word Watch

acute, right, obtuse angle, p. 382
acute, right, obtuse triangle, p. 382
equilateral, isosceles, scalene triangle, p. 382

Classifying Angles An angle can be classified by its measure.

Acute angle	Right angle	Obtuse angle
	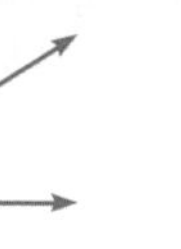	
Measure is less than 90°.	Measure is exactly 90°.	Measure is greater than 90° and less than 180°.

Notebook

Classifying Triangles

By Angles

An **acute triangle** has three acute angles.	A **right triangle** has one right angle.	An **obtuse triangle** has one obtuse angle.
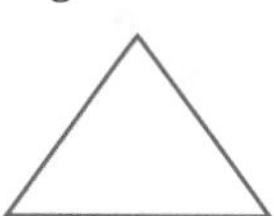		

By Sides

An **equilateral triangle** has three sides of equal length.	An **isosceles triangle** has at least two sides of equal length.	A **scalene triangle** has no sides of equal length.
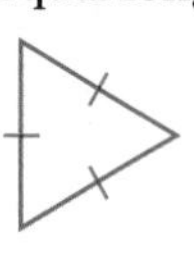	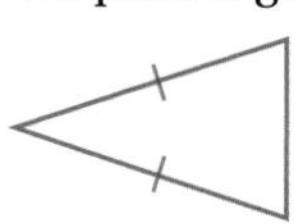	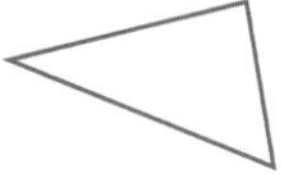

EXAMPLE 1 **Classifying a Triangle**

Classify the triangle by its side lengths.

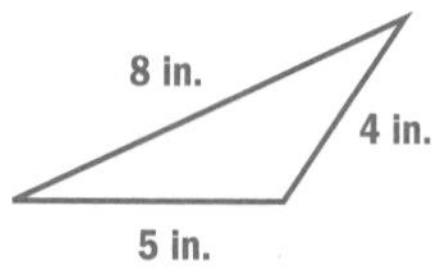

ANSWER The triangle has no sides of equal length. So, it is a scalene triangle.

ILLINOIS Standards and ISAT:
9.B.3; 7.A.3b

with Reading

Tick marks in a drawing show that side lengths are equal. Arc marks show that angle measures are equal.

EXAMPLE 2 Classifying a Triangle

Classify the triangle by its angles and by its side lengths.

ANSWER The triangle has one right angle and two sides of equal length. So, it is a right isosceles triangle.

Angles in a Triangle From the figures below, you can see that the sum of the angle measures in the triangle is 180°. This is true for all triangles.

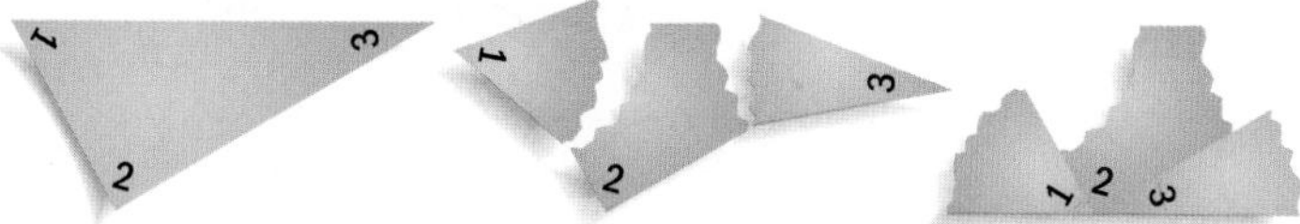

EXAMPLE 3 Finding an Unknown Angle Measure

Find the value of *x*. Then classify the triangle by its angles.

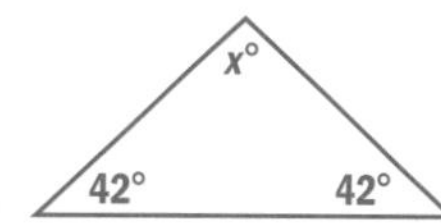

Solution

The sum of the angle measures in a triangle is 180°.

$x° + 42° + 42° = 180°$	Write an equation.
$x + 84 = 180$	Add.
$x + 84 - 84 = 180 - 84$	Subtract 84 from each side.
$x = 96$	Simplify.

ANSWER The triangle has one obtuse angle, so it is an obtuse triangle.

Your turn now **Find the value of *x*. Then classify the triangle by its angles.**

1. 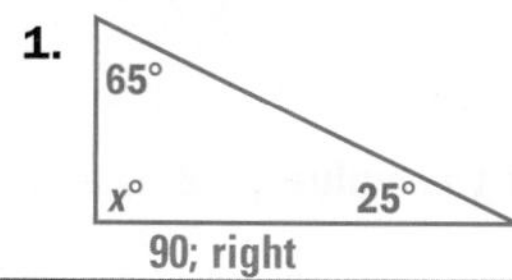

90; right

2. 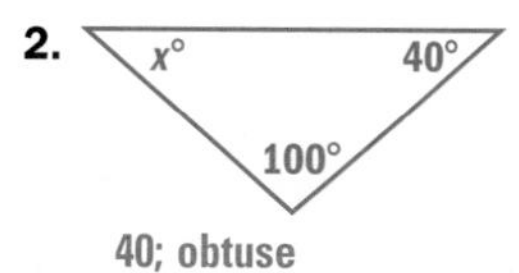

40; obtuse

EXTRA EXAMPLES

Example 1 Classify the triangle by its side lengths.

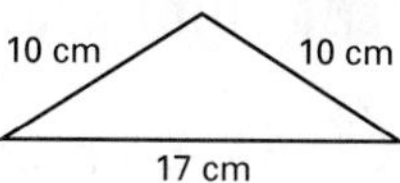

isosceles

Example 2 Classify the triangle by its angles and by its side lengths. **acute scalene**

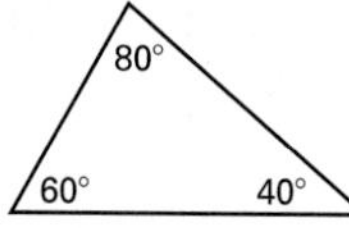

Example 3 Find the value of *x*. Then classify the triangle.

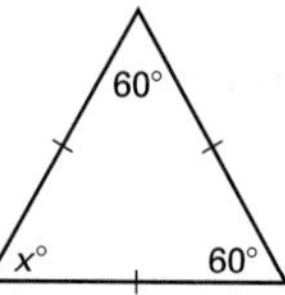

60; equilateral

CONCEPT CHECK

Can you draw a right equilateral triangle? Explain. **No; each angle of an equilateral triangle measures 60°.**

DAILY PUZZLER

A triangle has angle measures of x, y, and $z + 90$, where $x \neq y$ and $z > 0$. Classify the triangle by its angles and by its side lengths. **obtuse scalene**

3 APPLY

ASSIGNMENT GUIDE

Basic Course

Day 1: pp. 384–385 Exs. 6–15, 19–22, 25–30

Average Course

Day 1: pp. 384–385 Exs. 6–16, 19–23, 25–30

Advanced Course

Day 1: pp. 384–385 Exs. 8–13, 15–18, 20–30*

Block

pp. 384–385 Exs. 6–16, 19–23, 25–30 (with 8.3)

EXTRA PRACTICE

- Student Edition, p. 734
- Chapter 8 Resource Book, pp. 19–21
- Test and Practice Generator

TRANSPARENCY

Even-numbered answers are available on transparencies.

HOMEWORK CHECK

When you review students' homework for this lesson, go over the following exercises to check understanding of key concepts.
Basic: 9, 10, 12, 13, 19
Average: 9, 10, 12, 14, 20
Advanced: 10, 11, 13, 15, 21

TEACHING TIP

In Exercise 22, point out to students that an equiangular triangle is equilateral, and vice versa.

8.2 Exercises

More Practice, p. 734

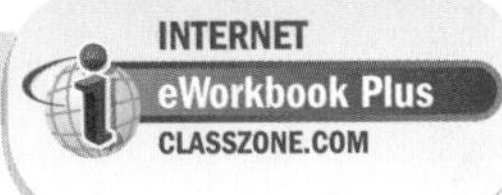

Getting Ready to Practice

Vocabulary **Copy and complete the statement.**

1. A(n) _?_ triangle has no sides of equal length. scalene

Classify the triangle by its side lengths.

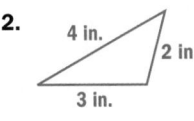

2. (triangle with sides 4 in., 2 in., 3 in.) scalene

3. (triangle with sides 3 ft, 3 ft, 3 ft) equilateral

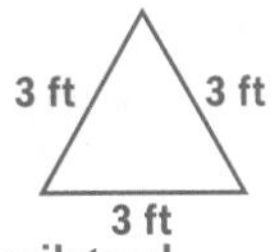

4. 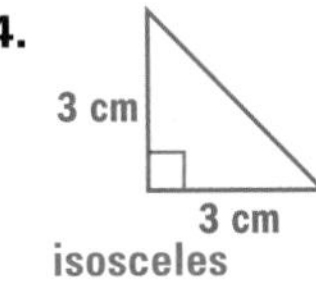

isosceles

5. **Find the Error** Describe and correct the error in the solution.
The triangle has one right angle, so it is a right triangle.

The triangle has an acute angle, so it is an acute triangle.

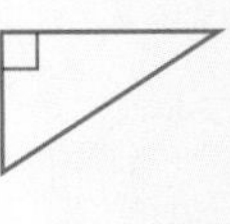

Practice and Problem Solving

HELP with Homework

Example	Exercises
1	9–11, 15
2	9–11
3	12–14

Online Resources CLASSZONE.COM
- More Examples
- eTutorial Plus

A Estimation **The referee is making calls during a hockey game. Classify the angle made by his arms as *acute*, *obtuse*, or *right*.**

6. Cross Checking

acute

7. Roughing

right

8. Delayed calling of penalty

obtuse

Classify the triangle by its side lengths.

9. (right triangle with sides 4 cm, 3 cm, 5 cm) scalene

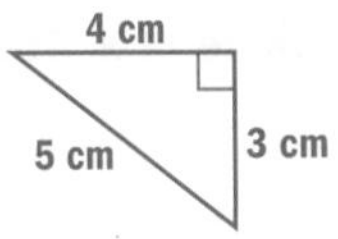

10. 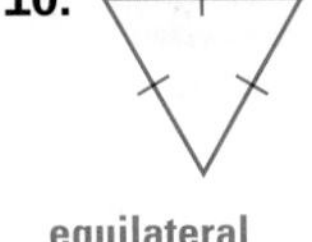
equilateral

11. (triangle with two marked equal sides) isosceles

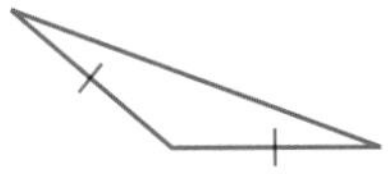

Measurement **Find the value of *x*. Classify the triangle by its angles.**

12. 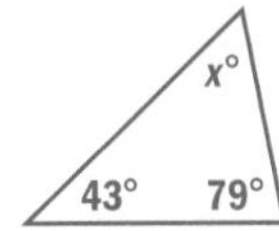

13. 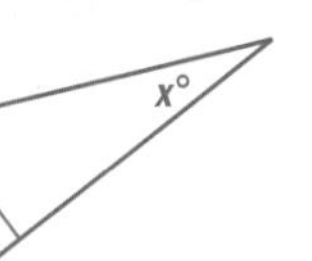

14. 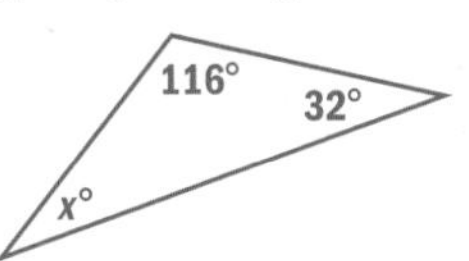

12. 58; acute
13. 24; right
14. 32; obtuse

House of Seven Gables in Salem, Massachusetts

16. No; the sum of the measures of the angles is 181°.

17. Yes; the sum of the measures of the angles is 180°.

18. Yes; the sum of the measures of the angles is 180°.

15. House of Seven Gables If the two side edges of this gable are the same length, what kind of triangle is formed? Explain.
Isosceles; an isosceles triangle has two sides of equal length.

Writing Can the angles in a triangle have the measures given? Explain.

16–18. See margin.

16. 43°, 48°, 90° **17.** 1.5°, 0.5°, 178° **18.** 21.3°, 56.7°, 102°

B **Algebra Find the measure of each angle in the triangle.**

19.

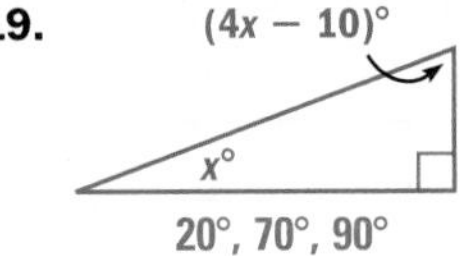

20°, 70°, 90°

20.

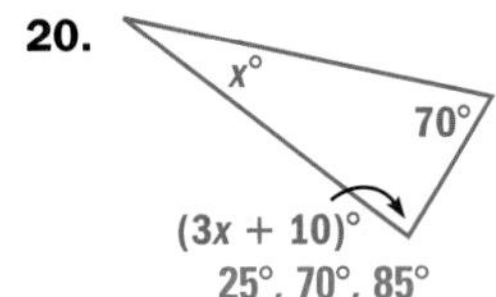

25°, 70°, 85°

21.

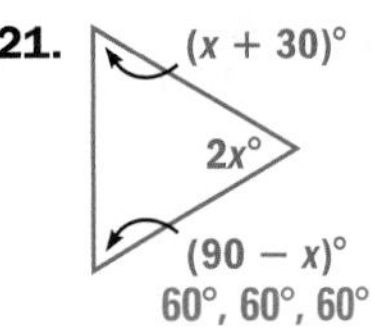

60°, 60°, 60°

22. Mental Math An *equiangular* triangle has three angles with equal measures. Find the measures of those angles.
Each angle measures 60°.

23. Measurement Find the measures of the numbered angles
$m\angle 1 = 75°$, $m\angle 2 = 35°$, $m\angle 3 = 70°$

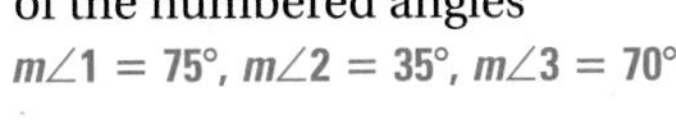

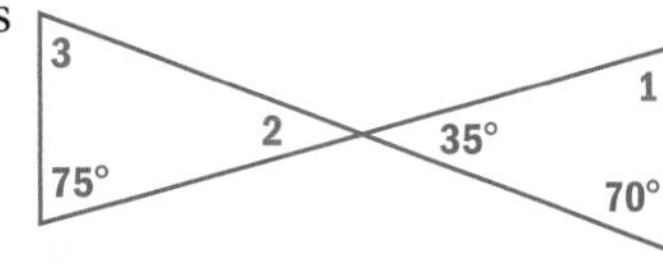

C **24. Challenge** Can two angles of a triangle be supplementary? Explain.
No. *Sample answer:* The sum of two supplementary angles is 180°, which is the same as the sum of all three angles of any triangle.

Mixed Review

Find the perimeter and area of the rectangle. *(Lesson 1.6)*

25. $l = 2$ yd, $w = 0.6$ yd 5.2 yd, 1.2 yd^2 **26.** $l = 13$ m, $w = 12$ m 50 m, 156 m^2

27. Geography Earth's surface is 29.2% land. The total surface area is 510,072,000 square kilometers. Find the total land area. *(Lesson 7.3)*
148,941,024 km^2

28. $\angle 3$ and $\angle 4$ are supplementary and $m\angle 4 = 19°$. Find $m\angle 3$. *(Lesson 8.1)*
161°

Test-Taking Practice

29. Multiple Choice Find the value of x. C

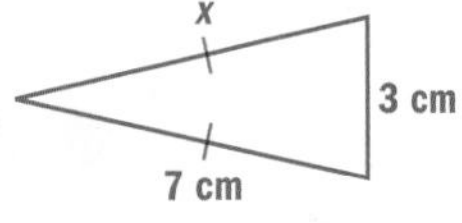

A. 3 cm **B.** 4 cm
C. 7 cm **D.** 10 cm

30. Multiple Choice The angles of a triangle measure 110°, 40°, and $x°$. Find the value of x. F

F. 30 **G.** 60 **H.** 70 **I.** 80

4 ASSESS

Assessment Resources

For more assessment resources, see:
- Assessment Book
- Test and Practice Generator

Mini-Quiz

1. Find the measure of each angle in the triangle. Then classify the triangle by its angles.

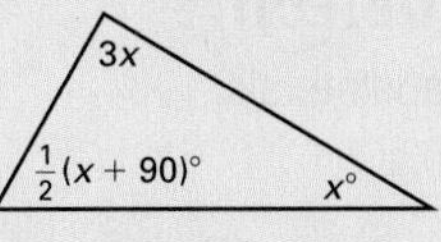

30°, 60°, 90°; right

2. What is a scalene triangle?
a triangle with no sides of equal length
3. What is an acute triangle?
a triangle with three acute angles
4. Can a right triangle be isosceles?
yes

5 FOLLOW-UP

Reteaching/Remediation

- Study Guide in Chapter 8 Resource Book, pp. 22-23
- Tutor Place, Geometry and Measurement Cards 3, 7, 8, 10
- eTutorial Plus Online
- Extra Practice, p. 734
- Lesson Practice in Chapter 8 Resource Book, pp. 19-21

Challenge/Enrichment

- Challenge Practice in Chapter 8 Resource Book, p. 24
- Teacher's Edition, p. 372F

English Learner Support

- Spanish Study Guide
- Multi-Language Glossary
- Chapter Audio Summaries CDs

1 PLAN

SKILL CHECK

Solve.

1. $185 + x = 360$ 175
2. $x + 321 = 360$ 39
3. $232 + x = 360$ 128
4. $455 - x = 360$ 95

LESSON OBJECTIVE

Classify quadrilaterals.

PACING

Suggested Number of Days
Basic Course: 2 days
Average Course: 2 days
Advanced Course: 2 days
Block: 0.5 block with 8.2
0.5 block with 8.4

TEACHING RESOURCES

For a complete list of Teaching Resources, see page 372B.

TRANSPARENCY

Warm-Up Exercises for this lesson are available on a transparency.

2 TEACH

MOTIVATING THE LESSON

To introduce the term *quadrilateral*, ask students if they can think of other words that begin with *quad-* and if they can describe how the number 4 relates to each term.

TIPS FOR NEW TEACHERS

Help students organize the different shapes using a concept map, Venn diagram, or other diagram. See Tips for New Teachers in the *Chapter 8 Resource Book.*

Quadrilaterals

BEFORE	Now	WHY?
You classified angles and triangles.	You'll classify quadrilaterals.	So you can analyze a design, as in Ex. 17.

Word Watch

quadrilateral, p. 386
trapezoid, p. 386
parallelogram, p. 386
rhombus, p. 386

Quadrilaterals A **quadrilateral** is a closed figure with four sides that are line segments. The figures below are special types of quadrilaterals.

Trapezoid

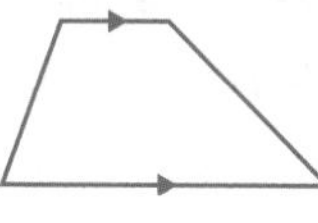

A **trapezoid** is a quadrilateral with exactly 1 pair of parallel sides.

Parallelogram

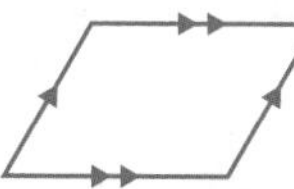

A **parallelogram** is a quadrilateral with both pairs of opposite sides parallel.

Rhombus

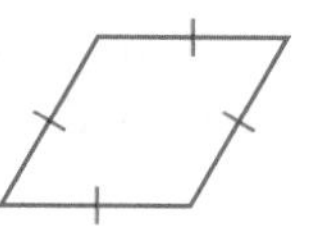

A **rhombus** is a parallelogram with 4 sides of equal length.

Rectangle

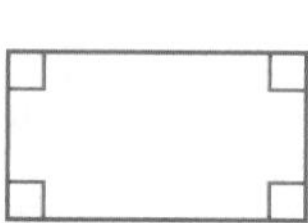

A rectangle is a parallelogram with 4 right angles.

Square

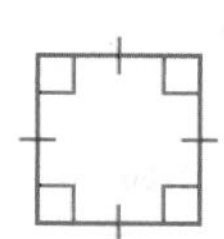

A square is a parallelogram with 4 sides of equal length and 4 right angles.

HELP with Notetaking

You can organize the definitions of quadrilaterals in your notebook using a concept map.

EXAMPLE 1 Classifying a Quadrilateral

Classify the quadrilateral.

5 cm 5 cm 5 cm 5 cm

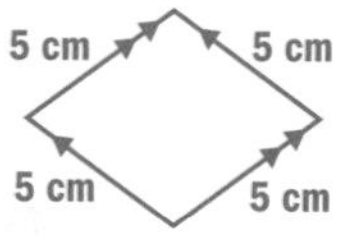

Solution

The quadrilateral is a parallelogram with 4 sides of equal length. So, it is a rhombus.

Your turn now **Classify the quadrilateral.**

1. 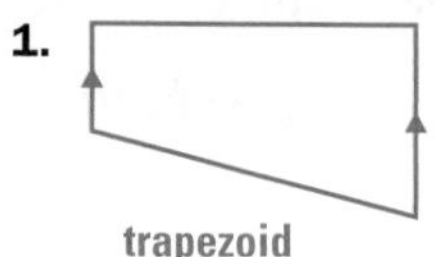
trapezoid

2. 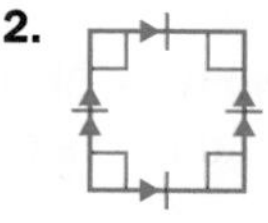

3. 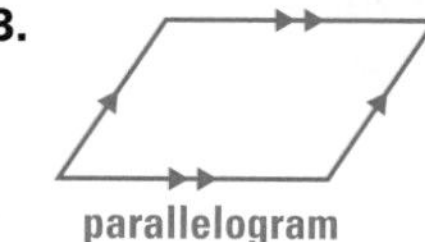
parallelogram

2. parallelogram, rectangle, rhombus, square

ILLINOIS Standards and ISAT:
9.B.3; 7.A.3b

Angle Measures The figures below show that the sum of the angle measures in a quadrilateral is 360°.

Cut a quadrilateral into 2 triangles.

The sum of the angle measures in each triangle is 180°.

The sum of the angle measures in a quadrilateral is $180° + 180° = 360°$.

EXAMPLE 2 Finding an Unknown Angle Measure

Find the value of *x*.

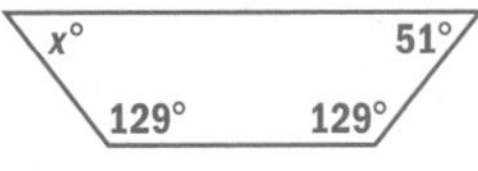

Solution

The sum of the angle measures in a quadrilateral is 360°.

$x° + 51° + 129° + 129° = 360°$ **Write an equation.**

$x + 309 = 360$ **Add.**

$x = 51$ **Subtract 309 from each side.**

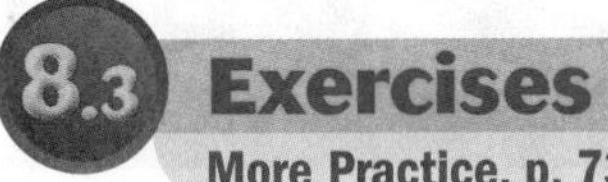

8.3 Exercises

More Practice, p. 734

Getting Ready to Practice

Vocabulary Copy and complete the statement.

1. A _?_ is a quadrilateral with both pairs of opposite sides parallel. parallelogram
2. A _?_ is a quadrilateral with exactly 1 pair of parallel sides. trapezoid
3. A parallelogram with 4 right angles is a _?_. rectangle

Classify the quadrilateral.

4. 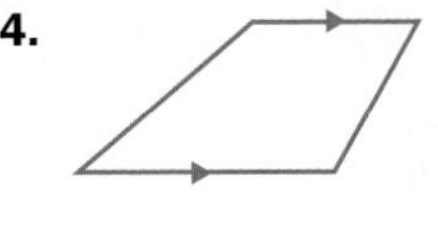

trapezoid

5. 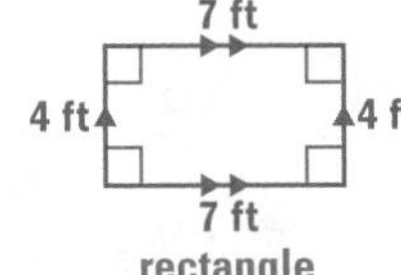

rectangle

6. 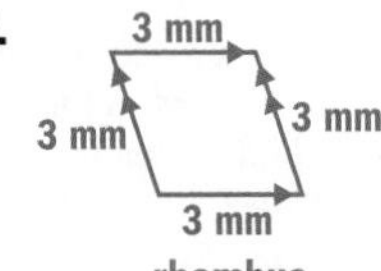

rhombus

7. The angles of a quadrilateral measure 85°, 74°, 110°, and $x°$. Find the value of x. 91

EXTRA EXAMPLES

Example 1 Classify the quadrilateral. rectangle

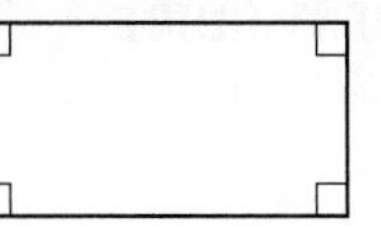

Example 2 Find the value of *x*.

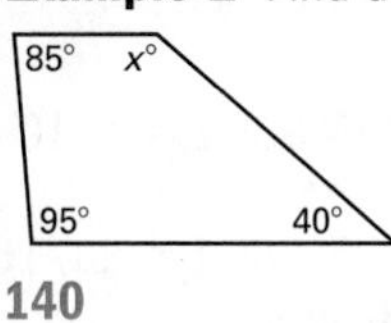

140

MATH REASONING

Have students make a 5-by-5 grid, with the names of the 5 quadrilaterals along the side and top. Have students shade the entries for trapezoid-trapezoid, etc. to exclude them. For each row, have students note in the grid whether the figure is *always*, *sometimes*, or *never* the quadrilateral appearing along the top. Make sure students can explain their reasoning.

CONCEPT CHECK

What distinguishes a trapezoid from a parallelogram? **A trapezoid has exactly 1 pair of parallel sides, while a parallelogram has 2 pairs of parallel sides.**

DAILY PUZZLER

Of the friends Alice, Ben, Celeste, and Diego, one has light brown hair, one dark brown hair, one blond hair, and one black hair. Celeste's hair is lighter than Ben's or Diego's. Alice used to have dark brown hair, and plans to change to blond soon. Ben does not have light brown hair, but his is lighter than Diego's. Match the friends with their hair colors.
Alice: light brown, Ben: dark brown, Celeste: blond, Diego: black

3 APPLY

ASSIGNMENT GUIDE

Basic Course

Day 1: pp. 388–389 Exs. 8–10, 18–20, 27–32

Day 2: pp. 388–389 Exs. 11–16, 21–23, 33–35

Average Course

Day 1: pp. 388–389 Exs. 8–10, 17–19, 27–32

Day 2: pp. 388–389 Exs. 11–16, 22–25, 33–35

Advanced Course

Day 1: pp. 388–389 Exs. 8–10, 17–19, 27–32

Day 2: pp. 388–389 Exs. 11–16, 23–26*, 33–35

Block

pp. 388–389 Exs. 8–10, 17–19, 27–32 (with 8.2)

pp. 388–389 Exs. 11–16, 22–25, 33–35 (with 8.4)

EXTRA PRACTICE

- Student Edition, p. 734
- Chapter 8 Resource Book, pp. 27–29
- Test and Practice Generator

TRANSPARENCY

Even-numbered answers are available on transparencies.

HOMEWORK CHECK

When you review students' homework for this lesson, go over the following exercises to check understanding of key concepts.

Basic: 8, 9, 11, 12, 14

Average: 8, 10, 11, 13, 14

Advanced: 8, 10, 12, 14, 15

HELP with Homework

Example	Exercises
1	8–10
2	11–16

Online Resources CLASSZONE.COM

- More Examples
- eTutorial Plus

Practice and Problem Solving

A Measurement **Measure the side lengths. Then classify the quadrilateral.**

8.

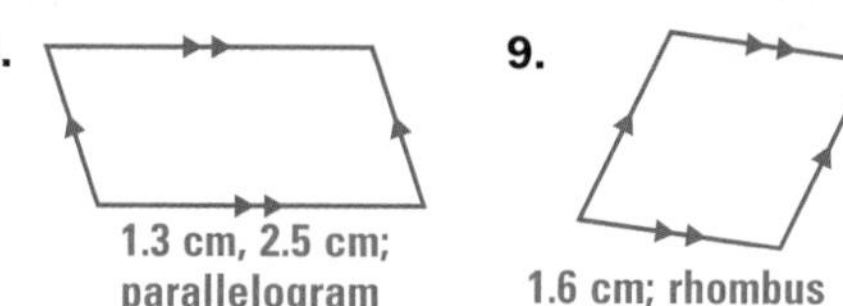

1.3 cm, 2.5 cm; parallelogram

9.

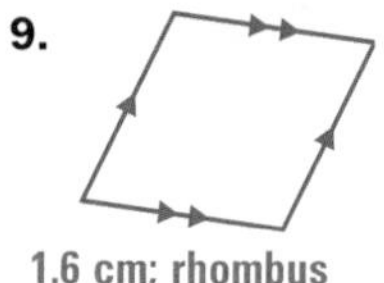

1.6 cm; rhombus

10.

1.3 cm; square

Find the value of *x*.

11.

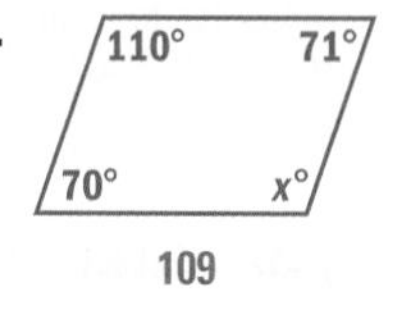

109

12.

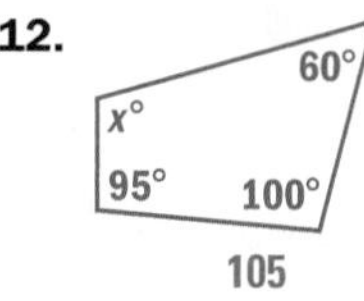

105

13.

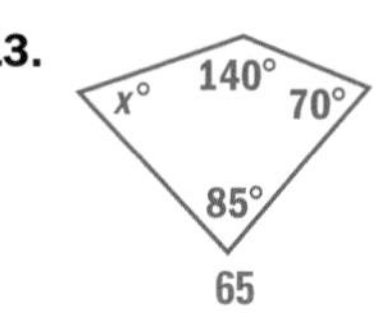

65

Find the values of *x* and *y*.

14. **15.** **16.**

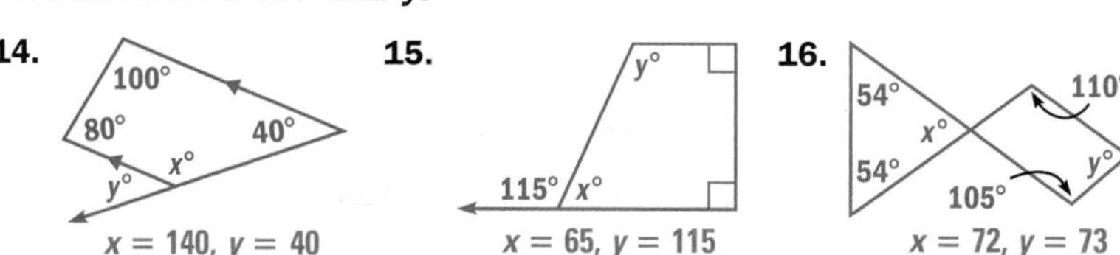

14. $x = 140$, $y = 40$ 15. $x = 65$, $y = 115$ 16. $x = 72$, $y = 73$

17. Classify each of the quadrilaterals in the design shown below.

17. dark blue rectangle
red square
green trapezoid
light blue parallelogram
purple parallelogram
yellow trapezoid

B **Tell whether the statement is *always*, *sometimes*, or *never* true.**

18. A rhombus is also a parallelogram. always

19. A rectangle is also a square. sometimes

20. A square is also a parallelogram. always

21. A triangle is also a quadrilateral. never

22. A quadrilateral is also a rectangle. sometimes

Find the value of *x* and the unknown angle measures.

23. **24.**

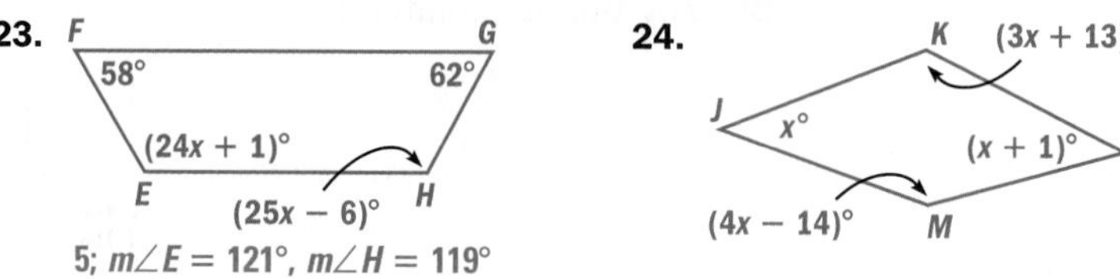

23. 5; $m\angle E = 121°$, $m\angle H = 119°$

24. 40; $m\angle J = 40°$, $m\angle K = 133°$, $m\angle L = 41°$, $m\angle M = 146°$

25. Critical Thinking What is the greatest number of obtuse angles that a quadrilateral can have? Explain your answer.

25. Three. *Sample answer:* If three angles are obtuse, the sum of their measures is greater than 3(90°), or greater than 270°, so the fourth angle measure must be less than 360° − 270°, or less than 90°, so it is acute.

C **26. Challenge** Find the value of x and y in the diagram. Explain your reasoning. **$x = 88$, $y = 58$. *Sample answer:* Because the sum of the angles in a quadrilateral is 360°, $x = 360 - (60 + 122 + 90) = 88$, and $y = 360 - [90 + (180 - 60) + (180 - 88)] = 58$.**

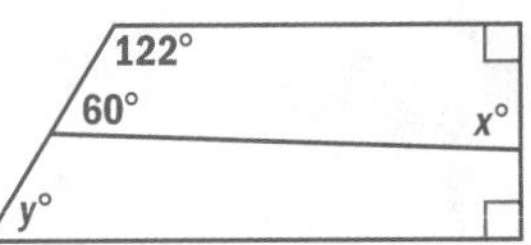

Mixed Review

In Exercises 27–29, solve the equation. *(Lesson 6.2)*

27. $3x + 12 = 7x - 8$ **5** **28.** $5x + 9 = 3x + 19$ **5** **29.** $-6x + 3 = 4x - 7$ **1**

30. Two lines intersect to form a 47° angle. Sketch the lines. Find the measure of each angle in the intersection. *(Lesson 8.1)* **See margin.**

Tell whether the statement is *always*, *sometimes*, or *never* true. *(Lessons 8.1, 8.2)*

31. The measures of complementary angles have a sum of 180°. **never**

32. An obtuse angle measures more than 90°. **always**

33. An isosceles triangle has three sides of equal length. **sometimes**

Test-Taking Practice 

INTERNET
State Test Practice
CLASSZONE.COM

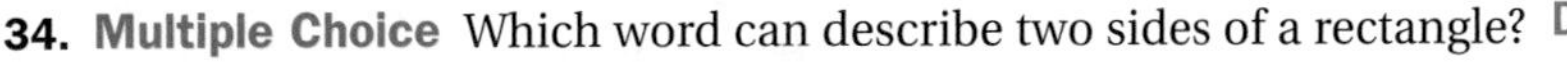

34. Multiple Choice Which word can describe two sides of a rectangle? **D**

A. vertical **B.** right **C.** acute **D.** perpendicular

35. Multiple Choice Three angles in a quadrilateral are acute. Classify the fourth angle. **H**

F. acute **G.** right **H.** obtuse **I.** straight

Buy Oval Car Vocabulary

Rearrange the letters to make a review word.

1. prizetoad **trapezoid**
2. bustoe **obtuse**
3. brushmo **rhombus**
4. tauce **acute**
5. allgrapemolar **parallelogram**
6. cleanse **scalene**
7. allearquiet **equilateral**
8. girth **right**
9. catliver **vertical**
10. includerapper **perpendicular**

Assessment Resources

For more assessment resources, see:
- Assessment Book
- Test and Practice Generator

Mini-Quiz

1. Find the value of x and the unknown angle measures.

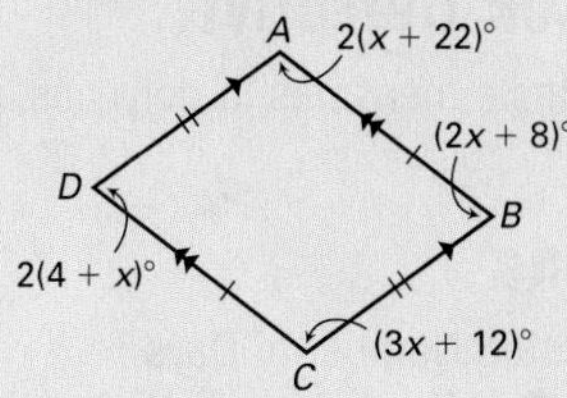

32; $m\angle A = m\angle C = 108°$, $m\angle B = m\angle D = 72°$

Tell whether the statement is *always*, *sometimes*, or *never* true.

2. A trapezoid is a square. **never**
3. A square is a rectangle. **always**

Reteaching/Remediation

- Study Guide in Chapter 8 Resource Book, pp. 30–31
- Tutor Place, Geometry and Measurement Cards 9, 10
- eTutorial Plus Online
- Extra Practice, p. 734
- Lesson Practice in Chapter 8 Resource Book, pp. 27–29

Challenge/Enrichment

- Challenge Practice in Chapter 8 Resource Book, p. 32
- Teacher's Edition, p. 372F

English Learner Support

- Spanish Study Guide
- Multi-Language Glossary
- Chapter Audio Summaries CDs

30. See Additional Answers beginning on page AA1.

SKILL CHECK

1. Evaluate $(n - 2) \cdot 180$ for $n = 10$. 1440
2. Evaluate $\frac{(n - 2) \cdot 180}{n}$ for $n = 12$. 150

LESSON OBJECTIVE

Find angle measures in polygons.

PACING

Suggested Number of Days
Basic Course: 1 day
Average Course: 1 day
Advanced Course: 1 day
Block: 0.5 block with 8.3

TEACHING RESOURCES

For a complete list of Teaching Resources, see page 372B.

TRANSPARENCY

Warm-Up Exercises for this lesson are available on a transparency.

MOTIVATING THE LESSON

Ask students if they can think of other words that begin with *pent-*, *hex-*, *hept-*, or *oct-*, and if they can identify the number that relates to each term.

ACTIVITY

Goal Find the sum of the angle measures in many-sided polygons.

Key Discovery The sum of the angle measures in a polygon is 180° times 2 less than the number of sides.

Polygons and Angles

BEFORE You found angle measures in triangles and quadrilaterals.

Now You'll find angle measures in polygons.

WHY? So you can explore a dome, as in Ex. 24.

Word Watch

polygon, p. 390
regular polygon, p. 390
pentagon, p. 390
hexagon, p. 390
heptagon, p. 390
octagon, p. 390

Activity You can use triangles to find the sum of the angle measures in other figures.

(1) Copy the table. Divide each figure into triangles by drawing as many diagonal lines as you can that begin at the point marked.

(2) Use your drawings to complete the table.

Shape	Quadrilateral	Pentagon	Hexagon	Octagon
Number of Sides	4	? 5	? 6	? 8
Number of Diagonal Lines	1	? 2	? 3	? 5
Number of Triangles Formed	2	? 3	? 4	? 6
Sum of Angle Measures	360°	? 540°	? 720°	? 1080°

(3) Use your results to complete a column for a figure with 10 sides.

Step 3: Number of Sides: 10; Number of Diagonal Lines: 7; Number of Triangles Formed: 8; Sum of Angle Measures: 1440°

Polygons A **polygon** is a closed figure whose sides are line segments that intersect only at their endpoints. In a **regular polygon**, all the angles have the same measure and all the sides have the same length.

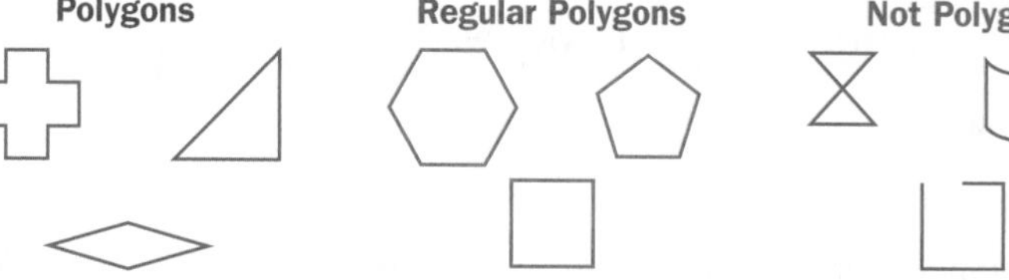

with Reading You can use n-gon, where n is the number of sides, to identify a polygon if you haven't learned its name. A 13-gon is a 13-sided polygon.

Polygons can be identified by the number of their sides.

Pentagon	Hexagon	Heptagon	Octagon	12-gon
5 sides	6 sides	7 sides	8 sides	12 sides

ILLINOIS Standards and ISAT: **9.B.3;** 7.A.3b, 8.B.3

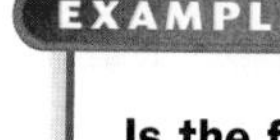

EXAMPLE 1 Identifying Figures

Is the figure a *polygon*, a *regular polygon*, or *not a polygon*? Explain.

a.

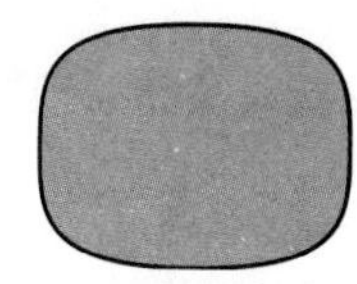

Not a polygon. The figure does not have line segments as sides.

b.

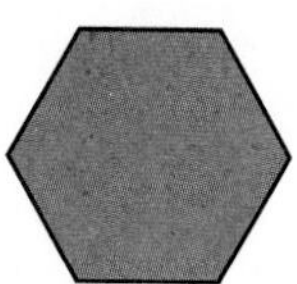

Regular polygon. Its angles have equal measures, and its sides have equal lengths.

Angles In the activity on page 390, you used triangles to find the sum of the angle measures in polygons. In a regular polygon, the measure of one angle is the sum of the angle measures divided by the number of sides.

Angle Measures in a Polygon

Sum of angle measures in an n-gon: $(n - 2) \cdot 180°$

Measure of one angle in a *regular* n-gon: $\dfrac{(n - 2) \cdot 180°}{n}$

EXAMPLE 2 Finding an Angle Measure

Find the measure of one angle in a regular octagon.

A regular octagon has 8 sides, so use $n = 8$.

$$\frac{(n-2) \cdot 180°}{n} = \frac{(8-2) \cdot 180°}{8} \quad \text{Substitute 8 for } n.$$

$$= \frac{1080°}{8} \quad \text{Simplify numerator.}$$

$$= 135° \quad \text{Divide.}$$

ANSWER The measure of one angle in a regular octagon is 135°.

Your turn now **Complete the exercise.**

1. Find the sum of the angle measures in a pentagon. 540°
2. Find the measure of one angle in a regular heptagon. Round to the nearest tenth of a degree. 128.6°

TIPS FOR NEW TEACHERS

Encourage students to draw pentagons, hexagons, and octagons with widely varying shapes. Point out that the sum of the angle measures does not change. See Tips for New Teachers in the *Chapter 8 Resource Book*.

EXTRA EXAMPLES

Example 1 Is the figure a *polygon*, a *regular polygon*, or *not a polygon*? Explain.

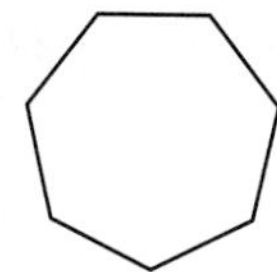

Regular polygon; all the angles have the same measure and all the sides have the same length.

Example 2 Find the measure of one angle in a regular 15-gon. **156°**

NOTETAKING

As students record the formulas on page 391, encourage them to show a worked example using each formula in their notebooks.

CONCEPT CHECK

What makes a polygon regular? **All angles have the same measure and all sides have the same length.**

DAILY PUZZLER

Draw a regular pentagon. Then draw lines connecting each vertex with every other vertex. You should have a five-pointed star inside your pentagon. How many different triangles are within the pentagon? **35 triangles**

3 APPLY

ASSIGNMENT GUIDE

Basic Course

Day 1: EP p. 727 Exs. 4–9; pp. 392–393 Exs. 11–16, 18–23, 29–36

Average Course

Day 1: pp. 392–393 Exs. 13–17, 20–24, 26–36

Advanced Course

Day 1: pp. 392–393 Exs. 13–17, 20–30*, 33–36

Block

pp. 392–393 Exs. 13–17, 20–24, 26–36 (with 8.3)

EXTRA PRACTICE

- Student Edition, p. 734
- Chapter 8 Resource Book, pp. 36–38
- Test and Practice Generator

TRANSPARENCY

Even-numbered answers are available on transparencies.

HOMEWORK CHECK

When you review students' homework for this lesson, go over the following exercises to check understanding of key concepts.

Basic: 11, 13, 14, 15, 16

Average: 13, 14, 15, 16, 17

Advanced: 13, 14, 15, 16, 17

COMMON ERROR

In Exercises 14–17, watch for students who find the sum of the angle measures in an *n*-gon instead of the measure of one angle.

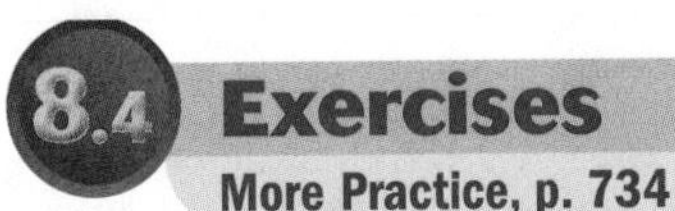

8.4 Exercises

More Practice, p. 734

Getting Ready to Practice

1. Vocabulary Copy and complete: A _?_ is a closed figure with sides that are line segments that intersect only at their endpoints. polygon

Tell whether the figure is a *polygon*, a *regular polygon*, or *not a polygon*.

2. polygon

3. not a polygon

4. 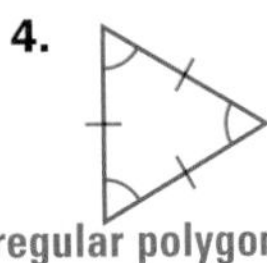 regular polygon

Find the sum of the angle measures in the polygon.

5. 10-gon 1440° **6.** 9-gon 1260° **7.** 11-gon 1620° **8.** 20-gon 3240°

9. Table A table has 7 sides of equal length and 7 equal angles. Find the measure of one angle to the nearest tenth of a degree. 128.6°

10. Find the Error Describe and correct the error in the solution.

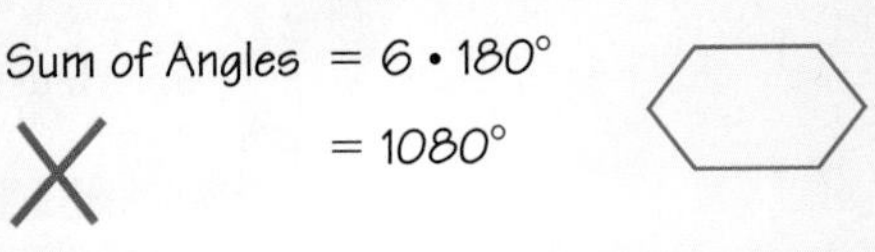

10. The sum of the angles is found by multiplying two less than the number of sides by 180: Sum of Angles = 4 • 180 = 720°.

Practice and Problem Solving

Example	Exercises
1	11–13
2	14–17

Online Resources CLASSZONE.COM
- More Examples
- eTutorial Plus

A Tell whether the swimming pool design is a polygon.

11. yes

12. 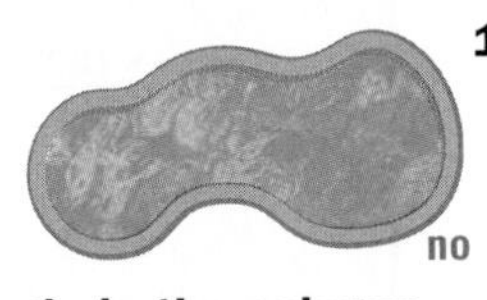 no

13. 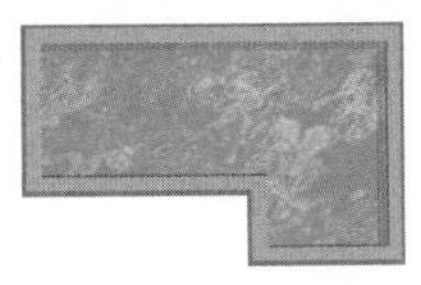 yes

Find the measure of one angle in the polygon.

14. regular 10-gon 144° **15.** regular 14-gon about 154° **16.** regular 15-gon 156°

17. Calculate Find the measure of one angle in a regular 115-gon. about 176.9°

Algebra **Find the value of *x*.**

18. 96

19. 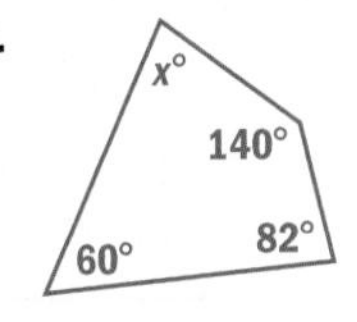

78

20. 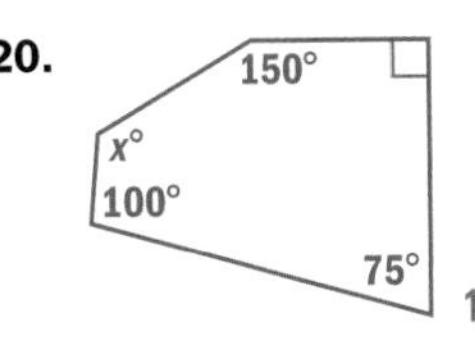

125

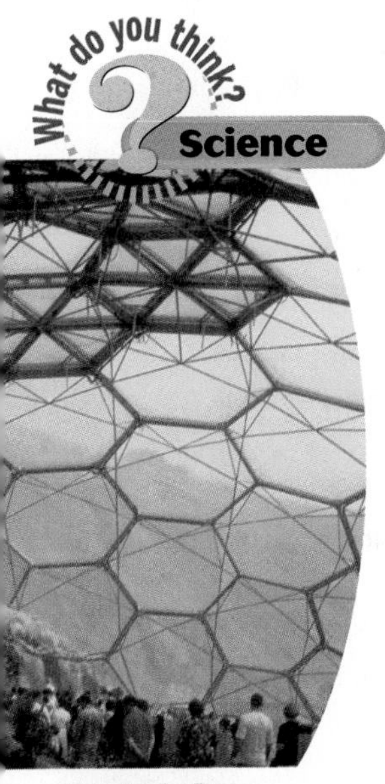

Geodesic Dome

The Eden Project is an environmental center in England made of connected geodesic domes. Its largest dome is 240 meters long. How many feet is this? (1 meter is equal to 3.281 feet.) about 787 ft

21. $x = 72$; $m\angle R = m\angle N = 72°$; $m\angle L = m\angle M = m\angle P = m\angle Q = 144°$

23. $x = 45$; $m\angle B = m\angle E = 135°$

INTERNET
State Test Practice
CLASSZONE.COM

B Critical Thinking Find the value of x and the unknown angle measures.

21. 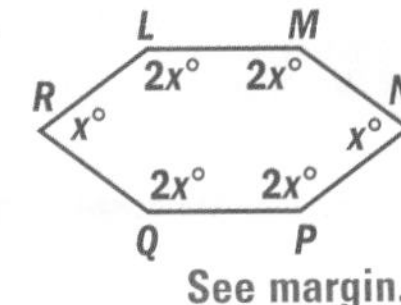

See margin.

22. 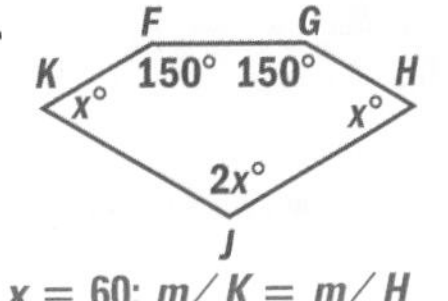

$x = 60$; $m\angle K = m\angle H = 60°$; $m\angle J = 120°$

23. 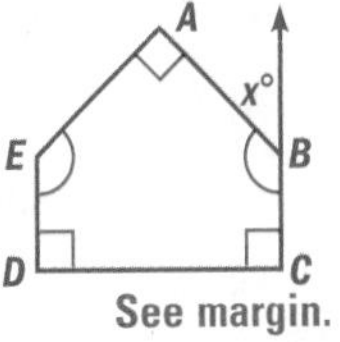

See margin.

24. Geodesic Dome A geodesic dome has some panels that are hexagons. Sketch a regular hexagon, and find the measure of one angle. See margin for art; 120°.

25. Challenge The sum of the angle measures in a polygon is 1980°. How many sides does it have? 13 sides

C Extended Problem Solving In Exercises 26–28, the angles marked with letters are called *exterior angles*.

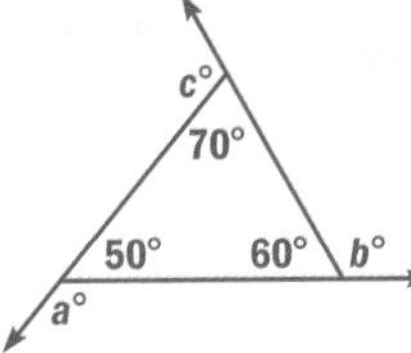

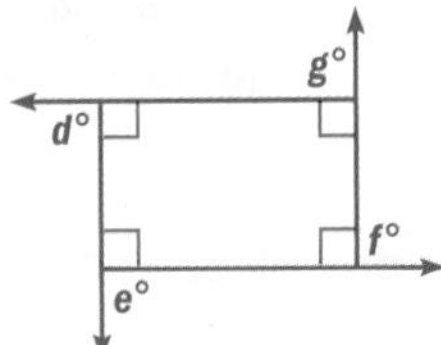

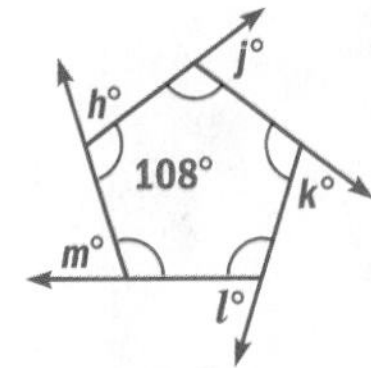

26. Evaluate Find the measures of the exterior angles of each polygon. $a = 130$, $b = 120$, $c = 110$, $d = e = f = g = 90$, $h = j = k = l = m = 72$

27. Calculate Find the sum of the exterior angle measures for each polygon. 360°; 360°; 360°

28. Patterns Describe a pattern in the sums you found in Exercise 27. They are all the same, 360°.

Mixed Review

Write the percent as a fraction in simplest form. *(Lesson 7.4)*

29. 98% $\frac{49}{50}$ **30.** 141.3% $1\frac{413}{1000}$ **31.** 0.14% $\frac{7}{5000}$ **32.** 82.5% $\frac{33}{40}$

33. The wholesale price of a pair of shoes is \$12.75. The retail price of the shoes is \$25.95. Find the percent markup. *(Lesson 7.6)* about 103.5%

34. $m\angle 1 = 56°$ and $m\angle 2 = 34°$. Are the angles supplementary? Explain your answer. *(Lesson 8.1)* No; their sum is 90°, not 180°.

Test-Taking Practice

35. Multiple Choice Find the measure of one angle in a regular 12-gon. D

A. 30° **B.** 60° **C.** 120° **D.** 150°

36. Multiple Choice Four angles in a pentagon measure 90°, 85°, 120°, and 130°. What is the measure of the fifth angle? G

F. 105° **G.** 115° **H.** 120° **I.** 165°

4 ASSESS

Assessment Resources

For more assessment resources, see:
- Assessment Book
- Test and Practice Generator

Mini-Quiz

Find the measure of one angle in the polygon to the nearest tenth.

1. regular 9-gon 140°
2. regular 11-gon 147.3°
3. regular 14-gon 154.3°
4. Find the value of x. 175

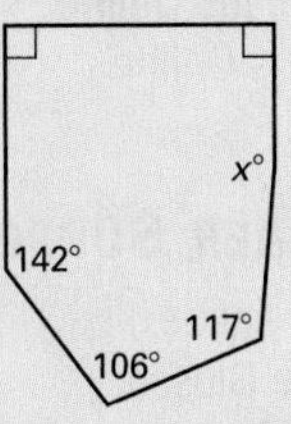

5 FOLLOW-UP

Reteaching/Remediation

- Study Guide in Chapter 8 Resource Book, pp. 39–40
- Tutor Place, Geometry and Measurement Cards 6, 10
- eTutorial Plus Online
- Extra Practice, p. 734
- Lesson Practice in Chapter 8 Resource Book, pp. 36–38

Challenge/Enrichment

- Challenge Practice in Chapter 8 Resource Book, p. 42
- Teacher's Edition, p. 372F

English Learner Support

- Spanish Study Guide
- Multi-Language Glossary
- Chapter Audio Summaries CDs

24. See Additional Answers beginning on page AA1.

Additional Resources

The following resources are available to help review the materials in Lessons 8.1–8.4.

Chapter 8 Resource Book
- Lesson Practice
- Study Guide

Assessment Book
- Chapter 8 Quiz 1

Technology
- Test and Practice Generator
- eTutorial CD-ROM

Internet
- Classzone
- eWorkbook Plus Online
- eTutorial Plus Online

English Learner Support

- Spanish Study Guide
- Multi-Language Glossary
- Chapter Audio Summaries CDs

Notebook Review

Review the vocabulary definitions in your notebook.

Copy the review examples in your notebook. Then complete the exercises.

Check Your Definitions

straight angle, right angle, p. 375
supplementary, complementary angles, p. 375
vertical angles, p. 376
perpendicular lines, p. 376
parallel lines, p. 377
acute, right, obtuse angle, p. 382
acute, right, obtuse triangle, p. 382
equilateral, isosceles, scalene triangle, p. 382
quadrilateral, p. 386
trapezoid, parallelogram, rhombus, p. 386
polygon, regular polygon, p. 390
pentagon, hexagon, heptagon, octagon, p. 390

Use Your Vocabulary

1. Vocabulary How many obtuse angles are in an obtuse triangle? one

8.1–8.2 Can you find and use angle measures?

EXAMPLE Refer to the diagram to answer parts (a) and (b).

a. Find $m\angle 2$.

The angle with measure 62° and $\angle 2$ are vertical angles, so their measures are equal.

62° 1 3 2 59° $x°$

ANSWER $m\angle 2 = 62°$

b. Find the value of x. Then classify the triangle.

$x° + 59° + 62° = 180°$	Sum of angle measures is 180°.
$x + 121 = 180$	Add.
$x = 59$	Subtract 121 from each side.

ANSWER The triangle is acute and isosceles.

Find the value of x. Classify the triangle by its angles.

2.

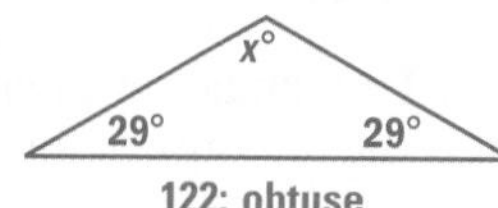

122; obtuse

3.

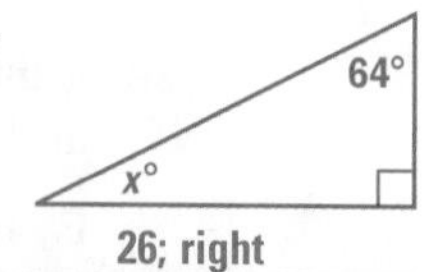

26; right

8.3–8.4 Can you find angle measures in polygons?

EXAMPLE Find the measure of one angle in a regular pentagon.

$\frac{(n-2) \cdot 180^\circ}{n}$	**Write the formula for measure of one angle in regular polygon.**
$= \frac{(5-2) \cdot 180^\circ}{5}$	**Substitute 5 for *n*.**
$= 108^\circ$	**Simplify.**

Find the angle measure.

4. Three angles in a quadrilateral measure 203°, 15°, and 90°. Find the measure of the fourth angle. 52°

5. Find the sum of the angle measures in a hexagon. 720°

Stop *and* Think about Lessons 8.1–8.4

6. **Writing** Can a hexagon have two right angles? Draw a diagram and explain your answer. See margin.

7. **Illustrate** How many pairs of vertical angles do two intersecting lines form? Draw a diagram and explain your answer. See margin.

Review Quiz 1

Tell whether the angles are *complementary*, *supplementary*, or *neither*.

1. $m\angle 1 = 32^\circ, m\angle 2 = 148^\circ$ supplementary

2. $m\angle 3 = 59^\circ, m\angle 4 = 41^\circ$ neither

3. $m\angle 5 = 12^\circ, m\angle 6 = 78^\circ$ complementary

4. $m\angle 7 = 116^\circ, m\angle 8 = 64^\circ$ supplementary

Can the angles in a triangle have the measures given? Explain. 5–7. See margin.

5. 23°, 57°, 95°

6. 64.6°, 77.3°, 38.1°

7. 155°, 24.9°, 0.1°

Find the value of *x*.

8.

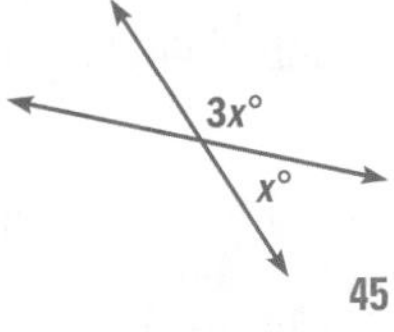

45

9. 50° 55° 130° x° 125

10.

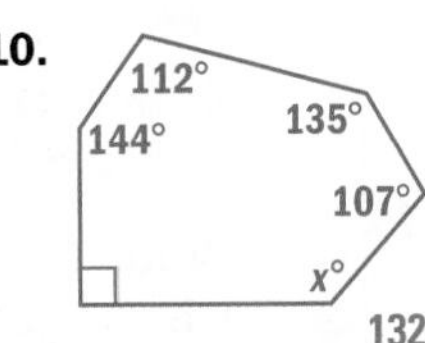

132

11. Two angles in a triangle measure 75° and 30°. Find the measure of the third angle. 75°

Notebook Review

6.

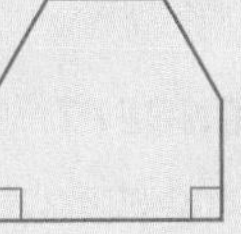

7.

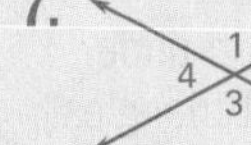

Notebook Review

6. Yes; see margin for art. *Sample answer:* The sum of the other four angles just needs to be 540°.

7. Two; see margin for art. *Sample answer:* There are two pairs of angles that do not share a side: ∠1 and ∠3, and ∠2 and ∠4.

Review Quiz 1

5. No; the measures add up to 175°.

6. Yes; the measures add up to 180°.

7. Yes; the measures add up to 180°.

EXPLORE THE CONCEPT

- Use a compass and straightedge to copy a triangle.
- This activity leads to an understanding of congruent triangles. In Lesson 8.5, students study congruent polygons.

MATERIALS

Each student will need a compass, straightedge, and protractor.

RECOMMENDED TIME

Work activity: 10 min
Discuss results: 5 min

GROUPING

Students should work individually.

 **TRANSPARENCY**

A support transparency is available for Exercise 4.

DISCUSSION

As students work through Step 2, ask them where relative to $\overrightarrow{PQ}$ they should draw their arcs.

 **KEY DISCOVERY**

If the corresponding sides of two triangles have the same lengths, then the triangles also have the same angle measures.

ASSESSMENT

1. How do you know that corresponding sides of the triangle and its copy have equal lengths? **The compass settings for corresponding arcs were the same.**

1–4. See Additional Answers beginning on page AA1.

8.5 Hands-on Activity

GOAL
Copy a triangle.

MATERIALS
- compass
- straightedge
- protractor

Copying a Triangle

You can use a compass and a straightedge to copy a triangle.

Explore **Use a compass and straightedge to copy a triangle.**

1. Draw a triangle with vertices *A, B,* and *C.* Draw a ray with endpoint *P.* Draw an arc with center *A* through point *C.* Use the same compass setting to draw an arc with center *P.* Label point *Q.*

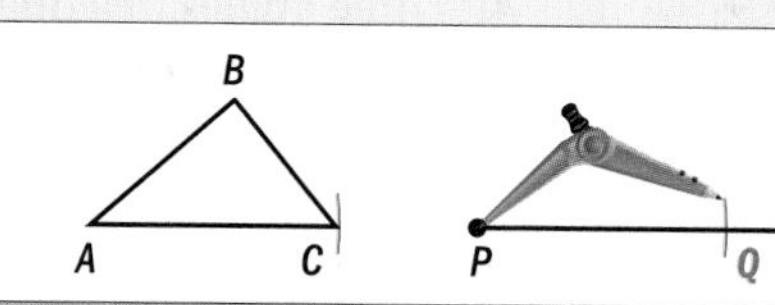

2. Draw an arc with center *C* through point *B.* Use the same compass setting to draw an arc with center *Q.*

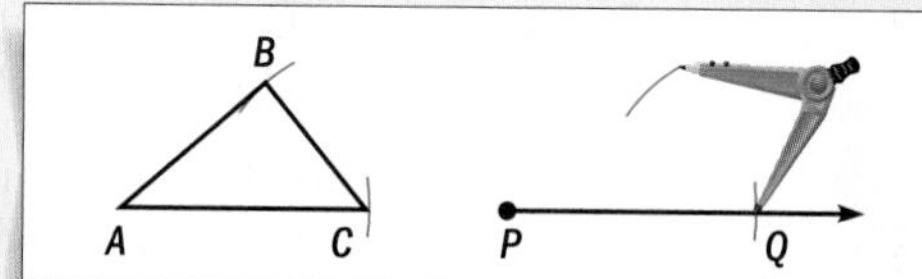

3. Draw an arc with center *A* through point *B.* Use the same compass setting to draw an arc with center *P.* Label point *R.* Connect *P* and *R.* Connect *R* and *Q.*

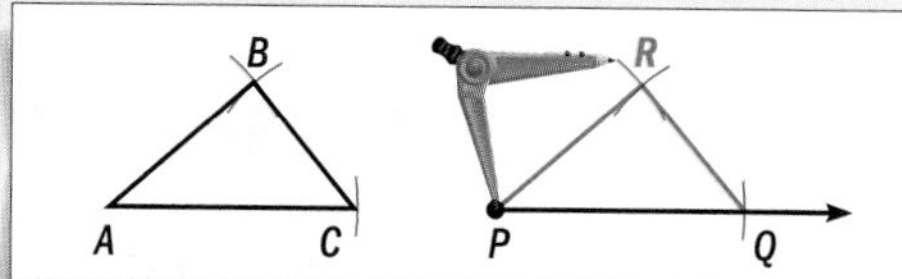

Your turn now **Draw a triangle that fits the description. Then use a compass and straightedge to copy the triangle.** **1–3. See margin.**

1. acute
2. obtuse
3. right

Stop and Think

4. **Critical Thinking** Measure the angles of each triangle you copied in Exercises 1–3. What do you notice? Explain. **See margin.**

5. **Writing** When you use a compass and straightedge to copy a triangle, what measures of the new triangle are identical to the old triangle? **The side lengths are the same and the angle measures are the same.**

ILLINOIS Standards and ISAT:
7.A.3a, 9.A.3a

Congruent Polygons

BEFORE You identified polygons.

Now You'll identify and name congruent polygons.

WHY? So you can measure kites, as in Exs. 13 and 14.

Word Watch

congruent sides, p. 397
congruent angles, p. 397
corresponding parts, p. 397

Congruent sides have equal lengths. **Congruent angles** have equal measures. The symbol ≅ means "is congruent to."

Congruent polygons have the same shape and size. Polygons are congruent if their *corresponding* angles and sides are congruent. **Corresponding parts** are in the same position in different figures. To name congruent polygons, list their corresponding vertices in the same order. In the diagram $\triangle KLM \cong \triangle PQR$.

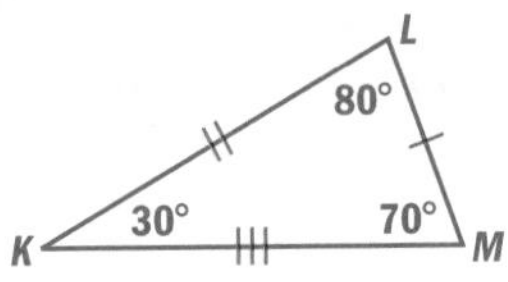

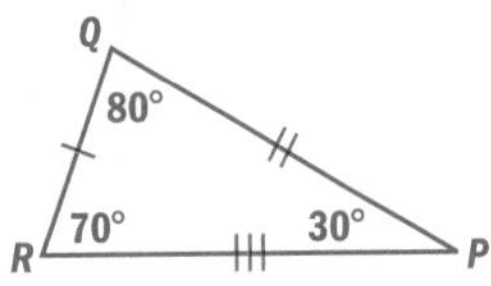

Corresponding angles are congruent.

$\angle K \cong \angle P$ $\angle L \cong \angle Q$ $\angle M \cong \angle R$

Corresponding sides are congruent.

$\overline{LM} \cong \overline{QR}$ $\overline{KL} \cong \overline{PQ}$ $\overline{KM} \cong \overline{PR}$

The side with endpoints *P* and *R*

EXAMPLE 1 Naming Corresponding Parts

In the frame below, quadrilateral *ABCD* ≅ quadrilateral *JKLM*. Name all pairs of corresponding angles and sides.

Solution

Corresponding angles are congruent.

$\angle A$, $\angle J$ $\angle B$, $\angle K$

$\angle C$, $\angle L$ $\angle D$, $\angle M$

Corresponding sides are congruent.

$\overline{AB}$, $\overline{JK}$ $\overline{BC}$, $\overline{KL}$

$\overline{CD}$, $\overline{LM}$ $\overline{DA}$, $\overline{MJ}$

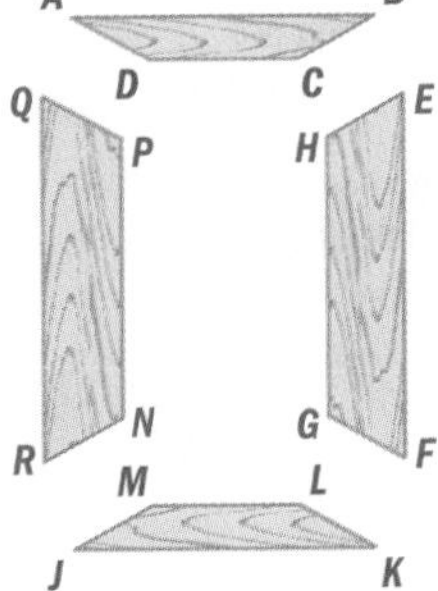

$\angle E, \angle Q; \angle F, \angle R; \angle G, \angle N; \angle H, \angle P; \overline{EF}, \overline{QR}; \overline{FG}, \overline{RN}; \overline{GH}, \overline{NP}; \overline{HE}, \overline{PQ}$

Your turn now **In Example 1, quadrilateral *EFGH* ≅ quadrilateral *QRNP*.**

1. Name all pairs of corresponding angles and sides.

ILLINOIS Standards and ISAT:
9.B.3

1 PLAN

SKILL CHECK

1. Solve 37 + 49 + x = 180 for x. 94
2. Solve 115 + x + 90 + 78 = 360 for x. 77

LESSON OBJECTIVE

Identify and name congruent polygons.

PACING

Suggested Number of Days
Basic Course: 1 day
Average Course: 1 day
Advanced Course: 1 day
Block: 0.5 block with 8.6

TEACHING RESOURCES

For a complete list of Teaching Resources, see page 372B.

TRANSPARENCY

Warm-Up Exercises for this lesson are available on a transparency.

2 TEACH

MOTIVATING THE LESSON

Ask what it means for polygons to have the same shape and size. Students should realize that having the same shape requires equal angles, and having the same size requires equal lengths.

TIPS FOR NEW TEACHERS

Make sure students correctly distinguish the congruence symbol from the "approximately equal to" symbol. See Tips for New Teachers in the *Chapter 8 Resource Book*.

EXTRA EXAMPLES

Example 1 Quadrilateral $HJKL \cong$ quadrilateral $MNPQ$. Name all pairs of congruent angles and sides.

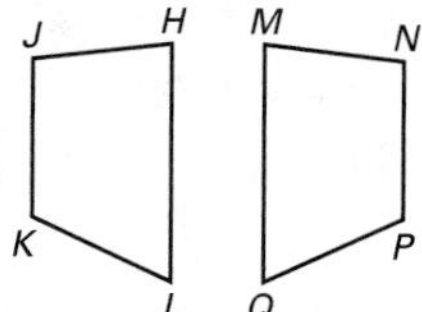

$\angle H \cong \angle M$, $\angle J \cong \angle N$, $\angle K \cong \angle P$, $\angle L \cong \angle Q$; $\overline{HJ} \cong \overline{MN}$, $\overline{JK} \cong \overline{NP}$, $\overline{KL} \cong \overline{PQ}$, $\overline{HL} \cong \overline{MQ}$

Example 2 $\triangle ABC \cong \triangle DEF$. Find $m\angle D$. **55°**

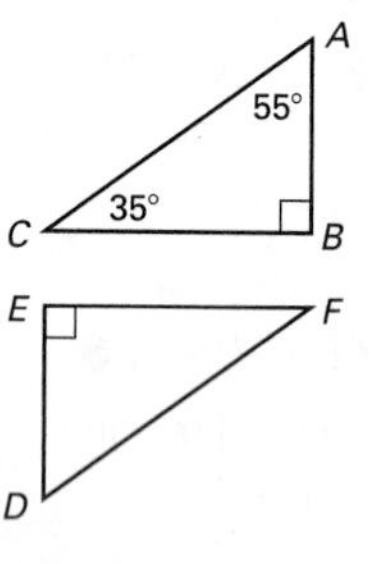

Multiple Representations

Work through the chart on this page row by row. Make sure students recognize how the abbreviation, the verbal description, and the figures are three different ways to represent the same rule. Point out the use of tick marks to indicate congruent sides and the use of arcs to indicate congruent angles.

Differentiating Instruction

Advanced Students Challenge advanced students to show that two triangles can have all corresponding angles congruent and each have a side of the same length and still not be congruent.

with Reading

$\triangle JKL$ is read "triangle JKL" and refers to the triangle with vertices J, K, and L.

EXAMPLE 2 Using Congruent Polygons

$\triangle JKL \cong \triangle TSR$
Find $m\angle S$.

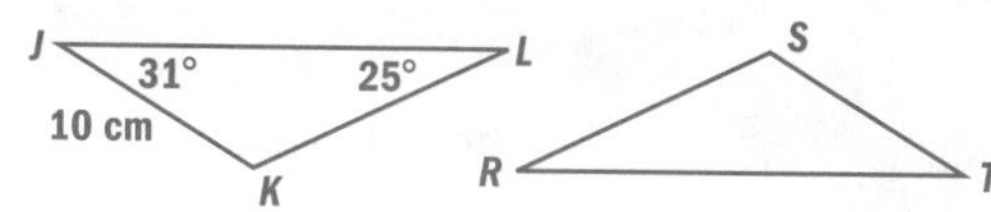

Solution

$\angle K$ and $\angle S$ are corresponding angles, so they have the same measure. Find $m\angle K$.

$m\angle J + m\angle K + m\angle L = 180°$	Sum of angle measures is 180°.
$31° + m\angle K + 25° = 180°$	Substitute given values.
$m\angle K + 56° = 180°$	Combine like terms.
$m\angle K = 124°$	Subtract 56° from each side.

ANSWER Because $m\angle K = m\angle S$, $m\angle S = 124°$.

Your turn now **Find the measure using the triangles in Example 2.**

2. length of $\overline{ST}$ **10 cm**
3. $m\angle T$ **31°**
4. $m\angle R$ **25°**

Congruent Triangles You can use the special rules in the chart to tell whether triangles are congruent.

HELP with Reading

The angle between two sides is sometimes called the *included* angle.
The side between two angles is sometimes called the *included* side.

Side-Side-Side (SSS)	If three sides of one triangle are congruent to three sides of another triangle, then the triangles are congruent.	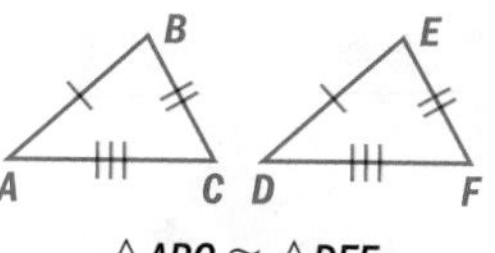 $\triangle ABC \cong \triangle DEF$
Side-Angle-Side (SAS)	If two sides and the angle between them in one triangle are congruent to two sides and the angle between them in another triangle, then the triangles are congruent.	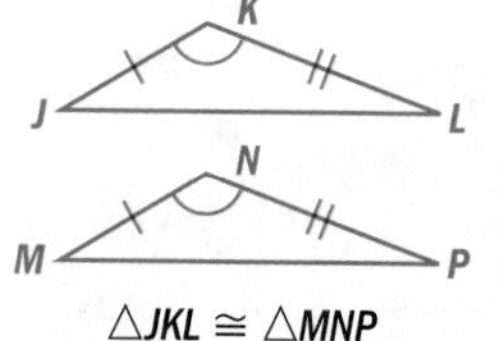 $\triangle JKL \cong \triangle MNP$
Angle-Side-Angle (ASA)	If two angles and the side between them in one triangle are congruent to two angles and the side between them in another triangle, then the triangles are congruent.	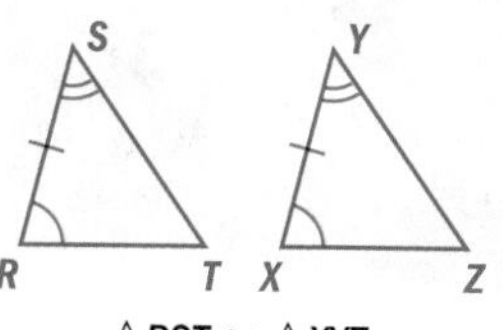 $\triangle RST \cong \triangle XYZ$

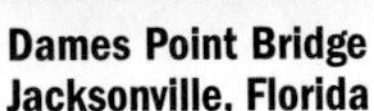

Dames Point Bridge
Jacksonville, Florida

EXAMPLE 3 Identifying Congruent Triangles

Name the congruent triangles formed by the bridge cables, and explain how you know that they are congruent.

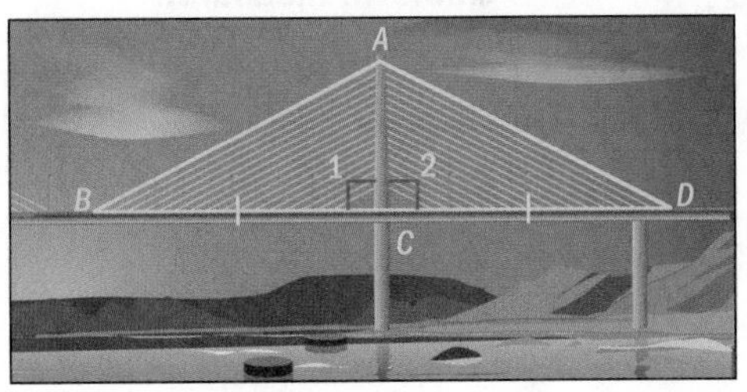

$\overline{CB} \cong \overline{CD}$	Sides are congruent.
$\overline{AC} \cong \overline{AC}$	Side is congruent to itself.
$\angle 1 \cong \angle 2$	Right angles are congruent.

ANSWER $\triangle ACB \cong \triangle ACD$ by Side-Angle-Side.

EXTRA EXAMPLES

Example 3 The face shown is part of a Jack-o'-lantern design. Tell whether the two teeth form congruent triangles. If they do, name the congruent triangles and explain why they are congruent.

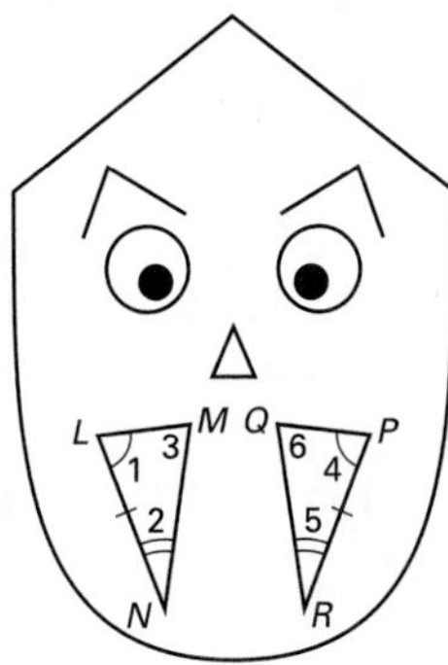

Yes; $\triangle LMN \cong \triangle PQR$ by Angle-Side-Angle, since $\angle 1 \cong \angle 4$, $\angle 2 \cong \angle 5$, and the sides between the congruent angles, $\overline{LN}$ and $\overline{PR}$, are congruent.

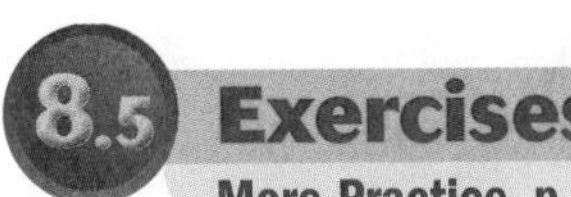

8.5 Exercises

More Practice, p. 734

Getting Ready to Practice

Vocabulary Copy and complete the statement.

1. Two angles with the same measure are ?. **congruent**
2. ? are in the same position in different figures. **Corresponding parts**

In the diagram, quadrilateral *KLMN* ≅ quadrilateral *SPQR*.

N, 60°, M, K, 13 in., L; P, S, 155°, Q, 12 in., R

3. Name four pairs of congruent angles.
4. Find $m\angle S$. **90°**
5. Find the length of $\overline{NK}$. **12 in.**
6. Find $m\angle R$. **60°**

3. $\angle K$ and $\angle S$, $\angle L$ and $\angle P$, $\angle M$ and $\angle Q$, $\angle N$ and $\angle R$

7. **Find the Error** Describe and correct the error in the solution. **The corresponding vertices are not listed in the correct order; $\triangle ABC \cong \triangle DFE$ by Side-Angle-Side.**

△ABC ≅ △DEF by Side-Angle-Side.

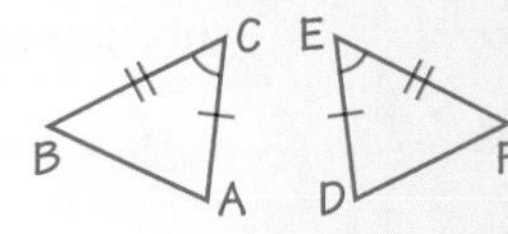

CONCEPT CHECK

What are three ways you can show that two triangles are congruent? **SSS, SAS, ASA**

DAILY PUZZLER

One right triangle has exactly three times the area of a smaller right triangle. The smallest angle in the smaller triangle is greater than the smallest angle in the larger triangle. The larger triangle has a 70° angle. Give an angle measure in the smaller triangle. **90°**

ASSIGNMENT GUIDE

Basic Course

Day 1: pp. 400–401 Exs. 8–15, 19, 22–32

Average Course

Day 1: pp. 400–401 Exs. 8–10, 13–20, 22–32

Advanced Course

Day 1: pp. 400–401 Exs. 8–10, 13–26*, 29–32

Block

pp. 400–401 Exs. 8–10, 13–20, 22–32 (with 8.6)

EXTRA PRACTICE

- Student Edition, p. 734
- Chapter 8 Resource Book, pp. 45–47
- Test and Practice Generator

TRANSPARENCY

Even-numbered answers are available on transparencies.

HOMEWORK CHECK

When you review students' homework for this lesson, go over the following exercises to check understanding of key concepts.
Basic: 8, 9, 10, 12, 14
Average: 8, 9, 10, 13, 14
Advanced: 8, 9, 10, 13, 14

COMMON ERROR

Exercise 7 illustrates an error that students frequently make. When identifying congruent polygons, students must always be careful to list corresponding vertices in the same order. Students may have to reflect or rotate figures in their minds to help identify corresponding vertices.

18. See Additional Answers beginning on page AA1.

with Homework

Example	Exercises
1	8-11
2	8-11
3	12-14

Online Resources
CLASSZONE.COM
· More Examples
· eTutorial Plus

15. Side-Side-Side; $x - 6 = 4$; 10

16. Angle-Side-Angle; $2x + 6 = 32$; 13

17. Angle-Side-Angle; $2x - 24 = x$; 24

Practice and Problem Solving

A Measurement **Quadrilateral *ABEF* ≅ quadrilateral *DGHC*. Find the unknown measure.**

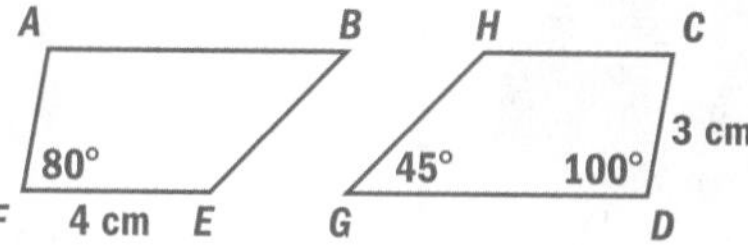

8. length of $\overline{AF}$ 3 cm

9. $m\angle C$ 80°

10. length of $\overline{HC}$ 4 cm

11. $m\angle A$ 100°

12. Name all the congruent triangles shown. Justify your answer. $\triangle ABC \cong \triangle LMK$ by Side-Angle-Side, $\triangle HGJ \cong \triangle QPN$ by Side-Side-Side

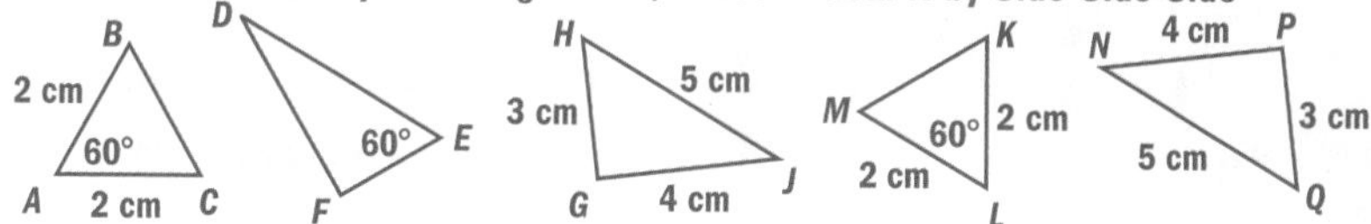

B Kites **Explain how you know the red triangles in the kite are congruent.**

13.

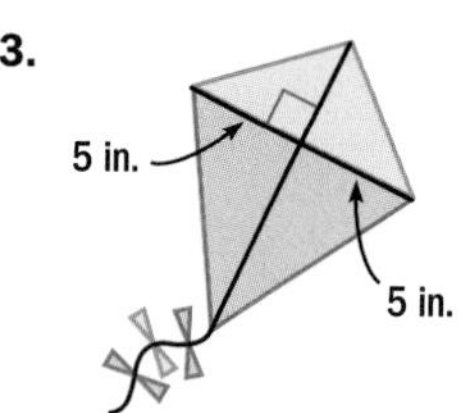

Side-Angle-Side

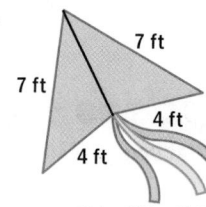

14. 7 ft, 7 ft, 4 ft, 4 ft

Side-Side-Side

Critical Thinking **Explain how you know the triangles are congruent. Then write an equation and solve for *x*.** 15–17. See margin.

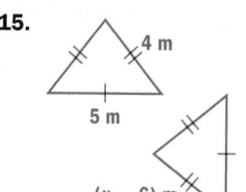

15. 4 m, 5 m, $(x - 6)$ m

16.

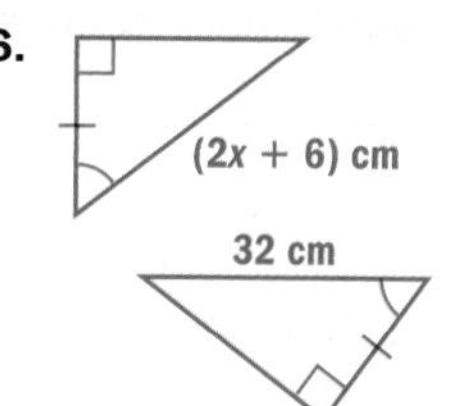

17.

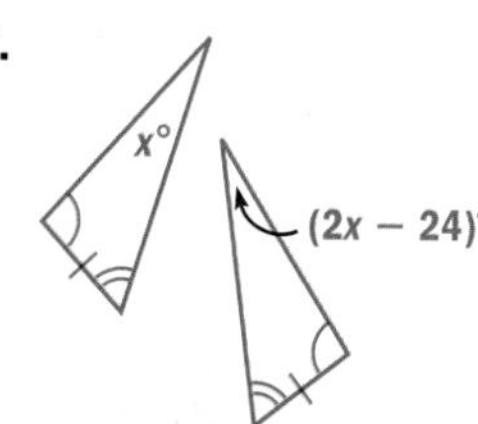

18. Soccer Field Some pieces of sod on a field are regular hexagons like the ones shown here. Explain how you know the regular hexagons are congruent. See margin.

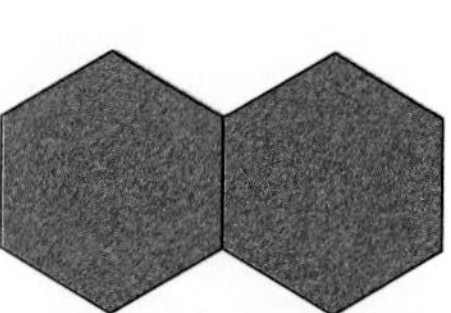

19. Pockets Two back pockets on a pair of jeans are congruent. Find $m\angle 1$.
127.5°

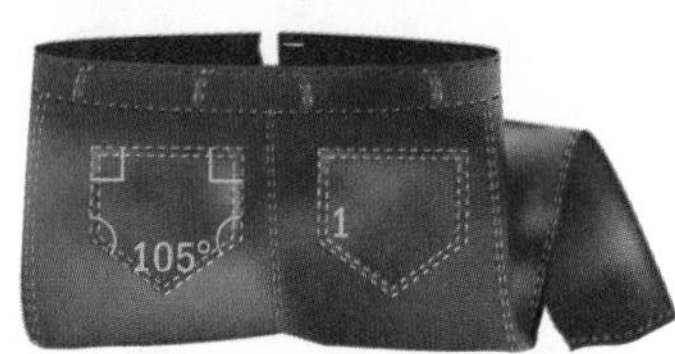

What do you think? Sports

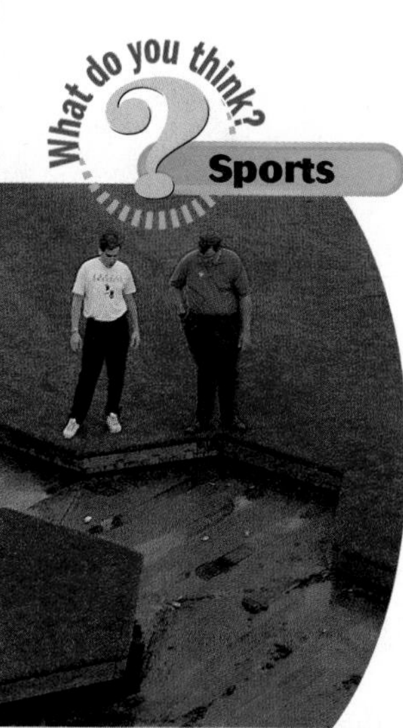

Soccer Field

In 1994, Michigan State University covered the floor of the Silverdome with natural grass for the World Cup tournament. Why do you think hexagons were used in the design? There are no gaps between them.

20. **Pod Shelters** The panels of the pod shelter shown are equilateral triangles. The sides of each triangle are 7 feet long. Explain how you know the panels are congruent triangles.
***Sample answer:* Since each pair of corresponding sides is congruent, the triangles are congruent by Side-Side-Side.**

C 21. **Challenge** Name the congruent triangles, and explain how you know that they are congruent.

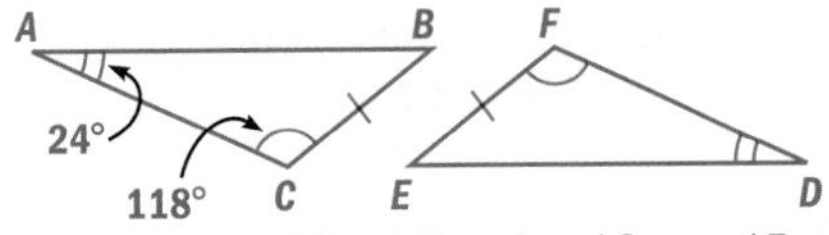

$\triangle ABC \cong \triangle DEF$. *Sample answer:* Since $m\angle A = m\angle D = 24°$ and $m\angle C = m\angle F = 118°$, then $m\angle B = m\angle E = 38°$. So the triangles are congruent by Angle-Side-Angle.

Mixed Review

22. Find 1.25% of 400. **5**

23. Find 65% of 91. *(Lesson 7.7)* **59.15**

24. If you pick a whole number at random from 1 to 100, what is the probability that the number is a multiple of 5? *(Lesson 7.8)* $\frac{1}{5}$

Find the value of *x*. *(Lessons 8.3, 8.4)*

25.

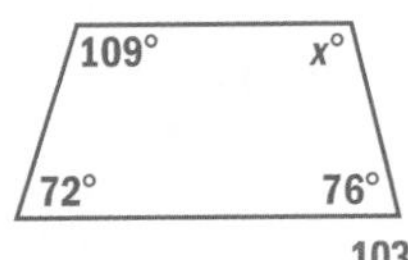

103

26.

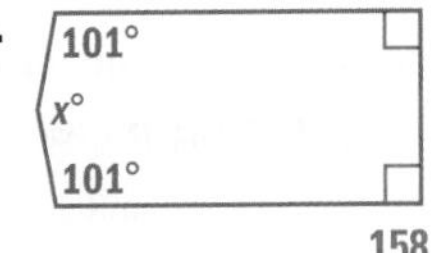

158

Basic Skills Plot the point in a coordinate plane. **27–30. See margin.**

27. $A(-9, 6)$ 28. $B(-3, -5)$ 29. $C(0, -4)$ 30. $D(4, -1)$

Test-Taking Practice

INTERNET
State Test Practice
CLASSZONE.COM

31. **Multiple Choice** Polygon $ABCD \cong$ polygon $EFGH$. Find $m\angle C$. **C**

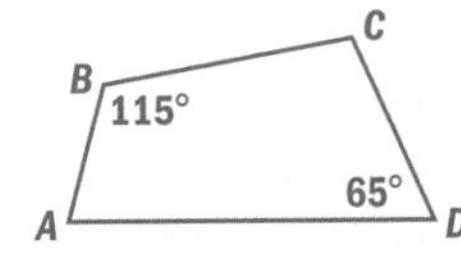

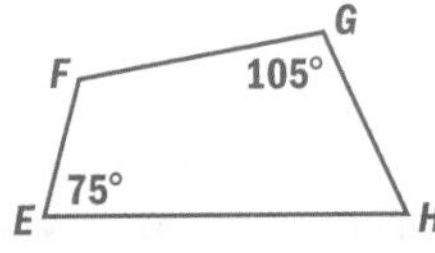

A. 65° **B.** 75° **C.** 105° **D.** 115°

32. **Short Response** Name the congruent triangles and explain how you know that they are congruent.

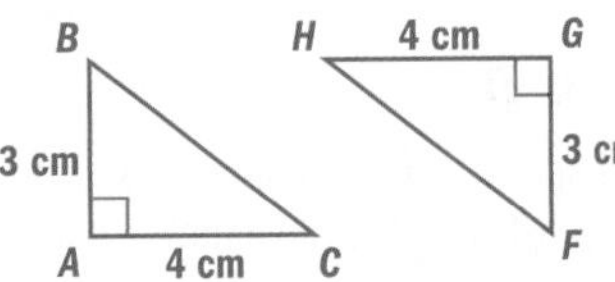

32. $\triangle ABC \cong \triangle GFH$ *Sample answer:* Two sides and the angle between them in $\triangle ABC$ are congruent to two sides and the angle between them in $\triangle GFH$, so the triangles are congruent by Side-Angle-Side.

4 ASSESS

ASSESSMENT RESOURCES

For more assessment resources, see:
- Assessment Book
- Test and Practice Generator

MINI-QUIZ

$\triangle RST \cong \triangle WXY$. Find the given measures.

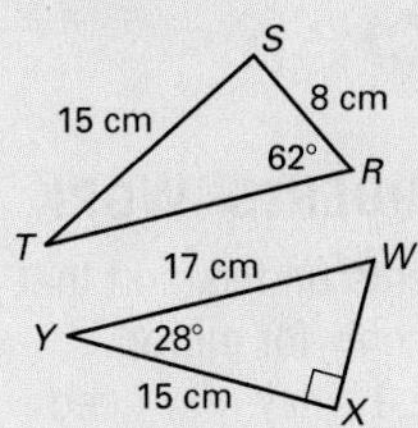

1. length of $\overline{XW}$ **8 cm**
2. $m\angle W$ **62°**
3. length of $\overline{RT}$ **17 cm**
4. $m\angle T$ **28°**

5 FOLLOW-UP

RETEACHING/REMEDIATION

- Study Guide in Chapter 8 Resource Book, pp. 48–49
- Tutor Place, Geometry and Measurement Card 17
- eTutorial Plus Online
- Extra Practice, p. 734
- Lesson Practice in Chapter 8 Resource Book, pp. 45–47

CHALLENGE/ENRICHMENT

- Challenge Practice in Chapter 8 Resource Book, p. 50
- Teacher's Edition, p. 372F

ENGLISH LEARNER SUPPORT

- Spanish Study Guide
- Multi-Language Glossary
- Chapter Audio Summaries CDs

27–30. See Additional Answers beginning on page AA1.

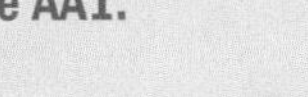

PLAN

STRATEGY BACKGROUND

The strategy Make a Model is helpful when the real-world objects can be easily created and when it is difficult to visualize the solution. It is useful for real-world problems that involve three-dimensional shapes.

TEACH

GUIDING STUDENTS' WORK

Make sure students understand that they are looking only for mirror images of shape 1. They may need help in deciding how to fold and refold the paper to test if the shapes line up.

EXTRA EXAMPLES

Example Which shapes are mirror images of shape 2?

5 6 7 8

4 3 2 1

shapes 3 and 7

8.6 Problem Solving Strategies

- Guess, Check, and Revise
- Look for a Pattern
- Draw a Diagram
- Write an Equation
- Make a Model
- Act It Out
- Work Backward

Make a Model

Problem You are looking at a picture of a kaleidoscope image. The image includes six red shapes. Tell which red shapes are mirror images of shape 1.

1 Read and Understand

Read the problem carefully.

You need to decide which red shapes are mirror images of shape 1.

2 Make a Plan

Decide on a strategy to use.

You can identify the mirror images by making a model. Trace the kaleidoscope image. Then fold your tracing paper to see if two shapes are mirror images.

3 Solve the Problem

Reread the problem and make a model of the kaleidoscope image using tracing paper.

Trace the outline of the kaleidoscope image and the six red shapes. Also trace the lines that divide the image into six equal parts. Cut out the circle.

Fold the paper once so that shape 1 lies on top of shape 2. You can see that shape 1 and shape 2 line up with each other exactly when you fold the paper. So, shape 2 is a mirror image of shape 1.

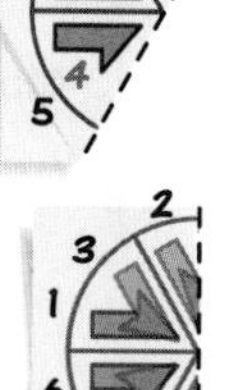

Unfold the paper. Now fold it once so that shape 1 lies on top of shape 3. You can see that shape 1 and shape 3 do not line up with each other exactly when you fold the paper. So, shape 3 is not a mirror image of shape 1. Continue to test shapes around the circle

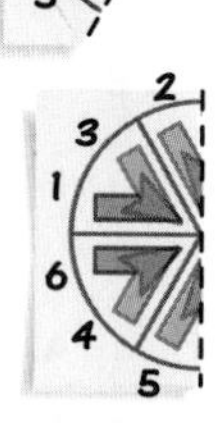

4 Look Back

Which shapes are a mirror images of shape 1? Did you do everything asked in the problem? **shape 2, shape 4, shape 6**

ILLINOIS Standards and ISAT:
7.C.3b; 6.B.3a, 6.C.3a

Practice the Strategy

Use the strategy *make a model*.

1. **Design** Sketch a kaleidoscope design that includes mirror images of a shape. Divide a circle into six equal parts to make your design. Identify the mirror images. See margin.

2. **Bowling Pins** Ten bowling pins are arranged in a triangle, as shown. Explain how you can make the triangle point to the left by moving only three pins. See margin.

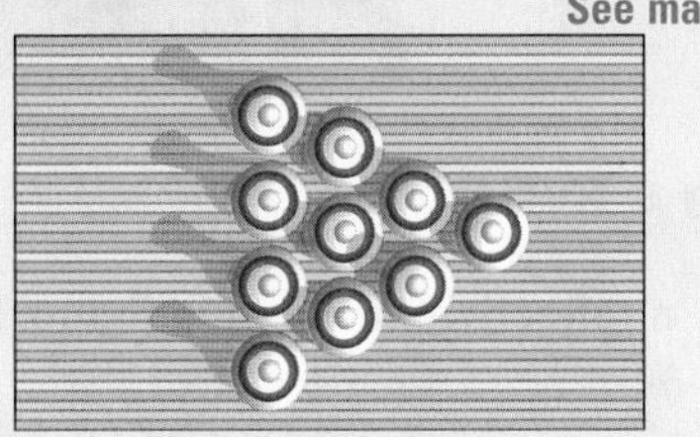

3. **Seating Arrangements** Alan, David, Mary, Peter, and Scott are sitting on a bench. Alan is between Scott and David. Mary is next to Peter. There is only one person between Mary and Alan, but Mary is not next to Scott. Find two possible seating arrangements. Scott, Alan, David, Mary, Peter; Scott, Alan, Peter, Mary, David

4. **Boxes** Four boxes of different sizes are stacked on a table, with the largest box on the bottom and the smallest box on the top. You need to move the entire stack of boxes to another table, but you can only move one box at a time. No box can touch the floor, and no box can support a larger box without breaking. You have one extra table to help you. List the moves it takes you to transfer the stack of boxes. See margin.

Mixed Problem Solving

Use any strategy to solve the problem.

5. **Hiking** You bring water on a hike. You drink a quarter of the water in the morning and a third of the remaining water at lunch time. In the afternoon, you drink two thirds of the water left in your container. When you get home, there are 16 fluid ounces of water. How much water did you bring on the hike? 96 oz

6. **Club Planning** The Spanish Club meets every other week. The members decided to have a party during the fifth meeting. The first meeting took place on October 2. Find the date of the party. November 27

7. **Test Scores** John has earned 92, 70, 95, 89, and 90 on his math tests this semester. What score must John receive on his next test to have a mean of 88? 92

8. **Numbers** You are helping your little sister with her math homework, but you can't read her writing very well. Her sevens and ones look exactly the same. She solved the problem below correctly. Decide which numerals are sevens and which are ones. See margin.

$$\begin{array}{r} 211 \\ +546 \\ \hline 811 \end{array}$$

APPLY

Transparency

Even-numbered answers are available on transparencies.

Teaching Tip

Bring a kaleidoscope to class, or encourage one or more students to bring a kaleidoscope to show to students who have never seen one.

Common Error

In Exercise 1, watch for students who confuse reflections with rotations or other transformations.

Suggested Strategies

You may wish to suggest the following strategies for the problems in the Mixed Problem Solving:

- Exercise 5: Work Backward; Guess, Check, and Revise
- Exercise 6: Draw a Diagram; Act It Out
- Exercise 7: Guess, Check, and Revise; Write an Equation
- Exercise 8: Guess, Check, and Revise; Look for a Pattern

1. *Sample:*

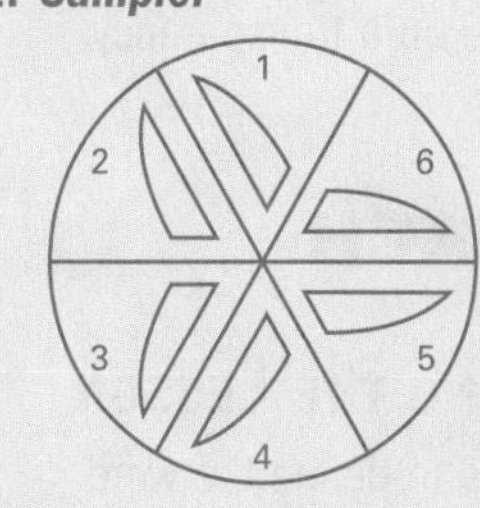

mirror images: 1 and 2, 3 and 4, 5 and 6, 1 and 6, 2 and 3, 4 and 5, 1 and 4, 2 and 5, 3 and 6

2. Move the top and bottom pins in the "column" on the left to similar positions in the third "column," and then move the single pin on the right to a similar position on the left.

4, 8. See Additional Answers beginning on page AA1.

1 PLAN

SKILL CHECK

Name the coordinates of each point.

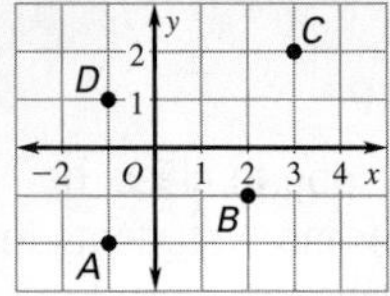

1. $A(-1, -2)$ **2.** $B(2, -1)$
3. $C(3, 2)$ **4.** $D(-1, 1)$

LESSON OBJECTIVE

Reflect figures and identify lines of symmetry.

PACING

Suggested Number of Days
Basic Course: 1 day
Average Course: 1 day
Advanced Course: 1 day
Block: 0.5 block with 8.5

TEACHING RESOURCES

For a complete list of Teaching Resources, see page 372B.

TRANSPARENCY

Warm-Up Exercises for this lesson are available on a transparency.

2 TEACH

MOTIVATING THE LESSON

Ask students to define the word *symmetry*, and to identify items in the classroom that exhibit symmetry.

TIPS FOR NEW TEACHERS

Give students plenty of practice reflecting in the *x*- and *y*-axes. See Tips for New Teachers in the *Chapter 8 Resource Book*.

Reflections and Symmetry

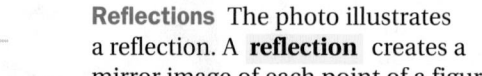

BEFORE You plotted points in a coordinate plane.

Now You'll reflect figures and identify lines of symmetry.

WHY? So you can find symmetry in starfish, as in Example 4b.

Word Watch

reflection, p. 404
transformation, p. 404
image, p. 404
line symmetry, p. 406

In the Real World

Reflections The photo illustrates a reflection. A **reflection** creates a mirror image of each point of a figure.

A reflection is a **transformation**, an operation that changes a figure into another figure. The new figure created is called the **image**.

EXAMPLE 1 Identifying a Reflection

Tell whether the red figure is a reflection of the blue figure.

a.

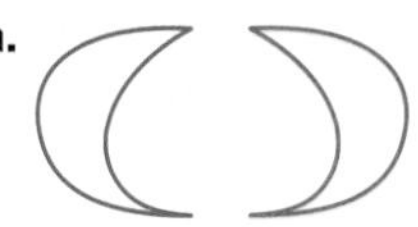

The figure is a reflection.

b.

The figure is *not* a reflection.

You can describe reflections of figures in a coordinate plane using coordinate notation. The notation $A \rightarrow A'$ is read "A goes to A prime."

EXAMPLE 2 Reflecting in the y-Axis

Quadrilateral *ABCD* has been reflected in the *y*-axis. Write the coordinates of each vertex of quadrilateral *ABCD* and its image, quadrilateral *A′B′C′D′*.

Solution

Original		Image
$A(-1, 1)$	$\rightarrow$	$A'(1, 1)$
$B(-3, 1)$	$\rightarrow$	$B'(3, 1)$
$C(-4, 3)$	$\rightarrow$	$C'(4, 3)$
$D(-2, 4)$	$\rightarrow$	$D'(2, 4)$

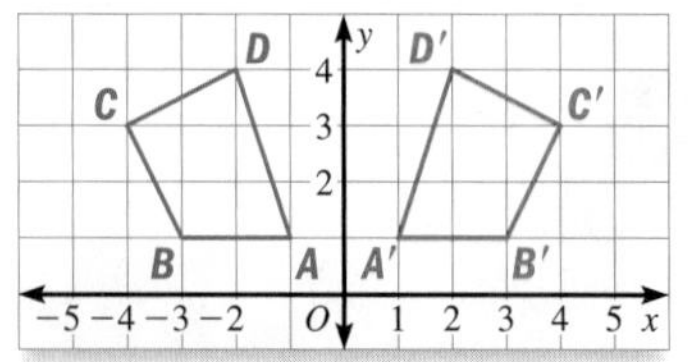

ILLINOIS Standards and ISAT:
9.A.3a, 9.A.3b, 9.A.3c

You may have noticed in Example 2 that when a point is reflected in the y-axis, its x-coordinate is multiplied by -1.

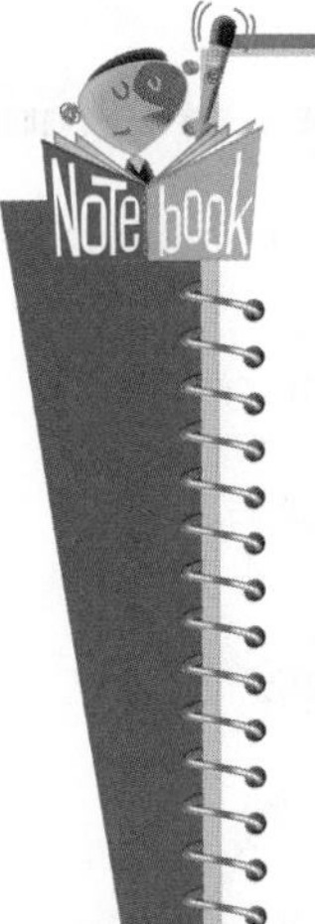

Reflections

Reflection in the x-axis

Words To reflect a point in the x-axis, multiply its y-coordinate by -1.

	Original		Image
Algebra	(x, y)	$\rightarrow$	$(x, -y)$

Reflection in the y-axis

Words To reflect a point in the y-axis, multiply its x-coordinate by -1.

	Original		Image
Algebra	(x, y)	$\rightarrow$	$(-x, y)$

EXAMPLE 3 Reflecting in the x-Axis

Reflect $\triangle PQR$ in the x-axis.

Solution

Multiply each y-coordinate by -1.

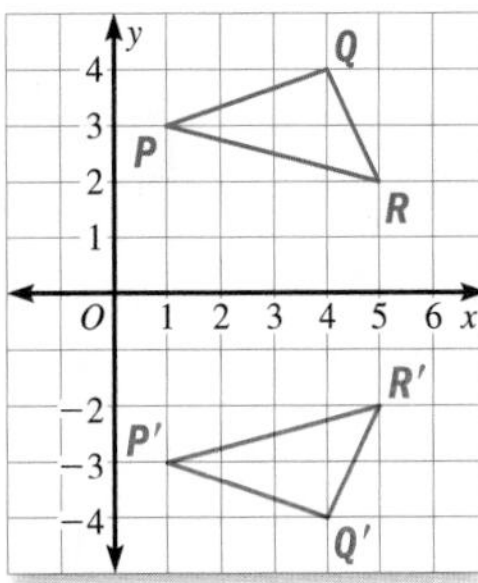

Original		Image
(x, y)	$\rightarrow$	$(x, -y)$
$P(1, 3)$	$\rightarrow$	$P'(1, -3)$
$Q(4, 4)$	$\rightarrow$	$Q'(4, -4)$
$R(5, 2)$	$\rightarrow$	$R'(5, -2)$

The graph shows $\triangle PQR$ and its reflection $\triangle P'Q'R'$.

Your turn now **Graph the polygon and its image.** 1–2. See margin.

1. Graph the triangle with vertices $J(0, 1)$, $K(0, 4)$, and $L(5, 2)$. Reflect the triangle in the y-axis.
2. Graph the quadrilateral with vertices $S(-3, 2)$, $T(-1, 4)$, $U(-4, 5)$, and $V(-5, 3)$. Reflect the quadrilateral in the x-axis.

EXTRA EXAMPLES

Example 1 Tell whether the triangles shown are reflections of each other. **no**

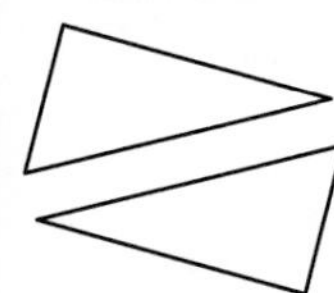

Example 2 Triangle FGH has been reflected in the y-axis. Write the coordinates of each vertex of $\triangle FGH$ and its image, $\triangle F'G'H'$.

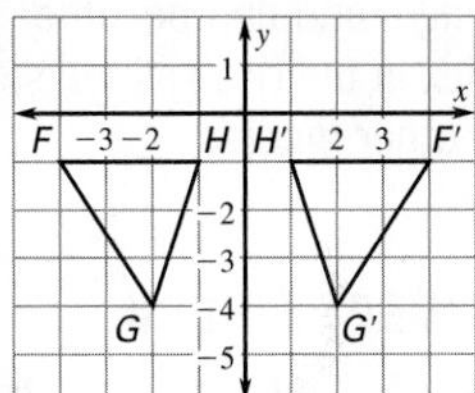

$F(-4, -1)$, $G(-2, -4)$, $H(-1, -1)$, $F'(4, -1)$, $G'(2, -4)$, $H'(1, -1)$

Example 3 Reflect the triangle in the x-axis.

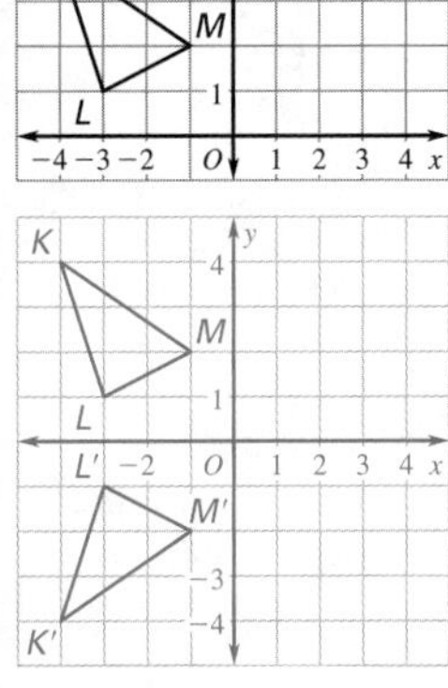

TRANSPARENCY

Support transparencies are available for Examples 2-3 and Your turn now Exercises 1-2.

1, 2. See Additional Answers beginning on page AA1.

EXTRA EXAMPLES

Example 4 How many lines of symmetry does the object have? **0**

CROSS-CURRICULUM

Art Symmetry, reflections, and transformations are all vitally important in art and design, and can become very complex in tile designs, rugs, quilts, and other media.

CONCEPT CHECK

When does a figure have symmetry? **When one half of the figure is a mirror image of the other half.**

DAILY PUZZLER

Which capital letters of the alphabet have at least two lines of symmetry? **H, I, O, X**

9.

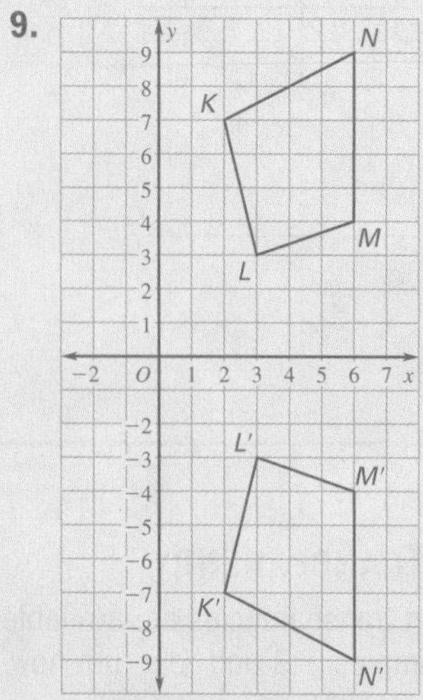

10. See Additional Answers beginning on page AA1.

Symmetry A figure has **line symmetry** if one half of the figure is a mirror image of the other half. A line of symmetry divides the figure into two congruent parts that are mirror images of each other.

EXAMPLE 4 Identifying Lines of Symmetry

How many lines of symmetry does the picture have?

a. one line of symmetry

b. five lines of symmetry

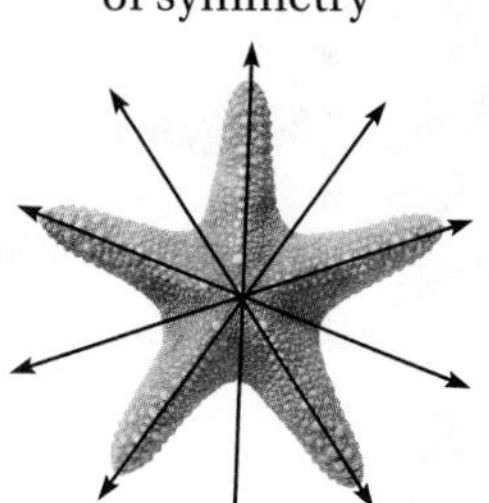

c. no lines of symmetry

8.6 Exercises

More Practice, p. 734

Getting Ready to Practice

Vocabulary Copy and complete the statement.

1. A(n) _?_ creates a mirror image of the original figure. **reflection**

2. A(n) _?_ is an operation that changes a figure into another figure. **transformation**

Tell whether the red figure is a reflection of the blue figure.

3. **no**

4. **yes**

5. **no**

How many lines of symmetry does the design have?

6. **one**

7. **none**

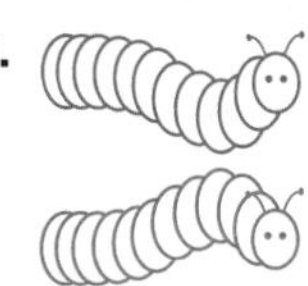

8. **two**

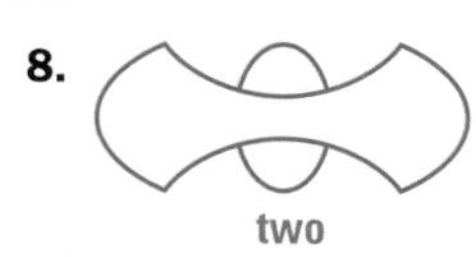

Graph the polygon. Then graph its reflection in the given axis. **9–10. See margin.**

9. $K(2, 7)$, $L(3, 3)$, $M(6, 4)$, $N(6, 9)$; x-axis

10. $F(-8, 8)$, $G(-4, 7)$, $H(-3, 3)$, $I(-7, 4)$; y-axis

with Homework

Example	Exercises
1	23
2	13-14
3	11-12
4	15-20

- More Examples
- eTutorial Plus

Practice and Problem Solving

A **Graph the polygon. Then graph its reflection in the given axis.** 11–14. See margin.

11. $A(3, 6)$, $B(6, 3)$, $C(5, 0)$, $D(1, 1)$; x-axis

12. $Q(-1, 3)$, $R(-3, 6)$, $S(-6, 4)$, $T(-6, 0)$; x-axis

13. $B(2, -1)$, $C(5, 0)$, $D(7, -2)$, $E(0, -6)$; y-axis

14. $P(0, 0)$, $Q(4, 1)$, $R(7, -3)$, $S(2, -7)$; y-axis

Sports How many lines of symmetry does the diagram have?

15. two

16.

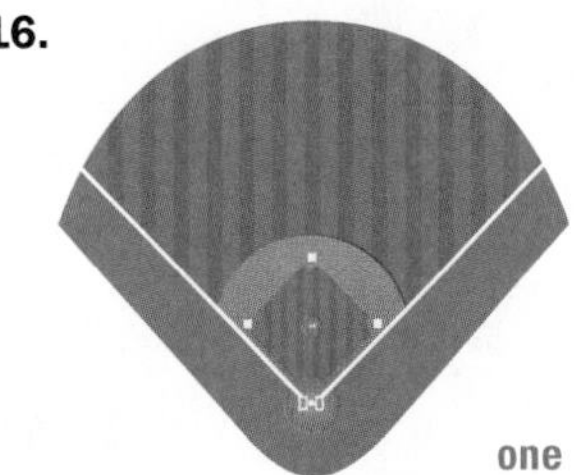

one

17. Illustrate Draw a quadrilateral with exactly four lines of symmetry. What kind of quadrilateral is this? See margin for art; square.

B **Extended Problem Solving For Exercises 18–20, use the table.**

Sides	3	4	5	6	8
Regular Polygon		?	?	?	?
Lines of Symmetry	? 3	? 4	? 5	? 6	? 8

18. Sketch Copy the table and sketch a regular polygon with the given number of sides in each column. Draw all the lines of symmetry. Check sketches.

19. Evaluate Count the lines of symmetry. Complete the table. See table.

20. Look for a Pattern How is the number of sides related to the number of lines of symmetry? They are the same.

21. Make a Model Write your name at the top of a piece of tracing paper. Fold the paper and trace your name to create a reflection. Unfold the paper to see your name and its reflection.

21. A good answer will include a clearly drawn reflection.

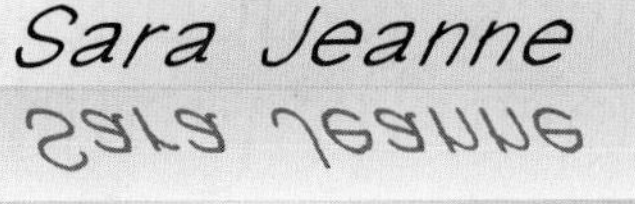

3 APPLY

ASSIGNMENT GUIDE

Basic Course

Day 1: EP p. 728 Exs. 44-47; pp. 407-408 Exs. 11-16, 18-20, 23-28

Average Course

Day 1: pp. 407-408 Exs. 11-15, 17-21, 23-29

Advanced Course

Day 1: pp. 407-408 Exs. 11-15, 17-23*, 25-29

Block

pp. 407-408 Exs. 11-15, 17-21, 23-29 (with 8.5)

EXTRA PRACTICE

- Student Edition, p. 734
- Chapter 8 Resource Book, pp. 54-56
- Test and Practice Generator

TRANSPARENCY

Even-numbered answers are available on transparencies. Support transparencies are available for Exercises 9-14, 22, and 23.

HOMEWORK CHECK

When you review students' homework for this lesson, go over the following exercises to check understanding of key concepts.

Basic: 11, 12, 13, 15, 23
Average: 11, 13, 14, 15, 23
Advanced: 11, 13, 14, 15, 23

TEACHING TIP

For Exercises 3-8, 15, and 16, expect to spend extra time with some students identifying lines of reflection and mirror images.

11-14, 17. See Additional Answers beginning on page AA1.

ASSESSMENT RESOURCES

For more assessment resources, see:

- Assessment Book
- Test and Practice Generator

MINI-QUIZ

1. How many lines of symmetry does a rectangle have? **2**
2. Reflect the triangle with vertices $A(0, 3)$, $B(3, 3)$, and $C(3, 0)$ in the y-axis. Graph the figure and its image.

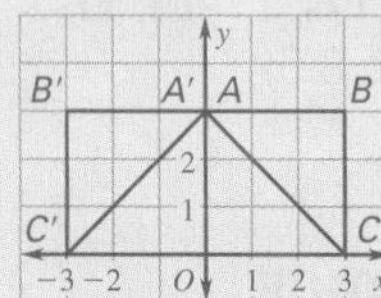

3. How many lines of symmetry does $\triangle ABC$ in Question 2 have? **1**

RETEACHING/REMEDIATION

- Study Guide in Chapter 8 Resource Book, pp. 57–58
- Tutor Place, Geometry and Measurement Cards 18, 19, Algebra Cards 17, 18
- eTutorial Plus Online
- Extra Practice, p. 734
- Lesson Practice in Chapter 8 Resource Book, pp. 54–46

CHALLENGE/ENRICHMENT

- Challenge Practice in Chapter 8 Resource Book, p. 60
- Teacher's Edition, p. 372F

ENGLISH LEARNER SUPPORT

- Spanish Study Guide
- Multi-Language Glossary
- Chapter Audio Summaries CDs

22, 23, 29. See Additional Answers beginning on page AA1.

C **22. Challenge** Graph the polygon with vertices $S(-6, 0)$, $T(0, 6)$, $V(6, 0)$, $W(2, -4)$, and $X(-2, -4)$. Reflect the polygon in the x-axis and graph its image in the same coordinate plane. **See margin.**

23. Critical Thinking A polygon has vertices $A(1, -2)$, $B(5, -1)$, $C(8, -4)$, $D(7, -7)$, and $E(4, -8)$. Reflect the polygon in the x-axis and find the vertices of its image. Then reflect the image in the y-axis. Graph the new image. Is the third polygon a reflection of the original? Explain. **See margin for art; no. *Sample answer:* It is not a mirror image of the original figure.**

Mixed Review 

In Exercises 24 and 25, find the number. *(Lesson 7.3)*

24. What is 0.8% of 500? **4**

25. 756 is what percent of 270? **280%**

26. Find the sum of the angle measures in a 9-gon. *(Lesson 8.4)* **1260°**

27. Find the measure of one angle in a regular 12-gon. *(Lesson 8.4)* **150°**

Test-Taking Practice 

INTERNET
State Test Practice
CLASSZONE.COM

28. Multiple Choice Which figure is a reflected image of figure D? **C**

A. figure A **B.** figure B

C. figure C **D.** none

29. Short Response Copy figure A and draw all its lines of symmetry. Where do the lines intersect? **See margin for art; in the center of the figure, (3, −3).**

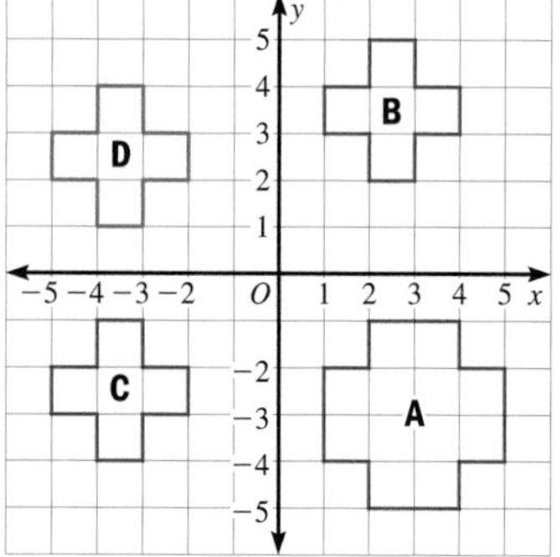

Deep Reflections

Use a mirror to read this quotation from William Shakespeare. **the eye sees not itself but by reflection**

Translations and Rotations

BEFORE
You reflected figures in a coordinate plane.

Now
You'll translate or rotate figures in a coordinate plane.

WHY?
So you can describe origami models, as in Exs. 5–6.

Word Watch

translation, p. 409
rotation, p. 410

Activity You can see how moving a triangle changes its vertices.

(1) Graph an image of *A* by moving it 7 units to the right and 2 units up. Plot the new vertex and label it *A′*. See margin.

(2) Repeat Step 1 with *B* and *C*. Then connect the vertices to form $\triangle A'B'C'$. See margin.

(3) How are the coordinates of *A*, *B*, and *C* related to *A′*, *B′*, and *C′*?

Step 3. 7 was added to each *x*-coordinate of the original figure and 2 was added to each *y*-coordinate of the original figure.

In the activity, you transformed $\triangle ABC$ by *sliding* it. A **translation** is a transformation that moves each point of a figure the same distance in the same direction. The image is congruent to the original figure.

To translate a figure in a coordinate plane, you change the coordinates of its points. When a and b are positive, you can use the guidelines below.

Slide up *b* units
$y \rightarrow y + b$

Slide to the left *a* units
$x \rightarrow x - a$

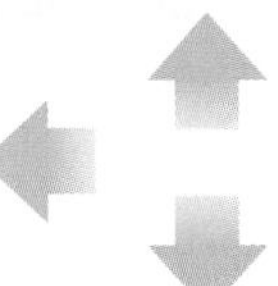

Slide to the right *a* units
$x \rightarrow x + a$

Slide down *b* units
$y \rightarrow y - b$

EXAMPLE 1 Using Coordinate Notation

Describe the translation from the blue figure to the red figure.

Solution

Each point moves 6 units to the right and 3 units down. The translation is

$(x, y) \rightarrow (x + 6, y - 3)$.

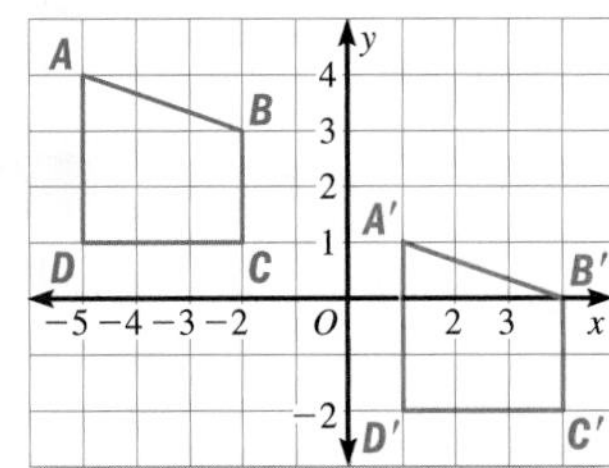

ILLINOIS Standards and ISAT:
9.A.3b, 9.A.3c

1 PLAN

SKILL CHECK

1. If $(x, y) = (-3, 5)$, find $(x + 1, y)$. **(−2, 5)**
2. If $(x, y) = (4, 6)$, find $(x, y - 8)$. **(4, −2)**

LESSON OBJECTIVE

Translate or rotate figures in a coordinate plane.

PACING

Suggested Number of Days
Basic Course: 2 days
Average Course: 2 days
Advanced Course: 2 days
Block: 1 block

TEACHING RESOURCES

For a complete list of Teaching Resources, see page 372B.

TRANSPARENCY

Warm-Up Exercises for this lesson are available on a transparency. Support transparencies are available for the Activity, Examples 1-3, and Your turn now Exercises 1-2.

2 TEACH

MOTIVATING THE LESSON

Perform translations of an object on a coordinate plane on the board or overhead. Ask students how the positions of different points on the object change.

Steps 1–2. See Additional Answers beginning on page AA1.

ACTIVITY

Goal To see how sliding a triangle on the coordinate plane changes the coordinates of the vertices.

Key Discovery A slide of a figure on the coordinate plane changes the coordinates of each point the same amount in the x- and/or y-directions.

TIPS FOR NEW TEACHERS

Rotations are harder for students to picture than translations. Using a yardstick, you can demonstrate rotations by attaching items to one end and rotating the yardstick with the other end fixed to act as the origin. See Tips for New Teachers in the *Chapter 8 Resource Book*.

EXTRA EXAMPLES

Example 1 Describe the translation from $EFGH$ to $E'F'G'H'$.

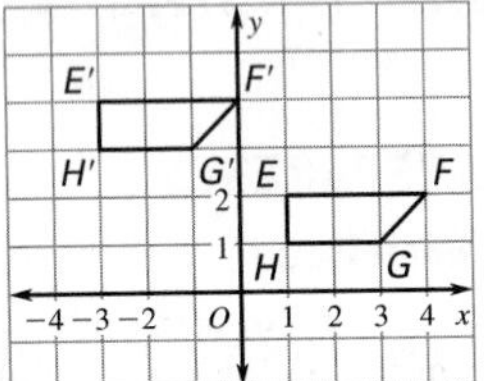

Each point moves 4 units to the left and 2 units up. The translation is $(x, y) \to (x - 4, y + 2)$.

Example 2 Rotate quadrilateral $KLMN$ 90° counterclockwise.

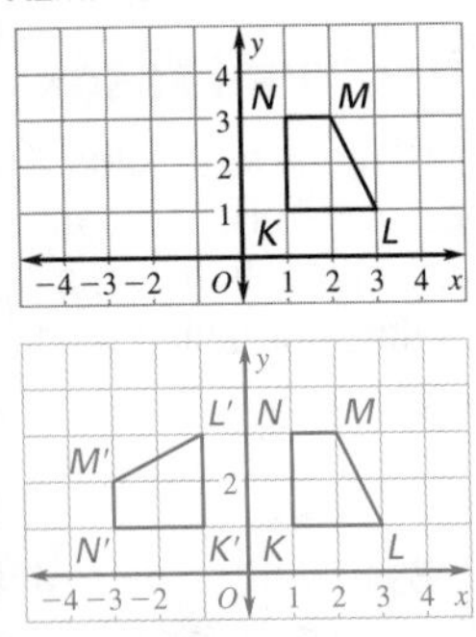

1, 2. See Additional Answers beginning on page AA1.

Rotations A **rotation** is a transformation that turns each point of a figure the same number of degrees around a common point. In this lesson, figures will always be turned around the origin.

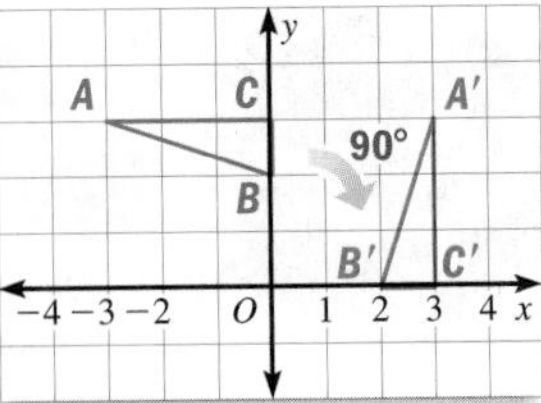

90° Rotations

90° Clockwise Rotation

Words To rotate a point 90° *clockwise*, switch the coordinates, then multiply the new y-coordinate by -1.

Numbers $P(6, 2) \to P'(2, -6)$ **Algebra** $P(x, y) \to P'(y, -x)$

90° Counterclockwise Rotation

Words To rotate a point 90° *counterclockwise*, switch the coordinates, then multiply the new x-coordinate by -1.

Numbers $P(5, 3) \to P'(-3, 5)$ **Algebra** $P(x, y) \to P'(-y, x)$

with Reading

Clockwise is the direction the hands on a clock turn. Counterclockwise is the opposite direction.

EXAMPLE 2 Rotating 90° Clockwise

Rotate quadrilateral *FGHJ* 90° clockwise.

Solution

Original		**Image**
(x, y)	$\to$	$(y, -x)$
$F(2, 2)$	$\to$	$F'(2, -2)$
$G(2, 4)$	$\to$	$G'(4, -2)$
$H(4, 4)$	$\to$	$H'(4, -4)$
$J(5, 2)$	$\to$	$J'(2, -5)$

The graph shows $FGHJ$ and $F'G'H'J'$.

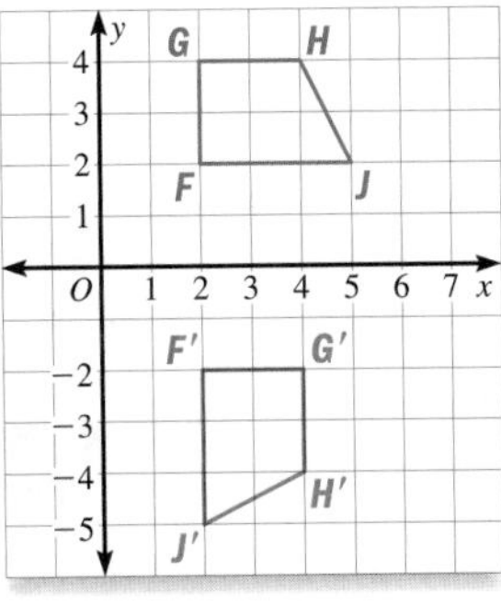

Your turn now **Graph the figure with the given vertices and its image after the rotation.** 1–2. See margin.

1. $A(1, 1)$, $B(3, 1)$, $C(3, 3)$, and $D(1, 4)$; 90° clockwise

2. $K(-1, 3)$, $L(1, 5)$, and $M(2, 3)$; 90° counterclockwise

180° Rotation

Words To rotate a point 180°, multiply its coordinates by −1.

Numbers $P(4, 1) \rightarrow P'(-4, -1)$ **Algebra** $P(x, y) \rightarrow P'(-x, -y)$

EXAMPLE 3 Rotating 180°

Rotate △*ABC* 180°.

Solution

Original		Image
(x, y)	→	$(-x, -y)$
$A(-6, 0)$	→	$A'(6, 0)$
$B(-5, 2)$	→	$B'(5, -2)$
$C(-1, 3)$	→	$C'(1, -3)$

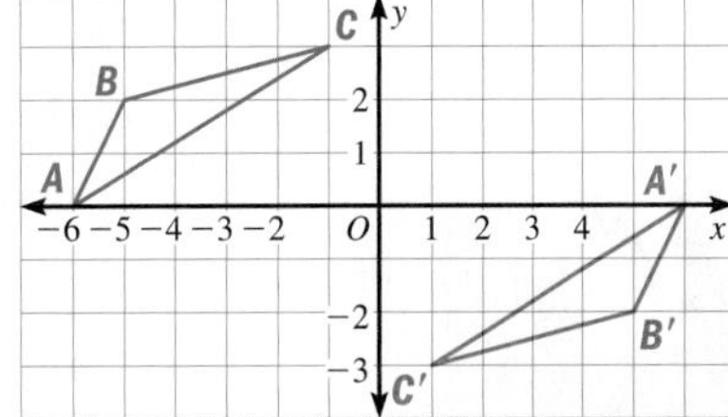

The graph shows △*ABC* and △*A′B′C′*.

8.7 Exercises

More Practice, p. 734

Getting Ready to Practice

with Vocabulary

Reflection is a **Fl**ip.
Rotation is a **T**urn.
Trans**l**ation is a **Sl**ide.

Vocabulary Name the transformation shown in the graph.

1. 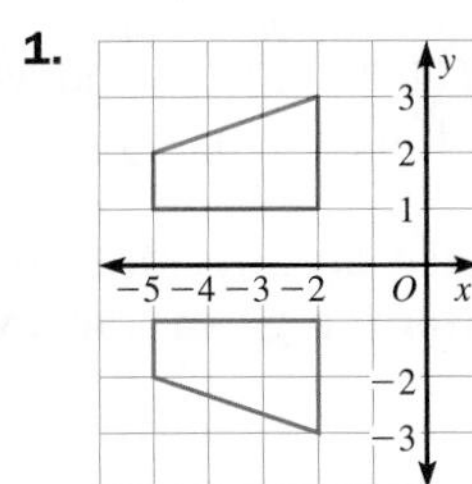
reflection

2. 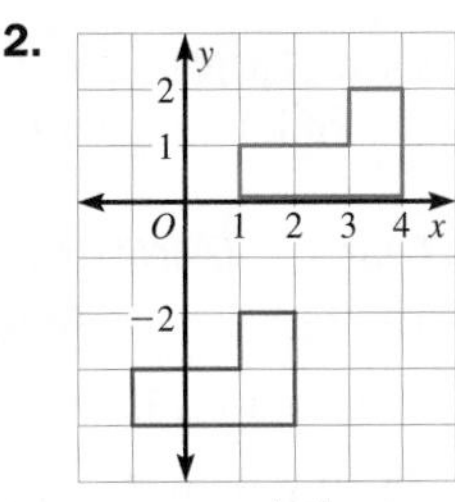
translation

3. 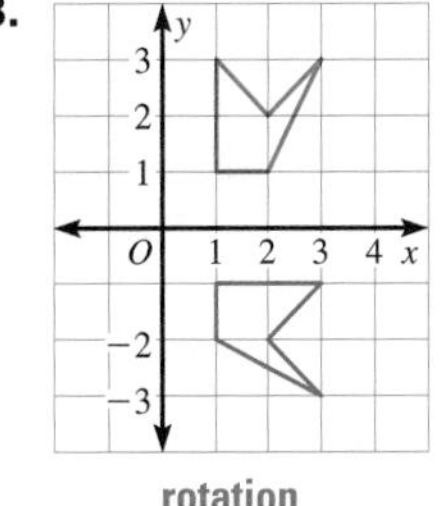
rotation

4. Guided Problem Solving Rotate △*RST* 90° counterclockwise.

(1) Graph △*RST* with vertices $R(-2, -1)$, $S(-5, -2)$, and $T(-4, 2)$. **See margin.**

(2) Find the vertices of the triangle's image. $R'(1, -2)$, $S'(2, -5)$, $T'(-2, -4)$

(3) Graph △*R′S′T′*, the image of △*RST* after rotation. **See margin.**

EXTRA EXAMPLES

Example 3 Rotate △*FGH* 180°.

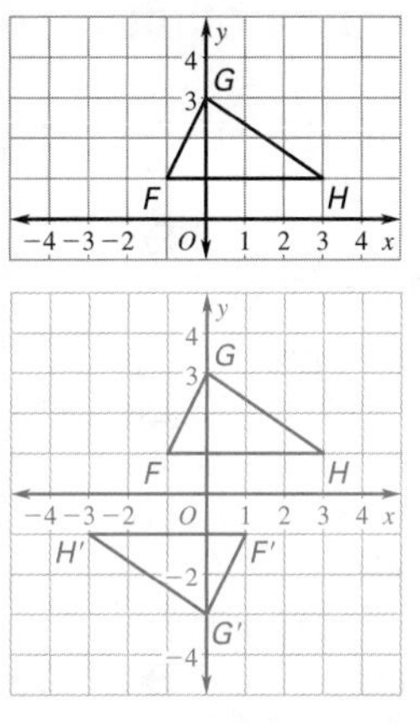

TEACHING TIP

Students may notice in Example 3, and in the box about a 180° rotation preceding it, that no mention is made of whether the rotation is clockwise or counterclockwise. Help students to come to see that the result is the same no matter the direction of the rotation.

CONCEPT CHECK

How do you change the coordinates of a point when you rotate a figure 90° clockwise about the origin? **Switch the coordinates and then multiply the new *y*-coordinate by −1.**

DAILY PUZZLER

Make a regular hexagon using 6 pencils or rods. By moving only 2 of the pencils and adding one more, show how you can form 2 rhombuses.

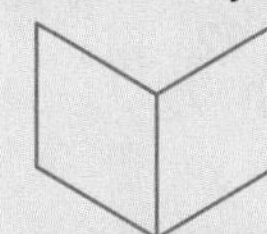

4. Steps 1, 3. See Additional Answers beginning on page AA1.

APPLY

ASSIGNMENT GUIDE

Basic Course

Day 1: pp. 412–413 Exs. 5–10, 16–18, 28–32

Day 2: pp. 412–413 Exs. 11–15, 19–24, 33–36

Average Course

Day 1: pp. 412–413 Exs. 5–10, 16–18, 25, 28–32

Day 2: pp. 412–413 Exs. 11–15, 19–22, 27, 33–36

Advanced Course

Day 1: pp. 412–413 Exs. 5–10, 16–18, 25–30*

Day 2: pp. 412–413 Exs. 11–15, 19–22, 31–36

Block

pp. 412–413 Exs. 5–22, 25, 27–36

EXTRA PRACTICE

- Student Edition, p. 734
- Chapter 8 Resource Book, pp. 63–65
- Test and Practice Generator

TRANSPARENCY

Even-numbered answers are available on transparencies. Support transparencies are available for Exercises 4 and 17–24.

HOMEWORK CHECK

When you review students' homework for this lesson, go over the following exercises to check understanding of key concepts.

Basic: 15, 16, 19, 20, 23

Average: 15, 16, 19, 20, 22

Advanced: 15, 16, 19, 20, 22

19–24. See Additional Answers beginning on page AA1.

HELP with Homework

Example	Exercises
1	15–16
2	20, 23
3	19, 22

Online Resources CLASSZONE.COM

- More Examples
- eTutorial Plus

Practice and Problem Solving

A Origami Describe the transformation shown in the origami model.

5.

reflection

6.

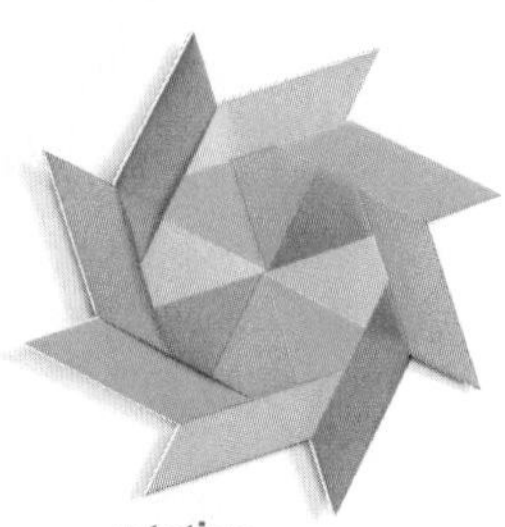

rotation

Name the type of transformation modeled by the action.

7. riding down an escalator translation

8. passing food around a table rotation

9. making a handprint in clay reflection

10. playing checkers translation

11. opening a combination lock rotation

12. going down a water slide translation

13. riding a carousel rotation

14. looking in a mirror reflection

Use coordinate notation to describe the translation from the blue figure to the red figure.

15. $(x + 5, y + 4)$

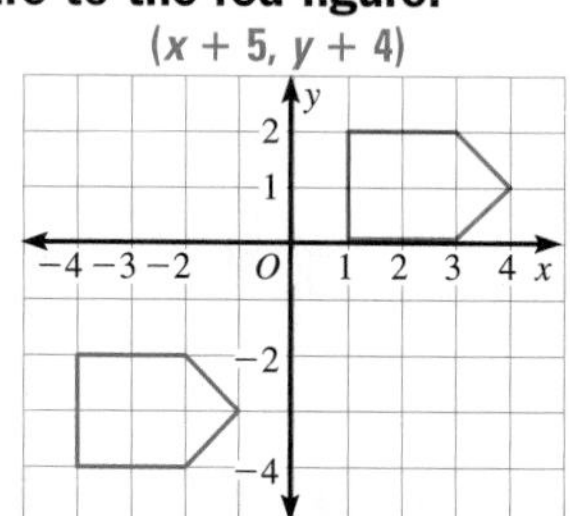

16. $(x - 5, y + 3)$

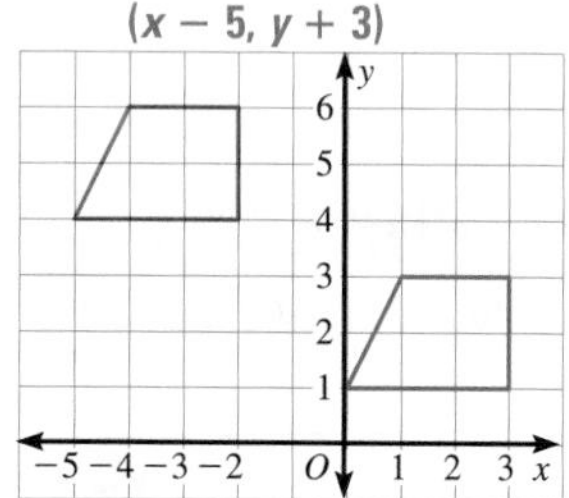

17. $\triangle PQR$ has vertices $P(0, -1)$, $Q(3, -1)$, and $R(5, -3)$. Find the vertices of its image after the translation $(x, y) \to (x - 5, y + 1)$. $P'(-5, 0)$, $Q'(-2, 0)$, $R'(0, -2)$

18. $\triangle LMN$ has vertices $L(4, 2)$, $M(0, 3)$, and $N(1, 1)$. Find the vertices of its image after the translation $(x, y) \to (x + 1, y - 6)$. $L'(5, -4)$, $M'(1, -3)$, $N'(2, -5)$

B Graph $\triangle LMN$ with vertices $L(2, 0)$, $M(2, 3)$, and $N(6, 0)$. Then graph its image after the given transformation. 19–24. See margin.

19. Rotate 180°.

20. Rotate 90° counterclockwise.

21. Translate using $(x, y) \to (x - 3, y - 4)$.

22. Rotate 180° then translate using $(x, y) \to (x + 1, y + 1)$.

23. Rotate 90° clockwise three times.

24. Translate using $(x, y) \to (x + 3, y)$ then rotate 180°.

For help with quadrants, see p. 91.

25. Quadrant IV; Quadrant III. *Sample answer:* A point in Quadrant II has a negative x-coordinate and a positive y-coordinate. To rotate 180°, you take the opposite of each coordinate, so the rotated point has a positive x-coordinate and a negative y-coordinate, and is in Quadrant IV. A point in Quadrant IV has a positive x-coordinate and a negative y-coordinate. To rotate 90° clockwise, you reverse the coordinates and take the opposite of the new y-coordinate, so the rotated point has a negative x-coordinate and a negative y-coordinate, and is in Quadrant III.

25. Writing Point A in Quadrant II is rotated 180°. Find the quadrant of point A'. Point B in Quadrant IV is rotated 90° clockwise. Find the quadrant of point B'. Explain your reasoning.

C **26. Challenge** The figure is the image of a triangle rotated 90° clockwise and reflected in the y-axis. Graph the original figure. See margin.

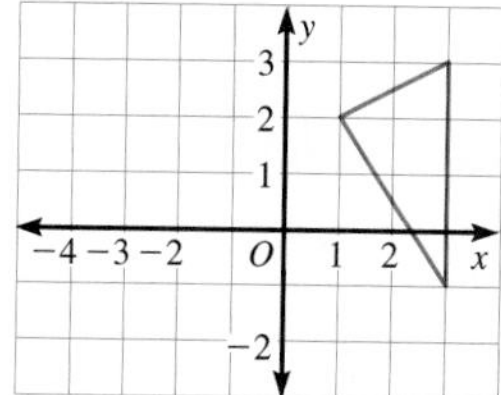

27. Multiple Methods Describe four different transformations of the blue square to the red square. You may include combinations of transformations. *Sample answer:* Reflect in the y-axis and then the x-axis; make two 90° clockwise rotations; make two 90° counterclockwise rotations; reflect in the x-axis and then the y-axis.

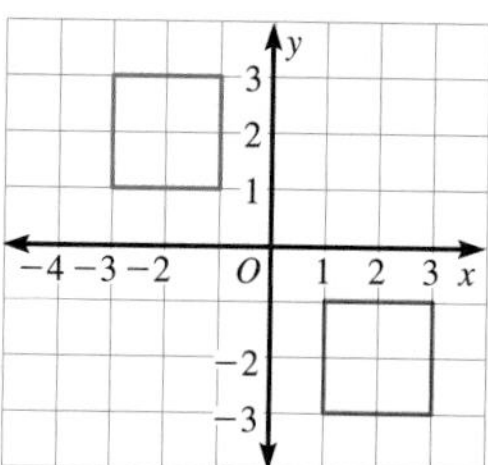

Mixed Review 

Solve the proportion. *(Lesson 7.2)*

28. $\frac{a}{25} = \frac{24}{200}$ 3

29. $\frac{32}{9} = \frac{c}{108}$ 384

30. $\frac{7}{60} = \frac{154}{d}$ 1320

Find the value of x. Classify the triangle by its angles. *(Lesson 8.2)*

31. 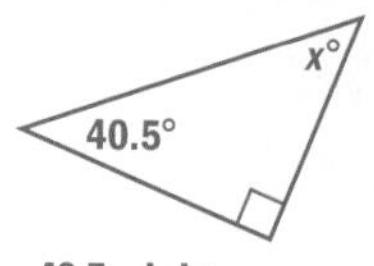

49.5; right

32. 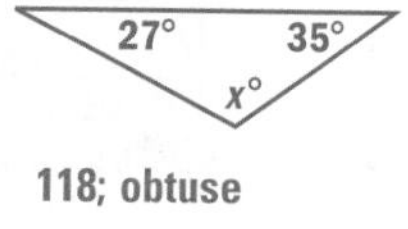

118; obtuse

33. 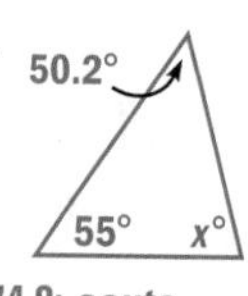

74.8; acute

Basic Skills Find the mean, median, and mode(s).

34. 39, 45, 43, 28, 45, 48, 39, 45 41.5, 44, 45

35. 110, 108, 118, 110, 105 110.2, 110, 110

Test-Taking Practice 

36. Extended Response Rotate the figure 90° clockwise. Reflect the image in the y-axis. Graph the final image. Complete the rule for the double transformation you performed.

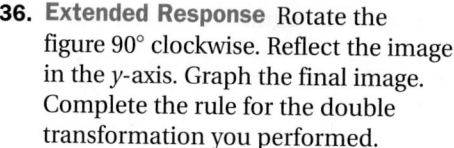

$(x, y) \rightarrow (\underline{?}, \underline{?})$ $-y, -x$

Explain your reasoning. See margin.

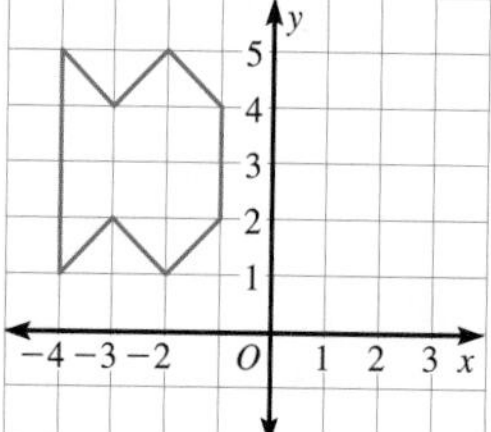

INTERNET
State Test Practice
CLASSZONE.COM

4 ASSESS

Assessment Resources

For more assessment resources, see:
- Assessment Book
- Test and Practice Generator

Mini-Quiz

1. $\triangle RST$ has vertices $R(-1, 4)$, $S(3, 4)$, and $T(2, -3)$. Find the vertices of its image after the translation $(x, y) \rightarrow (x - 4, y + 5)$. $R'(-5, 9)$, $S'(-1, 9)$, $T'(-2, 2)$
2. Graph $\triangle RST$ with vertices $R(0, 2)$, $S(3, 2)$, and $T(2, 0)$. Then graph its image after a 180° rotation.

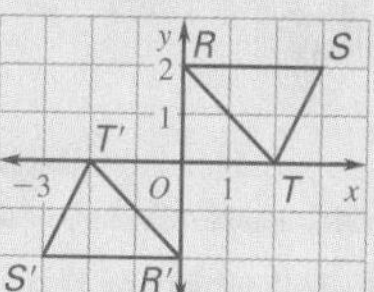

5 FOLLOW-UP

Reteaching/Remediation

- Study Guide in Chapter 8 Resource Book, pp. 66–67
- Tutor Place, Geometry and Measurement Card 19, Algebra Cards 17, 18
- eTutorial Plus Online
- Extra Practice, p. 734
- Lesson Practice in Chapter 8 Resource Book, pp. 63–65

Challenge/Enrichment

- Challenge Practice in Chapter 8 Resource Book, p. 68
- Teacher's Edition, p. 372F

English Learner Support

- Spanish Study Guide
- Multi-Language Glossary
- Chapter Audio Summaries CDs

26, 36. See Additional Answers beginning on page AA1.

PLAN

SKILL CHECK

How many sides does each polygon have?

1. trapezoid 4
2. pentagon 5
3. hexagon 6
4. parallelogram 4

LESSON OBJECTIVE

Decide if a shape tessellates and create tessellations.

TEACH

EXTRA EXAMPLES

Example 1 Tell whether the polygon tessellates.

a.

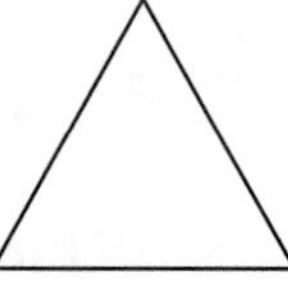

yes

b.

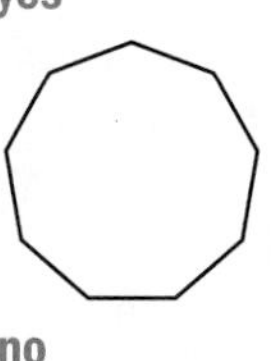

no

Example 2 Alter a hexagon to create a tessellation.

Sample:

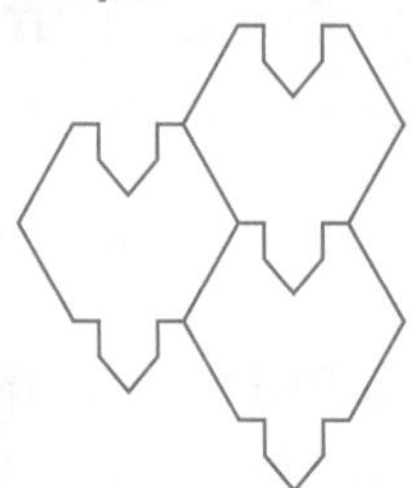

Tessellations

GOAL Decide if a shape tessellates. Create tessellations.

tessellation, p. 414

Tessellations You can use reflections, rotations, and translations to create a *tessellation*, like the one shown here. A **tessellation** is a repeating pattern of figures that covers a plane with no gaps or overlaps. If a figure can be used to create a tessellation, you say the figure *tessellates*.

EXAMPLE 1 Identifying Tessellating Polygons

Tell whether the polygon tessellates.

a.

Yes, you can create a tessellation by translating a rectangle.

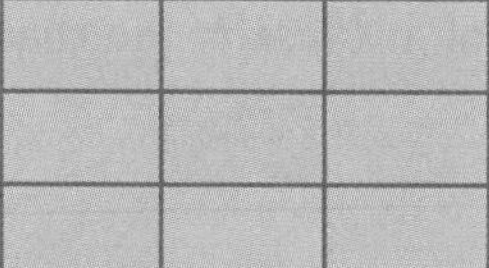

b.

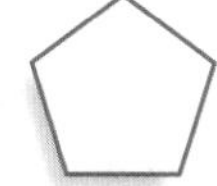

No, regular pentagons will not cover the plane without gaps or overlaps.

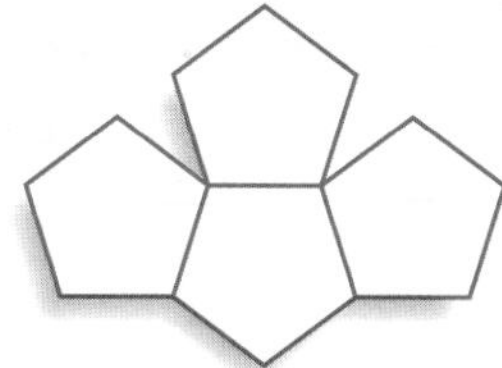

You can create a tessellation by altering a polygon that tessellates.

EXAMPLE 2 Creating a Tessellation

Alter a parallelogram to create a tessellation.

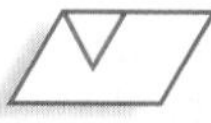

Cut a triangle from the parallelogram.

Slide the triangle to the opposite side.

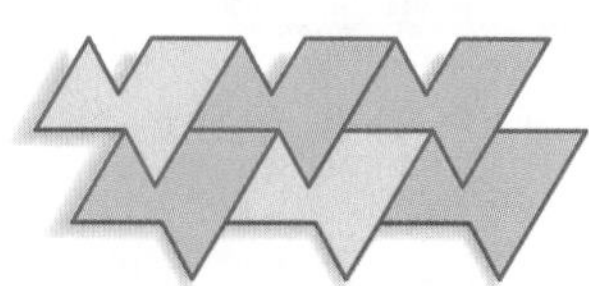

Translate the figure to create a tessellation.

ILLINOIS Standards and ISAT:
9.A.3b

EXAMPLE 3 Creating a Tessellation

Create a tessellation by altering an equilateral triangle.

Cut a piece from the triangle.

Slide the piece to another side.

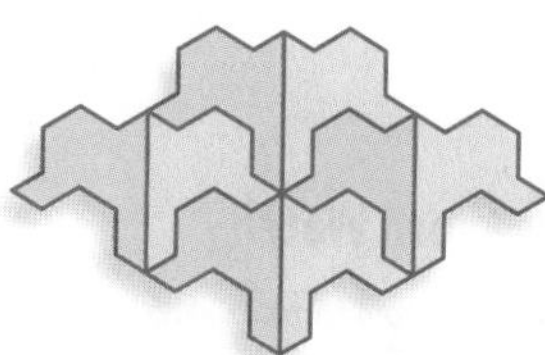

Reflect the figure then translate the pair.

Exercises

Tell whether the figure tessellates.

1. 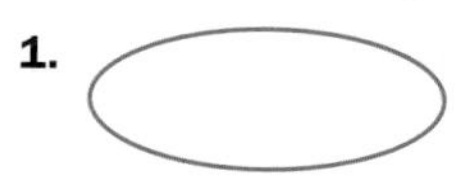
no

2. 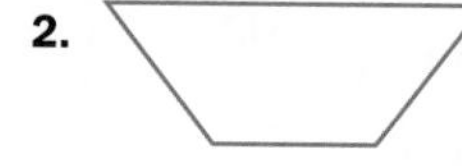
yes

3. 
no

4. Explain how you can transform the blue shape to create the tessellation. 90° counterclockwise rotation

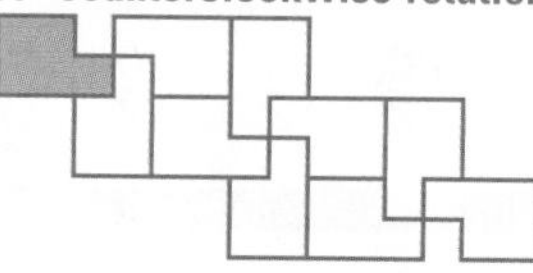

5. Copy and continue the pattern. Check work.

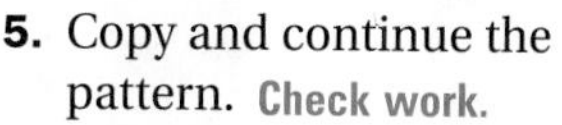

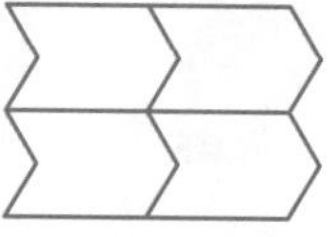

Copy the polygon and use it to create a tessellation. Describe how the polygon was transformed in your tessellation. 6–8. See margin for art.

6. 
translation

7. 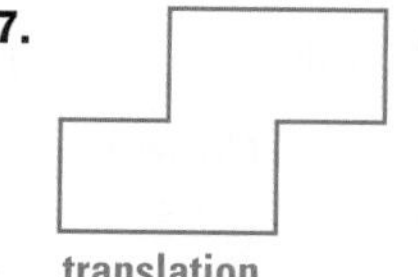
translation

8. 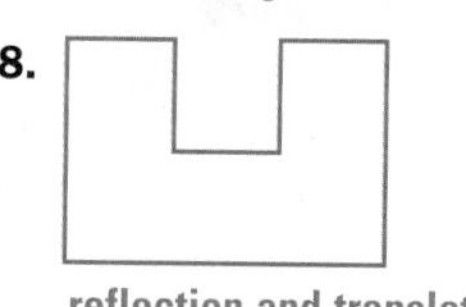
reflection and translation

9. **Make a Model** Create a tessellation by altering a rectangle.

10. Create a tessellation by altering a parallelogram that is not a rectangle.

11. Create two different tessellations using the shape at the right. See margin.

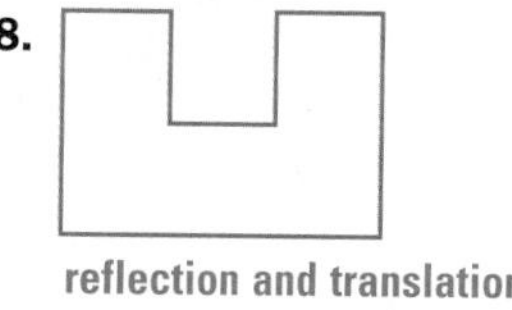

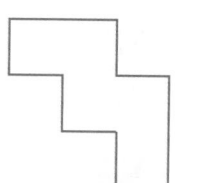

9. A good answer will include a rectangle with a piece cut from one side and slid to another side. The translation of that figure forms a tessellation.

10. A good answer will include the tessellation of a figure like the one in Example 2.

EXTRA EXAMPLES

Example 3 Create a tessellation by altering a rhombus.
Sample:

TEACHING TIP

In Example 3, students should notice that translations, rotations, and reflections are all used to tessellate the figure. All these transformations are permissible in making a tessellation. You may also want to point out that more than one tessellation can often be formed from the same shape. As an example, you can stack bricks one on top of the other or you can stagger them in various patterns.

3 APPLY

TRANSPARENCY

Even-numbered answers are available on transparencies.

TEACHING TIP

In Exercise 4, point out that the four middle tiles can be thought of as one larger tile shaped like a + symbol. Students may find it easier to visualize how to tessellate with the + shape than with the individual pieces.

6–8, 11. See Additional Answers beginning on page AA1.

1 PLAN

SKILL CHECK

1. Name the three pairs of congruent sides and the three pairs of congruent angles in the figure.

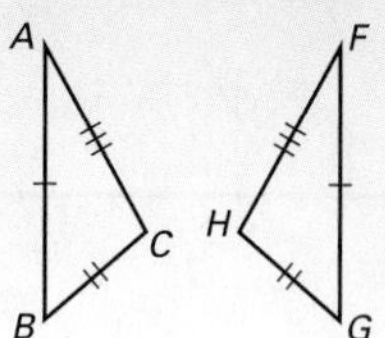

$\overline{AB} \cong \overline{FG}$, $\overline{BC} \cong \overline{GH}$, $\overline{AC} \cong \overline{FH}$; $\angle A \cong \angle F$, $\angle B \cong \angle G$, $\angle C \cong \angle H$

LESSON OBJECTIVE

Use similar polygons to find missing measures.

PACING

Suggested Number of Days
Basic Course: 2 days
Average Course: 2 days
Advanced Course: 2 days
Block: 1 block

TEACHING RESOURCES

For a complete list of Teaching Resources, see page 372B.

TRANSPARENCY

Warm-Up Exercises for this lesson are available on a transparency.

2 TEACH

MOTIVATING THE LESSON

Ask students to discuss the everyday meaning of "similar." Point out that mathematically, similar figures must have *exactly* the same shape, though the size can vary.

Similarity and Dilations

BEFORE
You used congruent polygons to find missing measures.

Now
You'll use similar polygons to find missing measures.

WHY?
So you can find the height of a sand castle, as in Ex. 14.

Word Watch

similar polygons, p. 416
dilation, p. 418
scale factor, p. 418

In the Real World

Television Screens The television screens shown here are different sizes, but they have the same shape. How are they related?

Similar polygons have the same shape, but they can be different sizes. The symbol ~ means "is similar to." When you name similar polygons, list their corresponding vertices in the same order.

Similar Polygons

$\triangle ABC \sim \triangle XYZ$

Corresponding angles are congruent.

$\angle A \cong \angle X \quad \angle B \cong \angle Y \quad \angle C \cong \angle Z$

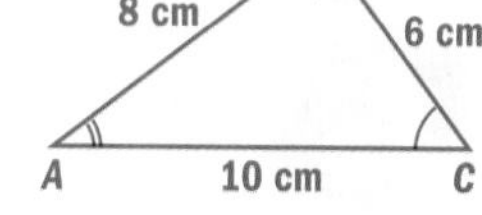

Corresponding side lengths are proportional.

$\frac{AB}{XY} = \frac{BC}{YZ} \quad \frac{BC}{YZ} = \frac{AC}{XZ} \quad \frac{AC}{XZ} = \frac{AB}{XY}$

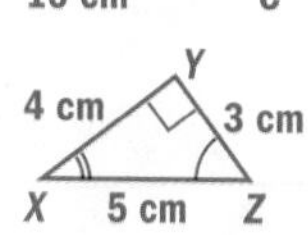

EXAMPLE 1 Identifying Similar Polygons

Tell whether the television screens are similar.

(1) Corresponding angles are congruent. Each angle measures 90°.
$\angle A \cong \angle E \quad \angle B \cong \angle F \quad \angle C \cong \angle G \quad \angle D \cong \angle H$

(2) Corresponding side lengths are proportional.

$$\frac{30 \text{ inches}}{18 \text{ inches}} = \frac{40 \text{ inches}}{24 \text{ inches}}$$

$$720 = 720$$

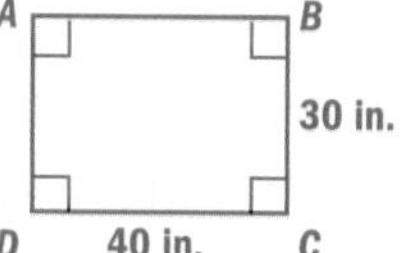

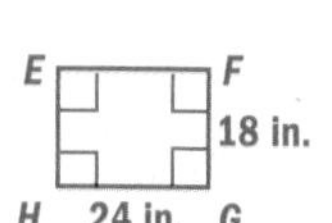

ANSWER Quadrilateral $ABCD \sim$ quadrilateral $EFGH$

ILLINOIS Standards and ISAT:
6.D.3, 9.A.3c, 9.B.3, 9.C.3b; 6.C.3b

with Review

For help with writing and solving proportions, see p. 322.

EXAMPLE 2 Using Similar Triangles

In the diagram, $\triangle KLM \sim \triangle NPQ$. Find the value of y.

Corresponding side lengths are proportional.

$\frac{KL}{NP} = \frac{LM}{PQ}$ **Write a proportion.**

$\frac{y}{12} = \frac{10}{5}$ **Substitute given values.**

$y = 24$ **Solve the proportion.**

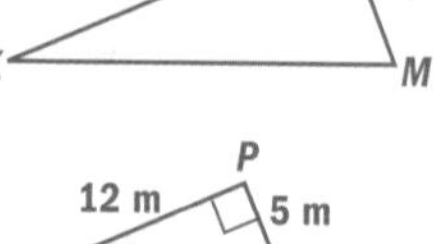

ANSWER The value of y is 24 meters.

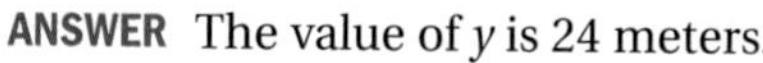

Your turn now **Find the value of x.**

1. Quadrilateral $ABCD \sim$ quadrilateral $FGHJ$ **8 m**

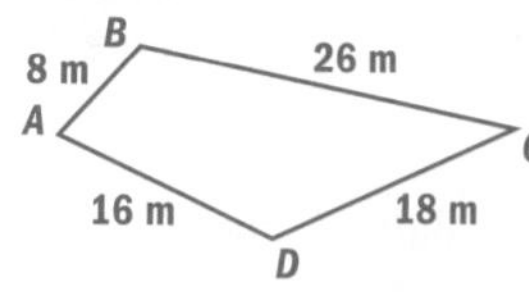

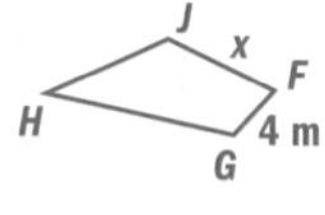

EXAMPLE 3 Using Indirect Measurement

Height Alma is 5 feet tall and casts a 7 foot shadow. At the same time, a tree casts a 14 foot shadow. The triangles formed are similar. Find the height of the tree.

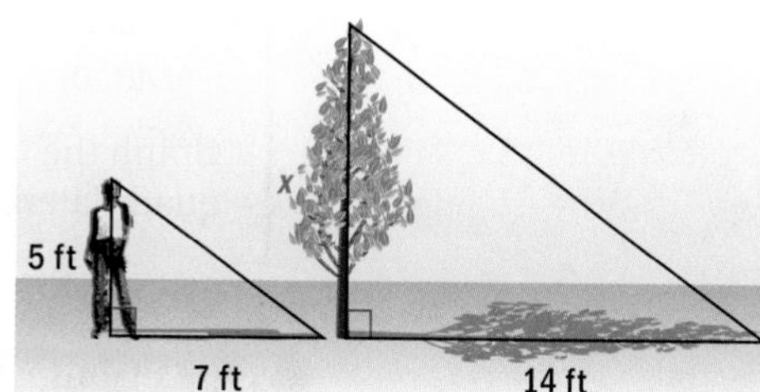

Solution

You can use a proportion to find the height of the tree.

$\frac{\text{Tree's height}}{\text{Alma's height}} = \frac{\text{Length of tree's shadow}}{\text{Length of Alma's shadow}}$ **Write a proportion.**

$\frac{x \text{ feet}}{5 \text{ feet}} = \frac{14 \text{ feet}}{7 \text{ feet}}$ **Substitute given values.**

$x = 10$ **Solve the proportion.**

ANSWER The tree is 10 feet tall.

TIPS FOR NEW TEACHERS

Students who have watched medical drama shows may have heard characters use expressions like "pupils fixed and dilated." They probably understand that "dilated" in this everyday sense means "enlarged." Make sure students understand that in mathematics, a dilation can refer either to an expansion or a shrinking. See Tips for New Teachers in the *Chapter 8 Resource Book*.

EXTRA EXAMPLES

Example 1 Tell whether the ramps are similar. Explain your reasoning.

Yes; corresponding angles are congruent and corresponding side lengths are proportional (the ratios all equal 0.5).

Example 2 In the diagram, $\triangle PQR \sim \triangle WXY$. Find the value of z. **18.75 in.**

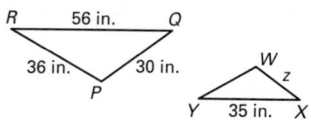

Example 3 Jan's banana plant is 8 feet tall and casts a 3 foot shadow. At the same time, Jan's house casts a shadow $11\frac{1}{4}$ feet. How high is Jan's house? **30 ft**

EXTRA EXAMPLES

Example 4 $\triangle RST$ has vertices $R(-1, 4)$, $S(3, 4)$, and $T(2, -3)$. Dilate using a scale factor of 2. Graph the triangle and its image.

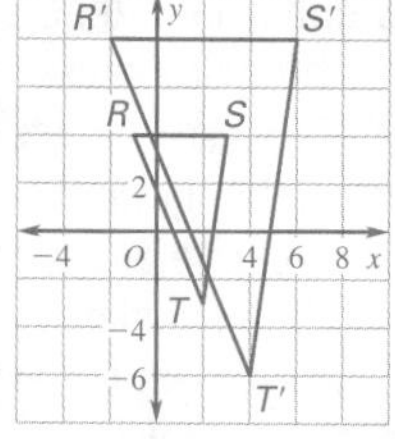

TEACHING TIP

In Example 4, students should notice that the dilation is not centered at the middle of the original figure. Making the center of the dilation the origin allows us to find the coordinates of the dilation simply by multiplying the coordinates of each vertex by the scale factor.

TRANSPARENCY

Support transparencies are available for Example 4 and Your turn now Exercises 2-5.

CONCEPT CHECK

Are congruent figures similar? Explain your reasoning. **Yes; corresponding angles are congruent, and corresponding side lengths all have the ratio 1 : 1.**

DAILY PUZZLER

Make eight equilateral triangles with 16 pencils or rods. Then show how you can remove 4 pencils or rods and leave only 4 equilateral triangles.

2–5. See Additional Answers beginning on page AA1.

Dilations A **dilation** stretches or shrinks a figure. The image created by a dilation is similar to the original figure. The **scale factor** of a dilation is the ratio of corresponding side lengths. In this course, the center of dilation will always be the origin.

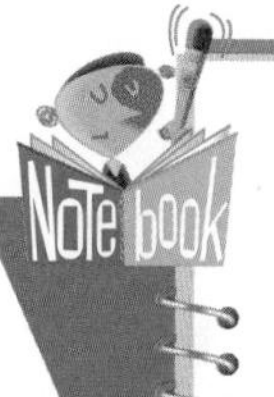

Dilation

Words To dilate a polygon, multiply the coordinates of each vertex by the scale factor k and connect the vertices.

Numbers $P(4, 1) \rightarrow P'(8, 2)$ **Algebra** $P(x, y) \rightarrow P'(kx, ky)$

Watch Out!

The scale factor is the ratio of corresponding side lengths:

$$\frac{\text{after dilation}}{\text{before dilation}}$$

EXAMPLE 4 Dilating a Polygon

Quadrilateral *ABCD* has vertices $A(-1, -1)$, $B(0, 1)$, $C(2, 2)$, and $D(3, 0)$. Dilate using a scale factor of 3.

Solution

Graph the quadrilateral. Find the vertices of the image.

Original		Image
(x, y)	$\rightarrow$	$(3x, 3y)$
$A(-1, -1)$	$\rightarrow$	$A'(-3, -3)$
$B(0, 1)$	$\rightarrow$	$B'(0, 3)$
$C(2, 2)$	$\rightarrow$	$C'(6, 6)$
$D(3, 0)$	$\rightarrow$	$D'(9, 0)$

Graph the image of the quadrilateral.

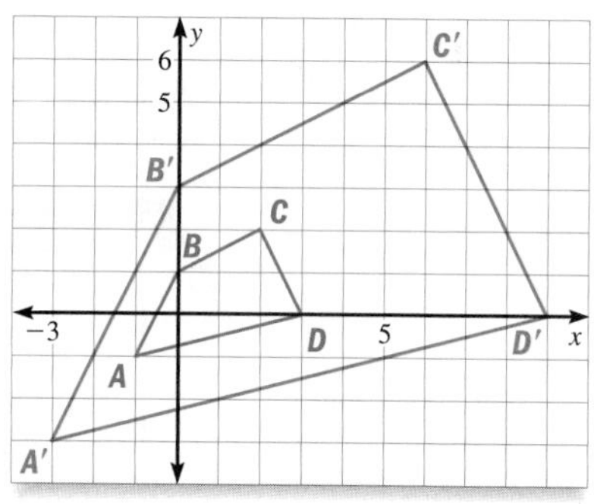

Your turn now **Graph the polygon with the given vertices. Then graph its image after dilation by the scale factor *k*.** **2–5. See margin.**

2. Triangle RST has vertices $R(1, 1)$, $S(3, 2)$, and $T(2, 3)$; $k = 2$.
3. Quadrilateral $MNPQ$ has vertices $M(1, 0)$, $N(0, -1)$, $P(-1, 0)$, and $Q(0, 1)$; $k = 4$.
4. Triangle JKL has vertices $J(0, 2)$, $K(6, 4)$, and $L(2, -2)$; $k = \frac{1}{2}$.
5. Quadrilateral $CDGH$ has vertices $C(-6, -6)$, $D(-3, -3)$, $G(0, -3)$, and $H(3, -6)$; $k = \frac{1}{3}$.

8.8 Exercises

More Practice, p. 734

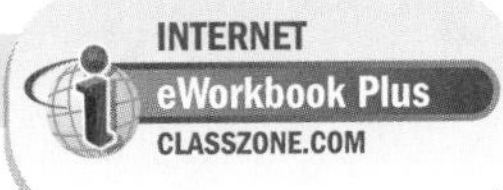

Getting Ready to Practice

Vocabulary **Copy and complete the statement.**

1. The _?_ of a dilation is the ratio of corresponding side lengths. scale factor
2. A figure and its image after dilation are always _?_. similar

Watch Out! Remember that corresponding parts are in the same position on different polygons.

Name the similar polygons.

3. 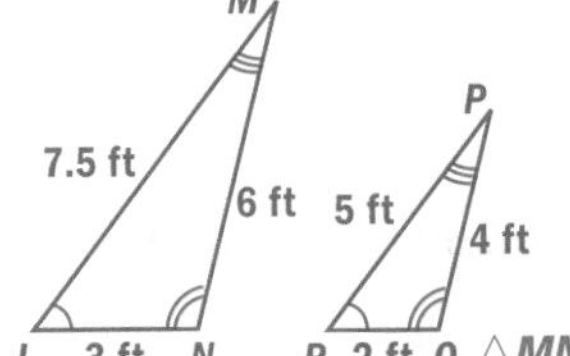

$\triangle MNL \sim \triangle PQR$

4. 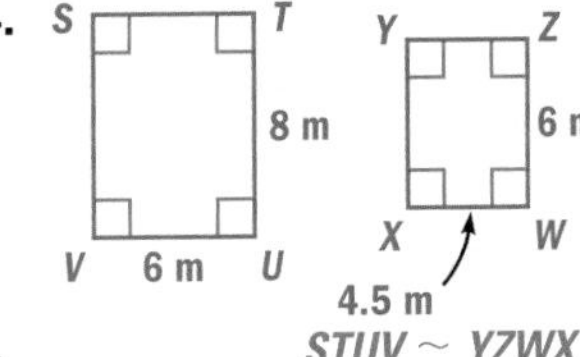

$STUV \sim YZWX$

5. **Guided Problem Solving** Dilate $\triangle ABC$ using a scale factor of $\frac{1}{3}$.
   (1 Graph $\triangle ABC$ with vertices $A(3, 6)$, $B(-3, -3)$, and $C(6, 0)$. See margin.
   (2 Find the vertices of its image using the scale factor. $A'(1, 2)$, $B'(-1, -1)$, $C'(2, 0)$
   (3 Graph the image. See margin.

Practice and Problem Solving

HELP with Homework

Example	Exercises
1	6-7
2	8-13
3	14, 21
4	15-19

Online Resources CLASSZONE.COM
- More Examples
- eTutorial Plus

A **In Exercises 6 and 7, name the similar polygons.**

6. D 6 yd E, 2.5 yd, 6.5 yd, F; A, 5 yd, 13 yd, B 12 yd C
$\triangle ABC \sim \triangle FED$

7. 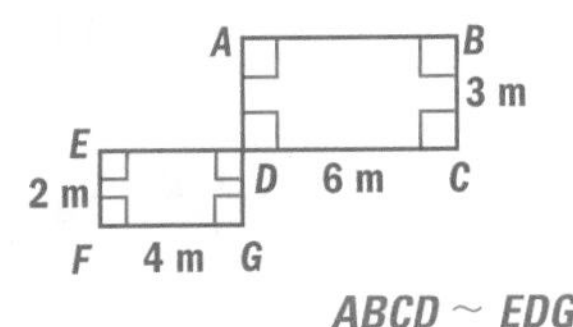

$ABCD \sim EDGF$

Use the similar triangles to find the value of *x*.

8. $\triangle ABC \sim \triangle DEF$ 4 in.

9. $\triangle GHJ \sim \triangle KHM$ 40

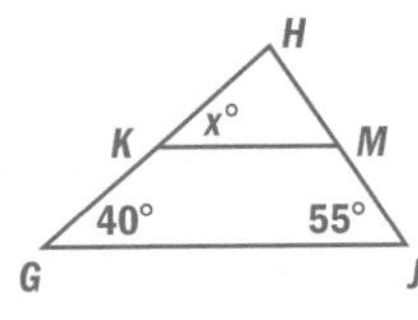

3 APPLY

ASSIGNMENT GUIDE

Basic Course
Day 1: EP p. 733 Exs. 7-10; pp. 419-421 Exs. 6-8, 12, 13, 23, 26-30
Day 2: pp. 419-421 Exs. 9-11, 14-21

Average Course
Day 1: pp. 419-421 Exs. 6-8, 12, 13, 22-24, 26-29
Day 2: pp. 419-421 Exs. 9-11, 14-21, 30

Advanced Course
Day 1: pp. 419-421 Exs. 6-8, 12, 13, 22-28*
Day 2: pp. 419-421 Exs. 9-11, 14-21, 30

Block
pp. 419-421 Exs. 6-24, 26-30

EXTRA PRACTICE
- Student Edition, p. 734
- Chapter 8 Resource Book, pp. 71-73
- Test and Practice Generator

TRANSPARENCY

Even-numbered answers are available on transparencies. Support transparencies are available for Exercises 5 and 15-19.

HOMEWORK CHECK

When you review students' homework for this lesson, go over the following exercises to check understanding of key concepts.
Basic: 6, 7, 8, 14, 15
Average: 6, 8, 10, 14, 15
Advanced: 6, 8, 11, 16, 21

5. Steps 1, 3. See Additional Answers beginning on page AA1.

15.

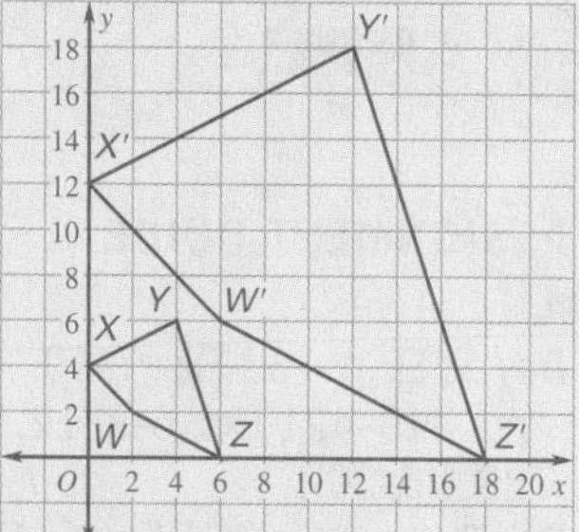

16.

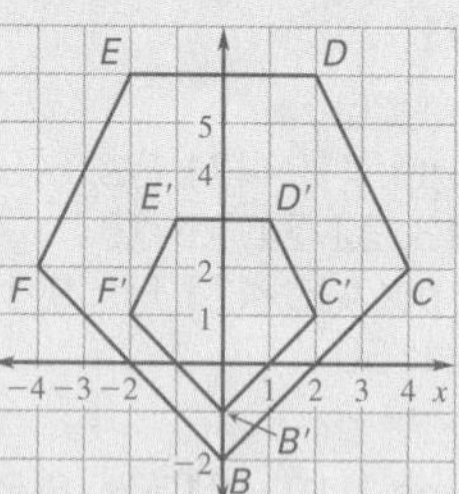

17.

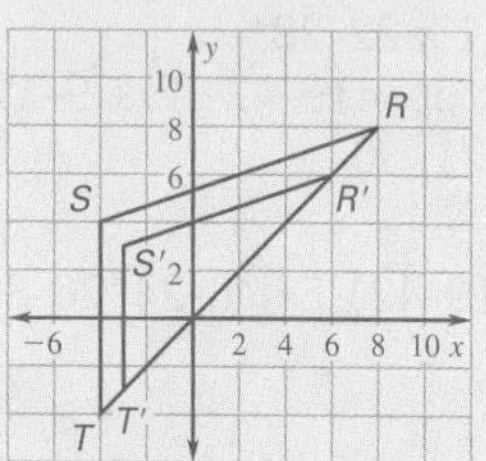

18. See Additional Answers beginning on page AA1.

19.

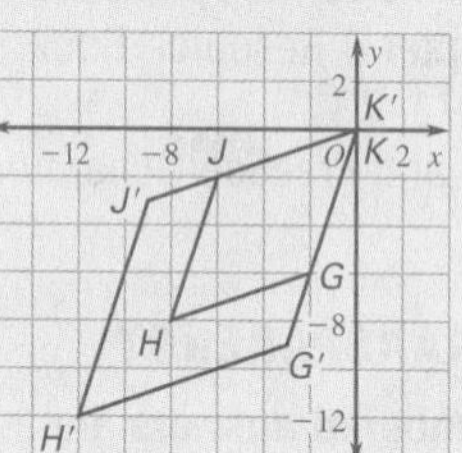

20. *K'* (43.38, 9.36), *L'* (8.82, 9.54), *M'* (12.24, 0.36), *N'* (5.94, 8.64), *P'* (46.44, 39.78)

22. *Sample Answer:* All squares have four right angles, so corresponding angles are congruent. Because all four sides of a square are the same length, the ratio of the side length of one square to the side length of another square will be the same for every pairing of sides.

Use the similar polygons to find the value of *x*.

10. Parallelogram *CDFG* is similar to parallelogram *HJLK*. $2\frac{1}{4}$ ft

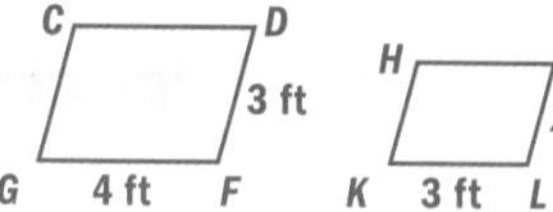

11. Trapezoid *MNPQ* is similar to trapezoid *RSTV*. 3 in.

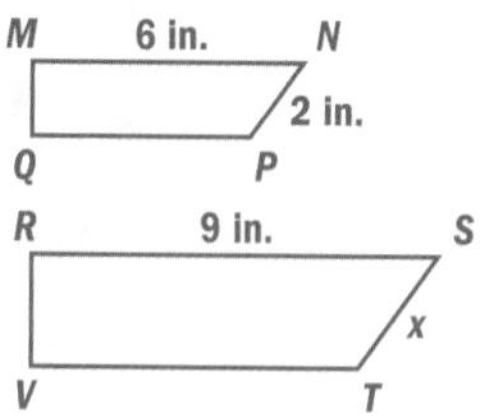

12. $\triangle LMN$ is similar to $\triangle PQR$. Find the value of *x*. 12 ft

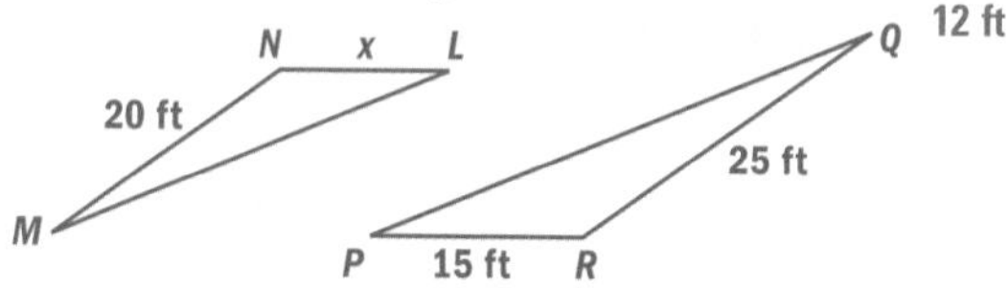

13. Pentagon *ABCDE* ~ pentagon *FGHJK*. Find the values of *x* and *y*. $x = 90$, $y = 6.75$ cm

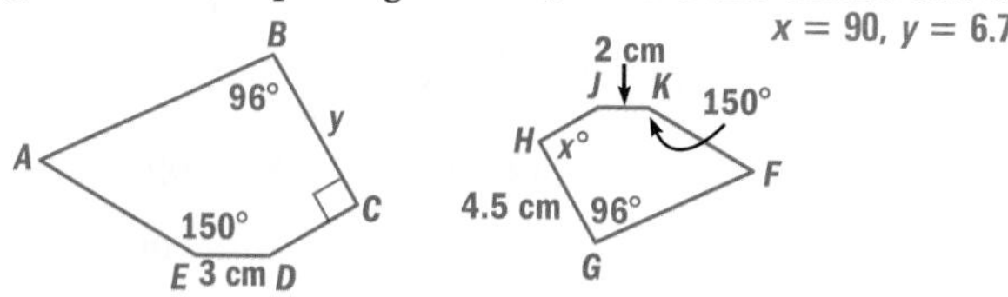

14. Indirect Measurement A sand castle casts an 18 foot shadow. At the same time, your 5 foot friend casts a 20 foot shadow. How tall is the sand castle? 4.5 ft

Graph the polygon with the given vertices. Then graph its image after dilation by the scale factor *k*. 15–19. See margin.

15. $W(2, 2)$, $X(0, 4)$, $Y(4, 6)$, $Z(6, 0)$; $k = 3$

16. $B(0, -2)$, $C(4, 2)$, $D(2, 6)$, $E(-2, 6)$, $F(-4, 2)$; $k = \frac{1}{2}$

17. $R(8, 8)$, $S(-4, 4)$, $T(-4, -4)$; $k = \frac{3}{4}$

18. $L(2, -2)$, $M(4, 2)$, $N(-3, 2)$, $P(-1, -2)$; $k = 4$

19. $G(-2, -6)$, $H(-8, -8)$, $J(-6, -2)$, $K(0, 0)$; $k = 1.5$

B **20. Calculate** Pentagon *KLMNP* has vertices $K(24.1, 5.2)$, $L(4.9, 5.3)$, $M(6.8, 0.2)$, $N(3.3, 4.8)$, and $P(25.8, 22.1)$. Use the scale factor 1.8 to find the vertices of its image after dilation. See margin.

21. Photo Reduction You reduce a 12 inch by 24 inch photo to $\frac{1}{3}$ of its original dimensions. What are the new dimensions of the photo? 4 in. by 8 in.

22. Writing Explain why all squares are similar.

24. Identical to. *Sample answer:* If you multiply both coordinates of each vertex by 1, the vertices will remain the same.

26. Vanilla and chocolate, vanilla and mint chip, vanilla and cookie crumble, vanilla and strawberry, chocolate and mint chip, chocolate and cookie crumble, chocolate and strawberry, mint chip and cookie crumble, mint chip and strawberry, cookie crumble and strawberry, vanilla and vanilla, chocolate and chocolate, mint chip and mint chip, cookie crumble and cookie crumble, strawberry and strawberry; 15. *Sample answer:* I used Make a List so I could write out all possible combinations.

23. Algebra Hexagon $ABCDEF$ is similar to hexagon $PQRSTU$. Find the values of x and y. $x = 44$, $y = 136$

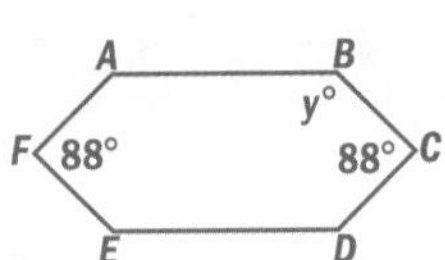

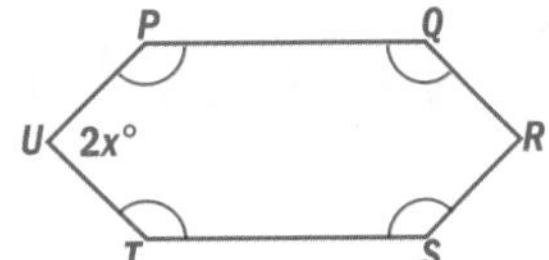

24. Analyze If a polygon is dilated by a scale factor of 1, will the image be *larger than, smaller than,* or *identical to* the original polygon? Explain.

C **25. Challenge** Name two similar polygons in the diagram. Find their scale factor. $\triangle ABF \sim \triangle ACE$; 2 or $\frac{1}{2}$

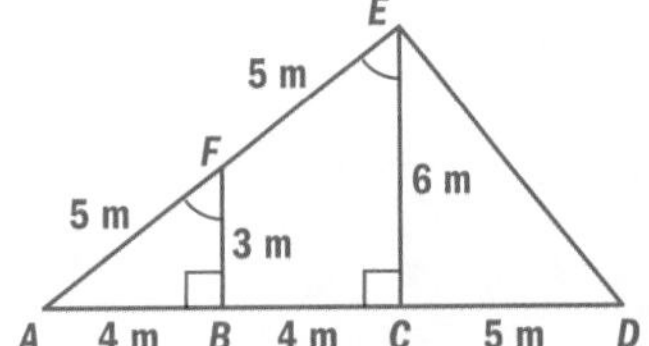

Mixed Review 

Choose a Strategy Use a strategy from the list to solve the following problem. Explain your choice of strategy.

26. An ice cream stand offers vanilla, chocolate, mint chip, cookie crumble, and strawberry ice cream. Write all the possible 2 scoop cones you can order. How many possibilities are there? See margin.

Problem Solving Strategies
- Look for a Pattern
- Draw a Diagram
- Make a List
- Make a Model

27. You sell your bike for \$50 but owe your parents 45% of the selling price. How much money do you have left after you repay your parents? *(Lesson 7.3)* \$27.50

28. Graph the polygon with vertices $A(0, 1)$, $B(3, 4)$, $C(9, 3)$, and $D(7, -3)$. Then graph its image after reflection in the x-axis. *(Lesson 8.6)* See margin.

Test-Taking Practice 

INTERNET
State Test Practice
CLASSZONE.COM

29. Multiple Choice Jenny is 5 feet tall and casts a 3 foot shadow. At the same time, a flagpole casts a 15 foot shadow. What mathematical idea can Jenny use to find the height of the flag pole? C

A. inequality **B.** congruence **C.** similarity **D.** symmetry

30. Multiple Choice Find the length of $\overline{AB}$. $\triangle ABD \sim \triangle BCD$. H

F. 6 cm **G.** 7.2 cm

H. 7.5 cm **I.** 11.25 cm

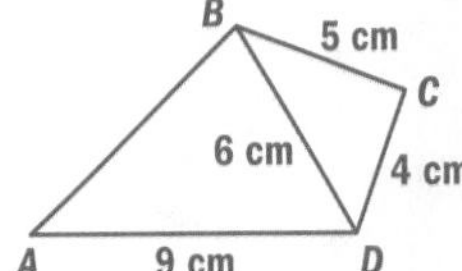

4 ASSESS

Assessment Resources

For more assessment resources, see:
- Assessment Book
- Test and Practice Generator

Mini-Quiz

1. Graph the polygon with vertices $V(0, 0)$, $W(-4, -6)$, and $X(4, -2)$. Dilate by the scale factor $\frac{1}{2}$, and graph the image.

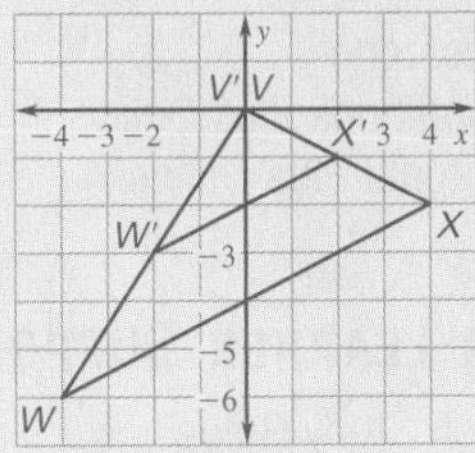

Reteaching/Remediation

- Study Guide in Chapter 8 Resource Book, pp. 74–75
- Tutor Place, Geometry and Measurement Card 17, Ratio, Proportion, and Percent Card 6, Algebra Cards 17, 18
- eTutorial Plus Online
- Extra Practice, p. 734
- Lesson Practice in Chapter 8 Resource Book, pp. 71–73

Challenge/Enrichment

- Challenge Practice in Chapter 8 Resource Book, p. 76
- Teacher's Edition, p. 372F

English Learner Support

- Spanish Study Guide
- Multi-Language Glossary
- Chapter Audio Summaries CDs

28. See Additional Answers beginning on page AA1.

ADDITIONAL RESOURCES

The following resources are available to help review the materials in Lessons 8.5–8.8.

Chapter 8 Resource Book
- Lesson Practice
- Study Guide

Assessment Book
- Chapter 8 Quiz 2

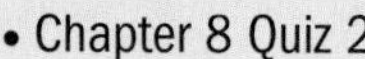

Technology
- Test and Practice Generator
- eTutorial CD-ROM

Internet
- Classzone
- eWorkbook Plus Online
- eTutorial Plus Online

ENGLISH LEARNER SUPPORT

- Spanish Study Guide
- Multi-Language Glossary
- Chapter Audio Summaries CDs

4.

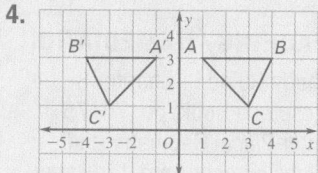

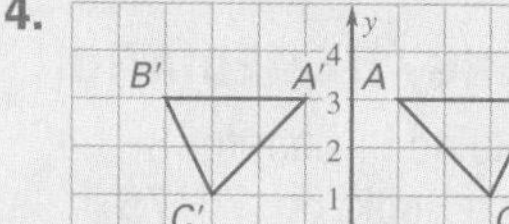

Notebook Review

Review the vocabulary definitions in your notebook.

Copy the review examples in your notebook. Then complete the exercises.

Check Your Definitions

congruent sides, angles, p. 397
corresponding parts, p. 397
reflection, p. 404
transformation, p. 404
image, p. 404
line symmetry, p. 406
translation, p. 409
rotation, p. 410
similar polygons, p. 416
dilation, p. 418
scale factor, p. 418

Use Your Vocabulary

Copy and complete the sentence with a review word.

1. A(n) ? creates a mirror image of a figure. reflection

2. A(n) ? is a transformation that slides a figure. translation

8.5 Can you name congruent polygons?

EXAMPLE Name the congruent triangles and explain how you know that they are congruent.

ANSWER $\triangle LMN \cong \triangle SRT$ by Angle-Side-Angle

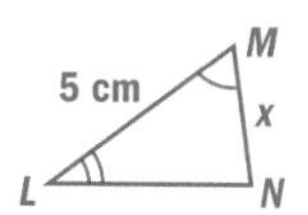

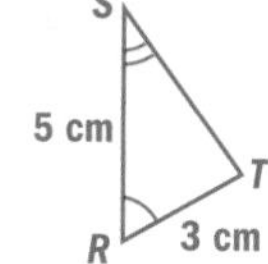

☑ **3.** Find the value of x using the triangles above. 3 cm

8.6–8.7 Can you reflect and rotate figures?

EXAMPLE Graph $\triangle ABC$ with vertices $A(1, 3)$, $B(4, 3)$, and $C(3, 1)$. Then graph its reflection in the x-axis.

Original		Image
(x, y)	$\rightarrow$	$(x, -y)$
$A(1, 3)$	$\rightarrow$	$A'(1, -3)$
$B(4, 3)$	$\rightarrow$	$B'(4, -3)$
$C(3, 1)$	$\rightarrow$	$C'(3, -1)$

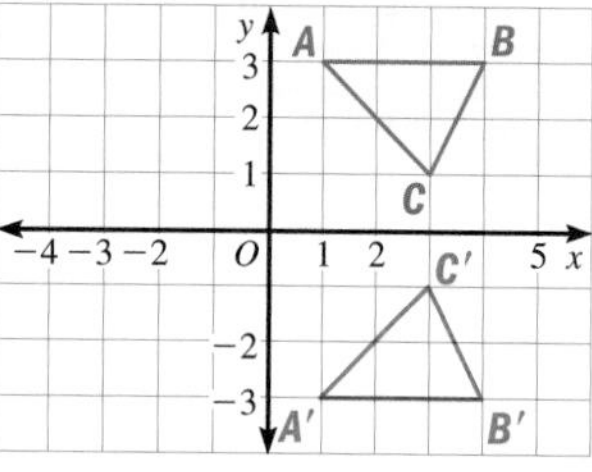

☑ **4.** Graph the reflection of $\triangle ABC$ in the y-axis. See margin.

EXAMPLE Rotate $\triangle KLM$ 90° counterclockwise.

Original		Image
(x, y)	$\rightarrow$	$(-y, x)$
$K(3, 1)$	$\rightarrow$	$K'(-1, 3)$
$L(1, 4)$	$\rightarrow$	$L'(-4, 1)$
$M(3, 3)$	$\rightarrow$	$M'(-3, 3)$

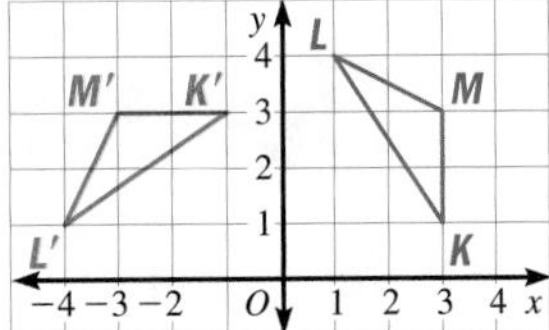

 **5.** Rotate $\triangle KLM$ 180°. See margin.

8.8 Can you use similarity to find measures?

EXAMPLE Polygons *ABCD* and *FGHJ* are similar. Find the value of x.

$\frac{AB}{FG} = \frac{BC}{GH}$ Write a proportion.

$\frac{16}{20} = \frac{x}{15}$ Substitute.

$x = 12$ Solve for x.

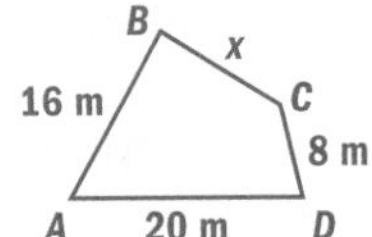

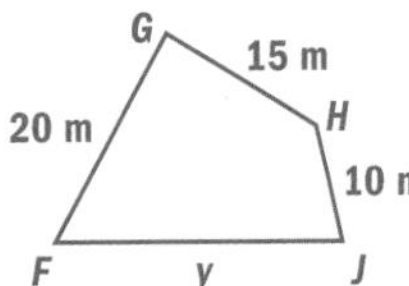

 **6.** Use the similar polygons to find the value of y. 25 m

Stop and Think about Lessons 8.5–8.8

 **7. Writing** Explain how dilation affects the perimeter of a figure. See margin.

8. Critical Thinking Give a real world example of a 180° rotation. *Sample answer*: A person turning around to face the opposite way

Review Quiz 2

1. In the diagram, $\triangle ABC \cong \triangle DEF$. Find $m\angle D$. 66°

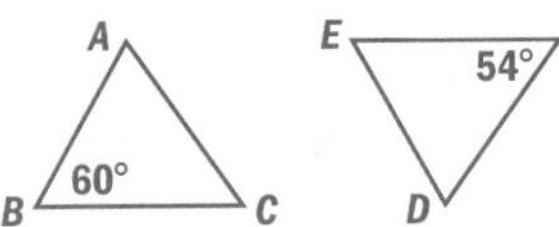

Name the type of transformation modeled by the action.

2. sledding downhill translation

3. leaving fingerprints reflection

4. spinning in place rotation

5. opening a drawer translation

6. Graph $\triangle ABC$ with vertices $A(1, 1)$, $B(2, 3)$, and $C(3, 0)$. Dilate the triangle using a scale factor of 4. See margin.

Notebook Review

7. *Sample answer*: The perimeter of the image is the product of the scale factor and the perimeter of the original figure.

Notebook Review

5.

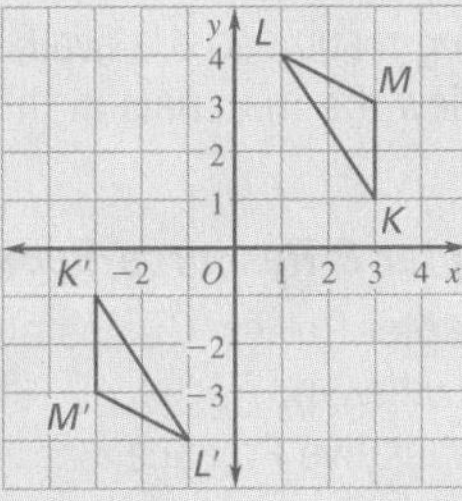

Review Quiz 2

6.

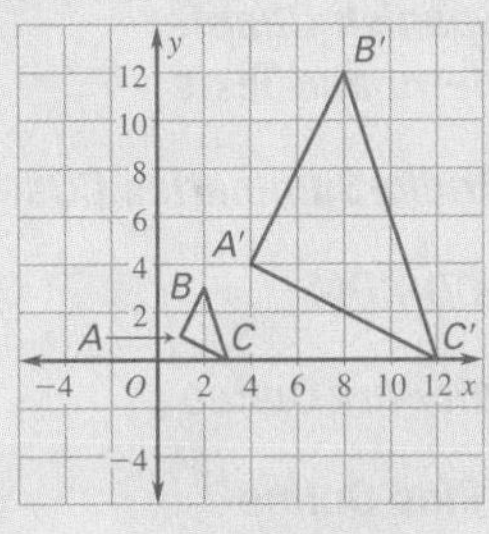

Additional Resources

The following resources are available to help review the materials in this chapter.

Chapter 8 Resource Book
- Chapter Review Games and Activities, p. 77
- Cumulative Practice, Chs. 1–8

English/Spanish Chapter Reviews and Tests

Chapter Audio Summaries CDs

eTutorial CD-ROM

eWorkbook Plus Online

eTutorial Plus Online

Chapter Review

Vocabulary

straight angle, right angle, p. 375
supplementary, complementary angles, p. 375
vertical angles, p. 376
perpendicular lines, p. 376
parallel lines, p. 377
acute, right, obtuse angle, p. 382
acute, right, obtuse triangle, p. 382
equilateral, isosceles, scalene triangle, p. 382
quadrilateral, p. 386
trapezoid, parallelogram, rhombus, p. 386
polygon, regular polygon, p. 390
pentagon, hexagon, heptagon, octagon, p. 390
congruent sides, angles, p. 397
corresponding parts, p. 397
reflection, p. 404
transformation, p. 404
image, p. 404
line symmetry, p. 406
translation, p. 409
rotation, p. 410
similar polygons, p. 416
dilation, p. 418
scale factor, p. 418

Vocabulary Review

Matching **Match each word with the correct definition.**

1. transformation G
2. reflection E
3. parallel lines F
4. complementary angles A
5. supplementary angles C
6. perpendicular lines H
7. translation D
8. dilation B

A. Two angles whose measures have a sum of 90°
B. A transformation that stretches or shrinks a figure
C. Two angles whose measures have a sum of 180°
D. A transformation that slides a figure
E. A transformation that creates a mirror image of a figure
F. Two lines in the same plane that do not intersect
G. An operation that changes one figure into another figure
H. Two lines that intersect to form a right angle

Review Questions

Find the measure of ∠1. *(Lesson 8.1)*

9. 109°, 109°, 1

10. 1, 50°, 130°

11. 65°, 1, 25°

Review Questions

Classify the polygon. *(Lessons 8.2, 8.3)*

12. 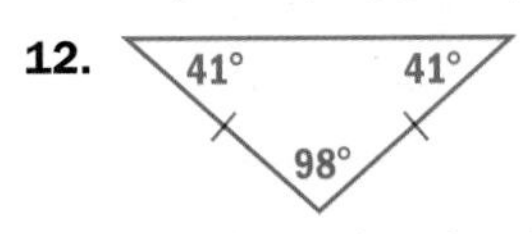

obtuse isosceles triangle

13. 4 in. 8 in. 4 in 8 in.

rectangle

14. 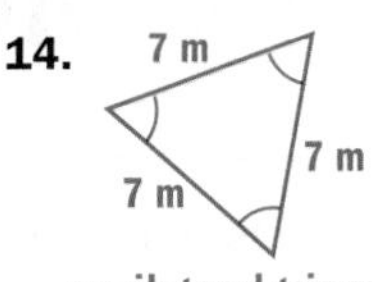

equilateral triangle

15. Find the sum of the angle measures in a heptagon. *(Lesson 8.4)* 900°

16. Find the measure of one angle in a regular pentagon. *(Lesson 8.4)* 108°

Pentagon *ABCDE* ≅ pentagon *PQRST*. *(Lesson 8.5)*
17–18. See margin.

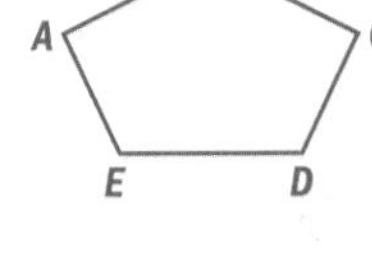

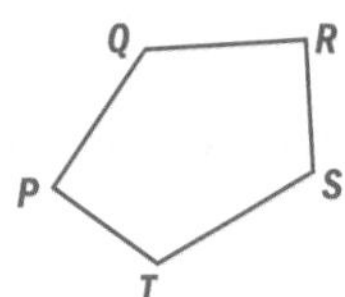

17. Name the congruent corresponding angles.

18. Name the congruent corresponding sides.

19. Name the congruent triangles and explain how you know they are congruent. *(Lesson 8.5)* See margin.

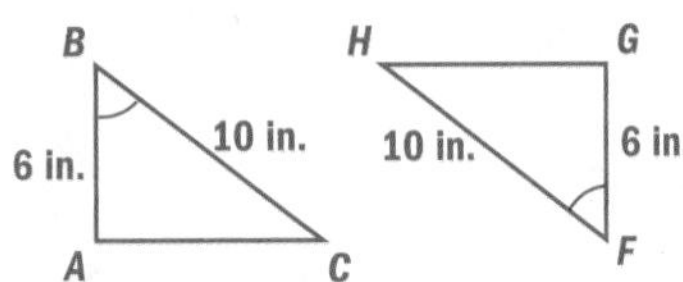

Tell whether the red figure is a reflection of the blue figure. *(Lesson 8.6)*

20. W W yes **21.** f ɟ no **22.** p p no **23.** g a no

24. $\triangle XYZ$ has vertices $X(-1, 1)$, $Y(-3, 1)$, and $Z(-2, 5)$. Reflect $\triangle XYZ$ in the y-axis. Find the vertices of the image. *(Lesson 8.6)* $X'(1, 1)$, $Y'(3, 1)$, $Z'(2, 5)$

Rotate the polygon 90° clockwise and graph its image. *(Lesson 8.7)* 25–27. See margin.

25. 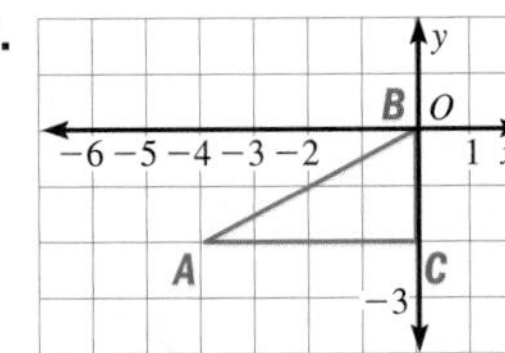

26. 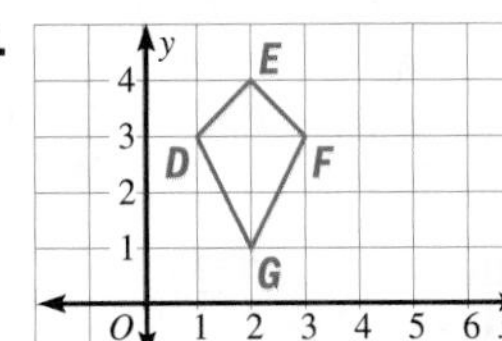

27. 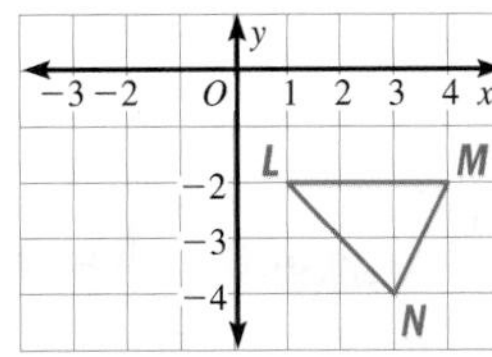

28. Building Height A 20 foot flagpole stands beside a building. The flagpole casts a shadow that is 25 feet long. At the same time, the building casts a shadow that is 60 feet long. How tall is the building? *(Lesson 8.8)* 48 ft

29. A polygon has vertices $A(-2, 0)$, $B(-2, 4)$, $C(-6, 8)$, and $D(-12, 6)$. Dilate it using a scale factor of 2. Find the vertices of the image. *(Lesson 8.8)* $A'(-4, 0)$, $B'(-4, 8)$, $C'(-12, 16)$, $D'(-24, 12)$

17. $\angle A \cong \angle P$, $\angle B \cong \angle Q$, $\angle C \cong \angle R$, $\angle D \cong \angle S$, $\angle E \cong \angle T$

18. $\overline{AB} \cong \overline{PQ}$, $\overline{BC} \cong \overline{QR}$, $\overline{CD} \cong \overline{RS}$, $\overline{DE} \cong \overline{ST}$, $\overline{AE} \cong \overline{PT}$

19. $\triangle ABC \cong \triangle GFH$; two sides and the included angle of one triangle are congruent to two sides and the included angle of the other triangle, so the triangles are congruent by Side-Angle-Side.

25. 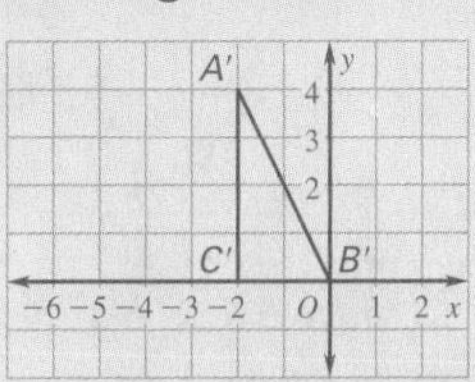

26. 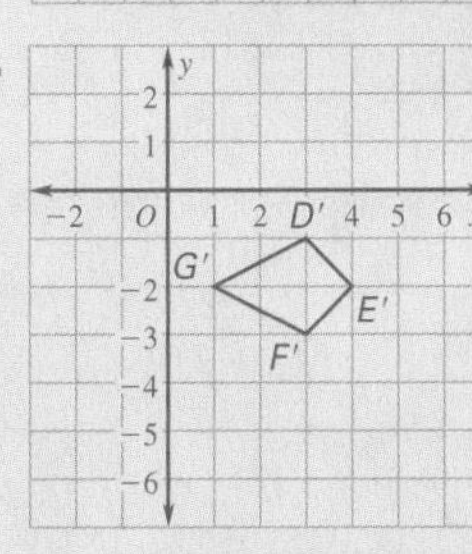

27. 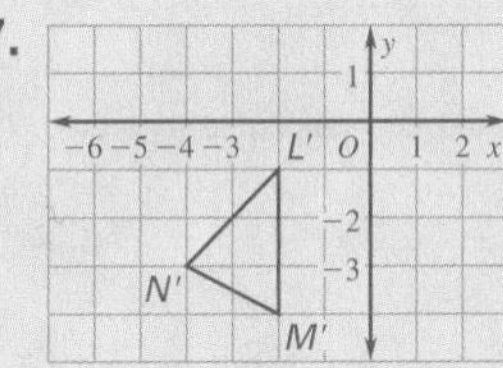

ADDITIONAL RESOURCES

Assessment Book

- Chapter Test (3 levels), pp. 90–103
- Standardized Chapter Test, p. 104
- Alternative Assessment, pp. 105–106

Test and Practice Generator

14.

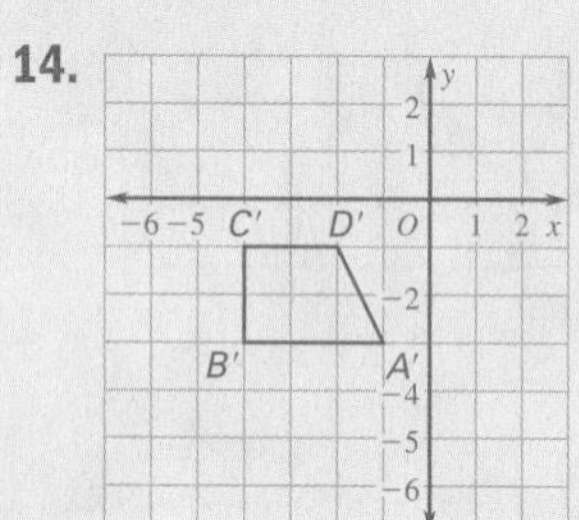

15.

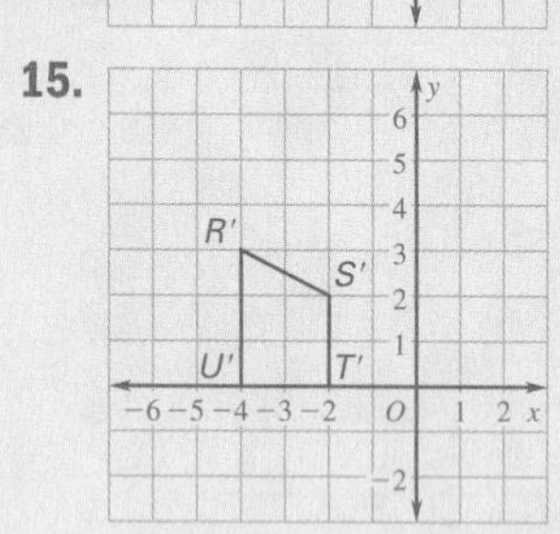

Chapter Test

Find the measures of the numbered angles.

1.

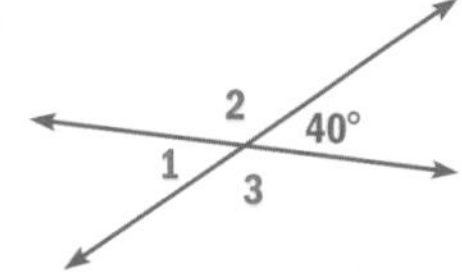

$m\angle 1 = 40°$, $m\angle 2 = m\angle 3 = 140°$

2.

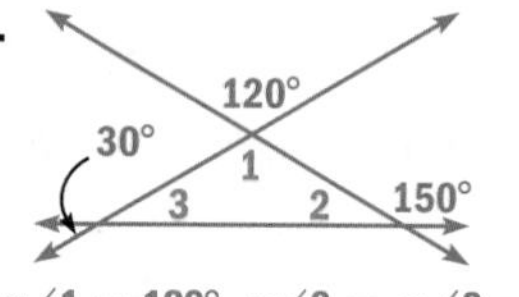

$m\angle 1 = 120°$, $m\angle 2 = m\angle 3 = 30°$

3.

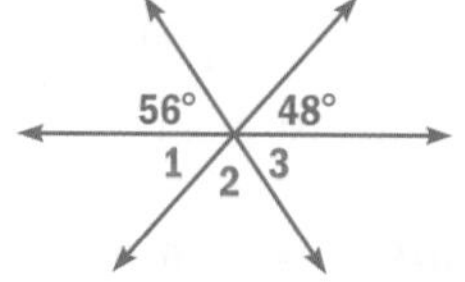

$m\angle 1 = 48°$, $m\angle 2 = 76°$, $m\angle 3 = 56°$

Classify the triangle by its angles.

4. 145°

obtuse

5.

right

6.

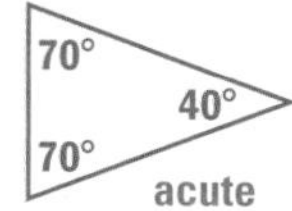

acute

Classify the quadrilateral.

7.

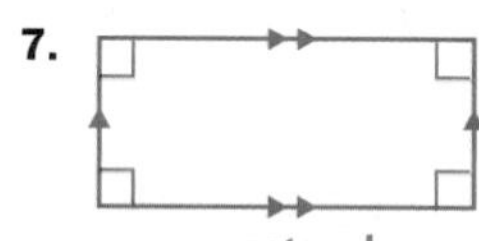

rectangle

8.

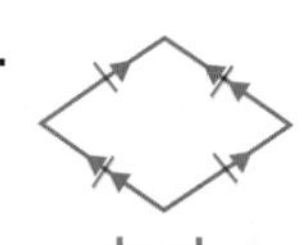

rhombus

9.

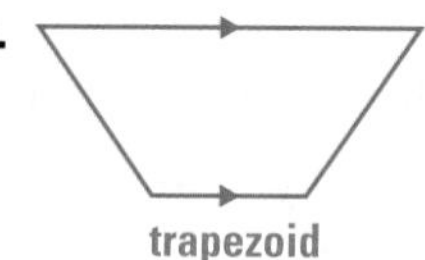

trapezoid

Find the measure of one angle in the polygon.

10. square 90°

11. regular octagon 135°

12. regular 9-gon 140°

13. Algebra Write and solve an equation to find the value of x. $5x - 2 = x + 6$; 2

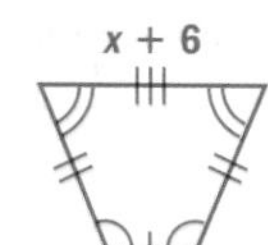

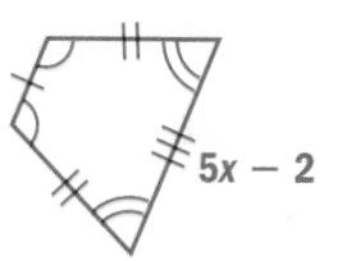

Graph the image of the given transformation. 14–15. See margin.

14. Rotate 180°.

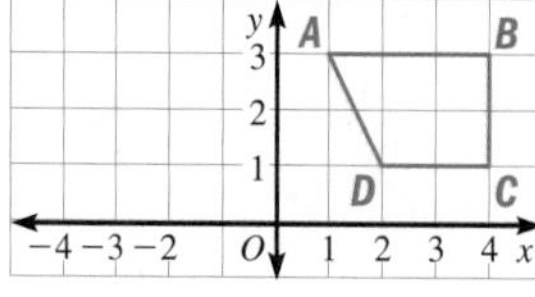

15. Translate using $(x, y) \rightarrow (x - 5, y + 3)$.

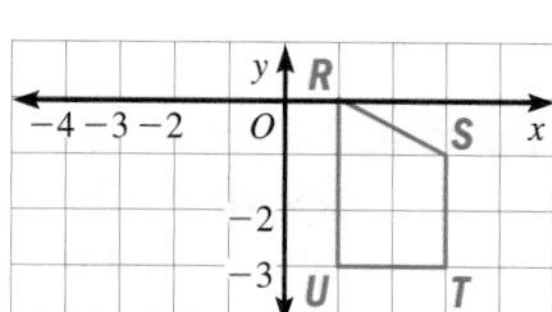

16. Shadows Joe is 72 inches tall and has a 108 inch shadow. At the same time, Martha has a 96 inch shadow. How tall is Martha? 64 in.

Chapter Standardized Test

Test-Taking Strategy **You can make notes, sketches, or graphs in your test booklet to help you solve problems, but you must keep your answer sheet neat.**

Multiple Choice

1. $\angle A$ is supplementary to $\angle B$ and $m\angle A = 62°$. What is $m\angle B$? B

A. 28° **B.** 118° **C.** 152° **D.** 298°

2. Which transformation takes the blue figure to the red figure? I

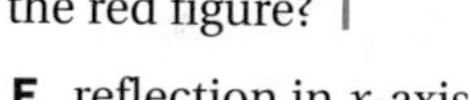

F. reflection in x-axis

G. 90° rotation

H. $(x, y) \rightarrow (x + 3, y + 2)$

I. $(x, y) \rightarrow (x - 3, y - 2)$

3. Which statement is *not* always true? B

A. A rhombus is a figure with four sides.

B. A rhombus has four right angles.

C. A rhombus has parallel opposite sides.

D. A rhombus has four sides of equal length.

4. What is the value of x? F

F. 108 **G.** 144

H. 180 **I.** 540

5. What is the sum of the angle measures in a 9-gon? A

A. 1260° **B.** 1620° **C.** 2520° **D.** 3240°

6. How many lines of symmetry does the figure have? I

F. 0 **G.** 1

H. 2 **I.** 4

7. Which diagram shows a reflection? C

A. A A **B.** B B

C. C Ɔ **D.** D D

8. $\triangle ABC \sim \triangle DEF$. What is the value of x? H

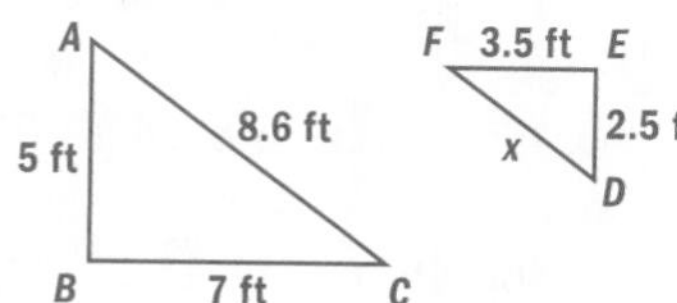

F. 2.5 ft **G.** 3.5 ft **H.** 4.3 ft **I.** 5.1 ft

9. Which statement is *always* true? D

A. Supplementary angles are congruent.

B. Complementary angles are congruent.

C. Acute angles are congruent.

D. Vertical angles are congruent.

Short Response

10. Find the value of x and explain your steps. See margin.

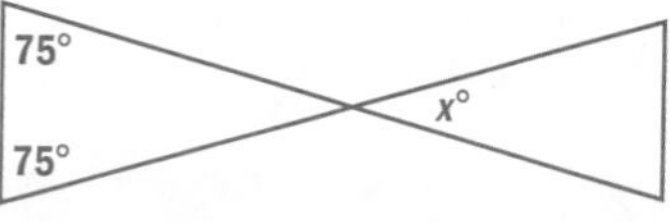

Extended Response

11. Graph $\triangle RST$ with vertices $R(1, 3)$, $S(3, 0)$, and $T(1, 0)$. Graph $\triangle BCA$ with vertices $A(-3, 0)$, $B(-1, 3)$, and $C(-1, 0)$. Explain how you know the two triangles are congruent. See margin.

ADDITIONAL RESOURCES

Assessment Book
- Standardized Chapter Test, p. 104

Test and Practice Generator

10. 30. *Sample answer:* The sum of the measures of the angles of a triangle is 180°, so the vertical angle to the angle with a measure of $x°$ has a measure of $180 - (75 + 75)$, or 30°. Since the angle measuring 30° and the angle measuring $x°$ are vertical angles, $x = 30$.

11.

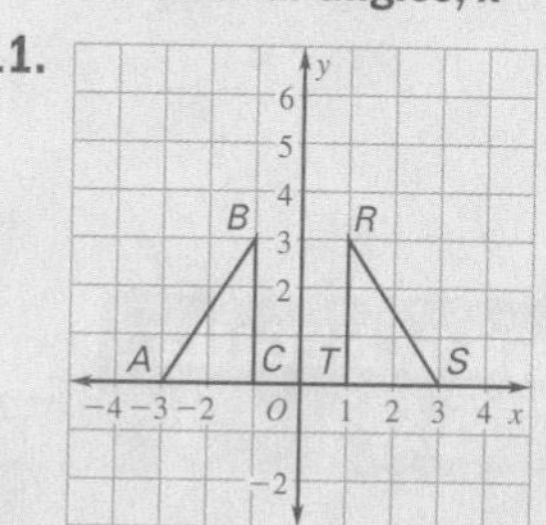

Sample answer: The vertical segment of each triangle has a length of 3, and the horizontal segment of each triangle has a length of 2. The included angle in each triangle is a right angle, so the triangles are congruent by Side-Angle-Side.

Pacing and Assignment Guide

REGULAR SCHEDULE

Lesson	Les. Day	BASIC	AVERAGE	ADVANCED
9.1	Day 1	EP p. 729 Exs. 1-4, 24; pp. 434-436 Exs. 15-29, 34-45, 50-52, 58-68	pp. 434-436 Exs. 17-24, 30-34, 38-55, 58-69	pp. 434-436 Exs. 17-24, 30-34, 38-63*, 67-69
9.2	Day 1	SRH p. 726 Exs. 1-4; pp. 440-441 Exs. 10-21, 25-30, 36-49	pp. 440-441 Exs. 12-15, 19-28, 31-34, 36-50	pp. 440-441 Exs. 12-15, 19-28, 31-40*, 45-50
9.3	Day 1	pp. 446-447 Exs. 11-19, 21-24, 26-30, 38-40	pp. 446-447 Exs. 14-21, 24-34, 38-41	pp. 446-447 Exs. 14-16, 19-21, 24-39*, 41
9.4	Day 1	EP p. 729 Exs. 20-22; pp. 452-453 Exs. 6-15, 17-20, 25-30	pp. 452-453 Exs. 8-11, 14-23, 25-30	pp. 452-453 Exs. 8-11, 14-25*, 28-30
9.5	Day 1	pp. 459-460 Exs. 6-8, 14-16, 24-29	pp. 459-460 Exs. 6-8, 14-18, 24-29	pp. 459-460 Exs. 6-8, 17-21, 28-30, 33
	Day 2	pp. 459-460 Exs. 9-11, 13, 17-20, 30-33	pp. 459-460 Exs. 9-13, 19-21, 30-34	pp. 459-460 Exs. 9-13, 22-27*, 34
9.6	Day 1	SRH p. 714 Exs. 16-20; pp. 466-468 Exs. 6-8, 15-18, 33-38	pp. 466-468 Exs. 6-8, 16-19, 30, 33-39	pp. 466-468 Exs. 7-10, 17-19, 27-31*, 40-42
	Day 2	pp. 466-468 Exs. 9-14, 20-24, 39-41	pp. 466-468 Exs. 11-14, 20-27, 32, 40-42	pp. 466-468 Exs. 13-16, 20-26, 32-36
Review	Day 1	pp. 472-473 Exs. 1-40	pp. 472-473 Exs. 1-40	pp. 472-473 Exs. 1-40
Assess	Day 1	Chapter 9 Test	Chapter 9 Test	Chapter 9 Test

YEARLY PACING Chapter 9 Total – **10 days** Chapters 1–9 Total – **104 days** Remaining – **56 days**

*Challenge Exercises EP = Extra Practice SRH = Skills Review Handbook EC = Extra Challenge

BLOCK SCHEDULE

DAY 1	DAY 2	DAY 3	DAY 4	DAY 5
9.1 pp. 434-436 Exs. 17-24, 30-34, 38-55, 58-69 **9.2** pp. 440-441 Exs. 12-15, 19-28, 31-34, 36-50	**9.3** pp. 446-447 Exs. 14-21, 24-34, 38-41 **9.4** pp. 452-453 Exs. 8-11, 14-23, 25-30	**9.5** pp. 459-460 Exs. 6-21, 24-34	**9.6** pp. 466-468 Exs. 6-8, 11-14, 16-27, 30, 32-42	**Review** pp. 472-473 Exs. 1-40 **Assess** Chapter 9 Test

YEARLY PACING Chapter 9 Total – **5 days** Chapters 1–9 Total – **52 days** Remaining – **28 days**

Support Materials

CHAPTER RESOURCE BOOK

CHAPTER SUPPORT			
Tips for New Teachers	p. 1	Parents as Partners	p. 3

LESSON SUPPORT	9.1	9.2	9.3	9.4	9.5	9.6
Lesson Plans (regular and block)	p. 6	p. 14	p. 22	p. 31	p. 41	p. 50
Technology Activities & Keystrokes				p. 33		p. 52
Activity Support Masters						
Activity Masters					p. 43	
Practice (3 levels)	p. 8	p. 16	p. 24	p. 35	p. 44	p. 53
Study Guide	p. 11	p. 19	p. 27	p. 38	p. 47	p. 56
Real-World Problem Solving			p. 29			p. 58
Challenge Practice	p. 13	p. 21	p. 30	p. 40	p. 49	p. 59

REVIEW			
Games Support Masters	p. 5	Cooperative Project with Rubric	p. 63
Chapter Review Games and Activities	p. 60	Extra Credit Project with Rubric	p. 65
Real-Life Project with Rubric	p. 61	Cumulative Practice	p. 67
		Resource Book Answers	A1

ASSESSMENT

Quizzes	p. 107	Alternative Assessments with Rubrics	p. 116
Chapter Tests (3 levels)	p. 109	Unit Test	p. 129
Standardized Test	p. 115	Cumulative Test	p. 131

TRANSPARENCIES

	9.1	9.2	9.3	9.4	9.5	9.6
Warm-Up / Daily Homework Quiz	✔	✔	✔	✔	✔	✔
Notetaking Guide	✔	✔	✔	✔	✔	✔
Teacher Support	✔	✔				
English/Spanish Problem Solving	✔			✔		
Answer Transparencies	✔	✔	✔	✔	✔	✔

TECHNOLOGY

- EasyPlanner CD-ROM
- Test and Practice Generator
- Electronic Lesson Presentations
- eTutorial CD-ROM
- Chapter Audio Summaries CDs
- Classzone.com
- eEdition Plus Online
- eWorkbook Plus Online
- eTutorial Plus Online
- EasyPlanner Plus Online

ADDITIONAL RESOURCES

- Worked-Out Solution Key
- Notetaking Guide
- Practice Workbook
- Tutor Place
- Professional Development Book
- Special Activities Book
- Posters
- Spanish Study Guide
- Exercises in Spanish
- English/Spanish Ch. Reviews/Tests
- Multi-Language Visual Glossary

Math Background and Teaching Strategies

Lesson 9.1

MATH BACKGROUND

For any positive number m, there are two numbers, its **square roots**, for which the product of the number with itself is m. The positive number for which this is true, the *principal* square root, is designated $\sqrt{m}$. The negative number for which this is true is $-\sqrt{m}$. A **perfect square** is a number whose square roots are rational, such as $1.96 = (\pm 1.4)^2$. To solve the square root equation $x^2 = c$, apply the definition of square root to obtain $x = \pm\sqrt{c}$.

TEACHING STRATEGIES

One point that often needs repeating to students about square roots is, for example, that though the square roots of 144 are -12 and 12, $\sqrt{144} = 12$ only. Emphasize that the radical sign itself indicates only the positive square root, so the square roots of 144 are $\pm\sqrt{144} = \pm 12$. Another area where students may need help is in gaining a feel for a reasonable starting point when estimating a square root. Inexperienced students may start by using half of a number, which is seldom appropriate. Encourage students to make a list or chart that indicates how quickly squares can grow, using values such as $\sqrt{1} = 1$, $\sqrt{4} = 2$, $\sqrt{25} = 5$, $\sqrt{100} = 10$, $\sqrt{2500} = 50$, and $\sqrt{10{,}000} = 100$. (Note that some students may hastily assume that $\sqrt{1000} = 100$.)

Lesson 9.2

MATH BACKGROUND

Unlike a rational number, an **irrational number** cannot be written as a quotient of integers. Unless a number is a perfect square, its square roots are irrational numbers, with decimal forms that do not terminate or repeat. The rational numbers and irrational numbers together comprise the **real numbers**.

TEACHING STRATEGIES

Students are often uncomfortable that the square root of a number between 0 and 1 is greater than the number. For example, they may assume that $\sqrt{\frac{1}{2}} = \frac{1}{4}$, though $\sqrt{\frac{1}{16}} = \frac{1}{4}$. You can use 10 by 10 grids scaled to represent the number 1 to provide a model of why this is true. For example, in the figure below, a unit square is divided into 100 squares each representing $\frac{1}{100}$. Point out that Square A has an area of 49 small squares, or $\frac{49}{100}$. The positive square root of $\frac{49}{100}$ is represented by the side length of Square A. Because the side of each small square is $\frac{1}{10}$, $\sqrt{\frac{49}{100}} = \frac{7}{10}$, and $\frac{7}{10} > \frac{49}{100}$ (since $0.7 > 0.49$).

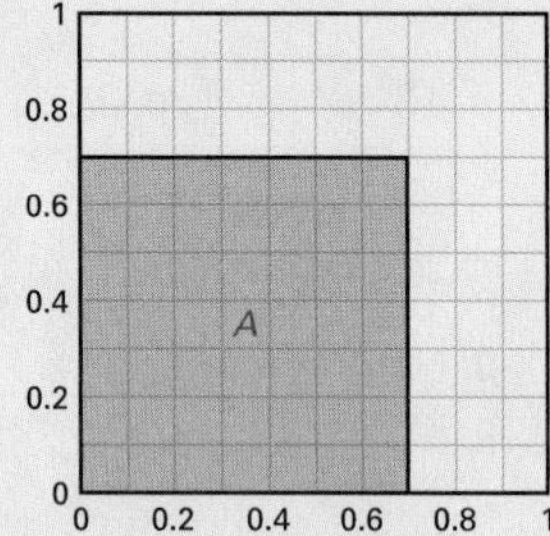

Also with this lesson, remind students of their work in Lesson 5.5 converting between repeating decimals and fractions to emphasize that numbers that can be represented using repeating decimals are rational.

Lesson 9.3

MATH BACKGROUND

RIGHT TRIANGLES About 2000 B.C, Egyptians devised a way to lay out square corners for their fields using a loop of rope knotted into 12 equal parts. They staked the rope to form a triangle with sides of three, four, and five units. This always gave a right angle opposite the longest side. About 1500 years later, the Greek philosophers called Pythagoreans generalized the relationship exhibited by the knotted rope to any right triangle. This relationship, which we now know as the **Pythagorean theorem**, states that the square of the length of the hypotenuse in a right triangle equals the sum of the squares of the lengths of the legs. The converse is also true: If the sum of the square of the lengths of two sides of a triangle equals the square of the length of the third side, then the triangle is a right triangle.

TEACHING STRATEGIES

Sketch the diagram below and ask students to find the missing value indicated by the question mark. To do so, they will first have to use the Pythagorean theorem to find the missing hypotenuse of the top triangle, which is 15, and then use this value and the Pythagorean theorem again to find that the missing leg length of the bottom triangle is 8.

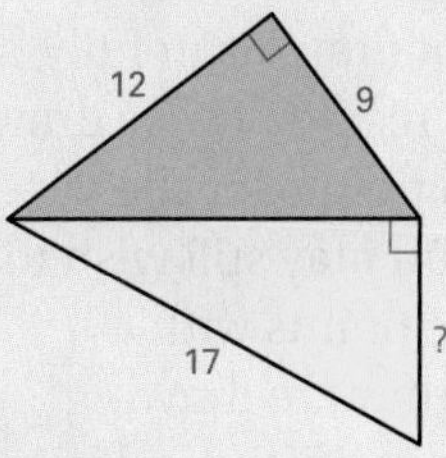

Lesson 9.4

MATH BACKGROUND

Applications of the Pythagorean theorem include finding measurements that cannot be made directly and in finding perimeter and area of triangles. A **Pythagorean triple** is a set of three positive integers, such as 3, 4, and 5, that satisfy the algorithm of the Pythagorean theorem, that is, for which $a^2 + b^2 = c^2$ is true. Any multiple of a Pythagorean triple is also a Pythagorean triple, since if $a^2 + b^2 = c^2$, then $(ka)^2 + (kb)^2 = k^2a^2 + k^2b^2 = k^2(a^2 + b^2) = k^2c^2 = (kc)^2$.

TEACHING STRATEGIES

Have students use a table such as the one below to generate Pythagorean triples. Point out that the method of this table only generates *some* of the Pythagorean triples. For example, the Pythagorean triple 5, 12, 13 is skipped. You may also want to point out to students that they can use the method of the table with decimal numbers that are greater than 1.

	Leg 1	Leg 2	Hypotenuse
n	$2n$	$n^2 - 1$	$n^2 + 1$
2	4	3	?
3	6	?	10
4	?	?	?
5	?	?	?
6	?	?	?

Lesson 9.5

MATH BACKGROUND

SPECIAL RIGHT TRIANGLES The lengths of the sides of "special" right triangles that have two 45° angles or a 30° and a 60° angle have ratios that can be expressed as whole numbers or simple radical expressions. In a 45°-45°-90° triangle, the lengths of the legs are the same, and the hypotenuse is $\sqrt{2}$ times the leg length. In a 30°-60°-90° triangle, the hypotenuse is twice the length of the leg opposite the 30° angle, and the length of the side opposite the 60° angle is $\sqrt{3}$ times the length of the leg opposite the 30° angle.

TEACHING STRATEGIES

Show students examples of how 45°-45°-90° triangles can be used to express the length of the diagonal of any square in terms of its side length. In 30°-60°-90° triangles, students may have a tendency to think that the longer leg is twice the length of the shorter leg, since the larger acute angle is twice the smaller acute angle. Remind them that it is the *hypotenuse* that is twice the length of the shorter leg.

Lesson 9.6

MATH BACKGROUND

The word *trigonometry* derives from the Greek words *trigon*, meaning "three-angled," and *metria*, meaning "measurement." Over 2000 years ago, the Greek astronomer Hipparchus charted the position of the stars using **trigonometric ratios**, ratios of the lengths of two sides of a right triangle. The three basic trigonometric ratios are **sine**, the ratio of the side opposite an acute angle to the hypotenuse, **cosine**, the ratio of the side adjacent an acute angle to the hypotenuse, and **tangent**, the ratio of the side opposite an acute angle to the side adjacent that angle.

TEACHING STRATEGIES

Many students have an easier time remembering the tangent ratio than the sine and cosine ratios, which they confuse. Encourage students to create and share their own mnemonics to help them remember the sine and cosine ratios. For example, to remember that the sine ratio involves the hypotenuse and the opposite side, one possibility might be "Sign says hip-hop tonight" for "sign" = sine, "hip" = hyp(otenuse), and "hop" = op(posite).

Differentiating Instruction

Strategies for Underachievers

USE MODELS AND MANIPULATIVES

In Lesson 9.1, make sure that students complete the Activity at the top of page 431. Many students may not yet even be proficient with the concept of squares. The concept of square roots, which requires a process of inverse thinking, will be even more challenging for these students, who may attempt to divide by two or employ some other incorrect method. For this activity, supply underachievers with graph paper so that they can draw the squares. You may want to have students draw squares with side lengths up to 10. Because it is helpful for students to have immediate recall of perfect squares and their roots, encourage them to create flash cards of perfect squares at least through 144 (for example, "$8^2 = 64$") as well as square roots (for example, "$\sqrt{64} = 8$").

COMPUTER SOFTWARE In conjunction with Hands-on Activity 9.3 and Lesson 9.4, it can be a great help to students to explore the Pythagorean theorem using geometric drawing software. Most such software packages come with instructions for completing helpful activities using the software.

In Lesson 9.5, some underachievers will certainly benefit from creating note cards to use as references when working with the special right triangles. To help students remember the relationships without having to use variable expressions, have them draw and label on their cards a 45°-45°-90° triangle with legs of 1 and a hypotenuse of $\sqrt{2}$, and a 30°-60°-90° triangle with legs of 1 and $\sqrt{3}$ and a hypotenuse of 2. These values make the relationships clear, while at the same time very easy to check for compliance with the Pythagorean theorem.

USE SCAFFOLDING

In Lesson 9.4, problems such as Example 2 on page 451 require many steps, as they involve first an application of the Pythagorean theorem followed by using the result in further calculations. You may wish to provide underachievers with templates to complete problems such as this.

In Hands-on Activity 9.6, you may wish to provide pre-drawn diagrams to some underachievers. Besides the fact that pre-drawing will save time, this activity will not be successful if students' diagrams are not drawn carefully, so pre-drawing can help ensure accurate results. These drawings could have the angles drawn with points for the vertices already marked and measured. You may still wish to have students connect the appropriate points with a straightedge so that they can see that they are drawing right triangles. You can also have them verify the indicated measurements.

CALCULATORS In Technology Activity 9.6, you may wish to supply students with detailed, step-by-step reference cards regarding the operation of their calculators. These cards can show how to find each trigonometric ratio and each inverse, and can also detail when a given operation should be used.

USE A CO-TEACHING MODEL

In Problem Solving Strategies 9.4, you may wish to co-teach with a Reading Specialist who can help students with language-based disabilities or limitations develop strategies for comprehending these problems and gleaning the important information from them.

Strategies for English Learners

VOCABULARY STUDY OF ROOTS

Many mathematical terms stem from a common root word, usually of Latin origins. Recognizing the Latin prefixes and roots can help students comprehend sophisticated mathematics vocabulary. Consider the roots and words in the table on the next page.

Latin Root	Mathematical Terms
aequus (even)	equal, equality, equate, equation, unequal, inequality
ex (out) and premere (to press)	express, expression
numerus (number)	number, numeral, numeration, numerical, numerator
radicare (to root)	radical, radicand
ratus (to think) and ration (to reason)	ratio, rational, irrational
simplex (simple)	simple, simplify, simple interest
solvere (solve, loosen, dissolve)	solve, solution, soluble, solvable, solubility
value	value, evaluate
variare (various, diverse)	vary, variance, variable, variation

Encourage students to look at the similarity between new words and known words. Recognizing, for example, that *irrational* has the word *ratio* in it, plus the prefix *ir*-, which generally means *not*, will help students remember that an irrational number is one that cannot be expressed as the ratio of two integers.

Strategies for Advanced Learners

INCREASE DEPTH AND COMPLEXITY

IMAGINARY NUMBERS In Lesson 9.1, a few advanced learners may be interested in investigating the concept of square roots of negative numbers. These students may be surprised to learn, for example, that though $\sqrt{-25}$ cannot possibly be a real number since there is no real number that can be multiplied by itself to yield -25, there is a number system, the *imaginary numbers system*, in which there is a number (actually, two numbers) whose square is -25. This number system is based on defining the quantity i as $i = \sqrt{-1}$. Furthermore, point out that there are many real-world applications of these numbers, such as in electrical engineering, even though these numbers are "imaginary." To encourage your advanced learners to explore the set of imaginary numbers further, help them choose appropriate resources for their exploration.

In Lesson 9.2, advanced learners should be able to understand that the decimal form of a number can have a *pattern*, but not a pattern that *repeats*. For example, the number 0.303003... in Exercise 12 on page 440 has a pattern, but it is irrational. Suggest to advanced students that they attempt to write this number as a rational number using the method from Lesson 5.5 of writing a repeating decimal as a fraction to convince themselves that it cannot be done. Also encourage these students to come up with other numbers whose decimal representations have different kinds of patterns, but that are irrational. An example is 0.123456789101112131415.... Also in conjunction with Lesson 9.2, you may suggest to some advanced learners to explore the mathematical meanings of the terms *dense*, *discrete*, and *continuous*.

INVESTIGATE HISTORY AND CONTEXT

HISTORY OF MATHEMATICS The problems and topics of Lessons 9.1–9.3 are rife with possibilities for student research regarding their history and development. The problem of finding square roots goes back into antiquity, as well as how to make sense of what we now know as irrational numbers. The relationship expressed by the Pythagorean theorem has a very rich history, with different insights provided by different cultures in different eras. The Pythagorean theorem has been proved in many different ways in many different contexts. It has also been proved by many different people, including some who are not usually associated with mathematics, including Leonardo da Vinci and United States President James A. Garfield.

Differentiating Instruction: Teaching Resources

Differentiating Assessment

McDougal Littell *Middle School Mathematics* offers a wide variety of assessment. This includes Level A, Level B, and Level C Chapter Tests, Standardized Tests, Cumulative Tests, and Quizzes from the *Assessment Book*, Daily Homework Quizzes from the *Warm-Up Transparencies*, and the *Test and Practice Generator*.

Assessment Book

The *Assessment Book* contains two quizzes, three levels of chapter tests, A (Basic), B (Average), and C (Advanced), and a standardized test for each chapter in the textbook. Also included are cumulative tests and unit tests.

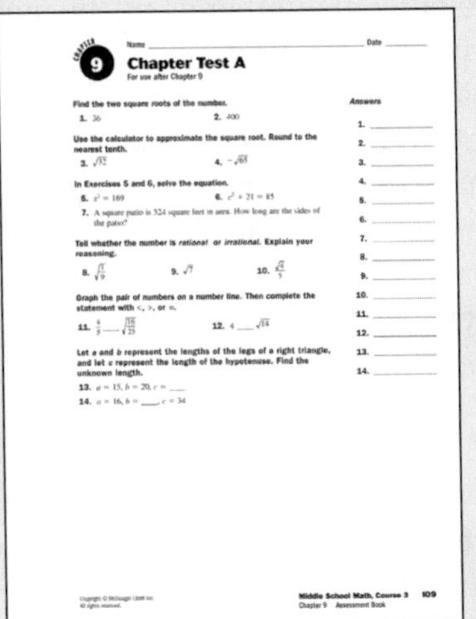

Chapter 9 Chapter Test A
For use after Chapter 9

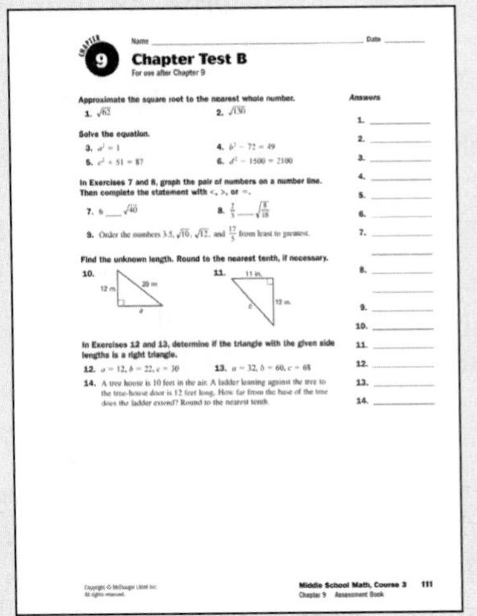

Chapter 9 Chapter Test B
For use after Chapter 9

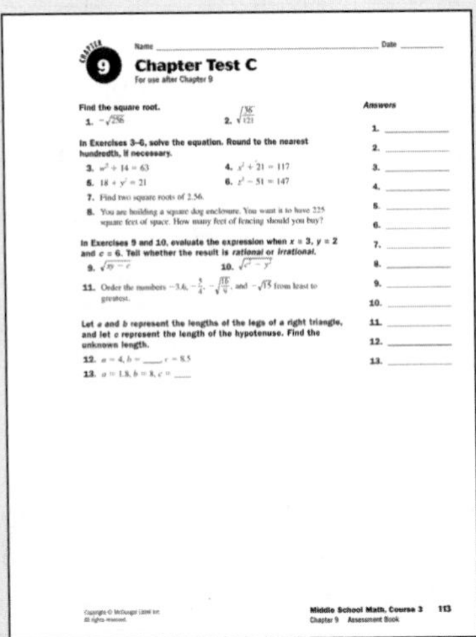

Chapter 9 Chapter Test C
For use after Chapter 9

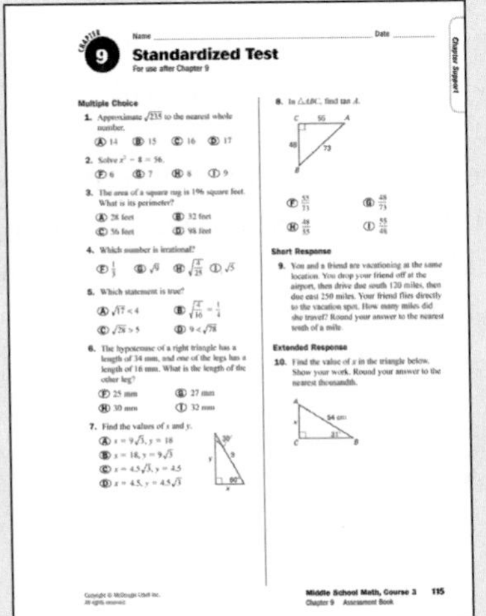

Chapter 9 Standardized Test
For use after Chapter 9

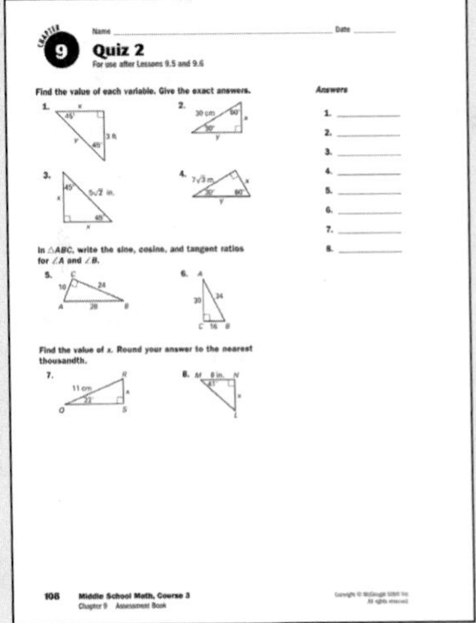

Chapter 9 Quiz 2
For use after Lessons 9.5 and 9.6

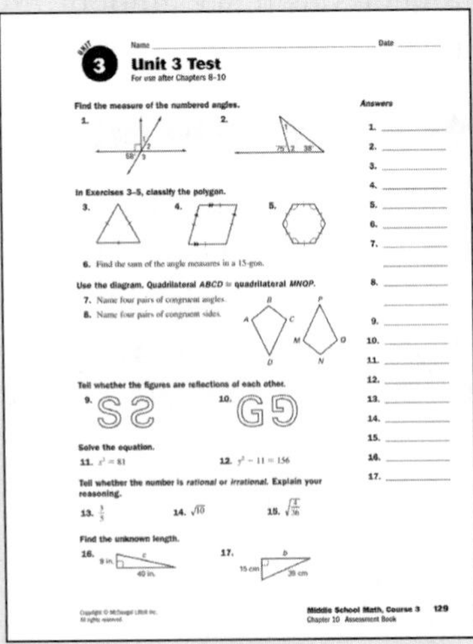

Unit 3 Unit 3 Test
For use after Chapters 8–10

Warm-Up Transparencies with Daily Homework Quiz

The *Warm-Up Transparencies with Daily Homework Quiz* contains a daily homework quiz for each lesson in the textbook. Each quiz appears with a set of warm-up exercises.

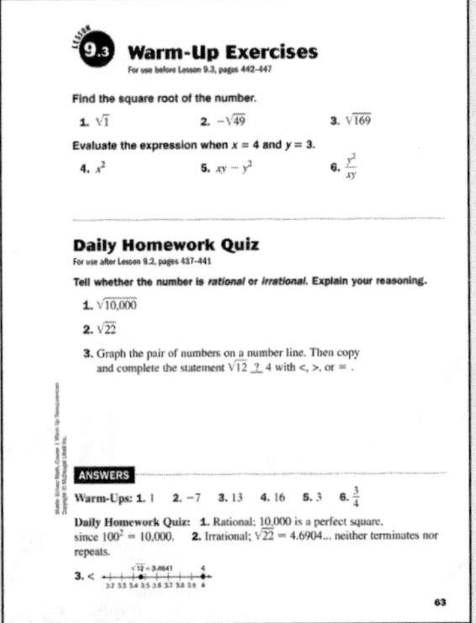

LESSON 9.3 **Warm-Up Exercises**

For use before Lesson 9.3, pages 442–447

Find the square root of the number.

1. $\sqrt{1}$ 2. $-\sqrt{49}$ 3. $\sqrt{169}$

Evaluate the expression when $x = 4$ and $y = 3$.

4. x^2 5. $xy - y^2$ 6. $\frac{y^2}{xy}$

Daily Homework Quiz

For use after Lesson 9.2, pages 437–441

Tell whether the number is *rational* or *irrational*. Explain your reasoning.

1. $\sqrt{10{,}000}$
2. $\sqrt{22}$
3. Graph the pair of numbers on a number line. Then copy and complete the statement $\sqrt{12}$ _?_ 4 with <, >, or = .

ANSWERS

Warm-Ups: 1. 1 **2.** −7 **3.** 13 **4.** 16 **5.** 3 **6.** $\frac{3}{4}$

Daily Homework Quiz: 1. Rational; 10,000 is a perfect square, since $100^2 = 10{,}000$. **2.** Irrational; $\sqrt{22} = 4.6904...$ neither terminates nor repeats.

3. <

63

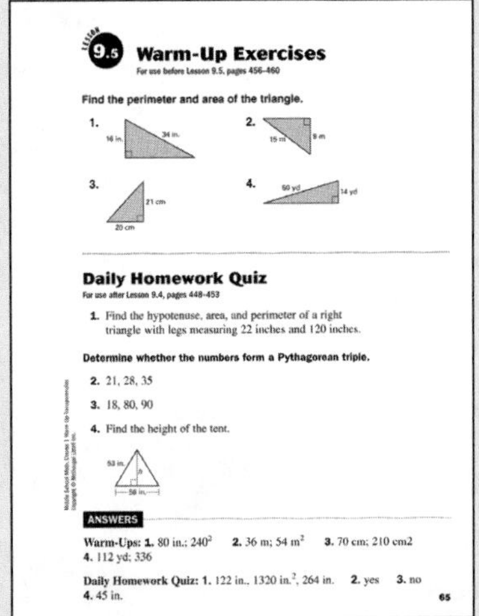

LESSON 9.5 **Warm-Up Exercises**

For use before Lesson 9.5, pages 456–460

Find the perimeter and area of the triangle.

1. 2. 3. 4.

Daily Homework Quiz

For use after Lesson 9.4, pages 448–453

1. Find the hypotenuse, area, and perimeter of a right triangle with legs measuring 22 inches and 120 inches.

Determine whether the numbers form a Pythagorean triple.

2. 21, 28, 35
3. 18, 80, 90
4. Find the height of the tent.

ANSWERS

Warm-Ups: 1. 80 in.; 240^2 **2.** 36 m; 54 m^2 **3.** 70 cm; 210 cm2 **4.** 112 yd; 336

Daily Homework Quiz: 1. 122 in., 1320 $in.^2$, 264 in. **2.** yes **3.** no **4.** 45 in.

65

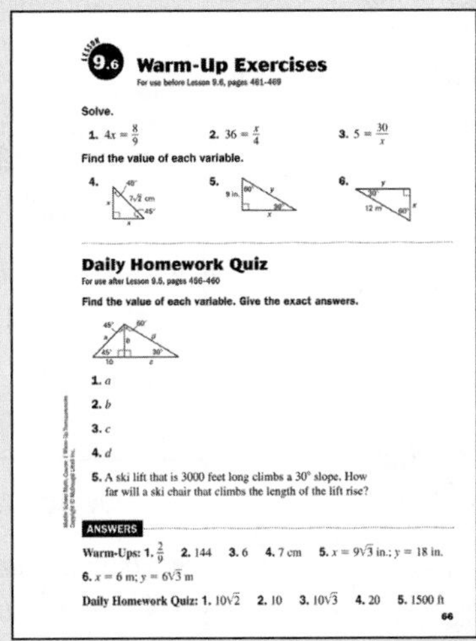

LESSON 9.6 **Warm-Up Exercises**

For use before Lesson 9.6, pages 461–469

Solve.

1. $4x = \frac{8}{9}$ 2. $36 = \frac{x}{4}$ 3. $5 = \frac{30}{x}$

Find the value of each variable.

4. 5. 6.

Daily Homework Quiz

For use after Lesson 9.5, pages 456–460

Find the value of each variable. Give the exact answers.

1. a
2. b
3. c
4. d
5. A ski lift that is 3000 feet long climbs a 30° slope. How far will a ski chair that climbs the length of the lift rise?

ANSWERS

Warm-Ups: 1. $\frac{2}{9}$ **2.** 144 **3.** 6 **4.** 7 cm **5.** $x = 9\sqrt{3}$ in.; $y = 18$ in. **6.** $x = 6$ m; $y = 6\sqrt{3}$ m

Daily Homework Quiz: 1. $10\sqrt{2}$ **2.** 10 **3.** $10\sqrt{3}$ **4.** 20 **5.** 1500 ft

66

Test and Practice Generator CD-ROM

The *Test and Practice Generator* can be used to create numerous quizzes and tests for each lesson and for each chapter using both static and algorithmic exercises.

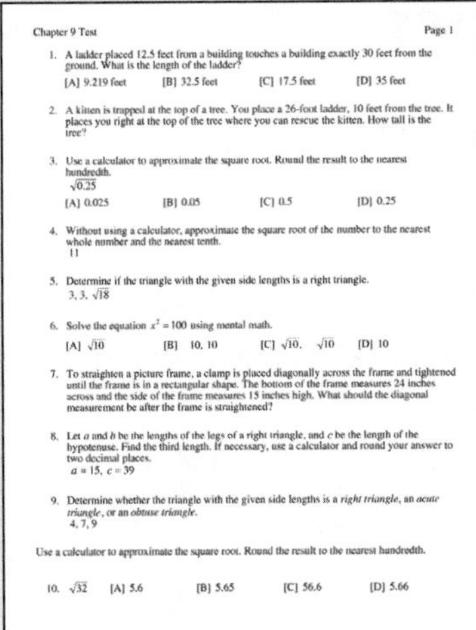

Chapter 9 Test Page 1

1. A ladder placed 12.5 feet from a building touches a building exactly 30 feet from the ground. What is the length of the ladder?
   [A] 9.219 feet [B] 32.5 feet [C] 17.5 feet [D] 35 feet
2. A kitten is trapped at the top of a tree. You place a 26-foot ladder, 10 feet from the tree. It places you right at the top of the tree where you can rescue the kitten. How tall is the tree?
3. Use a calculator to approximate the square root. Round the result to the nearest hundredth.
   $\sqrt{0.25}$
   [A] 0.025 [B] 0.05 [C] 0.5 [D] 0.25
4. Without using a calculator, approximate the square root of the number to the nearest whole number and the nearest tenth.
   11
5. Determine if the triangle with the given side lengths is a right triangle.
   3, 3, $\sqrt{18}$
6. Solve the equation $x^2 = 100$ using mental math.
   [A] $\sqrt{10}$ [B] 10, 10 [C] $\sqrt{10}$, $\sqrt{10}$ [D] 10
7. To straighten a picture frame, a clamp is placed diagonally across the frame and tightened until the frame is in a rectangular shape. The bottom of the frame measures 24 inches across and the side of the frame measures 15 inches high. What should the diagonal measurement be after the frame is straightened?
8. Let a and b be the lengths of the legs of a right triangle, and c be the length of the hypotenuse. Find the third length. If necessary, use a calculator and round your answer to two decimal places.
   $a = 15$, $c = 39$
9. Determine whether the triangle with the given side lengths is a *right triangle*, an *acute triangle*, or an *obtuse triangle*.
   4, 7, 9

Use a calculator to approximate the square root. Round the result to the nearest hundredth.

10. $\sqrt{32}$ [A] 5.6 [B] 5.65 [C] 56.6 [D] 5.66

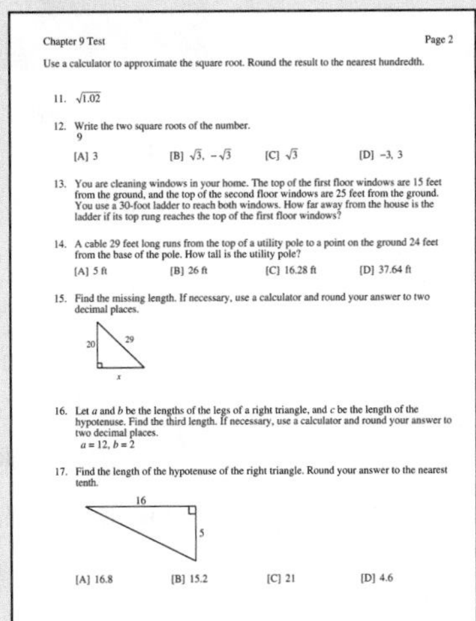

Chapter 9 Test Page 2

Use a calculator to approximate the square root. Round the result to the nearest hundredth.

11. $\sqrt{1.02}$
12. Write the two square roots of the number.
    9
    [A] 3 [B] $\sqrt{3}$, $-\sqrt{3}$ [C] $\sqrt{3}$ [D] −3, 3
13. You are cleaning windows in your home. The top of the first floor windows are 15 feet from the ground, and the top of the second floor windows are 25 feet from the ground. You use a 30-foot ladder to reach both windows. How far away from the house is the ladder if its top rung reaches the top of the first floor windows?
14. A cable 29 feet long runs from the top of a utility pole to a point on the ground 24 feet from the base of the pole. How tall is the utility pole?
    [A] 5 ft [B] 26 ft [C] 16.28 ft [D] 37.64 ft
15. Find the missing length. If necessary, use a calculator and round your answer to two decimal places.

16. Let a and b be the lengths of the legs of a right triangle, and c be the length of the hypotenuse. Find the third length. If necessary, use a calculator and round your answer to two decimal places.
    $a = 12$, $b = 2$
17. Find the length of the hypotenuse of the right triangle. Round your answer to the nearest tenth.

    [A] 16.8 [B] 15.2 [C] 21 [D] 4.6

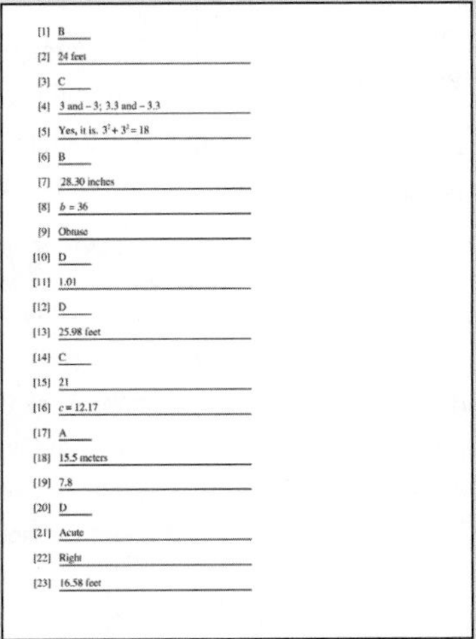

[1] B
[2] 24 feet
[3] C
[4] 3 and − 3; 3.3 and − 3.3
[5] Yes, it is. $3^2 + 3^2 = 18$
[6] B
[7] 28.30 inches
[8] $b = 36$
[9] Obtuse
[10] D
[11] 1.01
[12] D
[13] 25.98 feet
[14] C
[15] 21
[16] $c = 12.17$
[17] A
[18] 15.5 meters
[19] 7.8
[20] D
[21] Acute
[22] Right
[23] 16.58 feet

OVERVIEW

Main Ideas

In this chapter, students find and approximate square roots and classify real numbers as rational or irrational. Students solve real-world problems involving square roots, including problems that use the Pythagorean theorem and problems that involve special right triangles. Students also find the trigonometric ratios sine, cosine, and tangent, and use them to find missing side lengths in triangles.

Prerequisite Skills

The key skills reviewed in the games on these pages are:

- Evaluating powers
- Identifying angles in triangles

Additional practice with prerequisite skills can be found in the Review What You Need to Know exercises on page 430. Additional resources for reviewing prerequisite skills are:

- Skills Review Handbook, pp. 704–726
- Tutor Place
- eTutorial Plus

Managing the Games

Tips for Success

In *Spin Your Wheels*, it will be difficult for some students to perform the rotations mentally. Suggest that they copy and cut out the two "wheels" on paper so that they can rotate the wheels physically. Have them also write the evaluated powers on the left wheel. Students should realize that they are looking for the same three numbers in a row on each wheel, but that the direction in which they are counted is also important to make the match.

Real Numbers and Right Triangles

BEFORE

In previous chapters you've...

- Found the square of a number
- Investigated rational numbers

Now

In Chapter 9 you'll study...

- Finding square roots
- Classifying real numbers as rational or irrational
- Solving real-world problems using the Pythagorean theorem
- Using trigonometric ratios

WHY?

So you can solve real-world problems about...

- forest rangers, p. 435
- parasailing, p. 444
- softball, p. 456
- totem poles, p. 466

Internet Preview
CLASSZONE.COM

- eEdition Plus Online
- eWorkbook Plus Online
- eTutorial Plus Online
- State Test Practice
- More Examples

Chapter Warm-Up Games

Review skills you need for this chapter in these quick games.

Key Skill:
Evaluating powers

Spin the wheels until all three red lines connect equal values.

- You can turn the wheels one click at a time. Each click moves a wheel one space clockwise.
- How many clicks do you need to turn the left wheel?
  Turn the left wheel 4 times.
- How many clicks do you need to turn the right wheel?
  Turn the right wheel 6 times.

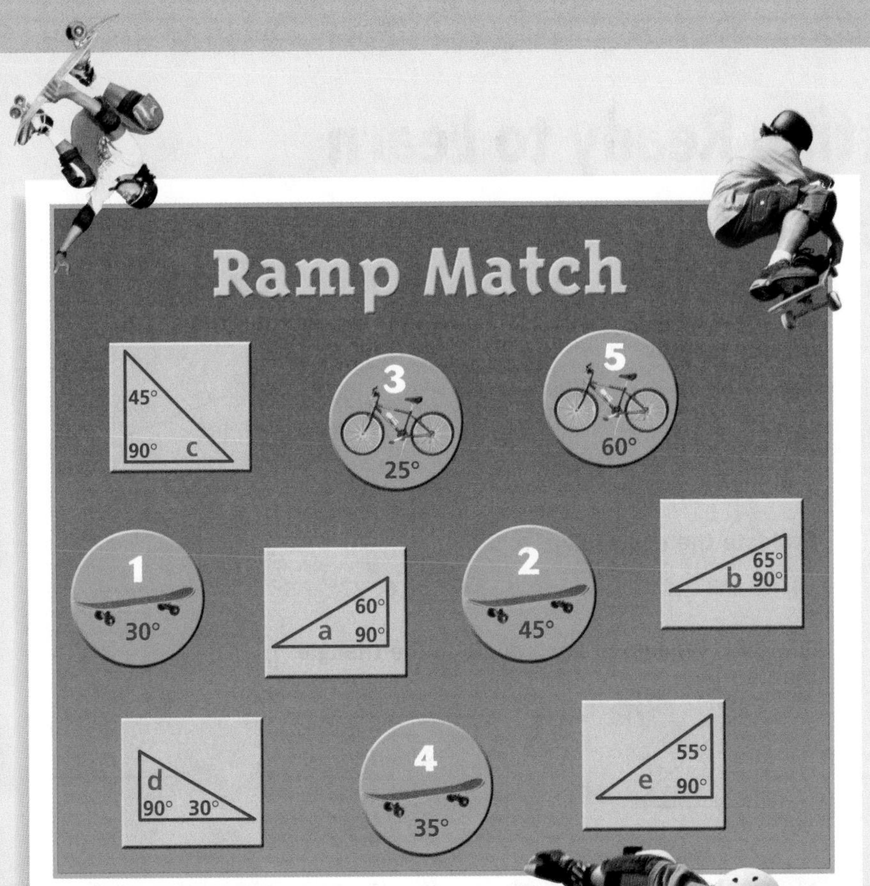

Ramp Match

45° 90° c

3 25°

5 60°

1 30°

60° a 90°

2 45°

65° b 90°

d 90° 30°

4 35°

55° e 90°

BrAIN GAME

Key Skill:
Identifying angles in triangles

Find the ramp each bike or skateboard matches.

- Match the angle on the bike or skateboard with the ramp it fits.
1 and a, 2 and c, 3 and b, 4 and e, 5 and d

Stop *and* Think

1. **Critical Thinking** How can you write 4^4 as a power of 2? Explain.
2. **Writing** Explain why a triangular ramp that has angles of 90°, 40°, and 55° cannot exist. **The sum of the measures of the angles of a triangle is 180°. The sum of the given angle measures is 185°, so these angles do not form a triangle.**

1. 2^8; $4^4 = 4 \cdot 4 \cdot 4 \cdot 4 = (2 \cdot 2) \cdot (2 \cdot 2) \cdot (2 \cdot 2) \cdot (2 \cdot 2) = 2^8$

Reflecting on the Games

Have students write an equation that describes the measure of an angle *A* in terms of the measure of an angle *B* in a right triangle if angle *C* is the right angle ($m\angle A = 90° - m\angle B$). Have students make a conjecture about the leg lengths in a right triangle that has two 45° angles (they are the same).

Chapter Resources

These resources are provided to help you prepare for the chapter and to customize review materials:

Chapter 9 Resource Book

- Tips for New Teachers, pp. 1-2
- Lesson Plan, pp. 6, 14, 22, 31, 41, 50
- Lesson Plan for Block Scheduling, pp. 7, 15, 23, 32, 42, 51

Technology

- EasyPlanner CD-ROM
- Test and Practice Generator
- Electronic Lesson Presentations CD-ROM
- eTutorial CD-ROM

Internet

- Classzone
- eEdition Plus Online
- eWorkbook Plus Online
- eTutorial Plus Online
- EasyPlanner Plus Online

English Learner Support

- Spanish Study Guide
- Multi-Language Glossary
- Chapter Audio Summaries CDs
- Teacher's Edition, pp. 428E–428F

PREPARE

DIAGNOSIS/REMEDIATION

Review What You Need to Know
The Review What You Need to Know exercises can help you diagnose whether students have the following skills needed in Chapter 9:

- Classifying triangles by their sides (Exs. 1-3)
- Evaluating exponential expressions (Exs. 4-7)
- Finding angle measures in triangles (Exs. 8-10)

Chapter 9 Resource Book

- Study Guide (Lessons 9.1-9.6)

Tutor Place

NOTETAKING STRATEGIES

When students enter examples or figures in their notebooks, encourage them to include all relevant information. For instance, their figures should be fully and clearly labeled, and the meaning of all variables noted. Students may think that their notes do not need to be so painstaking, and so make incomplete notes, only to realize later upon review that they do not understand all of their notes. Further suggestions for keeping a notebook can be found on page 443.

For more support on notetaking, see:

- Notetaking Guide Workbook
- Notetaking Transparencies

Getting Ready to Learn

Word Watch

Review Words

rational number, p. 242
right angle, p. 375
right triangle, p. 382
equilateral triangle, p. 382
isosceles triangle, p. 382
scalene triangle, p. 382

Review What You Need to Know 

Using Vocabulary **Use a review word to classify the triangle by its side lengths.**

1. 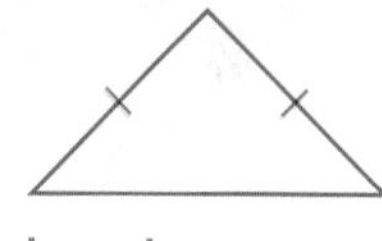 isosceles

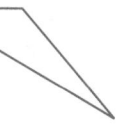

2. scalene

3. 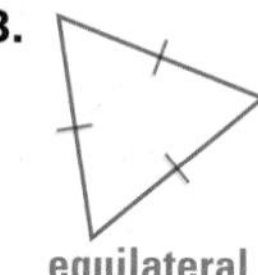 equilateral

Evaluate the expression. *(p. 20)*

4. $4^2 + 3^2$ 25 **5.** $14^2 - 5^2$ 171 **6.** $27^2 - 3^2$ 720 **7.** $2^2 + 6^2$ 40

Find the measure of each angle in the triangle. *(p. 382)*

8. 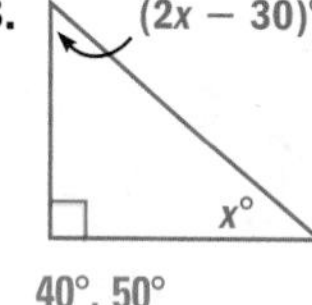

40°, 50°

9. 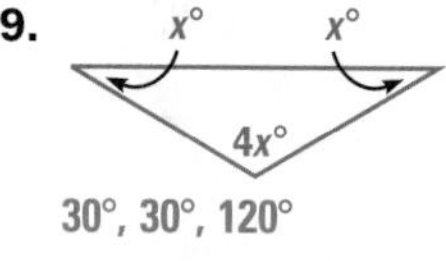

30°, 30°, 120°

10. 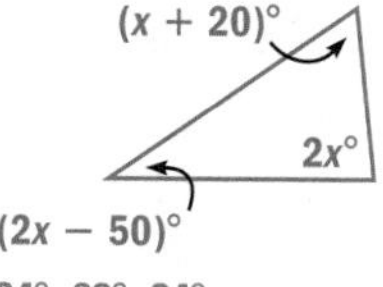

34°, 62°, 84°

You should include material that appears on a notebook like this in your own notes.

Know How to Take Notes

Illustrating with Examples When you learn a new concept or formula, write it in your notes along with examples and important information.

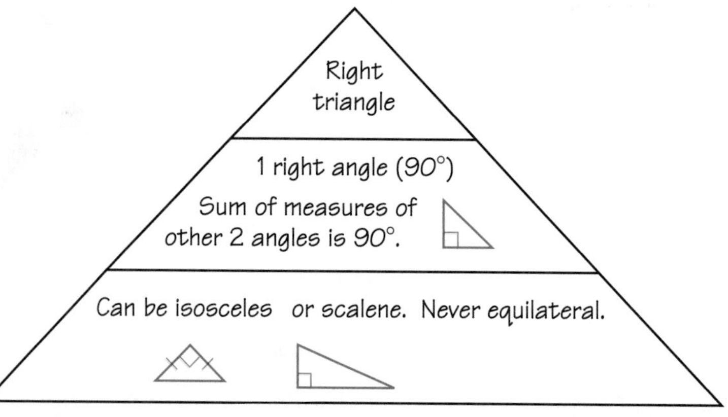

Right triangle
1 right angle (90°)
Sum of measures of other 2 angles is 90°.
Can be isosceles or scalene. Never equilateral.

In Lesson 9.3, you will learn a rule about right triangles that you should write in your notebook.

Square Roots

BEFORE	Now	WHY?
You found squares of numbers.	You'll find and approximate square roots of numbers.	So you can find the length of a side of a square pillow, as in Ex. 14.

Word Watch

square root, p. 431
radical expression, p. 431
perfect square, p. 432

Activity **You can find the length of a side of a square if you know its area.**

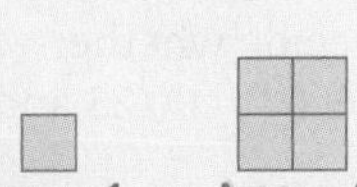
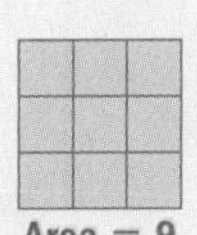

Area = 1 Area = 4 Area = 9

(1 Copy and complete the table.

Area of square (square units)	1	4	9	16	25	36
Side length (units)	1	2	3	? 4	? 5	? 6

(2 What is the length of each side of a square with an area of 49 square units? 64 square units? 100 square units? 400 square units?
7 units; 8 units; 10 units; 20 units

(3 What can you say about the length of a side of a square that has an area between 81 and 100 square units? It is between 9 and 10 units.

The numbers 5 and −5 are the *square roots* of 25 because $5^2 = 25$ and $(-5)^2 = 25$. If $m^2 = n$, then m is a **square root** of n.

Every positive number has a positive square root and a negative square root. The symbol $\sqrt{\ }$ is called a *radical sign*. It is used to represent the positive square root. A **radical expression** is an expression that involves a $\sqrt{\ }$.

$\sqrt{25} = 5$ positive square root

$-\sqrt{25} = -5$ negative square root

Zero has one square root, which is zero.

EXAMPLE 1 **Evaluating Square Roots**

a. $\sqrt{36} = 6$ because $6^2 = 36$. **b.** $-\sqrt{64} = -8$ because $(-8)^2 = 64$.

HELP with Solving

You may want to use the Table of Square Roots on p. 745.

Your turn now **Find the square root.**

1. $\sqrt{4}$ 2 **2.** $\sqrt{0}$ 0 **3.** $-\sqrt{36}$ −6 **4.** $-\sqrt{81}$ −9

ILLINOIS Standards and ISAT:
6.B.3c, 8.D.3c; 7.C.3b, 8.D.3b

1 PLAN

SKILL CHECK

1. $5^2 = \underline{?}$ 25
2. $-7^2 = \underline{?}$ −49
3. $10^2 = \underline{?}$ 100
4. $(-12)^2 = \underline{?}$ 144

Lesson Objective

Find and approximate square roots of numbers.

Pacing

Suggested Number of Days
Basic Course: 1 day
Average Course: 1 day
Advanced Course: 1 day
Block: 0.5 block with 9.2

Teaching Resources

For a complete list of Teaching Resources, see page 428B.

Transparency

Warm-Up Exercises for this lesson are available on a transparency.

2 TEACH

Motivating the Lesson

From solving equations, students are familiar with "undoing" addition by subtraction, multiplication by division, and so on. Point out that now they will explore how to "undo" squaring a number.

Activity

Goal Find the length of a side of a square given its area.

Key Discovery The side length of a square with a given area is the number that multiplied by itself gives the area.

TIPS FOR NEW TEACHERS

Students will likely need extra instruction about the "±" sign when they start solving equations with square roots. Remind them that any positive number has two square roots, so the equation $x^2 = c$ will have two solutions for positive c. Because the radical sign indicates the positive square root, its opposite indicates the negative square root. The "±" sign is just a shortcut for writing both roots. See Tips for New Teachers in the *Chapter 9 Resource Book*.

EXTRA EXAMPLES

Example 1 Find the square root of the number.

a. $\sqrt{49}$ **7**

b. $-\sqrt{144}$ **−12**

Example 2 Use a number line to estimate $\sqrt{150}$ to the nearest whole number. **12**

Example 3 Approximate the square root. Round to the nearest tenth, if necessary.

a. $\sqrt{841}$ **29**

b. $-\sqrt{18.49}$ **−4.3**

c. $\sqrt{12}$ **3.5**

d. $-\sqrt{964}$ **−31.0**

TRANSPARENCY

A support transparency is available for Example 2.

VISUALIZE

Throughout this lesson and beyond, you may need to revisit the activity at the lesson opener to help students visualize the relationship between a number and its square root.

Perfect Squares A **perfect square** is any number that has integer square roots. Some examples of perfect squares are 1, 4, 9, and 16. You can approximate the square roots of a number that is not a perfect square using a number line or a calculator.

EXAMPLE 2 Approximating a Square Root

You can use a number line to approximate $\sqrt{95}$ to the nearest whole number. You know that 95 is between 81 (or 9^2) and 100 (or 10^2), so $\sqrt{95}$ is between 9 and 10.

To decide whether $\sqrt{95}$ is closer to 9 or to 10, find 9.5^2. You can calculate that $9.5^2 = 90.25$ and $(\sqrt{95})^2 = 95$.

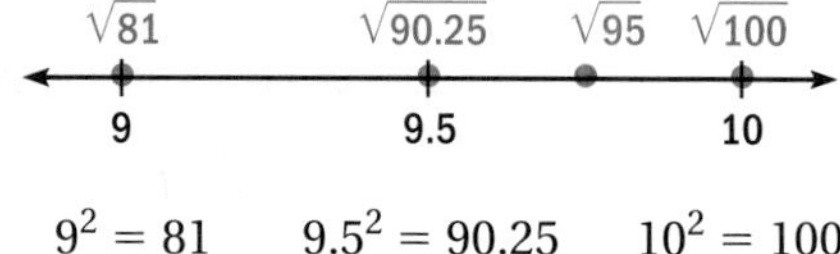

$9^2 = 81$ $9.5^2 = 90.25$ $10^2 = 100$

As shown on the number line, $\sqrt{95}$ is between $\sqrt{90.25}$ and $\sqrt{100}$, so it has a value between 9.5 and 10. Therefore, $\sqrt{95}$ is closer to 10 than it is to 9.

ANSWER To the nearest whole number, $\sqrt{95} \approx 10$.

EXAMPLE 3 Using a Calculator

Evaluate the square root. Round to the nearest tenth, if necessary.

a. $\sqrt{441}$ **b.** $-\sqrt{56.25}$ **c.** $\sqrt{8}$ **d.** $-\sqrt{1256}$

Solution

	Keystrokes	Display	Answer
a.	2nd [√‾] 441 =	21	21
b.	(−) 2nd [√‾] 56.25 =	−7.5	−7.5
c.	2nd [√‾] 8 =	2.828427125	2.8
d.	(−) 2nd [√‾] 1256 =	−35.44009029	−35.4

Your turn now **Approximate to the nearest whole number.**

5. $\sqrt{23}$ 5 **6.** $\sqrt{41}$ 6 **7.** $\sqrt{70}$ 8 **8.** $\sqrt{125}$ 11

Use a calculator to evaluate. Round to the nearest tenth.

9. $\sqrt{236}$ 15.4 **10.** $\sqrt{11}$ 3.3 **11.** $-\sqrt{20.96}$ −4.6 **12.** $-\sqrt{3590}$ −59.9

EXAMPLE 4 Using a Square Root Equation

Amusement Parks On an amusement park ride, riders stand against a circular wall that spins. At a certain speed, the floor drops out and the force of the rotation keeps the riders pinned to the wall.

The model $s = 4.95\sqrt{r}$ gives the speed needed to keep riders pinned to the wall. In the model, s is the speed in meters per second and r is the radius of the ride in meters. Find the speed necessary to keep riders pinned to the wall of a ride that has a radius of 2.61 meters.

Solution

$s = 4.95\sqrt{r}$	Write equation for speed of the ride.
$= 4.95\sqrt{2.61}$	Substitute 2.61 for r.
$\approx 4.95(1.62)$	Approximate the square root.
$= 8.019$	Multiply.

ANSWER The speed should be about 8.019 meters per second.

EXAMPLE 5 Solving Equations Using Square Roots

a.

$x^2 = 64$	Original equation
$x = \pm\sqrt{64}$	Definition of square root
$x = \pm 8$	Evaluate square roots.

ANSWER The solutions are 8 and −8.

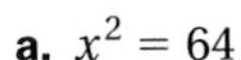

HELP with Reading

The symbol ± is read *plus or minus.* The statement $x = \pm 8$ means that 8 and −8 are the solutions of $x^2 = 64$.

b.

$z^2 + 14 = 20$	Original equation
$z^2 + 14 - 14 = 20 - 14$	Subtract 14 from each side.
$z^2 = 6$	Simplify.
$z = \pm\sqrt{6}$	Definition of square root
$z \approx \pm 2.45$	Approximate square roots.

ANSWER The solutions are about 2.45 and about −2.45.

Your turn now **Approximate the square root. Round to the nearest tenth.**

13. $\sqrt{5}$ 2.2 **14.** $\sqrt{12}$ 3.5 **15.** $\sqrt{15}$ 3.9 **16.** $\sqrt{23}$ 4.8

Solve the equation. Check your solutions.

17. $t^2 = 36$ ±6 **18.** $y^2 - 15 = 10$ ±5 **19.** $x^2 + 7 = 16$ ±3

EXTRA EXAMPLES

Example 4 The model $S = 5\sqrt{d}$ gives the speed S in miles per hour for a car that took d feet to stop. If it takes the car 160 feet to stop, how fast was it traveling to the nearest mile per hour? **63 mi/h**

Example 5 Solve the equation. Round to the nearest tenth, if necessary.

a. $a^2 = 169$ **±13**

b. $y^2 + 20 = 79$ **±7.7**

MATH REASONING

Make sure students can distinguish between the sentences "Find $\sqrt{100}$" and "Find the square root(s) of 100." The difference is not just in the hint in the second sentence that there could be more than one square root. Because of the radical symbol in the first sentence, that sentence does not translate in words to the second, but to "Find the positive (nonnegative) number that is a square root of 100."

Differentiating Instruction

Less Proficient Students

Suggest that students make a poster of squares with perfect square areas from 1 to 100. Have them also list the squares of all whole numbers from 1 to 20 or 1 to 30.

CONCEPT CHECK

Is $\sqrt{15}$ the only solution of $x^2 = 15$? Explain. **No; $\sqrt{15}$ is just the positive solution. There is also the solution $-\sqrt{15}$, since $(-\sqrt{15})^2 = 15$.**

DAILY PUZZLER

Find $\sqrt{\sqrt{16}}$. **2**

3 APPLY

ASSIGNMENT GUIDE

Basic Course

Day 1: EP p. 729 Exs. 1-4, 24; pp. 434-436 Exs. 15-29, 34-45, 50-52, 58-68

Average Course

Day 1: pp. 434-436 Exs. 17-24, 30-34, 38-55, 58-69

Advanced Course

Day 1: pp. 434-436 Exs. 17-24, 30-34, 38-63*, 67-69

Block

pp. 434-436 Exs. 17-24, 30-34, 38-55, 58-69 (with 9.2)

EXTRA PRACTICE

- Student Edition, p. 735
- Chapter 9 Resource Book, pp. 8-10
- Test and Practice Generator

TRANSPARENCY

Even-numbered answers are available on transparencies. A support transparency is available for Exercises 19-22.

HOMEWORK CHECK

When you review students' homework for this lesson, go over the following exercises to check understanding of key concepts.

Basic: 15, 19, 23, 27, 34
Average: 17, 20, 23, 30, 34
Advanced: 17, 21, 24, 30, 34

9.1 Exercises

More Practice, p. 735

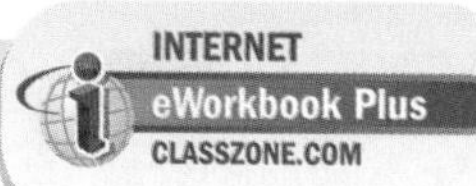

Getting Ready to Practice

1. **Vocabulary** Copy and complete: A number b is a square root of c if __?__. $b^2 = c$

Find the two square roots of the number.

2. 9 ±3
3. 16 ±4
4. 49 ±7
5. 121 ±11

Use a calculator to approximate the square root. Round to the nearest tenth.

6. $\sqrt{28}$ 5.3
7. $-\sqrt{482}$ −22.0
8. $-\sqrt{34.6}$ −5.9
9. $\sqrt{2440}$ 49.4

Solve the equation. Check your solutions.

10. $x^2 = 4$ ±2
11. $b^2 = 49$ ±7
12. $y^2 + 7 = 56$ ±7
13. $c^2 - 12 = 69$ ±9

14. **Guided Problem Solving** You want to make a square pillow. You have 729 square inches of material for the front of the pillow. If you use all the material, what is the length of one side of the pillow?
    (1) Write an equation. $x^2 = 729$
    (2) Use definition of square root to solve the equation. $x = \pm\sqrt{729}$
    (3) Evaluate the positive square root. $x = 27$ in.

Practice and Problem Solving

A **Find the square root.**

15. $-\sqrt{1}$ −1
16. $\sqrt{100}$ 10
17. $\sqrt{144}$ 12
18. $-\sqrt{900}$ −30

Approximate the square root to the nearest whole number.

19. $\sqrt{33}$ 6
20. $\sqrt{14}$ 4
21. $\sqrt{117}$ 11
22. $\sqrt{52}$ 7

Use a calculator to evaluate the square root. Round to the nearest tenth, if necessary.

23. $\sqrt{22}$ 4.7
24. $\sqrt{43.56}$ 6.6
25. $-\sqrt{1475}$ −38.4
26. $-\sqrt{6204}$ −78.8

Solve the equation. Check your solution(s).

27. $x^2 = 0$ 0
28. $y^2 = 81$ ±9
29. $z^2 - 169 = 0$ ±13
30. $n^2 - 27 = 94$ ±11
31. $a^2 + 12 = 48$ ±6
32. $m^2 + 21 = 421$ ±20

33. **Critical Thinking** Can you find $\sqrt{-25}$? Explain your answer.
No. *Sample answer:* There is no real number whose square is a negative number.

HELP with Homework

Example	Exercises
1	15-18
2	19-22
3	23-26
4	34
5	27-32

Online Resources CLASSZONE.COM
- More Examples
- eTutorial Plus

34. Fire Tower A forest ranger is stationed in a 53 foot tall fire tower. The equation for the distance in miles that the ranger can see is $d = \sqrt{1.5h}$, where h is the height in feet above the ground. Find the distance the ranger can see. Round your answer to the nearest tenth. 8.9 mi

HELP with Solving

You can use a calculator or the Table of Square Roots on p. 745 to solve Exercises 35–40.

B **Solve the equation. Round to the nearest hundredth, if necessary. Check your solutions.**

35. $x^2 + 8 = 49$ ±6.40 **36.** $y^2 - 31 = 36$ ±8.19 **37.** $62 + z^2 = 198$ ±11.66

38. $t^2 - 44 = 224$ ±16.37 **39.** $c^2 - 35 = 165$ ±14.14 **40.** $57 + m^2 = 253$ ±14

Evaluate the expression $\sqrt{x^2 - y^2}$ for the given values.

41. $x = 5, y = 3$ 4 **42.** $x = 10, y = 8$ 6 **43.** $x = 15, y = 12$ 9

Find the two square roots of the number.

44. 0.81 ±0.9 **45.** 1.44 ±1.2 **46.** 1.21 ±1.1 **47.** 1.96 ±1.4

48. Farming You want to put a fence around a square plot of land that has an area of 6250 square yards. Find the length of a side, to the nearest tenth of a yard, and then use it to approximate the perimeter of the plot of land. 79.1 yd; 316.4 yd

$A = 6250$ yd^2

49. Home Decorating You have a square table with an area of 34.5 square feet. You have a tablecloth that measures 60 inches by 60 inches. Is the tablecloth large enough to cover the table? Explain.

49. No. *Sample answer:* The table measures $\sqrt{34.5} \approx$ 5.9 feet on a side. Since 5.9 feet is over 70 inches, the tablecloth is not big enough.

C **50.** Evaluate the expression $\sqrt{\sqrt{16}}$. 2

EXAMPLE **Finding a Square Root of a Fraction**

$\sqrt{\frac{9}{16}} = \sqrt{\frac{3}{4} \cdot \frac{3}{4}} = \frac{3}{4}$ Definition of square root

In Exercises 51–55, find the square root.

51. $\sqrt{\frac{1}{4}}$ $\frac{1}{2}$ **52.** $\sqrt{\frac{16}{25}}$ $\frac{4}{5}$ **53.** $\sqrt{\frac{49}{64}}$ $\frac{7}{8}$ **54.** $\sqrt{\frac{81}{100}}$ $\frac{9}{10}$ **55.** $\sqrt{\frac{144}{169}}$ $\frac{12}{13}$

56. Look for a Pattern Find the positive square roots of 0.36, 0.0036, 0.000036, and 0.00000036. What pattern do you notice? Using the pattern, predict the positive square root of 0.0000000036.
0.6, 0.06, 0.006, 0.0006; each number is 0.1 times the previous number; 0.00006

57. Challenge In Example 2, you learned how to approximate the value of a square root to the nearest whole number without using a calculator. Explain how to approximate the value of a square root to the nearest tenth if you have a calculator that cannot evaluate square roots.

57. *Sample answer:* Choose two integers between which the square root lies. Guess the square root to the tenths' place using the relative distance of the original number from the squares of the two integers. Use the calculator to square your guess to see if it is too large or too small, and then adjust your guess accordingly. The one-place decimal whose square is closest to the original number is the best estimate.

TEACHING TIP

In Exercises 44 and 51–55, students will have a natural instinct to expect the positive square root to be less than the original number. You may want to have students use a calculator to find the square roots of several numbers between 0 and 1 to emphasize that in these cases the positive square root is actually greater than the original number.

ASSESS

ASSESSMENT RESOURCES

For more assessment resources, see:
- Assessment Book
- Test and Practice Generator

MINI-QUIZ

Find the square root of the number.

1. $\sqrt{196}$ **14**
2. $\sqrt{1600}$ **40**

Use a calculator to find the square root. Round to the nearest tenth.

3. $\sqrt{38}$ **6.2**
4. $\sqrt{95.8}$ **9.8**

Solve the equation. Round to the nearest hundredth, if necessary.

5. $p^2 + 21 = 190$ **±13**
6. $z^2 - 46 = 16$ **±7.87**
7. Find the two square roots of 2.25. **±1.5**
8. Evaluate $\sqrt{x^2 + y^2}$ for $x = 8$ and $y = 15$. **17**

FOLLOW-UP

RETEACHING/REMEDIATION

- Study Guide in Chapter 9 Resource Book, pp. 11–12
- eTutorial Plus Online
- Extra Practice, p. 735
- Lesson Practice in Chapter 9 Resource Book, pp. 8–10

CHALLENGE/ENRICHMENT

- Challenge Practice in Chapter 9 Resource Book, p. 13
- Teacher's Edition, p. 428F

ENGLISH LEARNER SUPPORT

- Spanish Study Guide
- Multi-Language Glossary
- Chapter Audio Summaries CDs

Mixed Review

58. Carnival Nikki is at a carnival and has \$6. She would like to buy some cotton candy for \$2.25 and use the rest of her money to go on the rides. Each ride costs \$.75. How many rides can she go on? *(Lesson 3.4)* **5 rides**

Tell whether the angles are *complementary*, *supplementary*, or *neither*. *(Lesson 8.1)*

59. $m\angle 1 = 89°$, $m\angle 2 = 31°$ **neither**

60. $m\angle 1 = 34°$, $m\angle 2 = 56°$ **complementary**

61. $m\angle 1 = 53°$, $m\angle 2 = 127°$ **supplementary**

62. $m\angle 1 = 78°$, $m\angle 2 = 102°$ **supplementary**

Choose a Strategy **Use a strategy from the list to solve the following problem. Explain your choice of strategy.**

Problem Solving Strategies
- Look for a Pattern
- Draw a Diagram
- Make a Model

63. In how many different ways can three postage stamps be torn from a 3 by 4 sheet of stamps so that the three stamps are still attached to one another?

63. 6 ways. *Sample answer:* I used the strategy Draw a Diagram so that I could draw all the ways that 3 stamps can be arranged and still be attached.

Basic Skills **Write the decimal as a mixed number.**

64. -1.25 $-1\frac{1}{4}$ **65.** 5.35 $5\frac{7}{20}$ **66.** 2.95 $2\frac{19}{20}$ **67.** -9.05 $-9\frac{1}{20}$

Test-Taking Practice

68. Multiple Choice Approximate $\sqrt{175}$ to the nearest whole number. **B**

A. 12 **B.** 13 **C.** 14 **D.** 15

69. Multiple Choice The area of the square base of a building is 2025 square feet. Find the perimeter of the base of the building. **I**

F. 25 feet **G.** 45 feet **H.** 90 feet **I.** 180 feet

BRAIN GAME

X-cellent Birthday

Augustus De Morgan, a nineteenth century English mathematician, was the first professor of Mathematics at University College, London.

Always interested in strange numerical facts, De Morgan once noted in his writings that he had the distinction of being x years old in the year x^2. If he was born between 1805 and 1815, in what year was he born? **1806**

Rational and Irrational Numbers

BEFORE	Now	WHY?
You investigated rational numbers.	You'll work with irrational numbers.	So you can determine how many stencils fill a wall, as in Ex. 24.

Word Watch

irrational number, p. 437
real number, p. 437

Recall that a *rational number* is a number that can be written as a quotient $\frac{a}{b}$, where a and b are integers and $b \neq 0$. An **irrational number** is a number that cannot be written as a quotient of two integers. If n is a positive integer and is not a perfect square, then $\sqrt{n}$ and $-\sqrt{n}$ are irrational numbers.

Together, rational numbers and irrational numbers make up the set of **real numbers**. The Venn diagram shows the relationships among numbers in the real number system.

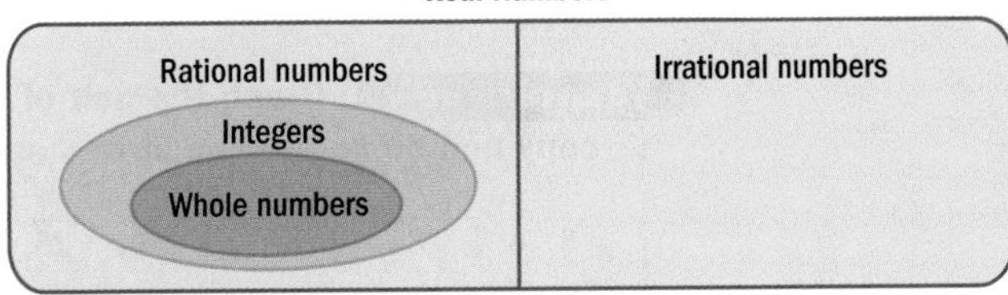

The decimal form of a rational number is either terminating or repeating. The decimal form of an irrational number neither terminates nor repeats.

HELP with Review

For help with writing a rational number as a decimal, see p. 242.

1–4. Sample explanations are given.
1. $\frac{5}{8} = 0.625$ and 0.625 is a terminating decimal.
2. 7 is not a perfect square.
3. $\frac{2}{9} = 0.\overline{2}$ and $0.\overline{2}$ is a repeating decimal.
4. $\sqrt{25} = 5$ and 5 is an integer.

EXAMPLE 1 Classifying Real Numbers

	Number	Type	Decimal Form	Type of Decimal
a.	$\frac{3}{4}$	Rational	$\frac{3}{4} = 0.75$	Terminating
b.	$\frac{1}{11}$	Rational	$\frac{1}{11} = 0.0909\ldots = 0.\overline{09}$	Repeating
c.	$\sqrt{3}$	Irrational	$\sqrt{3} = 1.7320508\ldots$	Nonrepeating and nonterminating

Your turn now Tell whether the number is *rational* or *irrational*. Explain your reasoning.

1. $\frac{5}{8}$ rational
2. $\sqrt{7}$ irrational
3. $\frac{2}{9}$ rational
4. $\sqrt{25}$ rational

ILLINOIS Standards and ISAT:
6.A.3, 6.B.3a, 8.D.3b

1 PLAN

SKILL CHECK

Write each fraction as a decimal.

1. $\frac{3}{4}$ 0.75
2. $\frac{5}{8}$ 0.625
3. $\frac{2}{5}$ 0.4
4. $\frac{4}{9}$ $0.\overline{4}$

LESSON OBJECTIVE

Work with irrational numbers.

PACING

Suggested Number of Days
Basic Course: 1 day
Average Course: 1 day
Advanced Course: 1 day
Block: 0.5 block with 9.1

TEACHING RESOURCES

For a complete list of Teaching Resources, see page 428B.

TRANSPARENCY

Warm-Up Exercises for this lesson are available on a transparency.

2 TEACH

MOTIVATING THE LESSON

Have students give examples of rational numbers, including integers as well as fractions whose decimal forms terminate and others whose decimal forms repeat.

TIPS FOR NEW TEACHERS

Encourage students to do Internet research to see to how many decimal places the value of π has been calculated. Emphasize that there is no repeating pattern. See Tips for New Teachers in the *Chapter 9 Resource Book*.

EXTRA EXAMPLES

Example 1 Tell whether the number is *rational* or *irrational*.

a. $\frac{3}{22}$ **rational**

b. $\sqrt{16}$ **rational**

c. $\sqrt{5}$ **irrational**

Example 2 Graph the pair of numbers on a number line. Then copy and complete the statement with <, >, or =.

a. $3 \underline{\ ?\ } \sqrt{10}$ <

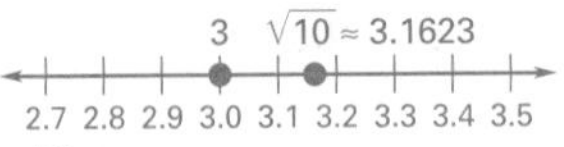

b. $\sqrt{\frac{1}{5}} \underline{\ ?\ } \frac{1}{5}$ >

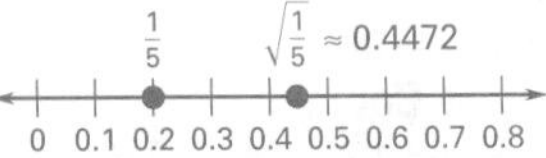

Example 3 Order the decimals 1.24, $1.2\overline{4}$, $1.2\overline{442}$, and $1.\overline{24}$ from least to greatest. **1.24, $1.\overline{24}$, $1.2\overline{442}$, $1.2\overline{4}$**

TEACHING TIP

When discussing Example 3, be sure students understand that just because a decimal does not terminate does not mean it is irrational. To be irrational, it must also never repeat. You may want to point out that the three repeating decimals given correspond to $\frac{43}{90}$, $\frac{474}{999}$, and $\frac{47}{99}$, respectively.

TRANSPARENCY

A support transparency is available for Example 2.

5. $\sqrt{8} \approx 2.8284$; 4
2 2.4 2.8 3.2 3.6 4

6.

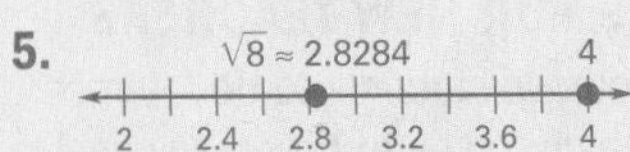

7.

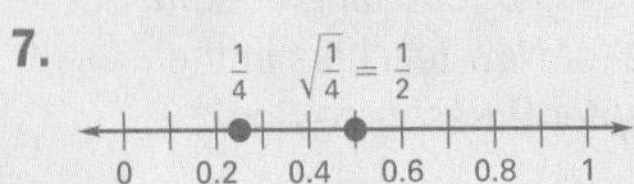

EXAMPLE 2 Comparing Real Numbers

Graph the pair of numbers on a number line. Then copy and complete the statement with <, >, or =.

a. $\sqrt{2} \underline{\ ?\ } 2$

b. $\sqrt{\frac{1}{2}} \underline{\ ?\ } \frac{1}{2}$

Solution

Use a calculator to approximate the square root and write any fractions as decimals. Then graph the numbers on a number line and compare.

a.

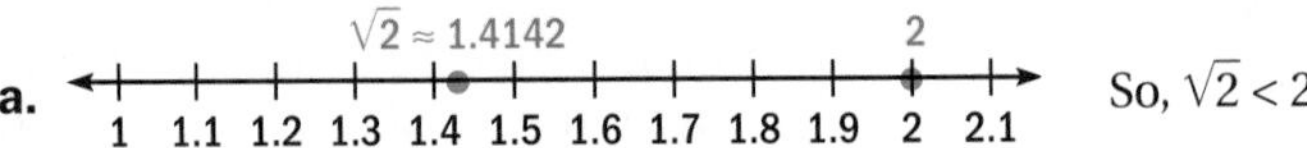

So, $\sqrt{2} < 2$.

b. $\frac{1}{2} = 0.5$ $\sqrt{\frac{1}{2}} \approx 0.7071$
0 0.1 0.2 0.3 0.4 0.5 0.6 0.7 0.8 0.9 1

So, $\sqrt{\frac{1}{2}} > \frac{1}{2}$.

Your turn now **Graph the pair of numbers on a number line. Then copy and complete the statement with <, >, or =.**

5–7. See margin for art.

5. $4 \underline{\ ?\ } \sqrt{8}$ >

6. $\sqrt{25} \underline{\ ?\ } 5$ =

7. $\frac{1}{4} \underline{\ ?\ } \sqrt{\frac{1}{4}}$ <

Watch Out! You may need to use parentheses when using a calculator to approximate a square root.

EXAMPLE 3 Ordering Decimals

Order the decimals $0.4\overline{7}$, $0.\overline{474}$, $0.\overline{47}$, and 0.477 from least to greatest.

Solution

1 Write each decimal out to six decimal places.

Notice that the first two digits after the decimal point are the same for each number.

$0.4\overline{7} = 0.477777...$

$0.\overline{474} = 0.474474...$

$0.\overline{47} = 0.474747...$

$0.477 = 0.477000$

Use the second pair of digits to order the decimals.

2 From least to greatest, the order of the numbers is $0.474474...$, $0.474747...$, 0.4770, and $0.477777...$.

ANSWER From least to greatest, the order is $0.\overline{474}$, $0.\overline{47}$, 0.477, and $0.4\overline{7}$.

EXAMPLE 4 Using an Irrational Number

Waves For large ocean waves, the wind speed s in knots and the height of the waves h in feet are related by the equation $s = \sqrt{\frac{h}{0.019}}$. If the waves are about 9.5 feet tall, what must the wind speed be? (1 knot is equivalent to 1.15 miles per hour.)

Solution

$s = \sqrt{\frac{h}{0.019}}$ Write original equation.

$= \sqrt{\frac{9.5}{0.019}}$ Substitute 9.5 for h.

$= \sqrt{500}$ Divide.

≈ 22.36 Approximate square root.

ANSWER The wind speed must be about 22.36 knots.

Your turn now Use the equation in Example 4.

8. Find the wind speed required to produce 15 foot waves. about 28.10 knots

9.2 Exercises

More Practice, p. 735

Getting Ready to Practice

1. **Vocabulary** Copy and complete: Numbers that cannot be written as a quotient of two integers are called _?_ numbers. irrational

Tell whether the number is *rational* or *irrational*. Explain your reasoning.

2. $\sqrt{36}$ 3. $\sqrt{5}$ 4. $\frac{\sqrt{3}}{8}$ 5. $\sqrt{\frac{25}{49}}$

Graph the pair of numbers on a number line. Then copy and complete the statement with <, >, or =. 6–8. See margin for art.

6. $\frac{5}{6}$ _?_ $\sqrt{\frac{5}{6}}$ < 7. $\frac{3}{5}$ _?_ $\sqrt{\frac{36}{100}}$ = 8. 5 _?_ $\sqrt{10}$ >

9. **Dimensions** The floor of a square room has an area of 90 square feet. What are the dimensions of the room to the nearest tenth of a foot? 9.5 ft by 9.5 ft

2–5. Sample explanations are given.

2. Rational; 36 is a perfect square, since $6^2 = 36$.

3. Irrational; 5 is not a perfect square.

4. Irrational; 3 is not a perfect square, so $\sqrt{3}$ is irrational. $\frac{\sqrt{3}}{8}$ cannot be written as the ratio of two integers.

5. Rational; $\sqrt{\frac{25}{49}} = \frac{5}{7}$, which is a quotient of two integers.

EXTRA EXAMPLES

Example 4 The equation $d = \sqrt{\frac{3h}{2}}$ models the distance d in miles that a person can see to the horizon from an eye-level height of h feet above the ground. If a woman with a normal eye level of 5 feet stands on a cliff 100 feet high, how far can she see to the horizon to the nearest tenth of a mile? **12.5 mi**

NOTETAKING

After students have worked Extra Example 3 on page 438, encourage them to record in their notebooks how they wrote out the decimals and then compared and ordered them.

CONCEPT CHECK

What is true about the decimal form of any irrational number? **It neither terminates nor repeats.**

DAILY PUZZLER

Tiffany dropped her textbook. The book fell open to two pages that had a product of page numbers of 4422. To what pages did the book fall open? **pages 66 and 67**

6.
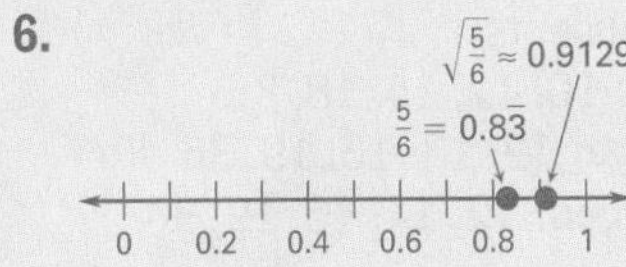

7.
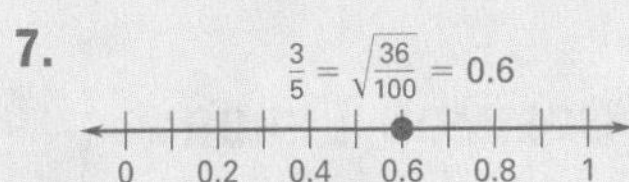

8.
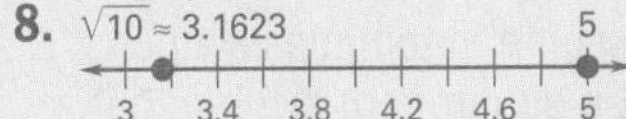

3 APPLY

ASSIGNMENT GUIDE

Basic Course

Day 1: SRH p. 726 Exs. 1–4; pp. 440–441 Exs. 10–21, 25–30, 36–49

Average Course

Day 1: pp. 440–441 Exs. 12–15, 19–28, 31–34, 36–50

Advanced Course

Day 1: pp. 440–441 Exs. 12–15, 19–28, 31–40*, 45–50

Block

pp. 440–441 Exs. 12–15, 19–28, 31–34, 36–50 (with 9.1)

EXTRA PRACTICE

- Student Edition, p. 735
- Chapter 9 Resource Book, pp. 16–18
- Test and Practice Generator

TRANSPARENCY

Even-numbered answers are available on transparencies. A support transparency is available for Exercises 6–8, 14–17, and 25–27.

HOMEWORK CHECK

When you review students' homework for this lesson, go over the following exercises to check understanding of key concepts.

Basic: 10, 12, 14, 18, 36

Average: 12, 13, 15, 19, 36

Advanced: 12, 14, 15, 19, 36

COMMON ERROR

In Exercise 10, watch for students who assume automatically upon seeing a square root symbol that a number is irrational.

14–17, 25–28, 33, 34. See Additional Answers beginning on page AA1.

with Homework

Example	Exercises
1	10–13
2	14–17
3	18–19
4	36

Online Resources
CLASSZONE.COM

- More Examples
- eTutorial Plus

10–13. Sample explanations are given.

10. Rational; 144 is a perfect square, since $12^2 = 144$.

11. Rational; $\frac{9}{46}$ is a quotient of two integers.

12. Rational; 0.30311 terminates.

13. Irrational; neither 3 nor 5 is a perfect square.

Practice and Problem Solving

A **Tell whether the number is *rational* or *irrational*. Explain your reasoning.** 10–13. See margin.

10. $\sqrt{144}$ **11.** $\frac{9}{46}$ **12.** 0.30311 **13.** $\sqrt{\frac{3}{5}}$

Graph the pair of numbers on a number line. Then copy and complete the statement with <, >, or =. 14–17. See margin for art.

14. $\sqrt{\frac{64}{121}}$? $\frac{8}{11}$ = **15.** $\sqrt{13}$? 3 > **16.** $\sqrt{21}$? 7 < **17.** -5 ? $-\sqrt{25}$ =

Order the decimals from least to greatest.

18. $0.1\overline{3}, 0.\overline{131}, 0.\overline{13}, 0.133$ — $0.\overline{131}, 0.\overline{13}, 0.133, 0.1\overline{3}$

19. $0.\overline{26}, 0.266, 0.2\overline{6}, 0.\overline{262}$ — $0.\overline{262}, 0.\overline{26}, 0.266, 0.2\overline{6}$

Evaluate the expression when *a* = 2, *b* = 4, and *c* = 9. Tell whether the result is *rational* or *irrational*.

20. $\sqrt{a+c}$ — $\sqrt{11}$; irrational **21.** $\sqrt{a^2}$ — $\sqrt{4} = 2$; rational **22.** $\sqrt{bc}$ — $\sqrt{36} = 6$; rational **23.** $\sqrt{a^2+b^2}$ — $\sqrt{20}$; irrational

24. Decorating You are decorating your room. You have a square wall stencil that has an area of 20.25 square inches. Find the length of a side of the stencil. The wall you are decorating is $7\frac{1}{2}$ feet high. How many stencils can you place in a column from the top to the bottom of your wall? 4.5 in.; 20 stencils

B **In Exercises 25–27, graph the pair of numbers on a number line. Then copy and complete the statement with <, >, or =.** 25–27. See margin for art.

25. $\sqrt{0.9}$? 0.9 > **26.** -7 ? $-\sqrt{7}$ < **27.** $\sqrt{2.25}$? $\frac{3.6}{2.4}$ =

28. Graph the numbers $-\sqrt{9}$, -8.69, $-\sqrt{45}$, and $-\frac{141}{25}$ on a number line. See margin.

Order the numbers from least to greatest.

29. 1.5, $\sqrt{8}$, −4, −3.75 — −4, −3.75, 1.5, $\sqrt{8}$

30. $\sqrt{81}$, 10.3, $\sqrt{220}$, −9 — −9, $\sqrt{81}$, 10.3, $\sqrt{220}$

31. $-\sqrt{12}, -\sqrt{\frac{1}{4}}, -3.5, -\frac{3}{4}$ — $-3.5, -\sqrt{12}, -\frac{3}{4}, -\sqrt{\frac{1}{4}}$

32. 1.02, $\sqrt{2.5}$, $\sqrt{1.25}$, $\frac{2}{5}$ — $\frac{2}{5}$, 1.02, $\sqrt{1.25}$, $\sqrt{2.5}$

33. Carpet Your aunt offers you a square piece of carpet that has an area of 110 square feet. You want to use the carpet in a bedroom that measures 10.5 feet by 11.2 feet. Will the carpet fit in the room? Will it be too small? too large? Explain. See margin.

C **34. Critical Thinking** Your friend gets a result of 2.645751311 on a calculator and says that it has to be an irrational number. Is your friend right? Explain your reasoning. See margin.

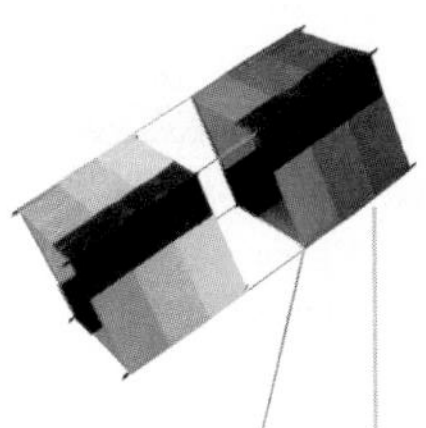

35. **Challenge** Find three rational numbers between $\frac{2}{3}$ and $\frac{3}{4}$. Can you write all of the rational numbers that are between these two numbers? Explain your reasoning. **See margin.**

36. **Box Kites** To calculate the minimum wind speed required to fly a box kite, you can use the formula $m = \sqrt{\frac{w}{A}}$, where m is the minimum wind speed in miles per hour, w is the weight in ounces, and A is the area in square feet of the surface used to lift the kite. Find the minimum wind speed required to lift a box kite with a weight of 5.6 ounces if the area used to lift the kite is 8.71 square feet. **about 0.8 mi/h**

Mixed Review 

Simplify. Write the expression using only positive exponents. *(Lessons 4.6, 4.7)*

37. $5a^2 \cdot 6a^9$ **$30a^{11}$**
38. $d^8 \cdot 4d^{-5}$ **$4d^3$**
39. $-5m^0$ **-5**
40. $n^{-7} \cdot n^5$ **$\frac{1}{n^2}$**
41. $\frac{c^5 \cdot c^3}{c^4}$ **c^4**
42. $\frac{24b^{14}}{8b^9}$ **$3b^5$**
43. $\frac{-8n^8}{12n^{12}}$ **$-\frac{2}{3n^4}$**
44. $\frac{24r^{-5}}{r^3}$ **$\frac{24}{r^8}$**

Describe the transformation from the blue figure to the red figure using coordinate notation. *(Lessons 8.6, 8.7)*

45. 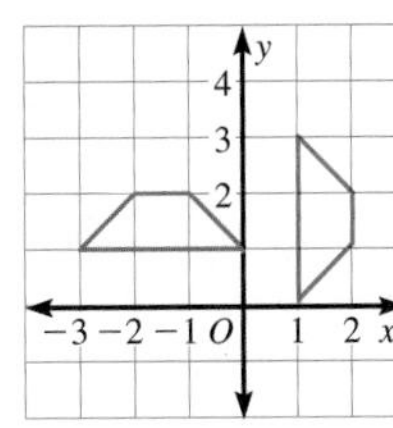
rotation; $(x, y) \rightarrow (y, -x)$

46. 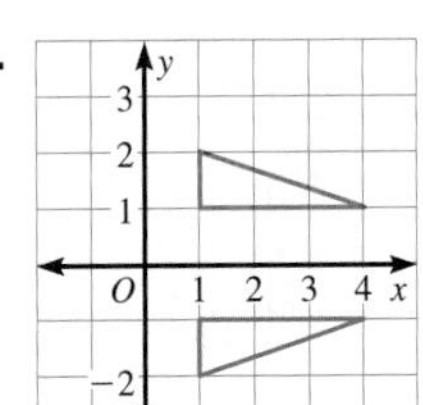
reflection; $(x, y) \rightarrow (x, -y)$

47. 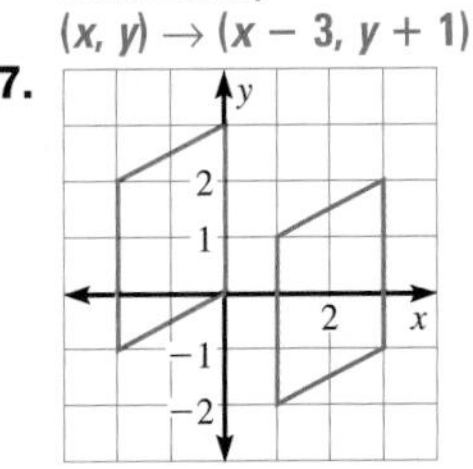
translation; $(x, y) \rightarrow (x - 3, y + 1)$

48. You draw a regular hexagon with side lengths of 2 centimeters on an overhead projector transparency. When it is projected, the hexagon is enlarged by a scale factor of 15. Find the perimeter of the image. *(Lesson 8.8)* **180 cm**

Test-Taking Practice 

INTERNET
State Test Practice
CLASSZONE.COM

49. **Multiple Choice** Which statement is *not* true? **D**

A. $\sqrt{12} < 4$ **B.** $8 > \sqrt{16}$ **C.** $\sqrt{169} = 13$ **D.** $\sqrt{30} < 5$

50. **Multiple Choice** Which of the following shows the numbers in order from least to greatest? **H**

F. $\sqrt{2}, \sqrt{5}, 1, 2, 3$ **G.** $1, \sqrt{2}, \sqrt{5}, 2, 3$

H. $1, \sqrt{2}, 2, \sqrt{5}, 3$ **I.** $1, \sqrt{2}, 2, 3, \sqrt{5}$

4 ASSESS

ASSESSMENT RESOURCES

For more assessment resources, see:
- Assessment Book
- Test and Practice Generator

MINI-QUIZ

Tell whether the number is *rational* or *irrational*. Explain your reasoning.

1. $\sqrt{10{,}000}$ **Rational; 10,000 is a perfect square, since $100^2 = 10{,}000$.**
2. $\sqrt{22}$ **Irrational; $\sqrt{22} = 4.6904...$ neither terminates nor repeats.**
3. Graph the pair of numbers on a number line. Then copy and complete the statement with <, >, or =. $\sqrt{12}$ _?_ 4 **<**

$\sqrt{12} \approx 3.4641$ 4
3.2 3.3 3.4 3.5 3.6 3.7 3.8 3.9 4

5 FOLLOW-UP

RETEACHING/REMEDIATION

- Study Guide in Chapter 9 Resource Book, pp. 19–20
- Tutor Place, Fractions Card 6
- eTutorial Plus Online
- Extra Practice, p. 735
- Lesson Practice in Chapter 9 Resource Book, pp. 16–18

CHALLENGE/ENRICHMENT

- Challenge Practice in Chapter 9 Resource Book, p. 21
- Teacher's Edition, p. 428F

ENGLISH LEARNER SUPPORT

- Spanish Study Guide
- Multi-Language Glossary
- Chapter Audio Summaries CDs

35. See Additional Answers beginning on page AA1.

EXPLORE THE CONCEPT

- Students will use graph paper to relate the side lengths of a right triangle.
- This activity leads into the study of the Pythagorean theorem in Lesson 9-3.

MATERIALS

Each student will need graph paper and a pen or pencil.

RECOMMENDED TIME

Work activity: 10 min
Discuss results: 5 min

GROUPING

Students should work individually.

TRANSPARENCY

A support transparency is available for this Activity.

TIPS FOR SUCCESS

Make sure in Step 2 that students understand that they are to match grid squares to the hypotenuse, not measure with a ruler, to find the area of the square on the hypotenuse.

KEY DISCOVERY

In a right triangle, the sum of the squares of the lengths of the legs equals the square of the length of the hypotenuse.

ASSESSMENT

1. How can you identify the hypotenuse of a right triangle? **It is opposite the right angle.**

9.3 Hands-on Activity

GOAL
Use graph paper to relate the side lengths of a right triangle.

MATERIALS
- graph paper
- pen or pencil

Modeling the Pythagorean Theorem

You can use graph paper to find the length of a right triangle's *hypotenuse*, which is the side opposite the right angle.

Explore **Find the length of the hypotenuse of a right triangle with side lengths of three units and four units.**

1 Draw the right triangle on graph paper. The sides of the triangle that form the right angle are called *legs*. For each leg, draw a square that has a leg as one side. What is the sum of the areas of these two squares? **25**

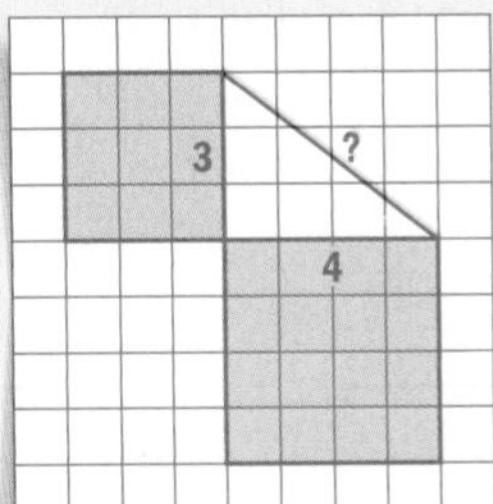

2 Measure the hypotenuse using graph paper. If you draw a square with the hypotenuse as one side, what is its area? **25**

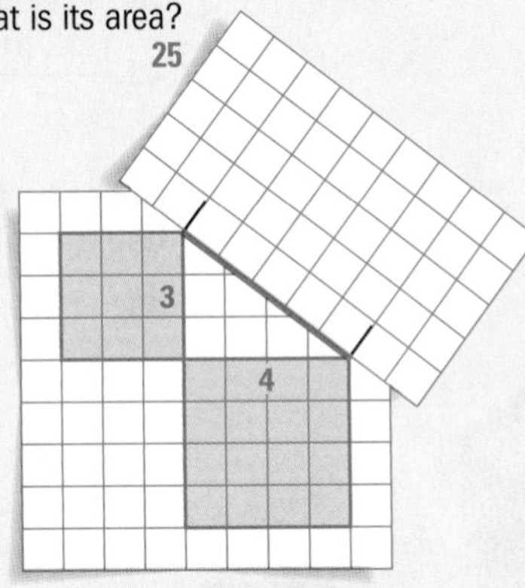

3 Compare the sum of the areas you found in Step 1 to the area you found in Step 2. What do you notice? **They are the same.**

Your turn now **Repeat Steps 1–3 for right triangles with legs of the given lengths.**

1. 5, 12 **169; 169; they are the same.** **2.** 6, 8 **100; 100; they are the same.** **3.** 8, 15 **289; 289; they are the same.**

Stop and Think

4. Let the lengths of the legs of a right triangle be a and b, and the length of the hypotenuse be c. Write a conjecture about the relationship between the lengths of the legs and the length of the hypotenuse. $a^2 + b^2 = c^2$

ILLINOIS Standards and ISAT:
7.C.3b, 9.D.3

The Pythagorean Theorem

BEFORE	Now	WHY?
You used formulas to solve problems.	You'll use the Pythagorean theorem to solve problems.	So you can find the length of a volleyball net support, as in Ex. 21.

Word Watch

leg, p. 443
hypotenuse, p. 443
Pythagorean theorem, p. 443
converse, p. 444

In a right triangle, the sides that form the right angle are called **legs**. The side opposite the right angle is the **hypotenuse**. The lengths of the legs and the hypotenuse are related by the **Pythagorean theorem**.

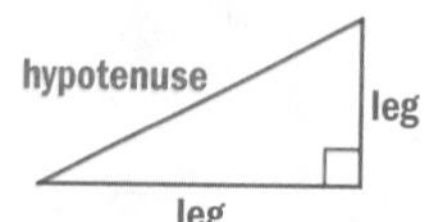

Pythagorean Theorem

Words For any right triangle, the sum of the squares of the lengths of the legs equals the square of the length of the hypotenuse.

$a = 3$, $b = 4$, $c = 5$

Algebra $a^2 + b^2 = c^2$

Numbers $3^2 + 4^2 = 5^2$

EXAMPLE 1 Finding the Length of a Hypotenuse

Find the length of the hypotenuse of a right triangle with leg lengths of 15 inches and 20 inches.

$a^2 + b^2 = c^2$	Pythagorean theorem
$15^2 + 20^2 = c^2$	Substitute 15 for a and 20 for b.
$225 + 400 = c^2$	Evaluate powers.
$625 = c^2$	Add.
$\sqrt{625} = c$	Take positive square root of each side.
$25 = c$	Evaluate square root.

ANSWER The length of the hypotenuse is 25 inches.

HELP with Notetaking

Be sure to write the Pythagorean theorem in your notebook.

Your turn now Complete the exercise.

1. Find the length of the hypotenuse of a right triangle with leg lengths of 28 inches and 45 inches. 53 in.

ILLINOIS Standards and ISAT:
7.C.3b, 9.D.3

1 PLAN

SKILL CHECK

Solve the equation.

1. $256 + 900 = x^2$ ± 34
2. $d^2 + 25 = 169$ ± 12
3. $54 + k^2 = 58$ ± 2

LESSON OBJECTIVE

Use the Pythagorean theorem to solve problems.

PACING

Suggested Number of Days
Basic Course: 1 day
Average Course: 1 day
Advanced Course: 1 day
Block: 0.5 block with 9.4

TEACHING RESOURCES

For a complete list of Teaching Resources, see page 428B.

TRANSPARENCY

Warm-Up Exercises for this lesson are available on a transparency.

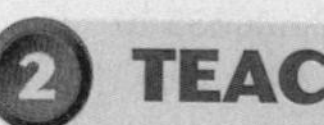

2 TEACH

MOTIVATING THE LESSON

Ask students how to check that a corner of the classroom is square using only a measuring tape to measure lengths of 3 feet, 4 feet, and 5 feet.

TIPS FOR NEW TEACHERS

Students should work with right triangles in many orientations so that they do not just think of the hypotenuse as the "slanted" side. See Tips for New Teachers in the *Chapter 9 Resource Book*.

EXTRA EXAMPLES

Example 1 Find the length of the hypotenuse of a right triangle with leg lengths of 28 centimeters and 45 centimeters. **53 cm**

Example 2 A community garden forms a square 160 feet on each side. Two diagonal paths cross the garden between opposite corners. What is the length of each path to the nearest foot? **226 ft**

TEACHING TIP

After working Example 1, have students draw a triangle that is clearly not a right triangle, and then use a ruler to show that the sum of the squares of the two shorter sides is not equal to the square of the longest side. Have them draw various triangles whose two shorter sides have these same lengths to show that the Pythagorean relationship holds only when the angle between the shorter sides is a right angle.

Differentiating Instruction

Advanced Students Invite students with Internet access to research web sites that give different methods for proving the Pythagorean theorem. Point out that U.S. president James A. Garfield even produced a proof of the theorem. Have these students present one or more of the simpler proof methods to the class.

In application problems, you usually need to take only the positive square root. For example, length, speed, and height are positive, so a negative square root would not give a reasonable answer.

EXAMPLE 2 Finding the Length of a Leg

Parasailing You are parasailing. After getting airborne and reaching cruising speed, you are 200 feet directly behind the boat. How high are you above the water to the nearest foot?

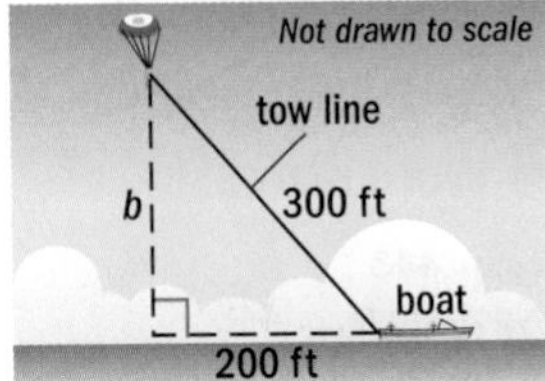

Solution

$a^2 + b^2 = c^2$	**Pythagorean theorem**
$200^2 + b^2 = 300^2$	**Substitute 200 for *a* and 300 for *c*.**
$40{,}000 + b^2 = 90{,}000$	**Evaluate powers.**
$b^2 = 50{,}000$	**Subtract 40,000 from each side.**
$b = \sqrt{50{,}000}$	**Take positive square root of each side.**
$b \approx 223.6068$	**Approximate square root.**

ANSWER You are about 224 feet above the water.

HELP with Solving

If you know the lengths of *any* two sides of a right triangle, you can use the Pythagorean theorem to find the length of the third side.

Your turn now **Find the unknown length. Round to the nearest tenth, if necessary.**

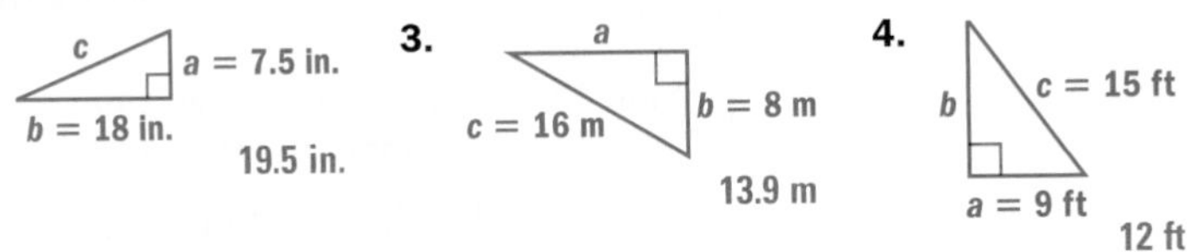

5. **Critical Thinking** Does it matter which leg of a right triangle is labeled a or b? Explain.

5. No. *Sample answer:* In the Pythagorean theorem, the leg lengths are both squared and then the sum of the squares is found. Since addition is commutative, the same sum results regardless of which leg length is chosen as a and which is chosen as b.

Converse of the Pythagorean Theorem The Pythagorean theorem can be written as an if-then statement with two parts.

Theorem If **a triangle is a right triangle**, then $a^2 + b^2 = c^2$.

When you reverse the parts of an if-then statement, the new statement is called the **converse** of the statement.

Converse If $a^2 + b^2 = c^2$, then **the triangle is a right triangle**.

The converse of a statement may or may not be true. The converse of the Pythagorean theorem is true. You can use the converse of the Pythagorean theorem to decide whether a triangle is a right triangle.

EXAMPLE 3 Identifying Right Triangles

Use the converse of the Pythagorean theorem to determine whether the triangle with the given side lengths is a right triangle.

a. $a = 6, b = 8, c = 10$

$a^2 + b^2 \stackrel{?}{=} c^2$

$6^2 + 8^2 \stackrel{?}{=} 10^2$

$36 + 64 \stackrel{?}{=} 100$

$100 = 100$ ✓

ANSWER A right triangle

b. $a = 10, b = 12, c = 16$

$a^2 + b^2 \stackrel{?}{=} c^2$

$10^2 + 12^2 \stackrel{?}{=} 16^2$

$100 + 144 \stackrel{?}{=} 256$

$244 \neq 256$ ✗

ANSWER Not a right triangle

9.3 Exercises

More Practice, p. 735

Getting Ready to Practice

1. **Vocabulary** Copy and complete: In a right triangle, the side opposite the right angle is called the _?_. hypotenuse

Let *a* and *b* represent the lengths of the legs of a right triangle, and let *c* represent the length of the hypotenuse. Find the unknown length.

2. $a = 12, b = ?, c = 20$ 16
3. $a = ?, b = 36, c = 39$ 15
4. $a = 9, b = ?, c = 41$ 40
5. $a = 7, b = 24, c = ?$ 25

Use the converse of the Pythagorean theorem to determine whether the triangle with the given side lengths is a right triangle.

6. $a = 3, b = 7, c = 9$ no
7. $a = 24, b = 45, c = 51$ yes
8. $a = 20, b = 48, c = 52$ yes
9. $a = 16, b = 18, c = 24$ no
10. **Ladders** A 13 foot ladder is leaning against a building. The bottom of the ladder is 5 feet from the building. How high is the top of the ladder? 12 ft

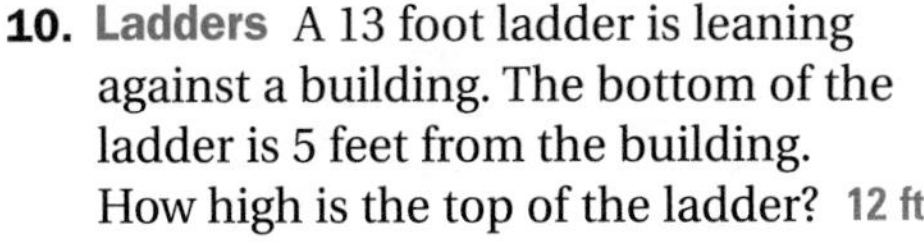

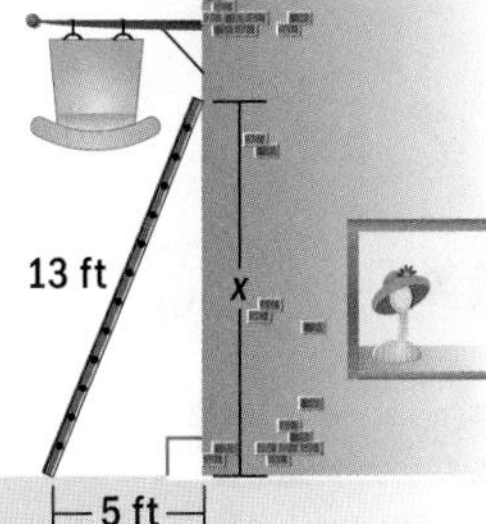

EXTRA EXAMPLES

Example 3 Use the converse of the Pythagorean theorem to determine whether the triangle with the given side lengths is a right triangle.

a. $a = 22, b = 120, c = 122$ yes

b. $a = 21, b = 70, c = 75$ no

CONCEPT CHECK

How can you tell by knowing the side lengths of a triangle whether it is a right triangle? **If the sum of the squares of the lengths of the two shorter sides equals the square of the length of the longest side, the triangle is a right triangle.**

DAILY PUZZLER

Paulo sees an Internet advertisement for a ranch that is in the shape of a triangle with side lengths of 2.5 miles, 4 miles, and 7.5 miles that is for sale for $1 per square mile. Paulo concludes the ad is a hoax. How does he know? **No triangle can be formed with the given side lengths because 7.5 miles is longer than the sum of the other two sides.**

APPLY

ASSIGNMENT GUIDE

Basic Course

Day 1: pp. 446–447 Exs. 11-19, 21-24, 26-30, 38-40

Average Course

Day 1: pp. 446–447 Exs. 14-21, 24-34, 38-41

Advanced Course

Day 1: pp. 446–447 Exs. 14-16, 19-21, 24-39*, 41

Block

pp. 446–447 Exs. 14-21, 24-34, 38-41 (with 9.4)

EXTRA PRACTICE

- Student Edition, p. 735
- Chapter 9 Resource Book, pp. 24-26
- Test and Practice Generator

TRANSPARENCY

Even-numbered answers are available on transparencies.

HOMEWORK CHECK

When you review students' homework for this lesson, go over the following exercises to check understanding of key concepts.

Basic: 11, 12, 14, 16, 17

Average: 14, 15, 16, 17, 21

Advanced: 14, 15, 16, 19, 21

COMMON ERROR

In Exercises 11-16, watch for students who hurriedly assume that the missing side of the triangle is always the hypotenuse. Make sure they take the time to examine each exercise to see whether the missing side is the hypotenuse or a leg.

HELP with Homework

Example	Exercises
1	11-16
2	11-16, 21
3	17-19

Online Resources CLASSZONE.COM

- More Examples
- eTutorial Plus

20. The 8 foot dimension is the hypotenuse, not a leg, so it should be substituted for c in the formula, not for b. This gives $6^2 + b^2 = 8^2$, $36 + b^2 = 64$, $b^2 = 28$, $b \approx 5.3$.

Practice and Problem Solving

A Find the unknown length. Round to the nearest tenth, if necessary.

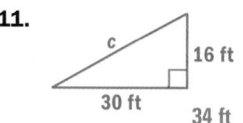

11. c; 16 ft; 30 ft — 34 ft

12. 40 m; 104 m; a — 96 m

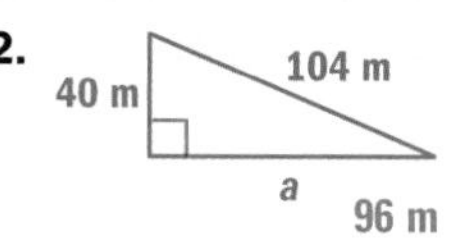

13. 46 ft; b; 50 ft — 19.6 ft

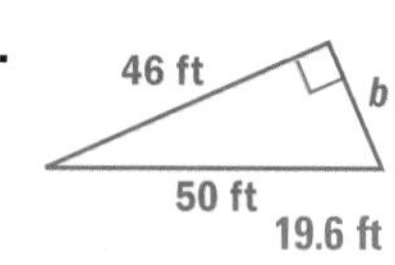

14. 90 cm; 150 cm; b — 120 cm

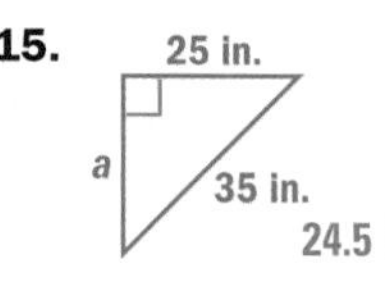

15. 25 in.; a; 35 in. — 24.5 in.

16. 24 in.; 18 in.; c — 30 in.

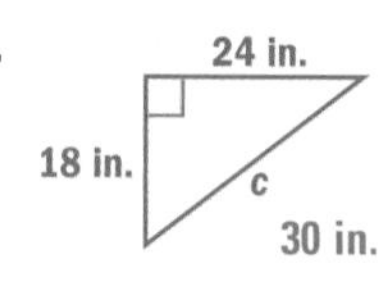

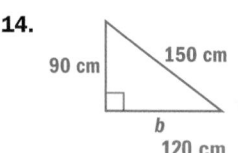

Determine whether the triangle with the given side lengths is a right triangle.

17. 44 m; 68 m; 52 m — no

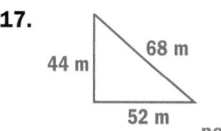

18. 50 in.; 64 in.; 80 in. — no

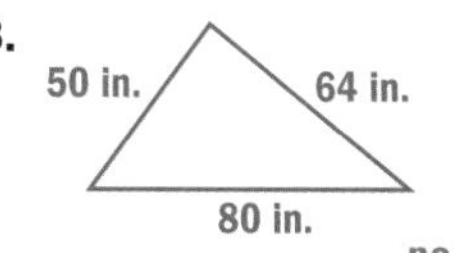

19. 221 ft; 204 ft; 85 ft — yes

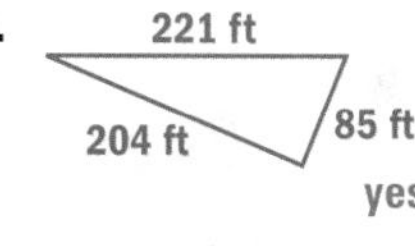

20. Find the Error Describe and correct the error in finding the length of the third side of the right triangle. Round to the nearest tenth of a foot.

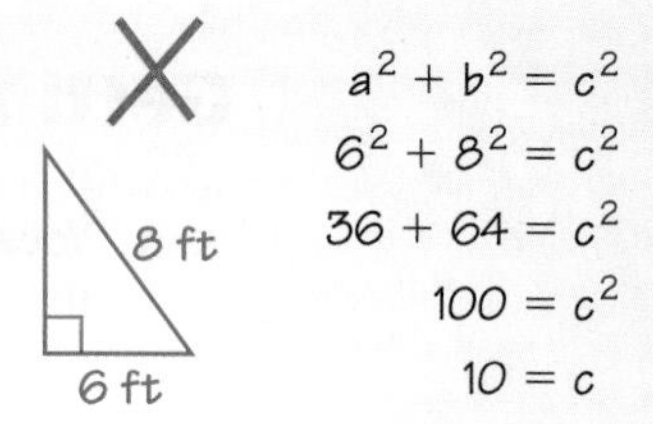

21. Volleyball Net You are setting up a volleyball net. There are two 8 foot poles that hold up the net. You are going to attach each pole to a stake in the ground using a piece of rope. Each stake should be 4 feet from the pole. Assume that the ropes are taut. How long should each rope be? Round to the nearest tenth of a foot. 8.9 ft

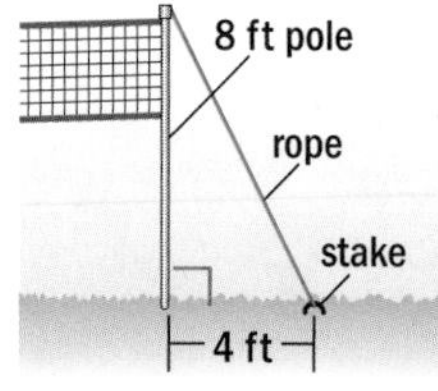

B Find the unknown length. Round to the nearest hundredth, if necessary.

22. a; 44.5 cm; 34.2 cm — 28.47 cm

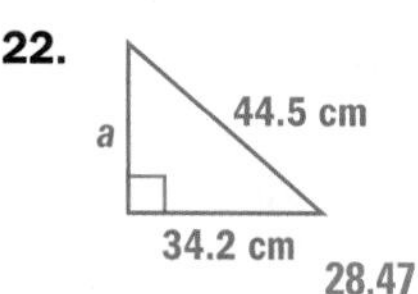

23. b; 10.2 m; 4.8 m — 9 m

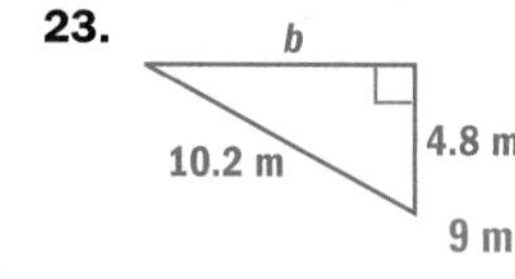

24. c; 1.6 ft; 1.6 ft — 2.26 ft

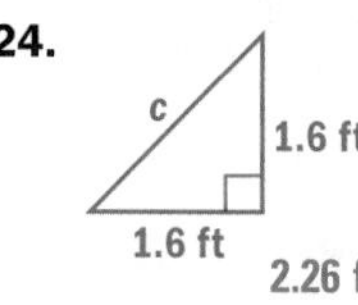

25. Critical Thinking An isosceles right triangle has a hypotenuse with a length of 6 feet. Find the length of each leg. Round to the nearest hundredth of a foot. 4.24 ft

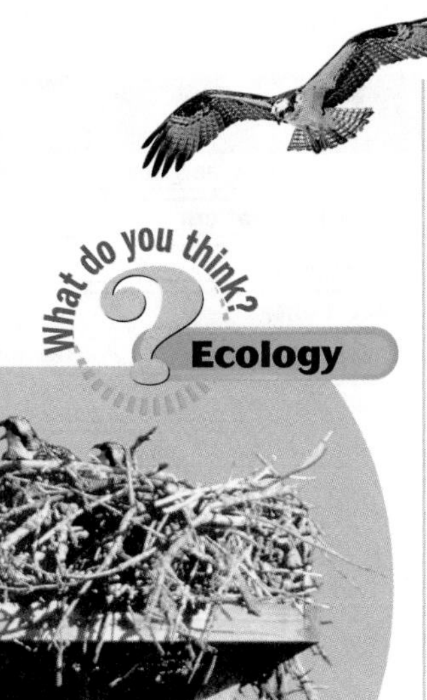

- **Utility Poles**

Several states have built nesting platforms on the tops of utility poles to provide safe nesting areas for birds. If a platform is 6 feet wide and the supports meet the pole 6 feet beneath the platform, how long are the supports? about 6.7 ft

Determine whether the triangle with the given side lengths is a right triangle.

26. $a = 0.65, b = 1.56, c = 1.69$ yes

27. $a = 2.88, b = 0.84, c = 3.2$ no

28. $a = 0.12, b = 0.16, c = 0.2$ yes

29. $a = 0.75, b = 0.4, c = 0.85$ yes

30. Utility Poles A guy wire with a length of 23.8 meters is attached to a utility pole. The wire is anchored to the ground 9 meters from the base of the pole. How high above the ground is the guy wire attached to the utility pole? Round to the nearest tenth of a meter. 22.0 m

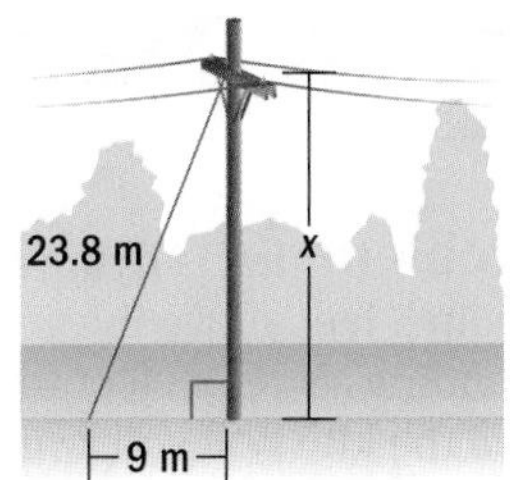

C **Let *a* and *b* represent the lengths of the legs of a right triangle, and let *c* represent the length of the hypotenuse. Find the unknown length.**

31. $a = 1.5, b = ?, c = 2.5$ 2

32. $a = ?, b = 123, c = 139.4$ 65.6

33. $a = 2.8, b = 4.5, c = ?$ 5.3

34. $a = 4.5, b = ?, c = 7.5$ 6

35. $a = \sqrt{8}, b = 1, c = ?$ 3

36. $a = ?, b = 2, c = \sqrt{13}$ 3

37. Challenge Draw several different obtuse triangles and measure the lengths of the legs. Let *a* and *b* represent the lengths of the two shorter sides and let *c* represent the length of the longest side. Make a conjecture about the relationship between the lengths of the sides of obtuse triangles.
Sample answer: The length of the longest side is always less than the sum of the lengths of the two shorter sides.

Mixed Review

38. In the figure, $ABCD \sim WXYZ$. Find $m\angle D$. *(Lesson 8.8)* 115°

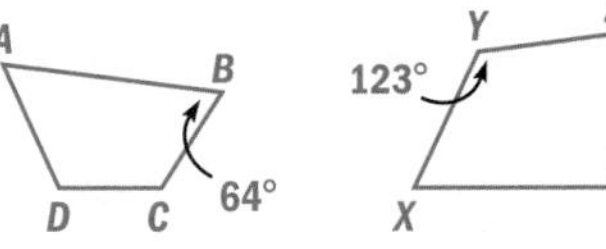

39. Triangle *LMN* has vertices $L(1, 5)$, $M(4, 2)$, and $N(0, 0)$. Dilate the triangle using a scale factor of 3. *(Lesson 8.8)* See margin.

Test-Taking Practice

40. Multiple Choice The hypotenuse of a right triangle has a length of 40 inches, and one of the legs has a length of 32 inches. What is the length of the other leg? C

A. 12 inches **B.** 21 inches **C.** 24 inches **D.** 39 inches

41. Short Response Determine whether a triangle with side lengths of 56 feet, 90 feet, and 106 feet is a right triangle. Explain.

41. Yes; $56^2 + 90^2 = 106^2$.

4 ASSESS

Assessment Resources

For more assessment resources, see:
- Assessment Book
- Test and Practice Generator

Mini-Quiz

Find the unknown length. Round to the nearest tenth, if necessary.

1. 12 cm

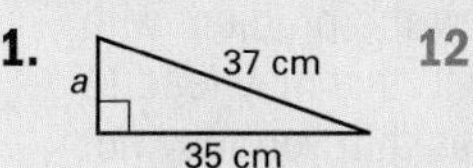

2. 73 ft

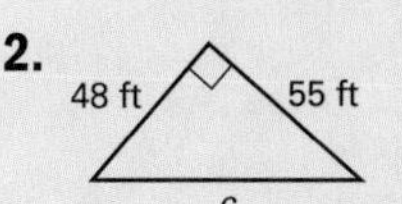

Determine whether the triangle with the given side lengths is a right triangle

3. $a = 14, b = 48, c = 50$ yes

4. $a = 32, b = 40, c = 48$ no

Reteaching/Remediation

- Study Guide in Chapter 9 Resource Book, pp. 27–28
- eTutorial Plus Online
- Extra Practice, p. 735
- Lesson Practice in Chapter 9 Resource Book, pp. 24–26

Challenge/Enrichment

- Challenge Practice in Chapter 9 Resource Book, p. 30
- Teacher's Edition, p. 428F

English Learner Support

- Spanish Study Guide
- Multi-Language Glossary
- Chapter Audio Summaries CDs

39. See Additional Answers beginning on page AA1.

1 PLAN

STRATEGY BACKGROUND

Draw a Diagram is an appropriate strategy when the words in the problem suggest a visual representation. Measurement and geometry problems are obvious applications of this strategy, but it is also useful for problems in logic, number theory, and probability. The strategy allows you to overview the problem with one glance, and this may lead to other strategies that you may not have considered.

2 TEACH

GUIDING STUDENTS' WORK

In Step 3, students will need to take careful note of the fact that the end of the kite string that Jeff is holding is 3 feet above the ground, and to indicate this on their drawing. Otherwise, they may assume that the height of the right triangle is the height of the kite above the ground.

EXTRA EXAMPLES

Example Tyrone climbed 26 feet up a tree to retrieve a ball. From there, he threw the ball 29 feet to his friend Aleesha, who was standing 21 feet from the base of the tree. How high above the ground were Aleesha's hands when she caught the ball? **6 ft**

9.4 Problem Solving Strategies

- Guess, Check, and Revise
- Look for a Pattern
- Make a List
- Act It Out
- Draw a Diagram
- Work Backward
- Solve a Simpler Problem

Draw a Diagram

Problem Jeff is flying a kite. He is holding the end of the kite string about 3 feet above the ground. The length of the string is 35 feet. He is standing about 28 feet from the base of a tree when the wind changes and the kite gets stuck in the tree. About how high off the ground is the kite when it is stuck in the tree?

1 Read and Understand

Read the problem carefully.

You know the height of Jeff's hands above the ground, the length of the kite string, and the distance to the tree. You need to find the height of the kite after it is in the tree.

2 Make a Plan

Decide on a strategy to use.

One way to solve the problem is to draw a diagram of the situation. Then you can use the Pythagorean theorem to find the height of the kite in the tree.

3 Solve the Problem

Reread the problem and draw a diagram.

Show the position of Jeff, the tree, and the kite.

Write known lengths on the diagram. The end of the kite string is about 3 feet above the ground, the string is 35 feet long, and the tree is about 28 feet from Jeff.

Next, use the Pythagorean theorem to find the missing length a.

$$a^2 + b^2 = c^2$$
$$a^2 + 28^2 = 35^2$$
$$a^2 + 784 = 1225$$
$$a^2 = 441$$
$$a = 21$$
$$21 + 3 = 24$$

Length is positive. Find positive square root.

ANSWER The kite is about 24 feet high.

4 Look Back

Be sure that you used all of the necessary information in the problem.

ILLINOIS Standards and ISAT:
9.A.3a; 9.D.3

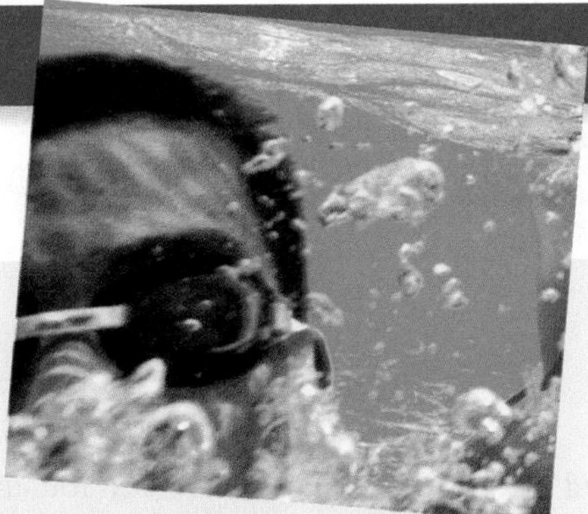

Practice the Strategy

Use the strategy *draw a diagram.*

1. **Utility Pole** A support wire 10 meters long is attached to the top of a utility pole 7 meters tall and is then stretched taut. How far from the base of the pole will the wire be attached to the ground? Round your answer to the nearest tenth of a meter. 7.1 m

2. **Hiking** Eric is hiking from his campsite to a creek. He walks 3.5 miles directly south, 4 miles directly east, then 1.5 miles directly south. Copy and complete the diagram to find how far he is from the campsite. See margin for art; about 6.4 mi.

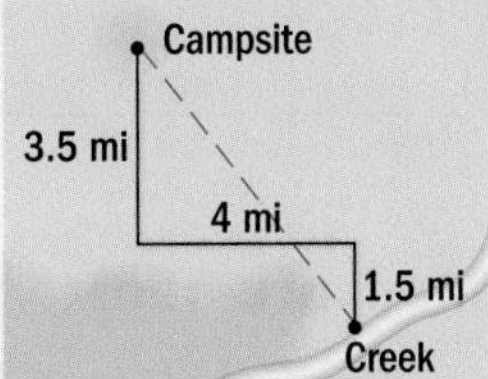

3. **Circus** A cable from the top of a circus tent pole is attached to the ground at a point 15 feet from the base of the pole. If the cable is 40 feet long, how high is the pole? Round your answer to the nearest foot. 37 ft

4. **Distance** You and your friend live on opposite corners of a square park. You usually ride your bike 1280 feet around the outside of the park to reach your friend's house. Today, you walk diagonally across the park to get to your friend's house. How much shorter is the walking distance than the biking distance? Round your answer to the nearest foot. 375 ft

5. **Moving** You are moving into a new house. The doorway is 78 inches high and 36 inches wide. Can a round table top with a diameter of 82 inches fit through the doorway? yes

Mixed Problem Solving

Use any strategy to solve the problem.

6. **Pool** To sanitize a swimming pool, you should use 2 parts per million of chlorine, which can also be written as

$$\frac{2 \text{ gallons chlorine}}{1{,}000{,}000 \text{ gallons water}}.$$

How much chlorine should there be in a pool that holds 20,000 gallons of water? 0.04 gal

7. **Advertising** A newspaper charges a base fee of $20 for a color ad plus a charge for each line. The table shows the total cost of several color ads. How much would you expect to pay for a 15 line color ad? $140

Number of lines	2	4	6	8	10
Total Cost	$36	$52	$68	$84	$100

8. **Money** Your grandmother gave you some money for your birthday. You put half of the money in the bank. Then you go to the mall and spend $12.50 on a DVD and give half of what's left to your younger brother. You now have $2.50 left. How much money did your grandmother give you? $35

9. **Banking** You have an ATM card for your savings account, but you have forgotten your four-digit personal identification number (PIN). You know the first digit is a 4 and the last three digits contain a 4, 2, and 7. How many possibilities are there for your PIN? 6 possibilities

3 APPLY

TRANSPARENCY

Even-numbered answers are available on transparencies.

TEACHING TIP

In Exercises 1–5, students will be drawing diagrams. Once they have drawn a diagram for a problem, encourage them to go back and re-read the problem carefully to make sure that their diagrams accurately represent the problem.

MATH REASONING

In Exercise 4, the key to the problem for students is recognizing that the distance 1280 feet is the sum of the lengths of two sides of a square. Because the sides must be equal, each is 1280 ÷ 2 = 640 feet long. Students must also recognize that the distance asked for is not the distance diagonally across the park, but the difference between that distance and the original riding distance.

SUGGESTED STRATEGIES

You may wish to suggest the following strategies for the problems in the Mixed Problem Solving:

- Exercise 6: Solve a Simpler Problem; Guess, Check, and Revise
- Exercise 7: Look for a Pattern
- Exercise 8: Work Backward
- Exercise 9: Make a List; Draw a Diagram

2. 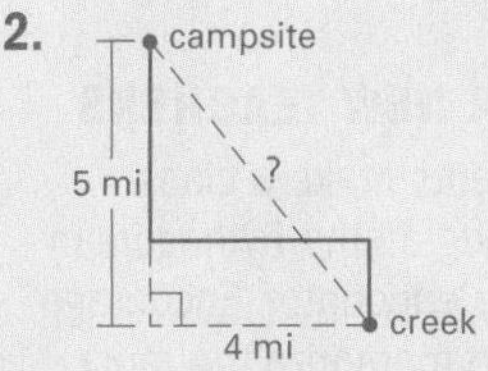

SKILL CHECK

Find the length of the hypotenuse of the right triangle with the given leg lengths.

1. 30 in., 40 in. **50 in.**
2. 18 m, 80 m **82 m**

LESSON OBJECTIVE

Solve real-life problems using the Pythagorean theorem.

PACING

Suggested Number of Days
Basic Course: 1 day
Average Course: 1 day
Advanced Course: 1 day
Block: 0.5 block with 9.3

TEACHING RESOURCES

For a complete list of Teaching Resources, see page 428B.

TRANSPARENCY

Warm-Up Exercises for this lesson are available on a transparency.

MOTIVATING THE LESSON

Ask students to think of distances they cannot measure directly that represent the hypotenuse of a right triangle whose legs can be measured.

TIPS FOR NEW TEACHERS

Have students make a class poster listing all the Pythagorean triples they encounter. Encourage students to memorize the most common triples. See Tips for New Teachers in the *Chapter 9 Resource Book*.

Using the Pythagorean Theorem

BEFORE	Now	WHY?
You found the side lengths of right triangles.	You'll solve real-life problems using the Pythagorean theorem.	So you can find the diagonal length of a swimming pool, as in Ex. 5.

Word Watch

Pythagorean triple, p. 451

In the Real World

Boating You and your friend live on opposite sides of a lake. To ride your bicycle to your friend's house, you travel 0.5 mile directly east, then 1.2 miles directly south. How far is it to your friend's house by boat?

One way to find the distance from your house to your friend's house by boat is to measure the distance *indirectly*. Because the bicycle and boat paths form a right triangle, you can do this using the Pythagorean theorem.

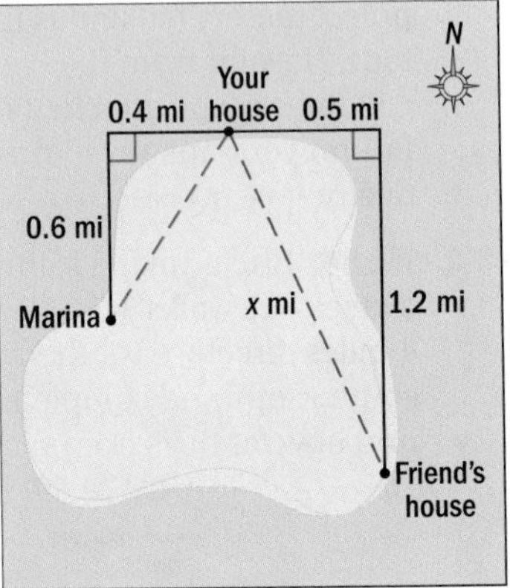

EXAMPLE 1 Using Indirect Measurement

Let a and b represent the lengths of the legs (bicycle paths) of the right triangle. Let x represent the length of the hypotenuse (boat path).

$a^2 + b^2 = x^2$	Pythagorean theorem
$0.5^2 + 1.2^2 = x^2$	Substitute 0.5 for a and 1.2 for b.
$0.25 + 1.44 = x^2$	Evaluate powers.
$1.69 = x^2$	Add.
$1.3 = x$	Take positive square root of each side.

ANSWER It is 1.3 miles to your friend's house by boat.

Your turn now **Use the information in the map.**

1. To get to the marina from your house, you travel 0.4 mile directly west, then 0.6 mile directly south. How far is it to the marina by boat? Round your answer to the nearest hundredth of a mile. **0.72 mi**

ILLINOIS Standards and ISAT:
7.C.3b, 9.D.3

EXAMPLE 2 Finding Perimeter and Area

Find the perimeter and area of the triangle.

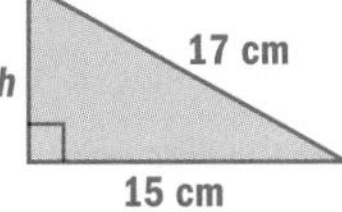

Solution

(1) Find the height of the triangle.

$h^2 + 15^2 = 17^2$	Pythagorean theorem
$h^2 + 225 = 289$	Evaluate powers.
$h^2 = 64$	Subtract 225 from each side.
$h = 8$	Take positive square root of each side.

(2) Use the height to find the perimeter and area.

Perimeter $= 8 + 15 + 17 = 40$

Area $= \frac{1}{2}bh$

$= \frac{1}{2}(15)(8)$

$= 60$

ANSWER The perimeter is 40 cm and the area is 60 cm^2.

with Review

For help with finding the perimeter and area of a triangle, see p. 134.

Your turn now **Complete the exercise.**

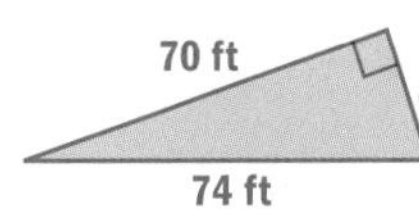

2. Find the perimeter and area of the triangle. 168 ft; 840 ft^2

Pythagorean Triples A **Pythagorean triple** is a set of three positive integers *a*, *b*, and *c* such that $a^2 + b^2 = c^2$. For example, the integers 3, 4, and 5 form a Pythagorean triple because $3^2 + 4^2 = 5^2$.

EXAMPLE 3 Identifying a Pythagorean Triple

Determine whether the side lengths of the triangle form a Pythagorean triple.

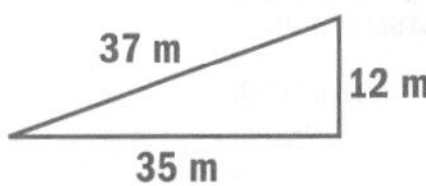

Solution

$a^2 + b^2 = c^2$	Definition of Pythagorean triple
$12^2 + 35^2 \stackrel{?}{=} 37^2$	Substitute 12 for *a*, 35 for *b*, and 37 for *c*.
$144 + 1225 \stackrel{?}{=} 1369$	Evaluate powers.
$1369 = 1369$	Add.

ANSWER Because $12^2 + 35^2 = 37^2$, the side lengths form a Pythagorean triple.

EXTRA EXAMPLES

Example 1 Jaime and Tara jog together in a park. Jaime is tired, and walks directly from *A* to *C*. Tara jogs from *A* to *B* and then to *C*. About how much farther does Tara go from *A* to *C* than Jaime? **about 382 m**

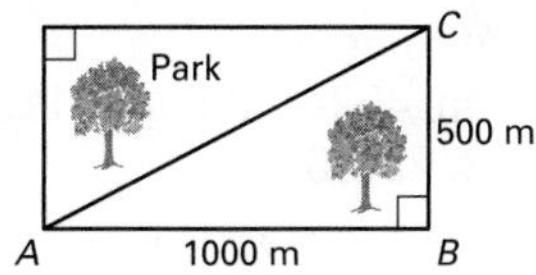

Example 2 Find the perimeter and area of the triangle.

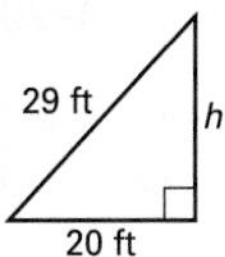

70 ft, 210 ft^2

Example 3 Determine whether the side lengths of a triangle with side lengths 96, 110, and 146 millimeters form a Pythagorean triple. **yes**

CONCEPT CHECK

In your own words, what is a Pythagorean triple? ***Sample answer:*** **A group of three positive integers such that the sum of the squares of two of the integers equals the square of the third**

DAILY PUZZLER

Rosita tiled her 9 foot by 11 foot patio with square tiles one foot on a side. To keep people off the patio while the glue was setting, she ran narrow strips of yellow tape across the patio between pairs of opposite corners. How many tiles had tape passing over them? **35 tiles**

ASSIGNMENT GUIDE

Basic Course

Day 1: EP p. 729 Exs. 20-22; pp. 452-453 Exs. 6-15, 17-20, 25-30

Average Course

Day 1: pp. 452-453 Exs. 8-11, 14-23, 25-30

Advanced Course

Day 1: pp. 452-453 Exs. 8-11, 14-25*, 28-30

Block

pp. 452-453 Exs. 8-11, 14-23, 25-30 (with 9.3)

EXTRA PRACTICE

- Student Edition, p. 735
- Chapter 9 Resource Book, pp. 35-37
- Test and Practice Generator

TRANSPARENCY

Even-numbered answers are available on transparencies.

HOMEWORK CHECK

When you review students' homework for this lesson, go over the following exercises to check understanding of key concepts.

Basic: 6, 8, 10, 12, 17
Average: 9, 10, 14, 15, 18
Advanced: 9, 11, 14, 15, 19

TEACHING TIP

In Exercise 16, students should realize that there is also a geometric justification. Multiplying each member of a Pythagorean triple by the same number represents multiplying each side length of a right triangle by the same number, so the resulting triangle is similar to the original triangle.

5. Steps 1-2. See Additional Answers beginning on page AA1.

9.4 Exercises

More Practice, p. 735

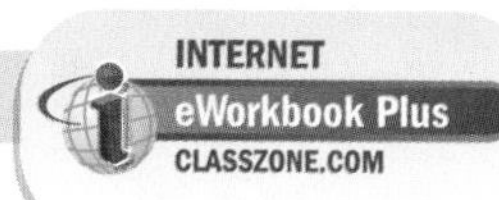

Getting Ready to Practice

1. **Vocabulary** Copy and complete: The integers 5, 12, and 13 form a _?_ because $5^2 + 12^2 = 13^2$. Pythagorean triple

Find the perimeter of the triangle.

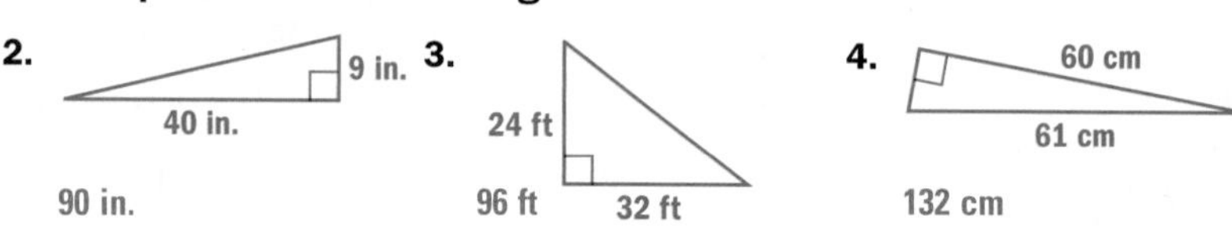

2. 90 in. 3. 96 ft 4. 132 cm

5. **Guided Problem Solving** A rectangular swimming pool has a length of 41 feet and a width of 11 feet. Tina swims the diagonal distance across the pool. About how far does she swim?
   1. Draw a diagram. Steps 1–2. See margin.
   2. Label the known distances.
   3. Use the Pythagorean theorem to find the unknown length. Round your answer to the nearest tenth of a foot. 42.4 ft

Practice and Problem Solving

with Homework

Example	Exercises
1	17-19
2	6-11
3	12-15

- More Examples
- eTutorial Plus

16. Row 2: 10, 24, 26; 14, 48, 50; Row 3: 9, 12, 15; 15, 36, 39; 21, 72, 75; Row 4: 30, 40, 50; 50, 120 130; 70, 240, 250; yes. *Sample answer:* Multiplying each number in a triple by the same number is equivalent to multiplying each side of the equation in the Pythagorean theorem by the same number.

A **Let a and b represent the lengths of the legs of a right triangle, and let c represent the length of the hypotenuse. Find the unknown length. Then find the area and perimeter.**

6. $a = 12$ cm, $b = 5$ cm, $c = ?$ 13 cm; 30 cm^2, 30 cm
7. $a = 8$ ft, $b = ?$, $c = 17$ ft 15 ft; 60 ft^2, 40 ft
8. $a = ?$, $b = 4.2$ km, $c = 5.8$ km 4 km; 8.4 km^2, 14 km
9. $a = 4.8$ in., $b = 3.6$ in., $c = ?$ 6 in.; 8.64 in.^{2}, 14.4 in.
10. $a = 60$ yd, $b = ?$, $c = 601.5$ yd 598.5 yd; 17,955 yd^2, 1260 yd
11. $a = ?$, $b = 117$ m, $c = 125$ m 44 m; 2574 m^2, 286 m

Determine whether the numbers form a Pythagorean triple.

12. 9, 36, 41 no
13. 55, 48, 73 yes
14. 39, 80, 89 yes
15. 45, 96, 104 no

16. **Critical Thinking** Copy and complete the table. Are the Pythagorean triples still Pythagorean triples after they are multiplied by another positive integer? Explain your reasoning.

Pythagorean Triples	3, 4, 5	5, 12, 13	7, 24, 25
Multiply by 2	6, 8, 10	?	?
Multiply by 3	?	?	?
Multiply by 10	?	?	?

B **Find the measure of x.**

17.

30 in.

18.

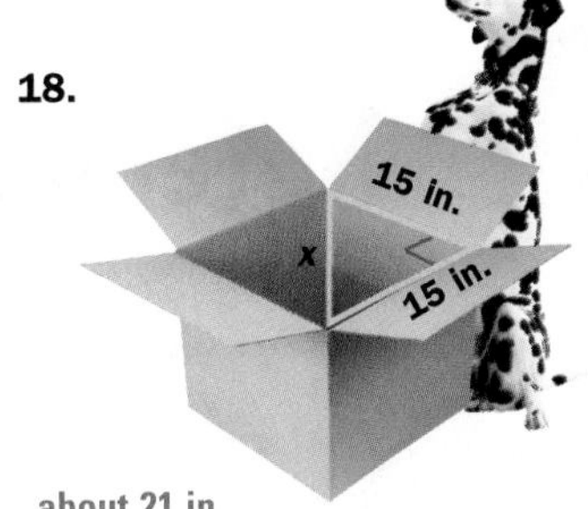

about 21 in.

19. Bookshelf You are making a bookshelf. Find x. Round to the nearest inch. 18 in.

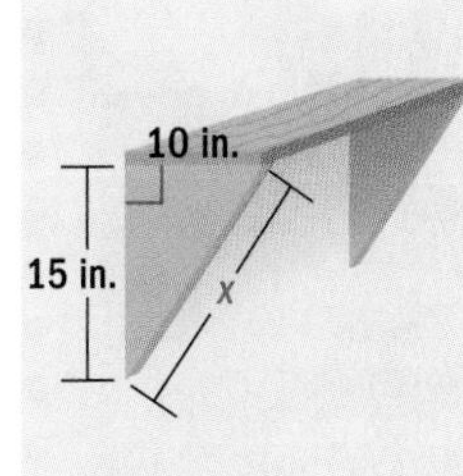

20. Draw a Diagram You are standing 500 feet from the Washington Monument. Using a laser range finder on the ground, you measure the distance to the top of the monument to be 747 feet. Find the height of the Washington Monument to the nearest foot. 555 ft

Washington Monument

Find the perimeter of the right triangle given its area and the length of one leg.

21. $a = 6$ m 24 m
Area $= 24$ m^2

22. $a = 8.8$ mi 33 mi
Area $= 46.2$ mi^2

23. $a = 84$ cm 182 cm
Area $= 546$ cm^2

C **24. Challenge** Find the area of the shaded region given $\triangle ABC \sim \triangle ADE$, $AB = 10$ ft, $AC = 6$ ft, and $DE = 16$ ft. 72 ft^2

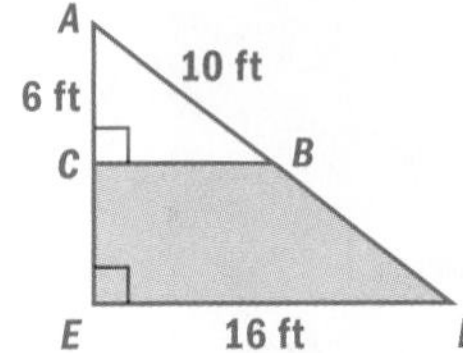

Mixed Review 

25. Reflect the polygon with the vertices $A(-3, 3)$, $B(-3, 6)$, $C(-5, 3)$, and $D(-6, 1)$ in the y-axis. Graph the figure and its image. *(Lesson 8.6)* See margin.

Find the square root. *(Lesson 9.1)*

26. $\sqrt{9}$ 3 **27.** $-\sqrt{144}$ −12 **28.** $-\sqrt{625}$ −25 **29.** $\sqrt{72.25}$ 8.5

Test-Taking Practice 

30. Extended Response Find the area and perimeter of $\triangle ABC$. Explain how you found your answers. Round your answers to the nearest tenth, if necessary. See margin.

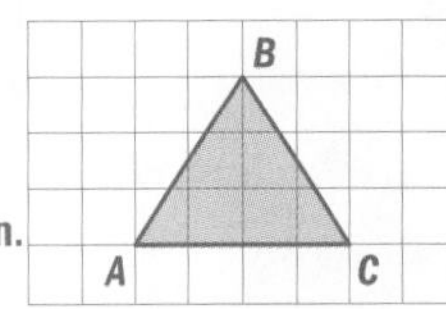

30. 6 units^2; 11.2 units. *Sample answer:* The base is 4 and the height is 3. I used the Pythagorean theorem to find that $AB = BC \approx 3.6$. I then used the area and perimeter formulas.

INTERNET
State Test Practice
CLASSZONE.COM

4 ASSESS

Assessment Resources

For more assessment resources, see:

- Assessment Book
- Test and Practice Generator

Mini-Quiz

1. Find the hypotenuse, area, and perimeter of a right triangle with legs measuring 22 inches and 120 inches. **122 in., 1320 in.^{2}, 264 in.**

Determine whether the numbers form a Pythagorean triple.

2. 21, 28, 35 yes

3. 18, 80, 90 no

4. Find the height of the tent. **45 in.**

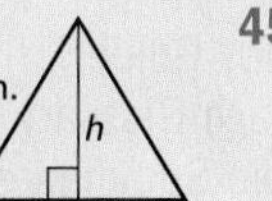

5 FOLLOW-UP

Reteaching/Remediation

- Study Guide in Chapter 9 Resource Book, pp. 38–39
- eTutorial Plus Online
- Extra Practice, p. 735
- Lesson Practice in Chapter 9 Resource Book, pp. 35–37

Challenge/Enrichment

- Challenge Practice in Chapter 9 Resource Book, p. 40
- Teacher's Edition, p. 428F

English Learner Support

- Spanish Study Guide
- Multi-Language Glossary
- Chapter Audio Summaries CDs

25. See Additional Answers beginning on page AA1.

ADDITIONAL RESOURCES

The following resources are available to help review the materials in Lessons 9.1–9.4.

Chapter 9 Resource Book
- Lesson Practice
- Study Guide

Assessment Book
- Chapter 9 Quiz 1

Technology
- Test and Practice Generator
- eTutorial CD-ROM

Internet
- Classzone
- eWorkbook Plus Online
- eTutorial Plus Online

ENGLISH LEARNER SUPPORT

- Spanish Study Guide
- Multi-Language Glossary
- Chapter Audio Summaries CDs

5. 4, $\sqrt{31} \approx 5.5678$ (number line from 4 to 6: 4, 4.4, 4.8, 5.2, 5.6, 6)

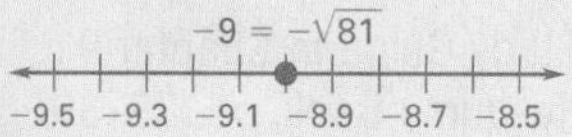

6. 7, $\sqrt{59} \approx 7.6811$ (number line from 7 to 8: 7, 7.2, 7.4, 7.6, 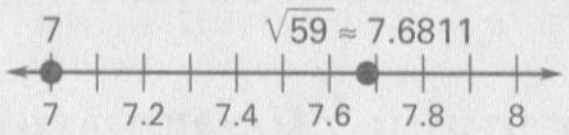 7.8, 8)

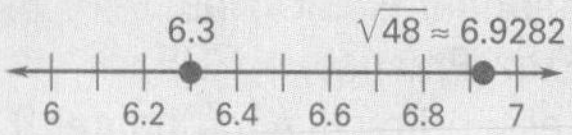

7. $-9 = -\sqrt{81}$ (number line: −9.5, −9.3, −9.1, −8.9, −8.7, −8.5)

8. 6.3, $\sqrt{48} \approx 6.9282$ (number line: 6, 6.2, 6.4, 6.6, 6.8, 7)

Notebook Review

Review the vocabulary definitions in your notebook.

Copy the review examples in your notebook. Then complete the exercises.

Check Your Definitions

square root, p. 431	real number, p. 437	converse, p. 444
radical expression, p. 431	leg, hypotenuse, p. 443	Pythagorean triple, p. 451
perfect square, p. 432	Pythagorean theorem, p. 443	
irrational number, p. 437		

Use Your Vocabulary

1. Copy and complete: Together, the rational numbers and the irrational numbers make up the set of _?_. real numbers

9.1 Can you solve equations using square roots?

EXAMPLE Solve the equation $x^2 - 18 = 4$.

$x^2 - 18 = 4$	Original equation
$x^2 = 22$	Add 18 to each side.
$x = \pm\sqrt{22}$	Definition of square root
$x \approx \pm 4.69$	Approximate square root.

Solve the equation.

2. $a^2 = 169$ ± 13 **3.** $b^2 - 20 = 101$ ± 11 **4.** $c^2 + 25 = 89$ ± 8

9.2 Can you compare two real numbers?

EXAMPLE Graph the numbers $\sqrt{7}$ and 3 on a number line. Then complete the statement $\sqrt{7}$ _?_ 3 with <, >, or =.

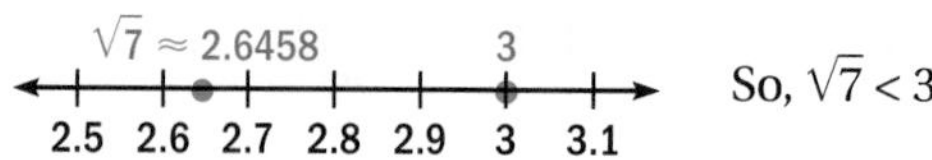

So, $\sqrt{7} < 3$.

Graph the pair of numbers on a number line. Then complete the statement with <, >, or =. 5–8. See margin for art.

5. $\sqrt{31}$ _?_ 4 > **6.** 7 _?_ $\sqrt{59}$ < **7.** −9 _?_ $-\sqrt{81}$ = **8.** $\sqrt{48}$ _?_ 6.3 >

9.3–9.4 Can you use the Pythagorean Theorem?

EXAMPLE Find the unknown length.

$a^2 + b^2 = c^2$ — **Pythagorean theorem**

$a^2 + 20^2 = 22^2$ — **Substitute 20 for *b* and 22 for *c*.**

$a^2 = 84$ — **Simplify.**

$a \approx 9.2$ in. — **Take positive square root of each side.**

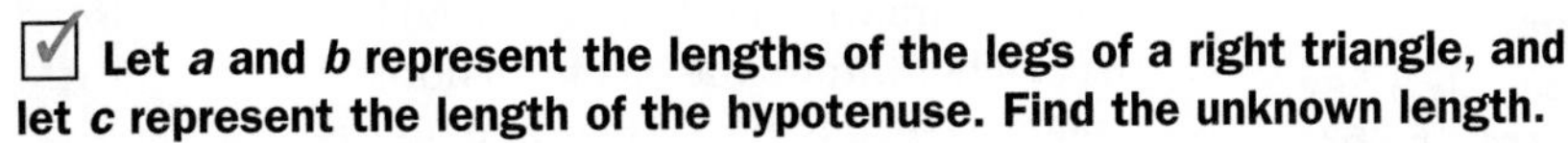

Let *a* and *b* represent the lengths of the legs of a right triangle, and let *c* represent the length of the hypotenuse. Find the unknown length.

9. $a = 8, c = 17$ 15 **10.** $b = 24, c = 40$ 32 **11.** $a = 2.4, b = 0.7$ 2.5

Stop *and* Think about Lessons 9.1–9.4

12. Writing Describe how the decimal forms of rational numbers are different from the decimal form of irrational numbers. Give examples to illustrate your answer.

Notebook Review

12. *Sample answer:* The decimal form of a rational number terminates or repeats, while the decimal form of an irrational number does neither. For example, $\frac{3}{4}$ and $\frac{1}{3}$ are rational because $\frac{3}{4} = 0.75$ (terminates) and $\frac{1}{3} = 0.\overline{3}$ (repeats), but $\pi \approx 3.1415926535\ldots$, which never terminates or repeats.

Review Quiz 1

Use a calculator to approximate the square root. Round to the nearest tenth.

1. $\sqrt{50}$ 7.1 **2.** $\sqrt{18}$ 4.2 **3.** $-\sqrt{160}$ −12.6 **4.** $\sqrt{462}$ 21.5

Solve the equation. Check your solutions.

5. $x^2 = 400$ ±20 **6.** $b^2 - 11 = -2$ ±3 **7.** $m^2 + 140 = 284$ ±12

8. Order the numbers 2.75, $\sqrt{5}$, $\frac{3}{2}$, and −1 from least to greatest. $-1, \frac{3}{2}, \sqrt{5}, 2.75$

9. Find the length of the hypotenuse of a right triangle with leg lengths of 12 meters and 16 meters. 20 m

10. Antenna How long must a wire be to connect the top of an 8 foot antenna to a hook 5 feet from the base of the antenna? Round your answer to the nearest tenth of a foot. 9.4 ft

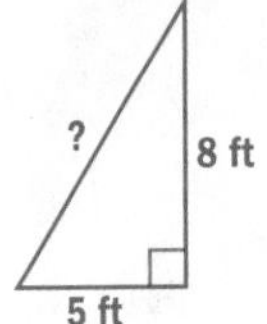

Determine whether the numbers form a Pythagorean triple.

11. 5, 12, 15 no **12.** 60, 91, 109 yes

1 PLAN

SKILL CHECK

1. A right triangle contains a 45° angle. What is the measure of the other acute angle? 45°
2. A right triangle contains a 60° angle. What is the measure of the other acute angle? 30°

LESSON OBJECTIVE

Use special right triangles to solve real-life problems.

PACING

Suggested Number of Days
Basic Course: 2 days
Average Course: 2 days
Advanced Course: 2 days
Block: 1 block

TEACHING RESOURCES

For a complete list of Teaching Resources, see page 428B.

TRANSPARENCY

Warm-Up Exercises for this lesson are available on a transparency.

2 TEACH

MOTIVATING THE LESSON

Ask students familiar with softball to describe the layout of the field.

TIPS FOR NEW TEACHERS

Have students use a triangle with leg lengths of 1 to illustrate a 45°-45°-90° triangle and a triangle with hypotenuse 2 and leg 1 to illustrate a 30°-60°-90° triangle. See Tips for New Teachers in the *Chapter 9 Resource Book*.

Special Right Triangles

BEFORE	Now	WHY?
You solved real-life problems using the Pythagorean theorem.	You'll use special right triangles to solve real-life problems.	So you can find the depth of a subway station, as in Ex. 13.

Word Watch

Review Words

equilateral triangle, p. 382
isosceles triangle, p. 382
right triangle, p. 382
scalene triangle, p. 382
leg, p. 443
hypotenuse, p. 443

In the Real World

Softball The infield of a softball field is a square with a side length of 60 feet. A catcher throws the ball from home plate to second base. How far does the catcher have to throw the ball?

To find missing side lengths of triangles whose angle measures are 45°-45°-90° or 30°-60°-90°, you can use the special relationships among the side lengths.

45°-45°-90° Triangle

Words In a 45°-45°-90° triangle, the length of the hypotenuse is the product of the length of a leg and $\sqrt{2}$.

Algebra hypotenuse = leg • $\sqrt{2}$

$= x\sqrt{2}$

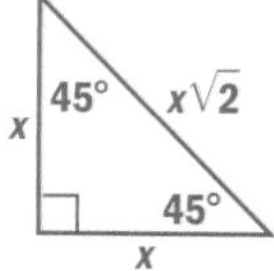

EXAMPLE 1 Using a 45°-45°-90° Triangle

To find the distance from home plate to second base, first draw a diagram. Then use the rule for a 45°-45°-90° triangle.

$$\begin{aligned} \text{hypotenuse} &= \text{leg} \cdot \sqrt{2} \\ &= 60 \cdot \sqrt{2} \\ &\approx 60(1.414) \\ &= 84.84 \end{aligned}$$

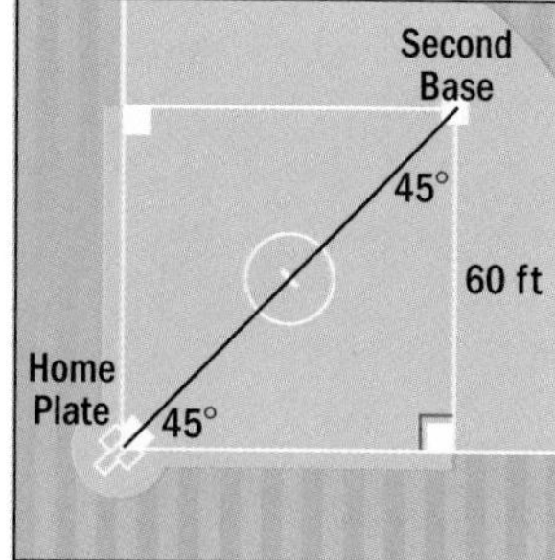

ANSWER A catcher has to throw the ball about 84.84 feet.

ILLINOIS Standards and ISAT:
9.C.3b

30°-60°-90° Triangle

Words In a 30°-60°-90° triangle, the hypotenuse is twice as long as the shorter leg. The length of the longer leg is the product of the length of the shorter leg and $\sqrt{3}$.

Algebra hypotenuse $= 2 \cdot$ shorter leg

$= 2x$

longer leg $=$ shorter leg $\cdot \sqrt{3}$

$= x\sqrt{3}$

Diagram

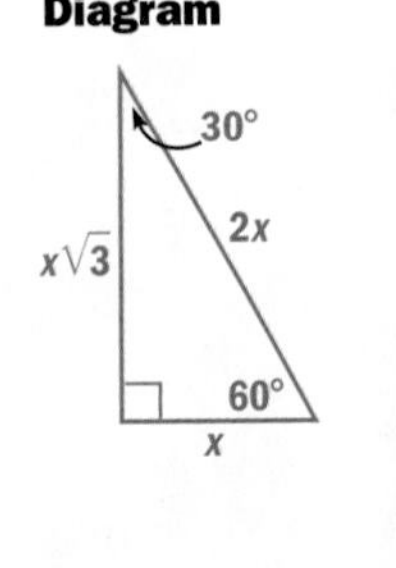

HELP with Solving

In a 30°-60°-90° triangle, the shorter leg is opposite the 30° angle, and the longer leg is opposite the 60° angle.

To give an *exact answer,* leave your answer as a radical expression.

EXAMPLE 2 Using a 30°-60°-90° Triangle

Find the value of each variable in the triangle. Give the exact answer.

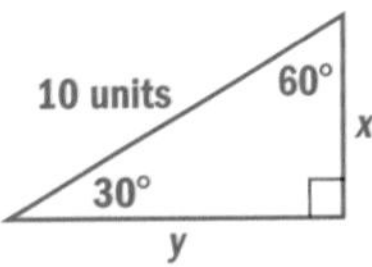

You need to find the length of the shorter leg first in order to find the length of the longer leg.

(1) Find the length of the shorter leg.

hypotenuse $= 2 \cdot$ shorter leg	**Rule for 30°-60°-90° triangle**
$10 = 2 \cdot x$	**Substitute.**
$5 = x$	**Divide each side by 2.**

(2) Find the length of the longer leg.

longer leg $=$ shorter leg $\cdot \sqrt{3}$	**Rule for 30°-60°-90° triangle**
$y = 5\sqrt{3}$	**Substitute.**

ANSWER The length of the shorter leg is 5 units. The length of the longer leg is $5\sqrt{3}$ units.

HELP with Solving

You can use the Pythagorean theorem to check the solutions in Examples 1 and 2.

Your turn now **Find the value of each variable. Give exact answers.**

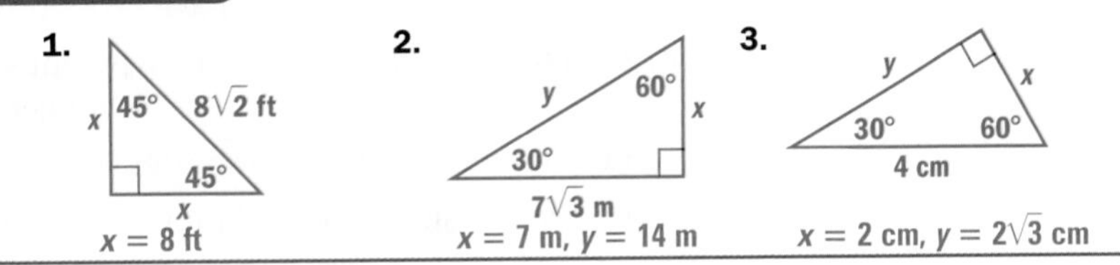

EXTRA EXAMPLES

Example 1 Find the height of the photograph to the nearest tenth of an inch. **11.3 in.**

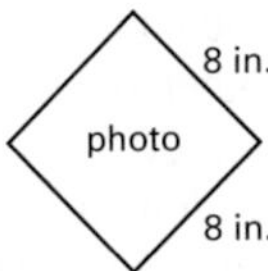

Example 2 Find the value of each variable in the triangle. Give the exact answers.

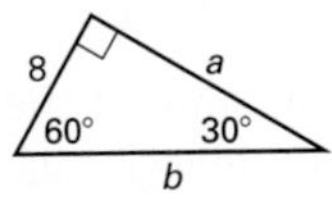

$a = 8\sqrt{3}$, $b = 16$ units

MULTIPLE REPRESENTATIONS

After discussing the 30°-60°-90° triangle in words and using algebra, encourage students to draw a 30°-60°-90° triangle on heavy paper, cut it out, measure it, and verify the side relationships. Students can write the angle and side measures on their models and add them to their notebooks.

Differentiating Instruction

Less Proficient Students Give groups of students five meter sticks and an oversize protractor. Have them arrange two meter sticks on the floor to form a 60° angle. Then have them extend one of these sides with an additional meter stick to form the hypotenuse of a 30°-60°-90° triangle. By using the remaining two meter sticks to measure the third side, students can show that it is about 1.73 times the length of the shortest side.

EXTRA EXAMPLES

Example 3 A school dance committee plans to suspend a giant paper dragon across the school hall from one corner diagonally to the other. The hall is 100 feet long and 60 feet wide. To the nearest foot, how long will the dragon need to be? **117 ft**

CONCEPT CHECK

How does the length of the shorter leg in a 30°-60°-90° triangle relate to the length of the hypotenuse? **It is one half the length of the hypotenuse.**

DAILY PUZZLER

Draw a large capital M. Show how you can draw three lines through the M to form 9 triangles.

Sample:

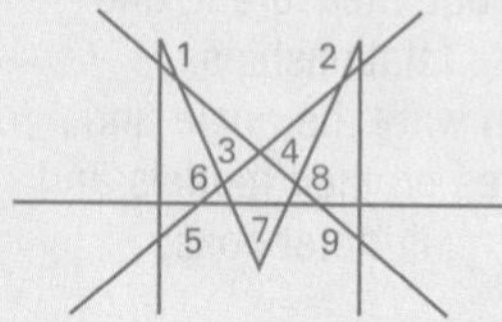

EXAMPLE 3 **Using a Special Right Triangle**

Water Ski Show The pyramid ski show is a common feature of water parks. Find the horizontal distance from the pyramid to the boat.

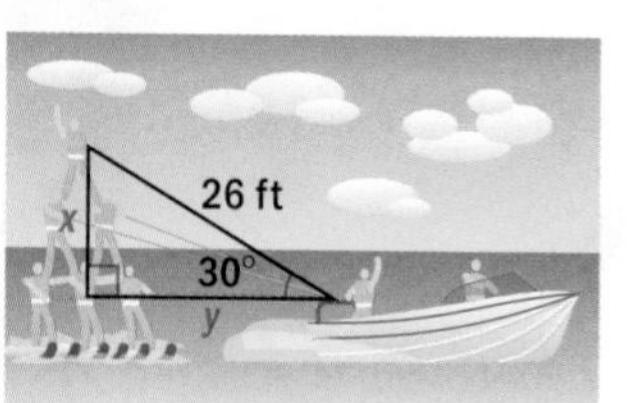

1. Find the length of the shorter leg.

   hypotenuse = 2 • **shorter leg**

   $26 = 2 \cdot x$

   $13 = x$

2. Find the length of the longer leg.

   longer leg = **shorter leg** • $\sqrt{3}$

   $y = 13 \cdot \sqrt{3}$

   ≈ 22.5166605

ANSWER The horizontal distance is about 23 feet.

9.5 Exercises

More Practice, p. 735

Getting Ready to Practice

1. **Vocabulary** Explain how the length of the hypotenuse in a 45°-45°-90° triangle is related to the length of a leg. **The length of the hypotenuse is $\sqrt{2}$ times the length of a leg.**

Find the value of the variable. Give the exact answer.

2. 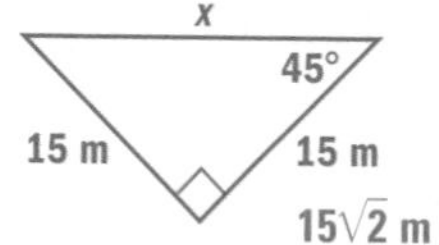

$15\sqrt{2}$ m

3. 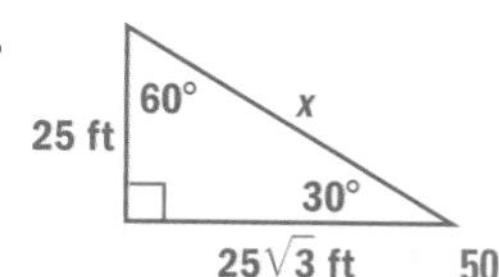

$25\sqrt{3}$ ft **50 ft**

4. **Find the Error** Describe and correct the error in the solution. **In a 45°-45°-90° triangle, the hypotenuse is $\sqrt{2}$ times the length of a leg, not $\sqrt{3}$ times the length of a leg. So, hypotenuse = leg • $\sqrt{2}$ = $8\sqrt{2}$.**

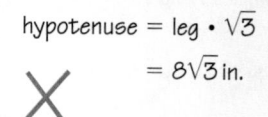

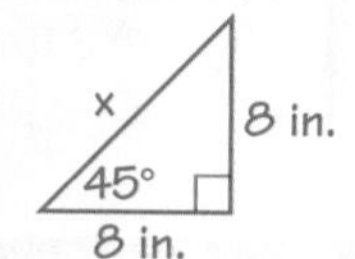

hypotenuse = leg • $\sqrt{3}$

= $8\sqrt{3}$ in.

5. **Guided Problem Solving** The hypotenuse of a 30°-60°-90° triangle is $5\sqrt{3}$ inches. Find the length of the longer leg.

   1. Find the length of the shorter leg. **$\frac{5\sqrt{3}}{2}$ in.**
   2. Use the shorter leg to find the length of the longer leg. **7.5 in.**

HELP with Homework

Example	Exercises
1	6-8
2	9-11
3	13

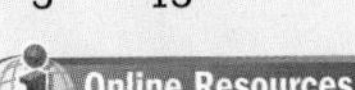

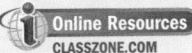

Online Resources
CLASSZONE.COM

- More Examples
- eTutorial Plus

Practice and Problem Solving

A Find the value of each variable. Give exact answers.

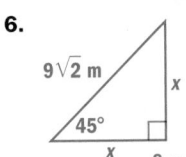

6. $9\sqrt{2}$ m, 45°, x, x 9 m

7. 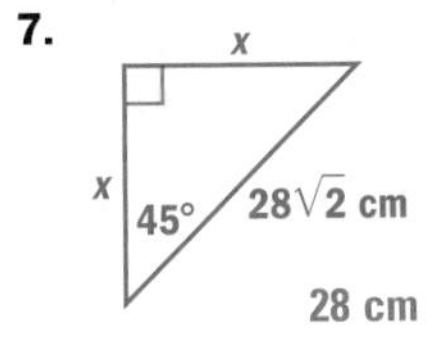

28 cm

8. 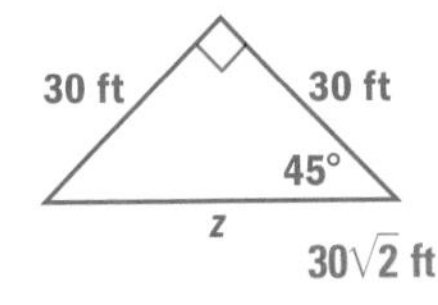

$30\sqrt{2}$ ft

9. 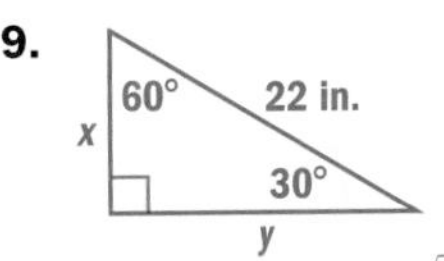

$x = 11$ in., $y = 11\sqrt{3}$ in.

10. 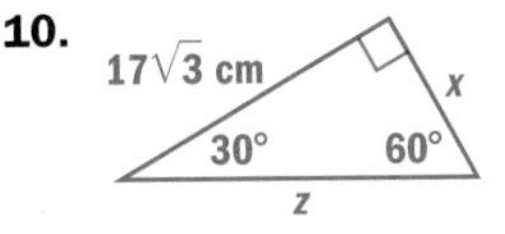

$x = 17$ cm, $z = 34$ cm

11. 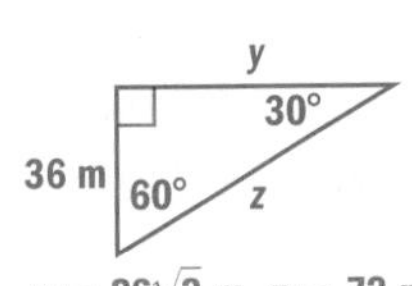

$y = 36\sqrt{3}$ m, $z = 72$ m

12. Critical Thinking Is it possible to have an equilateral right triangle? Explain your reasoning. See margin.

13. Escalator The escalator going down to the main floor of a subway station is 230 feet long and makes a 30° angle with the main floor. How many feet below ground is the subway station? 115 ft

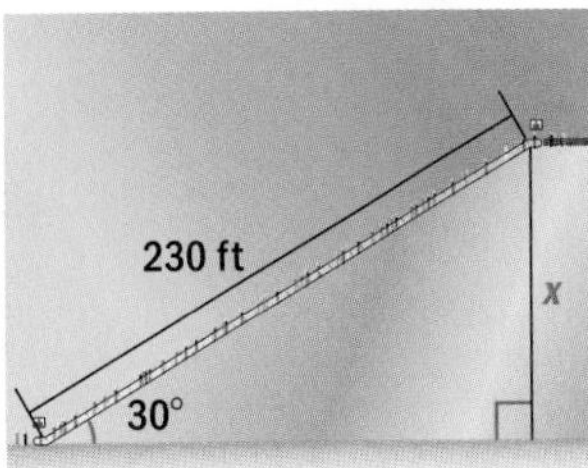

B Find the value of each variable. Give exact answers.

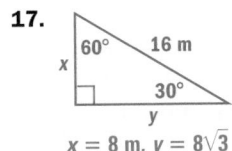

14. z, 45°, 6 cm, 6 cm
$6\sqrt{2}$ cm

15. x, $10\sqrt{2}$ in., 45°, x
10 in.

16. 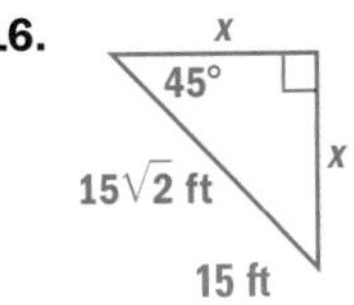

15 ft

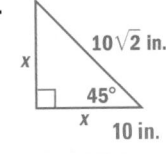

17. 60°, 16 m, x, 30°, y
$x = 8$ m, $y = 8\sqrt{3}$ m

18. 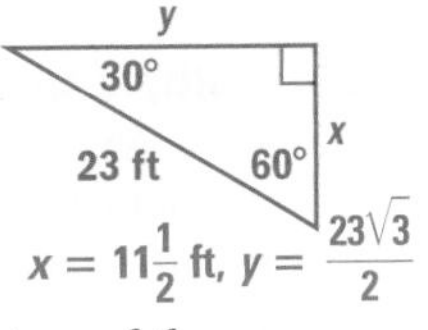

$x = 11\frac{1}{2}$ ft, $y = \frac{23\sqrt{3}}{2}$ ft

19. 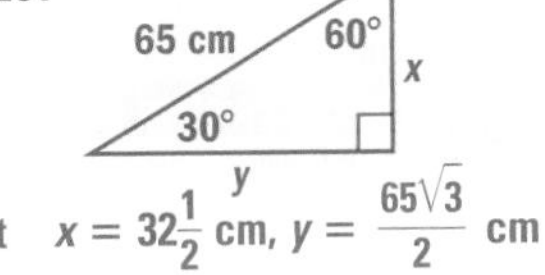

$x = 32\frac{1}{2}$ cm, $y = \frac{65\sqrt{3}}{2}$ cm

20. Quilting Find the perimeters of the five squares in the diagram of the Snail's Trail quilt pattern at the right. The triangles used in this pattern are 45°-45°-90° triangles. Round your answers to the nearest inch, if necessary.
from largest to smallest: 48 in., 34 in., 24 in., 17 in., 12 in.

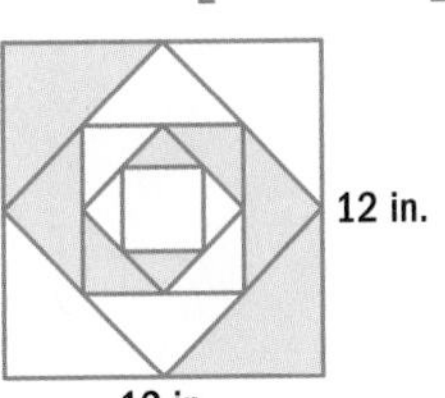

12. No. *Sample answer*: An equilateral triangle has three congruent angles which cannot all be right angles.

3 APPLY

ASSIGNMENT GUIDE

Basic Course
Day 1: pp. 459-460 Exs. 6-8, 14-16, 24-29
Day 2: pp. 459-460 Exs. 9-11, 13, 17-20, 30-33

Average Course
Day 1: pp. 459-460 Exs. 6-8, 14-18, 24-29
Day 2: pp. 459-460 Exs. 9-13, 19-21, 30-34

Advanced Course
Day 1: pp. 459-460 Exs. 6-8, 17-21, 28-30, 33
Day 2: pp. 459-460 Exs. 9-13, 22-27*, 34

Block
pp. 459-460 Exs. 6-21, 24-34

EXTRA PRACTICE

- Student Edition, p. 735
- Chapter 9 Resource Book, pp. 44-46
- Test and Practice Generator

TRANSPARENCY

Even-numbered answers are available on transparencies.

HOMEWORK CHECK

When you review students' homework for this lesson, go over the following exercises to check understanding of key concepts.
Basic: 6, 8, 9, 10, 13
Average: 6, 8, 9, 11, 13
Advanced: 7, 8, 9, 11, 13

TEACHING TIP

In Exercise 20, students can use the Pythagorean theorem several times to find a side length of each successive square, but encourage them to look for a pattern that will help them.

4 ASSESS

Assessment Resources

For more assessment resources, see:

- Assessment Book
- Test and Practice Generator

Mini-Quiz

Find the value of each variable. Give the exact answers.

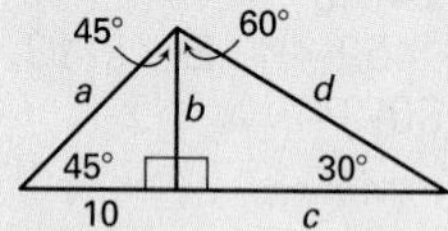

1. a $10\sqrt{2}$
2. b 10
3. c $10\sqrt{3}$
4. d 20
5. A ski lift that is 3000 feet long climbs a 30° slope. How far will a ski chair that climbs the length of the lift rise? 1500 ft

5 FOLLOW-UP

Reteaching/Remediation

- Study Guide in Chapter 9 Resource Book, pp. 47–48
- eTutorial Plus Online
- Extra Practice, p. 735
- Lesson Practice in Chapter 9 Resource Book, pp. 44–46

Challenge/Enrichment

- Challenge Practice in Chapter 9 Resource Book, p. 49
- Teacher's Edition, p. 428F

English Learner Support

- Spanish Study Guide
- Multi-Language Glossary
- Chapter Audio Summaries CDs

22. *Sample answer:* To find the height of the equilateral triangle, you can fold it in half and use the 30°-60°-90° relationship in the resulting triangle. Since the short leg after the fold measures 5 inches, the long leg (original height) is $5\sqrt{3} \approx 8.66$ inches. So the area of the equilateral triangle is about $\frac{1}{2}(10)(8.66) = 43.3$ square inches.

C 

21. Writing Use the Pythagorean theorem to verify that the 30°-60°-90° rule works. Give an example. $x^2 + (x\sqrt{3})^2 \stackrel{?}{=} (2x)^2$, $x^2 + 3x^2 \stackrel{?}{=} 4x^2$, $4x^2 = 4x^2$. *Sample answer:* $3^2 + (3\sqrt{3})^2 \stackrel{?}{=} 6^2$, $9 + 27 \stackrel{?}{=} 36$, $36 = 36$.

22. Critical Thinking How can you find the area of the triangle shown? (*Hint:* You can fold the triangle in half to create two congruent 30°-60°-90° triangles.)

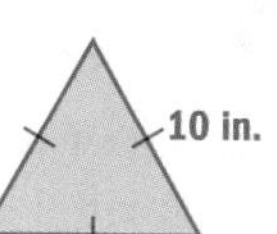

23. Challenge In the diagram below, $\triangle ABC \sim \triangle XYZ$. Find all unknown side lengths of the triangles. Give exact answers.

$AC = 11\sqrt{3}$ m, $BC = 22$ m, $XZ = 6\sqrt{3}$ m, $YZ = 12$ m

B, 11 m, 60°, 30°, A, C; Y, 6 m, X, Z

Mixed Review

Find the quotient. *(Lesson 5.4)*

24. $\frac{5}{11} \div \frac{5}{11}$ 1

25. $\frac{3}{10} \div \frac{1}{5}$ $1\frac{1}{2}$

26. $\frac{4}{15} \div \left(-\frac{12}{25}\right)$ $-\frac{5}{9}$

Write the rate as a unit rate. *(Lesson 7.1)*

27. $\frac{28 \text{ people}}{4 \text{ teams}}$ $\frac{7 \text{ people}}{1 \text{ team}}$

28. $\frac{60 \text{ meters}}{20 \text{ seconds}}$ $\frac{3 \text{ m}}{1 \text{ sec}}$

29. $\frac{488 \text{ rotations}}{8 \text{ minutes}}$ $\frac{61 \text{ rotations}}{1 \text{ min}}$

Basic Skills **Solve the equation.**

30. $165 = -5z$ -33

31. $77 = 7.7p$ 10

32. $19 = \frac{w}{4.2}$ 79.8

Test-Taking Practice

INTERNET
State Test Practice
CLASSZONE.COM

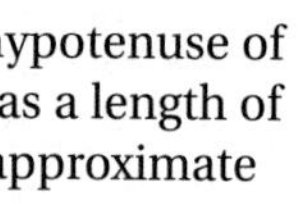

33. Multiple Choice The hypotenuse of a 45°-45°-90° triangle has a length of 20 inches. What is the approximate length of a leg? C

x, 20 in., 45°, x

A. 10 inches **B.** 12.5 inches

C. 14.1 inches **D.** 18 inches

34. Multiple Choice The hypotenuse of a 30°-60°-90° triangle has a length of $12\sqrt{3}$ feet. What is the length of the longer leg? H

60°, $12\sqrt{3}$ ft, x, 30°, y

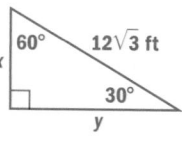

F. 6 feet **G.** $6\sqrt{3}$ feet

H. 18 feet **I.** $18\sqrt{3}$ feet

9.6 Hands-on Activity

GOAL
Find the sine and cosine ratios of right triangles.

MATERIALS
· metric ruler
· protractor

Exploring Trigonometric Ratios

You can use a protractor and metric ruler to find the ratios of the length of each leg of a right triangle to the hypotenuse.

Explore **Find ratios of side lengths of similar right triangles.**

1 Draw a 40° angle. Mark tick marks every 5 centimeters along one side. **Check work.**

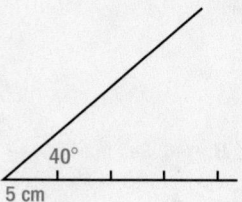

2 Draw perpendicular line segments from four of the tick marks to intersect with the other side of the angle. **Check work.**

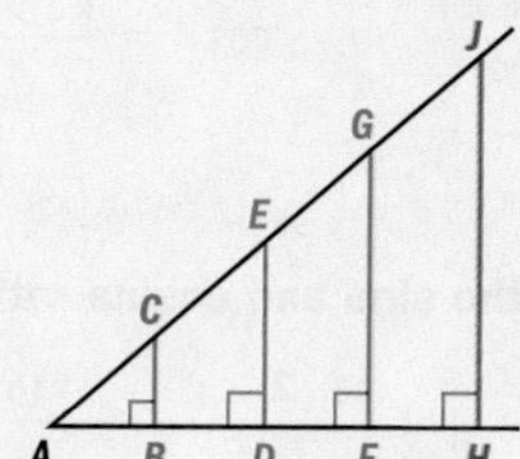

3 There are four similar triangles in your drawing. Measure the legs of each triangle in your drawing to the nearest tenth. Then copy and complete the table. Round your answers to the nearest hundredth.

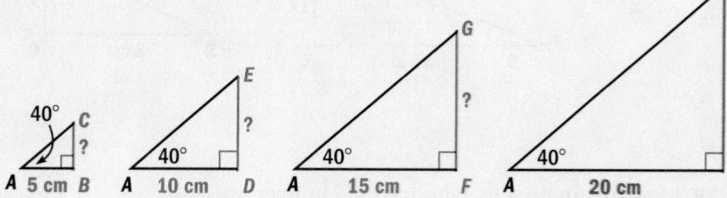

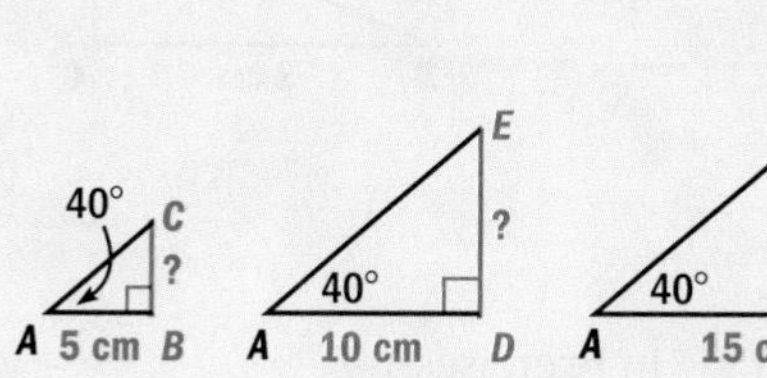

Triangle	Leg 1	Leg 2	Hypotenuse	$\frac{\text{Leg 1}}{\text{Hypotenuse}}$	$\frac{\text{Leg 2}}{\text{Hypotenuse}}$
$\triangle ABC$	5 cm	? 4.2 cm	? 6.5 cm	? 0.77	? 0.65
$\triangle ADE$	10 cm	? 8.4 cm	? 13.1 cm	? 0.76	? 0.64
$\triangle AFG$	15 cm	? 12.6 cm	? 19.6 cm	? 0.77	? 0.64
$\triangle AHJ$	20 cm	? 16.8 cm	? 26.1 cm	? 0.77	? 0.64

ILLINOIS Standards and ISAT:
9.D.3

1 PLAN

EXPLORE THE CONCEPT

- Students will use a metric ruler and protractor to find the sine and cosine ratios of right triangles.
- This activity leads into the study of the sine, cosine, and tangent ratios in Lesson 9.6.

MATERIALS

Each student or pair of students will need a protractor, a metric ruler, and a pen or pencil.

RECOMMENDED TIME

Work activity: 15 min
Discuss results: 10 min

GROUPING

Students can work individually or in pairs. If students work in pairs, they should each measure the sides of the triangles to make sure they agree.

TRANSPARENCY

Support transparencies are available for this Activity.

2 TEACH

ALTERNATIVE STRATEGY

Complete Steps 1 and 2 on the board. Then have students take turns measuring segments and completing parts of the table on the board. As a group, have students discuss their results and look for patterns.

TIPS FOR SUCCESS

In Step 2, students must be careful when drawing the perpendicular segments. In Step 6, help students understand that regardless of the size of the triangle, the ratios for a given angle will be the same, but that these ratios will differ for different angles.

3 CLOSE

KEY DISCOVERY

For a given acute angle in any right triangle, the ratio of the length of the leg opposite the angle to the length of the hypotenuse is the same, and the length of the leg adjacent to the angle to the length of the hypotenuse is the same.

ASSESSMENT

1. As the measure of an acute angle in a triangle increases, what happens to the ratio of the length of the side adjacent to that angle to the length of the hypotenuse? **It decreases.**
2. Can the ratio of the side opposite an acute angle to the length of the hypotenuse ever reach 1? Explain. **No; a ratio of 1 would mean that a leg of a right triangle is as long as the hypotenuse, which cannot occur.**

Step 6. (Step 3) row 2: 13.7 cm, 14.6 cm, 0.34, 0.94; row 3: 27.5 cm, 29.2 cm, 0.34, 0.94; row 4: 41.2 cm, 43.9 cm, 0.34, 0.94; row 5: 54.9 cm, 58.5 cm, 0.34, 0.94; (Step 4) Yes; they are all the same. (Step 5) Yes; they are all the same. (Step 6) the measures of its angles

1. $\sin A = \frac{12}{15}$, $\cos A = \frac{9}{15}$, $\sin B = \frac{9}{15}$, $\cos B = \frac{12}{15}$

2. $\sin A = \frac{6}{10}$, $\cos A = \frac{8}{10}$, $\sin B = \frac{8}{10}$, $\cos B = \frac{6}{10}$

3. $\sin A = \frac{15}{17}$, $\cos A = \frac{8}{17}$, $\sin B = \frac{8}{17}$, $\cos B = \frac{15}{17}$

4. $\sin A = \frac{24}{25}$, $\cos A = \frac{7}{25}$, $\sin B = \frac{7}{25}$, $\cos B = \frac{24}{25}$

5–7. See Additional Answers beginning on page AA1.

Hands-on Activity Continued

Explore **Look for a pattern.**

4 Is there a pattern in the ratios $\frac{\text{Leg 1}}{\text{Hypotenuse}}$? If so, what is it? **Yes; they are all about the same.**

5 Is there a pattern in the ratios $\frac{\text{Leg 2}}{\text{Hypotenuse}}$? If so, what is it? **Yes; they are all about the same.**

6 Repeat Steps 1-5 using a 70° angle. Based on your results, do the ratios depend on the lengths of the right triangles' sides or on the measures of their angles? **See margin.**

The ratios $\frac{\text{Leg 1}}{\text{Hypotenuse}}$ and $\frac{\text{Leg 2}}{\text{Hypotenuse}}$ have special names. They are called the *sine* and *cosine* ratios and can be defined as follows:

$$\sin A = \frac{\text{length of leg opposite } \angle A}{\text{length of hypotenuse}} \qquad \cos A = \frac{\text{length of leg adjacent to } \angle A}{\text{length of hypotenuse}}$$

Your turn now **Find the sine and cosine ratios for $\angle A$ and $\angle B$.** **1–6. See margin.**

1.
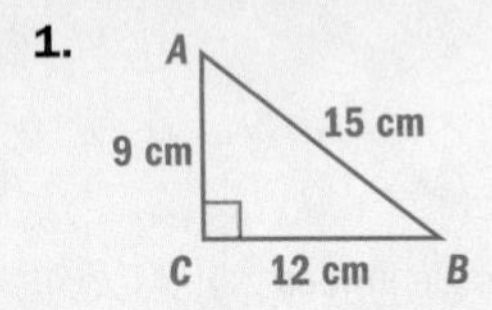

2.
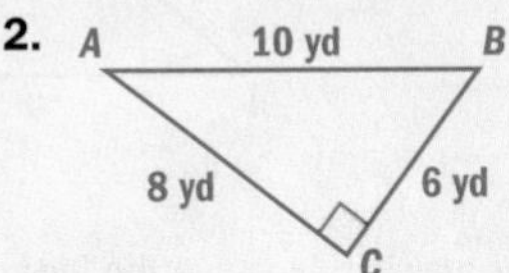

3.
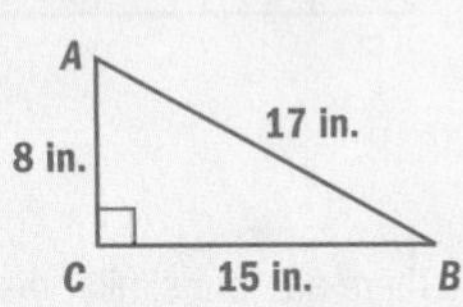

4.
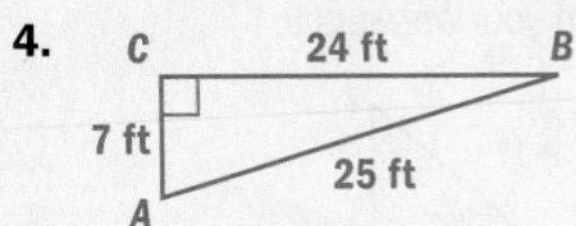

5.
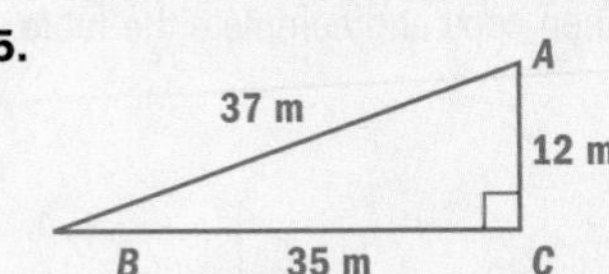

6.
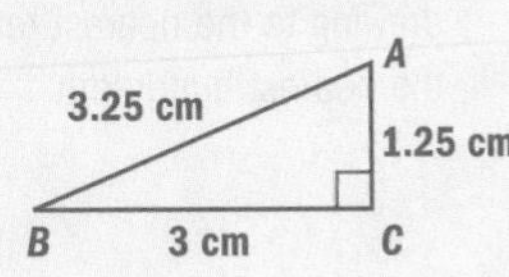

Stop and Think

7. **Critical Thinking** Measure angle A in each triangle in Exercises 1–6. Write the measures in order from least to greatest. Make a table that shows $m\angle A$, $\sin A$, and $\cos A$. Then copy and complete the following two statements using *increases* or *decreases*. **See margin for table.**

   a. As $m\angle A$ increases from 0° to 90°, the value of $\sin A$ __?__. **increases**

   b. As $m\angle A$ increases from 0° to 90°, the value of $\cos A$ __?__. **decreases**

Using Trigonometric Ratios

BEFORE	Now	WHY?
You found the side lengths of special right triangles.	You'll use trigonometric ratios to find the side lengths.	So you can find the height of a totem pole, as in Ex. 5.

Word Watch

trigonometric ratio, p. 463
sine, p. 463
cosine, p. 463
tangent, p. 463

In the Real World

Water Slide A water slide makes an angle of about 18° with the ground. The slide extends horizontally about 64.2 meters. What is the height of the slide? You will see how to solve this problem in Example 5.

You can find the height of the water slide using a *trigonometric ratio*. A **trigonometric ratio** is a ratio of the lengths of two sides of a right triangle. The three basic trigonometric ratios are **sine**, **cosine**, and **tangent**. These are abbreviated as *sin, cos,* and *tan*.

Note book: Trigonometric Ratios

$$\sin A = \frac{\text{side opposite } \angle A}{\text{hypotenuse}} = \frac{a}{c}$$

$$\cos A = \frac{\text{side adjacent to } \angle A}{\text{hypotenuse}} = \frac{b}{c}$$

$$\tan A = \frac{\text{side opposite } \angle A}{\text{side adjacent to } \angle A} = \frac{a}{b}$$

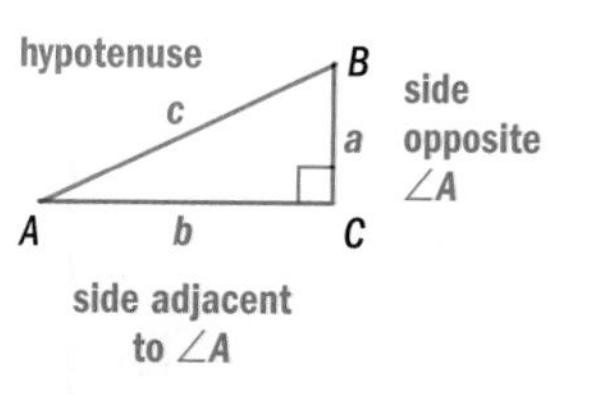

EXAMPLE 1 Finding Trigonometric Ratios

In $\triangle PQR$, write the sine, cosine, and tangent ratios for $\angle P$.

For $\angle P$, the length of the opposite side is 5 feet, and the length of the adjacent side is 12 feet. The length of the hypotenuse is 13 feet.

$$\sin P = \frac{\text{opposite}}{\text{hypotenuse}} = \frac{5}{13}$$

$$\cos P = \frac{\text{adjacent}}{\text{hypotenuse}} = \frac{12}{13}$$

$$\tan P = \frac{\text{opposite}}{\text{adjacent}} = \frac{5}{12}$$

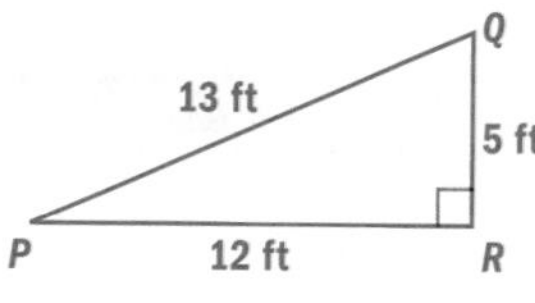

HELP with Solving

Determining the opposite and adjacent sides depends on the angle that is being used. For $\angle Q$, the length of the opposite side is 12 feet, and the length of the adjacent side is 5 feet.

ILLINOIS Standards and ISAT:
9.D.3

1 PLAN

SKILL CHECK

What is the value of the ratio?

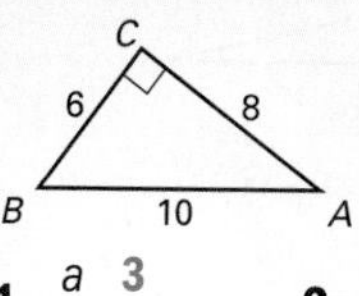

1. $\frac{a}{c}$ $\frac{3}{5}$
2. $\frac{b}{c}$ $\frac{4}{5}$
3. $\frac{a}{b}$ $\frac{3}{4}$
4. $\frac{b}{a}$ $\frac{4}{3}$

Lesson Objective

Use trigonometric ratios to find the side lengths.

Pacing

Suggested Number of Days
Basic Course: 2 days
Average Course: 2 days
Advanced Course: 2 days
Block: 1 block

Teaching Resources

For a complete list of Teaching Resources, see page 428B.

Transparency

Warm-Up Exercises for this lesson are available on a transparency.

2 TEACH

Motivating the Lesson

Ask students what kinds of angles they estimate water slides make with the ground.

TIPS FOR NEW TEACHERS

Challenge students to think of mnemonics they can use to help remember trigonometric ratios, such as "SOCA" for "Sine Opposite, Cosine Adjacent." See Tips for New Teachers in the *Chapter 9 Resource Book*.

EXTRA EXAMPLES

Example 1 In $\triangle GHJ$, write the sine, cosine, and tangent ratios for $\angle G$.

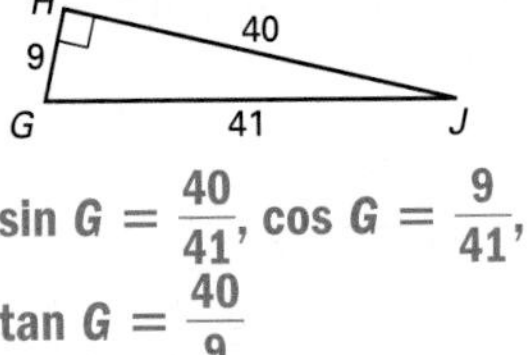

$\sin G = \frac{40}{41}$, $\cos G = \frac{9}{41}$, $\tan G = \frac{40}{9}$

Example 2 Use a calculator to find sine, cosine, and tangent of 65°. Round your answers to four decimal places. **sin 65° ≈ 0.9063, cos 65° ≈ 0.4226, tan 65° ≈ 2.1445**

Example 3 Find the value of x in the triangle. Round to the nearest tenth. **27.9 in.**

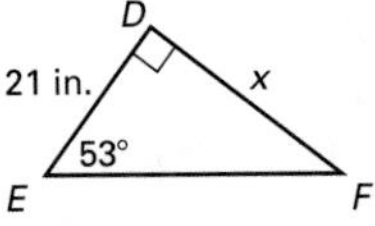

CROSS-CURRICULUM

Science The motion of waves can be modeled using functions based on the sine and cosine ratios. An understanding of sound waves has contributed to, for example, the development of sound-canceling headphones.

with Technology

When using a calculator to find trigonometric ratios of angles measured in degrees, be sure the calculator is in *degree mode*. You can test this by checking that tan 45° = 1.

1. $\sin A = \frac{8}{17}$, $\cos A = \frac{15}{17}$, $\tan A = \frac{8}{15}$, $\sin C = \frac{15}{17}$, $\cos C = \frac{8}{17}$, $\tan C = \frac{15}{8}$

EXAMPLE 2 Using a Calculator

Use a calculator to find sine, cosine, and tangent of 30°.

	Keystrokes	Display	Answer
a.	[2nd] [TRIG] [=] 30 [=]	0.5	sin 30° = 0.5
b.	[2nd] [TRIG] [▶] [▶] [=] 30 [=]	0.8660254	cos 30° ≈ 0.8660
c.	[2nd] [TRIG] [◀] [◀] [=] 30 [=]	0.5773503	tan 30° ≈ 0.5774

Your turn now **Complete the exercise.**

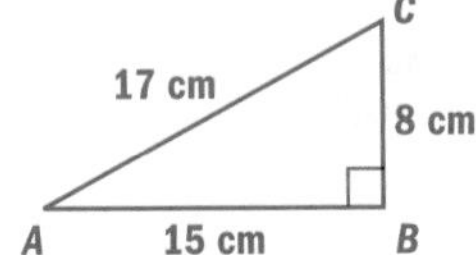

1. For $\triangle ABC$, write the sine, cosine, and tangent ratios for $\angle A$ and $\angle C$.

Use a calculator to approximate the given expression. Round your answer to four decimal places.

2. cos 70° 0.3420 **3.** tan 50° 1.1918 **4.** sin 25° 0.4226 **5.** cos 42° 0.7431 **6.** tan 7° 0.1228

EXAMPLE 3 Using a Cosine Ratio

Find the value of x in the triangle.

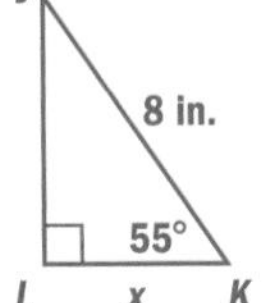

The length of the hypotenuse is 8 inches. The unknown side is adjacent to the given angle. Use cosine of $\angle K$.

$\cos K = \frac{\text{adjacent}}{\text{hypotenuse}}$ **Definition of cosine**

$\cos 55° = \frac{x}{8}$ **Substitute.**

$0.5736 \approx \frac{x}{8}$ **Use a calculator to approximate cos 55°.**

$0.5736 \cdot 8 \approx \frac{x}{8} \cdot 8$ **Multiply each side by 8.**

$4.5888 \approx x$ **Simplify.**

ANSWER The value of x is about 4.59 inches.

Your turn now **Complete the exercise.**

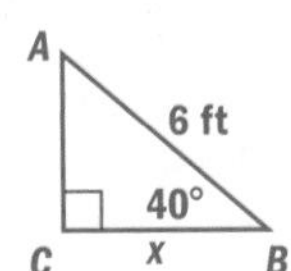

7. Find the value of x in the triangle. Round your answer to the nearest hundredth of a foot. 4.60 ft

EXAMPLE 4 Using a Sine Ratio

Ski Jump A ski jump is 380 feet long and makes a 27.6° angle with the ground. Find the height of the ski jump.

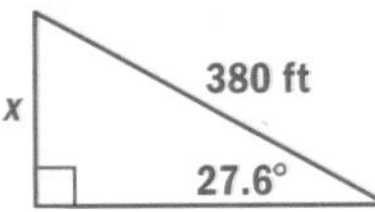

Solution

Use the sine ratio and a calculator to find the value of x.

$\sin 27.6° = \frac{\text{opposite}}{\text{hypotenuse}}$ **Definition of sine**

$\sin 27.6° = \frac{x}{380}$ **Substitute.**

$0.4633 \approx \frac{x}{380}$ **Use a calculator to approximate sin 27.6°.**

$0.4633 \cdot 380 \approx \frac{x}{380} \cdot 380$ **Multiply each side by 380.**

$176.054 \approx x$ **Simplify.**

ANSWER The ski jump is about 176 feet high.

EXAMPLE 5 Using a Tangent Ratio

Water Slide To find the height h of the water slide on page 463, use the tangent ratio.

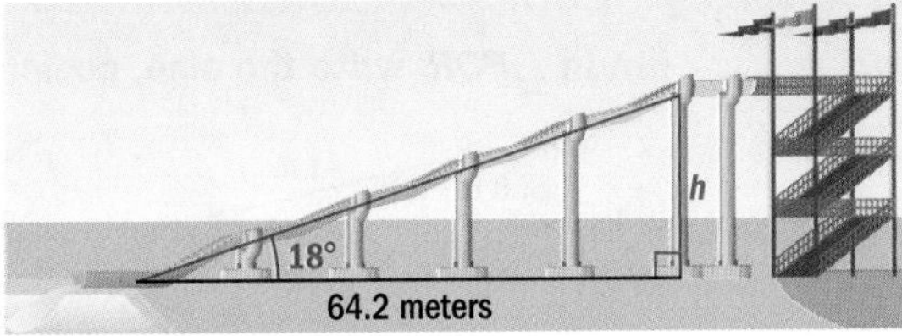

$\tan 18° = \frac{\text{opposite}}{\text{adjacent}}$ **Definition of tangent**

$\tan 18° = \frac{h}{64.2}$ **Substitute.**

$0.3249 \approx \frac{h}{64.2}$ **Use a calculator to approximate tan 18°.**

$0.3249 \cdot 64.2 \approx \frac{h}{64.2} \cdot 64.2$ **Multiply each side by 64.2.**

$20.85858 \approx h$ **Simplify.**

ANSWER The height of the water slide is about 21 meters.

EXTRA EXAMPLES

Example 4 A highway on-ramp is 500 yards long and climbs at a 5° angle. How much height does a car gain over the length of the on-ramp? **about 44 yd**

Example 5 Find the width w of the roof support to the nearest tenth of a meter. **64.3 m**

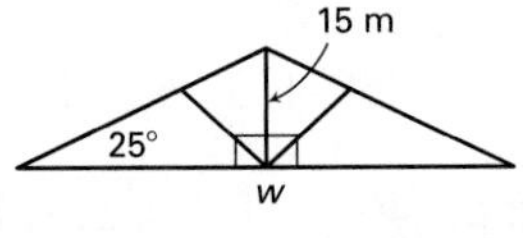

CONCEPT CHECK

Write in your own words how to find the sine, cosine, and tangent ratios in a right triangle. ***Sample answer:*** **For each acute angle, find the ratio of the side opposite the angle to the hypotenuse for sine, the ratio of the side adjacent to the angle to the hypotenuse for cosine, and the ratio of the side opposite the angle to the side adjacent to the angle for tangent.**

DAILY PUZZLER

Find x to the nearest hundredth.

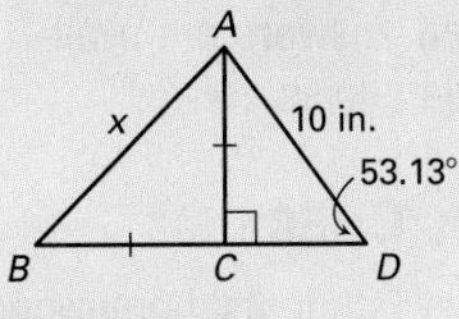

11.31 in.

3 APPLY

ASSIGNMENT GUIDE

Basic Course

Day 1: SRH p. 714 Exs. 16-20; pp. 466-468 Exs. 6-8, 15-18, 33-38

Day 2: pp. 466-468 Exs. 9-14, 20-24, 39-41

Average Course

Day 1: pp. 466-468 Exs. 6-8, 16-19, 30, 33-39

Day 2: pp. 466-468 Exs. 11-14, 20-27, 32, 40-42

Advanced Course

Day 1: pp. 466-468 Exs. 7-10, 17-19, 27-31*, 40-42

Day 2: pp. 466-468 Exs. 13-16, 20-26, 32-36

Block

pp. 466-468 Exs. 6-8, 11-14, 16-27, 30, 32-42

EXTRA PRACTICE

- Student Edition, p. 735
- Chapter 9 Resource Book, pp. 53-55
- Test and Practice Generator

TRANSPARENCY

Even-numbered answers are available on transparencies.

HOMEWORK CHECK

When you review students' homework for this lesson, go over the following exercises to check understanding of key concepts.

Basic: 6, 9, 13, 20, 24

Average: 7, 11, 14, 20, 24

Advanced: 8, 10, 15, 20, 25

TEACHING TIP

Have students write the meaning of each ratio in Exercises 6-8 in words before substituting numerical values.

5 (Step 1), 6-8, 16. See Additional Answers beginning on page AA1.

9.6 Exercises

More Practice, p. 735

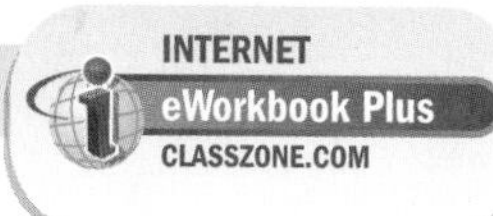

Getting Ready to Practice

Matching **Match the term with the correct ratio.**

1. sine B
2. cosine A
3. tangent C

A. $\frac{\text{adjacent}}{\text{hypotenuse}}$ B. $\frac{\text{opposite}}{\text{hypotenuse}}$ C. $\frac{\text{opposite}}{\text{adjacent}}$

4. Write the sine, cosine, and tangent ratios in simplest form, for $\angle A$ and $\angle B$ in $\triangle ABC$. See margin.

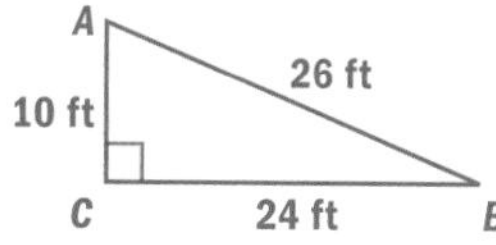

5. **Guided Problem Solving** You stand 50 feet from a totem pole that is perpendicular to the ground. The angle from the point where you stand to the top of the totem pole is 42°. How tall is the totem pole?
   1. Draw a diagram and identify the sides of the triangle. See margin.
   2. Write an equation using a trigonometric ratio. $\tan 42° = \frac{x}{50}$
   3. Solve the equation. Round your answer to the nearest foot. 45 ft

4. $\sin A = \frac{12}{13}$, $\cos A = \frac{5}{13}$, $\tan A = \frac{12}{5}$, $\sin B = \frac{5}{13}$, $\cos B = \frac{12}{13}$, $\tan B = \frac{5}{12}$

Practice and Problem Solving

A **In $\triangle PQR$, write the sine, cosine, and tangent ratios for $\angle P$ and $\angle R$.** 6–8. See margin.

6. 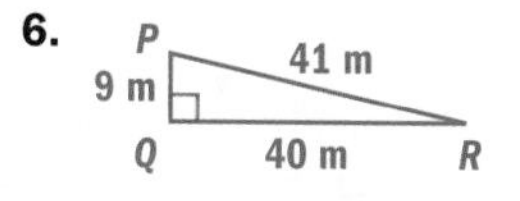

7. 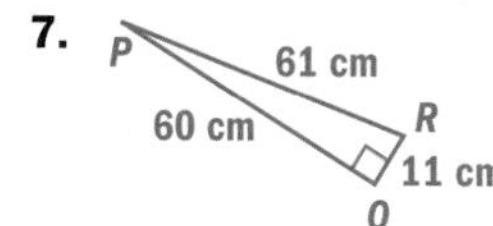

8. 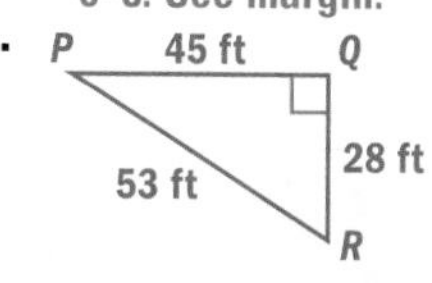

Use a calculator to approximate the given expression. Round your answer to four decimal places.

9. tan 51° 1.2349
10. sin 80° 0.9848
11. sin 36° 0.5878
12. cos 76° 0.2419

Find the value of *x*. Round your answer to the nearest thousandth.

13. 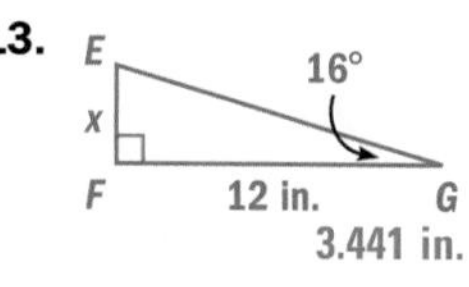

3.441 in.

14. 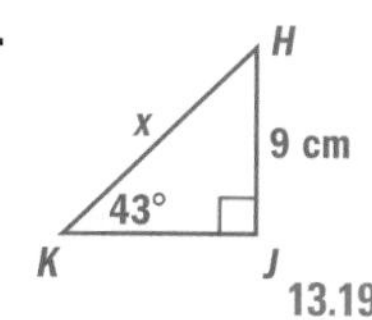

13.197 cm

15. 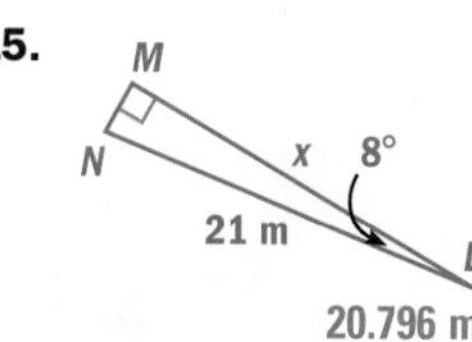

20.796 m

16. **Writing** Explain how to decide which trigonometric ratio (sine, cosine, or tangent) is best for solving a particular problem. See margin.

HELP with Homework

Example	Exercises
1	6-8
2	9-12
3	13-15
4	20, 24-26
5	20, 24-26

- More Examples
- eTutorial Plus

$18.\ \sin A = \frac{x+1}{2x-1},$

$\cos A = \frac{x}{2x-1},$

$\tan A = \frac{x+1}{x},$

$\sin B = \frac{x}{2x-1},$

$\cos B = \frac{x+1}{2x-1},$

$\tan B = \frac{x}{x+1}$

21. $m\angle C = 60°$, $AC = 10$ in.;

$\sin A = \frac{1}{2}$, $\cos A = \frac{8.7}{10}$,

$\tan A = \frac{5}{8.7}$

22. $m\angle C = 54°$, $AB \approx 9.3$ m;

$\sin A = \frac{6.8}{11.5}$, $\cos A = \frac{9.3}{11.5}$,

$\tan A = \frac{6.8}{9.3}$

23. $m\angle A = 19.7°$, $BC \approx 17.2$ cm;

$\sin A = \frac{17.2}{51}$, $\cos A = \frac{48}{51}$,

$\tan A = \frac{17.2}{48}$

17. Draw a Diagram Sketch right triangle *ABC* that has the given trigonometric ratios: $\tan A = \frac{15}{8}$ and $\cos B = \frac{15}{17}$. Label each side with its length. See margin.

18. Algebra Write the trigonometric ratios for $\angle A$ and $\angle B$ in $\triangle ABC$.

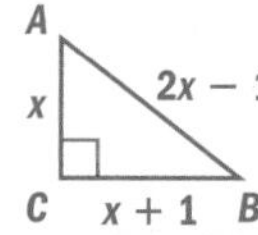

19. Find the Error Describe and correct the error in the solution.
The tangent ratio is the length of the opposite side over the length of the adjacent side, not over the length of the hypotenuse. So $\tan 25° = \frac{x}{13}$, and $x \approx 6$ cm.

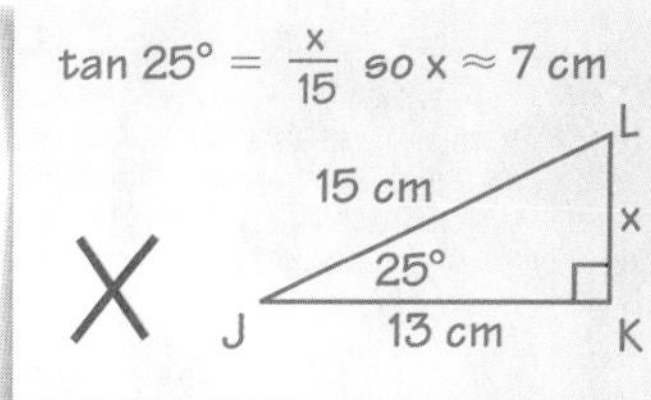

20. Cats You are constructing a scratching post and platform for your cat. Find the length *x* of the scratching post. Round your answer to the nearest tenth of a foot. 3.5 ft

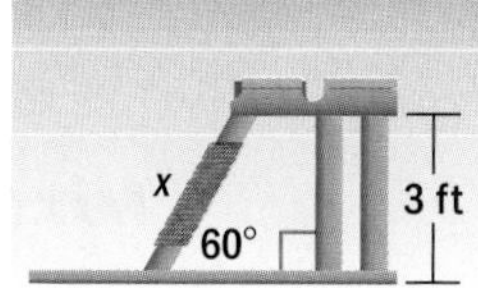

B **Find the value of the unknown angle and side. Then write three trigonometric ratios for $\angle A$.**

21.

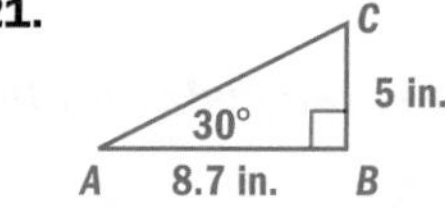

22.

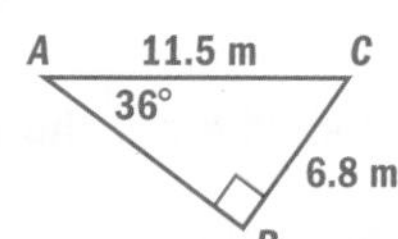

23.

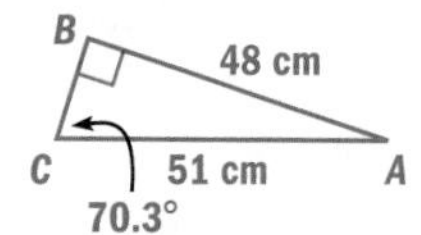

Extended Problem Solving In Exercises 24–26, use the following information. Round your answer to the nearest whole number.

Some whales have been known to dive down to a depth of 3000 meters in search of their favorite food.

24. Calculate The whale shown finds food after swimming 2000 m. How deep is the water where the whale found its food? about 845 m

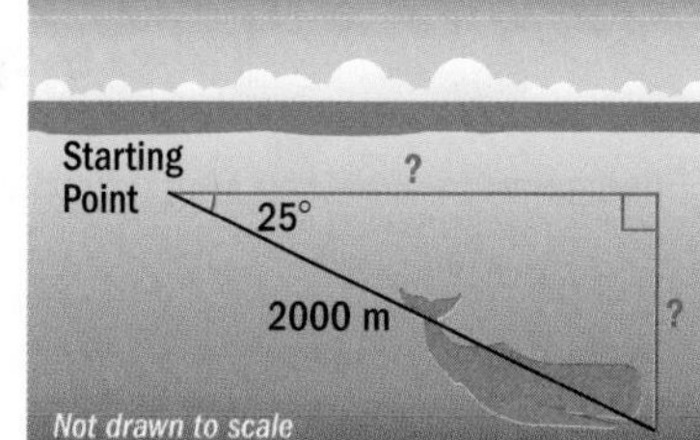

25. Calculate How far is the whale along the ocean surface from the point where it started to the point directly above the spot where it found its food? about 1813 m

26. Compare Did this whale dive more or less than $\frac{1}{2}$ of the deepest known dive? less

TEACHING TIP

After working Exercise 21, have students write the sine and cosine ratios for $\angle C$ so that they can see that $\cos 60° = \sin 30°$ and $\sin 60° = \cos 30°$. Have them also find these ratios for Exercises 22 and 23 so that they can see that the sine of one acute angle is the cosine of the other acute angle.

17.

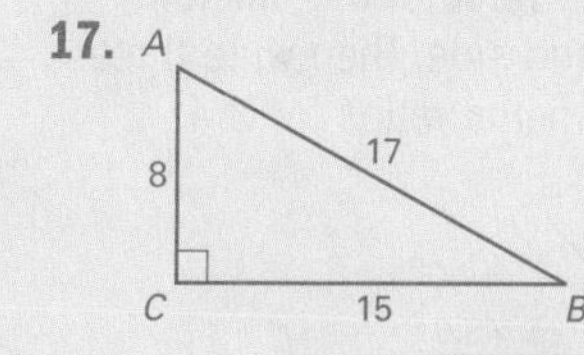

ASSESS

Assessment Resources

For more assessment resources, see:
- Assessment Book
- Test and Practice Generator

Mini-Quiz

1. Find the value of the unknown angle and side. Then write three trigonometric ratios for $\angle A$.

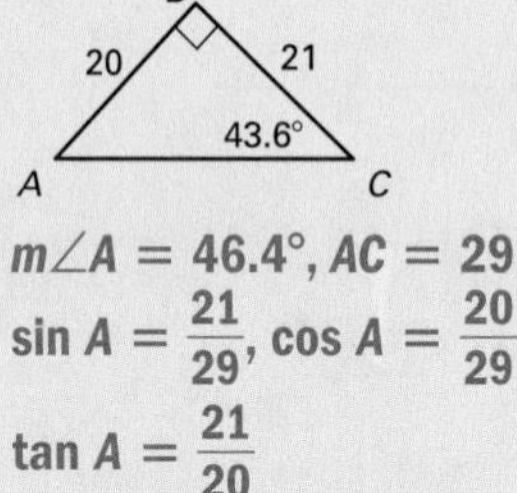

$m\angle A = 46.4°$, $AC = 29$;
$\sin A = \frac{21}{29}$, $\cos A = \frac{20}{29}$,
$\tan A = \frac{21}{20}$

Use a calculator to approximate the given expression. Round your answer to four decimal places.

2. tan 15° **0.2679**

3. sin 88° **0.9994**

4. cos 25° **0.9063**

FOLLOW-UP

Reteaching/Remediation

- Study Guide in Chapter 9 Resource Book, pp. 56–57
- eTutorial Plus Online
- Extra Practice, p. 735
- Lesson Practice in Chapter 9 Resource Book, pp. 53–55

Challenge/Enrichment

- Challenge Practice in Chapter 9 Resource Book, p. 59
- Teacher's Edition, p. 428F

English Learner Support

- Spanish Study Guide
- Multi-Language Glossary
- Chapter Audio Summaries CDs

30. No. *Sample answer:* The hypotenuse is always greater than the length of either leg, so the ratios will always be less than 1.

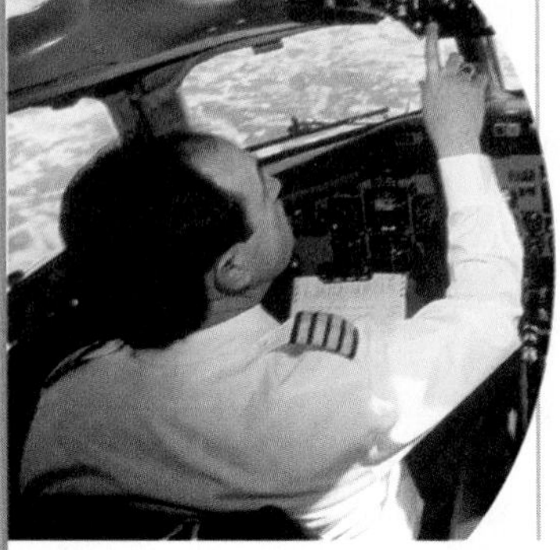

Find the perimeter of the triangle. Round your answer to the nearest tenth.

27. 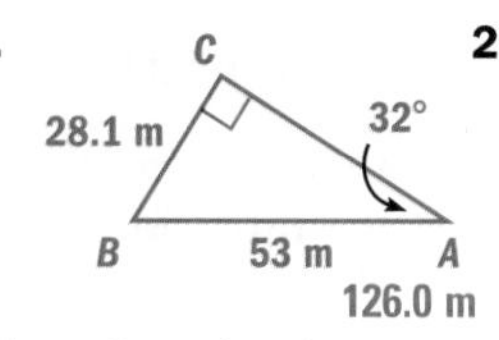

84.4 in.

28.

126.0 m

29. 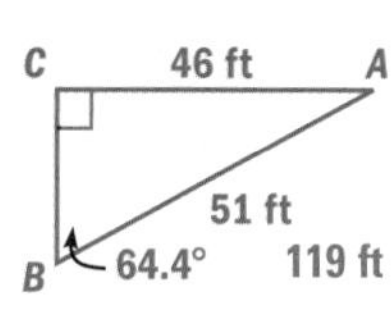

119 ft

30. Critical Thinking Can the values for the sine or cosine of one of the acute angles in a right triangle be greater than or equal to 1? Explain.

31. Challenge Find the area of the isosceles triangle. Round your answer to the nearest tenth. $17.7\ cm^2$

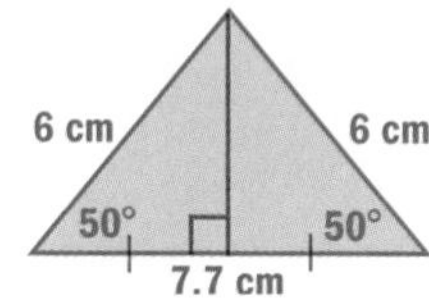

32. Aviation An airplane is at an altitude of 33,000 feet when the pilot starts the descent to the airport. The pilot wants the plane to descend at an angle of 3°. How many miles away from the airport must the descent begin? Round your answer to the nearest mile. **119 mi**

Mixed Review

35–38. Sample explanations are given.

35. Rational; 484 is a perfect square, since $22^2 = 484$.

36. Irrational; 99 is not a perfect square.

37. Irrational; neither 17 nor 29 is a perfect square.

38. Rational; $\sqrt{\frac{144}{225}} = \frac{12}{15}$, which is a quotient of two integers.

33. Find the sum of 9.87 and $\frac{43}{50}$. Write your answer in decimal form. *(Lessons 5.5, 5.6)* **10.73**

34. What type of transformation is modeled by a merry-go-round? *(Lesson 8.7)* **rotation**

Tell whether the number is *rational* or *irrational*. Explain. *(Lesson 9.2)*

35. $\sqrt{484}$ **36.** $\sqrt{99}$ **37.** $\sqrt{\frac{17}{29}}$ **38.** $\sqrt{\frac{144}{225}}$

Basic Skills Use the distance formula to find the rate.

39. $d = 145$ mi, $t = 40$ h **3.625 mi/h** **40.** $d = 78$ m, $t = 20$ sec **3.9 m/sec**

Test-Taking Practice

INTERNET
State Test Practice
CLASSZONE.COM

41. Multiple Choice What is the cosine of $\angle E$? **B**

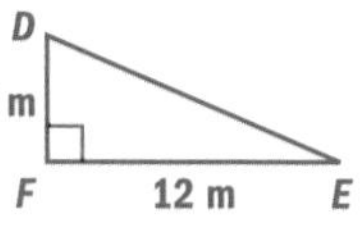

A. $\frac{5}{13}$ **B.** $\frac{12}{13}$ **C.** $\frac{13}{5}$ **D.** 13

42. Multiple Choice What is the approximate length of side AC? **G**

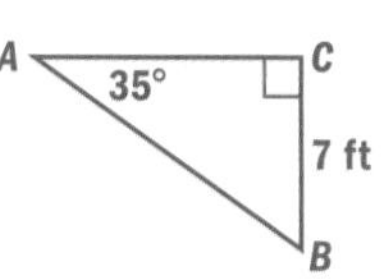

F. 7 ft **G.** 10 ft **H.** $7\sqrt{3}$ ft **I.** 14 ft

CALCULATOR

9.6 Technology Activity

Finding an Angle Measure

GOAL Use a calculator to find an angle measure using the inverse of a trigonometric ratio.

In some situations, you need to find a particular angle of a given triangle. You can use the inverse of a trigonometric ratio to find the measure of the angle. For example, you can use the inverse tangent feature of your calculator to solve the following problem. The inverse tangent formula is:

$$\text{If } \tan x° = \frac{a}{b}, \text{ then } x° = \tan^{-1}\left(\frac{a}{b}\right).$$

Example **In the 1870s, a cable car system was built in San Francisco. A section of California Street has a vertical height of 76 feet and a horizontal length of 420 feet. Find the angle of the hill, $x°$.**

Solution

To find the angle, use inverse tangent.

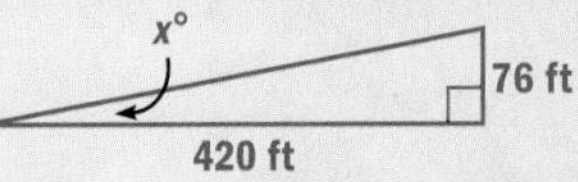

$\tan x° = \frac{\text{opposite}}{\text{adjacent}}$	**Definition of tangent**
$\tan x° = \frac{76}{420}$	**Substitute.**
$x° = \tan^{-1}\left(\frac{76}{420}\right)$	**Definition of inverse tangent**
$x \approx 10.3$	**Use your calculator to approximate.**

ANSWER The angle of the hill is about 10°.

Your turn now **Use a calculator to approximate the expression. Round to the nearest tenth of a degree.**

1. $\tan^{-1}(0.25)$ 14.0°
2. $\tan^{-1}(0.14)$ 8.0°
3. $\tan^{-1}(0.92)$ 42.6°
4. $\tan^{-1}(1.05)$ 46.4°
5. $\tan^{-1}(24.65)$ 87.7°
6. $\tan^{-1}(64.25)$ 89.1°
7. **Critical Thinking** Given $\tan^{-1}(0.18)$ and $\tan^{-1}(32.46)$, which one would you expect to represent the largest angle? Why?

with Technology

To evaluate an inverse tangent on your calculator, press the 2nd key. Then press the [TRIG] key. Use the right or left arrow to highlight the inverse tangent feature and then press =. Enter the ratio and press = again. The result is the angle measure.

7. $\tan^{-1}(32.46)$. *Sample answer:* The greater the tangent of an angle, the larger the angle.

ILLINOIS Standards and ISAT:
9.D.3

1 PLAN

LEARN THE METHOD

- Students will use a calculator to find an angle measure using the inverse of a trigonometric ratio.
- Once students understand finding inverse trigonometric ratios, have them return to Example 1 in Lesson 9.6 to find the measures of the acute angles.

2 TEACH

TIPS FOR SUCCESS

Emphasize that $\tan^{-1}$ is an angle, not a ratio. Have students practice reading $\tan^{-1} x$ as "the angle whose tangent is x" to keep the relationship clear in their minds.

EXTRA EXAMPLES

Example A handicapped-access ramp rises 2 feet over a horizontal distance of 25 feet. Find the angle that the ramp rises from the horizontal. **about 4.6°**

3 CLOSE

ASSESSMENT

1. Use a calculator to evaluate $\tan^{-1}(14.3)$. Round to the nearest tenth of a degree. **86.0°**
2. Explain why it must be true that $\tan^{-1}(1) = 45°$. ***Sample answer:*** **If the tangent ratio is 1, then the legs of a right triangle have the same length. This is only true when the acute angles are also equal, that is, when their measures are 45°.**

ADDITIONAL RESOURCES

The following resources are available to help review the materials in Lessons 9.5–9.6.

Chapter 9 Resource Book
- Lesson Practice
- Study Guide

Assessment Book
- Chapter 9 Quiz 2

Technology
- Test and Practice Generator
- eTutorial CD-ROM

Internet
- Classzone
- eWorkbook Plus Online
- eTutorial Plus Online

ENGLISH LEARNER SUPPORT

- Spanish Study Guide
- Multi-Language Glossary
- Chapter Audio Summaries CDs

Notebook Review

Review the vocabulary definitions in your notebook.

Copy the review examples in your notebook. Then complete the exercises.

Check Your Definitions

trigonometric ratio, p. 463	cosine, p. 463
sine, p. 463	tangent, p. 463

Use Your Vocabulary

1. Copy and complete: To write the sine ratio for a given acute angle of a right triangle, you need to know the length of the side _?_ the angle and the length of the _?_. **opposite; hypotenuse**

9.5 Can you find side lengths of special right triangles?

EXAMPLE Find the length of the hypotenuse. Give the exact answer.

hypotenuse = leg • $\sqrt{2}$ **Rule for 45°-45°-90° triangle**

$= 26\sqrt{2}$ **Substitute.**

26 ft, x, 45°, 26 ft

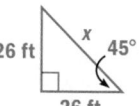

ANSWER The length of the hypotenuse is $26\sqrt{2}$ feet.

☑ **Find the value of each variable. Give the exact answer.**

2.

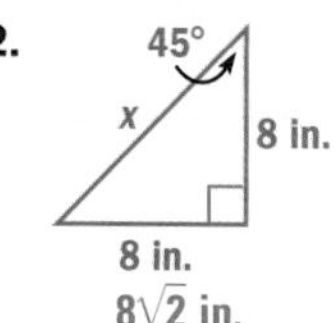

$8\sqrt{2}$ in.

3.

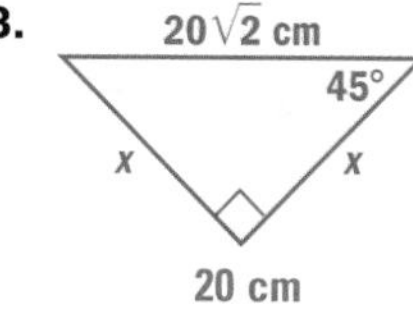

20 cm

4.

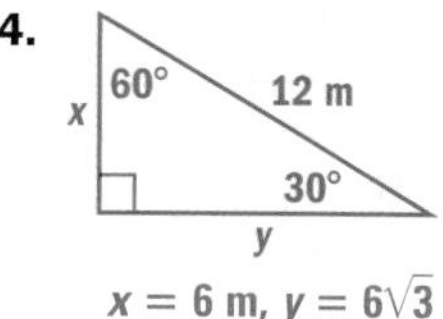

$x = 6$ m, $y = 6\sqrt{3}$ m

9.6 Can you use trigonometric ratios?

EXAMPLE In $\triangle ABC$, write the sine, cosine, and tangent ratios for $\angle A$.

$$\sin A = \frac{\text{opposite}}{\text{hypotenuse}} = \frac{12}{37}$$

$$\cos A = \frac{\text{adjacent}}{\text{hypotenuse}} = \frac{35}{37}$$

$$\tan A = \frac{\text{opposite}}{\text{adjacent}} = \frac{12}{35}$$

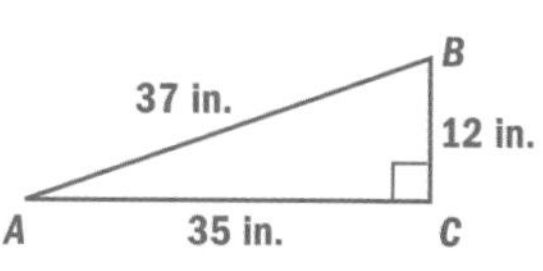

 **In $\triangle ABC$, write the sine, cosine, and tangent ratios for $\angle A$ and $\angle B$.** 5–7. See margin.

5. 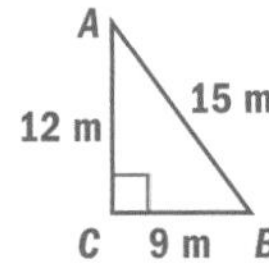

6. 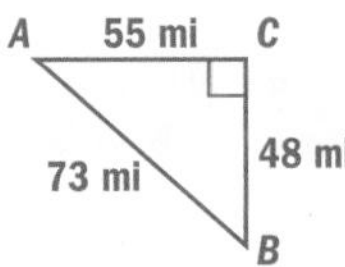

7. 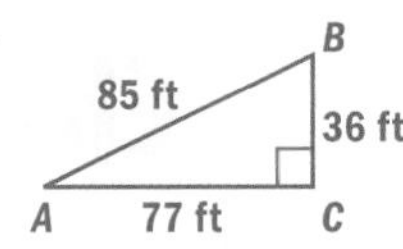

Stop and Think about Lessons 9.5–9.6

8. Writing Describe how to find the cosine ratio for one of the acute angles of a right triangle when you know that its sine ratio is $\frac{3}{5}$. See margin.

Review Quiz 2

Find the value of each variable. Give exact answers.

1. 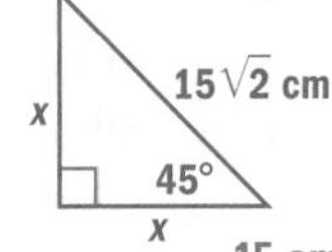

15 cm

2. 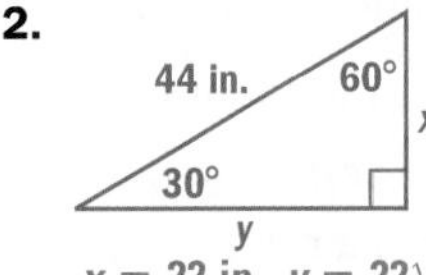

$x = 22$ in., $y = 22\sqrt{3}$ in.

3. 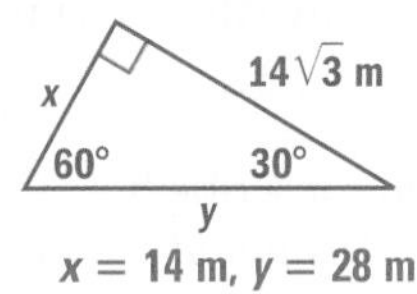

$x = 14$ m, $y = 28$ m

In $\triangle ABC$, write the sine, cosine, and tangent ratios for $\angle A$ and $\angle B$.

4. 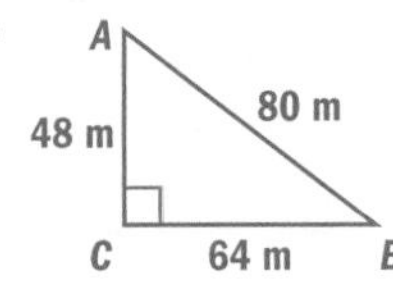

5. 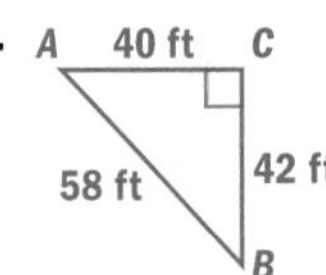

6. 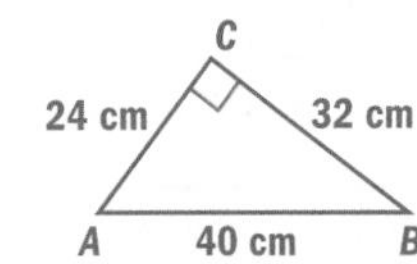

7. Aviation If a plane flies 1° off course for 2000 miles, how far away will the plane be from the correct path? Round to the nearest tenth of a mile. 34.9 mi

BRAIN GAME

A Real Winner

Replace each expression with the letter of its decimal approximation to find the name of a person who won the Nobel Prize in both physics and chemistry. MARIE CURIE

cos 15° sin 52° cos 85° sin 60° cos 45°

tan 30° tan 12° sin 5° cos 30° sin 45°

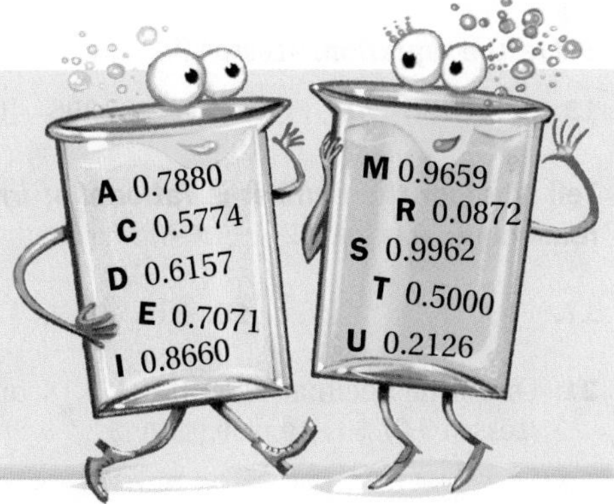

Review Quiz 2

4. $\sin A = \frac{4}{5}$, $\cos A = \frac{3}{5}$, $\tan A = \frac{4}{3}$, $\sin B = \frac{3}{5}$, $\cos B = \frac{4}{5}$, $\tan B = \frac{3}{4}$

5. $\sin A = \frac{21}{29}$, $\cos A = \frac{20}{29}$, $\tan A = \frac{21}{20}$, $\sin B = \frac{20}{29}$, $\cos B = \frac{21}{29}$, $\tan B = \frac{20}{21}$

6. $\sin A = \frac{4}{5}$, $\cos A = \frac{3}{5}$, $\tan A = \frac{4}{3}$, $\sin B = \frac{3}{5}$, $\cos B = \frac{4}{5}$, $\tan B = \frac{3}{4}$

Notebook Review

5. $\sin A = \frac{3}{5}$, $\cos A = \frac{4}{5}$, $\tan A = \frac{3}{4}$, $\sin B = \frac{4}{5}$, $\cos B = \frac{3}{5}$, $\tan B = \frac{4}{3}$

6. $\sin A = \frac{48}{73}$, $\cos A = \frac{55}{73}$, $\tan A = \frac{48}{55}$, $\sin B = \frac{55}{73}$, $\cos B = \frac{48}{73}$, $\tan B = \frac{55}{48}$

7. $\sin A = \frac{36}{85}$, $\cos A = \frac{77}{85}$, $\tan A = \frac{36}{77}$, $\sin B = \frac{77}{85}$, $\cos B = \frac{36}{85}$, $\tan B = \frac{77}{36}$

8. *Sample answer:* Use the Pythagorean theorem to find that the length of the other leg is 4 units. Use this fact to find the cosine ratio, $\frac{4}{5}$.

Additional Resources

The following resources are available to help review the materials in this chapter.

Chapter 9 Resource Book
- Chapter Review Games and Activities, p. 60
- Cumulative Practice, Chs. 1-9

English/Spanish Chapter Reviews and Tests

Chapter Audio Summaries CDs

eTutorial CD-ROM

eWorkbook Plus Online

eTutorial Plus Online

1. *Sample answer:* A rational number can be written as a quotient of two integers, while an irrational number cannot. A rational number has a decimal representation that either terminates or repeats, while an irrational number does not.

17–20. Sample explanations are given.

17. Rational; 100 is a perfect square, since $10^2 = 100$.
18. Rational; $0.\overline{6} = \frac{2}{3}$, which is the quotient of two integers.
19. Rational; $\frac{16}{25}$ is the quotient of two integers.
20. Irrational; 6 is not a perfect square.

Chapter Review

Vocabulary

square root, p. 431
radical expression, p. 431
perfect square, p. 432
irrational number, p. 437
real number, p. 437
leg, p. 443
hypotenuse, p. 443
Pythagorean theorem, p. 443
converse, p. 444
Pythagorean triple, p. 451
trigonometric ratio, p. 463
sine, p. 463
cosine, p. 463
tangent, p. 463

Vocabulary Review

1. Describe the difference between a *rational number* and an *irrational number*.
2. Give three examples of rational numbers. *Sample answer:* 3, $\sqrt{4}$, $\frac{4}{5}$
3. Give three examples of irrational numbers. *Sample answer:* $\sqrt{2}$, π, $\sqrt{7}$
4. Describe how the *lengths of the legs* and *the length of the hypotenuse* of a right triangle are related. The sum of the squares of the lengths of the legs equals the square of the length of the hypotenuse.

Copy and complete the statement.

5. A(n) _?_ is any number that has integer square roots. perfect square
6. In a right triangle, the side opposite the right angle is the _?_. hypotenuse
7. In a 30°-60°-90° triangle, the _?_ leg is opposite the 30° angle. shorter
8. Sine, cosine, and tangent are _?_ ratios. trigonometric

Review Questions

Use a calculator to approximate the square root. Round to the nearest hundredth, if necessary. *(Lesson 9.1)*

9. $\sqrt{94.09}$ 9.7
10. $-\sqrt{784}$ −28
11. $-\sqrt{2118}$ −46.02
12. $\sqrt{941}$ 30.68

Solve the equation. *(Lesson 9.1)*

13. $m^2 = 196$ ±14
14. $a^2 - 1296 = 0$ ±36
15. $c^2 - 28 = 36$ ±8
16. $x^2 + 15 = 51$ ±6

Tell whether the number is *rational* or *irrational*. Explain your reasoning. *(Lesson 9.2)* 17–20. See margin.

17. $\sqrt{100}$
18. $0.\overline{6}$
19. $\frac{16}{25}$
20. $\sqrt{6}$

21. Order the decimals $0.1\overline{8}$, $0.\overline{181}$, $0.\overline{18}$, and 0.188 from least to greatest. *(Lesson 9.2)* $0.\overline{181}$, $0.\overline{18}$, 0.188, $0.1\overline{8}$

Review Questions

Find the unknown length. *(Lesson 9.3)*

22. 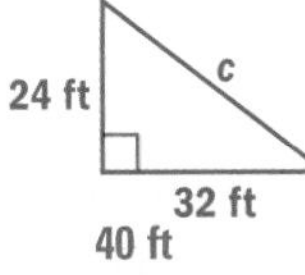

40 ft

23. 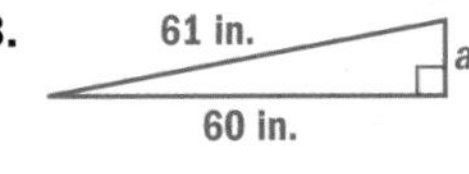

11 in.

24. 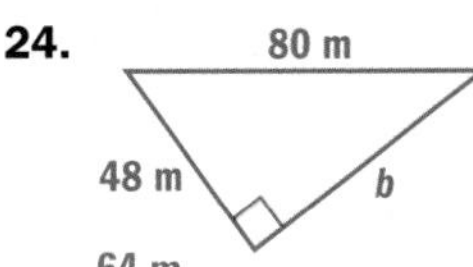

64 m

Determine whether the numbers form a Pythagorean triple. *(Lesson 9.4)*

25. 9, 40, 45 no **26.** 24, 10, 28 no **27.** 72, 54, 90 yes **28.** 133, 156, 205 yes

29. Ski Lift A ski lift has a horizontal length of 662 meters and a vertical height of 152 meters. Find the length of the ski lift. Round to the nearest hundredth of a meter. *(Lesson 9.4)* 679.23 m

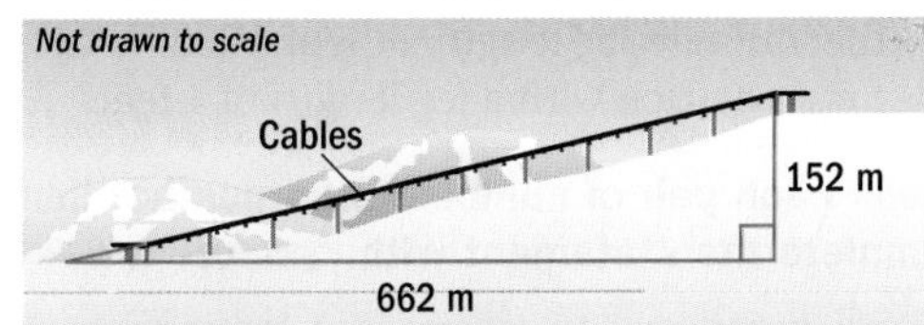

Find the value of each variable. Give exact answers. *(Lesson 9.5)*

30. 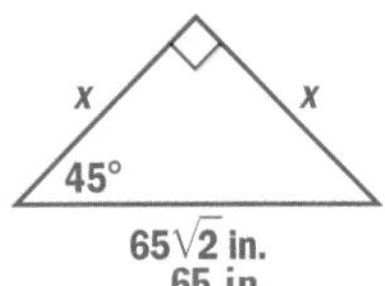

65 in.

31. 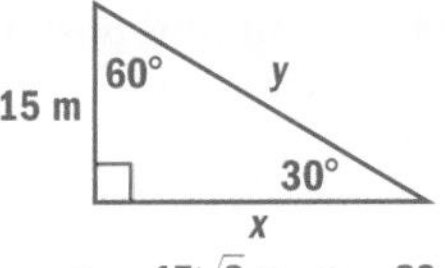

$x = 15\sqrt{3}$ m, $y = 30$ m

32. 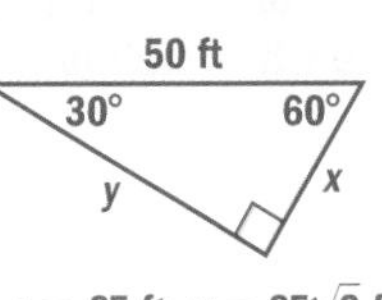

$x = 25$ ft, $y = 25\sqrt{3}$ ft

In $\triangle PQR$, write the sine, cosine, and tangent ratios for $\angle P$ and $\angle Q$.
(Lesson 9.6) 33–35. See margin.

33. 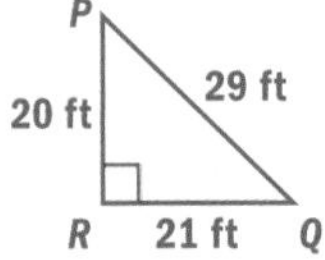

34. 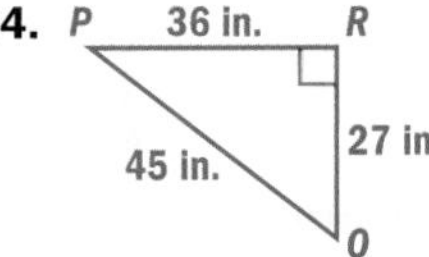

35. 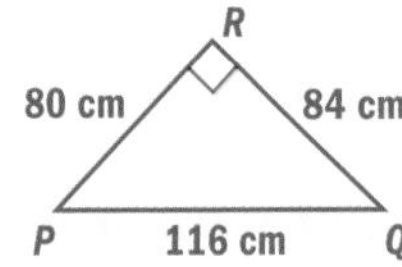

Use a calculator to approximate the given expression. Round your answer to four decimal places. *(Lesson 9.6)*

36. sin 72° 0.9511 **37.** tan 18.5° 0.3346 **38.** cos 49° 0.6561 **39.** tan 40° 0.8391

40. Skateboard Ramp You are constructing a skateboard ramp like the one shown in the diagram. Find the lengths of the legs of the triangle that supports the ramp. Round your answers to the nearest tenth of a foot. *(Lesson 9.6)* $x \approx 2.7$ ft, $y \approx 7.5$ ft

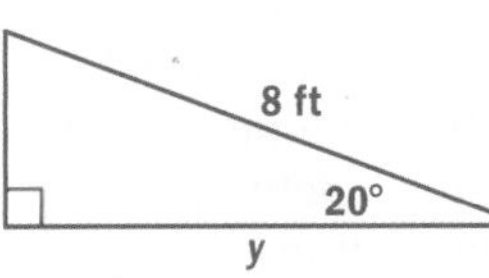

33. $\sin P = \frac{21}{29}$, $\cos P = \frac{20}{29}$, $\tan P = \frac{21}{20}$, $\sin Q = \frac{20}{29}$, $\cos Q = \frac{21}{29}$, $\tan Q = \frac{20}{21}$

34. $\sin P = \frac{3}{5}$, $\cos P = \frac{4}{5}$, $\tan P = \frac{3}{4}$, $\sin Q = \frac{4}{5}$, $\cos Q = \frac{3}{5}$, $\tan Q = \frac{4}{3}$

35. $\sin P = \frac{21}{29}$, $\cos P = \frac{20}{29}$, $\tan P = \frac{21}{20}$, $\sin Q = \frac{20}{29}$, $\cos Q = \frac{21}{29}$, $\tan Q = \frac{20}{21}$

ADDITIONAL RESOURCES

Assessment Book

- Chapter Test (3 levels), pp. 109–114
- Standardized Chapter Test, p. 115
- Alternative Assessment, pp. 116–117

Test and Practice Generator

6. 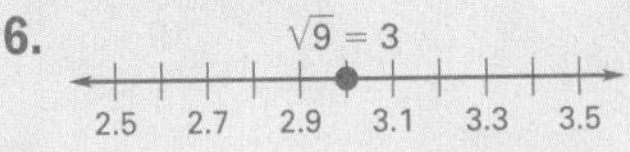

7. 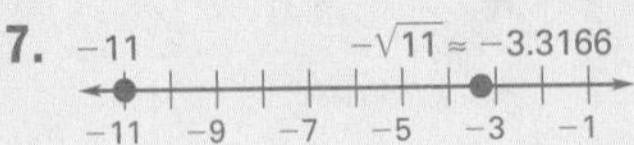

8. 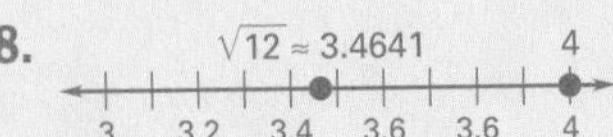

Chapter 9 Chapter Test

Solve the equation.

1. $x^2 = 49$ ±7
2. $m^2 + 41 = 162$ ±11
3. $n^2 - 63 = 162$ ±15
4. $a^2 + 88 = 232$ ±12

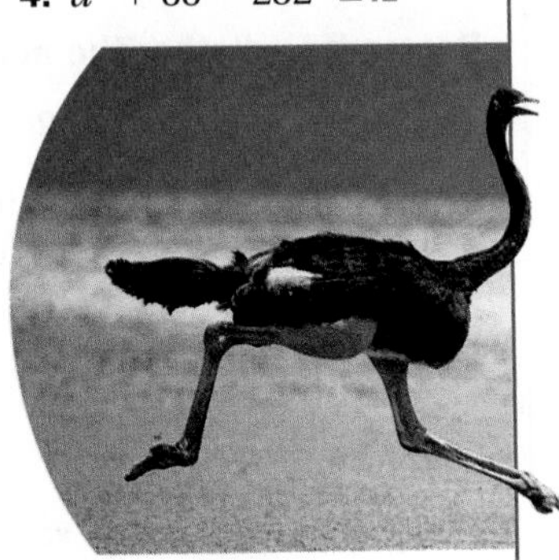

5. **Zoology** Dr. R. McNeill Alexander studies the motion of animals. From his studies, he determined that the maximum walking speed s, in feet per second, that an animal can walk is $s = 5.66\sqrt{l}$ where l is the animal's leg length, in feet. What is the maximum walking speed for an ostrich with a leg length of 4 feet? 11.32 ft/sec

Graph each pair of numbers on a number line. Then copy and complete the statement with <, >, or =. 6–8. See margin for art.

6. $\sqrt{9}$ _?_ 3 =
7. -11 _?_ $-\sqrt{11}$ <
8. $\sqrt{12}$ _?_ 4 <

Find the length of the unknown side of the right triangle. Round to the nearest tenth, if necessary. Then find the area and perimeter.

9. 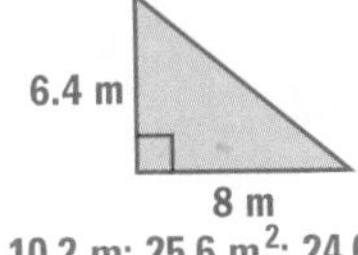

10.2 m; 25.6 m²; 24.6 m

10. 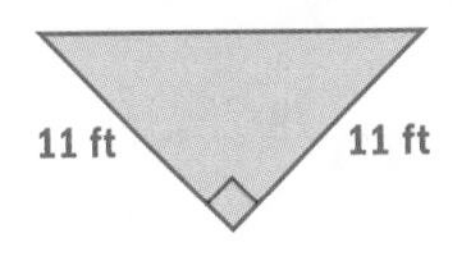

15.6 ft; 60.5 ft²; 37.6 ft

11. 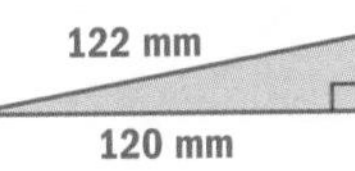

22 mm; 1320 mm²; 264 mm

Determine whether the triangle with the given side lengths is a right triangle.

12. $a = 28, b = 96, c = 100$ yes
13. $a = 22.5, b = 30, c = 37.5$ yes
14. $a = 1.8, b = 6.2, c = 41.68$ no

Find the value of each variable. Give exact answers.

15. 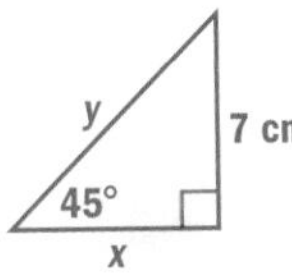

$x = 7$ cm, $y = 7\sqrt{2}$ cm

16. 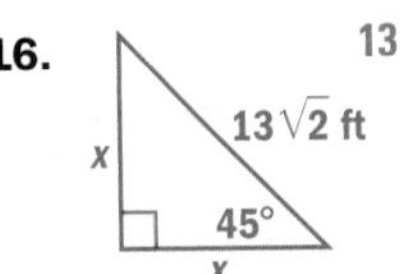

13 ft

17. 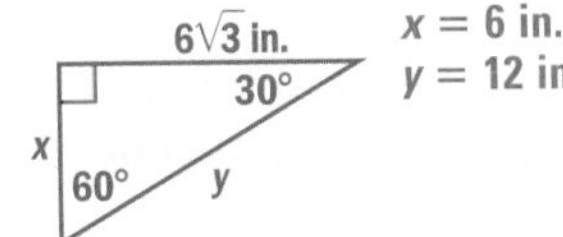

$x = 6$ in., $y = 12$ in.

18. **Incline** In the 1870s, a motorized incline was built in Pittsburgh, PA, to climb the steep hill known as Mt. Washington located at the mouth of the Monongahela River. The track of the incline is 793 feet long and makes a 30° angle with the ground. Find the height of the boarding platform at the top of the incline. 396.5 ft

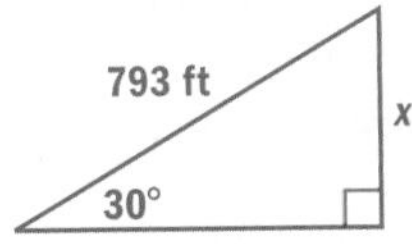

Chapter Standardized Test

Test-Taking Strategy **Some questions involve more than one step. Read each question carefully to be sure you are answering the right question.**

Multiple Choice

1. What is the positive square root of 81? C

A. −18 **B.** −9 **C.** 9 **D.** 18

2. Find the value of $\sqrt{x+y}$ when $x = 12$ and $y = 13$. G

F. 1 **G.** 5 **H.** 25 **I.** 156

3. The area of the square base of a building is 2704 square feet. Find the perimeter of the base of the building. C

A. 52 feet **B.** 104 feet

C. 208 feet **D.** 1352 feet

4. Which number is irrational? H

F. $\frac{2}{5}$ **G.** $\sqrt{4}$ **H.** $\sqrt{7}$ **I.** $\sqrt{49}$

5. Which list *is* in order from least to greatest? B

A. $-1.5, -\sqrt{15}, -\sqrt{5}, -1$

B. $-\sqrt{15}, -\sqrt{5}, -1.5, -1$

C. $-\sqrt{15}, -1.5, -\sqrt{5}, -1$

D. $-1, -1.5, -\sqrt{5}, -\sqrt{15}$

6. Find the length of the hypotenuse of the right triangle below. H

F. 23 cm **G.** 26 cm

H. 29 cm **I.** 32 cm

7. Find the length of the legs of the right triangle. Lengths are given in feet. A

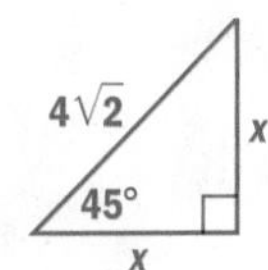

A. 4 feet **B.** 8 feet

C. $8\sqrt{2}$ feet **D.** 16 feet

8. In $\triangle ABC$, find $\sin A$. F

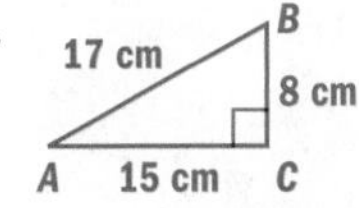

F. $\frac{8}{17}$ **G.** $\frac{8}{15}$ **H.** $\frac{15}{17}$ **I.** $\frac{15}{8}$

Short Response

9. **Space Needle** You are standing 400 feet from the base of the Space Needle in Seattle, Washington. Using a laser range finder, you measure the distance to the top of the Space Needle to be 725 feet. Find the height of the Space Needle to the nearest foot. 605 ft

Extended Response

10. **Quilting** Jenwa is making a quilt using a design based on the pattern shown below. This pattern is a spiral design using right triangles. It is called the Wheel of Theodorus. Working from left to right, use the Pythagorean theorem in each right triangle to find the values of r, s, t, and u. Then identify the 45°-45°-90° triangle in the figure.

$r = \sqrt{2}$, $s = \sqrt{3}$, $t = 2$, $u = \sqrt{5}$; the triangle with hypotenuse r

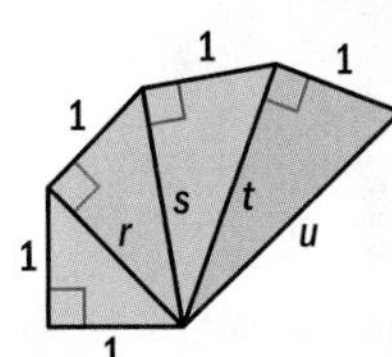

Additional Resources

Assessment Book
- Standardized Chapter Test, p. 115

Test and Practice Generator

PLAN

Explore the Concept

- Students apply their knowledge of the sine ratio.
- The sine ratio was studied in Lesson 6 of Chapter 9.
- Earth's atmosphere interferes with a telescope's view of celestial objects.

Science Background

The purpose of a telescope is to gather as much light from the observed object as possible, without gathering other light that interferes. Observatories are built far from cities so there is less man-made light and on top of mountains so there is less atmosphere above the telescope. The Hubble telescope was placed in space to avoid the interference caused by man-made light and the atmosphere.

TEACH

Tips for Success

Students need to check that their calculators are in DEGREE mode. Make sure they understand how the formula for d follows from the formula for $\sin x^\circ$. Discuss Exercise 2 with the class before students continue the Activity to make sure they follow the reasoning.

Guiding Students' Work

If students are having difficulty understanding why increasing the angle of elevation decreases d, you may want to have them insert a row for $\sin x^\circ$ in the table between the given rows. In Exercise 4, point out that the atmosphere is much denser near Earth's surface, with half of the air below about 5.5 kilometers.

2, 4. See Additional Answers beginning on page AA1.

Viewing the STARS

Aiming a Telescope

Earth's atmosphere extends about 1000 kilometers from its surface. As light from stars passes through the atmosphere, some of it is absorbed or scattered by the molecules in the air. Without atmospheric interference, the stars in the night sky would appear much brighter.

An astronomer can minimize this interference by aiming a telescope so that star light passes through as little atmosphere as possible. If you know a star's *angle of elevation*, you can use trigonometry to find how far its light travels through the atmosphere to reach the telescope.

Angle of Elevation In the diagram, light from a star travels a distance of d kilometers through Earth's atmosphere to the telescope. The measure of the star's *angle of elevation* above Earth's surface is x°.

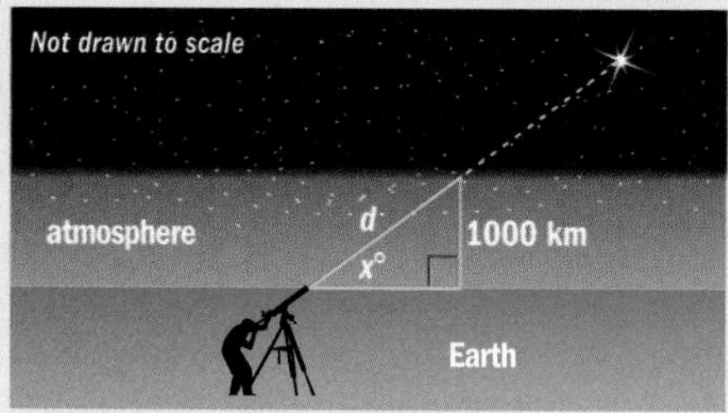

1. Because $\sin x^\circ = \frac{1000}{d}$, you can use the equation $d = \frac{1000}{\sin x^\circ}$ to find d. Copy and complete the table below.

angle of elevation x°	10°	20°	30°	40°	50°	60°	70°	80°
distance d (km)	?	?	?	?	?	?	?	?

5758.8 2923.8 2000 1555.7 1305.4 1154.7 1064.2 1015.4

2. **Critical Thinking** At what angle should you aim a telescope to look through the least amount of atmosphere? Explain your reasoning. **See margin.**

Comparing Observatories

Observatories, buildings devoted to observing the night sky, are often placed at high elevations. Hanle Observatory in India, the world's highest, is about 4.5 kilometers above sea level.

How does raising a telescope's elevation affect the distance a star's light travels through the atmosphere for a given angle of elevation? Use the formula from the previous page to find out.

Telescope at Sea Level

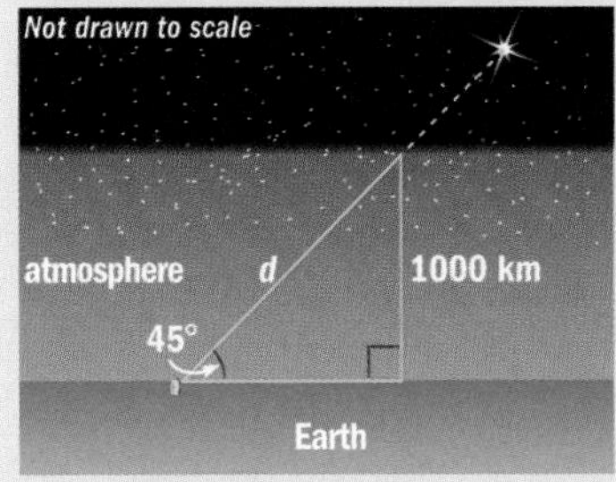

Telescope at Hanle Observatory

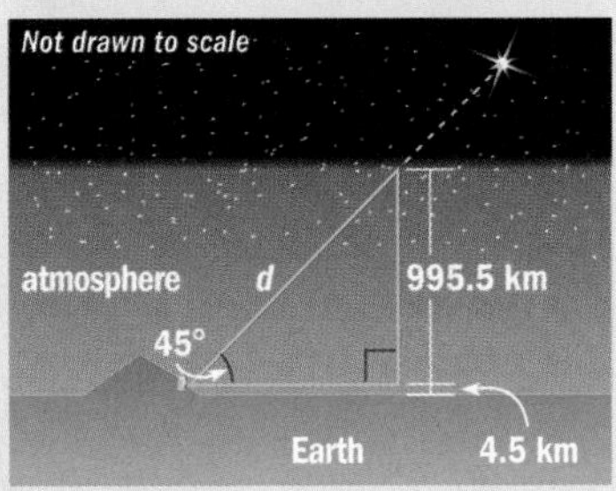

3. Find the distance d, in kilometers, that light travels through the atmosphere to reach a telescope at sea level, given an angle of elevation of 45°. Then find the value of d for Hanle Observatory. **1414.2 km; 1407.8 km**

4. **Critical Thinking** Compare the distances you found in Exercise 3. How does a change in elevation affect d? Do you think this difference is significant? Explain. **See margin.**

Project IDEAS

- **Experiment** Measure an object's shadow. Draw a diagram to explain how to use trigonometry to find the object's height if you know the shadow's length and the sun's angle of elevation. Present your findings to the class.
- **Extension** Locate some major astronomical observatories placed at high elevations, and find out why these locations were chosen. Present your findings to the class.
- **Research** The angle of elevation of the moon above Earth's horizon may affect its apparent color. Find out how and why an object's apparent color changes as it moves across the sky. Present your findings to the class.
- **Career** What subjects would you study if you were preparing to be an astronomer? Present your findings to the class.

3 APPLY

Reflecting on the Activity

The distance through the atmosphere that a star's light passes can be found by using the angle of elevation and the thickness of the atmosphere to write a sine ratio.

Project Ideas

For additional information on the Project Ideas and for suggestions for more projects, go to classzone.com

4 ASSESS

The rubric below can be used to assess the projects on the pupil page. For more information on rubrics, see the Professional Development Book.

4 The student fully achieves the mathematical and project goals. The student shows understanding of why a steeper angle of elevation should be used, and supports her or his decision about the significance of placing an observatory at a high elevation. All work is complete and accurate.

3 The student substantially achieves the mathematical and project goals. Explanations to Critical Thinking questions show some understanding, but may be incomplete. There may be some minor misunderstanding of content or errors in computation.

2 The student partially achieves the mathematical and project goals. The student is able to complete most computations, but provides inadequate explanations. Some of the work may be incomplete, misdirected, or unclear.

1 The student makes little progress toward accomplishing the goals of the project because of a lack of understanding or lack of effort. The student is unable to provide adequate work beyond finding table values.

CHAPTER 10

Pacing and Assignment Guide

REGULAR SCHEDULE

Lesson	Les. Day	BASIC	AVERAGE	ADVANCED
10.1	Day 1	SRH p. 713 Exs. 11-15; pp. 483-485 Exs. 8-13, 29, 35, 40-42	pp. 483-485 Exs. 10-12, 21-23, 30-32, 40-43	pp. 483-485 Exs. 10-12, 22-26, 32-36
	Day 2	pp. 483-485 Exs. 15-23, 31, 43, 44	pp. 483-485 Exs. 14-17, 24-27, 33-35, 44, 45	pp. 483-485 Exs. 14-17, 28-30, 37-39*, 43-45
10.2	Day 1	EP p. 732 Exs. 19-22; pp. 488-490 Exs. 6-12, 19-25, 29-31, 36-39	pp. 488-490 Exs. 7-9, 13-18, 22, 25-29, 32-34, 36-40	pp. 488-490 Exs. 7-9, 13-18, 22, 26-28, 31-36*, 38-40
10.3	Day 1	pp. 494-495 Exs. 7-11, 13-17, 19-21, 24-27	pp. 494-495 Exs. 9-18, 21-27	pp. 494-495 Exs. 9-11, 13-26, EC: TE p. 478D*
10.4	Day 1	SRH p. 705 Exs. 11-15; pp. 505-506 Exs. 5-8, 18-21, 30-34	pp. 505-506 Exs. 5-8, 18-20, 26-32	pp. 505-506 Exs. 5-8, 18-20, 26-31
	Day 2	pp. 505-506 Exs. 9-17, 26-29	pp. 505-506 Exs. 9-16, 22-24, 33-35	pp. 505-506 Exs. 10-16, 22-25*, 33-35
10.5	Day 1	pp. 510-511 Exs. 6-11, 14-20, 23-28, 32-37	pp. 510-511 Exs. 8-13, 16-22, 24-30, 32-38	pp. 510-511 Exs. 8-13, 16-20, 22-26, 28-33*, 36-38
10.6	Day 1	pp. 516-517 Exs. 6-10, 13-15, 19-26, 33-38	pp. 516-517 Exs. 9-12, 16-18, 21-24, 27-31, 33-38	pp. 516-517 Exs. 9-12, 16-18, 22-24, 27-38*
10.7	Day 1	pp. 522-523 Exs. 8-16, 26, 35-37	pp. 522-523 Exs. 10-15, 26-28, 35-37	pp. 522-523 Exs. 10-14, 26-30, 35-37
	Day 2	pp. 522-523 Exs. 17-25, 27, 38-40	pp. 522-523 Exs. 18-23, 29-31, 38-40	pp. 522-523 Exs. 18-23, 31-34*, 38-40
Review	Day 1	pp. 526-527 Exs. 1-35	pp. 526-527 Exs. 1-35	pp. 526-527 Exs. 1-35
Assess	Day 1	Chapter 10 Test	Chapter 10 Test	Chapter 10 Test

YEARLY PACING Chapter 10 Total – **12 days** Chapters 1–10 Total – **116 days** Remaining – **44 days**

*Challenge Exercises EP = Extra Practice SRH = Skills Review Handbook EC = Extra Challenge

BLOCK SCHEDULE

DAY 1	DAY 2	DAY 3	DAY 4	DAY 5	DAY 6
10.1 pp. 483-485 Exs. 10-12, 14-17, 21-27, 30-35, 40-45	**10.2** pp. 488-490 Exs. 7-9, 13-18, 22, 25-29, 32-34, 36-40 **10.3** pp. 494-495 Exs. 9-18, 21-27	**10.4** pp. 505-506 Exs. 5-16, 18-20, 22-24, 26-35	**10.5** pp. 510-511 Exs. 8-13, 16-22, 24-30, 32-38 **10.6** pp. 516-517 Exs. 9-12, 16-18, 21-24, 27-31, 33-38	**10.7** pp. 522-523 Exs. 10-15, 18-23, 26-31, 35-40	**Review** pp. 526-527 Exs. 1-35 **Assess** Chapter 10 Test

YEARLY PACING Chapter 10 Total – **6 days** Chapters 1–10 Total – **58 days** Remaining – **22 days**

Support Materials

CHAPTER RESOURCE BOOK

CHAPTER SUPPORT							
Tips for New Teachers	p. 1			Parents as Partners			p. 3

LESSON SUPPORT	10.1	10.2	10.3	10.4	10.5	10.6	10.7
Lesson Plans (regular and block)	p. 7	p. 15	p. 25	p. 34	p. 42	p. 50	p. 59
Technology Activities & Keystrokes		p. 17					p. 61
Activity Support Masters							
Activity Masters			p. 27				
Practice (3 levels)	p. 9	p. 18	p. 28	p. 36	p. 44	p. 52	p. 63
Study Guide	p. 12	p. 21	p. 31	p. 39	p. 47	p. 55	p. 66
Real-World Problem Solving		p. 23				p. 57	
Challenge Practice	p. 14	p. 24	p. 33	p. 41	p. 49	p. 58	p. 68

REVIEW			
Games Support Masters	p. 5	Cooperative Project with Rubric	p. 72
Chapter Review Games and Activities	p. 69	Extra Credit Project with Rubric	p. 74
Real-Life Project with Rubric	p. 70	Cumulative Practice	p. 76
		Resource Book Answers	A1

ASSESSMENT

Quizzes	p. 118	Alternative Assessments with Rubrics	p. 127
Chapter Tests (3 levels)	p. 120	Unit Test	p. 129
Standardized Test	p. 126	Cumulative Test	p. 131

TRANSPARENCIES

	10.1	10.2	10.3	10.4	10.5	10.6	10.7
Warm-Up / Daily Homework Quiz	✔	✔	✔	✔	✔	✔	✔
Notetaking Guide	✔	✔	✔	✔	✔	✔	✔
Teacher Support	✔						
English/Spanish Problem Solving	✔	✔		✔			✔
Answer Transparencies	✔	✔	✔	✔	✔	✔	✔

TECHNOLOGY

- EasyPlanner CD-ROM
- Test and Practice Generator
- Electronic Lesson Presentations
- eTutorial CD-ROM
- Chapter Audio Summaries CDs
- Classzone.com
- eEdition Plus Online
- eWorkbook Plus Online
- eTutorial Plus Online
- EasyPlanner Plus Online

ADDITIONAL RESOURCES

- Worked-Out Solution Key
- Notetaking Guide
- Practice Workbook
- Tutor Place
- Professional Development Book
- Special Activities Book
- Posters
- Spanish Study Guide
- Exercises in Spanish
- English/Spanish Ch. Reviews/Tests
- Multi-Language Visual Glossary

Math Background and Teaching Strategies

Lesson 10.1

MATH BACKGROUND

AREAS OF PARALLELOGRAMS AND TRAPEZOIDS The region bounded by any parallelogram can be transformed into a rectangular region with the same base and height by cutting off and repositioning a triangular region. So, the area of a parallelogram is the product of its base and height, where the base can be any side and the height is the perpendicular distance between the base and its opposite side. By duplicating any trapezoidal region and rearranging the two copies, you can form a parallelogram with the same height whose base is the sum of the bases (the parallel sides) of the trapezoid. So, the area of a trapezoid is one half the product of the sum of its bases and its height.

TEACHING STRATEGIES

To help students avoid confusing the height of a parallelogram with a side adjacent a base, point out as shown below that you can "squash" a parallelogram without changing the base or the side adjacent a base. Clearly, the area decreases. But if the height is a perpendicular segment of a given length, the parallelogram can no longer be squashed.

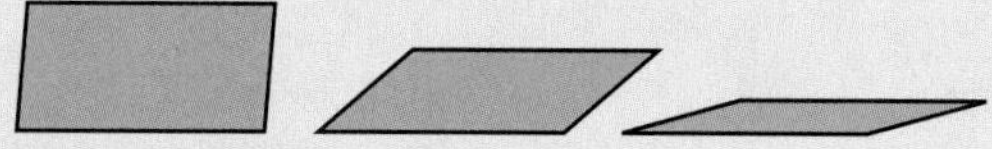

You may also want to have students draw parallelograms with the same base and height, but with different degrees of slant. By cutting and rearranging, students can see that the same rectangle can be formed, so the parallelograms have the same area.

Lesson 10.2

MATH BACKGROUND

One way to estimate the area of a circle is to inscribe regular polygons with an increasing number of sides in the circle and use their areas as closer and closer approximations. But as with the formula for the circumference of a circle, the formula for the area of a circle requires the irrational number π. Specifically, the area of a circle is the product of π and the square of the radius of the circle.

TEACHING STRATEGIES

Students sometimes confuse the area and circumference formulas for circles. Remind them that area is measured in *square* units, which corresponds to the *square* of the radius in the formula $A = \pi r^2$. Also watch for students who use the diameter in the area formula instead of the radius. You may want to ask students what the effect of using diameter instead of radius in the area formula would be. By substituting $2r$ for r in the area formula, they should be able to discern that the result would be a value for the area that is 4 times the actual value.

Lesson 10.3

MATH BACKGROUND

SOLIDS A **polyhedron** is a solid enclosed by polygons, which form its **faces**. A **prism** is a polyhedron that has two polygonal bases that are parallel and congruent. Its other faces are rectangles. A **pyramid** is a polyhedron that has a single polygonal base. Its other faces are triangles that meet at a single vertex. Prisms and pyramids are classified by the shape of their bases. Some other solids are a **cylinder**, which has two circular bases that are parallel and congruent, a **cone**, which has one circular base and a single vertex, and a **sphere**, which is the locus of points equidistant from a single point in space.

TEACHING STRATEGIES

Have students complete the chart below to help them learn to identify the characteristics of a polyhedron. You can add solids to those named in the chart, and, if you wish, use a "random" order instead of the one shown.

Polyhedron	No. of bases	Base shape	No. of faces	Face shape
Trang. prism				
Trang. pyr.				
Rect. prism				
Rect. pyr.				
Square prism				
Square pyr.				
Pentag. prism				
Pentag. pyr.				

Lesson 10.4

MATH BACKGROUND

The **surface area** of a polyhedron is the sum of the areas of its faces. For a prism, this can be found more simply by adding twice the area of the polygon that forms the base to the product of the perimeter of a base and the height of the prism. The algorithm for finding the surface area of a cylinder is the same as that for finding the surface area of a prism, but with "perimeter" replaced by "circumference."

TEACHING STRATEGIES

NETS By working with physical objects, students can better understand nets and surface area. For example, students can cut a label from a canned good and flatten it to see that the length of the rectangle formed matches the circumference of the can. They can also cut circles for the ends of the can and use these as part of the net for the can. Students can also cut an empty cereal box and flatten it, and observe how the net formed relates to the perimeter of a base of the box.

Lesson 10.5

MATH BACKGROUND

PYRAMIDS AND CONES Finding a simple algorithm for the surface area of a pyramid parallels doing so for a prism, but with some twists. First, there is only one base. Second, the faces are triangles, not rectangles, and third, in a prism the height of each face matches that of the prism, but the height of each face in a pyramid, the **slant height**, does not match the height of the pyramid. To find the surface area of a pyramid, add the base area to half the product of the perimeter of the base and the slant height. For a cone, this translates to the surface area formula $S = \pi r^2 + \pi rl$.

TEACHING STRATEGIES

Make sure students can connect the formula for the surface area of a cone, $S = \pi r^2 + \pi rl$, to the formula for the surface area of a pyramid, $S = B + \frac{1}{2}Pl$. They should notice that B and πr^2 correspond directly. In the formula for a pyramid, $\frac{1}{2}P$ is half the perimeter of the base. The "perimeter" of a circle is its circumference, or $2\pi r$, so half of $2\pi r$ is πr, which appears in the formula for the surface area of the cone.

Lesson 10.6

MATH BACKGROUND

The **volume** of a solid is a measure of the space it occupies. The volume of a prism or a cylinder is just the product of the area of its base and its height. Volume is measured in cubic units, since the volume of space any solid occupies can be represented to any desired degree of accuracy as the sum of the volumes of a number of cubes.

TEACHING STRATEGIES

Make sure students understand the idea of volume in the Hands-on Activity preceding this lesson. The volume formulas for prisms and cylinders will likely be easier for students to remember than their surface area formulas. Remind students that a prism does not have to be resting on a base, and that the height is the measure perpendicular to the base, and so may not be a vertical measure.

Lesson 10.7

MATH BACKGROUND

The volume of a pyramid or cone is one third the volume of the prism or cylinder that has the same base and height, that is, the volume of a pyramid or cone is $V = \frac{1}{3}Bh$. In the case of a cylinder, this translates to $V = \frac{1}{3}\pi r^2 h$.

TEACHING STRATEGIES

Students often expect the volume of a pyramid to be one half the volume of the prism with the same base and height, and may be surprised at the results of the Hands-on Activity preceding the lesson. You can use the diagram below to show that it takes more than two pyramids to fill a prism. By cutting two wedges from the prism as shown and repositioning them, two tent-shaped solids are formed. Since it would require two more cuts in each tent-shaped solid to form pyramids with the same base and height as the original prism, the prism clearly "contains" more than two pyramids.

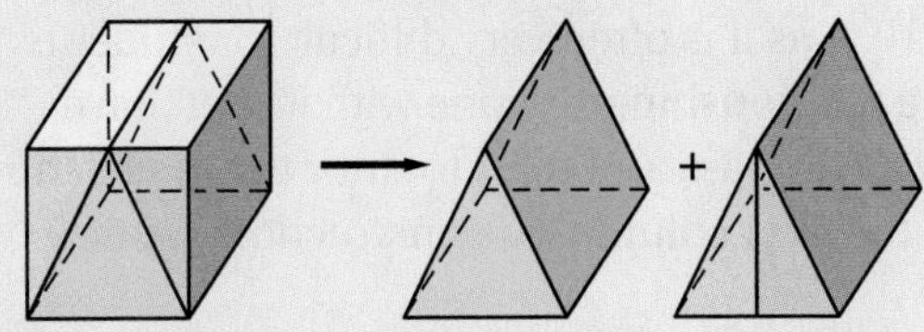

CHAPTER 10 Differentiating Instruction

Strategies for Underachievers

USE MODELS AND MANIPULATIVES

Beginning with Lesson 10.3, because students at the level of this course may have little or no experience working with and classifying geometric solids, it is a great help to have models of solids available in the classroom, whether they are specifically designed for this purpose or just classroom or household objects like cans, cereal boxes, conical paper cups, and so on. It may be very helpful for some students to be allowed to create solids out of modeling clay. Encourage students to list the differences and similarities they find among the solids as they manipulate them.

For the Special Topic section on sketching solids that begins on page 496, underachievers especially will benefit from access to building blocks, multi-link cubes, centimeter cubes, or unifix cubes. You can have students draw the three views of their construction and then have a partner try to build a model out of the cubes that satisfies all of the conditions of the drawing. Ask students to examine whether there is more than one model that meets the conditions of the given views, and, if so, to build any such additional models. Students should also practice building different models with the cubes and then sketching the views on grid paper.

SOLIDS AND NETS In Lesson 10.4, students can increase their ability to visualize the relationship between solids and nets by outlining the faces of solids on paper. For example, to draw the net of a pyramid, students can first outline the base. Then, without otherwise moving the pyramid, students can tilt the pyramid onto one of its faces, outline that face, and then tilt the pyramid back to its base. By repeating this process for each side, students can draw a net. Also beginning with Lesson 10.4, you may wish to bring in pre-made nets of various solids that students can fold and unfold.

In Lesson 10.5, as it is often very difficult for students to picture the relationship of a cone with its net, have students use a compass and ruler to draw the figure shown at the top of the next column on construction paper.

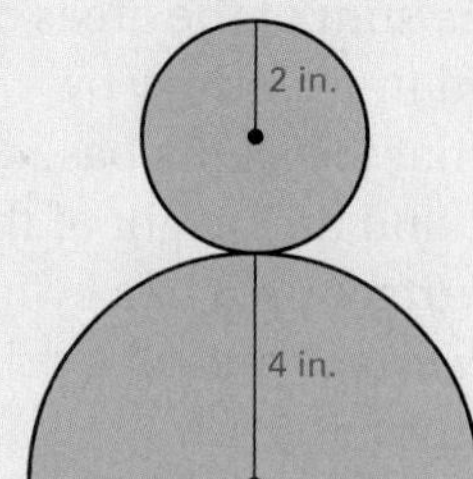

Have students make the calculations to verify that the circumference of the circle is equal to the length of the arc of the semicircle. Point out that this is always true in a cone because the edge of the side of the cone has to wrap all the way around the circle that forms the base. Students can then cut out the net (leaving the circle and semicircle connected at their point of tangency) and fold and tape it to form a cone. Have students work in pairs to help each other fold and tape. Students can further explore nets of cones by removing sectors of various sizes from paper circles and then folding and taping the fan shapes that remain to form the lateral surface of cones. Students should notice that the greater the arc of the circle that remains, the shorter and wider is the cone.

MAKE REAL-WORLD CONNECTIONS

Some students may enjoy investigating product packaging. For example, why are some canned foods in short, fat, cans (e.g., tuna), while others are in taller cylinders? Why are products like cereal in tall, wide prisms when a cube would take less packaging to hold the same volume?

Strategies for English Learners

VOCABULARY STUDY OF ROOTS

The analysis of Greek and Latin roots in mathematical terms and common English words is a good activity for all students because it helps them figure out the meanings of new words. Students who speak a language in addition to English may find words in other languages that are derived from Greek and Latin roots. This word study could be covered in a few minutes each week during math class or in a more extended way during the language arts period.

First review words that describe shapes, such as circle, triangle, square, rectangle, quadrilateral, vertices, angle, prism, polygon, pentagon, hexagon, octagon, trapezoid, isosceles triangle, right triangle, right angle, rectangular solid, sphere, pyramid, and cylinder. Then have students look at the following table of Greek and Latin roots.

Greek or Latin Root	Mathematical Terms
congruere (Latin, *to agree*)	*congru*ent, *congru*ence, *congru*ity, *congru*ous
polys (Greek, *many*)	*poly*gon, *poly*hedron, *poly*hedral
hedra (Greek, *surface*)	poly*hedr*on, octa*hedr*al
circum (Latin, *around*)	*circum*ference
circulus (Latin, *circle* or *ring*)	*circl*e, *circul*ar
ferre (Latin, *bear, carry*)	circum*fere*nce, peri*pher*y
secare (Latin, *to cut*)	inter*sect*, inter*sect*ion
capere (Latin, *to seize* or *stop*)	inter*cept*, inter*cept*ion

PREFIXES Some common Greek and Latin prefixes are listed below:

bi- (from the Latin for *two*)
co-, com-, cum- (from the Latin for *with*)
dis-, di-, dif- (from the Latin for *away from* or *out of, apart*)
in- (from the Latin for *in* or *not, without*)
inter- (from the Latin for *between*)
iso- (from the Greek for *equal*)
mono- (from the Greek for *single* or *alone*)
multi- (from the Latin for *many*)
para- (from the Greek for *beside*)
per- (from the Latin for *through*, or *by means of*)
poly- (from the Greek for *many*)
pre- (from the Latin for *before*)
re- (from the Latin for *again* or *backward*)
sub- (from the Latin for *under, beneath*)
quad- (from the Latin for *four*)
tri- (from the Latin for *three*)

Strategies for Advanced Learners

INCREASE DEPTH AND COMPLEXITY

TANGRAMS After Lesson 10.1 you may wish to have some advanced students investigate tangram puzzles. Their investigation should include a discussion of the relationship of the areas of the pieces of tangrams.

In conjunction with Lesson 10.3, you may wish to have advanced students investigate the *Platonic solids*, the regular tetrahedron (4 sides), the cube (6 sides), the regular octahedron (8 sides), the regular dodecahedron (12 sides), and the regular icosahedron (20 sides), which have the rather surprising property of being the only regular polyhedrons that can be formed.

In conjunction with Lesson 10.5, you can have advanced learners further investigate the nets of cones. Copy the diagram below for them (for a 90° central angle, R must be 4 times r.)

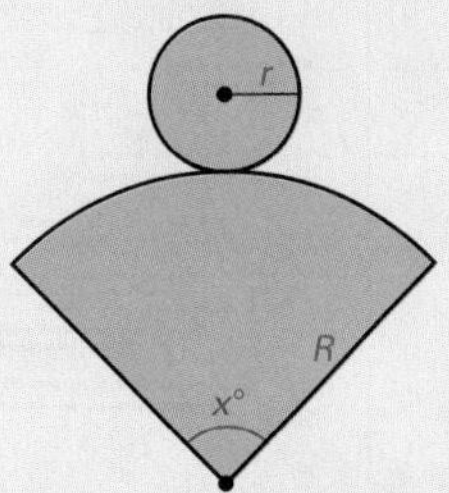

Ask students to find an expression for the value of x that involves R and r by writing a proportion that relates the circumference of circles with radius R and r. You may need to remind them that the circumference of the circle must equal the length of the arc shown. One such proportion is $\frac{x}{360} = \frac{2\pi r}{2\pi R}$, which simplifies to $x = 360 \cdot \frac{r}{R}$.

The following problem, which is an extension of Exercise 18 on page 495, can be used with **Lesson 10.3**:

- **Challenge** Write formulas for the number of edges, vertices, and faces for a pyramid in terms of s, where s is the number of sides of a polygon that forms the base. Then use these expressions to show that Euler's formula holds for prisms. $E = 3s, V = 2s, F = s + 2; F + V - 2 = (s + 2) + 2s - 2 = (s + 2s) + (2 - 2) = 3s = E$

Differentiating Instruction: Teaching Resources

Differentiating Alternative Assessment

McDougal Littell *Middle School Mathematics* offers teachers a wide variety of alternative assessment for all levels of students. Pictured here are facsimiles of the alternative assessment pages from the *Assessment Book*, and the various types of chapter projects available in the *Chapter 10 Resource Book*.

Assessment Book

The *Assessment Book* contains two pages of alternative assessment for each chapter in the textbook.

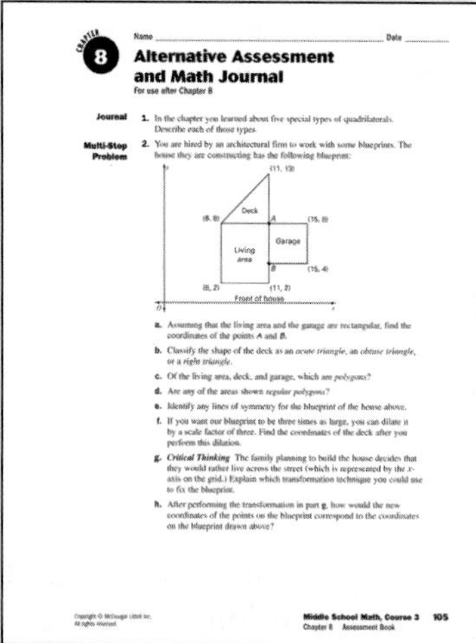

CHAPTER 8

Name ______________________ Date ________

Alternative Assessment and Math Journal

For use after Chapter 8

Journal 1. In the chapter you learned about five special types of quadrilaterals. Describe each of those types.

Multi-Step Problem 2. You are hired by an architectural firm to work with some blueprints. The house they are constructing has the following blueprint:

a. Assuming that the living area and the garage are rectangular, find the coordinates of the points *A* and *B*.

b. Classify the shape of the deck as an *acute triangle*, an *obtuse triangle*, or a *right triangle*.

c. Of the living area, deck, and garage, which are *polygons*?

d. Are any of the areas shown *regular polygons*?

e. Identify any lines of symmetry for the blueprint of the house above.

f. If you want our blueprint to be three times as large, you can dilate it by a scale factor of three. Find the coordinates of the deck after you perform this dilation.

g. ***Critical Thinking*** The family planning to build the house decides that they would rather live across the street (which is represented by the *x*-axis on the grid.) Explain which transformation technique you could use to fix the blueprint.

h. After performing the transformation in part g, how would the new coordinates of the points on the blueprint correspond to the coordinates on the blueprint drawn above?

Copyright © McDougal Littell Inc. All rights reserved.

Middle School Math, Course 3 105
Chapter 8 Assessment Book

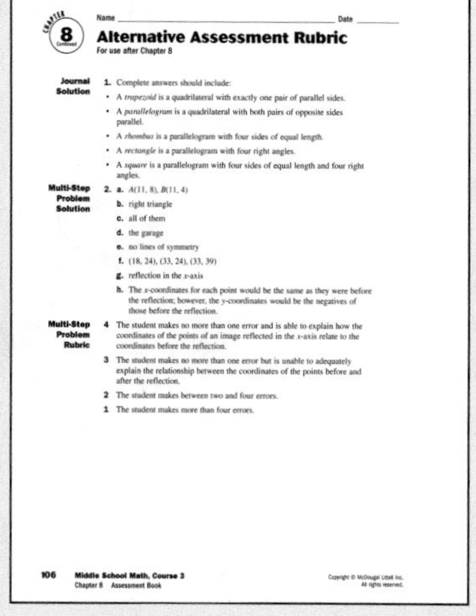

CHAPTER 8 Continued

Name ______________________ Date ________

Alternative Assessment Rubric

For use after Chapter 8

Journal Solution 1. Complete answers should include:

- A *trapezoid* is a quadrilateral with exactly one pair of parallel sides.
- A *parallelogram* is a quadrilateral with both pairs of opposite sides parallel.
- A *rhombus* is a parallelogram with four sides of equal length.
- A *rectangle* is a parallelogram with four right angles.
- A *square* is a parallelogram with four sides of equal length and four right angles.

Multi-Step Problem Solution 2. a. *A*(11, 8), *B*(11, 4)

b. right triangle

c. all of them

d. the garage

e. no lines of symmetry

f. (18, 24), (33, 24), (33, 39)

g. reflection in the *x*-axis

h. The *x*-coordinates for each point would be the same as they were before the reflection; however, the *y*-coordinates would be the negatives of those before the reflection.

Multi-Step Problem Rubric

4 The student makes no more than one error and is able to explain how the coordinates of the points of an image reflected in the *x*-axis relate to the coordinates before the reflection.

3 The student makes no more than one error but is unable to adequately explain the relationship between the coordinates of the points before and after the reflection.

2 The student makes between two and four errors.

1 The student makes more than four errors.

106 Middle School Math, Course 3
Chapter 8 Assessment Book

Copyright © McDougal Littell Inc. All rights reserved.

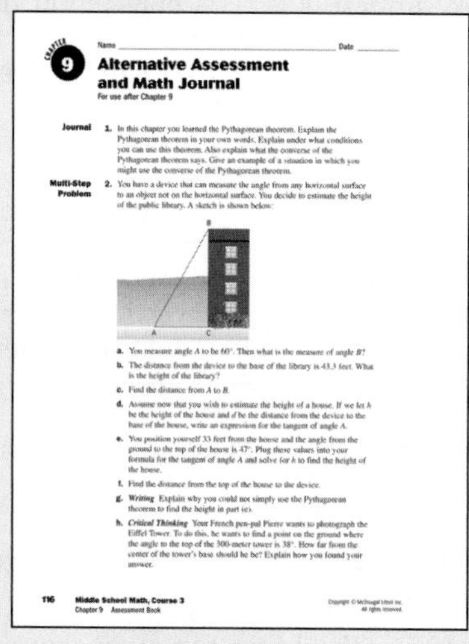

CHAPTER 9

Name ______________________ Date ________

Alternative Assessment and Math Journal

For use after Chapter 9

Journal 1. In this chapter you learned the Pythagorean theorem. Explain the Pythagorean theorem in your own words. Explain under what conditions you can use this theorem. Also explain what the converse of the Pythagorean theorem says. Give an example of a situation in which you might use the converse of the Pythagorean theorem.

Multi-Step Problem 2. You have a device that can measure the angle from any horizontal surface to an object not on the horizontal surface. You decide to estimate the height of the public library. A sketch is shown below:

a. You measure angle *A* to be 60°. Then what is the measure of angle *B*?

b. The distance from the device to the base of the library is 43.3 feet. What is the height of the library?

c. Find the distance from *A* to *B*.

d. Assume now that you wish to estimate the height of a house. If we let *h* be the height of the house and *d* be the distance from the device to the base of the house, write an expression for the tangent of angle *A*.

e. You position yourself 33 feet from the house and the angle from the ground to the top of the house is 47°. Plug these values into your formula for the tangent of angle *A* and solve for *h* to find the height of the house.

f. Find the distance from the top of the house to the device.

g. ***Writing*** Explain why you could not simply use the Pythagorean theorem to find the height in part (e).

h. ***Critical Thinking*** Your French pen-pal Pierre wants to photograph the Eiffel Tower. To do this, he wants to find a point on the ground where the angle to the top of the 300-meter tower is 38°. How far from the center of the tower's base should he be? Explain how you found your answer.

116 Middle School Math, Course 3
Chapter 9 Assessment Book

Copyright © McDougal Littell Inc. All rights reserved.

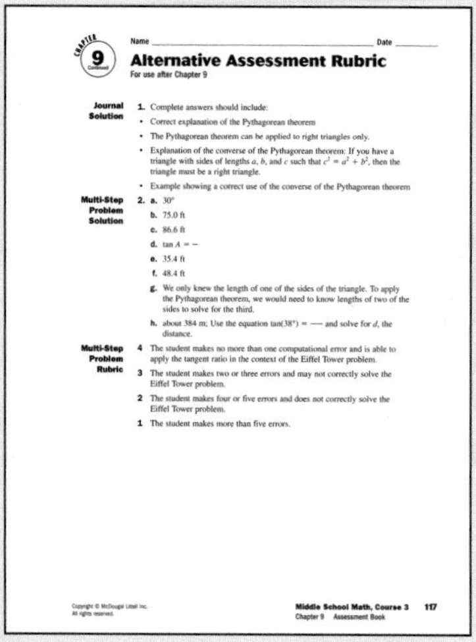

CHAPTER 9 Continued

Name ______________________ Date ________

Alternative Assessment Rubric

For use after Chapter 9

Journal Solution 1. Complete answers should include:

- Correct explanation of the Pythagorean theorem
- The Pythagorean theorem can be applied to right triangles only.
- Explanation of the converse of the Pythagorean theorem: If you have a triangle with sides of lengths *a*, *b*, and *c* such that $c^2 = a^2 + b^2$, then the triangle must be a right triangle.
- Example showing a correct use of the converse of the Pythagorean theorem

Multi-Step Problem Solution 2. a. 30°

b. 75.0 ft

c. 86.6 ft

d. $\tan A = -$

e. 35.4 ft

f. 48.4 ft

g. We only knew the length of one of the sides of the triangle. To apply the Pythagorean theorem, we would need to know lengths of two of the sides to solve for the third.

h. about 384 m; Use the equation tan(38°) = —— and solve for *d*, the distance.

Multi-Step Problem Rubric

4 The student makes no more than one computational error and is able to apply the tangent ratio in the context of the Eiffel Tower problem.

3 The student makes two or three errors and may not correctly solve the Eiffel Tower problem.

2 The student makes four or five errors and does not correctly solve the Eiffel Tower problem.

1 The student makes more than five errors.

Copyright © McDougal Littell Inc. All rights reserved.

Middle School Math, Course 3 117
Chapter 9 Assessment Book

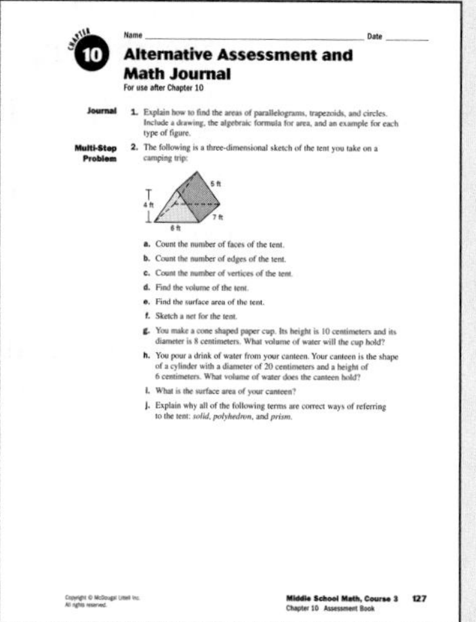

CHAPTER 10

Name ______________________ Date ________

Alternative Assessment and Math Journal

For use after Chapter 10

Journal 1. Explain how to find the areas of parallelograms, trapezoids, and circles. Include a drawing, the algebraic formula for area, and an example for each type of figure.

Multi-Step Problem 2. The following is a three-dimensional sketch of the tent you take on a camping trip:

a. Count the number of faces of the tent.

b. Count the number of edges of the tent.

c. Count the number of vertices of the tent.

d. Find the volume of the tent.

e. Find the surface area of the tent.

f. Sketch a net for the tent.

g. You make a cone shaped paper cup. Its height is 10 centimeters and its diameter is 8 centimeters. What volume of water will the cup hold?

h. You pour a drink of water from your canteen. Your canteen is the shape of a cylinder with a diameter of 20 centimeters and a height of 6 centimeters. What volume of water does the canteen hold?

i. What is the surface area of your canteen?

j. Explain why all of the following terms are correct ways of referring to the tent: *solid*, *polyhedron*, and *prism*.

Copyright © McDougal Littell Inc. All rights reserved.

Middle School Math, Course 3 127
Chapter 10 Assessment Book

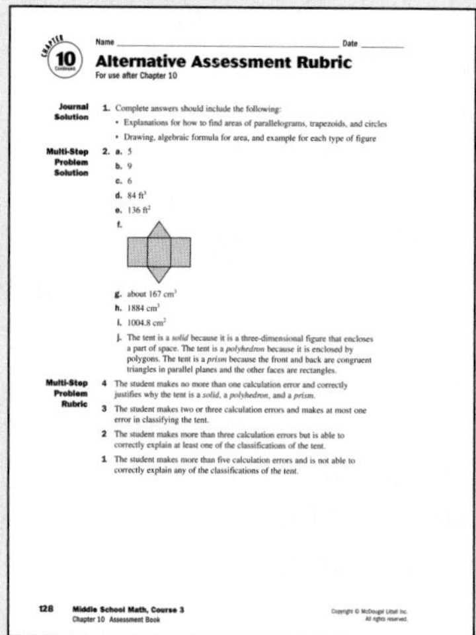

CHAPTER 10 Continued

Name ______________________ Date ________

Alternative Assessment Rubric

For use after Chapter 10

Journal Solution 1. Complete answers should include the following:

- Explanations for how to find areas of parallelograms, trapezoids, and circles
- Drawing, algebraic formula for area, and example for each type of figure

Multi-Step Problem Solution 2. a. 5

b. 9

c. 6

d. 84 ft^3

e. 136 ft^2

f.

g. about 167 cm^3

h. 1884 cm^3

i. 1004.8 cm^2

j. The tent is a *solid* because it is a three-dimensional figure that encloses a part of space. The tent is a *polyhedron* because it is enclosed by polygons. The tent is a *prism* because the front and back are congruent triangles in parallel planes and the other faces are rectangles.

Multi-Step Problem Rubric

4 The student makes no more than one calculation error and correctly justifies why the tent is a *solid*, a *polyhedron*, and a *prism*.

3 The student makes two or three calculation errors and makes at most one error in classifying the tent.

2 The student makes more than three calculation errors but is able to correctly explain at least one of the classifications of the tent.

1 The student makes more than five calculation errors and is not able to correctly explain any of the classifications of the tent.

128 Middle School Math, Course 3
Chapter 10 Assessment Book

Copyright © McDougal Littell Inc. All rights reserved.

RESOURCE BOOK

The *Chapter Resource Books* contain three different projects for each chapter: Real Life, Cooperative, and Independent Extra Credit. Each project is accompanied by a scoring rubric. Shown below are the three projects for Chapter 10 with their rubrics. A complete discussion of rubrics is available in the *Professional Development Book.*

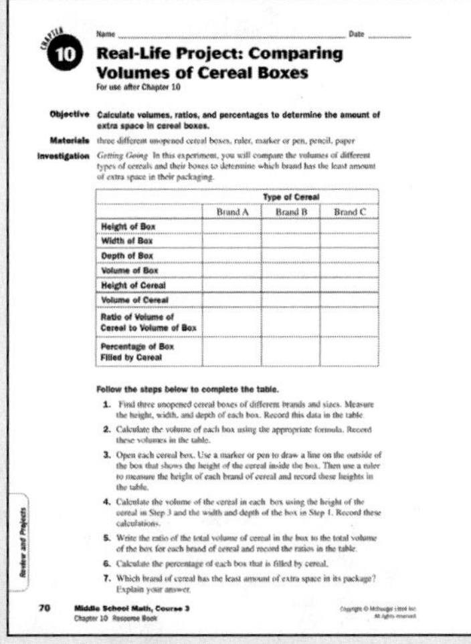

CHAPTER 10 Name ______ Date ______

Real-Life Project: Comparing Volumes of Cereal Boxes

For use after Chapter 10

Objective **Calculate volumes, ratios, and percentages to determine the amount of extra space in cereal boxes.**

Materials three different unopened cereal boxes, ruler, marker or pen, pencil, paper

Investigation *Getting Going* In this experiment, you will compare the volumes of different types of cereals and their boxes to determine which brand has the least amount of extra space in their packaging.

	Type of Cereal		
	Brand A	Brand B	Brand C
Height of Box			
Width of Box			
Depth of Box			
Volume of Box			
Height of Cereal			
Volume of Cereal			
Ratio of Volume of Cereal to Volume of Box			
Percentage of Box Filled by Cereal			

Follow the steps below to complete the table.

1. Find three unopened cereal boxes of different brands and sizes. Measure the height, width, and depth of each box. Record this data in the table.
2. Calculate the volume of each box using the appropriate formula. Record these volumes in the table.
3. Open each cereal box. Use a marker or pen to draw a line on the outside of the box that shows the height of the cereal inside the box. Then use a ruler to measure the height of each brand of cereal and record these heights in the table.
4. Calculate the volume of the cereal in each box using the height of the cereal in Step 3 and the width and depth of the box in Step 1. Record these calculations.
5. Write the ratio of the total volume of cereal in the box to the total volume of the box for each brand of cereal and record the ratios in the table.
6. Calculate the percentage of each box that is filled by cereal.
7. Which brand of cereal has the least amount of extra space in its package? Explain your answer.

Review and Projects

70 **Middle School Math, Course 3** Chapter 10 Resource Book — Copyright © McDougal Littell Inc. All rights reserved.

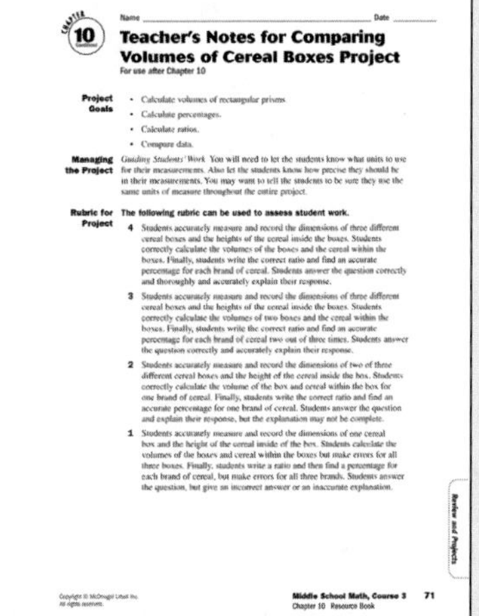

CHAPTER 10 Name ______ Date ______

Teacher's Notes for Comparing Volumes of Cereal Boxes Project

For use after Chapter 10

Project Goals

- Calculate volumes of rectangular prisms.
- Calculate percentages.
- Calculate ratios.
- Compare data.

Managing the Project *Guiding Students' Work* You will need to let the students know what units to use for their measurements. Also let the students know how precise they should be in their measurements. You may want to tell the students to be sure they use the same units of measure throughout the entire project.

Rubric for Project **The following rubric can be used to assess student work.**

4 Students accurately measure and record the dimensions of three different cereal boxes and the heights of the cereal inside the boxes. Students correctly calculate the volumes of the boxes and the cereal within the boxes. Finally, students write the correct ratio and find an accurate percentage for each brand of cereal. Students answer the question correctly and thoroughly and accurately explain their response.

3 Students accurately measure and record the dimensions of three different cereal boxes and the heights of the cereal inside the boxes. Students correctly calculate the volumes of two boxes and the cereal within the boxes. Finally, students write the correct ratio and find an accurate percentage for each brand of cereal two out of three times. Students answer the question correctly and accurately explain their response.

2 Students accurately measure and record the dimensions of two of three different cereal boxes and the height of the cereal inside the box. Students correctly calculate the volume of the box and cereal within the box for one brand of cereal. Finally, students write the correct ratio and find an accurate percentage for one brand of cereal. Students answer the question and explain their response, but the explanation may not be complete.

1 Students accurately measure and record the dimensions of one cereal box and the height of the cereal inside of the box. Students calculate the volumes of the boxes and cereal within the boxes but make errors for all three boxes. Finally, students write a ratio and then find a percentage for each brand of cereal, but make errors for all three brands. Students answer the question, but give an incorrect answer or an inaccurate explanation.

Review and Projects

Copyright © McDougal Littell Inc. All rights reserved. — **Middle School Math, Course 3** Chapter 10 Resource Book 71

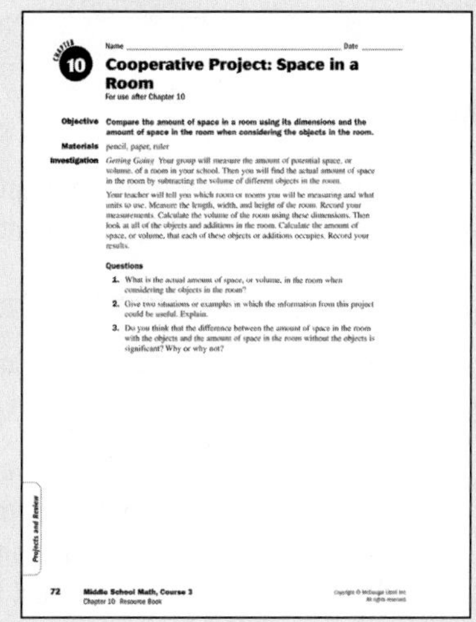

CHAPTER 10 Name ______ Date ______

Cooperative Project: Space in a Room

For use after Chapter 10

Objective **Compare the amount of space in a room using its dimensions and the amount of space in the room when considering the objects in the room.**

Materials pencil, paper, ruler

Investigation *Getting Going* Your group will measure the amount of potential space, or volume, of a room in your school. Then you will find the actual amount of space in the room by subtracting the volume of different objects in the room.

Your teacher will tell you which room or rooms you will be measuring and what units to use. Measure the length, width, and height of the room. Record your measurements. Calculate the volume of the room using these dimensions. Then look at all of the objects and additions in the room. Calculate the amount of space, or volume, that each of these objects or additions occupies. Record your results.

Questions

1. What is the actual amount of space, or volume, in the room when considering the objects in the room?
2. Give two situations or examples in which the information from this project could be useful. Explain.
3. Do you think that the difference between the amount of space in the room with the objects and the amount of space in the room without the objects is significant? Why or why not?

Projects and Review

72 **Middle School Math, Course 3** Chapter 10 Resource Book — Copyright © McDougal Littell Inc. All rights reserved.

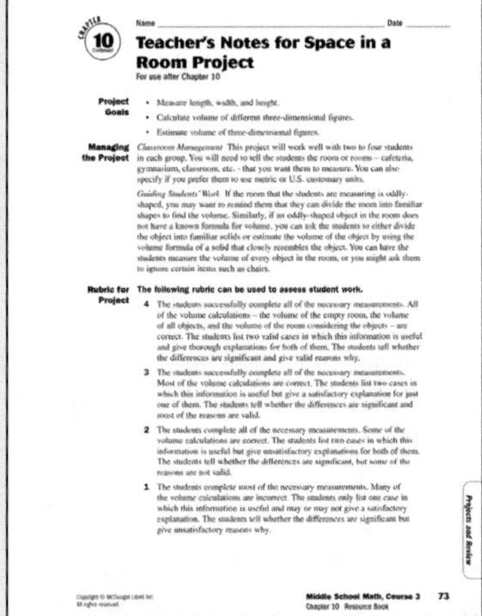

CHAPTER 10 Name ______ Date ______

Teacher's Notes for Space in a Room Project

For use after Chapter 10

Project Goals

- Measure length, width, and height.
- Calculate volume of different three-dimensional figures.
- Estimate volume of three-dimensional figures.

Managing the Project *Classroom Management* This project will work well with two to four students in each group. You will need to tell the students the room or rooms – cafeteria, gymnasium, classroom, etc. – that you want them to measure. You can also specify if you prefer them to use metric or U.S. customary units.

Guiding Students' Work If the room that the students are measuring is oddly-shaped, you may want to remind them that they can divide the room into familiar shapes to find the volume. Similarly, if an oddly-shaped object in the room does not have a known formula for volume, you can ask the students to either divide the object into familiar solids or estimate the volume of the object by using the volume formula of a solid that closely resembles the object. You can have the students measure the volume of every object in the room, or you might ask them to ignore certain items such as chairs.

Rubric for Project **The following rubric can be used to assess student work.**

4 The students successfully complete all of the necessary measurements. All of the volume calculations – the volume of the empty room, the volume of all objects, and the volume of the room considering the objects – are correct. The students list two valid cases in which this information is useful and give thorough explanations for both of them. The students tell whether the differences are significant and give valid reasons why.

3 The students successfully complete all of the necessary measurements. Most of the volume calculations are correct. The students list two cases in which this information is useful but give a satisfactory explanation for just one of them. The students tell whether the differences are significant and most of the reasons are valid.

2 The students complete all of the necessary measurements. Some of the volume calculations are correct. The students list two cases in which this information is useful but give unsatisfactory explanations for both of them. The students tell whether the differences are significant, but some of the reasons are not valid.

1 The students complete most of the necessary measurements. Many of the volume calculations are incorrect. The students only list one case in which this information is useful and may or may not give a satisfactory explanation. The students tell whether the differences are significant but give unsatisfactory reasons why.

Projects and Review

Copyright © McDougal Littell Inc. All rights reserved. — **Middle School Math, Course 3** Chapter 10 Resource Book 73

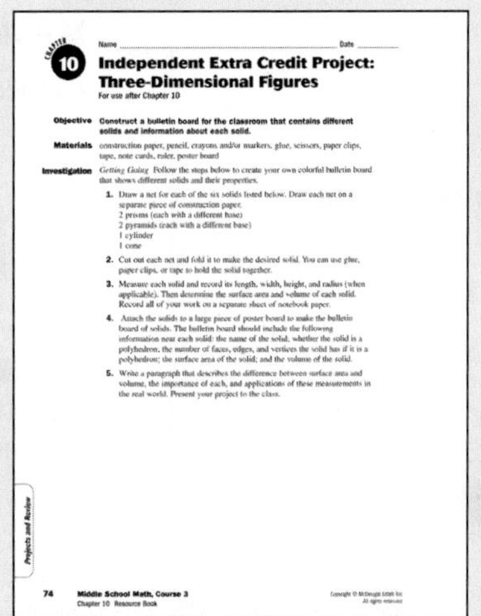

CHAPTER 10 Name ______ Date ______

Independent Extra Credit Project: Three-Dimensional Figures

For use after Chapter 10

Objective **Construct a bulletin board for the classroom that contains different solids and information about each solid.**

Materials construction paper, pencil, crayons and/or markers, glue, scissors, paper clips, tape, note cards, ruler, poster board

Investigation *Getting Going* Follow the steps below to create your own colorful bulletin board that shows different solids and their properties.

1. Draw a net for each of the six solids listed below. Draw each net on a separate piece of construction paper.
   2 prisms (each with a different base)
   2 pyramids (each with a different base)
   1 cylinder
   1 cone
2. Cut out each net and fold it to make the desired solid. You can use glue, paper clips, or tape to hold the solid together.
3. Measure each solid and record its length, width, height, and radius (when applicable). Then determine the surface area and volume of each solid. Record all of your work on a separate sheet of notebook paper.
4. Attach the solids to a large piece of poster board to make the bulletin board of solids. The bulletin board should include the following information near each solid: the name of the solid; whether the solid is a polyhedron; the number of faces, edges, and vertices the solid has if it is a polyhedron; the surface area of the solid; and the volume of the solid.
5. Write a paragraph that describes the difference between surface area and volume, the importance of each, and applications of these measurements in the real world. Present your project to the class.

Projects and Review

74 **Middle School Math, Course 3** Chapter 10 Resource Book — Copyright © McDougal Littell Inc. All rights reserved.

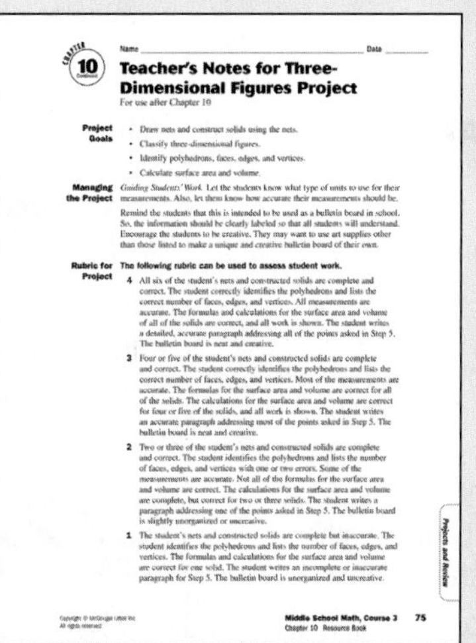

CHAPTER 10 Name ______ Date ______

Teacher's Notes for Three-Dimensional Figures Project

For use after Chapter 10

Project Goals

- Draw nets and construct solids using the nets.
- Classify three-dimensional figures.
- Identify polyhedrons, faces, edges, and vertices.
- Calculate surface area and volume.

Managing the Project *Guiding Students' Work* Let the students know what type of units to use for their measurements. Also, let them know how accurate their measurements should be.

Remind the students that this is intended to be used as a bulletin board in school. So, the information should be clearly labeled so that all students will understand. Encourage the students to be creative. They may want to use art supplies other than those listed to make a unique and creative bulletin board of their own.

Rubric for Project **The following rubric can be used to assess student work.**

4 All six of the student's nets and constructed solids are complete and correct. The student correctly identifies the polyhedrons and lists the correct number of faces, edges, and vertices. All measurements are accurate. The formulas and calculations for the surface area and volume of all of the solids are correct, and all work is shown. The student writes a detailed, accurate paragraph addressing all of the points asked in Step 5. The bulletin board is neat and creative.

3 Four or five of the student's nets and constructed solids are complete and correct. The student correctly identifies the polyhedrons and lists the correct number of faces, edges, and vertices. Most of the measurements are accurate. The formulas for the surface area and volume are correct for all of the solids. The calculations for the surface area and volume are correct for four or five of the solids, and all work is shown. The student writes an accurate paragraph addressing most of the points asked in Step 5. The bulletin board is neat and creative.

2 Two or three of the student's nets and constructed solids are complete and correct. The student identifies the polyhedrons and lists the number of faces, edges, and vertices with one or two errors. Some of the measurements are accurate. Not all of the formulas for the surface area and volume are correct. The calculations for the surface area and volume are complete, but correct for two or three solids. The student writes a paragraph addressing one of the points asked in Step 5. The bulletin board is slightly unorganized or uncreative.

1 The student's nets and constructed solids are complete but inaccurate. The student identifies the polyhedrons and lists the number of faces, edges, and vertices. The formulas and calculations for the surface area and volume are correct for one solid. The student writes an incomplete or inaccurate paragraph for Step 5. The bulletin board is unorganized and uncreative.

Projects and Review

Copyright © McDougal Littell Inc. All rights reserved. — **Middle School Math, Course 3** Chapter 10 Resource Book 75

OVERVIEW

Main Ideas

In this chapter, students find the areas of parallelograms, trapezoids, and circles. Students identify solids and sketch solids including by using front, top, and side views and by making isometric drawings. Students draw nets of prisms, pyramids, cylinders, and cones and use them to find the surface areas of these solids. Students also use formulas to find the volumes of these solids.

Prerequisite Skills

The key skills reviewed in the games on these pages are:

- Finding the perimeter, area, or circumference of squares, rectangles, triangles, and circles.

Additional practice with prerequisite skills can be found in the Review What You Need to Know exercises on page 480. Additional resources for reviewing prerequisite skills are:

- Skills Review Handbook, pp. 704–726
- Tutor Place
- eTutorial Plus

Managing the Game

Tips for Success

Before beginning the game, you may want to draw and label a square, a rectangle, a triangle, and a circle on the board or overhead and have students find the area and perimeter or circumference of each so that they can review the formulas. When a student removes a "match," have the other student verify that it is indeed a match.

Reflecting on the Game

After students play the game and answer the questions, challenge them to draw various figures for different Picture Cards that would match the given Answer Cards.

Measurement, Area, and Volume

BEFORE

In previous chapters you've...

- Found the areas of rectangles
- Identified and sketched polygons

Now

In Chapter 10 you'll study...

- Finding the areas of circles, parallelograms, and trapezoids
- Identifying and sketching three-dimensional figures
- Finding the surface areas and volumes of solids

WHY?

So you can solve real-world problems about...

- architecture, p. 482
- hockey, p. 487
- recycling, p. 515
- swimming pools, p. 517

Internet Preview
CLASSZONE.COM

- eEdition Plus Online
- eWorkbook Plus Online
- eTutorial Plus Online
- State Test Practice
- More Examples

Chapter Warm-Up Game

Review skills you need for this chapter in this quick game. Work with a partner.

Key Skills:
Finding the perimeter, area, or circumference of squares, rectangles, triangles, and circles

MEASURE MATCH

MATERIALS

- 15 Picture Cards
- 15 Measure Cards

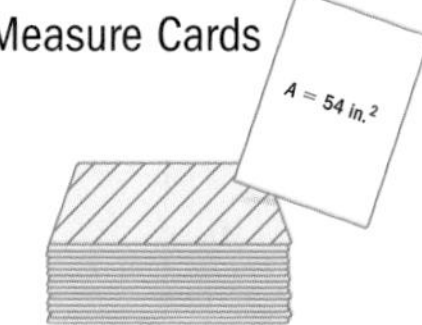

PREPARE Place all cards face down and mix them up. On your turn follow the steps on the next page.

1 TURN over two cards.

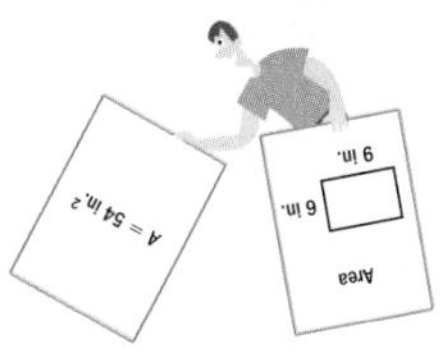

2 DECIDE whether the two cards match. Cards match when you turn over a Picture Card and a Measure Card that describes the picture. If the cards match, you may keep them. Otherwise, turn them back over.

3 REMEMBER where the cards are so you can find matching pairs on future turns.

HOW TO WIN

Be the player with the most cards once all the cards have been matched.

Stop *and* Think

1. **Writing** If the Measure Cards did not have *A*, *P*, or *C* on them, would you still be able to tell what was being measured? Explain. See margin.
2. **Extension** Design six new cards for *Measure Match*. Three should be Picture Cards and three should be Measure Cards. Make sure each Picture Card matches a Measure Card. Check work.

CHAPTER RESOURCES

These resources are provided to help you prepare for the chapter and to customize review materials:

Chapter 10 Resource Book

- Tips for New Teachers, pp. 1–2
- Lesson Plan, pp. 7, 15, 25, 34, 42, 51, 59
- Lesson Plan for Block Scheduling, pp. 8, 16, 26, 35, 43, 52, 60

Technology

- EasyPlanner CD-ROM
- Test and Practice Generator
- Electronic Lesson Presentations CD-ROM
- eTutorial CD-ROM

Internet

- Classzone
- eEdition Plus Online
- eWorkbook Plus Online
- eTutorial Plus Online
- EasyPlanner Plus Online

ENGLISH LEARNER SUPPORT

- Spanish Study Guide
- Multi-Language Glossary
- Chapter Audio Summaries CDs
- Teacher's Edition, pp. 478E–478F

1. No. *Sample answer:* You could tell area from circumference and perimeter because area is measured in square units and circumference and perimeter are measured in units. However, you might not be able to tell a perimeter from a circumference if the side lengths of a triangle or rectangle were decimal measures.

PREPARE

Diagnosis/Remediation

Review What You Need to Know
The Review What You Need to Know exercises can help you diagnose whether students have the following skills needed in Chapter 10:
- Identifying figures (Exs. 1–3)
- Finding areas (Exs. 4–6)

Chapter 10 Resource Book
- Study Guide (Lessons 10.1–10.7)

Tutor Place

Notetaking Strategies

Discuss the concept grid. Point out that the four boxes around the concept of rectangle contain a definition, relevant vocabulary, and the area and perimeter formulas for a rectangle. Further suggestions for keeping a notebook can be found on page 486.

For more support on notetaking, see:
- Notetaking Guide Workbook
- Notetaking Transparencies

Getting Ready to Learn

Word Watch

Review Words
area, p. 33
base, p. 134
height, p. 134
circle, p. 290
radius, p. 290
pi (π), p. 290
trapezoid, p. 386
parallelogram, p. 386
rhombus, p. 386

Review What You Need to Know 

Using Vocabulary **Classify the figure indicated using a review word.**

1. quadrilateral *ABCD*

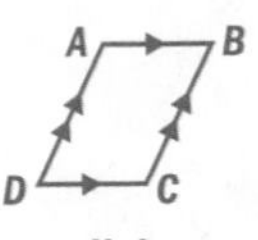

parallelogram

2. $\overline{PQ}$

radius

3. quadrilateral *JKLM*

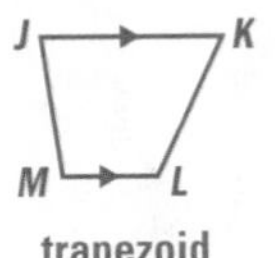

trapezoid

Find the area of the shaded region. *(Lessons 1.6, 3.5)*

4.

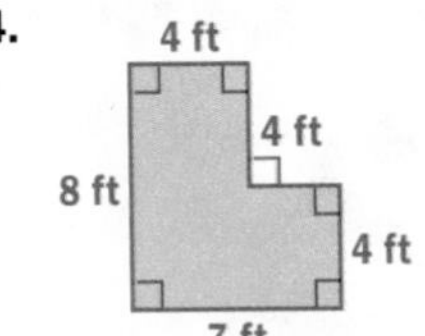

44 ft^2

5.

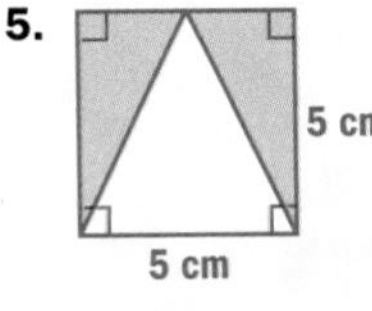

12.5 cm^2

6.

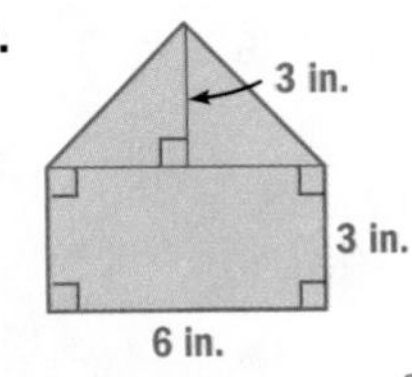

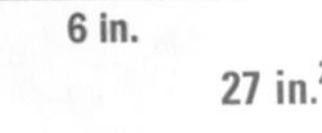
27 in.^2

You should include material that appears on a notebook like this in your own notes.

Know How to Take Notes

Using a Concept Grid You can use a concept grid to organize what you know about a topic.

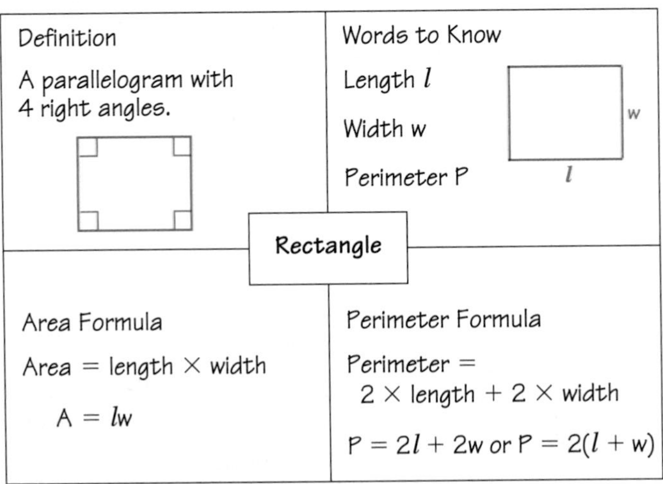

Definition
A parallelogram with 4 right angles.
Words to Know
Length l
Width w
Perimeter P
w
l
Rectangle
Area Formula
Area = length × width
$A = lw$
Perimeter Formula
Perimeter = 2 × length + 2 × width
$P = 2l + 2w$ or $P = 2(l + w)$

In Lesson 10.2, you will learn the formula for the area of a circle. Then you can make a concept grid for circles.

Areas of Parallelograms and Trapezoids

BEFORE	Now	WHY?
You found the areas of triangles and rectangles.	You'll find the areas of parallelograms and trapezoids.	So you can find the area of one side of a podium, as in Ex. 32.

Word Watch

base of a parallelogram, p. 481
height of a parallelogram, p. 481
bases of a trapezoid, p. 482
height of a trapezoid, p. 482

The **base of a parallelogram** can be any one of its sides. The **height of a parallelogram** is the perpendicular distance between the base and the opposite side.

The diagram below shows how to change a parallelogram into a rectangle with the same base, height, and area.

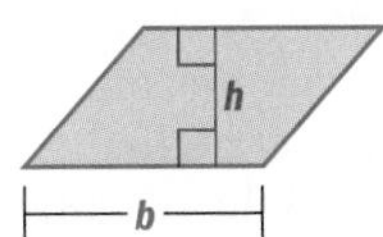

Start with any parallelogram.

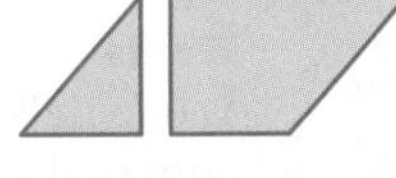

Cut the parallelogram to form a right triangle and a trapezoid.

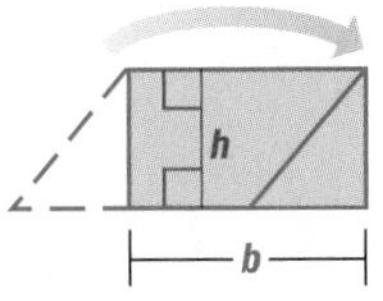

Move the triangle to form a rectangle.

The area of the rectangle is the product of the base and the height, so the formula for the area of the parallelogram is $A = bh$.

Area of a Parallelogram

Words The area of a parallelogram is the product of the base and the height.

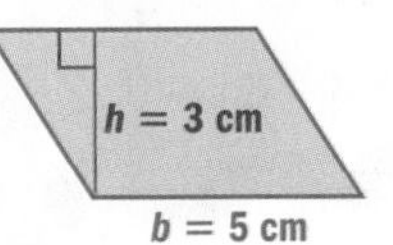

Algebra $A = bh$ **Numbers** $A = 5 \cdot 3 = 15\text{ cm}^2$

EXAMPLE 1 Finding the Area of a Parallelogram

Find the area of the parallelogram.

10 in.
8 in.

$A = bh$ Write formula for area.

$= 8 \cdot 10$ Substitute 8 for b and 10 for h.

$= 80$ Multiply.

ANSWER The parallelogram has an area of 80 square inches.

ILLINOIS Standards and ISAT:
7.C.3b, 8.D.3b; 7.A.3b, 7.C.3a

1 PLAN

SKILL CHECK

1. What is the area of a triangle with base 4 cm and height 6 cm? **12 cm²**
2. Find the area of a rectangle with length 5 in. and width 3 in. **15 in.²**

LESSON OBJECTIVE

Find the areas of parallelograms and trapezoids.

PACING

Suggested Number of Days
Basic Course: 2 days
Average Course: 2 days
Advanced Course: 2 days
Block: 1 block

TEACHING RESOURCES

For a complete list of Teaching Resources, see page 478B.

TRANSPARENCY

Warm-Up Exercises for this lesson are available on a transparency.

2 TEACH

MOTIVATING THE LESSON

Draw a parallelogram on the board. Ask students what real-world object the shape could model.

TIPS FOR NEW TEACHERS

Draw many differently-shaped trapezoids on the board so students understand that trapezoids are not all the same shape. See Tips for New Teachers in the *Chapter 10 Resource Book*.

EXTRA EXAMPLES

Example 1 Find the area of the parallelogram. **60 cm²**

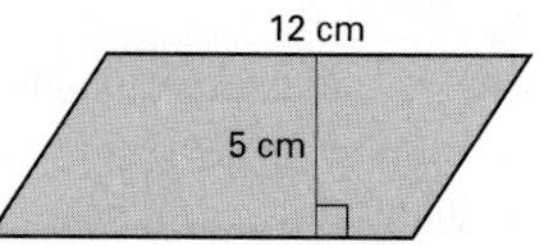

Example 2 This trapezoid is part of a mural on the side of the school gym. Find the area of the shape. **45 ft²**

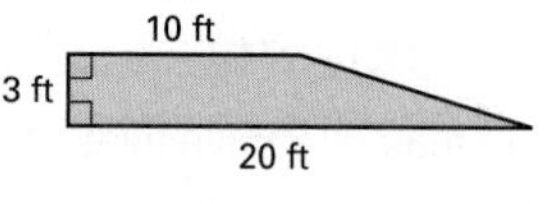

MATH REASONING

Remind students how to find the mean. Point out that another way to think about the formula for the area of a trapezoid is as the mean length of the bases times the height.

CONCEPT CHECK

Find the area of a trapezoid with bases 2 centimeters and 5 centimeters and height 10 centimeters. **35 cm²**

DAILY PUZZLER

Find the area of the design. **288 in.²**

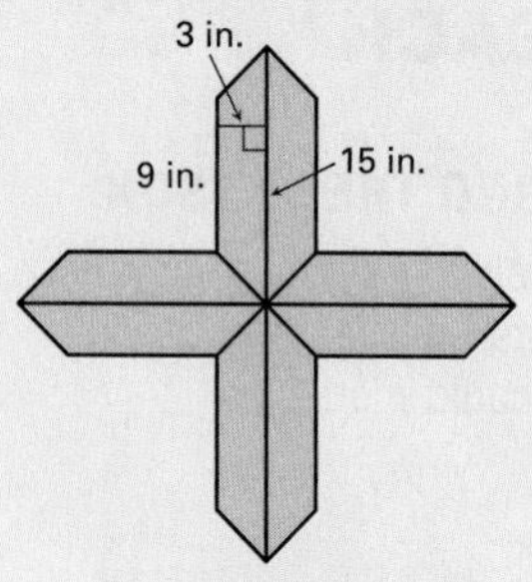

1, 2. See Additional Answers beginning on page AA1.

with Reading

The bases of a trapezoid are labeled b_1 and b_2. You read these labels as "*b* sub one" and "*b* sub two." For help with trapezoids, see p. 386.

Trapezoids The **bases of a trapezoid** are its parallel sides. The **height of a trapezoid** is the perpendicular distance between the bases. The diagram below shows how two congruent trapezoids with height h and bases b_1 and b_2 can form a parallelogram with height h and base $b_1 + b_2$.

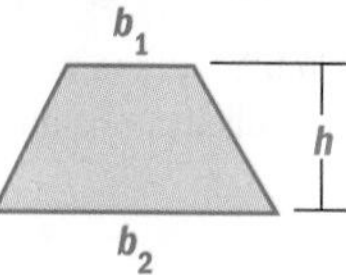

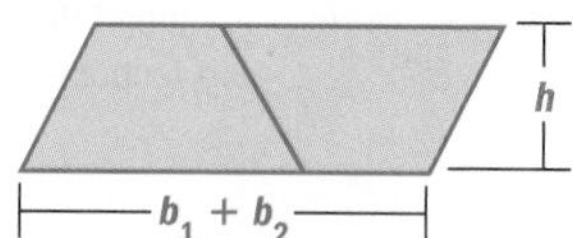

The area of the parallelogram is $(b_1 + b_2)h$, so the area of each trapezoid is $\frac{1}{2}(b_1 + b_2)h$.

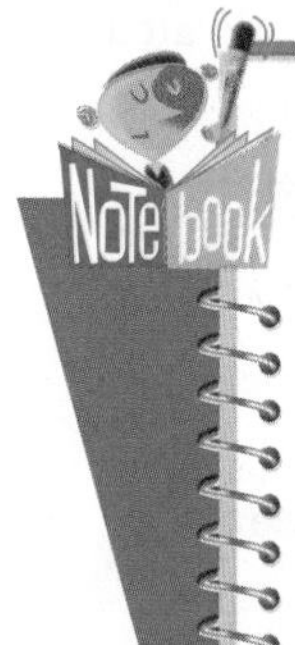

Area of a Trapezoid

Words The area of a trapezoid is one half the product of the sum of the bases and the height.

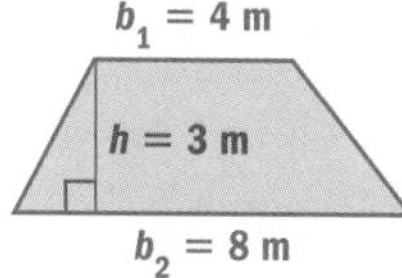

Algebra $A = \frac{1}{2}(b_1 + b_2)h$ **Numbers** $A = \frac{1}{2}(4 + 8)3 = 18 \text{ m}^2$

The Winslow House in River Forest, Illinois

EXAMPLE 2 Finding the Area of a Trapezoid

Architecture The Winslow House was designed by Frank Lloyd Wright. The front part of the roof is a trapezoid. What is its area?

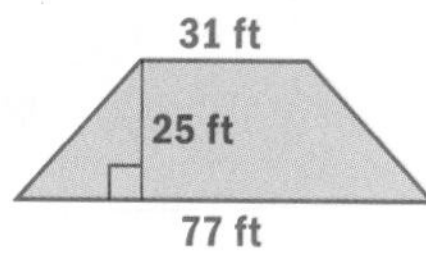

Solution

$A = \frac{1}{2}(b_1 + b_2)h$ Write formula for area of a trapezoid.

$= \frac{1}{2}(31 + 77)25$ Substitute values for b_1, b_2, and h.

$= 1350$ Multiply.

ANSWER The front part of the roof has an area of 1350 square feet.

Your turn now **Sketch the quadrilateral and find its area.** 1–2. See margin for art.

1. A parallelogram with base 20 meters and height 9 meters **180 m²**
2. A trapezoid with bases of 17 feet and 14 feet and height 6 feet **93 ft²**

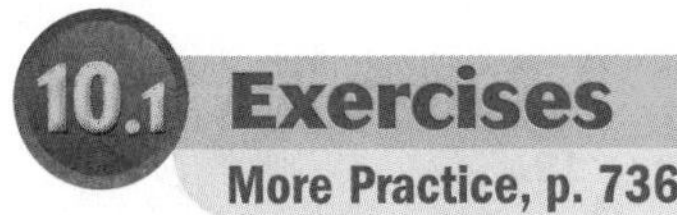

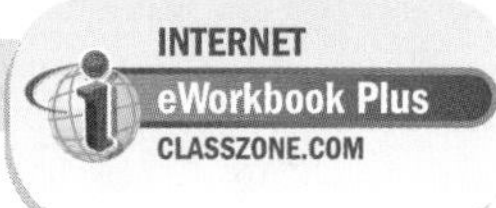

Getting Ready to Practice

Vocabulary Write the area formula for the polygon.

1. parallelogram $A = bh$
2. triangle $A = \frac{1}{2}bh$
3. trapezoid $A = \frac{1}{2}(b_1 + b_2)h$

Find the area of the parallelogram or trapezoid.

4.  81 cm^2

5. 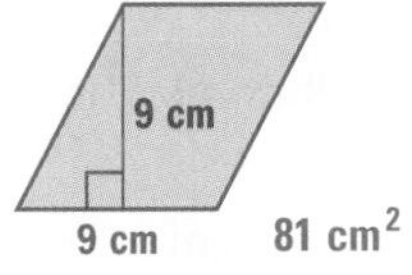 56 in.^{2}

6. 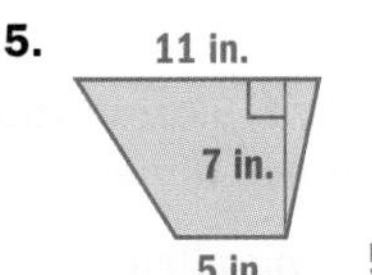 16 m^2

7. Step 2: trapezoid: $49\frac{1}{2}$ ft^2, parallelogram: 72 ft^2

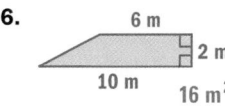

7. **Guided Problem Solving** You are designing a putting green for a miniature golf course, as shown. Find the area of the green.

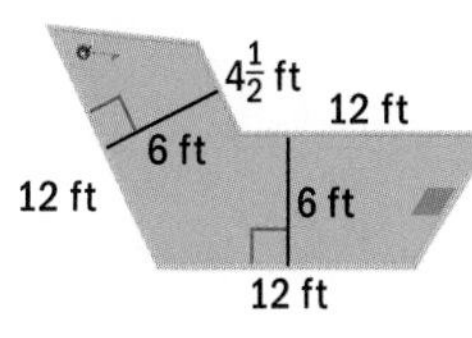

(1) Copy the shape and divide it into a trapezoid and a parallelogram. See margin for art.
(2) Find the area of each quadrilateral. See margin.
(3) Add the two areas to find the total area. $121\frac{1}{2}$ ft^2

Practice and Problem Solving

Example	Exercises
1	8-13, 20
2	15-19

Online Resources
CLASSZONE.COM
· More Examples
· eTutorial Plus

A **Sketch a parallelogram with base b and height h and find its area.** 8–10. See margin for art.

8. $b = 12$ in., $h = 8$ in. 96 in.^{2}
9. $b = 9$ ft, $h = 14$ ft 126 ft^2
10. $b = 10$ cm, $h = 22$ cm 220 cm^2

Find the area of the parallelogram.

11. 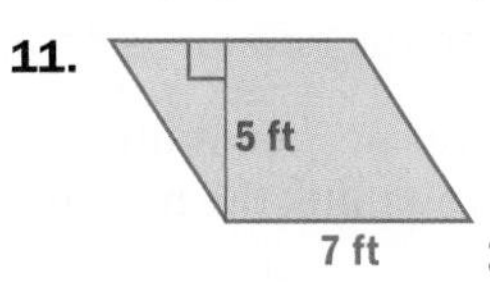 35 ft^2

12. 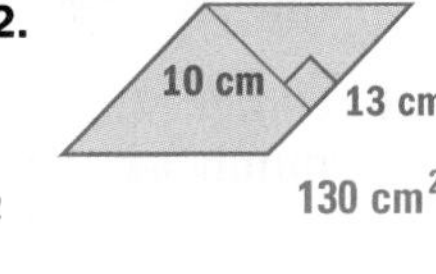 130 cm^2

13. 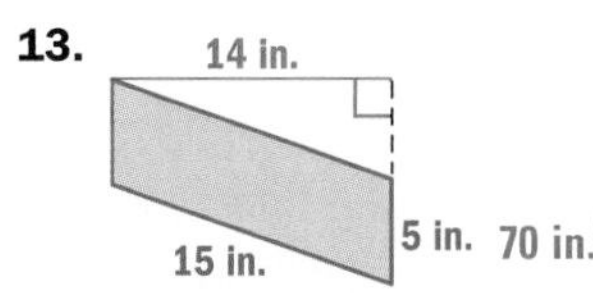 70 in.^{2}

14. **Find the Error** Describe and correct the error in the solution.

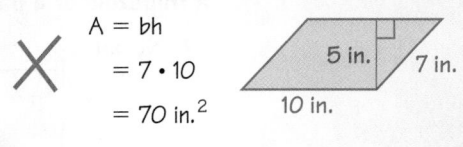

X
$A = bh$
$= 7 \cdot 10$
$= 70$ in.^{2}

14. The height of the parallelogram is 5 inches, not 7 inches; $A = bh = 10 \cdot 5 = 50$ in.^{2}.

Sketch a trapezoid with bases b_1 and b_2 and height h and find its area. 15–16. See margin for art.

15. $b_1 = 13$ ft, $b_2 = 7$ ft, $h = 6$ ft 60 ft^2
16. $b_1 = 8$ m, $b_2 = 16$ m, $h = 11$ m 132 m^2

3 APPLY

ASSIGNMENT GUIDE

Basic Course

Day 1: SRH p. 713 Exs. 11-15; pp. 483-485 Exs. 8-13, 29, 35, 40-42

Day 2: pp. 483-485 Exs. 15-23, 31, 43, 44

Average Course

Day 1: pp. 483-485 Exs. 10-12, 21-23, 30-32, 40-43

Day 2: pp. 483-485 Exs. 14-17, 24-27, 33-35, 44, 45

Advanced Course

Day 1: pp. 483-485 Exs. 10-12, 22-26, 32-36

Day 2: pp. 483-485 Exs. 14-17, 28-30, 37-39*, 43-45

Block

pp. 483-485 Exs. 10-12, 14-17, 21-27, 30-35, 40-45

EXTRA PRACTICE

- Student Edition, p. 736
- Chapter 10 Resource Book, pp. 9-11
- Test and Practice Generator

TRANSPARENCY

Even-numbered answers are available on transparencies.

HOMEWORK CHECK

When you review students' homework for this lesson, go over the following exercises to check understanding of key concepts.
Basic: 8, 11, 12, 15, 17
Average: 10, 12, 15, 16, 17
Advanced: 10, 12, 15, 16, 17

7-10, 15, 16. See Additional Answers beginning on page AA1.

MATH REASONING

Exercises 23–26 should help dispel the notion that doubling or tripling a polygon's dimensions doubles or triples its area. Students should realize that multiplying each original dimension by k results in the original area being multiplied by k^2.

TRANSPARENCY

A support transparency is available for Exercises 35–36.

21.

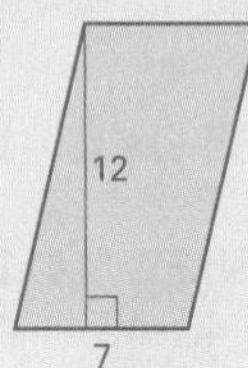

22.

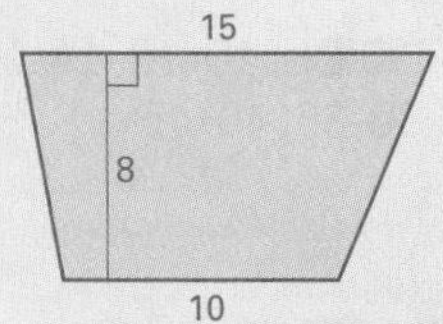

Find the area of the trapezoid.

17.

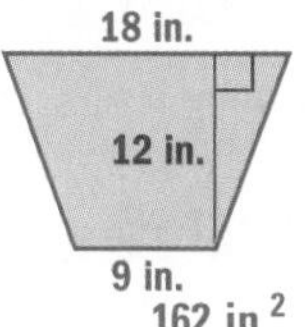

162 in.^2

18. **19.**

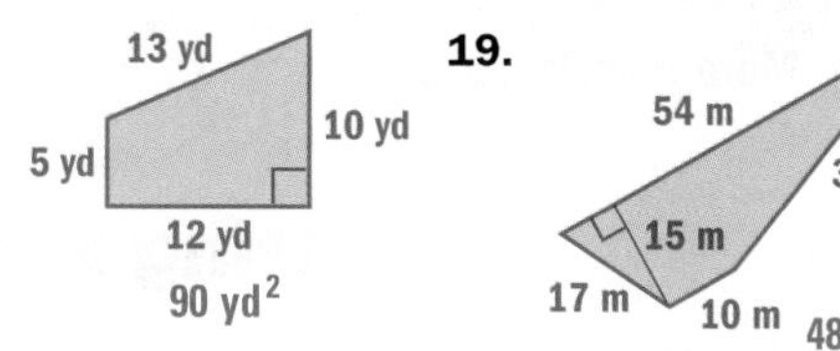

90 yd^2 480 m^2

20. Measurement Use a metric ruler to measure the dimensions of the parallelogram in millimeters. Then find the area. $b = 26$ mm, $h = 13$ mm, $A = 338\text{ mm}^2$

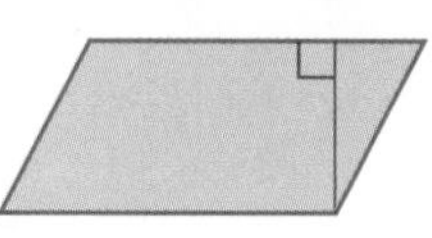

Algebra Sketch the quadrilateral. Then use an area formula to find the unknown dimension. 21–22. See margin for art.

21. A parallelogram has an area of 84 square units. Its height is 12 units. Find the base. 7 units

22. A trapezoid has an area of 100 square units. Its bases are 10 units and 15 units. Find the height. 8 units

Extended Problem Solving In Exercises 23–26, use the parallelogram and trapezoid shown.

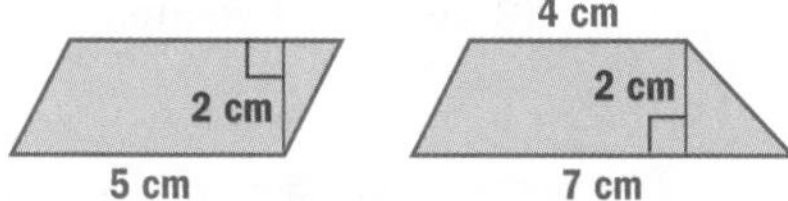

B **23. Calculate** Find the areas of the parallelogram and trapezoid. 10 cm^2, 11 cm^2

24. Compare Double each dimension of the quadrilaterals. Find the new areas. How do the new areas compare to the original areas? 40 cm^2, 44 cm^2; the new areas are four times the original areas.

25. Compare Triple each dimension of the original quadrilaterals and find the new areas. How do the new areas compare to the original areas? 90 cm^2, 99 cm^2; the new areas are nine times the original areas.

26. Critical Thinking Suppose you multiply each dimension by a positive number k. What do you think the new areas would be? $10k^2\text{ cm}^2$, $11k^2\text{ cm}^2$

Estimation Use the given scale and the formula for the area of a trapezoid or a parallelogram to estimate the area of the state. 27–28. Estimates may vary.

27. Nevada **28.** Tennessee

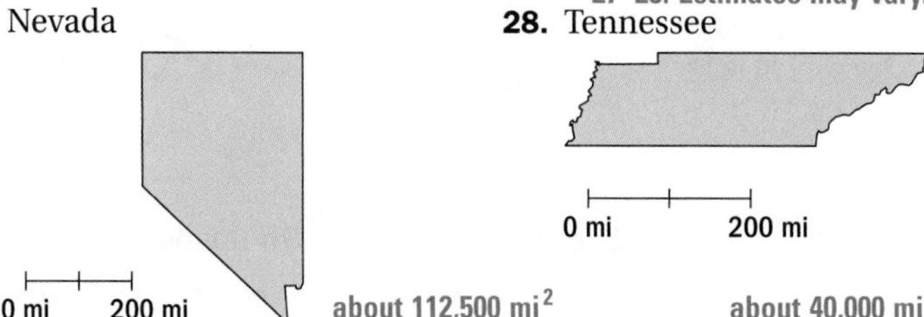

about $112{,}500\text{ mi}^2$ about $40{,}000\text{ mi}^2$

Find the area of the polygon.

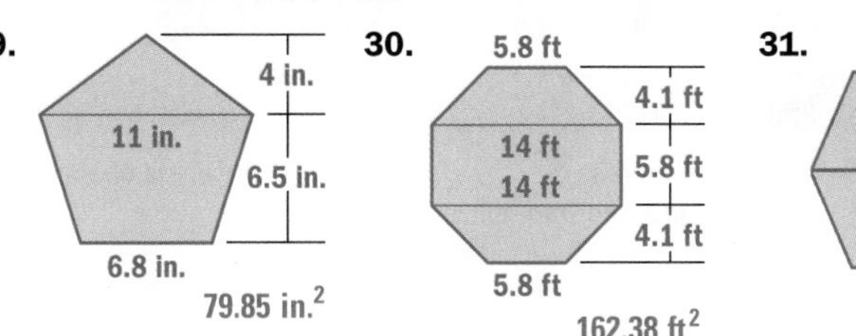

Find the area of the polygon.

32. 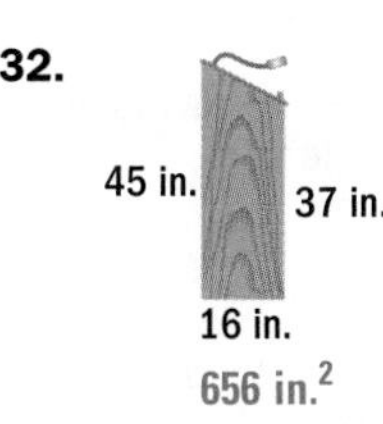

33. 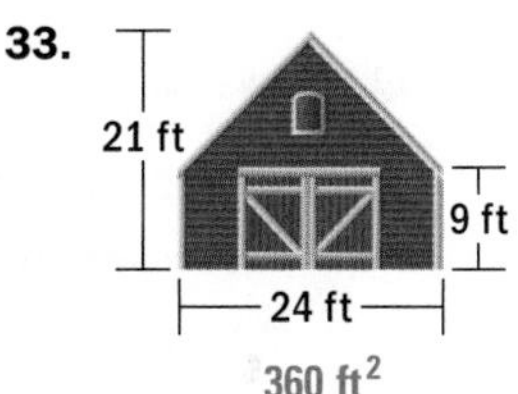

34. 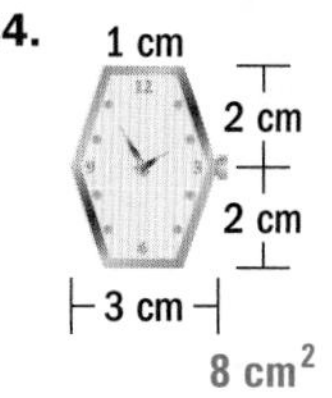

Plot the points in a coordinate plane and connect them to form a parallelogram. Then find the area of the parallelogram.

35–36. See margin for art.

C **35.** $(-3, -1), (0, 4), (6, 4), (3, -1)$ 30 units²

36. $(8, 0), (11, -5), (-2, -5), (-5, 0)$ 65 units²

Challenge Find the area of the parallelogram or trapezoid.

37. 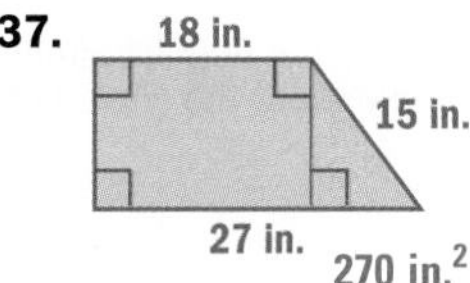

38. 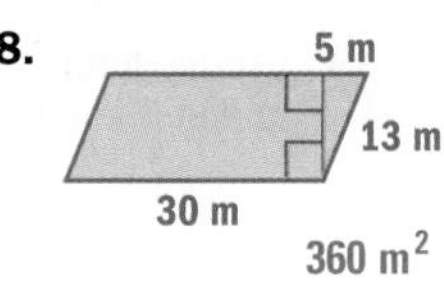

39. 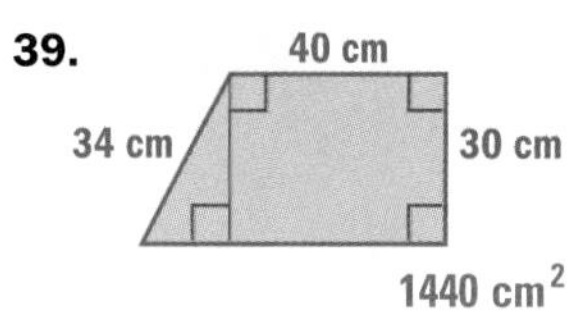

Mixed Review 

Find the product. *(Lesson 5.3)*

40. $-\frac{3}{4} \cdot 1\frac{5}{9}$ $-1\frac{1}{6}$

41. $-7 \cdot \left(-\frac{5}{3}\right)$ $11\frac{2}{3}$

42. $2\frac{3}{8} \cdot \left(-\frac{6}{7}\right)$ $-2\frac{1}{28}$

43. In $\triangle PQR$, write the sine, cosine, and tangent ratios for $\angle P$ and $\angle R$. *(Lesson 9.6)*
$\sin P = \frac{8}{17}$, $\cos P = \frac{15}{17}$, $\tan P = \frac{8}{15}$, $\sin R = \frac{15}{17}$, $\cos R = \frac{8}{17}$, $\tan R = \frac{15}{8}$

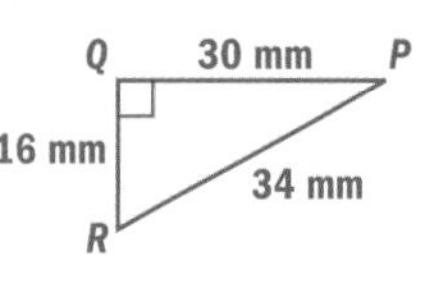

Test-Taking Practice 

INTERNET
State Test Practice
CLASSZONE.COM

44. Multiple Choice A trapezoid has bases of 14 feet and 8 feet and a height of 5 feet. What is the area of the trapezoid? A

A. 55 ft² **B.** 76 ft² **C.** 91 ft² **D.** 110 ft²

45. Short Response Sketch a trapezoid and a parallelogram, each with an area of 54 square feet. Label the dimensions needed to find each area. See margin.

4 ASSESS

Assessment Resources

For more assessment resources, see:
- Assessment Book
- Test and Practice Generator

Mini-Quiz

1. Find the area of a parallelogram with base 15 centimeters and height 10 centimeters. **150 cm²**
2. Find the area of a trapezoid with height 5 inches and bases 10 inches and 12 inches. **55 in.²**
3. A parallelogram has an area of 240 square meters. Its height is 12 meters. Find the base. **20 m**
4. A trapezoid has an area of 564 square feet. Its bases are 42 feet and 52 feet. Find the height. **12 ft**

5 FOLLOW-UP

Reteaching/Remediation

- Study Guide in Chapter 10 Resource Book, pp. 12–13
- eTutorial Plus Online
- Extra Practice, p. 736
- Lesson Practice in Chapter 10 Resource Book, pp. 9–11

Challenge/Enrichment

- Challenge Practice in Chapter 10 Resource Book, p. 14
- Teacher's Edition, p. 478F

English Learner Support

- Spanish Study Guide
- Multi-Language Glossary
- Chapter Audio Summaries CDs

35, 36, 45. See Additional Answers beginning on page AA1.

1 PLAN

SKILL CHECK

1. Find the radius of a circle if its diameter is 10 inches. **5 in.**
2. Evaluate x^2 when $x = 12$. **144**
3. If $2y = 18$, what is the value of y^2? **81**

LESSON OBJECTIVE

Find the areas of circles.

PACING

Suggested Number of Days
Basic Course: 1 day
Average Course: 1 day
Advanced Course: 1 day
Block: 0.5 block with 10.3

TEACHING RESOURCES

For a complete list of Teaching Resources, see page 478B.

TRANSPARENCY

Warm-Up Exercises for this lesson are available on a transparency.

2 TEACH

MOTIVATING THE LESSON

Have students name ten circular objects. Then ask students to think of three scenarios in which a person would need to know the area of a circle.

ACTIVITY

Goal Use a model to find the area of a circle.

Key Discovery The formula for the area of a circle is $A = \pi r^2$.

Areas of Circles

BEFORE	Now	WHY?
You found the areas of parallelograms and trapezoids.	You'll find the areas of circles.	So you can find the area of a yard watered by a sprinkler, as in Ex. 22.

Word Watch

Review Words
area, p. 33
circle, p. 290
radius, p. 290
diameter, p. 290
circumference, p. 290
pi (π), p. 290

Activity You can use a model to find the area of a circle.

1. Draw a circle and cut it into 8 congruent parts. Arrange the pieces of the circle to resemble a parallelogram, as shown below.

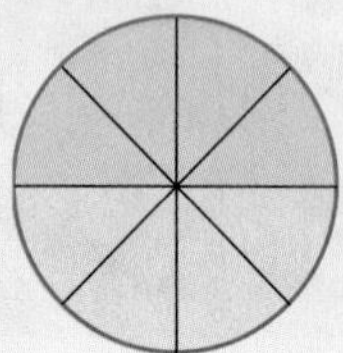

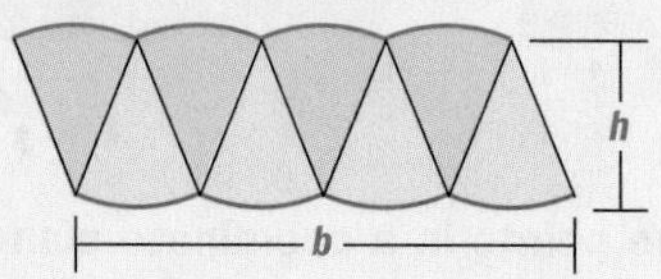

2. Copy and complete: The height of the parallelogram is equal to the __?__ of the circle, and the base of the parallelogram is about equal to one half of the __?__ of the circle. radius; circumference

3. Use the formula for the area of a parallelogram and your answer from Step 2 to find the formula for the area of the circle in terms of r. $A = \pi r^2$

The activity suggests the formula given below.

Area of a Circle

Words The area of a circle is the product of π and the square of the radius.

Algebra $A = \pi r^2$ **Numbers** $A = \pi(6)^2$

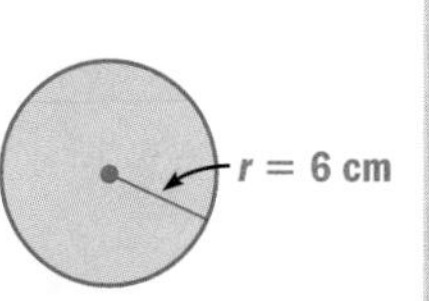

EXAMPLE 1 Finding the Area of a Circle

Find the area of a circle with a diameter of 10 inches.

$A = \pi r^2$ Write formula for area of a circle.

$\approx 3.14(5)^2$ Substitute 3.14 for π and 5 for r.

$= 78.5$ Evaluate using a calculator.

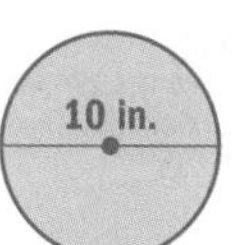

ANSWER The area is about 78.5 square inches.

HELP with Notetaking

To help you organize information about circles, you may want to make a concept grid.

ILLINOIS Standards and ISAT:
7.C.3b, 8.D.3b; 7.B.3, 6.C.3b

EXAMPLE 2 Finding the Radius of a Circle

Find the radius of a circle that has an area of 530.66 square feet.

$A = \pi r^2$	Write formula for area of a circle.
$530.66 \approx (3.14)r^2$	Substitute 530.66 for *A* and 3.14 for π.
$169 \approx r^2$	Use a calculator to divide each side by 3.14.
$\sqrt{169} \approx r$	Take positive square root of each side.
$13 \approx r$	Evaluate square root.

ANSWER The radius of the circle is about 13 feet.

Your turn now **Find the unknown area or radius of the circle. Use 3.14 for π.**

1. $r = 7$ ft, $A = \underline{?}$ 154 ft^2 **2.** $d = 3$ km, $A = \underline{?}$ 7.07 km^2 **3.** $A = 628$ cm^2, $r = \underline{?}$ 14.1 cm

EXAMPLE 3 Using the Area of a Circle

Hockey Find the combined area of the two face-off circles of an ice hockey rink.

Solution

The distance between the centers is 44 feet and there is 14 feet between the circles. So,

$r + 14 + r = 44$ and $r = 15$.

Now use the formula for the area of a circle.

$A = 2\pi r^2$	Area of two circles
$\approx 2(3.14)(15)^2$	Substitute 3.14 for π and 15 for *r*.
$= 1413$	Evaluate using a calculator.

ANSWER The area of the face-off circles is about 1413 square feet.

Your turn now **Find the area of the shaded region. Use 3.14 for π.**

4.

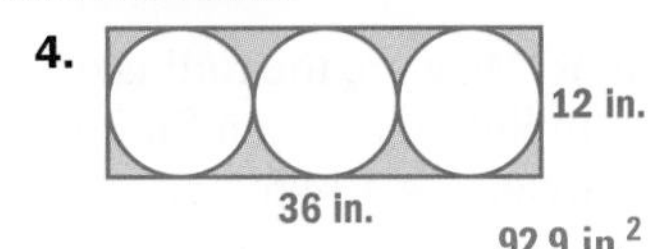

92.9 in.^{2}

5.

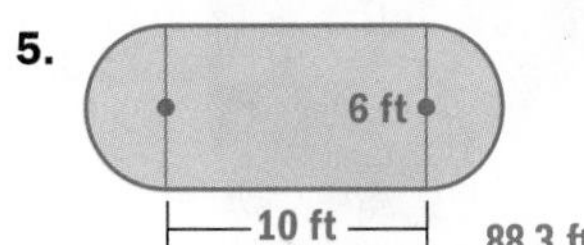

88.3 ft^2

TIPS FOR NEW TEACHERS

Remind students often to use the correct units when writing area. Students often forget to use square units, or they forget to include any unit at all. See Tips for New Teachers in the *Chapter 10 Resource Book*.

EXTRA EXAMPLES

Example 1 Find the area of a circle with a diameter of 30 feet. **about 707 ft^2**

Example 2 Find the radius of a circle that has an area of 12,070 square meters. **about 62 m**

Example 3 Find the combined area of four CDs if each CD has a radius of 6 centimeters.

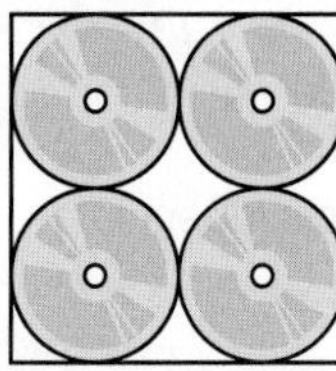

about 452 cm^2

CONCEPT CHECK

Explain how you would find the area of a circle with radius 4 meters. **Square 4 meters and multiply times π.**

DAILY PUZZLER

To the nearest whole number, what percent of this square is covered by the circle? (*Hint:* First write the areas for the square and the circle in terms of *r*.) **about 79%**

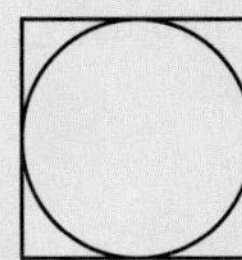

3 APPLY

ASSIGNMENT GUIDE

Basic Course

Day 1: EP p. 732 Exs. 19-22; pp. 488-490 Exs. 6-12, 19-25, 29-31, 36-39

Average Course

Day 1: pp. 488-490 Exs. 7-9, 13-18, 22, 25-29, 32-34, 36-40

Advanced Course

Day 1: pp. 488-490 Exs. 7-9, 13-18, 22, 26-28, 31-36*, 38-40

Block

pp. 488-490 Exs. 7-9, 13-18, 22, 25-29, 32-34, 36-40 (with 10.3)

EXTRA PRACTICE

- Student Edition, p. 736
- Chapter 10 Resource Book, pp. 18-20
- Test and Practice Generator

TRANSPARENCY

Even-numbered answers are available on transparencies.

HOMEWORK CHECK

When you review students' homework for this lesson, go over the following exercises to check understanding of key concepts.

Basic: 6, 10, 19, 20, 22
Average: 7, 13, 16, 17, 22
Advanced: 7, 13, 16, 18, 22

COMMON ERROR

In Exercises 8, 9, and 13-15, watch for students who find the area using diameter instead of radius.

10.2 Exercises

More Practice, p. 736

Getting Ready to Practice

1. Vocabulary Copy and complete: The area of a circle is the product of π and the square of the _?_. radius

Find the area of the circle. Use 3.14 for π.

2. 2 ft — $12.6\ ft^2$

3. 10 cm — $314\ cm^2$

4. 50 yd — $1960\ yd^2$

5. Find the radius of a circle that has an area of 154 square meters. Use 3.14 for π. about 7 m

Practice and Problem Solving

HELP with Homework

Example	Exercises
1	6-15
2	16-21
3	22

- More Examples
- eTutorial Plus

Find the area of the circle. Use 3.14 for π.

A **6.** 11 yd — $380\ yd^2$

7. 13.3 m — $555\ m^2$

8.

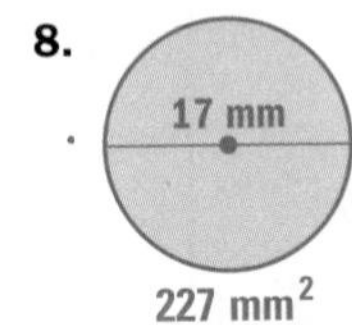

$227\ mm^2$

9.

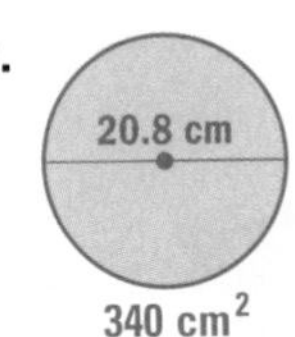

$340\ cm^2$

Find the area of the circle with the given radius or diameter. Use 3.14 for π.

10. $r = 9$ cm $254\ cm^2$ **11.** $r = 10$ ft $314\ ft^2$ **12.** $r = 30$ m $2830\ m^2$

13. $d = 28$ mm $615\ mm^2$ **14.** $d = 6$ yd $28.3\ yd^2$ **15.** $d = 40$ in. $1260\ in.^2$

Find the radius of the circle with the given area. Use 3.14 for π.

16. $A = 28.26\ ft^2$ 3 ft **17.** $A = 3.14\ m^2$ 1 m **18.** $A = 200.96\ yd^2$ 8 yd

19. $A = 113.04\ in.^2$ 6 in. **20.** $A = 12.56\ mm^2$ 2 mm **21.** $A = 254.34\ cm^2$ 9 cm

22. Sprinklers You are using a rotating sprinkler to water your yard. The sprinkler rotates in a complete circle. It sprays water a distance of 12 feet. Find the area of the yard that is watered. Use 3.14 for π. about $452\ ft^2$

B **23. Measurement** Measure the radius of the circle in millimeters. Then find the area of the circle. Use 3.14 for π. 10 mm; $314\ mm^2$

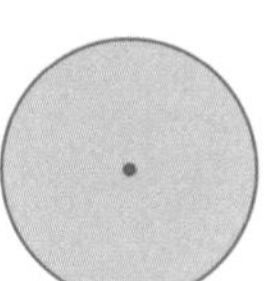

■ **Tennis Center**

The roof of the New South Wales Tennis Center has a mass of 70,000 kilograms. The roof was designed using 24 separate panels. What is the mass of each panel? about 2917 kg

29. $18.84 = 2(3.14)r$; 3 ft; 28.3 ft^2

30. $81.64 = 2(3.14)r$; 13 m; 531 m^2

31. $37.68 = 2(3.14)r$, 6 cm; 113 cm^2

33. Larger square: 400 mm^2, smaller square: 200 mm^2, estimate: 300 mm^2; actual: 314 mm^2. *Sample answer:* The estimate is close to the actual area of the circle.

Find the area of the shaded region. Use 3.14 for π.

24. 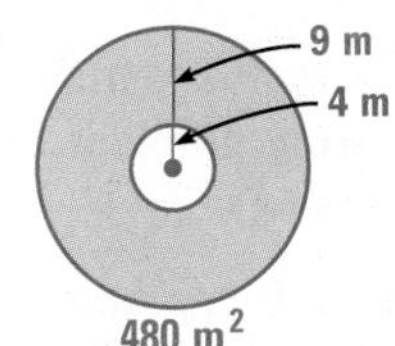

480 m^2

25. 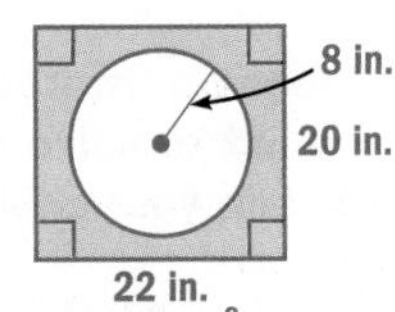

239 in.^{2}

26. 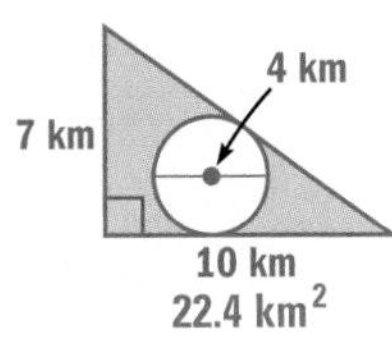

22.4 km^2

27. Mental Math If the area of a circle is 25π square feet, what is the radius? 5 ft

28. Tennis Center The roof of the New South Wales Tennis Center in Sydney, Australia, can be approximated by a circle. A level of seats is covered by the ring-shaped roof whose outer diameter is about 100 meters and inner diameter is about 65 meters. What is the area of the roof? Use 3.14 for π. about 4530 m^2

Algebra Write and solve an equation to find the radius of the circle given its circumference *C*. Then use the radius to find the area of the circle. Use 3.14 for π. 29–31. See margin.

29. $C = 18.84$ ft **30.** $C = 81.64$ m **31.** $C = 37.68$ cm

32. Critical Thinking Copy and complete the table. Leave your answers in terms of π. What happens to the area of a circle when the radius is multiplied by a number? The area is multiplied by the square of the number.

Radius r	Area of a circle with radius r	Area of a circle with radius $2r$	Area of a circle with radius $3r$	Area of a circle with radius $4r$
2 in.	4π in.^{2}	? 16π in.^{2}	? 36π in.^{2}	? 64π in.^{2}
3 in.	? 9π in.^{2}	? 36π in.^{2}	? 81π in.^{2}	? 144π in.^{2}
5 in.	? 25π in.^{2}	? 100π in.^{2}	? 225π in.^{2}	? 400π in.^{2}

C **33. Estimation** The diameter of the circle equals the side length of the larger square and the diagonal of the smaller square. The diameter of the circle is 20 millimeters. Find the area of each square and use the areas to estimate the area of the circle. Then calculate the area of the circle and compare it to your estimate. Use 3.14 for π. See margin.

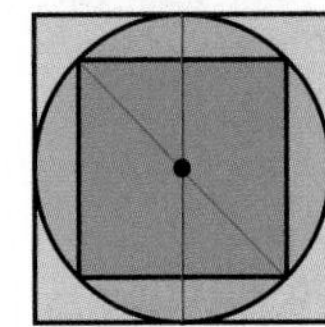

34. Disk Sanders You are using a disk sander to sand a porch that has an area of 11,520 square inches. One disk for the sander has a diameter of 7 inches. Another disk has a diameter of 10 inches. You can sand a surface with the area of five disks in one minute. About how much time would you save by sanding with the larger disk? Round your answer to the nearest minute. Use 3.14 for π. about 31 min

35. Challenge Find the area of the shaded region. Use 3.14 for π. 84.3 mm^2

VISUALIZE

You may wish to do this activity in conjunction with Exercise 33. Point out that the value r^2 can be thought of as the area of a square with side r. Have students draw and cut out a circle on plain white paper. Then ask them to cut out three colored squares with sides the length of their circle's radius. Students can cut and piece the three squares inside the circle to help them visualize the area of a circle as being a little more than three times the area of a square with side r.

ASSESS

ASSESSMENT RESOURCES

For more assessment resources, see:
- Assessment Book
- Test and Practice Generator

MINI-QUIZ

Find the area of the circle given its radius r or diameter d. Use 3.14 for π.

1. $r = 20$ in. about 1256 in.^{2}
2. $d = 44$ m about 1520 m^2
3. Determine the radius of a circle with an area of 1134 square feet. Use 3.14 for π. 19 ft
4. A traffic circle is 120 feet across. How many square feet of wildflowers could the city plant on the circle? Use 3.14 for π. about 11,304 ft^2

FOLLOW-UP

RETEACHING/REMEDIATION

- Study Guide in Chapter 10 Resource Book, pp. 21–22
- Tutor Place, Geometry and Measurement Card 16
- eTutorial Plus Online
- Extra Practice, p. 736
- Lesson Practice in Chapter 10 Resource Book, pp. 18–20

CHALLENGE/ENRICHMENT

- Challenge Practice in Chapter 10 Resource Book, p. 24
- Teacher's Edition, p. 478F

ENGLISH LEARNER SUPPORT

- Spanish Study Guide
- Multi-Language Glossary
- Chapter Audio Summaries CDs

36. 33 quarters. *Sample answer:* I used Work Backward because I could find the number of quarters needed, 7, by dividing 100 by 15 and rounding up, then subtracting 7 from 40, the original number of quarters in the roll.

Mixed Review

Problem Solving Strategies
- Make a Table
- Work Backward
- Act It Out

Choose a Strategy Use a strategy from the list to solve the following problem. Explain your choice of strategy.

36. For each quarter you put in a parking meter you can park your car for 15 minutes. You know you'll be away from your car for up to an hour and 40 minutes. If you have a \$10 roll of quarters, how many quarters will you have after you put the necessary amount in the meter?

Tell whether the side lengths form a right triangle. *(Lesson 9.3)*

37. $a = 0.5, b = 0.9, c = 1.06$ no

38. $a = 3.6, b = 4.8, c = 6$ yes

Test-Taking Practice 

39. Multiple Choice What is the approximate diameter of a circle with an area of 201 square millimeters? Use 3.14 for π. B

A. 8 mm **B.** 16 mm **C.** 32 mm **D.** 64 mm

40. Short Response Ty is helping to paint his school's basketball court. Find the total area of the figure and explain how you found it. Use 3.14 for π.

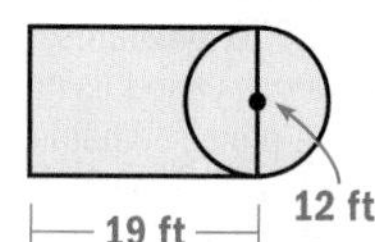

40. 285 ft^2; I found the area of the rectangle and half the area of the circle, then added to find the total area.

BRAIN GAME

What's the Score?

The center circle of the target has a radius of 3 inches and each ring is 3 inches wide. Find the area of each region in terms of π. Then use the formula below to find the score for each region. Round to the nearest whole number.

$$score = \frac{225\pi}{area}$$

For example, the yellow region has an area of $\pi(3)^2$, or 9π square inches. The score in the yellow region is

$$\frac{225\pi}{area} = \frac{225\pi}{9\pi} = 25.$$

Which player, Greg or Jamie, has a higher score?

area from center outward: 9π in.^{2}, 27π in.^{2}, 45π in.^{2}, 63π in.^{2}, 81π in.^{2}; score from center outward: 25, 8, 5, 4, 3; Greg.

Greg 

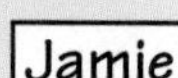

10.2 Technology Activity

SPREADSHEET

Comparing Radii of Circles

GOAL Use a spreadsheet to find how the radius of a circle changes when its area changes.

Example **How does the radius of a circle change when its area is multiplied by 4?**

1. Create a spreadsheet with an original circle area in cell A1 and the multiplier 4 in cell A2. Enter formulas for the Area column that refer to these cells, as shown.

2. The radius of a circle with area A is given by $\sqrt{\frac{A}{\pi}}$. Enter formulas for the Radius column, as shown.

3. Compare the radii of the two circles by dividing the second radius by the first radius. Enter a formula for this quotient in the Ratio column, as shown.

Comparing Radii

	A	B	C
1	1	Original circle area	
2	4	Multiplier	
3			
4	Area	Radius	Ratio
5	=A1	=SQRT(A5/PI())	
6	=A5*A2	=SQRT(A6/PI())	=B6/B5

4. Change the value of the original circle area in cell A1 several times. What do you notice about the ratio of the radii?

	A	B	C
1	1	Original circle area	
2	4	Multiplier	
3			
4	Area	Radius	Ratio
5	1	0.564190	
6	4	1.128379	2

	A	B	C
1	5	Original circle area	
2	4	Multiplier	
3			
4	Area	Radius	Ratio
5	5	1.261566	
6	20	2.523133	2

	A	B	C
1	15	Original circle area	
2	4	Multiplier	
3			
4	Area	Radius	Ratio
5	15	2.185097	
6	60	4.370194	2

ANSWER When the area of a circle is multiplied by 4, the radius is multiplied by 2.

Your turn now **Find how the radius of a circle changes when its area is multiplied by the given number.**

1. 9 **multiplied by 3** **2.** 16 **multiplied by 4** **3.** 25 **multiplied by 5** **4.** 36 **multiplied by 6**

5. Critical Thinking How does the radius of a circle change when its area is doubled? tripled? Explain. **Multiplied by $\sqrt{2}$; multiplied by $\sqrt{3}$. *Sample answer:* If the area of a circle is multiplied by n, then the radius is multiplied by $\sqrt{n}$.**

6. Explain why $r = \sqrt{\frac{A}{\pi}}$ is the formula for the radius of a circle with area A. **See margin.**

ILLINOIS Standards and ISAT:
8.B.3; 8.D.3b

1 PLAN

LEARN THE METHOD

- Students will use a spreadsheet to find how the radius of a circle changes when its area changes.
- In Exercise 32 of Lesson 10.2, students examine the relationship between change in radius and change in area.

2 TEACH

ALTERNATIVE STRATEGY

Have students close their books. Draw two circles on the board so that the area of one circle is twice the area of the other circle. Do not tell students that the radius of the larger circle is about 1.4 times the radius of the smaller one. Challenge students to think about the relationship between the radii, make conjectures, and explain their reasoning.

EXTRA EXAMPLES

Example If you triple the area of a circle, by how much does the diameter of the circle increase? **about 1.73**

3 CLOSE

ASSESSMENT

1. Find $\sqrt{2}$. **about 1.414**

2. How does this square root relate to the ratio of the areas in the Example? **The ratio of the areas is $x^2 = 2$, so $x = \sqrt{2}$ or about 1.414.**

6. See Additional Answers beginning on page AA1.

1 PLAN

SKILL CHECK

1. Is a circle a polygon? Explain. **No; the sides are not segments.**
2. Name a polygon with three sides. **triangle**

LESSON OBJECTIVE

Classify and sketch solids.

PACING

Suggested Number of Days
Basic Course: 1 day
Average Course: 1 day
Advanced Course: 1 day
Block: 0.5 block with 10.2

TEACHING RESOURCES

For a complete list of Teaching Resources, see page 478B.

TRANSPARENCY

Warm-Up Exercises for this lesson are available on a transparency.

2 TEACH

MOTIVATING THE LESSON

Bring solid polyhedra to class for students to see and handle.

TIPS FOR NEW TEACHERS

Students' spatial skills vary. Some students are quick to visualize and mentally manipulate three-dimensional objects while others need considerable practice. Have models on hand for students to manipulate. See Tips for New Teachers in the *Chapter 10 Resource Book.*

Lesson 10.3 Three-Dimensional Figures

BEFORE	Now	WHY?
You classified and sketched polygons.	You'll classify and sketch solids.	So you can classify solids that form structures, as in Exs. 19–21.

Word Watch

solid, polyhedron, p. 492
face, p. 492
prism, p. 492
pyramid, p. 492
cylinder, p. 492
cone, p. 492
sphere, p. 492
edge, vertex, p. 492

A **solid** is a three-dimensional figure that encloses a part of space. A **polyhedron** is a solid that is enclosed by polygons. A polyhedron has only flat surfaces. The polygons that form a polyhedron are called **faces**.

Classifying Solids

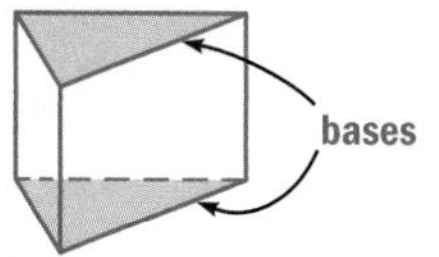

A **prism** is a polyhedron. Prisms have two congruent bases that lie in parallel planes. The other faces are rectangles.

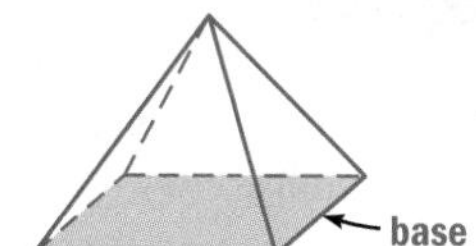

A **pyramid** is a polyhedron. Pyramids have one base. The other faces are triangles.

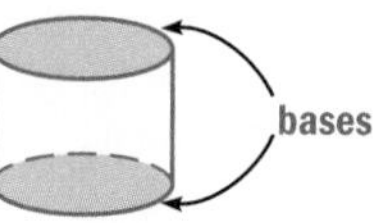

A **cylinder** is a solid with two congruent circular bases that lie in parallel planes.

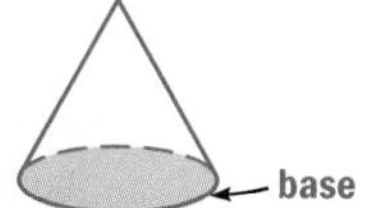

A **cone** is a solid with one circular base.

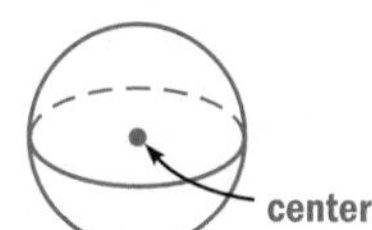

A **sphere** is a solid formed by all points in space that are the same distance from a fixed point called the center.

EXAMPLE 1 Classifying Solids

Classify the solid. Then tell whether it is a polyhedron.

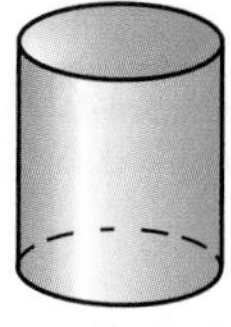

The solid has two congruent circular bases that lie in parallel planes, so it is a cylinder. It is not a polyhedron, because circles are not polygons.

with Vocabulary

The plural of vertex is *vertices*.

The segments where faces meet are called **edges**. A **vertex** of a polyhedron is a point where three or more edges meet.

ILLINOIS Standards and ISAT:
9.A.3a, 9.B.3

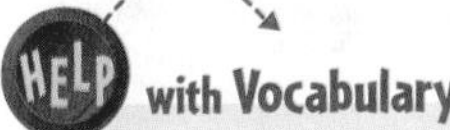

HELP with Vocabulary

You can name a prism or pyramid using the shape of its base. For example, in Example 2 the base is a pentagon, so the solid is called a pentagonal pyramid.

EXAMPLE 2 Counting Faces, Edges, and Vertices

Classify the solid. Then count the number of faces, edges, and vertices.

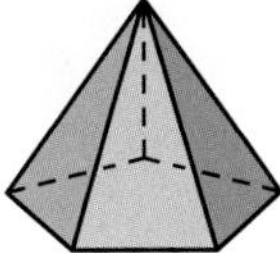

The solid is a pentagonal pyramid.

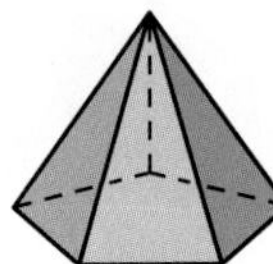

6 faces

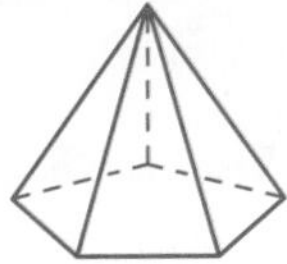

10 edges

6 vertices

EXAMPLE 3 Sketching a Solid

Show two ways to represent a triangular prism.

Method 1 Sketch the solid.

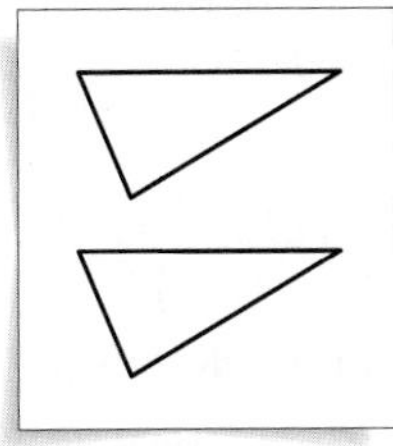

(1) **Sketch two congruent bases.**

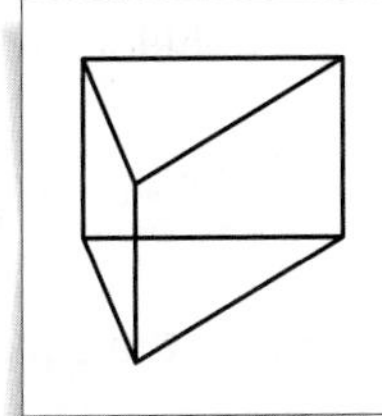

(2) **Connect the vertices of the bases.**

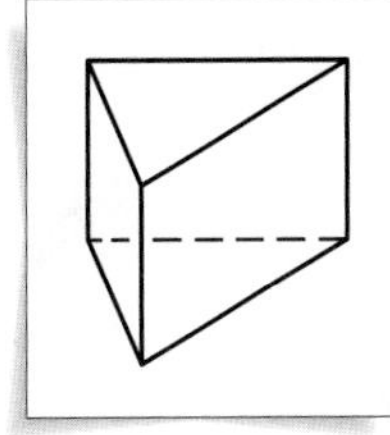

(3) **Make any hidden lines dashed.**

Method 2 Sketch the top, front, and side views of the solid.

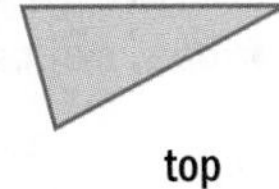

top

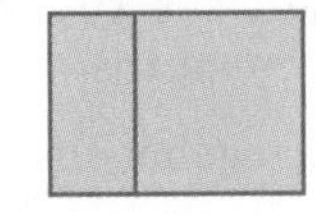

front

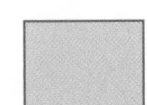

side

Your turn now **Classify the solid. Then tell whether it is a polyhedron.**

1. 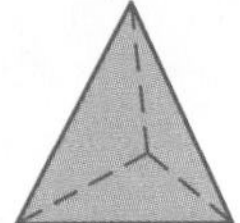

triangular pyramid; yes

2. 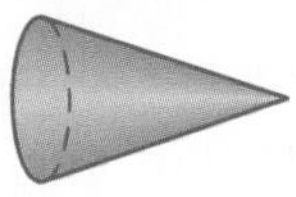

cone; no

3. 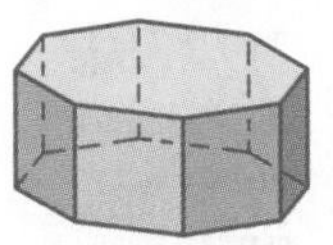

octagonal prism; yes

4. Show two ways to represent a rectangular pyramid. Then count the number of faces, edges, and vertices.
See margin for art; 5 faces, 8 edges, 5 vertices.

EXTRA EXAMPLES

Example 1 Classify the solid. Then tell whether it is a polyhedron. **cone; no**

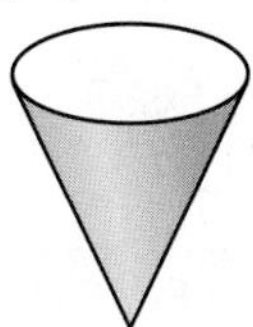

Example 2 Classify the solid. Then count the number of faces, edges, and vertices.

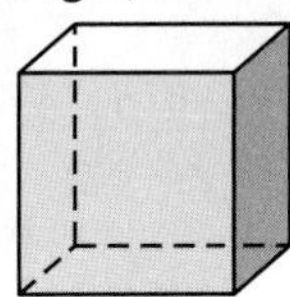

rectangular prism; 6 faces, 12 edges, 8 vertices

Example 3 Show two ways to represent a cylinder.

top

front

side

CONCEPT CHECK

Name the two solids that have two congruent bases. Which one is a polyhedron and why? **A prism and a cylinder; a prism is a polyhedron because it is a solid that is enclosed by polygons. A cylinder is not a polyhedron because its bases are circles.**

DAILY PUZZLER

Name a solid whose top, front, and side views are identical. ***Sample answers:*** **cube, sphere**

4. See Additional Answers beginning on page AA1.

3 APPLY

ASSIGNMENT GUIDE

Basic Course

Day 1: pp. 494–495 Exs. 7-11, 13-17, 19-21, 24-27

Average Course

Day 1: pp. 494–495 Exs. 9-18, 21-27

Advanced Course

Day 1: pp. 494–495 Exs. 9-11, 13-26, EC: TE p. 478D*

Block

pp. 494–495 Exs. 9-18, 21-27 (with 10.2)

EXTRA PRACTICE

- Student Edition, p. 736
- Chapter 10 Resource Book, pp. 28-30
- Test and Practice Generator

TRANSPARENCY

Even-numbered answers are available on transparencies.

HOMEWORK CHECK

When you review students' homework for this lesson, go over the following exercises to check understanding of key concepts.
Basic: 7, 10, 11, 13, 17
Average: 9, 10, 11, 13, 18
Advanced: 9, 10, 11, 14, 18

4.

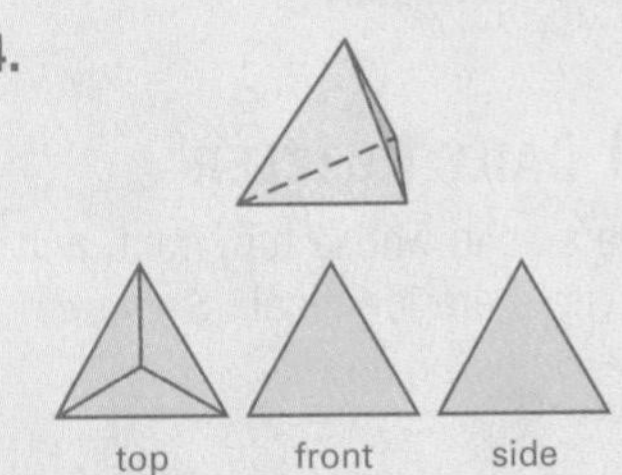

5, 6 (Steps 1-3), 10, 11. See Additional Answers beginning on page AA1.

10.3 Exercises

More Practice, p. 736

Getting Ready to Practice

Vocabulary **Classify the solid. Then tell whether it is a polyhedron.**

1.  cylinder; no

2. 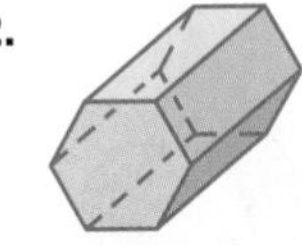 hexagonal prism; yes

3. 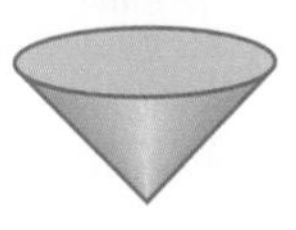 cone; no

Show two ways to represent the solid. Then count the number of faces, edges, and vertices. 4–5. See margin for art.

4. triangular pyramid 4 faces, 6 edges, 4 vertices
5. pentagonal prism 7 faces, 15 edges, 10 vertices
6. **Guided Problem Solving** Sketch a square pyramid. Steps 1–3. See margin.
   (1) Sketch a parallelogram for the square base.
   (2) Draw a dot centered above the parallelogram.
   (3) Connect the vertices of the parallelogram to the dot. Make any hidden lines dashed.

Practice and Problem Solving

A **Classify the solid. Then tell whether it is a polyhedron.**

7. 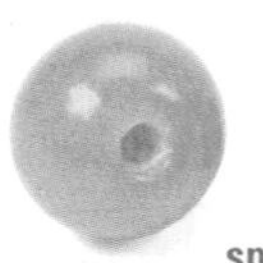 sphere; no

8.  rectangular prism; yes

9.  cylinder; no

In Exercises 10 and 11, show two ways to represent the solid. Then count the number of faces, edges, and vertices. 10–11. See margin for art.

10. octagonal prism 10 faces, 24 edges, 16 vertices
11. hexagonal prism 8 faces, 18 edges, 12 vertices
12. **Writing** Give examples of cylinders, cones, and square prisms that you find in your classroom or at home. *Sample answer:* cylinders: cans, oatmeal boxes; cones: ice cream cones, funnels; square prisms: boxes, note cubes

B Matching **Match the description with the solid.**

13. one circular base D
14. two rectangular bases C
15. no edges or bases E
16. three rectangular faces A
17. four triangular faces B

A. triangular prism
B. rectangular pyramid
C. rectangular prism
D. cone
E. sphere

HELP with Homework

Example	Exercises
1	7-9, 13-17
2	10-11, 18
3	10-11

Online Resources
CLASSZONE.COM
- More Examples
- eTutorial Plus

18. **Critical Thinking** Copy and complete the table. Use the pattern to write a formula that gives the number of edges in terms of the number of faces and vertices. This is called Euler's Formula. $E = F + V - 2$

Figure	Number of faces F	Number of vertices V	Number of edges E	$F + V$
pentagonal pyramid	6	6	10	12
rectangular pyramid	? 5	? 5	? 8	? 10
triangular prism	? 5	? 6	? 9	? 11
rectangular prism	? 6	? 8	? 12	? 14
pentagonal prism	? 7	? 10	? 15	? 17

Classify the solids that form the structure.

19. 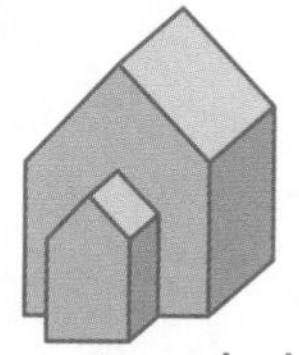
pentagonal prisms

20. 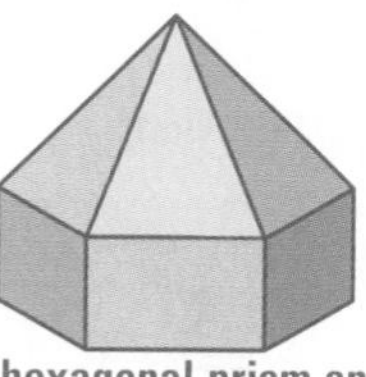
hexagonal prism and hexagonal pyramid

21. 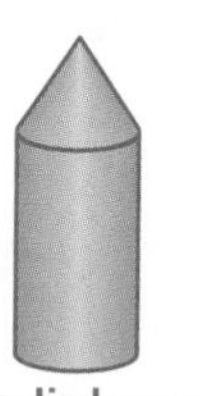
cylinder and cone

Sketch the solid with the given views. 22–23. See margin.

C 22. 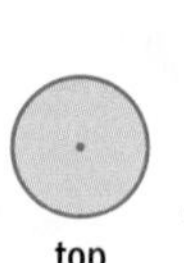  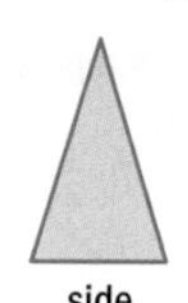
top front side

23. 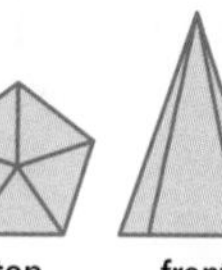 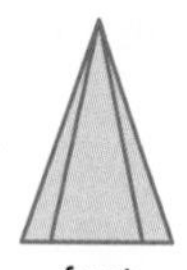 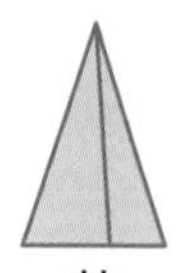
top front side

Mixed Review 

24. Find the value of h. Then find the perimeter and area of the triangle. *(Lesson 9.4)* 15 cm; 90 cm, 270 cm^2

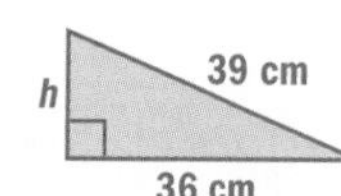

25. Find the area of a circle whose diameter is 21 inches. Use 3.14 for π. *(Lesson 10.2)* 346 in.^{2}

Test-Taking Practice 

INTERNET State Test Practice CLASSZONE.COM

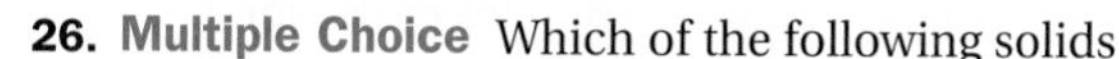

26. **Multiple Choice** Which of the following solids is a polyhedron? D

A. sphere **B.** cylinder **C.** cone **D.** pyramid

27. **Multiple Choice** What is the name of the solid shown? H

F. cone **G.** triangle

H. triangular pyramid **I.** triangular prism

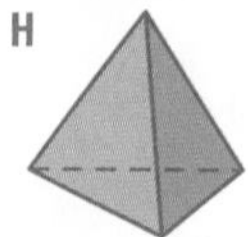

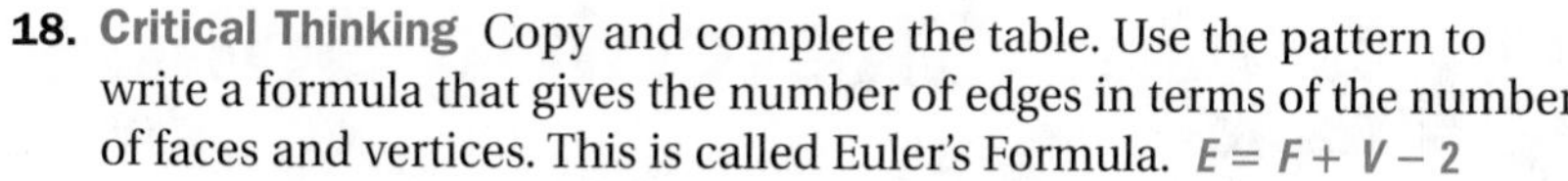

4 ASSESS

Assessment Resources

For more assessment resources, see:
- Assessment Book
- Test and Practice Generator

Mini-Quiz

1. Classify the solid. Then tell whether it is a polyhedron. sphere; no

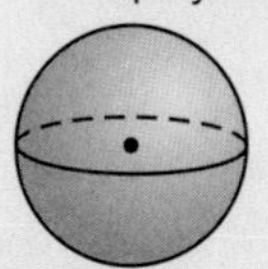

Count the number of faces, edges, and vertices of each solid.

2. triangular pyramid
4 faces, 6 edges, 4 vertices
3. hexagonal prism
8 faces, 18 edges, 12 vertices

5 FOLLOW-UP

Reteaching/Remediation

- Study Guide in Chapter 10 Resource Book, pp. 31–32
- Tutor Place, Geometry and Measurement Card 20
- eTutorial Plus Online
- Extra Practice, p. 736
- Lesson Practice in Chapter 10 Resource Book, pp. 28–30

Challenge/Enrichment

- Challenge Practice in Chapter 10 Resource Book, p. 33
- Teacher's Edition, p. 478F

English Learner Support

- Spanish Study Guide
- Multi-Language Glossary
- Chapter Audio Summaries CDs

22, 23. See Additional Answers beginning on page AA1.

1 PLAN

SKILL CHECK

Sketch the top, front, and side view of the cone.

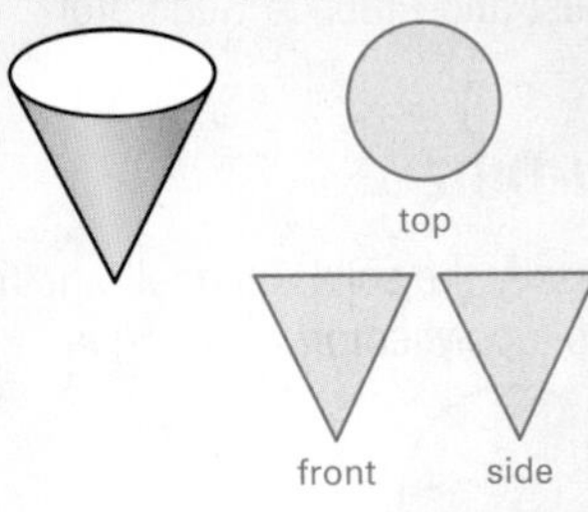

LESSON OBJECTIVE

Draw views of solids and make isometric drawings.

2 TEACH

EXTRA EXAMPLES

Example 1 Draw the top, front, and side views of the solid.

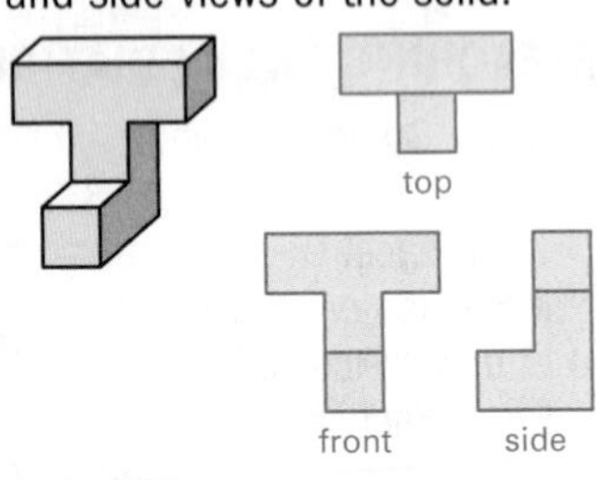

Example 2 Create an isometric drawing of the solid from Example 1.

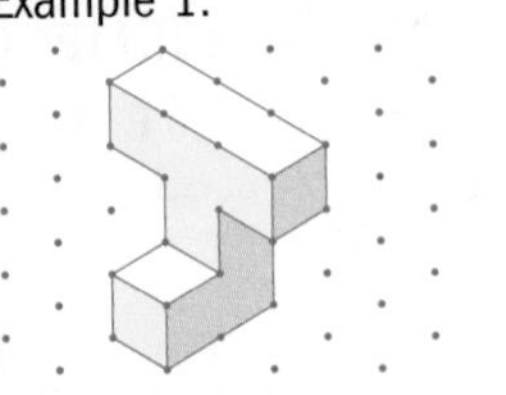

TRANSPARENCY

A support transparency is available for this Special Topic. A blackline master is also available in the *Chapter 10 Resource Book.*

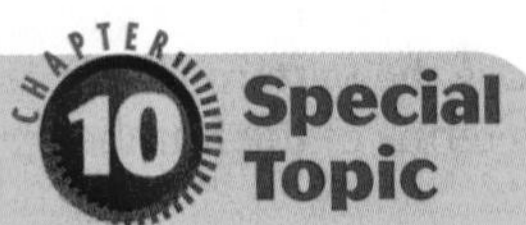

Sketching Solids

GOAL Draw views of solids and make isometric drawings.

Word Watch

isometric drawing, p. 496

In Lesson 10.3, you drew the top, front, and side views of several common solids. In the following examples, you will see how to draw the top, front, and side views of more complicated solids.

EXAMPLE 1 Drawing Views of a Solid

Draw the top, front, and side views of the solid.

Solution

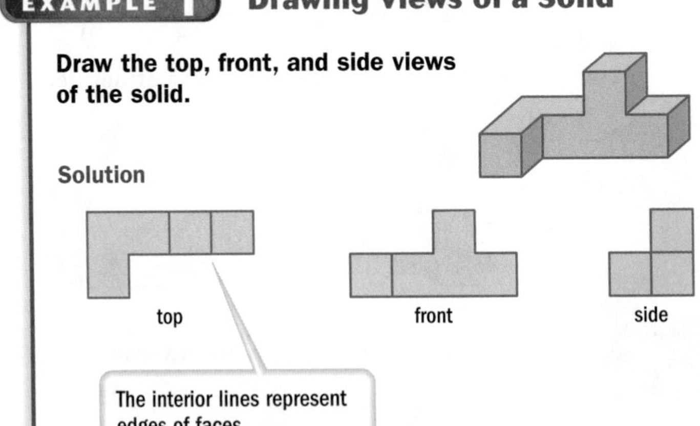

Isometric Drawings An **isometric drawing** is a two-dimensional drawing of a three-dimensional figure. You can create isometric drawings using a grid of dots and a set of three axes that intersect to form 120° angles. Use the dots to guide your drawing.

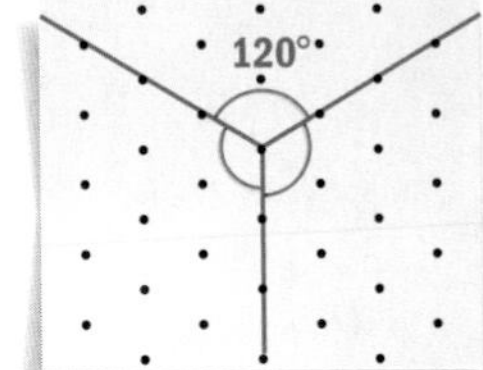

EXAMPLE 2 Creating an Isometric Drawing

Create an isometric drawing of the solid from Example 1.

Solution

The isometric drawing is shown at the right. Each vertical edge of the solid is represented by a vertical line segment.

Add depth to the drawing by shading the top, front, and sides differently.

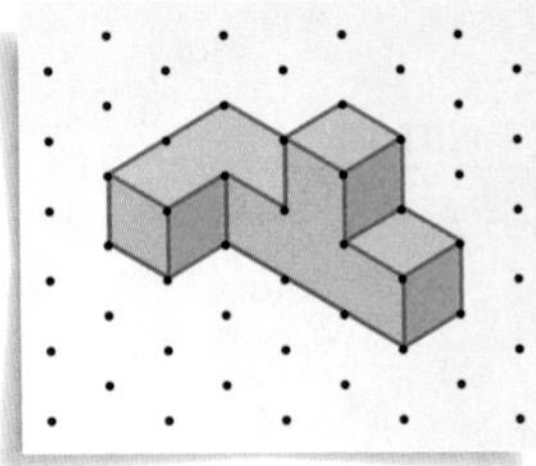

ILLINOIS Standards and ISAT:
9.A.3a

EXAMPLE 3 Interpreting an Isometric Drawing

Draw the top, front, and side views of the solid.

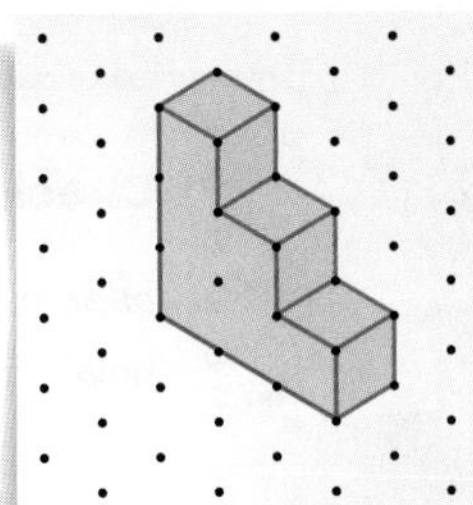

Solution

You can arrange the views this way.

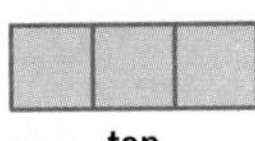
top

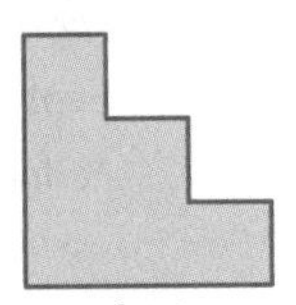
front

side

Exercises

Draw the top, front, and side views of the solid. 1–3. See margin.

1. 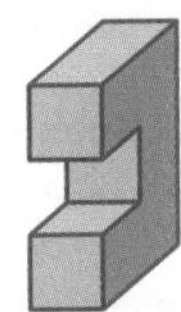

2. 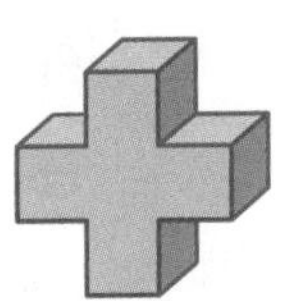

3. 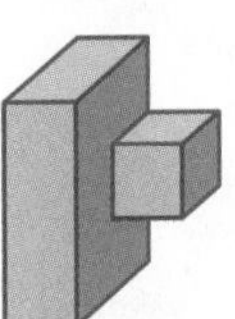

Create an isometric drawing of the solid. 4–6. See margin.

4. 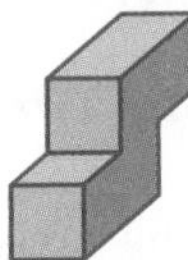

5. 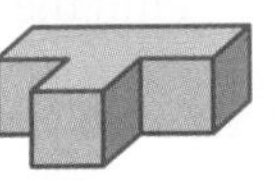

6. 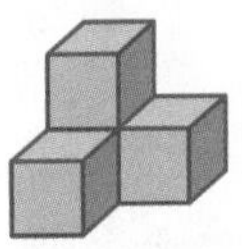

Draw the top, front, and side views of the solid. 7–9. See margin.

7. 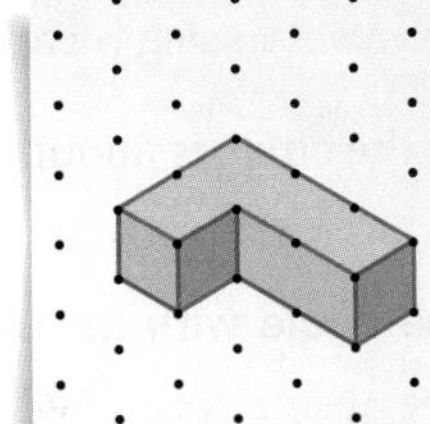

8. 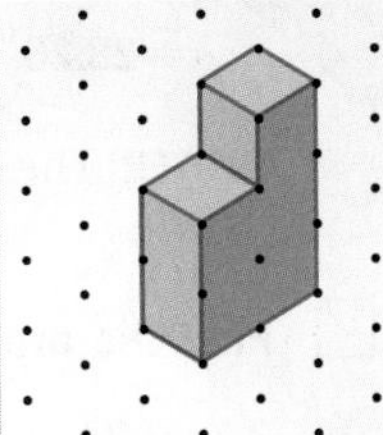

9. 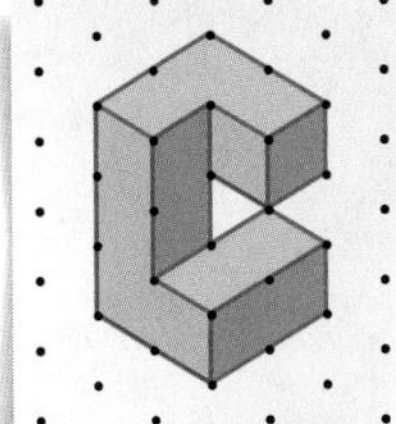

HELP with Solving

For the solids shown here, assume there are no cubes hidden from view except those needed to support the visible ones.

COMMON ERROR

Students may confuse the front view with the side view. Discuss the convention of the front view being the face that is facing toward the left.

TEACHING TIP

Construct a three-dimensional representation of the irregular solid to help students visualize the three views of the solid.

EXTRA EXAMPLES

Example 3 Draw the top, front, and side views of the solid.

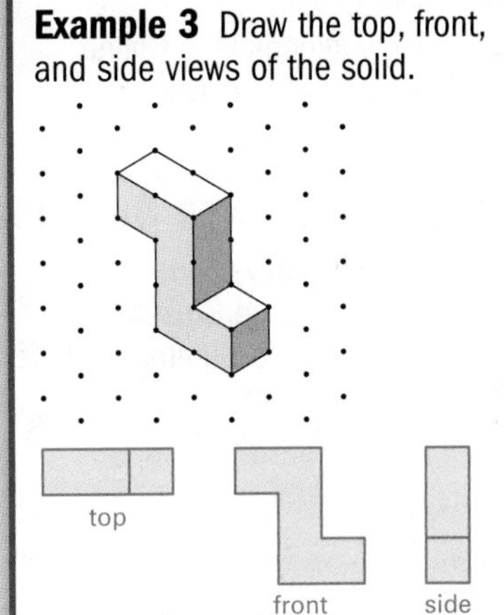

top

front

side

3 APPLY

TRANSPARENCY

Even-numbered answers are available on transparencies.

TEACHING TIP

In Exercise 3, make sure students pay careful attention to the location of the single cube.

1–9. See Additional Answers beginning on page AA1.

ADDITIONAL RESOURCES

The following resources are available to help review the materials in Lessons 10.1–10.3.

Chapter 10 Resource Book

- Lesson Practice
- Study Guide

Assessment Book

- Chapter 10 Quiz 1

Technology

- Test and Practice Generator
- eTutorial CD-ROM

Internet

- Classzone
- eWorkbook Plus Online
- eTutorial Plus Online

ENGLISH LEARNER SUPPORT

- Spanish Study Guide
- Multi-Language Glossary
- Chapter Audio Summaries CDs

Notebook Review

Review the vocabulary definitions in your notebook.

Copy the review examples in your notebook. Then complete the exercises.

Check Your Definitions

base of a parallelogram, p. 481	prism, p. 492
height of a parallelogram, p. 481	pyramid, p. 492
bases of a trapezoid, p. 482	cylinder, p. 492
height of a trapezoid, p. 482	cone, p. 492
solid, polyhedron, p. 492	sphere, p. 492
face, p. 492	edge, vertex, p. 492

Use Your Vocabulary

1. A(n) _?_ is a solid that is enclosed by polygons. polyhedron

10.1 Can you find the area of a parallelogram or trapezoid?

EXAMPLE Find the area of the trapezoid.

$A = \frac{1}{2}(b_1 + b_2)h$ — **Write formula for area.**

$= \frac{1}{2}(12 + 18)(5) = 75$ — **Substitute values for b_1, b_2, and h.**

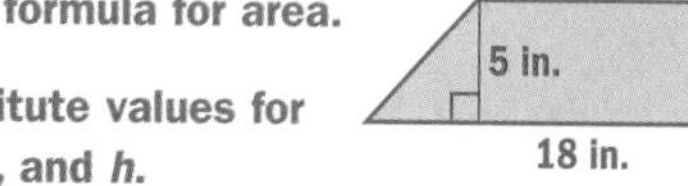

ANSWER The area of the trapezoid is 75 square inches.

☑ **2.** Find the area of a parallelogram with base 20 feet and height 8 feet. 160 ft²

10.2 Can you find the area of a circle?

EXAMPLE Find the area of the circle. Use 3.14 for π.

$A = \pi r^2$ — **Write formula for area of a circle.**

$\approx 3.14(3)^2$ — **Substitute 3.14 for π and 3 for r.**

$= 28.26$ — **Evaluate using a calculator.**

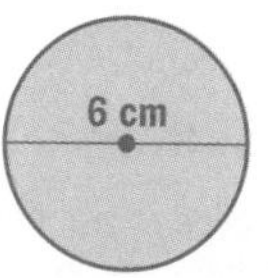

ANSWER The area of the circle is about 28.26 square centimeters.

☑ **Find the area of the circle with radius r or diameter d. Use 3.14 for π.**

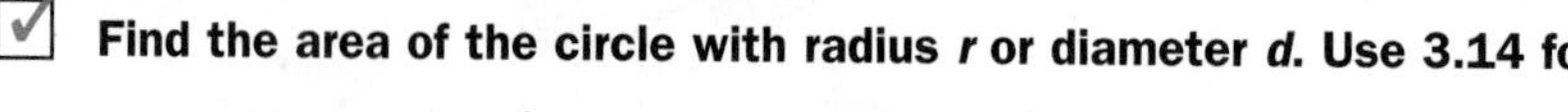

3. $r = 24$ in. 1810 in.² **4.** $r = 4$ mm 50.2 mm² **5.** $d = 18$ yd 254 yd²

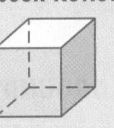

10.3 Can you classify three-dimensional figures?

EXAMPLE Count the faces, edges, and vertices of a triangular pyramid.

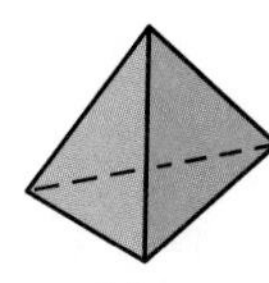

4 faces

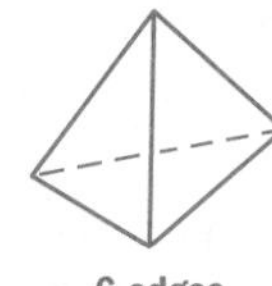

6 edges

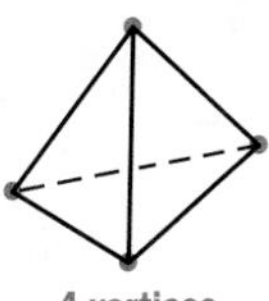

4 vertices

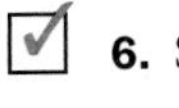

6. Show two ways to represent a square prism. See margin.

Stop and Think about Lessons 10.1–10.3

7. **Compare** Explain how a cone and a cylinder are alike and how they are different. Then explain how a cylinder and a prism are alike and how they are different. See margin.

8. **Critical Thinking** Can the number of vertices of a prism be odd? Explain. See margin.

Notebook Review

7. *Sample answer:* A cone and a cylinder both have circular bases, but a cone has only one circular base while a cylinder has two. A cross-section of either solid parallel to a base is a circle, but for the cone these circles get smaller toward the vertex, while for the cylinder they are all the same size. A cylinder and a prism both have two parallel bases, but the bases of a cylinder are circles, while the bases of a prism are polygons.

8. No. *Sample answer:* The only vertices of a prism are on its bases. Because the bases are two congruent polygons, the total number of vertices is twice the number on one base, so it is an even number.

Review Quiz 1

Find the area of the parallelogram or trapezoid.

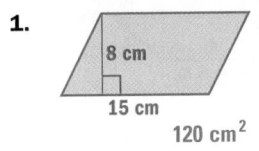

1. (parallelogram: 8 cm, 15 cm) 120 cm^2

2. (parallelogram: 12 ft, 6 ft) 72 ft^2

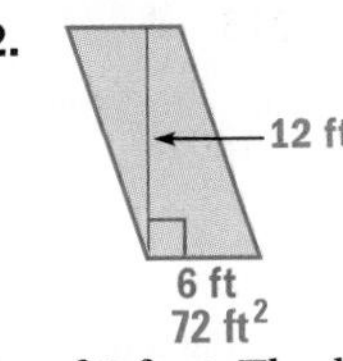

3. (trapezoid: 4.5 cm, 6 cm, 9 cm) 40.5 cm^2

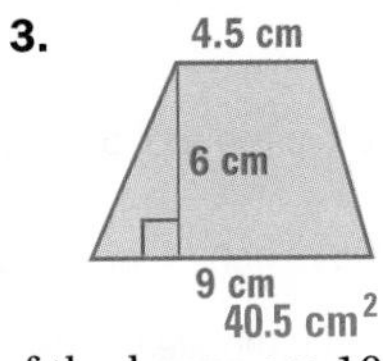

4. A trapezoid has a height of 8 feet. The lengths of the bases are 10 feet and 14 feet. Find the area of the trapezoid. 96 ft^2

5. Find the area of a circle with diameter 22 feet. Use 3.14 for π. 380 ft^2

Find the radius of the circle with the given area. Use 3.14 for π.

6. $A = 254.34 \text{ ft}^2$ 9 ft
7. $A = 452.16 \text{ cm}^2$ 12 cm
8. $A = 78.5 \text{ m}^2$ 5 m

9. Classify the solid. Then tell whether it is a polyhedron. rectangular pyramid; yes

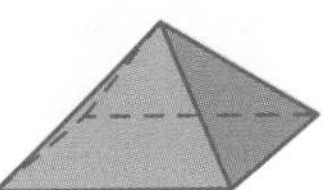

10. Show two ways to represent a pentagonal pyramid. Then count the number of faces, edges, and vertices. See margin for art; 6 faces, 10 edges, 6 vertices.

Notebook Review

6.

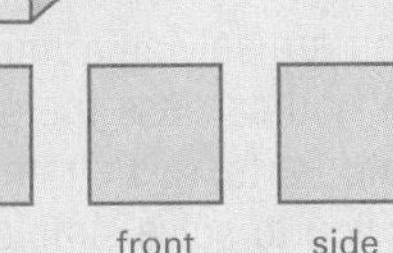

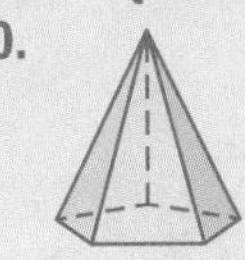

Review Quiz 1

10.

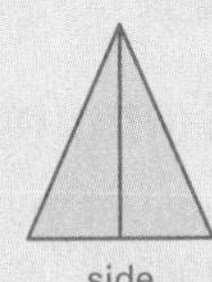

1 PLAN

STRATEGY BACKGROUND

When you are solving a multi-step problem, you can use the strategy Break into Parts. This strategy enables you to solve simpler problems whose solutions together solve the original problem.

2 TEACH

GUIDING STUDENTS' WORK

Suggest that students first list all the areas to be found before doing the calculations.

EXTRA EXAMPLES

Example You are carpeting your walkway and deck in your back yard. How much carpet do you need? **112 ft^2**

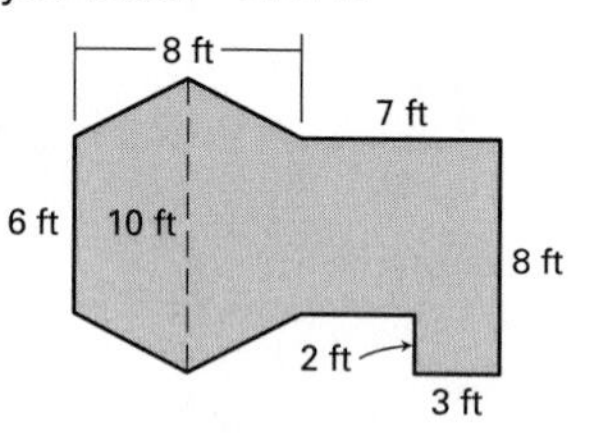

10.4 Problem Solving Strategies

- Guess, Check, and Revise
- Draw a Diagram
- Make a List
- Act It Out
- Break into Parts
- Work Backward
- Make a Table

Break into Parts

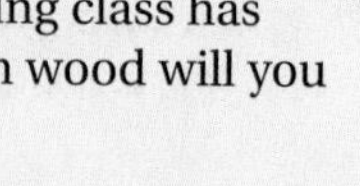

Problem Each student in your woodworking class has been assigned to make a mailbox. How much wood will you need to make the mailbox?

1 Read and Understand

Read the problem carefully.

You need to find the amount of wood needed to make the mailbox.

2 Make a Plan

Decide on a strategy to use.

You can solve this problem by breaking it into parts. Find the area of each side of the mailbox. Then add the areas together.

3 Solve the Problem

Reread the problem and break the problem into smaller parts.

3 in.
5 in.
$h = 6$ in.
$l = 18$ in.
$w = 8$ in.

Area of bottom: $lw = 18(8)$

$= 144$

Area of left and right sides: $2lh = 2(18)(6)$

$= 216$

Area of two roof pieces: $2(5)(18) = 180$

Area of front door and back door:

Add the area of the two triangles to the area of the two rectangles.

Area of the two triangles: $2\left(\frac{1}{2}\right)(8)(3) = 24$

Area of the two rectangles: $2(8)(6) = 96$

Find the sum of the areas: $A = 144 + 216 + 180 + 24 + 96$

$= 660 \text{ in.}^2$

4 Look Back

Have you found the area of every side of the mailbox? Did you find the total of these areas?

ILLINOIS Standards and ISAT:
6.B.3a, 6.C.3a

Practice the Strategy

Use the strategy *Break into Parts.*

1. **Mailbox** As an extra credit project, you are making a mailbox with a flat top. The new mailbox is 6 inches wide, 7 inches high, and 12 inches long. How much wood do you need to make this mailbox? **396 in.²**

2. **Tiling** You are tiling the L-shaped room shown below. Each tile is 6 inches long by 6 inches wide. How many tiles do you need to tile the room? **1200 tiles**

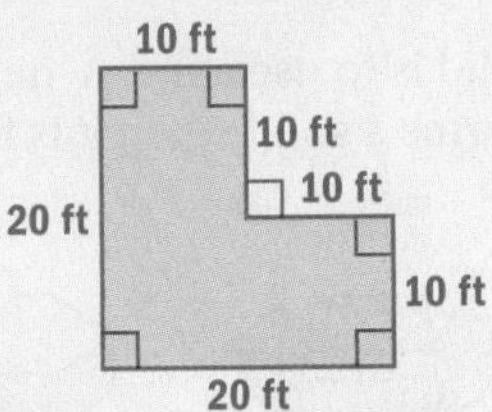

3. **Digits** You are making numbers to hang outside the classrooms in your school. The rooms are numbered 1–100. How many of each digit from 0–9 do you need? **11 0's, 21 1's, 20 of each of the digits 2–9**

4. **Lawn Mowing** You need about 2 hours to mow 3 acres of land. The total land area in the diagram is one acre, or 43,560 square feet. The house and surrounding plants have an area of 1500 square feet. The driveway is 12 feet wide and 50 feet long. How much time would you need to mow the remaining land area? Round your answer to the nearest minute. **about 38 min**

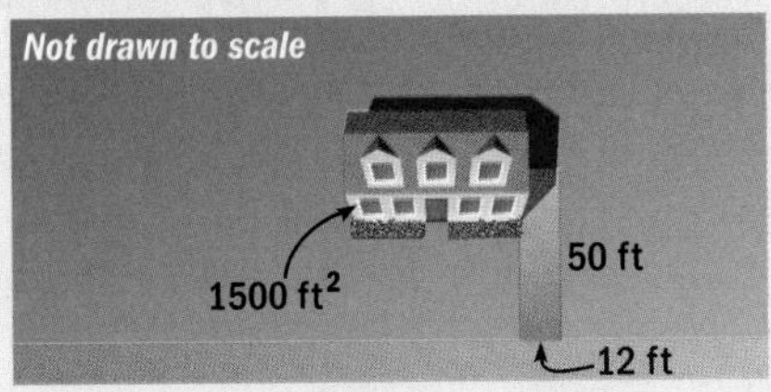

Mixed Problem Solving

Use any strategy to solve the problem.

5. **Food** Paula is making a sandwich with one type of meat, one type of cheese, and one dressing. How many different kinds of sandwiches can she make using the items in the list? **12 sandwiches**

Meat	Cheese	Dressing
Ham	Swiss	Mayonnaise
Turkey	American	Italian dressing
	Cheddar	

6. **Traveling** Ryan left his house at 7:00 A.M. and traveled in his car. He drove 3 miles north, 2.5 miles east, 1 mile south, 1 mile east, 4 miles south, 1.5 miles west, 2 miles north, and 1.5 miles west. At the end of this trip, how far from home was Ryan? **0.5 mi**

7. **Numbers** The sum of two numbers is 17. The product of the numbers is 52. Find the two numbers. **4 and 13**

8. **Clock** One chime of a clock takes 2.5 seconds to complete. At 1:00 the clock chimes once. At 2:00 the clock chimes twice. If the clock chimes in this way every hour, how many seconds will it spend chiming from 1:00 A.M. to 1:05 P.M.? **197.5 sec**

3 APPLY

Transparency

Even-numbered answers are available on transparencies.

Teaching Tip

In Exercise 2, students should assume that the tiles are square. Suggest that students check units as one part of solving the problem.

Math Reasoning

In Exercise 2, point out that the area of the L-shaped room can also be found by subtracting the area of the small square in the top right corner from the area of a square 20 feet on a side.

Suggested Strategies

You may wish to suggest the following strategies for the problems in the Mixed Problem Solving:

- Exercise 5: Draw a Diagram; Act It Out
- Exercise 6: Make a List
- Exercise 7: Guess, Check, and Revise; Make a List
- Exercise 8: Make a List; Break into Parts; Make a Table

PLAN

SKILL CHECK

1. Find $2xy + 3xz$ when $x = 12, y = 11$, and $z = 20$. 984
2. Find the area of a triangle with base 3 meters and height 5 meters. 7.5 m^2

Lesson Objective

Find the surface areas of prisms and cylinders.

Pacing

Suggested Number of Days
Basic Course: 2 days
Average Course: 2 days
Advanced Course: 2 days
Block: 1 block

Teaching Resources

For a complete list of Teaching Resources, see page 478B.

Transparency

Warm-Up Exercises for this lesson are available on a transparency.

TEACH

Motivating the Lesson

Ask students who have wrapped gifts how they estimate how much wrapping paper they will need.

TIPS FOR NEW TEACHERS

It is hard for many students to visualize the relation of a net and a solid. Bring several models and nets to class for students to manipulate. See Tips for New Teachers in the *Chapter 10 Resource Book*.

Surface Areas of Prisms and Cylinders

BEFORE	Now	WHY?
You classified prisms and cylinders.	You'll find the surface areas of prisms and cylinders.	So you can compare two caramels, as in Ex. 18.

Word Watch

net, p. 502
surface area, p. 503

In the Real World

Storage Chest You are painting a storage chest. Before you begin painting the chest, you need to find the *surface area*. What is the *surface area* of the chest? You'll find the answer in Example 2.

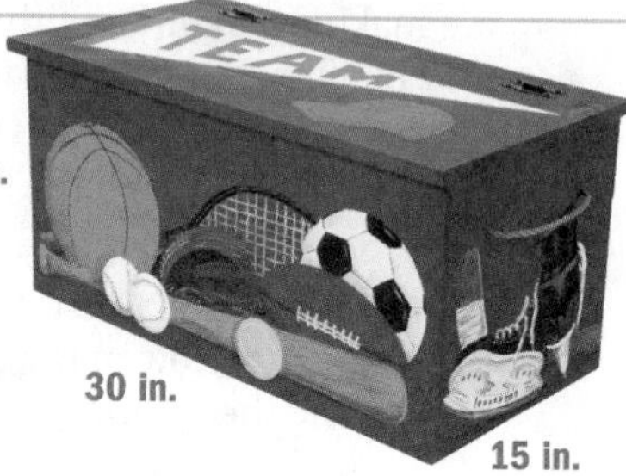

Nets One way to represent a solid is to use a *net*. A **net** is a two-dimensional pattern that forms a solid when it is folded.

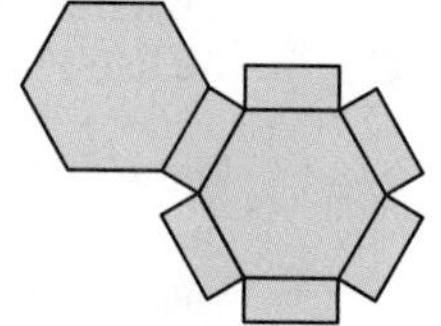

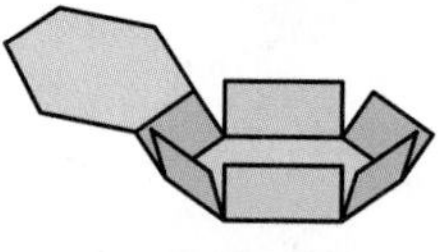

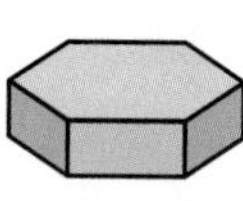

Each polygon of the net represents one face of the solid. There are usually several different possible nets for a given solid.

EXAMPLE 1 Drawing a Net

Draw a net of the triangular prism.

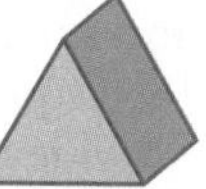

Solution

Method 1 Draw one base with a rectangle adjacent to each side. Draw the other base adjacent to one of the rectangles.

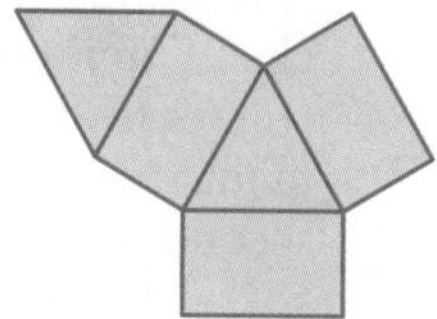

Method 2 For the rectangular faces, draw adjacent rectangles. Draw the bases on opposite sides of one rectangle.

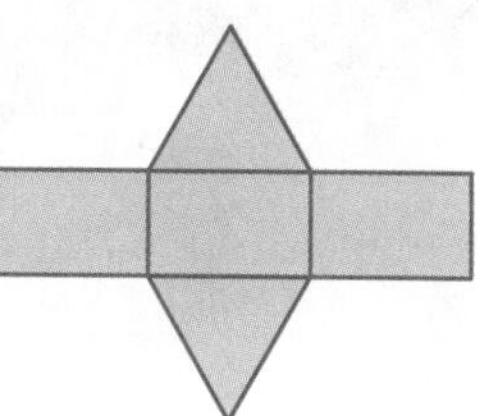

ILLINOIS Standards and ISAT:
7.C.3b, 8.D.3b

The **surface area** of a polyhedron is the sum of the areas of its faces.

EXAMPLE 2 Using a Net to Find Surface Area

Storage Chest Find the surface area of the storage chest shown on page 502. The chest is 30 inches long, 15 inches wide, and 15 inches high.

Solution

Draw a net of the chest.

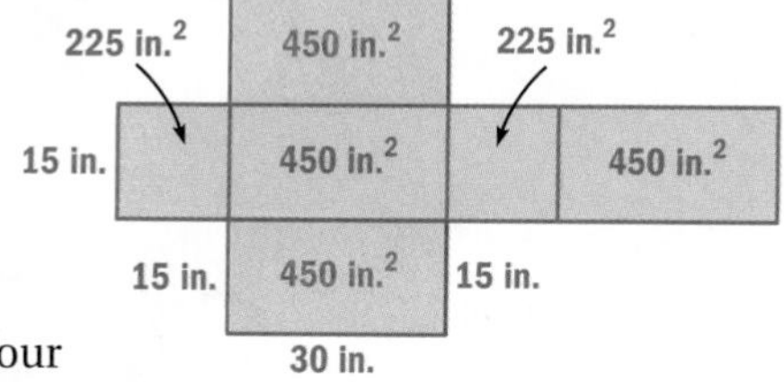

The area of each square face is 15 in. • 15 in. = **225 in.²**

The area of the rectangular face is 30 in. • 15 in. = **450 in.²**

There are two square faces and four rectangular faces, so the surface area is 2 • **225 in.²** + 4 • **450 in.²** = 2250 in.²

ANSWER The surface area of the storage chest is 2250 square inches.

Notice that in Example 2 the four blue faces form a rectangle that has length equal to the perimeter of the base.

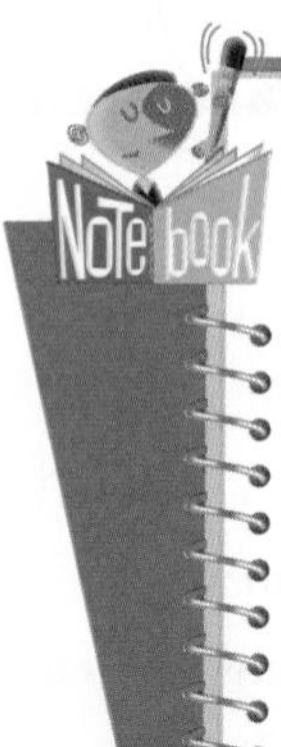

Surface Area of a Prism

Words The surface area of a prism is the sum of twice the area of a base and the product of the base's perimeter and the height.

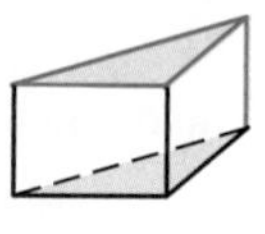

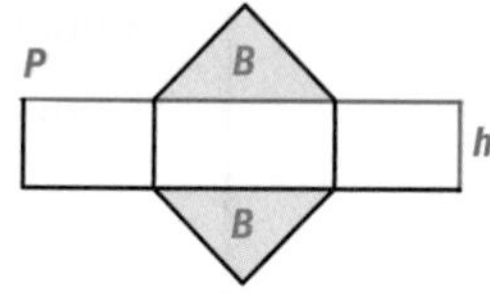

Algebra $S = 2B + Ph$

EXAMPLE 3 Using a Formula to Find Surface Area

Find the surface area of the triangular prism.

$S = 2B + Ph$

$= 2\left(\frac{1}{2} \cdot 10 \cdot 12\right) + (13 + 13 + 10)15$

$= 660$

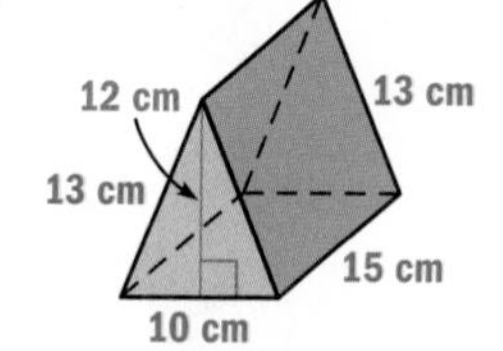

ANSWER The surface area of the prism is 660 square centimeters.

EXTRA EXAMPLES

Example 1 Draw a net of the triangular prism.

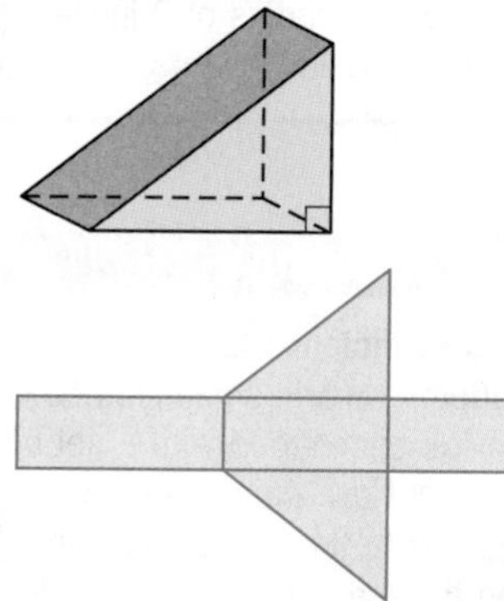

Example 2 Find the surface area of a rectangular prism that is 3 centimeters wide, 10 centimeters long, and 2 centimeters high. **112 cm²**

Example 3 A block of cheese is in the shape of a triangular prism as shown below. Find the surface area of the cheese block. **36 in.²**

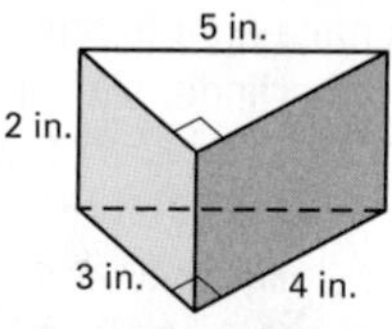

NOTETAKING

Have students record in their own words what a net is and sketch an example. Also have them record the surface area formulas for a prism and a cylinder and show a worked-out example of each.

EXTRA EXAMPLES

Example 4 Find the surface area of a closed tube 50 inches long with a radius of 2 inches. **about 653 in.^{2}**

Differentiating Instruction

Less Proficient Students Have students work in small groups. Provide each group with a net of a prism. Have the students work together to find the dimensions and the area of each face of the prism from the net and add these together to find the total surface area. Then lead them to find the surface area of the prism using the formula in this lesson. Have students compare their results and summarize how using the formula is more efficient.

CONCEPT CHECK

How are the surface area formulas for a prism and a cylinder similar and different? **They are similar in that both formulas include twice the area of the base. They are different in that the rest of the prism's surface area is found by perimeter times height, while the rest of the cylinder's surface area is found by circumference times height.**

DAILY PUZZLER

Imagine a cube that is one inch on each side. Now imagine gluing six other one inch cubes to each of the six faces of your initial cube. What is the surface area of the resulting solid? **30 in.^{2}**

1–3. See Additional Answers beginning on page AA1.

Cylinders The net of a cylinder has two circles for the bases. The curved surface of the cylinder becomes a rectangle in the net. The width of the rectangle is the height of the cylinder, and the length of the rectangle is the circumference of the base.

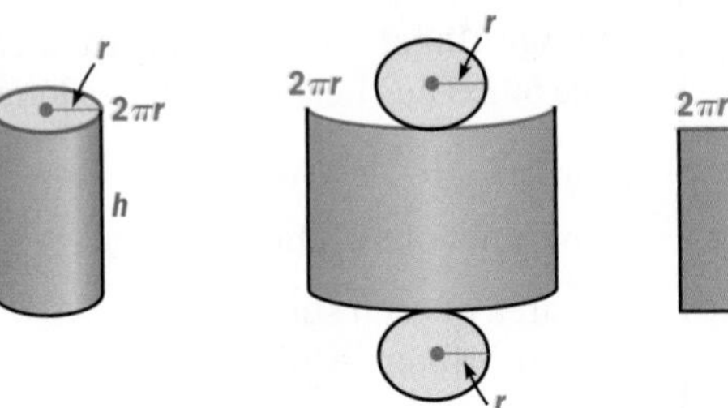

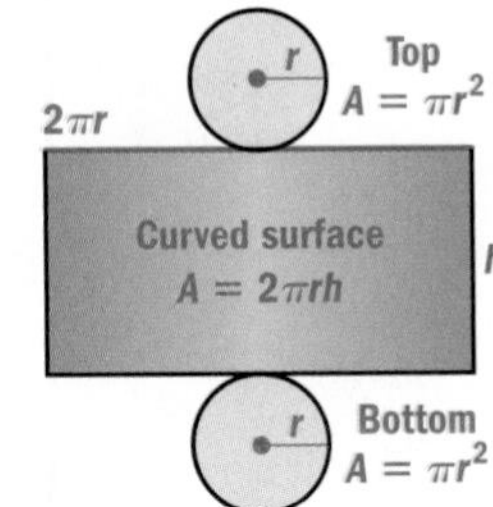

Surface Area of a Cylinder

Words The surface area of a cylinder is the sum of twice the area of a base and the product of the base's circumference and the height.

Algebra $S = 2B + Ch = 2\pi r^2 + 2\pi rh$

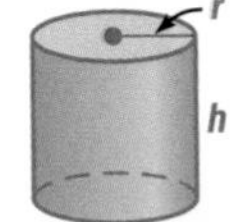

Finding the Surface Area of a Cylinder

Sloppy Joe Find the surface area of the can of sloppy joe sauce.

Solution

The radius is one half the diameter, so $r = 4$ cm.

$S = 2\pi r^2 + 2\pi rh$	**Write formula for surface area of a cylinder.**
$= 2\pi(4)^2 + 2\pi(4)(10.7)$	**Substitute 4 for *r* and 10.7 for *h*.**
≈ 369.45	**Evaluate using a calculator.**

ANSWER The surface area of the can is about 369 square centimeters.

HELP with Technology

You can use the π key on your calculator instead of 3.14 when evaluating formulas.

Your turn now **Draw a net of the solid. Then find the surface area. Round to the nearest tenth.** **1–3. See margin for art.**

1. 3 ft, 5 ft, 12 ft **222 ft^2**

2. 10 m, 6 m, 14 m, 8 m **384 m^2**

3.

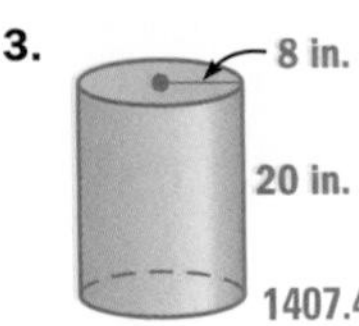

1407.4 in.^{2}

10.4 Exercises

More Practice, p. 736

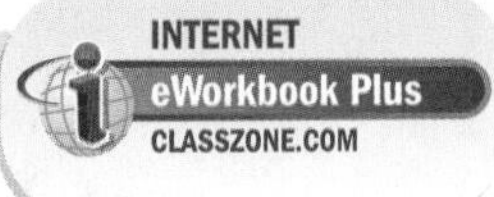
INTERNET eWorkbook Plus CLASSZONE.COM

Getting Ready to Practice

1. Vocabulary In your own words, explain what surface area is. *Sample answer:* Surface area is the sum of the areas of all the faces and lateral surfaces of a solid.

Draw a net. Then find the surface area. Round to the nearest tenth. 2–4. See margin for art.

2. 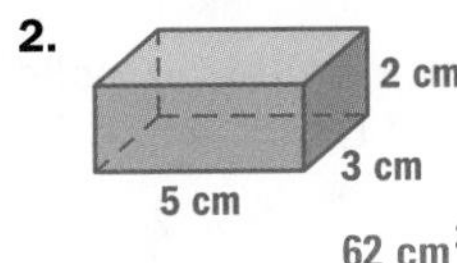

62 cm²

3. 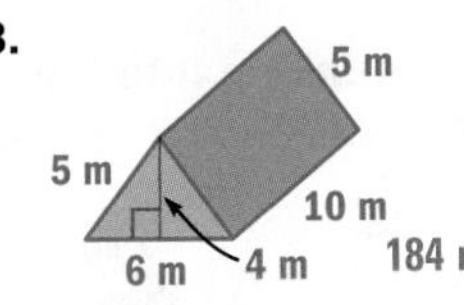

184 m²

4. 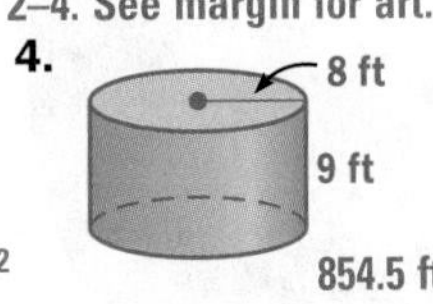

854.5 ft²

Practice and Problem Solving

HELP with Homework

Example	Exercises
1	15-17
2	12-17
3	5-8
4	9-17

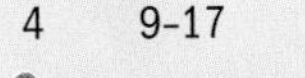

Online Resources CLASSZONE.COM
- More Examples
- eTutorial Plus

A **Find the surface area of the prism, where *B* is the area of the base, *P* is the perimeter of the base, and *h* is the height.**

5. $B = 4 \text{ in.}^2$, $P = 8$ in., $h = 5$ in. 48 in.²

6. $B = 20 \text{ cm}^2$, $P = 12$ cm, $h = 3$ cm 76 cm²

7. $B = 45 \text{ yd}^2$, $P = 30$ yd, $h = 2$ yd 150 yd²

8. $B = 19.3 \text{ m}^2$, $P = 16$ m, $h = 0.5$ m 46.6 m²

Sketch a cylinder with radius *r* and height *h*. Then find its surface area. Round to the nearest tenth. 9–11. See margin for art.

9. $r = 6$ m, $h = 2$ m 301.6 m²

10. $r = 1$ ft, $h = 7$ ft 50.3 ft²

11. $r = 10$ cm, $h = 20$ cm 1885.0 cm²

Find the surface area of the net. Round to the nearest tenth.

12. 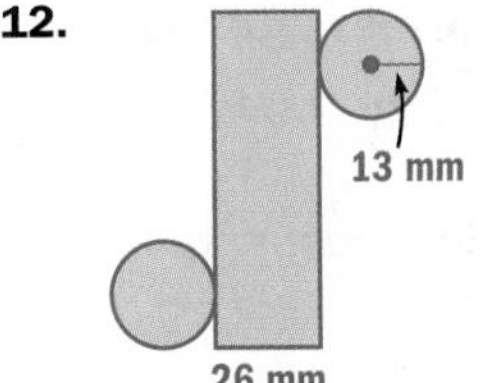

3185.6 mm²

13. 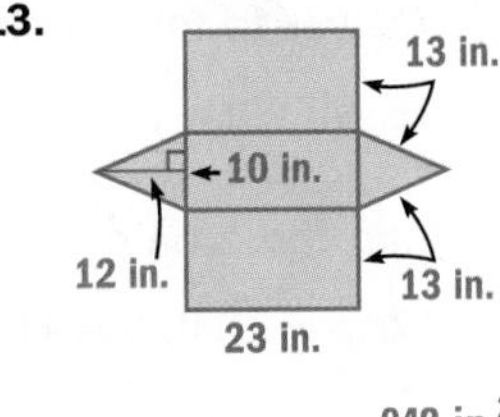

948 in.²

14. 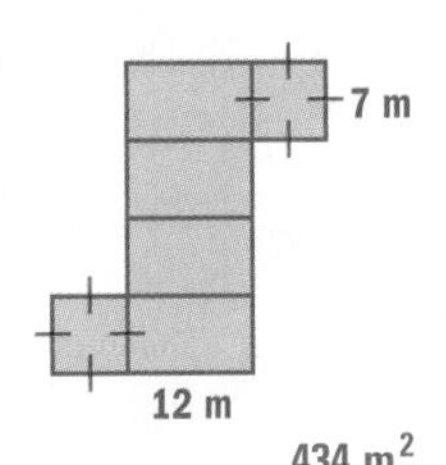

434 m²

Draw a net. Then find the surface area. Round to the nearest tenth. 15–17. See margin for art.

15. 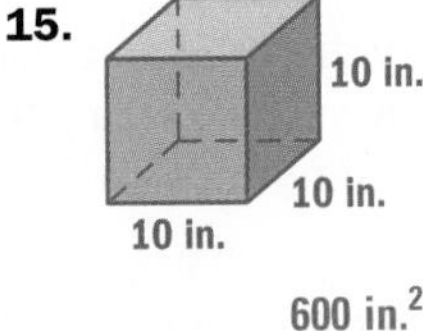

600 in.²

16. 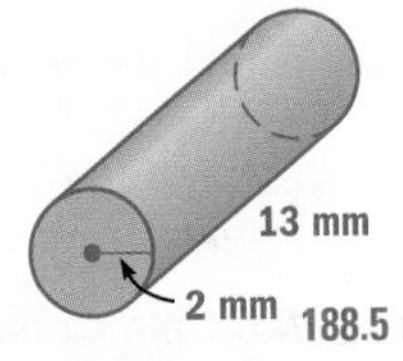

188.5 mm²

17. 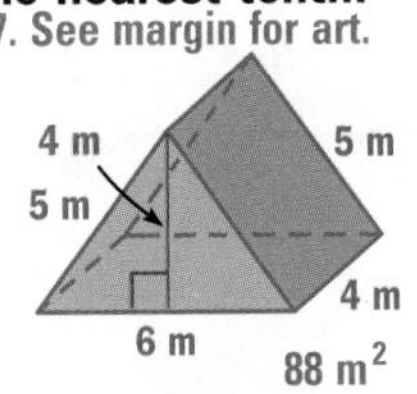

88 m²

B **18. Chocolates** You are dipping caramels into chocolate. Some of the caramels are 1 inch cubes. Others are cylinders that are 1 inch high and 1 inch in diameter. Which shape will require more chocolate? cube

3 APPLY

ASSIGNMENT GUIDE

Basic Course

Day 1: SRH p. 705 Exs. 11-15; pp. 505-506 Exs. 5-8, 18-21, 30-34

Day 2: pp. 505-506 Exs. 9-17, 26-29

Average Course

Day 1: pp. 505-506 Exs. 5-8, 18-20, 26-32

Day 2: pp. 505-506 Exs. 9-16, 22-24, 33-35

Advanced Course

Day 1: pp. 505-506 Exs. 5-8, 18-20, 26-31

Day 2: pp. 505-506 Exs. 10-16, 22-25*, 33-35

Block

pp. 505-506 Exs. 5-16, 18-20, 22-24, 26-35

EXTRA PRACTICE

- Student Edition, p. 736
- Chapter 10 Resource Book, pp. 36-38
- Test and Practice Generator

TRANSPARENCY

Even-numbered answers are available on transparencies.

HOMEWORK CHECK

When you review students' homework for this lesson, go over the following exercises to check understanding of key concepts.

Basic: 5, 7, 9, 12, 15
Average: 5, 7, 9, 13, 16
Advanced: 6, 7, 10, 13, 16

COMMON ERROR

In Exercise 3, watch for students who think the base is a rectangle.

2-4, 9-11, 15-17. See Additional Answers beginning on page AA1.

ASSESS

Assessment Resources

For more assessment resources, see:
- Assessment Book
- Test and Practice Generator

Mini-Quiz

1. Find the surface area of a prism with base area 5 square inches, base perimeter 14 inches, and height 8 inches. **122 in.^{2}**
2. Find the surface area of a cylinder with radius 2 feet and height 14 feet. Use 3.14 for π. Round to the nearest tenth. **201.0 in.^{2}**
3. Identify the solid shown by the net. Then find its surface area. Use 3.14 for π. Round to the nearest tenth. **cylinder; 29.8 m^2**

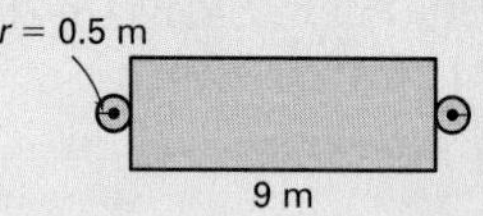

FOLLOW-UP

Reteaching/Remediation

- Study Guide in Chapter 10 Resource Book, pp. 39–40
- Tutor Place, Geometry and Measurement Card 21
- eTutorial Plus Online
- Extra Practice, p. 736
- Lesson Practice in Chapter 10 Resource Book, pp. 36–38

Challenge/Enrichment

- Challenge Practice in Chapter 10 Resource Book, p. 41
- Teacher's Edition, p. 478F

English Learner Support

- Spanish Study Guide
- Multi-Language Glossary
- Chapter Audio Summaries CDs

23, 24, 34. See Additional Answers beginning on page AA1.

The Crystal Bridge

Find the surface area of the solid. Round to the nearest tenth.

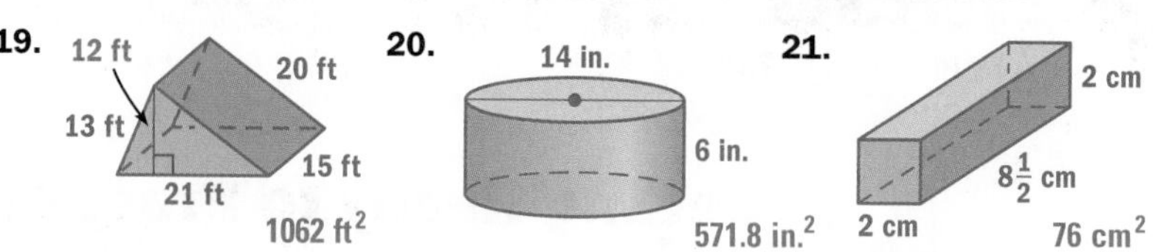

19. 1062 ft^2 20. 571.8 in.^{2} 21. 76 cm^2

22. **Crystal Bridge** At the Myriad Botanical Gardens in Oklahoma City, there is a tropical conservatory that bridges a small lake. The Crystal Bridge is a cylinder 224 feet long and 70 feet in diameter. Find the surface area of the Crystal Bridge. Round to the nearest tenth. **56,957.1 ft^2**

Breaking into Parts **Draw a net of the solid. Then find the surface area. Round to the nearest tenth.** 23–24. See margin for art.

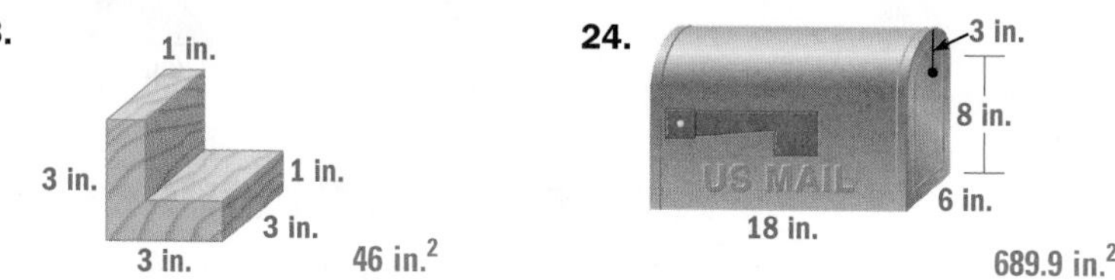

23. 46 in.^{2} 24. 689.9 in.^{2}

25. **Challenge** Find the surface area of a triangular prism whose edge lengths are all 1 foot. (*Hint*: Each triangular base can be divided into two 30°-60°-90° triangles.) **about 3.866 ft^2**

Mixed Review

Tell whether the side lengths form a right triangle. *(Lesson 9.3)*

26. $a = 10, b = 24, c = 26$ **yes**
27. $a = 28, b = 45, c = 53$ **yes**

Use your calculator to approximate the given value. Round your answer to four decimal places. *(Lesson 9.6)*

28. sin 78° **0.9781** 29. tan 23° **0.4245** 30. cos 14° **0.9703** 31. sin 66° **0.9135**

Find the area of a parallelogram with base *b* and height *h*. *(Lesson 10.1)*

32. $b = 16$ ft, $h = 11$ ft **176 ft^2**
33. $b = 12$ in., $h = 18$ in. **216 in.^{2}**

Test-Taking Practice

INTERNET
State Test Practice
CLASSZONE.COM

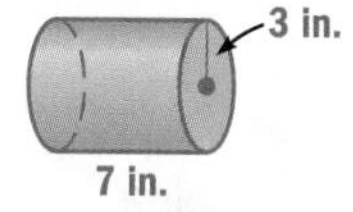

34. **Short Response** Classify the solid. Draw a net of the solid. Then find the surface area of the solid. Round to the nearest tenth. **Cylinder; see margin for art; 188.5 in.^{2}**

35. **Multiple Choice** What is the surface area of a rectangular prism that is 3 feet long, 2 feet wide, and 9 feet high? **D**

A. 14 ft^2 **B.** 54 ft^2 **C.** 61 ft^2 **D.** 102 ft^2

Surface Areas of Pyramids and Cones

BEFORE	Now	WHY?
You found the surface areas of prisms and cylinders.	You'll find the surface areas of pyramids and cones.	So you can find the surface area of icicles, as in Exs. 25–28.

Word Watch

slant height, p. 507

The height of a pyramid is the perpendicular distance between the vertex and the base.

The **slant height** l of a regular pyramid is the height of any face that is not the base.

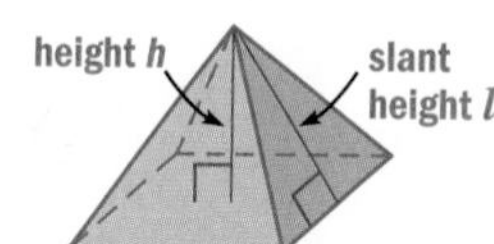

The net for a regular pyramid has a regular polygon as the base and congruent isosceles triangles on each side of the base.

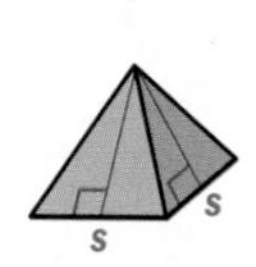

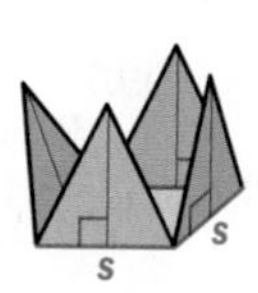

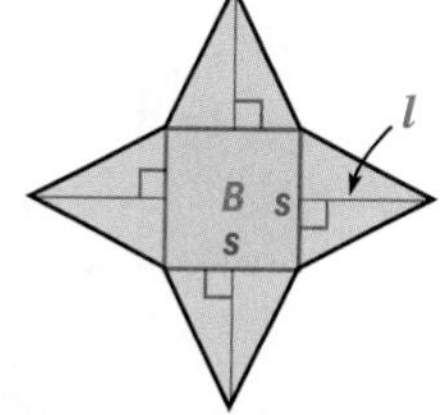

You can use the net of a pyramid to find the surface area of the pyramid.

HELP with Solving

All the pyramids in this lesson have a regular polygon as a base and congruent isosceles triangles as the other faces. The slant height is the same on any face that is not the base.

		Base area		Area of other faces		
Surface area	=	Area of base	+	Number of triangles	×	Area of each triangle
	=	B	+	4	×	$\left(\frac{1}{2}sl\right)$

$$= B + \frac{1}{2}(4s)l$$

$$= B + \frac{1}{2}Pl$$

The product of the number of triangles and the side length of the base is the perimeter of the base.

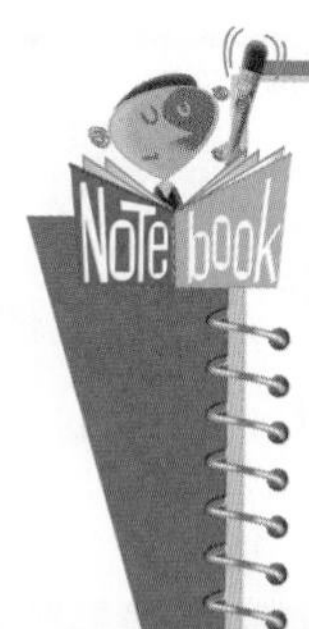

Surface Area of a Pyramid

Words The surface area of a regular pyramid is the sum of the area of the base and one half the product of the base perimeter and the slant height.

Algebra $S = B + \frac{1}{2}Pl$

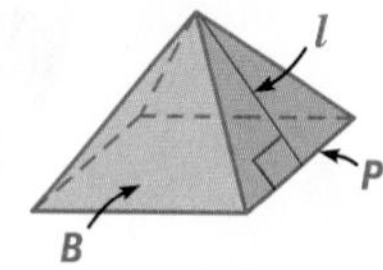

ILLINOIS Standards and ISAT:
7.C.3b, 8.D.3b

1 PLAN

SKILL CHECK

What shape is the base of each of these solids?

1. cylinder **circle**
2. square pyramid **square**
3. cone **circle**
4. hexagonal pyramid **hexagon**

Lesson Objective

Find the surface areas of pyramids and cones.

Pacing

Suggested Number of Days
Basic Course: 1 day
Average Course: 1 day
Advanced Course: 1 day
Block: 0.5 block with 10.6

Teaching Resources

For a complete list of Teaching Resources, see page 478B.

Transparency

Warm-Up Exercises for this lesson are available on a transparency.

2 TEACH

Motivating the Lesson

Using a model of a pyramid, demonstrate how to measure the slant height and the height. Discuss which is longer and why.

TIPS FOR NEW TEACHERS

Challenge students to make cones from a sheet of paper. After students have experimented, lead them to recognize that a flat fan shape rolls into a cone. See Tips for New Teachers in the *Chapter 10 Resource Book*.

EXTRA EXAMPLES

Example 1 Find the surface area of the regular pyramid.

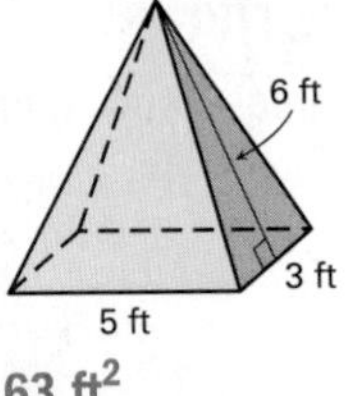

63 ft²

MULTIPLE REPRESENTATIONS

Give each student a net of a pyramid and a net of a cone. Throughout the lesson, as you discuss concepts, have students make notes on their nets. Students can also fold the nets into the solid to help them visualize the concept.

EXAMPLE 1 Finding the Surface Area of a Pyramid

Find the surface area of the regular pyramid.

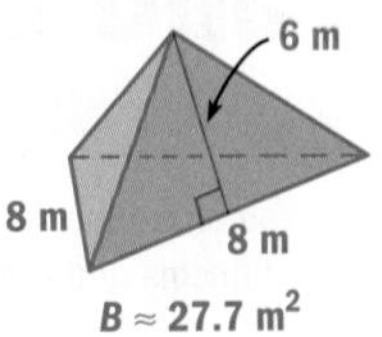

(1) Find the perimeter of the base.

$P = 8 + 8 + 8 = 24$

(2) Substitute into the formula for surface area.

$S = B + \frac{1}{2}Pl$	**Write formula for surface area of a pyramid.**
$\approx 27.7 + \frac{1}{2}(24)(6)$	**Substitute 27.7 for *B*, 24 for *P*, and 6 for *l*.**
$= 99.7$	**Simplify.**

ANSWER The surface area is about 99.7 square meters.

Cones You can use the net of a cone to find its surface area. The curved surface of a cone is part of a circle with radius l, the slant height of the cone. The area of this surface is $A = \pi rl$, where r is the radius of the base of the cone.

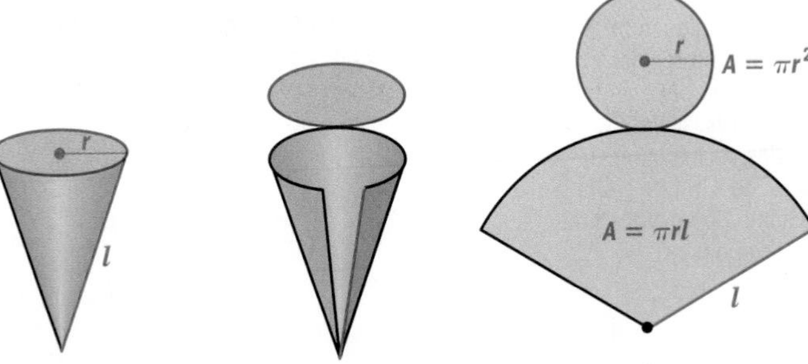

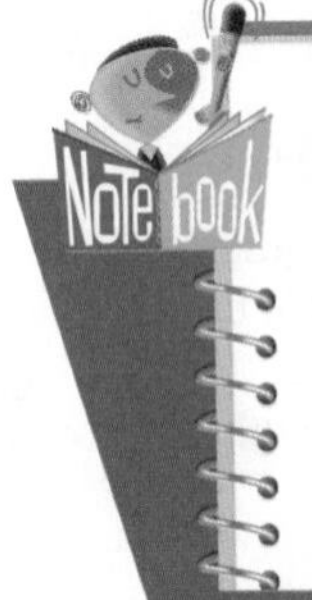

Surface Area of a Cone

Words The surface area of a cone is the sum of the area of the base and the product of pi, the radius of the base, and the slant height.

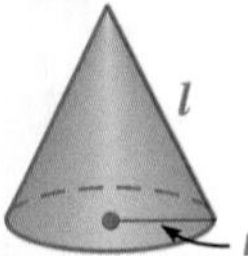

Algebra $S = \pi r^2 + \pi rl$

EXAMPLE 2 Finding the Surface Area of a Cone

Find the surface area of a cone with radius 4 meters and slant height 9 meters.

$S = \pi r^2 + \pi rl$	**Write formula for surface area of a cone.**
$= \pi(4)^2 + \pi(4)(9)$	**Substitute 4 for *r* and 9 for *l*.**
≈ 163.36	**Evaluate using a calculator.**

ANSWER The surface area is about 163.36 square meters.

Your turn now **Find the surface area. Round to the nearest tenth.**

1.

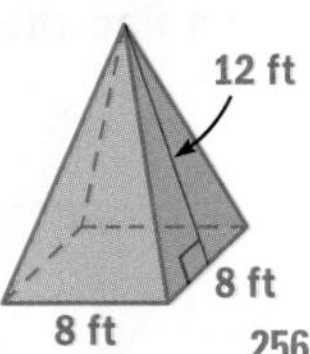

256 ft²

2.

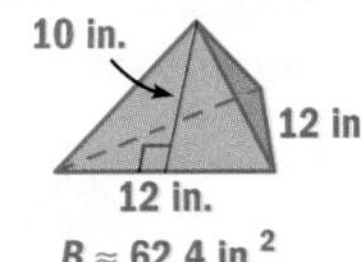

$B \approx 62.4$ in.²

242.4 in.²

3.

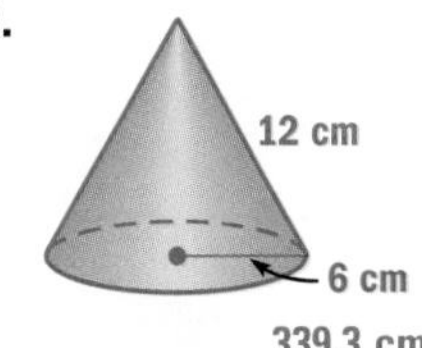

339.3 cm²

10.5 Exercises

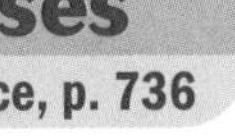

More Practice, p. 736

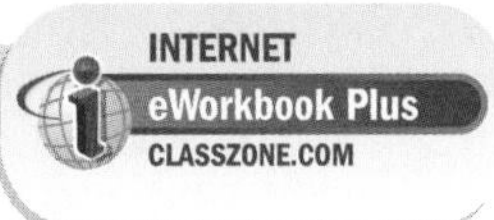

Getting Ready to Practice

1. **Vocabulary** Draw a square pyramid. Label the height h, slant height l, and base B of the pyramid. See margin.

Draw a net of the solid. Then find the surface area. Round to the nearest tenth. 2–4. See margin for art.

2.

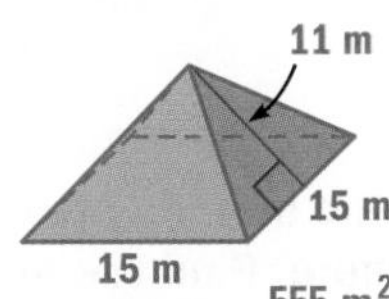

555 m²

3.

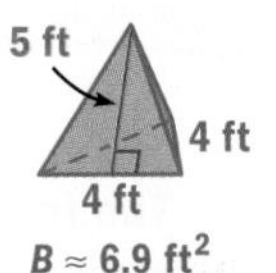

$B \approx 6.9$ ft²

36.9 ft²

4.

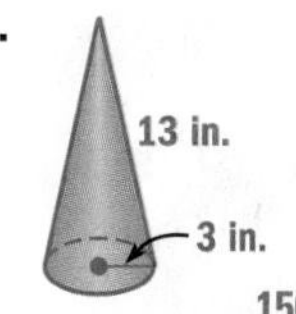

150.8 in.²

5. **Guided Problem Solving** Use the figure below to find the surface area of an ice cream cone with an open base.

   (1) Write the formula for the surface area of a cone and subtract the area of the base from the formula.

   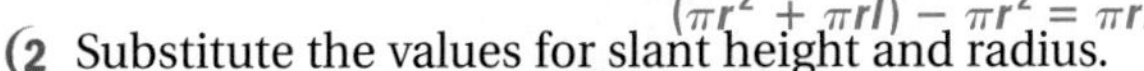

   $(\pi r^2 + \pi rl) - \pi r^2 = \pi rl$

   (2) Substitute the values for slant height and radius.

   (3) Evaluate and round to the nearest tenth. $\pi(1)\left(4\frac{1}{4}\right)$ 13.4 in.²

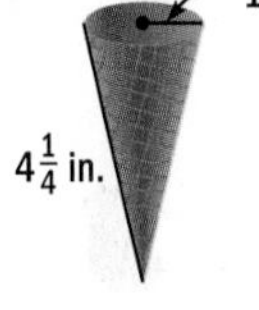

EXTRA EXAMPLES

Example 2 Find the surface area of a cone with radius 4 centimeters and slant height 10 centimeters. **about 176 cm²**

Differentiating Instruction

Advanced Students Ask students to define height and slant height. Then ask how the two are related. Challenge students to write the formula for the surface area of a pyramid if the height is known and the slant height is unknown.

CONCEPT CHECK

What is the surface area of a solid with one circular base if the diameter of the base is 18 feet and the slant height of the solid is 16 feet? Explain your reasoning. Use 3.14 for π. **About 707 ft²; a solid with one circular base must be a cone. Halve the diameter to get a radius of 9 ft, and find the area of the circular base to be 81π ft². Find the surface area of the rest of the cone by multiplying π, the radius of the base, and the slant height. The result is 144π ft². Add 81π and 144π to get 225π ft². Substitute 3.14 for π to get 706.5 ft², and round to three significant digits.**

DAILY PUZZLER

Write a formula for the surface area of this solid. **$S = Pl$**

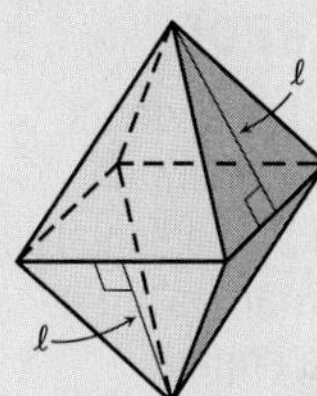

1–4. See Additional Answers beginning on page AA1.

ASSIGNMENT GUIDE

Basic Course

Day 1: pp. 510–511 Exs. 6–11, 14–20, 23–28, 32–37

Average Course

Day 1: pp. 510–511 Exs. 8–13, 16–22, 24–30, 32–38

Advanced Course

Day 1: pp. 510–511 Exs. 8–13, 16–20, 22–26, 28–33*, 36–38

Block

pp. 510–511 Exs. 8–13, 16–22, 24–30, 32–38 (with 10.6)

EXTRA PRACTICE

- Student Edition, p. 736
- Chapter 10 Resource Book, pp. 44–46
- Test and Practice Generator

TRANSPARENCY

Even-numbered answers are available on transparencies.

HOMEWORK CHECK

When you review students' homework for this lesson, go over the following exercises to check understanding of key concepts.

Basic: 6, 10, 11, 14, 17
Average: 8, 12, 16, 17, 18
Advanced: 8, 12, 16, 17, 19

COMMON ERROR

In Exercise 18, watch for students who ignore the value of B written underneath the figure and calculate surface area based on an assumption that the base is a square.

14–16. See Additional Answers beginning on page AA1.

with Homework

Example	Exercises
1	6-9, 14-19
2	10-19

Online Resources
CLASSZONE.COM

- More Examples
- eTutorial Plus

Practice and Problem Solving

Find the surface area of the square pyramid with base side length s and slant height l.

A **6.** $s = 4$ in., $l = 11$ in. 104 in.^{2}

7. $s = 6$ m, $l = 9$ m 144 m^2

8. $s = 5$ cm, $l = 4.2$ cm 67 cm^2

9. $s = 15$ yd, $l = 10$ yd 525 yd^2

Find the surface area of the cone with radius r and slant height l. Round to the nearest tenth.

10. $r = 3$ ft, $l = 8$ ft 103.7 ft^2

11. $r = 2$ in., $l = 20$ in. 138.2 in.^{2}

12. $r = 12$ m, $l = 6.5$ m 697.4 m^2

13. $r = 4$ mm, $l = 5.5$ mm 119.4 mm^2

Draw a net of the solid. Then find the surface area. Round to the nearest tenth. 14–16. See margin for art.

14.

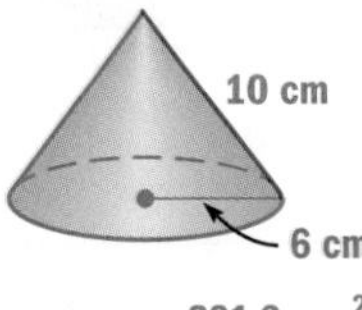

301.6 cm^2

15.

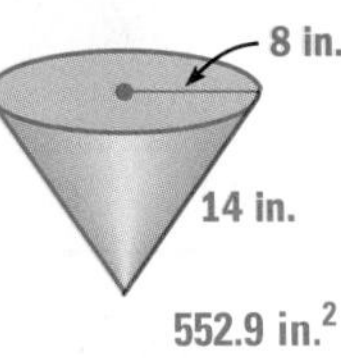

552.9 in.^{2}

16.

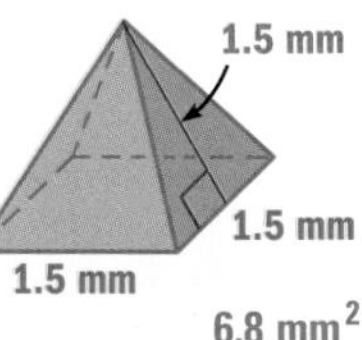

6.8 mm^2

Find the surface area of the solid. Round to the nearest tenth.

17.

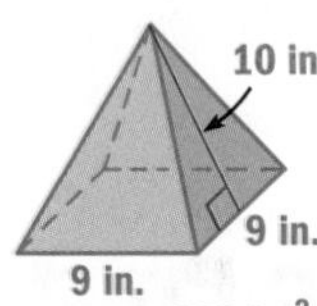

261 in.^{2}

18.

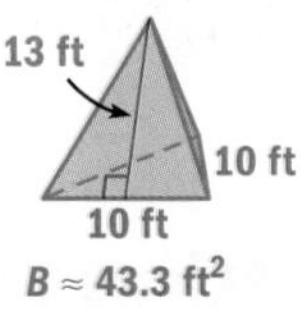

238.3 ft^2

19.

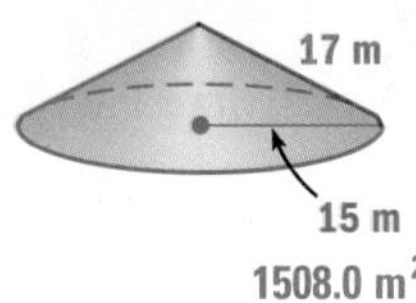

1508.0 m^2

Find the surface area of the net. Round to the nearest tenth.

20.

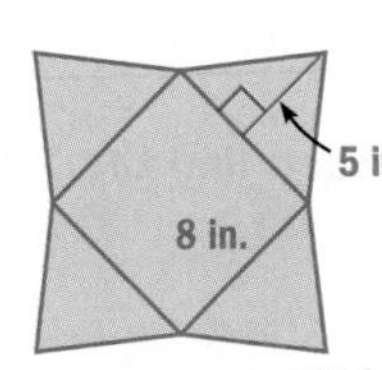

144 in.^{2}

21.

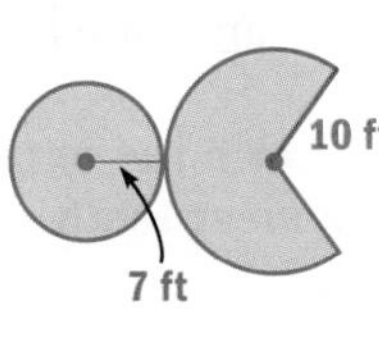

373.8 ft^2

22.

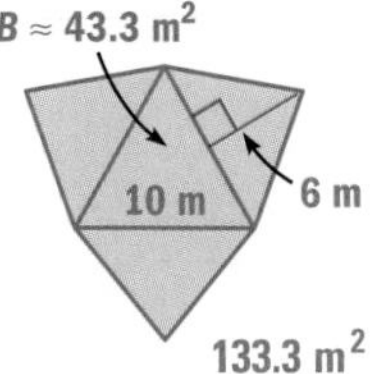

133.3 m^2

Sports **The formula for the surface area of a sphere is $S = 4\pi r^2$ where r is the radius of the sphere. Find the surface area of the sphere. Round to the nearest tenth.**

B **23.**

243.3 in.^{2}

24.

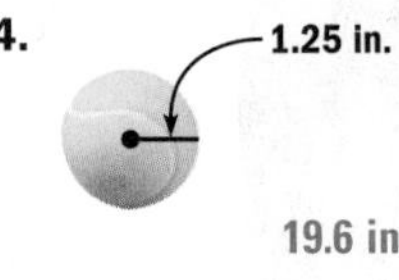

19.6 in.^{2}

Icicles In Exercises 25–28, use the following information. Find the surface area of the icicle, not including the base, in terms of π. Icicles are shaped like cones. As they melt, icicles change size but stay similar in shape.

25. $r = 1$ in., $l = 6$ in. 6π in.^{2} **26.** $r = 2$ in., $l = 12$ in. 24π in.^{2} **27.** $r = 3$ in., $l = 18$ in. 54π in.^{2}

28. Look for a Pattern Describe the pattern developed in Exercises 25–27. Then predict the surface area of an icicle with a radius of 4 inches and a slant height of 24 inches. When both r and l are multiplied by the same number, the surface area is multiplied by the square of that number; 96π in.^{2}

C **29. Critical Thinking** Think of a cone as a special type of pyramid. Substitute the formulas for the area and circumference of a circle into the formula for the surface area of a pyramid. Simplify the expression. What do you notice? See margin.

29. $S = B + \frac{1}{2}Pl = \pi r^2 + \frac{1}{2}(2\pi r)l = \pi r^2 + \pi rl$; the simplified expression is the same as the formula for the surface area of a cone.

30. Number Sense Which has a greater surface area: a square pyramid with a slant height of 12 units and a base side length of 10 units, or a cone with a slant height of 12 units and a diameter of 10 units? square pyramid

31. Challenge Find the surface area of the regular hexagonal pyramid shown. In the diagram of its base, all the triangles are congruent. 363.6 cm^2

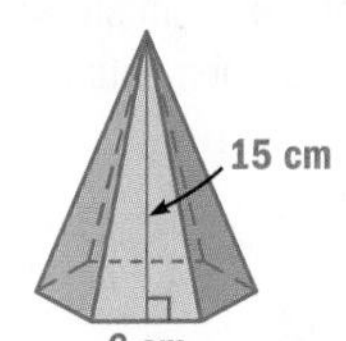

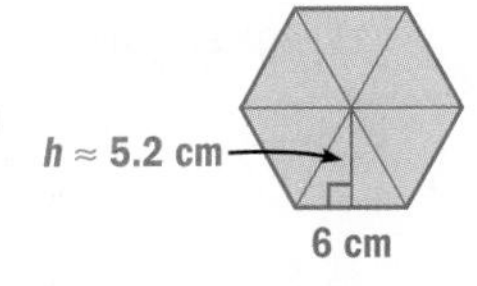

Mixed Review 

Tell whether the number is *rational* or *irrational*. *(Lesson 9.2)*

32. $\sqrt{169}$ rational **33.** $\frac{4}{21}$ rational **34.** $\frac{\sqrt{7}}{2}$ irrational **35.** $\sqrt{\frac{3}{2}}$ irrational

36. Find the surface area of a cylinder with a radius of 3 inches and a height of 8 inches. Round to the nearest tenth. *(Lesson 10.4)* 207.3 in.^{2}

Test-Taking Practice 

37. Multiple Choice What is the surface area of the square pyramid at the right? C

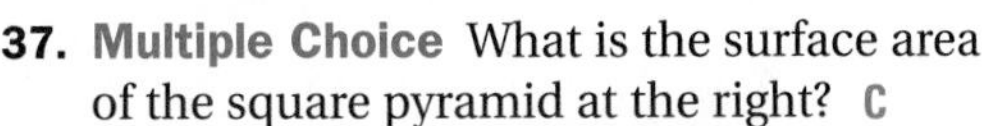

A. 70 m^2 **B.** 95 m^2

C. 119 m^2 **D.** 150.5 m^2

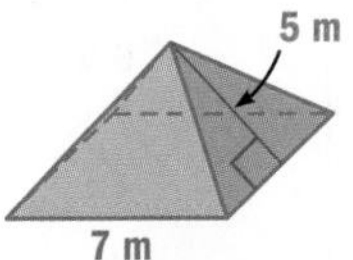

38. Short Response Pablo makes a party hat that is a cone with no base. It has a radius of 4 inches and a slant height of 7 inches. What is the surface area of Pablo's party hat? Monica makes a larger party hat that has a radius and slant height that are twice the lengths of those on Pablo's hat. What is the surface area of Monica's party hat? Round to the nearest tenth. 88.0 in.^{2}; 351.9 in.^{2}

4 ASSESS

Assessment Resources

For more assessment resources, see:
- Assessment Book
- Test and Practice Generator

Mini-Quiz

1. Find the surface area of a square pyramid with base side length 25 millimeters and slant height 50 millimeters. 3125 mm^2
2. Find the surface area of a cone with radius 15 feet and slant height 22 feet. Use 3.14 for π. about 1740 ft^2
3. Find the surface area of the solid.

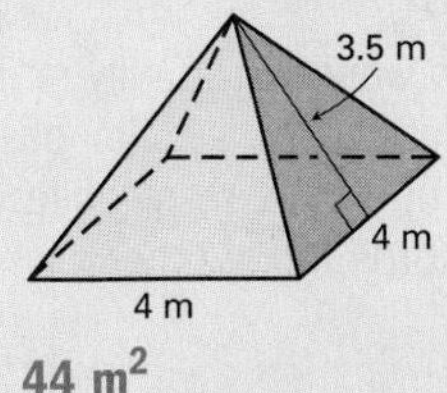

44 m^2

5 FOLLOW-UP

Reteaching/Remediation

- Study Guide in Chapter 10 Resource Book, pp. 47-48
- eTutorial Plus Online
- Extra Practice, p. 736
- Lesson Practice in Chapter 10 Resource Book, pp. 44-46

Challenge/Enrichment

- Challenge Practice in Chapter 10 Resource Book, p. 49
- Teacher's Edition, p. 478F

English Learner Support

- Spanish Study Guide
- Multi-Language Glossary
- Chapter Audio Summaries CDs

1 PLAN

Explore the Concept

- Students will find the volume of a rectangular prism.
- This activity leads into the study of prism volume in Lesson 10.6.

Materials

Each student or pair of students will need sugar cubes.

Recommended Time

Work activity: 10 min
Discuss results: 10 min

Grouping

Students can work individually or in pairs. If students work in pairs, one student can build the prism while the other records the number of cubes used.

2 TEACH

Alternative Strategy

If you have access to large, equal-sized, cubical boxes, you can have students build larger prisms, and then discuss how much space is inside the prisms.

3 CLOSE

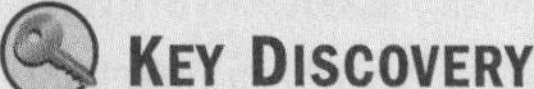

Key Discovery

The volume of a rectangular prism is length times width times height.

Assessment

1. Does the volume of a prism change if you rotate it? Explain. **No; the number of cubes in the prism is still the same.**

10.6 Hands-on Activity

GOAL
Find the volume of a rectangular prism.

MATERIALS
- sugar cubes

Exploring Volume

The *volume* of a solid is a measure of how much space it occupies. Volume is measured in cubic units. One cubic unit is the amount of space occupied by a cube that measures one unit on each side. This cube is called the *unit cube.*

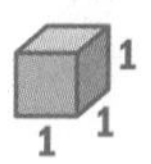

Explore **Find the volume of the rectangular prism.**

To find the volume of the prism shown, first build the prism using sugar cubes to represent unit cubes. Then count the number of cubes you used.

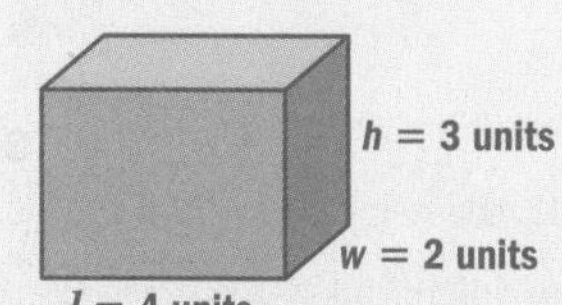

1. It takes 2 rows of 4 cubes, or 8 cubes, to make the bottom of the prism.

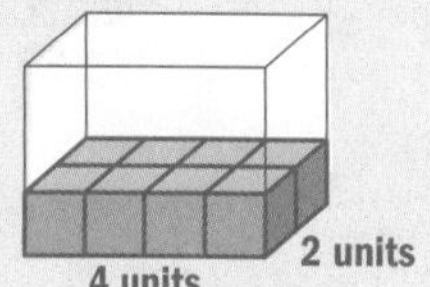

2. It takes 3 layers of 8 cubes, or 24 cubes, to make the prism the right height.

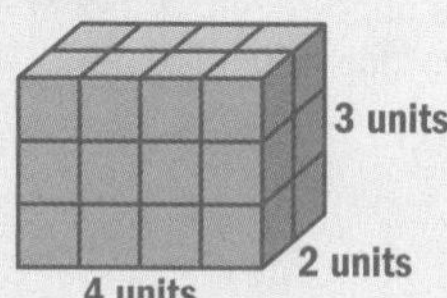

3. Because each cube is 1 cubic unit, the volume of the prism is 24 cubic units.

Your turn now **Use cubes to model the volume of rectangular prisms.**

1. Copy and complete the table to find the volume of the rectangular prism with the given dimensions.

Dimensions of the prism	Cubes to cover the bottom of the prism	Layers of cubes to make the prism	Volume of the prism
4 × 3 × 3	12	3	36
6 × 1 × 2	? 6	? 2	? 12
7 × 5 × 3	? 35	? 3	? 105
4 × 2 × 8	? 8	? 8	? 64

Stop and Think

2. **Critical Thinking** Write a formula for the number of cubes that will make a prism of length l, width w, and height h. $V = lwh$

ILLINOIS Standards and ISAT:
7.C.3b; 8.B.3

Volumes of Prisms and Cylinders

BEFORE

You found the surface areas of prisms and cylinders.

Now

You'll find the volumes of prisms and cylinders.

WHY?

So you can compare the volumes of pools, as in Ex. 28.

In the Real World

Word Watch

volume, p. 513

Recycling Residents of a community can choose between two recycling bins. Which recycling bin holds more? You will find the answer in Example 3.

The **volume** of a solid is a measure of the amount of space it occupies. Volume is measured in cubic units. One cubic unit is the amount of space occupied by a cube that measures one unit on each side.

Volume of a Prism

Words The volume of a prism is the product of the area of the base and the height.

Algebra $V = Bh$

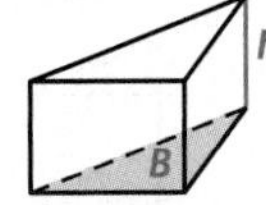

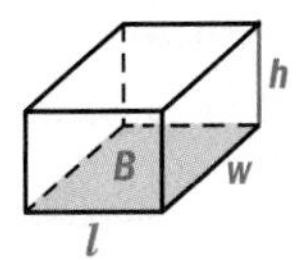

EXAMPLE 1 **Finding Volumes of Prisms**

Find the volume of the prism.

a.

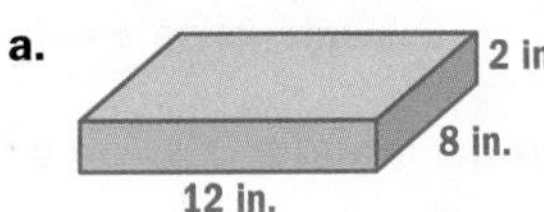

$V = Bh$

$= lwh$

$= 12(8)(2)$

$= 192$

ANSWER The volume is 192 cubic inches.

b.

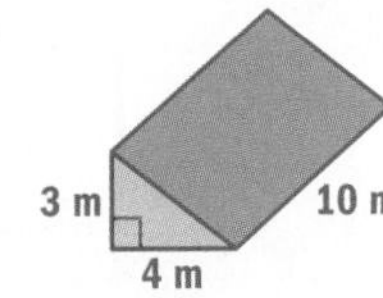

$V = Bh$

$= \frac{1}{2}(4)(3)(10)$

$= 60$

ANSWER The volume is 60 cubic meters.

Watch Out!

When you find the volume of a triangular prism, be careful not to confuse the height of the prism with the height of the triangular base.

ILLINOIS Standards and ISAT:
7.C.3b, 8.D.3b; 9.C.3a

1 PLAN

SKILL CHECK

1. Write the formula for the area of a triangle. $A = \frac{1}{2}bh$
2. What is the area of a circle with radius 9 inches? Use 3.14 for π. about 254 in.^{2}

LESSON OBJECTIVE

Find the volumes of prisms and cylinders.

PACING

Suggested Number of Days
Basic Course: 1 day
Average Course: 1 day
Advanced Course: 1 day
Block: 0.5 block with 10.5

TEACHING RESOURCES

For a complete list of Teaching Resources, see page 478B.

TRANSPARENCY

Warm-Up Exercises for this lesson are available on a transparency.

2 TEACH

MOTIVATING THE LESSON

Ask students to define volume. Ask them for different ways to describe how much a container can hold.

TIPS FOR NEW TEACHERS

Help students recognize that area is a measure of a flat surface and volume is a measure of a three-dimensional space. See Tips for New Teachers in the *Chapter 10 Resource Book*.

EXTRA EXAMPLES

Example 1 Find the volume of the prism.

a.

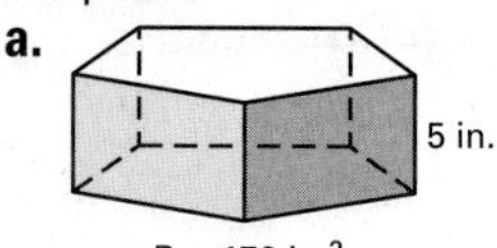

$B = 172$ in.^{2}

860 in.^{3}

b.

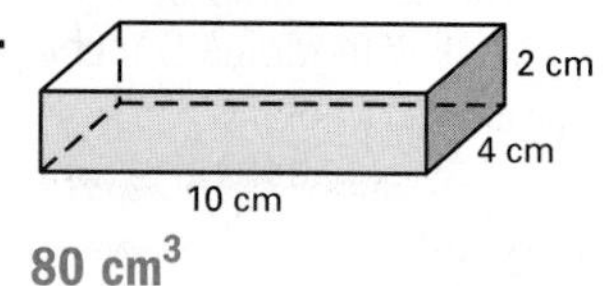

80 cm^3

Example 2 Find the volume of the cylinder. **about 1257 mm^3**

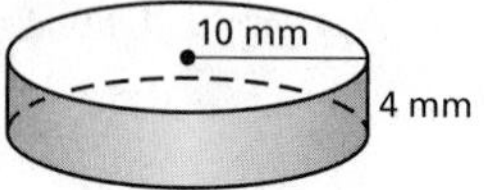

TEACHING TIP

In Example 1b, point out that the base of a prism is not always the surface resting on the floor in a figure. Make sure students can explain how to correctly identify the base of a prism.

Differentiating Instruction

Advanced Students Ask students to think about whether an increase in surface area means an increase in volume. Have students think about the surface area and volume of a cube and compare that to the surface area and volume of a sheet of plywood. Encourage students to discuss their theories using correct mathematical language in order to familiarize all students with the concepts of area and volume and how they relate.

Because the base of the cylinder is a circle, its area is πr^2.

Volumes of Cylinders The formula for the volume of a cylinder is similar to the formula for the volume of a prism.

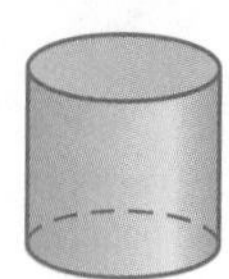 = 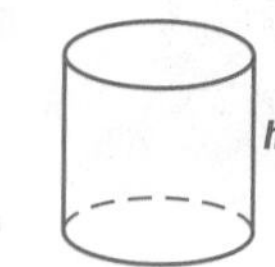

Volume of a cylinder = Area of base × Height

Volume of a Cylinder

Words The volume of a cylinder is the product of the area of a base and the height.

Algebra $V = Bh$

$= \pi r^2 h$

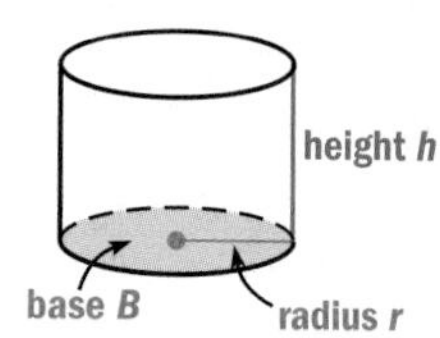

EXAMPLE 2 Finding the Volume of a Cylinder

Find the volume of the cylinder.

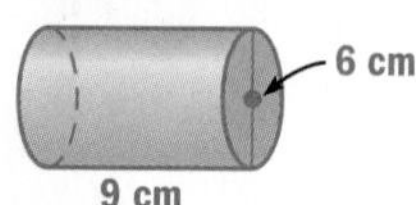

The radius is one half the diameter, so $r = 3$ cm.

$V = Bh$	Write formula for volume.
$= \pi r^2 h$	Write formula for volume of a cylinder.
$= \pi(3)^2(9)$	Substitute 3 for r and 9 for h.
$= 81\pi$	Simplify.
≈ 254.469	Evaluate using a calculator.

ANSWER The volume is about 254 cubic centimeters.

Your turn now Find the volume of the solid. Round to the nearest tenth.

1. 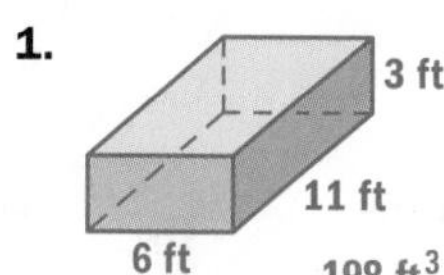

198 ft^3

2. 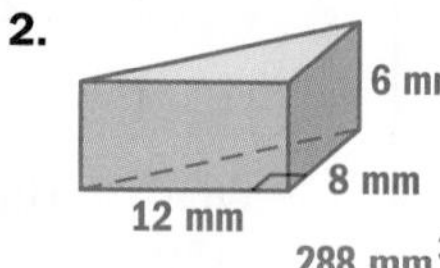

288 mm^3

3. 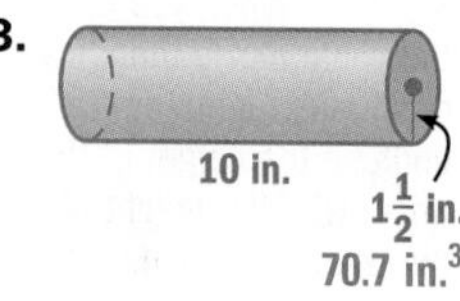

70.7 in.^{3}

with Reading

When the abbreviation for a unit of measure has an exponent of 3, you read the 3 as "cubic."

ft^3 = cubic feet
cm^3 = cubic centimeters

EXAMPLE 3 Comparing Capacities

Recycling To decide which recycling bin on page 513 can hold more, find the capacity of each bin.

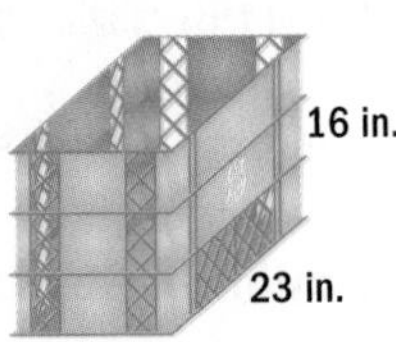

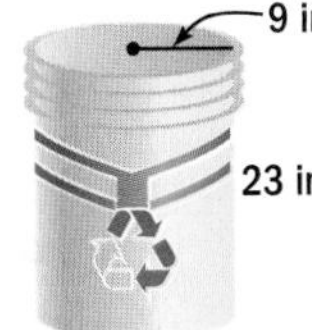

Prism	Cylinder
$V = Bh$	$V = Bh$
$= lwh$	$= \pi r^2 h$
$= 14(23)(16)$	$= \pi(9)^2(23)$
$= 5152 \text{ in.}^3$	$\approx 5852.8 \text{ in.}^3$

ANSWER The cylindrical recycling bin holds more.

EXTRA EXAMPLES

Example 3 A company is comparing two kinds of packaging for shipping dog food. Which container holds more?

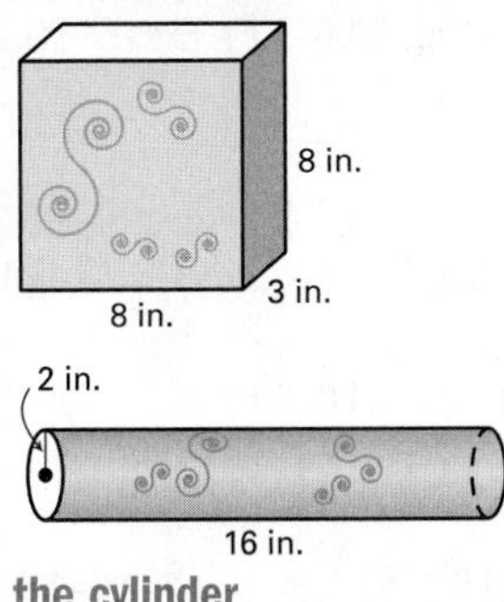

the cylinder

CONCEPT CHECK

Which has more volume, a rectangular prism with length 12 feet, width 12 feet, and height 14 feet or a cylinder with diameter 12 feet and height 14 feet? Use the π key on a calculator and round to two decimal places if necessary. **The volume of the rectangular prism is 2016 square feet, and the volume of the cylinder is about 1583 square feet. The rectangular prism has more volume.**

10.6 Exercises

More Practice, p. 736

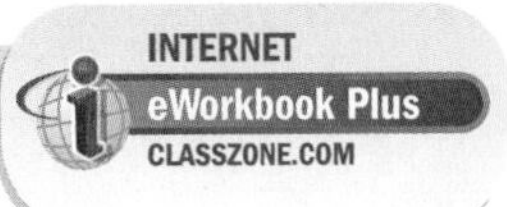

Getting Ready to Practice

1. **Vocabulary** Explain the difference between area and volume.

1. ***Sample answer:* Area is the measure of the region inside a two-dimensional shape, while volume is the measure of the space inside a solid.**

Find the volume of the solid. Round to the nearest tenth.

2\.
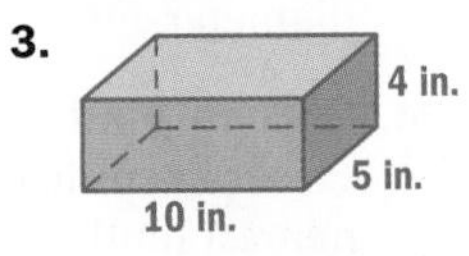

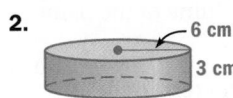

339.3 cm^3

3\.
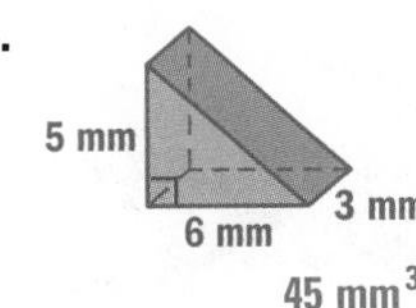

200 $in.^3$

4\.

45 mm^3

5. **Find the Error** Describe and correct the error in finding the volume of the cylinder. **The area of the base is πr^2, not $2\pi r$; $V = Bh = \pi r^2 h = \pi(4^2)5 \approx 251.3 \text{ m}^3$.**

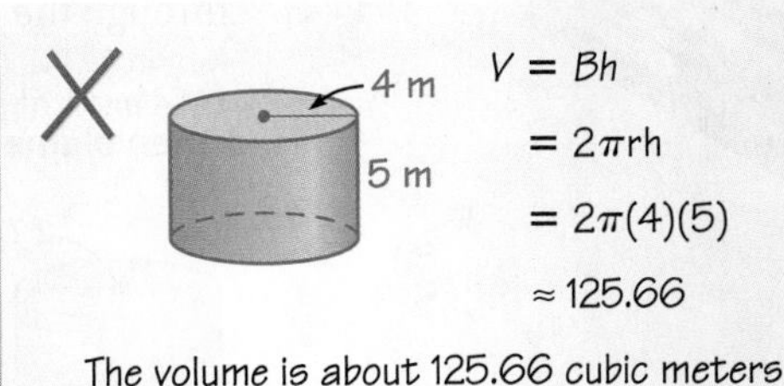

4 m
5 m
V = Bh
= 2πrh
= 2π(4)(5)
≈ 125.66
The volume is about 125.66 cubic meters.

DAILY PUZZLER

Three balls with radius 1 inch fit exactly into a tube. What percent of the tube's volume is air? (The volume of each ball is $\frac{4}{3}\pi r^3$.) **$33\frac{1}{3}$ %**

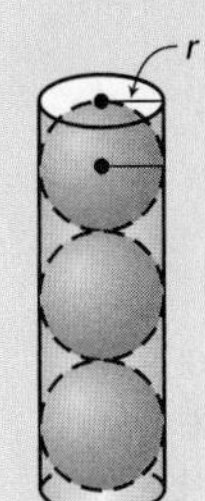

ASSIGNMENT GUIDE

Basic Course

Day 1: pp. 516–517 Exs. 6–10, 13–15, 19–26, 33–38

Average Course

Day 1: pp. 516–517 Exs. 9–12, 16–18, 21–24, 27–31, 33–38

Advanced Course

Day 1: pp. 516–517 Exs. 9–12, 16–18, 22–24, 27–38*

Block

pp. 516–517 Exs. 9–12, 16–18, 21–24, 27–31, 33–38 (with 10.5)

EXTRA PRACTICE

- Student Edition, p. 736
- Chapter 10 Resource Book, pp. 52–54
- Test and Practice Generator

TRANSPARENCY

Even-numbered answers are available on transparencies.

HOMEWORK CHECK

When you review students' homework for this lesson, go over the following exercises to check understanding of key concepts.
Basic: 6, 10, 13, 14, 24
Average: 9, 11, 16, 23, 24
Advanced: 9, 12, 18, 23, 24

TEACHING TIP

In Exercises 17 and 18, make sure students notice that there are two different units in each of the two figures.

HELP with Homework

Example	Exercises
1	6-9, 13-18
2	10-18, 23
3	24

· More Examples
· eTutorial Plus

Practice and Problem Solving

Find the volume of the rectangular prism.

A **6.** $l = 6$ m, $w = 2$ m, $h = 11$ m 132 m³ **7.** $l = 7$ in., $w = 7$ in., $h = 7$ in. 343 in.³

8. $l = 3$ cm, $w = 3.8$ cm, $h = 1.2$ cm 13.68 cm³ **9.** $l = 16$ ft, $w = 3$ ft, $h = 2\frac{1}{2}$ ft 120 ft³

Find the volume of the cylinder. Round to the nearest tenth.

10. $r = 4$ ft, $h = 11$ ft 552.9 ft³ **11.** $r = 3$ cm, $h = 9$ cm 254.5 cm³ **12.** $r = 1.2$ m, $h = 4.5$ m 20.4 m³

Find the volume of the solid. If two units of measure are used, give your answer in the smaller units. Round to the nearest tenth.

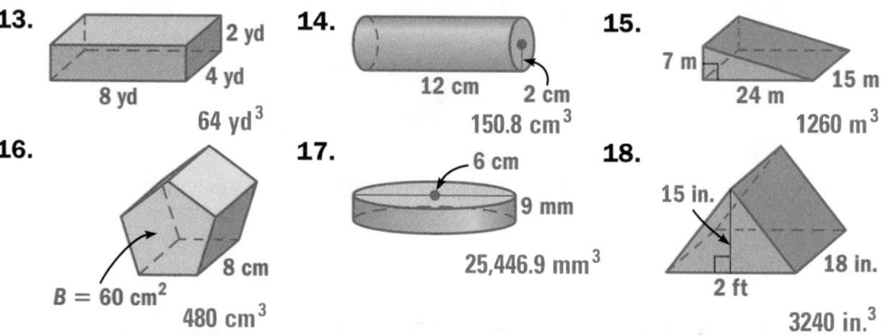

Critical Thinking **In Exercises 19–22, tell whether you would need to calculate *surface area* or *volume* to find the quantity.**

19. The amount of wrapping paper needed to wrap a gift surface area

20. The amount of cereal that will fit in a box volume

21. The amount of water needed to fill a watering can volume

22. The amount of frosting needed to decorate a cake surface area

23. Paint A paint can is a cylinder 19 centimeters tall and 16 centimeters in diameter. Find the volume of the paint can. Round to the nearest tenth. 3820.2 cm³

24. Erasers Find the volume of each eraser in cubic millimeters to the nearest tenth. How many pencil-top erasers would you go through in the time it takes you to go through the larger eraser? larger: 10,400 mm³, pencil-top: 141.4 mm³; about 74 erasers

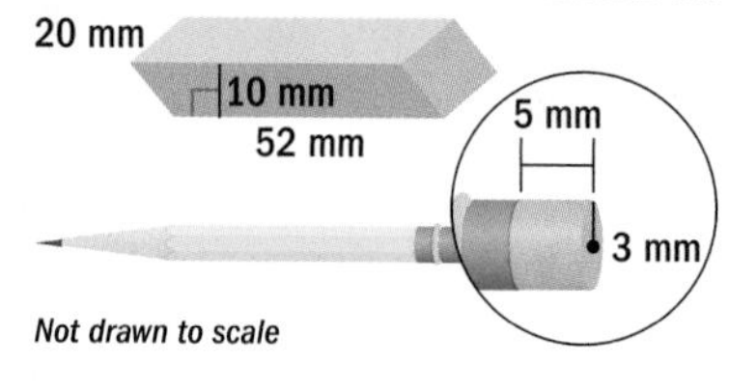

Find the volume of the solid. Round to the nearest tenth.

B **25.** 2.7 mm, 1.5 mm — 8.6 mm³

26. 3 ft, 5 ft, 9 ft, 7 ft — 409.5 ft³

27. 11 m, 4 m, 6 m, 17 m — 336 m³

28. Swimming Pools A rectangular in-ground pool is 40 feet long, 16 feet wide, and 4 feet deep. A cylindrical above-ground pool has a radius of 12 feet and is 6 feet deep. How many cubic feet of water does each pool hold? Round to the nearest tenth. Which pool holds more?
rectangular: 2560 ft^3, cylindrical: 2714.3 ft^3; cylindrical

29. Salt Shakers You buy a cylindrical container of salt that has a diameter of 4 inches and a height of 6 inches. Your salt shaker is a rectangular prism that is $1\frac{1}{2}$ inches by $1\frac{1}{2}$ inches by 3 inches. How many times can the salt in the container fill the salt shaker? 11 times

C **30. Number Sense** Which would have a greater effect on the volume of a cylinder: *doubling the height* or *doubling the radius*? Explain. See margin.

31. Number Sense Which would have a greater effect on the volume of a long, thin, short box: *doubling the length* or *doubling the width*? Explain. See margin.

32. Challenge Find the volume of the solid at the right. 337.5 ft^3

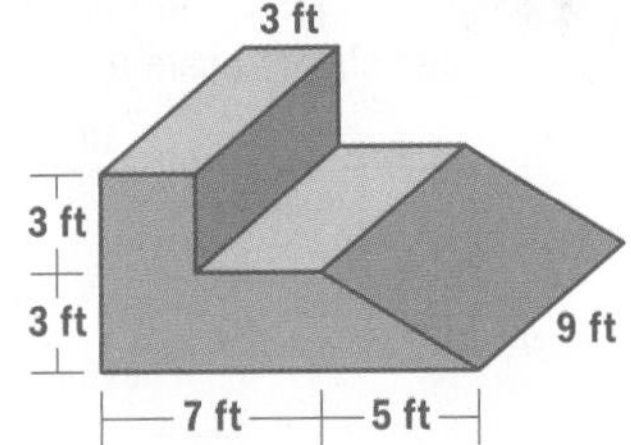

30. Doubling the radius. *Sample answer:* The radius is squared in the volume formula, but the height is not.

31. They would have the same effect. *Sample answer:* Since $V = lwh$, if any dimension is doubled, the volume is doubled.

Mixed Review 

Let a and b represent the lengths of the legs of the right triangle, and let c represent the length of the hypotenuse. Find the unknown length. *(Lesson 9.3)*

33. $a = 15, b = ?, c = 39$ 36

34. $a = 16, b = 63, c = ?$ 65

Find the surface area of the solid to the nearest tenth. *(Lesson 10.5)*

35.

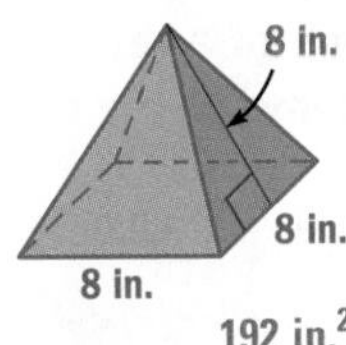

192 $in.^2$

36.

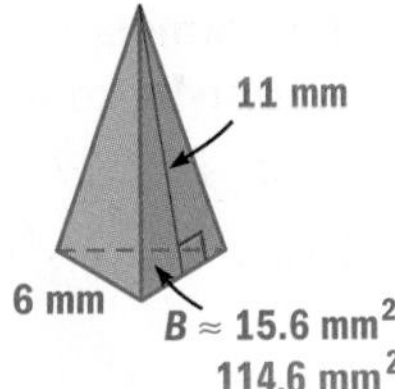

114.6 mm^2

37.

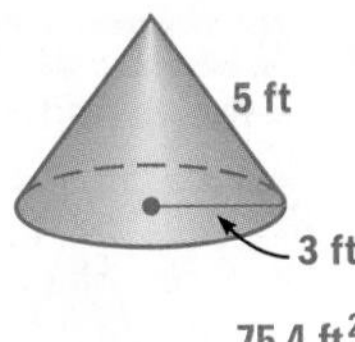

75.4 ft^2

Test-Taking Practice 

38. Extended Response Find the surface area and volume of the cylinder shown in terms of π. Then triple the radius and height of the cylinder and find the new surface area and volume. Compare the surface area and volume of the new cylinder to the original cylinder. How did the surface area and the volume change?

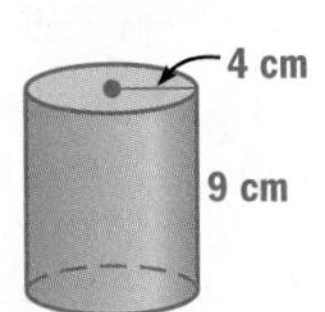

INTERNET
State Test Practice
CLASSZONE.COM

38. 104π cm^2, 144π cm^3; 936π cm^2, 3888π cm^3; the surface area was multiplied by 9 and the volume by 27.

4 ASSESS

Assessment Resources

For more assessment resources, see:

- Assessment Book
- Test and Practice Generator

Mini-Quiz

1. Find the volume of a rectangular prism with length 24 millimeters, width 12 millimeters, and height 8 millimeters. 2304 mm^3
2. To the nearest whole number, find the volume of a cylinder with radius 18 inches and height 108 inches. Use the π key on your calculator. about 109,931 $in.^3$
3. Find the volume of the solid.

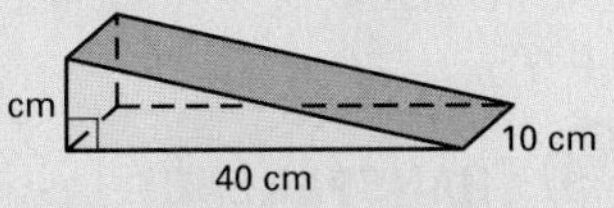

1800 cm^3

5 FOLLOW-UP

Reteaching/Remediation

- Study Guide in Chapter 10 Resource Book, pp. 55–56
- Tutor Place, Geometry and Measurement Card 21
- eTutorial Plus Online
- Extra Practice, p. 736
- Lesson Practice in Chapter 10 Resource Book, pp. 52–54

Challenge/Enrichment

- Challenge Practice in Chapter 10 Resource Book, p. 58
- Teacher's Edition, p. 478F

English Learner Support

- Spanish Study Guide
- Multi-Language Glossary
- Chapter Audio Summaries CDs

PLAN

EXPLORE THE CONCEPT

- Students will compare the volumes of a prism and a pyramid.
- This activity leads into the study of the volumes of pyramids and cones in Lesson 10.7.

MATERIALS

Each student or pair of students will need tape, scissors, a metric ruler, thin cardboard, and popcorn kernels.

RECOMMENDED TIME

Work activity: 15 min
Discuss results: 5 min

GROUPING

Students can work individually or in pairs.

TRANSPARENCY

A support transparency is available for Exercise 4.

TEACH

ALTERNATIVE STRATEGY

Make a pair of nets ahead of time, have the class measure them, and have volunteers pour the popcorn. Have students predict how much popcorn is needed.

CLOSE

KEY DISCOVERY

A square pyramid has one third the volume of a square prism with the same side length and height.

ASSESSMENT

1. A prism has the same base as a pyramid that is three times as tall. How do their volumes compare? They are equal.

10.7 Hands-on Activity

GOAL

Compare the volumes of a prism and a pyramid.

MATERIALS

- tape
- scissors
- metric ruler
- thin cardboard
- popcorn kernels

Comparing Volumes

Compare the volume of a pyramid to the volume of a prism.

Explore **Compare pyramids and prisms.**

1 On cardboard, draw the nets shown. Then cut out the nets and use tape to make an open square prism and an open square pyramid.

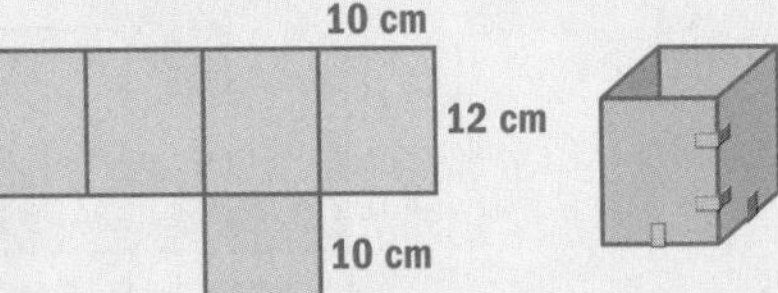

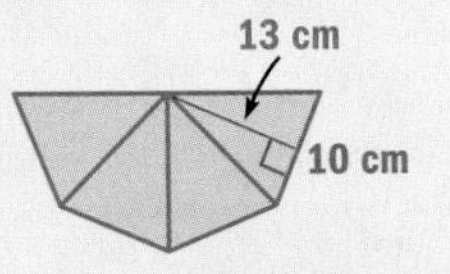

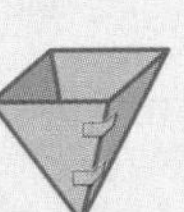

2 Compare the height of the prism to the height of the pyramid. Then compare the base of the prism to the base of the pyramid. What do you notice? The heights are the same and the bases are the same.

3 Fill the pyramid with popcorn kernels and pour the contents into the prism. Repeat until the prism is full. How many times did you have to empty the pyramid into the prism? Use this number to write the ratio of the volume of the pyramid to the volume of the prism. 3; 1 : 3

Your turn now **Use the formula for the volume of a rectangular prism and the ratio found in the activity to find the volume of the square pyramid.**

1. 4 cm, 2 cm, 2 cm — $5.\overline{3}$ cm^3

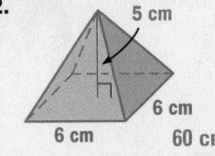

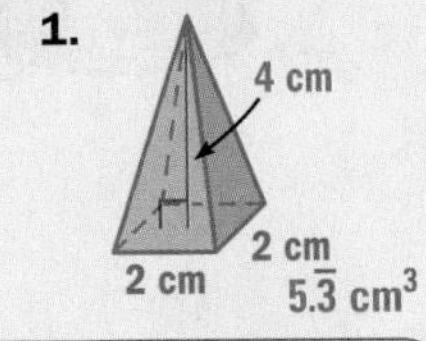

2. 60 cm^3

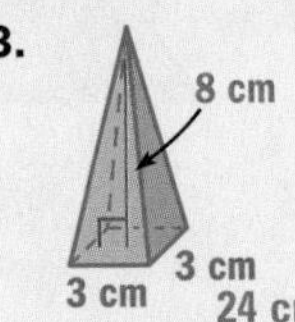

3. 24 cm^3

Stop and Think

4. Make a Model Use the nets shown to make an open cylinder and an open cone. Find the ratio of their volumes. 1:3

5 cm, 12 cm, 31.4 cm

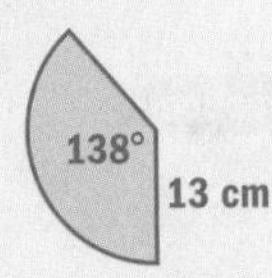

ILLINOIS Standards and ISAT:
7.C.3b, 8.D.3b

Volumes of Pyramids and Cones

BEFORE

You found the volumes of prisms and cylinders.

Now

You'll find the volumes of pyramids and cones.

WHY?

So you can find the amount of space lit by a spotlight, as in Ex. 26.

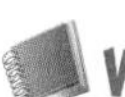

Word Watch

Review Words

pyramid, p. 492
cone, p. 492
volume, p. 513

In the Real World

Famous Buildings The Rainforest Pyramid in Galveston Island, Texas, is the home of many plants, butterflies, fish, and reptiles. This square pyramid has a height of 100 feet, and each side of its base measures 200 feet. What is the volume of the Rainforest Pyramid?

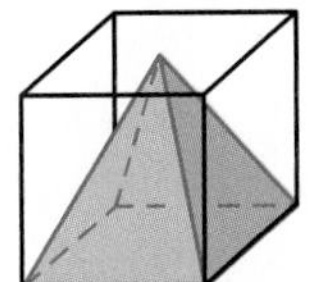

The volumes of a pyramid and a prism with the same base area and the same height are related. The volume of the pyramid is exactly one third the volume of the prism.

Volume of a Pyramid

Words The volume of a pyramid is one third the product of the area of the base and the height.

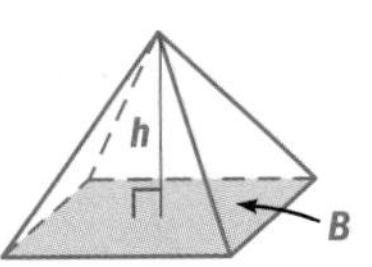

Algebra $V = \frac{1}{3}Bh$

EXAMPLE 1 Finding the Volume of a Pyramid

Find the volume of the Rainforest Pyramid described above using the diagram.

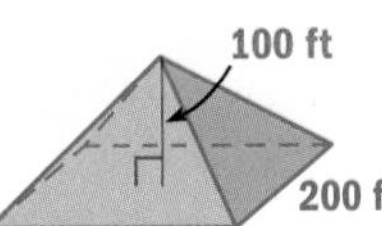

Solution

$V = \frac{1}{3}Bh$ — Write formula for volume of a pyramid.

$= \frac{1}{3}(200^2)(100)$ — The base is a square, so $B = s^2$.

$= 1{,}333{,}333.\overline{3}$ — Evaluate using a calculator.

ANSWER The Rainforest Pyramid has a volume of about 1,300,000 cubic feet.

ILLINOIS Standards and ISAT:
7.C.3b, 8.D.3b

1 PLAN

SKILL CHECK

Find each area. Use 3.14 for π.

1. a circle with diameter 105 meters **8655 m²**
2. a circle with radius 8 millimeters **201 mm²**

LESSON OBJECTIVE

Find volumes of pyramids and cones.

PACING

Suggested Number of Days
Basic Course: 2 days
Average Course: 2 days
Advanced Course: 2 days
Block: 1 block

TEACHING RESOURCES

For a complete list of Teaching Resources, see page 478B.

TRANSPARENCY

Warm-Up Exercises for this lesson are available on a transparency.

2 TEACH

MOTIVATING THE LESSON

Have students discuss the pros and cons of living in a house shaped like a pyramid.

TIPS FOR NEW TEACHERS

Remind students that they use height, not slant height, for calculating volume in pyramids and cones. See Tips for New Teachers in the *Chapter 10 Resource Book*.

EXTRA EXAMPLES

Example 1 Find the volume of the pyramid. **400 m³**

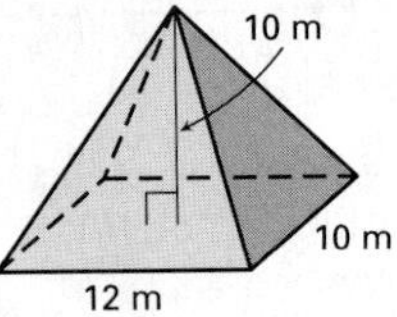

Example 2 Find the volume of the pyramid. **128 in.³**

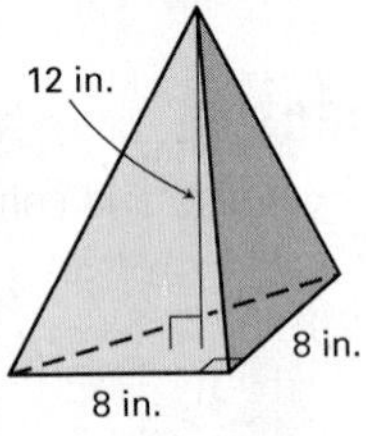

Differentiating Instruction

Alternative Teaching Approach
Bring a cone and a cylinder with the same radius and the same height to class. The cone should be thin enough to fit inside the cylinder. Demonstrate that three cones of popcorn kernels are needed to fill the cylinder. Empty the cylinder. Then measure out two cones of kernels into a separate container. Invert the cone point side up and place it inside the cylinder. Next, empty the two cones of kernels on top and around the point of the cone to demonstrate that the cone takes up one third the volume of the cylinder.

EXAMPLE 2 Finding the Volume of a Pyramid

Find the volume of the pyramid.

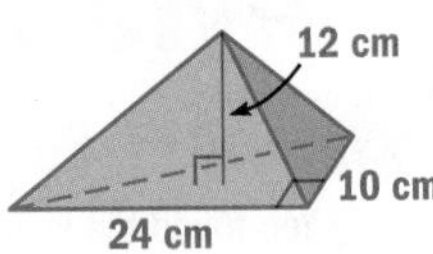

$V = \frac{1}{3}Bh$	**Write formula for volume of a pyramid.**
$= \frac{1}{3}\left(\frac{1}{2} \cdot 24 \cdot 10\right)(12)$	**The base is a triangle, so $B = \frac{1}{2}bh$.**
$= 480$	**Multiply.**

ANSWER The pyramid has a volume of 480 cubic centimeters.

Your turn now **Find the volume of the pyramid.**

1.

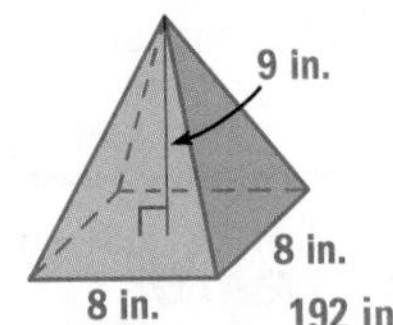

192 in.³

2.

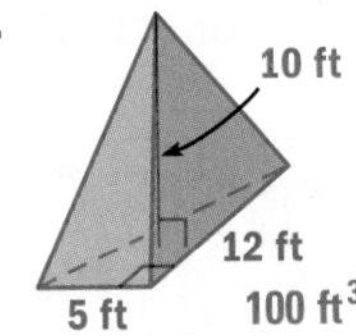

100 ft³

3.

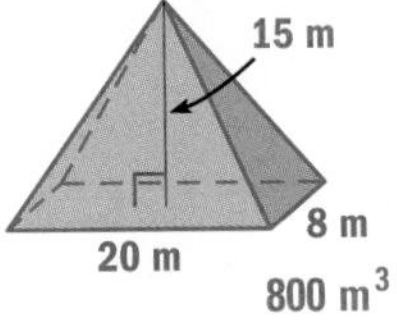

800 m³

4. Critical Thinking Explain how you found the area of the base of each figure in Exercises 1–3.

4. *Sample answer:* For Exercise 1, the base is a square, so I multiplied the length of a side of the base by itself. For Exercise 2, the base is a right triangle, so I found half the product of the legs. For Exercise 3, the base is a rectangle, so I multiplied its length by its width.

Volumes of Cones The volume of a cone is related to the volume of a cylinder in the same way the volume of a pyramid is related to the volume of a prism. That is, the volume of a cone is one third the volume of a cylinder with the same base and height.

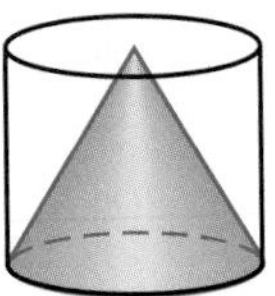

Volume of a Cone

Words The volume of a cone is one third the product of the area of the base and the height.

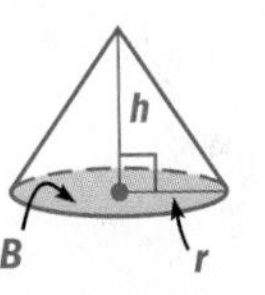

Algebra $V = \frac{1}{3}Bh = \frac{1}{3}\pi r^2 h$

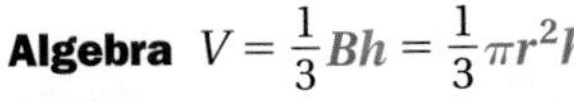

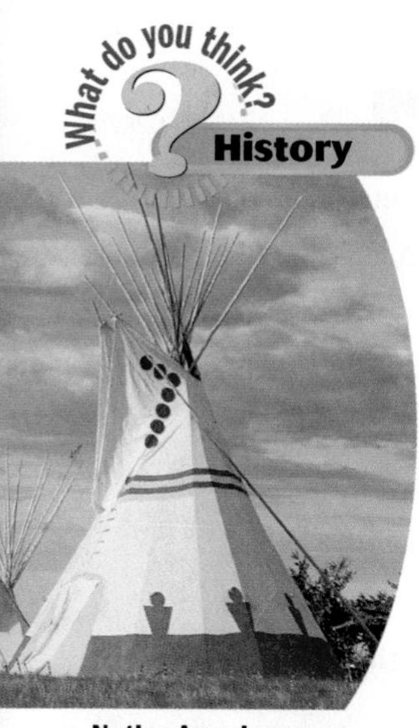

Native Americans

In the United States, 26 of the 50 states have names that originated from Native American languages. What percent is this? 52%

EXAMPLE 3 Finding the Volume of a Cone

Native Americans Many Native American tribes built tepees that were cone-shaped. A tepee has a height of 12 feet and a base diameter of 12 feet. Approximate the volume of the tepee.

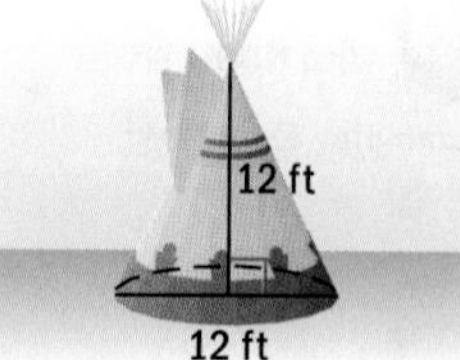

Solution

The radius is one half the diameter, so $r = \frac{1}{2} \cdot 12 = 6$ ft.

$V = \frac{1}{3}\pi r^2 h$	**Write formula for volume of a cone.**
$= \frac{1}{3}\pi(6)^2(12)$	**Substitute 6 for *r* and 12 for *h*.**
$= 144\pi$	**Simplify.**
≈ 452.389	**Evaluate using a calculator.**

ANSWER The tepee has a volume of about 450 cubic feet.

Your turn now **Find the volume of the cone with radius *r* and height *h*. Round to the nearest tenth.**

5. $r = 24$ m, $h = 18$ m 10,857.3 m^3
6. $r = 4$ in., $h = 16$ in. 268.1 $in.^3$
7. $r = 15$ ft, $h = 28$ ft 6597.3 ft^3

10.7 Exercises

More Practice, p. 736

INTERNET
eWorkbook Plus
CLASSZONE.COM

Getting Ready to Practice

Matching **Match each solid with the *best* formula for its volume.**

1. prism D
2. cylinder B
3. pyramid A
4. cone C

A. $V = \frac{1}{3}Bh$ **B.** $V = \pi r^2 h$ **C.** $V = \frac{1}{3}\pi r^2 h$ **D.** $V = Bh$

Find the volume of the solid. Round to the nearest tenth.

5. 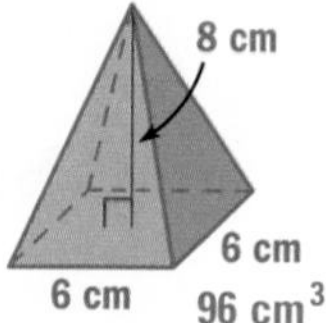

96 cm^3

6. 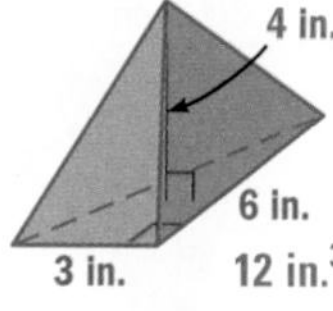

12 $in.^3$

7. 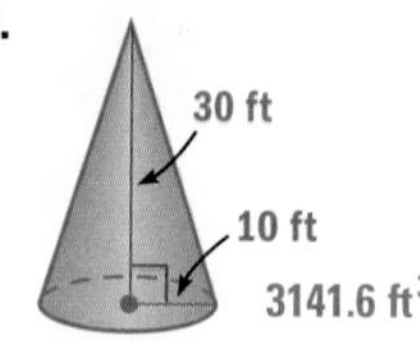

3141.6 ft^3

EXTRA EXAMPLES

Example 3 Find the volume of bird seed that this conical bird feeder can hold. about 12.6 ft^3

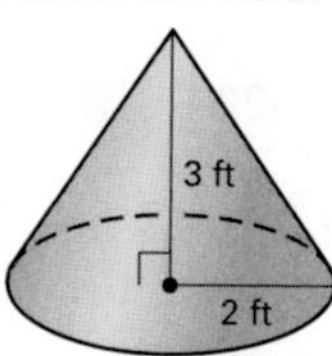

CONCEPT CHECK

A cone and a pyramid each have base area 131 square centimeters and height 12 centimeters. Find the two volumes and explain any similarities or differences. The volume of the cone is 524 square centimeters, and the volume of the pyramid is 524 square centimeters. The volumes are the same because the two solids have the same base area and the same height.

DAILY PUZZLER

How many small square pyramids with a base of 2 inches by 2 inches and a height of 2 inches have the equivalent volume of a large square pyramid with a base of 10 inches by 10 inches and a height of 10 inches? 125 small square pyramids

ASSIGNMENT GUIDE

Basic Course

Day 1: pp. 522–523 Exs. 8–16, 26, 35–37

Day 2: pp. 522–523 Exs. 17–25, 27, 38–40

Average Course

Day 1: pp. 522–523 Exs. 10–15, 26–28, 35–37

Day 2: pp. 522–523 Exs. 18–23, 29–31, 38–40

Advanced Course

Day 1: pp. 522–523 Exs. 10–14, 26–30, 35–37

Day 2: pp. 522–523 Exs. 18–23, 31–34*, 38–40

Block

pp. 522–523 Exs. 10–15, 18–23, 26–31, 35–40

EXTRA PRACTICE

- Student Edition, p. 736
- Chapter 10 Resource Book, pp. 63–65
- Test and Practice Generator

TRANSPARENCY

Even-numbered answers are available on transparencies.

HOMEWORK CHECK

When you review students' homework for this lesson, go over the following exercises to check understanding of key concepts.

Basic: 8, 11, 14, 17, 20

Average: 10, 12, 15, 18, 22

Advanced: 10, 13, 14, 19, 23

TEACHING TIP

Students may need to review how to find the area of a trapezoid for Exercise 28.

Example	Exercises
1	14–16
2	8–16
3	17–25

- More Examples
- eTutorial Plus

Practice and Problem Solving

Find the volume of the pyramid with base area *B* and height *h*.

A **8.** $B = 9 \text{ in.}^2$, $h = 4$ in. 12 in.^{3} **9.** $B = 12 \text{ ft}^2$, $h = 15$ ft 60 ft^3 **10.** $B = 1.5 \text{ m}^2$, $h = 0.6$ m 0.3 m^3

Find the volume of the pyramid.

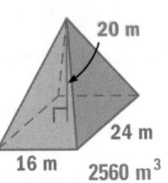

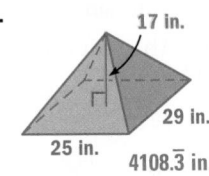

11. 20 m, 24 m, 16 m 2560 m^3

12. 17 in., 29 in., 25 in. 4108.$\overline{3}$ in.^{3}

13.

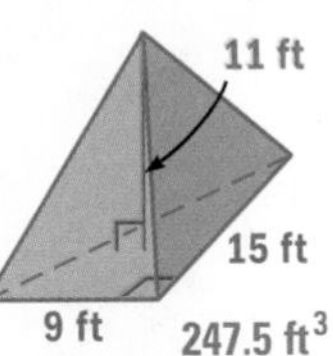

Find the volume of the square pyramid with base side length *s* and height *h*.

14. $s = 5$ m, $h = 4$ m 33.$\overline{3}$ m^3 **15.** $s = 12$ yd, $h = 3$ yd 144 yd^3 **16.** $s = 6$ in., $h = \frac{1}{2}$ in. 6 in.^{3}

Find the volume of the cone. If two units of measure are used, give your answer in the smaller units. Round to the nearest tenth.

17. **18.** **19.**

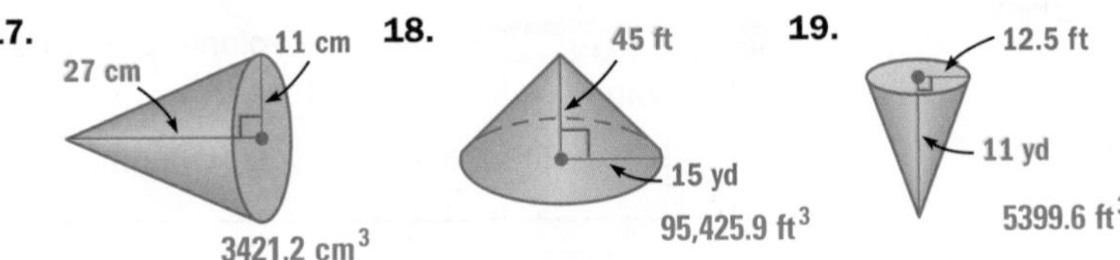

Find the volume of the cone with the given dimensions. If two units of measure are used, give your answer in the smaller units. Round to the nearest tenth.

20. $r = 3$ in., $h = 7$ in. 66.0 in.^{3} **21.** $r = 11$ ft, $h = 4$ ft 506.8 ft^3 **22.** $r = 1.2$ m, $h = 45$ cm 678,584.0 cm^3

23. $d = 8$ m, $h = 8$ m 134.0 m^3 **24.** $d = 5$ cm, $h = 9$ cm 58.9 cm^3 **25.** $d = 3$ ft, $h = 10$ yd 70.7 ft^3

26. **Spotlight** The light from a spotlight reaches out in a cone shape from the bulb. The light of the beam extends 24 feet before it hits the floor under the spotlight and creates a circle with a radius of 10 feet. What is the volume of the space directly lit by the spotlight? Round to the nearest tenth. 2513.3 ft^3

Find the volume of the pyramid with the given height and the base shown. Round to the nearest tenth.

B **27.** $h = 1.8$ cm

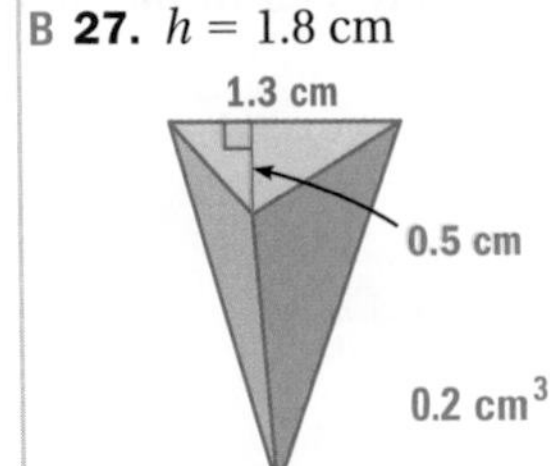

28. $h = 8$ m

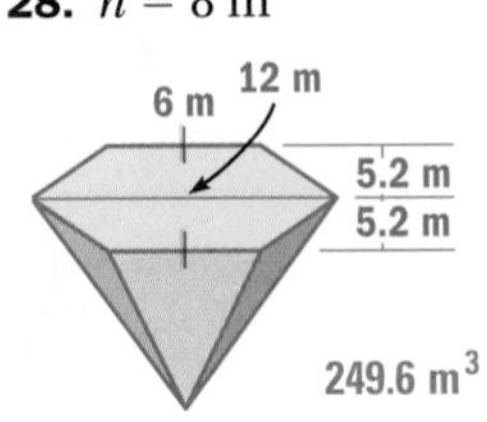

29. **Critical Thinking** Which would affect the volume of a cone more: *doubling the height* or *doubling the radius*? Explain your reasoning.

Writing **Write a sentence describing how to find the volume of the solid. Then write a formula for the volume of the solid.**

30.

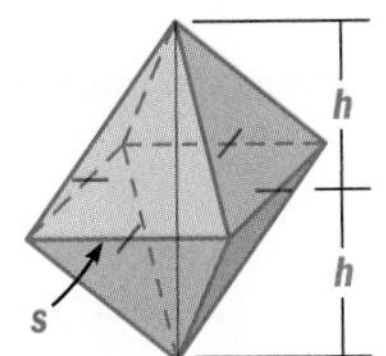

31.

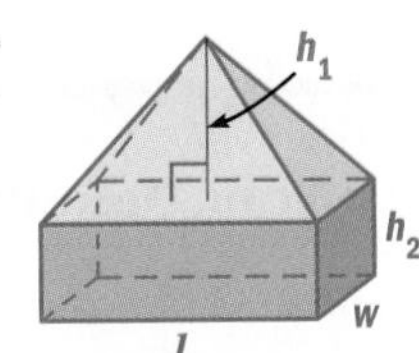

32.

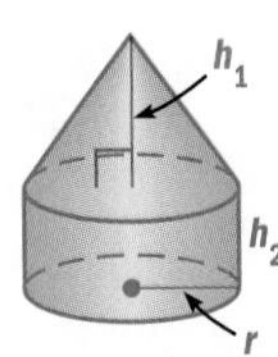

33. **Construction** A rectangular prism-shaped hole 10 feet by 12 feet by 8 feet is dug into the ground. How tall a pyramid can the excavated dirt form if the base is 10 feet by 10 feet? How tall a cone can it form if the base has a radius of 5 feet? Round your answers to the nearest tenth. **28.8 ft; 36.7 ft**

C 34. **Challenge** A cone-shaped cup has a height of 11 centimeters and a radius of 4 centimeters. You pour water into the cup until it is 2 centimeters from the top. Sketch the cone. How many fluid ounces of water are in the cup? Round to the nearest tenth. (*Hint*: Use similar triangles and the fact that 1 $cm^3 \approx 0.0338$ fl oz.) **See margin for art; 3.4 fl oz.**

Mixed Review

Show two ways to represent the solid. *(Lesson 10.3)* **35–36. See margin.**

35. hexagonal prism

36. square pyramid

37. Find the volume of a cylinder with radius 7 inches and height 18 inches. Round to the nearest tenth. *(Lesson 10.6)* **2770.9 $in.^3$**

38. **Basic Skills** The table shows the average high temperatures in Alexandria, Egypt, during the months April through September. Make a bar graph of the data. **See margin.**

Month	April	May	June	July	August	September
Temperature	75° F	79° F	83° F	84° F	86° F	84° F

Test-Taking Practice

39. **Multiple Choice** What is the volume of the cone? **C**

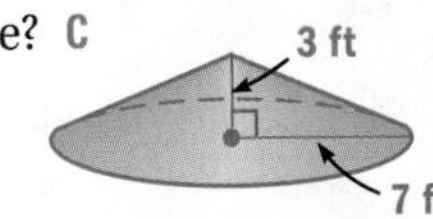

A. 10π ft^3 **B.** 21π ft^3

C. 49π ft^3 **D.** 147π ft^3

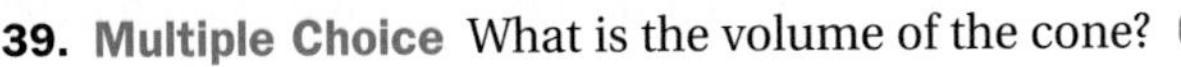

40. **Multiple Choice** What is the volume of a square pyramid with base side length 8 centimeters and height 9 centimeters? **G**

F. 72 cm^3 **G.** 192 cm^3 **H.** 576 cm^3 **I.** 648 cm^3

29. **Doubling the radius.** *Sample answer:* The radius is squared in the volume formula, but the height is not.

30. Find the volume of one of the square pyramids and double it; $V = \frac{2}{3}s^2h$.

31. Find the volume of the rectangular pyramid and the volume of the rectangular prism and add; $V = \frac{1}{3}lwh_1 + lwh_2$.

32. Find the volume of the cone and the volume of the cylinder and add; $V = \frac{1}{3}\pi r^2h_1 + \pi r^2h_2$.

INTERNET
State Test Practice
CLASSZONE.COM

4 ASSESS

Assessment Resources

For more assessment resources, see:

- Assessment Book
- Test and Practice Generator

Mini-Quiz

Find the volume of the pyramid with base area *B* and height *h*. Round to the nearest tenth.

1. $B = 14$ cm^2, $h = 16$ cm **74.7 cm^3**
2. $B = 7.5$ ft^2, $h = 6.5$ ft **16.3 ft^3**

Find the volume of the cone with the given dimensions. Use 3.14 for π. Round to the nearest tenth.

3. $r = 4$ cm, $h = 8$ cm **134.0 cm^3**
4. $d = 10.2$ ft, $h = 13$ ft **353.9 ft^3**

5 FOLLOW-UP

Reteaching/Remediation

- Study Guide in Chapter 10 Resource Book, pp. 66-67
- eTutorial Plus Online
- Extra Practice, p. 736
- Lesson Practice in Chapter 10 Resource Book, pp. 63-65

Challenge/Enrichment

- Challenge Practice in Chapter 10 Resource Book, p. 68
- Teacher's Edition, p. 478F

English Learner Support

- Spanish Study Guide
- Multi-Language Glossary
- Chapter Audio Summaries CDs

34-36, 38. See Additional Answers beginning on page AA1.

ADDITIONAL RESOURCES

The following resources are available to help review the materials in Lessons 10.4–10.7.

Chapter 10 Resource Book

- Lesson Practice
- Study Guide

Assessment Book

- Chapter 10 Quiz 2

Technology

- Test and Practice Generator
- eTutorial CD-ROM

Internet

- Classzone
- eWorkbook Plus Online
- eTutorial Plus Online

ENGLISH LEARNER SUPPORT

- Spanish Study Guide
- Multi-Language Glossary
- Chapter Audio Summaries CDs

Notebook Review

Review the vocabulary definitions in your notebook.

Copy the review examples in your notebook. Then complete the exercises.

Check Your Definitions

net, p. 502	slant height, p. 507
surface area, p. 503	volume, p. 513

Use Your Vocabulary

1. In your own words, explain what slant height is. For a regular pyramid, it is the height of a face that is not a base; for a cone, it is the length of any segment joining the base to the top point of the cone.

10.4–10.5 Can you find surface areas?

EXAMPLE Find the surface area of the cylinder.

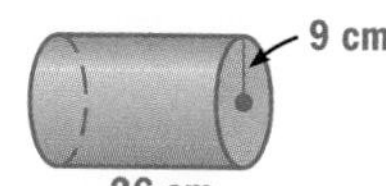

$S = 2\pi r^2 + 2\pi rh$

$= 2\pi(9)^2 + 2\pi(9)(26) \approx 509 + 1470 = 1979$

ANSWER The surface area of the cylinder is about 1979 square centimeters.

EXAMPLE Find the surface area of the square pyramid.

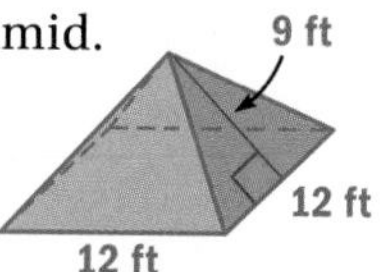

$S = B + \frac{1}{2}Pl$

$= 12^2 + \frac{1}{2}(4 \cdot 12)(9) = 144 + 216 = 360$

ANSWER The surface area of the pyramid is 360 square feet.

☑ **Find the surface area of the solid. Round to the nearest tenth.**

2. a cylinder with radius 5 meters and height 10 meters $471.2\ m^2$

3. a rectangular prism with length 5 inches, width 2 inches, and height 9 inches $146\ in.^2$

4. a square pyramid with base side length 7 meters and slant height 4 meters $105\ m^2$

5. a cone with diameter 20 feet and slant height 15 feet $785.4\ ft^2$

10.6–10.7 Can you find volumes?

EXAMPLE Find the volume of the prism.

$$V = Bh = \frac{1}{2}(7 \cdot 14)(21) = 49 \cdot 21 = 1029$$

ANSWER The volume is 1029 cubic inches.

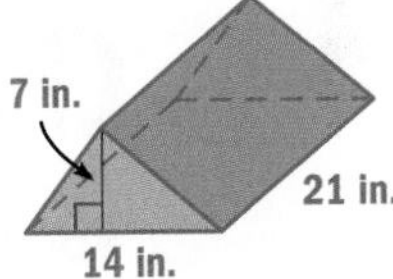

EXAMPLE Find the volume of the cone.

$$V = \frac{1}{3}\pi r^2 h = \frac{1}{3}\pi(7)^2(18) = 294\pi \approx 923.628$$

ANSWER The cone has a volume of about 924 cubic feet.

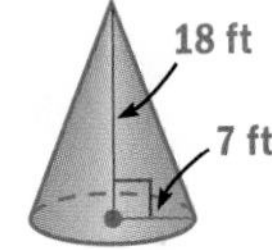

6. Find the volume of a pyramid with base area 27 square meters and height 14 meters. 126 m^3

Stop and Think about Lessons 10.4–10.7

7. Writing What is the difference between area and surface area? See margin.

Notebook Review

7. *Sample answer:* Area is the measure of the region inside a two-dimensional figure, while surface area is the sum of the areas of all faces or surfaces of a solid.

Review Quiz 2

Find the surface area of the solid. Round to the nearest tenth.

1.

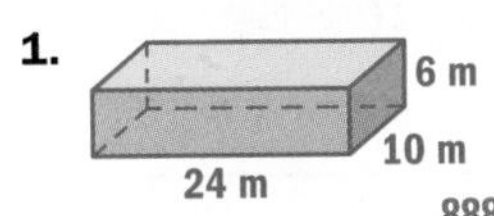

888 m^2

2.

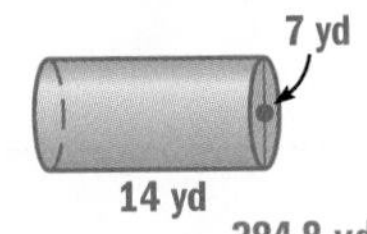

384.8 yd^2

3.

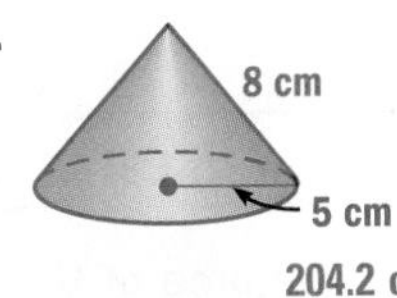

204.2 cm^2

Find the volume of the solid. Round to the nearest tenth.

4.

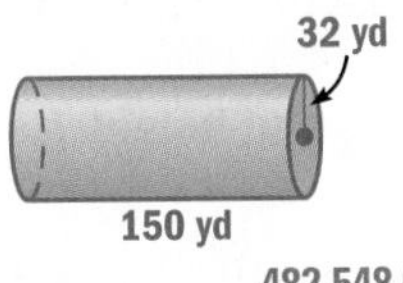

$482{,}548.6 \text{ yd}^3$

5.

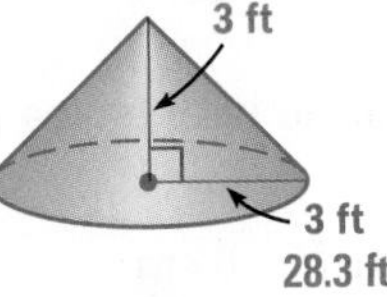

28.3 ft^3

6.

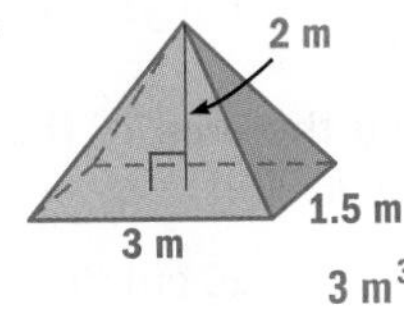

3 m^3

7. Ramp How much cement is needed to make the ramp shown?

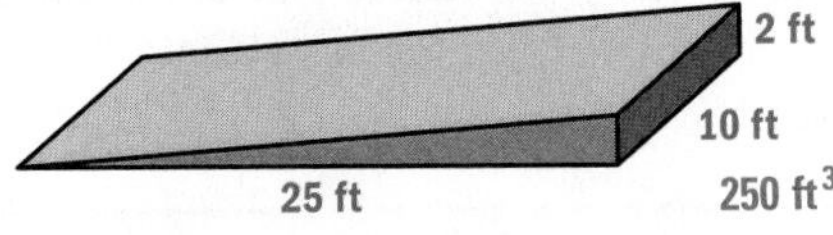

250 ft^3

The following resources are available to help review the materials in this chapter.

Chapter 10 Resource Book
- Chapter Review Games and Activities, p. 69
- Cumulative Practice, Chs. 1–10

English/Spanish Chapter Reviews and Tests

Chapter Audio Summaries CDs

eTutorial CD-ROM

eWorkbook Plus Online

eTutorial Plus Online

5. ***Sample:***

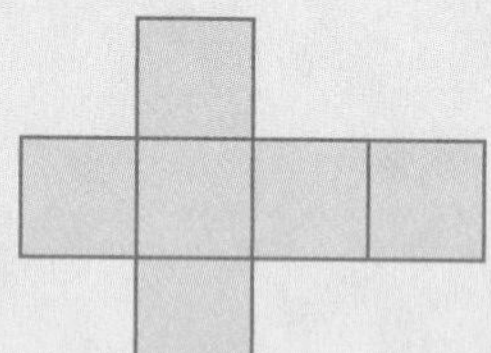

Chapter Review

Vocabulary

base of a parallelogram, p. 481
height of a parallelogram, p. 481
bases of a trapezoid, p. 482
height of a trapezoid, p. 482
solid, polyhedron, p. 492
face, p. 492
prism, p. 492
pyramid, p. 492
cylinder, p. 492
cone, p. 492
sphere, p. 492
edge, vertex, p. 492
net, p. 502
surface area, p. 503
slant height, p. 507
volume, p. 513

Vocabulary Review

Match the figure with its area formula.

1. (triangle) B **2.** (circle) A **3.** (trapezoid) D **4.** (parallelogram) C

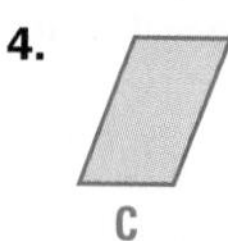

A. $A = \pi r^2$ **B.** $A = \frac{1}{2}bh$

C. $A = bh$ **D.** $A = \frac{1}{2}(b_1 + b_2)h$

5. Draw a net of a square prism. **See margin.**

6. How many faces, edges, and vertices does a triangular pyramid have? **4 faces, 6 edges, 4 vertices**

Write the formulas for the surface area and the volume of the figure.

7. cylinder **8.** cone

9. pyramid **10.** prism

7. $S = 2\pi r^2 + 2\pi rh$; $V = \pi r^2 h$ *8.* $S = \pi r^2 + \pi rl$; $V = \frac{1}{3}\pi r^2 h$

9. $S = B + \frac{1}{2}Pl$; $V = \frac{1}{3}Bh$ *10.* $S = 2B + Ph$; $V = Bh$

Review Questions

Find the area of the parallelogram with base *b* and height *h*.
(Lesson 10.1)

11. $b = 16$ ft, $h = 7$ ft **112 ft²** **12.** $b = 63$ m, $h = 5.2$ m **327.6 m²** **13.** $b = 8\frac{1}{4}$ in., $h = 6\frac{5}{11}$ in. **$53\frac{1}{4}$ in.²**

Find the area of the trapezoid with bases b_1 and b_2 and height *h*.
(Lesson 10.1)

14. $b_1 = 20$ cm, $b_2 = 12$ cm, $h = 8$ cm **128 cm²** **15.** $b_1 = 6$ yd, $b_2 = 9$ yd, $h = 12$ yd **90 yd²**

Find the area of the circle with radius *r* or diameter *d*. Use 3.14 for π.
(Lesson 10.2)

16. $r = 3$ ft **28.3 ft²** **17.** $r = 15$ yd **707 yd²** **18.** $d = 80$ cm **5020 cm²** **19.** $d = 1.5$ m **1.77 m²**

Review Questions

20. Show two ways to represent a hexagonal prism. Then count the number of faces, edges, and vertices. *(Lesson 10.3)* **See margin for art; 8 faces, 18 edges, 12 vertices.**

21. Draw a net for an octagonal pyramid. How many faces, edges, and vertices does the octagonal pyramid have? *(Lessons 10.3, 10.4)* **See margin for art; 9 faces, 16 edges, 9 vertices.**

Find the surface area of the solid. Round to the nearest tenth. *(Lessons 10.4, 10.5)*

22. 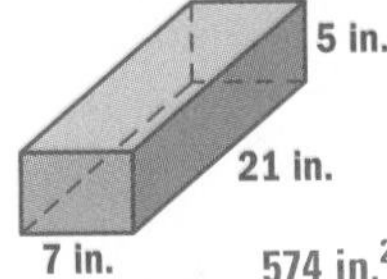

574 in.²

23. 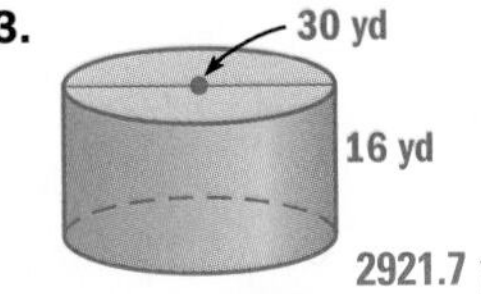

2921.7 yd²

24. 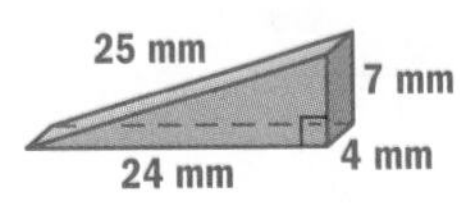

392 mm²

25. 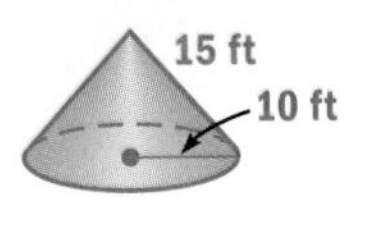

785.4 ft²

26. 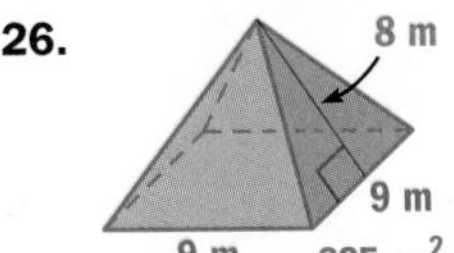

225 m²

27. 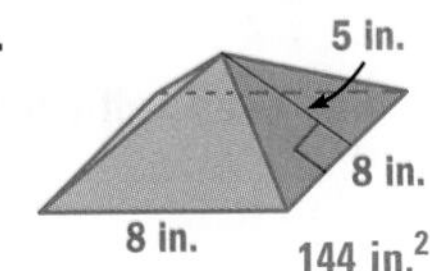

144 in.²

Find the volume of the solid. Round to the nearest tenth. *(Lessons 10.6, 10.7)*

28. 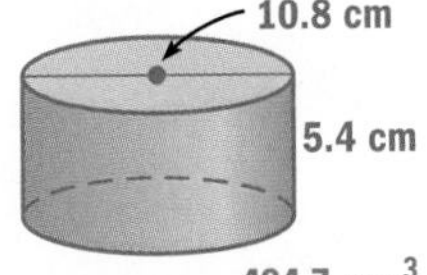

494.7 cm³

29. 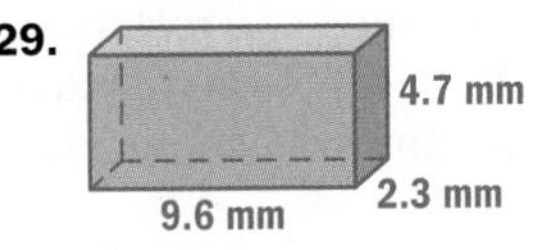

103.8 mm³

30. 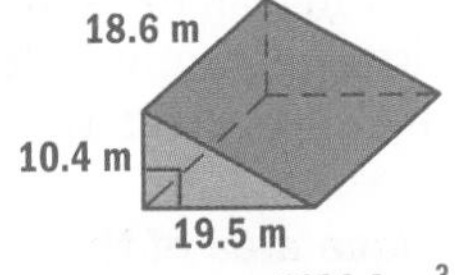

1886.0 m³

31. 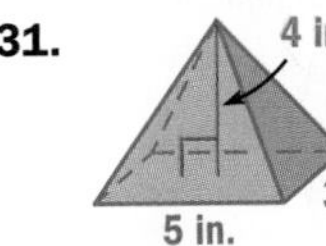

20 in.³

32. 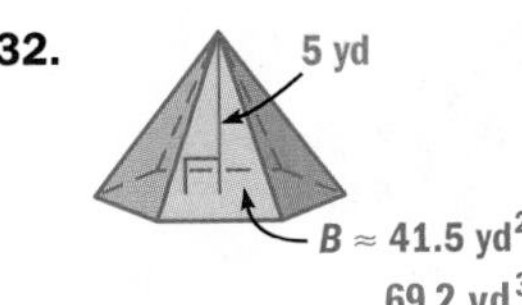

69.2 yd³

33. 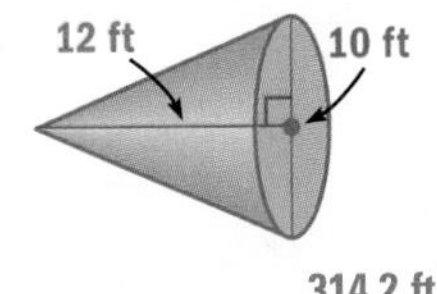

314.2 ft³

34. Containers A cylinder with a radius of 6 centimeters and a height of 7 centimeters has about the same volume as a rectangular prism with a length of 9 centimeters, a width of 8 centimeters, and a height of 11 centimeters. Which container uses less material to hold the same amount? About how much less material? Round to the nearest tenth. *(Lessons 10.4, 10.6)* **the cylinder; 27.9 cm²**

35. Candles You have 12 cubic inches of candle wax. You have a mold for a square pyramid candle that has a base side length of 3 inches and a height of 5 inches. Do you have enough wax to make this candle? Explain. *(Lesson 10.7)* **See margin.**

20. 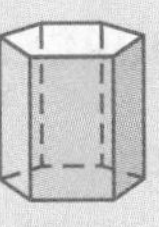

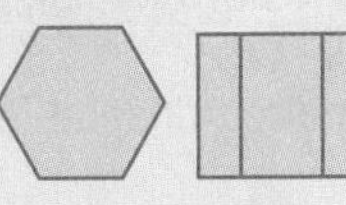

21. ***Sample:***

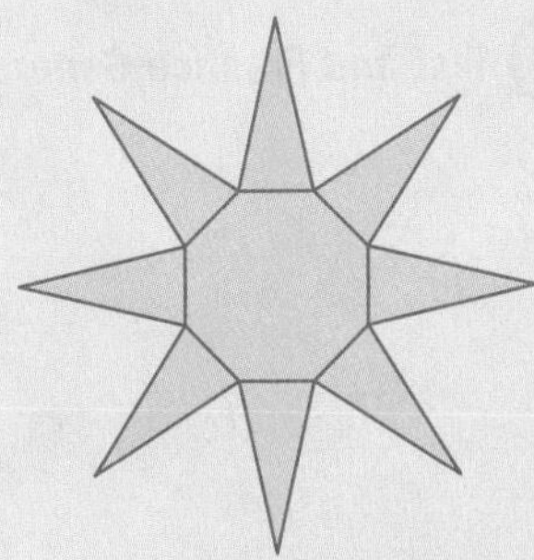

35. No. *Sample answer:* The volume of the pyramid is 15 cubic inches, which is greater than the 12 cubic inches of candle wax.

ADDITIONAL RESOURCES

Assessment Book

- Chapter Test (3 levels), pp. 120–125
- Standardized Chapter Test, p. 126
- Alternative Assessment, pp. 127–128

Test and Practice Generator

Chapter Test

Find the area of the parallelogram or trapezoid.

1. 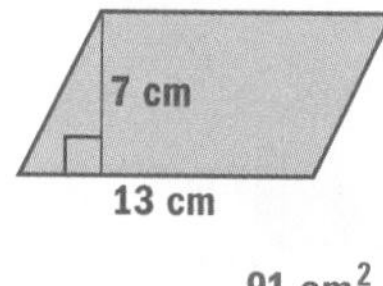

91 cm^2

2. 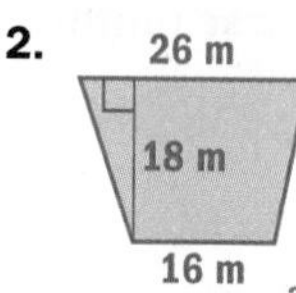

378 m^2

3. 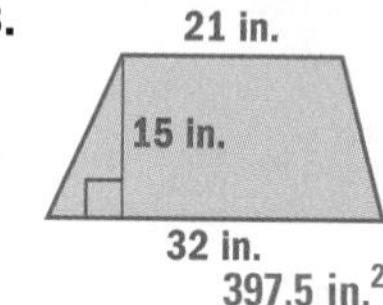

397.5 in.^{2}

Determine the radius of the circle given its area. Use 3.14 for π.

4. $A = 3.7994 \text{ ft}^2$ 1.1 ft

5. $A = 0.785 \text{ m}^2$ 0.5 m

6. $A = 94.985 \text{ yd}^2$ 5.5 yd

Classify the solid. Then tell whether it is a polyhedron.

7. 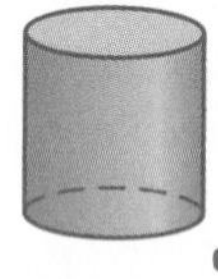
cylinder; no

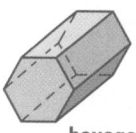

8. 
hexagonal prism; yes

9. 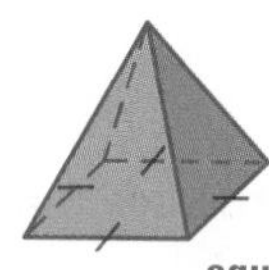
square pyramid; yes

10. Painting You plan to paint the 4 walls and ceiling of a rectangular room with dimensions 15 feet by 12 feet by 8 feet. A can of paint covers 400 square feet. How many cans of paint will you need? 2 cans

Find the surface area of the solid. Round to the nearest tenth.

11. 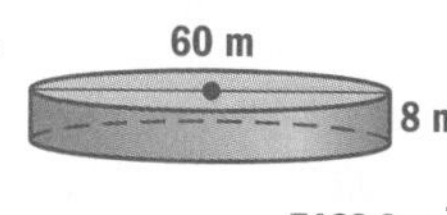

7162.8 m^2

12. 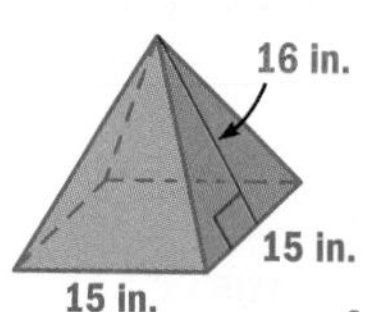

705 in.^{2}

13. 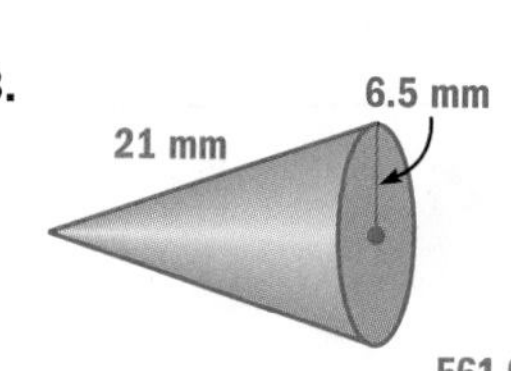

561.6 mm^2

14. Pepperoni A stick of pepperoni is a cylinder, with a radius of 2 centimeters and a length of 12 centimeters. If a slice of pepperoni is 1 cubic centimeter, how many whole slices can be made? 150 slices

Find the volume of the solid. Round to the nearest tenth.

15. 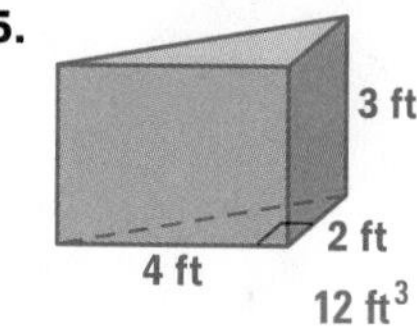

12 ft^3

16. 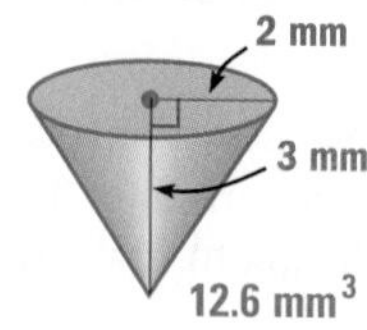

12.6 mm^3

17. 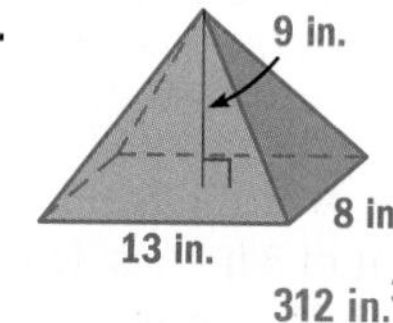

312 in.^{3}

ADDITIONAL RESOURCES

Assessment Book

- Standardized Chapter Test, p. 126

Test and Practice Generator

Chapter Standardized Test

Test-Taking Strategy **Go back and check as many of your answers as you can.**

Multiple Choice

1. A parallelogram has an area of 14 square inches and a base length of 2 inches. What is the height? B

A. 2 in. **B.** 7 in. **C.** 12 in. **D.** 16 in.

2. The diameter of a nickel is 2 centimeters. What is the area of one side of the coin? Use 3.14 for π. F

F. 3.14 cm^2 **G.** 12.56 cm^2

H. 25.12 cm^2 **I.** 50.24 cm^2

3. How many faces does the figure have? C

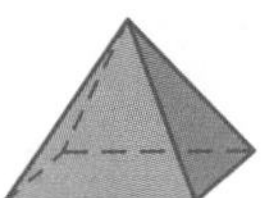

A. 3 **B.** 4 **C.** 5 **D.** 6

4. Which of the following statements is true of the prisms? G

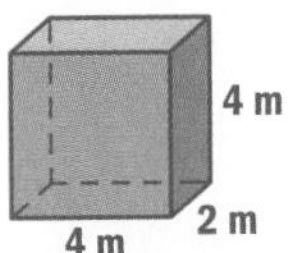

Prism A

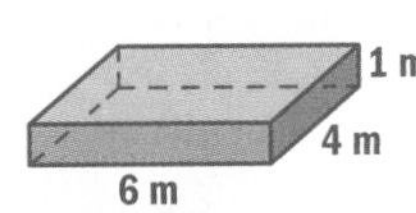

Prism B

F. Prism A has a greater surface area than Prism B.

G. Prism B has a greater surface area than Prism A.

H. Prism A and Prism B have equal surface areas.

I. Prism A and Prism B have equal volumes.

5. What is the surface area of a square pyramid with base side length 6 meters and slant height 10 meters? D

A. 36 m^2 **B.** 42 m^2 **C.** 96 m^2 **D.** 156 m^2

6. A pool has a rectangular base measuring 30 feet by 20 feet and is 12 feet deep. What is the volume of the pool? I

F. 240 ft^3 **G.** 600 ft^3

H. 6000 ft^3 **I.** 7200 ft^3

7. What is the volume of a square pyramid that has a height of 9 feet and a perimeter of 24 feet? C

A. 36 ft^3 **B.** 72 ft^3 **C.** 108 ft^3 **D.** 216 ft^3

8. What is the diameter of a cone with a height of 10 yards and a volume of 92.4 cubic yards? Round to the nearest whole number. G

F. 3 yd **G.** 6 yd **H.** 9 yd **I.** 12 yd

Short Response

9. How does multiplying each dimension by 3 affect the surface area of a cylinder?
The surface area is multiplied by 9.

Extended Response

10. A company is making two types of aluminum containers. One is a cylinder with a height of 1.25 feet and a diameter of 1 foot. The other is a rectangular prism with a length of 0.75 foot, a width of 0.75 foot, and a height of 1 foot. Aluminum costs $.02 per square foot. How much will it cost to produce each type of container? Round to the nearest cent. Which container holds more? **$.11 for the cylinder; $.08 for the prism; the cylinder holds more.**

TEST-TAKING TIP

Encourage students to read the questions thoroughly. Remind them that some information in context-based questions may not be needed when solving the problem.

COMMON ERROR

Students will sometimes make assumptions based on the appearance of a figure that is provided with a question. Emphasize that properties of a figure, such as congruence or parallelism, must be specifically indicated on a figure. For example, two angles of a triangle may appear to be congruent but if they are not marked with matching arcs in the figure, then congruence should not be assumed.

UNIT 3 Chapters 8–10

BUILDING **Test-Taking Skills**

Strategies for Answering

Context-Based Multiple Choice Questions

Some of the information you need to solve a context-based multiple choice question may appear in a table, a diagram, or a graph.

Problem 1

Ali plants a flower garden in a circle around a tree. The outer edge of the garden has twice the radius of the inner edge. Find the area of the flower garden.

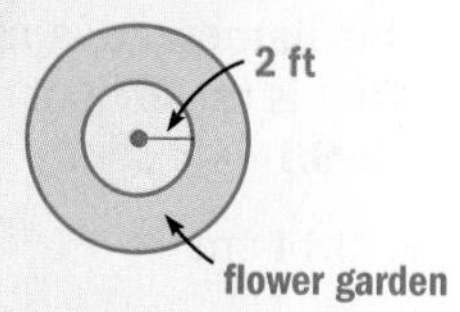

A. 12.56 ft^2 **B.** 25.12 ft^2 **C.** 37.68 ft^2 **D.** 50.24 ft^2

Solution

Read the problem carefully. Decide how you can use the information you are given to solve the problem.

1) You know that the radius of the inner circle is 2 feet and the radius of the outer circle is double the radius of the inner circle, or 4 feet.

Use the areas of both circles to find the area of the garden.

Find the areas of the two circles.

2) Area of inner circle:

radius = 2 ft

$$A = \pi r^2 = \pi \cdot 2^2 = 4\pi$$

Area of outer circle:

radius = 4 ft

$$A = \pi r^2 = \pi \cdot 4^2 = 16\pi$$

Use the areas of the circles to find the area of the garden.

3) Area of garden = Area of outer circle − Area of inner circle

$$A = 16\pi - 4\pi = 12\pi \approx 12 \times 3.14 = 37.68$$

The area of the flower garden is about 37.68 ft^2. The correct answer is C.

Use one of the strategies on pages 156–157.

4) Check to see that the answer is reasonable. Estimate that 16π is about 48 and 4π is about 12. Because $48 - 12 = 36$, C is the most reasonable choice.

Problem 2

Jim walks diagonally across a field. Martha walks along its length and width. The rectangular field is 300 feet wide and 400 feet long. How many feet less does Jim walk than Martha?

F. 1200 feet **G.** 700 feet **H.** 500 feet **I.** 200 feet

Solution

Read the problem carefully. Remember that the field is a rectangle.

1) Use the information in the problem to make a sketch.

Jim's path
300 ft
400 ft

Use the Pythagorean theorem to find the length of Jim's path. Add to find the length of Martha's path.

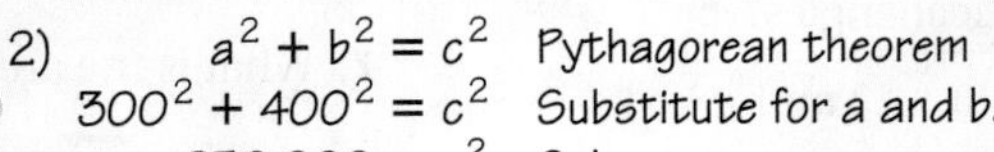

2) $a^2 + b^2 = c^2$ Pythagorean theorem
$300^2 + 400^2 = c^2$ Substitute for a and b.
$250{,}000 = c^2$ Solve.
$500 = c$ Evaluate positive square root.

The length of Jim's path is 500 feet.
The length of Martha's path is 300 + 400 = 700 feet.

Find the difference of the two distances.

3) Martha's distance − Jim's distance
= 700 − 500
= 200

Jim walks 200 feet less than Martha. The correct answer is I.

Your turn now

Watch Out! Be sure that you know what question you are asked to answer. Some choices given may be intended to distract you.

1. In Problem 2, Jim and Martha both walk at the rate of 250 ft/min. How many minutes less does Jim walk than Martha? C

A. 0.2 min **B.** 0.25 min **C.** 0.8 min **D.** 1.25 min

In Exercises 2–3, use the diagram.

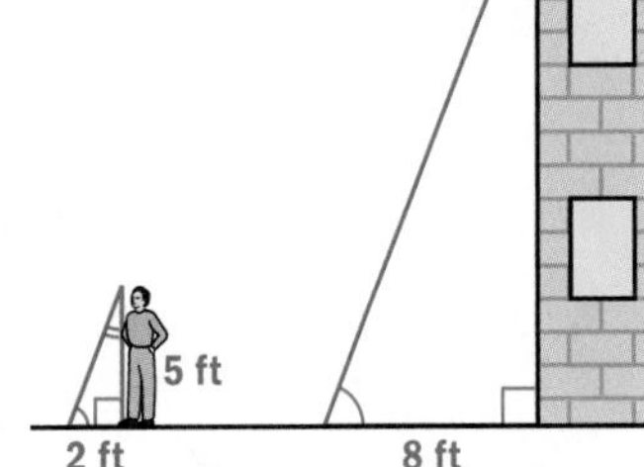

2. What is the height of the building? H

F. 10 feet **G.** 16 feet
H. 20 feet **I.** 40 feet

3. How long will the person's shadow be when the building's shadow is 14 feet long? B

A. 3 feet **B.** 3.5 feet
C. 4 feet **D.** 7 feet

GO ON

UNIT 3 Chapters 8–10

PRACTICING Test-Taking Skills

Multiple Choice

In Exercises 1 and 2, use the diagram below.

1. Which angles are complementary? C

A. ∠1 and ∠2
B. ∠2 and ∠3
C. ∠3 and ∠4
D. ∠1 and ∠4

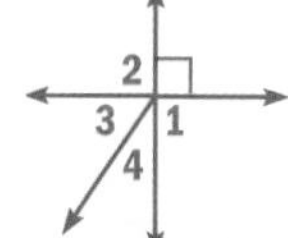

2. Which angles are vertical angles? F

F. ∠1 and ∠2 G. ∠2 and ∠4
H. ∠3 and ∠1 I. ∠1 and ∠3

In Exercises 3 and 4, use the diagram below.

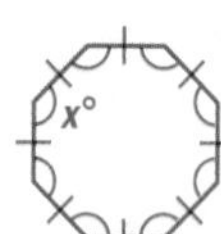

3. What is the value of x? C

A. 45 B. 90 C. 135 D. 360

4. How many lines of symmetry does the figure have? H

F. 1 G. 4 H. 8 I. 16

5. ∠B and ∠A are supplementary. What is m∠B? C

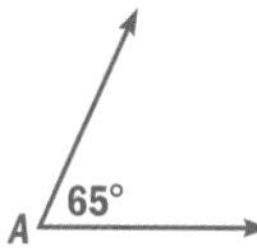

A. 25° B. 35° C. 115° D. 125°

6. Ben has a rectangular garden that is 12 feet long and 5 feet wide. He plants a row of marigolds along the diagonal of the garden. How long is the row of marigolds? G

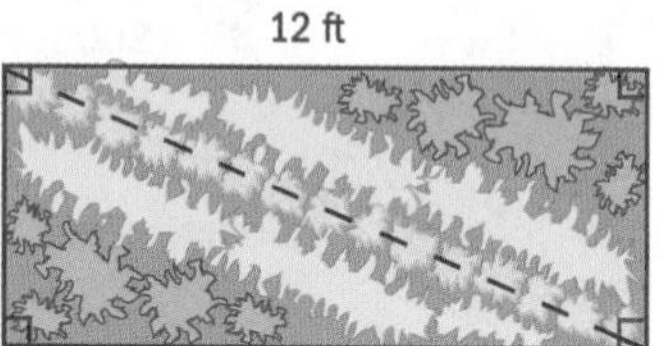

F. 12 ft G. 13 ft H. 14 ft I. 15 ft

7. What is the area of the parallelogram? D

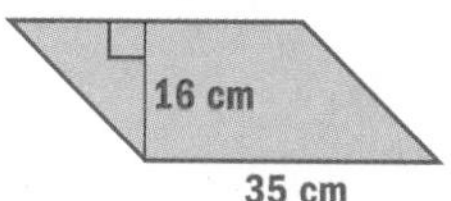

A. 16 cm^2 B. 102 cm^2
C. 280 cm^2 D. 560 cm^2

In Exercises 8 and 9, use the diagram below. The Giant Ocean Tank at the New England Aquarium is a cylinder that is 23 feet deep and 40 feet in diameter.

8. Find the area of the curved wall of the tank. H

F. 920 ft^2 G. 80π ft^2
H. 920π ft^2 I. 1840π ft^2

9. What is the volume of the tank? C

A. 920π ft^3 B. 1720π ft^3
C. 9200π ft^3 D. $18{,}400\pi$ ft^3

Test-Taking Skills

Short Response

10. Find the value of x and explain your steps. See margin.

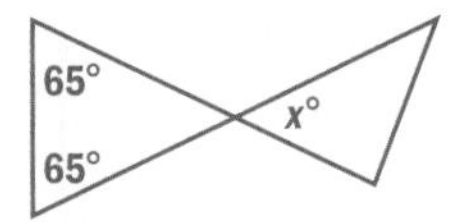

11. An 11 foot ladder leans against a building. The top of the ladder is 7 feet high. How far is the bottom of the ladder from the base of the building? about 8.5 ft

12. Your town purchases a new fire truck with a 100 foot extension ladder. How close can the fire truck come to a building if the ladder is fully extended at an angle of 45°? Draw a diagram and explain how you found your answer. See margin.

13. You stand 15 feet from a flagpole that is perpendicular to the ground. The angle from the point where you stand to the top of the flagpole is 60°. How tall is the flagpole? Explain how you found your answer. See margin.

14. The Inuit people of the Arctic use blocks of snow to build igloos in the shape of a half sphere. An igloo is 15 feet in diameter. Find the area of the igloo's floor to the nearest square foot. 177 ft^2

15. A radio broadcasts to a circular region with an area of 182 square miles. What is the radius of the region? Round your answer to the nearest tenth of a mile. about 7.6 mi

Extended Response

16. A boarding ramp extends down from a dock to a ship. The angle of the ramp to the dock changes with the tide. At high tide, the 10 foot ramp meets the dock at an angle of 12°. At low tide, it meets the dock at an angle of 18°. What is the difference in water level to the nearest foot between high tide and low tide? 1 ft

Draw a diagram and explain how you found your answer. See margin.

17. A high school running track surrounds a field that needs to be watered. Write an equation that you can use to find the area enclosed by the track. Explain your reasoning. See margin.

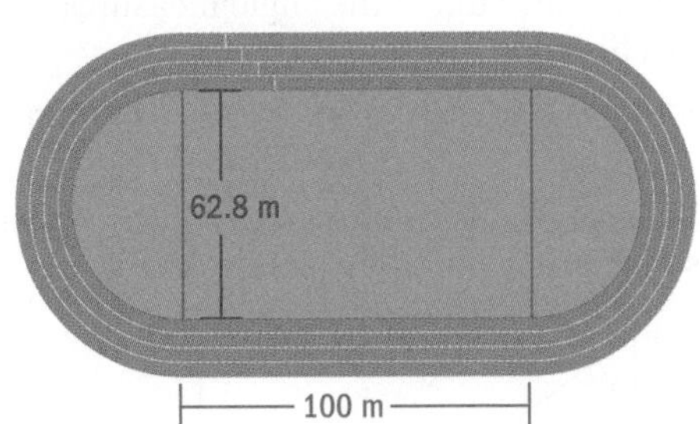

Solve the equation to find the area enclosed by the track. about 9380 ft^2

If you water the field at a rate of about $1\frac{1}{4}$ gallons per square foot, about how much water will be used to water the field? about 11,700 gal

GO ON

10. 50; the measure of the third angle in the triangle on the left is 50°. Since that angle and the angle labeled $x°$ are vertical angles, they are congruent. So $x = 50$.

12. about 70.7 ft;

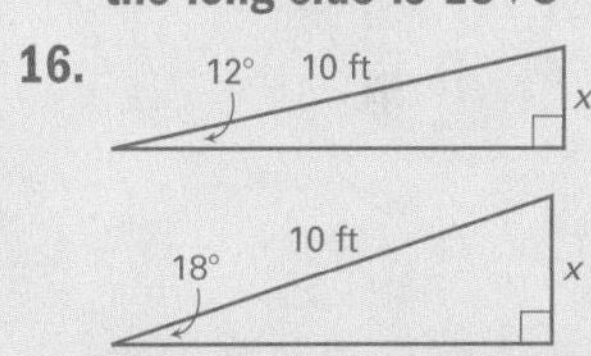

The right triangle formed is a 45°-45°-90° triangle so the legs are $\frac{100}{\sqrt{2}} \approx 70.7$.

13. About 26 ft; the right triangle formed is a 30°-60°-90° triangle. The side given is the short side and the side that needs to be found is the long side, so the long side is $15\sqrt{3} \approx 26$.

16.

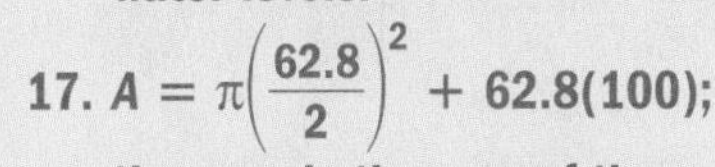

Solve the equation $\sin 12° = \frac{x}{10}$ to find the water level at low tide and $\sin 18° = \frac{x}{10}$ to find the water level at high tide. Then subtract the two water levels.

17. $A = \pi\left(\frac{62.8}{2}\right)^2 + 62.8(100)$; the area is the sum of the areas of the two semicircles on the ends and the area of the rectangle in the middle.

Additional Resources

The following resources are available to help review the materials in this unit:

Chapter Resource Books

- Chapter 8 CRB, Cumulative Practice, pp. 84–85
- Chapter 9 CRB, Cumulative Practice, pp. 67–68
- Chapter 10 CRB, Cumulative Practice, pp. 76–77

Assessment Book

- Unit Test, pp. 129–130
- Cumulative Test, pp. 131–134

8. 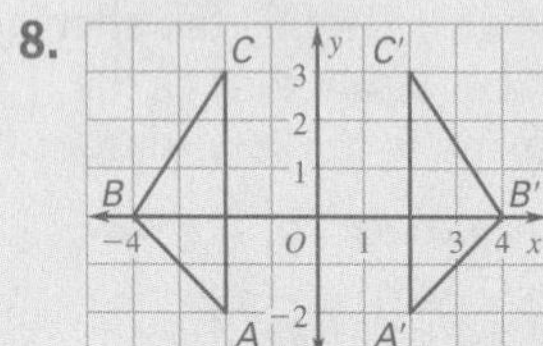

UNIT 3 Chapters 8–10 PRACTICING **Test-Taking Skills**

Cumulative Practice for Chapters 8–10

Chapter 8

Multiple Choice In Exercises 1–7, choose the letter of the correct answer.

1. $\angle 1$ and $\angle 2$ are complementary, and $m\angle 1 = 62°$. What is $m\angle 2$? *(Lesson 8.1)* A

   A. 28° **B.** 38° **C.** 118° **D.** 128°

2. What is the value of x? *(Lesson 8.2)* F

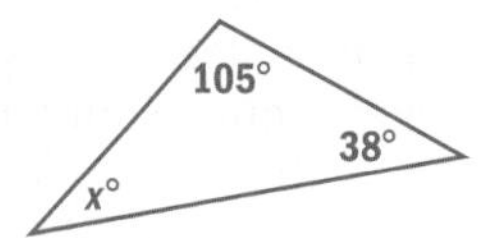

   F. 37 **G.** 67 **H.** 117 **I.** 143

3. Classify the quadrilateral. *(Lesson 8.3)* D

   A. rectangle
   B. rhombus
   C. trapezoid
   D. parallelogram

4. What is the sum of the angle measures in a hexagon? *(Lesson 8.4)* H

   F. 180° **G.** 540° **H.** 720° **I.** 1080°

5. Triangle ABC is congruent to $\triangle EDF$. Which statement is *not* true? *(Lesson 8.5)* C

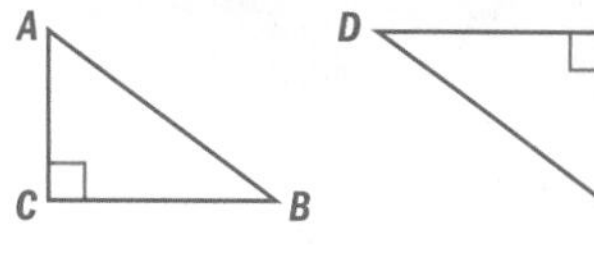

   A. $\overline{AC} \cong \overline{EF}$ **B.** $\overline{CB} \cong \overline{FD}$
   C. $\overline{AB} \cong \overline{DF}$ **D.** $\angle A \cong \angle E$

6. Which transformation is shown? *(Lessons 8.6–8.8)* F

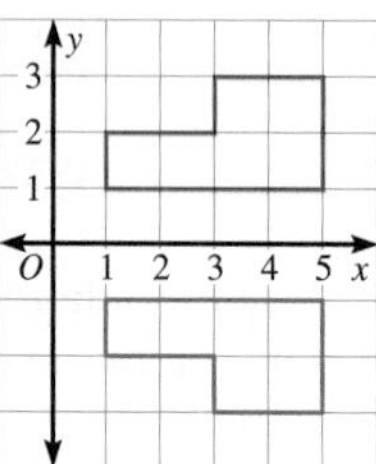

   F. reflection
   G. rotation
   H. translation
   I. dilation

7. You reduce a 20 inch by 36 inch photo to $\frac{1}{4}$ of its original dimensions. What are the new dimensions of the photo? *(Lesson 8.8)* D

   A. 4 inch by 6 inch **B.** 4 inch by 9 inch
   C. 5 inch by 6 inch **D.** 5 inch by 9 inch

8. **Short Response** Triangle ABC has vertices $A(-2, -2)$, $B(-4, 0)$, and $C(-2, 3)$. Reflect $\triangle ABC$ in the y-axis. What are the vertices of the image? *(Lesson 8.6)* **See margin for art; $A'(2, -2)$, $B'(4, 0)$, $C'(2, 3)$**

9. **Extended Response** In baseball and softball, home plate is a pentagon with three right angles and two congruent obtuse angles. *(Lesson 8.4)*

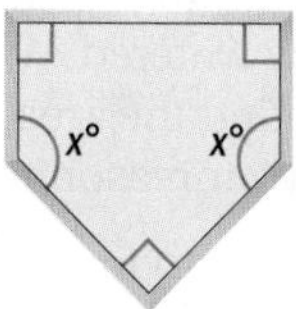

   a. Find the sum of the angle measures of a pentagon. 540°

   b. Write an equation that you can use to find the measure of each obtuse angle. $2x + 270 = 540$

   c. Solve the equation to find the measure of each obtuse angle. 135°

Chapter 9

Multiple Choice In Exercises 10–17, choose the letter of the correct answer.

10. In 1891, Captain Dansey of the British Royal Artillery designed a square kite for rescuing shipwreck victims. The kite has an area of 81 square feet. What are the dimensions of the kite? *(Lesson 9.1)* **B**

A. 3 ft by 3 ft **B.** 9 ft by 9 ft

C. 18 ft by 18 ft **D.** 81 ft by 81 ft

11. What are the values of a in the equation $a^2 - 81 = 115$? *(Lesson 9.1)* **I**

F. $a = \pm 5.8$ **G.** $a = \pm 9$

H. $a = \pm 10.7$ **I.** $a = \pm 14$

12. Which list shows the numbers in order from least to greatest? *(Lesson 9.2)* **B**

A. $2, \sqrt{3}, \sqrt{7}, \sqrt{11}, 5.5$

B. $\sqrt{3}, 2, \sqrt{7}, \sqrt{11}, 5.5$

C. $2, \sqrt{3}, 5.5, \sqrt{7}, \sqrt{11}$

D. $2, \sqrt{3}, \sqrt{7}, 5.5, \sqrt{11}$

13. What is the value of c? *(Lesson 9.3)* **H**

F. 28 feet

G. 39 feet

H. 45 feet

I. 55 feet

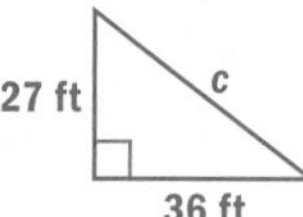

14. The size of a television screen is given by the length of the diagonal of the screen. What size is a television screen that is 28 inches wide and 21 inches high? *(Lesson 9.4)* **C**

A. 24 in. **B.** 32 in. **C.** 35 in. **D.** 40 in.

15. Which set of numbers *is not* a Pythagorean triple? *(Lesson 9.4)* **I**

F. 5, 12, 13 **G.** 9, 40, 41

H. 8, 15, 17 **I.** 6, 24, 25

16. What is the value of x? *(Lesson 9.5)* **B**

A. 7.5 inches

B. 15 inches

C. 21.2 inches

D. 30 inches

17. In $\triangle ABC$, what is $\tan A$? *(Lesson 9.6)* **F**

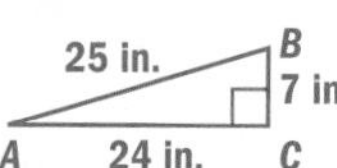

F. $\frac{7}{24}$ **G.** $\frac{7}{25}$ **H.** $\frac{24}{25}$ **I.** $\frac{24}{7}$

18. Short Response Julie designs a wheelchair ramp that reaches a door 2 feet above the ground. The ramp makes an angle of 4.76° with the ground. What is the length of the ramp's base to the nearest foot? Draw a diagram and explain your steps. *(Lesson 9.6)*
See margin.

19. Extended Response A jet takes off at an angle of 15° with the ground. The jet's speed is 300 feet per second. *(Lesson 9.6)*

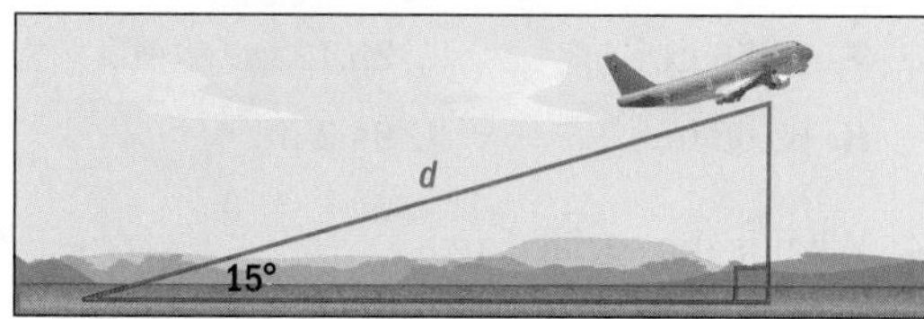

a. How far does the jet travel in 10 seconds? **3000 ft**

b. Find the height of the jet 10 seconds after take off. **about 776 ft**

c. Find the horizontal distance the jet travels after 10 seconds. **about 2898 ft**

18. 24 ft;

4.76°
2 ft
x

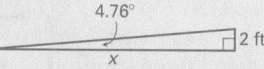

Solve the equation $\tan 4.76° = \frac{2}{x}$ to find the length of the ramp's base.

$\tan 4.76° = \frac{2}{x}$ Use the tangent ratio.

$0.0833 = \frac{2}{x}$ Use a calculator.

$0.0833x = 2$ Multiply each side by x.

$x \approx 24$ Divide each side by 0.0833.

28c. The large container. *Sample answer:* You need to buy three small containers for $6 to equal the amount of popcorn in the large container, which costs $4.

Cumulative Practice continued

Chapter 10

Multiple Choice In Exercises 20–26, choose the letter of the correct answer.

20. What is the area of the trapezoid? *(Lesson 10.1)* B

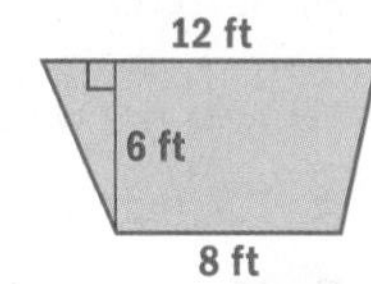

A. 48 ft^2 **B.** 60 ft^2 **C.** 72 ft^2 **D.** 120 ft^2

21. What is the area of the circle? Use 3.14 for π. *(Lesson 10.2)* H

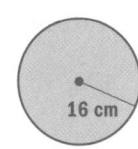

16 cm

F. 50.24 cm^2 **G.** 256 cm^2
H. 803.84 cm^2 **I.** 4096 cm^2

22. Identify the solid. *(Lesson 10.3)* A

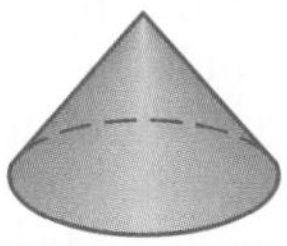

A. cone
B. cylinder
C. pyramid
D. triangular prism

23. What is the approximate surface area of the cylinder? *(Lesson 10.4)* I

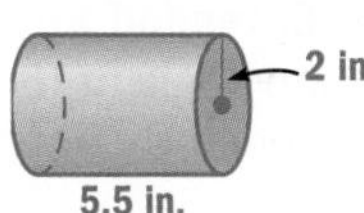

F. 12.56 $in.^2$ **G.** 25.12 $in.^2$
H. 69.08 $in.^2$ **I.** 94.2 $in.^2$

24. What is the surface area of the square pyramid? *(Lesson 10.5)* C

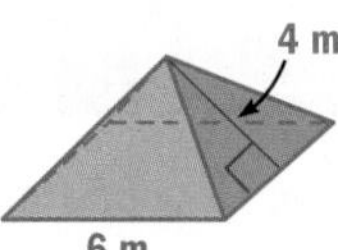

A. 36 m^2 **B.** 48 m^2
C. 84 m^2 **D.** 132 m^2

25. What is the volume of the prism? *(Lesson 10.6)* I

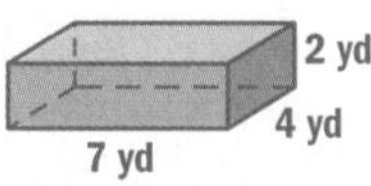

F. 8 yd^2 **G.** 14 yd^2 **H.** 28 yd^3 **I.** 56 yd^3

26. What is the approximate volume of the cone? B *(Lesson 10.7)*

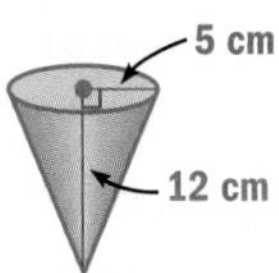

A. 78.5 cm^3 **B.** 314 cm^3
C. 753.6 cm^3 **D.** 942 cm^3

27. Short Response Identify the solid. Then count the number of faces, edges, and vertices. *(Lesson 10.3)* Triangular prism; 5 faces, 9 edges, 6 vertices

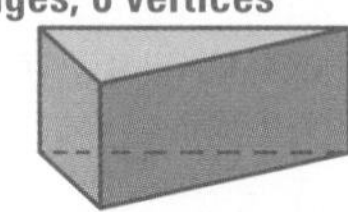

28. Extended Response A movie theater serves a small size of popcorn in a conical container and a large size of popcorn in a cylindrical container. *(Lessons 10.6, 10.7)*

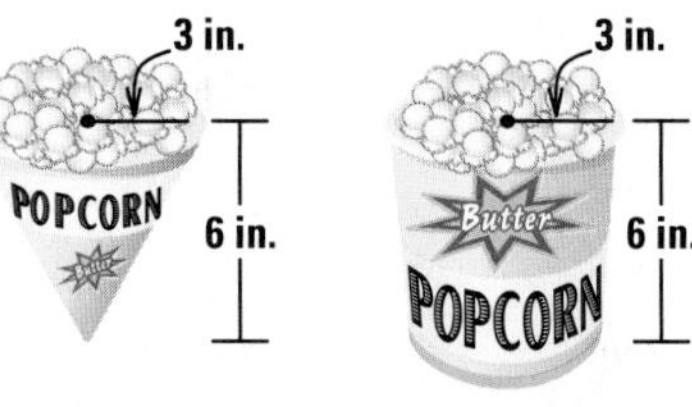

a. What is the volume of the small container? about 57 $in.^3$

b. What is the volume of the large container? about 170 $in.^3$

c. Which container gives you more popcorn for your money? Explain your reasoning? See margin.

Advanced Algebra Topics

Chapter 11 Linear Equations and Graphs

- Write and use functions to predict outcomes.
- Write and solve equations and inequalities.
- Write, evaluate, and graph functions.

Chapter 12 Data Analysis and Probability

- Make and interpret data displays. Choose an appropriate display for a data set.
- Use tree diagrams, the counting principle, and permutations and combinations to solve problems.
- Find probabilities of independent and dependent events.

Chapter 13 Polynomials and Functions

- Simplify and evaluate expressions using exponents.
- Evaluate and graph non-linear equations.

From Chapter 13, p. 679
How many e-mail jokes are sent?

Unit Resources

These resources are provided to help you prepare for the unit and to customize review materials:

 ***Chapter Resource Books***
- Chapter 11
- Chapter 12
- Chapter 13

 ***Assessment Book***
- Chapters 11–13, pp. 135–173

 ***Technology***
- EasyPlanner CD-ROM
- Test and Practice Generator
- Electronic Lesson Presentations CD-ROM
- eTutorial CD-ROM

 ***Internet***
- Classzone
- eEdition Plus Online
- eWorkbook Plus Online
- eTutorial Plus Online
- EasyPlanner Plus Online

English Learner Support

- Spanish Study Guide
- Multi-Language Glossary
- Chapter Audio Summaries CDs
- Teacher's Edition
  Chapter 11, pp. 538E–538F
  Chapter 12, pp. 594E–594F
  Chapter 13, pp. 654E–654F

Pacing and Assignment Guide

REGULAR SCHEDULE

Lesson	Les. Day	BASIC	AVERAGE	ADVANCED
11.1	Day 1	pp. 543-544 Exs. 9-18, 20-22, 25-28	pp. 543-544 Exs. 10-23, 25-29	pp. 543-544 Exs. 10-14, 17-29*
11.2	Day 1	SRH p. 725 Exs. 1-3; pp. 547-548 Exs. 3-12, 15-25	pp. 547-548 Exs. 5-13, 15-26	pp. 547-548 Exs. 5-20, 24-26, EC: TE p. 538D*
11.3	Day 1	pp. 551-553 Exs. 7-15, 19-22, 31-33, 43-45, 51	pp. 551-553 Exs. 9-15, 19-22, 31-33, 42-47	pp. 551-553 Exs. 9-15, 19-22, 33-39, 50
	Day 2	pp. 551-553 Exs. 16-18, 23-29, 34-38, 46-49	pp. 551-553 Exs. 16-18, 23-29, 34-40, 48-51	pp. 551-553 Exs. 16-18, 23-30, 40-46*, 51
11.4	Day 1	pp. 559-560 Exs. 8-10, 17-22, 30-32, 41-46	pp. 559-560 Exs. 8-10, 17-22, 33-39, 48-50	pp. 559-560 Exs. 8-10, 17-22, 33-39, 48-50
	Day 2	pp. 559-560 Exs. 11-16, 23-28, 33-37, 47-49	pp. 559-560 Exs. 11-16, 23-29, 41-47	pp. 559-560 Exs. 11-16, 23-29, 40-45*
11.5	Day 1	pp. 566-567 Exs. 5-10, 16-18, 30-33	pp. 566-567 Exs. 5-10, 16-21, 30-32	pp. 566-567 Exs. 8-10, 15-18, 25-31
	Day 2	pp. 566-567 Exs. 11-14, 19-24, 34-36	pp. 566-567 Exs. 11-15, 25-28, 33-37	pp. 566-567 Exs. 11-14, 22-24, 32-37, EC: TE p. 538D*
11.6	Day 1	pp. 573-574 Exs. 10, 11, 13-15, 28, 36-42	pp. 573-574 Exs. 10, 13-15, 27-30, 40-44	pp. 573-574 Exs. 10, 13-15, 27-32*, 42-44
	Day 2	pp. 573-574 Exs. 12, 16-26, 35, 43	pp. 573-574 Exs. 12, 19-26, 35-39	pp. 573-574 Exs. 12, 19-26, 33-37*
11.7	Day 1	pp. 579-580 Exs. 9-14, 22, 28-31	pp. 579-580 Exs. 9-14, 23-26, 33-35	pp. 579-580 Exs. 9-14, 24-27*, 33-35
	Day 2	pp. 579-580 Exs. 15-21, 23, 32-35	pp. 579-580 Exs. 15-22, 28-32	pp. 579-580 Exs. 15-22, 28-32
11.8	Day 1	pp. 586-587 Exs. 11-14, 23-28, 38-41	pp. 586-587 Exs. 11-15, 26-31, 38-40	pp. 586-587 Exs. 11-15, 26-31, 38-40
	Day 2	pp. 586-587 Exs. 16-22, 32-34, 42-44	pp. 586-587 Exs. 16-22, 32-36, 43-45	pp. 586-587 Exs. 16-22, 32-37*, 44, 45
Review	Day 1	pp. 590-591 Exs. 1-26	pp. 590-591 Exs. 1-26	pp. 590-591 Exs. 1-26
Assess	Day 1	Chapter 11 Test	Chapter 11 Test	Chapter 11 Test

YEARLY PACING Chapter 11 Total – **16 days** Chapters 1-11 Total – **132 days** Remaining – **28 days**

*Challenge Exercises EP = Extra Practice SRH = Skills Review Handbook EC = Extra Challenge

BLOCK SCHEDULE

DAY 1	DAY 2	DAY 3	DAY 4	DAY 5	DAY 6	DAY 7	DAY 8
11.1 pp. 543-544 Exs. 10-23, 25-29 **11.2** pp. 547-548 Exs. 5-13, 15-26	**11.3** pp. 551-553 Exs. 9-29, 31-40, 42-51	**11.4** pp. 559-560 Exs. 8-29, 33-39, 41-50	**11.5** pp. 566-567 Exs. 5-21, 25-28, 30-37	**11.6** pp. 573-574 Exs. 10, 12-15, 19-30, 35-44	**11.7** pp. 579-580 Exs. 9-26, 28-35	**11.8** pp. 586-587 Exs. 11-22, 26-36, 38-40, 43-45	**Review** pp. 590-591 Exs. 1-26 **Assess** Chapter 11 Test

YEARLY PACING Chapter 11 Total – **8 days** Chapters 1-11 Total – **66 days** Remaining – **14 days**

Support Materials

CHAPTER RESOURCE BOOK

CHAPTER SUPPORT			
Tips for New Teachers	p. 1	Parents as Partners	p. 3

LESSON SUPPORT	11.1	11.2	11.3	11.4	11.5	11.6	11.7	11.8
Lesson Plans (regular and block)	p. 6	p. 14	p. 25	p. 35	p. 44	p. 52	p. 60	p. 68
Technology Activities & Keystrokes		p. 16		p. 37				
Activity Support Masters								
Activity Masters			p. 27					
Practice (3 levels)	p. 8	p. 18	p. 28	p. 38	p. 46	p. 54	p. 62	p. 70
Study Guide	p. 11	p. 21	p. 31	p. 41	p. 49	p. 57	p. 65	p. 73
Real-World Problem Solving		p. 23	p. 33					
Challenge Practice	p. 13	p. 24	p. 34	p. 43	p. 51	p. 59	p. 67	p. 75

REVIEW			
Games Support Masters	p. 5	Cooperative Project with Rubric	p. 79
Chapter Review Games and Activities	p. 76	Extra Credit Project with Rubric	p. 81
Cooperative Project with Rubric	p. 77	Cumulative Practice	p. 83
		Resource Book Answers	A1

ASSESSMENT

Quizzes	p. 135	Alternative Assessments with Rubrics	p. 144
Chapter Tests (3 levels)	p. 137	Unit Test	p. 168
Standardized Test	p. 143	Cumulative Test	p. 170

TRANSPARENCIES

	11.1	11.2	11.3	11.4	11.5	11.6	11.7	11.8
Warm-Up / Daily Homework Quiz	✔	✔	✔	✔	✔	✔	✔	✔
Notetaking Guide	✔	✔	✔	✔	✔	✔	✔	✔
Teacher Support	✔	✔	✔	✔	✔	✔	✔	✔
English/Spanish Problem Solving	✔		✔	✔	✔		✔	✔
Answer Transparencies	✔	✔	✔	✔	✔	✔	✔	✔

TECHNOLOGY

- EasyPlanner CD-ROM
- Test and Practice Generator
- Electronic Lesson Presentations
- eTutorial CD-ROM
- Chapter Audio Summaries CDs
- Classzone.com
- eEdition Plus Online
- eWorkbook Plus Online
- eTutorial Plus Online
- EasyPlanner Plus Online

ADDITIONAL RESOURCES

- Worked-Out Solution Key
- Notetaking Guide
- Practice Workbook
- Tutor Place
- Professional Development Book
- Special Activities Book
- Posters
- Spanish Study Guide
- Exercises in Spanish
- English/Spanish Ch. Reviews/Tests
- Multi-Language Visual Glossary

Math Background and Teaching Strategies

Lesson 11.1

MATH BACKGROUND

A **relation** is any set of ordered pairs. The y-coordinates, which form the **range** of the relation, are often related to the x-coordinates, which form the **domain** of the relation, by a rule for which the x-coordinates are the **inputs** and the y-coordinates are the **outputs**. If the rule assigns each element of the domain of a relation to exactly one number in the range, the relation is a **function**.

TEACHING STRATEGIES

Present the table below to students.

Vehicle	Axles	Wheels	Lug nuts
car	2	4	16
heavy pick-up	2	6	24
car pulling boat	4	8	32
tractor/trailer rig	5	18	72

Ask whether the relations (axles, wheels) and (wheels, lug nuts) represent functions. In the first case, the answer is "no." Because 2 is paired with 4 and 6, there is no rule for which inputting the number of axles guarantees a single output for the number of wheels. In the second case, the answer is "yes." For each number of wheels, the rule "multiply by 4" gives a unique number of lug nuts.

Lesson 11.2

MATH BACKGROUND

A **scatter plot** is a graph of a set of ordered pairs. If the y-coordinates of the points tend to increase as the x-coordinates increase, the plot indicates a *positive relationship* between x and y. If the y-coordinates tend to decrease as the x-coordinates increase, the plot indicates a *negative relationship*. If there is no pattern between the coordinates, the plot indicates *no relationship* between x and y.

TEACHING STRATEGIES

Have students brainstorm examples of quantities that might show a positive relationship, a negative relationship, or no relationship. Following are some samples.

positive: fuel use and distance driven, height and weight, temperature at a soccer game and amount of water players drink

negative: distance to an object and apparent size, altitude and temperature, volume of boxes and number that will fit in a closet

no relationship: grades and shoe size in a class, minutes until next Old Faithful eruption and number of tourists in Yellowstone Park

Lesson 11.3

MATH BACKGROUND

TWO-VARIABLE EQUATIONS A linear equation in one variable, such as $2x + 4 = -3x - 6$, has a single solution except in the case of an identity or contradiction. A linear equation in two variables, such as $2x - y = -1$, has infinitely many solutions, which can be seen by writing the equation in function form, in this case $y = 2x + 1$. For any value of x that is chosen, there is a corresponding value of y. The solutions of this equation are the ordered pairs $(x, 2x + 1)$.

TEACHING STRATEGIES

In this lesson, students must change their mindset from looking for *the* value that makes an equation true to a situation in which there are *infinitely* many solutions to an equation. Stress the importance of the function form of an equation, since students can see that it gives a rule for taking *any* input value and assigning to it an output value. Students may need to review using the addition and multiplication properties of equality.

Lesson 11.4

MATH BACKGROUND

GRAPHING The equations in Lesson 11.3 were all **linear equations** in two variables. The graphs of the ordered pairs that satisfy a linear equation all lie along a line, and *every* ordered pair corresponding to a point on the line satisfies the equation. The graph of $y = a$ is a horizontal line through $(0, a)$; the graph of $x = b$ is a vertical line through $(b, 0)$.

TEACHING STRATEGIES

Encourage students to plot at least three points when graphing a linear equation to provide a check on their work. Make sure students understand why the graph of $y = 4$ represents a function, while that of $x = 4$ does not. Also make sure students understand why the graph of $x = 4$ is a *vertical* line when the x-axis is *horizontal*, and why the graph of $y = 4$ is a *horizontal* line when the y-axis is *vertical*.

Lesson 11.5

MATH BACKGROUND

GRAPHING WITH INTERCEPTS Because two points determine a line, a quick way to graph a nonvertical/nonhorizontal line, especially when its equation is in the form $ax + by = c$, is to plot the **x-intercept**, the x-coordinate of the point where the line crosses the x-axis, and the **y-intercept**, the y-coordinate of the point where the line crosses the y-axis. To find the y-intercept, substitute 0 for x and solve for y. To find the x-intercept, substitute 0 for y and solve for x.

TEACHING STRATEGIES

Students often confuse for which variable to substitute 0 to find which intercept. You may want to tell them at first just to make sure they substitute 0 for each variable in turn and solve for the other. For example, in $2x + 3y = 6$, setting $x = 0$ and solving gives $y = 2$; setting $y = 0$ and solving gives $x = 3$. So, the points (0, 2) and (3, 0) are on the graph. Point out that this method is especially useful for linear equations not in function form. For equations in function form, students can substitute 0 for x to find the y-intercept, then find a second ordered pair by substituting any other value for x.

Lesson 11.6

MATH BACKGROUND

The importance of **slope** lies in its interpretation as a rate of change. The slope of a line representing a linear equation is constant, and is just the ratio of the differences $y_2 - y_1$ and $x_2 - x_1$ for any two points (x_1, y_1) and (x_2, y_2) that lie on the line. The slope of a horizontal line is 0, since the numerator of the slope ratio is always 0, and the slope of a vertical line cannot be defined, since the denominator of the slope ratio is always 0. In differential calculus, the idea of slope is extended to finding rates of change for curves at given points.

TEACHING STRATEGIES

Emphasize that the slope formula expresses how much the y-coordinate of a line changes for a given change in its x-coordinates. This relates to rate problems. For example, weighing out 5 pounds of oranges and paying $4.75 is equivalent to the unit rate $.95 per pound, which expresses a change of cost of $.95 for each 1 pound increase in weight.

Lesson 11.7

MATH BACKGROUND

GRAPHING WITH SLOPE By writing a linear equation in two variables in *slope-intercept form*, $y = mx + b$, it can be graphed without any computation because b will be the y-intercept and m the slope. So, you can plot $(0, b)$ and then use the slope to locate a second point on the graph.

TEACHING STRATEGIES

Students must be able to apply the slope of a line correctly once they have plotted the y-intercept. Have students graph $y = 2x + 2$, $y = -2x + 2$, $y = \frac{1}{2}x + 2$, and $y = -\frac{1}{2}x + 2$ on the same coordinate plane. They will begin by plotting (0, 2), the common point of the graphs. Make sure students can identify the proper rise and run to count off on the graph.

Lesson 11.8

MATH BACKGROUND

The graph of a linear inequality in *one* variable is a ray whose *endpoint*, which may (≤, ≥) or may not (<, >) be included in the graph, divides the *number line* into two halves. The graph of a linear inequality in *two* variables is a **half-plane** whose *boundary line*, which may (≤, ≥) or may not (<, >) be included in the graph, divides the *coordinate plane* into two halves.

TEACHING STRATEGIES

It can help students deepen their understanding to learn the "above or below" method for deciding which half-plane to shade. For a horizontal line, this is simple, since, for example, "$y >$" clearly indicates to shade above a value. For an inequality whose boundary line has a steep slope, such as $y > 3x$, this may be less clear to students, but help them see that *for any given value* of x, the y-values above the graph of the boundary are greater than those below the boundary.

Differentiating Instruction

Strategies for Underachievers

FOCUS ON VOCABULARY

In Lesson 11.1, it is imperative that students learn and feel comfortable with the terms *input, output, relation, function, domain,* and *range.* You may wish to have underachieving students develop note cards with the definition of each term along with examples of the term. The card for the term *function* should include examples of relations that are functions as well as relations that are not functions. Additionally, this card should compare relations that match two or more inputs with the same output (function) to relations that match two or more outputs with the same input (not a function). Make sure that students understand that all functions are also relations, while some relations are not functions. Having students include a Venn diagram like the one below with their cards may help.

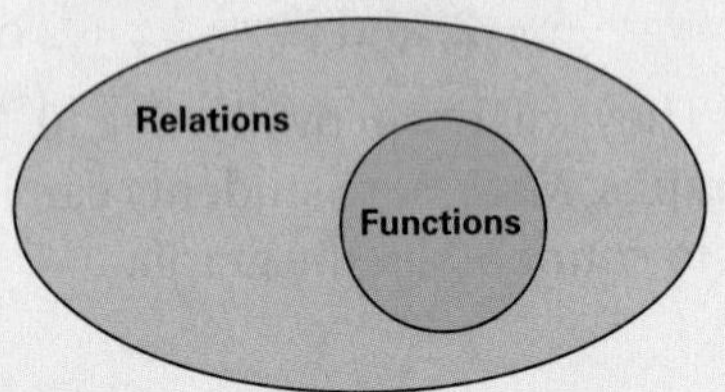

USE TECHNOLOGY

In conjunction with Lessons 11.4–11.6, it can be very helpful for underachievers to have access or at least exposure to using technology for graphing linear equations in two variables. Often, computer operating systems include applications, perhaps a "graphing calculator" program, that allow you to enter an equation in either standard or function form and then view its graph. If students are allowed to change one parameter of an equation at a time, such as slope, it can help them greatly in understanding the role of the parameter. If your students have any familiarity with graphing calculators, they can also use them to graph lines, though students will have to enter equations in function form. Also, students at this level should not graph any lines whose graphs fall outside the standard viewing window. Note that graphing calculators also have the ability to make tables of values for functions.

USE SCAFFOLDING

SCATTER PLOTS In Lesson 11.2, you may wish to provide some underachievers with graph paper with coordinate axes and scales already on them for a few examples until they become comfortable plotting points using the different scales. Then, you can introduce them to the concept of choosing appropriate scales, including when it might be appropriate to use a "broken" scale that does not start at 0, such as for Exercises 6 and 7 on page 547.

In Lesson 11.3, solving linear equations for *y*, especially when involving fractions, may be difficult for underachievers. At the start, make sure that these students work solely with equations that are already solved for *y* until they are confident. Then, you may wish to provide students with a reference sheet to give examples that serve as templates for their work with equations that are not solved for *y*. The reference sheet should address the various situations in which the variables are on one side or the other or both, in which terms are positive or negative, and in which fractions are or are not involved. The reference sheet should have a step-by-step solution worked out for each sample equation.

In Lesson 11.5, you may wish to provide for students (or have students create) note cards that illustrate the step-by-step process of graphing a line using intercepts. These cards should contain several examples that involve a variety of sign combinations.

SLOPE In Lesson 11.6, you may wish to have underachievers make a set of reference note cards corresponding to the "Summary of Slope" table at the top of page 572. For each type of slope shown, students should have a line drawn with two points marked on it. Students should show the numerical calculation involved in finding the slope for each line shown. Have students pay particular attention to the case of the vertical line, where an attempt at the calculation of slope will cause division by zero, which is undefined.

Strategies for English Learners

PRETEACH VOCABULARY

Introduce the students to more difficult verbs that they will find in texts and on tests. Examples of these types of verbs are listed in the following chart. Which of these words may be used as a noun or a verb, and which ones require a new suffix to change the verb to a noun? You can use a chart to show the verb and noun forms of each.

Verb	Noun
apply	application
assume	assumption
conclude	conclusion
define	definition
demonstrate	demonstration
display	display
generalize	generalization
graph	graph
investigate	investigation
model	model
plot	plot
predict	prediction
solve	solution
substitute	substitution
summarize	summary
observe	observation
prove	proof

Strategies for Advanced Learners

INVESTIGATE REAL-WORLD APPLICATIONS

In conjunction with Lesson 11.6, you may wish to challenge some advanced students to consider and report on the applications of slope in the real world. One example might be the importance of slope with regard to the aesthetics and functionality of stairs in architecture. Other applications might include the importance of the concept of slope in road building, handicapped-access ramps, designing and building roofs, and rating ski and snowboard trails in terms of difficulty at a ski resort. Students should explain the connection of other measures of steepness, such as percent grade and pitch (in regard to roofs) to the mathematical definition of slope. Students might also want to investigate the use of the word *slope* in relation to the golf handicap system, and what, if any, relationship it has to the concept of slope introduced in the lesson. One resource for the use of slope in golf is the web site http://www.usga.org/handicap.

Here is an activity to use in conjunction with **Lesson 11.2.**

- **Challenge** Have students find examples of and make scatter plots of data that exhibit a positive relationship, a negative relationship, and no relationship. Have students give their qualitative evaluation of the positive and negative relationships as to whether the relationships are very strong or more modest. Also, have students present their hypotheses of why the related data show the relationship that they do. For example, does a change in one data measure cause a change in the other, or are changes in both measures caused by some outside influence that is not indicated? Check work.

The following problems, the first of which can be used with **Lesson 11.5**, and the second of which can be used with **Lesson 11.7**, investigate the general form of a linear equation in two variables.

- **Challenge** The *general form* of a linear equation in two variables is $Ax + By = C$, where A, B, and C are real numbers and A and B are not both equal to 0. Use the general form to find expressions for the x-intercept and the y-intercept of a linear equation in two variables.
  x-intercept: $\frac{C}{A}$, y-intercept: $\frac{C}{B}$

- **Challenge** Use the general form of a linear equation in two variables to write an equation for the function form of the linear equation. $y = -\frac{A}{B}x + \frac{C}{B}$

Differentiating Instruction: Teaching Resources

Differentiating Review, Reteaching, and Remediation

McDougal Littell *Middle School Mathematics* offers teachers a wide variety of reteaching and remediation resources. Pictured here are facsimiles of various pages from the *Notetaking Guide*, the Study Guide pages from the *Chapter 11 Resource Book*, and remediation cards from *Tutor Place*.

NOTETAKING GUIDE

The *Notetaking Guide* easily allows students to take notes on and review each lesson in the textbook by using guided examples and Your Turn Now exercises. The *Notetaking Guide* is available on transparencies also.

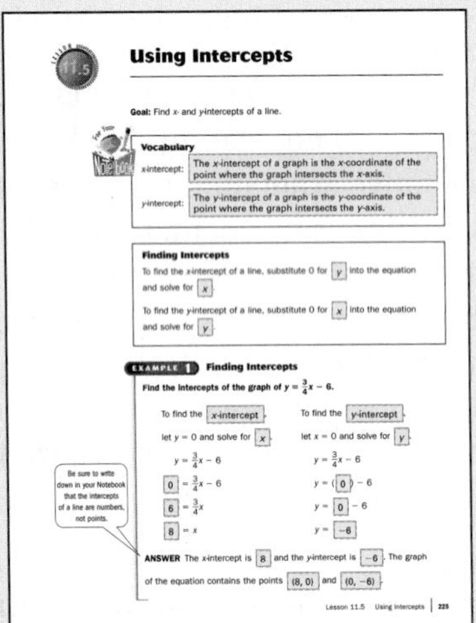

11.5 **Using Intercepts**

Goal: Find x- and y-intercepts of a line.

Vocabulary

x-intercept: The x-intercept of a graph is the x-coordinate of the point where the graph intersects the x-axis.

y-intercept: The y-intercept of a graph is the y-coordinate of the point where the graph intersects the y-axis.

Finding Intercepts

To find the x-intercept of a line, substitute 0 for y into the equation and solve for x.

To find the y-intercept of a line, substitute 0 for x into the equation and solve for y.

EXAMPLE 1 Finding Intercepts

Find the intercepts of the graph of $y = \frac{3}{4}x - 6$.

To find the x-intercept, let $y = 0$ and solve for x.	To find the y-intercept, let $x = 0$ and solve for y.
$y = \frac{3}{4}x - 6$	$y = \frac{3}{4}x - 6$
$0 = \frac{3}{4}x - 6$	$y = \frac{3}{4}(0) - 6$
$6 = \frac{3}{4}x$	$y = 0 - 6$
$8 = x$	$y = -6$

Be sure to write down in your Notebook that the intercepts of a line are numbers, not points.

ANSWER The x-intercept is 8 and the y-intercept is −6. The graph of the equation contains the points (8, 0) and (0, −6).

Lesson 11.5 Using Intercepts | 225

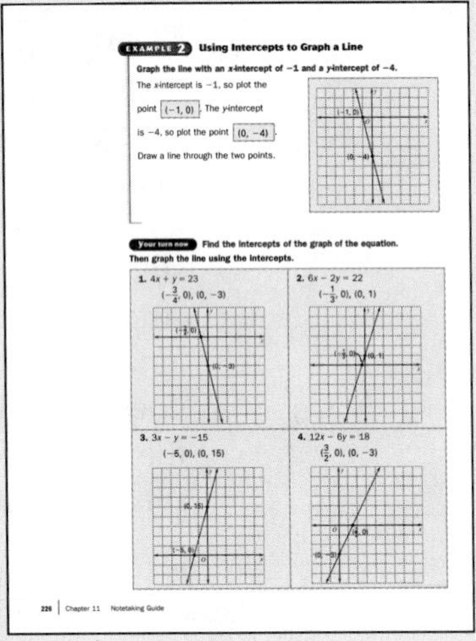

EXAMPLE 2 Using Intercepts to Graph a Line

Graph the line with an x-intercept of −1 and a y-intercept of −4.

The x-intercept is −1, so plot the point (−1, 0). The y-intercept is −4, so plot the point (0, −4).

Draw a line through the two points.

Your turn now **Find the intercepts of the graph of the equation. Then graph the line using the intercepts.**

1. $4x + y = 23$ — $(-\frac{3}{4}, 0)$, (0, −3)
2. $6x - 2y = 22$ — $(-\frac{1}{3}, 0)$, (0, 1)
3. $3x - y = -15$ — (−5, 0), (0, 15)
4. $12x - 6y = 18$ — $(\frac{3}{2}, 0)$, (0, −3)

226 | Chapter 11 Notetaking Guide

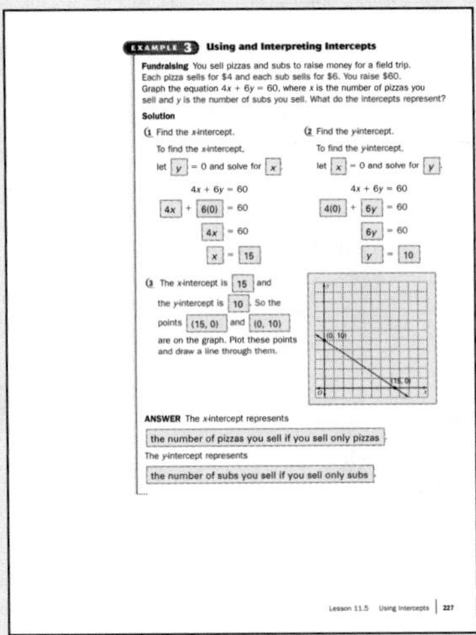

EXAMPLE 3 Using and Interpreting Intercepts

Fundraising You sell pizzas and subs to raise money for a field trip. Each pizza sells for $4 and each sub sells for $6. You raise $60. Graph the equation $4x + 6y = 60$, where x is the number of pizzas you sell and y is the number of subs you sell. What do the intercepts represent?

Solution

1. Find the x-intercept. To find the x-intercept, let y = 0 and solve for x.
$4x + 6y = 60$
$4x + 6(0) = 60$
$4x = 60$
$x = 15$
2. Find the y-intercept. To find the y-intercept, let x = 0 and solve for y.
$4x + 6y = 60$
$4(0) + 6y = 60$
$6y = 60$
$y = 10$
3. The x-intercept is 15 and the y-intercept is 10. So the points (15, 0) and (0, 10) are on the graph. Plot these points and draw a line through them.

ANSWER The x-intercept represents the number of pizzas you sell if you sell only pizzas. The y-intercept represents the number of subs you sell if you sell only subs.

Lesson 11.5 Using Intercepts | 227

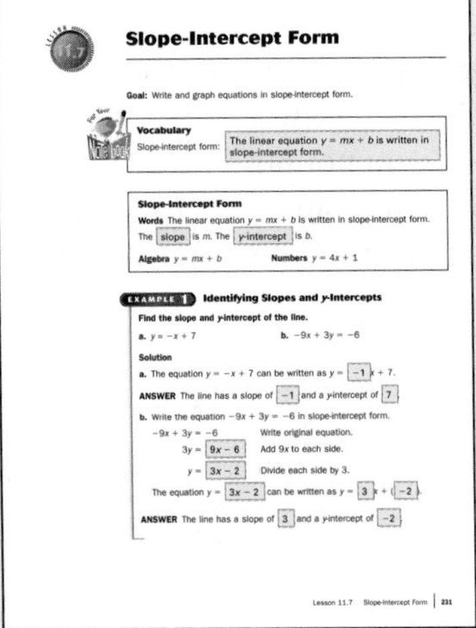

11.7 **Slope-Intercept Form**

Goal: Write and graph equations in slope-intercept form.

Vocabulary

Slope-intercept form: The linear equation $y = mx + b$ is written in slope-intercept form.

Slope-Intercept Form

Words The linear equation $y = mx + b$ is written in slope-intercept form. The slope is m. The y-intercept is b.

Algebra $y = mx + b$ **Numbers** $y = 4x + 1$

EXAMPLE 1 Identifying Slopes and y-Intercepts

Find the slope and y-intercept of the line.

a. $y = -x + 7$ **b.** $-9x + 3y = -6$

Solution

a. The equation $y = -x + 7$ can be written as $y = -1x + 7$.

ANSWER The line has a slope of −1 and a y-intercept of 7.

b. Write the equation $-9x + 3y = -6$ in slope-intercept form.

$-9x + 3y = -6$	Write original equation.
$3y = 9x - 6$	Add 9x to each side.
$y = 3x - 2$	Divide each side by 3.

The equation $y = 3x - 2$ can be written as $y = 3x + (-2)$.

ANSWER The line has a slope of 3 and a y-intercept of −2.

Lesson 11.7 Slope-Intercept Form | 231

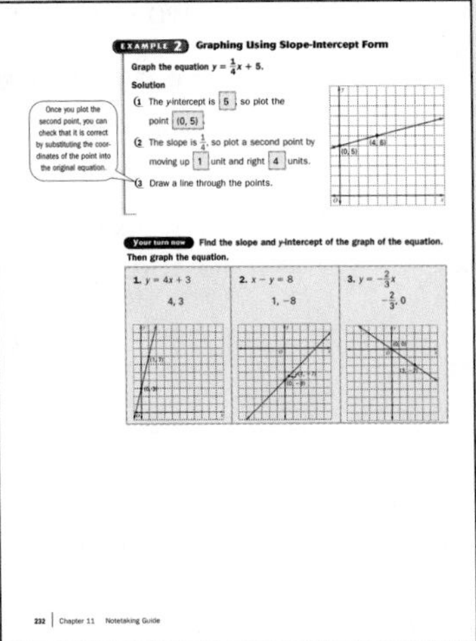

EXAMPLE 2 Graphing Using Slope-Intercept Form

Graph the equation $y = \frac{1}{4}x + 5$.

Solution

1. The y-intercept is 5, so plot the point (0, 5).
2. The slope is $\frac{1}{4}$, so plot a second point by moving up 1 unit and right 4 units.
3. Draw a line through the points.

Once you plot the second point, you can check that it is correct by substituting the coordinates of the point into the original equation.

Your turn now **Find the slope and y-intercept of the graph of the equation. Then graph the equation.**

1. $y = 4x + 3$ — 4, 3
2. $x - y = 8$ — 1, −8
3. $y = -\frac{2}{3}x$ — $-\frac{2}{3}$, 0

232 | Chapter 11 Notetaking Guide

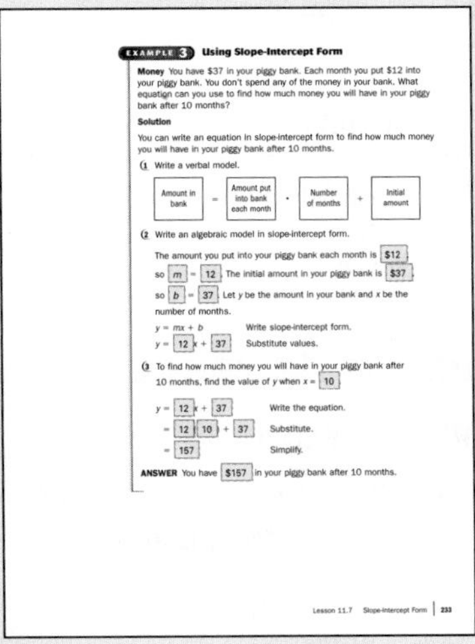

EXAMPLE 3 Using Slope-Intercept Form

Money You have $37 in your piggy bank. Each month you put $12 into your piggy bank. You don't spend any of the money in your bank. What equation can you use to find how much money you will have in your piggy bank after 10 months?

Solution

You can write an equation in slope-intercept form to find how much money you will have in your piggy bank after 10 months.

1. Write a verbal model.
Amount in bank = Amount put into bank each month · Number of months + Initial amount
2. Write an algebraic model in slope-intercept form.
The amount you put into your piggy bank each month is $12, so m = 12. The initial amount in your piggy bank is $37, so b = 37. Let y be the amount in your bank and x be the number of months.
$y = mx + b$ Write slope-intercept form.
$y = 12x + 37$ Substitute values.
3. To find how much money you will have in your piggy bank after 10 months, find the value of y when x = 10.
$y = 12x + 37$ Write the equation.
$= 12(10) + 37$ Substitute.
$= 157$ Simplify.

ANSWER You have $157 in your piggy bank after 10 months.

Lesson 11.7 Slope-Intercept Form | 233

Resource Book

The *Chapter Resource Books* contain Study Guide pages with reteaching examples and exercises for each lesson in the textbook. Pictured below are Study Guide pages from the *Chapter 11 Resource Book*. (The Study Guide pages are also available in Spanish in the *Spanish Study Guide*.)

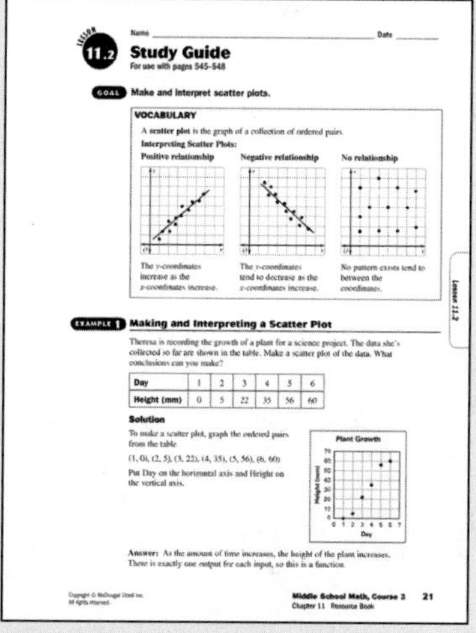

Lesson 11.2

Name ______________________ Date ________

Study Guide

For use with pages 545–548

GOAL Make and interpret scatter plots.

VOCABULARY

A **scatter plot** is the graph of a collection of ordered pairs.

Interpreting Scatter Plots:

Positive relationship	Negative relationship	No relationship
The y-coordinates increase as the x-coordinates increase.	The y-coordinates tend to decrease as the x-coordinates increase.	No pattern exists tend to between the coordinates.

EXAMPLE 1 Making and Interpreting a Scatter Plot

Theresa is recording the growth of a plant for a science project. The data she's collected so far are shown in the table. Make a scatter plot of the data. What conclusions can you make?

Day	1	2	3	4	5	6
Height (mm)	0	5	22	35	56	60

Solution

To make a scatter plot, graph the ordered pairs from the table.

(1, 0), (2, 5), (3, 22), (4, 35), (5, 56), (6, 60)

Put Day on the horizontal axis and Height on the vertical axis.

Plant Growth

Answer: As the amount of time increases, the height of the plant increases. There is exactly one output for each input, so this is a function.

Middle School Math, Course 3 21
Chapter 11 Resource Book

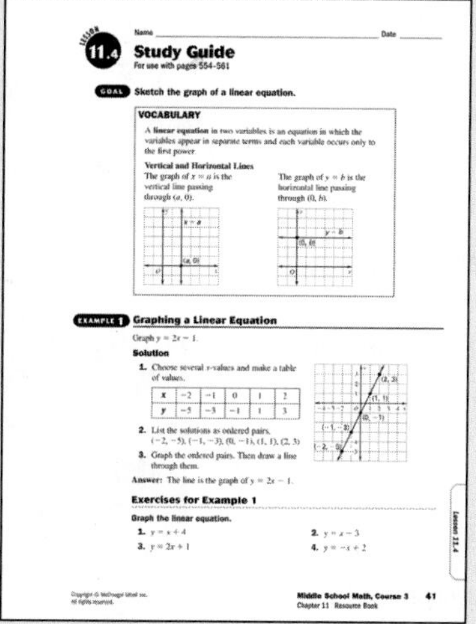

Lesson 11.4

Name ______________________ Date ________

Study Guide

For use with pages 554–561

GOAL Sketch the graph of a linear equation.

VOCABULARY

A **linear equation** in two variables is an equation in which the variables appear in separate terms and each variable occurs only to the first power.

Vertical and Horizontal Lines

The graph of $x = a$ is the vertical line passing through $(a, 0)$.

The graph of $y = b$ is the horizontal line passing through $(0, b)$.

EXAMPLE 1 Graphing a Linear Equation

Graph $y = 2x - 1$.

Solution

1. Choose several x-values and make a table of values.

x	−2	−1	0	1	2
y	−5	−3	−1	1	3

2. List the solutions as ordered pairs. (−2, −5), (−1, −3), (0, −1), (1, 1), (2, 3)
3. Graph the ordered pairs. Then draw a line through them.

Answer: The line is the graph of $y = 2x - 1$.

Exercises for Example 1

Graph the linear equation.

1. $y = x + 4$
2. $y = x - 3$
3. $y = 2x + 1$
4. $y = -x + 2$

Middle School Math, Course 3 41
Chapter 11 Resource Book

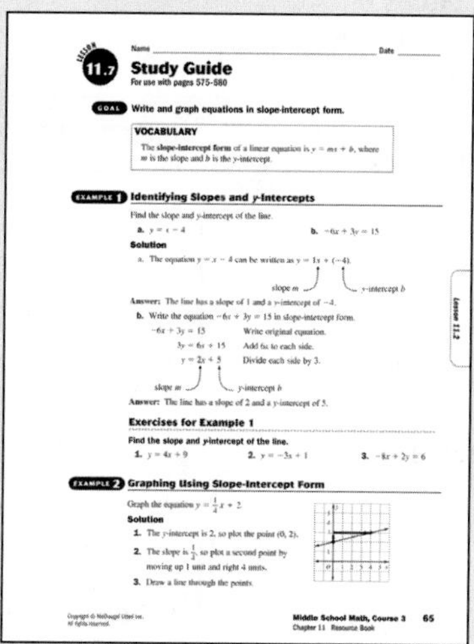

Lesson 11.7

Name ______________________ Date ________

Study Guide

For use with pages 575–580

GOAL Write and graph equations in slope-intercept form.

VOCABULARY

The **slope-intercept form** of a linear equation is $y = mx + b$, where m is the slope and b is the y-intercept.

EXAMPLE 1 Identifying Slopes and y-Intercepts

Find the slope and y-intercept of the line.

a. $y = x - 4$

b. $-6x + 3y = 15$

Solution

a. The equation $y = x - 4$ can be written as $y = 1x + (-4)$.

slope m y-intercept b

Answer: The line has a slope of 1 and a y-intercept of −4.

b. Write the equation $-6x + 3y = 15$ in slope-intercept form.

$-6x + 3y = 15$ Write original equation.

$3y = 6x + 15$ Add $6x$ to each side.

$y = 2x + 5$ Divide each side by 3.

slope m y-intercept b

Answer: The line has a slope of 2 and a y-intercept of 5.

Exercises for Example 1

Find the slope and y-intercept of the line.

1. $y = 4x + 9$
2. $y = -3x + 1$
3. $-8x + 2y = 6$

EXAMPLE 2 Graphing Using Slope-Intercept Form

Graph the equation $y = \frac{1}{4}x + 2$.

Solution

1. The y-intercept is 2, so plot the point (0, 2).
2. The slope is $\frac{1}{4}$, so plot a second point by moving up 1 unit and right 4 units.
3. Draw a line through the points.

Middle School Math, Course 3 65
Chapter 11 Resource Book

Tutor Place

Tutor Place helps students practice and master essential topics. Instruction is provided by 104 cards containing examples and two sets of practice exercises. Answers are provided in a handy answer key.

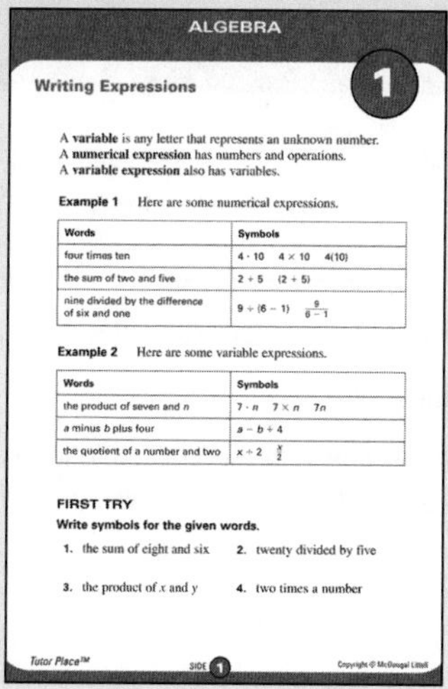

ALGEBRA

Writing Expressions 1

A **variable** is any letter that represents an unknown number.
A **numerical expression** has numbers and operations.
A **variable expression** also has variables.

Example 1 Here are some numerical expressions.

Words	Symbols
four times ten	$4 \cdot 10$ 4×10 $4(10)$
the sum of two and five	$2 + 5$ $(2 + 5)$
nine divided by the difference of six and one	$9 \div (6 - 1)$ $\frac{9}{6 - 1}$

Example 2 Here are some variable expressions.

Words	Symbols
the product of seven and n	$7 \cdot n$ $7 \times n$ $7n$
a minus b plus four	$a - b + 4$
the quotient of a number and two	$x \div 2$ $\frac{x}{2}$

FIRST TRY

Write symbols for the given words.

1. the sum of eight and six
2. twenty divided by five
3. the product of x and y
4. two times a number

Tutor Place™ SIDE 1

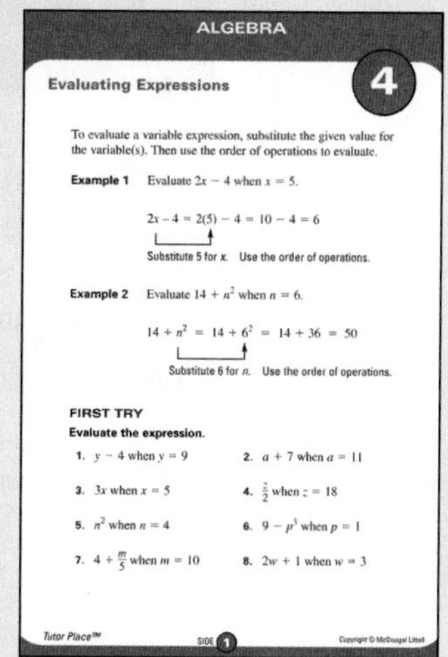

ALGEBRA

Evaluating Expressions 4

To evaluate a variable expression, substitute the given value for the variable(s). Then use the order of operations to evaluate.

Example 1 Evaluate $2x - 4$ when $x = 5$.

$2x - 4 = 2(5) - 4 = 10 - 4 = 6$

Substitute 5 for x. Use the order of operations.

Example 2 Evaluate $14 + n^2$ when $n = 6$.

$14 + n^2 = 14 + 6^2 = 14 + 36 = 50$

Substitute 6 for n. Use the order of operations.

FIRST TRY

Evaluate the expression.

1. $y - 4$ when $y = 9$
2. $a + 7$ when $a = 11$
3. $3x$ when $x = 5$
4. $\frac{z}{2}$ when $z = 18$
5. n^2 when $n = 4$
6. $9 - p^3$ when $p = 1$
7. $4 + \frac{m}{5}$ when $m = 10$
8. $2w + 1$ when $w = 3$

Tutor Place™ SIDE 1

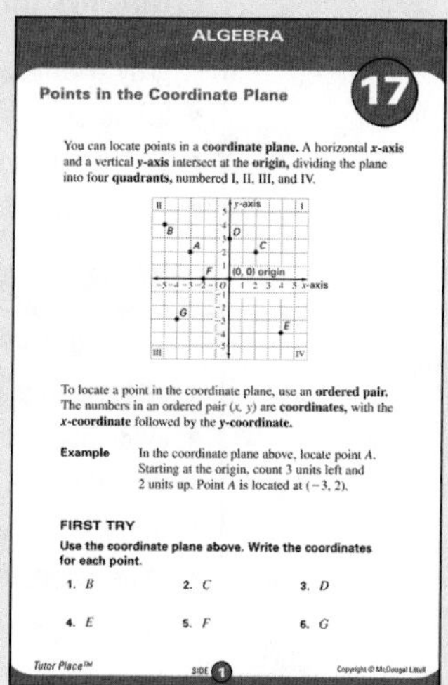

ALGEBRA

Points in the Coordinate Plane 17

You can locate points in a **coordinate plane.** A horizontal **x-axis** and a vertical **y-axis** intersect at the **origin,** dividing the plane into four **quadrants,** numbered I, II, III, and IV.

To locate a point in the coordinate plane, use an **ordered pair.** The numbers in an ordered pair (x, y) are **coordinates,** with the **x-coordinate** followed by the **y-coordinate.**

Example In the coordinate plane above, locate point A. Starting at the origin, count 3 units left and 2 units up. Point A is located at (−3, 2).

FIRST TRY

Use the coordinate plane above. Write the coordinates for each point.

1. B
2. C
3. D
4. E
5. F
6. G

Tutor Place™ SIDE 1

OVERVIEW

Main Ideas

In this chapter, students identify and write functions, represent them with tables, and evaluate them. Students make and interpret scatter plots and use them to identify relationships between data sets. Students find solutions of equations in two variables, identify linear equations, and sketch their graphs using tables of values and using *x*- and *y*-intercepts. Students find and interpret slope, and write and graph linear equations in slope-intercept form. Students also graph linear inequalities.

Prerequisite Skills

The key skills reviewed in the games on these pages are:

- Solving equations in one variable
- Plotting points on a coordinate grid

Additional practice with prerequisite skills can be found in the Review What You Need to Know exercises on page 540. Additional resources for reviewing prerequisite skills are:

- Skills Review Handbook, pp. 704–726
- Tutor Place
- eTutorial Plus

Managing the Games

Tips for Success

As students begin *Sidewalk Scramble*, remind them that the goal is to get the variable alone on one side of the equation, and that as a first step (or second step in the equation corresponding to the letter H), they should eliminate a variable expression from one side of the equation. In *Plot the Picture*, remind students to connect the points as they go so that they connect the proper points.

Linear Equations and Graphs

BEFORE

In previous chapters you've...

- Translated verbal sentences into mathematical statements
- Solved equations in one variable

Now

In Chapter 11 you'll study...

- Constructing and interpreting scatter plots
- Finding solutions of equations in two variables
- Writing and graphing equations

WHY?

So you can solve real-world problems about...

- gray whales, p. 543
- inline skates, p. 549
- elevators, p. 552
- hiking, p. 577

Internet Preview

CLASSZONE.COM

- eEdition Plus Online
- eWorkbook Plus Online
- eTutorial Plus Online
- State Test Practice
- More Examples

Chapter Warm-Up Games

Review skills you need for this chapter in these quick games.

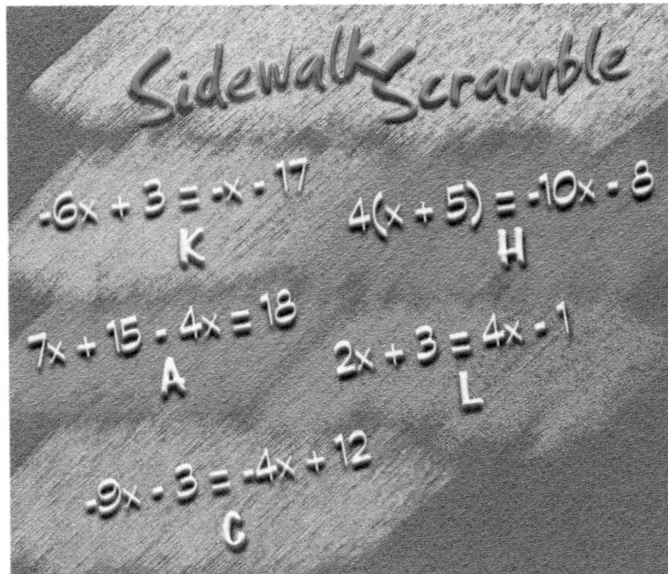

Key Skill:
Solving equations in one variable

Solve the scramble to spell a word associated with sidewalk art.

- Find the solution of each equation. K: 4; H: −2; A: 1; L: 2; C−3
- Order the equations so that the one with the least solution is first and the one with the greatest solution is last. This will unscramble the letters. CHALK

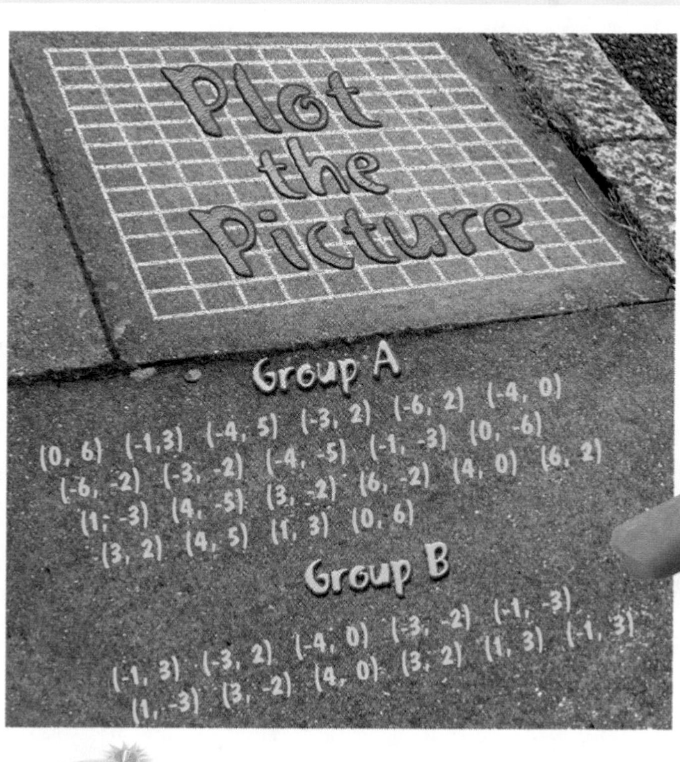

Plot the Picture
Group A
(0, 6) (-1, 3) (-4, 5) (-3, 2) (-6, 2) (-4, 0)
(-6, -2) (-3, -2) (-4, -5) (-1, -3) (0, -6)
(1, -3) (4, -5) (3, -2) (6, -2) (4, 0) (6, 2)
(3, 2) (4, 5) (1, 3) (0, 6)
Group B
(-1, 3) (-3, 2) (-4, 0) (-3, -2) (-1, -3)
(1, -3) (3, -2) (4, 0) (3, 2) (1, 3) (-1, 3)

BRAIN GAME

Key Skill:
Plotting points on a coordinate grid

Create a piece of sidewalk art. **See margin.**

- Plot the points listed in Group A on a coordinate grid. Connect each point with a line to the point that follows it.
- Now find and connect the points in Group B in order.

1. The first step in solving the equation $-6x + 3 = -x - 17$ is to add the opposite of $-x$ to both sides of the equation. Since the opposite of $-x$ is x, you need to add x to both sides.

Stop *and* Think

1. **Writing** A student says that in *Sidewalk Scramble* the first step in solving the equation $-6x + 3 = -x - 17$ is to subtract x from both sides. Explain why the student is wrong.
2. **Extension** Design your own piece of sidewalk art. Write directions for making your sidewalk art using points on a coordinate grid. **Check work.**

Reflecting on the Games

After answering the Stop & Think question for *Sidewalk Scramble*, have students use the equation corresponding to the letter H to write the steps in solving any equation such as this in which there is a variable on each side and the distributive property is used.

Chapter Resources

These resources are provided to help you prepare for the chapter and to customize review materials:

Chapter 11 Resource Book

- Tips for New Teachers, pp. 1–2
- Lesson Plan, pp. 6, 14, 25, 35, 44, 52, 60, 68
- Lesson Plan for Block Scheduling, pp. 7, 15, 26, 36, 45, 53, 61, 69

Technology

- EasyPlanner CD-ROM
- Test and Practice Generator
- Electronic Lesson Presentations CD-ROM
- eTutorial CD-ROM

Internet

- Classzone
- eEdition Plus Online
- eWorkbook Plus Online
- eTutorial Plus Online
- EasyPlanner Plus Online

English Learner Support

- Spanish Study Guide
- Multi-Language Glossary
- Chapter Audio Summaries CDs
- Teacher's Edition, pp. 538E–538F

Brain Game. See Additional Answers beginning on page AA1.

PREPARE

DIAGNOSIS/REMEDIATION

Review What You Need to Know
The Review What You Need to Know exercises can help you diagnose whether students have the following skills needed in Chapter 11:
- Use vocabulary relating to coordinate grids (Exs. 1–2)
- Plot points in coordinate planes (Exs. 3–6)
- Solve equations (Exs. 7–9)
- Solve inequalities (Exs. 10–12)

Chapter 11 Resource Book
- Study Guide (Lessons 11.1–11.8)

Tutor Place

NOTETAKING STRATEGIES

Students might understand how a formula or equation works, but not how to apply it to an exercise. Encourage students to write questions identifying any exercise that is causing them trouble. Tell them to highlight their questions for easy review. Further suggestions for keeping a notebook can be found on page 565.

For more support on notetaking, see:
- Notetaking Guide Workbook
- Notetaking Transparencies

1.
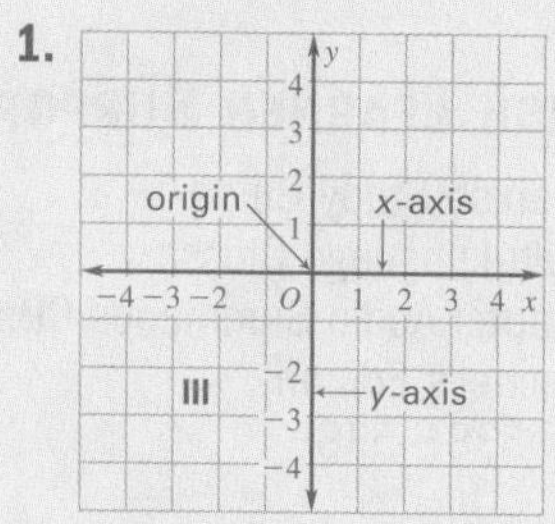

3–6.
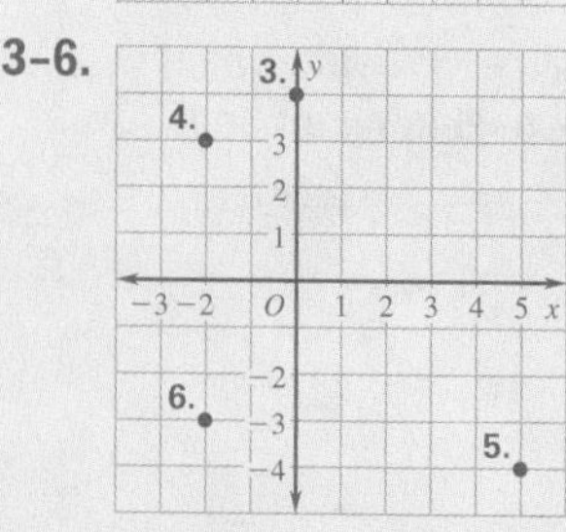

Getting Ready to Learn

Word Watch

Review Words
- coordinate plane, p. 91
- x-axis, p. 91
- y-axis, p. 91
- origin, p. 91
- quadrant, p. 91
- ordered pair, p. 91
- inequality, p. 140
- ratio, p. 317

Review What You Need to Know 

1. Using Vocabulary Draw a coordinate plane and label the x-axis, y-axis, origin, and third quadrant. **See margin.**

2. Write the ordered pair for each labeled point in the coordinate plane.
A(0, 3), B(2, −2), C(−2, 0), D(2, 1)

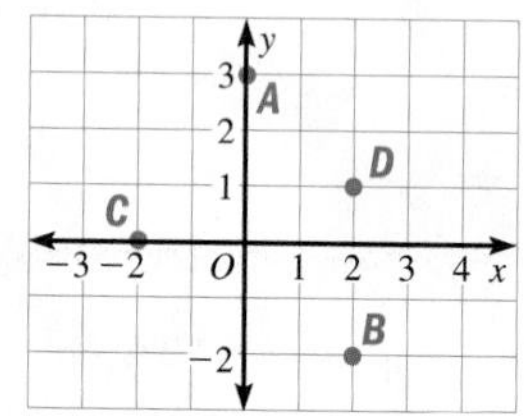

Plot the point in a coordinate plane. *(p. 91)* **3–6. See margin.**

3. (0, 4) **4.** (−2, 3) **5.** (5, −4) **6.** (−2, −3)

Solve the equation. *(p. 119)*

7. $3 = 9x - 24$ 3 **8.** $7 - 8x = 3$ $\frac{1}{2}$ **9.** $6x + 9 = -45$ −9

Solve the inequality. *(p. 295)*

10. $3x - 4 \le 5$ $x \le 3$ **11.** $-4x - 3 \ge 12$ $x \le -3\frac{3}{4}$ **12.** $6 + 2x < 2$ $x < -2$

You should include material that appears on a notebook like this in your own notes.

Know How to Take Notes

Write Questions About Homework If you don't know how to solve a homework problem, make a note in you notebook. Leave room to write the answer to your question.

What is the distance from A to C?

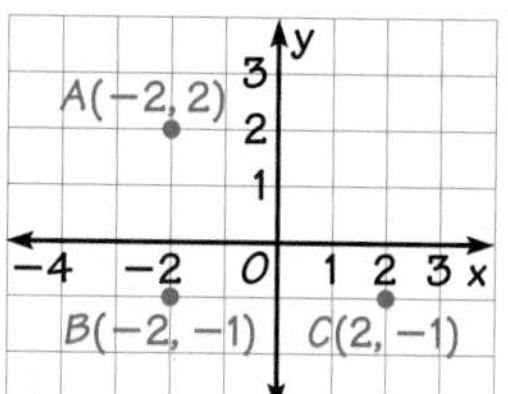

I can't count along the grid from A to C, so how do I solve this?

Use the Pythagorean theorem. AB = 3, BC = 4, and △ABC is a right triangle, so AC = 5.

In Chapter 11, you will learn how the coordinate plane is related to equations. Be sure to find answers to any questions you have.

Relations and Functions

BEFORE	Now	WHY?
You translated verbal sentences into algebraic models.	You'll use tables to represent functions.	So you can find the amount of formula consumed, as in Ex. 8.

In the Real World

relation, p. 541
input, p. 541
output, p. 541
function, p. 541
domain, p. 542
range, p. 542

Fundraisers Your soccer team is selling glow sticks to raise money. The team paid \$50 for a case of 48 glow sticks and sells each glow stick for \$3. How many glow sticks does the team need to sell to start earning a profit? You will answer this question in Example 2.

A **relation** is a set of ordered pairs that relates an **input** to an **output**. A relation can be written as a set of ordered pairs or by using an *input-output table.*

(Input, Output)

(2, 5)
(4, 7)
(−1, 15)
(0, 0)

Input	Output
2	5
4	7
−1	15
0	0

A relation is a **function** if for each input there is exactly one output. In a function, you can say that the output is a *function of* the input.

EXAMPLE 1 Identifying Functions

Tell whether the relation is a function. Explain your answer.

a. (0, 2), (1, 4), (2, 6), (3, 8)

ANSWER The relation is a function. Each input has exactly one output.

b.

Input	9	9	25	25
Output	3	−3	5	−5

ANSWER The relation is *not* a function. Both 9 and 25 have two outputs.

Watch Out!

In a function, two different inputs can have the same output, but each input must have *exactly one* output.

Tell whether the relation is a function.

1. (−2, 4), (2, 4), (4, 2), (−2, −4) no

2.

Input	−2	0	2	4
Output	4	0	4	16

yes

ILLINOIS Standards and ISAT:
8.A.3b, 8.B.3, 8.D.3b

1 PLAN

SKILL CHECK

1. $2(0) - 10 = \underline{?}$ −10
2. $2(5) - 10 = \underline{?}$ 0
3. $2(10) - 10 = \underline{?}$ 10

LESSON OBJECTIVE

Use tables to represent functions.

PACING

Suggested Number of Days
Basic Course: 1 day
Average Course: 1 day
Advanced Course: 1 day
Block: 0.5 block with 11.2

TEACHING RESOURCES

For a complete list of Teaching Resources, see page 538B.

Warm-Up Exercises for this lesson are available on a transparency. A support transparency is available for Examples 1 and 3.

2 TEACH

MOTIVATING THE LESSON

Have students describe any fundraisers they have helped with. Ask them what items their group bought and sold. See if they recall cost, selling price, and profit per item.

TIPS FOR NEW TEACHERS

Many students may have difficulty remembering the definition of a function. Ask students to suggest different ways to remember how to tell whether a relation is a function. See Tips for New Teachers in the *Chapter 11 Resource Book*.

EXTRA EXAMPLES

Example 1 Tell whether the relation is a function. Explain your answer.

a. (5, 1), (5, 3), (7, 1), (8, 4)
No; 5 has two outputs.

b.

Input	10	12	14	16
Output	12	12	16	20

Yes; each input has exactly one output.

Example 2 An online company sells cardboard puzzles for \$5 per puzzle and charges a flat shipping fee of \$10 to deliver the puzzles to your home. Use the function $c = 5p + 10$, where c is cost and p is the number of puzzles you plan to buy. Find the range for $p = 5$, 10, and 15. How many puzzles can you buy for \$60? **range: 35, 60, 85; 10 puzzles**

Example 3 Write a function rule that relates x and y.

Input x	−2	−1	0	1	2
Output y	−5	−3	−1	1	3

$y = 2x - 1$

CONCEPT CHECK

Which relation cannot be a function, one that has outputs of 5 and 7 for an input of 2, or one that has an output of 2 for inputs of both 5 and 7? Explain. **The one that has outputs of 5 and 7 for an input of 2; a function cannot have two different outputs for one input.**

DAILY PUZZLER

What is the next number in the sequence?
2, 5, 10, 17, 26, 37, ... **50**

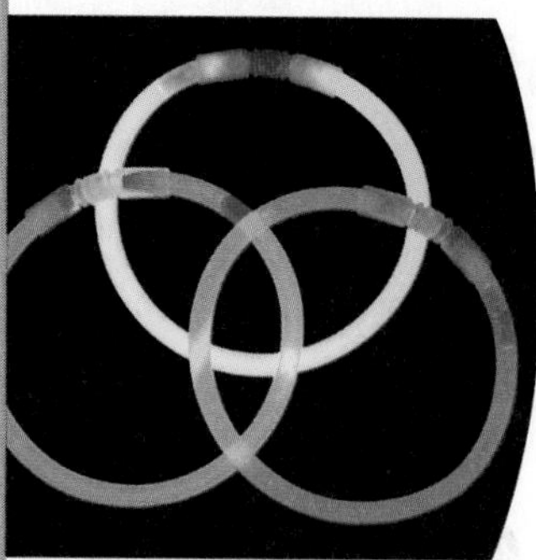

Domain and Range The **domain** of a function is the set of all possible input values. The **range** of a function is the set of all possible output values. A *function rule* assigns each number in the domain to exactly one number in the range.

EXAMPLE 2 Evaluating a Function

Fundraising To solve the problem on page 541, use the function rule $P = 3g - 50$, where P is the profit in dollars and g is the number of glow sticks your team sells.

Solution

First, make a table to determine how many glow sticks your soccer team needs to sell to start earning a profit.

Input g	Function	Output P
0	$P = 3(0) - 50$	−50
10	$P = 3(10) - 50$	−20
16	$P = 3(16) - 50$	−2
17	$P = 3(17) - 50$	1

There are 48 glow sticks, so the domain is 0, 1, 2, 3, . . . , 48. The range is −50, −47, −44, −41, . . . , 94.

ANSWER Your soccer team needs to sell at least 17 glow sticks.

HELP with Solving

In Example 2, a negative output value indicates a loss of money for the team.

EXAMPLE 3 Writing a Function Rule

Write a function rule that relates x and y.

Input x	−4	−2	0	2	4
Output y	1	3	5	7	9

(Inputs: +2, +2, +2, +2; Outputs: +2, +2, +2, +2)

To write a function rule, try to find an equation of the form $y = ax + b$. You can look at differences in the function to find values of a and b.

1. The value of a is $\frac{\text{change in output}}{\text{change in input}}$.

   $a = \frac{2}{2} = 1$ $\qquad y = 1x + b$

2. To find b, choose an input-output pair to substitute for x and y.

   Let $(x, y) = (0, 5)$ $\qquad 5 = 1(0) + b$, so $b = 5$

ANSWER A function rule that relates x and y is $y = x + 5$.

✓**Check** $3 = -2 + 5$ **Substitute (−2, 3) in function rule.**

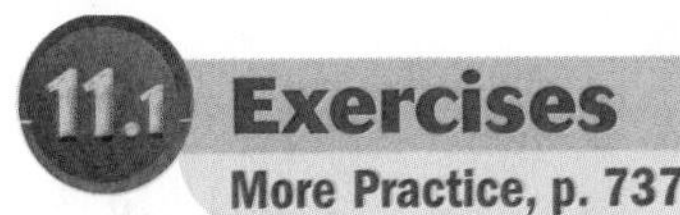

11.1 Exercises

More Practice, p. 737

Getting Ready to Practice

1. **Vocabulary** Copy and complete: A relation that has exactly one output value for each input is a(n) _?_. function

Tell whether the relation is a function.

2. (3, 0), (0, 6), (1, 5), (3, 7) (−1, 2), (5, 1), (−3, 0) no

3.

Input	−2	3	8	13
Output	0	0	0	0

yes

Copy and complete the table of values for the function rule.

Input x	−1	0	1	2
Output y	?	?	?	?

4. $y = x - 3$ −4, −3, −2, −1

5. $5x + y = 13$ 18, 13, 8, 3

Write a function rule that relates x and y.

6.

Input x	−1	0	1	2
Output y	5	6	7	8

$y = x + 6$

7.

Input x	0	1	2	3
Output y	0	−5	−10	−15

$y = -5x$

8. **Whale Calf** A gray whale calf was nursed back to health with milk-based formula. The table shows the amounts of formula, in gallons, the whale consumed every 3 to 4 hours. Use the table to write a function rule. $y = 2x$

Number of times fed	Total amount consumed (gal)
1	2
2	4
3	6
4	8

9. No; one input, 4, has two output values.
10. Yes; each input has exactly one output value.
11. Yes; each input has exactly one output value.
12. No; one input, 4, has two output values.

Practice and Problem Solving

HELP with Homework

Example	Exercises
1	9-12
2	13-16
3	17-18

- More Examples
- eTutorial Plus

Tell whether the relation is a function. Explain your answer. 9–12. See margin.

A 9. (4, 5), (2, −3), (4, 9), (−2, −3)

10. (−3, 7), (3, 7), (7, 3), (−7, −3)

11.

Input	−3	−2	0	2
Output	9	4	0	4

12.

Input	4	4	2	5
Output	2	−2	5	−5

Make an input-output table for the function rule. Use a domain of −2, −1, 0, 1, and 2. Identify the range. 13–16. See margin.

13. $y = x - 1$ 14. $y = -\frac{1}{4}x$ 15. $y = 5x$ 16. $y = x^2$

3 APPLY

ASSIGNMENT GUIDE

Basic Course

Day 1: pp. 543-544 Exs. 9-18, 20-22, 25-28

Average Course

Day 1: pp. 543-544 Exs. 10-23, 25-29

Advanced Course

Day 1: pp. 543-544 Exs. 10-14, 17-29*

Block

pp. 543-544 Exs. 10-23, 25-29 (with 11.2)

EXTRA PRACTICE

- Student Edition, p. 737
- Chapter 11 Resource Book, pp. 8-10
- Test and Practice Generator

TRANSPARENCY

Even-numbered answers are available on transparencies. A support transparency is available for Exercises 4, 5, and 13-16.

HOMEWORK CHECK

When you review students' homework for this lesson, go over the following exercises to check understanding of key concepts.
Basic: 9, 11, 13, 14, 17
Average: 10, 11, 13, 14, 17
Advanced: 10, 12, 13, 17, 18

COMMON ERROR

In Exercises 21 and 22, watch for students who find a function rule that works for only some pairs in the table. Remind students that the rule must work for every pair in the table, not just some of them.

13–16. See Additional Answers beginning on page AA1.

Assessment Resources

For more assessment resources, see:

- Assessment Book
- Test and Practice Generator

Mini-Quiz

Tell whether the relation is a function. Explain your answer.

1. (2, 7), (−1, 3), (2, 12), (4, 6)
   No; 2 has more than one output.
2. (−4, 1), (−3, 1), (−2, 0), (1, 3)
   Yes; each input has only one output.
3. Make a table of values for the function $y = 2x + 3$. Use a domain of −1, 0, 1, and 2. Identify the range.

Input	−1	0	1	2
Output	1	3	5	7

The range is 1, 3, 5, 7.

Reteaching/Remediation

- Study Guide in Chapter 11 Resource Book, pp. 11–12
- Tutor Place, Algebra Cards 1, 4
- eTutorial Plus Online
- Extra Practice, p. 737
- Lesson Practice in Chapter 11 Resource Book, pp. 8–10

Challenge/Enrichment

- Challenge Practice in Chapter 11 Resource Book, p. 13
- Teacher's Edition, p. 538F

English Learner Support

- Spanish Study Guide
- Multi-Language Glossary
- Chapter Audio Summaries CDs

20. Yes. *Sample answer:* For any number of tickets, there is only one corresponding total cost, the number of tickets times the cost per ticket.

Write a function rule that relates *x* and *y*.

17.

Input x	1	2	3	4
Output y	5	10	15	20

$y = 5x$

18.

Input x	−3	−2	−1	0
Output y	−12	−8	−4	0

$y = 4x$

19. **Recycling** Stanley receives $.75 per pound of aluminum cans he recycles. Is the weight of cans he recycles a function of the number of cans? Explain. **No; the weight of the cans that Stanley recycles is a function of the amount of money.**

20. **Tickets** Ashley is buying movie tickets that are all the same price. Is the total cost a function of the number of tickets? Explain. **See margin.**

Write a function rule that relates *r* and *t*.

B 21.

Input r	1	2	3	4
Output t	1	4	7	10

$t = 3r - 2$

22.

Input r	0	1	2	3
Output t	2	1.5	1	0.5

$t = -0.5r + 2$

23. **Writing** Your friend says that the input-output table below represents a function. Is your friend correct? Explain why or why not. **Yes; each input has exactly one output value.**

Input x	−9	−4.5	0	4.5	9
Output y	81	20.25	0	20.25	81

C 24. **Challenge** Explain why the distance you travel on your bike is not always a function of the time you spend riding your bike. Describe a situation when it would be a function. ***Sample answer:* Sometimes you will travel different distances in the same amount of time. If you always traveled at a steady speed, the situation would be a function.**

Mixed Review

Find the surface area of the solid. *(Lessons 10.4–10.5)*

25.

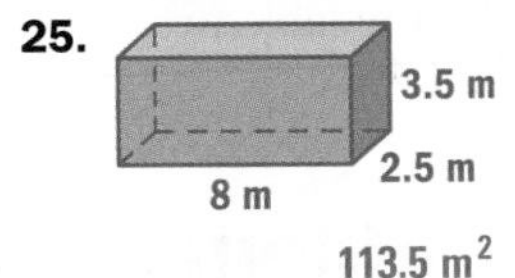

$113.5\ m^2$

26.

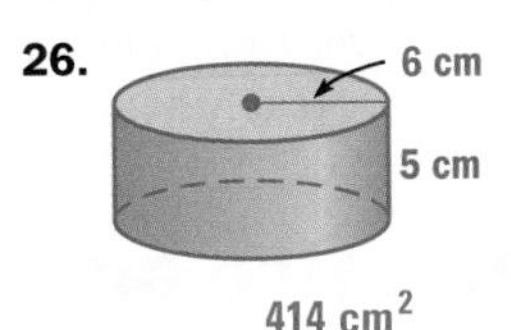

$414\ cm^2$

27.

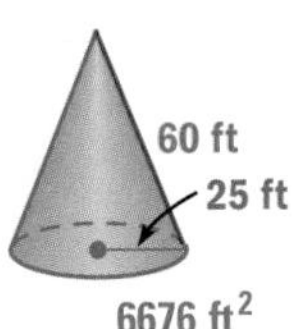

$6676\ ft^2$

Test-Taking Practice

INTERNET
State Test Practice
CLASSZONE.COM

28. **Multiple Choice** The function rule $y = 3x$ relates x and y in which set of ordered pairs? **B**

A. (0, 0), (3, 1), (6, 2), (9, 3)
B. (0, 0), (1, 3), (2, 6), (3, 9)
C. (0, 3), (1, 4), (2, 5), (3, 6)
D. (0, −3), (1, −2), (2, −1), (3, 0)

29. **Multiple Choice** Which of the following relations is *not* a function? **I**

F. (2, 3), (4, 3), (6, 7), (9, 2)
G. (2, 3), (4, 5), (6, 4), (5, 4)
H. (−1, 8), (0, 11), (1, 8), (5, 4)
I. (3, 5), (4, 3), (4, 6), (6, 9)

Scatter Plots

BEFORE	Now	WHY?
You found a function rule given a table of values.	You'll make and interpret scatter plots.	So you can compare study time to test score, as in Ex. 6.

In the Real World

Word Watch

scatter plot, p. 545

NASA NASA's Crawler Transporter is a large vehicle that moves the space shuttle and its launch platform to the launch pad. The crawler uses about 126 gallons of fuel to travel 1 mile.

The table below shows the amount of fuel that is used to travel different numbers of miles. How can you present this information using a graph?

Distance (miles)	1	2	3	4	5	6
Amount of fuel (gallons)	126	252	378	504	630	756

You can represent the information using a *scatter plot*. A **scatter plot** is the graph of a collection of ordered pairs.

EXAMPLE 1 Making and Interpreting a Scatter Plot

You can represent and make conclusions about the information above using a scatter plot.

To make a scatter plot, graph the ordered pairs from the table.

(1, 126), (2, 252), (3, 378),

(4, 504), (5, 630), (6, 756)

Put *Distance* on the horizontal axis and *Fuel used* on the vertical axis.

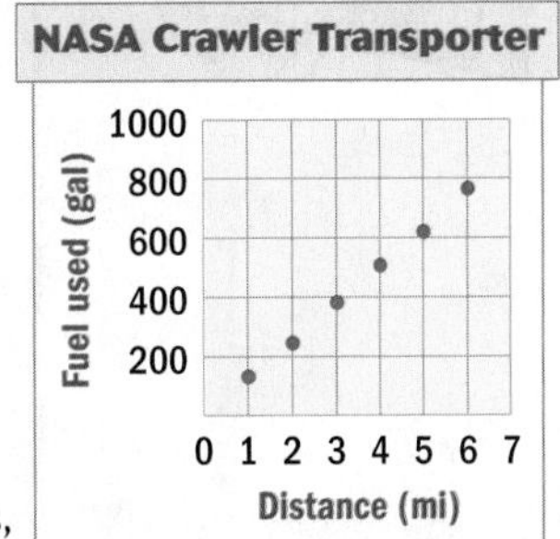

ANSWER As the distance traveled increases, the amount of fuel used increases. There is exactly one output for each input, so this is a function.

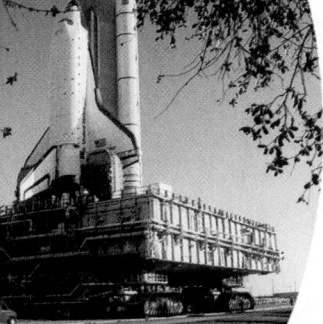

NASA's Crawler Transporter

Your turn now Make a scatter plot of the data.

1–2. See margin.

1.

c	-2	-1	0	1
d	-5	-4	-3	-2

2.

x	0	3	6	9
y	-2	-4	-6	-8

ILLINOIS Standards and ISAT:
8.B.3, 8.D.3a

1 PLAN

SKILL CHECK

Graph each point on a coordinate grid.

1. (0, 4) **2.** (1, 2)

3. (2, 1) **4.** (3, 0)

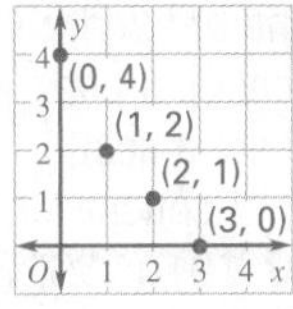

LESSON OBJECTIVE

Make and interpret scatter plots.

PACING

Suggested Number of Days

Basic Course: 1 day

Average Course: 1 day

Advanced Course: 1 day

Block: 0.5 block with 11.1

TEACHING RESOURCES

For a complete list of Teaching Resources, see page 538B.

TRANSPARENCY

Warm-Up Exercises for this lesson are available on a transparency. Support transparencies are available for Examples 1-2 and Your turn now Exercises 1-2.

2 TEACH

MOTIVATING THE LESSON

Challenge students to do further research about the Crawler.

1, 2. See Additional Answers beginning on page AA1.

TIPS FOR NEW TEACHERS

Remind students not to connect the points in a scatter plot. See Tips for New Teachers in the *Chapter 11 Resource Book*.

EXTRA EXAMPLES

Example 1 The ordered pairs (x, y) give the cost per copy, y, for x copies. Make a scatter plot of the data. What conclusion can you make? (10, 10), (100, 7), (200, 5), (300, 4)

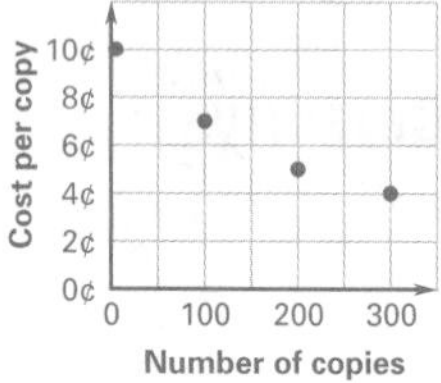

Cost per copy decreases as number of copies increases.

Example 2 The ordered pairs (x, y) give the tip, y, that Shelby earned from dinners costing x dollars. (12, 2), (15, 2), (22, 3), (24, 5), (29, 5), (45, 6)

a. Make a scatter plot of the data. Do x and y have a *positive, negative*, or *no* relationship? **positive**

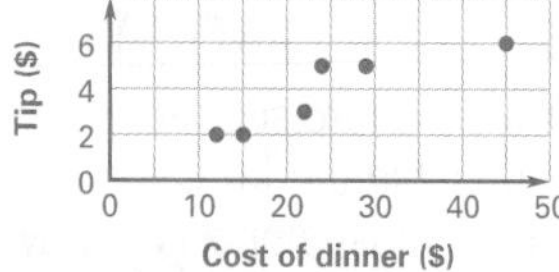

b. Estimate the tip Shelby would earn on a dinner costing $50. ***Sample answer:* $7**

CONCEPT CHECK

How do you decide if a scatter plot shows a positive relationship? **The y-coordinates increase as the x-coordinates increase.**

DAILY PUZZLER

Find two integers, a and b, both less than 10 such that $a^2 + b^2 + ab$ is a perfect square. **3, 5; or 7, 8**

Interpreting Scatter Plots Scatter plots show what kind of relationship exists between two sets of data.

Positive relationship

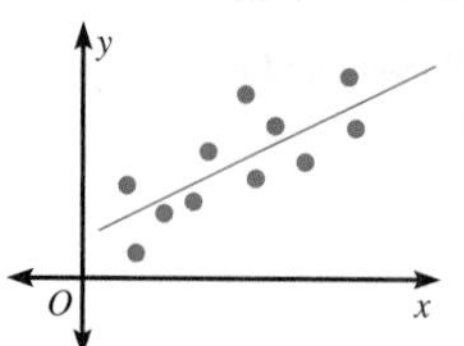

The y-coordinates tend to increase as the x-coordinates increase.

Negative relationship

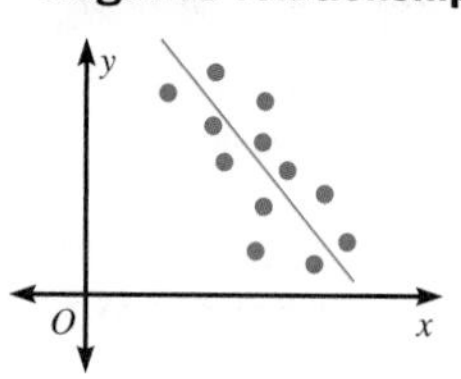

The y-coordinates tend to decrease as the x-coordinates increase.

No relationship

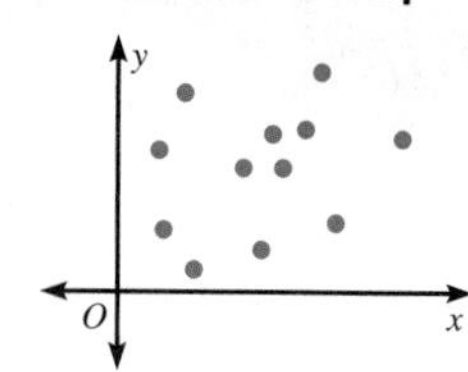

No pattern exists between the coordinates.

EXAMPLE 2 Interpreting a Scatter Plot

Shipping and Handling The table shows the cost y of shipping and handling per item when you buy x items.

Number of items x	1	2	3	4	5	6
Cost per item y	\$6.58	\$3.37	\$2.37	\$1.79	\$1.46	\$1.24

a. Make a scatter plot of the data. Tell whether x and y have a *positive relationship*, a *negative relationship*, or *no relationship*.

b. Estimate the cost of shipping and handling per item if you buy eight items.

Solution

a. In the scatter plot, the y-coordinates decrease as the x-coordinates increase.

ANSWER The quantities have a negative relationship.

b. To estimate the shipping and handling cost per item to buy eight items, draw a curve that shows the overall pattern of the data, as shown. The curve looks like it will pass through the point (8, 1).

ANSWER The shipping and handling cost per item, if you buy eight items, is about \$1.

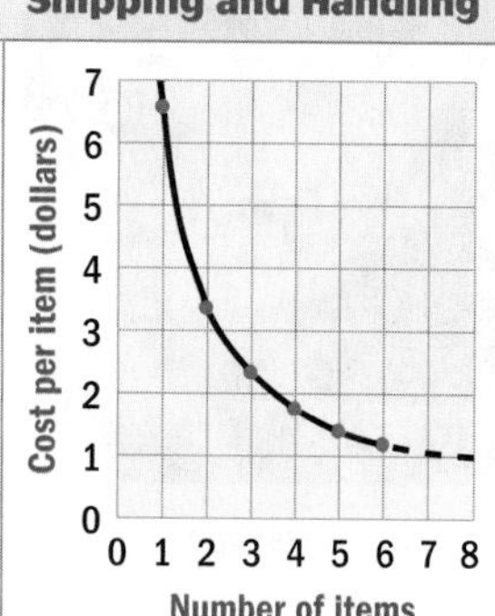

11.2 Exercises

More Practice, p. 737

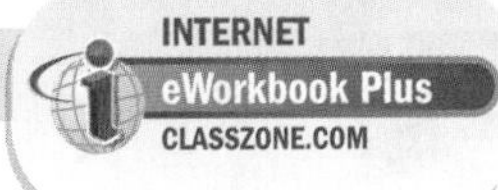

Getting Ready to Practice

1. **Vocabulary** Copy and complete: A(n) _?_ is a graph of a collection of ordered pairs. scatter plot

2. **Guided Problem Solving** The table shows the number of cookbooks sold at a bookstore in each of the six years it has been open. Predict the number of cookbooks that will be sold in the ninth year.

Year x	1	2	3	4	5	6
Books y	450	650	700	800	1100	1250

(1) Make a scatter plot. See margin.

(2) Describe the relationship between the variables. There is a positive relationship.

(3) Estimate the number of cookbooks that will be sold in the ninth year by sketching a curve that follows the trend of the data. *Sample answer*: about 1600 cookbooks

Practice and Problem Solving

HELP with Homework

Example	Exercises
1	6-9
2	3-5, 8-9

Online Resources
CLASSZONE.COM
· More Examples
· eTutorial Plus

Tell whether x and y have a *positive relationship*, a *negative relationship*, or *no relationship*.

A 3. 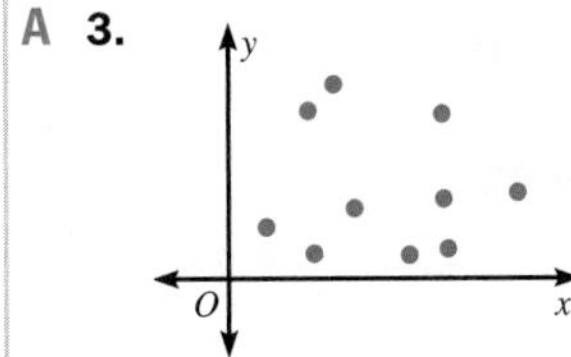
no relationship

4. 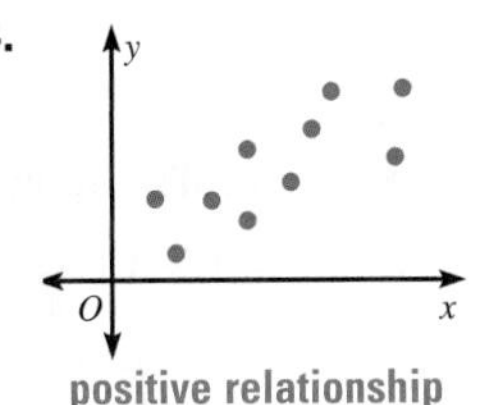
positive relationship

5. 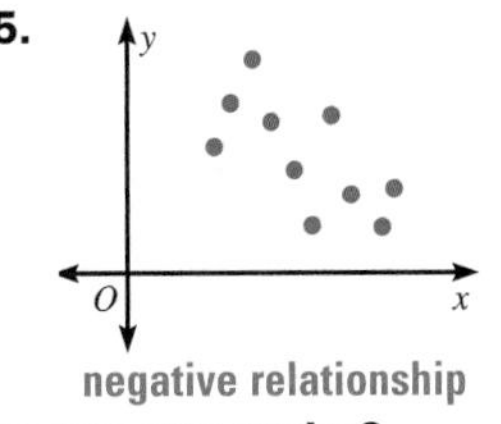
negative relationship

Make a scatter plot of the data. What conclusions can you make? 6–7. See margin.

6.

Hours spent studying	Test score (percent)
1	70
2	80
3	85

7. 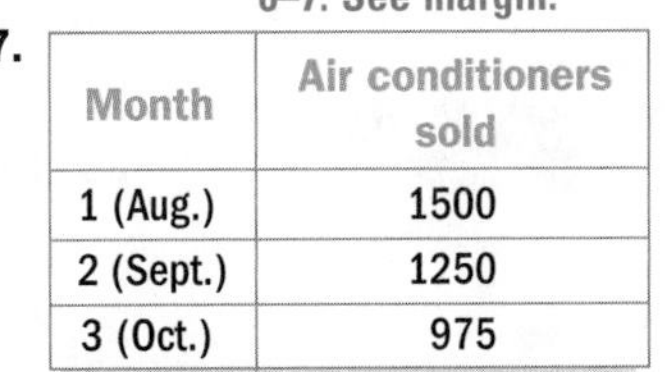

Month	Air conditioners sold
1 (Aug.)	1500
2 (Sept.)	1250
3 (Oct.)	975

Make a scatter plot of the data. Describe the relationship between the variables. Use the relationship to find the next ordered pair. 8–9. See margin.

8.

x	1	2	3	4	5
y	5	10	15	20	?

9. 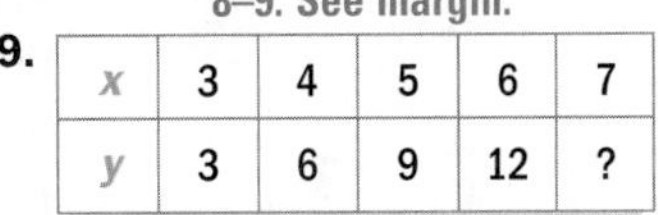

x	3	4	5	6	7
y	3	6	9	12	?

3 APPLY

ASSIGNMENT GUIDE

Basic Course
Day 1: SRH p. 725 Exs. 1-3; pp. 547-548 Exs. 3-12, 15-25

Average Course
Day 1: pp. 547-548 Exs. 5-13, 15-26

Advanced Course
Day 1: pp. 547-548 Exs. 5-20, 24-26, EC: TE p. 538D*

Block
pp. 547-548 Exs. 5-13, 15-26 (with 11.1)

Extra Practice

- Student Edition, p. 737
- Chapter 11 Resource Book, pp. 18-20
- Test and Practice Generator

Transparency

Even-numbered answers are available on transparencies. Support transparencies are available for Exercises 2, 6-9, and 14.

Homework Check

When you review students' homework for this lesson, go over the following exercises to check understanding of key concepts.
Basic: 3, 4, 6, 7, 8
Average: 5, 6, 7, 8, 9
Advanced: 5, 6, 7, 8, 9

2. Step 1:

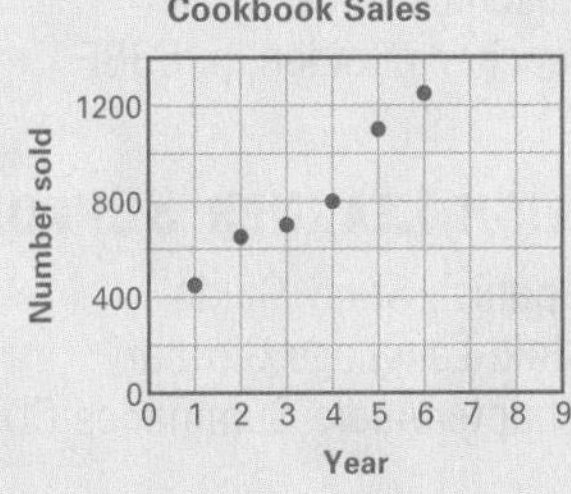

6-9. See Additional Answers beginning on page AA1.

4 ASSESS

ASSESSMENT RESOURCES

For more assessment resources, see:

- Assessment Book
- Test and Practice Generator

MINI-QUIZ

1. Tell whether x and y have a *positive*, *negative*, or *no* relationship. **positive**

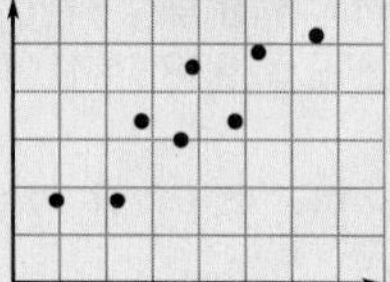

What type of relationship might you expect for the given data?

2. The number of hours of batting practice and the number of successful hits **positive**
3. The number of people sharing the cost of renting a tour bus and the cost per person **negative**

5 FOLLOW-UP

RETEACHING/REMEDIATION

- Study Guide in Chapter 11 Resource Book, pp. 21-22
- Tutor Place, Algebra Card 17
- eTutorial Plus Online
- Extra Practice, p. 737
- Lesson Practice in Chapter 11 Resource Book, pp. 18-20

CHALLENGE/ENRICHMENT

- Challenge Practice in Chapter 11 Resource Book, p. 24
- Teacher's Edition, p. 538F

ENGLISH LEARNER SUPPORT

- Spanish Study Guide
- Multi-Language Glossary
- Chapter Audio Summaries CDs

14, 17-20. See Additional Answers beginning on page AA1.

13. *Sample answer:* When the weather is nicer, more people will vote; no, because it would be hard to find a single measure that would accurately indicate how "nice" the weather is.

In Exercises 10–12, what type of relationship might you expect for the given data?

B **10.** The height of a student in 8th grade and a test score of the student **no relationship**

11. The size of a pizza and the price of a pizza **positive relationship**

12. The amount of money you give back to your friend and the amount you still owe **negative relationship**

C **13. Writing** A newspaper claims there is a strong relationship between the weather on the day of an election and voter turnout. What do you think the newspaper means? Could the newspaper use a scatter plot to support its claim? If so, what would the labels on each axis be? **See margin.**

14. Geometry Make a table showing several values of length and width of a rectangle whose perimeter is 12 inches. Make a scatter plot of the data. Draw a curve that shows the overall pattern of the data. Predict the width of a rectangle when the length is 3.5 inches. **See margin for art; 2.5 in.**

Mixed Review

Find the area of a trapezoid with bases b_1 and b_2 and height h. *(Lesson 10.1)*

15. $b_1 = 14$ m, $b_2 = 16$ m, $h = 6$ m **90 m²**

16. $b_1 = 21$ ft, $b_2 = 32$ ft, $h = 18$ ft **477 ft²**

17. Draw the net of a triangular pyramid. *(Lesson 10.3)* **See margin.**

Make a table of values for the function. Use a domain of −2, −1, 0, 1, and 2. Identify the range. *(Lesson 11.1)* **18–20. See margin.**

18. $y = 0.7x$ **19.** $y = 3x + 4$ **20.** $y = 0.4x - 1$

Basic Skills Solve the equation.

21. $t - 4 = 15$ **19** **22.** $6 + x = 27$ **21** **23.** $z + 17 = 36$ **19** **24.** $w - 13 = 42$ **55**

Test-Taking Practice

INTERNET
State Test Practice
CLASSZONE.COM

Use the information in the table.

25. Multiple Choice Describe the relationship shown in the data. **A**

A. positive **B.** negative
C. none **D.** not enough information

26. Multiple Choice Predict how many points a player who is 77 inches tall could make. **F**

F. 15 **G.** 25 **H.** 65 **I.** 85

Basketball	
Height (in inches)	Avg. points per game
71	3
73	10
75	4
83	19
84	20
90	24

Equations in Two Variables

BEFORE	Now	WHY?
You found solutions of equations in one variable.	You'll find solutions of equations in two variables.	So you can find how long it takes to pay back a loan, as in Ex. 29.

Word Watch

solution of an equation in two variables, p. 549

In the Real World

In-line Skates At a sports store, it costs \$7 per hour to rent in-line skates plus \$10 for the safety equipment. The total cost can be modeled by the equation $C = 10 + 7h$, where C is the total cost in dollars and h is the number of hours skated. What are some possible costs for renting in-line skates?

A **solution of an equation in two variables** is an ordered pair whose values make the equation true. For example, (2, 3) is a solution of $x + y = 5$ because $2 + 3 = 5$.

EXAMPLE 1 Evaluating an Equation in Two Variables

a. Make a table for $C = 10 + 7h$ to find some possible costs for renting in-line skates.

b. How many hours can you skate if you have \$35?

Solution

a. Substitute several values of h into the equation and solve for C.

h-value	Substitute for *h*.	Solve for *C*.	Solution
$h = 1$	$C = 10 + 7(1)$	$C = 17$	(1, 17)
$h = 2$	$C = 10 + 7(2)$	$C = 24$	(2, 24)
$h = 3$	$C = 10 + 7(3)$	$C = 31$	(3, 31)
$h = 4$	$C = 10 + 7(4)$	$C = 38$	(4, 38)

Use the solutions to make a table.

Hours skated *h*	1	2	3	4
Total cost *C*	\$17	\$24	\$31	\$38

b. If you have \$35, you can rent in-line skates for about $3\frac{1}{2}$ hours.

ILLINOIS Standards and ISAT:
8.A.3b, 8.D.3a

PLAN

SKILL CHECK

1. $4(-2) + 7 = \underline{?}$ -1
2. $7(3) + 10 = \underline{?}$ 31
3. $8(-4) - 5 = \underline{?}$ -37
4. $15 - 6(0) = \underline{?}$ 15

LESSON OBJECTIVE

Find solutions of equations in two variables.

PACING

Suggested Number of Days
Basic Course: 2 days
Average Course: 2 days
Advanced Course: 2 days
Block: 1 block

TEACHING RESOURCES

For a complete list of Teaching Resources, see page 538B.

TRANSPARENCY

Warm-Up Exercises for this lesson are available on a transparency. A support transparency is available for Example 1.

TEACH

MOTIVATING THE LESSON

Ask students who have rented sports equipment or facilities what they remember about the costs.

TIPS FOR NEW TEACHERS

Some students may have difficulty adjusting to the idea that an equation can have more than one solution. See Tips for New Teachers in the *Chapter 11 Resource Book*.

EXTRA EXAMPLES

Example 1 Jan is considering a cell phone plan that costs \$21 each month plus a one-time activation fee of \$35. She has budgeted \$120 for cell phone costs for the year.

a. Make a table for $C = 35 + 21m$ to find some possible costs for the cell phone plan.

Months m	Cost (\$)
1	56
2	77
3	98
4	119

b. How many months can Jan use the cell phone with her budget of \$120? **4 mo**

Example 2 Tell whether (4, 7) is a solution of $2x + 3y = 29$. **yes**

Example 3 Solve the equation $5x - y = 9$ for y. List four solutions. $y = 5x - 9$; *Sample answer:* (−1, −14), (0, −9), (1, −4), (2, 1)

COMMON ERROR

Watch for students who substitute ordered pairs mentally, make arithmetic mistakes, and so err on whether or not an ordered pair is a solution.

CONCEPT CHECK

Find the value of C to make (4, 5) a solution of the equation $7x + 5y = C$. Explain your reasoning. **53; $7(4) + 5(5) = C$ must be true to make (4, 5) a solution of the equation, so C must be 53.**

DAILY PUZZLER

Is $(x, y, z) = (3, 1, 0)$ a solution of $2x - 6y = 9z$? **yes**

EXAMPLE 2 Checking Solutions

Tell whether (7, −6) is a solution of $x + 3y = 14$.

$x + 3y = 14$	Write original equation.
$7 + 3(-6) \stackrel{?}{=} 14$	Substitute 7 for x and −6 for y.
$7 + (-18) \stackrel{?}{=} 14$	Simplify.
$-11 \neq 14$ ✗	Solution does not check.

ANSWER The ordered pair (7, −6) is *not* a solution of $x + 3y = 14$.

When finding solutions of an equation, it can be helpful to rewrite the equation in *function form*. When an equation is in function form it is solved for y.

Function form	Not function form
$y = -2x + 15$	$2x + y = 15$

HELP with Solving

Generally, an equation involving two variables has an infinite number of solutions.

EXAMPLE 3 Finding Solutions of an Equation

Solve the equation $4x + y = 15$ for y. List four solutions.

(1) Rewrite the equation in function form.

$4x + y = 15$	Write original equation.
$y = 15 - 4x$	Subtract $4x$ from each side.

(2) Evaluate the equation for several x-values.

x-value	Substitute for x.	Solve for y.	Solution
$x = -1$	$y = 15 - 4(-1)$	$y = 19$	(−1, 19)
$x = 0$	$y = 15 - 4(0)$	$y = 15$	(0, 15)
$x = 1$	$y = 15 - 4(1)$	$y = 11$	(1, 11)
$x = 2$	$y = 15 - 4(2)$	$y = 7$	(2, 7)

ANSWER Four solutions are (−1, 19), (0, 15), (1, 11), and (2, 7).

Your turn now **Tell whether the ordered pair is a solution of the equation.**

1. $y = 3x - 7$; (6, 5) **no**
2. $-2x - 4y = 12$; (−4, −1) **yes**

List four solutions of the equation. 3–4. Sample answers are given.

3. $y = -2x + 6$ (−1, 8), (0, 6), (1, 4), (2, 2)
4. $15x + 3y = 12$ (0, 4), (1, −1), (2, −6), (3, −11)

Exercises

More Practice, p. 737

Getting Ready to Practice

5. The x-value was substituted for y and the y-value was substituted for x. The second step should be $2(-5) + 3(4) \stackrel{?}{=} -7$, followed by $-10 + 12 \stackrel{?}{=} -7$ and $2 \neq -7$. So, $(-5, 4)$ is not a solution.

1. **Vocabulary** Copy and complete: A(n) _?_ of an equation in two variables is an ordered pair. solution

Rewrite the equation in function form.

2. $3x + y = 19$ $y = 19 - 3x$
3. $-4x + 2y = 8$ $y = 2x + 4$
4. $-10x - 5y = -15$ $y = 3 - 2x$

5. **Find the Error** Describe and correct the error made when a student was asked to decide whether $(-5, 4)$ is a solution of $2x + 3y = -7$.

$$2x + 3y = -7$$
$$2(4) + 3(-5) \stackrel{?}{=} -7$$
$$8 + (-15) \stackrel{?}{=} -7$$
$$-7 = -7 \checkmark$$
So, $(-5, 4)$ is a solution.

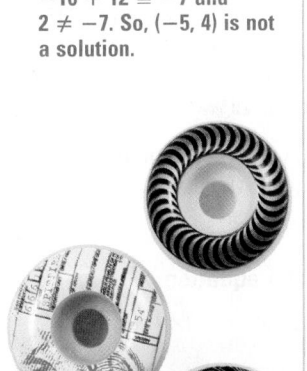

6. **Skateboard Wheels** Your skateboard club decides to replace each club member's wheels for a competition. Sets of four wheels sell for \$24 plus a \$14 shipping and handling cost added to the total. Use the equation $C = 24n + 14$, where C is the total cost in dollars and n is the number of sets of wheels ordered. If the final cost is \$182, how many sets of wheels were bought? 7 sets

Practice and Problem Solving

HELP with Homework

Example	Exercises
1	7-9, 29
2	10-15, 19-22
3	16-18, 23-28

Online Resources CLASSZONE.COM
- More Examples
- eTutorial Plus

Copy and complete the table for the equation.

x	-5	0	5	10
y	?	?	?	?

A 7. $y = x + 8$ 3, 8, 13, 18
8. $y = 4 - 3x$ 19, 4, −11, −26
9. $y = -20 + x$ −25, −20, −15, −10

Tell whether the ordered pair is a solution of the equation.

10. $y = 4x + 2$; $(2, 10)$ yes
11. $y = -2x + 5$; $(7, 5)$ no
12. $y = 6 - x$; $(-3, 3)$ no
13. $y = 13 - 5x$; $(4, -7)$ yes
14. $y = 6x + 7$; $(2, 21)$ no
15. $y = 3x - 26$; $(6, -8)$ yes

List four solutions of the equation. 16–18. Sample answers are given.

16. $y = -2x + 5$ (−1, 7), (0, 5), (1, 3), (2, 1)
17. $y = -10 + (-4x)$
18. $y = \frac{1}{2}x - 1$

17. (−1, −6), (0, −10), (1, −14), (2, −18)

18. (−2, −2), (0, −1), (2, 0), (4, 1)

3 APPLY

ASSIGNMENT GUIDE

Basic Course

Day 1: pp. 551-553 Exs. 7-15, 19-22, 31-33, 43-45, 51

Day 2: pp. 551-553 Exs. 16-18, 23-29, 34-38, 46-49

Average Course

Day 1: pp. 551-553 Exs. 9-15, 19-22, 31-33, 42-47

Day 2: pp. 551-553 Exs. 16-18, 23-29, 34-40, 48-51

Advanced Course

Day 1: pp. 551-553 Exs. 9-15, 19-22, 33-39, 50

Day 2: pp. 551-553 Exs. 16-18, 23-30, 40-46*, 51

Block

pp. 551-553 Exs. 9-29, 31-40, 42-51

EXTRA PRACTICE

- Student Edition, p. 737
- Chapter 11 Resource Book, pp. 28-30
- Test and Practice Generator

TRANSPARENCY

Even-numbered answers are available on transparencies. A support transparency is available for Exercises 7-9.

HOMEWORK CHECK

When you review students' homework for this lesson, go over the following exercises to check understanding of key concepts.

Basic: 7, 9, 10, 16, 19

Average: 9, 10, 16, 19, 23

Advanced: 9, 10, 17, 20, 24

TEACHING TIP

In Exercises 19–22, have students estimate their answers before using a calculator.

23–28. Sample answers are given.

23. (−1, −15), (0, −13), (1, −11), (2, −9)

24. (−1, 8), (0, 24), (1, 40), (2, 56)

25. (−1, 8), (0, 3), (1, −2), (2, −7)

26. (−1, 18), (0, 17), (1, 16), (2, 15)

27. (−1, −45), (0, −51), (1, −57), (2, −63)

28. (−3, −6), (0, −5), (3, −4), (6, −3)

31–36. Sample solutions are given.

31. $y = -x + 8$; (−1, 9), (0, 8), (1, 7), (2, 6)

32. $y = -4x + 42$; (−1, 46), (0, 42), (1, 38), (2, 34)

33. $y = 3x + 33$; (−1, 30), (0, 33), (1, 36), (2, 39)

34. $y = 2x + 3$; (−1, 1), (0, 3), (1, 5), (2, 7)

35. $y = 2 - 3x$; (−1, 5), (0, 2), (1, −1), (2, −4)

36. $y = \frac{1}{3}x + 2\frac{2}{3}$; (−2, 2), (1, 3), (4, 4), (7, 5)

Calculator Tell whether the ordered pair is a solution of the equation.

19. $3x - y = 71.2$; (−4.6, 8.2) no **20.** $8x + y = 25$; (2.25, 1.75) no

21. $x + 4y = 28.75$; (3.23, 6.38) yes **22.** $x - 2y = -10.42$; (−5.22, −7.82) no

List four solutions of the equation.

23. $y = 2x - 13$ **24.** $y = 16x + 24$ **25.** $-5x + 3 = y$

26. $y = -x + 17$ **27.** $y = -51 - 6x$ **28.** $y = \frac{1}{3}x - 5$

B **29. Loan** Your friend agrees to lend you \$15 to buy a toy rocket. You promise to pay your friend \$.75 each week until you have paid back the full \$15. Use the equation $P = 15 - 0.75n$, where P is the amount of money in dollars that you have left to pay and n is the number of weeks, to find the number of weeks it takes to pay back your friend. 20 wk

30. Critical Thinking In Example 3 of the lesson, you solved the equation for y before substituting the x-values. Will you get the same solutions if you substitute the x-values before solving for y? yes

Solve the equation for *y*. List four solutions of the equation.

31. $x + y = 8$ **32.** $42 = 4x + y$ **33.** $33 = -3x + y$

34. $4y = 8x + 12$ **35.** $5y + 15x = 10$ **36.** $-32 = 4x - 12y$

Write an equation in two variables for the values in the table.

37.

x	−1	0	1	2
y	2	4	6	8

$y = 2x + 4$

38.

x	0	2	4	6
y	2	3	4	5

$y = \frac{1}{2}x + 2$

39. Estimation Estimate the values of $9x$ and $8y$ to explain why $\left(\frac{8}{3}, \frac{-7}{10}\right)$ is not a solution of $9x + 8y = 16$. *Sample answer:* $9x = 24$ and $8y \approx -6$, so $9x + 8y \approx 18$, which is greater than 16.

40. Glass Elevator An elevator is at a height of 800 feet. It is descending at a rate of 150 feet per minute. Use the equation $h = 800 - 150m$, where h is the height of the elevator in feet and m is the time in minutes. What is the height of the elevator after 5 minutes? How long will it take the elevator to reach a height of 0 feet? 50 ft; $5\frac{1}{3}$ min

C **41. Challenge** Find the ordered pair that is the solution of both of the equations $y = -2x + 3$ and $y = 0.5x - 2$. (2, −1)

42. Carnival You can go to the carnival for 2 hours. You know that each ride takes about 10 minutes (including the wait in line), and you also want to spend time playing games. Write an equation in two variables to model this situation. If you go on 8 rides, how long can you play games? $120 = 10x + y$; 40 min

Mixed Review

43. Plot (2, 3), (−6, 0), (−5, −1), and (8, −4) in a coordinate plane. *(Lesson 2.8)* **See margin.**

44. Find the area of a circle whose diameter is 25 inches. Use 3.14 for π. *(Lesson 10.2)* **491 in.^{2}**

Make a table of values for the function. Use a domain of −2, −1, 0, 1, and 2. Identify the range. *(Lesson 11.1)* **45–47. See margin.**

45. $4x + 8y = 16$
46. $6x + 3y = 36$
47. $14x + 7y = 56$

Basic Skills Solve the equation.

48. $6x - 4.25 = 3.55$ **1.3**
49. $14.98 + 2.4y = -6.02$ **−8.75**

Test-Taking Practice

INTERNET
State Test Practice
CLASSZONE.COM

50. **Short Response** To join the summer movie club at your local theater, you pay a fee of \$25. Then each movie you see is only \$3. This situation can be modeled by the equation $C = 25 + 3m$, where C is the total cost in dollars and m is the number of movies you see. Copy and complete the table. If you can spend \$60 on the movie club this summer, how many movies can you see? **11 movies**

Movies seen m	Total cost C
1	? 28
5	? 40
10	? 55
25	? 100

51. **Multiple Choice** Which ordered pair is a solution of the equation $y = -3x + 11$? **A**

A. (−2, 17) B. (0, −11) C. (2, 3) D. (−1, −14)

BRAIN GAME

Late Night Show

Each ordered pair is a solution of exactly one lettered equation. Write the appropriate letters in the blanks to find what kind of show the boy can expect to see. **PLANETARIUM**

?	?	?	?	?	?	?	?	?	?	?
(4, 1)	(9, 12)	(1, 9)	(3, 2)	(2, 5)	(4, 4)	(1, 9)	(17, 9)	(7, 24)	(0, 2)	(8, 15)

L. $y = 2x - 6$ **A.** $x + y = 10$ **T.** $4x + y = 20$ **E.** $y = 2x + 1$

I. $6x - y = 18$ **N.** $2y = 6x - 14$ **R.** $y = x - 8$ **U.** $y = \frac{1}{3}x + 2$

M. $x + 3y = 53$ **P.** $y = \frac{3}{2}x - 5$ **S.** $x + y = 6$ **O.** $y = x + 1$

4 ASSESS

Assessment Resources

For more assessment resources, see:
- Assessment Book
- Test and Practice Generator

Mini-Quiz

1. List four solutions of the equation $y = -6 + 5x$. ***Sample answer:* (−1, −11), (0, −6), (1, −1), (2, 4)**

Tell whether the ordered pair is a solution of the equation.

2. $y = -x + 12$; (−1, 12) **no**
3. $y = -17 + 3x$; (5, −2) **yes**
4. Write an equation in two variables for the values in the table.

x	0	1	2	3
y	−2	1	4	7

$y = 3x - 2$

5 FOLLOW-UP

Reteaching/Remediation
- Study Guide in Chapter 11 Resource Book, pp. 31-32
- Tutor Place, Algebra Card 4
- eTutorial Plus Online
- Extra Practice, p. 737
- Lesson Practice in Chapter 11 Resource Book, pp. 28-30

Challenge/Enrichment
- Challenge Practice in Chapter 11 Resource Book, p. 34
- Teacher's Edition, p. 538F

English Learner Support
- Spanish Study Guide
- Multi-Language Glossary
- Chapter Audio Summaries CDs

43, 45–47. See Additional Answers beginning on page AA1.

1 PLAN

Strategy Background

The strategy Make a Table helps students visualize and analyze data. They can use the table to identify patterns or properties of the entries in the table. Before making a table, students should always take time to think about the headings for the table.

2 TEACH

Guiding Students' Work

Have students read the problem several times. Make sure they understand from the wording of the problem that the number of laps John swims is increasing every week.

EXTRA EXAMPLES

Example Zuhneida is learning to type. On the first day, she made 20 mistakes on one page. On the second day, she made 2 fewer mistakes on one page than the first day. If Zuhneida continues at this rate, on what day of class will she make no mistakes on one page? **day 11**

11.4 Problem Solving Strategies

- Guess, Check, and Revise
- Look for a Pattern
- Draw a Diagram
- Act It Out
- Make a Table
- Work Backward
- Make a Model

Make a Table

Problem At the beginning of swimming class John can swim 4 laps. Starting after the first week, his swimming teacher wants him to swim 2 laps more than the week before until the end of the 7 week class. At this rate, how many laps will John be able to swim during the last week of class?

1 Read and Understand

Read the problem carefully.

You need to use the pattern to find the number of laps John can swim after a given number of weeks.

2 Make a Plan

Decide on a strategy to use.

One way to solve the problem is to make a table of values. Then extend the pattern until you find the answer.

3 Solve the Problem

Reread the problem and make a table.

First, make a table and enter the information given.

In week 1, John swims 4 laps. In week 2, he swims $4 + 2$, or 6 laps. Each week he swims 2 more laps.

You know that the swimming class is 7 weeks long, so extend your table following the pattern to fill it in.

ANSWER John will be swimming 16 laps during the last week of the 7 week class.

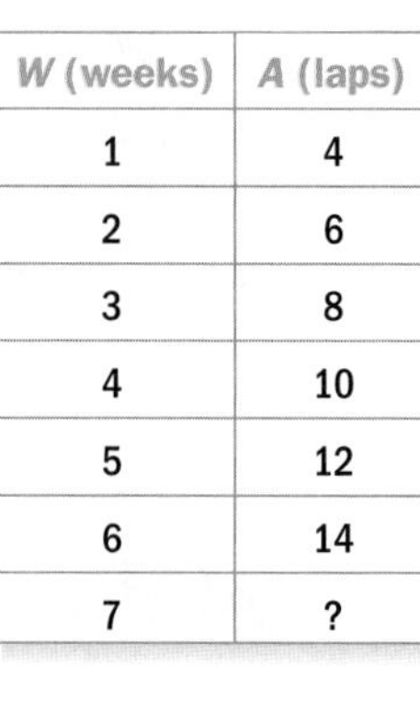

W (weeks)	*A* (laps)
1	4
2	6
3	8
4	10
5	12
6	14
7	?

4 Look Back

Compare the information in your table to the original problem to be sure you've used the information correctly.

ILLINOIS Standards and ISAT:
6.B.3a, 6.C.3a, 8.B.3

Practice the Strategy

Use the strategy *make a table.*

1. **Diving** Copy and complete the table below representing the depth in feet of a deep-sea diver, currently 160 feet below the surface, ascending at a rate of 20 feet every 4 minutes.

Time (minutes)	4	8	12	16
Depth (feet)	?	?	?	?

140 120 100 80

2. **Training** Extend the table below using the pattern to find out how many miles you will run in week 10 of training for a race. 7.5 mi

Week	1	2	3	4
Distance (miles)	3	3.5	4	4.5

3. **Hot-Air Balloon** A hot-air balloon has just taken off. The balloon is currently 10 feet off the ground and is rising at a rate of 2 feet per second. What is the height of the balloon after 25 seconds? 60 ft

4. **Reading** You were assigned to read a book over your 2 week spring vacation. The book has 256 pages, so you decide to read 32 pages each day. At this rate when will you finish the book? in 8 days

5. **DVD Players** Casey and Krystal are each saving money to buy a DVD player that costs $160. Casey already has $55 saved. He will add $7 every week to his fund. Krystal does not have any money saved. She will put $16 in her fund every week until she can afford it. Who will be able to purchase a DVD player first? Krystal

Mixed Problem Solving

Use any strategy to solve the problem.

6. **Number Sense** The cube of what number is 3375? 15

7. **Folding** You are trying to divide a sheet of paper into rectangles by folding it into thirds. You fold the paper 3 times into thirds without opening it. How many of the smallest rectangles do you have as a result? How many of the smallest rectangles will you have if you fold the paper into thirds one more time? 27 rectangles; 81 rectangles

8. **Clothing** The sale price of a rack of sweaters is 80% of the original price. A month later, the sweaters sold for $23.20 each, which is two dollars less than 70% of the sale price. What is the original price of one of the sweaters? $45

9. **Running** Leslie and Todd each ran in a race. Leslie ran in the girls' 12–16 year old division on a 10 mile track and Todd ran in the boys' 10–12 year old division on an 8 mile track. Leslie came in second place with a time of 1 hour and 20 minutes. Todd came in first place with a time of 1 hour and 8 minutes. Who ran faster? Leslie

10. **Surface Area** Find the surface area of the solid shown below. about 452 yd^2

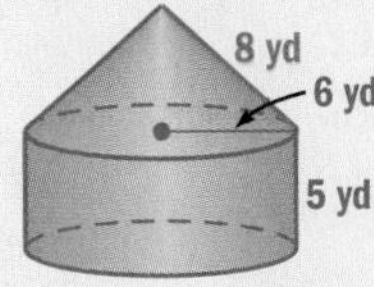

3 APPLY

TRANSPARENCY

Even-numbered answers are available on transparencies.

TEACHING TIP

In the Example on the previous page, students had to extend the pattern to find the solution. In Exercise 1, students do not need to extend the pattern because they can study what they already have to compute the depth for 10 minutes.

MATH REASONING

In Exercise 3, have students write an equation for the height h after s seconds. ($h = 10 + 2s$)

SUGGESTED STRATEGIES

You may wish to suggest the following strategies for the problems in the Mixed Problem Solving:

- Exercise 6: Guess, Check, and Revise
- Exercise 7: Draw a Diagram; Make a Model; Act It Out
- Exercise 8: Work Backward
- Exercise 9: Break into Parts
- Exercise 10: Break into Parts

1 PLAN

SKILL CHECK

Graph each ordered pair on a coordinate grid.

1. (2, −1) **2.** (3, 1)
3. (−2, −2) **4.** (−1, −3)

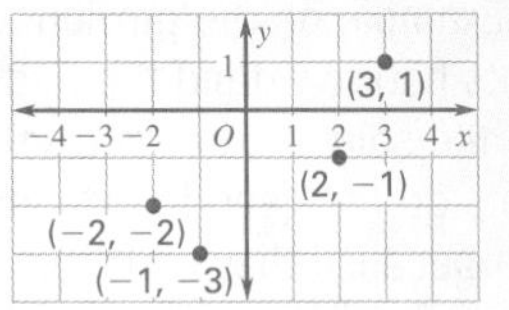

LESSON OBJECTIVE

Learn to sketch the graph of a linear equation.

PACING

Suggested Number of Days
Basic Course: 2 days
Average Course: 2 days
Advanced Course: 2 days
Block: 1 block

TEACHING RESOURCES

For a complete list of Teaching Resources, see page 538B.

TRANSPARENCY

Warm-Up Exercises for this lesson are available on a transparency. Support transparencies are available for the Activity and Examples 1-3.

2 TEACH

MOTIVATING THE LESSON

Ask students what *linear* means, and how a linear equation relates to the word *line*.

ACTIVITY

Goal Plot ordered pairs.

Key Discovery The graph of a linear equation forms a line.

Graphs of Linear Equations

BEFORE	Now	WHY?
You found solutions of equations in two variables.	You'll learn to sketch the graph of a linear equation.	So you can find the amount you pay on a payment plan, as in Ex. 28.

Word Watch

linear equation, p. 556

Activity You can graph a function by plotting ordered pairs from a table of values.

(1) Copy and complete the table of values using the equation $y = 3x + 2$.

x	−4	−2	0	2	4
y	−10	? −4	2	? 8	? 14

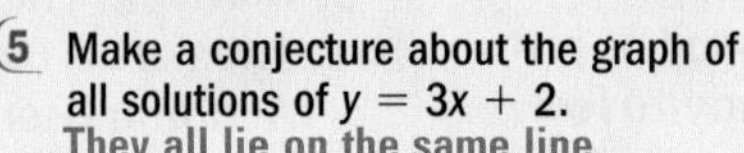

(2) Graph each ordered pair (x, y) in a coordinate plane.
(−4, −10), (−2, ?), (0, 2), (2, ?), (4, ?) See margin.

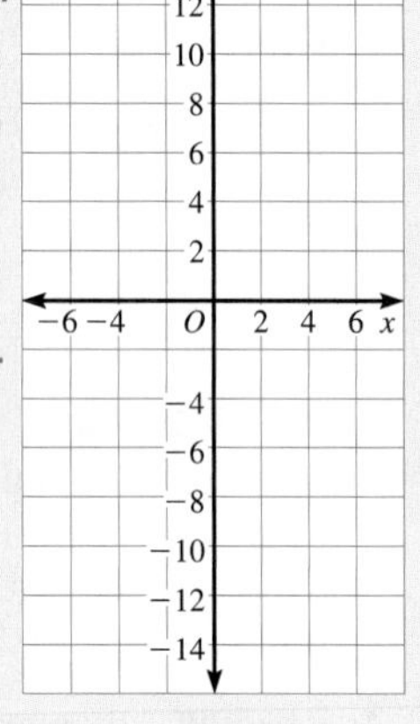

(3) Connect the points. What pattern do you notice?
They form a line.

(4) Find several more solutions of $y = 3x + 2$. Locate each solution in your coordinate plane. What do you notice?
Sample answer: (−1, −1), (1, 5); they are on the line.

(5) Make a conjecture about the graph of all solutions of $y = 3x + 2$.
They all lie on the same line.

Linear Equations In the activity, you graphed solutions of a *linear equation.* A **linear equation** in two variables is an equation in which the variables appear in separate terms and each variable occurs only to the first power. The graph of a linear equation is a line.

Linear equations	Not linear equations
$y = x - 1$	$24 = rt$
$3p + 5q = 16$	$a^2 + b^2 = c^2$
$s = 0.2t$	

The equation $24 = rt$ is not linear because it has two variables in the same term. The equation $a^2 + b^2 = c^2$ is not linear because the variables are squared.

ILLINOIS Standards and ISAT:
8.B.3, 8.D.3a

with Solving

The arrowheads on the graph in Example 1 indicate that the line extends forever in both directions.

EXAMPLE 1 Graphing a Linear Equation

Graph $y = \frac{1}{2}x + 1$.

Solution

(1) Choose several x-values and make a table of values.

x	−4	−2	0	2	4
y	−1	0	1	2	3

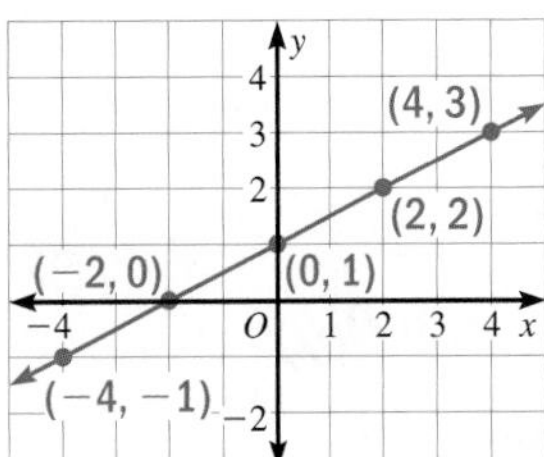

(2) List the solutions as ordered pairs.

(−4, −1), (−2, 0), (0, 1), (2, 2), (4, 3)

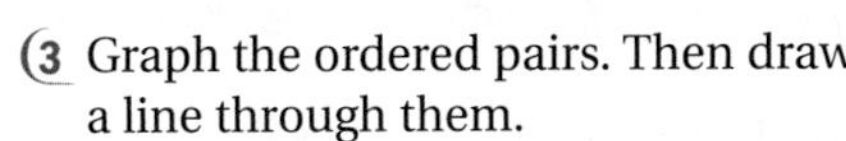

(3) Graph the ordered pairs. Then draw a line through them.

ANSWER The line is the graph of $y = \frac{1}{2}x + 1$.

Your turn now **Graph the linear equation.** 1–4. See margin.

1. $y = x + 4$ **2.** $y = -2x - 3$ **3.** $y = \frac{1}{2}x - 7$ **4.** $y - x = 6$

EXAMPLE 2 Using the Graph of a Linear Equation

Hair Sue's hair is 3 inches long. If her hair grows $\frac{1}{2}$ inch per month, you can model the length l of her hair in inches using the equation $l = \frac{1}{2}m + 3$ where m is the time in months.

a. Graph $l = \frac{1}{2}m + 3$.

b. Estimate how many months it will take Sue to grow her hair to $5\frac{1}{2}$ inches.

Solution

a. Make a table of values.

m	0	1	2	3
l	3	$3\frac{1}{2}$	4	$4\frac{1}{2}$

Then graph each solution and draw a ray through the points.

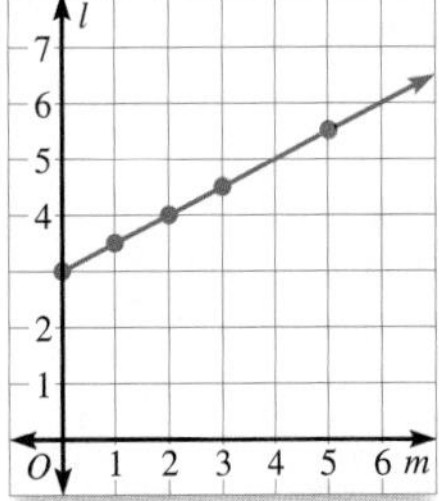

b. The graph shows that it will take about 5 months for Sue to grow her hair to $5\frac{1}{2}$ inches.

What do you think? Biology

Hair Growth

If human hair grows at a rate of $\frac{1}{2}$ inch per month, how much does your hair grow in one year? in one and a half years? **6 in.; 9 in.**

TIPS FOR NEW TEACHERS

Some students may need extra practice plotting points before graphing lines. See Tips for New Teachers in the *Chapter 11 Resource Book*.

EXTRA EXAMPLES

Example 1 Graph $y = -x + 2$.

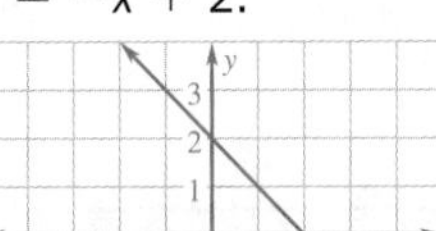

Example 2 Teofono's puppy weighs 10 pounds and is gaining a pound every week. You can model the weight, p, of the puppy using the equation $p = 10 + w$, where w is the time in weeks.

a. Graph $p = 10 + w$.

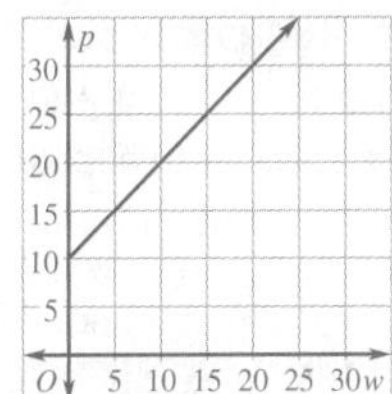

b. Estimate how many weeks it will take the puppy to weigh 25 pounds. **15 wk**

Differentiating Instruction

Less Proficient Students Have a small group of students graph simple equations, such as $y = x$, $y = x + 1$, and so on. One student can make the table and graph while the others direct the student's work. Then progress the group to slightly more difficult equations, such as $y = \frac{1}{2}x + 3$, $y = -x + 1$, and so on.

Step 2, 1–4. See Additional Answers beginning on page AA1.

EXTRA EXAMPLES

Example 3

a. Graph $x = 3$.

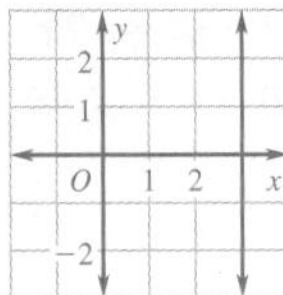

b. Graph $y = -1$.

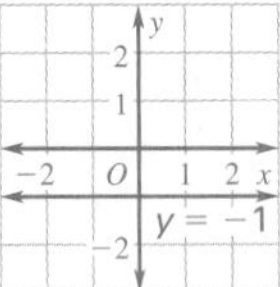

CONCEPT CHECK

Which is a linear equation in two variables, $7x + 9y = 19$ or $y(7x + 9) = 19$? What do you know about the graph of a linear equation, and what steps could you take to draw its graph? **$7x + 9y = 19$; it forms a line. You can choose several x-values, find corresponding y-values to make ordered pairs, plot the ordered pairs, and then draw a line through the plotted points.**

DAILY PUZZLER

How many horizontal lines pass through the point (154, 77)? **one**

2–4. Sample answers are given.

2.

Input x	−2	−1	0	1	2
Output y	−4	−1	2	5	8

3.

Input x	−2	−1	0	1	2
Output y	−4	−4	−4	−4	−4

4.

Input x	−2	−1	0	1	2
Output y	2	5	8	11	14

Vertical and Horizontal Lines Some linear equations have only one variable. The graphs of these equations are vertical or horizontal lines.

Vertical and Horizontal Lines

The graph of $x = a$ is the vertical line passing through $(a, 0)$.

The graph of $y = b$ is the horizontal line passing through $(0, b)$.

Watch Out! A vertical line *does not* represent a function, because one input has infinitely many outputs. A horizontal line *does* represent a function.

EXAMPLE 3 **Graphing Vertical and Horizontal Lines**

a. The graph of $x = -2$ is the vertical line through $(-2, 0)$.

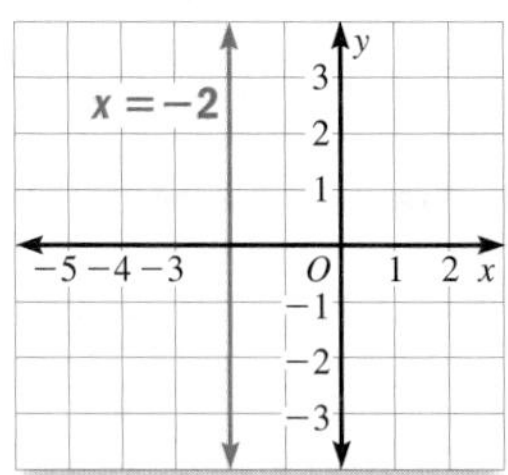

For all values of y, the x-value is -2.

b. The graph of $y = 4$ is the horizontal line through $(0, 4)$.

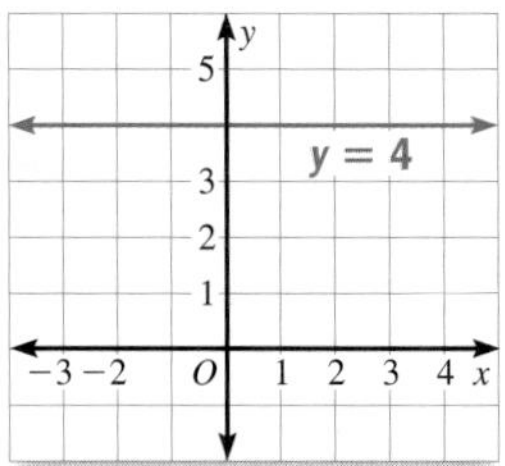

For all values of x, the y-value is 4.

11.4 Exercises

More Practice, p. 737

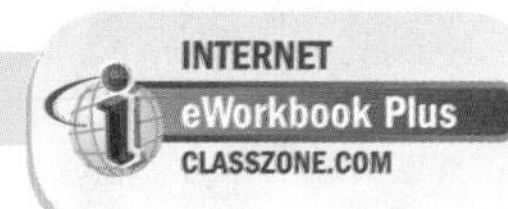

Getting Ready to Practice

1. Vocabulary Copy and complete: When you graph the solutions of a linear equation, the points form a(n) __?__. **line**

Make a table of values for the equation. 2–4. See margin.

2. $3x - y = -2$ **3.** $y + 4 = 0$ **4.** $-6x + 2y = 16$

Match the equation with the description of its graph.

5. $y = -16$ **B** **6.** $x = 20$ **A** **7.** $y = x + 1$ **C**

A. vertical line **B.** horizontal line **C.** slanted line

Practice and Problem Solving

with Homework

Example	Exercises
1	14-25
2	28
3	14-27, 29

Online Resources
CLASSZONE.COM

- More Examples
- eTutorial Plus

Tell whether the equation is a linear equation.

A **8.** $3x + y = 8$ yes **9.** $2y - 5x = 10$ yes **10.** $9x^2 = y + 4$ no

Find three ordered pairs that are solutions of the given equation. 11–13. Sample answers are given.

11. $y = x - 2$ (−1, −3), (0, −2), (1, −1) **12.** $y = 3x + 4$ (−1, 1), (0, 4), (1, 7) **13.** $y = 6$ (−1, 6), (0, 6), (1, 6)

Graph the linear equation. 14–25. See margin.

14. $y = x + 9$ **15.** $y = x + 10$ **16.** $y = x - 14$

17. $y = 8x$ **18.** $y = -2x + 1$ **19.** $y = -7x + 8$

20. $y = -5x - 6$ **21.** $y = \frac{1}{2}x + 5$ **22.** $y = -\frac{1}{4}x + 12$

23. $y = 9$ **24.** $x = 8$ **25.** $x = -17$

Critical Thinking **Write the equation of the line.**

B **26.**

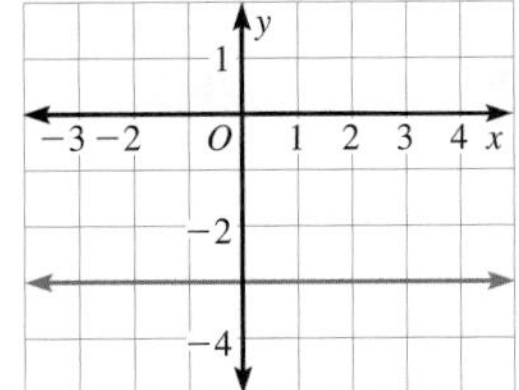

$y = -3$

27.

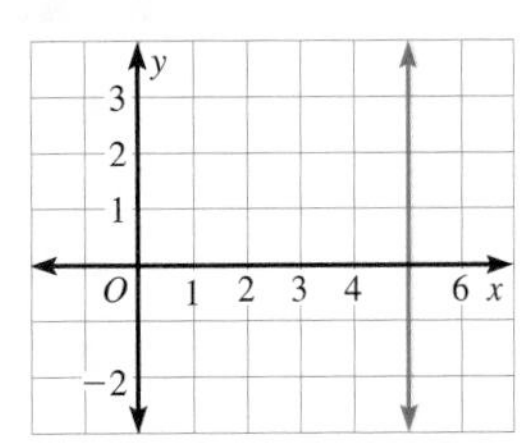

$x = 5$

28. Buying a Camera You are taking a photography class and need a digital camera. The payment plan for the camera can be modeled by the equation $C = 10m + 50$, where C is the total amount paid and m is the number of months. Graph the equation and then estimate how much you pay in 12 months. See margin for art; $170.

29. Critical Thinking Graph the equations $x = -3$ and $y = 5$ on the same coordinate grid. Then write the coordinates of the point where the lines intersect. Explain how you can find the coordinates of this point without graphing. See margin for art; (−3, 5). *Sample answer:* Since $x = -3$ and $y = 5$, (−3, 5) will be the coordinates of the point of intersection.

Graph the linear equation. 30–35. See margin.

30. $x - y = 0$ **31.** $10x = -2y$ **32.** $16x - 4y = 8$

33. $9x + 3y = 18$ **34.** $x - 5y = -5$ **35.** $3x - 2y = 6$

36. Savings Account Janet is saving money for a vacation. She has $80 saved and plans to add $15.50 to her savings each month. The equation $y = 15.50x + 80$, where y is the amount of money Janet has saved and x is the number of months, models this situation. Make a table of values and graph the equation. Use your graph to estimate when Janet will have $250. See margin for art; in 11 mo.

ASSIGNMENT GUIDE

Basic Course

Day 1: pp. 559-560 Exs. 8-10, 17-22, 30-32, 41-46

Day 2: pp. 559-560 Exs. 11-16, 23-28, 33-37, 47-49

Average Course

Day 1: pp. 559-560 Exs. 8-10, 17-22, 33-39, 48-50

Day 2: pp. 559-560 Exs. 11-16, 23-29, 41-47

Advanced Course

Day 1: pp. 559-560 Exs. 8-10, 17-22, 33-39, 48-50

Day 2: pp. 559-560 Exs. 11-16, 23-29, 40-45*

Block

pp. 559-560 Exs. 8-29, 33-39, 41-50

EXTRA PRACTICE

- Student Edition, p. 737
- Chapter 11 Resource Book, pp. 38-40
- Test and Practice Generator

TRANSPARENCY

Even-numbered answers are available on transparencies. Support transparencies are available for Exercises 2-4, 14-25, 28, 30-36, and 40.

HOMEWORK CHECK

When you review students' homework for this lesson, go over the following exercises to check understanding of key concepts.

Basic: 14, 20, 23, 27, 28

Average: 15, 21, 23, 27, 28

Advanced: 16, 21, 24, 26, 29

14-25, 28-36. See Additional Answers beginning on page AA1.

4 ASSESS

Assessment Resources

For more assessment resources, see:

- Assessment Book
- Test and Practice Generator

Mini-Quiz

Find three ordered pairs that are solutions of the given equation.

1. $y = 4 + x$ ***Sample answer:*** **(0, 4), (2, 6), (3, 7)**
2. $y = 3x - 10$ ***Sample answer:*** **(0, −10), (3, −1), (5, 5)**
3. Graph the equation $y = -2x + 3$.

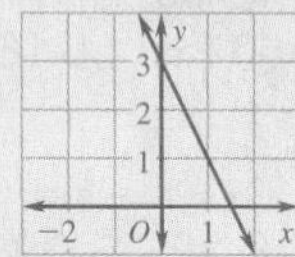

4. Tell whether $xy = 3$ is a linear equation. Explain your reasoning. **No; the variables are not in separate terms.**

5 FOLLOW-UP

Reteaching/Remediation

- Study Guide in Chapter 11 Resource Book, pp. 41–42
- Tutor Place, Algebra Card 17
- eTutorial Plus Online
- Extra Practice, p. 737
- Lesson Practice in Chapter 11 Resource Book, pp. 38–40

Challenge/Enrichment

- Challenge Practice in Chapter 11 Resource Book, p. 43
- Teacher's Edition, p. 538F

English Learner Support

- Spanish Study Guide
- Multi-Language Glossary
- Chapter Audio Summaries CDs

40, 50. See Additional Answers beginning on page AA1.

C **37.** Write the equation of the horizontal line that passes through point A. **$y = 2$**

38. Write the equation of the vertical line that passes through point B. **$x = -5$**

39. Writing Explain how to find the equation of a line that is parallel to the x-axis and lies 8.6 units below it.

39. ***Sample answer:*** **The line must be horizontal and contain all points with a y-coordinate of −8.6, so the equation of the line is $y = -8.6$.**

40. Challenge Copy and complete the table for the equation $y = x^2$. Then graph the equation. How can you tell that $y = x^2$ is not a linear equation from looking at the graph? How can you tell from the equation that it is not a linear equation?

x	−2	−1	0	1	2
y	? 4	? 1	0	? 1	? 4

See margin for art. *Sample answer:* The graph is not a line; the equation contains a variable term that is squared.

Mixed Review

Find the area of the parallelogram with height *h* and base *b*. *(Lesson 10.1)*

41. $h = 10, b = 14$ **140 square units** **42.** $h = 17, b = 23$ **391 square units** **43.** $h = 32, b = 33$ **1056 square units**

44. Decide whether the relation is a function: (0, 0), (1, −1), (−1, −1), (2, −2). *(Lesson 11.1)* **yes**

45. Copy and complete the table for the equation $6x - 2y = 4$. *(Lesson 11.3)*

x	−4	−2	0	1	2	5
y	?	?	−2	?	?	?
	−14	−8		1	4	13

Basic Skills Solve the equation.

46. $-8n = -240$ **30** **47.** $\frac{x}{6} = -42$ **−252** **48.** $\frac{z}{12} = 4$ **48**

Test-Taking Practice

INTERNET
State Test Practice
CLASSZONE.COM

49. Multiple Choice Which equation is not linear? **C**

A. $y = \frac{1}{2}x + 6$ **B.** $2x + 3y = 6$ **C.** $y = x^2 - 6$ **D.** $2x = 6 - 3y$

50. Short Response The monthly charge for a local cell phone calling plan can be modeled by the linear equation $C = 0.05t + 5.95$, where C is the total monthly cost in dollars and t is the number of minutes used per month. Make a table of values and graph the equation. **See margin.**

Technology Activity

GRAPHING CALCULATOR

Graphing Linear Functions

GOAL Use a graphing calculator to graph linear functions.

Example **Graph the equation $x - 2y = 6$.**

Solution

1 Rewrite the equation so that it is in function form: $y = \frac{1}{2}x - 3$.

2 Use the following keystrokes on a graphing calculator to enter the function:

Keystrokes

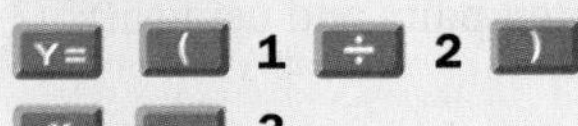

Display

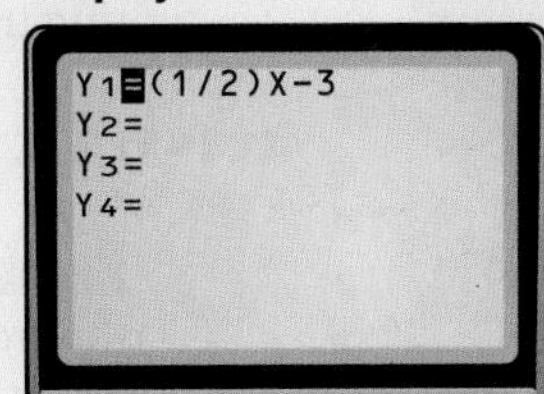

Use the WINDOW feature to set the size of the graph.

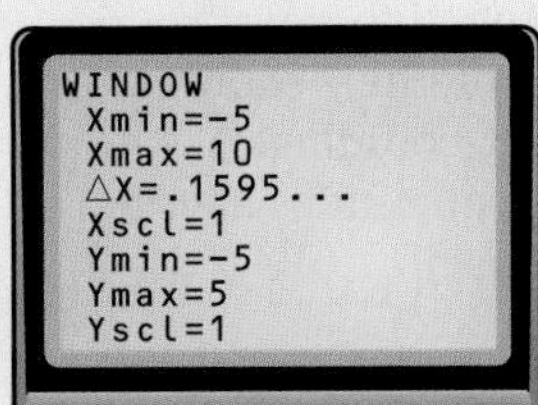

View the graph by pressing the GRAPH button.

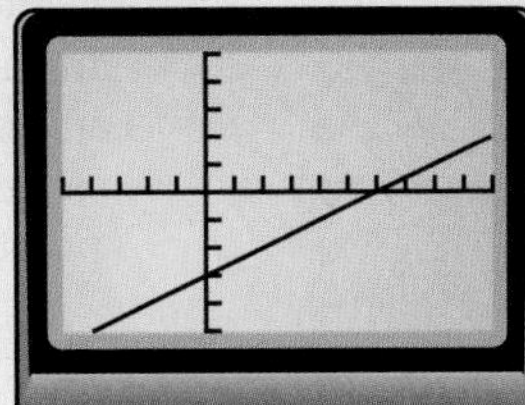

Your turn now **Use a calculator to graph the equation.** 1–4. See margin.

1. $y = 2x - 5$ **2.** $y = 5x + 10$ **3.** $x - y = 11$ **4.** $x + y = 6$

Tell whether the viewing window is appropriate for the graph of the equation. If not, give an appropriate window for it.

5. $y = 4x + 5$ **yes**

Xmin=-5
Xmax=5
ΔX=.1063...
Ymin=-5
Ymax=5

6. $y = 2x + 14$ **No. *Sample answer:* Xmin = −10 Xmax = 5 Ymin = −5 Ymax = 15**

Xmin=-5
Xmax=5
ΔX=.1063...
Ymin=-5
Ymax=5

ILLINOIS Standards and ISAT:
8.B.3, 8.D.3a

1 PLAN

Learn the Method

- Students will use a graphing calculator to graph linear functions.
- Students can use their calculators to verify their graphs for Exercises 14–25 in Lesson 11.4.

2 TEACH

Discussion

As students work through Step 1, you may wish to ask them why the equation must be rewritten. Also ask students why there are parentheses entered around $1 \div 2$.

EXTRA EXAMPLES

Example Graph the equation $3y = x + 6$.

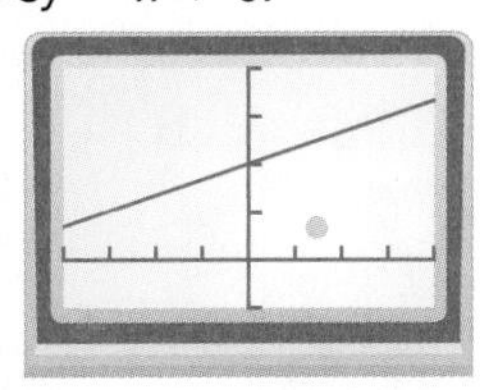

3 CLOSE

Assessment

1. What types of graphs are visible in the calculator's default window? **graphs that pass through or close to the origin**
2. How would you graph the equation $y - 3 = 0$ on a graphing calculator? **Enter $y = 3$ in the calculator and press the GRAPH button.**

1–4. See Additional Answers beginning on page AA1.

Additional Resources

The following resources are available to help review the materials in Lessons 11.1–11.4.

Chapter 11 Resource Book
- Lesson Practice
- Study Guide

Assessment Book
- Chapter 11 Quiz 1

Technology
- Test and Practice Generator
- eTutorial CD-ROM

Internet
- Classzone
- eWorkbook Plus Online
- eTutorial Plus Online

English Learner Support

- Spanish Study Guide
- Multi-Language Glossary
- Chapter Audio Summaries CDs

4.

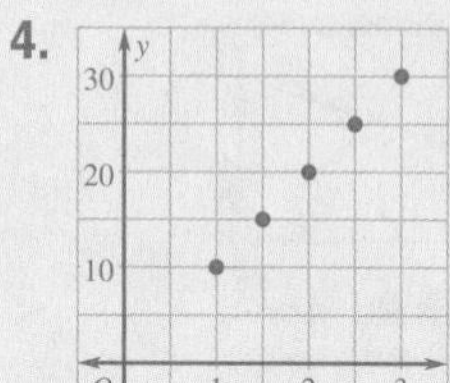

5.

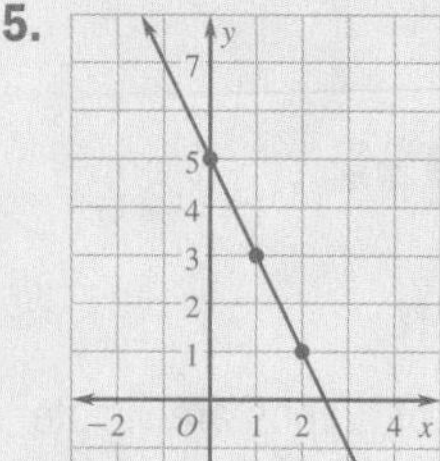

Notebook Review

Review the vocabulary definitions in your notebook.

Copy the review examples in your notebook. Then complete the exercises.

Check Your Definitions

relation, p. 541
input, p. 541
output, p. 541
function, p. 541
domain, p. 542
range, p. 542
scatter plot, p. 545
solution of an equation in two variables, p. 549
linear equation, p. 556

Use Your Vocabulary

1. Vocabulary Copy and complete: Two ways to represent a relation are writing the ordered pairs and using a(n) _?_. **input-output table**

11.1–11.2 Can you write and plot a function rule?

EXAMPLE Write a function rule that relates x and y. Then make a scatter plot of the data.

Input x	-1	0	1	2
Output y	-6	-5	-4	-3

ANSWER Because each output is 5 less than the corresponding input, a rule for this function is $y = x - 5$. In the scatter plot, the y-coordinates increase as the x-coordinates increase. So the quantities have a positive relationship.

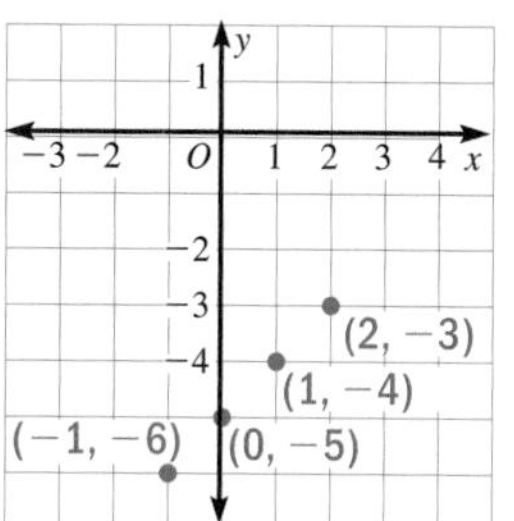

Write a function rule that relates x and y.

2.

x	-2	-1	0	1	2
y	8	4	0	-4	-8

$y = -4x$

3.

x	-6	-3	0	3	6
y	-3	0	3	6	9

$y = x + 3$

4. Make a scatter plot of the data. Describe the relationship.

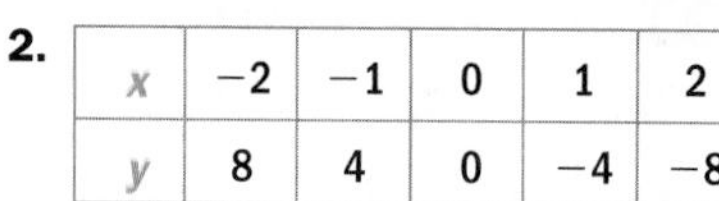

x	1	1.5	2	2.5	3
y	10	15	20	25	30

See margin for art; the data have a positive relationship, with every increase of 0.5 in x there is a corresponding increase of 5 in y.

11.3–11.4 Can you graph linear equations?

EXAMPLE Graph the equation $y = 2x + 1$.

Choose 3 values for x. Substitute each value into the equation and solve for y.

x-value	Substitute for x.	Solve for y.	Solution
$x = -1$	$y = 2(-1) + 1$	$y = -1$	$(-1, -1)$
$x = 0$	$y = 2(0) + 1$	$y = 1$	$(0, 1)$
$x = 1$	$y = 2(1) + 1$	$y = 3$	$(1, 3)$

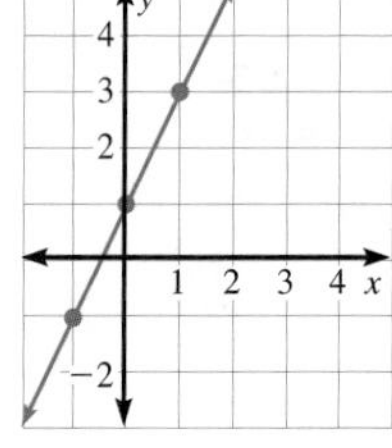

List three solutions of the equation and then graph it.

5–7. Sample answers are given; see margin for art.

5. $2x + y = 5$ (0, 5), (1, 3), (2, 1)

6. $-9x + 3y = -18$ (0, −6), (1, −3) (2, 0)

7. $4y - x = 16$ (0, 4), (4, 5), (8, 6)

about Lessons 11.1–11.4

8. Writing The ordered pair (2, 3) is a solution of $8 = 2y + x$. It is also a solution of $4y = -2x + 16$. Explain why every solution of $8 = 2y + x$ is also a solution of $4y = -2x + 16$. See margin.

Notebook Review

8. *Sample answer:* $4y = -2x + 16$ can be rewritten as $16 = 2x + 4y$, or $8 = x + 2y$, so the equations are equivalent and have the same solutions.

Review Quiz 1

1. Make a table of values for $y = -\frac{1}{3}x$. Use a domain of 0, 1, 2, and 3. Identify the range. See margin.

2. Is (5, −4) a solution of the equation $x - 6y = 29$? yes

List three solutions of the equation and then graph it.

3–5. Sample solutions are given; see margin for art.

3. $7y + x = 21$ (−7, 4), (0, 3), (7, 2)

4. $-5x - 2y = -20$ (−2, 15), (0, 10), (2, 5)

5. $-3x + 9y = -18$ (−3, −3), (0, −2), (3, −1)

Write a function rule that relates x and y.

6. (−2, 0), (−1, 1), (0, 2), (1, 3), (2, 4) $y = x + 2$

7. (−3, −5), (0, 1), (3, 7), (6, 13), (9, 19) $y = 2x + 1$

8. Fundraising An art club raised \$120 for supplies by selling pottery made by students. Mugs cost \$4 and bowls cost \$2. Make an input-output table and a graph for the equation $4x + 2y = 120$, where x is the number of mugs sold and y is the number of bowls sold. Suppose the art club sold 20 mugs. How many bowls did it sell? See margin.

Notebook Review

6.

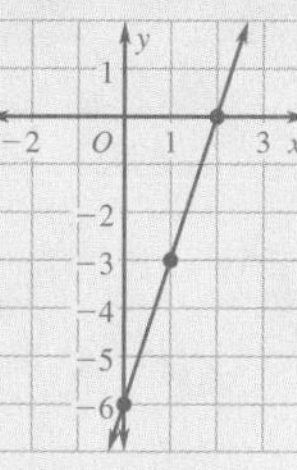

7.

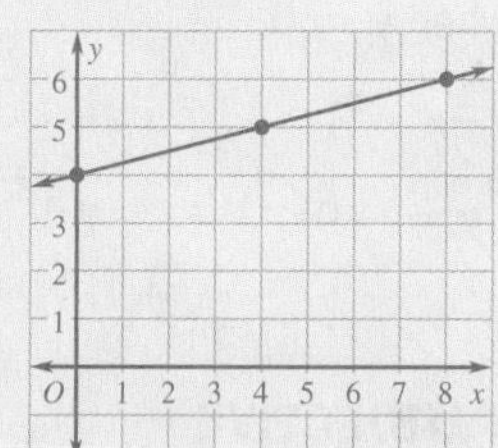

Review Quiz 1

1.

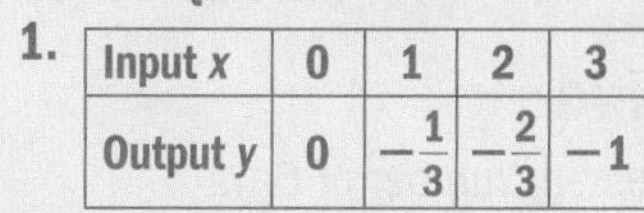

Input x	0	1	2	3
Output y	0	$-\frac{1}{3}$	$-\frac{2}{3}$	-1

range: $-1, -\frac{2}{3}, -\frac{1}{3}, 0$

3.

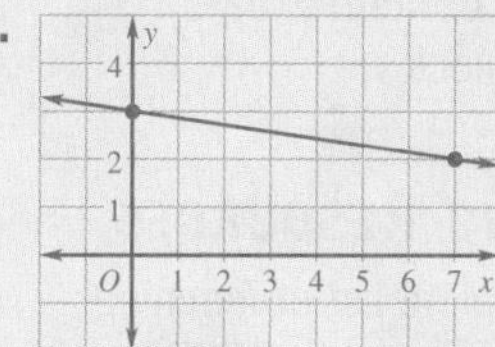

4.

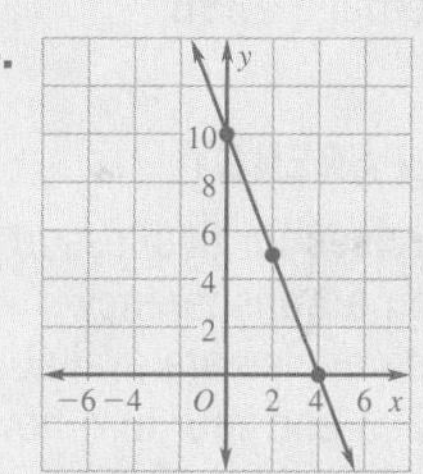

5.

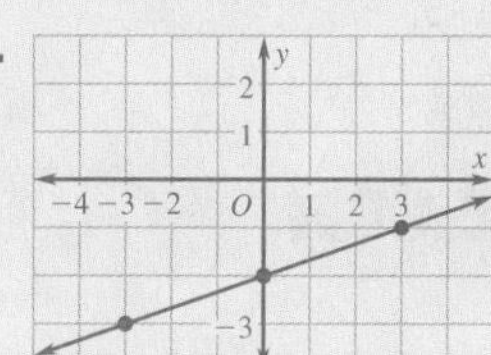

8.

Input x	5	10	15	20
Output y	50	40	30	20

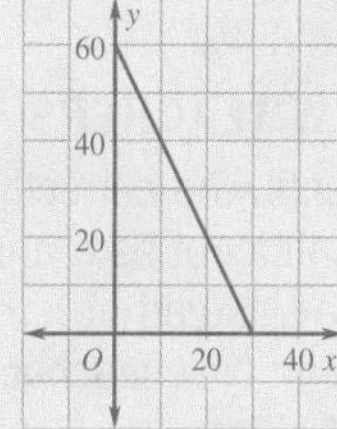

20 bowls

PLAN

SKILL CHECK

Find y when $x = 0$.

1. $y = 4x + 1$ — 1
2. $y = -x$ — 0

Find x when $y = 0$.

3. $y = \frac{1}{2}x + 3$ — −6
4. $x + y = -9$ — −9

LESSON OBJECTIVE

Find x- and y-intercepts of a line.

PACING

Suggested Number of Days
Basic Course: 2 days
Average Course: 2 days
Advanced Course: 2 days
Block: 1 block

TEACHING RESOURCES

For a complete list of Teaching Resources, see page 538B.

TRANSPARENCY

Warm-Up Exercises for this lesson are available on a transparency. Support transparencies are available for Examples 2–3 and Your turn now Exercises 1–3.

TEACH

MOTIVATING THE LESSON

Ask students what it means to intercept something.

TIPS FOR NEW TEACHERS

Watch for students who correctly calculate an x-intercept as a and then graph $(0, a)$ instead of $(a, 0)$. See Tips for New Teachers in the *Chapter 11 Resource Book*.

Using Intercepts

BEFORE	Now	WHY?
You graphed linear equations.	You'll find x- and y-intercepts of a line.	So you can find the number of CDs you can buy, as in Ex. 4.

Word Watch

x-intercept, p. 564
y-intercept, p. 564

Intercepts The **x-intercept** of a graph is the x-coordinate of the point where the graph crosses the x-axis. The graph of $2x + 3y = 12$ crosses the x-axis at (6, 0), so its x-intercept is 6.

The **y-intercept** is the y-coordinate of the point where the graph intersects the y-axis. The graph of $2x + 3y = 12$ crosses the y-axis at (0, 4), so its y-intercept is 4.

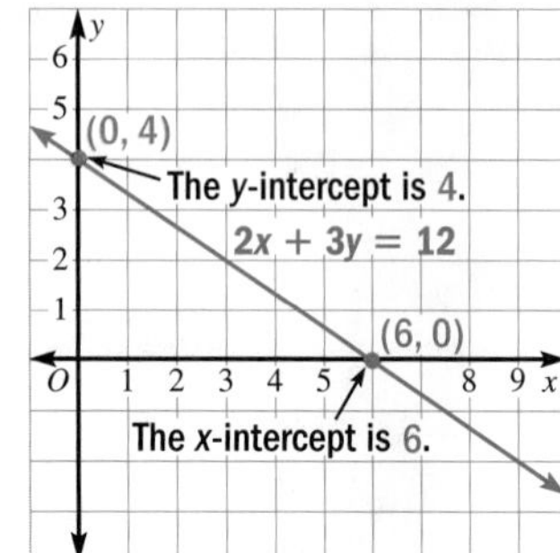

Finding Intercepts

To find the x-intercept of a line, substitute 0 for y into the equation and solve for x.

To find the y-intercept of a line, substitute 0 for x into the equation and solve for y.

EXAMPLE 1 Finding Intercepts

Find the intercepts of the graph of $y = \frac{1}{2}x - 5$.

To find the x-intercept, let $y = 0$ and solve for x.

$$y = \frac{1}{2}x - 5$$
$$0 = \frac{1}{2}x - 5$$
$$5 = \frac{1}{2}x$$
$$10 = x$$

To find the y-intercept, let $x = 0$ and solve for y.

$$y = \frac{1}{2}x - 5$$
$$y = \frac{1}{2}(0) - 5$$
$$y = 0 - 5$$
$$y = -5$$

ANSWER The x-intercept is 10 and the y-intercept is −5. The graph of the equation contains the points (10, 0) and (0, −5).

ILLINOIS Standards and ISAT:
8.B.3, 8.D.3a

Graphing The intercepts tell you the points where a line intersects the x-axis and the y-axis. You can use these points to graph a line.

with Notetaking

Be sure to write down in your notebook that the intercepts of a line are numbers, not points.

EXAMPLE 2 Using Intercepts to Graph a Line

Graph the line with an x-intercept of -3 and a y-intercept of 2.

The x-intercept is -3, so plot the point $(-3, 0)$. The y-intercept is 2, so plot the point $(0, 2)$.

Draw a line through the two points.

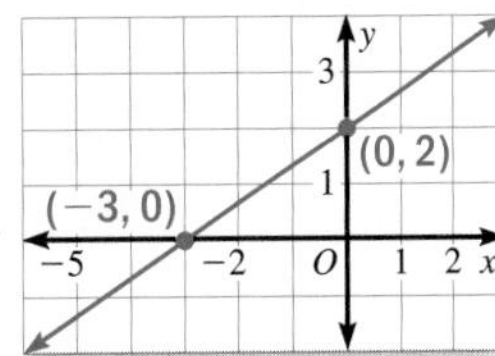

Your turn now **Find the intercepts of the graph of the equation. Then graph the line using the intercepts.** 1–3. See margin for art.

1. x-intercept: $3\frac{3}{5}$, y-intercept: 6
2. x-intercept: 5, y-intercept: -10
3. x-intercept: $-\frac{1}{3}$, y-intercept: -1

1. $5x + 3y = 18$ **2.** $-2x + y = -10$ **3.** $3x + y = -1$

EXAMPLE 3 Using and Interpreting Intercepts

Fitness Pamela runs and walks with her dog on a trail that is 8 miles long. She can run 4 miles per hour and walk 2 miles per hour. Graph the equation $4x + 2y = 8$, where x is the number of hours running and y is the number of hours walking. What do the intercepts represent?

Solution

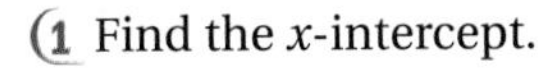

1 Find the x-intercept.

To find the x-intercept, let $y = 0$ and solve for x.

$$4x + 2y = 8$$
$$4x + 2(0) = 8$$
$$4x = 8$$
$$x = 2$$

2 Find the y-intercept.

To find the y-intercept, let $x = 0$ and solve for y.

$$4x + 2y = 8$$
$$4(0) + 2y = 8$$
$$2y = 8$$
$$y = 4$$

3 The x-intercept is 2 and the y-intercept is 4. So the points $(2, 0)$ and $(0, 4)$ are on the graph. Plot these points and draw a line through them.

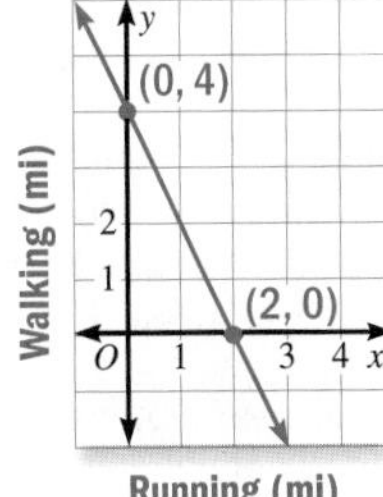

ANSWER The x-intercept represents how many hours it would take if Pamela runs the entire time. The y-intercept represents how many hours it would take if Pamela walks the entire time.

EXTRA EXAMPLES

Example 1 Find the intercepts of the graph of $y = -8x + 4$.
x-intercept: $\frac{1}{2}$, y-intercept: 4

Example 2 Graph the line with an x-intercept of -2 and a y-intercept of -1.

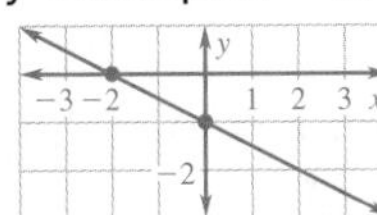

Example 3 James is spending \$24 for cookies and ice cream for a party. Each box of cookies costs \$3 and each carton of ice cream costs \$4. Graph $3x + 4y = 24$, where x is the number of cookie boxes and y is the number of ice-cream cartons. What do the intercepts represent?

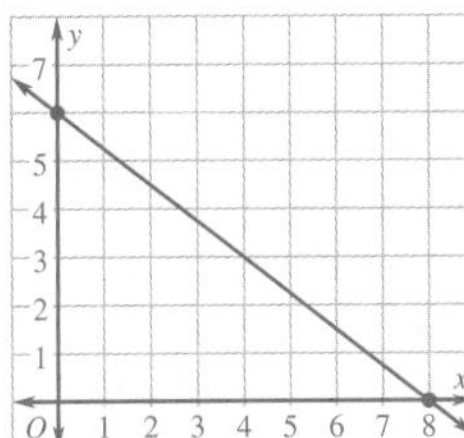

The y-intercept represents the 6 cartons of ice cream James can buy if he buys no cookies. The x-intercept represents the 8 boxes of cookies James can buy if he buys no ice cream.

CONCEPT CHECK

What steps would you take to find the y-intercept of $12x + 35y = 70$? **Substitute $x = 0$ into the equation and solve for y. The result is 2.**

DAILY PUZZLER

Write an equation that has the same x- and y-intercepts. ***Sample answer:* $y = x$**

1–3. See Additional Answers beginning on page AA1.

APPLY

ASSIGNMENT GUIDE

Basic Course

Day 1: pp. 566–567 Exs. 5–10, 16–18, 30–33

Day 2: pp. 566–567 Exs. 11–14, 19–24, 34–36

Average Course

Day 1: pp. 566–567 Exs. 5–10, 16–21, 30–32

Day 2: pp. 566–567 Exs. 11–15, 25–28, 33–37

Advanced Course

Day 1: pp. 566–567 Exs. 8–10, 15–18, 25–31

Day 2: pp. 566–567 Exs. 11–14, 22–24, 32–37, EC: TE p. 538D*

Block

pp. 566–567 Exs. 5–21, 25–28, 30–37

EXTRA PRACTICE

- Student Edition, p. 737
- Chapter 11 Resource Book, pp. 45–47
- Test and Practice Generator

TRANSPARENCY

Even-numbered answers are available on transparencies. Support transparencies are available for Exercises 4, 11–14, and 19–24.

HOMEWORK CHECK

When you review students' homework for this lesson, go over the following exercises to check understanding of key concepts.
Basic: 5, 8, 11, 12, 14
Average: 6, 8, 11, 12, 14
Advanced: 8, 10, 12, 13, 14

TEACHING TIP

In Exercise 14, after students have graphed the equation, have them label the axes with x and y. Then ask them to label the appropriate axes with "minutes" and "miles."

11.5 Exercises

More Practice, p. 737

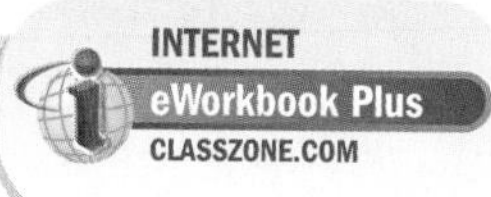

Getting Ready to Practice

1. Vocabulary Copy and complete: A line passes through the points (3, 0) and (0, 5). So, the _?_ is 5 and the _?_ is 3. **y-intercept, x-intercept**

Identify the x-intercept and the y-intercept.

2.

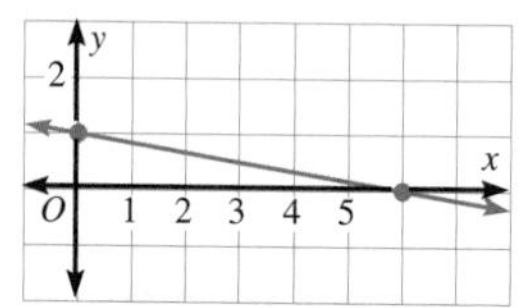

x-intercept: 6, y-intercept: 1

3.

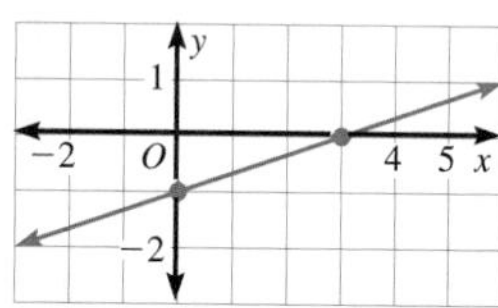

x-intercept: 3, y-intercept: -1

4. Guided Problem Solving You have $60 to spend. CDs are $12 each and videos are $10 each. The number of each item you can buy is modeled by the equation $12x + 10y = 60$. Graph the equation and explain what the intercepts represent.

(1) Find the intercepts. **x-intercept: 5, y-intercept: 6**

(2) Graph the equation. **See margin.**

(3) Decide what x and y represent in the equation. Explain what the intercepts represent. **x represents the number of CDs you buy, y represents the number of videos you buy; the x-intercept represents the number of CDs you buy if you do not buy any videos, the y-intercept represents the number of videos you buy if you do not buy any CDs.**

Practice and Problem Solving

Find the intercepts of the graph of the equation. **5–10. See margin.**

A **5.** $y = 6x - 3$ **6.** $y = 2x + 4$ **7.** $y = 5x + 10$

8. $x + 9y = 18$ **9.** $4x + 5y = 20$ **10.** $7x - 9y = -63$

Graph the line that has the given intercepts. **11–13. See margin.**

11. x-intercept: 9, y-intercept: 4

12. x-intercept: -3, y-intercept: 1

13. x-intercept: 6, y-intercept: -10

14. Riding the Bus You are riding the bus home from school. After x minutes, the number of miles from home y is given by $2x + 3y = 18$. Find the intercepts. Then graph the equation. What do the intercepts represent?

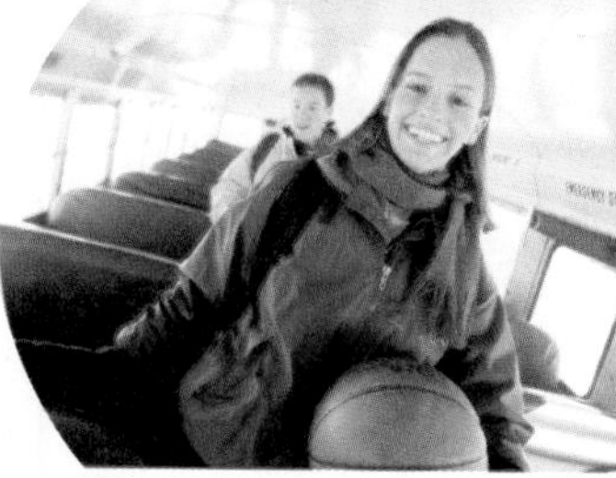

5. x-intercept: $\frac{1}{2}$, y-intercept: -3

6. x-intercept: -2, y-intercept: 4

7. x-intercept: -2, y-intercept: 10

8. x-intercept: 18, y-intercept: 2

9. x-intercept: 5, y-intercept: 4

10. x-intercept: -9, y-intercept: 7

HELP with Homework

Example	Exercises
1	5–10
2	11–13
3	14

- More Examples
- eTutorial Plus

14. x-intercept: 9, y-intercept: 6; see margin for art; the x-intercept represents the number of minutes it takes to get home and the y-intercept represents the number of miles from school to home.

15. Up. *Sample answer:* The x-intercept will be on the positive side of the x-axis and the y-intercept will be on the negative side of the y-axis, so the line will slant up from left to right.

B **15. Critical Thinking** If the x-intercept of a line is positive and the y-intercept is negative, does the line slant up or down from left to right? Explain your reasoning.

Find the intercepts of the graph of the equation.

16. $y = 9$ x-intercept: none, y-intercept: 9

17. $y = 14$ x-intercept: none, y-intercept: 14

18. $x = 21$ x-intercept: 21, y-intercept: none

Graph the equation using intercepts. 19–24. See margin.

19. $y = 5x - 15$

20. $y = -2.5x + 6.5$

21. $8x + 10y = 30$

22. $y = \frac{1}{2}x + 1$

23. $y = -\frac{2}{3}x + 2$

24. $y = \frac{3}{4}x - \frac{1}{2}$

25. x-intercept: 1.71, y-intercept: 3.65

26. x-intercept: 6.18, y-intercept: −12.05

27. x-intercept: −3.64, y-intercept: −15.01

Find the intercepts of the graph of the equation. Round to the nearest hundredth.

C **25.** $y = -2.14x + 3.65$

26. $y = 1.95x - 12.05$

27. $y = -4.12x - 15.01$

28. Critical Thinking What kind of line has no y-intercept? any vertical line with an equation of the form $x = a$, $a \neq 0$

29. s-intercept: 5000, c-intercept: 2000; the s-intercept represents the amount needed in the savings account only to earn \$100 interest and the c-intercept represents the amount needed in the certificate of deposit only to earn \$100 interest.

29. Investing A bank offers a savings account at a 2% simple annual interest rate and a certificate of deposit at a 5% simple annual interest rate. You want to earn \$100 in interest the first year. The equation $0.02s + 0.05c = 100$ models the situation. Find the intercepts of the graph of the equation. What do they represent in terms of the situation?

Mixed Review

30. Evaluate the expression $\frac{6a^2b}{2ab^2}$ when $a = 9$ and $b = 4$. *(Lesson 4.3)* 6.75

Graph the equation. *(Lesson 11.4)* 31–33. See margin.

31. $y = \frac{3}{4}x + 5$

32. $y = 2x - 6$

33. $y = -7x + 4$

Basic Skills **Use the formula $d = rt$ to find the rate.**

34. $d = 460$ mi, $t = 8$ h 57.5 mi/h

35. $d = 720$ km, $t = 12$ h 60 km/h

Test-Taking Practice

36. Multiple Choice What is the y-intercept of the graph of $2x - y = 4$? A

A. −4 **B.** −1 **C.** 2 **D.** 4

37. The x-intercept tells her the number of T-shirts she can buy if she buys 0 CD gift certificates, and the y-intercept tells her the number of CD gift certificates she can buy if she buys 0 T-shirts.

37. Short Response Melissa needs to have a total of 10 prizes for a school contest. She has two choices: school T-shirts that come in orders of 4, and CD gift certificates that come in packs of 2. Melissa knows that the number of each prize group she can buy is represented by the equation $4x + 2y = 10$. Melissa graphs the line. What do the intercepts tell her about the prizes she can buy? See margin.

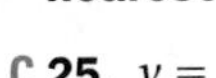

4 ASSESS

Assessment Resources

For more assessment resources, see:
- Assessment Book
- Test and Practice Generator

Mini-Quiz

Find the intercepts of the graph of the equation.

1. $y = -5x + 8$ $(0, 8), \left(\frac{8}{5}, 0\right)$
2. $3x - 6y = 10$ $\left(0, -\frac{5}{3}\right), \left(\frac{10}{3}, 0\right)$
3. Graph the equation $y = -\frac{1}{2}x + 2$ using intercepts.

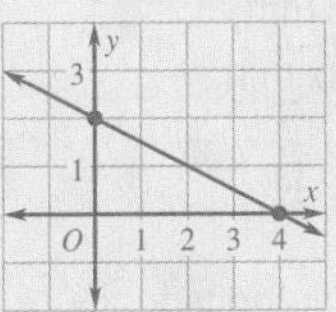

5 FOLLOW-UP

Reteaching/Remediation

- Study Guide in Chapter 11 Resource Book, pp. 49–50
- eTutorial Plus Online
- Extra Practice, p. 737
- Lesson Practice in Chapter 11 Resource Book, pp. 46–48

Challenge/Enrichment

- Challenge Practice in Chapter 11 Resource Book, p. 51
- Teacher's Edition, p. 538F

English Learner Support

- Spanish Study Guide
- Multi-Language Glossary
- Chapter Audio Summaries CDs

4 (Step 2), 11–14, 19–24, 31–33. See Additional Answers beginning on page AA1.

PLAN

EXPLORE THE CONCEPT

- Students will understand slope as a measure of steepness.
- This activity leads into the study of slope in Lesson 11.6. Once students understand slope, they can graph equations using the slope and y-intercept of an equation.

MATERIALS

Each student or pair of students will need a pencil and graph paper.

RECOMMENDED TIME

Work activity: 10 min
Discuss results: 5 min

GROUPING

Students can work individually or in pairs. In pairs, they can work together to plot points and find rise and run.

TRANSPARENCY

Support transparencies are available for this Activity.

TEACH

TIPS FOR SUCCESS

Most students will have a natural tendency to always measure run from left to right, so for a nonvertical line, the run will be positive. Help students realize that if a line falls from left to right, then the run is still positive, but the "rise" is negative, and so the slope is negative.

1. Step 1:

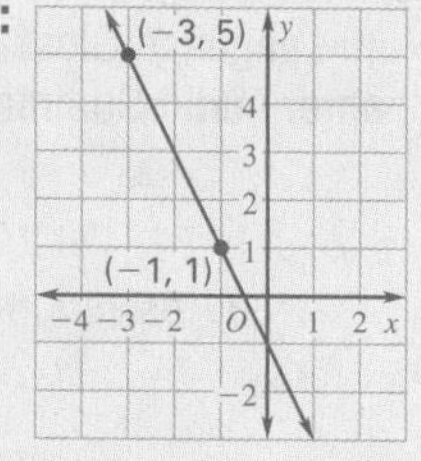

11.6 Hands-on Activity

GOAL
Understand slope as a measure of steepness.

MATERIALS
- pencil
- graph paper

Finding the Slope of a Line

You can describe the steepness of a line using its *slope*, or ratio of vertical change (rise) to horizontal change (run) in any two points on a line. You can find slope using the formula: $slope = \frac{rise}{run}$.

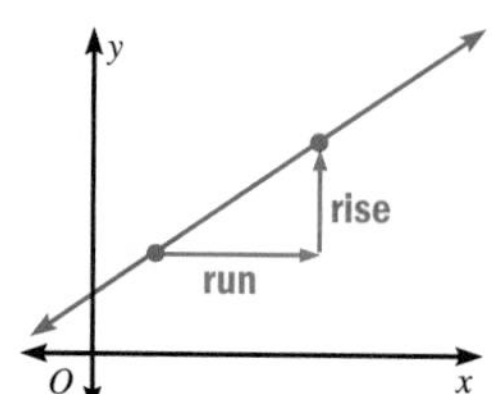

Explore 1 **Find the slope of the line passing through the points (2, 3) and (6, 5).**

1 Plot the points (2, 3) and (6, 5) on a coordinate grid. Using a straightedge draw a line through the points.

(6, 5)
rise = 2
(2, 3)
run = 4

2 Find the rise. Then find the run. Substitute for rise and run in the formula for slope.

$$\text{slope} = \frac{\text{rise}}{\text{run}} = \frac{2}{4} = \frac{1}{2}$$

The slope of the line passing through the points (2, 3) and (6, 5) is $\frac{1}{2}$.

Your turn now **Use the formula for slope.**

1. Find the slope of the line passing through the points $(-1, 1)$ and $(-3, 5)$.

(1) Plot the points $(-1, 1)$ and $(-3, 5)$ on a coordinate plane using graph paper. Then draw a line through the points. **See margin.**

(2) Find the rise. Then find the run. Substitute for rise and run in the formula for slope. **rise: 4; run: −2; slope = −2**

2. Using the points (5, 6) and $(-2, 3)$, what operation can you perform on the y-coordinates to find the rise? What operation can you perform on the x-coordinates to find the run? **subtraction; subtraction**

ILLINOIS Standards and ISAT:
8.D.3a, 8.D.3b

Explore 2 **Use two points to find the slope of a line.**

1. Copy the graph.

2. Choose two points on the line. Find the rise and run. Calculate the slope. **rise: 2, run: 1; slope: 2**

3. Choose a different pair of points on the line. Find the rise and run. Calculate the slope. **rise: 2, run: 1; slope: 2**

4. What pattern do you notice in your answers to Steps 2 and 3? Make a conjecture about the slope of a line.
Sample answer: The slope is the same no matter what two points are chosen. The slope of a line can be found using any two different points on the line.

Your turn now **Find the slope of the line passing through the points.**

3. (1, 4), (4, 2) $-\frac{2}{3}$ **4.** (1, −3), (5, −2) $\frac{1}{4}$ **5.** (−3, 4), (0, 6) $\frac{2}{3}$

6. (7, 8), (−1, −5) $\frac{13}{8}$ **7.** (−2, 6), (0, −3) $-\frac{9}{2}$ **8.** (−9, 3), (3, −9) −1

9. If a line falls from left to right, what can you say about the rise and run? **One of them is negative.**

10. If a line rises from left to right, what can you say about the rise and run? **Either both are positive or both are negative.**

11. Compare a line with slope greater than 1 to a line with slope between 0 and 1. **A line with a slope greater than 1 will rise more steeply than a line with slope between 0 and 1.**

Find the slope of the line.

12. $\frac{2}{3}$

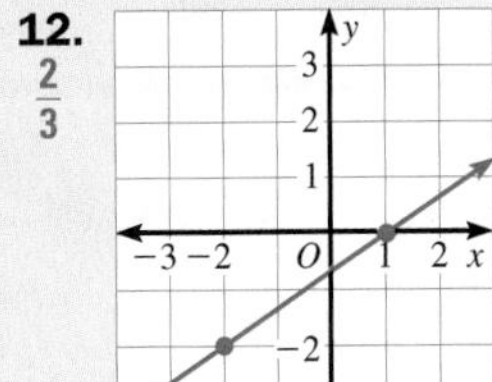

13. $-\frac{1}{4}$

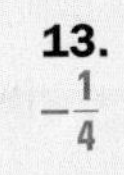

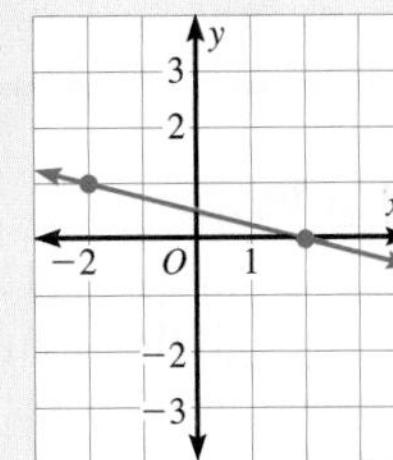

14. −3

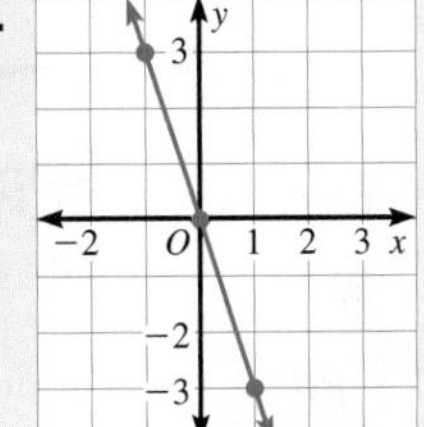

Stop and Think

15. Challenge What is the slope of the line passing through the points (a, b) and (c, d)? $\frac{d-b}{c-a}$ or $\frac{b-d}{a-c}$

DISCUSSION

Ask students in terms of what axis the rise is measured (*y*-axis) and in terms of what axis the run is measured (*x*-axis). When students are working Exercise 2 on page 568, ask them if it matters which point they use first when they perform the operations on the *x*- and *y*-coordinates, and tell them to form a conjecture. Then have them test their conjectures as they complete Exercises 3–8 on page 569.

3 CLOSE

KEY DISCOVERY

You can use rise over run to find slope.

ASSESSMENT

1. Does the value of slope relate to the steepness of the line? How? **Accept all reasonable answers. Students should observe that as the absolute value of the slope increases, the line becomes steeper.**

2. Do you think a line could have zero slope? Why or why not? **Accept all reasonable answers. Students should reason that for the slope of a line to be zero, its "rise" must be zero. This is allowable in the formula as long as the run is not zero.**

1 PLAN

SKILL CHECK

1. $\dfrac{7-7}{-8+21}$ 0
2. $\dfrac{2-3}{6-8}$ $\dfrac{1}{2}$
3. $\dfrac{0-4}{2-0}$ -2

LESSON OBJECTIVE

Find and interpret slopes of lines.

PACING

Suggested Number of Days
Basic Course: 2 days
Average Course: 2 days
Advanced Course: 2 days
Block: 1 block

TEACHING RESOURCES

For a complete list of Teaching Resources, see page 538B.

TRANSPARENCY

Warm-Up Exercises for this lesson are available on a transparency.

2 TEACH

MOTIVATING THE LESSON

Ask students to describe some ways they could quantify how steep a hill or a staircase is.

TIPS FOR NEW TEACHERS

Explain that in the real world, a hill is steep regardless of which direction you travel up the hill. In mathematics, however, the direction of travel affects whether the slope is positive or negative. See Tips for New Teachers in the *Chapter 11 Resource Book*.

Slope

BEFORE	Now	WHY?
You graphed linear equations.	You'll find and interpret slopes of lines.	So you can find the slope of the roof of a birdhouse, as in Ex. 9.

Word Watch

slope, p. 570
rise, p. 570
run, p. 570

In the Real World

Cogwheel Railways The Mount Pilatus Railway in the Swiss Alps is the steepest cogwheel railway in the world. The track rises about 20 feet vertically for every 50 feet it runs horizontally. What is the steepness of the track?

You can describe steepness using *slope*. The **slope** of a nonvertical line is the ratio of its vertical change, called the **rise**, to its horizontal change, called the **run**.

EXAMPLE 1 **Finding Slope**

The diagram shows the rise and the run of the Mount Pilatus Railway.

$$\text{slope} = \frac{\text{rise}}{\text{run}} = \frac{20 \text{ ft}}{50 \text{ ft}} = \frac{2}{5}$$

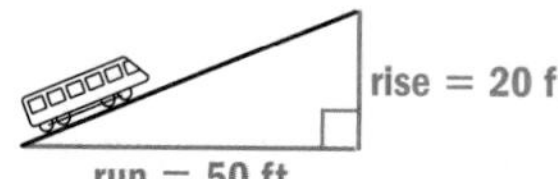

ANSWER The railway has a slope of $\frac{2}{5}$.

with Vocabulary

The rise is the change in *y* and the run is the change in *x*.

Slope of a Line

The slope m of a nonvertical line passing through the points (x_1, y_1) and (x_2, y_2) is

$$m = \frac{\text{rise}}{\text{run}} = \frac{y_2 - y_1}{x_2 - x_1}$$

The slope of a line is the same no matter which two points you choose to use in the formula.

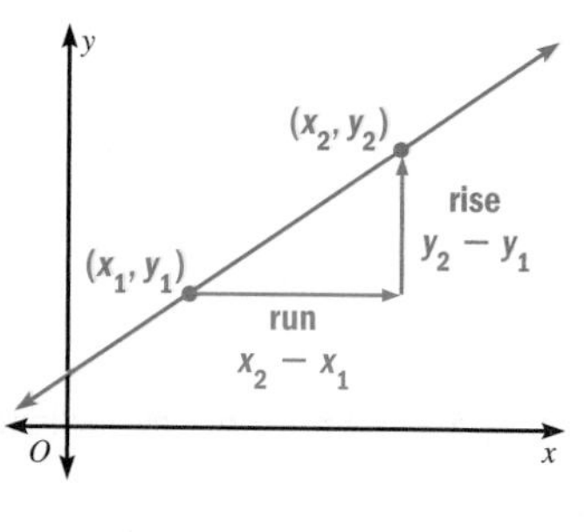

ILLINOIS Standards and ISAT:
8.D.3a, 8.D.3b; 9.A.3a

EXAMPLE 2 Positive and Negative Slope

Find the slope of the line.

a.

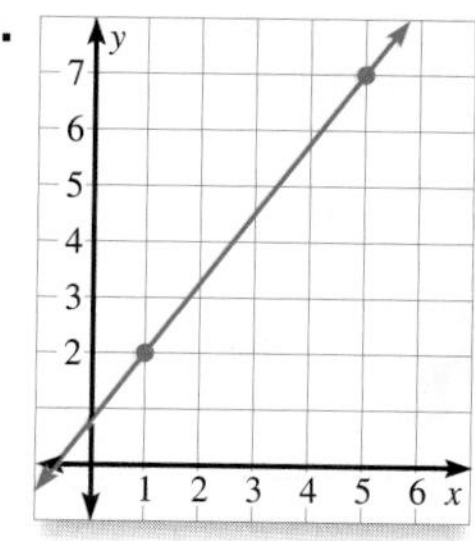

$$m = \frac{\text{rise}}{\text{run}} = \frac{y_2 - y_1}{x_2 - x_1}$$
$$= \frac{7 - 2}{5 - 1}$$
$$= \frac{5}{4}$$

ANSWER The slope is $\frac{5}{4}$.

b.

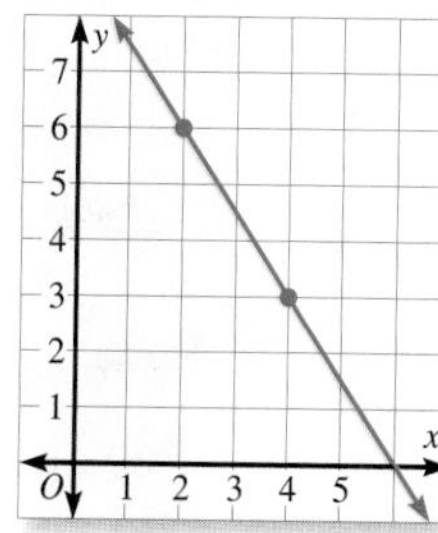

$$m = \frac{\text{rise}}{\text{run}} = \frac{y_2 - y_1}{x_2 - x_1}$$
$$= \frac{3 - 6}{4 - 2}$$
$$= \frac{-3}{2}, \text{ or } -\frac{3}{2}.$$

ANSWER The slope is $-\frac{3}{2}$.

HELP with Review

For help with subtracting integers, see p. 63.

Your turn now **Find the slope of the line passing through the points.**

1. (2, 1), (6, 4) $\frac{3}{4}$ **2.** (0, 6), (10, 0) $-\frac{3}{5}$ **3.** (−3, −4), (5, 2) $\frac{3}{4}$

EXAMPLE 3 Zero and Undefined Slope

Find the slope of the line.

a.

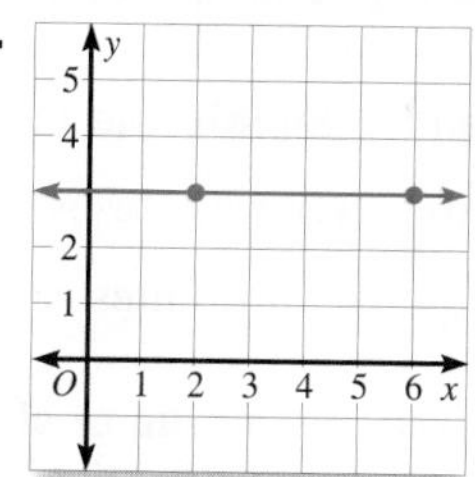

$$m = \frac{\text{rise}}{\text{run}} = \frac{y_2 - y_1}{x_2 - x_1}$$
$$= \frac{3 - 3}{6 - 2} = \frac{0}{4} = 0$$

ANSWER The slope is 0.

b.

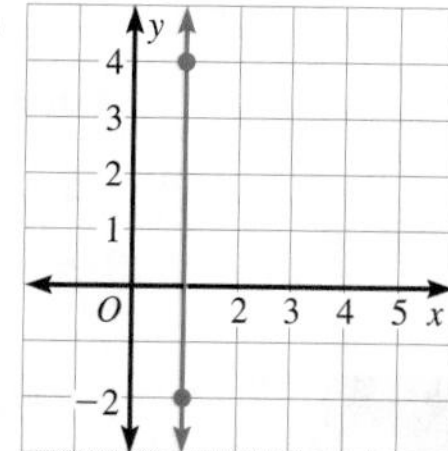

$$m = \frac{\text{rise}}{\text{run}} = \frac{y_2 - y_1}{x_2 - x_1}$$
$$= \frac{4 - (-2)}{1 - 1} = \frac{6}{0}$$

ANSWER The slope is undefined.

Watch Out!

When finding the slope of a line, make sure that you are using the x- and y-coordinates in the same order.

EXTRA EXAMPLES

Example 1 The diagram shows a ramp at a loading dock. What is the slope of the ramp? $\frac{1}{3}$

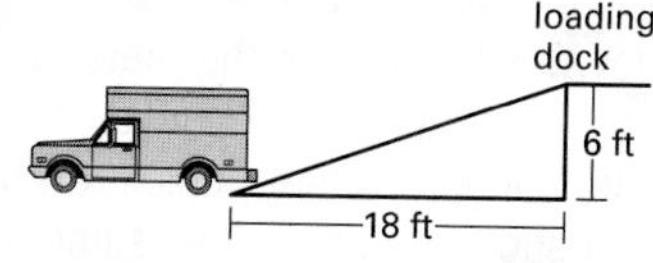

Example 2 Find the slope of the line.

a.

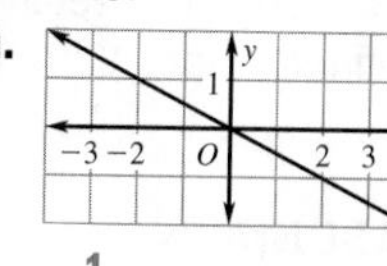

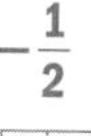

$-\frac{1}{2}$

b.

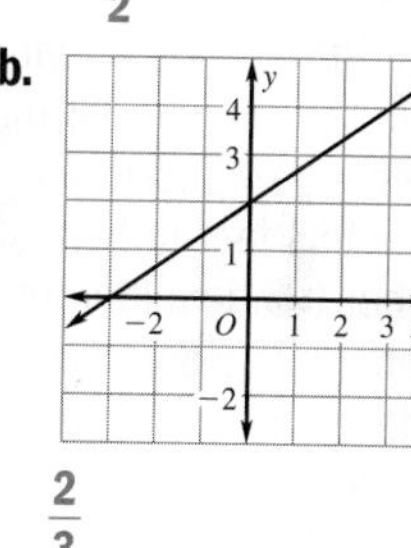

$\frac{2}{3}$

Example 3 Find the slope of the line.

a.

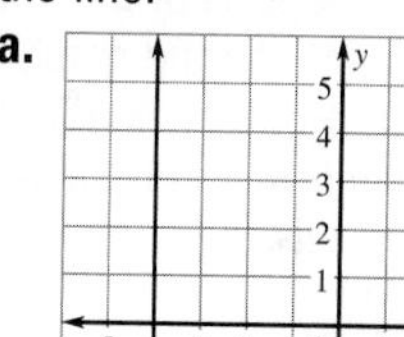

undefined

b.

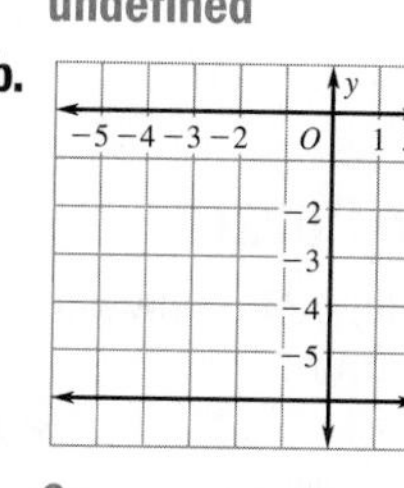

0

TRANSPARENCY

Support transparencies are available for Examples 2–3.

VISUALIZE

As you discuss the summary on page 572, draw axes on the board and use a meter stick to model lines with each slope. Demonstrate how you can place a quarter or some other small object on the meter stick when it has positive, negative, or zero slope, but you cannot place it on the meter stick when its slope is undefined. Ask students to suggest other ways to remember which of horizontal and vertical graphs has zero slope or undefined slope.

MATH REASONING

Ask students where else in math they have heard the term *undefined* used. Students may remember that division by zero is referred to as undefined. Use this fact to help students remember the definition of an undefined slope. If the denominator is zero, then the run is zero, so the line must be vertical.

CONCEPT CHECK

The slope of a line is 7, and the rise between two points on the graph of the line is 10.5. How can you find the run of the line between these two points? **Substitute 7 for slope and 10.5 for rise in the equation slope $= \frac{\text{rise}}{\text{run}}$, and solve for the run, which is $\frac{10.5}{7}$, or 1.5.**

DAILY PUZZLER

What is the slope of a line with the same rise and run? **1**

3-6. See Additional Answers beginning on page AA1.

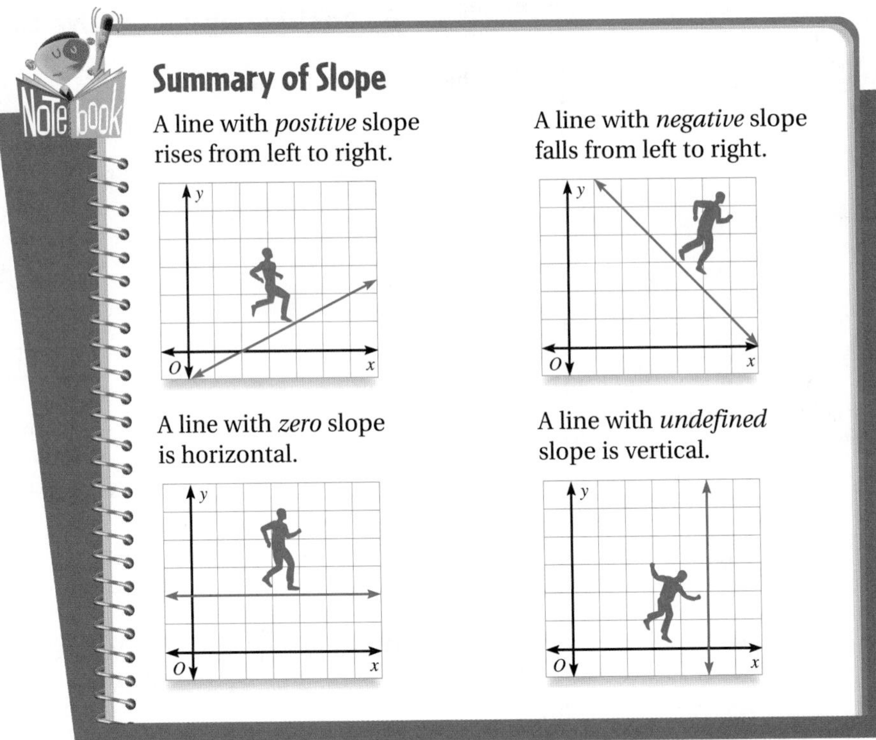

Notebook
Summary of Slope
A line with *positive* slope rises from left to right.
A line with *negative* slope falls from left to right.
A line with *zero* slope is horizontal.
A line with *undefined* slope is vertical.

11.6 Exercises

More Practice, p. 737

Getting Ready to Practice

Vocabulary Copy and complete the statement.

1. The change in the y-coordinates is called the _?_. **rise**
2. The change in the x-coordinates is called the _?_. **run**

Sketch a line with the given type of slope. **3–6. See margin.**

3. negative
4. undefined
5. positive
6. zero

Birdhouse Use the red line on the diagram of a birdhouse.

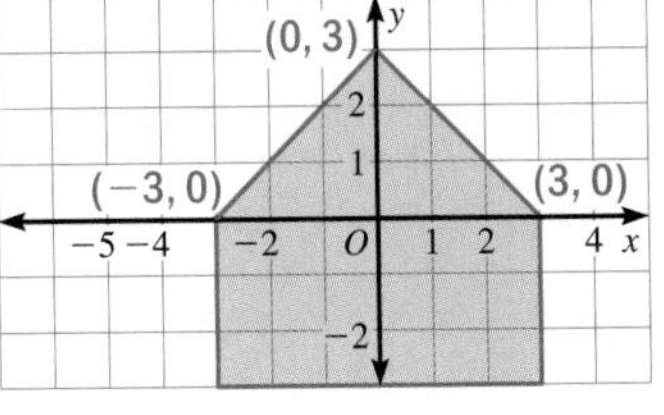

7. What is the rise of the roof? **3**
8. What is the run of the roof? **3**
9. What is the slope of the roof? **$\frac{3}{3}$ or 1**

Practice and Problem Solving

with Homework

Example	Exercises
1	26
2	10-26
3	10-25

Online Resources
CLASSZONE.COM

- More Examples
- eTutorial Plus

Write the coordinates of the two points on the line. Then find the slope.

A **10.**

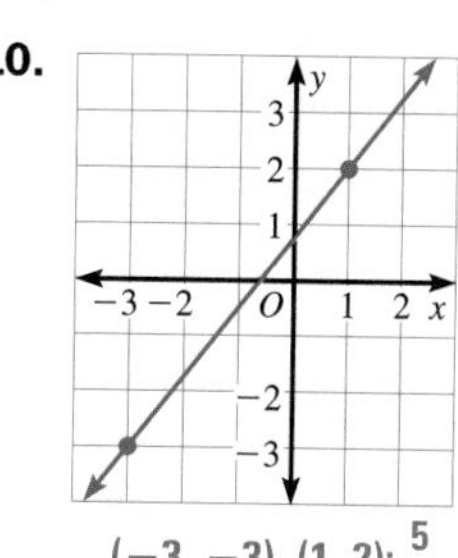

$(-3, -3), (1, 2); \frac{5}{4}$

11.

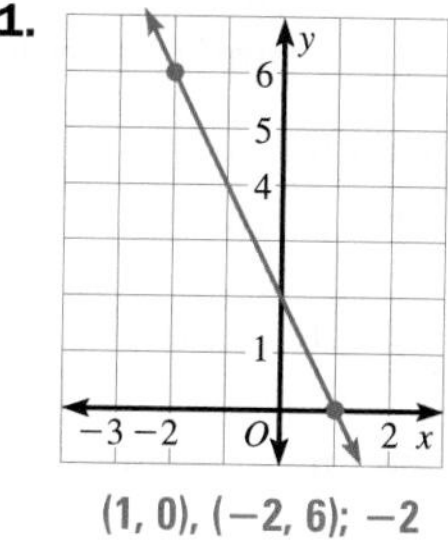

$(1, 0), (-2, 6); -2$

12.

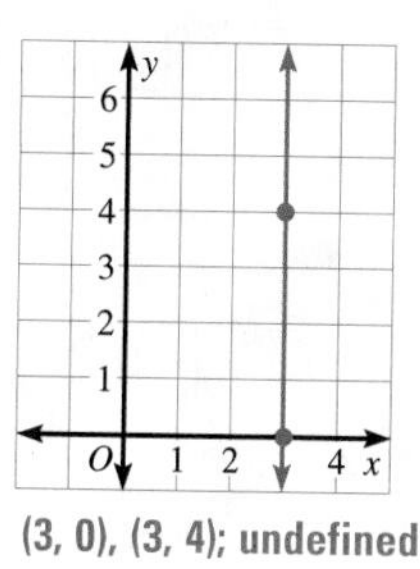

$(3, 0), (3, 4)$; undefined

Find the slope of the line passing through the points.

13. $(-4, 8), (6, 6)$ $-\frac{1}{5}$

14. $(1, 4), (1, -7)$ undefined

15. $(-2, -4), (4, 2)$ 1

16. $(-5, 4), (3, 4)$ 0

17. $(5, 8), (0, 5)$ $\frac{3}{5}$

18. $(-3, 1), (-3, -2)$ undefined

19. $(-6, -2), (6, -7)$ $-\frac{5}{12}$

20. $(9, -8), (15, -8)$ 0

21. $(12, 22), (-20, 19)$ $\frac{3}{32}$

The three points are vertices of a triangle. Plot and connect the points. Then find the slope of each side of the triangle. 22–25. See margin for art.

22. $A(0, 0), B(0, 8), C(6, 0)$

23. $D(-3, 4), E(4, 1), F(-1, -7)$

24. $G(0, 6), H(4, 0), J(-4, 0)$

25. $K(-5, 1), L(-1, -4), M(-2, 4)$

26. Tides The pictures show a floating dock at low and high tide. Find the slopes of the ramp in both pictures. Is the ramp steeper at high tide or at low tide? $\frac{36}{77}, \frac{13}{84}$; low tide

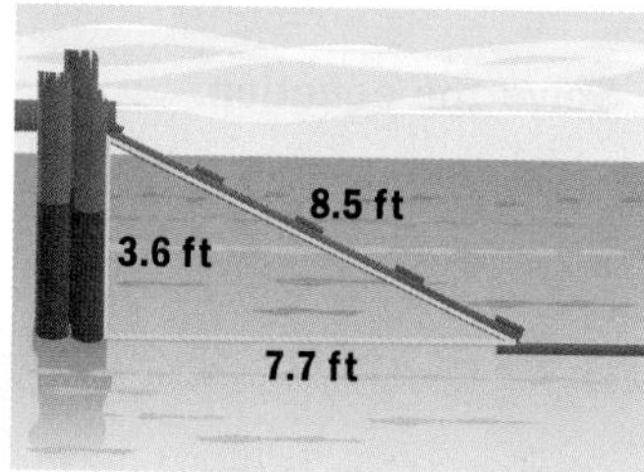

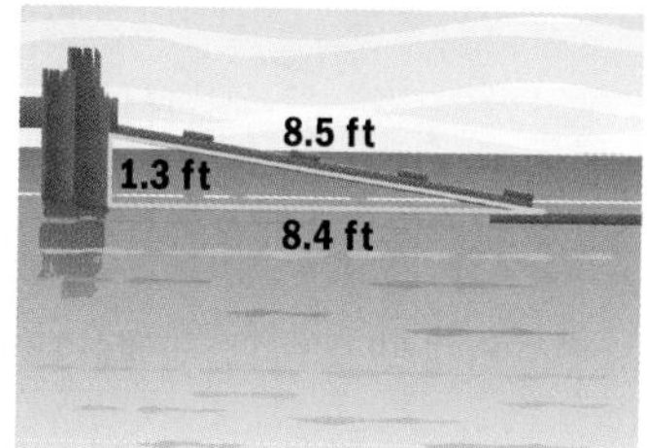

27. Writing One line passes through the points $M(1, 1)$ and $N(3, 4)$ and another line passes through the points $P(2, 5)$ and $Q(5, 8)$. Which line has a greater slope? Explain how you can tell by graphing the two lines. Explain how you can tell by calculating the slopes of the lines. See margin.

B

28. Algebra A line contains the points (p, q) and $(p + 2, q + 2)$. Find the slope of the line. 1

29. Critical Thinking When you have selected two points on a line to find its slope, does it matter which is (x_1, y_1) and which is (x_2, y_2)? Explain. Give examples to justify your reasoning.

22. slope of $\overline{AB}$: undefined, slope of $\overline{BC}$: $\frac{4}{3}$, slope of $\overline{CA}$: 0

23. slope of $\overline{DE}$: $-\frac{3}{7}$, slope of $\overline{EF}$: $\frac{8}{5}$, slope of $\overline{FD}$: $-\frac{11}{2}$

24. The slope of $\overline{GH}$: $-\frac{3}{2}$, slope of $\overline{HJ}$: 0, slope of $\overline{GJ}$: $\frac{3}{2}$

25. slope of $\overline{KL}$: $-\frac{5}{4}$, slope of $\overline{LM}$: -8, slope of $\overline{MK}$: 1

27. The line through (1, 1) and (3, 4); the line with the greater slope is steeper; the line with the greater slope has a greater number for the slope.

29. No. *Sample answer:* The rise and the run using one ordered pair first will both be the opposite of the rise and the run using the other ordered pair first, so the quotient of the rise and the run will remain the same; the slope of the line containing (1, 2) and (−3, 4) is $\frac{4-2}{-3-1} = \frac{2}{-4} = -\frac{1}{2}$ or $\frac{2-4}{1-(-3)} = -\frac{2}{4} = -\frac{1}{2}$.

3 APPLY

ASSIGNMENT GUIDE

Basic Course

Day 1: pp. 573-574 Exs. 10, 11, 13-15, 28, 36-42

Day 2: pp. 573-574 Exs. 12, 16-26, 35, 43

Average Course

Day 1: pp. 573-574 Exs. 10, 13-15, 27-30, 40-44

Day 2: pp. 573-574 Exs. 12, 19-26, 35-39

Advanced Course

Day 1: pp. 573-574 Exs. 10, 13-15, 27-32*, 42-44

Day 2: pp. 573-574 Exs. 12, 19-26, 33-37*

Block

pp. 573-574 Exs. 10, 12-15, 19-30, 35-44

Extra Practice

- Student Edition, p. 737
- Chapter 11 Resource Book, pp. 54-56
- Test and Practice Generator

Transparency

Even-numbered answers are available on transparencies. Support transparencies are available for Exercises 22-25.

Homework Check

When you review students' homework for this lesson, go over the following exercises to check understanding of key concepts.

Basic: 10, 13, 16, 22, 26
Average: 10, 13, 20, 22, 26
Advanced: 10, 14, 20, 22, 26

22-25. See Additional Answers beginning on page AA1.

4 ASSESS

ASSESSMENT RESOURCES

For more assessment resources, see:
- Assessment Book
- Test and Practice Generator

MINI-QUIZ

Find the slope of the line passing through the points.

1. (1, 1), (4, 6) $\frac{5}{3}$

2. (0, 1), (9, 0) $-\frac{1}{9}$

3. Find the slope of each side of the triangle.

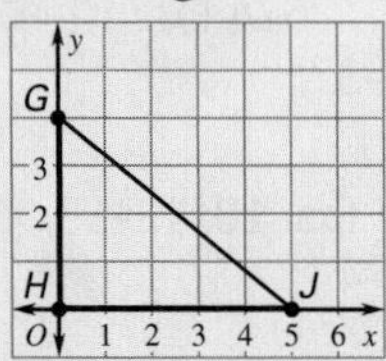

$\overline{GH}$: undefined, $\overline{HJ}$: 0, $\overline{GJ}$: $-\frac{4}{5}$

5 FOLLOW-UP

RETEACHING/REMEDIATION

- Study Guide in Chapter 11 Resource Book, pp. 57–58
- eTutorial Plus Online
- Extra Practice, p. 737
- Lesson Practice in Chapter 11 Resource Book, pp. 54–56

CHALLENGE/ENRICHMENT

- Challenge Practice in Chapter 11 Resource Book, p. 59
- Teacher's Edition, p. 538F

ENGLISH LEARNER SUPPORT

- Spanish Study Guide
- Multi-Language Glossary
- Chapter Audio Summaries CDs

35. See Additional Answers beginning on page AA1.

30. Ski Jump A ski slope has a starting altitude of 2800 meters and an ending altitude of 1886 meters. The length of the ski slope is about 3299 meters. What is the approximate slope of the ski slope? Round to the nearest hundredth. 0.28

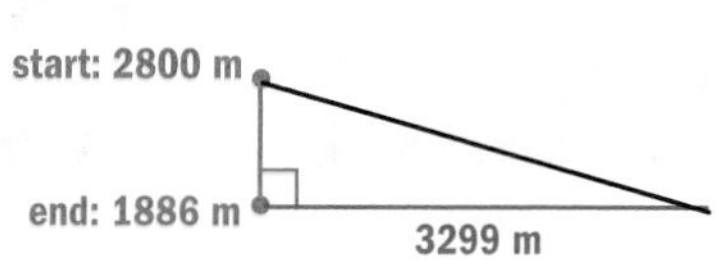

Challenge Find the missing value(s) using the given slope and points.

C **31.** $m = \frac{7}{4}$ and $(x, -7)$, $(16, 0)$ $x = 12$

32. $m = 0$ and $(0, 7)$, $(3, y)$ $y = 7$

33. $m = \frac{1}{2}$ and $(0, 0)$, $(x, 2)$, $(6, y)$ $x = 4$, $y = 3$

34. $m = -3$ and $(2, -6)$, $(x, 9)$, $(-1, y)$ $x = -3$, $y = 3$

Mixed Review

35. The table shows the number of runs scored in each inning of a seven-inning softball game. Make a scatter plot of the data. Tell whether the two quantities have a *positive relationship*, a *negative relationship*, or *no relationship*. *(Lesson 11.2)* See margin for art; no relationship.

Inning	1	2	3	4	5	6	7
Runs	0	0	4	2	1	0	1

Tell whether the ordered pair is a solution of the equation $y = -x + 5$. *(Lesson 11.3)*

36. (4, 1) yes **37.** (−9, 14) yes **38.** (10, 15) no **39.** (−31, −26) no

Basic Skills Solve the equation.

40. $-7r + 15 = 29$ −2 **41.** $42 = \frac{t}{3} + 21$ 63 **42.** $6s - 5 = 2s$ $1\frac{1}{4}$

Test-Taking Practice

INTERNET
State Test Practice
CLASSZONE.COM

43. Multiple Choice What is the slope of the line shown in the graph? C

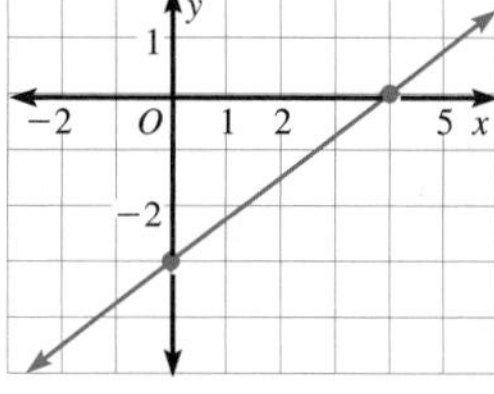

A. $-\frac{4}{3}$ **B.** $-\frac{3}{4}$

C. $\frac{3}{4}$ **D.** $\frac{4}{3}$

44. Multiple Choice A line passes through the points (10, 0) and $(x, -5)$ and has a slope of $\frac{1}{2}$. What is the value of x? H

F. −20 **G.** −5 **H.** 0 **I.** 5

11.7 Hands-on Activity

GOAL
Find how slope, y-intercept, and an equation can relate.

MATERIALS
- pencil
- graph paper

Slope-Intercept Form

You can find the slope and y-intercept of a line by looking at its equation in *slope-intercept form.*

Explore 1 **Find the slope and y-intercept of $y = 4x + 3$.**

1. Make a table of values for the equation $y = 4x + 3$.

x	0	1	2
y	3	7	11

2. Plot points and draw a line.

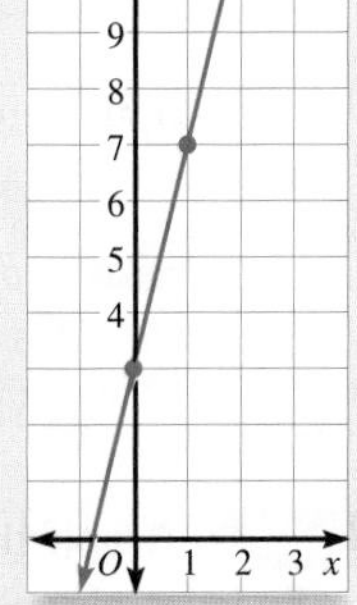

3. Use the graph to find the slope and y-intercept of $y = 4x + 3$.

slope $= \frac{4}{1} = 4$ y-intercept $= 3$

Your turn now **Use a graph to answer Exercises 1–3.**

1. Copy and complete the table of values for $y = -2x - 1$.

x	−1	0	1
y	?	?	?
	1	−1	−3

2. Plot the points and draw a line. See margin.
3. Use the graph to find the slope and y-intercept. −2, −1
4. Copy and complete the table.

Equation	Slope	y-intercept
$y = 4x + 3$	? 4	? 3
$y = -2x - 1$	? −2	? −1

ILLINOIS Standards and ISAT:
8.B.3, 8.D.3a

1 PLAN

Explore the Concept

- Students will find how slope, y-intercept, and an equation can relate.
- This activity leads into using slope-intercept form to graph equations in Lesson 11.7.

Materials

Each student or pair of students will need a pencil and graph paper.

Recommended Time

Work activity: 10 min
Discuss results: 5 min

Grouping

Students can work individually or in pairs. If students work in pairs, one can make a table of values while the other plots points and draws the line. Students can work together to find the slope and y-intercept.

Transparency

Support transparencies are available for this Activity.

2 TEACH

Tips for Success

If the points plotted do not form a straight line, students should reexamine their work, as all the equations provided are of lines.

Alternative Strategy

After the Explore activities, write the equation $y = -x + 3$ on the board and draw its graph. Have students find the y-intercept and slope and then test some points to show that the graph matches the equation.

2. See Additional Answers beginning on page AA1.

CLOSE

KEY DISCOVERY

Without graphing, you can use the equation of a line written in the form $y = mx + b$ to easily pinpoint the slope and y-intercept of the line.

ASSESSMENT

1. What is the slope of the line whose equation is $y = -5x + 2$? **-5**
2. Does every line have a y-intercept? **Accept all reasonable answers. Students should realize that every line with positive, negative, or zero slope has a y-intercept, but vertical lines do not have y-intercepts if they do not lie on the y-axis.**

5. 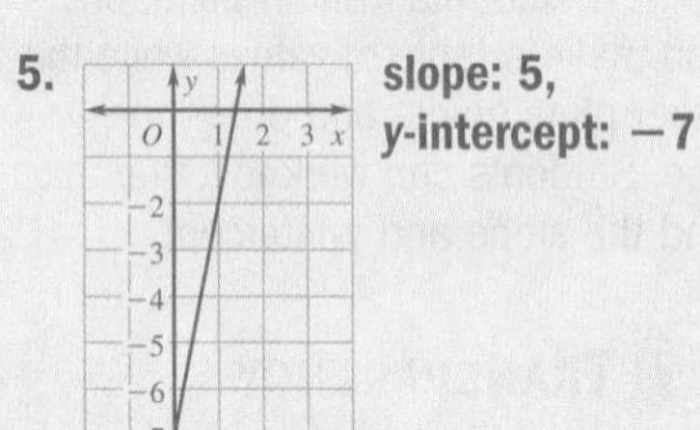 **slope: 5, y-intercept: -7**

6. 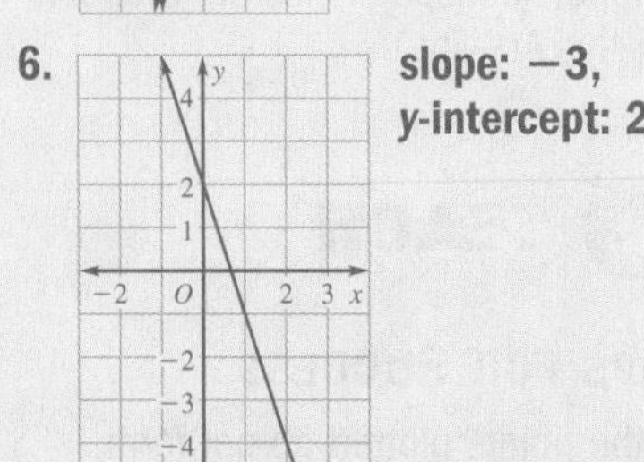 **slope: -3, y-intercept: 2**

7. 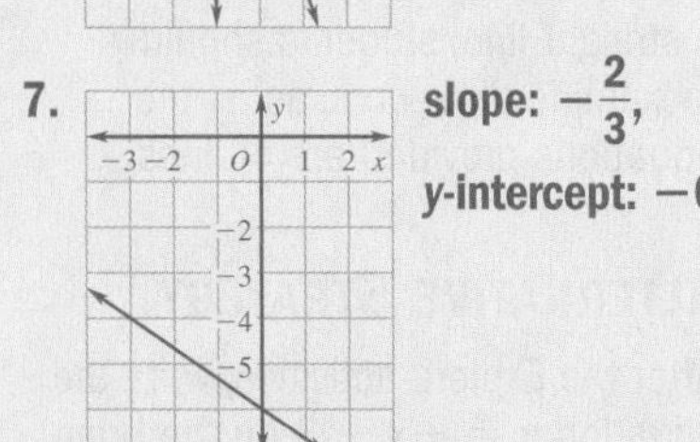 **slope: $-\frac{2}{3}$, y-intercept: -6**

8–12. See Additional Answers beginning on page AA1.

Hands-on Activity Continued

Explore 2 **Find the slope and y-intercept of $y = 3x + 5$.**

1 Make a table of values for the equation $y = 3x + 5$.

x	1	2	3
y	8	11	14

2 Calculate the slope of the line from the points.

$$m = \frac{y_2 - y_1}{x_2 - x_1} = \frac{11 - 8}{2 - 1} = 3$$

3 Calculate the y-intercept by substitution.

$$y = 3x + 5 = 3(0) + 5 = 5$$

4 Add $y = 3x + 5$ to your table from Exercise 4. **slope: 3; y-intercept: 5**

5 Use your table to make a conjecture about using an equation of a line to find the slope and y-intercept of the line. ***Sample answer:* When a linear equation is solved for y, the slope is the coefficient of x and the y-intercept is the constant term.**

Your turn now **Graph the line using a table of values. Then use the graph to find the slope and y-intercept.** **5–8. See margin.**

5. $y = 5x - 7$ **6.** $y = -3x + 2$ **7.** $y = -\frac{2}{3}x - 6$ **8.** $y = \frac{5}{4}x + 1$

Solve the equation for y. Make a table of values for the equation. Calculate the slope and y-intercept. **9–12. See margin.**

9. $y + 2 = \frac{1}{2}x$ **10.** $3y = -2x + 9$ **11.** $y + 4x = -5$ **12.** $6x - 2y = 10$

13. Does your conjecture in Step 5 still seem to be true? **yes**

Stop and Think

14. What does m stand for in the equation $y = mx + b$? What does b stand for in the equation $y = mx + b$? **slope; y-intercept**

Slope-Intercept Form

BEFORE

You graphed equations using intercepts.

Now

You'll write and graph equations in slope-intercept form.

WHY?

So you can determine how many bracelets you must sell, as in Ex. 21.

In the Real World

Word Watch

slope-intercept form, p. 577

Hiking You are hiking a trail on Mount Rainier in Washington. At the base of the trail, the temperature is 50.9°F. The temperature changes at a rate of −0.005°F per foot as you hike up. What equation can you use to find the temperature after you hike up 1000 feet?

One way to write an equation is to use *slope-intercept form.*

Slope-Intercept Form

Words The linear equation $y = mx + b$ is written in **slope-intercept form**. The slope is m. The y-intercept is b.

Algebra $y = mx + b$ **Numbers** $y = 3x + 2$

EXAMPLE 1 Identifying Slopes and y-Intercepts

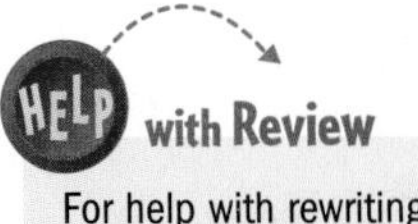

with Review

For help with rewriting equations, see p. 549.

Find the slope and y-intercept of the line.

a. $y = x - 3$ **b.** $-4x + 2y = 16$

Solution

a. The equation $y = x - 3$ can be written as $y = 1x + (-3)$.

ANSWER The line has a slope of 1 and a y-intercept of −3.

b. Write the equation $-4x + 2y = 16$ in slope-intercept form.

$-4x + 2y = 16$ Write original equation.

$2y = 4x + 16$ Add $4x$ to each side.

$y = 2x + 8$ Divide each side by 2.

ANSWER The line has a slope of 2 and a y-intercept of 8.

ILLINOIS Standards and ISAT:
8.A.3b, 8.D.3a; 8.D.3b

1 PLAN

SKILL CHECK

Write the equation $y = mx + b$ for the values of m and b.

1. $m = 3, b = 5$
$y = 3x + 5$

2. $m = -1, b = 2$
$y = -x + 2$

LESSON OBJECTIVE

Write and graph equations in slope-intercept form.

PACING

Suggested Number of Days
Basic Course: 2 days
Average Course: 2 days
Advanced Course: 2 days
Block: 1 block

TEACHING RESOURCES

For a complete list of Teaching Resources, see page 538B.

TRANSPARENCY

Warm-Up Exercises for this lesson are available on a transparency.

2 TEACH

MOTIVATING THE LESSON

Ask students if it gets hotter or colder as you climb a mountain and why.

TIPS FOR NEW TEACHERS

Remind students to write an equation in slope-intercept form to identify slope and y-intercept. For example, in $2x + 6y = 9$, some students may conclude that the slope is 2 and the y-intercept is 9. Illustrate that this conclusion is incorrect. See Tips for New Teachers in the *Chapter 11 Resource Book.*

EXTRA EXAMPLES

Example 1 Find the slope and y-intercept of the line.

a. $y = 2x + 7$ **2, 7**

b. $4x + 3y = 12$ **$-\frac{4}{3}$, 4**

Example 2 Graph the equation $y = -\frac{1}{3}x + 1$.

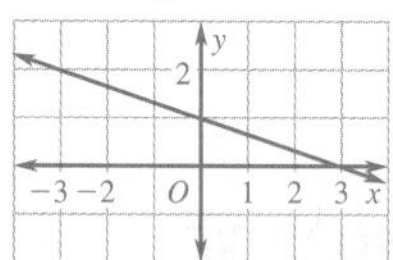

Example 3 A 7 foot long python is growing $\frac{1}{2}$ foot per year. Write an equation for its length in x years. Use your equation to calculate its length in 10 years. **$y = \frac{1}{2}x + 7$; 12 ft**

TRANSPARENCY

Support transparencies are available for Example 2 and Your turn now Exercises 1–3.

NOTETAKING

Suggest students write a note for this lesson that refers them to their notes for Lesson 11.6 about finding slope.

CONCEPT CHECK

What do m and b represent in the slope-intercept form? **m is the slope and b is the y-intercept.**

DAILY PUZZLER

Graph $y = mx + m$ for a few values of m. What do all the graphs have in common? **They all intercept the x-axis at $(-1, 0)$.**

1–3. See Additional Answers beginning on page AA1.

EXAMPLE 2 Graphing Using Slope-Intercept Form

Graph the equation $y = \frac{1}{2}x + 3$.

Solution

1. The y-intercept is 3, so plot the point (0, 3).
2. The slope is $\frac{1}{2}$, so plot a second point by moving up 1 unit and right 2 units.
3. Draw a line through the points.

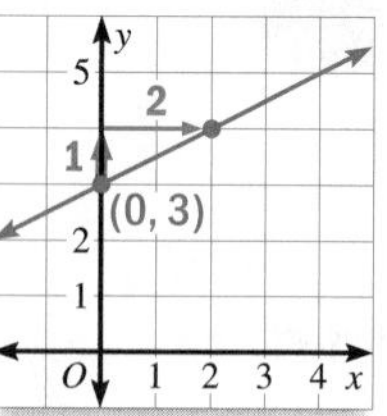

Your turn now **Find the slope and y-intercept of the graph of the equation. Then graph the equation.** **1–3. See margin for art.**

1. $y = 2x + 5$ **2, 5** **2.** $-x + y = 6$ **1, 6** **3.** $y = \frac{1}{4}x$ **$\frac{1}{4}$, 0**

EXAMPLE 3 Using Slope-Intercept Form

To answer the question on page 577, you can write an equation in slope-intercept form to find the temperature after hiking up 1000 feet.

Solution

1. Write a verbal model.

Temperature	=	Rate of temperature change	•	Increase in altitude	+	Initial temperature

2. Write an algebraic model in slope-intercept form.

The temperature changes at a rate of -0.005°F per foot, so $m = -0.005$. The initial temperature is 50.9°F, so $b = 50.9$. Let y be the temperature and x be the change in altitude.

$y = mx + b$ **Write slope-intercept form.**

$y = -0.005x + 50.9$ **Substitute -0.005 for m and 50.9 for b.**

3. To find the temperature after hiking up 1000 feet, find the value of y when $x = 1000$.

$y = -0.005x + 50.9$ **Write the equation.**

$= -0.005 \cdot (1000) + 50.9$ **Substitute 1000 for x.**

$= 45.9$ **Simplify.**

ANSWER The temperature after hiking up 1000 feet is 45.9°F.

11.7 Exercises

More Practice, p. 737

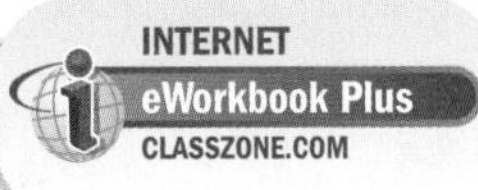

INTERNET
eWorkbook Plus
CLASSZONE.COM

Getting Ready to Practice

1. **Vocabulary** Identify the slope and y-intercept of the graph of the equation $y = -5x + 7$. $-5, 7$

Rewrite the equation in slope-intercept form.

2. $x - y = -2$ $y = x + 2$
3. $2x = y + 5$ $y = 2x - 5$
4. $8x - 4y = 32$ $y = 2x - 8$

Find the slope and y-intercept of the graph of the equation.

5. $y = x + 3$ $1, 3$
6. $y = 6 - x$ $-1, 6$
7. $1 = 2x - y$ $2, -1$

8. **Find the Error** Describe and correct the error made by a student while graphing the equation $y = -2x - 1$.
The y-intercept is -1, so the corresponding ordered pair is $(0, -1)$; see margin for art.

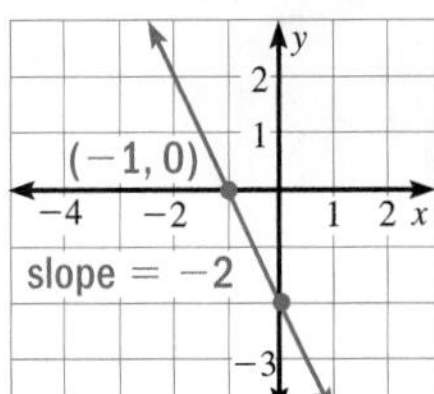

Practice and Problem Solving

Find the slope and y-intercept of the graph of the equation. Then graph the equation. 9–14. See margin for art.

A
9. $y = x - 8$ $1, -8$
10. $y = 3$ $0, 3$
11. $y = -x + 7$ $-1, 7$
12. $y = x - \frac{1}{2}$ $1, -\frac{1}{2}$
13. $y = \frac{2}{3}x - 4$ $\frac{2}{3}, -4$
14. $y = \frac{1}{5}x$ $\frac{1}{5}, 0$

Rewrite in slope-intercept form. Then find the slope and y-intercept of the line.

15. $y = 10 - 6x$
16. $y - 9 = -\frac{3}{4}x$
17. $\frac{2}{3}x - y = 3$
18. $2y + 2x = 12$
19. $y + 12x = 0$
20. $13x - 11y = 143$

21. **Bracelets** You make and sell bracelets. You buy \$28 in supplies and sell the bracelets for \$3.50 each. Your profit can be modeled by $p = 3.50b - 28$ where p is the profit and b is the number of bracelets sold. Graph the equation. How many bracelets do you need to sell to make a profit?
See margin for art; 9 bracelets.

HELP with Homework

Example	Exercises
1	9-20
2	9-14
3	21

Online Resources
CLASSZONE.COM
- More Examples
- eTutorial Plus

15. $y = -6x + 10$; $-6, 10$
16. $y = -\frac{3}{4}x + 9$; $-\frac{3}{4}, 9$
17. $y = \frac{2}{3}x - 3$; $\frac{2}{3}, -3$
18. $y = -x + 6$; $-1, 6$
19. $y = -12x$; $-12, 0$
20. $y = \frac{13}{11}x - 13$; $\frac{13}{11}, -13$

3 APPLY

ASSIGNMENT GUIDE

Basic Course
Day 1: pp. 579-580 Exs. 9-14, 22, 28-31
Day 2: pp. 579-580 Exs. 15-21, 23, 32-35

Average Course
Day 1: pp. 579-580 Exs. 9-14, 23-26, 33-35
Day 2: pp. 579-580 Exs. 15-22, 28-32

Advanced Course
Day 1: pp. 579-580 Exs. 9-14, 24-27*, 33-35
Day 2: pp. 579-580 Exs. 15-22, 28-32

Block
pp. 579-580 Exs. 9-26, 28-35

EXTRA PRACTICE
- Student Edition, p. 737
- Chapter 11 Resource Book, pp. 62-64
- Test and Practice Generator

TRANSPARENCY

Even-numbered answers are available on transparencies. Support transparencies are available for Exercises 9-14, 21, 25, and 26.

HOMEWORK CHECK

When you review students' homework for this lesson, go over the following exercises to check understanding of key concepts.
Basic: 10, 13, 15, 18, 21
Average: 10, 13, 16, 19, 21
Advanced: 10, 13, 17, 20, 21

TEACHING TIP

In Exercises 10 and 14, discuss with students what is missing from each equation and what this means.

8-14, 21. See Additional Answers beginning on page AA1.

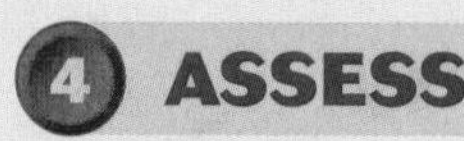

ASSESSMENT RESOURCES

For more assessment resources, see:

- Assessment Book
- Test and Practice Generator

MINI-QUIZ

1. Find the slope and y-intercept of the line $y = -3x + 11$. **−3, 11**
2. Rewrite $4x - 2y + 5 = 0$ in slope-intercept form. Then find the slope and y-intercept of the line. $y = 2x + \frac{5}{2}$; **2,** $\frac{5}{2}$
3. Write the equation of the graph in slope-intercept form.

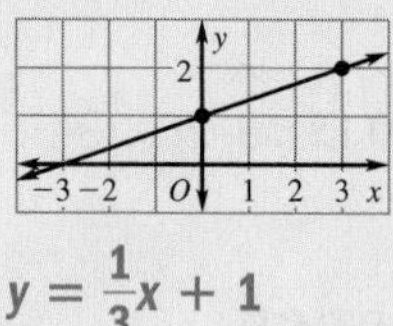

$y = \frac{1}{3}x + 1$

RETEACHING/REMEDIATION

- Study Guide in Chapter 11 Resource Book, pp. 65-66
- eTutorial Plus Online
- Extra Practice, p. 737
- Lesson Practice in Chapter 11 Resource Book, pp. 62-64

CHALLENGE/ENRICHMENT

- Challenge Practice in Chapter 11 Resource Book, p. 67
- Teacher's Edition, p. 538F

ENGLISH LEARNER SUPPORT

- Spanish Study Guide
- Multi-Language Glossary
- Chapter Audio Summaries CDs

25, 26, 32–35. See Additional Answers beginning on page AA1.

Write the equation of the graph in slope-intercept form.

B 22.

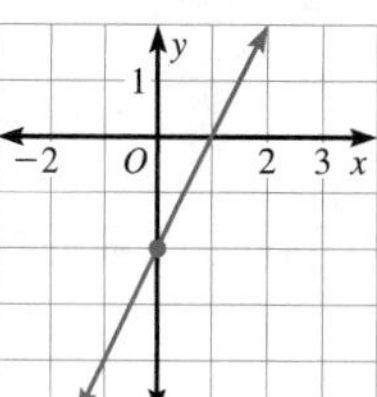

$y = 2x - 2$

23.

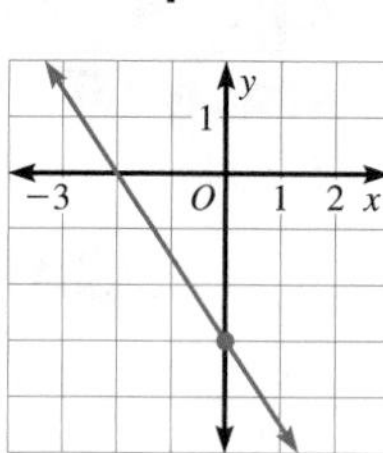

$y = -\frac{3}{2}x - 3$

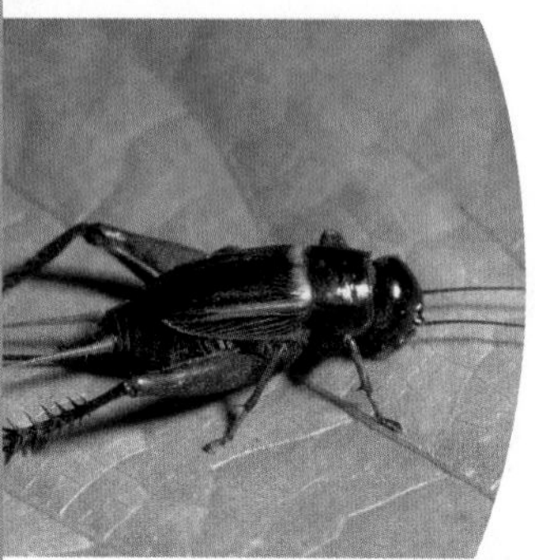

26. $y = -\frac{1}{2}x + 8$; see margin for art.

24. Critical Thinking Write the equations of two lines that have the same slope but different y-intercepts. *Sample answer:* $y = 2x + 2$, $y = 2x - 1$

25. Crickets The number of chirps per minute made by a cricket can be modeled by the equation $c = 4t - 156$, where c is the number of chirps per minute and t is the temperature in degrees Fahrenheit. Graph the equation. What does the x-intercept mean in terms of the temperature and the number of chirps per minute? **See margin for art; at 39°F, the number of chirps per minute is 0.**

C 26. Critical Thinking When two lines are perpendicular and neither has a slope of zero, the product of their slopes is -1. Write the equation of the line that is perpendicular to and has the same y-intercept as the line $y = 2x + 8$. Then graph both lines to check that they are perpendicular.

27. Challenge Write the equation $ax + by + c = 0$, where b is not equal to 0, in slope-intercept form. $y = -\frac{a}{b}x - \frac{c}{b}$

Mixed Review

Write the sentence as an inequality, letting x represent the variable. Then solve the inequality. *(Lesson 6.6)*

28. Six is less than a number plus 8. $6 < x + 8$; $x > -2$

29. Five times a number is greater than or equal to thirty-five. $5x \geq 35$; $x \geq 7$

Find the volume of the figure. *(Lessons 10.6, 10.7)*

30. A cylinder with radius 3 inches and height 7 inches **198 in.^{3}**

31. A pyramid with base area 25 square feet and height 9 feet **75 ft^3**

Basic Skills Solve the inequality. Then graph its solution. **32–34. See margin for art.**

32. $a + 3 \leq -7$ $a \leq -10$ **33.** $8 < 2 + t$ $t > 6$ **34.** $n - 4 > 7$ $n > 11$

Test-Taking Practice

INTERNET
State Test Practice
CLASSZONE.COM

35. Extended Response You and two friends decide to rent one canoe. It costs \$9 an hour to rent the canoe and \$12 for a ride back to the starting point. Graph the equation $c = 9h + 12$ to see the possible costs of renting a canoe. If the maximum amount that each of you wants to spend is \$16, for how many hours can you rent a canoe? **See margin for art; 4h.**

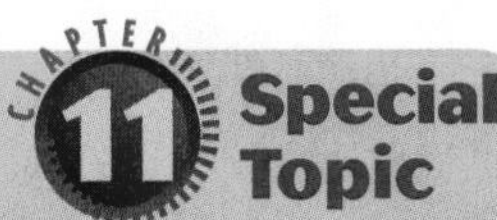

Systems of Equations

GOAL Solve systems of linear equations.

Word Watch

system of linear equations, p. 581
solution of a linear system, p. 581

A **system of linear equations** is a set of two or more linear equations with the same variables. A **solution of a linear system** is an ordered pair that is a solution of each equation in the system.

In the system of equations below, (3, 2) is a solution.

System of equations	Check
$2x + 4y = 14$	$2(3) + 4(2) = 6 + 8 = 14$ ✓
$3x - 5y = -1$	$3(3) - 5(2) = 9 - 10 = -1$ ✓

If a system of linear equations has a solution, then the graphs of the equations intersect.

EXAMPLE 1 Solving a System of Equations by Graphing

Solve the linear system: $x + y = 5$ **Equation 1**

$y = 2x - 1$ **Equation 2**

Solution

1. Write each equation in slope-intercept form.

Equation 1	Equation 2
$x + y = 5$	$y = 2x - 1$
$y = -x + 5$	

2. Graph both equations.

3. Estimate the point of intersection using the graph. It appears that the point of intersection is (2, 3).

4. Check whether (2, 3) is the solution by substituting 2 for x and 3 for y in each of the equations.

Equation 1	Equation 2
$x + y = 5$	$y = 2x - 1$
$2 + 3 \stackrel{?}{=} 5$	$3 \stackrel{?}{=} 2(2) - 1$
$5 = 5$ ✓	$3 = 3$ ✓

ANSWER The solution is (2, 3).

ILLINOIS Standards and ISAT:
8.A.3b, 8.D.3a

1 PLAN

SKILL CHECK

Write each equation in slope-intercept form.

1. $4x + y = 12$ $y = -4x + 12$
2. $2y = -6 + x$ $y = \frac{1}{2}x - 3$
3. $y + 20 = 3x$ $y = 3x - 20$
4. $7x + y = 0$ $y = -7x$

LESSON OBJECTIVE

Solve systems of linear equations.

2 TEACH

EXTRA EXAMPLES

Example 1 Solve the linear system:
$y = 3x + 1$
$x + y = 1$

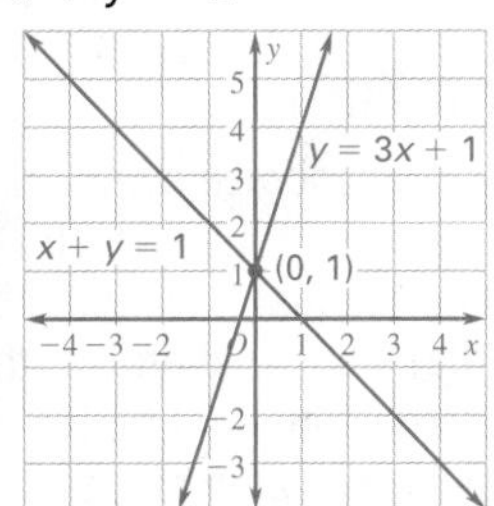

The solution is (0, 1).

TRANSPARENCY

Support transparencies are available for Example 1.

EXTRA EXAMPLES

Example 2 Solve the linear system:
$y = -2x + 3$
$2y = x - 4$
(2, −1)

COMMON ERROR

Watch for students who substitute an expression back into its original equation and end up with $-6 = -6$ or something similar. Encourage students to label the equations 1 and 2 or A and B, and advise them to make sure they substitute an expression from one equation into the other equation.

APPLY

TRANSPARENCY

Even-numbered answers are available on transparencies. Support transparencies are available for Exercises 1–3 and 7.

TEACHING TIP

In Exercise 6, encourage some students to substitute the second equation into the first, while others substitute the first equation into the second. Demonstrate that both methods yield the same results.

1.
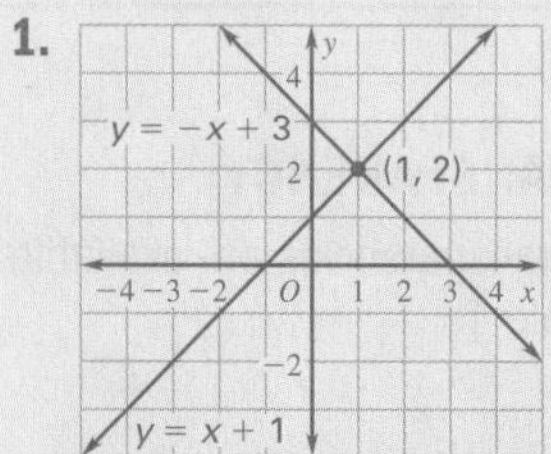

2, 3, 7. See Additional Answers beginning on page AA1.

Special Topic Continued

with Solving

When solving by substitution, solve for the variable that is easier to isolate. You will get the same solution whether you begin by solving for *x* or for *y*.

EXAMPLE 2 Solving Linear Systems by Substitution

Solve the linear system: $x + 4y = 4$ **Equation 1**
$x - y = -6$ **Equation 2**

Solution

1. Choose an equation to solve for one of the variables.

$x - y = -6$	Write Equation 2.
$x = y - 6$	Add y to each side.

2. Substitute $y - 6$ for x in Equation 1. Then solve for y.

$x + 4y = 4$	Write Equation 1.
$(y - 6) + 4y = 4$	Substitute $y - 6$ for x.
$5y - 6 = 4$	Combine like terms.
$5y = 10$	Add 6 to each side.
$y = 2$	Divide each side by 5.

3. Substitute 2 for y in the original Equation 2 and solve for x.

$x - y = -6$	Write Equation 2.
$x - 2 = -6$	Substitute 2 for y.
$x = -4$	Add 2 to each side.

ANSWER The solution is $(-4, 2)$.

Exercises

Estimate the solution of the linear system using a graph. Then check the solution using algebra. 1–3. See margin for art.

1. $y = -x + 3$ (1, 2)
$y = x + 1$

2. $x - y = 1$ (−4, −5)
$5x - 4y = 0$

3. $y = 2x - 15$ (6, −3)
$x = -2y$

Solve the linear system by substitution.

4. $x = 4$ (4, −2)
$x + y = 2$

5. $a + b = 4$ (−1, 5)
$4a + b = 1$

6. $2w - z = -2$ (3, 8)
$4w + z = 20$

7. Trading Cards You have 100 trading cards and your friend has 20. Every day you give your friend one card. Use the equations $c = 100 - d$ and $c = 20 + d$ to model this situation. Graph the two equations and find when you both will have the same number of cards. See margin for art; in 40 days.

Graphs of Linear Inequalities

BEFORE
You graphed linear equations.

Now
You'll graph linear inequalities.

WHY?
So you can find how much water you can bring on a trip, as in Ex. 34.

Word Watch

linear inequality, p. 583
solution of a linear inequality, p. 583
half-plane, p. 584

Activity You can use a graph to model linear inequalities.

1. Sketch the graph of $y = x - 1$.

2. Graph and label the following points in your coordinate plane.

   $A(0, 0), B(-3, -2), C(4, -3), D(0, -4)$

3. Which of the points in Step 2 make the inequality $y < x - 1$ true? Draw a circle around these points. *C and D*

   Steps 3–4. See margin for art.

4. Which of the points in Step 2 make the inequality $y > x - 1$ true? Draw a square around these points. *A and B*

5. Make a conjecture about the solutions of $y < x - 1$ and the solutions of $y > x - 1$.

Step 5. All solutions for $y < x - 1$ are below the line $y = x - 1$, and all solutions for $y > x - 1$ are above the line $y = x - 1$.

In the activity, you investigated solutions of linear inequalities. Some examples of **linear inequalities** in two variables are $y \le 2x + 5$, $2x + 5y < 7$, and $4x + y \ge -6$.

An ordered pair (x, y) is a **solution of a linear inequality** if the inequality is true when the values of x and y are substituted into the inequality.

EXAMPLE 1 **Checking Solutions of a Linear Inequality**

Tell whether the point is a solution of $3x - 4y \le -8$.

(x, y)	$3x - 4y$	$3x - 4y \overset{?}{\le} -8$	Conclusion
a. $(0, 0)$	$3(0) - 4(0) = 0$	$0 \not\le -8$	$(0, 0)$ is *not* a solution.
b. $(-1, 4)$	$3(-1) - 4(4) = -19$	$-19 \le -8$	$(-1, 4)$ is a solution.

HELP with Solving

The symbol $\not\le$ means *not less than or equal to*. It is equivalent to the symbol $>$, which means *greater than*.

Your turn now Is the ordered pair a solution of $2x + 3y < 5$?

1. $(0, 0)$ yes
2. $(-4, 2)$ yes
3. $(5, -1)$ no
4. $(1, 1)$ no

ILLINOIS Standards and ISAT:
8.A.3b, 8.D.3a

1 PLAN

SKILL CHECK

Determine if the point is on the line $y = 3x - 8$.

1. $(-1, -11)$ yes
2. $(0, -5)$ no

Lesson Objective

Graph linear inequalities.

Pacing

Suggested Number of Days
Basic Course: 2 days
Average Course: 2 days
Advanced Course: 2 days
Block: 1 block

Teaching Resources

For a complete list of Teaching Resources, see page 538B.

Transparency

Warm-Up Exercises for this lesson are available on a transparency. Support transparencies are available for the Activity.

2 TEACH

Motivating the Lesson

Have students give pairs of numbers whose sum is greater than 10. Stress that you cannot plot all such pairs, so shading is used to represent them.

Activity

Goal Graph a linear inequality.

Key Discovery All points whose coordinates satisfy a linear inequality are on one side of the graph of the corresponding linear equation. The points on the line may or may not satisfy the inequality.

Steps 3–4. See Additional Answers beginning on page AA1.

TIPS FOR NEW TEACHERS

To help students understand why they are shading a half-plane, graph an inequality line, mark several points in the half-plane, and confirm that they satisfy the inequality and that points in the other half-plane do not. Then shade the rest of the half-plane to show that the shading is a shortcut for plotting every single possible point that satisfies the inequality. See Tips for New Teachers in the *Chapter 11 Resource Book*.

EXTRA EXAMPLES

Example 1 Tell whether the point is a solution of $5x - 2y \geq 10$.

a. $(0, -5)$ yes

b. $(3, 3)$ no

Example 2 Graph $y < \frac{1}{2}x - 1$.

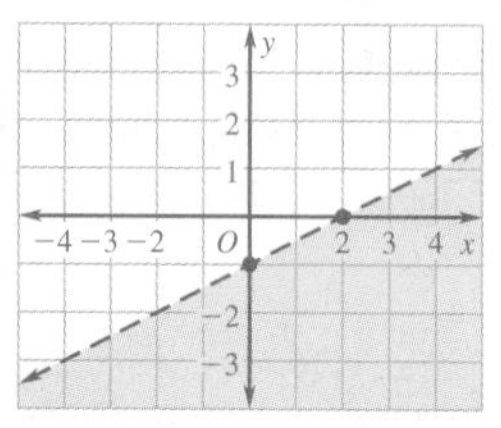

TRANSPARENCY

Support transparencies are available for Examples 2–3 and Your turn now Exercises 5–8.

MULTIPLE REPRESENTATIONS

Write the symbols $\leq, <, =, >$, and $\geq$ on the board. Ask students to describe what each represents and how the symbols differ from each other. Then show the opposite of each symbol, such as $\neq$, and have students identify the symbol above that is equivalent to each opposite.

5–8. See Additional Answers beginning on page AA1.

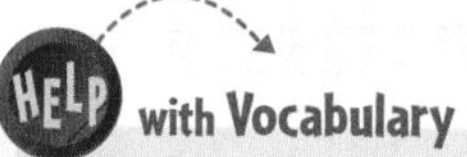

HELP with Vocabulary

A line divides a coordinate plane into two half-planes.

The graph of a linear inequality in two variables is a **half-plane**. The shaded region includes all the solutions of the inequality.

A solid line indicates that points on the line *are* solutions of an inequality. A dashed line indicates that points on the line are *not* solutions.

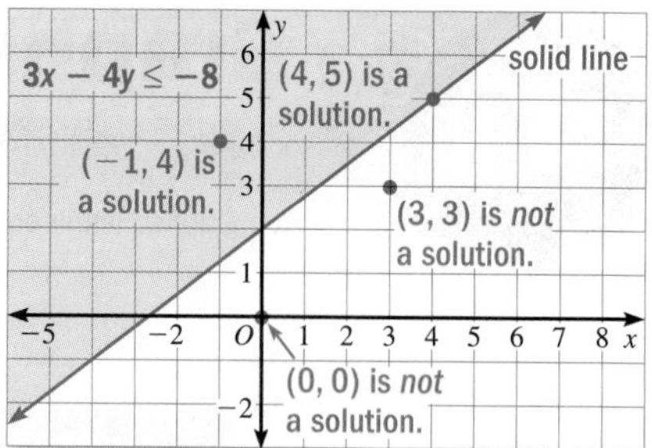

Graphing Linear Inequalities

1. Change the inequality symbol to "=." Graph the equation. Use a dashed line for < or >. Use a solid line for ≤ or ≥.

2. Test a point in one of the half-planes to check whether it is a solution of the inequality.

3. If the test point is a solution, shade its half-plane. If the test point is not a solution, shade the other half-plane.

EXAMPLE 2 Graphing a Linear Inequality

Graph $y - 2x > 3$.

1 Change > to = and write the equation in slope-intercept form.

$y - 2x = 3$ **Replace > with = sign.**

$y = 2x + 3$ **Add $2x$ to each side.**

Graph the line that has a slope of 2 and a y-intercept of 3. Because the inequality is >, use a dashed line.

HELP with Solving

You can use any point not on the line as a test point. Using (0, 0) is convenient because 0 is substituted for each variable.

2 Use (0, 0) as a test point.

$y > 2x + 3$

$0 \stackrel{?}{>} 2(0) + 3$

$0 \not> 3$ **(0, 0) is not a solution.**

3 Shade the half-plane that does *not* contain (0, 0).

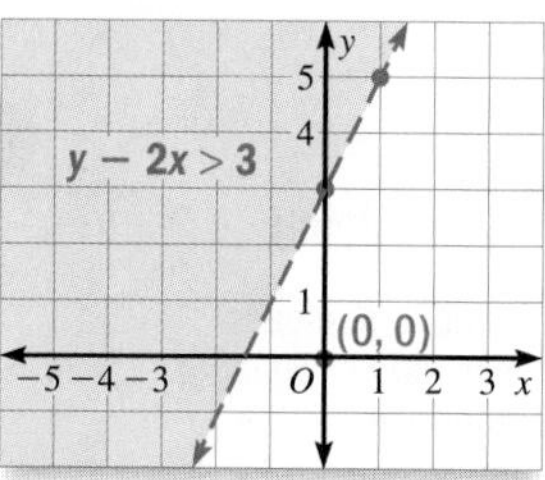

Your turn now **Graph the inequality.** 5–8. See margin.

5. $y < x + 1$ **6.** $3x + y \geq 3$ **7.** $x - 2y \geq -1$ **8.** $y \geq -2$

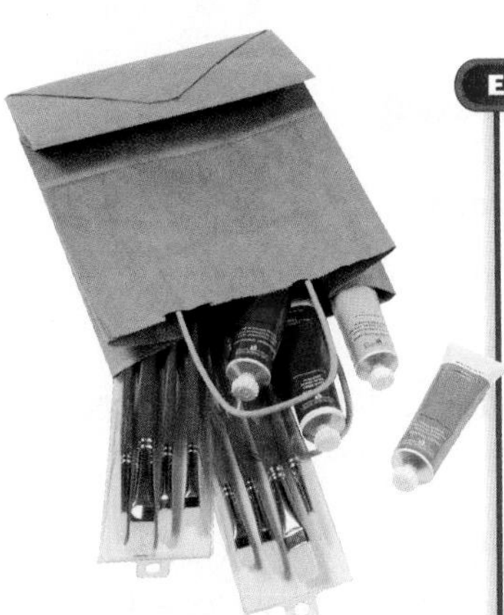

EXAMPLE 3 Using the Graph of a Linear Inequality

Art Supplies You are buying art supplies for your art club. You have $40 to spend. Tubes of paint cost $6 each and brushes cost $4 each. The inequality $6x + 4y \le 40$, where x represents the number of tubes of paint and y represents the number of brushes, models this situation. How many tubes of paint and how many brushes can you buy with $40?

a. Graph the inequality.

b. Use the graph to find a solution. Then interpret the solution.

Solution

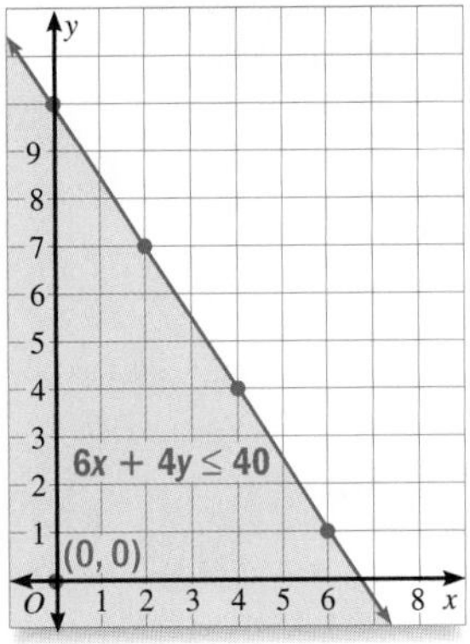

a. Graph the equation $y = -\frac{3}{2}x + 10$.

Use a solid line.

Use (0, 0) as a test point.

$$6(0) + 4(0) \overset{?}{\le} 40$$

$$0 \le 40 \checkmark$$

Shade the half-plane that contains (0, 0).

b. One solution is (4, 4). This means that you can buy 4 tubes of paint and 4 brushes.

HELP with Solving

In Example 3, all points in the shaded region and on the line are solutions of the inequality. However, negative and fractional solutions do not make sense. You cannot buy a negative number of items, and you cannot buy part of an item.

EXTRA EXAMPLES

Example 3 A video store rents new releases for $4 each and family specials for $1.50 each. Chad has $12 to rent videos. The inequality $4x + 1.5y \le 12$, where x represents the number of new releases and y represents the number of family specials, models this situation. How many new releases and how many family specials can Chad rent?

a. Graph the inequality.

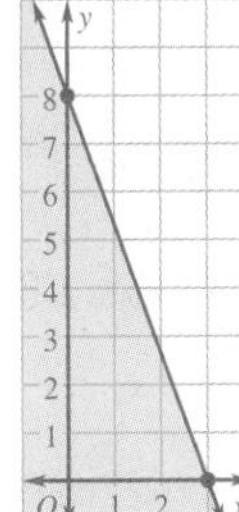

b. Use the graph to find a solution. Then interpret the solution. ***Sample answer:* (3, 0); Chad can rent 3 new releases and 0 family specials.**

11.8 Exercises

More Practice, p. 737

INTERNET eWorkbook Plus CLASSZONE.COM

Getting Ready to Practice

1. **Vocabulary** When graphing the inequality $y < 2x + 1$, the graphed dashed line divides the coordinate plane into two __?__. **half-planes**

Tell whether the point is a solution of the inequality $6x + 3y > 24$.

2. (2, 3) **no**
3. (4, 5) **yes**
4. (5, 4) **yes**
5. (3, 2) **no**

Graph the inequality. **6–9. See margin.**

6. $y > 14 - 4x$
7. $y < x + 5$
8. $3x - 4 \ge y$
9. $y + 3 \ge 4x$

10. **Trail Mix** You are making a trail mix of peanuts and raisins. You have $6.00 to spend on trail mix. Peanuts cost $2.00 per pound and raisins cost $1.50 per pound. How much of each item can you buy? Graph the inequality $2x + 1.50y \le 6$ to find different combinations of pounds of peanuts and raisins that you could buy to use in your trail mix. **See margin.**

CONCEPT CHECK

Can you use a solution to the equation of a line as a test point in a half-plane? Explain. **No; a point representing a solution to the equation of a line lies on the line and so does not indicate which side of the line must be shaded.**

DAILY PUZZLER

Which pair of inequalities has a solution set where all the x- and y-coordinates are negative?
$x \le 3$ and $y = -2$
$x \le -5$ and $y > -21$
$x < 0$ and $y \le -0.5$
$x < 0$ and $y \le -0.5$

6–10. See Additional Answers beginning on page AA1.

ASSIGNMENT GUIDE

Basic Course

Day 1: pp. 586–587 Exs. 11–14, 23–28, 38–41

Day 2: pp. 586–587 Exs. 16–22, 32–34, 42–44

Average Course

Day 1: pp. 586–587 Exs. 11–15, 26–31, 38–40

Day 2: pp. 586–587 Exs. 16–22, 32–36, 43–45

Advanced Course

Day 1: pp. 586–587 Exs. 11–15, 26–31, 38–40

Day 2: pp. 586–587 Exs. 16–22, 32–37*, 44, 45

Block

pp. 586–587 Exs. 11–22, 26–36, 38–40, 43–45

EXTRA PRACTICE

- Student Edition, p. 737
- Chapter 11 Resource Book, pp. 70–72
- Test and Practice Generator

Even-numbered answers are available on transparencies. Support transparencies are available for Exercises 6–10, 20–31, 33, and 34.

HOMEWORK CHECK

When you review students' homework for this lesson, go over the following exercises to check understanding of key concepts.

Basic: 11, 16, 20, 26, 32

Average: 12, 17, 21, 30, 32

Advanced: 13, 18, 22, 31, 32

20–31, 33. See Additional Answers beginning on page AA1.

Example	Exercises
1	11–14, 16–19
2	16–31
3	32–34

Online Resources CLASSZONE.COM

- More Examples
- eTutorial Plus

Practice and Problem Solving

Tell whether the point is a solution of the inequality.

A **11.** $5x + y \leq 17$; (1, 2) yes

12. $3x + 7y < 20$; (−11, 2) yes

13. $9x + 12y > 26$; (3, −4) no

14. $11x + 18y \geq 31$; (−6, −7) no

15. Writing Explain how you can tell when to use a solid line and when to use a dashed line when graphing an inequality. Use a dashed line when the inequality symbol is < or >. Use a solid line when the inequality symbol is ≤ or ≥.

Matching **Match the inequality with its graph.**

16. $y \leq 2x + 1$ D **17.** $y < 2x + 1$ A **18.** $y > 2x + 1$ B **19.** $y \geq 2x + 1$ C

A. 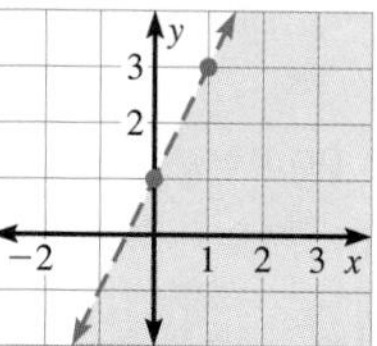

B. 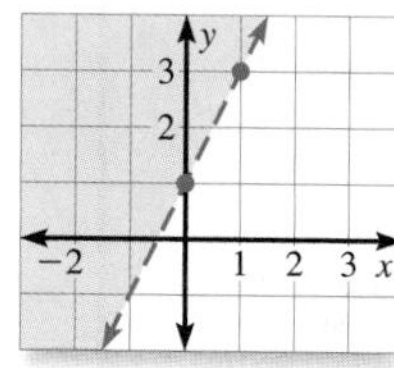

C. 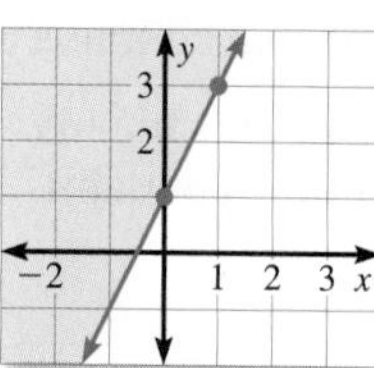

D. 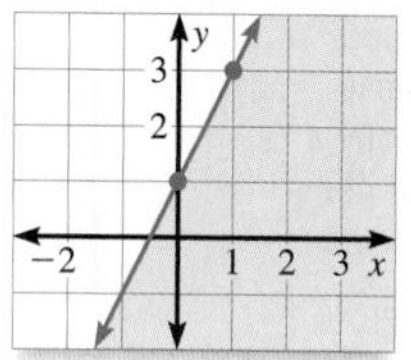

Graph the inequality. 20–31. See margin.

20. $y < x + 6$ **21.** $y > 9 - 2x$ **22.** $y \geq 3x - 7$

23. $y \leq 4x - 12$ **24.** $y < 7x + 19$ **25.** $4x - 13 > y$

26. $5x \leq 45$ **27.** $22 < 2x$ **28.** $6y > 36$

29. $8y > 64$ **30.** $-96 \leq -3x$ **31.** $-2y \geq 74$

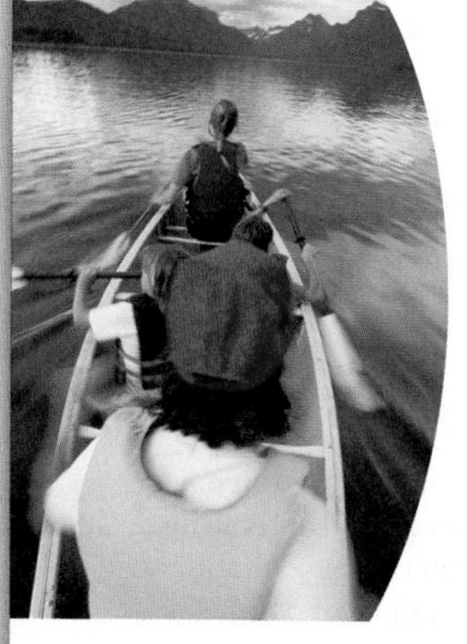

Extended Problem Solving **In Exercises 32–34, use the information about Catherine's canoe trip.**

Catherine is going on a canoe trip. She has to carry a backpack containing the food and water she will need. Catherine can take no more than 10 pounds in her backpack. A bottle of water weighs 16 ounces and a sandwich and fruit weigh 12 ounces.

B **32.** The inequality $16x + 12y \leq 160$ models the situation, where x is the number of water bottles and y is the number of meals. How many meals can Catherine take with her if she brings 4 bottles of water? 8 meals

33. Graph the inequality. See margin.

34. Using the graph, find the maximum number of bottles of water Catherine can carry when she packs 2 meals in her backpack. 8 bottles

35. *Sample answer:* The half-plane representing points that are not solutions of the given inequality cannot contain the line $5x + y = 2$, but contains points on the other side of the line, so use the < symbol: $5x + y < 2$.

36. No; the points on the line $y = x + 3$ are not included in either graph.

35. Writing Explain how you can write an inequality that represents the half-plane that is *not* the solution of the inequality $5x + y \geq 2$.

36. Critical Thinking If you graph the inequalities $y < x + 3$ and $y > x + 3$, do you cover all of the points in the plane? Explain.

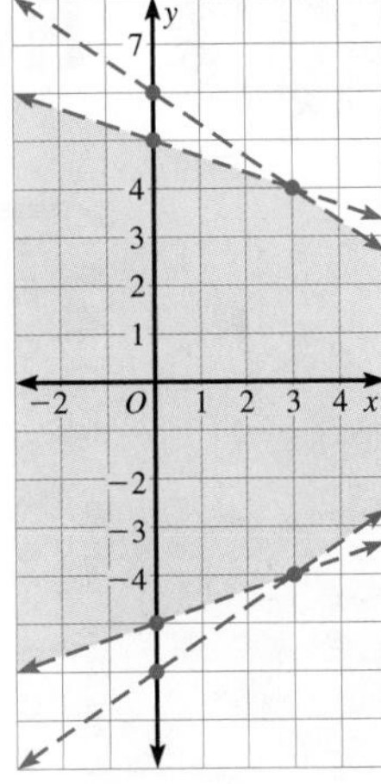

C **37. Challenge** The graph at the right represents all the points that are solutions to four inequalities. The equations used to graph the inequalities are

$y = -\frac{1}{3}x + 5$, $y = \frac{1}{3}x - 5$, $y = \frac{2}{3}x - 6$, and

$y = -\frac{2}{3}x + 6$. What are the four inequalities?

$y < -\frac{1}{3}x + 5$; $y > \frac{1}{3}x - 5$; $y > \frac{2}{3}x - 6$; $y < -\frac{2}{3}x + 6$

Mixed Review 

38. Find the intercepts of $4x + 18y = 36$. *(Lesson 11.5)* x-intercept: 9, y-intercept: 2

39. Find the slope of the line that passes through $(-3, -4)$ and $(7, 8)$. *(Lesson 11.6)* $\frac{6}{5}$

Basic Skills Write the decimal as a fraction in simplest form.

40. 1.34 $1\frac{17}{50}$ **41.** 3.75 $3\frac{3}{4}$ **42.** 8.125 $8\frac{1}{8}$ **43.** 7.164 $7\frac{41}{250}$

Test-Taking Practice

INTERNET
State Test Practice
CLASSZONE.COM

44. Multiple Choice The graph shows how many child tickets y and how many adult tickets x need to be sold at a fundraiser to meet the goal. Which inequality describes the graph? D

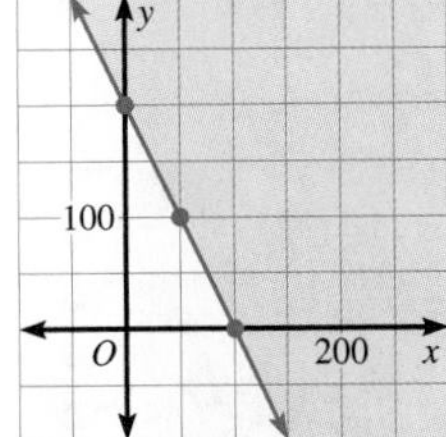

A. $y \leq 2x + 200$ **B.** $y \geq 2x + 200$

C. $y \leq -2x + 200$ **D.** $y \geq -2x + 200$

45. Multiple Choice Sonya can spend up to \$125 on decorations for a dance. A bag of balloons costs \$4 and a roll of streamers costs \$2. She uses $4x + 2y \leq 125$ to find how much she can buy, where x is the number of bags of balloons and y is the number of rolls of streamers. Which of the following is a solution? I

F. (30, 6) **G.** (30, 4) **H.** (25, 15) **I.** (25, 12)

4 ASSESS

Assessment Resources

For more assessment resources, see:
- Assessment Book
- Test and Practice Generator

Mini-Quiz

Determine whether the ordered pair is a solution of the inequality.

1. $4x + 2y < 9$; (0, 1) yes
2. $10x - 3y \geq 12$; (2, 3) no
3. $3x - 4y \leq 5$; (4, 0) no
4. Graph the inequality $y > \frac{1}{3}x + 2$.

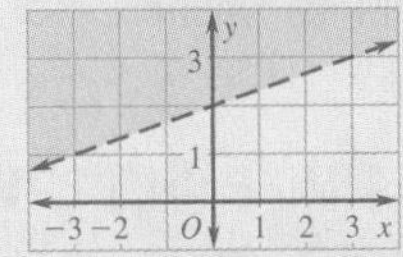

5 FOLLOW-UP

Reteaching/Remediation
- Study Guide in Chapter 11 Resource Book, pp. 73–74
- eTutorial Plus Online
- Extra Practice, p. 737
- Lesson Practice in Chapter 11 Resource Book, pp. 70–72

Challenge/Enrichment
- Challenge Practice in Chapter 11 Resource Book, p. 75
- Teacher's Edition, p. 538F

English Learner Support
- Spanish Study Guide
- Multi-Language Glossary
- Chapter Audio Summaries CDs

Additional Resources

The following resources are available to help review the materials in Lessons 11.5–11.8.

Chapter 11 Resource Book
- Lesson Practice
- Study Guide

Assessment Book
- Chapter 11 Quiz 2

Technology
- Test and Practice Generator
- eTutorial CD-ROM

Internet
- Classzone
- eWorkbook Plus Online
- eTutorial Plus Online

English Learner Support

- Spanish Study Guide
- Multi-Language Glossary
- Chapter Audio Summaries CDs

5.

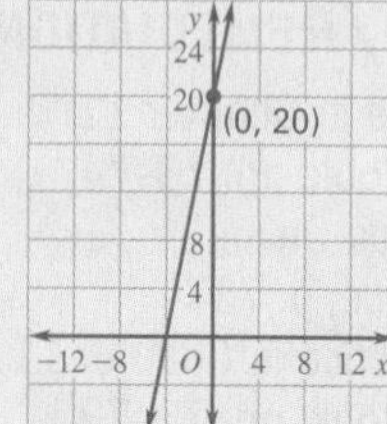

6.

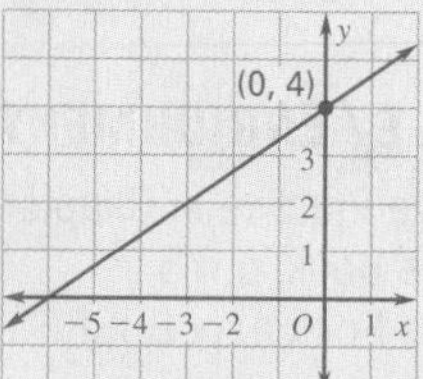

7.

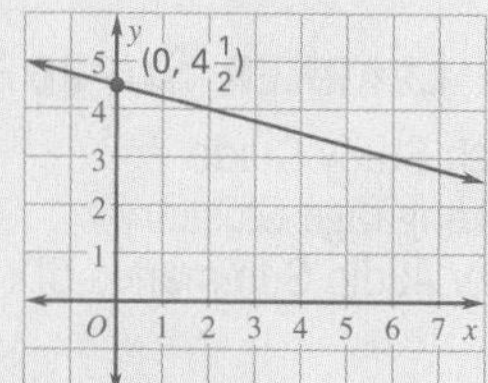

Notebook Review

Review the vocabulary definitions in your notebook.

Copy the review examples in your notebook. Then complete the exercises.

Check Your Definitions

x-intercept, p. 564	rise, run, p. 570	linear inequality, solution, p. 583
y-intercept, p. 564	slope-intercept form, p. 577	half-plane, p. 584
slope, p. 570		

Use Your Vocabulary

1. Vocabulary Copy and complete: In the equation $y = 4x - 9$, 4 is the _?_ and -9 is the _?_. slope; *y*-intercept

11.5–11.7 Can you use slope and y-intercepts?

EXAMPLE Find the slope of the line passing through (0, 3) and (4, 6).

The slope can be found by calculating

$$\frac{y_2 - y_1}{x_2 - x_1} = \frac{6 - 3}{4 - 0} = \frac{3}{4}$$

Find the slope of the line passing through the two points.

2. $(-1, 0)$ and $(5, 8)$ $\frac{4}{3}$ **3.** $(8, 7)$ and $(-2, 3)$ $\frac{2}{5}$ **4.** $(0, 11)$ and $(6, 1)$ $-\frac{5}{3}$

EXAMPLE Graph $y = \frac{3}{4}x + 3$.

Since $y = \frac{3}{4}x + 3$ is already in slope-intercept form, you know that $\frac{3}{4}$ is the slope and 3 is the *y*-intercept of the graph of the equation. To graph the equation, first plot the point (0, 3). Then use the slope to find another point on the line.

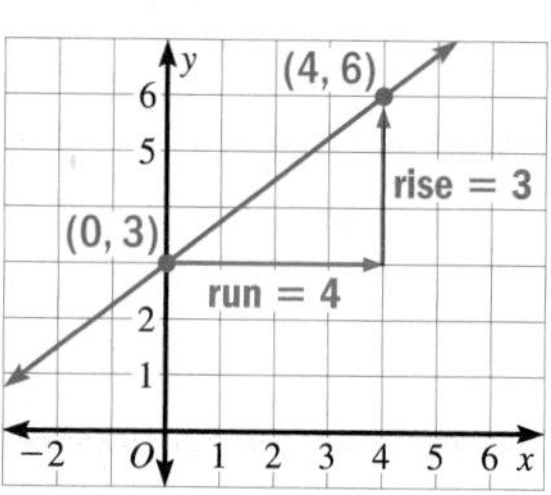

Find the slope and *y*-intercept of the graph of the equation. Then graph the equation. 5–7. See margin for art.

5. $y = 5x + 20$ 5, 20 **6.** $2x - 3y = -12$ $\frac{2}{3}$, 4 **7.** $x + 4y = 18$ $-\frac{1}{4}$, $4\frac{1}{2}$

11.8 Can you graph linear inequalities?

EXAMPLE Graph $y > -2x + 4$.

The graph of $y = -2x + 4$ has a slope of -2 and a y-intercept of 4.

Because the inequality is >, use a dashed line.

Use (0, 0) as a test point:

$0 \overset{?}{>} -2(0) + 4$

$0 \not> 4$ **(0, 0) is not a solution.**

Shade the half-plane that does not include (0, 0).

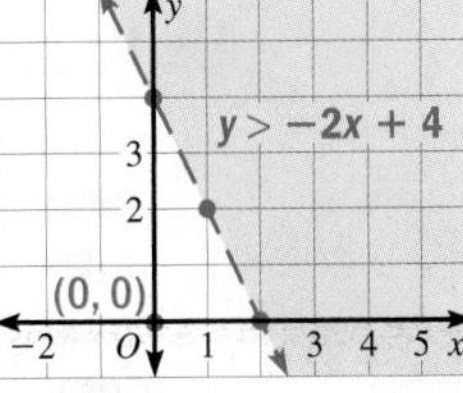

☑ **Graph the inequality.** 8–11. See margin.

8. $y < x - 4$ **9.** $y \geq 2x - 3$ **10.** $x + y > 6$ **11.** $x - y \leq -5$

Stop and Think about Lessons 11.5–11.8

12. Critical Thinking Graph $y = 3x + 5$ and $y = 3x - 2$. What do you notice about the lines? See margin for art; they are parallel to each other.

Review Quiz 2

Find the intercepts of the graph of the equation.

1. $y = 2x + 3$ **2.** $2y + x = 6$ **3.** $x = 3$

Find the slope of the line passing through the points.

4. (3, 4), (5, 7) $\frac{3}{2}$ **5.** (−1, −3), (0, 0) 3 **6.** (−5, 3), (4, 3) 0

Find the slope and y-intercept of the graph of the equation. Then sketch its graph. 7–9. See margin for art.

7. $y = \frac{6}{5}x - 2$ $\frac{6}{5}$, −2 **8.** $-5x - 5y = -20$ −1, 4 **9.** $y = -x$ −1, 0

Graph the inequality. Then list three solutions of the inequality. 10–12. See margin for art; sample solutions are given.

10. $y > x - 3$ (−1, 0), (0, −2), (1, −1) **11.** $x - 3y \leq -9$ (−3, 4), (0, 5), (3, 7) **12.** $6x + 7y < -21$ (−7, −10), (0, −5), (7, −12)

13. Car Wash Your club holds a car wash for three hours to raise money for a charity. The equation $10x + 15y = 180$ describes the amount of time it takes to wash small and large vehicles respectively. Find the intercepts of the equation. What do they represent? Graph the equation.

1. x-intercept: $-\frac{3}{2}$, y-intercept: 3
2. x-intercept: 6, y-intercept: 3
3. x-intercept: 3, y-intercept: none

13. x-intercept: 18, y-intercept: 12; the x-intercept represents the number of small vehicles that can be washed if no large vehicles are washed and the y-intercept represents the number of large vehicles that can be washed if no small vehicles are washed; see margin for art.

Notebook Review

8. $y < x - 4$

9. $y \geq 2x - 3$

10. $x + y > 6$

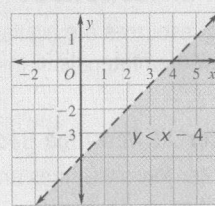

11. $x - y \leq -5$

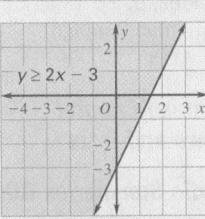

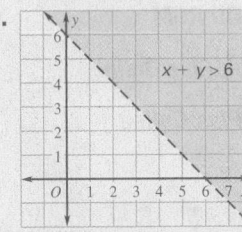

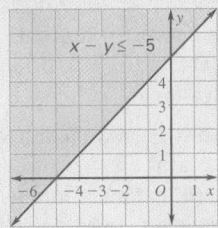

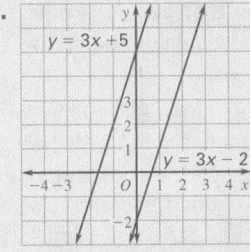

12. $y = 3x + 5$, $y = 3x - 2$

Review Quiz 2

7. (0, −2)

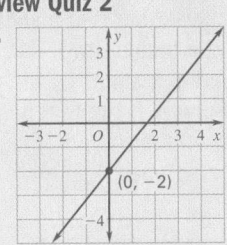

8–13. See Additional Answers beginning on page AA1.

ADDITIONAL RESOURCES

The following resources are available to help review the materials in this chapter.

Chapter 11 Resource Book

- Chapter Review Games and Activities, p. 76
- Cumulative Practice, Chs. 1–11

English/Spanish Chapter Reviews and Tests

Chapter Audio Summaries CDs

eTutorial CD-ROM

eWorkbook Plus Online

eTutorial Plus Online

4. *Sample answer:* To find the *x*-intercept, substitute 0 for *y* and solve for *x*; to find the *y*-intercept, substitute 0 for *x* and solve for *y*.
5. A good answer will include a situation that changes over time, such as time and distance traveled, and an explanation that the slope tells you how quickly something changes.
6. *Sample answer:* Replace the inequality symbol with "=" and graph the equation. Use a dashed line for < or >. Use a solid line for ≤ or ≥. Test a point in one of the half-planes to check whether it is a solution of the inequality. If the test point is a solution, shade its half-plane. If the test point is not a solution, shade the other half-plane.

10.

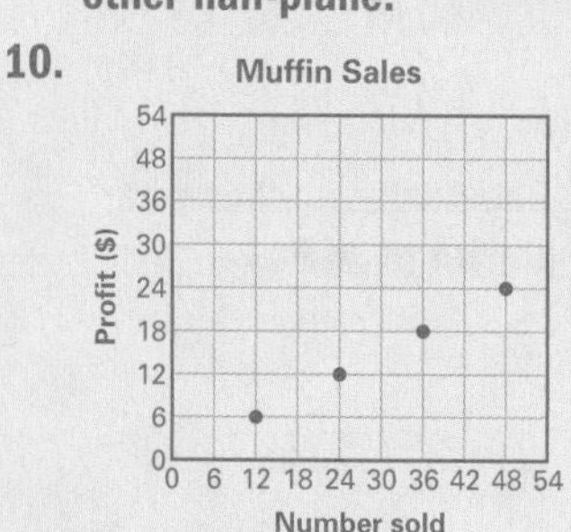

Chapter Review

Vocabulary

relation, p. 541
input, p. 541
output, p. 541
function, p. 541
domain, p. 542
range, p. 542
scatter plot, p. 545
solution of an equation in two variables, p. 549
linear equation, p. 556
x-intercept, p. 564
y-intercept, p. 564
slope, p. 570
rise, run, p. 570
slope-intercept form, p. 577
linear inequality, solution, p. 583
half-plane, p. 584

Vocabulary Review

In Exercises 1–3, copy and complete the statement.

1. The graph of a linear inequality in two variables is a(n) _?_. **half-plane**
2. For a function, the set of all possible input values is called the _?_, and the set of all possible output values is called the _?_. **domain, range**
3. The slope of a nonvertical line is the ratio of its _?_ to its _?_. **rise, run**
4. Explain in your own words how to find the *x*-intercept and the *y*-intercept of the graph of an equation. **See margin.**
5. Describe a real-life situation that can be represented by a linear equation. What does the slope of the line tell you about the situation? **See margin.**
6. Write the steps you would take to graph a linear inequality. **See margin.**

Review Questions

Tell whether the relation is a function. Explain your answer. *(Lesson 11.1)*

7. (0, 6), (2, 6), (4, 7), (0, 3), (2, 3), (4, 8) **No; each input has more than one output.**

8.

Input	Output
0	−8
1	−11
2	−14
3	−17

Yes; each input has exactly one output.

9.

Input	Output
−4	12
−2	12
0	12
2	12

Yes; each input has exactly one output.

10. Make a scatter plot of the data. Then describe the relationship. *(Lesson 11.2)* **See margin for art.**

Number of muffins sold	12	24	36	48
Profit	\$6	\$12	\$18	\$24

The relationship is positive, with each increase of 12 muffins sold corresponding to an increase of \$6 in profit.

Review Questions

11. Model Plane You buy a battery operated model plane for \$45. It costs you about \$8 each month to replace the batteries. The equation $C = 45 + 8m$, where C is the total cost in dollars and m is the number of months, describes this situation. About how much has the plane cost you in the first year? *(Lesson 11.3)* **\$141**

Matching Match the equation with its graph. *(Lesson 11.4)*

12. $y = -2x$ **B** **13.** $y = -2$ **C** **14.** $x = -2$ **A**

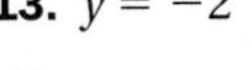

A.

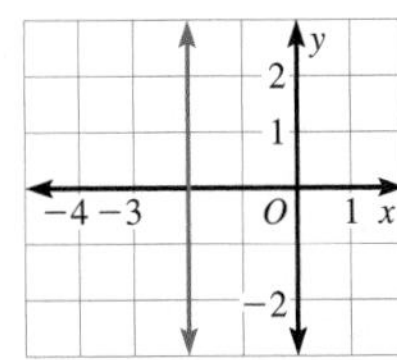

B.

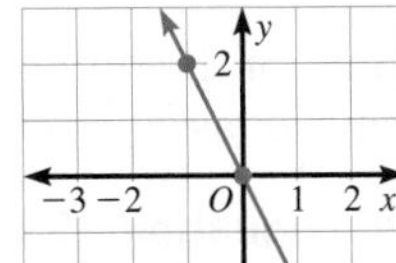

C.

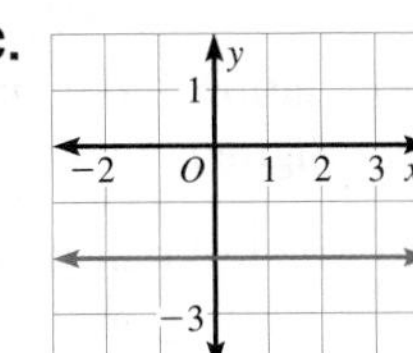

Graph the linear equation. *(Lesson 11.4)* **15–17. See margin for art.**

15. $y = x + 2$ **16.** $y = -\frac{3}{2}x - 1$ **17.** $y = 8$

18. Taxes The approximate amount of taxes collected by the Internal Revenue Service from 1980 to 1990 can be modeled by $y = 57.1x + 488$, where y represents taxes, in billions of dollars, and x represents the number of years since 1980. What is the y-intercept of the graph of this equation? What does the y-intercept represent? *(Lesson 11.5)*
488; the billions of dollars in taxes collected by the Internal Revenue Service in 1980

Write the coordinates of two points on the line. Then find the slope of the line. *(Lesson 11.6)* **19–20. Sample answers are given.**

19.

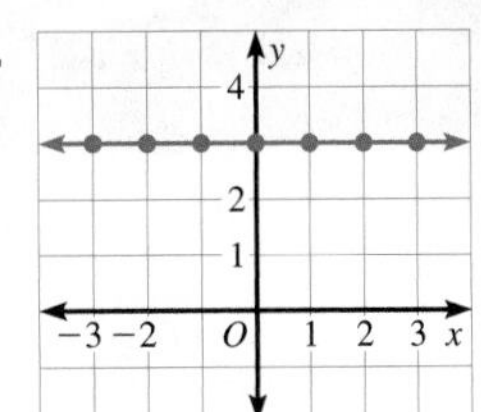

(−2, 3), (2, 3); 0

20.

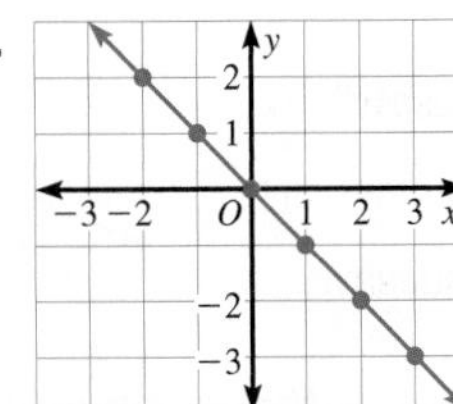

(−1, 1), (1, −1); −1

Rewrite the equation in slope-intercept form. Then find the slope and y-intercept of the graph of the equation. *(Lesson 11.7)*

21. $y - 4x = 10$ **$y = 4x + 10$; 4, 10** **22.** $2y + 6 = x$ **$y = \frac{1}{2}x - 3$; $\frac{1}{2}$, −3** **23.** $-3x - 7y = 21$ **$y = -\frac{3}{7}x - 3$; $-\frac{3}{7}$, −3**

Graph the inequality. *(Lesson 11.8)* **24–26. See margin.**

24. $6x + 10y < -30$ **25.** $3x - 7y \geq 21$ **26.** $4x + 8y \leq 32$

15.

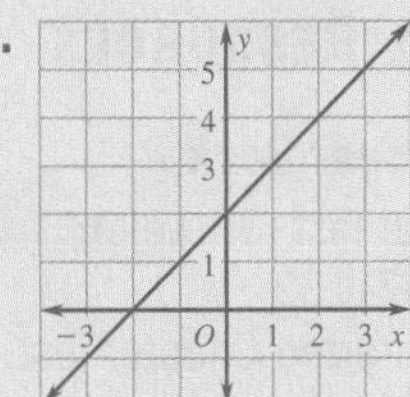

16.

17.

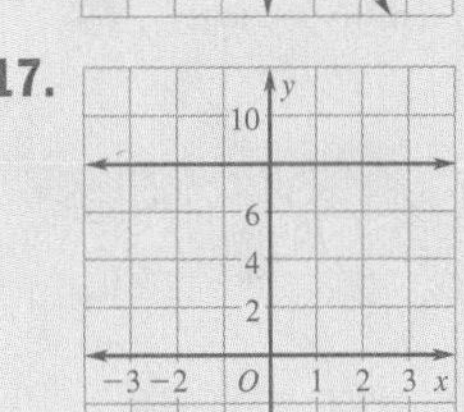

24.

$6x + 10y < -30$

25.

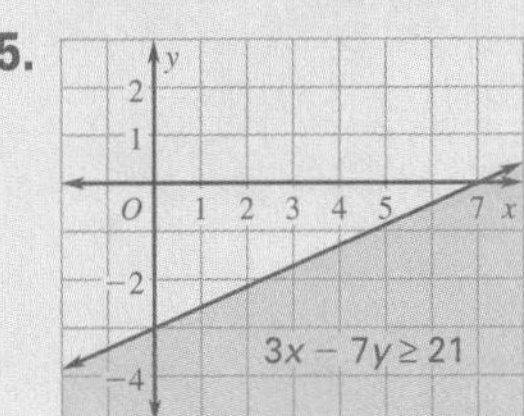

26.

$4x + 8y \leq 32$

ADDITIONAL RESOURCES

Assessment Book

- Chapter Test (3 levels), pp. 137–139
- Standardized Chapter Test, p. 143
- Alternative Assessment, pp. 144–145

Test and Practice Generator

9.

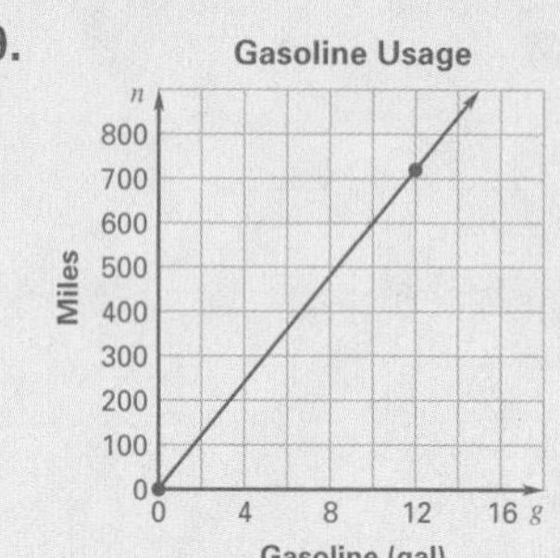

13.

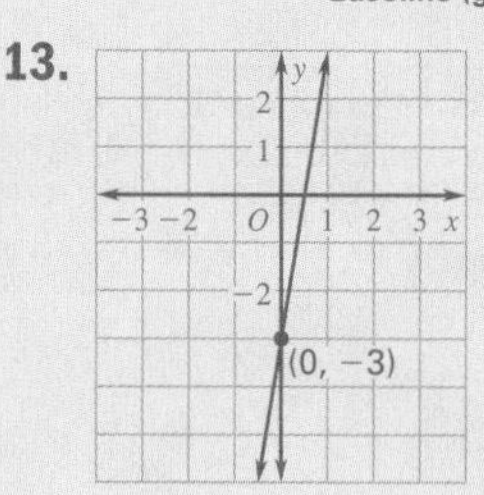

14.

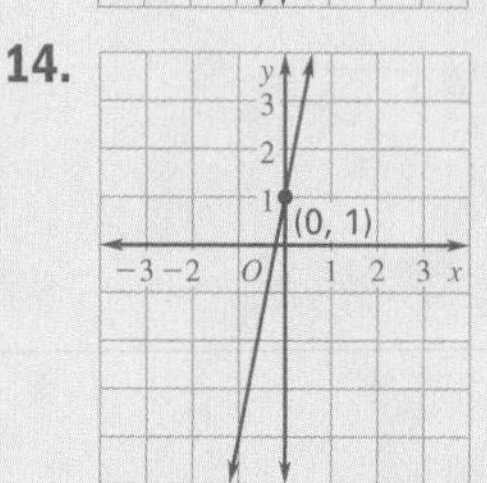

15.

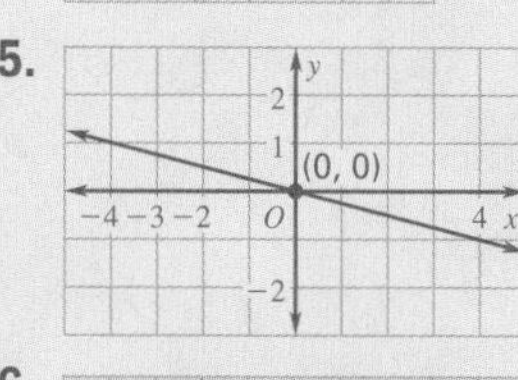

16.

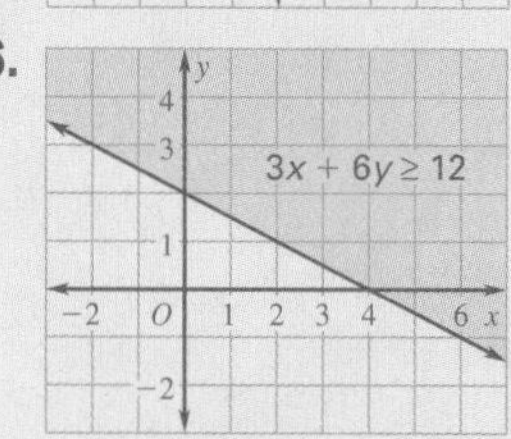

17–19. See Additional Answers beginning on page AA1.

Chapter Test

In Exercises 1 and 2, write a function rule that relates *x* and *y*.

1.

Input x	0	1	2	3
Output y	0	−0.25	−0.5	−0.75

$y = -0.25x$

2.

Input x	−2	−1	0	1
Output y	−9	−3	3	9

$y = 6x + 3$

3. What type of relationship do you expect to find for the number of problems assigned and the time spent doing an assignment? positive relationship

Tell whether the ordered pair is a solution of the equation $12x + 3y = 21$.

4. $(-1, 11)$ yes **5.** $(-4, -9)$ no **6.** $(2, -15)$ no **7.** $(6, -17)$ yes

8. Temperature To change a temperature in degrees Celsius C to degrees Fahrenheit F, use the formula $F = \frac{9}{5}C + 32$. Your friend tells you that 45°C is equal to 77°F. Is your friend correct? If not, find the temperature in degrees Fahrenheit. no; 113°F

9. Gasoline A scooter uses 1 gallon of gasoline per 60 miles. A linear equation that models the relationship between the number of miles driven n and the amount of gasoline used in gallons g is $n = 60g$. Graph the function and then estimate the number of miles traveled using 12 gallons of gasoline. See margin for art; 720 mi

Use the diagram of a seesaw.

10. What is the run of the seesaw? 12

11. What is the rise of the seesaw? 5

12. What is the slope of the seesaw? $\frac{5}{12}$

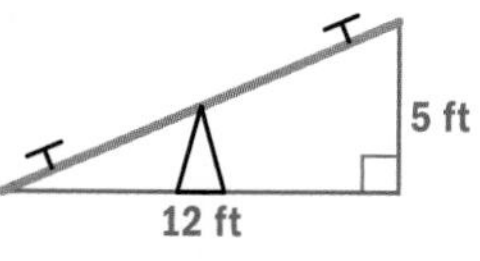

Find the slope and *y*-intercept of the graph of the equation. Then graph the equation. 13–15. See margin for art.

13. $y = 6x - 3$ 6, −3 **14.** $-5x + y = 1$ 5, 1 **15.** $y = -\frac{1}{4}x$ $-\frac{1}{4}$, 0

Graph the inequality. 16–18. See margin.

16. $3x + 6y \geq 12$ **17.** $7x - y \leq 49$ **18.** $8x - 15y > 30$

19. Gift Card Ken got a \$25 movie gift card. Matinee shows cost \$4 and evening shows cost \$7. Graph the inequality $4x + 7y \leq 25$. Using the graph, find the greatest number of movies Ken can see. See margin for art; 6 movies.

Chapter Standardized Test

Test-Taking Strategy **When you check your answers, try to use a method other than the one you originally used, to avoid repeating the same mistake.**

Multiple Choice

1. Which of the following relations is *not* a function? C

A. (5, 6), (6, 5), (−3, 7), (2, 6) **B.** (−5, 6), (5, 6), (−3, 7), (2, 4)

C. (5, 6), (7, 7), (1, −1), (5, 0) **D.** (3, 2), (−3, −2), (2, 3), (−2, −3)

2. The scatter plot below shows the average test score of each class on a recent English exam. Describe the relationship shown in the data. H

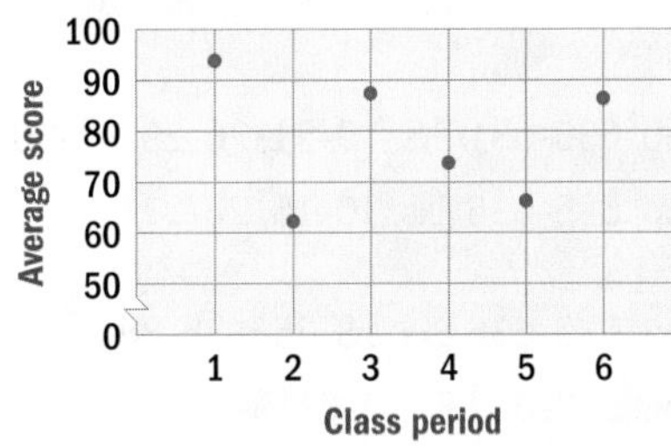

F. positive **G.** negative

H. none **I.** not enough information

3. Which of the ordered pairs is a solution of the equation $y = 4x - 5$? A

A. (−2, −13) **B.** (0, 5)

C. (3, 17) **D.** (7, 3)

4. What is the slope of the line passing through points (−3, 2) and (4, −5)? G

F. −3 **G.** −1 **H.** $\frac{1}{3}$ **I.** 1

5. Which is the slope-intercept form of $9x - 3y = 12$? D

A. $-3y = -9x + 12$ **B.** $x = \frac{1}{3}y + \frac{4}{3}$

C. $y = 3x + 4$ **D.** $y = 3x - 4$

6. Which equation is represented by the graph? F

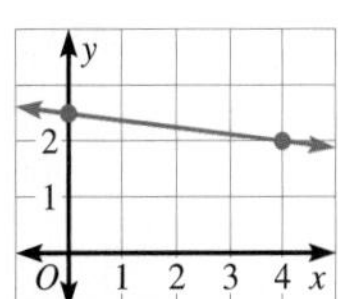

F. $y = -\frac{1}{8}x + 2.5$ **G.** $y = \frac{1}{8}x + 2.5$

H. $y = -8x + 2.5$ **I.** $y = 8x + 2.5$

7. What is the value for y in the function table representing $y = x - 7$, when x is 7? B

x	3	5	7	9
y	−4	−2	?	2

A. −1 **B.** 0 **C.** 1 **D.** 4

Short Response

8. Graph the inequalities $x + y \le 5$, $x \ge 0$, and $y \ge 0$. Find the area of the solution region. See margin for art; 12.5 square units.

Extended Response

9. Your class needs to raise $120 selling hats and T-shirts. The equation $6x + 5y = 120$, where x is the number of hats sold and y is the number of T-shirts sold, represents the situation. What are the intercepts of the equation? What do they mean in this context? See margin.

ADDITIONAL RESOURCES

Assessment Book

- Standardized Chapter Test, p. 143

Test and Practice Generator

8.

9. *x*-intercept: 20, *y*-intercept: 24; the *x*-intercept represents the number of hats that must be sold if no T-shirts are sold, and the *y*-intercept represents the number of T-shirts that must be sold if no hats are sold.

Pacing and Assignment Guide

REGULAR SCHEDULE

Lesson	Les. Day	BASIC	AVERAGE	ADVANCED
12.1	Day 1	SRH p. 723 Exs. 1-5; pp. 599-600 Exs. 7-9, 14, 15, 23-25	pp. 599-600 Exs. 7-9, 13-15, 23-25	pp. 599-600 Exs. 7-9, 13-15, 20-23
	Day 2	pp. 599-600 Exs. 10-12, 16-20, 26	pp. 599-600 Exs. 10-12, 16-21, 26	pp. 599-600 Exs. 10-12, 16-19, 24-26, EC: TE p. 594D*
12.2	Day 1	EP p. 731 Exs. 45-47; pp. 603-604 Exs. 3-5, 9-11, 19-22	pp. 603-604 Exs. 3-5, 9-11, 19-22	pp. 603-604 Exs. 3-5, 9-11, 18-21*
	Day 2	pp. 603-604 Exs. 6-8, 12-16, 23	pp. 603-604 Exs. 6-8, 12-17, 23	pp. 603-604 Exs. 6-8, 12-17, 23
12.3	Day 1	SRH p. 721 Exs. 1-4, EP p. 733 Exs. 19, 20; pp. 608-609 Exs. 9-16, 18-20, 23-27	pp. 608-609 Exs. 9-14, 16-21, 23-28	pp. 608-609 Exs. 9-14, 16-23*, 26-28
12.4	Day 1	pp. 621-622 Exs. 8-13, 15-18, 24-29	pp. 621-622 Exs. 10-18, 20-22, 24-29	pp. 621-622 Exs. 10-14, 16-24*, 27-29
12.5	Day 1	pp. 625-626 Exs. 11-15, 25, 28-30	pp. 625-626 Exs. 11-15, 26, 29-32	pp. 625-626 Exs. 11-15, 28-32
	Day 2	pp. 625-626 Exs. 16-22, 31, 32	pp. 625-626 Exs. 16-24, 28	pp. 625-626 Exs. 18-27*
12.6	Day 1	pp. 630-631 Exs. 9-15, 22-24, 34-37	pp. 630-631 Exs. 9-13, 22-25, 30-32, 40, 41	pp. 630-631 Exs. 9-13, 22-25, 30-32, 40, 41
	Day 2	pp. 630-631 Exs. 16-21, 26-30, 38-40	pp. 630-631 Exs. 18-21, 26-29, 34-39	pp. 630-631 Exs. 19-21, 26-29, 33-39*
12.7	Day 1	EP p. 733 Exs. 32, 33; pp. 635-636 Exs. 10-15, 21-24, 36-38	pp. 635-636 Exs. 10-15, 26-32	pp. 635-636 Exs. 10-15, 26-31
	Day 2	pp. 635-636 Exs. 16-20, 29-35	pp. 635-636 Exs. 18-24, 33-38	pp. 635-636 Exs. 18-25*, 35-38
12.8	Day 1	pp. 642-643 Exs. 4-6, 16-21	pp. 642-643 Exs. 4-6, 16-22	pp. 642-643 Exs. 4-6, 15-19*
	Day 2	pp. 642-643 Exs. 7-13, 22	pp. 642-643 Exs. 7-14, 23	pp. 642-643 Exs. 9-14, 21-23
Review	Day 1	pp. 648-649 Exs. 1-23	pp. 648-649 Exs. 1-23	pp. 648-649 Exs. 1-23
Assess	Day 1	Chapter 12 Test	Chapter 12 Test	Chapter 12 Test

YEARLY PACING Chapter 12 Total – **16 days** Chapters 1–12 Total – **148 days** Remaining – **12 days**

*Challenge Exercises EP = Extra Practice SRH = Skills Review Handbook EC = Extra Challenge

BLOCK SCHEDULE

DAY 1	DAY 2	DAY 3	DAY 4	DAY 5	DAY 6	DAY 7	DAY 8
12.1 pp. 599-600 Exs. 7-21, 23-25	**12.2** pp. 603-604 Exs. 3-17, 19-23	**12.3** pp. 608-609 Exs. 9-14, 16-21, 23-28 **12.4** pp. 621-622 Exs. 10-18, 20-22, 24-29	**12.5** pp. 625-626 Exs. 11-24, 26, 28-32	**12.6** pp. 630-631 Exs. 9-13, 18-32, 34-41	**12.7** pp. 635-636 Exs. 10-15, 18-24, 26-38	**12.8** pp. 642-643 Exs. 4-14, 16-23	**Review** pp. 648-649 Exs. 1-23 **Assess** Chapter 12 Test

YEARLY PACING Chapter 12 Total – **8 days** Chapters 1–12 Total – **74 days** Remaining – **6 days**

Support Materials

CHAPTER RESOURCE BOOK

CHAPTER SUPPORT

Tips for New Teachers	p. 1	Parents as Partners	p. 3

LESSON SUPPORT	12.1	12.2	12.3	12.4	12.5	12.6	12.7	12.8
Lesson Plans (regular and block)	p. 5	p. 13	p. 21	p. 31	p. 39	p. 48	p. 58	p. 66
Technology Activities & Keystrokes			p. 23			p. 50		
Activity Support Masters								
Activity Masters					p. 41			
Practice (3 levels)	p. 7	p. 15	p. 24	p. 33	p. 42	p. 52	p. 60	p. 68
Study Guide	p. 10	p. 18	p. 27	p. 36	p. 45	p. 55	p. 63	p. 71
Real-World Problem Solving			p. 29					p. 73
Challenge Practice	p. 12	p. 20	p. 30	p. 38	p. 47	p. 57	p. 65	p. 74

REVIEW

Chapter Review Games and Activities	p. 75	Extra Credit Project with Rubric	p. 80
Real-Life Project with Rubric	p. 76	Cumulative Practice	p. 82
Cooperative Project with Rubric	p. 78	Resource Book Answers	A1

ASSESSMENT

Quizzes	p. 146	Alternative Assessments with Rubrics	p. 155
Chapter Tests (3 levels)	p. 148	Unit Test	p. 168
Standardized Test	p. 154	Cumulative Test	p. 170

TRANSPARENCIES

	12.1	12.2	12.3	12.4	12.5	12.6	12.7	12.8
Warm-Up / Daily Homework Quiz	✔	✔	✔	✔	✔	✔	✔	✔
Notetaking Guide	✔	✔	✔	✔	✔	✔	✔	✔
Teacher Support		✔	✔					
English/Spanish Problem Solving	✔	✔						
Answer Transparencies	✔	✔	✔	✔	✔	✔	✔	✔

TECHNOLOGY

- EasyPlanner CD-ROM
- Test and Practice Generator
- Electronic Lesson Presentations
- eTutorial CD-ROM
- Chapter Audio Summaries CDs
- Classzone.com
- eEdition Plus Online
- eWorkbook Plus Online
- eTutorial Plus Online
- EasyPlanner Plus Online

ADDITIONAL RESOURCES

- Worked-Out Solution Key
- Notetaking Guide
- Practice Workbook
- Tutor Place
- Professional Development Book
- Special Activities Book
- Posters
- Spanish Study Guide
- Exercises in Spanish
- English/Spanish Ch. Reviews/Tests
- Multi-Language Visual Glossary

Math Background and Teaching Strategies

Lesson 12.1

MATH BACKGROUND

A **stem-and-leaf** plot is a data display that lists all data values in a set in order. The data are grouped in rows by their **stems**, which consist of the larger place value digits of the data. To each stem correspond its **leaves**, which are the remaining (smaller place value) digits of the data.

TEACHING STRATEGIES

Be sure students know that the advantage of a stem-and-leaf-plot over a histogram is that it shows all data values. To emphasize this, have students find the mean, median, and mode of one data set given in the Examples in this lesson. Make sure they know how to order the leaves when making a double stem-and-leaf plot. It may confuse students that the leaves to the left of a stem increase to the left, while those to the right of the stem increase to the right.

Lesson 12.2

MATH BACKGROUND

A **box-and-whisker plot** is a visual display to scale along a number line of five statistics of a data set: the **lower extreme**, or least value; the **lower quartile**, or median of the lower half of the data; the median; the **upper quartile**, or median of the upper half of the data; and the **upper extreme**, or greatest value. A box-and-whisker plot also gives a quick visual of the center, distribution, and range of a data set, and is useful for visually comparing two data sets plotted next to each other using the same scale.

TEACHING STRATEGIES

Point out the following facts about box-and-whisker plots:

- For an odd number of data values: The median is *the* middle data value. The overall median *is not included* as a data value when finding the quartiles.
- For an even number of data values: The median is the *mean* of the *two* middle data values. Each quartile is the middle value of its respective half of the data values.
- The box represents half of the data values. Each whisker represents one quarter of the data values.

Lesson 12.3

MATH BACKGROUND

USING DATA DISPLAYS Stem-and-leaf plots and box-and-whisker plots have their own uses and advantages, while bar graphs and histograms have their appropriate uses: the first for categorical data and the second to compare frequency of occurrence of data values in equal intervals. A **circle graph** represents data as parts of a whole by relating the number of data points in a category within a set to the proportional part of a circle. A **line graph** represents data that change over time by segments that connect ordered pairs.

TEACHING STRATEGIES

The process of constructing circle graphs can confuse students. If students have difficulty understanding how to set up the proportions that relate categorical numbers of data values to degrees in a circle directly, point out that they can alternately use a two-step process. First, for each category write the ratio of data values to total data values as a percent. Then multiply this percent by 360° to find the corresponding part of a circle.

Lesson 12.4

MATH BACKGROUND

COUNTING METHODS A **tree diagram** models all possibilities that can result from successive choices or events. A more efficient way to count possibilities is to use the **fundamental counting principle**, which states that the number of ways a sequence of events can occur is the product of the number of ways that each of the events in the sequence can occur.

TEACHING STRATEGIES

Students often fail to leave enough space for successive branches of tree diagrams, and may need guidance in this regard. You may want to point out how the rapid growth in tree diagrams is related to powers. For example, if a tree diagram has 3 possibilities at each step, the total number of possibilities is 3^n, where n is the number of steps. So, after only four steps there are $3^4 = 81$ branches.

Lesson 12.5

MATH BACKGROUND

ORDERED ARRANGEMENTS The counting principle can be used to find the number of **permutations**, or ordered arrangements, of a set or subset of objects. Because ordering removes an item at each step, there is one less item available with each application of the counting principle. **Factorial** notation is used to indicate such a process, where $n! = n \cdot (n-1) \cdot (n-2) \cdot \ldots \cdot 1$. The formula ${}_nP_r = \frac{n!}{(n-r)!}$ gives the number of permutations of a set of n objects when a subset of r of the n objects is taken at a time.

TEACHING STRATEGIES

The formula for permutations will likely be difficult for students. Though students need to be able to evaluate the formula, stress that the result of the formula is to find the first r factors of $n!$ For example, ${}_9P_3$ indicates to find the first 3 factors of 9!, or $9 \cdot 8 \cdot 7$. Thinking of the formula in these terms will be most useful for application problems, where it gives students a more intuitive sense of the problem and allows them to check for reasonableness in their calculations.

Lesson 12.6

MATH BACKGROUND

In a **combination**, order is not important. The formula ${}_nC_r = \frac{{}_nP_r}{r!}$, or ${}_nC_r = \frac{n!}{(n-r)!r!}$, gives the number of combinations of a set of n objects when a subset of r of the n objects is taken at a time. It is the number of permutations divided by the number of ways that the subset of r items can be ordered.

TEACHING STRATEGIES

It may help to show a concrete example of why the number of combinations is the number of permutations divided by $r!$. For example, the number of permutations of 2 tea bags chosen from 4 tea bags with different flavors, mint (m), black (b), green (g), and chamomile (c), is ${}_4P_2 = 12$. They are:

mb, bm, mg, gm, mc, cm, bg, gb, bc, cb, gc, cg.

If we are interested only in combinations of the flavors, the order is not important. Notice that for *each* flavor combination, there are $2! = 2$ possible orders. So, the number of combinations is the number of permutations divided by 2!.

Lesson 12.7

MATH BACKGROUND

Two events are **complementary** if one or the other must occur in a probability experiment, but both cannot occur. The sum of the probabilities of complementary events is 1. So, one way to find the probability of an event is to subtract the probability of its complement from 1. **Odds** and probability both express likelihood. While probability expresses the ratio of favorable to total outcomes, the odds in favor of an event expresses the ratio of favorable to unfavorable outcomes.

TEACHING STRATEGIES

Use this example with students: Jené has made 55 of 80 free-throw attempts. What are the odds in favor of and the probability that Jené makes her next attempt? Students should be able to find the probability $\frac{55}{80} = \frac{11}{16}$. Make sure students understand that the number of unfavorable outcomes is just the total number of outcomes minus the number of favorable outcomes. So, the odds in favor of making the free throw are $\frac{55}{80-55} = \frac{55}{25} = \frac{11}{5}$. Point out that the probability $\frac{11}{16}$ is read "11 out of 16," while the odds $\frac{11}{5}$ are read "11 to 5."

Lesson 12.8

MATH BACKGROUND

PROBABILITY OF COMPOUND EVENTS The probability of a compound event consisting of two or more events depends on whether the occurrence of one simple event affects the occurrence of another. If it does not, the events are **independent**. If it does, the events are **dependent**. The probability of two independent events occurring is the product of the individual probabilities. The probability of two dependent events occurring is the product of the probability of the first and the probability of the second *given that* the first occurs.

TEACHING STRATEGIES

Give as many examples as possible where students identify events as independent or dependent. Drawing objects with or without replacement provides one example of the distinction. Students must realize that an event's occurrence can change the possible number of outcomes and the number of favorable outcomes of an event that depends on it.

Differentiating Instruction

Strategies for Underachievers

USE MODELS AND MANIPULATIVES

In Lesson 12.1, it could help some underachieving students to use a very concrete approach to making a stem-and-leaf plot. Give students sets of data values, and have them copy the numbers, writing them large and well spaced out. Students can then cut out and order the numbers. Next, have them decide on appropriate stems. Then, students can cut each number into its stem and leaf and physically form the plot, placing stems that are the same on top of each other.

For Lesson 12.3, you may want to have different circle graphs drawn for students that illustrate different central angles and their degree measures. The graphs should also have the corresponding percent measure for each section. This should help students gain a better "feel" for interpreting a circle graph. For example, one sample circle graph could have three sections measuring and labeled 180°, 120°, and 60°, with the corresponding percents of a circle—50%, $33\frac{1}{3}$%, and $16\frac{2}{3}$%—also labeled.

REAL-LIFE MODELING In Lesson 12.5, students may have a hard time believing how many possibilities there are, for example, of arranging a penny, a nickel, a dime, and a quarter, or even arranging pairs of these four coins. You may want to have students model possibilities like this (perhaps using different shapes instead of coins) as a class, with each student modeling a different ordered arrangement from an ordered list that the class has made. Students should verify that all the models are indeed different. Note that there are 24 possibilities for the 4 coins, so if you have a smaller class size, you may want to modify the example. You can continue this modeling process into Lesson 12.6 so that students can see that the ordered arrangements do not all represent different combinations of the objects.

In Lessons 12.7 and 12.8, whenever possible, try to have students use an experimental approach when exploring probabilities and odds. It can be especially helpful to use experimental probability to verify calculations of theoretical probabilities. For these lessons, you may wish to have chips, counters, spinners, number cubes, marbles, cards, coins, or other physical objects that students can use to perform probability experiments. For example, you might have students work in pairs and give each pair 4 blue counters, 3 red counters, 2 green counters, and 1 yellow counter. Students can put the counters in a bag or box and shake it before selecting a counter and recording its color. Students can then perform many repetitions of experiments both with and without replacement so that they can compare the results. Pairs of students can write the results of their experiments on the board for comparison. Students can also combine their results and see how classroom results compare to the results of individual pairs. You may need to begin at a very basic level for underachievers. For example, you may want to ask them before they perform any experiments if they are more or less likely to draw blue than yellow and to explain why.

USE SCAFFOLDING

In Lesson 12.2, to give students familiarity with interpreting box-and-whisker plots, you may want to give them ordered data sets, perhaps already organized into stem-and-leaf plots. For each data set, have a few different box-and-whisker plots drawn on an appropriate scale for that set. Have students try to decide without finding the median or quartiles which plot they think represents the data set. Students can then find the quartiles and median to verify their choices.

TEMPLATES In Lesson 12.4, you may wish to provide templates for tree diagrams with various branching schemes, such as 2 • 4 • 2 or 3 • 3 • 3, already drawn out with rules drawn where students can then write the possibilities. You can offer examples that will fit each branching scheme or have students work together to come up with examples. These templates will help with students' tendency not to leave enough space when drawing tree diagrams as well as let them concentrate on identifying the different choices.

Strategies for English Learners

DISSECT WORD PROBLEMS

Most of the word problems in *Concepts and Skills* follow the basic format discussed earlier. Throughout this chapter, students will be asked to express their thinking in words as well as in mathematical symbols. For example, at the end of a word problem they may be told, "Explain your answer;" "Give an example;" "Explain your thinking;" "Write your findings;" "Justify your ideas;" or "Describe the rule." Some word problems will be open-ended, where students are expected not just to solve the problem and produce the right answer but to discuss how they solved the problem, show their steps, and explain their thinking.

OPEN-ENDED PROBLEMS Open-ended word problems present three challenges for English learners: (1) understanding what is being asked; (2) being able to develop a solution and perform the computations; and (3) finding the right English to explain their thinking. Reassure students that they are not required to write English perfectly. As a general rule, mathematics tests are not scored in terms of English grammar. Furthermore, many open-ended word problems can be explained by showing the mathematical steps that led you to a logical conclusion. Use of the English language can be minimal. Drawing a picture, in many cases, really can be worth a thousand words.

MORE PRACTICE Have students practice reading open-ended prompts (such as the ones below) and discussing what is asked for. Then have them respond by using pictures or standard phrases to express their thinking. If students are asked to label their steps, make sure they do so with numerals or using words such as *first, second, third,* or *finally.* Words that are useful to show conclusions are *thus, and so, in conclusion,* and the Latin abbreviation QED (*quod erat demonstrandum*), which is put at the end of a proof.

Here is a sample of word problems that ask students to do more than find a right answer:

Page 600, Exercise 18. . . . Can you make a stem-and-leaf plot from a frequency table? Why or Why not?

Page 642, Exercise 15. . . . Which statement leads you to think that investing money today is independent of past events? Which statement suggests the opposite? Explain.

Have students work in small groups to brainstorm how these questions could be answered using mathematical explanations and a minimum of English.

Strategies for Advanced Learners

INCREASE DEPTH AND COMPLEXITY

In Lesson 12.2, direct students who quickly master box-and-whisker plots to the Brain Game challenge at the bottom of page 615. After completing this activity, challenge students to write their own puzzles similar to this one. When they are sure that their puzzles are correct, these students can challenge each other with their puzzles.

USE CROSS-CURRICULAR CONNECTIONS

MISLEADING GRAPHS In conjunction with the Special Topic about misleading graphs that begins on page 612, you may wish to have students look for graphs in newspapers, magazines, or the Internet that they think are misleading. Have students then bring these graphs to class to explain why they think the graph is misleading and have them make a conjecture as to why the graph was used the way that it was in its original context. You may want to encourage students to look for graphs that match topics in other classes such as a social studies or science class.

In conjunction with the Special Topic about samples that begins on page 644, you might wish to work with the advisor to the school newspaper to help students develop unbiased questions that could be used to poll the student body. You might also wish to involve a social studies teacher to help students incorporate current events or social studies topics presently being covered into their questions. This could be especially appropriate if elections are occurring during the term. Students may also want to research using the Internet or other resources the various methods that pollsters use to help ensure that their questions are unbiased.

The following problem can be used with **Lesson 12.1**:

- **Challenge** A set of data has 10 values that have a range of 4.7 and a median of 56.5. Create a data set that matches these criteria and make a stem-and-leaf plot for your data. Check work.

Differentiating Instruction: Teaching Resources

Differentiating Technology

McDougal Littell *Middle School Mathematics* offers teachers a wide variety of technology, ranging from calculator activities in the *Chapter Resource Books* to the *Test and Practice Generator CD-ROM* to interactive, online resources and products accessed at Classzone.com.

CLASSZONE.COM

Classzone.com provides helpful online resources for students and teachers, including More Examples, Vocabulary Support, and State Test Practice. Classzone.com is also the access point for the following online products: *eEdition Plus Online*, an interactive, online version of the textbook; *eWorkbook Plus Online*, an interactive practice workbook correlated to the textbook; *eTutorial Plus Online*, an Internet tutorial that makes it easier than ever to help students master skills and concepts; and *EasyPlanner Plus Online*, an online resource with teacher tools and a lesson planner.

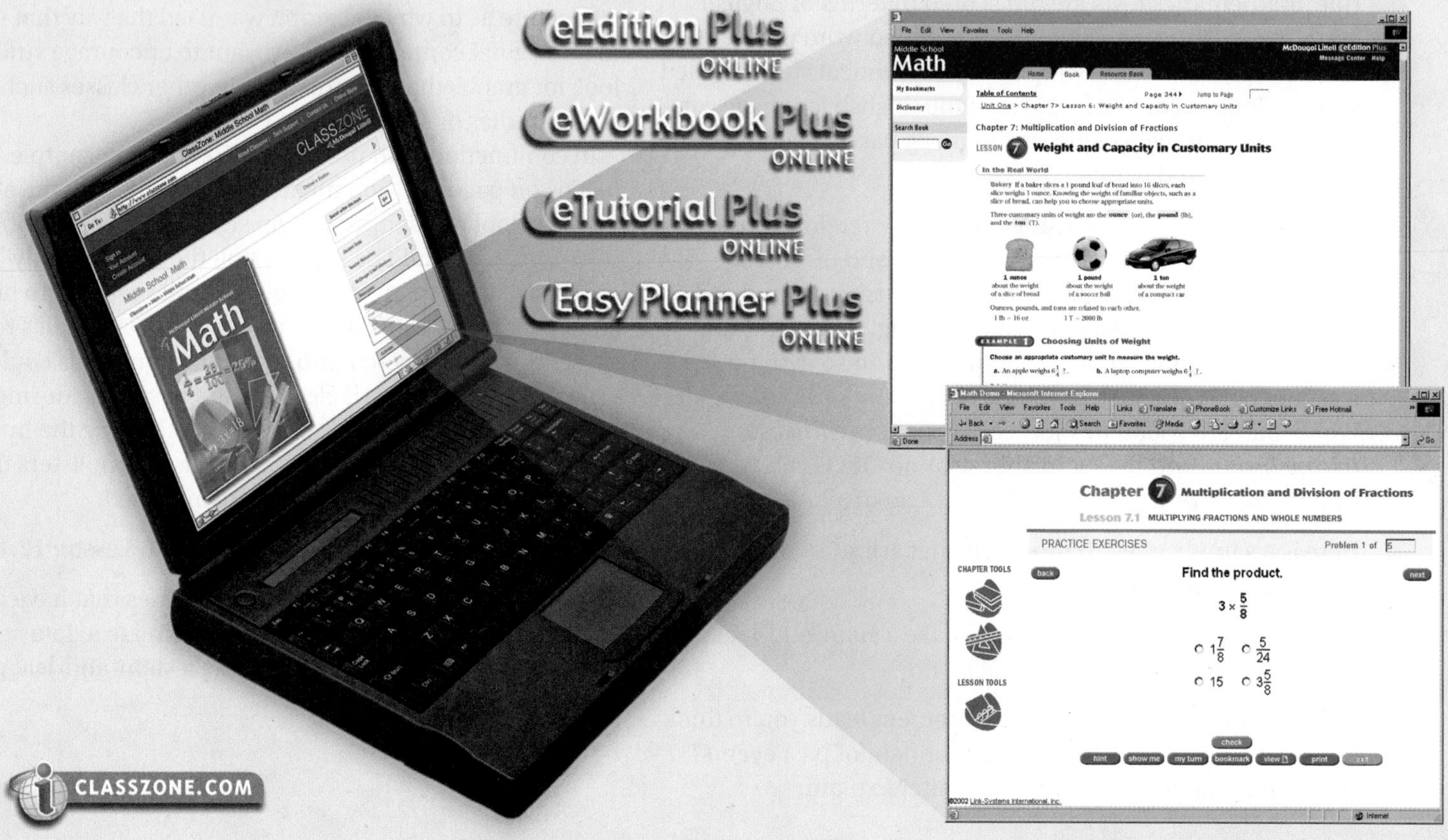

eEdition Plus ONLINE

eWorkbook Plus ONLINE

eTutorial Plus ONLINE

Easy Planner Plus ONLINE

CLASSZONE.COM

Test and Practice Generator CD-ROM

The *Test and Practice Generator* can be used to create numerous practice sheets and quizzes for each lesson and tests for each chapter using both static and algorithmic exercises. Information about creating and editing questions is provided.

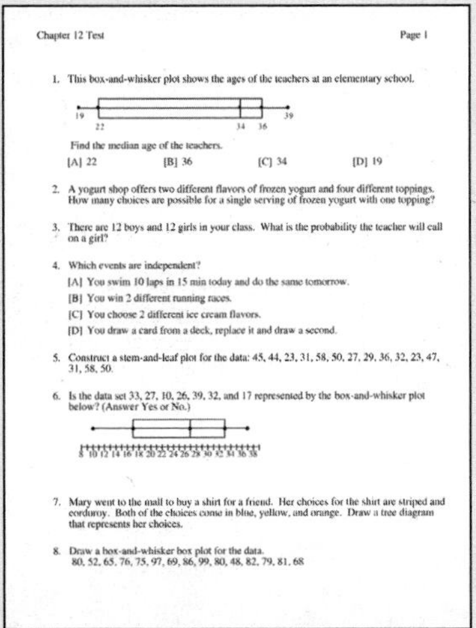

Chapter 12 Test　　Page 1

1. This box-and-whisker plot shows the ages of the teachers at an elementary school.

Find the median age of the teachers.

[A] 22　[B] 36　[C] 34　[D] 19

2. A yogurt shop offers two different flavors of frozen yogurt and four different toppings. How many choices are possible for a single serving of frozen yogurt with one topping?

3. There are 12 boys and 12 girls in your class. What is the probability the teacher will call on a girl?

4. Which events are independent?
[A] You swim 10 laps in 15 min today and do the same tomorrow.
[B] You win 2 different running races.
[C] You choose 2 different ice cream flavors.
[D] You draw a card from a deck, replace it and draw a second.

5. Construct a stem-and-leaf plot for the data: 45, 44, 23, 31, 58, 50, 27, 29, 36, 32, 23, 47, 31, 58, 50.

6. Is the data set 33, 27, 10, 26, 39, 32, and 17 represented by the box-and-whisker plot below? (Answer Yes or No.)

7. Mary went to the mall to buy a shirt for a friend. Her choices for the shirt are striped and corduroy. Both of the choices come in blue, yellow, and orange. Draw a tree diagram that represents her choices.

8. Draw a box-and-whisker box plot for the data.
80, 52, 65, 76, 75, 97, 69, 86, 99, 80, 48, 82, 79, 81, 68

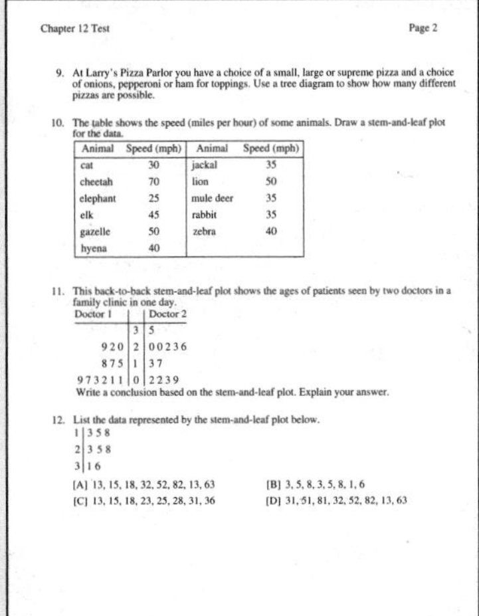

Chapter 12 Test　　Page 2

9. At Larry's Pizza Parlor you have a choice of a small, large or supreme pizza and a choice of onions, pepperoni or ham for toppings. Use a tree diagram to show how many different pizzas are possible.

10. The table shows the speed (miles per hour) of some animals. Draw a stem-and-leaf plot for the data.

Animal	Speed (mph)	Animal	Speed (mph)
cat	30	jackal	35
cheetah	70	lion	50
elephant	25	mule deer	35
elk	45	rabbit	35
gazelle	50	zebra	40
hyena	40		

11. This back-to-back stem-and-leaf plot shows the ages of patients seen by two doctors in a family clinic in one day.

Doctor 1		Doctor 2
	3	5
9 2 0	2	0 0 2 3 6
8 7 5	1	3 7
9 7 3 2 1 1	0	2 2 3 9

Write a conclusion based on the stem-and-leaf plot. Explain your answer.

12. List the data represented by the stem-and-leaf plot below.

1 | 3 5 8
2 | 3 5 8
3 | 1 6

[A] 13, 15, 18, 32, 52, 82, 13, 63　[B] 3, 5, 8, 3, 5, 8, 1, 6
[C] 13, 15, 18, 23, 25, 28, 31, 36　[D] 31, 51, 81, 32, 52, 82, 13, 63

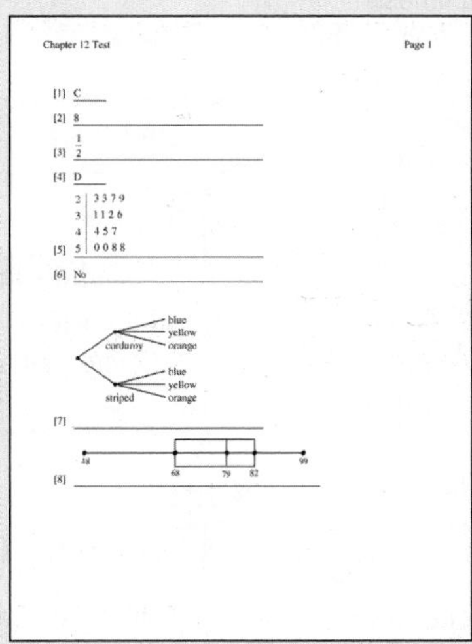

Chapter 12 Test　　Page 1

[1] C
[2] 8
[3] $\frac{1}{2}$
[4] D

[5]
2 | 3 3 7 9
3 | 1 1 2 6
4 | 4 5 7
5 | 0 0 8 8

[6] No

[7]

[8]

Resource Book

The *Chapter Resource Books* contain technology activities that are different from the activities given in the textbook. Also included, where appropriate, are calculator keystrokes that can be used to do the technology activities and exercises that appear in the textbook and in the *Chapter Resource Books*.

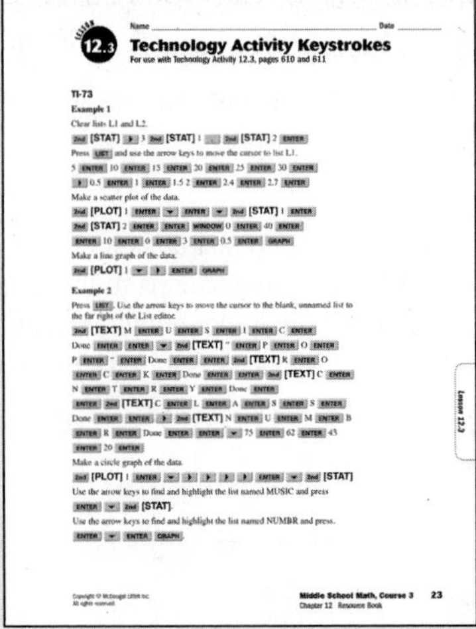

LESSON 12.3　Name ______ Date ______

Technology Activity Keystrokes
For use with Technology Activity 12.3, pages 610 and 611

TI-73

Example 1

Clear lists L1 and L2.

2nd [STAT] ► 3 2nd [STAT] 1 , 2nd [STAT] 2 ENTER

Press LIST and use the arrow keys to move the cursor to list L1.

5 ENTER 10 ENTER 15 ENTER 20 ENTER 25 ENTER 30 ENTER

► 0.5 ENTER 1 ENTER 1.5 2 ENTER 2.4 ENTER 2.7 ENTER

Make a scatter plot of the data.

2nd [PLOT] 1 ENTER ▼ ENTER ▼ 2nd [STAT] 1 ENTER

2nd [STAT] 2 ENTER ENTER WINDOW 0 ENTER 40 ENTER

ENTER 10 ENTER 0 ENTER 3 ENTER 0.5 ENTER GRAPH

Make a line graph of the data.

2nd [PLOT] 1 ▼ ► ENTER GRAPH

Example 2

Press LIST. Use the arrow keys to move the cursor to the blank, unnamed list to the far right of the List editor.

2nd [TEXT] M ENTER U ENTER S ENTER I ENTER C ENTER

Done ENTER ENTER ▼ 2nd [TEXT] " ENTER P ENTER O ENTER

P ENTER " ENTER Done ENTER ENTER 2nd [TEXT] R ENTER O

ENTER C ENTER K ENTER Done ENTER ENTER 2nd [TEXT] C ENTER

N ENTER T ENTER R ENTER Y ENTER Done ENTER

ENTER 2nd [TEXT] C ENTER L ENTER A ENTER S ENTER S ENTER

Done ENTER ENTER ► 2nd [TEXT] N ENTER U ENTER M ENTER B

ENTER R ENTER Done ENTER ENTER ▼ 75 ENTER 62 ENTER 43

ENTER 20 ENTER

Make a circle graph of the data.

2nd [PLOT] 1 ENTER ▼ ► ► ► ► ENTER ▼ 2nd [STAT]

Use the arrow keys to find and highlight the list named MUSIC and press

ENTER ▼ 2nd [STAT].

Use the arrow keys to find and highlight the list named NUMBR and press.

ENTER ▼ ENTER GRAPH.

Lesson 12.3

Copyright © McDougal Littell Inc. All rights reserved.　　Middle School Math, Course 3　23
Chapter 12 Resource Book

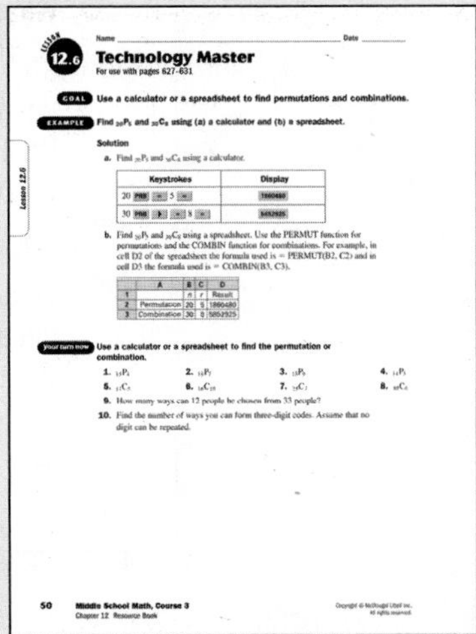

LESSON 12.6　Name ______ Date ______

Technology Master
For use with pages 627–631

GOAL Use a calculator or a spreadsheet to find permutations and combinations.

EXAMPLE Find $_{20}P_5$ and $_{30}C_8$ using (a) a calculator and (b) a spreadsheet.

Solution

a. Find $_{20}P_5$ and $_{30}C_8$ using a calculator.

Keystrokes	Display
20 PRB = 5 =	1860480
30 PRB ► = 8 =	5852925

b. Find $_{20}P_5$ and $_{30}C_8$ using a spreadsheet. Use the PERMUT function for permutations and the COMBIN function for combinations. For example, in cell D2 of the spreadsheet the formula used is = PERMUT(B2, C2) and in cell D3 the formula used is = COMBIN(B3, C3).

	A	B	C	D
1		n	r	Result
2	Permutation	20	5	1860480
3	Combination	30	8	5852925

your turn now Use a calculator or a spreadsheet to find the permutation or combination.

9. How many ways can 12 people be chosen from 33 people?
10. Find the number of ways you can form three-digit codes. Assume that no digit can be repeated.

Lesson 12.6

50　Middle School Math, Course 3　Chapter 12 Resource Book　　Copyright © McDougal Littell Inc. All rights reserved.

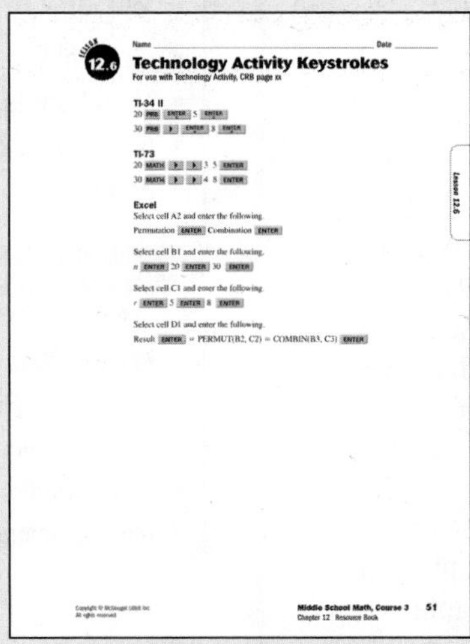

LESSON 12.6　Name ______ Date ______

Technology Activity Keystrokes
For use with Technology Activity, CRB page xx

TI-34 II

20 PRB ENTER 5 ENTER

30 PRB ► ENTER 8 ENTER

TI-73

20 MATH ► ► 3 5 ENTER

30 MATH ► ► 4 8 ENTER

Excel

Select cell A2 and enter the following.

Permutation ENTER Combination ENTER

Select cell B1 and enter the following.

n ENTER 20 ENTER 30 ENTER

Select cell C1 and enter the following.

r ENTER 5 ENTER 8 ENTER

Select cell D1 and enter the following.

Result ENTER = PERMUT(B2, C2) = COMBIN(B3, C3) ENTER

Lesson 12.6

Copyright © McDougal Littell Inc. All rights reserved.　　Middle School Math, Course 3　51
Chapter 12 Resource Book

OVERVIEW

Main Ideas

In this chapter, students make and interpret stem-and-leaf plots, box-and-whisker plots, circle graphs, and line graphs, and decide which graph or plot is most appropriate for a data set. Students use tree diagrams, the counting principle, permutations, and combinations to count choices or possibilities. Students apply these counting methods to find the probability and odds of simple events. Students also learn to distinguish between and find the probabilities of independent and dependent events.

Prerequisite Skills

The key skills reviewed in the games on these pages are:

- Interpreting bar and circle graphs

Additional practice with prerequisite skills can be found in the Review What You Need to Know exercises on page 596. Additional resources for reviewing prerequisite skills are:

- Skills Review Handbook, pp. 704–726
- Tutor Place
- eTutorial Plus

Managing the Game

Tips for Success

When students compare lengths of bars in the first question of the game, suggest that they estimate the size of each island first and then write a ratio instead of trying to compare lengths by measuring them. As they will learn in the chapter, sometimes bar graphs can be misleading, and they can avoid problems by first finding a value corresponding to each bar. For the circle graph, remind students that they will need to find the total number of species first.

Data Analysis and Probability

BEFORE

In previous chapters you've...

- Found the median and range of a data set
- Found probabilities of events

Now

In Chapter 12 you'll study...

- Interpreting data displays
- Using permutations and combinations to count possibilities
- Finding the probability of independent and dependent events

WHY?

So you can solve real-world problems about...

- electricity, p. 599
- skateboards, p. 619
- poetry, p. 624
- archery, p. 636

Internet Preview
CLASSZONE.COM

- eEdition Plus Online
- eWorkbook Plus Online
- eTutorial Plus Online
- State Test Practice
- More Examples

Chapter Warm-Up Game

Review skills you need for this chapter in this quick game.

Key Skill:
Interpreting bar and circle graphs

GALAPAGOS GRAPHS

HOW TO PLAY

1 USE the data displays to answer each question. Record the letter for each correct answer.

About how many times larger is Santa Cruz than San Cristobal? A
A. 2 **B.** 3 **C.** 4

What is the area of Isabela? E
D. 1680 mi^2 **E.** 1771 mi^2 **F.** 1800 mi^2

What percent of the land vertebrate species in the Galapagos Islands are reptiles? H
G. 10% **H.** 26% **I.** 30%

2 WRITE the letters of the correct answers to the questions in order. Find the number that corresponds to the letter. Put all three numbers together in the order of the answers. This will tell you the age of the oldest Galapagos tortoise on record. 152 years ol

A. 1 **B.** 2 **C.** 0 **D.** 9 **E.** 5
F. 2 **G.** 7 **H.** 2 **I.** 5

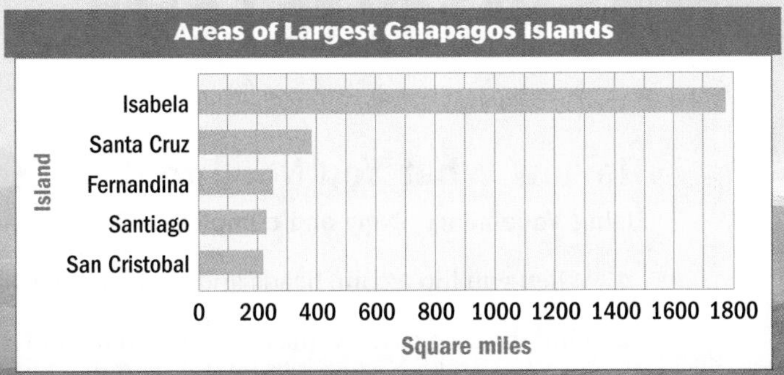

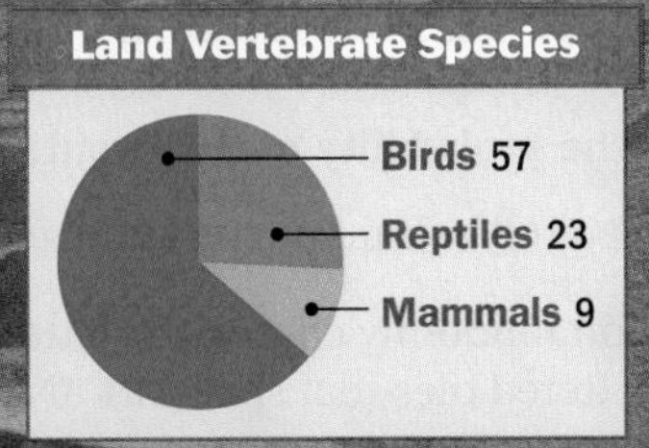

Areas of Largest Galapagos Islands

Land Vertebrate Species

Great Frigatebird

Giant Galapagos Tortoise

Galapagos Sea Lion

Stop *and* Think

1. **Writing** Describe one way the circle graph would change if you included the ocean life of the Galapagos Islands. *Sample answer:* The number of sections on the graph would change.
2. **Critical Thinking** Is the area of Isabela greater than the total area of the next four largest islands? Explain. Yes. *Sample answer:* The area of Isabela is about 1771 square miles while the total area of the next four largest islands is about 1225 square miles, and 1771 > 1225.

Reflecting on the Game

Have students state other relationships that they can identify from the graphs. You may also want to have students find the angle measures of each sector in the circle graph.

Chapter Resources

These resources are provided to help you prepare for the chapter and to customize review materials:

 ***Chapter 12 Resource Book***

- Tips for New Teachers, pp. 1–2
- Lesson Plan, pp. 6, 13, 21, 31, 39, 48, 58, 66
- Lesson Plan for Block Scheduling, pp. 7, 14, 22, 32, 40, 49, 59, 62

 ***Technology***

- EasyPlanner CD-ROM
- Test and Practice Generator
- Electronic Lesson Presentations CD-ROM
- eTutorial CD-ROM

 ***Internet***

- Classzone
- eEdition Plus Online
- eWorkbook Plus Online
- eTutorial Plus Online
- EasyPlanner Plus Online

English Learner Support

- Spanish Study Guide
- Multi-Language Glossary
- Chapter Audio Summaries CDs
- Teacher's Edition, pp. 594E–594F

PREPARE

Diagnosis/Remediation

Review What You Need to Know
The Review What You Need to Know exercises can help you diagnose whether students have the following skills needed in Chapter 12:
- Using vocabulary (Exs. 1–3)
- Finding mean and median of a data set (Exs. 4–5)
- Finding simple probability (Exs. 6–7)

 ***Chapter 12 Resource Book***
- Study Guide (Lessons 12.1–12.8)

 ***Tutor Place***

Notetaking Strategies

Encourage students to record in their notebooks any single words that they do not initially know the meaning of or that they find confusing. Then they can write helpful hints to remember the meanings of these words. Further suggestions for keeping a notebook can be found on page 629.

For more support on notetaking, see:
- Notetaking Guide Workbook
- Notetaking Transparencies

Chapter 12 Getting Ready to Learn

Word Watch

Review Words
data, p. 5
mean, p. 257
median, p. 257
range, p. 258
outcome, p. 354
probability of an event, p. 354

Review What You Need to Know 

Using Vocabulary Copy and complete using a review word.

1. When you flip a coin, heads and tails are the two possible _?_. outcomes
2. Find the sum of the values of a set of data and then divide by the number of data values to find the _?_ of the data. mean
3. The _?_ is a measure of how likely it is that the event will occur. probability

Find the mean and the median of the data set. *(p. 257)*

4. 23, 27, 13, 24, 19, 21, 25, 25, 12 21, 23
5. 0.2, 0.35, 1.33, 1.32, 0.05, 0.5 0.625, 0.425

Find the probability of the event. *(p. 354)*

6. You roll a number cube and get a number greater than 4. $\frac{1}{3}$
7. You randomly choose the letter A from a bag holding the eight lettered tiles that spell ARKANSAS. $\frac{3}{8}$

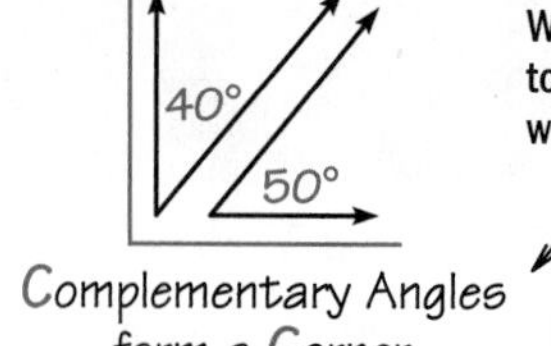

You should include material that appears on a notebook like this in your own notes.

Know How to Take Notes

Contrasting Terms When words have similar meanings, you should emphasize their differences in your notes.

Pairs of Angles

Complementary Angles: The sum of the angle measures is 90°.

Supplementary Angles: The sum of the angle measures is 180°.

40° 50°
Complementary Angles form a Corner

Write hints to remember word meanings.

130° 50°
Supplementary Angles form a Straight line

In Lesson 12.6, you should note the difference between combinations and permutations.

596

Stem-and-Leaf Plots

BEFORE

You organized data using bar graphs and histograms.

Now

You will make and interpret stem-and-leaf plots.

WHY?

So you can analyze waiting times at a restaurant, as in Ex. 14.

Word Watch

stem-and-leaf plot, p. 597

1.
1	0 2 5 5 9
2	0 4 4 5 7 9 9
3	0 5 6 9
4	0 3 7
5	0 1

Key: 3 | 0 = 30

In the Real World

Track Hurdlers entering the 200 meter hurdles at a track meet were ranked according to their qualifying times, in seconds, shown below.

28.6, 29.2, 28.1, 27.5, 29.8, 28.7,
30.2, 29.3, 28.3, 28.9, 29.9, 28.4

How can the data be displayed to show the distribution of the times?

A **stem-and-leaf plot** is a data display that helps you see how data are distributed. You can use a stem-and-leaf plot to order data.

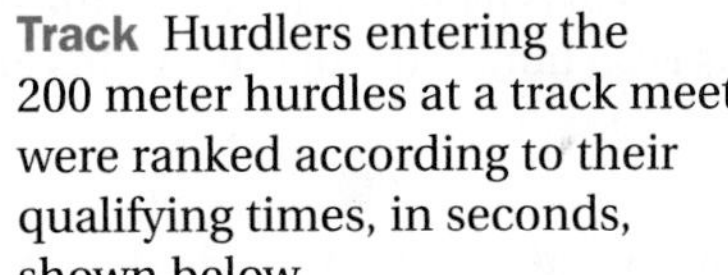

EXAMPLE 1 Making a Stem-and-Leaf Plot

You can display the hurdlers' times given above in a stem-and-leaf plot.

(1) The times range from 27.5 to 30.2. Let the stems be the digits in the tens' and ones' places. Let the leaves be the tenths' digits.

(2) Write the stems first. Then record each time by writing its tenths' digit on the same line as its corresponding stem. Include a key that shows what the stems and leaves represent.

(3) Make an ordered stem-and-leaf plot.

Unordered Plot

27	5
28	6 1 7 3 9 4
29	2 8 3 9
30	2

Key: 27 | 5 = 27.5

Ordered Plot

27	5
28	1 3 4 6 7 9
29	2 3 8 9
30	2

Key: 27 | 5 = 27.5

The leaves for each stem are listed in order from least to greatest.

Your turn now **Make an ordered stem-and-leaf plot of the data.**

1. Video game prices: \$40, \$15, \$10, \$19, \$12, \$24, \$15, \$39, \$51, \$50, \$35, \$20, \$47, \$36, \$30, \$25, \$27, \$29, \$24, \$43, \$29 See margin.

ILLINOIS Standards and ISAT:
10.A.3a

1 PLAN

SKILL CHECK

List each set of numbers in order from least to greatest.

1. 5.1, 5.05, 5.15, 5.01
5.01, 5.05, 5.1, 5.15
2. 113, 103, 131, 138, 118
103, 113, 118, 131, 138

LESSON OBJECTIVE

Make and interpret stem-and-leaf plots.

PACING

Suggested Number of Days
Basic Course: 2 days
Average Course: 2 days
Advanced Course: 2 days
Block: 1 block

TEACHING RESOURCES

For a complete list of Teaching Resources, see page 594B.

TRANSPARENCY

Warm-Up Exercises for this lesson are available on a transparency.

2 TEACH

MOTIVATING THE LESSON

Ask students whether any of them has kept a record of any personal athletic data.

TIPS FOR NEW TEACHERS

Some students will need extra practice choosing appropriate units for stems and leaves in data sets. See Tips for New Teachers in the *Chapter 12 Resource Book*.

EXTRA EXAMPLES

Example 1 Hue recorded the following plant heights. Make an ordered stem-and-leaf plot.
62, 71, 82, 65, 73, 84, 62, 77, 68, 77, 60, 77

Stem	Leaves
6	0 2 2 5 8
7	1 3 7 7 7
8	2 4

Key: 6 | 0 = 60

Example 2 The stem-and-leaf plot shows the weights of packages in pounds. Describe the data. What interval includes the most weights?

Stem	Leaves
1	8
2	2 3 3 5 5
3	1 2 2

Key: 1 | 8 = 1.8

The lightest weighs 1.8 pounds and the heaviest weighs 3.2 pounds, so the range is 1.4 pounds; 2.0–2.9.

Example 3 The data give the number of customers daily for two weeks in each of two stores. Make a double stem-and-leaf plot. Which store had more customers during this period?

Store A: 28, 38, 48, 37, 47, 35, 46, 35, 44, 33, 32, 42, 42, 41

Store B: 21, 32, 41, 47, 23, 36, 41, 24, 38, 42, 24, 38, 25, 42

Store A		Store B
8	2	1 3 4 4 5
8 7 5 5 3 2	3	2 6 8 8
8 7 6 4 2 2 1	4	1 1 2 2 7

Key: 8 | 2 | 1 = 28 and 21

Store A

CONCEPT CHECK

When would you use a double stem-and-leaf plot? **when you want to compare two sets of data**

DAILY PUZZLER

Every number in a data set is doubled. How is the number of leaves in a stem-and-leaf plot affected? **It remains the same.**

with Solving

In a stem-and-leaf plot, a stem can be one or more digits. A leaf is usually a single digit.

EXAMPLE 2 Interpreting a Stem-and-Leaf Plot

Biology The stem-and-leaf plot at the right shows the lengths, in millimeters, of young fish in a tank. Use the stem-and-leaf plot to describe the data. What interval includes the most lengths?

Stem	Leaves
4	9
5	
6	1 2 4 7 8 8
7	6 8
8	4

Key: 6 | 8 = 68

Solution

The longest fish is 84 mm and the shortest fish is 49 mm, so the range of lengths is 35 mm. Most of the lengths are in the 60–69 interval.

Double Stem-and-Leaf Plots A double stem-and-leaf plot can be used to compare two sets of data. You read to the left of the stems for one set of data and to the right for the other.

EXAMPLE 3 Making a Double Stem-and-Leaf Plot

Test Scores The data below show the test scores for Beth's class and Marisa's class. Overall, which class had the better test scores?

Beth's class: 95, 86, 79, 79, 58, 68, 90, 63, 71, 81, 82, 94, 64, 76, 77, 79, 83, 91, 83, 68, 74, 71

Marisa's class: 95, 73, 76, 84, 84, 89, 67, 82, 88, 86, 93, 97, 96, 84, 60, 75, 91, 87, 89, 86, 76, 93

Solution

You can use a double stem-and-leaf plot to compare the test scores.

Beth's Class		Marisa's Class
8	5	
8 8 4 3	6	0 7
9 9 9 7 6 4 1 1	7	3 5 6 6
6 3 3 2 1	8	2 4 4 4 6 6 7 8 9 9
5 4 1 0	9	1 3 3 5 6 7

Key: 0 | 9 | 1 represents 90 and 91.

ANSWER Marisa's class; it had more scores in the eighties and nineties.

Your turn now **Complete the following exercises.**

2. Make an ordered double stem-and-leaf plot to compare the lengths, in minutes, of the last 10 phone calls made by two friends.

   Kenyon: 12, 8, 17, 5, 23, 29, 21, 34, 16, 28
   Jason: 31, 28, 7, 5, 11, 5, 13, 16, 11, 24

3. In general, who made longer calls, Kenyon or Jason? **Kenyon**

2.

Kenyon		Jason
8 5	0	5 5 7
7 6 2	1	1 1 3 6
9 8 3 1	2	4 8
4	3	1

Key: 1 | 2 | 4 = 21 and 24

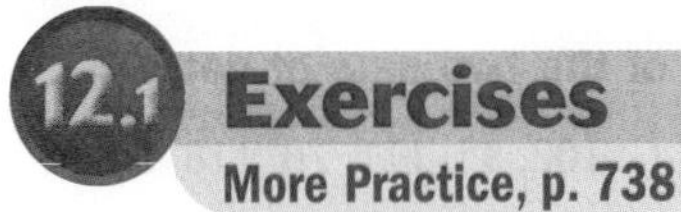

12.1 Exercises

More Practice, p. 738

INTERNET
eWorkbook Plus
CLASSZONE.COM

Getting Ready to Practice

1. **Vocabulary** Copy and complete: The key for a stem-and-leaf plot says $7|4 = 74$. In the plot, 7 is the _?_ and 4 is the _?_. stem, leaf

Write the number as it would appear in a stem-and-leaf plot. Identify the stem and the leaf.

2. 80 8 | 0; stem: 8, leaf: 0 **3.** 117 11 | 7; stem: 11, leaf: 7 **4.** 12.9 12 | 9; stem: 12, leaf: 9 **5.** 4.6 4 | 6; stem: 4, leaf: 6

6. **Guided Problem Solving** The data show the times, in minutes, it takes ten students to get ready for school. Make an ordered stem-and-leaf plot of the data. What interval includes the most time values?

   25, 10, 25, 15, 30, 18, 35, 40, 28, 20

   (1 Identify the range of the data. 30

   (2 Make the stem-and-leaf plot. Include a key. See margin.

   (3 Use the plot to find where most of the times fall. in the 20–29 minute interval

6. Step 2:

1	0 5 8
2	0 5 5 8
3	0 5
4	0

Key: 3 | 0 = 30

7.

4	5 8
5	0
6	3 5 7
7	4
8	2

Key: 5 | 0 = 50

60–69

Practice and Problem Solving

Make an ordered stem-and-leaf plot of the data. Identify the interval that includes the most data values. 7–12. See margin.

A

7. 45, 48, 65, 50, 67, 82, 74, 63
8. 33, 12, 8, 14, 35, 9, 26, 37, 4, 6
9. 108, 95, 89, 112, 109, 94, 103
10. 461, 492, 439, 467, 501, 485
11. 20.2, 22.6, 18.3, 18.7, 22.5, 18.1
12. 5.1, 4.0, 5.3, 3.2, 5.7, 6.9, 5.3
13. **Writing** Explain how you can use an ordered stem-and-leaf plot to find the median value of a set of data. See margin.
14. **Restaurants** The stem-and-leaf plot shows the average waiting times, in minutes, to be seated for fifteen restaurants. What are the shortest and longest waiting times? Which interval has the fewest number of waiting times?
    5 min, 45 min; 30–39 minute range

0	5 6 9
1	2 5 5
2	0 0 5 8
3	2 8
4	0 5 5

Key: 2|5 = 25

15. **Electricity** The data show the amounts, in dollars, of a family's electric bills for twelve months. Make an ordered stem-and-leaf plot. What is the range? Are the bills more often greater or less than $60? See margin.

    95, 58, 47, 78, 43, 65, 84, 72, 55, 84, 96, 59

HELP with Homework

Example	Exercises
1	7-12
2	13-15, 18
3	16-17, 19

Online Resources
CLASSZONE.COM
· More Examples
· eTutorial Plus

3 APPLY

ASSIGNMENT GUIDE

Basic Course

Day 1: SRH p. 723 Exs. 1-5; pp. 599-600 Exs. 7-9, 14, 15, 23-25

Day 2: pp. 599-600 Exs. 10-12, 16-20, 26

Average Course

Day 1: pp. 599-600 Exs. 7-9, 13-15, 23-25

Day 2: pp. 599-600 Exs. 10-12, 16-21, 26

Advanced Course

Day 1: pp. 599-600 Exs. 7-9, 13-15, 20-23

Day 2: pp. 599-600 Exs. 10-12, 16-19, 24-26, EC: TE p. 594D*

Block

pp. 599-600 Exs. 7-21, 23-25

EXTRA PRACTICE

- Student Edition, p. 738
- Chapter 12 Resource Book, pp. 7-9
- Test and Practice Generator

TRANSPARENCY

Even-numbered answers are available on transparencies.

HOMEWORK CHECK

When you review students' homework for this lesson, go over the following exercises to check understanding of key concepts.
Basic: 7, 10, 11, 14, 16
Average: 7, 11, 13, 14, 16
Advanced: 7, 12, 14, 15, 16

8-13, 15. See Additional Answers beginning on page AA1.

ASSESSMENT RESOURCES

For more assessment resources, see:

- Assessment Book
- Test and Practice Generator

MINI-QUIZ

1. Make a stem-and-leaf plot of the data. Identify the interval that includes the most data values.
72, 68, 88, 74, 61, 89, 72, 79

6	1 8
7	2 2 4 9
8	8 9

Key: 6 | 1 = 61

70–79

2. Make a double stem-and-leaf plot of the two sets of data.
A: 215, 221, 231, 223, 227
B: 211, 222, 213, 223, 228

Set A		Set B
5	21	1 3
7 3 1	22	2 3 8
1	23	

Key: 5 | 21 | 1 = 215 and 211

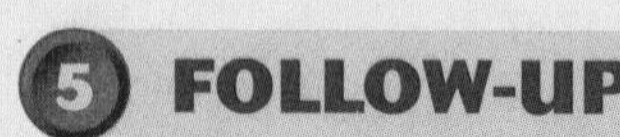

RETEACHING/REMEDIATION

- Study Guide in Chapter 12 Resource Book, pp. 10–11
- eTutorial Plus Online
- Extra Practice, p. 738
- Lesson Practice in Chapter 12 Resource Book, pp. 7-9

CHALLENGE/ENRICHMENT

- Challenge Practice in Chapter 12 Resource Book, p. 12
- Teacher's Edition, p. 594F

ENGLISH LEARNER SUPPORT

- Spanish Study Guide
- Multi-Language Glossary
- Chapter Audio Summaries CDs

19, 20, 22. See Additional Answers beginning on page AA1.

Make an ordered double stem-and-leaf plot of the two sets of data. 16–17. See margin.

B **16.** Set A: 16, 19, 8, 22, 18, 20, 32, 5
Set B: 12, 8, 25, 42, 31, 15, 16, 9

17. Set C: 102, 98, 111, 70, 118, 92, 77
Set D: 115, 88, 87, 102, 65, 95, 93

18. Critical Thinking Can you make a stem-and-leaf plot from a frequency table? Why or why not? No; specific data values are not given in a frequency table.

19. Football The total points that the Cleveland Browns scored in each game of a recent season are given below. Red numbers represent wins and blue numbers represent losses. Make an ordered double stem-and-leaf plot of the data. Describe the relationship between points scored and the outcome of the game. See margin.

6, 24, 23, 20, 14, 24, 21, 12, 27, 18, 15, 16, 10, 7, 41, 7

16.

Set A		Set B
8 5	0	8 9
9 8 6	1	2 5 6
2 0	2	5
2	3	1
	4	2

Key: 6 | 1 | 2 = 16 and 12

17.

Set C		Set D
	6	5
7 0	7	
	8	7 8
8 2	9	3 5
2	10	2
8 1	11	5

Key: 2 | 9 | 3 = 92 and 93

Extended Problem Solving **In Exercises 20–22, use the data below, which show the average monthly temperatures in degrees Fahrenheit (°F) for Los Angeles, California.**

56.8, 57.6, 58.0, 60.1, 62.7, 65.7, 69.1, 70.5, 69.9, 66.8, 61.6, 56.9

C **20. Plot** Make an ordered stem-and-leaf plot of the data. What is the range? See margin for art; 13.7.

21. Convert Convert the data to degrees Celsius (°C) using the formula $C = \frac{5}{9}(F - 32)$. Round to the nearest tenth of a degree. 13.8, 14.2, 14.4, 15.6, 17.1, 18.7, 20.6, 21.4, 21.1, 19.3, 16.4, 13.8

22. Compare Make an ordered stem-and-leaf plot of the converted data. Compare the two plots. In what ways are they different? Explain. See margin.

Mixed Review

23. Find the mean, median, mode(s), and range of the data. *(Lesson 5.8)*

−22, 14, 12, 6, −10, 14, 20, 16, −7, −5, 6, −2 3.5, 6, 6 and 14, 42

24. Find the slope and y-intercept of the line $7x + 4y = 24$. *(Lesson 11.7)* $-\frac{7}{4}$, 6

Test-Taking Practice 

The stem-and-leaf plot shows the ages of people at a birthday party. Use the plot to answer Exercises 25 and 26.

0	6
1	3 7 9
2	0 1 4 5
3	
4	7 9
5	0 1 2 2 2

Key: 4 | 7 = 47

25. Multiple Choice What is the age of the oldest person? A

A. 52 **B.** 59 **C.** 60 **D.** 79

26. Multiple Choice What is the median age? I

F. 52 **G.** 35 **H.** 30 **I.** 25

Box-and-Whisker Plots

BEFORE	Now	WHY?
You found the median and range of a data set.	You will make and interpret box-and-whisker plots.	So you can analyze camera prices, as in Ex. 12.

Word Watch

box-and-whisker plot, p. 601
lower quartile, p. 601
upper quartile, p. 601
lower extreme, p. 601
upper extreme, p. 601

In the Real World

Bridges The lengths, in meters, of the world's ten longest suspension bridges are listed below. How can you display these data to show how the lengths are distributed?

1280 1118 1990 1074 1298
1067 1624 1158 1090 1410

A **box-and-whisker plot** is a data display that organizes data values into four parts. Ordered data are divided into lower and upper halves by the median. The **lower quartile** is the median of the lower half of the data set. The **upper quartile** is the median of the upper half of the data set.

The **lower extreme** is the least data value and the **upper extreme** is the greatest data value.

HELP with Solving

If a data set has an odd number of values, then the median is not included in either half of the data when determining the quartile values. For help with finding a median, see p. 257.

EXAMPLE 1 Making a Box-and-Whisker Plot

To display the bridge lengths above in a box-and-whisker plot, first order the data to find the median and the quartiles.

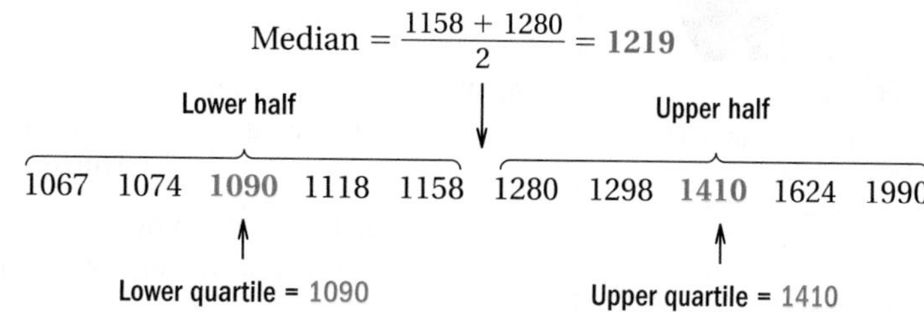

Plot these values below a number line that includes the extremes.

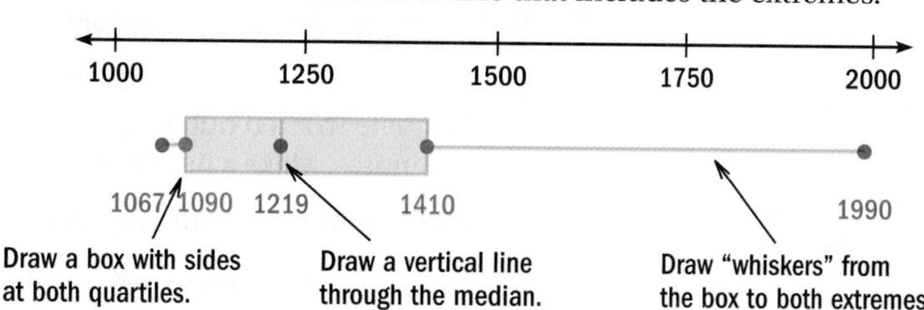

ILLINOIS Standards and ISAT:
10.A.3a; 10.A.3b

1 PLAN

SKILL CHECK

Find the average of each pair of numbers.

1. 1158, 1280 **1219**
2. 623, 627 **625**
3. 582, 771 **676.5**

LESSON OBJECTIVE

Construct and interpret box-and-whisker plots.

PACING

Suggested Number of Days
Basic Course: 2 days
Average Course: 2 days
Advanced Course: 2 days
Block: 1 block

TEACHING RESOURCES

For a complete list of Teaching Resources, see page 594B.

TRANSPARENCY

Warm-Up Exercises for this lesson are available on a transparency. A support transparency is available for Examples 1–2 and Your turn now Exercises 1–3.

2 TEACH

MOTIVATING THE LESSON

Have students list questions to ask about a set of data.

TIPS FOR NEW TEACHERS

Be sure to show how to make box-and-whisker plots with both odd and even numbers of data values. See Tips for New Teachers in the *Chapter 12 Resource Book*.

EXTRA EXAMPLES

Example 1 Fran recorded how many minutes she walked each day. Make a box-and-whisker plot of the data.
25, 45, 48, 48, 52, 52, 55, 57, 65, 75

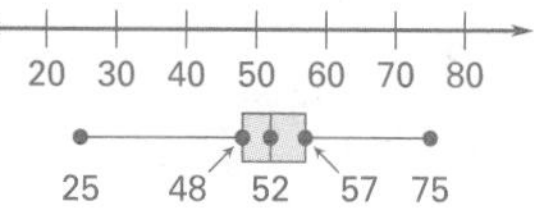

Example 2 A class is studying what effect television viewing has on their quiz scores. One group of students watched no television for two weeks before a quiz. The second group watched television during this time. The box-and-whisker plot shows the quiz scores for each group.

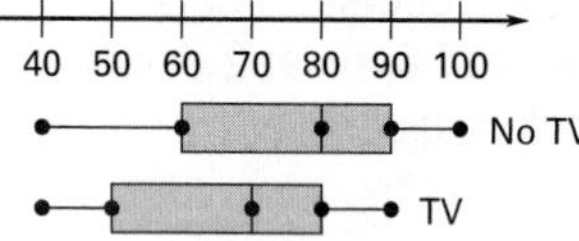

a. About what fraction of the "No TV" group scored better than anyone in the "TV" group? $\frac{1}{4}$

b. About what fraction of the "TV" group scored between 50 and 80 on the quiz? $\frac{1}{2}$

CONCEPT CHECK

Which whisker would be longer on the box-and-whisker plot for these data? Explain. 27.2, 28, 4.5, 25.6, 17, 30.5, 25, 22.3, 32.1 **The left whisker; there would be a larger gap between 4.5 and 19.65 than between 29.25 and 32.1 on a number line.**

DAILY PUZZLER

What number can be inserted into the data set 2, 3, 4, 4, 5, 7, 10, so that the new data set will have an upper quartile value of 8? **9**

1. See Additional Answers beginning on page AA1.

Interpreting a Box-and-Whisker Plot A box-and-whisker plot helps to show how varied, or spread out, the data are. The points divide the data into four parts. Each part represents about one quarter of the data.

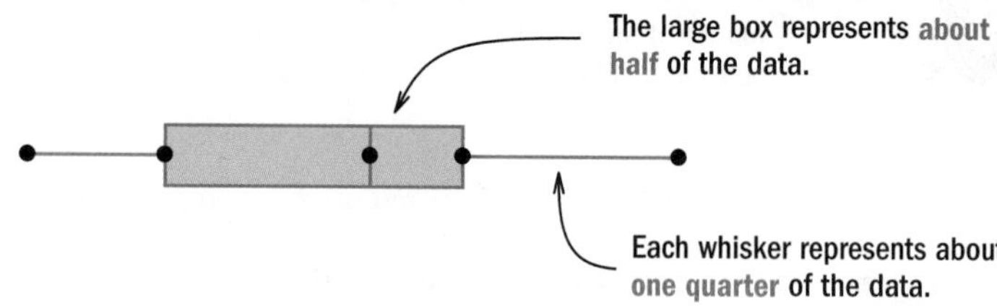

You can use box-and-whisker plots to compare two or more data sets.

EXAMPLE 2 Interpreting Box-and-Whisker Plots

Food Science You are testing whether a fertilizer helps tomato plants grow. You give fertilizer to the plants in Group 2, but not to Group 1. The box-and-whisker plots show how much the plants grew, in centimeters, for each group of plants after two weeks.

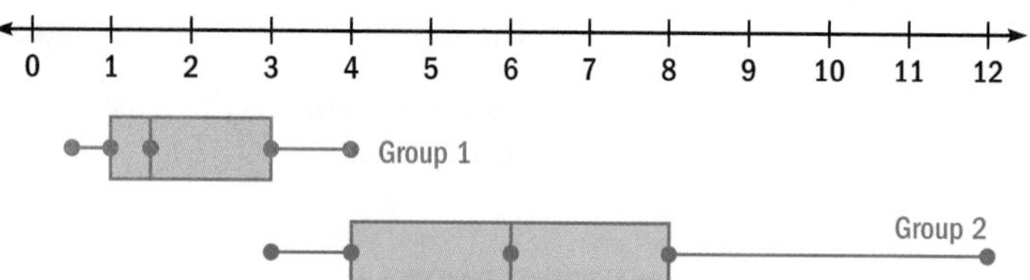

a. About what fraction of the unfertilized plants grew as much as any of the fertilized plants?

b. About what fraction of the fertilized plants grew 4 to 8 centimeters?

Solution

a. Notice that the right whisker for Group 1 overlaps the left whisker for Group 2. So about one quarter of the unfertilized plants grew as much as the any of the fertilized plants.

b. The large box in the plot for Group 2 ranges from 4 to 8, so about one half of the fertilized plants grew 4 to 8 centimeters.

Food Science

It takes about 24 pounds of tomatoes to make 7 pints of ketchup. At this rate, how many pounds of tomatoes are used to make a 2 pint bottle of ketchup? **6.9 lb**

Your turn now Use a box-and-whisker plot.

1. Ming worked out for 34, 27, 26, 15, 24, 21, 30, 23, 24, and 35 minutes. Chantelle worked out for 26, 33, 36, 21, 41, 36, 29, 25, 34, and 35 minutes. Make a box-and-whisker plot of the data for each person. **See margin.**
2. Who usually works out longer? Explain.
3. About how often does each person work out for 25–35 minutes? **about half the time for each**

2. **Chantelle. *Sample answer:* The median workout time for Chantelle is longer than the third quartile time for Ming, and almost as long as the upper extreme for Ming.**

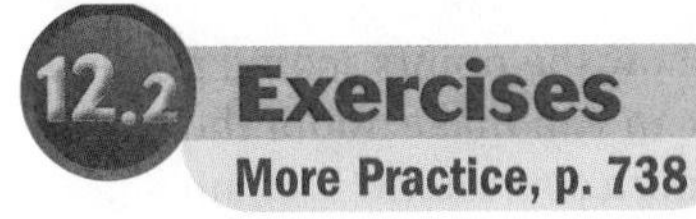

Exercises

More Practice, p. 738

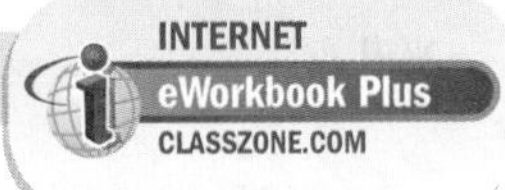

INTERNET eWorkbook Plus CLASSZONE.COM

Getting Ready to Practice

2. Step 2: median: 227, lower quartile: 197, upper quartile: 306; extremes: 141 and 351

12. $179.99, $229.99, $259.99, $259.99, $284.99, $299.99, $329.99, $379.99, $399.99; see margin for art. *Sample answer:* The median camera price is $284.99, with about half of the cameras costing between $244.99 and $354.99.

1. **Vocabulary** The median of the lower half of a data set is the _?_ and the median of the upper half of a data set is the _?_. lower quartile; upper quartile

2. **Guided Problem Solving** You had the following scores while playing a math game: 306, 211, 235, 197, 351, 141, and 227. Make a box-and-whisker plot of your scores. Then predict your next score.
   1. Find the range and draw a number line. 210; see margin for art.
   2. Find the median, quartiles, and extremes. See margin.
   3. Draw the box-and-whisker plot. See margin.
   4. Predict a range for your next score. Explain your reasoning. *Sample answer:* Between 197 and 306; half of the scores are between the lower and upper quartiles, which are 197 and 306.

Practice and Problem Solving

HELP with Homework

Example	Exercises
1	3-13
2	12-15

Online Resources CLASSZONE.COM
- More Examples
- eTutorial Plus

In Exercises 3–5, make a box-and-whisker plot of the data. 3–5. See margin.

A 3. $67, $53, $41, $33, $52, $28, $70, $56

4. 327 ft, 419 ft, 9 ft, 299 ft, 111 ft, 0 ft

5. 26 m, 389 m, 878 m, 144 m, 515 m, 404 m

The box-and-whisker plot shows the lengths, in inches, of the jumps of frogs in a frog-jumping contest. Estimate the following values.

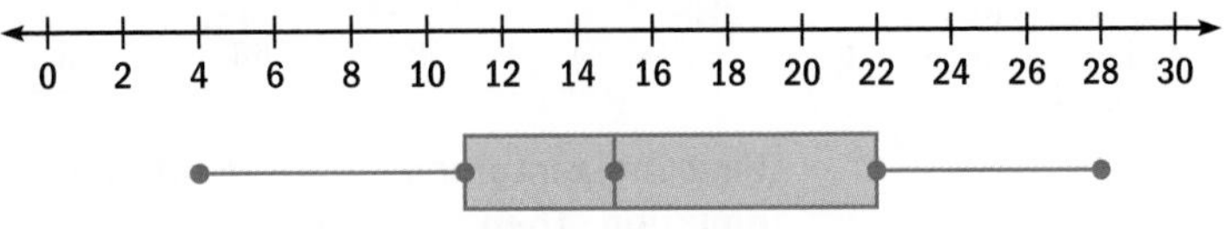

6. range 24 in.
7. median 15 in.
8. lower quartile 11 in.
9. upper quartile 22 in.
10. lower extreme 4 in.
11. upper extreme 28 in.

12. **Camera Prices** The prices of several cameras are $179.99, $329.99, $229.99, $284.99, $399.99, $379.99, $299.99, $259.99, and $259.99. Organize the list of prices from least to greatest. Then make a box-and-whisker plot of the data. What conclusions can you make? See margin.

13. **Pumpkins** The weights, in pounds, of 10 giant pumpkins were 853, 811.5, 785, 1020, 826.5, 789, 838, 810, 731, and 822.5. Make a box and-whisker plot of the data. Describe what the plot shows.

B 14. **Critical Thinking** Explain how making a stem-and-leaf plot can help you to make a box-and-whisker plot.

13. See margin for art. *Sample answer:* The middle half of the pumpkin weights clustered within about a 50 pound range, from 789 pounds to 838 pounds, but the range was much wider, nearly 300 pounds.

14. *Sample answer:* A stem-and-leaf plot gives all the data in order, so finding the extremes, the median, and the upper and lower quartiles is easy.

3 APPLY

ASSIGNMENT GUIDE

Basic Course

Day 1: EP p. 731 Exs. 45-47; pp. 603-604 Exs. 3-5, 9-11, 19-22

Day 2: pp. 603-604 Exs. 6-8, 12-16, 23

Average Course

Day 1: pp. 603-604 Exs. 3-5, 9-11, 19-22

Day 2: pp. 603-604 Exs. 6-8, 12-17, 23

Advanced Course

Day 1: pp. 603-604 Exs. 3-5, 9-11, 18-21*

Day 2: pp. 603-604 Exs. 6-8, 12-17, 23

Block

pp. 603-604 Exs. 3-17, 19-23

EXTRA PRACTICE

- Student Edition, p. 738
- Chapter 12 Resource Book, pp. 15-17
- Test and Practice Generator

TRANSPARENCY

Even-numbered answers are available on transparencies. A support transparency is available for Exercises 2-5, 12, 13, 16, and 17.

HOMEWORK CHECK

When you review students' homework for this lesson, go over the following exercises to check understanding of key concepts.

Basic: 3, 6, 7, 9, 12

Average: 4, 7, 8, 12, 13

Advanced: 5, 7, 10, 12, 15

2 (Steps 1, 3), 3-5, 12, 13. See Additional Answers beginning on page AA1.

4 ASSESS

Assessment Resources

For more assessment resources, see:
- Assessment Book
- Test and Practice Generator

Mini-Quiz

The box-and-whisker plot shows the number of visitors to a museum each day of one month. Estimate the following values.

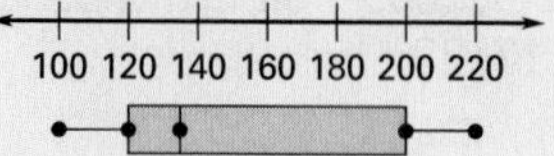

1. range 120
2. median 135
3. lower quartile 120
4. upper quartile 200
5. lower extreme 100
6. upper extreme 220

5 FOLLOW-UP

Reteaching/Remediation

- Study Guide in Chapter 12 Resource Book, pp. 18–19
- eTutorial Plus Online
- Extra Practice, p. 738
- Lesson Practice in Chapter 12 Resource Book, pp. 15–17

Challenge/Enrichment

- Challenge Practice in Chapter 12 Resource Book, p. 20
- Teacher's Edition, p. 594F

English Learner Support

- Spanish Study Guide
- Multi-Language Glossary
- Chapter Audio Summaries CDs

15–23. See Additional Answers beginning on page AA1.

Lake Area

Three of the world's 10 largest lakes are Great Lakes. The 6 quadrillion gallons in the Great Lakes are 18% of the world's fresh water supply. One quadrillion is equal to one million billions. How much fresh water does the world have? **33.3 quadrillion gal**

17. See margin for art. *Sample answer:* The outlier does not have much of an effect on the quartiles, but it makes a whisker very long and thus greatly increases the range.

INTERNET
State Test Practice
CLASSZONE.COM

15. Basketball The box-and-whisker plots show the points scored per game for two players. What conclusions can you make about the players' performances? Which player is more consistent? Explain. **See margin.**

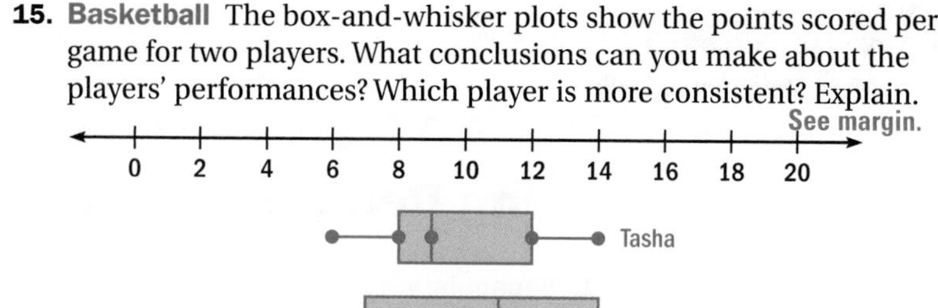

Lake Area In Exercises 16 and 17, use the areas, in square kilometers, of the world's ten largest lakes: 371,000, 84,500, 64,500, 63,500, 62,940, 58,020, 32,000, 31,500, 31,400, and 28,400.

An *outlier* is a data value that is much less or much greater than most of the other values in the data set.

16. Make a box-and-whisker plot of the data. Which value is an outlier? **See margin for art; 371,000.**

C **17.** Remove the outlier and then make another box-and-whisker plot. Describe how an outlier affects a box-and-whisker plot. **See margin.**

18. Challenge Change one value in the data set 3, 4, 5, 7, 9, 11, 13, 15, 17, 18, 21 so that the median of the set is 13, the lower quartile is 7, and the upper quartile is 17. Explain how you got your answer. **See margin.**

Mixed Review

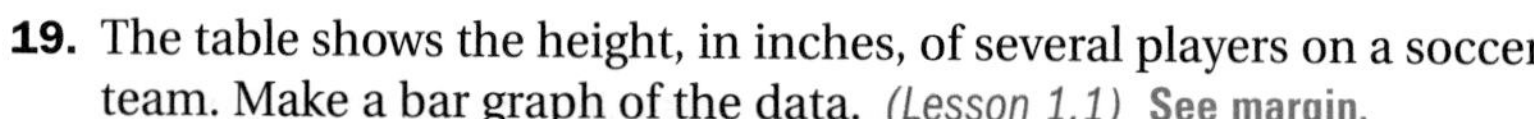

19. The table shows the height, in inches, of several players on a soccer team. Make a bar graph of the data. *(Lesson 1.1)* **See margin.**

Name	Ally	Nate	Bob	Inez	Dan	Lisa
Height	68	66	73	66	60	62

Find the *x*-intercept, *y*-intercept, and slope of the graph of the equation. Then graph the line. *(Lessons 11.5, 11.6)* **20–22. See margin for art.**

20. $y = 24$ **x-intercept: none, y-intercept: 24, slope: 0**

21. $3x - 5y = 30$ **x-intercept: 10, y-intercept: −6, slope: $\frac{3}{5}$**

22. $x = -4$ **x-intercept: −4, y-intercept: none, slope: undefined**

Test-Taking Practice

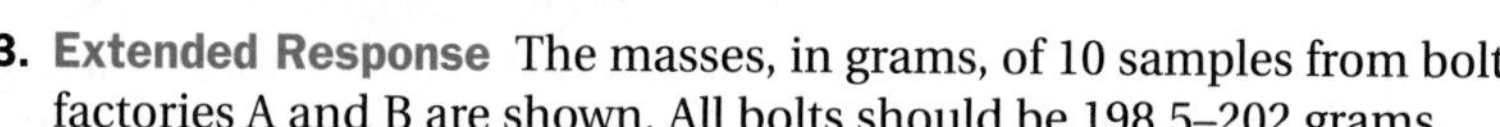

23. Extended Response The masses, in grams, of 10 samples from bolt factories A and B are shown. All bolts should be 198.5–202 grams.

Factory A: 199, 201, 200, 198.5, 200.5, 202, 201, 200.8, 200.9, 198.5

Factory B: 201, 200.4, 203, 200.8, 201, 203.4, 200.6, 201, 200.9, 203.1

Make box-and-whisker plots comparing the samples. Describe how well each factory makes bolts within the desired mass range, based on the samples. Then use the plots to compare the factories' performances. **See margin.**

Using Data Displays

BEFORE	Now	WHY?
You organized data using box-and-whisker plots.	You will organize data using circle graphs and line graphs.	So you can represent the areas of boroughs of New York, as in Ex. 13.

Word Watch

circle graph, p. 605
line graph, p. 606

Circle Graphs A survey asked, "How well can you whistle?" The results are shown in the *circle graph* below. It shows that three out of four people can whistle a tune.

A **circle graph** represents data as sections of a circle. Each section can be labeled using a fraction, decimal, or percent. Because the graph represents all the data, the sum of the sections must equal 1, or 100%.

How Well Can You Whistle?

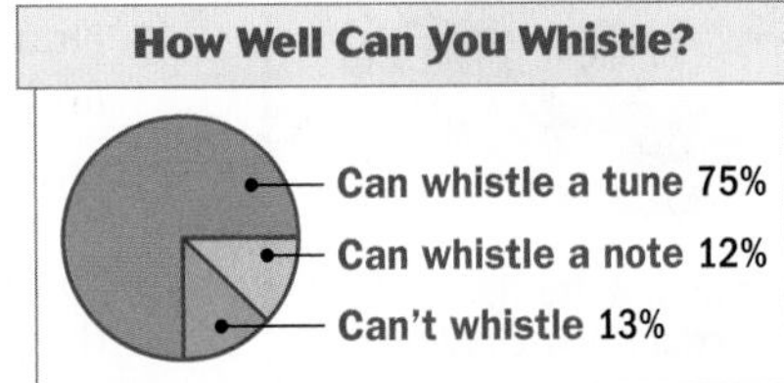

To make a circle graph, find the angle measure to the nearest degree that represents each data value's portion of the whole. The sum of all the angle measures must equal 360°, the number of degrees in a circle.

EXAMPLE 1 Making a Circle Graph

E-mail A survey asked, "How often do you check your e-mail?" Of the 100 people asked, 4 answered *less than weekly*, 23 answered *weekly*, and 73 answered *every day*. You can display the data in a circle graph.

HELP with Solving

In Example 1, you can draw the 14° and 83° angles first. Then the remaining section of the circle will have a measure of 263°.

(1) Use a proportion to find the number of degrees to use to represent each response as a section in a circle graph.

Less than weekly	Weekly	Every day
$\frac{4}{100} = \frac{a}{360°}$	$\frac{23}{100} = \frac{b}{360°}$	$\frac{73}{100} = \frac{c}{360°}$
$a = 14.4° \approx 14°$	$b = 82.8° \approx 83°$	$c = 262.8° \approx 263°$

(2) Draw a circle.

(3) Use a protractor to draw the first angle measure. Then label the section.

(4) Draw and label remaining sections. Include a title.

Check Your E-mail?

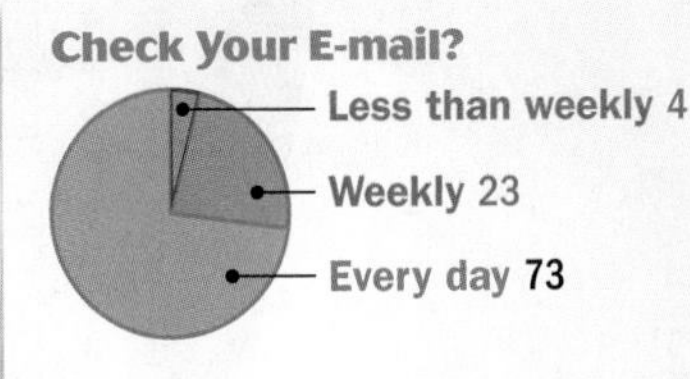

ANSWER The graph shows that the majority of people check their e-mail every day.

ILLINOIS Standards and ISAT:
10.A.3a; 10.A.3c

1 PLAN

SKILL CHECK

Find each fraction of 360°.

1. $\frac{1}{2}$ 180° **2.** $\frac{1}{4}$ 90°

3. $\frac{1}{8}$ 45° **4.** $\frac{2}{3}$ 240°

LESSON OBJECTIVE

Organize data using circle graphs and line graphs.

PACING

Suggested Number of Days
Basic Course: 1 day
Average Course: 1 day
Advanced Course: 1 day
Block: 0.5 block with 12.4

TEACHING RESOURCES

For a complete list of Teaching Resources, see page 594B.

TRANSPARENCY

Warm-Up Exercises for this lesson are available on a transparency.

2 TEACH

MOTIVATING THE LESSON

Collect data on the whistling ability of students in the class and discuss how your class data compare to the data in the text.

TIPS FOR NEW TEACHERS

Ask students to suggest ways to keep from confusing the number of degrees in a circle section with the percent of a data set that is being graphed. See Tips for New Teachers in the *Chapter 12 Resource Book*.

EXTRA EXAMPLES

Example 1 A survey of 100 people asked how many times a week they exercised. Of the 100 people, 28 exercised daily, 16 exercised twice a week, 23 exercised 3 times a week, and 33 exercised once a week or less. Make a circle graph of the data.

How Often Do You Exercise?

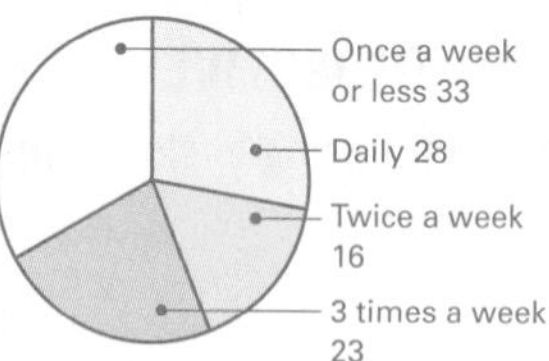

Example 2 The table shows the number of empty units in an apartment complex for the first six months of a year. Make a line graph of the data.

Month	Number
Jan	5
Feb	7
Mar	12
Apr	20
May	15
Jun	15

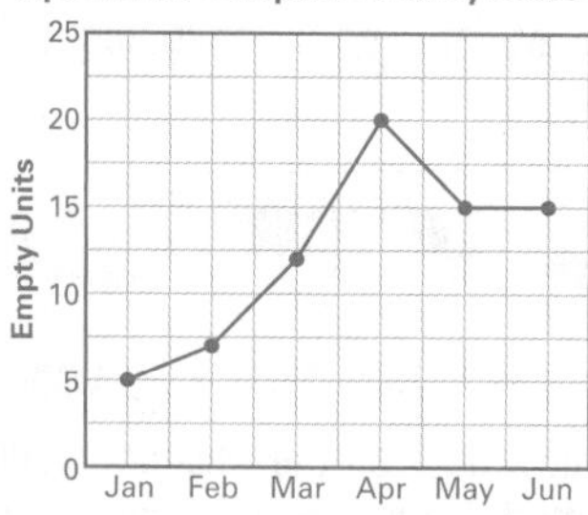

TRANSPARENCY

Support transparencies are available for Examples 1–2 and Your turn now Exercises 1–2.

1, 2. See Additional Answers beginning on page AA1.

Line Graphs A **line graph** represents data that change over time.

EXAMPLE 2 Making a Line Graph

Karner Blue Butterfly, endangered since 1992

Environment The table shows the number of insect species on the United States endangered species list. Make a line graph of the data.

Year	1995	1996	1997	1998	1999	2000	2001
Number	20	20	28	28	28	33	35

(1) Draw and label the horizontal and vertical scales.

(2) Plot a point for each data pair.

(3) Draw line segments to connect the points.

(4) The graph shows an increase over time.

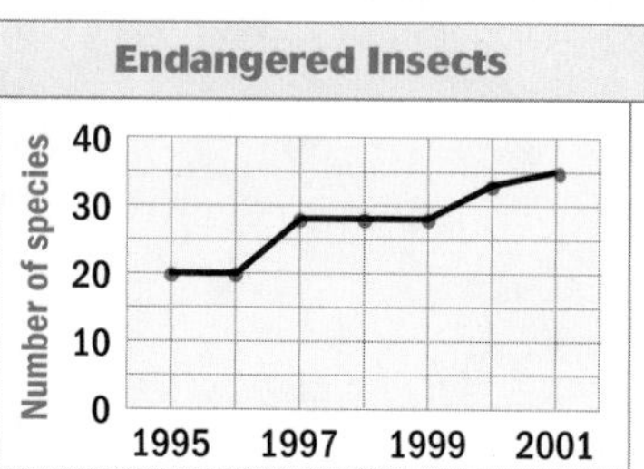

Your turn now **Use the table of polling data.** 1–2. See margin for art.

1. Make a circle graph of the data for Week 1. What does the graph show?
More people would vote for Ben in week 1.
2. Make a line graph of the data for Ben. What does the graph show?
The percent of people who would vote for Ben decreased from Week 1 to Week 3 while the percent who would vote for Alice increased.

Who Will You Vote For?			
Week	1	2	3
Ben	55%	50%	40%
Alice	45%	50%	60%

Using appropriate data displays helps you make meaningful conclusions.

Using Appropriate Data Displays

- Use a *circle graph* to represent data as parts of a whole.
- Use a *line graph* to display data over time.
- Use a *stem-and-leaf plot* to order a data set.
- Use a *box-and-whisker plot* to show the data's distribution in quarters, using the median, quartiles, and extremes.
- Use a *bar graph* to display data in distinct categories.
- Use a *histogram* to compare the frequencies of data that are grouped in equal intervals.

EXAMPLE 3 **Choosing a Data Display**

Choose an appropriate display for the data.

a. The table below shows the results of a survey that asked students if they are going away during summer vacation.

Response	Percent
Yes	48%
No	37%
Don't know	15%

b. The table below shows the results of a survey that asked students about ways they use the Internet.

Purpose	Percent
Research	62%
Shopping	34%
E-mail	45%
News	10%
Browsing	18%

Solution

a. The data add up to 100%, so a circle graph is appropriate.

b. The percents in the categories add up to more than 100%. An appropriate display for the data is a bar graph.

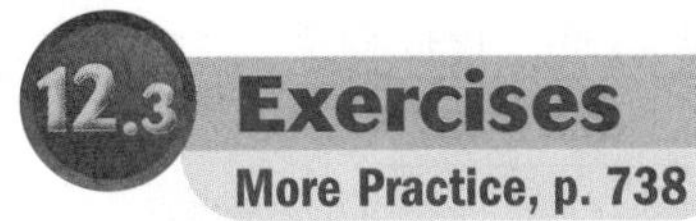

12.3 Exercises

More Practice, p. 738

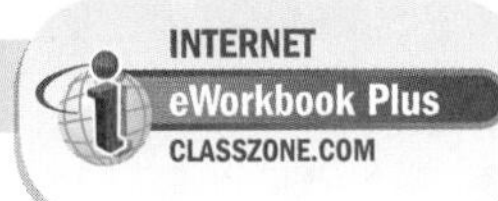

INTERNET eWorkbook Plus CLASSZONE.COM

Getting Ready to Practice

Vocabulary **Copy and complete the statement.**

1. You can use a _?_ to display data as parts of a whole. **circle graph**
2. You can use a _?_ to display changes in a quantity over time. **line graph**

Convert the value into an angle measure for display in a circle graph.

3. 31% **112°**
4. $\frac{3}{8}$ **135°**
5. 14% **50°**
6. 27 out of 60 **162°**

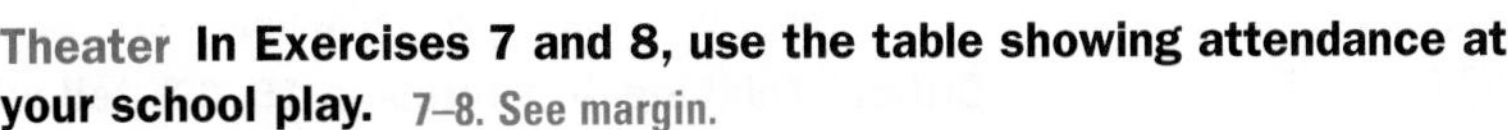

Theater **In Exercises 7 and 8, use the table showing attendance at your school play.** **7–8. See margin.**

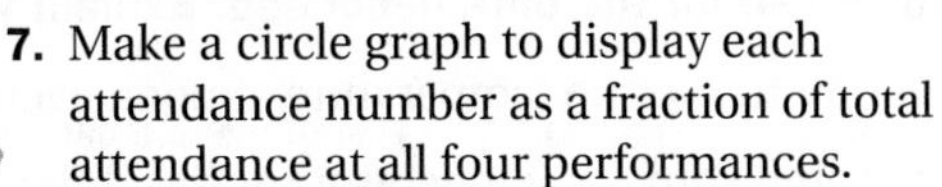

7. Make a circle graph to display each attendance number as a fraction of total attendance at all four performances.
8. Tickets cost $7 each. Make a line graph that shows how much money was collected from each performance.

Play Attendance	
Friday	130
Saturday (2 P.M.)	231
Saturday (8 P.M.)	291
Sunday	185

EXTRA EXAMPLES

Example 3 Choose an appropriate display for the data.

a. The table below shows the results of a survey that asked students what kind of pet they owned.

Pet	Percent
dog/cat	62
bird/reptile	14
Other	8
None	16

The data add up to 100%, so a circle graph is appropriate.

b. The table below shows the results of a survey that asked moviegoers their age.

Ages	Number
0–19	57
20–39	42
40–59	37
60–79	12

The data fall in equal intervals, so a histogram is appropriate.

CONCEPT CHECK

Explain the differences between a line graph and a bar graph. **A line graph displays data that change over time. From it, you can see rising or falling trends. A bar graph displays data in distinct categories, so you can visually compare and contrast the amounts in each category.**

DAILY PUZZLER

A circle graph has four sections. The second section is half the measure of the first, the third is half the measure of the second, and the fourth is half the measure of the third. What are the measures of the four sections? **192°, 96°, 48°, 24°**

7, 8. See Additional Answers beginning on page AA1.

3 APPLY

ASSIGNMENT GUIDE

Basic Course

Day 1: SRH p. 721 Exs. 1-4, EP p. 733 Exs. 19, 20; pp. 608-609 Exs. 9-16, 18-20, 23-27

Average Course

Day 1: pp. 608-609 Exs. 9-14, 16-21, 23-28

Advanced Course

Day 1: pp. 608-609 Exs. 9-14, 16-23*, 26-28

Block

pp. 608-609 Exs. 9-14, 16-21, 23-28 (with 12.4)

EXTRA PRACTICE

- Student Edition, p. 738
- Chapter 12 Resource Book, pp. 24-26
- Test and Practice Generator

TRANSPARENCY

Even-numbered answers are available on transparencies. Support transparencies are available for Exercises 7-11, 13, and 18.

HOMEWORK CHECK

When you review students' homework for this lesson, go over the following exercises to check understanding of key concepts.

Basic: 9, 10, 12, 13, 15
Average: 9, 10, 12, 13, 16
Advanced: 9, 10, 12, 16, 17

TEACHING TIP

Point out the Help with Solving note for Exercise 13. Discuss round-off error with students, as they may not be familiar with this concept.

9-11, 13. See Additional Answers beginning on page AA1.

HELP with Homework

Example	Exercises
1	9, 12-17
2	10-11, 15-17
3	15-17

Online Resources CLASSZONE.COM
- More Examples
- eTutorial Plus

10. See margin for art. ***Sample answer:*** **There is an overall increase in the number of houses sold over time, though there was a slight decrease during the period from 1998 to 2000.**

HELP with Solving

The sum of the rounded angle measures in Exercise 13 will not equal 360°. This is the result of *round-off error*. The sum of the unrounded values is 360°.

11. See margin for art. ***Sample answer:*** **The number of people who attend symphony orchestra concerts increased rapidly from 1994 to 1995, and then at a slower rate from 1995 to 1998.**

12. The Bronx: 14%, Queens: 36%, Brooklyn: 24%, Staten Island: 18%, Manhattan: 8%

Practice and Problem Solving

A **9. Snacking** The table shows the results of a survey asking students to describe how often they snack. Represent the data in a circle graph. **See margin.**

How Often Do You Snack?	
Never	10%
Rarely	45%
Sometimes	35%
Often	10%

10. New Houses The table below shows the number, in thousands, of new single-family houses sold in the United States each year from 1997 to 2001. Make a line graph of the data. Describe how the data change over time.

Year	1997	1998	1999	2000	2001
Houses sold (thousands)	804	886	880	877	900

11. Music The table below shows the number of people, in millions, who attended symphony orchestra concerts in the United States each year from 1994 to 1998. Make a line graph of the data. What trend does the graph show? **See margin.**

Year	1994	1995	1996	1997	1998
Attendees (millions)	24.4	30.9	31.1	31.9	32.2

New York City **The map shows the land area, in square miles, of each of the five boroughs of New York City.**

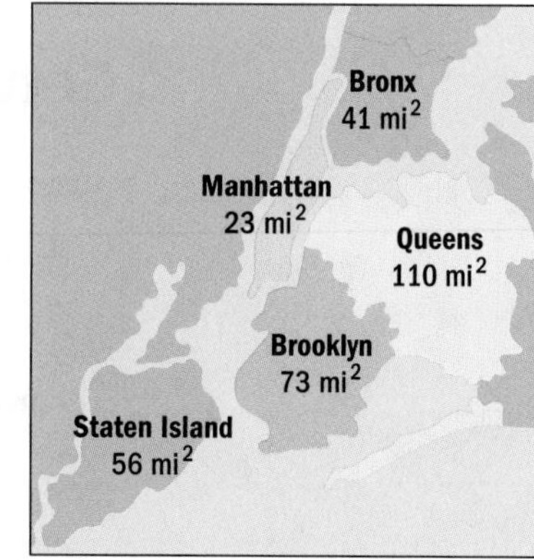

12. Find the percent of the total area of New York City that each borough covers. **See margin.**

13. Represent the data using a circle graph. **See margin.**

14. Use the graph to compare the areas of the boroughs.
Sample answer: **Queens is the largest borough, followed in order by Brooklyn, Staten Island, The Bronx, and Manhattan.**

Critical Thinking **In Exercises 15–17, tell which type of display you would use for the data described. Explain your reasoning.**

15. You record the temperature at noon every day for a month.
Line graph; the data is collected over time.

16. You record the temperature at five different locations.
Bar graph; the data is collected at distinct locations.

17. You record the high temperature every day for a month, and find how often the daily high temperature falls within each 10 degree temperature interval. ***Sample answer:*** **Histogram; the data is the frequency of occurrence in equal intervals for a certain range.**

20. *Sample answer:* By comparing the graphs; it is easier to see which categories increased and decreased the most from the graph.

Car Color In Exercises 18 and 19, use the table. It shows the percent of people who liked the given color for sports and compact cars.

Color	Silver	Black	Dark blue	White	Dark green	Red	Other
2000	25.4%	14.5%	11.3%	9.8%	6.7%	12.7%	19.6%
2001	22.3%	14.4%	5.0%	11.4%	9.7%	15.8%	21.4%

B **18.** Make a circle graph of the data for 2000 and for 2001. See margin.

19. From 2000 to 2001, which color had the largest percent increase? The largest percent decrease? red; dark blue

20. Critical Thinking Is it easier to answer Exercise 19 by comparing the graphs or by using the table? Explain. See margin.

C **21. Camping** The data in the circle graph show the percent of people who chose each reason for camping. Can you display the data in a line graph? Why or why not? Can you display the data in a bar graph? Why or why not? See margin.

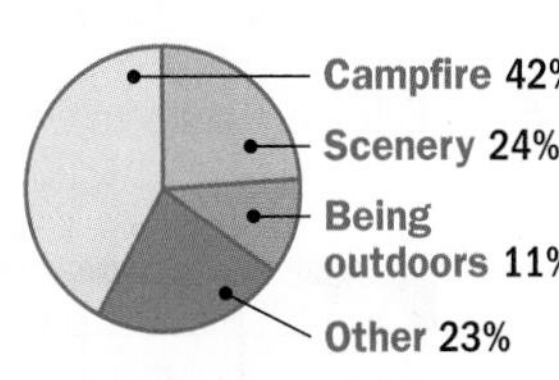

22. Challenge Describe a set of data that could be displayed in three different types of data display. Explain how to display it in each. See margin.

21. No; it does not show a change in data over time; yes; it shows data in distinct categories.

Mixed Review

Graph the equation using intercepts. *(Lesson 11.5)* 23–25. See margin.

23. $5x + 2y = 10$ **24.** $8x - 3y = 24$ **25.** $9y - 18x = 27$

26. Make an ordered stem-and-leaf plot of the following data: 17, 10, 11, 15, 21, 34, 26, 16, 36, 24, 37, 20, 18, 31, 39, 29, 28. *(Lesson 12.1)*

26.
1	0 1 5 6 7 8
2	0 1 4 6 8 9
3	1 4 6 7 9

Key: 3 | 1 = 31

Test-Taking Practice

27. Multiple Choice Use the line graph. It shows the numbers, in millions, of black-and-white TVs sold from 1965 to 1995. In which time period is the decrease the greatest? A

A. 1965–1970 **B.** 1975–1980

C. 1985–1990 **D.** 1990–1995

Black-and-white TV Sales

Sales (millions): 0, 2, 4, 6, 8, 10; years: 1965, 1975, 1985, 1995

28. Short Response You ask 100 people a yes or no question. The possible answers are *yes, no,* and *no answer*. What types of display would be appropriate for this type of data? Explain your reasoning.

28. Circle graph or bar graph. *Sample answer:* A circle graph shows what part of the whole each answer represents and a bar graph displays the three answers as distinct categories, so either is appropriate.

4 ASSESS

Assessment Resources

For more assessment resources, see:
- Assessment Book
- Test and Practice Generator

Mini-Quiz

1. The table below shows the favorite city park to walk dogs. Make a circle graph to display the data.

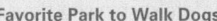

City Park	Percent
Schenck	42
Umstead	18
Johnson	26
Fairgrounds	14

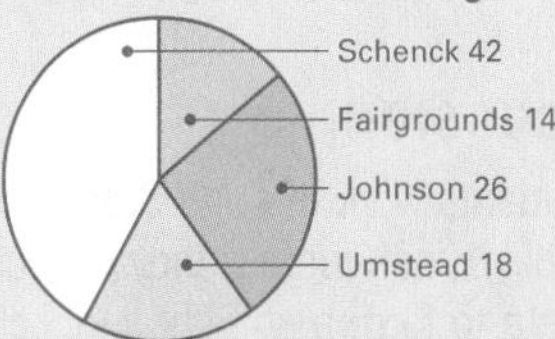

5 FOLLOW-UP

Reteaching/Remediation
- Study Guide in Chapter 12 Resource Book, pp. 27-28
- Tutor Place, Ratio, Proportion and Percent Card 17
- eTutorial Plus Online
- Extra Practice, p. 738
- Lesson Practice in Chapter 12 Resource Book, pp. 24-26

Challenge/Enrichment
- Challenge Practice in Chapter 12 Resource Book, p. 30
- Teacher's Edition, p. 594F

English Learner Support
- Spanish Study Guide
- Multi-Language Glossary
- Chapter Audio Summaries CDs

18, 22-25. See Additional Answers beginning on page AA1.

1 PLAN

Learn the Method

- Students will use a graphing calculator to create data displays.
- Students can recreate the line graphs they drew for Exercises 10 and 11 in Lesson 12.3 and compare the calculator displays to their hand-drawn graphs.

2 TEACH

Tips for Success

Remind students to enter the data carefully and check that the data are correct before displaying their graphs.

Discussion

As students work through Step 1 of Example 1, ask them if they expect the data to form a straight line. Lead students to recognize that the cost interval differs between each 5-minute difference, so the slope will not be the same for all parts of the graph.

Extra Examples

Example 1 The table shows the average wait time, in minutes, for the number of park visitors waiting for a ride. Make a line graph on your calculator.

Riders	Wait Time
10	1
20	1.5
30	2.5
40	3

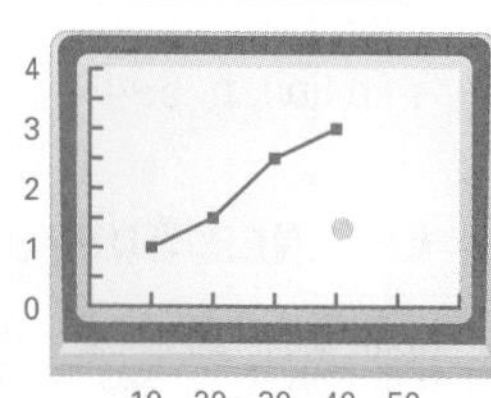

1. See Additional Answers beginning on page AA1.

12.3 Technology Activity

GRAPHING CALCULATOR

Making Data Displays

GOAL Use a graphing calculator to create data displays.

Example 1 **The table shows the cost, in dollars, of a phone call, based on the length, in minutes, of the call. Make a scatter plot or a line graph on your calculator.**

Minutes	Cost
5	0.5
10	1
15	1.5
20	2
25	2.4
30	2.7

Solution

1 Enter the data into two lists.

L1	L2	L3
5	.5	
10	1	
15	1.5	
20	2	
25	2.4	
30	2.7	

L2(5)=2.4

2 Choose maximums and minimums for the window.

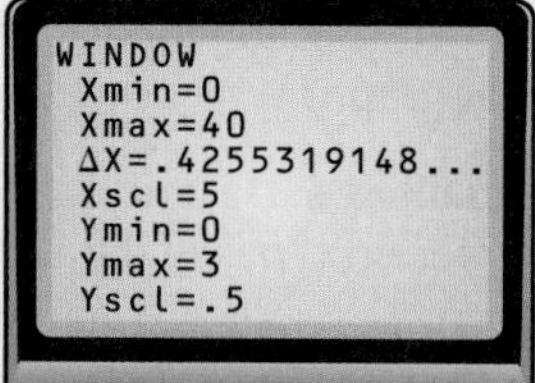

3 Choose a display from the PLOT menu and set the Xlist and Ylist.

Choose [scatter icon] for a scatter plot or [line icon] for a line graph.

4 Press GRAPH to show the display you have chosen.

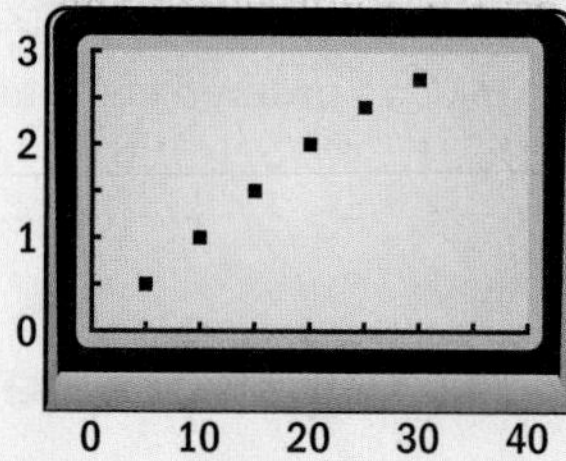

Your turn now **Make a scatter plot and a line graph of the data.** See margin.

1.

Year	1997	1998	1999	2000	2001
Rainfall (in.)	21.4	39.8	34.5	26.1	44.9

ILLINOIS Standards and ISAT:
10.A.3a

Example 2

The table shows the number of people out of 200 surveyed who prefer each type of music. You can use a graphing calculator to make a circle graph of the data.

Pop	75
Rock	62
Country	43
Classical	20

Solution

1 Press LIST. Then use the TEXT menu to name a list and its categories. Use quotation marks for the first item, so the calculator recognizes that the list is *categorical* (contains words).

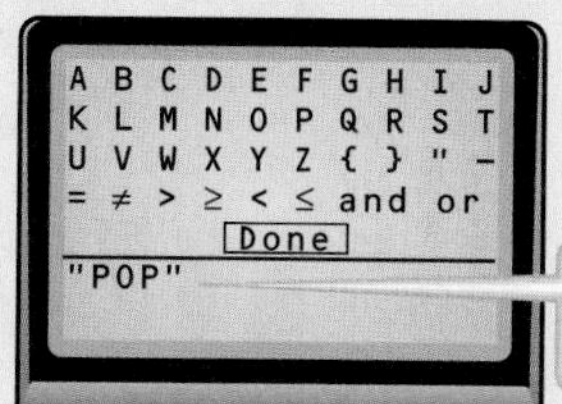

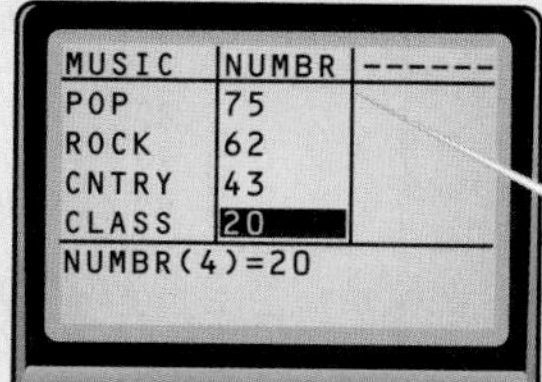

2 Use the PLOT menu to choose the two lists.

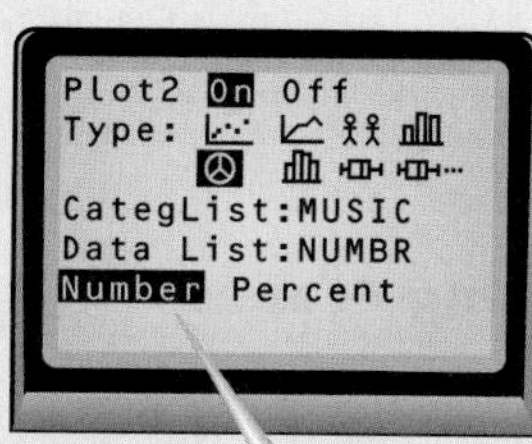

3 Press GRAPH to display the circle graph.

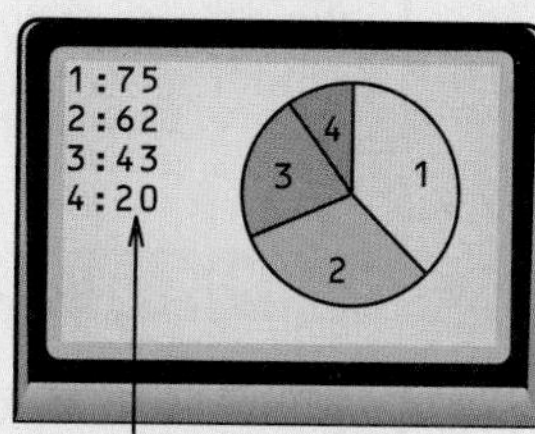

Your turn now **Make a circle graph of the survey data.** 2–3. See margin.

2.

Did You Get Enough Sleep?	
Need more	541
Need less	167
Just right	282
Don't know	21

3.

The last movie I saw I watched...	
in a theater.	410
on a television.	483
on a computer.	21

EXTRA EXAMPLES

Example 2 The table shows the number of people out of 200 surveyed who preferred each type of vacation. Use a graphing calculator to make a circle graph of the data.

Destination	Number
Camping	26
Beach	82
Skiing	54
Theme park	38

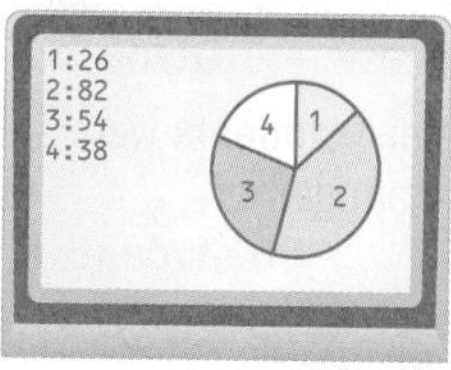

3 CLOSE

Assessment

1. Explain why you do not need to calculate degree measures when you make circle graphs on a calculator. **The calculator finds the degree measures based on the data you enter.**
2. Do the data totals have to sum to 100 when you make circle graphs on a calculator? Why or why not? **No; the data total does not matter for a circle graph.**

2.

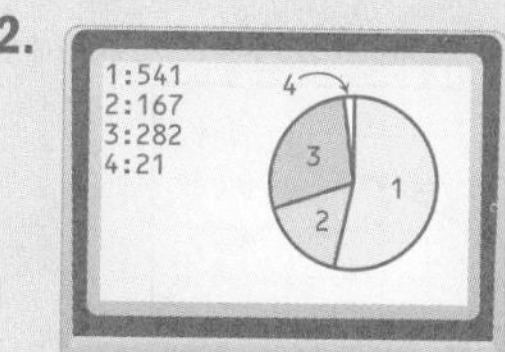

3.

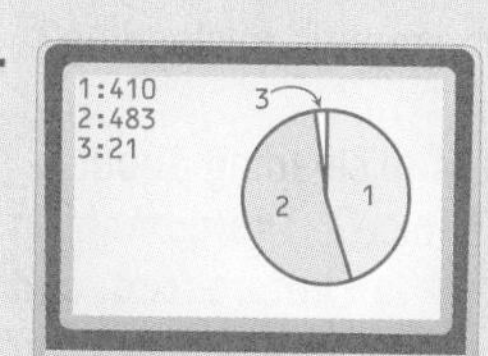

1 PLAN

SKILL CHECK

Use the bar graph to answer the questions.

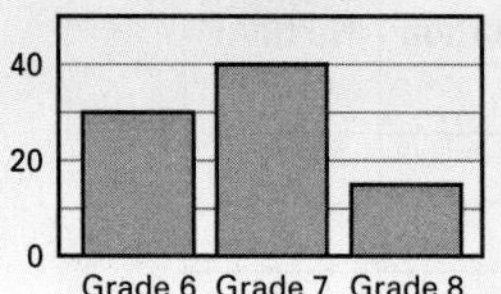

1. Which grade had the most absentees? **Grade 7**
2. How many students were absent altogether? **85 students**

LESSON OBJECTIVE

Identify and analyze misleading graphs.

2 TEACH

EXTRA EXAMPLES

Examples 1 and 2 The line graphs below display the increase in subscribers to an online service.

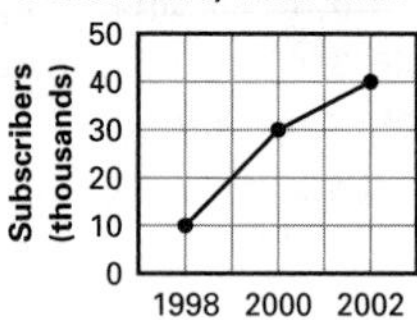

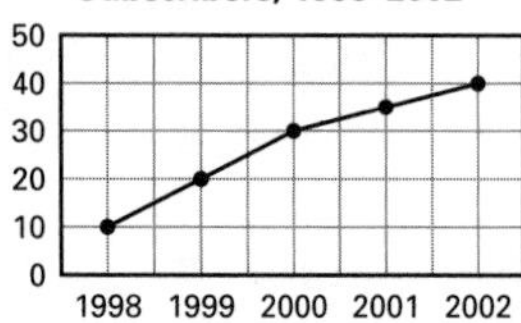

a. Which graph is misleading? **graph A**

b. What is misleading about your choice? **The domain in graph A is compressed, and every other year is excluded so the graph rises faster.**

Misleading Graphs

GOAL Identify and analyze misleading graphs.

Word Watch

Review Words

bar graph, p. 5
line graph, p. 606

When you analyze a graph to make conclusions based on the data displayed, it is important to be aware that the display may be misleading.

EXAMPLE 1 Identifying a Misleading Graph

Attendance Which of the bar graphs that show attendance at an annual rock festival from 1998 to 2002 could be misleading?

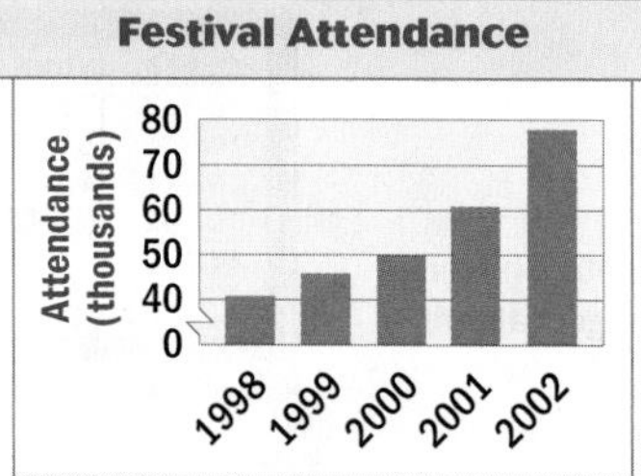

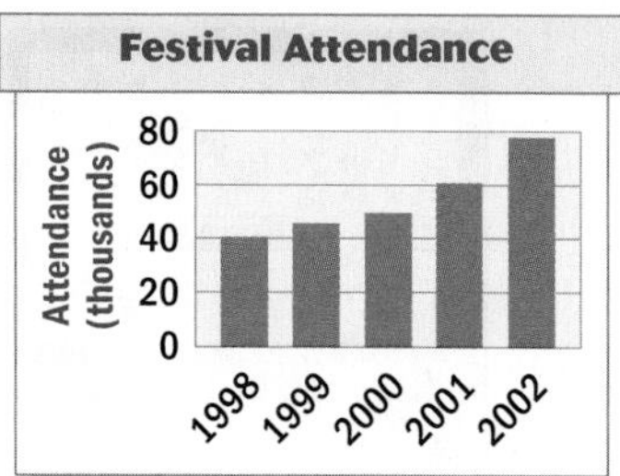

HELP with Solving

Remember that the broken axis symbol indicates that some of the values in the axis have been left out.

The first graph has a break in the vertical axis, so comparing the bars may lead to incorrect conclusions. It looks as if attendance in 2002 was about three times as great as in 1998, but attendance only doubled during this time. The second graph is less likely to mislead.

EXAMPLE 2 Analyzing Misleading Graphs

Business The line graphs below display a company's profits and sales for each year from 1998 to 2002. What is misleading about each graph?

a.

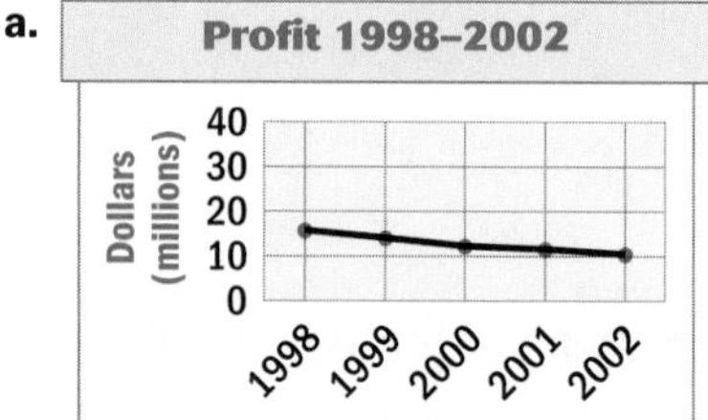

b.

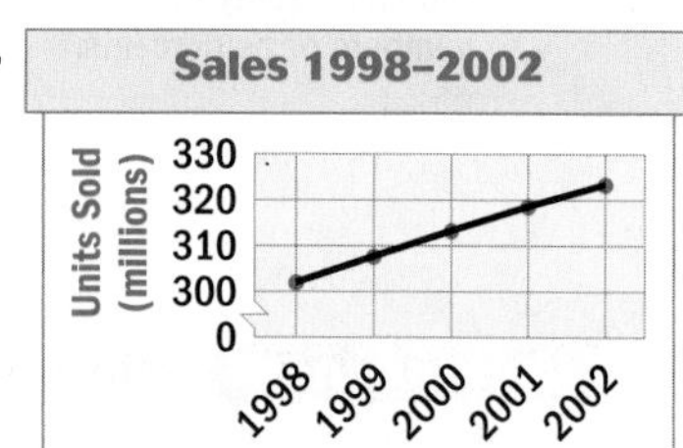

Solution

a. The range of values on the vertical scale is larger than needed. The graph suggests that profits have decreased only slightly, when they have decreased by a third.

b. Because the vertical axis starts at 300, it looks as if sales have risen rapidly. An unbroken axis would show that sales have risen slowly, at less than 2% per year.

ILLINOIS Standards and ISAT:
10.A.3a, 10.A.3c

EXAMPLE 3 Misleading Comparisons

Compare the average monthly temperatures at two resorts.

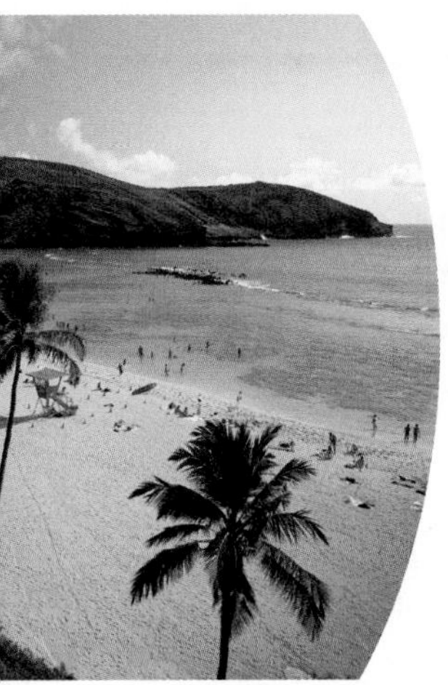

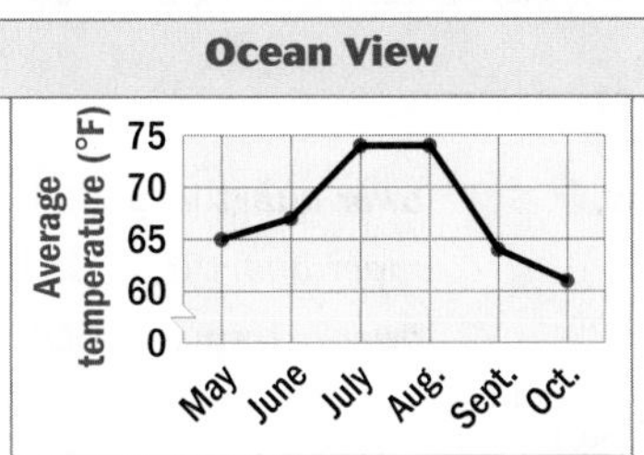

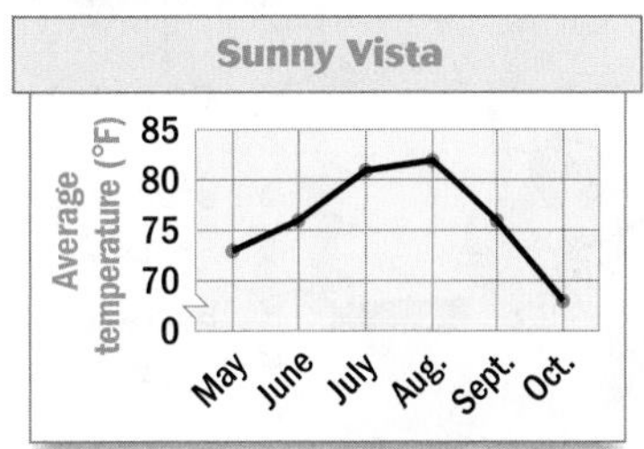

At a glance, the displays suggest that the temperatures are about the same, but the vertical axes are different. When data for both resorts are graphed together, it becomes clear that Sunny Vista has warmer temperatures.

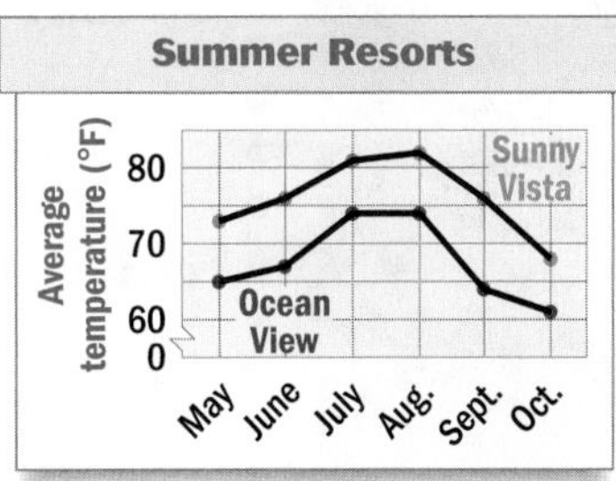

EXTRA EXAMPLES

Example 3 The line graphs below compare the sales for two competitors. Explain what is misleading about the comparison. How would you combine the graphs so they are not misleading?

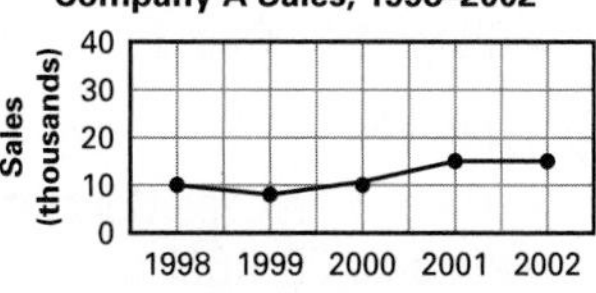

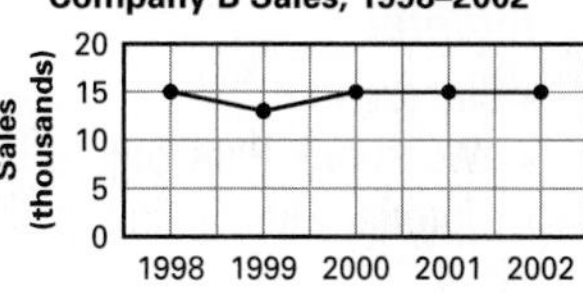

The graphs have different vertical scales. If company B's data were added to company A's graph, the difference in sales would be shown to be much less significant.

Exercises

Tell whether the data are represented clearly. If the graph is misleading, explain why. Then redraw the graph so that it is not misleading.

1.

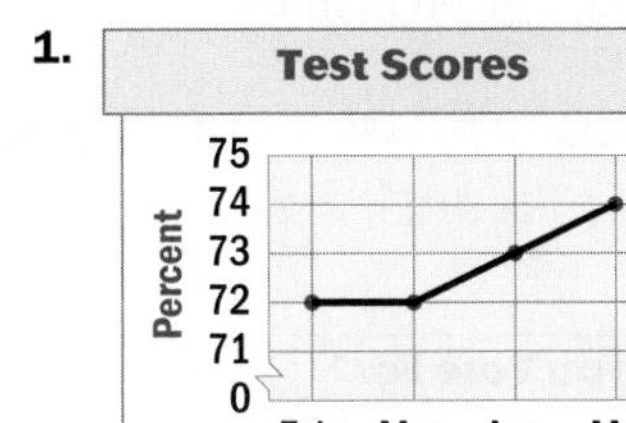

2.

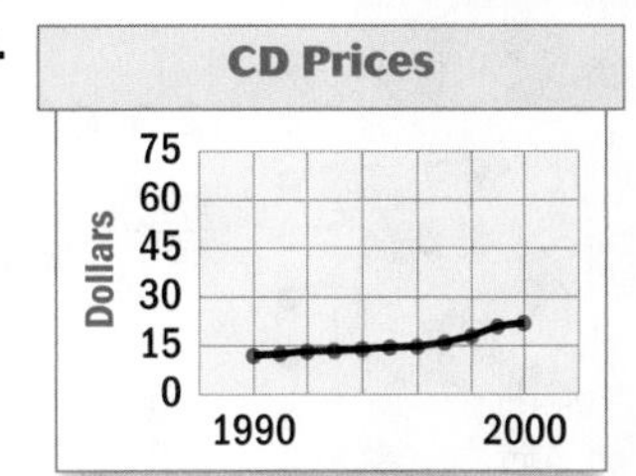

3. Baseball The table below shows a baseball pitcher's wins and losses per season. Make a graph that shows a positive performance. Then make another graph that shows a negative performance. **See margin.**

Year	1998	1999	2000	2001	2002
Wins	6	8	10	12	16
Losses	7	9	9	13	14

1. No. *Sample answer:* **There is a break in the vertical scale, so the relative change is smaller than it appears. See margin for art.**
2. No. *Sample answer:* **The range of values on the vertical axis is greater than needed. It appears that the price rises are slight, but prices have nearly doubled during the period shown. See margin for art.**

3 APPLY

TRANSPARENCY

Even-numbered answers are available on transparencies. Support transparencies are available for Exercise 3.

TEACHING TIP

In Exercise 2, students may need help understanding why this graph is misleading. Ask students whether \$0–\$75 is a reasonable range for CD prices between 1990 and 2000.

1–3. See Additional Answers beginning on page AA1.

ADDITIONAL RESOURCES

The following resources are available to help review the materials in Lessons 12.1–12.3.

Chapter 12 Resource Book
- Lesson Practice
- Study Guide

Assessment Book
- Chapter 12 Quiz 1

Technology
- Test and Practice Generator
- eTutorial CD-ROM

Internet
- Classzone
- eWorkbook Plus Online
- eTutorial Plus Online

ENGLISH LEARNER SUPPORT

- Spanish Study Guide
- Multi-Language Glossary
- Chapter Audio Summaries CDs

2.

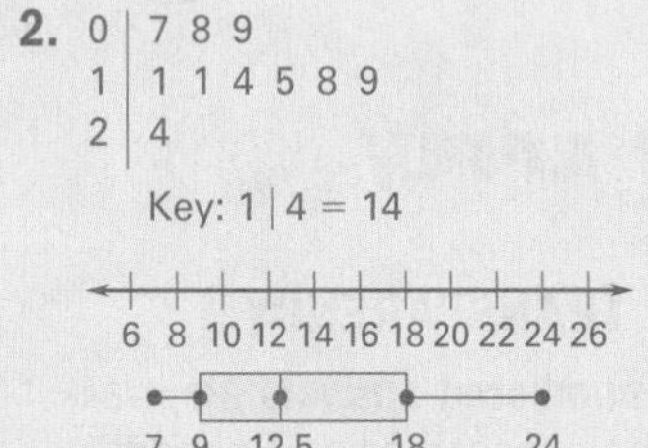

Notebook Review

Review the vocabulary definitions in your notebook.

Copy the review examples in your notebook. Then complete the exercises.

Check Your Definitions

stem-and-leaf plot, p. 597
box-and-whisker plot, p. 601
lower quartile, p. 601
upper quartile, p. 601
lower extreme, p. 601
upper extreme, p. 601
circle graph, p. 605
line graph, p. 606

Use Your Vocabulary

1. Copy and complete: The _?_ is the least value in a data set and the _?_ is the greatest value in the data set. **lower extreme, upper extreme**

12.1–12.2 Can you order and display data?

EXAMPLE Order the data set 24, 29, 35, 32, 22, 20, 43, 27, 41, 31, 26 in a stem-and-leaf plot. Then make a box-and-whisker plot of the data.

2 | 0 2 4 6 7 9
3 | 1 2 5
4 | 1 3
Key: 4 | 1 = 41

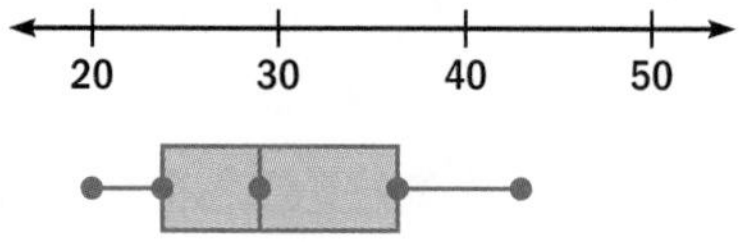

(Box-and-whisker plot on number line: 20, 30, 40, 50)

2. Make an ordered stem-and-leaf plot and a box-and-whisker plot of the wind speed data, given in miles per hour: 9, 15, 8, 19, 11, 18, 11, 24, 7, 14. **See margin.**

12.3 Can you use appropriate data displays?

EXAMPLES

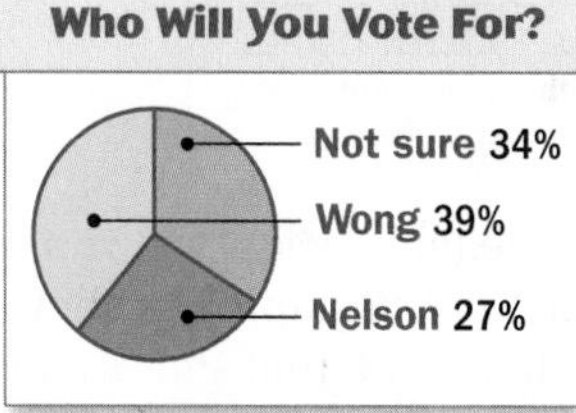

Use a circle graph to represent data as parts of a whole.

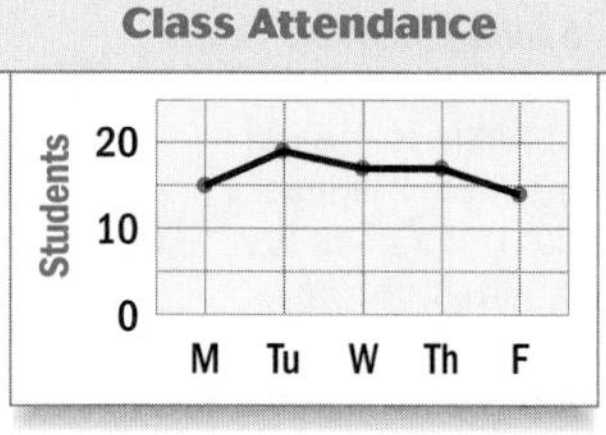

Use a line graph to display changes in a quantity over time.

 **3.** Make a circle graph of survey results where 24% of the people surveyed said *no*, 47% said *yes*, and the rest said *not sure.* **See margin.**

4. The hourly temperatures, in degrees Celsius, starting at 1 P.M. were 33°C, 33°C, 34°C, 37°C, 37°C, and 36°C. Make a line graph of the data. **See margin.**

Stop and Think about Lessons 12.1–12.3

5. Writing Describe some real-world data that a double stem-and-leaf plot would help you analyze. ***Sample answer:* Movie attendance each night for two weeks**

6. Critical Thinking Could you display the data from Exercise 3 in a line graph? Explain. What other type of display could be useful? **No; it does not show data that vary over time; bar graph.**

Review Quiz 1

1. Attendance Make an ordered double stem-and-leaf plot comparing the ballpark attendance data below for April and June. Then make a pair of box-and-whisker plots that compare the data. Use the displays to compare April attendance to June attendance. **See margin.**

April: 1025, 1058, 1030, 997, 990, 1116, 1001, 995, 1122, 1099

June: 1056, 1125, 1151, 1048, 1123, 1097, 1042, 1164, 1125, 1131

2. Nuts Consumption of peanuts per person in the United States was as follows: 1995, 5.7 lb; 1996, 5.7 lb; 1997, 5.9 lb; 1998, 5.9 lb; 1999, 6.4 lb. Make a circle graph or a line graph of the data. Explain your choice. **See margin.**

Safe Cracker

Use the box-and-whisker plot to find the missing leaves in the stem-and-leaf plot of the same group of eight numbers. Take the numbers that the missing leaves represent, and put them in order from least to greatest to find the combination that opens the safe. **6, 4, 6; 16-24-36**

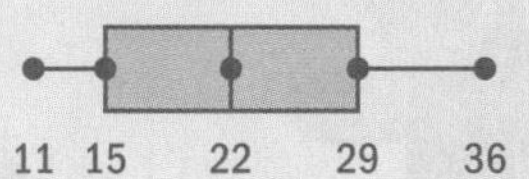

1	1 4 ?
2	0 ? 7
3	1 ?

Key: 1 | 4 = 14

Notebook Review

3.

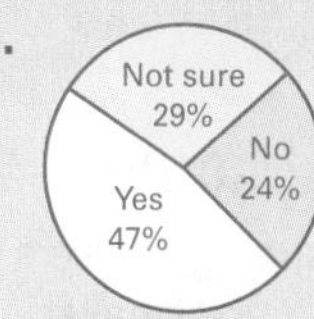

4.

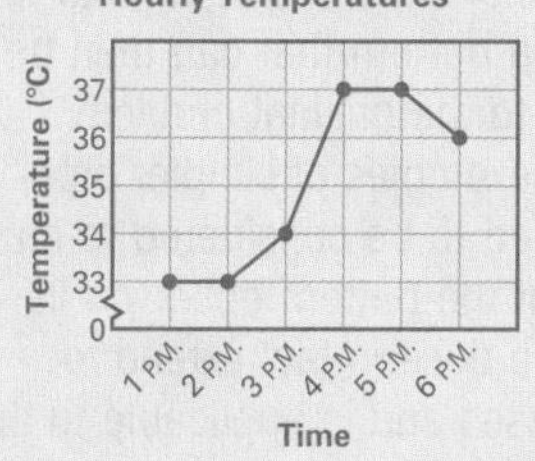

Review Quiz 1

1.

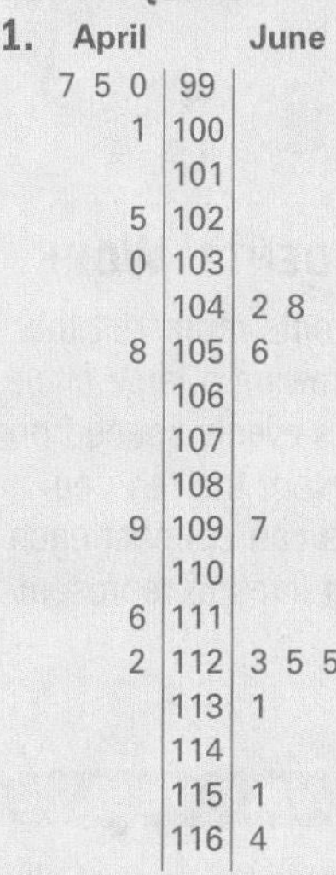

April		June
7 5 0	99	
1	100	
	101	
5	102	
0	103	
	104	2 8
8	105	6
	106	
	107	
	108	
9	109	7
	110	
6	111	
2	112	3 5 5
	113	1
	114	
	115	1
	116	4

Key: 2 | 112 | 3 = 1122 and 1123

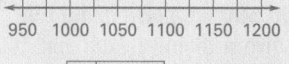

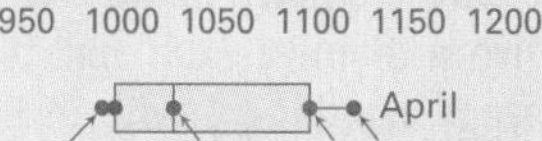

June
1042 1056 1124 1131 1164

***Sample answer:* As a whole, June had higher attendance than April. It had the 5 highest attendances, while April had the 5 lowest attendances.**

2. See Additional Answers beginning on page AA1.

1 PLAN

STRATEGY BACKGROUND

The purpose of the strategy Solve a Simpler Problem is to use smaller numbers or simpler diagrams to identify a pattern that can then be applied to the original problem. Several examples of simpler problems need to be considered to make sure that the pattern observed in one case does in fact extend to other cases and is applicable to the original problem.

2 TEACH

GUIDING STUDENTS' WORK

Suggest that students represent the handshakes by drawing a large circle and placing points evenly spaced on the circle to represent the ten people. Then students can connect each pair of points with lines to represent each handshake.

EXTRA EXAMPLES

Example What is the sum of all the numbers from 1 to 1000? **500,500 (To solve using the "Solve a Simpler Problem" strategy, combine 1 with 999, 2 with 998, etc., down to 499 + 501, which gives you 499,000. Then add 500 and 1000 to get 500,500.)**

12.4 Problem Solving Strategies

- Guess, Check, and Revise
- Look for a Pattern
- Draw a Diagram
- Act It Out
- Solve a Simpler Problem
- Work Backward
- Make a Table

Solve a Simpler Problem

Problem There are 10 people in a room. They introduce themselves to each other by shaking every other person's hand one time. How many handshakes occur?

1 Read and Understand

Read the problem carefully.

You know that 10 people in a room each shake every other person's hand.

You want to find the total number of handshakes.

2 Make a Plan

Decide on a strategy to use.

By solving a series of simpler problems, you can identify a pattern in the number of handshakes. Then you can extend the pattern to find how many handshakes occur among 10 people.

3 Solve the Problem

Reread the problem and solve a simpler problem.

First, find the number of handshakes between 2 people, 3 people, and so on. You can do this by drawing a diagram. Make a table of your results.

Number of people	2	3	4	5
Number of handshakes	1	3	6	10
Pattern		+2	+3	+4

Extend the pattern to find the number of handshakes among 10 people.

1, 3, 6, 10, 15, 21, 28, 36, 45

+5 +6 +7 +8 +9

ANSWER So, 45 handshakes occur when 10 people shake hands.

4 Look Back

Double-check your calculations to be sure you didn't make any mistakes. You can also use the strategy *act it out* to check your answer.

ILLINOIS Standards and ISAT:
6.B.3a, 6.C.3a

Practice the Strategy

Use the strategy *solve a simpler problem*.

1. **Restaurants** A restaurant has 28 square tables that seat one person per side. You can join tables together. How many people can fit at two long tables made from all 28 tables? Will it make a difference if the tables are not divided equally? **60 people; no**

2. **Triangular Numbers** The dots arranged in a triangle represent triangular numbers.

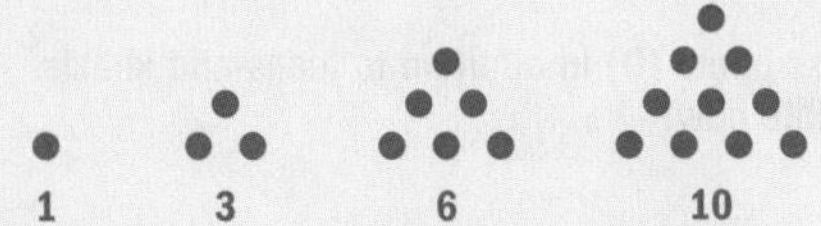

Predict the number of dots in the eighth triangular number. **36 dots**

3. **Tournament** You are planning a small tournament for a chess club. If each of five members plays one game against each of the other members, how many games must you schedule? **10 games**

4. **House Numbers** The houses on Stanford Street are numbered consecutively from 10 to 132. How many of each digit do you need to form all the house numbers? **23 0's, 66 1's, 33 2's, 25 3's, 22 each of 4–9**

5. **Odd Numbers** Find the sum of the first 50 odd whole numbers. **2500**

6. **Marching Band** A marching band is in a triangular formation. There is 1 band member in the front row. Each of the other rows contains 2 more band members than the row in front of it. There are 11 rows in all. How many band members are there? **121 band members**

7. **Palindromes** A palindrome is a number that reads the same backward and forward. For example, the number 1 and the number 414 are both palindromes. How many palindromes are there from 1 to 500? **58 palindromes**

Mixed Problem Solving

Use any strategy to solve the problem.

8. **Walking** Jay and Paul start walking in opposite directions. Jay walks 0.75 mile every 12 minutes, and Paul walks 2.5 miles every 30 minutes. How far apart are they after 1.5 hours? **13.125 mi**

9. **Games** What is the total number of squares on the checkerboard? Include squares of all sizes. **55 squares**

10. **Prisms** How does doubling the height of each base of a triangular prism affect its volume? How does halving the height of each base affect the volume? **It doubles the volume; it halves the volume.**

11. **Calendars** What day of the week is the 3117th day after Thursday? **Saturday**

12. **Checking Account** The list below shows deposits and withdrawals this month. If Rodney has $57.68 in his checking account now, how much money did he have before Week 1? **$103.18**

Week 1: He bought a shirt for $18 and a pair of pants for $26.

Week 2: He bought a CD for $14 and lunch for $7.50.

Week 3: He deposited $20.

3 APPLY

Transparency

Even-numbered answers are available on transparencies.

Teaching Tip

In Exercise 2, suggest that students write the triangular numbers across a page in a line. Then underneath and between each pair of numbers, students can record the difference between the pairs. Encourage students to write out their conjectures.

Common Error

In Exercise 7, students may think that a palindrome means a number that appears the same in a mirror, as the number 1 can. Address this possible misunderstanding and point out that all the single digits are palindromes.

Suggested Strategies

You may wish to suggest the following strategies for the problems in the Mixed Problem Solving:

- Exercise 8: Draw a Diagram; Solve a Simpler Problem
- Exercise 9: Make a Table; Draw a Diagram; Solve a Simpler Problem
- Exercise 10: Guess, Check, and Revise; Draw a Diagram
- Exercise 11: Look for a Pattern; Solve a Simpler Problem
- Exercise 12: Work Backward

SKILL CHECK

Evaluate.

1. 14^2 196
2. $2^5 \cdot 26^3$ 562,432
3. $\frac{1}{5} \cdot \frac{1}{5} \cdot \frac{1}{5}$ $\frac{1}{125}$
4. $\frac{4}{6^4}$ $\frac{1}{324}$

LESSON OBJECTIVE

Use counting methods to count the number of choices.

PACING

Suggested Number of Days

Basic Course: 1 day

Average Course: 1 day

Advanced Course: 1 day

Block: 0.5 block with 12.3

TEACHING RESOURCES

For a complete list of Teaching Resources, see page 594B.

Warm-Up Exercises for this lesson are available on a transparency.

MOTIVATING THE LESSON

Ask students to describe a time when they were overwhelmed with the number of possible choices they had to choose from.

ACTIVITY

Goal Count choices using a list.

Key Discovery A large number of choices can be displayed and organized using a list.

Counting Methods

BEFORE	Now	WHY?
You found theoretical and experimental probability.	You will use counting methods to count the number of choices.	So you can count the outcomes of an election, as in Ex. 12.

Word Watch

tree diagram, p. 618

Activity You can count choices using an organized list.

You are choosing an outfit. You can choose a T-shirt (T), a button-down shirt (B), or a sweater (S) as a top and jeans (J) or khakis (K) for pants.

jeans (J) khakis (K)  T-shirt (T)  button-down (B)  sweater (S)

1. Use the letters to represent possible outfits. One possible outfit is JT, which means jeans and a T-shirt. Make a list of all possible outfits. JT, JB, JS, KT, KB, KS
2. You decide to consider dress pants (D) in addition to jeans and khakis. How many outfits are possible now? 9 outfits
3. You also decide to include socks as part of the outfit. You can choose between red (R) and green (G). How many outfits are possible now? 18 outfits

In the activity, you made lists to count the number of choices. Another way to count the number of choices is to use a **tree diagram**.

EXAMPLE 1 **Making a Tree Diagram**

You can use a tree diagram to count the number of possible outfits in Step 2 of the activity above.

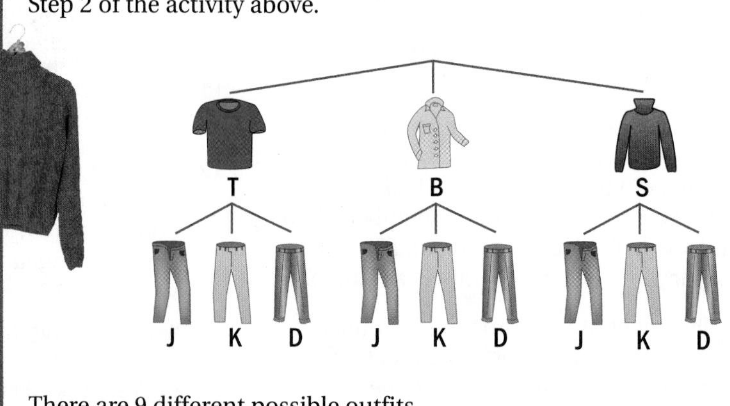

There are 9 different possible outfits.

ILLINOIS Standards and ISAT:
10.C.3a

Another way to count choices is to use the *counting principle.*

The Counting Principle

If one event can occur in m ways, and for each of these a second event can occur in n ways, then the number of ways that the two events can occur together is $m \cdot n$.

This principle can be extended to three or more events.

EXAMPLE 2 Using the Counting Principle

Skateboards To build a skateboard, you can choose one deck and one type of wheel assembly from those shown. To count the number of different skateboards you can build, use the counting principle.

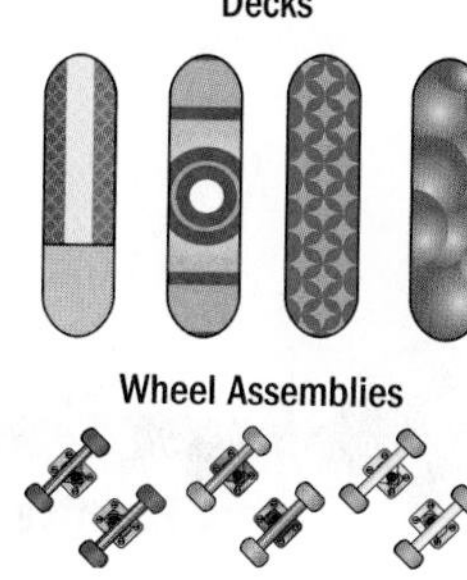

$\underset{\text{decks}}{4} \cdot \underset{\text{wheel assemblies}}{3} = 12$ **Counting principle**

ANSWER You can build 12 different skateboards.

EXAMPLE 3 Using the Counting Principle

Passwords You are choosing a password that starts with 3 letters and then has 2 digits. How many different passwords are possible?

Solution

$\underbrace{26 \cdot 26 \cdot 26}_{\text{letters}} \cdot \underbrace{10 \cdot 10}_{\text{digits}} = 1{,}757{,}600$ **Counting principle**

ANSWER There are 1,757,600 different possible passwords.

Your turn now **Count the choices.**

1. Your soccer team's uniform choices include yellow and green shirts, white, black, and green shorts, and four colors of socks. Use a tree diagram to find how many different uniforms are possible. **24 uniforms**
2. In Example 3, suppose that the passwords may not start with an A or use the digit 0. How many different passwords are possible? Explain. **1,368,900 passwords. *Sample answer:* There are 25 choices for the first letter, 26 for each of the next two letters, and 9 for each of the digits.**

TIPS FOR NEW TEACHERS

Stress the importance of thinking methodically about how to represent and list choices. See Tips for New Teachers in the *Chapter 12 Resource Book*.

EXTRA EXAMPLES

Example 1 A sandwich cart offers 3 types of bread, 2 types of filling, and 2 types of drink. Make a tree diagram to count the number of possible sandwich-drink combinations.

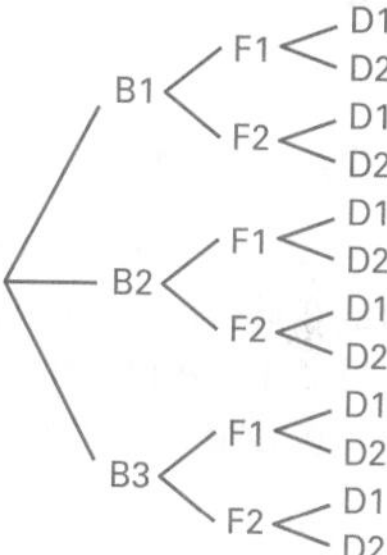

12 combinations

Example 2 There are 4 possible flights Saraj can take to Boston on Thursday and 6 possible flights she can take home. Use the counting principle to find the number of different trips she can choose from. **24 trips**

Example 3 You are choosing a personal identification number (PIN) for a debit card. The PIN must be four digits long. How many different PINs are possible? **10^4, or 10,000 PINs**

MULTIPLE REPRESENTATIONS

Using an example in the text, work a problem twice on the board first using a tree diagram and then the counting principle. Point out the connection between the two methods. Work a more complicated problem with the counting principle, and have students predict how large the corresponding tree diagram would be.

EXTRA EXAMPLES

Example 4 You roll a number cube five times in a row. What is the probability that you roll a 4 each time? $\frac{1}{7776}$

CONCEPT CHECK

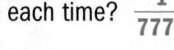

Madison is using the counting principle, and she writes $d \cdot g$. What do d and g represent? **The d represents the number of times the first event can occur, and the g represents the number of times the second event can occur.**

DAILY PUZZLER

You roll a number cube three times in a row. Is it more likely that you roll a 5 each time or a 1 the first time, a 2 the second time, and a 3 the third time? **Each case is equally likely.**

EXAMPLE 4 Finding a Probability

Number Cubes You and three friends each roll a number cube. What is the probability that you each roll the same number?

(1) List the *favorable* outcomes. There are 6:

1-1-1-1 2-2-2-2 3-3-3-3 4-4-4-4 5-5-5-5 6-6-6-6

(2) Use the counting principle to find the number of *possible* outcomes.

$$\underbrace{6 \cdot 6 \cdot 6 \cdot 6}_{\text{4 number cubes}} = 1296$$

(3) Then use the formula for finding probability.

$$\frac{\text{Number of favorable outcomes}}{\text{Number of possible outcomes}} = \frac{6}{1296} = \frac{1}{216}$$

ANSWER The probability that you each roll the same number is $\frac{1}{216}$.

with Review

For help with probability, see p. 354.

12.4 Exercises

More Practice, p. 738

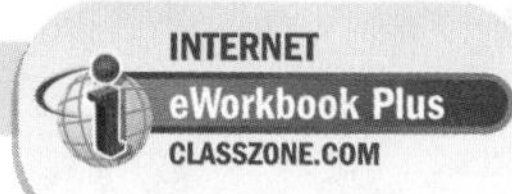

Getting Ready to Practice

1. **Vocabulary** Copy and complete: If there are m ways that one event can occur and for each of those there are n ways that a second event can occur, then there are _?_ ways that the two events can occur together. $m \cdot n$

Make a tree diagram to find the number of choices that are possible. Then check your answer using the counting principle.

2. Choose apple, blueberry, lemon, or cherry pie with juice or tea. **8 choices**
3. Choose a small, medium, or large shirt in red, yellow, or blue. **9 choices**
4. Choose a car or truck with a tape player or a CD player. **4 choices**
5. Choose a hat or scarf in gray, white, or black. **6 choices**
6. **Weekend Plans** You would like to go to the movies, a play, or the zoo. You can invite your cousin or your best friend. You can go on Friday or Saturday. Make a tree diagram to list all of the possibilities. Then use the counting principle to check your answer. **12 possibilities**
7. **Movies** You and three friends all go to the movies on Friday night. You each pick a movie at random from the four choices. What is the probability that you all pick the same movie to see? $\frac{1}{64}$

Practice and Problem Solving

with Homework

Example	Exercises
1	8-12, 14, 17
2	8-14, 18
3	8-14, 18
4	15-16

Online Resources
CLASSZONE.COM
- More Examples
- eTutorial Plus

In Exercises 8–11, make a tree diagram to find the number of choices that are possible. Then check your answer using the counting principle.

A **8.** Choose a red, green, blue, or gray ball with a black or silver racquet. 8 choices

9. Choose one of 6 DVDs and one of 4 CDs. 24 choices

10. Choose one of 5 essays and one of 3 extra credit questions. 15 choices

11. Choose a city tour or a park tour with passes to the art or science museum and a trip to the zoo, baseball game, movies, or mall. 16 choices

12. Class Election The lists show the candidates for offices in a class election. Make a tree diagram to find the number of different ways a president, treasurer, and secretary can be chosen. Then use the counting principle to check your answer. 30 ways

President	Treasurer	Secretary
☐ Amy	☐ Jessica	☐ Scott
☐ Hector	☐ Michael	☐ Nicole
	☐ Carson	☐ Thomas
		☐ Angela
		☐ Isabel

13. Banking You open a bank account and need to choose a password with 4 characters that can repeat. The password starts with 3 digits and then has 1 letter. How many different passwords are possible? 26,000 passwords

14. Writing There are 5 CDs and 4 books that you are interested in buying. Describe how to find the number of different pairs of 1 CD and 1 book that you can buy. *Sample answer:* Draw a tree diagram to list and then count all of the possibilities or use the counting principle.

15. Coins Six people all flip a coin. What is the probability that they all get heads? $\frac{1}{64}$

B **16. States** You and Terry randomly choose the name of a state. What is the probability that you both choose a state whose name starts with a T? (Tennessee and Texas are the two states that start with the letter T.) $\frac{1}{625}$

Extended Problem Solving You are at a grocery store buying flavored water. You can choose lime, lemon, cherry, or orange. You can choose a 0.5-liter, 1-liter, or 2-liter bottle.

17. Draw Make a tree diagram that shows all of the different bottles of flavored water that you can choose. See margin.

18. Multiply How many total different bottles can you choose from if 5 new flavors become available? 27 bottles

19. Challenge The sign shows the prices for each bottle size. What are the different total prices that you could be charged for three bottles? What is largest total quantity of water you can buy if you have only $2.60?

Water Sale
0.5 liter — $0.59
1 liter — $0.69
2 liter — $0.99

19. $1.77, $1.87, $1.97, $2.07, $2.17, $2.27, $2.37, $2.57, $2.67, $2.97; two 2-liter bottles and one 0.5-liter bottle

3 APPLY

ASSIGNMENT GUIDE

Basic Course
Day 1: pp. 621-622 Exs. 8-13, 15-18, 24-29

Average Course
Day 1: pp. 621-622 Exs. 10-18, 20-22, 24-29

Advanced Course
Day 1: pp. 621-622 Exs. 10-14, 16-24*, 27-29

Block
pp. 621-622 Exs. 10-18, 20-22, 24-29 (with 12.3)

Extra Practice

- Student Edition, p. 738
- Chapter 12 Resource Book, pp. 33-35
- Test and Practice Generator

Transparency

Even-numbered answers are available on transparencies.

Homework Check

When you review students' homework for this lesson, go over the following exercises to check understanding of key concepts.
Basic: 8, 10, 13, 15, 17
Average: 10, 12, 14, 15, 17
Advanced: 10, 12, 14, 16, 18

17.

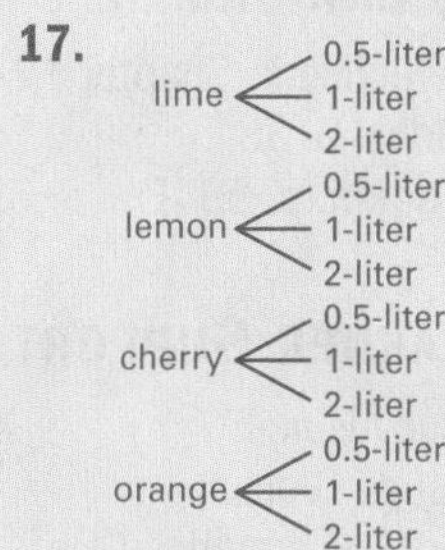

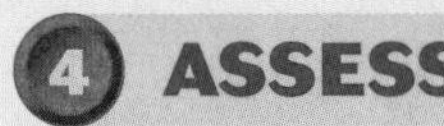

Assessment Resources

For more assessment resources, see:
- Assessment Book
- Test and Practice Generator

Mini-Quiz

1. Cedric is choosing from three apartment layouts, each with or without a washer/dryer. How many apartment choices does he have? **6 choices**
2. A DVD has three audio channels and four language subtitles. How many channel and subtitle choices are there? **12 choices**
3. A supplier offers three sizes of inkjet cartridges. If Jeff and Tia each choose a cartridge at random, what is the probability both choose the smallest cartridge? $\frac{1}{9}$

Reteaching/Remediation

- Study Guide in Chapter 12 Resource Book, pp. 36–37
- Tutor Place, Fractions Cards 19, 20, Ratio, Proportion, and Percent Card 16
- eTutorial Plus Online
- Extra Practice, p. 738
- Lesson Practice in Chapter 12 Resource Book, pp. 33–35

Challenge/Enrichment

- Challenge Practice in Chapter 12 Resource Book, p. 38
- Teacher's Edition, p. 594F

English Learner Support

- Spanish Study Guide
- Multi-Language Glossary
- Chapter Audio Summaries CDs

27, 29. See Additional Answers beginning on page AA1.

20. $\frac{2}{3}$. *Sample answer:* There are 6 possible outcomes, 2 of which are all boys or all girls, so $6 - 2 = 4$ include at least one boy and one girl.

23. Yes; the number of symbols possible with 5 raised dots and 1 position without a dot is 6, because there are 6 different positions that could possibly be without a dot. The number of symbols possible with 1 raised dot and 5 positions without a dot is also 6, because there are 6 different positions for the single raised dot.

20. **Solve a Simpler Problem** If you have 5 cousins, and the probability that a cousin is a boy is 0.5, what is the probability that there is at least one boy and at least one girl among the cousins? Explain how you used a simpler problem to get your answer. (*Hint:* How many of the possible outcomes do *not* include both a boy and a girl?)

21. **Critical Thinking** A restaurant has 36 possible meal specials that you can choose. A meal has a main course, a vegetable, and a dessert. The restaurant has 6 different main courses and 2 different vegetables. How many different desserts does it have? **3 desserts**

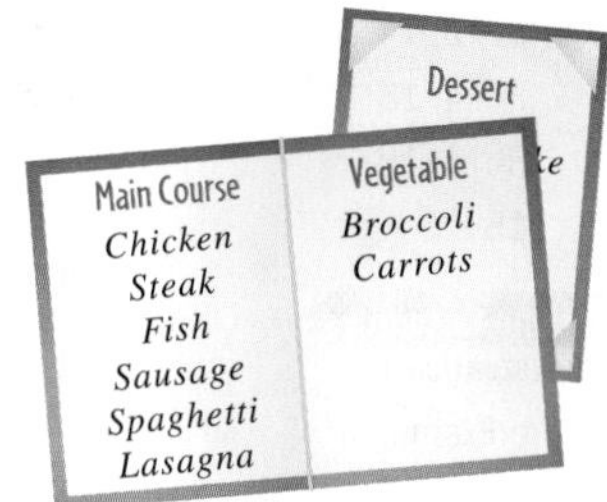

Braille In Exercises 22 and 23, use the following information.

Braille uses arrangements of raised dots to form symbols that represent letters, numbers, and punctuation marks. Braille is read by touching the symbols. Each symbol is a cell of 6 dots arranged in 3 rows of 2. In the cell, certain dots are raised to make a particular symbol.

C 22. How many different Braille symbols are possible? How many symbols are possible with no raised dots? With 6 raised dots? **64 symbols; 1 symbol; 1 symbol**

23. Are the number of symbols possible with one raised dot the same as the number of symbols possible with 5 raised dots? Explain.

Mixed Review 

Find the slope of the line passing through the points. *(Lesson 11.6)*

24. (5, 2), (−4, 2) **0**
25. (−2, 3), (4, 6) $\frac{1}{2}$
26. (3, 1), (7, −2) $-\frac{3}{4}$
27. The ages, in years, of youth group members are 12, 9, 8, 16, 12, 13, 8, 10, 11, and 17. Make a box-and-whisker plot of the data. *(Lesson 12.2)* **See margin.**

Test-Taking Practice 

28. **Multiple Choice** Your computer password has three digits. Which of the expressions would you use to find the total number of possible passwords? **B**

    A. $10 + 10 + 10$ **B.** $10 \cdot 10 \cdot 10$ **C.** $10 + 3$ **D.** $10 \cdot 3$

29. **Short Response** You would like a sandwich, a side order, and a drink for lunch. You have a choice of a turkey, tuna, ham, or roast beef sandwich. You may have fruit, salad, or soup as a side order. You may choose juice or iced tea to drink. Make a tree diagram to show all the possible lunches that you can have. Write and evaluate an expression to find the total number of possible lunches. **See margin for art; $4 \cdot 3 \cdot 2 = 24$ lunches.**

Permutations

BEFORE	Now	WHY?
You used the counting principle to count possibilities.	You will use permutations to count possibilities.	So you can count the ways you can knit a hat, as in Ex. 20.

Word Watch

permutation, p. 623
factorial, p. 623

In some arrangements of groups, order is important. For example, the diagram shows the different ways that a group of three dogs could finish first, second, and third at a dog show.

Each arrangement lists the same dogs, but the orders are different. Arrangements such as these are called *permutations.* A **permutation** is an arrangement in which order is important. You can use the counting principle to count permutations.

EXAMPLE 1 Counting Permutations

Music You have five CDs. You can use the counting principle to count the number of permutations of 5 CDs. This is the number of different orders in which you can listen to the CDs.

Choices for 1st CD		Choices for 2nd CD		Choices for 3rd CD		Choices for 4th CD		Choices for 5th CD	
5	•	4	•	3	•	2	•	1	= 120

ANSWER You can listen to the CDs in 120 different orders.

HELP with Solving

You can use $n!$ to find the number of permutations of n objects.

Factorials In Example 1, you evaluated $5 \cdot 4 \cdot 3 \cdot 2 \cdot 1$. You can write $5 \cdot 4 \cdot 3 \cdot 2 \cdot 1$ as 5!, which is read "5 **factorial**."

$5! = 5 \cdot 4 \cdot 3 \cdot 2 \cdot 1$ $\qquad$ $n! = n \cdot (n-1) \cdot (n-2) \cdot \ldots \cdot 1$

The value of 0! is defined to be 1.

Your turn now **Evaluate the factorial.**

1. 3! 6
2. 4! 24
3. 6! 720
4. 1! 1

ILLINOIS Standards and ISAT:
10.C.3a

1 PLAN

SKILL CHECK

1. $7 \cdot 6 \cdot 5$ 210
2. $5 \cdot 4 \cdot 3$ 60
3. $10 \cdot 9 \cdot 8$ 720

LESSON OBJECTIVE

Use permutations to count possibilities.

PACING

Suggested Number of Days
Basic Course: 2 days
Average Course: 2 days
Advanced Course: 2 days
Block: 1 block

TEACHING RESOURCES

For a complete list of Teaching Resources, see page 594B.

TRANSPARENCY

Warm-Up Exercises for this lesson are available on a transparency.

2 TEACH

MOTIVATING THE LESSON

Ask students how the problem of arranging dogs is different from the problem of choosing between different outfits of pants, tops, and shoes.

TIPS FOR NEW TEACHERS

Expect students to wonder why they cannot use tree diagrams in this lesson. Point out that an arrangement in which order is important differs from a random list. See Tips for New Teachers in the *Chapter 12 Resource Book.*

EXTRA EXAMPLES

Example 1 Andre has to read four books this summer. How many different ways can he read the books? **24 ways**

Example 2 Use the counting principle to count how many ways a club president and vice president can be chosen from 72 members. **5112 ways**

Example 3 Four students are selected from 30 band members to receive first, second, third, and fourth place in a music competition. In how many ways can the students be chosen? **657,720 ways**

TEACHING TIP

Students may wonder why $0! = 1$. Point out that when $n = r$ in the permutations formula, ${}_nP_r = \frac{n!}{(n-r)!}$, the denominator becomes 0. By defining 0! as 1, ${}_nP_n = \frac{n!}{0!} = \frac{n!}{1} = n!$ Then, for example, the number of permutations of 5 objects is the same as the number of permutations of 5 objects taken 5 at a time.

CONCEPT CHECK

How can you find the number of permutations of 8 objects taken 2 at a time? **The formula for ${}_8P_2$ gives $\frac{8!}{(8-2)!}$, or $\frac{8!}{6!}$. Cancel 6! from the numerator and denominator to get $8 \cdot 7$, or 56.**

DAILY PUZZLER

Marlene is taking three dogs, Buster, Izzy, and Casey, to the veterinarian. Two dogs can ride on the back seat, and the third can ride up front. How many different ways can Marlene arrange the dogs if Casey and Izzy must be kept apart? **4 ways**

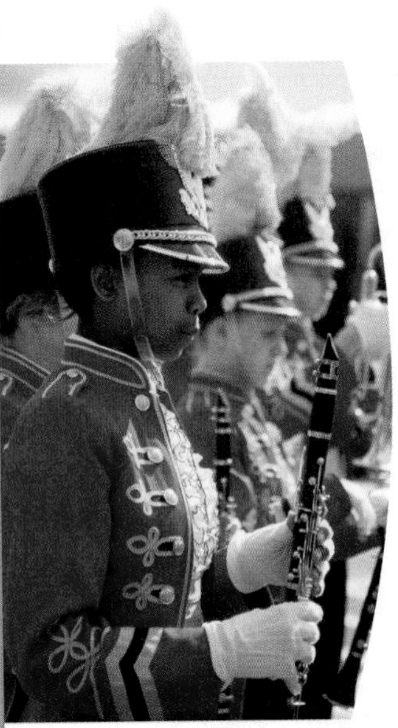

EXAMPLE 2 Counting Permutations

Band Competition Twelve marching bands are entered in a competition. You can use the counting principle to count how many ways first, second, and third places can be awarded.

Choices for 1st place		Choices for 2nd place		Choices for 3rd place		
12	•	11	•	10	= 1320	**Counting principle**

ANSWER There are 1320 ways to award the three places.

Permutation Notation Example 2 shows how to find the number of permutations of 12 objects taken 3 at a time. This is written ${}_{12}P_3$.

Permutations

Algebra The number of permutations of n objects taken r at a time can be written as ${}_nP_r$ and evaluated using $\frac{n!}{(n-r)!}$.

Numbers ${}_7P_3 = \frac{7!}{(7-3)!} = \frac{7!}{4!} = \frac{7 \cdot 6 \cdot 5 \cdot \cancel{4} \cdot \cancel{3} \cdot \cancel{2} \cdot \cancel{1}}{\cancel{4} \cdot \cancel{3} \cdot \cancel{2} \cdot \cancel{1}} = 7 \cdot 6 \cdot 5$

HELP with Solving

In Example 3, you can write 6! as $6 \cdot 5 \cdot 4!$ and cancel both 4 factorials.

$\frac{6 \cdot 5 \cdot 4!}{4!} = 6 \cdot 5$

EXAMPLE 3 Evaluating a Permutation

Poetry Two students are chosen from a group of 6 to read the first and second poems at the school's poetry reading. To find how many different ways the students can be chosen, find ${}_6P_2$.

$${}_6P_2 = \frac{6!}{(6-2)!} = \frac{6!}{4!} \quad \textbf{Use formula.}$$

$$= \frac{6 \cdot 5 \cdot \cancel{4} \cdot \cancel{3} \cdot \cancel{2} \cdot \cancel{1}}{\cancel{4} \cdot \cancel{3} \cdot \cancel{2} \cdot \cancel{1}} \quad \textbf{Divide out common factors.}$$

$$= 30 \quad \textbf{Multiply.}$$

ANSWER There are 30 ways the speakers can be chosen.

Your turn now **Find the number of permutations.**

5. ${}_5P_3$ **60** **6.** ${}_6P_6$ **720** **7.** ${}_8P_7$ **40,320** **8.** ${}_{100}P_2$ **9900**

9. In Example 1 on page 623, you found the number of permutations of 5 CDs taken how many at a time? Explain.

9. 5 at a time. *Sample answer:* You found the number of permutations of 5 CDs taken 5 at a time, or ${}_5P_5$.

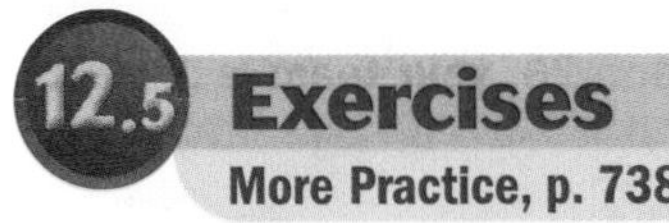

12.5 Exercises

More Practice, p. 738

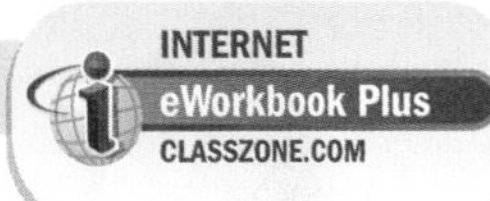

INTERNET eWorkbook Plus CLASSZONE.COM

Getting Ready to Practice

1. **Vocabulary** Copy and complete: The number of permutations of 15 objects taken 7 at a time can be written as _?_. $_{15}P_7$

Evaluate.

2. 2! 2
3. 0! 1
4. 7! 5040
5. 9! 362,880
6. $_4P_2$ 12
7. $_9P_6$ 60,480
8. $_{10}P_7$ 604,800
9. $_5P_5$ 120

10. You have three things to do after you wake up tomorrow. You need to take a shower, eat breakfast, and call your friend. Find the number of permutations and list them.

10. 6 permutations; take a shower, eat breakfast, call your friend; take a shower, call your friend, eat breakfast; eat breakfast, take a shower, call your friend; eat breakfast, call your friend, take a shower; call your friend, take a shower, eat breakfast; call your friend, eat breakfast, take a shower

Practice and Problem Solving

HELP with Homework

Example	Exercises
1	11
2	20–22, 24
3	12–22, 24

Online Resources CLASSZONE.COM
- More Examples
- eTutorial Plus

A 11. **Movies** You rent four movies. In how many different orders can you watch the movies? 24 orders

Find the number of permutations.

12. $_3P_1$ 3
13. $_5P_2$ 20
14. $_3P_2$ 6
15. $_9P_3$ 504
16. $_{12}P_6$ 665,280
17. $_7P_4$ 840
18. $_{15}P_5$ 360,360
19. $_{20}P_3$ 6840

20. **Knitting** You are knitting a hat, and you want it to have 3 different colored stripes. You have 6 different colors of yarn. How many different hats could you knit? 120 hats

21. **Softball** Your softball team has 15 players. Find the number of different ways that the first, second, third, fourth, and fifth batters can be chosen. 360,360 ways

22. **After School** You are given a list of 10 activities you can do after school. You are asked to pick your first, second, third, and fourth choices. How many different permutations are possible? 5040 arrangements

B 23. **Critical Thinking** Your friend says that 11! = 11 • 10!. Is your friend correct? Explain. Yes; 11! = 11 • 10 • 9 • 8 • 7 • 6 • 5 • 4 • 3 • 2 • 1 = 11 • 10!

24. **Gardening** You are planning a garden with 3 rows. Each row will have one type of flower, and none of the rows will be the same. You can choose from the flowers below. Find the number of permutations. 210 permutations

Day Lily

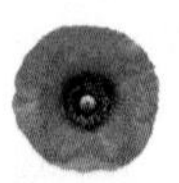
Poppy

Gladiolus

Daffodil

Rose

Sunflower

Tulip

3 APPLY

ASSIGNMENT GUIDE

Basic Course

Day 1: pp. 625-626 Exs. 11-15, 25, 28-30

Day 2: pp. 625-626 Exs. 16-22, 31, 32

Average Course

Day 1: pp. 625-626 Exs. 11-15, 26, 29-32

Day 2: pp. 625-626 Exs. 16-24, 28

Advanced Course

Day 1: pp. 625-626 Exs. 11-15, 28-32

Day 2: pp. 625-626 Exs. 18-27*

Block

pp. 625-626 Exs. 11-24, 26, 28-32

EXTRA PRACTICE
- Student Edition, p. 738
- Chapter 12 Resource Book, pp. 42-44
- Test and Practice Generator

TRANSPARENCY

Even-numbered answers are available on transparencies.

HOMEWORK CHECK

When you review students' homework for this lesson, go over the following exercises to check understanding of key concepts.

Basic: 11, 12, 16, 20, 22
Average: 11, 12, 17, 20, 22
Advanced: 11, 14, 18, 22, 24

4 ASSESS

Assessment Resources

For more assessment resources, see:
- Assessment Book
- Test and Practice Generator

Mini-Quiz

Find the number of permutations.

1. ${}_{9}P_{4}$ 3024
2. ${}_{14}P_{2}$ 182
3. How many different ways can you select and arrange 3 photographs from a portfolio of 7 photographs? 210 ways
4. Find the number of different ways that you could choose 2 kittens to adopt from 18 at a shelter. 306 ways

5 FOLLOW-UP

Reteaching/Remediation

- Study Guide in Chapter 12 Resource Book, pp. 45–46
- eTutorial Plus Online
- Extra Practice, p. 738
- Lesson Practice in Chapter 12 Resource Book, pp. 42–44

Challenge/Enrichment

- Challenge Practice in Chapter 12 Resource Book, p. 47
- Teacher's Edition, p. 594F

English Learner Support

- Spanish Study Guide
- Multi-Language Glossary
- Chapter Audio Summaries CDs

29, 30. See Additional Answers beginning on page AA1.

Extended Problem Solving In Exercises 25 and 26, your team is 1 of 15 in a cheerleading competition.

25. If trophies are awarded for first, second, third, and fourth places, in how many different ways can the trophies be awarded? 32,760 ways

26. **Compare and Contrast** Suppose the four teams that perform best are all given *excellence* medals instead of first, second, third, and fourth place trophies. In this case, are there more or fewer ways to give the awards than in Exercise 25? Explain. See margin.
C

27. **Challenge** You choose a 6-letter password for your e-mail. Write an expression to represent the number of different passwords you could choose. Explain how this expression changes if you can use each letter only once. See margin.

26. Fewer. *Sample answer:* If order does not matter, then there will be fewer ways to give the awards.

27. 26 • 26 • 26 • 26 • 26 • 26. *Sample answer:* If each letter is used only once, there would be one less letter available at each step, and the expression would change to 26 • 25 • 24 • 23 • 22 • 21.

Mixed Review

28. Find the surface area of a cone that has a slant height of 24 inches and a diameter of 10 inches. Round to the nearest tenth. *(Lesson 10.5)* 455.3 in.^{2}

29. The table shows the results of a survey that asked students to choose their favorite color. Make a circle graph of the data. *(Lesson 12.3)* See margin.

Red	25%
Green	12%
Blue	40%
Other	23%

30. You are making a cake for your younger sister's birthday. You can make vanilla or chocolate cake. You can have white, yellow, or blue frosting. You can make a balloon design or a flower design for the top of the cake. Make a tree diagram to show all of the possible cakes that you could make. *(Lesson 12.4)* See margin.

Test-Taking Practice

INTERNET
State Test Practice
CLASSZONE.COM

31. **Multiple Choice** You go to the cafeteria with five friends. In how many different orders can you and your friends get into the lunch line? D

A. 6 **B.** 30 **C.** 120 **D.** 720

32. **Short Response** When you come back from vacation, you want to call Ed, Sue, Ty, and Nestor. You have time to make only two calls. Find the number of different orders in which you can call two friends. Then make a list to show all the different orders. See margin.

32. 12 orders; Ed and Sue, Ed and Ty, Ed and Nestor, Sue and Ed, Ty and Ed, Nestor and Ed, Sue and Ty, Ty and Sue, Sue and Nestor, Nestor and Sue, Ty and Nestor, Nestor and Ty

LESSON 12.6

Combinations

BEFORE	Now	WHY?
You used permutations to count possibilities.	You will use combinations to count possibilities.	So you can count the ways a team can choose captains, as in Ex. 22.

Word Watch

combination, p. 627

In Lesson 12.5, you studied permutations, which are arrangements in which order is important.

A **combination** is a group of items whose order is *not* important. For example, suppose you go to lunch with a friend. You choose milk, soup, and a salad. Your friend chooses soup, a salad, and milk. The order in which the items are chosen does not matter. You both have same meal.

The two meals are the same.

EXAMPLE 1 Listing Combinations

County Fair You have 4 tickets to the county fair and can take 3 of your friends. You can choose from Abby (A), Brian (B), Chloe (C), and David (D). How many different choices of groups of friends do you have?

Solution

List all possible arrangements of three friends. Then cross out any duplicate groupings that represent the same group of friends.

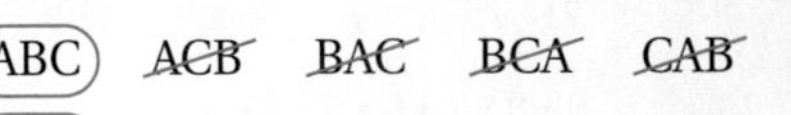

(ABC)	~~ACB~~	~~BAC~~	~~BCA~~	~~CAB~~	~~CBA~~
(ABD)	~~ADB~~	~~BAD~~	~~BDA~~	~~DAB~~	~~DBA~~
(ACD)	~~ADC~~	~~CAD~~	~~CDA~~	~~DAC~~	~~DCA~~
(BCD)	~~BDC~~	~~CBD~~	~~CDB~~	~~DBC~~	~~DCB~~

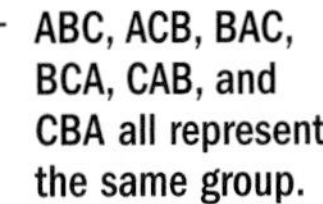

← ABC, ACB, BAC, BCA, CAB, and CBA all represent the same group.

ANSWER You have 4 different choices of groups to take to the fair.

Your turn now

1. In Example 1, the complete list shows the number of *permutations* of 4 items chosen 3 at a time. How many items would be in the complete list if you had to choose from 8 friends? 336 items

ILLINOIS Standards and ISAT:
10.C.3a

1 PLAN

SKILL CHECK

Evaluate.

1. ${}_7P_2$ 42 **2.** $\frac{{}_5P_3}{3!}$ 10

LESSON OBJECTIVE

Use combinations to count possibilities.

PACING

Suggested Number of Days
Basic Course: 2 days
Average Course: 2 days
Advanced Course: 2 days
Block: 1 block

TEACHING RESOURCES

For a complete list of Teaching Resources, see page 594B.

TRANSPARENCY

Warm-Up Exercises for this lesson are available on a transparency.

2 TEACH

MOTIVATING THE LESSON

Have students imagine choosing 4 of 10 novels to take on vacation. It does not matter in what order the novels are chosen, only the order in which they are read.

TIPS FOR NEW TEACHERS

Throughout this lesson, revisit permutations and ask students to describe the similarities and differences between combinations and permutations. See Tips for New Teachers in the *Chapter 12 Resource Book*.

EXTRA EXAMPLES

Example 1 Marie has 4 mallard ducks and wants to enter two of them at a state fair competition. How many choices of ducks does she have?
6 choices

Example 2 Find the number of combinations.

a. ${}_7C_4$ 35

b. ${}_{10}C_8$ 45

NOTETAKING

Students may need extra practice determining if problems should be solved using permutations or combinations. Have students record in their notebooks the formulas for permutations and combinations. Then have students list an example of a problem that can be solved by finding the number of combinations. Challenge students to change the conditions for the problem so that it has to be solved by finding the number of permutations. They may repeat this notetaking technique for more examples.

VISUALIZE

Using four different colored objects, such as four beach balls, demonstrate how the four objects, taken two at a time, can make 6 combinations. Have a student record and count the combinations on the board using variables to represent each colored object. Next, show how you can find the number of combinations for the objects by using the combination formula.

Combination Notation In Example 1, after you cross out the duplicate groupings, you are left with the number of combinations of 4 items chosen 3 at a time. Using notation, this is written ${}_4C_3$.

Combination Notation

Words To find the number of combinations of n objects taken r at a time, divide the number of permutations of n objects taken r at a time by $r!$.

Numbers ${}_9C_4 = \frac{{}_9P_4}{4!}$ **Algebra** ${}_nC_r = \frac{{}_nP_r}{r!}$

EXAMPLE 2 Evaluating Combinations

Find the number of combinations.

a. ${}_8C_3$ **b.** ${}_9C_7$

Solution

a. ${}_8C_3 = \frac{{}_8P_3}{3!}$ Combination formula

$= \frac{8 \cdot 7 \cdot 6}{3!}$ ${}_8P_3 = \frac{8!}{(8-3)!} = 8 \cdot 7 \cdot 6$

$= \frac{8 \cdot 7 \cdot \cancel{6}}{\cancel{3} \cdot \cancel{2} \cdot 1}$ Expand. $3! = 3 \cdot 2 \cdot 1$. Divide out common factors.

$= 56$ Simplify.

b. ${}_9C_7 = \frac{{}_9P_7}{7!}$ Combination formula

$= \frac{9 \cdot 8 \cdot 7 \cdot 6 \cdot 5 \cdot 4 \cdot 3}{7!}$ ${}_9P_7 = \frac{9!}{(9-7)!} = 9 \cdot 8 \cdot 7 \cdot 6 \cdot 5 \cdot 4 \cdot 3$

$= \frac{9 \cdot \overset{4}{\cancel{8}} \cdot \cancel{7} \cdot \cancel{6} \cdot \cancel{5} \cdot \cancel{4} \cdot \cancel{3}}{\cancel{7} \cdot \cancel{6} \cdot \cancel{5} \cdot \cancel{4} \cdot \cancel{3} \cdot \underset{1}{\cancel{2}} \cdot 1}$ Expand 7!. Divide out common factors.

$= 36$ Simplify.

Your turn now Find the number of combinations.

2. ${}_8C_8$ 1 **3.** ${}_8C_7$ 8 **4.** ${}_7C_2$ 21 **5.** ${}_6C_1$ 6

EXAMPLE 3 Permutations and Combinations

Tell whether the possibilities can be counted using a *permutation* or *combination*. Then write an expression for the number of possibilities.

a. Swimming There are 8 swimmers in the 400 meter freestyle race. In how many ways can the swimmers finish first, second, and third?

b. Track Your track team has 6 runners available for the 4-person relay event. How many different 4-person teams can be chosen?

Solution

a. Because the swimmers can finish first, second, or third, order is important. So the possibilities can be counted by evaluating ${}_8P_3$.

b. Order is not important in choosing the team members, so the possibilities can be counted by evaluating ${}_6C_4$.

HELP with Notetaking

Mutate means to change. For *permutations*, you count changes in the order of items. For *combinations*, objects *combined* in any order represent the same group. You may wish to copy this hint into your notebook.

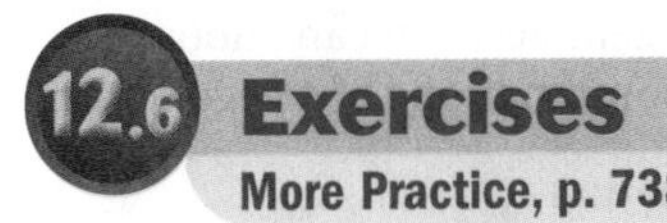

12.6 Exercises

More Practice, p. 738

Getting Ready to Practice

1. **Vocabulary** Copy and complete: The expression ${}_9C_5$ represents the number of combinations of _?_ objects taken _?_ at a time. **9; 5**

2. **Find the Error** You choose 3 art projects from the following list: clay, plaster, wood, wire, drawing, painting. Describe and correct the error below in finding the number of possible combinations of 3 projects. **See margin.**

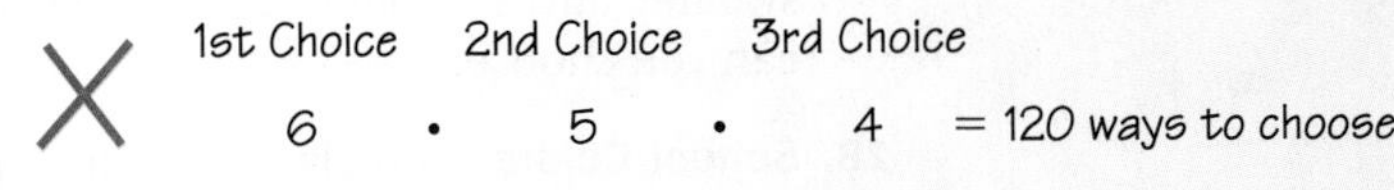

Find the number of combinations.

3. ${}_4C_1$ **4**
4. ${}_4C_4$ **1**
5. ${}_7C_6$ **7**
6. ${}_5C_2$ **10**

Tell whether the possibilities should be counted using a *permutation* or *combination*. Then find the answer.

7. **Party** You are buying balloons for a party. The store has four different colors, and you would like to choose two different colors. How many different pairs of balloon colors can be chosen? **combination; 6 pairs**

8. **Homework** You must do homework in math, history, science, and geography. In how many different orders can you do your homework? **permutation; 24 orders**

EXTRA EXAMPLES

Example 3 Tell whether the possibilities can be counted using a *permutation* or *combination*. Then write an expression for the number of possibilities.

a. Find how many ways a secretary and treasurer of a homeowner association can be chosen from 40 homeowners. **permutation; ${}_{40}P_2$**

b. An artist has a collection of 25 paintings. How many ways can he choose 3 paintings to submit for an art show? **combination; ${}_{25}C_3$**

CONCEPT CHECK

How is the number of combinations of *n* objects taken *r* at a time related to the number of permutations of the same objects? **The number of combinations is the number of permutations divided by $r!$.**

DAILY PUZZLER

Three boys and three girls at camp want to cross a river in one canoe that holds only two people. None of the boys want to be left alone with two girls, and the river is too cold to swim in. Out of the six campers, only one boy and one girl are strong enough to paddle the canoe. How can they all get across the river? **Use B b b and G g g to represent the campers.**
G g go, G returns
G g go, G returns
B b go, B g return
B G go, B g return
B b go, G returns
G g go, G returns
G g go

2. See Additional Answers beginning on page AA1.

3 APPLY

ASSIGNMENT GUIDE

Basic Course

Day 1: pp. 630-631 Exs. 9-15, 22-24, 34-37

Day 2: pp. 630-631 Exs. 16-21, 26-30, 38-40

Average Course

Day 1: pp. 630-631 Exs. 9-13, 22-25, 30-32, 40, 41

Day 2: pp. 630-631 Exs. 18-21, 26-29, 34-39

Advanced Course

Day 1: pp. 630-631 Exs. 9-13, 22-25, 30-32, 40, 41

Day 2: pp. 630-631 Exs. 19-21, 26-29, 33-39*

Block

pp. 630-631 Exs. 9-13, 18-32, 34-41

EXTRA PRACTICE

- Student Edition, p. 738
- Chapter 12 Resource Book, pp. 52-54
- Test and Practice Generator

TRANSPARENCY

Even-numbered answers are available on transparencies.

HOMEWORK CHECK

When you review students' homework for this lesson, go over the following exercises to check understanding of key concepts.

Basic: 9, 10, 19, 22, 26

Average: 9, 12, 19, 23, 27

Advanced: 9, 13, 24, 27, 28

HELP with Homework

Example	Exercises
1	9
2	10-21, 22-25
3	26-29

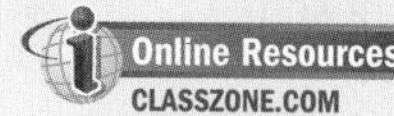

Online Resources
CLASSZONE.COM

- More Examples
- eTutorial Plus

9. 1, 2 ~~1, 3~~ ~~1, 4~~ ~~1, 5~~
~~2, 1~~ 2, 3 ~~2, 4~~ ~~2, 5~~
3, 1 ~~3, 2~~ 3, 4 ~~3, 5~~
4, 1 4, 2 ~~4, 3~~ 4, 5
5, 1 5, 2 5, 3 ~~5, 4~~

Practice and Problem Solving

A **9. Essays** For a test, you can choose any 2 essay questions to answer from the 5 questions asked. Make a list and cross out the duplicate choices to show how many different pairs of essay questions you could answer. See margin for list; 10 pairs.

Find the number of combinations.

10. ${}_6C_5$ 6	**11.** ${}_6C_6$ 1	**12.** ${}_{11}C_9$ 55	**13.** ${}_8C_4$ 70
14. ${}_8C_6$ 28	**15.** ${}_8C_1$ 8	**16.** ${}_{10}C_8$ 45	**17.** ${}_9C_5$ 126
18. ${}_{11}C_3$ 165	**19.** ${}_{13}C_{11}$ 78	**20.** ${}_9C_2$ 36	**21.** ${}_{100}C_{99}$ 100

22. Hockey Your hockey team is choosing 2 team captains from its 18 members. Find the number of combinations that are possible. 153 combinations

23. Debating A debate team has 5 members. Your debating club has 12 students. How many different teams can be chosen? 792 teams

24. Gardening You want to grow 4 different vegetables. You can choose from 9 types of seed. Find the number of combinations of 4 vegetables. 126 combinations

25. Writing Is it possible to evaluate a combination such as ${}_3C_4$, ${}_2C_6$, or ${}_1C_{10}$? Explain why or why not. No. *Sample answer:* You cannot choose more items that you have to start with, that is, *r* must be less than or equal to *n*.

In Exercises 26–29, tell whether the possibilities should be counted using a *permutation* or *combination*. Then find the number of possibilities.

B **26. Music** You want to know the number of ways you can play your four favorite songs. permutation; 24 ways

27. Shopping You are shopping for a trip and want to buy three sweaters from among a red sweater, a blue sweater, a plaid sweater, a striped sweater, and a turtleneck sweater. How many sets of three sweaters can you choose? combination; 10 sets

28. School Colors Your class is voting for the new school colors. You are asked to choose 2 colors from a list of 8 colors. How many possibilities are there? combination; 28 possibilities

29. Geography You are coloring the map shown at the right. You want each state to be a different color, and you have 10 possible colors. In how many ways can you color the map? In how many ways can you choose 8 colors? permutation; 1,814,400 ways; combination; 45 ways

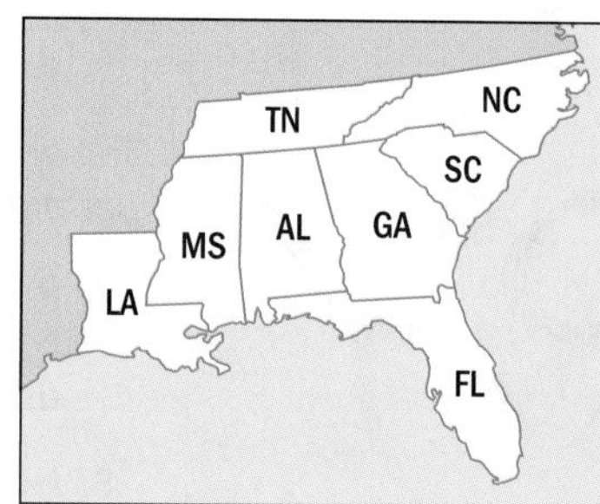

30. *Sample answer:* The numbers form a symmetrical pattern increasing from 1 to 35, then decreasing from 35 to 1. It appears that if two values of r in ${}_7C_r$ have a sum of seven, then the corresponding values of ${}_7C_r$ are the same.

32. 153. *Sample answer:* Since two games are already chosen, you are choosing 2 games from 18 games, so ${}_{18}C_2 = 153$.

34. $192 for paint, $336 for wallpaper. *Sample answer:* I used Draw a Diagram to draw a net of the walls so I could easily find the area and compute the cost.

41. ${}_6C_2 = 15$ ways; 20 ways

30. Look for a Pattern Copy the table. Complete the table by finding the number of combinations. Then describe the pattern. See margin.

${}_7C_0$	${}_7C_1$	${}_7C_2$	${}_7C_3$	${}_7C_4$	${}_7C_5$	${}_7C_6$	${}_7C_7$
? 1	? 7	? 21	? 35	? 35	? 21	? 7	? 1

Video Games In Exercises 31 and 32, your friend has a collection of 20 video games.

31. You want to borrow four games from your friend. How many different groups of four games can you choose? 4845 groups

C **32.** If you are already sure about two of the game choices, how many different groups of four games can you choose? Explain. See margin.

33. Challenge What is the value of ${}_nC_r$ when $r = n$? What is the value of ${}_nC_r$ when $n - r = 1$? Explain.
1; n. *Sample answer:* ${}_nP_n = n!$, so ${}_nC_n = 1$; when $n - r = 1$, ${}_nP_r = n!$ and $\frac{n!}{r!} = n$.

Mixed Review 

Choose a Strategy Use a strategy from the list to solve the following problem. Explain your choice of strategy.

> Problem Solving Strategies
> - Act It Out
> - Solve a Simpler Problem
> - Draw a Diagram
> - Make a Table

34. A rectangular room is 20 feet by 12 feet, with walls 7.5 feet high. A decorator charges $.40 per square foot to use paint and $.70 per square foot for wallpaper. Find the cost to decorate the room with each material. See margin.

Find the number of permutations. *(Lesson 12.5)*

35. ${}_{10}P_5$ 30,240 **36.** ${}_{11}P_4$ 7920 **37.** ${}_{18}P_3$ 4896 **38.** ${}_{21}P_2$ 420

39. Basic Skills You spin the spinner at the right. What is the probability that the spinner lands on blue? $\frac{1}{3}$

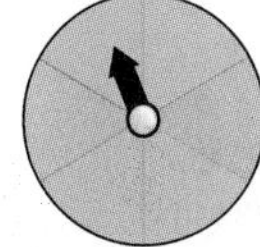

Test-Taking Practice 

40. Multiple Choice You are at a fair with four friends. All of you want to ride the roller coaster, but only three people can fit in the first car. How many different groups of three can you and your friends make? C

A. 60 **B.** 24 **C.** 10 **D.** 4

41. Short Response You have 6 different sweatshirts, and you want to donate some to a charity. Draw a diagram or write an expression so that you can find the number of ways you can donate 2 sweatshirts. Then find the number of ways you can donate 3 sweatshirts.

4 ASSESS

Assessment Resources

For more assessment resources, see:
- Assessment Book
- Test and Practice Generator

Mini-Quiz

Find the number of combinations.

1. ${}_{12}C_5$ 792 **2.** ${}_{25}C_2$ 300

Tell whether the possibilities can be counted using a *permutation* or *combination*. Then write an expression for the number of possibilities.

3. You want to use a set of 8 lamps for a window display. Find how many sets you can choose from 25 lamps in the stock room. combination; ${}_{25}C_8$

4. How many different ways can you select a preferred color and a substitute color from a mail-order catalog offering 12 colors of slacks? permutation; ${}_{12}C_2$

5 FOLLOW-UP

Reteaching/Remediation

- Study Guide in Chapter 12 Resource Book, pp. 55–56
- eTutorial Plus Online
- Extra Practice, p. 738
- Lesson Practice in Chapter 12 Resource Book, pp. 52–54

Challenge/Enrichment

- Challenge Practice in Chapter 12 Resource Book, p. 57
- Teacher's Edition, p. 594F

English Learner Support

- Spanish Study Guide
- Multi-Language Glossary
- Chapter Audio Summaries CDs

1 PLAN

SKILL CHECK

You roll a number cube. Use the counting principle to find each probability.

1. You roll a 6. $\frac{1}{6}$
2. You roll a 5 or 6. $\frac{1}{3}$
3. You roll an 8. 0

LESSON OBJECTIVE

Find the odds in favor of events.

PACING

Suggested Number of Days
Basic Course: 2 days
Average Course: 2 days
Advanced Course: 2 days
Block: 1 block

TEACHING RESOURCES

For a complete list of Teaching Resources, see page 594B.

TRANSPARENCY

Warm-Up Exercises for this lesson are available on a transparency.

2 TEACH

MOTIVATING THE LESSON

Ask students where they have heard people ask about the odds of something happening.

ACTIVITY

Goal Use a spinner to explore probability.

Key Discovery You can find the probability of something not occurring as well as something occurring.

Probability and Odds

BEFORE
You found the probability of events.

Now
You will find the odds in favor of events.

WHY?
So you can find the odds of a goalie's save, as in Ex. 18.

Word Watch

complementary events, p. 632
unfavorable outcome, p. 633
odds, p. 633

Activity You can use a spinner to explore probability.

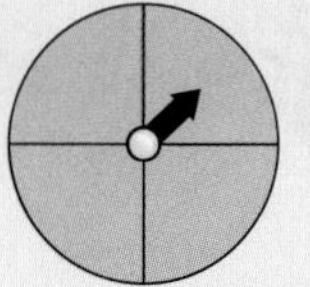

1. What is the probability of the spinner landing on blue? What is the probability of the spinner landing on red? $\frac{1}{4}$; $\frac{3}{4}$
2. Is it more likely that the spinner will land on blue than red? no
3. Find each ratio. Use the ratios to compare the chances of landing on red and on blue. See margin.

   a. $\frac{\text{number of red sections}}{\text{number of blue sections}}$ b. $\frac{\text{number of blue sections}}{\text{number of red sections}}$

4. Explain how to find the probability of the spinner *not* landing on red. Find the probability of the spinner landing on blue.

Step 3. a. $\frac{3}{1}$; it is 3 times more likely the spinner will land on red than on blue.
b. $\frac{1}{3}$; it is $\frac{1}{3}$ as likely the spinner will land on blue as on red.

In the activity, the spinner will land on either red or blue. Two events are **complementary** when one event or the other (but not both) must occur. The sum of the probabilities of complementary events is always 1.

When Events A and B are complementary, $P(\text{Event A}) = 1 - P(\text{Event B})$.

HELP with Solving

The probability that Event A occurs and the probability that Event A does *not* occur have a sum of 1 because they are complementary events.

For help with probability, see p. 354.

EXAMPLE 1 Finding Probabilities

Gifts You and seven friends contribute money for a gift. Everyone's name is put in a hat. The person whose name is chosen picks the gift.

a. What is the probability that your name is randomly chosen?

b. What is the probability that your name is randomly *not* chosen?

Solution

a. $P(\text{your name is chosen}) = \frac{\text{Number of favorable outcomes}}{\text{Number of possible outcomes}} = \frac{1}{8}$

b. $P(\text{your name is not chosen}) = 1 - P(\text{your name is chosen})$

$= 1 - \frac{1}{8}$

$= \frac{7}{8}$

ILLINOIS Standards and ISAT:
10.C.3a

Your turn now **You are given the probability that an event will occur. Find the probability that the event will not occur.**

1. $P(A) = \frac{3}{4}$ $\frac{1}{4}$
2. $P(A) = 0.45$ 0.55
3. $P(A) = 32\%$ 68%
4. $P(A) = \frac{7}{10}$ $\frac{3}{10}$
5. The 11 letters in the word MISSISSIPPI are each written on pieces of paper and put in a bag. What is the probability of randomly drawing an S from the bag? What is the probability of randomly *not* drawing an S? $\frac{4}{11}, \frac{7}{11}$

Odds Once you specify the event for which you are finding the probability, outcomes for that event are called *favorable outcomes*. The other outcomes are **unfavorable outcomes**.

When all outcomes are equally likely, the **odds** in favor of an event are equal to the ratio of favorable outcomes to unfavorable outcomes.

$$\textbf{Odds} = \frac{\textbf{Number of favorable outcomes}}{\textbf{Number of unfavorable outcomes}}$$

EXAMPLE 2 Finding Odds

You do a survey asking your class to rank three ice cream flavors. Results for vanilla are shown at the right. What are the odds in favor of a randomly chosen student from your class ranking vanilla first?

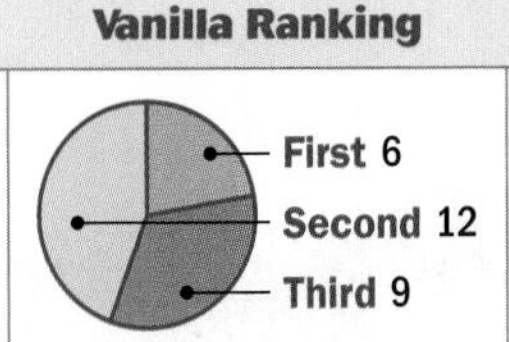

Solution

Vanilla was ranked first by 6 students, so there are 6 favorable outcomes.

It was ranked second by 12 students, and ranked third by 9 students, so there are $12 + 9 = 21$ unfavorable outcomes.

$$\text{Odds} = \frac{\text{Number of favorable outcomes}}{\text{Number of unfavorable outcomes}}$$

$$= \frac{6}{21}$$

$$= \frac{2}{7}$$

ANSWER The odds in favor of a randomly chosen student ranking vanilla first are 2 to 7.

HELP with Reading

Odds are always read as a ratio. For example, $\frac{5}{2}$ is read "five to two," not "five halves."

Your turn now **You choose a card at random from a set of cards numbered 1 to 24. Find the odds in favor of the event.**

6. You choose a 10. $\frac{1}{23}$
7. You choose an odd number greater than 7. $\frac{1}{2}$

TIPS FOR NEW TEACHERS

As students explore mathematical concepts such as *unfavorable outcomes*, stress that the word *unfavorable* has nothing to do with whether the student would personally prefer the event to occur. See Tips for New Teachers in the *Chapter 12 Resource Book*.

EXTRA EXAMPLES

Example 1 You are one of 20 shoppers who are eligible for a store prize. The winner is chosen at random.

a. What is the probability that you are chosen? $\frac{1}{20}$

b. What is the probability that you are *not* chosen? $\frac{19}{20}$

Example 2 You do a survey asking 50 students how they will spend their vacation time. Results are shown in the graph. What are the odds that a randomly chosen student is traveling this summer? $\frac{6}{19}$

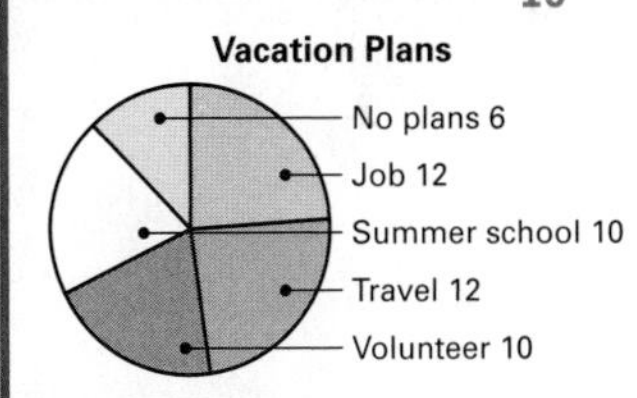

EXTRA EXAMPLES

Example 3 A performing dog successfully jumps through a hoop 70% of the time. What are the odds that the dog will make her next jump successfully? **7 to 3**

CONCEPT CHECK

If the odds of an event are represented by $\frac{1}{2}$, and you expect to have 15 favorable outcomes for this event, how many unfavorable outcomes would you expect to have for the event? Explain. **30 unfavorable outcomes; write the ratio $\frac{1}{2} = \frac{15}{u}$, where u is the number of unfavorable outcomes, and solve for u.**

DAILY PUZZLER

The population of the United States is about 280 million people. If the odds are "one-in-a-million" that someone experiences a particular event, how many people in the United States would you expect to experience this event? **280 people**

Probability and Odds If you know the probability of an event, you can use the following formula to find the odds in favor of that event.

$$\textbf{Odds} = \frac{\textbf{Probability event will occur}}{\textbf{Probability event will not occur}} = \frac{\textbf{Probability event will occur}}{\textbf{1 − Probability event will occur}}$$

EXAMPLE 3 **Finding Odds Using Probability**

Basketball Sean makes 65% of his free throws. What are the odds in favor of Sean making a free throw?

Solution

$\text{Odds} = \frac{0.65}{1 - 0.65}$ **Write percents as decimals.**

$= \frac{0.65}{0.35}$ **Subtract.**

$= \frac{65}{35}$ **Multiply numerator and denominator by 100.**

$= \frac{13}{7}$ **Simplify.**

ANSWER Sean's odds in favor of making a free throw are 13 to 7.

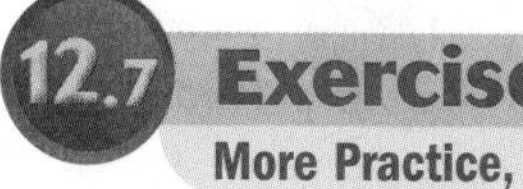

12.7 Exercises

More Practice, p. 738

INTERNET eWorkbook Plus CLASSZONE.COM

Getting Ready to Practice

1. **Vocabulary** Copy and complete: Find the ratio of the number of favorable outcomes to the number of unfavorable outcomes to find the _?_ of an event. **odds in favor**

You are given the probability that an event will occur. Find the probability that the event will not occur.

2. $P(A) = 84\%$ **16%** 3. $P(A) = \frac{2}{5}$ $\frac{3}{5}$ 4. $P(A) = 0.37$ **0.63** 5. $P(A) = \frac{9}{10}$ $\frac{1}{10}$

You randomly draw a letter tile from a bag. The 8 letters in the word GEOMETRY are in the bag. Find the odds in favor of the event.

6. You choose a G. $\frac{1}{7}$ 7. You choose an E. $\frac{1}{3}$ 8. You choose an S. $\frac{0}{8} = 0$

9. **Weather** The weather forecast says that there is a 30 percent probability of rain. What are the odds in favor of rain? $\frac{3}{7}$

Practice and Problem Solving

HELP with Homework

Example	Exercises
1	10-13, 19-20
2	10-20
3	18, 20

Online Resources CLASSZONE.COM

- More Examples
- eTutorial Plus

Find the probability of randomly choosing a red marble from the bag of marbles described. Then find the odds in favor of randomly choosing a blue marble.

A **10.** 3 red and 7 blue marbles $\frac{3}{10}; \frac{7}{3}$ **11.** 4 red and 9 blue marbles $\frac{4}{13}; \frac{9}{4}$

12. 6 red and 5 blue marbles $\frac{6}{11}; \frac{5}{6}$ **13.** 6 red, 5 blue, and 3 green marbles $\frac{3}{7}; \frac{5}{9}$

Find the odds in favor of the event described when rolling a number cube.

14. Roll a 3. $\frac{1}{5}$ **15.** Roll a number less than 6. $\frac{5}{1}$

16. Roll a number greater than 2. $\frac{2}{1}$ **17.** Roll an odd number less than 5. $\frac{1}{2}$

18. Hockey A hockey goalie has a save percentage of 93%. What are the odds that he makes a save? $\frac{93}{7}$

19. Compare Sam finds the probability of Event A is 0.2. Jan finds the odds in favor of Event A are 1 to 4. Can they both be right? Explain. See margin.

20. Socks In your sock drawer, you have 20 socks. You have 2 pairs of patterned socks, 4 pairs of gym socks, 3 pairs of striped socks, and 1 pair of black socks. What is the probability that you randomly pull a gym sock from the drawer? What are the odds? $\frac{2}{5}; \frac{2}{3}$

Pizza In Exercises 21–23, use the circle graph. It shows the number of people ordering pizza that order each type of crust.

What kind of crust?

B **21.** What is the probability that a randomly chosen pizza order is for thin crust? $\frac{7}{25}$

22. What are the odds in favor of a randomly chosen pizza order being for regular crust? $\frac{13}{12}$

23. What are the odds in favor of a randomly chosen pizza order *not* being for stuffed crust? $\frac{4}{1}$

Odds Against In Exercises 24 and 25, use the following information. In this lesson, you learned how to find the *odds in favor* of an event. You can also find the *odds against* an event.

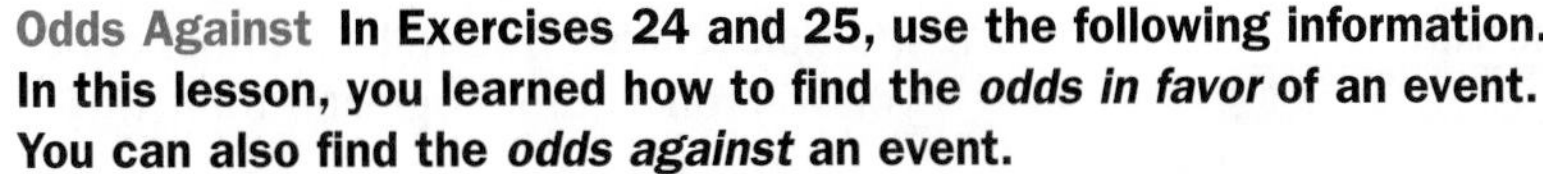

$$\text{Odds against} = \frac{\text{Number of unfavorable outcomes}}{\text{Number of favorable outcomes}}$$

24. You choose a chip from a bag of 6 blue, 3 red, and 5 green chips. Find the odds in favor of choosing a green chip. Then find the odds against choosing a green chip. $\frac{5}{9}; \frac{9}{5}$

25. Challenge You hear a friend claim that "the odds that you get hit by lightning are a million to one." Is your friend talking about *odds in favor* or *odds against*? Explain your reasoning.

19. Yes. *Sample answer:* A probability of 0.2 describes a situation where there is one favorable outcome for every four unfavorable outcomes, which also describes an event where the odds in favor are 1 to 4.

25. Odds against. *Sample answer:* If a million to one are the odds in favor of getting hit by lightning, that means a million people get hit for every one who does not get hit, which is not true.

3 APPLY

ASSIGNMENT GUIDE

Basic Course

Day 1: EP p. 733 Exs. 32, 33; pp. 635-636 Exs. 10-15, 21-24, 36-38

Day 2: pp. 635-636 Exs. 16-20, 29-35

Average Course

Day 1: pp. 635-636 Exs. 10-15, 26-32

Day 2: pp. 635-636 Exs. 18-24, 33-38

Advanced Course

Day 1: pp. 635-636 Exs. 10-15, 26-31

Day 2: pp. 635-636 Exs. 18-25*, 35-38

Block

pp. 635-636 Exs. 10-15, 18-24, 26-38

Extra Practice

- Student Edition, p. 738
- Chapter 12 Resource Book, pp. 60-62
- Test and Practice Generator

Transparency

Even-numbered answers are available on transparencies.

Homework Check

When you review students' homework for this lesson, go over the following exercises to check understanding of key concepts.

Basic: 10, 12, 14, 17, 18
Average: 10, 12, 14, 18, 20
Advanced: 10, 13, 15, 18, 20

Common Error

In Exercise 8, watch for students who are unsure how to proceed when the odds are 0. Assure students that odds of 0 to 8 and odds of 8 to 0 are both valid mathematically.

ASSESS

Assessment Resources

For more assessment resources, see:
- Assessment Book
- Test and Practice Generator

Mini-Quiz

Find the probability and the odds of choosing one yellow marble from the bag of marbles described.

1. a bag of 7 yellow and 8 green marbles **probability: $\frac{7}{15}$; odds: 7 to 8**

2. a bag of 3 yellow, 4 white, and 5 black marbles **probability: $\frac{1}{4}$; odds: 1 to 3**

Find the odds of the outcome described when rolling a number cube.

3. a 4 or a 6 **1 to 2**

4. a number greater than 2 **2 to 1**

5. an odd number **1 to 1**

FOLLOW-UP

Reteaching/Remediation

- Study Guide in Chapter 12 Resource Book, pp. 63–64
- Tutor Place, Fractions Card 19, Ratio, Proportion, and Percent Card 16
- eTutorial Plus Online
- Extra Practice, p. 738
- Lesson Practice in Chapter 12 Resource Book, pp. 60–62

Challenge/Enrichment

- Challenge Practice in Chapter 12 Resource Book, p. 65
- Teacher's Edition, p. 594F

English Learner Support

- Spanish Study Guide
- Multi-Language Glossary
- Chapter Audio Summaries CDs

Extended Problem Solving In Exercises 26–28, use the following information.

You make an archery target like the one shown. Assume that when an arrow is shot and hits the target, the arrow is equally likely to hit any point on the target. The probability that an arrow lands within the red bull's-eye circle is given by the following equation.

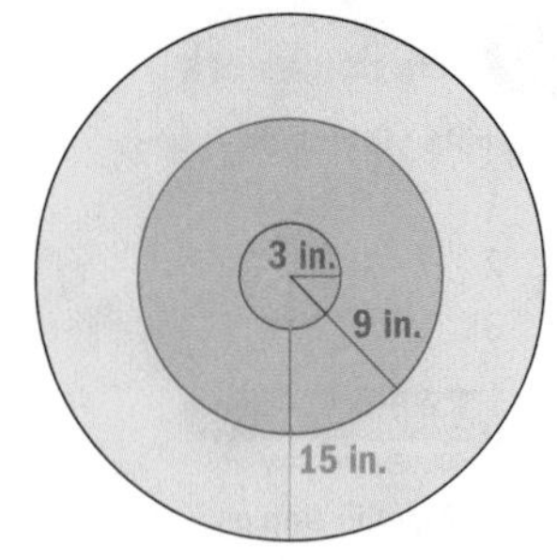

$$P = \frac{\text{Area of bull's-eye}}{\text{Area of target}}$$

C **26. Geometry** What is the area of the bull's-eye? What is the total area of the target? Leave your answers in terms of π. **9π; 225π**

27. Probability What is the probability that an arrow that hits the target lands within the bull's-eye? **0.04**

28. Odds What are the odds that an arrow that hits the target lands on the blue region? **$\frac{8}{17}$**

Mixed Review

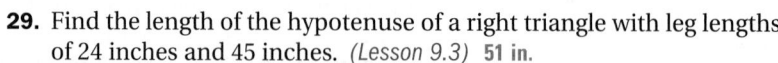

29. Find the length of the hypotenuse of a right triangle with leg lengths of 24 inches and 45 inches. *(Lesson 9.3)* **51 in.**

Find the slope of the line passing through the points. *(Lesson 11.6)*

30. $(-8, 12), (9, 2)$ **$-\frac{10}{17}$** **31.** $(7, 5), (-3, 6)$ **$-\frac{1}{10}$** **32.** $(-1, -5), (-4, -10)$ **$\frac{5}{3}$**

Basic Skills Find the product.

33. $\frac{4}{5} \cdot \frac{7}{12}$ **$\frac{7}{15}$** **34.** $\frac{5}{9} \cdot \frac{3}{5}$ **$\frac{1}{3}$** **35.** $\frac{1}{8} \cdot \frac{3}{7}$ **$\frac{3}{56}$** **36.** $\frac{9}{13} \cdot \frac{5}{6}$ **$\frac{15}{26}$**

Test-Taking Practice

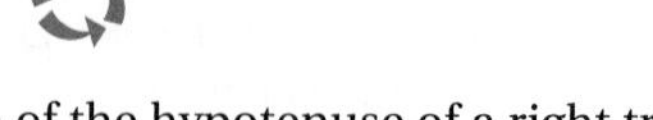

37. Multiple Choice You roll a number cube. What is the probability that you will roll a number greater than 4? **B**

A. $\frac{1}{4}$ **B.** $\frac{1}{3}$ **C.** $\frac{1}{2}$ **D.** $\frac{2}{3}$

38. Multiple Choice While playing for your baseball team, you have hit the ball 14 out of 21 times at bat. Based on this record, what are the odds in favor of hitting the ball the next time you are at bat? **I**

F. $\frac{14}{35}$ **G.** $\frac{1}{2}$ **H.** $\frac{2}{3}$ **I.** $\frac{2}{1}$

12.8 Hands-on Activity

GOAL
Use a simulation to explore probability.

MATERIALS
- index cards
- calculator

Probability and Simulations

You can use a simulation to explore probability. A *simulation* is an experiment done to explore the probability of an event.

Explore 1 **Simulate a real-world situation.**

Do a simulation to find an experimental probability that you and a friend are the 2 students randomly chosen from a group of 8 students. **Steps 1–3. A good answer will include an accurate recording of the results for drawing 10 pairs of cards.**

1 Label eight index cards as shown. Use 1 to represent yourself, 2 to represent your friend, and 3, 4, 5, 6, 7, and 8 to represent the other students.

1	2	3	4
5	6	7	8

2 Shuffle the cards. Randomly draw a card, and then another, without replacing the first. Record whether or not the results represent you and your friend being chosen. Replace the cards.

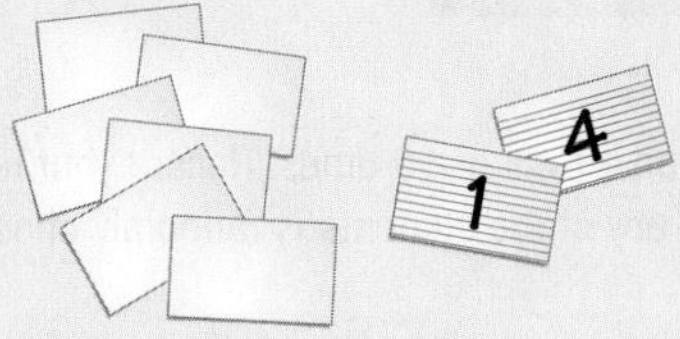

3 Repeat drawing a pair of cards. Draw a total of 10 pairs. For each pair of cards drawn, record the results.

Use the ratio $\frac{\text{you and friend are chosen}}{\text{total number of pairs drawn}}$ to find the experimental probability that you and your friend are chosen.

Pair	Times Drawn
5, 8	I
7, 2	II
1, 4	I

Your turn now **Use your results from the simulation above.**

1. Combine all the class results. Based on these results, what is the experimental probability that you and your friend are chosen? **Answers will vary. Check class results.**

ILLINOIS Standards and ISAT:
10.B.3, 10.C.3a

1 PLAN

Explore the Concept

- Students will use a simulation to explore probability.
- This activity leads into the study of dependent events in Lesson 12.8. Sometimes a simulation can be used to verify a probability calculation when it seems unreasonable.

Materials

Each student or pair of students will need index cards and a calculator.

Recommended Time

Work activity: 15 min
Discuss results: 10 min

Grouping

Students can work individually or in pairs. If students work in pairs, one student can record the results while the partner selects the cards.

2 TEACH

Tips for Success

Make sure students understand that this activity is only studying the probability of both 1 and 2 being chosen, so a partial result, such as 1 and 5, must be counted as an unfavorable result.

Discussion

As students work through Step 2, ask them why they need to replace the cards. Lead students to recognize that they must randomly choose two students from a group of eight each time they simulate the activity.

CLOSE

KEY DISCOVERY

Sufficient numbers of simulations can give a reasonable approximation of a probability.

ASSESSMENT

1. When would you use a simulation? ***Sample answer:*** **When you could feasibly perform an experiment to determine the likelihood of an event**
2. Were everybody's results for the activity the same? Why or why not? **Everybody's results differed because simulations rely on chance.**

5. ***Sample answer:*** **In the simulation above, (1, 1), (2, 2), (3, 3), (4, 4), (5, 5), (6, 6), (7, 7), and (8, 8) are all favorable outcomes. The probability that you are the person chosen twice in a row is lower than the probability that any student is chosen twice in a row, so consider only (1, 1) a favorable outcome.**

Explore 2 **Use technology to simulate a real-world situation.**

Use your calculator's random integer function to simulate randomly choosing 1 student from a group of 8. Find the experimental probability that any of the students is randomly chosen twice in a row.

1. Use 1, 2, 3, 4, 5, 6, 7, and 8 to represent the students.

2. Clear your calculator screen. Press MATH and choose the PRB menu. Select *randInt(*, the random integer function.

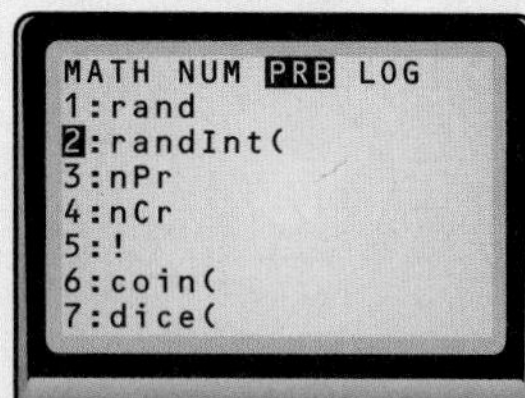

3. Enter **1** , **8** ENTER) to select an integer at random from 1 to 8. Press ENTER again to simulate choosing a student again. Record whether your results represent a match.

4. Do the simulation a total of 10 times. Record your results. What is the experimental probability that any of the students is randomly chosen twice in a row? **Actual results may vary. The theoretical probability is $\frac{8}{64}$ or $\frac{1}{8}$.**

Your turn now **Design a simulation of the situation.**

2. You randomly choose to go to the library, from the choices mall, library, or bowling lanes. ***Sample answer:*** **Assign random numbers 1, 2, and 3 to the choices and simulate the situation by using a calculator to generate a random integer of 1, 2, or 3.**
3. You and your friend Chris are randomly chosen from a group of 10 team members to be co-captains. ***Sample answer:*** **Write the numbers 1 through 10 on index cards. Simulate choosing co-captains by drawing two cards. Do not replace the first card before drawing the second card.**

Stop and Think

4. **Critical Thinking** Refer to Exercise 1 on page 637. Which results do you think are more likely to be close to the theoretical probability that you and your friend are chosen, your results or the class results? Explain. **The class results. *Sample answer:* There were more trials.**
5. **Writing** Explain how the simulation above would be different if you wanted to find the probability that you are randomly chosen twice in a row from a group of eight people. **See margin.**

Independent and Dependent Events

BEFORE	Now	WHY?
You found the probability of an event.	You will study independent and dependent events.	So you can find the probability of winning a free snack, as in Ex. 13.

Word Watch

independent events, p. 639
dependent events, p. 639

Two events are **independent events** if the occurrence of one event does *not* affect the probability that the other event will occur. Two events are **dependent events** if the occurrence of one event *does* affect the probability that the other event will occur.

Suppose you randomly choose two gumballs one at a time from the jar below. The probability of choosing two red gumballs with replacement is different than the probability without replacement.

Independent Events

First Event

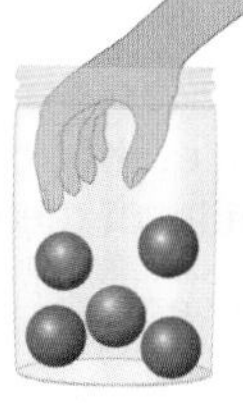

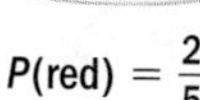

$P(\text{red}) = \frac{2}{5}$

Second Event

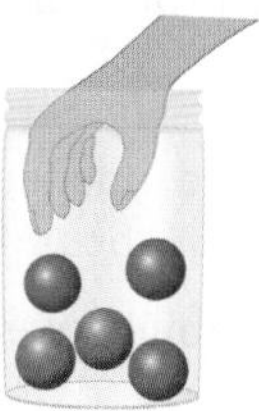

$P(\text{red}) = \frac{2}{5}$

If you replace the gumball, the probability of choosing a red gumball is the same for each choice.

Dependent Events

First Event

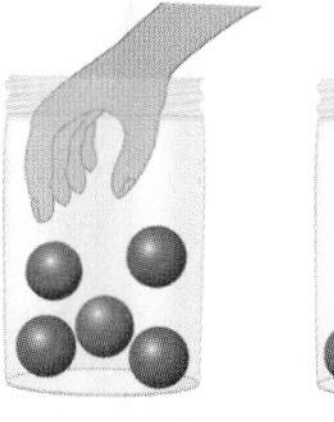

$P(\text{red}) = \frac{2}{5}$

Second Event

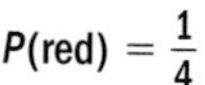

$P(\text{red}) = \frac{1}{4}$

If you don't replace the gumball after choosing, the probability changes.

EXAMPLE 1 Independent and Dependent Events

Tell whether the events are *independent* or *dependent*.

a. You roll a number cube. Then you roll the number cube again.

b. You randomly draw a number from a bag. Then you randomly draw a second number without putting the first number back.

Solution

a. The result of the first roll does not affect the result of the second roll, so the events are independent.

b. There is one fewer number in the bag for the second draw, so the events are dependent.

ILLINOIS Standards and ISAT:
10.C.3a

1 PLAN

SKILL CHECK

1. $\frac{4}{5} \cdot \frac{3}{4}$ $\frac{3}{5}$

2. $\frac{1}{25} \cdot \frac{1}{25}$ $\frac{1}{625}$

3. $\frac{2}{12} \cdot \frac{1}{11}$ $\frac{1}{66}$

LESSON OBJECTIVE

Study independent and dependent events.

PACING

Suggested Number of Days
Basic Course: 2 days
Average Course: 2 days
Advanced Course: 2 days
Block: 1 block

TEACHING RESOURCES

For a complete list of Teaching Resources, see page 594B.

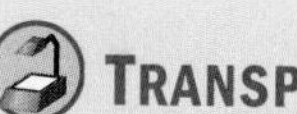

TRANSPARENCY

Warm-Up Exercises for this lesson are available on a transparency.

2 TEACH

MOTIVATING THE LESSON

Bring gumballs or marbles to class to demonstrate the lesson opener for students.

TIPS FOR NEW TEACHERS

For each example in this lesson, make sure students are clear about whether the events are independent or dependent. See Tips for New Teachers in the *Chapter 12 Resource Book*.

EXTRA EXAMPLES

Example 1 Tell whether the events are *independent* or *dependent*.

a. You choose a boy from a group of ten boys and send him on an errand. Then you choose another boy. **There are fewer boys to choose from the second time, so the events are dependent.**

b. You toss a coin four times and get heads each time. Then you toss the coin a fifth time. **Each toss does not affect the others, so the events are independent.**

Example 2 Each day ten colleagues put their names in a bag, and someone draws a name at random. The person whose name is drawn answers the phones during lunch while the others go out for lunch. What is the probability that one colleague answers the phones two days in a row? $\frac{1}{100}$

COMMON ERROR

In Example 3, clarify that the probability of the second number is found by *assuming* that the first number has been successfully called.

Differentiating Instruction

Advanced Students Some students, while less interested in the mathematics of chance, may be highly motivated by and interested in the psychology of chance. Encourage students to do research on *gambler's fallacy* and *clustering illusion* and to share their findings with the class.

Multiple Events To find the probability that Event A *and* Event B happen, you multiply probabilities. Because the occurrence of an event may affect the probability of another event, you should determine whether the events are independent or dependent before multiplying.

Probability of Independent Events

For two independent events, the probability that both occur is the product of the probabilities of the events.

$P(\text{A and B}) = P(\text{A}) \cdot P(\text{B})$ **Events A and B are independent.**

EXAMPLE 2 Probability of Independent Events

School Fair Your class is raising money by operating a ball toss game. You estimate that about 1 out of every 25 balls tossed results in a win. What is the probability that someone will win on two tosses in a row?

Solution

The tosses are independent events, because the outcome of a toss does not affect the probability of the next toss resulting in a win.

So the probability of each event is $\frac{1}{25}$.

$$P(\text{win and win}) = P(\text{win}) \cdot P(\text{win}) = \frac{1}{25} \cdot \frac{1}{25} = \frac{1}{625}$$

ANSWER The probability of two winning tosses in a row is $\frac{1}{625}$.

Dependent Events If A and B are dependent events, the probability that B occurs given that A also occurs is not the same as the probability of B. So, you should use $P(\text{B given A})$ instead of $P(\text{B})$ to represent the probability that B occurs given that A also occurs.

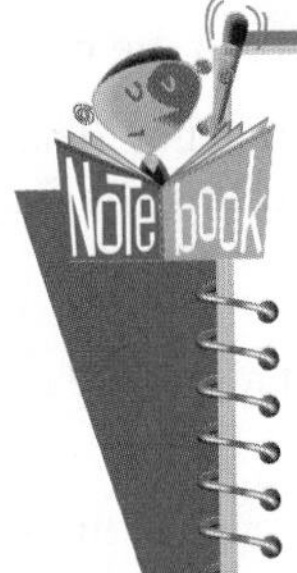

Probability of Dependent Events

For two dependent events, the probability that both events occur is the product of the probability of the first event and the probability of the second event given that the first event also occurs.

$P(\text{A and B}) = P(\text{A}) \cdot P(\text{B given A})$ **A and B are dependent.**

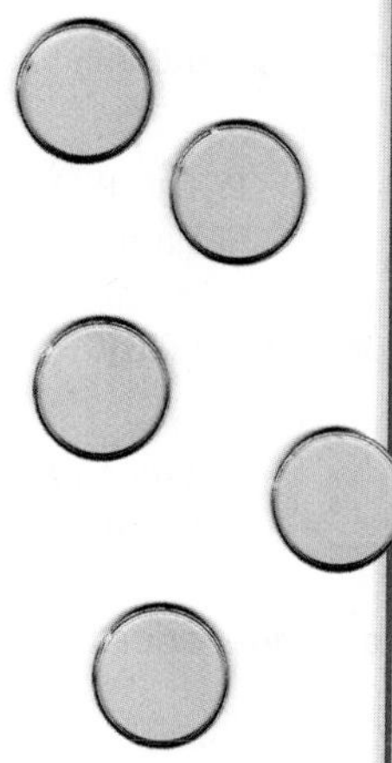

EXAMPLE 3 Finding Probability of Dependent Events

Bingo You are playing the bingo card shown. The caller has 50 numbers left to call. What is the probability that you will get bingo on the next 2 numbers called?

B	I	N	G	O
12	18	41	51	66
7	26	44	54	70
6	27	FREE SPACE	58	63
5	23	39	52	73
3	30	36	57	75

Solution

You need B7 and N44 for bingo. Find the probability of success when each of the next 2 numbers is drawn. Then multiply.

$P(\text{B7 or N44}) = \frac{2}{50} = \frac{1}{25}$ **There are 50 numbers left to call.**

$P(\text{remaining number}) = \frac{1}{49}$ **There are 49 numbers left to call.**

$P(\text{both numbers}) = \frac{1}{25} \cdot \frac{1}{49} = \frac{1}{1225}$ **Multiply the probabilities.**

ANSWER The probability is $\frac{1}{1225}$, or about 0.0008.

Your turn now **Find the probability.**

1. You toss a coin twice. Find the probability of getting two heads. $\frac{1}{4}$
2. Find the probability for Example 3 if there are 36 numbers left to call.

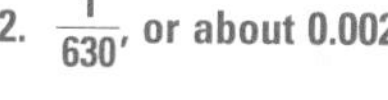

2. $\frac{1}{630}$, or about 0.002

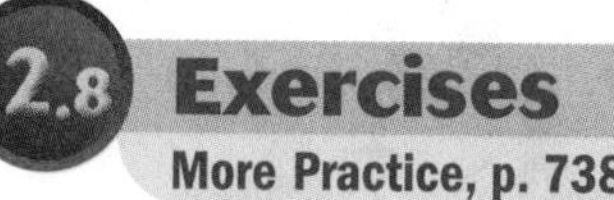

12.8 Exercises

More Practice, p. 738

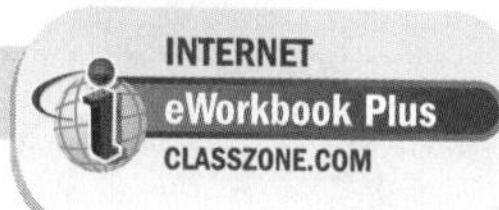

Getting Ready to Practice

1. **Vocabulary** Copy and complete: When the occurrence of an event does not affect the probability of the next event, the events are _?_. **independent**

Tell whether the events are *independent* or *dependent*. Then find the probability.

2. You randomly choose a green marble from a jar of 8 green and 3 blue marbles. You replace the marble and randomly choose another green marble. **independent;** $\frac{64}{121}$
3. Your teacher randomly chooses you to give a report. She then randomly chooses Pam from the 22 remaining students. **dependent;** $\frac{1}{506}$

EXTRA EXAMPLES

Example 3 Teofono must make two dentist appointments in September. He writes the numbers from 1 to 30 on papers to represent the days that he could go to the dentist, puts them in a bag, and pulls two papers at random from the bag without replacement. What is the probability that both appointments will be within the first seven days of September? **$\frac{7}{145}$, or about 0.048**

CONCEPT CHECK

How is finding the probability of A and B different if B is independent from or dependent on A? **If A and B are independent, then the probability of A and B is P(A) multiplied by P(B). If B is dependent on A, then the probability of A and B is P(A) multiplied by P(B after A has occurred).**

DAILY PUZZLER

Alex, Basil, Cassandra, and Dyron are standing in line to walk through the Haunted House at a theme park. Basil does not want to be the first of the four to walk through. Cassandra does not want to be first or last. What is the probability that Dyron will be the first to walk through the Haunted House? **$\frac{1}{2}$, or 0.5**

ASSIGNMENT GUIDE

Basic Course

Day 1: pp. 642-643 Exs. 4-6, 16-21

Day 2: pp. 642-643 Exs. 7-13, 22

Average Course

Day 1: pp. 642-643 Exs. 4-6, 16-22

Day 2: pp. 642-643 Exs. 7-14, 23

Advanced Course

Day 1: pp. 642-643 Exs. 4-6, 15-19*

Day 2: pp. 642-643 Exs. 9-14, 21-23

Block

pp. 642-643 Exs. 4-14, 16-23

EXTRA PRACTICE

- Student Edition, p. 738
- Chapter 12 Resource Book, pp. 68-70
- Test and Practice Generator

TRANSPARENCY

Even-numbered answers are available on transparencies.

HOMEWORK CHECK

When you review students' homework for this lesson, go over the following exercises to check understanding of key concepts.

Basic: 4, 6, 7, 10, 11

Average: 4, 7, 9, 10, 12

Advanced: 5, 9, 10, 12, 13

TEACHING TIP

As students work Exercises 10-15, advise them to look for words that indicate independent events, such as *equally likely*, and words that indicate dependent events, such as *without replacement*.

HELP with Homework

Example	Exercises
1	10-14
2	4-6, 10-14
3	7-14

Online Resources CLASSZONE.COM

- More Examples
- eTutorial Plus

14. $\frac{1}{128}$; $\frac{1}{2}$

15. The last statement; the first statement. *Sample answer:* The last statement says that what happens in the future does not depend on what happened in the past; the first statement indicates that what has happened in the past 5 years has depended on what happened in the previous years.

Practice and Problem Solving

Events A and B are independent. Find the missing probability.

A **4.** $P(A) = 0.4$, $P(B) = 0.6$, $P(A \text{ and } B) = \underline{?}$ 0.24

5. $P(A) = 0.9$, $P(B) = \underline{?}$ 0.1, $P(A \text{ and } B) = 0.09$

6. $P(A) = \underline{?}$, $P(B) = 0.6$ 0.2, $P(A \text{ and } B) = 0.12$

Events A and B are dependent. Find the missing probability.

7. $P(A) = 0.75$, $P(B \text{ given } A) = 0.5$, $P(A \text{ and } B) = \underline{?}$ 0.375

8. $P(A) = 0.8$, $P(B \text{ given } A) = \underline{?}$ 0.4, $P(A \text{ and } B) = 0.32$

9. $P(A) = \underline{?}$ 0.13, $P(B \text{ given } A) = 0.3$, $P(A \text{ and } B) = 0.039$

In Exercises 10–12, tell whether the events are *independent* or *dependent*. Then find the probability.

10. Banquet At a banquet, you can order a main course of a chef's salad, salmon and potatoes, ham and beans, or steak and rice. You can drink water, juice, milk, coffee, or iced tea. If all choices are equally likely, what is the probability that a randomly chosen person orders a chef's salad and juice? independent; $\frac{1}{20}$

11. Cookies You have a jar filled with 5 oatmeal cookies, 6 sugar cookies, 8 frosted cookies, and 9 chocolate cookies. You randomly choose a cookie, keep it, and then choose another. What is the probability that you pick a frosted cookie and then a chocolate cookie? dependent; $\frac{2}{21}$

12. Buttons You draw a button at random from the jar at the right. Without replacing the first button, you draw another. What is the probability that you draw a red button and then a yellow button? dependent; $\frac{1}{19}$

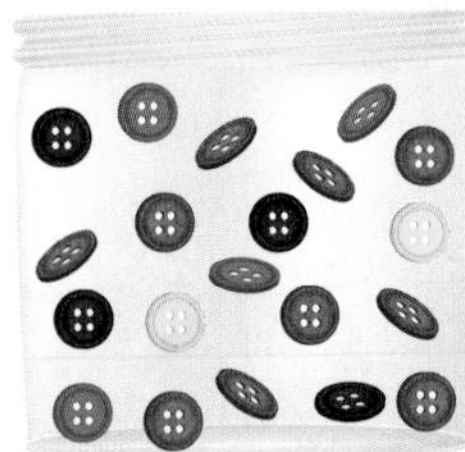

B **13. Lucky Plate** Each day, the person who gets the lucky plate wins a free snack from the school cafeteria. The cafeteria sells 127 lunches on Wednesday and 134 lunches on Thursday. What is the probability that you win on both days if you buy lunch both days? $\frac{1}{17{,}018}$

14. Critical Thinking What is the probability that when you toss a coin you get heads 7 times in a row? If you have already gotten heads 6 times in a row, what is the probability that you will get heads on the next toss? See margin.

C **15. Challenge** A brochure says, "If you invested money with us 5 years ago, that money grew by an average of 20%." The brochure also says, "Past performance is no guarantee of future results." Which statement leads you to think that investing money today is independent of past events? Which statement suggests the opposite? Explain. See margin.

16. Elections A town's election for mayor drew 75% of the town's 800 eligible voters. What is the probability that two different randomly selected people both voted in the election? 0.562

Mixed Review 

17. See margin for art. *Sample answer:* About 46 min; if you extend the graph, it passes through 46 on Saturday.

17. The table shows the amount of time, in minutes, that Cindy ran on the treadmill each day. Make a line graph of the data. Predict how long Cindy will run on Saturday. Explain your reasoning. *(Lesson 12.3)*

Monday	20
Tuesday	25
Wednesday	25
Thursday	35
Friday	41

Basic Skills **Evaluate the expression.**

18. $5 \cdot (11 - 4)$ 35 **19.** $3 + 9 \cdot 6$ 57 **20.** $35 - 21 \div 3$ 28 **21.** $\frac{35}{9 - 2}$ 5

Test-Taking Practice 

22. Multiple Choice Suppose you spin the spinner at the right twice. What is the probability of landing on a blue region both times? C

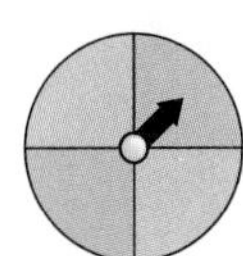

A. $\frac{1}{16}$ **B.** $\frac{1}{8}$ **C.** $\frac{1}{4}$ **D.** $\frac{1}{2}$

23. Short Response Your teacher is giving away two prizes by random drawing. She puts 25 students' names into a hat. She draws the first name. Then she chooses a second name without replacing the first name. What is the probability that your name will be chosen first? Does the probability that your name will be chosen second depend on the first outcome? Explain why or why not.
$\frac{1}{25}$; yes. *Sample answer:* After one name is drawn, there are only 24 left, so the first drawing affects the second drawing.

Brain Game

Lucky Numbers

Two balls will be randomly chosen without replacement from the globe shown.

Bo wins if the first ball is blue, and the next ball is a 3 or a 4.

Sherry wins if the first ball is an even number and the next ball is green.

Eva wins if both balls are red.

Who has the best chance of winning? Bo

4 ASSESS

Assessment Resources

For more assessment resources, see:
- Assessment Book
- Test and Practice Generator

Mini-Quiz

Find the missing probability.

1. Events A and B are independent. $P(A) = 0.3$, $P(B) = 0.5$, $P(A \text{ and } B) = \underline{?}$ 0.15
2. Events A and B are dependent. $P(A) = 0.75$, $P(B \text{ given } A) = \underline{?}$, $P(A \text{ and } B) = 0.3$. 0.4
3. A bag contains ten cards numbered 1 through 10. You pick one card and then another without replacement. What is the probability that both cards display a value of 6 or higher? $\frac{2}{9}$, or $0.\overline{2}$

5 FOLLOW-UP

Reteaching/Remediation

- Study Guide in Chapter 12 Resource Book, pp. 71–72
- Tutor Place, Fractions Card 19, Ratio, Proportion, and Percent Card 16
- eTutorial Plus Online
- Extra Practice, p. 738
- Lesson Practice in Chapter 12 Resource Book, pp. 68–70

Challenge/Enrichment

- Challenge Practice in Chapter 12 Resource Book, p. 74
- Teacher's Edition, p. 594F

English Learner Support

- Spanish Study Guide
- Multi-Language Glossary
- Chapter Audio Summaries CDs

17. See Additional Answers beginning on page AA1.

1 PLAN

SKILL CHECK

Identify who is excluded in each survey group.

1. a group of car drivers **people who do not drive**
2. a poll of 2000 parents **people who do not have children**
3. members of a warehouse club **nonmembers of the club**

LESSON OBJECTIVE

Identify biased samples and surveys.

2 TEACH

EXTRA EXAMPLES

Example 1 A fast-food franchise is trying to decide whether to open a new restaurant at a specific location. A sample of residents will be surveyed. Tell whether the survey method could result in a biased sample. Explain.

a. Survey customers in a diner. **This method could result in a biased survey because diner customers may be more likely to favor a new fast-food restaurant.**

b. Survey patrons in a library. **This method is less likely to result in a biased survey because library patrons are neither more or less likely to favor a new fast-food restaurant.**

c. Survey customers in a grocery store. **This method could result in a biased survey because grocery-store customers could be less likely to favor a new fast-food restaurant.**

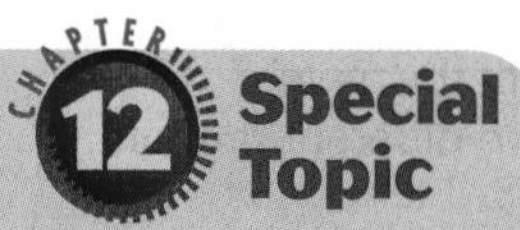

Samples

GOAL Identify biased samples and surveys.

Word Watch

population, p. 644
sample, p. 644
random sample, p. 644
biased sample, p. 644

One way to collect data about a group is by doing a survey. A **population** is the entire group of people or objects that you want information about. When it is difficult to survey an entire population, a **sample**, or a part of the entire group, is surveyed.

In a **random sample**, each person or object has an equally likely chance of being selected. A non-random sample can result in a **biased sample** that is not representative of the population.

EXAMPLE 1 Identifying Potentially Biased Samples

Costume Dance The student council wants students to help decide on a theme for a costume dance. Students can choose one of the council's three ideas from the options listed at the right.

Which dance theme do you prefer?
Choose one:
☐ movies
☐ famous historical figures
☐ sports and games

Surveying all of the students will take too long, so a sample will be surveyed. Tell whether the survey method could result in a biased sample. Explain.

a. Survey members of the movie club.

b. Survey students as they enter the school.

c. Survey students on the football team.

Solution

a. This method could result in a biased sample because this group is more likely to favor the movie theme.

b. This method is not likely to result in a biased sample because a wide range of students will be surveyed.

c. This method could result in a biased sample because the football players are more likely to favor sports and games.

Survey Questions When you do a survey, you need to phrase the questions so that the responses of the people surveyed accurately reflect their opinions or actions. If not, claims based on the survey results may be biased.

ILLINOIS Standards and ISAT:
10.A.3c

5–8. Sample explanations are given.

5. Yes; this question suggests the mall is noisy and crowded. It encourages respondents to favor staying at home. So, the question could lead to biased results.

6. Yes; this question suggests that dogs are messy and dangerous. It encourages a response of no. So, the question could lead to biased results.

7. No; this question is straight forward with no suggestions. It is not likely to lead to biased results.

EXAMPLE 2 Identifying Potentially Biased Questions

Tell whether the question could produce biased results. Explain.

a. *Do you support the unfair policy of requiring students to do a time-consuming community project?* YES ☐ NO ☐

b. *Do you like our new apple-nut yogurt flavor, now on sale in stores everywhere?* YES ☐ NO ☐

Solution

a. This question suggests that the policy is unfair and that the project is time-consuming. It encourages a response of *no*. So, the question could lead to biased results.

b. The question assumes that the person responding has tried the new yogurt flavor. Those who have not tried the new flavor may not give an accurate opinion. So, the question could lead to biased results.

Exercises

Stadiums In Exercises 1–3, a city wants to know whether residents favor using public funds to pay for a new baseball stadium. Tell whether the method could result in a biased sample. Explain.

1. Ask people that call in to a sports radio talk show.
   Yes; people who call in to a sports talk show are likely to favor sports.
2. Ask every tenth person listed in the phone book.
   No; people chosen from the phone book should provide a wide range of responses.
3. Ask every fifth person who enters the sporting goods store in town.
   Yes; people who enter a sporting goods store are likely to favor sports.
4. **Food** A restaurant wants to know what kinds of food to add to its menu to attract new customers. Describe a sampling method that the restaurant can use that is not likely to result in a biased sample.
   ***Sample answer:* Ask every tenth person listed in the phone book.**

Tell whether the survey question could produce biased results. Explain your reasoning. 5–8. See margin.

5. Would you rather relax at home while reading a book, or go to a noisy, crowded mall?
6. Allowing messy, dangerous dogs into the park will cause safety and health problems. Will you vote to allow dogs into the park?
7. How often do you buy lunch in the school cafeteria?
8. Do you agree with this store's policy for returning purchases?

8. Yes; the question assumes that persons responding know what the store's policy is. This could lead to biased results unless a description of the policy is also given.

EXTRA EXAMPLES

Example 2 Tell whether the question could produce biased results. Explain.

a. How many hours of television do you watch per day? **This question may not produce biased results.**

b. Do you think filthy rich people should pay more in taxes? **This question encourages a response of *yes* by using emotional language to describe rich people, so the question could lead to biased results.**

COMMON ERROR

In part b of Example 2, some students may not understand why this question is considered biased. Lead students to understand that if the question were to appear in a random store or on a web site, it would be best broken into two parts, first asking if the customer has tried the new flavor and then asking the customer's opinion of the flavor. Then ask students if the question would be as biased if it were included in a package of the apple-nut yogurt.

3 APPLY

TEACHING TIP

For Exercises 1–3, advise students to think about the people who would be excluded by the survey. Then students can critically examine whether the included and excluded groups are significantly different in a way that would bias the survey results.

ADDITIONAL RESOURCES

The following resources are available to help review the materials in Lessons 12.4–12.8.

Chapter 12 Resource Book
- Lesson Practice
- Study Guide

Assessment Book
- Chapter 12 Quiz 2

Technology
- Test and Practice Generator
- eTutorial CD-ROM

Internet
- Classzone
- eWorkbook Plus Online
- eTutorial Plus Online

ENGLISH LEARNER SUPPORT

- Spanish Study Guide
- Multi-Language Glossary
- Chapter Audio Summaries CDs

Notebook Review

Review the vocabulary definitions in your notebook.

Copy the review examples in your notebook. Then complete the exercises.

Check Your Definitions

tree diagram, p. 618
permutation, p. 623
factorial, p. 623
combination, p. 627
complementary events, p. 632
unfavorable outcome, p. 633
odds, p. 633
independent events, p. 639
dependent events, p. 639

Use Your Vocabulary

1. **Vocabulary** Copy and complete: A(n) _?_ is an arrangement in which order is important. permutation

12.4 Can you use the counting principle?

EXAMPLE You need to choose one of 3 birdhouse designs and one of 6 possible colors. How many different birdhouses can you build?

ANSWER $3 \cdot 6 = 18$, so you can build 18 different birdhouses.

2. You have 5 designs of birdhouses and 4 colors from which to choose. How many different birdhouses can you build? 20 birdhouses

12.5–12.6 Can you find permutations and combinations?

EXAMPLE At a swim meet, 10 swimmers are in an event. In how many ways can first, second, third, and fourth place medals be awarded?

The order is important, so find the number of permutations.

$${}_{10}P_4 = \frac{10!}{(10-4)!} = \frac{10!}{6!} = 10 \cdot 9 \cdot 8 \cdot 7 = 5040$$

ANSWER There are 5040 ways to award the medals.

3. You are making a braided rope out of three different colors of yarn. You have seven colors of yarn. In how many ways can you choose the colors so the rope has three different colors? 210 ways

Review Quiz 2

1.

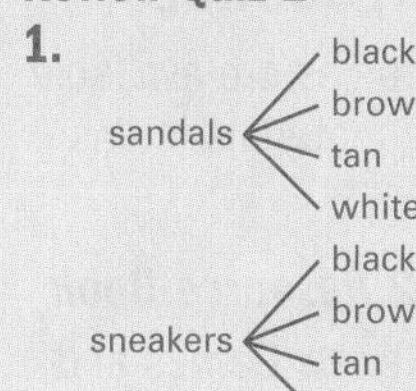

12.7 Can you find odds?

EXAMPLE You have a bag of 6 red, 5 blue, and 3 white marbles. What are the odds in favor of randomly drawing a red marble from the bag?

ANSWER $\text{Odds} = \dfrac{\text{Number of favorable outcomes}}{\text{Number of unfavorable outcomes}} = \dfrac{6}{8} = \dfrac{3}{4}$

☑ **4.** What are the odds in favor of randomly drawing a white marble? $\frac{3}{11}$

12.8 Can you calculate probabilities?

EXAMPLE Tiles with each of the 11 letters in PROBABILITY are in a bag. You randomly draw a tile, replace it, and then randomly draw a second tile. What is the probability that both tiles are I's?

ANSWER $P(\text{I and I}) = P(\text{I}) \cdot P(\text{I}) = \frac{2}{11} \cdot \frac{2}{11} = \frac{4}{121}$

☑ **5.** What is the probability that the first tile is B and the second is L? $\frac{2}{121}$

Stop and Think about Lessons 12.4–12.8

6. Writing Give a real-world example of a situation where you use combinations to count possibilities. *Sample answer:* Ordering toppings on a pizza

Review Quiz 2

1. **Shoes** You can buy sandals or sneakers in black, brown, tan, or white. Make a tree diagram to show the possible choices for shoes. See margin.
2. **Camp** You are scheduling swimming, crafts, canoeing, and softball. How many different schedules of four different activities are possible? 24 schedules
3. **Hockey** Find the number of ways two players can be chosen from 20 team members. 190 ways
4. **Rain** If the probability that it will rain today is 0.4, what are the odds in favor of rain? What is the probability that it will *not* rain? $\frac{2}{3}$; 0.6

Find the probability.

5. You roll a 5 on a 6-sided number cube. Then you roll another 5. $\frac{1}{36}$
6. A bag has 3 red and 5 blue tiles. You randomly draw a red tile, keep it, and then randomly draw a blue tile. $\frac{15}{56}$

ADDITIONAL RESOURCES

The following resources are available to help review the materials in this chapter.

Chapter 12 Resource Book

- Chapter Review Games and Activities, p. 75
- Cumulative Practice, Chs. 1–12

English/Spanish Chapter Reviews and Tests

Chapter Audio Summaries CDs

eTutorial CD-ROM

eWorkbook Plus Online

eTutorial Plus Online

7.

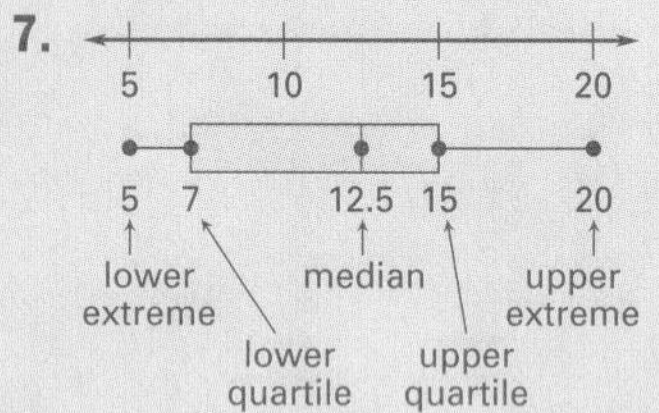

8.

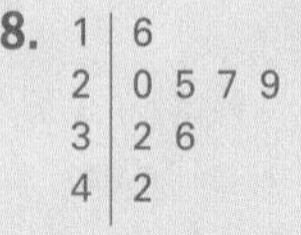

1	6
2	0 5 7 9
3	2 6
4	2

Key: 2 | 0 = 20

20–29

9.

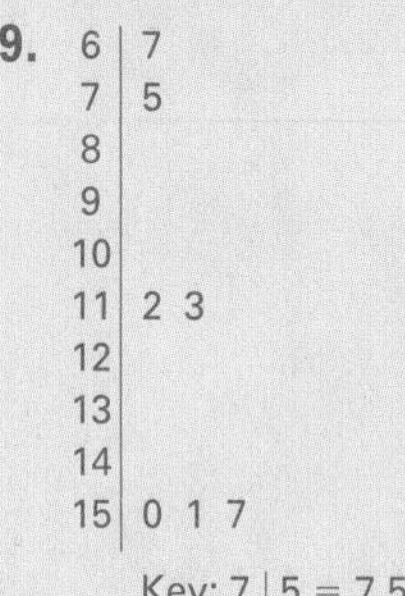

6	7
7	5
8	
9	
10	
11	2 3
12	
13	
14	
15	0 1 7

Key: 7 | 5 = 7.5

15.0–15.9

10.

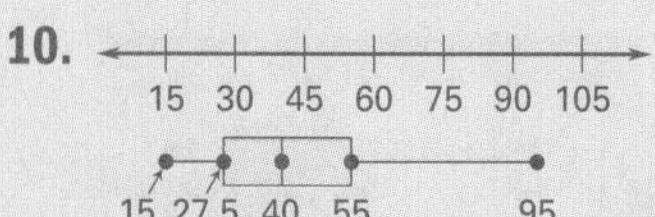

Sample answer: **About half of the chess sets are priced between $27.50 and $55. The $95 set lies well beyond the third quartile, and appears to be an outlier.**

Chapter Review

Vocabulary

stem-and-leaf plot, p. 597
box-and-whisker plot, p. 601
lower quartile, p. 601
upper quartile, p. 601
lower extreme, p. 601
upper extreme, p. 601
circle graph, p. 605
line graph, p. 606
tree diagram, p. 618
permutation, p. 623
factorial, p. 623
combination, p. 627
complementary events, p. 632
unfavorable outcome, p. 633
odds, p. 633
independent events, p. 639
dependent events, p. 639

Vocabulary Review

Matching In Exercises 1–6, match the description with the correct word(s).

1. An arrangement in which order is important F
2. An arrangement in which order is not important E
3. A graph to display data that fall into distinct categories A
4. A graph used to display changes in a quantity over time B
5. A plot used to order a data set D
6. A plot used to summarize a data set C

A. bar graph
B. line graph
C. box-and-whisker plot
D. stem-and-leaf plot
E. combination
F. permutation

7. Copy the box-and-whisker plot at the right. Label the median, upper and lower quartiles, and upper and lower extremes. **See margin.**

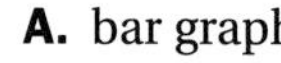

Review Questions

Make an ordered stem-and-leaf plot to organize the data. Identify the interval that includes the most data values. *(Lesson 12.1)* **8–9. See margin.**

8. 20, 25, 36, 16, 29, 32, 27, 42
9. 11.2, 7.5, 15.1, 15.7, 15.0, 6.7, 11.3

10. **Chess** The prices of several chess sets are $15, $20, $38, $95, $60, $45, $40, $35, and $50. Make a box-and-whisker plot of the data. What conclusions can you make? *(Lesson 12.2)* **See margin.**

Review Questions

11. Summer Treats The table shows the favorite summer treats of students surveyed. Represent the data in a circle graph. *(Lesson 12.3)* **See margin.**

Ice Cream	50%
Frozen fruit	25%
Ices	10%
Other	15%

12. Election Your class is having an election for president, vice president, and secretary. For president there are 4 candidates, for vice president there are 5 candidates, and for secretary there are 3 candidates. No one is running for more than one office. How many groups of winners are possible? *(Lesson 12.4)* **60 groups**

Evaluate the expression. *(Lessons 12.5, 12.6)*

13. ${}_8P_4$ 1680 **14.** ${}_{10}P_3$ 720 **15.** ${}_9C_2$ 36 **16.** ${}_6C_1$ 6

17. Photograph You and six friends are posing for a photograph. In how many ways can you line up for the photograph if you line up in one row? *(Lesson 12.5)* **5040 ways**

In Exercises 18 and 19, tell whether the situation describes a *combination* or a *permutation*. Then find the answer. *(Lessons 12.5, 12.6)*

18. Pizza In how many ways can you select 4 different pizza toppings from 12 toppings? **combination; 495 ways**

19. Bobblehead Dolls You have six different bobblehead dolls, and you want to choose three to give as gifts to Ali, Lin, and Rhea. How many different ways can you do this? **permutation; 120 ways**

20. Contest The probability that you will win a contest is 76%. What is the probability that you will lose the contest? What are the odds that you will lose the contest? *(Lesson 12.7)* **24%; $\frac{6}{19}$**

21. Softball A softball player has a batting average of 0.350, which means she gets a hit 35% of her times at bat. What are the odds that she will get a hit in her next at bat? *(Lesson 12.7)* $\frac{7}{13}$

22. Weather The weather forecaster says there is a 60% chance that it will snow on Wednesday and a 25% chance that it will snow on Thursday. Find the probability that it will snow on both Wednesday and Thursday. *(Lesson 12.8)* **15%**

23. Cards Two cards are dealt randomly, one after another, from a deck of cards numbered from 1 through 20. The first card is not returned to the deck before the second is dealt. Find the probability that the first card is a 7 and the second card is a 4. *(Lesson 12.8)* $\frac{1}{380}$

11. Favorite Summer Treat

Ice cream 50%
Frozen fruit 25%
Other 15%
Ices 10%

ADDITIONAL RESOURCES

Assessment Book

- Chapter Test (3 levels), pp. 148–153
- Standardized Chapter Test, p. 154
- Alternative Assessment, pp. 155–156

Test and Practice Generator

1.

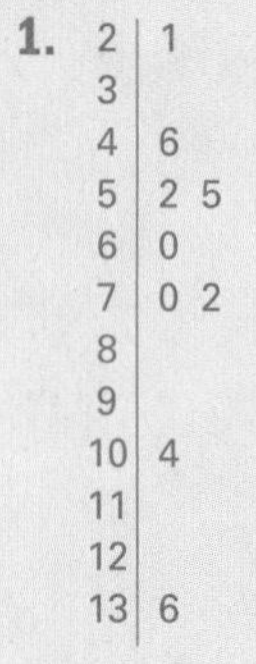

Key: 4 | 6 = 46

50–59 and 70–79

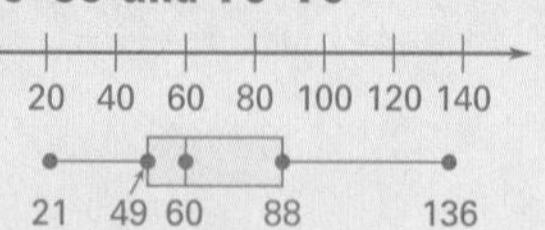

2.

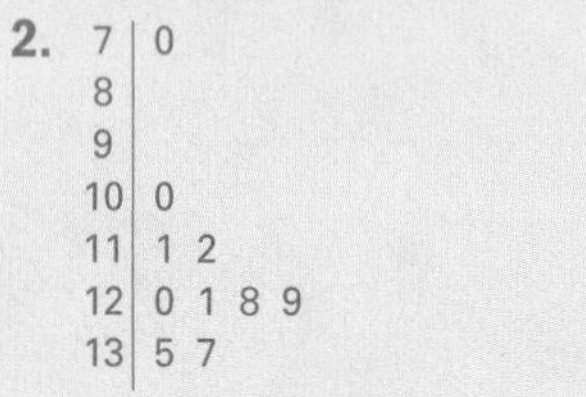

Key: 10 | 0 = 10.0

12.0–12.9

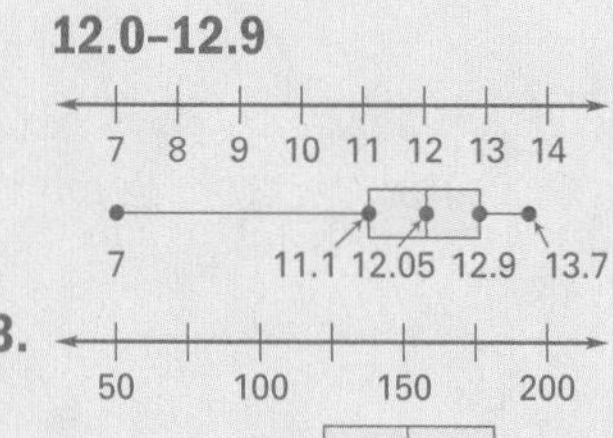

4, 6. See Additional Answers beginning on page AA1.

Chapter Test

In Exercises 1 and 2, make a stem-and-leaf plot. Tell which interval includes the most values. Then make a box-and-whisker plot. 1–2. See margin.

1. 46 kg, 70 kg, 21 kg, 136 kg, 55 kg, 60 kg, 72 kg, 104 kg, 52 kg

2. 12.1 in., 13.5 in., 12.8 in., 10 in., 7 in., 11.2 in., 12.9 in., 11.1 in., 12 in., 13.7 in.

3. Academy Awards The lengths, in minutes, of the Best Picture Academy Award winning movies for the years 1990–1999 are 99, 118, 122, 131, 142, 160, 177, 183, 194, and 197. Make a box-and-whisker plot of the data. See margin.

4. Temperature The record low temperatures in Miami, Florida, are given in the table. Display the data in an appropriate graph. See margin.

Month	Jan.	Feb.	Mar.	Apr.	May	Jun.	Jul.	Aug.	Sep.	Oct.	Nov.	Dec.
Temp (°F)	30	32	32	46	53	60	69	68	68	51	39	30

5. Golf There are five members on a golf team. Make a tree diagram to count the number of ways you can select a captain and an assistant. 20 ways

6. Movies You and four friends are going to a movie. In how many different orders can you pick your friends up? List all the possible orders. See margin.

7. School Dance You are making a banner for a school dance and have a choice of 8 colors. You want to use 4 different colors. How many different combinations are possible? 70 combinations

In Exercises 8 and 9, use the circle graph. It shows student replies to *Which animal career would you enjoy?*

Animal Careers

Veterinarian 35%
Pet store owner 22%
Zookeeper 21%
Rodeo star 13%
Circus animal trainer 9%

8. What is the probability that a randomly chosen student replied *veterinarian*? 35%

9. What are the odds in favor of a randomly chosen student replying *zookeeper*? $\frac{21}{79}$

Tell whether the events are *independent* or *dependent*. Then find the probability.

10. You roll a 6 on a number cube. Then you roll again and roll a 2. independent; $\frac{1}{36}$

11. You have 8 blue marbles and 12 red marbles in a bag. You randomly pick a blue marble on the first draw. Then you randomly pick another blue marble without replacing the first one. dependent; $\frac{14}{95}$

Chapter Standardized Test

Test-Taking Strategy Learn as much as you can about a test ahead of time, such as the types of questions and the topics the test will cover.

Multiple Choice

1. When the number 29 is plotted on a stem-and-leaf plot, the 9 is which of the following? B

   A. stem **B.** leaf **C.** key **D.** median

2. What does the number 56 represent on the box-and-whisker plot? G

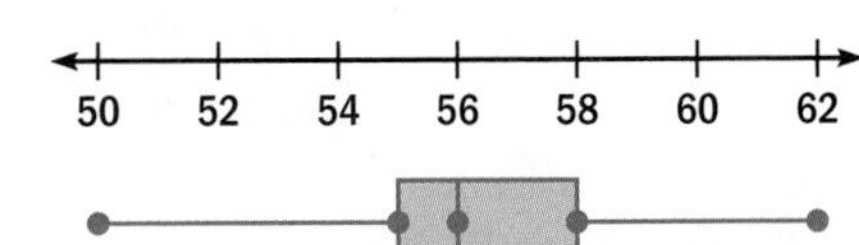

   F. upper quartile **G.** median
   H. lower quartile **I.** lower extreme

3. Which is an appropriate display for the data in the table below? A

Favorite sport	Percent of students
Football	17%
Baseball	28%
Basketball	39%
Soccer	8%

   A. bar graph **B.** line graph
   C. circle graph **D.** histogram

4. You are asked to enter a 4-character password for a video game. The password must begin with a letter and end with 3 digits. How many different passwords are possible if you can repeat digits? G

   F. 56 **G.** 26,000
   H. 175,760 **I.** 456,976

5. An ice cream parlor has 8 different flavors of ice cream. You would like a dish with 3 scoops of different flavors. How many different dishes can you pick? B

   A. 36 **B.** 56
   C. 336 **D.** 40,320

6. There are 200 raffle tickets and 5 are winning tickets. What are the odds in favor of winning with one ticket? G

   F. 1 to 40 **G.** 1 to 39
   H. 1 to 199 **I.** 1 to 200

7. You pick randomly from a jar of 12 green, 18 yellow, and 20 red mints. You pick a mint, eat it, and pick another mint. What is the probability that you pick a green mint and then a yellow mint? C

   A. $\frac{99}{1225}$ **B.** $\frac{54}{625}$ **C.** $\frac{108}{1225}$ **D.** $\frac{27}{152}$

Short Response

8. There are 30 students auditioning for new openings in a chorus. How many ways can you choose 4 students to be in the chorus? **27,405 ways**

Extended Response

9. You asked 100 students whether they had shirts of the following colors: blue, yellow, orange. Your results were blue: 94%, yellow: 68%, orange: 43%. Use an appropriate form to display these data. Explain your choice. Then identify another type of display that would not be a good choice for these data. Explain why it would not be a good choice. **See margin.**

Additional Resources

Assessment Book
- Standardized Chapter Test, p. 154

Test and Practice Generator

9. **Shirt Color Survey**

Color	Percent
Blue	94
Yellow	68
Orange	43

Sample answer: **A bar graph was used because the data is in categories; a line graph is not a good choice because the data does not change over time.**

Explore the Concept

- Students apply their knowledge of finding simple probability.
- Finding simple probability was studied in Lesson 8 of Chapter 7.
- Robins use their senses to locate worms.

Science Background

Animals often have highly developed, specialized senses for locating their food, such as the sonar of bats, the acute sense of smell of dogs, the night vision of owls, and the ability of mosquitoes to detect the heat and carbon dioxide given off by prey.

Tips for Success

Review the general probability ratio $\frac{\text{\# of favorable outcomes}}{\text{\# of possible outcomes}}$ with students to show how it applies to geometric probability. To provide an image of finding something at random, have students imagine placing a marble anywhere on a field that has a treasure chest buried in it, with no clues, and having the marble be directly over the chest.

Guiding Students' Work

Exercise 5 may prove difficult for students. Point out that the experiment is to see if the probability that a robin locates a square with a worm in it is greater than the geometric probability of choosing that square randomly. If so, something must be at work besides geometric probability, so a hypothesis is made as to what else is at work. Blocking a robin's sight or hearing tests the hypothesis that a robin uses sight and sound to locate worms.

EXPLORING MATH IN SCIENCE

INVESTIGATING Robins

Geometric Probability

When a robin hunts for worms, does it search randomly, or can it sense a worm's location? Scientists used geometric probability to investigate this. Geometric probability is based on area. For events dependent on area, you can find the *geometric probability* using the following formula:

$$P(\text{event}) = \frac{\text{Area representing favorable outcomes}}{\text{Area representing possible outcomes}}$$

There are 4 treasure chests buried in a 5 yard by 10 yard field. Each chest has an area of 1 square yard. Use geometric probability to describe the expected results of searching a randomly chosen spot in the field.

1 Find the area of the treasure chests.

$$4 \text{ chests} \cdot \frac{1 \text{ square yard}}{\text{chest}} = 4 \text{ square yards}$$

2 Find the area of the field.

$$5 \text{ yards} \cdot 10 \text{ yards} = 50 \text{ square yards}$$

3 Find the geometric probability of finding a treasure chest by random search.

$$P(\text{finding a chest}) = \frac{\text{Area of treasure chests}}{\text{Area of field}}$$

$$= \frac{4}{50} = 0.08$$

10 yd

5 yd

So, the geometric probability of finding a chest by random search is 8%.

1. Suppose there are 6 treasure chests in the field. What is the geometric probability of finding a chest by random search? 0.12, or 12%
2. Suppose there are 9 treasure chests in the field, and each has an area of 2 square feet. Find the geometric probability of finding a chest by random search. Remember to measure the field in the same units as the chests. 0.04, or 4%

How Robins Find Worms

To investigate how robins find worms, scientists did a series of experiments. They buried four worms in pans of soil that were marked into a 10 by 10 grid and calculated the geometric probability of a robin finding a worm at random.

Then they let robins search the pan and recorded the percent of the time a worm was found. A robin was counted as finding a worm if the square that it searched contained a worm. The experiment was repeated under different conditions.

Condition	Correct Finds
Robins could use all senses.	90%
Robins prevented from using visual clues.	50%
White noise decreased robins' ability to hear worms.	59%

3. Find the geometric probability of finding a worm by searching randomly. Write the probability as a percent. **0.04, or 4%**

4. The table above shows the percent of attempts in which the robins found worms under each condition. For each condition, compare the percent of correct finds to the geometric probability of randomly finding a worm. **See margin.**

5. **Critical Thinking** What can you conclude from the results of the experiment? How do the results suggest that robins don't search randomly for worms but instead use their senses? **See margin.**

Project IDEAS

- **Experiment** Design and perform an experiment or a search involving geometric probability. Compare the theoretical and experimental geometric probabilities. Explain any discrepancies. Present your findings to the class.
- **Investigate** Learn more about how different birds find food. Present your findings.
- **Research** Look up information about search and rescue techniques. What techniques do people use to increase the probability of finding something? Present your findings.
- **Career** Learn about people who study animal behavior. What sorts of careers do they have? Present your findings.

APPLY

REFLECTING ON THE ACTIVITY

Robins are much more accurate at locating worms than random geometric probability would indicate, and are apparently using their senses, including sight and hearing.

PROJECT IDEAS

For additional information on the Project Ideas and for suggestions for more projects, go to classzone.com

ASSESS

The rubric below can be used to assess the projects on the pupil page. For more information on rubrics, see the Professional Development Book.

4 The student fully achieves the mathematical and project goals. The student gives logical reasoning for her or his conclusions. All work is complete and accurate.

3 The student substantially achieves the mathematical and project goals. The student may have some difficulty explaining the results of the experiment. There may be some minor misunderstanding of content or errors in computation.

2 The student partially achieves the mathematical and project goals. The student is able to find geometric probabilities, but has trouble with comparisons and conclusions. Some of the work may be incomplete, or unclear.

1 The student makes little progress toward accomplishing the goals of the project because of a lack of understanding or lack of effort. The student is not able to find the geometric probabilities.

4, 5. See Additional Answers beginning on page AA1.

Pacing and Assignment Guide

REGULAR SCHEDULE

Lesson	Les. Day	BASIC	AVERAGE	ADVANCED
13.1	Day 1	pp. 659–660 Exs. 12–22, 41–43	pp. 659–660 Exs. 12–22, 40–44	pp. 659–660 Exs. 14–24, 41–44
	Day 2	pp. 659–660 Exs. 23–31, 44–49	pp. 659–660 Exs. 25–35, 45–49	pp. 659–660 Exs. 29–40*, 47–49
13.2	Day 1	EP p. 728 Exs. 7–9; pp. 664–665 Exs. 9–14, 21–26, 39–41	pp. 664–665 Exs. 9–14, 21–24, 34–36, 43–45	pp. 664–665 Exs. 11–14, 21–24, 34–36, 43–45
	Day 2	pp. 664–665 Exs. 15–20, 29–33, 42–45	pp. 664–665 Exs. 15–20, 27–31, 39–42	pp. 664–665 Exs. 17–20, 27–29, 37–42*
13.3	Day 1	pp. 669–670 Exs. 9–20, 40–42, 54–59	pp. 669–670 Exs. 12–21, 40–47, 54–56	pp. 669–670 Exs. 12–21, 39–45, 54–58
	Day 2	pp. 669–670 Exs. 22–37, 45–48, 60, 61	pp. 669–670 Exs. 26–38, 48–50, 57–61	pp. 669–670 Exs. 26–37, 48–53*, 59–61
13.4	Day 1	pp. 676–677 Exs. 9–14, 24–27, 40–43	pp. 676–677 Exs. 12–17, 23–25, 31–36	pp. 676–677 Exs. 14–17, 23–25, 32–38
	Day 2	pp. 676–677 Exs. 15–20, 22, 32–39	pp. 676–677 Exs. 18–22, 26–28, 37–43	pp. 676–677 Exs. 18–22, 27–31*, 41–43
13.5	Day 1	EP p. 737 Exs. 1, 8–11; pp. 682–684 Exs. 8–14, 23–25, 36–42	pp. 682–684 Exs. 10–13, 23–25, 35–42	pp. 682–684 Exs. 10–13, 26–30, 36–42
	Day 2	pp. 682–684 Exs. 15–20, 26–30, 43–49	pp. 682–684 Exs. 18–22, 29–32, 43–49	pp. 682–684 Exs. 18–22, 32–35*, 43–49
Review	Day 1	pp. 688–689 Exs. 1–57	pp. 688–689 Exs. 1–57	pp. 688–689 Exs. 1–57
Assess	Day 1	Chapter 13 Test	Chapter 13 Test	Chapter 13 Test

YEARLY PACING Chapter 13 Total – **12 days** Chapters 1–13 Total – **160 days** Remaining – **0 days**

*Challenge Exercises EP = Extra Practice SRH = Skills Review Handbook EC = Extra Challenge

BLOCK SCHEDULE

DAY 1	DAY 2	DAY 3	DAY 4	DAY 5	DAY 6
13.1 pp. 659–660 Exs. 12–22, 25–35, 40–49	**13.2** pp. 664–665 Exs. 9–24, 27–31, 34–36, 39–45	**13.3** pp. 669–670 Exs. 12–21, 26–38, 40–50, 54–61	**13.4** pp. 676–677 Exs. 12–28, 31–43	**13.5** pp. 682–684 Exs. 10–13, 18–25, 29–32, 35–49	**Review** pp. 688–689 Exs. 1–57 **Assess** Chapter 13 Test

YEARLY PACING Chapter 13 Total – **6 days** Chapters 1–13 Total – **80 days** Remaining – **0 days**

Support Materials

CHAPTER RESOURCE BOOK

CHAPTER SUPPORT

Tips for New Teachers	p. 1	Parents as Partners	p. 3

LESSON SUPPORT	13.1	13.2	13.3	13.4	13.5
Lesson Plans (regular and block)	p. 5	p. 15	p. 24	p. 33	p. 41
Technology Activities & Keystrokes		p. 17			
Activity Support Masters					
Activity Masters	p. 7				
Practice (3 levels)	p. 8	p. 18	p. 26	p. 35	p. 43
Study Guide	p. 11	p. 21	p. 29	p. 38	p. 46
Real-World Problem Solving	p. 13		p. 31		
Challenge Practice	p. 14	p. 23	p. 32	p. 40	p. 48

REVIEW

Chapter Review Games and Activities	p. 49	Extra Credit Project with Rubric	p. 54
Real-Life Project with Rubric	p. 50	Cumulative Practice	p. 56
Cooperative Project with Rubric	p. 52	Resource Book Answers	A1

ASSESSMENT

Quizzes	p. 157	Alternative Assessments with Rubrics	p. 166
Chapter Tests (3 levels)	p. 159	Unit Test	p. 168
Standardized Test	p. 165	Cumulative Test	p. 170

TRANSPARENCIES

	13.1	13.2	13.3	13.4	13.5
Warm-Up / Daily Homework Quiz	✔	✔	✔	✔	✔
Notetaking Guide	✔	✔	✔	✔	✔
Teacher Support		✔		✔	✔
English/Spanish Problem Solving		✔		✔	✔
Answer Transparencies	✔	✔	✔	✔	✔

TECHNOLOGY

- EasyPlanner CD-ROM
- Test and Practice Generator
- Electronic Lesson Presentations
- eTutorial CD-ROM
- Chapter Audio Summaries CDs
- Classzone.com
- eEdition Plus Online
- eWorkbook Plus Online
- eTutorial Plus Online
- EasyPlanner Plus Online

ADDITIONAL RESOURCES

- Worked-Out Solution Key
- Notetaking Guide
- Practice Workbook
- Tutor Place
- Professional Development Book
- Special Activities Book
- Posters
- Spanish Study Guide
- Exercises in Spanish
- English/Spanish Ch. Reviews/Tests
- Multi-Language Visual Glossary

Math Background and Teaching Strategies

Lesson 13.1

MATH BACKGROUND

A *monomial* is a constant, a variable, or the product of a constant and one or more variables. A **polynomial** is a monomial or the sum of one or more monomials. Each monomial in a polynomial is called a *term* of the polynomial. To write a polynomial in **standard form**, write the terms so that the exponents of the variable decrease from left to right. To simplify a polynomial, combine like terms by adding their coefficients. This process may include one or more applications of the distributive property.

TEACHING STRATEGIES

You may want to model some polynomials with students using algebra tiles in anticipation of the use of algebra tiles to perform operations with polynomials in the following lessons. This is also a good time to review the use of the distributive property, especially how it is used with negative numbers and subtraction. Remind students when evaluating a term that is to the second power or higher to include the negative sign in the exponentiation operation, for example, z^2 for $z = -3$ corresponds to $(-3)^2$, not -3^2.

Lesson 13.2

MATH BACKGROUND

ADDING AND SUBTRACTING POLYNOMIALS Adding and subtracting polynomials is just like simplifying a polynomial, in that you find and combine the like terms. You can add and subtract polynomials using either a vertical format, in which terms of the same power are aligned, or horizontally. When subtracting polynomials, you add the opposite. So, the first step in polynomial subtraction is to use the distributive property to multiply each of the terms of the polynomial to be subtracted by -1.

TEACHING STRATEGIES

The Activity at the beginning of this lesson shows an example of using algebra tiles to model polynomial addition involving only positive terms. You may also want to use algebra tiles to model polynomial addition involving negative terms. You will need to make sure that students understand the concept of forming and removing zero pairs. You can also model polynomial subtraction with algebra tiles. The first step will be replacing the subtraction sign with an addition sign and replacing the tiles for the subtracted polynomial with their opposites. Also in this lesson, make sure that students understand that taking the opposite of each term is just an application of the distributive property, as shown in the example below.

$$\begin{aligned}&(4x^2 - 3x + 6) - (-7x^2 + 5x + 3)\\ &\quad = (4x^2 - 3x + 6) + (-1)(-7x^2 + 5x + 3)\\ &\quad = (4x^2 - 3x + 6) + [(-1)(-7x^2) + (-1)5x + (-1)3]\\ &\quad = (4x^2 - 3x + 6) + (7x^2 - 5x - 3)\end{aligned}$$

Lesson 13.3

MATH BACKGROUND

MONOMIALS AND POWERS The product of powers property, which was presented earlier in this text, states that the product of powers with the same base is the power whose base is the original power and whose exponent is the sum of the exponents of the original powers. For example, $j^2 \cdot j^3 = j^{2+3}$. This lesson presents two new properties of powers. First, the *power of a product property* states that a power of a product is the product of the powers of the factors. For example, $(3j)^3 = 3^3 \cdot j^3$. Second, the *power of a power property* states that a power of a power is the power whose base is that of the original power and whose exponent is the product of the exponents involved. For example, $(j^3)^3 = j^{3 \cdot 3}$.

TEACHING STRATEGIES

It is easy for students to confuse the properties of exponents and to make other mistakes involving powers. Some examples of mistakes might be $j^2 \cdot j^3 = j^{2 \cdot 3}$, $(3j)^3 = 9 \cdot j^3$, or $(j^3)^3 = j^{3+3}$. You will need to spend extra time with students to be sure they understand when each property applies and how to apply it. You may want to go back with students to the definition of a power in terms of repeated multiplication, for example, $j^2 \cdot j^3 = (j \cdot j) \cdot (j \cdot j \cdot j)$, or $(j^3)^3 = j^3 \cdot j^3 \cdot j^3$, to refresh students' memories and to help them better understand the properties.

Lesson 13.4

MATH BACKGROUND

MULTIPLYING BINOMIALS As with multiplying a polynomial by a monomial, multiplying two binomials is an application of the distributive property, but it is more complicated, since it requires a compound application. For example, you can think of the binomial product $(ax + b)(cx + d)$ as $(ax + b) \cdot y$, where $y = (cx + d)$. So, applying the distributive property gives $ax \cdot y + b \cdot y$, or $ax(cx + d) + b(cx + d)$. Then, applying the distributive property twice more gives $acx^2 + adx + bcx + bd$. Notice that this is the same result that is given using the **FOIL** method:

First: $ax \cdot cx = acx^2$
Outer: $ax \cdot d = adx$
Inner: $b \cdot cx = bcx$
Last: $b \cdot d = bd$

TEACHING STRATEGIES

You may want to extend the modeling work with algebra tiles at the beginning of this lesson to multiplying binomials that include a negative constant term. Again, students will need to understand the concept of zero pairs. Emphasize to students that all of the methods that are shown in Examples 1–4 in this lesson are just different ways to show the application of the distributive property to multiplying two binomials. They should notice that in each of the Examples, there are four products, which correspond to the four terms that result when each of the two terms of a binomial is multiplied by each of the two terms of the other.

Lesson 13.5

MATH BACKGROUND

NON-LINEAR FUNCTIONS In **function notation**, the dependent variable is stated explicitly as a function of the independent variable. For example, writing the function $y = -3x - 4$ in function notation as $f(x) = -3x - 4$ states that y is a function of x. Because a function assigns a unique value to any input, you can identify the graph of a function using the **vertical line test**, which states that if any vertical line intersects a graph at more than one point, the graph does not represent a function.

TEACHING STRATEGIES

It often takes students a while to become comfortable with function notation, and they are often unsure why it is needed. You may want to point out that one advantage comes in evaluating functions for a value of a variable, as in Example 1. Function notation makes it very clear what value is substituted as well as which is the dependent quantity. When students start graphing second-degree functions, you may want to point out that these are called *quadratic functions*, and that the graph of any function of the form $f(x) = ax^2 + bx + c$ for $a \neq 0$ will have a U-shaped graph. Using technology to graph quadratic functions, such as in the Technology Activity following this lesson, will help students gain an understanding of the effect of changing parameters on the graphs of quadratic functions.

Differentiating Instruction

Strategies for Underachievers

FOCUS ON VOCABULARY

In Lesson 13.1, it will help students understand the vocabulary terms *monomial*, *binomial*, *trinomial*, and *polynomial* to connect the use of the prefixes involved to their use in everyday words. Have students brainstorm words that use the prefixes *mono-*, *bi-*, *tri-*, and *poly-*, such as monoplane, monologue, monopoly, bicycle, bipedal, binary, tricycle, triangle, triceratops, polygon, polychrome, and polyester.

USE MODELS AND MANIPULATIVES

ALGEBRA TILES In Lesson 13.2, plan on spending a considerable amount of time with the Activity at the top of page 661. Students should each be given their own set of algebra tiles. If you have access to a translucent overhead set of tiles, you can model addition and subtraction for students. For some underachievers, you may wish to start at a more basic level by adding just 1-tiles, then by adding just x-tiles, and then by adding just x^2-tiles. From there, you can extend into adding polynomials with tiles. As noted in the Teaching Strategies for this lesson, you can extend the use of algebra tiles to model polynomial subtraction as well as addition. Some underachievers should be allowed to continue using algebra tiles until they are ready to make their own natural break from them.

Again, in Hands-on Activity 13.4, plan on allowing students substantial time to practice modeling binomial multiplication with algebra tiles. Students should also be shown models involving negative constant terms and allowed to practice modeling binomials with negative terms on their own. Point out that a zero pair can involve a positive and a negative x-tile as well as a positive and a negative 1-tile. Multiplying binomials that contain negative terms will also give students additional practice in using the sign rules for multiplication.

DECREASE COMPLEXITY

The four Examples of Lesson 13.4 illustrate four methods of multiplying two binomials (in addition to using algebra tile models). It may be confusing for some underachievers to have so many options. For these students, you may want to concentrate just on one method. The FOIL method is a good common denominator, since it is mnemonic in nature, but students with different learning styles and needs may benefit from employing one of the other methods, at least until they are comfortable and ready to move on.

USE SCAFFOLDING

In Lesson 13.2, for application problems such as Example 4 on page 663, you may wish to provide students with templates that will guide them through solving such problems step by step. Some underachievers may possess the cognitive ability to understand such problems but lack the organizational ability to navigate their way through the required steps.

EXPONENTS In Lesson 13.3, after completing the table in the Activity at the top of page 666, you may wish to have students create note cards to have as a reference when needed for the various properties of exponents. These cards should include the product of powers property, the power of a product property, and the power of a power property. Each card should have the property stated both in words and in algebraic language, and should have examples illustrating the use of the property.

FOIL METHOD For Lesson 13.4, you may wish to provide students templates for applying the FOIL method for multiplying binomials. At the top, the template could include a model binomial for which first, outer, inner, and last terms are indicated. Then blanks could be provided and labeled in which students could fill in the appropriate products. You can also provide templates if desired for students to use in multiplying binomials by the vertical and horizontal methods.

Strategies for English Learners

FOCUS ON MATHEMATICAL SYMBOLS

In spite of the fact that the English used in the text is becoming increasingly abstract, part of students' developing competence in mathematics is being able to learn the language of the discipline. Some of the new phrases are:

standard form (p. 657)
binomial (p. 657)
Power of a Product Property (p. 667)

For English learners, however, you may want to express the concepts in mathematical symbols first and follow with a discussion of the verbal description. For example, when teaching the power of a product property, teachers may want to start by putting this expression from page 667 on the board:

$$(ab)^m = a^m b^m$$

Next, substitute numbers for variables, so that students can see that the rule works. Then discuss the explanation in English on that same page.

Students should be reassured that even though they are working with mathematical expressions and equations that are more complex, logical mathematical reasoning underlies all of mathematics. Everything can be explained, although some explanations have to be taken at face value at this point, because students are still learning the mathematics they need to be able to understand the proofs. The same basic rules, including the associative property, the distributive property, and the commutative property, still apply. The same basic strategies for evaluating polynomials, such as combining like terms and removing factors of one, still apply.

Strategies for Advanced Learners

INCREASE DEPTH AND COMPLEXITY

PATTERNS In Lesson 13.4, in Exercises 18–21 on page 676, students explore the pattern in multiplying binomials that are the sum and difference of the same two terms. You may wish to have students perform a similar investigation of any patterns they can find when a binomial is squared. Students should square binomials both with positive and negative constant terms to explore the patterns. Also in Lesson 13.4, in conjunction with Exercise 29 on page 677, you may wish to further challenge some advanced students by giving them other polynomials to multiply, for example $(2x - 5)(3x^2 + 5x - 4)$, which has product $6x^3 - 5x^2 - 33x + 20$, or $(x^2 - x + 6)(x^2 + 3x + 9)$, which has product $x^4 + 2x^3 + 12x^2 + 9x + 54$. Point out to students that they can use any of the methods of Examples 1–3 from Lesson 13.5. Ask students to predict how many terms will be produced by each multiplication before like terms are collected. Through the two examples given and their exploration of other products, students should be able to see that the number of products before simplification is just the product of the number of terms in each polynomial, since polynomial multiplication involves using the distributive property to multiply each term of one polynomial by each term of the other.

In Technology Activity 13.5, encourage advanced students to extend their exploration of quadratic functions to find other patterns that result from varying the parameters of the functions. For example, students can explore the graphs of functions of the form $y = (x - h)^2$ for varying values of h, and then include the effect of k to explore graphs of $y = (x - h)^2 + k$. Students can also explore the graphs of cubic functions and quartic functions, as well as rational functions of the form $y = \frac{a}{x}$ for varying values of a or exponential functions of the form $y = a^x$ for various positive values of a, including values between 0 and 1. If students have access to graphing software, they can pursue their investigations using a computer instead of a graphing calculator.

Differentiating Instruction: Teaching Resources

Differentiating Enrichment and Activities

McDougal Littell *Middle School Mathematics* offers teachers enrichment for all levels of students. Pictured on these pages are facsimiles of the Real-World Problem Solving pages, Chapter Review Games, and Chapter Projects from the *Chapter 13 Resource Book* and a number of activities from the *Special Activities Book*. Also available is the *Poster Package* containing large, full-color posters, one for each unit.

RESOURCE BOOK

The *Chapter Resource Books* contain Real-World Problem Solving activities for various lessons in the textbook, Chapter Review Games for a motivating review of each chapter, and Chapter Projects with rubrics that apply the mathematics of the chapter.

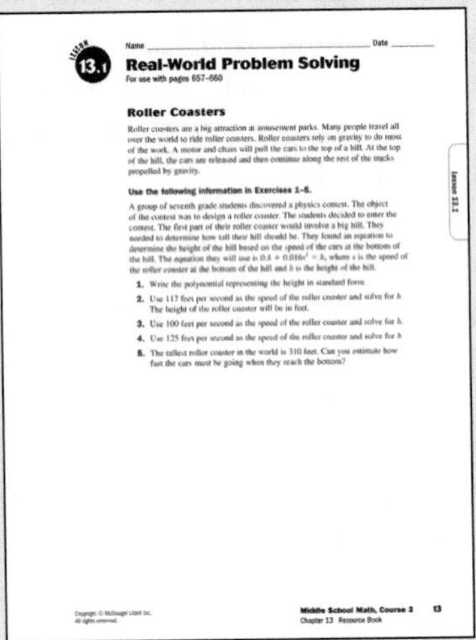

LESSON 13.1 Name ______ Date ______

Real-World Problem Solving

For use with pages 657–660

Roller Coasters

Roller coasters are a big attraction at amusement parks. Many people travel all over the world to ride roller coasters. Roller coasters rely on gravity to do most of the work. A motor and chain will pull the cars to the top of a hill. At the top of the hill, the cars are released and then continue along the rest of the tracks propelled by gravity.

Use the following information in Exercises 1–5.

A group of seventh grade students discovered a physics contest. The object of the contest was to design a roller coaster. The students decided to enter the contest. The first part of their roller coaster would involve a big hill. They needed to determine how tall their hill should be. They found an equation to determine the height of the hill based on the speed of the cars at the bottom of the hill. The equation they will use is $0.4 + 0.016s^2 = h$, where s is the speed of the roller coaster at the bottom of the hill and h is the height of the hill.

1. Write the polynomial representing the height in standard form.
2. Use 117 feet per second as the speed of the roller coaster and solve for h. The height of the roller coaster will be in feet.
3. Use 100 feet per second as the speed of the roller coaster and solve for h.
4. Use 125 feet per second as the speed of the roller coaster and solve for h.
5. The tallest roller coaster in the world is 310 feet. Can you estimate how fast the cars must be going when they reach the bottom?

Lesson 13.1

Copyright © McDougal Littell Inc. All rights reserved.

Middle School Math, Course 3 Chapter 13 Resource Book 13

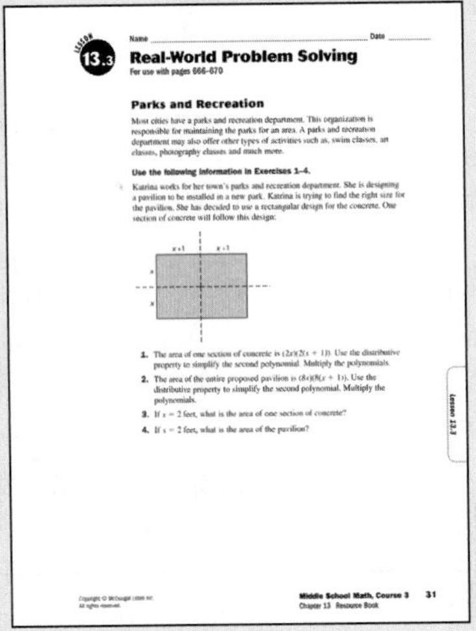

LESSON 13.3 Name ______ Date ______

Real-World Problem Solving

For use with pages 666–670

Parks and Recreation

Most cities have a parks and recreation department. This organization is responsible for maintaining the parks for an area. A parks and recreation department may also offer other types of activities such as, swim classes, art classes, photography classes and much more.

Use the following information in Exercises 1–4.

Katrina works for her town's parks and recreation department. She is designing a pavilion to be installed in a new park. Katrina is trying to find the right size for the pavilion. She has decided to use a rectangular design for the concrete. One section of concrete will follow this design:

1. The area of one section of concrete is $(2x)(2(x + 1))$. Use the distributive property to simplify the second polynomial. Multiply the polynomials.
2. The area of the entire proposed pavilion is $(8x)(8(x + 1))$. Use the distributive property to simplify the second polynomial. Multiply the polynomials.
3. If $x = 2$ feet, what is the area of one section of concrete?
4. If $x = 2$ feet, what is the area of the pavilion?

Lesson 13.3

Copyright © McDougal Littell Inc. All rights reserved.

Middle School Math, Course 3 Chapter 13 Resource Book 31

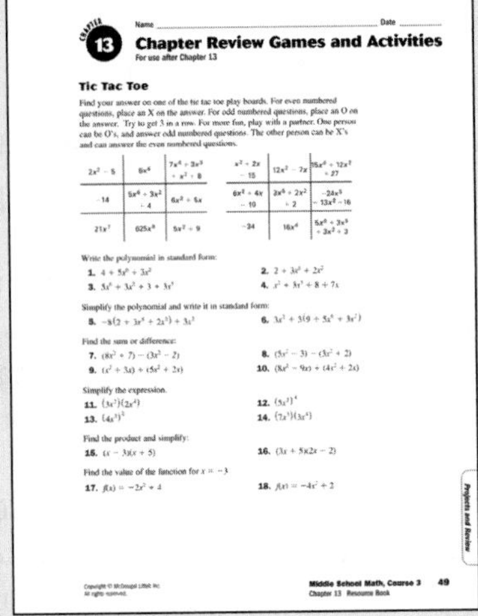

CHAPTER 13 Name ______ Date ______

Chapter Review Games and Activities

For use after Chapter 13

Tic Tac Toe

Find your answer on one of the tic tac toe play boards. For even numbered questions, place an X on the answer. For odd numbered questions, place an O on the answer. Try to get 3 in a row. For more fun, play with a partner. One person can be O's, and answer odd numbered questions. The other person can be X's and can answer the even numbered questions.

$2x^2 - 5$	$6x^5$	$7x^4 + 2x^3 + x^2 + 8$
-14	$5x^6 + 3x^2 - 4$	$6x^2 + 5x$
$21x^7$	$625x^8$	$5x^2 + 9$

$x^2 + 2x - 15$	$12x^2 - 7x$	$15x^4 + 12x^2 + 27$
$6x^2 + 4x - 10$	$2x^5 + 2x^2 + 2$	$-24x^3 - 13x^2 - 16$
-24	$16x^4$	$5x^6 + 3x^5 + 3x^2 + 3$

Write the polynomial in standard form:

1. $4 + 5x^6 + 3x^2$
2. $2 + 3x^3 + 2x^2$
3. $5x^6 + 3x^2 + 3 + 3x^5$
4. $x^2 + 8x^3 + 8 + 7x$

Simplify the polynomial and write it in standard form:

5. $-8(2 + 3x^5 + 2x^3) + 3x^3$
6. $3x^3 + 3(9 + 5x^4 + 3x^2)$

Find the sum or difference:

7. $(8x^2 + 7) - (3x^2 - 2)$
8. $(5x^2 - 3) - (3x^2 + 2)$
9. $(x^2 + 3x) + (5x^2 + 2x)$
10. $(8x^2 - 9x) + (4x^2 + 2x)$

Simplify the expression.

11. $(3x^3)(2x^4)$
12. $(5x^2)^4$
13. $(4x^3)^2$
14. $(7x^3)(3x^4)$

Find the product and simplify:

15. $(x - 3)(x + 5)$
16. $(3x + 5)(2x - 2)$

Find the value of the function for $x = -3$

17. $f(x) = -2x^2 + 4$
18. $f(x) = -4x^2 + 2$

Projects and Review

Copyright © McDougal Littell Inc. All rights reserved.

Middle School Math, Course 3 Chapter 13 Resource Book 49

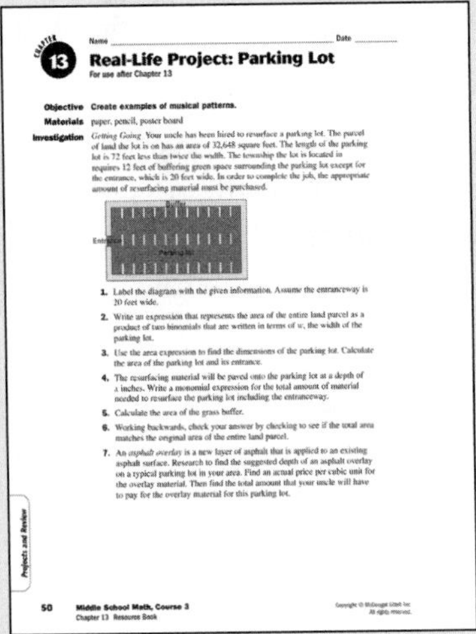

CHAPTER 13 Name ______ Date ______

Real-Life Project: Parking Lot

For use after Chapter 13

Objective **Create examples of musical patterns.**

Materials paper, pencil, poster board

Investigation *Getting Going* Your uncle has been hired to resurface a parking lot. The parcel of land the lot is on has an area of 32,648 square feet. The length of the parking lot is 72 feet less than twice the width. The township the lot is located in requires 12 feet of buffering green space surrounding the parking lot except for the entrance, which is 20 feet wide. In order to complete the job, the appropriate amount of resurfacing material must be purchased.

1. Label the diagram with the given information. Assume the entranceway is 20 feet wide.
2. Write an expression that represents the area of the entire land parcel as a product of two binomials that are written in terms of w, the width of the parking lot.
3. Use the area expression to find the dimensions of the parking lot. Calculate the area of the parking lot and its entrance.
4. The resurfacing material will be paved onto the parking lot at a depth of x inches. Write a monomial expression for the total amount of material needed to resurface the parking lot including the entranceway.
5. Calculate the area of the grass buffer.
6. Working backwards, check your answer by checking to see if the total area matches the original area of the entire land parcel.
7. An *asphalt overlay* is a new layer of asphalt that is applied to an existing asphalt surface. Research to find the suggested depth of an asphalt overlay on a typical parking lot in your area. Find an actual price per cubic unit for the overlay material. Then find the total amount that your uncle will have to pay for the overlay material for this parking lot.

Projects and Review

50 Middle School Math, Course 3 Chapter 13 Resource Book

Copyright © McDougal Littell Inc. All rights reserved.

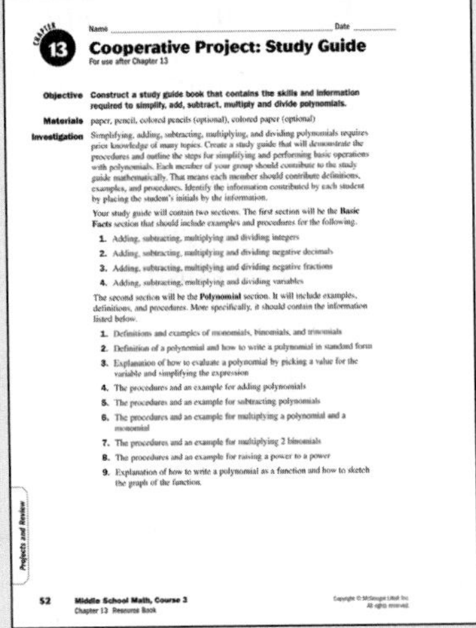

CHAPTER 13 Name ______ Date ______

Cooperative Project: Study Guide

For use after Chapter 13

Objective **Construct a study guide book that contains the skills and information required to simplify, add, subtract, multiply and divide polynomials.**

Materials paper, pencil, colored pencils (optional), colored paper (optional)

Investigation Simplifying, adding, subtracting, multiplying, and dividing polynomials requires prior knowledge of many topics. Create a study guide that will demonstrate the procedures and outline the steps for simplifying and performing basic operations with polynomials. Each member of your group should contribute to the study guide mathematically. That means each member should contribute definitions, examples, and procedures. Identify the information contributed by each student by placing the student's initials by the information.

Your study guide will contain two sections. The first section will be the **Basic Facts** section that should include examples and procedures for the following.

1. Adding, subtracting, multiplying and dividing integers
2. Adding, subtracting, multiplying and dividing negative decimals
3. Adding, subtracting, multiplying and dividing negative fractions
4. Adding, subtracting, multiplying and dividing variables

The second section will be the **Polynomial** section. It will include examples, definitions, and procedures. More specifically, it should contain the information listed below.

1. Definitions and examples of monomials, binomials, and trinomials
2. Definition of a polynomial and how to write a polynomial in standard form
3. Explanation of how to evaluate a polynomial by picking a value for the variable and simplifying the expression
4. The procedures and an example for adding polynomials
5. The procedures and an example for subtracting polynomials
6. The procedures and an example for multiplying a polynomial and a monomial
7. The procedures and an example for multiplying 2 binomials
8. The procedures and an example for raising a power to a power
9. Explanation of how to write a polynomial as a function and how to sketch the graph of the function.

Projects and Review

52 Middle School Math, Course 3 Chapter 13 Resource Book

Copyright © McDougal Littell Inc. All rights reserved.

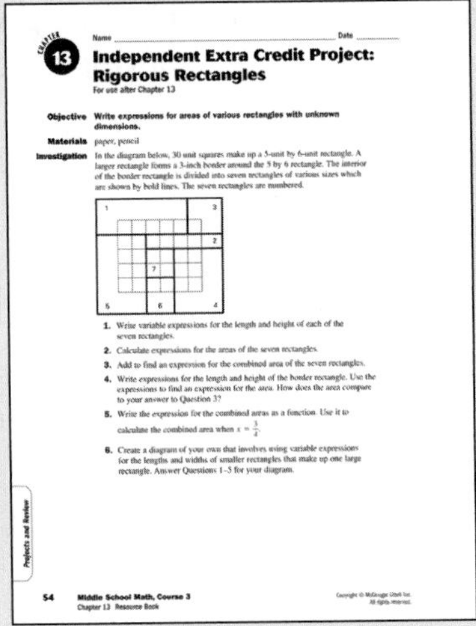

CHAPTER 13 Name ______ Date ______

Independent Extra Credit Project: Rigorous Rectangles

For use after Chapter 13

Objective **Write expressions for areas of various rectangles with unknown dimensions.**

Materials paper, pencil

Investigation In the diagram below, 30 unit squares make up a 5-unit by 6-unit rectangle. A larger rectangle forms a 3-inch border around the 5 by 6 rectangle. The interior of the border rectangle is divided into seven rectangles of various sizes which are shown by bold lines. The seven rectangles are numbered.

1. Write variable expressions for the length and height of each of the seven rectangles.
2. Calculate expressions for the areas of the seven rectangles.
3. Add to find an expression for the combined area of the seven rectangles.
4. Write expressions for the length and height of the border rectangle. Use the expressions to find an expression for the area. How does the area compare to your answer to Question 3?
5. Write the expression for the combined areas as a function. Use it to calculate the combined area when $x = \frac{3}{4}$.
6. Create a diagram of your own that involves using variable expressions for the lengths and widths of smaller rectangles that make up one large rectangle. Answer Questions 1–5 for your diagram.

Projects and Review

54 Middle School Math, Course 3 Chapter 13 Resource Book

Copyright © McDougal Littell Inc. All rights reserved.

SPECIAL ACTIVITIES BOOK

The *Special Activities Book* contains numerous activities including activities for the start of school, activities for substitute teachers, activities for use before holiday breaks, and short change-of-pace activities.

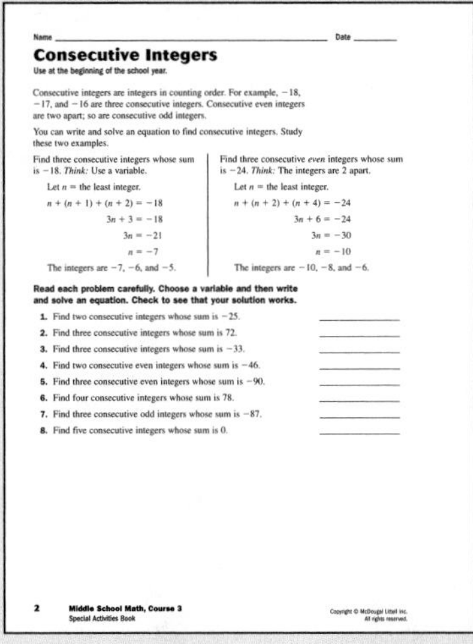

Name ______________________ Date ________

Consecutive Integers

Use at the beginning of the school year.

Consecutive integers are integers in counting order. For example, −18, −17, and −16 are three consecutive integers. Consecutive even integers are two apart; so are consecutive odd integers.

You can write and solve an equation to find consecutive integers. Study these two examples.

Find three consecutive integers whose sum is −18. *Think:* Use a variable.

Let n = the least integer.

$n + (n + 1) + (n + 2) = -18$

$3n + 3 = -18$

$3n = -21$

$n = -7$

The integers are −7, −6, and −5.

Find three consecutive *even* integers whose sum is −24. *Think:* The integers are 2 apart.

Let n = the least integer.

$n + (n + 2) + (n + 4) = -24$

$3n + 6 = -24$

$3n = -30$

$n = -10$

The integers are −10, −8, and −6.

Read each problem carefully. Choose a variable and then write and solve an equation. Check to see that your solution works.

1. Find two consecutive integers whose sum is −25. ________
2. Find three consecutive integers whose sum is 72. ________
3. Find three consecutive integers whose sum is −33. ________
4. Find two consecutive even integers whose sum is −46. ________
5. Find three consecutive even integers whose sum is −90. ________
6. Find four consecutive integers whose sum is 78. ________
7. Find three consecutive odd integers whose sum is −87. ________
8. Find five consecutive integers whose sum is 0. ________

2 **Middle School Math, Course 3**
Special Activities Book

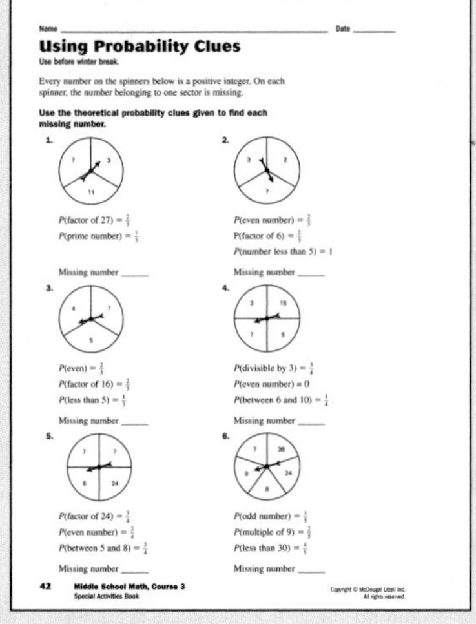

Name ______________________ Date ________

Using Probability Clues

Use before winter break.

Every number on the spinners below is a positive integer. On each spinner, the number belonging to one sector is missing.

Use the theoretical probability clues given to find each missing number.

1. Spinner: ?, 3, 11

$P(\text{factor of } 27) = \frac{2}{3}$

$P(\text{prime number}) = \frac{1}{3}$

Missing number ______

2. Spinner: 3, 2, ?

$P(\text{even number}) = \frac{2}{3}$

$P(\text{factor of } 6) = \frac{2}{3}$

$P(\text{number less than } 5) = 1$

Missing number ______

3. Spinner: 4, ?, 5

$P(\text{even}) = \frac{2}{3}$

$P(\text{factor of } 16) = \frac{2}{3}$

$P(\text{less than } 5) = \frac{1}{3}$

Missing number ______

4. Spinner: 3, 15, ?, 5

$P(\text{divisible by } 3) = \frac{3}{4}$

$P(\text{even number}) = 0$

$P(\text{between 6 and 10}) = \frac{1}{4}$

Missing number ______

5. Spinner: ?, 7, 6, 24

$P(\text{factor of } 24) = \frac{3}{4}$

$P(\text{even number}) = \frac{3}{4}$

$P(\text{between 5 and 8}) = \frac{3}{4}$

Missing number ______

6. Spinner: ?, 36, 9, 24, 8

$P(\text{odd number}) = \frac{1}{5}$

$P(\text{multiple of } 9) = \frac{2}{5}$

$P(\text{less than } 30) = \frac{4}{5}$

Missing number ______

42 **Middle School Math, Course 3**
Special Activities Book

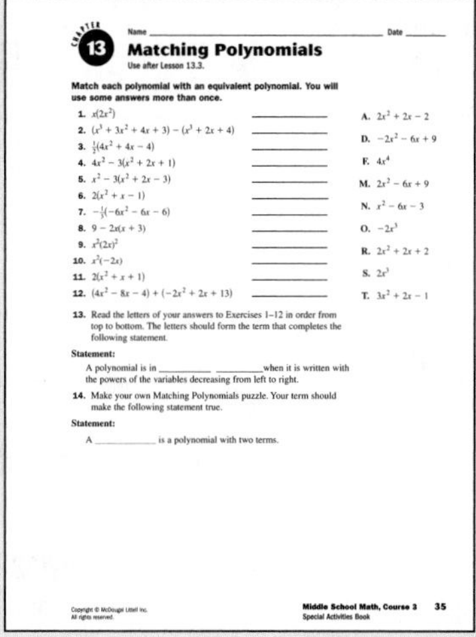

CHAPTER 13

Name ______________________ Date ________

Matching Polynomials

Use after Lesson 13.3.

Match each polynomial with an equivalent polynomial. You will use some answers more than once.

1. $x(2x^2)$ ________
2. $(x^3 + 3x^2 + 4x + 3) - (x^3 + 2x + 4)$ ________
3. $\frac{1}{2}(4x^2 + 4x - 4)$ ________
4. $4x^2 - 3(x^2 + 2x + 1)$ ________
5. $x^2 - 3(x^2 + 2x - 3)$ ________
6. $2(x^2 + x - 1)$ ________
7. $-\frac{1}{3}(-6x^2 - 6x - 6)$ ________
8. $9 - 2x(x + 3)$ ________
9. $x^2(2x)^2$ ________
10. $x^2(-2x)$ ________
11. $2(x^2 + x + 1)$ ________
12. $(4x^2 - 8x - 4) + (-2x^2 + 2x + 13)$ ________

A. $2x^2 + 2x - 2$
D. $-2x^2 - 6x + 9$
F. $4x^4$
M. $2x^2 - 6x + 9$
N. $x^2 - 6x - 3$
O. $-2x^3$
R. $2x^2 + 2x + 2$
S. $2x^3$
T. $3x^2 + 2x - 1$

13. Read the letters of your answers to Exercises 1–12 in order from top to bottom. The letters should form the term that completes the following statement.

Statement:

A polynomial is in __________ __________ when it is written with the powers of the variables decreasing from left to right.

14. Make your own Matching Polynomials puzzle. Your term should make the following statement true.

Statement:

A __________ is a polynomial with two terms.

Middle School Math, Course 3 35
Special Activities Book

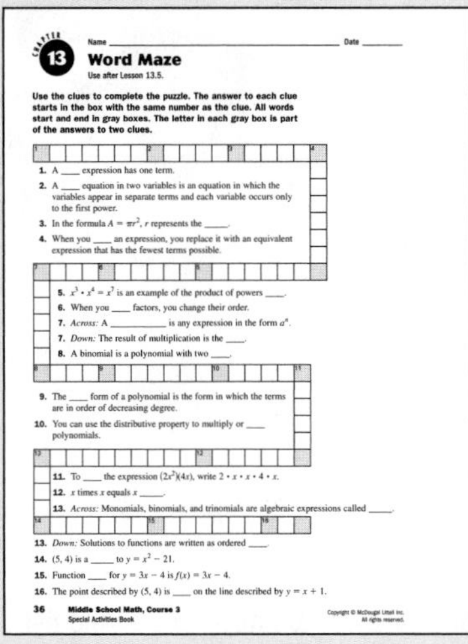

CHAPTER 13

Name ______________________ Date ________

Word Maze

Use after Lesson 13.5.

Use the clues to complete the puzzle. The answer to each clue starts in the box with the same number as the clue. All words start and end in gray boxes. The letter in each gray box is part of the answers to two clues.

1. A ____ expression has one term.
2. A ____ equation in two variables is an equation in which the variables appear in separate terms and each variable occurs only to the first power.
3. In the formula $A = \pi r^2$, r represents the _____.
4. When you ____ an expression, you replace it with an equivalent expression that has the fewest terms possible.
5. $x^3 \cdot x^4 = x^7$ is an example of the product of powers ____.
6. When you ____ factors, you change their order.
7. *Across:* A __________ is any expression in the form a^n.
7. *Down:* The result of multiplication is the ____.
8. A binomial is a polynomial with two ____.
9. The ____ form of a polynomial is the form in which the terms are in order of decreasing degree.
10. You can use the distributive property to multiply or ____ polynomials.
11. To ____ the expression $(2x^2)(4x)$, write $2 \cdot x \cdot x \cdot 4 \cdot x$.
12. x times x equals x _____.
13. *Across:* Monomials, binomials, and trinomials are algebraic expressions called _____.
13. *Down:* Solutions to functions are written as ordered ____.
14. (5, 4) is a _____ to $y = x^2 - 21$.
15. Function ____ for $y = 3x - 4$ is $f(x) = 3x - 4$.
16. The point described by (5, 4) is ____ on the line described by $y = x + 1$.

36 **Middle School Math, Course 3**
Special Activities Book

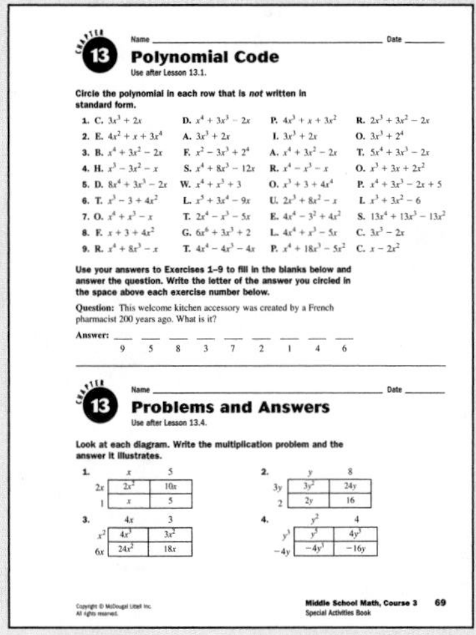

CHAPTER 13

Name ______________________ Date ________

Polynomial Code

Use after Lesson 13.1.

Circle the polynomial in each row that is *not* written in standard form.

1.	C. $3x^3 + 2x$	D. $x^4 + 3x^3 - 2x$	P. $4x^3 + x + 3x^2$	R. $2x^3 + 3x^2 - 2x$
2.	E. $4x^2 + x + 3x^4$	A. $3x^3 + 2x$	I. $3x^3 + 2x$	O. $3x^3 + 2^4$
3.	B. $x^4 + 3x^2 - 2x$	F. $x^2 - 3x^3 + 2^4$	A. $x^4 + 3x^2 - 2x$	T. $5x^4 + 3x^3 - 2x$
4.	H. $x^3 - 3x^2 - x$	S. $x^4 + 8x^3 - 12x$	R. $x^4 - x^3 - x$	O. $x^3 + 3x + 2x^2$
5.	D. $8x^4 + 3x^3 - 2x$	W. $x^4 + x^3 + 3$	O. $x^3 + 3 + 4x^4$	P. $x^4 + 3x^3 - 2x + 5$
6.	T. $x^3 - 3 + 4x^2$	L. $x^5 + 3x^4 - 9x$	U. $2x^3 + 8x^2 - x$	I. $x^3 + 3x^2 - 6$
7.	O. $x^4 + x^3 - x$	T. $2x^4 - x^3 - 5x$	E. $4x^4 - 3^2 + 4x^2$	S. $13x^4 + 13x^3 - 13x^2$
8.	F. $x + 3 + 4x^2$	G. $6x^6 + 3x^3 + 2$	L. $4x^4 + x^3 - 5x$	C. $3x^3 - 2x$
9.	R. $x^4 + 8x^3 - x$	T. $4x^4 - 4x^3 - 4x$	P. $x^4 + 18x^3 - 5x^2$	C. $x - 2x^2$

Use your answers to Exercises 1–9 to fill in the blanks below and answer the question. Write the letter of the answer you circled in the space above each exercise number below.

Question: This welcome kitchen accessory was created by a French pharmacist 200 years ago. What is it?

Answer: ___ ___ ___ ___ ___ ___ ___ ___ ___
9 5 8 3 7 2 1 4 6

CHAPTER 13

Name ______________________ Date ________

Problems and Answers

Use after Lesson 13.4.

Look at each diagram. Write the multiplication problem and the answer it illustrates.

1.

	x	5
$2x$	$2x^2$	$10x$
1	x	5

2.

	y	8
$3y$	$3y^2$	$24y$
2	$2y$	16

3.

	$4x$	3
x^2	$4x^3$	$3x^2$
$6x$	$24x^2$	$18x$

4.

	y^2	4
y^3	y^5	$4y^3$
$-4y$	$-4y^3$	$-16y$

Middle School Math, Course 3 69
Special Activities Book

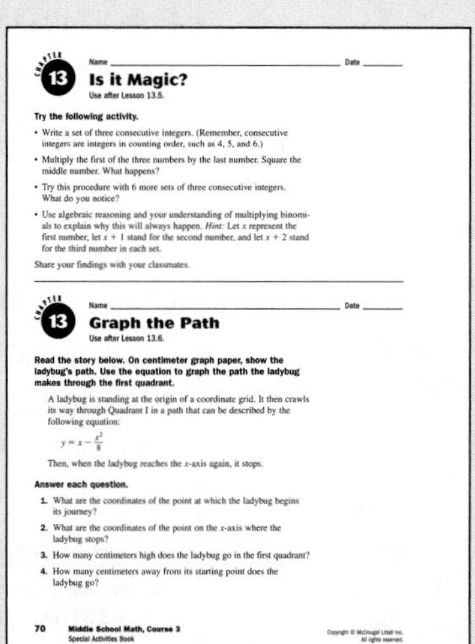

CHAPTER 13

Name ______________________ Date ________

Is it Magic?

Use after Lesson 13.5.

Try the following activity.

- Write a set of three consecutive integers. (Remember, consecutive integers are integers in counting order, such as 4, 5, and 6.)
- Multiply the first of the three numbers by the last number. Square the middle number. What happens?
- Try this procedure with 6 more sets of three consecutive integers. What do you notice?
- Use algebraic reasoning and your understanding of multiplying binomials to explain why this will always happen. *Hint:* Let x represent the first number, let $x + 1$ stand for the second number, and let $x + 2$ stand for the third number in each set.

Share your findings with your classmates.

CHAPTER 13

Name ______________________ Date ________

Graph the Path

Use after Lesson 13.6.

Read the story below. On centimeter graph paper, show the ladybug's path. Use the equation to graph the path the ladybug makes through the first quadrant.

A ladybug is standing at the origin of a coordinate grid. It then crawls its way through Quadrant I in a path that can be described by the following equation:

$$y = x - \frac{x^2}{8}$$

Then, when the ladybug reaches the x-axis again, it stops.

Answer each question.

1. What are the coordinates of the point at which the ladybug begins its journey?
2. What are the coordinates of the point on the x-axis where the ladybug stops?
3. How many centimeters high does the ladybug go in the first quadrant?
4. How many centimeters away from its starting point does the ladybug go?

70 **Middle School Math, Course 3**
Special Activities Book

OVERVIEW

Main Ideas

In this chapter, students identify polynomials by the number of terms, simplify them by combining like terms, and evaluate them. Students add and subtract polynomials, including by using algebra tiles. Students apply properties of exponents to monomials and multiply them. Students multiply binomials by several methods, including the FOIL method. Students also use function notation, graph non-linear functions, and apply the vertical line test.

Prerequisite Skills

The key skills reviewed in the games on these pages are:

- Using properties of exponents
- Combining like terms

Additional practice with prerequisite skills can be found in the Review What You Need to Know exercises on page 656. Additional resources for reviewing prerequisite skills are:

- Skills Review Handbook, pp. 704–726
- Tutor Place
- eTutorial Plus

Managing the Games

Tips for Success

Have students recall the order of operations and the properties of exponents before playing *Piñata Punch*. Before they play *Unmasking Expressions*, you may want to work an example with students in which the distributive property is used with a negative factor, since students often have trouble with this.

Polynomials and Functions

BEFORE

In previous chapters you've...

- Simplified expressions by combining like terms
- Graphed linear functions

Now

In Chapter 13 you'll study...

- Simplifying polynomials
- Adding and subtracting polynomials
- Multiplying binomials
- Graphing non-linear functions

WHY?

So you can solve real-world problems about...

- treehouses, p. 663
- baseball, p. 676
- stage design, p. 677
- juggling, p. 680

Internet Preview
CLASSZONE.COM

- eEdition Plus Online
- eWorkbook Plus Online
- eTutorial Plus Online
- State Test Practice
- More Examples

Chapter Warm-Up Games

Review skills you need for this chapter in these quick games.

PIÑATA PUNCH

$(5 - 11)^3 \cdot 2 \cdot (-6)^{-2}$

$\frac{4^7}{(9 - 5)^3}$

$3^{-3} \cdot 3^8 + 5$

$2^5 \cdot 7 \cdot 2^{-1}$

$\frac{(7 + 1)^6}{8^4}$

18, 12, 250, 112, 8, -64

Key Skill:
Using properties of exponents

To break open the piñata on your turn, you need to pick the right stick.

- Evaluate the expression under each stick. −12; 256, 248; 112; 64
- A stick breaks the piñata if it has the same value as one of the spots.
- Which stick breaks the piñata? Which spot should you hit?
  The stick above the expression $2^5 \cdot 7 \cdot 2^{-1}$; the spot labeled 112.

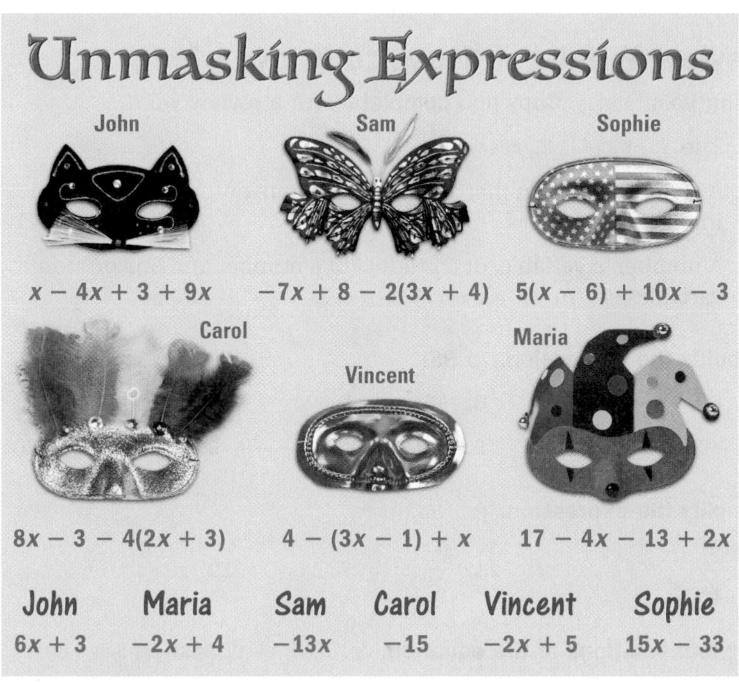

Key Skill:
Combining like terms

Find who is behind each of the masks.

- Match the expression under the mask with the correct simplified expression below a name.

1. *Sample answer:* The first step is to use the distributive property to simplify $-2(3x + 4)$. Then add and subtract from left to right to combine like terms.

Stop and Think

1. **Writing** Explain the steps for simplifying the expression $-7x + 8 - 2(3x + 4)$.
2. **Critical Thinking** Write $2^5 \cdot 7 \cdot 2^{-1}$ as an expression with only positive exponents. $2^4 \cdot 7$

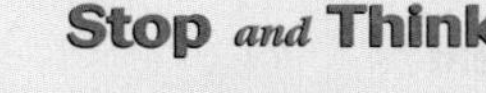

Reflecting on the Games

Have students simplify the fraction $\frac{(7-1)^6}{8^4}$ from *Unmasking Expressions* by factoring and then canceling to obtain $\frac{3^6}{2^6}$. Ask them how they can know without evaluating this expression that the stick it represents cannot break the piñata. They should realize that the value of the expression cannot be a whole number.

Chapter Resources

These resources are provided to help you prepare for the chapter and to customize review materials:

Chapter 13 Resource Book

- Tips for New Teachers, pp. 1–2
- Lesson Plan, pp. 5, 15, 24, 33, 41
- Lesson Plan for Block Scheduling, pp. 6, 16, 25, 34, 42

Technology

- EasyPlanner CD-ROM
- Test and Practice Generator
- Electronic Lesson Presentations CD-ROM
- eTutorial CD-ROM

Internet

- Classzone
- eEdition Plus Online
- eWorkbook Plus Online
- eTutorial Plus Online
- EasyPlanner Plus Online

English Learner Support

- Spanish Study Guide
- Multi-Language Glossary
- Chapter Audio Summaries CDs
- Teacher's Edition, pp. 654E–654F

PREPARE

Diagnosis/Remediation

Review What You Need to Know
The Review What You Need to Know exercises can help you diagnose whether students have the following skills needed in Chapter 13:

- Using vocabulary (Exs. 1-3)
- Simplifying expressions (Exs. 4-12)
- Solving linear equations (Exs. 13-15)

 ***Chapter 13 Resource Book***

- Study Guide (Lessons 13.1-13.5)

 ***Tutor Place***

Notetaking Strategies

As students begin the chapter, encourage them to look through the entire chapter with an eye to what material will be covered. This will help them to recognize important material to enter into their notebooks and will help them to anticipate the connections in the material. Further suggestions for keeping a notebook can be found on page 674.

For more support on notetaking, see:

- Notetaking Guide Workbook
- Notetaking Transparencies

Getting Ready to Learn

Review What You Need to Know 

Word Watch

Review Words
power, p. 20
exponent, p. 20
like terms, p. 86
coefficient, p. 86
monomial, p. 170
function, p. 541

Using Vocabulary Copy and complete with a review word.

1. The _?_ of $2x^3$ is 2. **coefficient**
2. A(n) _?_ is a relation that assigns exactly one output value to each input value. **function**
3. A number, a variable, or a product of a number and one or more variables is a(n) _?_. **monomial**

Simplify the expression. *(p. 85)*

4. $6x - 4 + 4x - 3$ **$10x - 7$**
5. $-5(2x + 3) - 4x$ **$-14x - 15$**
6. $7(3x - 5) - (-x)$ **$22x - 35$**
7. $-2x - (-5x)$ **$3x$**
8. $-2(-4x - 8)$ **$8x + 16$**
9. $-3(3x) + 18x$ **$9x$**

Simplify the expression. *(p. 196)*

10. $\frac{y^4}{y^6}$ **$\frac{1}{y^2}$ or y^{-2}**
11. $\frac{5^{37}}{5^{35}}$ **$5^2 = 25$**
12. $x^4 \cdot x^5$ **x^9**

List four solutions of the equation. *(p. 550)* **13–15. Answers may vary.**

13. $y = 3x - 5$ **(0, −5), (1, −2), (2, 1), (3, 4)**
14. $y = -2x + 1$ **(0, 1), (1, −1), (2, −3), (3, −5)**
15. $y = \frac{1}{2}x$ **(0, 0), (2, 1), (4, 2), (6, 3)**

You should include material that appears on a notebook like this in your own notes.

Know How to Take Notes

Summarizing Material Summarize the main ideas from different lessons in your notebook. This will help you to see how key ideas are related.

Exponent Rules

Product of Powers

$x^2 \cdot x^3 = x^{2+3}$

$= x^5$

Quotient of Powers

$\frac{x^5}{x^2} = x^{5-2}$

$= x^3$

Zero Exponent

for $x \neq 0$,

$x^0 = 1$

Negative Exponents

for $x \neq 0$,

$x^{-4} = \frac{1}{x^4}$

In Lesson 13.4, you can summarize key ideas about algebra in your notebook.

656

Polynomials

BEFORE	Now	WHY?
You simplified expressions by combining like terms.	You will simplify polynomials by combining like terms.	So you can find the height of a falling pinecone, as in Example 3.

Word Watch

polynomial, p. 657
binomial, p. 657
trinomial, p. 657
standard form, p. 657

A **polynomial** is a monomial or a sum of monomials. Each monomial in a polynomial is called a *term*. Polynomials are classified by the number of their terms. If a polynomial has more than three terms, it is simply called a polynomial.

Monomial (1 term)	**Binomial** (2 terms)	**Trinomial** (3 terms)
$-2x$	$3x - 2$	$-2a^2 + 3a + 1$
4	$-s^4 + 6s^3$	$3 + 5r - 7r^2$

A polynomial is written in **standard form** if the exponents of the variable decrease from left to right.

Standard Form	Not Standard Form
$3x^3 - 2x^2 + 4$	$3 + 5y$
$-2m^6 + 5m^3 - m$	$7t^4 - t^7 - 2t^2 + 3t$

EXAMPLE 1 Writing Polynomials in Standard Form

Write the polynomial in standard form. Classify the polynomial.

a. $x - 9 + 5x^2$

$= x + (-9) + 5x^2$ Write subtraction as addition.

$= 5x^2 + x + (-9)$ Order terms with decreasing exponents.

ANSWER The polynomial $5x^2 + x - 9$ has 3 terms, so it is a trinomial.

b. $2x - 3x^3$

$= 2x + (-3x^3)$ Write subtraction as addition.

$= -3x^3 + 2x$ Order terms with decreasing exponents.

ANSWER The polynomial $-3x^3 + 2x$ has 2 terms, so it is a binomial.

Watch Out!

If you do not see an exponent with a variable, then its exponent is 1.

$2x = 2x^1$

Your turn now Write the polynomial in standard form and classify it.

1. $4 + b^2 - 8b$ $b^2 - 8b + 4$; trinomial
2. $-5 + 3x^2$ $3x^2 - 5$; binomial
3. $11 + 2n^4 - 7n + 5n^2$ $2n^4 + 5n^2 - 7n + 11$; polynomial

ILLINOIS Standards and ISAT:
8.A.3a, 8.D.3a

1 PLAN

SKILL CHECK

Simplify.

1. $2x + 6 + 3x$ $5x + 6$

2. $-4y + 3 - y - 8$ $-5y - 5$

Lesson Objective

Simplify polynomials by combining like terms.

Pacing

Suggested Number of Days
Basic Course: 2 days
Average Course: 2 days
Advanced Course: 2 days
Block: 1 block

Teaching Resources

For a complete list of Teaching Resources, see page 654B.

Transparency

Warm-Up Exercises for this lesson are available on a transparency.

2 TEACH

Motivating the Lesson

Have students name words they can think of that begin with the prefix "poly-." Lead students to understand that "poly" means "many."

TIPS FOR NEW TEACHERS

Emphasize that writing polynomials in standard form is the first step in solving equations that contain polynomials, which occur very frequently in real-world applications. See Tips for New Teachers in the *Chapter 13 Resource Book*.

EXTRA EXAMPLES

Example 1 Write the polynomial in standard form and classify it.

a. $12 + x^2 - x^3$
$-x^3 + x^2 + 12$, trinomial

b. $6a + 22a^2$
$22a^2 + 6a$, binomial

Example 2 Simplify the polynomial, and write it in standard form.

a. $3y + 5y^2 + 3y - 5$
$5y^2 + 6y - 5$

b. $7(a^2 - 2) + a^2 - a$
$8a^2 - a - 14$

Example 3 A skydiver jumps from an airplane 13,000 feet above the ground. Her height in feet after freefalling for t seconds can be found using the polynomial $-16t^2 + 13,000$. Find the skydiver's height after 10 seconds of freefall. **11,400 ft**

VISUALIZE

Using the board or overhead, write a polynomial and have students use colored chalk or markers to highlight or underline like terms.

CONCEPT CHECK

Explain in your own words how to simplify a polynomial and write it in standard form. ***Sample answer:* First combine like terms by adding their coefficients. Then write the terms so that the exponents are decreasing from left to right.**

DAILY PUZZLER

The polynomial $-16t^2 + 225$ gives the height in feet after t seconds of a rock falling from a cliff that rises 225 feet from a field. Where is the rock after 6 seconds of falling?
on the ground

Simplifying Polynomials Remember that *like terms* have the same variables raised to the same powers. To simplify a polynomial, combine like terms by adding their coefficients.

HELP with Review

Remember that $x^2 = 1x^2$. For help with like terms, see p. 85.

EXAMPLE 2 Simplifying Polynomials

Simplify the polynomial and write it in standard form.

a. $3x^2 + 4x^2 - 2x - 3$

$= (3x^2 + 4x^2) - 2x - 3$ — Group like terms.

$= 7x^2 - 2x - 3$ — Simplify.

b. $x^2 + 2 + 4(x^2 - 2x)$

$= x^2 + 2 + 4x^2 - 8x$ — Use the distributive property.

$= (x^2 + 4x^2) + 2 - 8x$ — Group like terms.

$= 5x^2 + 2 - 8x$ — Simplify.

$= 5x^2 - 8x + 2$ — Write in standard form.

Your turn now **Simplify the polynomial and write it in standard form.**

4. $7p + 5p^2 - 2 - 3p^2$ **$2p^2 + 7p - 2$**
5. $10s^4 - 3s + s^4 - 1$ **$11s^4 - 3s - 1$**
6. $2(a^2 + 3a - 1) + 2a^2$ **$4a^2 + 6a - 2$**
7. $8x + 3(2x^2 - x + 1)$ **$6x^2 + 5x + 3$**

EXAMPLE 3 Evaluating a Polynomial Expression

Pinecone You drop a pinecone from a 150 foot bridge. The height of the pinecone, in feet, after t seconds of falling, can be found using the polynomial $-16t^2 + 150$. Find the pinecone's height after 2 seconds.

Solution

$-16t^2 + 150 = -16(2)^2 + 150$ — Substitute 2 for t.

$= -16(4) + 150$ — Evaluate the power.

$= -64 + 150$ — Multiply.

$= 86$ — Add.

ANSWER The pinecone's height after 2 seconds is 86 feet.

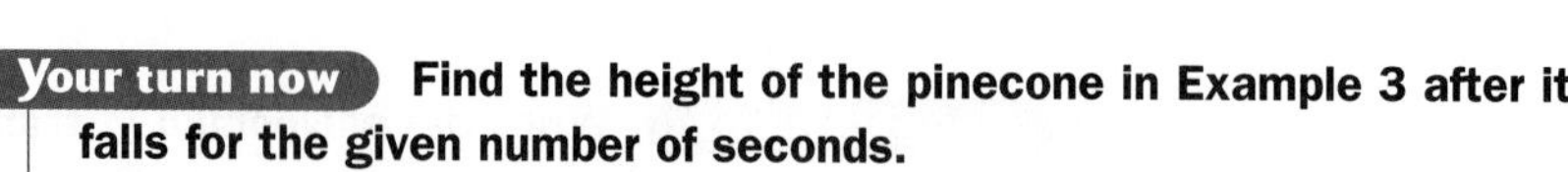

Your turn now **Find the height of the pinecone in Example 3 after it falls for the given number of seconds.**

8. 0.5 sec **146 ft** **9.** 1 sec **134 ft** **10.** 1.5 sec **114 ft** **11.** 3 sec **6 ft**

13.1 Exercises

More Practice, p. 739

ASSIGNMENT GUIDE

Basic Course

Day 1: pp. 659-660 Exs. 12-22, 41-43

Day 2: pp. 659-660 Exs. 23-31, 44-49

Average Course

Day 1: pp. 659-660 Exs. 12-22, 40-44

Day 2: pp. 659-660 Exs. 25-35, 45-49

Advanced Course

Day 1: pp. 659-660 Exs. 14-24, 41-44

Day 2: pp. 659-660 Exs. 29-40*, 47-49

Block

pp. 659-660 Exs. 12-22, 25-35, 40-49

Getting Ready to Practice

Vocabulary **Classify the polynomial as a *monomial*, a *binomial*, or a *trinomial*.**

1. $x^2 + 3x - 7$ trinomial **2.** $y - 5$ binomial **3.** $8s^2t$ monomial **4.** $2a^2 + 9a^3 + a$ trinomial

Write the polynomial in standard form.

5. $7 + 3m$ $3m + 7$ **6.** $5n - 1 - n^2$ $-n^2 + 5n - 1$ **7.** $4b - 4 + 6b^3$ $6b^3 + 4b - 4$

Simplify the polynomial and write it in standard form.

8. $3x + x^2 - 2x$ $x^2 + x$ **9.** $4 + 5y - 5$ $5y - 1$ **10.** $-9 + 7m^3 - 2m^3$ $5m^3 - 9$

11. **Find the Error** Describe and correct the error in simplifying the polynomial. $-3x^2$ and $-20x$ are not like terms and cannot be combined. The expression $-3x^2 - 20x - 4$ cannot be simplified.

$$-3x^2 - 4(5x + 1)$$
$$= -3x^2 - 20x - 4$$
$$= -23x - 4$$

Practice and Problem Solving

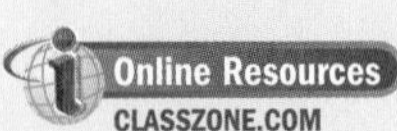

HELP with Homework

Example	Exercises
1	12-14
2	15-20, 23-26
3	27-30

Online Resources CLASSZONE.COM
- More Examples
- eTutorial Plus

A Write the polynomial in standard form. Classify the polynomial.

12. $2 - 5y + y^2$ $y^2 - 5y + 2$; trinomial **13.** $-13x^3 + 4x^{10}$ $4x^{10} - 13x^3$; binomial **14.** $3 - r^4 + r + 2r^3$ $-r^4 + 2r^3 + r + 3$; polynomial

Simplify the polynomial and write it in standard form.

15. $3x - 4 + x$ $4x - 4$ **16.** $2c^2 - c^2 + 5c$ $c^2 + 5c$

17. $4q^3 - 7q^5 + 3q - q^3$ $-7q^5 + 3q^3 + 3q$ **18.** $7 - 4d^2 - 3d^2 + d$ $-7d^2 + d + 7$

19. $12 + 3b - 6b + 5$ $-3b + 17$ **20.** $g^3 - 10 + 2g^2 - 5g^3$ $-4g^3 + 2g^2 - 10$

Measurement **Write a polynomial expression for the perimeter. Simplify the polynomial and write it in standard form.**

21.

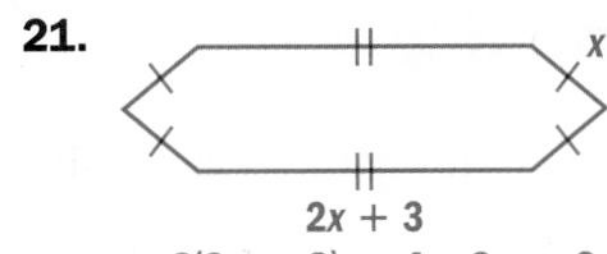

$2(2x + 3) + 4x$; $8x + 6$

22. x, $2(x + 1)$

$2[2(x + 1)] + 2x$; $6x + 4$

Simplify the polynomial and write it in standard form.

23. $1 + 12m^2 - 5m + 6m - 7$ $12m^2 + m - 6$ **24.** $7 - p^3 - 5p^3 + 3p + p - p^3$ $-7p^3 + 4p + 7$

25. $3x^2 + 5(x^2 - 3x + 6)$ $8x^2 - 15x + 30$ **26.** $-6(2y^3 - 4y^2 + 1) + 10y^2$ $-12y^3 + 34y^2 - 6$

EXTRA PRACTICE

- Student Edition, p. 739
- Chapter 13 Resource Book, pp. 8-10
- Test and Practice Generator

Even-numbered answers are available on transparencies.

HOMEWORK CHECK

When you review students' homework for this lesson, go over the following exercises to check understanding of key concepts.

Basic: 12, 14, 15, 23, 27
Average: 12, 14, 15, 25, 27
Advanced: 14, 16, 20, 24, 29

COMMON ERROR

In Exercises 26, 31, 32, 38, and 39, watch for students who distribute the negative sign incorrectly.

ASSESSMENT RESOURCES

For more assessment resources, see:
- Assessment Book
- Test and Practice Generator

MINI-QUIZ

Simplify the polynomial, and write it in standard form.

1. $4 + k^2 - 3k + 5$ $k^2 - 3k + 9$
2. $a + 4a^2 - a + 2$ $4a^2 + 2$
3. $3(x^2 + 2) - x^2$ $2x^2 + 6$
4. $2x^3 + x - 3x^3 + 4x - 5 + x^2$ $-x^3 + x^2 + 5x - 5$
5. $-2(4 + 2y + 5y^2) + 9y^2$ $-y^2 - 4y - 8$
6. A rectangle has a length of $2x^2 - 2x + 4$ inches and a width of $x + 1$ inches. Write a polynomial expression for the perimeter of the rectangle. $4x^2 - 2x + 10$ **in.**

RETEACHING/REMEDIATION

- Study Guide in Chapter 13 Resource Book, pp. 11–12
- Tutor Place, Algebra Card 4
- eTutorial Plus Online
- Extra Practice, p. 739
- Lesson Practice in Chapter 13 Resource Book, pp. 8–10

CHALLENGE/ENRICHMENT

- Challenge Practice in Chapter 13 Resource Book, p. 14
- Teacher's Edition, p. 654F

ENGLISH LEARNER SUPPORT

- Spanish Study Guide
- Multi-Language Glossary
- Chapter Audio Summaries CDs

Baseball

A player hits a ball 60 mi/h into right field. The ball has the same height after 2 seconds as it has after 3.5 seconds. How is this possible? **Each height the ball passes through on its way up, it passes through again on its way down.**

B Baseball A player hits a ball 60 mi/h, or 88 ft/sec, toward right field. Evaluate the polynomial $-16t^2 + 88t + 2$ to find the ball's height, in feet, after t seconds.

27. $t = 1.5$ 98 ft **28.** $t = 2$ 114 ft **29.** $t = 2.5$ 122 ft **30.** $t = 3$ 122 ft

Simplify the polynomial and write it in standard form.

31. $-4(t - 3t^2 + 8 - 4t) + 6t^2 - 5$ $18t^2 + 12t - 37$ **32.** $-3(-s^4 + 2s - 6 - s) - 8s + s^4$ $4s^4 - 11s + 18$

Critical Thinking Tell whether the statement is *always*, *sometimes*, or *never* true.

33. The terms of a trinomial are monomials. always

34. A monomial has one factor. sometimes

35. A binomial has more than two terms. never

C Challenge Simplify the polynomial.

36. $3x^2 - 2y + 5x^2 - 4$ $8x^2 - 2y - 4$ **37.** $-16t - 7h + 3t^2 + 4h$ $3t^2 - 16t - 3h$

38. $5a - 4(3b + 6) + 4b$ $5a - 8b - 24$ **39.** $-z^2 + 3z - 2(4y - 5z)$ $-z^2 + 13z - 8y$

40. Make a Connection Find the meaning of the prefix *poly*. Explain what this tells you about the words *polygon* and *polynomial*. *Sample answer:* "Poly" means more than one or many. A polygon has at least three sides, and all polynomials, except monomials, have more than one term.

Mixed Review

41. The letters in the word FUNCTION are put in a bag. Find the probability of drawing the letter N at random. *(Lesson 7.8)* $\frac{1}{4}$

42. Find the volume of the cylinder. Round to the nearest hundredth of a cubic meter. *(Lesson 10.6)* 251 m^3

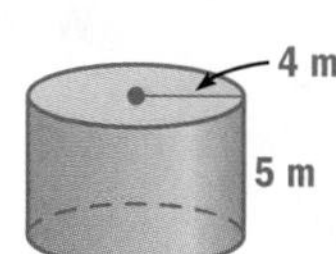

43. Make a stem-and-leaf plot of the data. *(Lesson 12.1)*
38.6, 35.8, 36.3, 34.2, 37.6, 37.5, 36.4, 36.2, 38.6, 36.6

43.

Stem	Leaves
34	2
35	8
36	2 3 4 6
37	5 6
38	6 6

Key: 35 | 8 = 35.8

Basic Skills Evaluate the expression.

44. $8(3 + 9)$ 96 **45.** $-3(11 - 4)$ -21 **46.** $-5(7 + 2)$ -45 **47.** $12(6 - 1)$ 60

Test-Taking Practice

INTERNET
State Test Practice
CLASSZONE.COM

48. Multiple Choice Simplify the polynomial $5(x^2 - 2x - 3) - 9x^2$. D

A. $4x^2 + 10x - 15$ **B.** $-4x^2 + 10x - 15$
C. $-4x^2 - 15x - 10x$ **D.** $-4x^2 - 10x - 15$

49. Multiple Choice Find the value of $-2x^2 - 4x + 7$ when $x = -2$. G

F. -9 **G.** 7 **H.** 15 **I.** 23

Adding and Subtracting Polynomials

BEFORE

You simplified polynomials.

Now

You'll add and subtract polynomials.

WHY?

So you can find the area of clay coasters, as in Ex. 29.

Word Watch

Review Words

opposite, p. 54
like terms, p. 86

Activity You can model polynomial addition with algebra tiles.

You can model polynomials with algebra tiles.

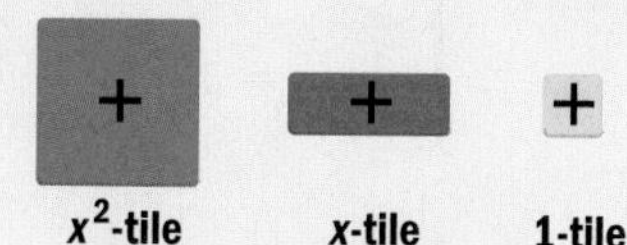

(1) Write the two polynomials represented by the algebra tiles. $2x^2 + 3x + 5$ and $x^2 + 4x + 1$

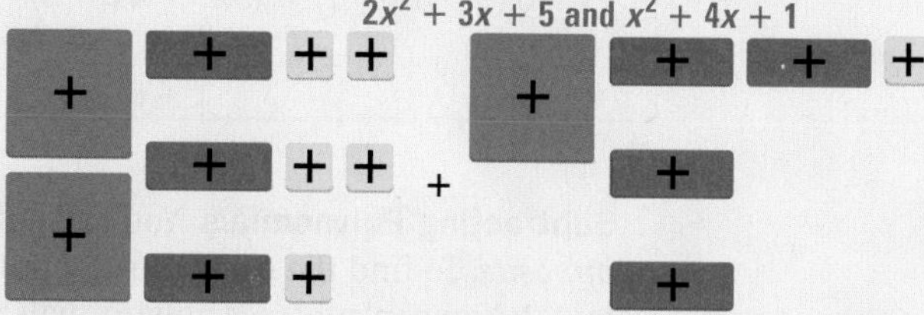

(2) Group the algebra tiles to model the sum of the polynomials. Draw your model. Write the polynomial that your drawing represents. See margin for art; $3x^2 + 7x + 6$.

(3) Use algebra tiles to model the sum of the polynomials below. Write the polynomial that your model represents.

a. $(3x^2 + 6x + 1) + (x^2 + x)$ $4x^2 + 7x + 1$

b. $(2x^2 + 3x + 1) + (4x^2 + x)$ $6x^2 + 4x + 1$

In the activity, you used algebra tiles to add two polynomials. You add polynomials by combining like terms.

EXAMPLE 1 Adding Polynomials Vertically

Find the sum $(-4x^3 + x^2 - 3x - 1) + (4x^2 - 7x + 5)$.

Solution

$-4x^3 + x^2 - 3x - 1$	Write the second polynomial under the first.
$+ \quad 4x^2 - 7x + 5$	Arrange like terms in columns.
$-4x^3 + 5x^2 - 10x + 4$	Add like terms.

ILLINOIS Standards and ISAT:
8.D.3a; 7.C.3b

SKILL CHECK

Simplify.

1. $-4x^3 + 5x^3$ x^3
2. $6b^2 - 16b^2$ $-10b^2$
3. $8a^3 - 8a^3$ 0

LESSON OBJECTIVE

Add and subtract polynomials.

PACING

Suggested Number of Days
Basic Course: 2 days
Average Course: 2 days
Advanced Course: 2 days
Block: 1 block

TEACHING RESOURCES

For a complete list of Teaching Resources, see page 654B.

TRANSPARENCY

Warm-Up Exercises for this lesson are available on a transparency. Support transparencies are available for the Activity.

MOTIVATING THE LESSON

Have students add 450 and 505 in vertical format. Point out that they are adding like terms: units to units, tens to tens, and hundreds to hundreds.

ACTIVITY

Goal Model polynomial addition with algebra tiles.

Key Discovery You can model polynomial addition with algebra tiles by combining and counting like tiles.

Step 2. See Additional Answers beginning on page AA1.

TIPS FOR NEW TEACHERS

Until students are proficient, they should rewrite polynomial subtraction as addition of the opposite. Make sure students are comfortable with rewriting polynomial subtraction as addition both in vertical and horizontal formats. See Tips for New Teachers in the *Chapter 13 Resource Book*.

EXTRA EXAMPLES

Example 1 Find the sum $(5x^2 - 2x + 3) + (x^3 + 2x^2 - 5x + 1)$. $x^3 + 7x^2 - 7x + 4$

Example 2 Find the sum $(4a^2 - 7a + 5) + (2a^2 + 3a - 4)$. $6a^2 - 4a + 1$

Example 3 Find the difference $(6k^3 - 2k^2 + k - 9) - (3k^3 + 5k - 2)$. $3k^3 - 2k^2 - 4k - 7$

MATH REASONING

To show that the opposite of a polynomial is found by writing the opposite of each term (multiplying each term by -1), have students write a trinomial, find its opposite, and then add the two trinomials to show that the sum is zero, the additive identity.

Differentiating Instruction

Alternative Teaching Approach Give each student a card with a different polynomial written on it. Divide the class in half and have students form two concentric circles. Have students in one circle rotate until you say "stop." Then have students nearest each other in the different circles find the sum of the polynomials on their cards.

In Example 1, you combined like terms vertically. You can also add polynomials by combining like terms horizontally.

with Solving

When you regroup terms, you must move a subtraction or addition sign with the term that follows it.

EXAMPLE 2 Adding Polynomials Horizontally

Find the sum $(2y^2 - 4y + 6) + (y^2 + 3y - 2)$.

Solution

$(2y^2 - 4y + 6) + (y^2 + 3y - 2)$

$= 2y^2 + y^2 - 4y + 3y + 6 - 2$ **Group like terms.**

$= 3y^2 - y + 4$ **Combine like terms.**

Your turn now **Find the sum.**

1. $(6x^2 - 3x + 1) + (3x^2 + 4x - 5)$ $9x^2 + x - 4$
2. $(5n^2 + 2n - 9) + (3n^2 - n + 4)$ $8n^2 + n - 5$
3. $(y^2 - y + 1) + (-2y^2 + 2y - 1)$ $-y^2 + y$
4. $(3p^2 - p - 1) + (p^2 + p - 4)$ $4p^2 - 5$

Subtracting Polynomials You can subtract a polynomial by adding its *opposite*. To find the opposite of a polynomial, multiply each of its terms by -1. You can subtract polynomials vertically or horizontally.

EXAMPLE 3 Subtracting Polynomials Vertically

Find the difference $(4x^3 + 5x^2 - 2x - 5) - (3x^3 - 4x + 2)$.

Solution

(1) Find the opposite of the second polynomial.

$-(3x^3 - 4x + 2) = -3x^3 + 4x - 2$

(2) Find the sum $(4x^3 + 5x^2 - 2x - 5) + (-3x^3 + 4x - 2)$.

$4x^3 + 5x^2 - 2x - 5$	**Write the second polynomial under the first.**
$+ -3x^3 \qquad\quad + 4x - 2$	**Arrange like terms in columns.**
$x^3 + 5x^2 + 2x - 7$	**Add like terms.**

Your turn now **Find the difference.**

5. $(4r^2 - r + 8) - (r^2 + 6r - 1)$ $3r^2 - 7r + 9$
6. $(6m^2 + 2m - 3) - (7m^2 + 4)$ $-m^2 + 2m - 7$
7. $(5t^2 + 4t + 1) - (2t^2 + 8t + 11)$ $3t^2 - 4t - 10$
8. $(x^2 + 5x + 7) - (3x^2 - 4x - 2)$ $-2x^2 + 9x + 9$

EXAMPLE 4 Finding the Area of a Tree House

Tree House The design for a tree house calls for a rectangular hole in the floor. Write a polynomial expression for the area of the tree house floor.

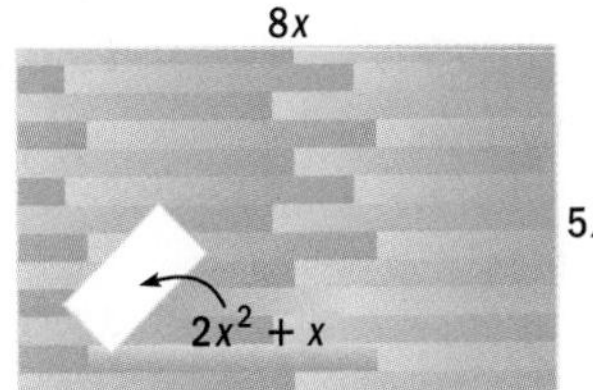

Solution

To find the area of the floor, use the area of the two rectangles.

Area of Large Rectangle	**Area of Small Rectangle**
$8x \cdot 5x = 40x^2$	$2x^2 + x$

Area of floor = Area of large rectangle − Area of small rectangle

$= 40x^2 - (2x^2 + x)$

$= 40x^2 - 2x^2 - x$ **Distributive property**

$= 38x^2 - x$ **Combine like terms.**

ANSWER A polynomial expression for the area of the floor is $38x^2 - x$.

13.2 Exercises

More Practice, p. 739

Getting Ready to Practice

1. **Vocabulary** Copy and complete: To add polynomials, you should combine _?_. **like terms**

Find the sum or difference.

2. $(8y + 5) + (4y - 3)$ **$12y + 2$**
3. $(7x + 10) - (x - 2)$ **$6x + 12$**
4. $(x - 6) + (2x + 9)$ **$3x + 3$**
5. $(4p + 1) - (p - 7)$ **$3p + 8$**
6. $(5n^2 + 2n + 1) - (4n^2 - 1)$ **$n^2 + 2n + 2$**
7. $(-3a + 10) + (2a - 4)$ **$-a + 6$**
8. **Find the Error** Describe and correct the error(s) in the solution.

$$\begin{array}{r} -4x^3 + 5x^2 - 7x + 2 \\ +\quad 2x^3 - 6x + 10 \\ \hline -2x^3 - x^2 + 3x + 2 \end{array}$$

8. **In some cases, the coefficients of terms that are not like terms were combined.**

$$\begin{array}{r} -4x^3 + 5x^2 - 7x + 2 \\ +2x^3 \qquad - 6x + 10 \\ \hline -2x^3 + 5x^2 - 13x + 12 \end{array}$$

EXTRA EXAMPLES

Example 4 An L-shaped porch has the dimensions shown. Write a polynomial expression for the area of the porch.

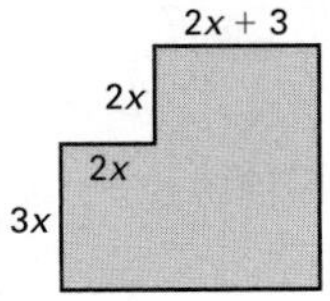

(Figure labels: $2x + 3$; $2x$; $2x$; $3x$)

$16x^2 + 15x$

CONCEPT CHECK

Explain in your own words how to subtract one polynomial from another. ***Sample answer:*** **To subtract one polynomial from another, first find its opposite by multiplying each of its terms by −1. Then add the result to the first polynomial.**

DAILY PUZZLER

Two trinomials are added. What are all the possible numbers of terms that the result can have? **1, 2, 3, 4, 5, or 6 terms**

APPLY

ASSIGNMENT GUIDE

Basic Course

Day 1: EP p. 728 Exs. 7-9; pp. 664-665 Exs. 9-14, 21-26, 39-41

Day 2: pp. 664-665 Exs. 15-20, 29-33, 42-45

Average Course

Day 1: pp. 664-665 Exs. 9-14, 21-24, 34-36, 43-45

Day 2: pp. 664-665 Exs. 15-20, 27-31, 39-42

Advanced Course

Day 1: pp. 664-665 Exs. 11-14, 21-24, 34-36, 43-45

Day 2: pp. 664-665 Exs. 17-20, 27-29, 37-42*

Block

pp. 664-665 Exs. 9-24, 27-31, 34-36, 39-45

EXTRA PRACTICE

- Student Edition, p. 739
- Chapter 13 Resource Book, pp. 18-20
- Test and Practice Generator

TRANSPARENCY

Even-numbered answers are available on transparencies.

HOMEWORK CHECK

When you review students' homework for this lesson, go over the following exercises to check understanding of key concepts.

Basic: 9, 12, 13, 15, 29

Average: 9, 12, 14, 16, 29

Advanced: 11, 13, 14, 19, 29

COMMON ERROR

In Exercises 30, 33, and 35, students may make mistakes trying to subtract polynomials and apply the distributive property at the same time.

with Homework

Example	Exercises
1	9-14
2	9-14
3	15-20
4	29

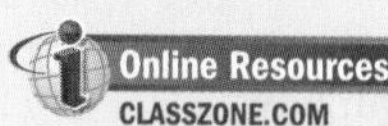

Online Resources
CLASSZONE.COM

- More Examples
- eTutorial Plus

Practice and Problem Solving

A **Find the sum.**

9. $(4x + 7) + (x - 3)$ $5x + 4$

10. $(-2a - 9) + (a + 4)$ $-a - 5$

11. $(3n - 7) + (4n + 5)$ $7n - 2$

12. $(t^2 + 3t) + (3t^2 + 8t)$ $4t^2 + 11t$

13. $(-g^2 + g + 9) + (7g^2 - 6)$ $6g^2 + g + 3$

14. $(3z^2 - 2z + 1) + (4z^3 + 3z)$ $4z^3 + 3z^2 + z + 1$

Find the difference.

15. $(-5d - 1) - (5d + 6)$ $-10d - 7$

16. $(7y + 1) - (3y - 2)$ $4y + 3$

17. $(2h^2 + 9h) - (13h^2 - h)$ $-11h^2 + 10h$

18. $(4x^2 + 9x) - (x^2 + 7x - 1)$ $3x^2 + 2x + 1$

19. $(6r^2 + 2r - 5) - (3r^2 - 9)$ $3r^2 + 2r + 4$

20. $(-4b^3 - 9b + 2) - (b^3 - b + 3)$ $-5b^3 - 8b - 1$

Geometry **Write a polynomial expression for the perimeter of the figure. Simplify the polynomial.**

21.

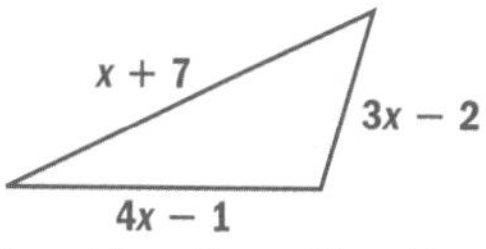

$(x + 7) + (3x - 2) + (4x - 1)$; $8x + 4$

22.

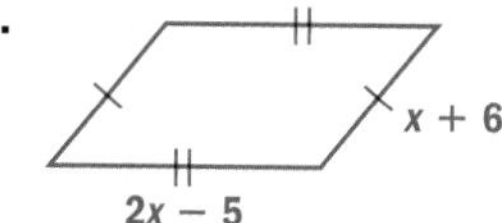

$2(2x - 5) + 2(x + 6)$; $6x + 2$

Find the sum or difference.

23. $(2k^2 + 5k) + (4k^2 - 5k)$ $6k^2$

24. $(5a^2 + 3a + 8) - (2a^2 - 2a - 9)$ $3a^2 + 5a + 17$

25. $(6x^3 - 12x + 1) + (8x^2 - 4)$ $6x^3 + 8x^2 - 12x - 3$

26. $(4p^3 + p^2 - 8) - (7p^3 + 2p + 5)$ $-3p^3 + p^2 - 2p - 13$

27. $(4n - 3) + (9n + 5) - (n - 1)$ $12n + 3$

28. $(-8m + 1) - (2m - 6) + 5m$ $-5m + 7$

B **29. Coasters** To make a set of coasters, you cut identical circles out of a square piece of clay. Write a polynomial expression for the area of clay that remains after you remove the circles. Simplify the polynomial. Is there enough clay left over to make another coaster of the same radius and thickness? Explain your answer.

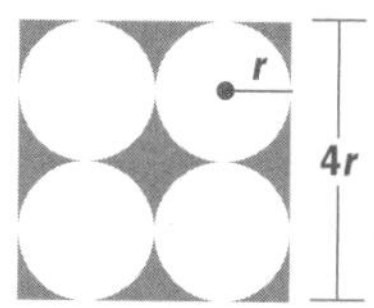

$16r^2 - 4(\pi r^2)$; $3.44r^2$; yes; one coaster needs $3.14r^2$ of clay, which is less than what is left over.

Perform the indicated operations.

30. $-2(5y + 3) - 9(y + 1)$ $-19y - 15$

31. $4(-3s^2 + s - 4) + (5s^2 + s + 7)$ $-7s^2 + 5s - 9$

32. $3(q^2 - q) + 2(7q^2 - 2q)$ $17q^2 - 7q$

33. $6(t^3 - t^2 + 3t) - 4(5t^3 + t^2 - t)$ $-14t^3 - 10t^2 + 22t$

34. $5(4x^3 - 2x^2 + 1) + 3(7x^2 - 5x)$ $20x^3 + 11x^2 - 15x + 5$

35. $-7(2v^4 + 3v^2 - 1) - 5(-3v^3 - 6)$ $-14v^4 + 15v^3 - 21v^2 + 37$

C **36. Critical Thinking** Can the sum of two trinomials be a binomial? Give an example to justify your answer.
Yes. *Sample answer:* $(x^2 + 2x + 1) + (2x^2 - 2x + 3) = 3x^2 + 4$

37. Challenge Solve the equation $(2x^2 - 3x + 4) - (2x^2 + x - 8) = 0$. 3

with Review

For help with surface area of a pyramid, see p. 507.

38. Science Fair You are constructing two wooden pyramids using the designs shown. Write a simplified polynomial expression for the total surface area of the two pyramids.
$2b^2 + 10b$

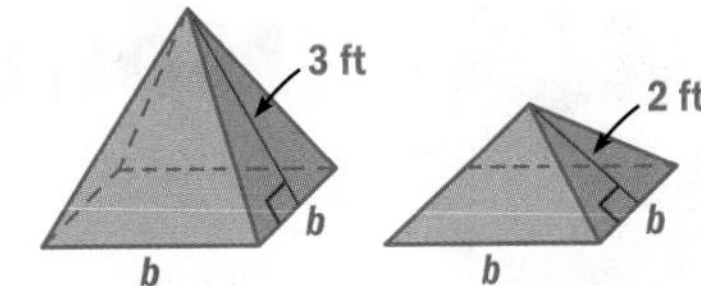

Mixed Review

Simplify the expression. *(Lesson 4.6)*

39. $b^3 \cdot b^7$ b^{10} **40.** $\frac{x^{12}}{x^5}$ x^7 **41.** $\frac{m^4n^5}{n^2}$ m^4n^3 **42.** $\frac{a^2 \cdot a^6}{a^3}$ a^5

43. How many different passwords can be made using 4 digits from 0 to 9? *(Lesson 12.4)* **10,000 passwords**

Test-Taking Practice

INTERNET
State Test Practice
CLASSZONE.COM

44. Multiple Choice Find the sum $(-7x^3 + 4x^2 - 1) + (x^3 - 9x + 3)$. **A**

A. $-6x^3 + 4x^2 - 9x + 2$ **B.** $-8x^3 + 4x^2 - 9x - 4$

C. $-6x^3 + 5x^2 + 2$ **D.** $-8x^3 - 5x^2 + 4$

45. Short Response Explain how to find the difference. **See margin.**
$(x^4 - 3x^3 + 5x + 3) - (x^4 + 2x^3 - 9x^2)$ **A**

Brain Game. Fish Oil and Nail Polish = $x^2 + 6x - 7$; Fish Oil and Muck = $7x - 5$; Green Slime and Nail Polish = $-2x - 2$; Dog Biscuits and Cotton Balls = $-8x$; Green Slime and Fish Oil = $5x^2 + 2x - 3$; Cotton Balls and Green Slime = $x^2 - 9x - 1$

Brain Game

Polynomial Potions

You need to make six potions using the six ingredients in the laboratory. Each potion is made by adding two ingredients together. Use the list of ingredients and the potion labels to find the secret formulas.

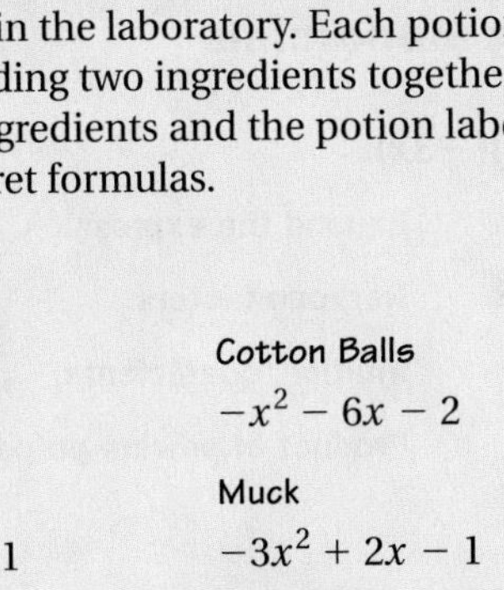

Ingredients

Dog Biscuits $x^2 - 2x + 2$	Cotton Balls $-x^2 - 6x - 2$
Green Slime $2x^2 - 3x + 1$	Muck $-3x^2 + 2x - 1$
Fish Oil $3x^2 + 5x - 4$	Nail Polish $-2x^2 + x - 3$

4 ASSESS

Assessment Resources

For more assessment resources, see:
- Assessment Book
- Test and Practice Generator

Mini-Quiz

Find the sum or difference.

1. $(3a^2 - 4) + (4a^2 - 3)$
$7a^2 - 7$

2. $(6y + 2) + (y^2 + y + 4)$
$y^2 + 7y + 6$

3. $(5f^2 + 2f - 4) - (3f^2 - f + 6)$
$2f^2 + 3f - 10$

4. $(-k^3 + k^2) - (2k^2 + k)$
$-k^3 - k^2 - k$

5. A rectangle with a length of $2x^2 + 3x - 3$ centimeters is shortened by $2x + 1$ centimeters. What is the length of the resulting rectangle? **$2x^2 + x - 4$ cm**

5 FOLLOW-UP

Reteaching/Remediation

- Study Guide in Chapter 13 Resource Book, pp. 21–22
- eTutorial Plus Online
- Extra Practice, p. 739
- Lesson Practice in Chapter 13 Resource Book, pp. 18–20

Challenge/Enrichment

- Challenge Practice in Chapter 13 Resource Book, p. 23
- Teacher's Edition, p. 654F

English Learner Support

- Spanish Study Guide
- Multi-Language Glossary
- Chapter Audio Summaries CDs

45. See Additional Answers beginning on page AA1.

1 PLAN

SKILL CHECK

Simplify. Write your answer as a power.

1. $x^2 \cdot x$ x^3
2. $2^3 \cdot 2^2$ 2^5
3. $n^3 \cdot n^3$ n^6

LESSON OBJECTIVE

Apply properties of exponents to monomials.

PACING

Suggested Number of Days
Basic Course: 2 days
Average Course: 2 days
Advanced Course: 2 days
Block: 1 block

TEACHING RESOURCES

For a complete list of Teaching Resources, see page 654B.

TRANSPARENCY

Warm-Up Exercises for this lesson are available on a transparency.

2 TEACH

MOTIVATING THE LESSON

Have students recall the product of powers property in their own words and give examples of its use.

ACTIVITY

Goal Use the properties of exponents to simplify monomials.

Key Discovery To multiply monomial factors that have the same base, add the exponents and multiply the coefficients.

Step 1. See Additional Answers beginning on page AA1.

LESSON 13.3 Monomials and Powers

BEFORE You added and subtracted polynomials.

Now You will apply properties of exponents to monomials.

WHY? So you can find the volume of Saturn, as in Ex. 48.

Word Watch

Review Words
power, p. 20
exponent, p. 20
coefficient, p. 86
monomial, p. 170

Activity You can use the properties of exponents to simplify monomials.

1. Copy and complete the table by expanding each expression, regrouping factors, and simplifying. See margin.

Expression	Expand	Regroup	Simplify
$(3x)(4x^2)$	$3 \cdot x \cdot 4 \cdot x \cdot x$	$3 \cdot 4 \cdot x \cdot x \cdot x$	$12x^3$
$(-2x)(5x^4)$	?	?	?
$(xy)^3$	$xy \cdot xy \cdot xy$	$x \cdot x \cdot x \cdot y \cdot y \cdot y$	x^3y^3
$(4x)^2$	?	?	?
$(-3x)^3$	?	?	?

2. What patterns do you notice in the table?

3. Use your results to simplify the expressions $(5x)(2x^3)$ and $(3pq)^2$. $10x^4$; $9p^2q^2$

Step 2. *Sample answer:* To multiply monomials that have the same base, you can multiply the coefficients and add the exponents of the base. To find the power of a product, you can multiply the exponent of each factor by the power.

In the activity, you used properties of exponents that you learned in Lesson 4.6 to multiply monomials. To multiply factors that have the same base, add their exponents. Multiply their coefficients.

HELP with Review
For help with rules of exponents, see p. 196.

EXAMPLE 1 Multiplying Monomials

Simplify the expression $(2x^3)(-3x)$.

$(2x^3)(-3x) = 2 \cdot x^3 \cdot (-3) \cdot x$ — Expand the expression.

$= 2 \cdot (-3) \cdot x^3 \cdot x$ — Regroup factors.

$= -6 \cdot x^3 \cdot x$ — Multiply coefficients.

$= -6x^4$ — Product of powers property

Your turn now Simplify the expression.

1. $4a(a^2)$ $4a^3$
2. $(-2m)(7m^2)$ $-14m^3$
3. $(-x)(8x^2)$ $-8x^3$
4. $(y^5)(5y)$ $5y^6$

ILLINOIS Standards and ISAT:
8.A.3a, 8.D.3c

You can use the distributive property and the properties of exponents to find the product of a monomial and a binomial.

EXAMPLE 2 Using the Distributive Property

Simplify the expression $2n(4n^2 - 5)$.

$2n(4n^2 - 5) = (2n)(4n^2) - (2n)(5)$ — Distributive property

$= 8n^3 - 10n$ — Product of powers property

Your turn now **Simplify the expression.**

5. $p(2p + 3)$ $2p^2 + 3p$
6. $-t^2(-2t + 8)$ $2t^3 - 8t^2$
7. $n^2(5n^2 - 3)$ $5n^4 - 3n^2$
8. $2x(3x - 4)$ $6x^2 - 8x$

In the activity on page 666, you found powers of products. You can use the rule below to simplify a power of a product.

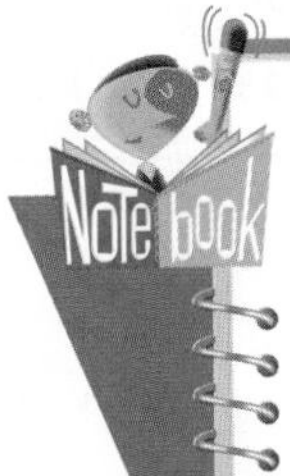

Power of a Product Property

Words To simplify a power of a product, find the power of each factor and multiply.

Algebra $(ab)^m = a^m \cdot b^m$ **Numbers** $(5 \cdot 2)^3 = 5^3 \cdot 2^3$

EXAMPLE 3 Simplifying a Power of a Product

Container The radius of a container is twice its height. Write an expression for the volume of the container. Use the formula $V = \pi r^2 h$.

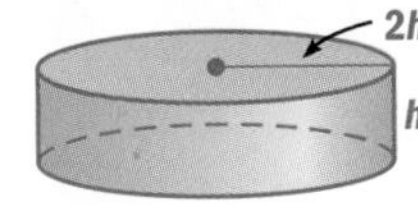

Solution

The radius is twice the height, so $r = 2h$.

$V = \pi(2h)^2h$ — Substitute $2h$ for r.

$= \pi(2^2 \cdot h^2)h$ — Power of a product property

$= \pi \cdot 4 \cdot h^2 \cdot h$ — Evaluate the power.

$= 4\pi h^3$ — Product of powers property.

ANSWER An expression for the volume of the container is $V = 4\pi h^3$.

TIPS FOR NEW TEACHERS

It will be easy for many students to confuse the product of powers property and the power of a power property, so you may need to spend extra time emphasizing when to apply each property. You may want to have students offer their own examples that use the different properties, and have them explain why a given property applies to the example. See Tips for New Teachers in the *Chapter 13 Resource Book*.

EXTRA EXAMPLES

Example 1 Simplify the expression $7b(3b^2)$. $21b^3$

Example 2 Simplify the expression $6d(d^2 - 3d)$. $6d^3 - 18d^2$

Example 3 Using the formula $V = lwh$, write an expression for the volume of a box with dimensions $l = 2x$, $w = 2x$, and $h = x^2 - 1$. $4x^4 - 4x^2$

TEACHING TIP

Before Example 2, review the distributive property with simpler expressions, such as $2(b - 1)$ and $-3(15 - n)$. It is especially important to review the use of the distributive property with a negative factor.

Differentiating Instruction

Less Proficient Students Work step by step through each type of problem in this lesson, encouraging student participation. Think aloud as you work the problems. To help students distinguish among the properties, have them call out the justification for each step as it is carried out.

EXTRA EXAMPLES

Example 4 Simplify the expression $(3e^3)^4$. **$81e^{12}$**

CONCEPT CHECK

When do you multiply exponents to simplify an expression? When do you add exponents? **when you are finding a power of a power; when you are finding the product of powers that have the same base**

DAILY PUZZLER

What is $((x^2)^3)^4$? x^{24}

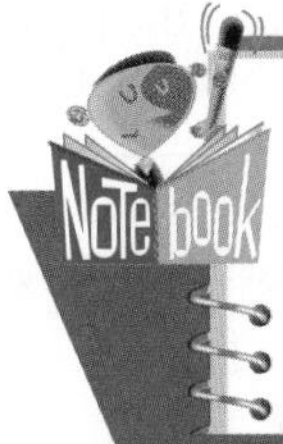

Power of a Power Property

Words To simplify a power of a power, multiply exponents.

Algebra $(a^m)^n = a^{mn}$ **Numbers** $(5^3)^2 = 5^{3 \cdot 2} = 5^6$

EXAMPLE 4 Simplifying a Power of a Power

Simplify the expression $(2y^2)^3$.

$(2y^2)^3 = 2^3 \cdot (y^2)^3$	Power of a product property
$= 8 \cdot y^{2 \cdot 3}$	Power of a power property
$= 8y^6$	Simplify.

Your turn now **Simplify the expression.**

9. $(2^4)^2$ 256 **10.** $(x^6)^2$ x^{12} **11.** $(5m^3)^2$ $25m^6$ **12.** $(a^2b)^2$ a^4b^2

13.3 Exercises

More Practice, p. 739

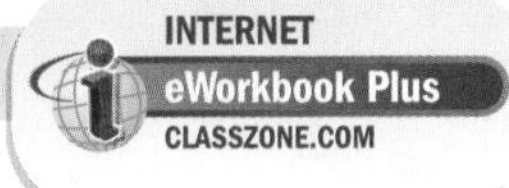

Getting Ready to Practice

Vocabulary **Match the expression with the rule used to simplify it.**

1. $(2y)^5$ B

2. $(x^2)^7$ A

3. $3 \cdot x^4 \cdot x^6$ C

A. power of a power property

B. power of a product property

C. product of powers property

Simplify the expression.

4. $(5x)(7x^6)$ $35x^7$ **5.** $2x(x^2 - 1)$ $2x^3 - 2x$ **6.** $(4y)^3$ $64y^3$ **7.** $(z^4)^4$ z^{16}

8. Guided Problem Solving Simplify the expression $\left(\frac{x}{y}\right)^4$.

(1) Write the expression in expanded form.

(2) Simplify by multiplying numerators and multiplying denominators.

(3) Write a rule you could use to find the power of a quotient.

Step 1. $\frac{x}{y} \cdot \frac{x}{y} \cdot \frac{x}{y} \cdot \frac{x}{y}$

Step 2. $\frac{x \cdot x \cdot x \cdot x}{y \cdot y \cdot y \cdot y} = \frac{x^4}{y^4}$

Step 3. *Sample answer:* Find the power of the numerator and the power of the denominator.

with Homework

Example	Exercises
1	9-14
2	15-20
3	22-29
4	30-37

Online Resources
CLASSZONE.COM

- More Examples
- eTutorial Plus

Practice and Problem Solving

A Simplify the expression by multiplying the monomials.

9. $(-4x)(5x^3)$ $-20x^4$ **10.** $(-16t)(-3t^9)$ $48t^{10}$ **11.** $(-x^2)(-3x)$ $3x^3$

12. $(3s)(-2s^3)$ $-6s^4$ **13.** $(-b^3)(-b^8)$ b^{11} **14.** $(-y^2)(y^3)$ $-y^5$

Simplify the expression by using the distributive property.

15. $m(m + 4)$ $m^2 + 4m$ **16.** $2w(3w + 1)$ $6w^2 + 2w$ **17.** $-t(t^2 - 4)$ $-t^3 + 4t$

18. $-8x(x^5 + x)$ $-8x^6 - 8x^2$ **19.** $w^2(-2w - 1)$ $-2w^3 - w^2$ **20.** $3k^2(12 - k^5)$ $36k^2 - 3k^7$

21. Seat Cushion You need fabric for a window seat cushion. Use the trapezoid pattern shown to write a polynomial expression for the area of the top of the cushion. Simplify the expression. $\frac{1}{2}(b - 6)(3b + b)$; $2b^2 - 12b$

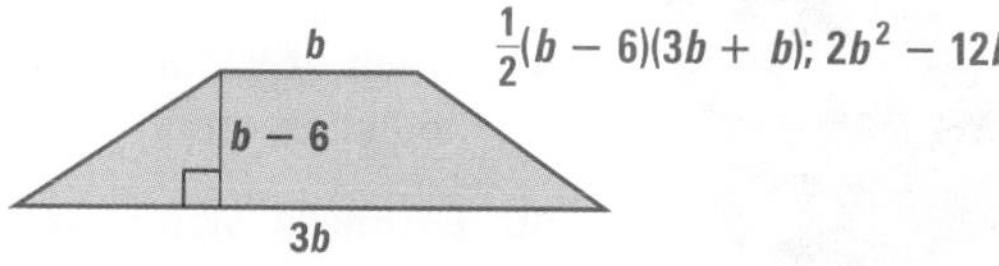

Simplify the expression by using the power of a product property.

22. $(5z)^3$ $125z^3$ **23.** $(xyz)^5$ $x^5y^5z^5$ **24.** $(2ab)^4$ $16a^4b^4$ **25.** $(-6z)^3$ $-216z^3$

26. $(-dt)^4$ d^4t^4 **27.** $(3rs)^2$ $9r^2s^2$ **28.** $(-3xy)^3$ $-27x^3y^3$ **29.** $(10bh)^5$ $100{,}000b^5h^5$

Simplify the expression by using the power of a power property.

30. $(t^4)^2$ t^8 **31.** $(y^2)^2$ y^4 **32.** $(c^2)^9$ c^{18} **33.** $(x^2)^{10}$ x^{20}

34. $(ab^3)^2$ a^2b^6 **35.** $(x^2y^2)^3$ x^6y^6 **36.** $(3a^2)^2$ $9a^4$ **37.** $(2r^3)^3$ $8r^9$

38. Compare and Contrast Explain why $(4y)^2$ is different from $4y^2$. In $(4y)^2$, both 4 and y are squared. In $4y^2$, only y is squared.

39. Photo Albums You are making photo albums in different sizes. Each page is twice as long as it is wide and needs a 2 inch margin for binding. Write a polynomial expression for the total area of one page. $(2w^2 + 4w)$ in.^{2}

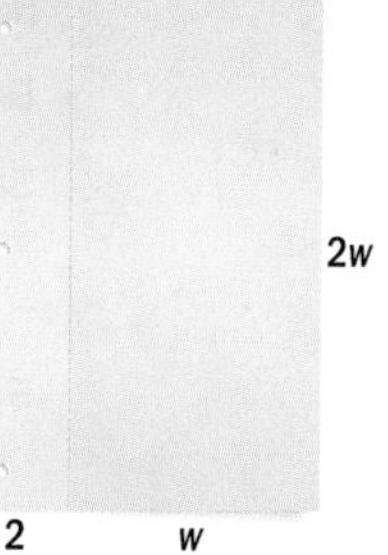

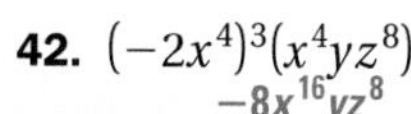

B Simplify the expression.

40. $2(5mn^4)^3$ $250m^3n^{12}$ **41.** $-3a^{10}(a^4b^2c)^4$ $-3a^{26}b^8c^4$ **42.** $(-2x^4)^3(x^4yz^8)$ $-8x^{16}yz^8$

43. Critical Thinking Write a ratio comparing the area of the circle to the area of the square. Simplify the ratio. Leave your answer in terms of π. $\frac{\pi r^2}{(2r)^2}$; $\frac{\pi}{4}$

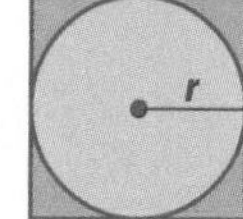

3 APPLY

ASSIGNMENT GUIDE

Basic Course

Day 1: pp. 669-670 Exs. 9-20, 40-42, 54-59

Day 2: pp. 669-670 Exs. 22-37, 45-48, 60, 61

Average Course

Day 1: pp. 669-670 Exs. 12-21, 40-47, 54-56

Day 2: pp. 669-670 Exs. 26-38, 48-50, 57-61

Advanced Course

Day 1: pp. 669-670 Exs. 12-21, 39-45, 54-58

Day 2: pp. 669-670 Exs. 26-37, 48-53*, 59-61

Block

pp. 669-670 Exs. 12-21, 26-38, 40-50, 54-61

EXTRA PRACTICE

- Student Edition, p. 739
- Chapter 13 Resource Book, pp. 26-28
- Test and Practice Generator

TRANSPARENCY

Even-numbered answers are available on transparencies.

HOMEWORK CHECK

When you review students' homework for this lesson, go over the following exercises to check understanding of key concepts.

Basic: 9, 13, 15, 22, 30

Average: 12, 14, 16, 26, 32

Advanced: 13, 17, 18, 28, 37

COMMON ERROR

In Exercises 45-47, watch for students who forget to apply the power to the coefficient or who forget to rewrite the expression with a coefficient between 1 and 10.

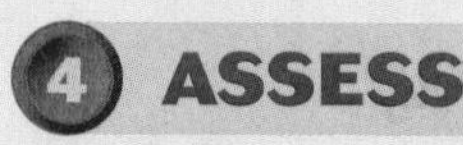

ASSESSMENT RESOURCES

For more assessment resources, see:
- Assessment Book
- Test and Practice Generator

MINI-QUIZ

Simplify the expression.

1. $(-5k)(7k^4)$ $-35k^5$
2. $(12g^6)(-2g^6)$ $-24g^{12}$
3. $c^3(c^2 - 4c)$ $c^5 - 4c^4$
4. $-d(d^3 - 3)$ $-d^4 + 3d$
5. $(3r^2)^4$ $81r^8$
6. $(4wx)^3$ $64w^3x^3$
7. A cube has a side length of $5xy^2$. Write an expression for the volume of the cube. $125x^3y^6$

RETEACHING/REMEDIATION
- Study Guide in Chapter 13 Resource Book, pp. 29–30
- Tutor Place, Algebra Cards 2, 6
- eTutorial Plus Online
- Extra Practice, p. 739
- Lesson Practice in Chapter 13 Resource Book, pp. 26–28

CHALLENGE/ENRICHMENT
- Challenge Practice in Chapter 13 Resource Book, p. 32
- Teacher's Edition, p. 654F

ENGLISH LEARNER SUPPORT
- Spanish Study Guide
- Multi-Language Glossary
- Chapter Audio Summaries CDs

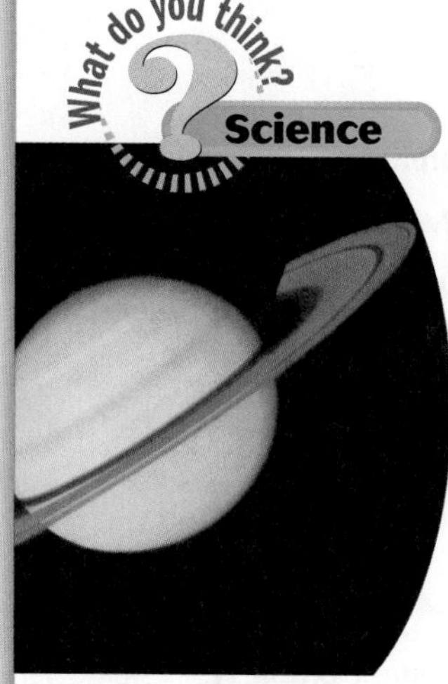

Saturn

The moon Pan orbits within a gap in Saturn's rings. Pan's radius is about 10 kilometers. Compare the volumes of Pan and Saturn. **The volume of Saturn is about 1.96×10^{11} times the volume of Pan.**

50. $\dfrac{\frac{4}{3}\pi(6.0 \times 10^4)^3}{\frac{4}{3}\pi(5.6 \times 10^2)^3} = \dfrac{2.16 \times 10^{14}}{1.76 \times 10^8}$; about 1,230,000 times

44. **Volume** Write and simplify a polynomial expression for the volume of the square pyramid. $3x^3$

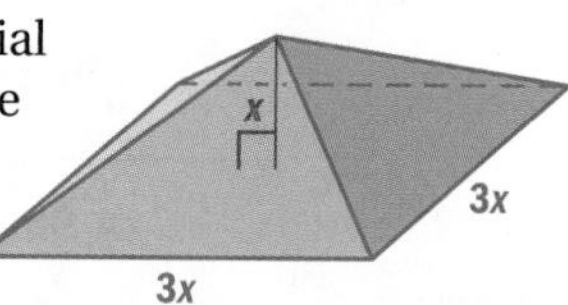

Scientific Notation **Simplify the expression and write it in scientific notation.**

45. $(3 \times 10^4)^3$ 2.7×10^{13} 46. $(9 \times 10^{10})^3$ 7.29×10^{32} 47. $(5 \times 10^7)^4$ 6.25×10^{30}

Extended Problem Solving **In Exercises 48–50, use the formula $V = \frac{4}{3}\pi r^3$ for the volume of a sphere to find the volumes of spherical objects in our solar system.**

48. **Saturn** The radius of Saturn is about 6.0×10^4 kilometers. about 9.04×10^{14} km^3
49. **Moon of Saturn** The radius of Saturn's moon Dione is about 560 kilometers. about 7.35×10^8 km^3
50. **Estimate** Write a ratio comparing the volume of Saturn to the volume of Dione. Use this ratio to estimate how many times larger Saturn is than Dione. See margin.

C **Challenge** **Simplify the expression.**

51. $3[(a^4b^3)^4 \cdot a^8b]^3$ $3a^{72}b^{39}$ 52. $\left(\dfrac{2x^2}{x}\right)^3$ $8x^3$ 53. $\dfrac{(-2xy)^2}{(x^2)^3}$ $\dfrac{4y^2}{x^4}$

Mixed Review

In Exercises 54–57, write the percent as a fraction in simplest form. *(Lesson 7.4)*

54. 55% $\frac{11}{20}$ 55. 71% $\frac{71}{100}$ 56. 29% $\frac{29}{100}$ 57. 18% $\frac{9}{50}$

58. In one out of every eight holes of mini-golf, you get a hole in one. Find the odds of getting a hole in one on the next hole that you play. *(Lesson 12.7)* $\frac{1}{8}$
59. Find the probability of rolling first a 2 and then a 4 if you roll a number cube twice. *(Lesson 12.8)* $\frac{1}{36}$

Test-Taking Practice

60. **Multiple Choice** Simplify the expression $4a^2(3a + 1)$. D
    A. $7a^3 + 1$ B. $12a^3 + 4a$ C. $7a^3 + 4a^2$ D. $12a^3 + 4a^2$
61. **Multiple Choice** Simplify the expression $(-2b^4)^3$. F
    F. $-8b^{12}$ G. $8b^7$ H. $8b^{12}$ I. $-8b^7$

Notebook Review

LESSONS 13.1 TO 13.3

Review the vocabulary definitions in your notebook.

Copy the review examples in your notebook. Then complete the exercises.

Check Your Definitions

polynomial, p. 657
binomial, p. 657
trinomial, p. 657
standard form, p. 657

Use Your Vocabulary

Copy and complete the statement.

1. A polynomial with one term is called a _?_. monomial
2. A _?_ is a monomial or a sum of monomials. polynomial

13.1 Can you simplify polynomials?

EXAMPLE Simplify the polynomial $4x^2 - 5(x^2 - x + 3 - 2x)$.

$4x^2 - 5(x^2 - x + 3 - 2x)$

$= 4x^2 - 5x^2 + 5x - 15 + 10x$ Distributive property

$= -x^2 + 15x - 15$ Combine like terms.

Simplify the polynomial and write it in standard form.

3. $10 - 3a^2 + 4a^2 + 8$ $a^2 + 18$
4. $6 + z^2 - 3z + z^2 - 5$ $2z^2 - 3z + 1$

13.2 Can you add and subtract polynomials?

EXAMPLE Find the sum $(3x^2 - 2x + 7) + (5x - 9)$.

$$\begin{array}{r} 3x^2 - 2x + 7 \\ + \qquad\quad 5x - 9 \\ \hline 3x^2 + 3x - 2 \end{array}$$

Write the second polynomial under the first.
Arrange like terms in columns.
Combine like terms.

Find the sum or difference.

5. $(n^3 + 4n^2 - 9) + (n^3 + n^2 - 2n + 6)$ $2n^3 + 5n^2 - 2n - 3$
6. $(2x^2 + 3x - 1) - (7x^2 - x - 5)$ $-5x^2 + 4x + 4$

Additional Resources

The following resources are available to help review the materials in Lessons 13.1–13.3.

Chapter 13 Resource Book
- Lesson Practice
- Study Guide

Assessment Book
- Chapter 13 Quiz 1

Technology
- Test and Practice Generator
- eTutorial CD-ROM

Internet
- Classzone
- eWorkbook Plus Online
- eTutorial Plus Online

English Learner Support

- Spanish Study Guide
- Multi-Language Glossary
- Chapter Audio Summaries CDs

13.3 Can you multiply monomials?

EXAMPLE Simplify the expression $(x^3)(3x)^2$.

$(x^3)(3x)^2 = x^3(3^2 \cdot x^2)$ **Power of a product property**

$= x^3 \cdot 9 \cdot x^2$ **Evaluate the power.**

$= 9x^5$ **Product of powers property**

☑ **Simplify the expression.**

7. $(8x^8)(6x^2)$ $48x^{10}$ **8.** $(6n^3m)^2$ $36n^6m^2$ **9.** $(2ab)^4$ $16a^4b^4$ **10.** $(4r^2)(r - 5)$ $4r^3 - 20r^2$

Stop and Think about Lessons 13.1–13.3

11. Writing Simplify the expression $(2x)(x^2y)$ and explain your steps. See margin.

12. Critical Thinking The radius of a cylinder is three times its height. Write a polynomial expression for the surface area of the cylinder using only one variable. Use the formula $S = 2\pi r^2 + 2\pi rh$. $24\pi h^2$ or $\frac{8\pi r^2}{3}$

Notebook Review

11. *Sample answer*: By the associative property of multiplication, $(2x)(x^2y) = 2(x \cdot x^2)y$. By the product of powers property, $2(x \cdot x^2)y = 2x^3y$. So $(2x)(x^2y) = 2x^3y$.

Review Quiz 1

Simplify the polynomial and write it in standard form.

1. $5x^2 + 4x - 3x^2 - 11$ $2x^2 + 4x - 11$

2. $-9y^2 + 7y - 2y + 10 - y$ $-9y^2 + 4y + 10$

3. $-5k^3 + 2(3k^3 + k - 4)$ $k^3 + 2k - 8$

4. $8r^3 - 4r - 5r^3 - 3r + 1$ $3r^3 - 7r + 1$

Find the sum or difference.

5. $(6n^3 - 2n^2) + (n^3 + 7n^2 - 4n)$ $7n^3 + 5n^2 - 4n$

6. $(4b^2 - 3b + 8) - (2b^2 - 6)$ $2b^2 - 3b + 14$

7. $(x^2 + 6x + 1) - (2x^2 - 8x + 4)$ $-x^2 + 14x - 3$

8. $(3m^2 + m - 9) + (7m^2 + 2)$ $10m^2 + m - 7$

9. Area Write a polynomial expression for the area of the floor surrounding the rug in the diagram. Simplify the polynomial. $2x \cdot 3x - x(x - 3) = 5x^2 + 3x$

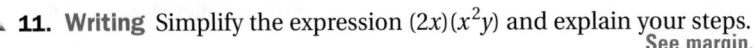

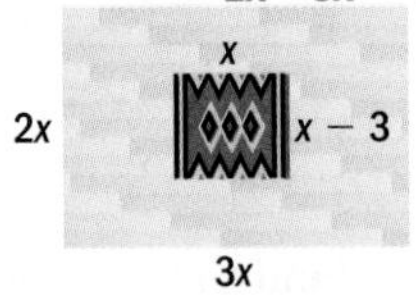

Simplify the expression.

10. $(x^3)(-5x)$ $-5x^4$ **11.** $(3t^4)(4t^2)$ $12t^6$ **12.** $(2c^3)^4$ $16c^{12}$

13. $(-2y)^4$ $16y^4$ **14.** $r^3(3r - 4)$ $3r^4 - 4r^3$ **15.** $-5d(3d^2 + 2)$ $-15d^3 - 10d$

13.4 Hands-on Activity

GOAL

Multiply binomials using algebra tiles.

MATERIALS

- algebra tiles

Multiplying Binomials

You can model binomial multiplication with algebra tiles.

Explore **Model the product $(x + 3)(3x + 2)$ with algebra tiles.**

1. Model each binomial with algebra tiles. Arrange the first binomial vertically and the second binomial horizontally, as shown.

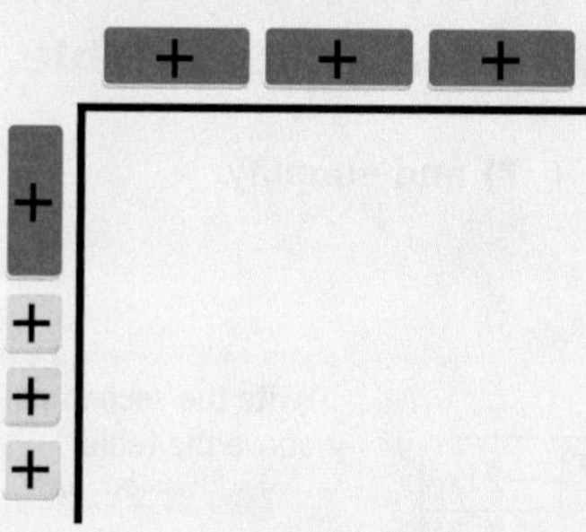

2. The binomials define a rectangular area with length $(3x + 2)$ units and width $(x + 3)$ units. Fill in the region with the appropriate tiles.

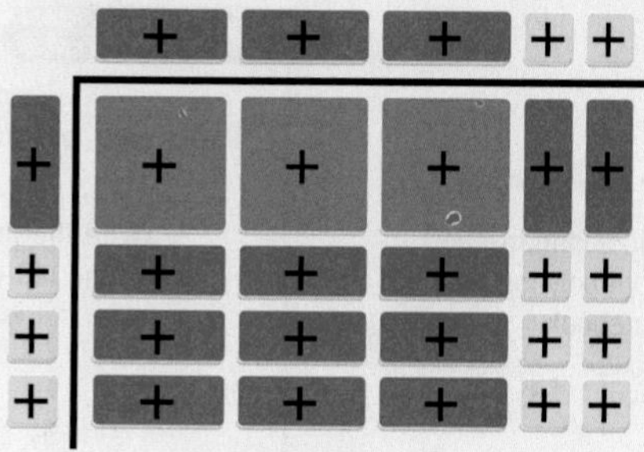

3. The rectangle on the inside of the model represents $3x^2 + 11x + 6$. This is the product of the binomials.

Your turn now **Find the product with algebra tiles. Draw your model.** 1–3. See margin for art.

1. $(x + 1)(x + 2)$ $x^2 + 3x + 2$
2. $(x + 4)(x + 4)$ $x^2 + 8x + 16$
3. $(x + 2)(2x + 2)$ $2x^2 + 6x + 4$

Stop and Think

Model the expression with algebra tiles. Arrange the tiles in a rectangle. Find the two binomials that have this product. 4–6. See margin for art.

4. $x^2 + 5x + 6$ $(x + 3)(x + 2)$
5. $x^2 + 2x + 1$ $(x + 1)(x + 1)$
6. $3x^2 + 8x + 4$ $(x + 2)(3x + 2)$

ILLINOIS Standards and ISAT:
8.D.3a

1 PLAN

Explore the Concept

- Students will multiply binomials using algebra tiles.
- This activity leads into multiplying binomials using the FOIL method in Lesson 13.4.

Materials

Each student will need algebra tiles.

Recommended Time

Work activity: 10 min
Discuss results: 5 min

Grouping

Students should work individually.

Transparency

Support transparencies are available for this Activity.

2 TEACH

Alternative Strategy

Demonstrate the activity using an overhead. Think aloud as you model one example. Find other products by having students direct you.

3 CLOSE

Key Discovery

Simple binomial multiplication can be modeled with algebra tiles by filling in a rectangular area represented by the binomials.

Assessment

1. If two binomials each contain an x-term, what do you know about the product? **It will contain an x^2 term.**

1–6. See Additional Answers beginning on page AA1.

PLAN

SKILL CHECK

Simplify.

1. $2(x + 7)$ $\quad 2x + 14$
2. $-3(4 - y)$ $\quad 3y - 12$
3. $k^3(9k - k^2)$ $\quad -k^5 + 9k^4$

Lesson Objective

Multiply binomials.

Pacing

Suggested Number of Days

Basic Course: 2 days
Average Course: 2 days
Advanced Course: 2 days
Block: 1 block

Teaching Resources

For a complete list of Teaching Resources, see page 654B.

Transparency

Warm-Up Exercises for this lesson are available on a transparency. Support transparencies are available for the beginning of this lesson.

TEACH

Motivating the Lesson

Multiply 72 and 23 using a vertical format on the board. Point out the four multiplications: 3(2), 3(7), 2(2), and 2(7). Stress that these are the products formed when multiplying the binomials 70 + 2 and 20 + 3.

TIPS FOR NEW TEACHERS

Stress that the FOIL method is the distributive property applied to the product of two binomials. See Tips for New Teachers in the *Chapter 13 Resource Book*.

Multiplying Binomials

BEFORE	Now	WHY?
You multiplied monomials and polynomials.	You'll multiply binomials.	So you can find an account balance after 2 years, as in Ex. 22.

Word Watch

Review words

polynomial, p. 657
binomial, p. 657

You can use a visual model to multiply binomials. The model below shows that the product $(x + 2)(3x + 1)$ equals $3x^2 + 7x + 2$.

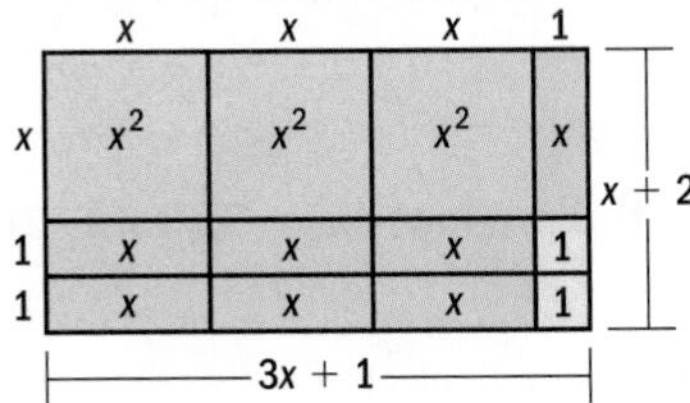

You can multiply two binomials using a table or a vertical method.

HELP with Notetaking

You should summarize key ideas about polynomials in your notebook.

EXAMPLE 1 Multiplying Binomials with a Table

Find the product $(-3x + 2)(8x + 7)$ and simplify.

Write the first polynomial on the left of the table.

Write the second polynomial above the table.

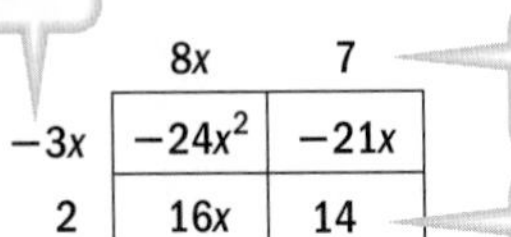

	$8x$	7
$-3x$	$-24x^2$	$-21x$
2	$16x$	14

Multiply to fill in the table.

The product is $-24x^2 - 21x + 16x + 14$. Combine like terms.

ANSWER The product is $-24x^2 - 5x + 14$.

EXAMPLE 2 Multiplying Binomials Vertically

Find the product $(2x - 5)(3x + 4)$ and simplify.

$2x - 5$	Write the first binomial.
$\times \quad 3x + 4$	Write the second binomial.
$8x - 20$	Multiply $4(2x - 5)$.
$6x^2 - 15x$	Multiply $3x(2x - 5)$. Line up like terms.
$6x^2 - 7x - 20$	Add $8x - 20$ and $6x^2 - 15x$.

ILLINOIS Standards and ISAT:
8.D.3a

with Vocabulary

Compound interest is earned on the original amount of money in an account and on the interest already earned.

EXAMPLE 3 Multiplying Binomials Horizontally

Banking You deposit $1 into a savings account with interest compounded annually. The balance of the account after two years can be found using the expression $(1 + r)^2$, where r represents the interest rate. Expand this expression and simplify.

Solution

To expand the expression, multiply 2 binomials.

$(1 + r)^2 = (1 + r)(1 + r)$	$(1 + r)^2$ means $(1 + r)(1 + r)$.
$= 1(1 + r) + r(1 + r)$	Distributive property
$= 1 + r + r + r^2$	Distributive property
$= 1 + 2r + r^2$	Combine like terms.
$= r^2 + 2r + 1$	Write in standard form.

Your turn now Find the product and simplify.

1. $(x + 1)(x + 3)$ $x^2 + 4x + 3$
2. $(b - 4)(b - 3)$ $b^2 - 7b + 12$
3. $(3t - 4)(t + 2)$ $3t^2 + 2t - 8$

The FOIL Method The letters in the word FOIL can help you remember how to multiply binomials. The letters should remind you of the words **F**irst, **O**uter, **I**nner, and **L**ast.

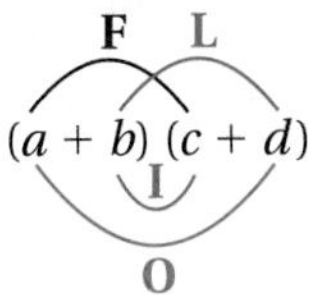

EXAMPLE 4 Multiplying with the FOIL Method

Find the product $(2x + 3)(3x - 1)$ and simplify.

F		O		I		L	
First	+	Outer	+	Inner	+	Last	
$2x \cdot 3x$	+	$2x \cdot (-1)$	+	$3 \cdot 3x$	+	$3 \cdot (-1)$	Group terms.
$6x^2$	+	$(-2x)$	+	$9x$	+	(-3)	Multiply.
		$6x^2 + 7x - 3$					Combine like terms.

Your turn now Find the product and simplify.

4. $(d + 6)(d + 5)$ $d^2 + 11d + 30$
5. $(x - 3)(x - 1)$ $x^2 - 4x + 3$
6. $(5s + 3)(2s - 4)$ $10s^2 - 14s - 12$

EXTRA EXAMPLES

Example 1 Find the product $(5a + 2)(a - 3)$ and simplify. $5a^2 - 13a - 6$

Example 2 Find the product $(4b - 5)(-b + 2)$ and simplify. $-4b^2 + 13b - 10$

Example 3 A flower garden has a length of $5x + 8$ meters and a width of $4x - 2$ meters. Write an expression that represents the area of the garden. Expand the expression. $(5x + 8)(4x - 2)$; $20x^2 + 22x - 16$

Example 4 Find the product $(4x - 3)(3x + 7)$ and simplify. $12x^2 + 19x - 21$

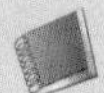

NOTETAKING

Encourage students to write a binomial multiplication problem in their notebooks and perform the multiplication using each method from Examples 1–4. This will help them to see that the methods are closely related.

CONCEPT CHECK

Describe the FOIL method in your own words. ***Sample answer:* To multiply two binomials, multiply the First terms, then the Outer terms (the first term of the first binomial and the last term of the second), then the Inner terms (the last term of the first binomial and the first term of the second), and finally the Last terms. Then combine like terms.**

DAILY PUZZLER

A binomial product of the form $(x + a)(x - a)$ simplifies to $x^2 - a^2$. Use this information to find the product 1009(991) without using a calculator. **999,919**

3 APPLY

ASSIGNMENT GUIDE

Basic Course

Day 1: pp. 676–677 Exs. 9–14, 24–27, 40–43

Day 2: pp. 676–677 Exs. 15–20, 22, 32–39

Average Course

Day 1: pp. 676–677 Exs. 12–17, 23–25, 31–36

Day 2: pp. 676–677 Exs. 18–22, 26–28, 37–43

Advanced Course

Day 1: pp. 676–677 Exs. 14–17, 23–25, 32–38

Day 2: pp. 676–677 Exs. 18–22, 27–31*, 41–43

Block

pp. 676–677 Exs. 12–28, 31–43

EXTRA PRACTICE

- Student Edition, p. 739
- Chapter 13 Resource Book, pp. 35–37
- Test and Practice Generator

TRANSPARENCY

Even-numbered answers are available on transparencies.

HOMEWORK CHECK

When you review students' homework for this lesson, go over the following exercises to check understanding of key concepts.

Basic: 9, 11, 12, 16, 22

Average: 12, 14, 16, 17, 22

Advanced: 14, 15, 16, 17, 22

13.4 Exercises

More Practice, p. 739

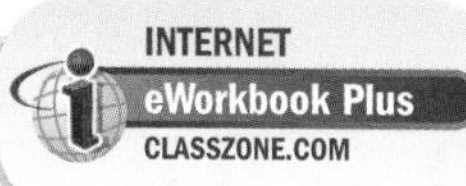

Getting Ready to Practice

HELP with Homework

Example	Exercises
1	9-17
2	9-17
3	22
4	9-17

Online Resources CLASSZONE.COM
- More Examples
- eTutorial Plus

1. Vocabulary Copy and complete: A polynomial with two terms is called a _?_. binomial

Find the product and simplify.

2. $3x(x - 4)$ $3x^2 - 12x$ **3.** $2m(3m + 1)$ $6m^2 + 2m$ **4.** $-2y(y + 5)$ $-2y^2 - 10y$

5. $(y - 4)(y + 1)$ $y^2 - 3y - 4$ **6.** $(g + 3)(g + 7)$ $g^2 + 10g + 21$ **7.** $(z + 4)(z - 2)$ $z^2 + 2z - 8$

8. Find the Error Describe and correct the error in the solution.

$(x + 2)(x - 4)$
$= x \cdot x + x \cdot 4 + 2 \cdot x + 2 \cdot (-4)$
$= x^2 + 4x + 2x - 8$
$= x^2 + 6x - 8$ ✗

In the second term of the expansion, x should be multiplied by -4, not 4: $(x + 2)(x - 4) = x \cdot x + x \cdot (-4) + 2 \cdot x + 2 \cdot (-4) = x^2 - 4x + 2x - 8 = x^2 - 2x - 8$.

Practice and Problem Solving

A Find the product and simplify.

9. $(x + 9)(x - 2)$ $x^2 + 7x - 18$ **10.** $(p + 6)(p + 4)$ $p^2 + 10p + 24$ **11.** $(a + 10)(a - 4)$ $a^2 + 6a - 40$

12. $(2m + 3)(m - 7)$ $2m^2 - 11m - 21$ **13.** $(3q - 1)(q - 1)$ $3q^2 - 4q + 1$ **14.** $(b - 3)(9b + 4)$ $9b^2 - 23b - 12$

15. $(6r + 7)(r - 1)$ $6r^2 + r - 7$ **16.** $(t - 1)(-3t - 4)$ $-3t^2 - t + 4$ **17.** $(-x - 5)(11x - 12)$ $-11x^2 - 43x + 60$

Critical Thinking **Find the product and simplify.**

18. $(x + 3)(x - 3)$ $x^2 - 9$ **19.** $(x - 4)(x + 4)$ $x^2 - 16$ **20.** $(x + 1)(x - 1)$ $x^2 - 1$

21. Look for a Pattern Describe the pattern in the binomials and their products in Exercises 18–20. See margin.

21. *Sample answer:* One binomial in each product is the sum of two terms. The other binomial in each product is the difference of the same two terms. The product of these two binomials is the square of the first term minus the square of the second term.

22. Savings Account You deposit \$50 into a savings account with interest compounded annually. The expression $50(1 + r)^2$, where r is the interest rate, gives the account balance after 2 years. Expand this expression and simplify. Find the account balance for $r = 0.03$. $50 + 100r + 50r^2$; \$53.05

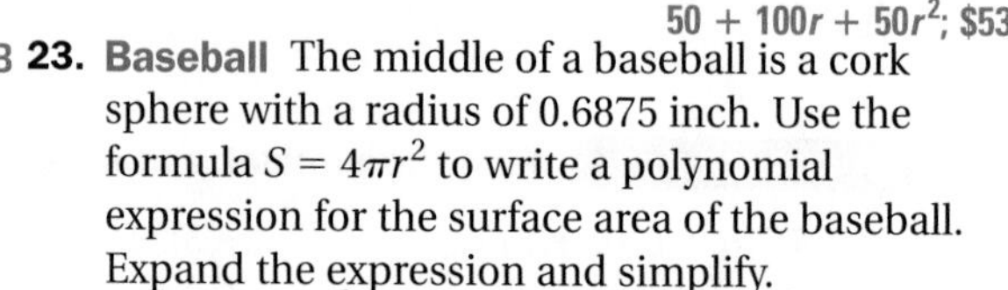

B 23. Baseball The middle of a baseball is a cork sphere with a radius of 0.6875 inch. Use the formula $S = 4\pi r^2$ to write a polynomial expression for the surface area of the baseball. Expand the expression and simplify.
$4\pi(0.6875 + x)^2 = 4\pi(0.4727 + 1.375x + x^2) = 1.8908\pi + 5.5\pi x + 4\pi x^2$

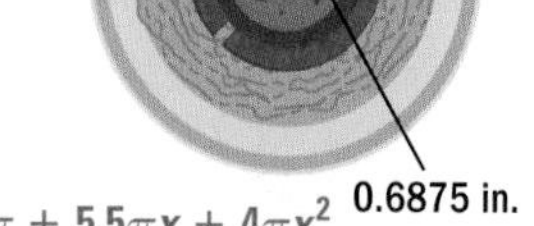

Find the product and simplify.

24. $\left(\frac{1}{2}x + 2\right)(4x - 6)$ $2x^2 + 5x - 12$

25. $(9b - 12)\left(\frac{1}{3}b - 6\right)$ $3b^2 - 58b + 72$

26. $(n^2 - 2)(n^2 + 1)$ $n^4 - n^2 - 2$

27. Stage Design You are building a platform on stage for a school talent show. Write and simplify a polynomial expression for the area of the platform using the design shown. Then find the area when x is 5 feet. $(30 - 2x)(20 - x) = 600 - 70x + 2x^2$; 300 ft^2

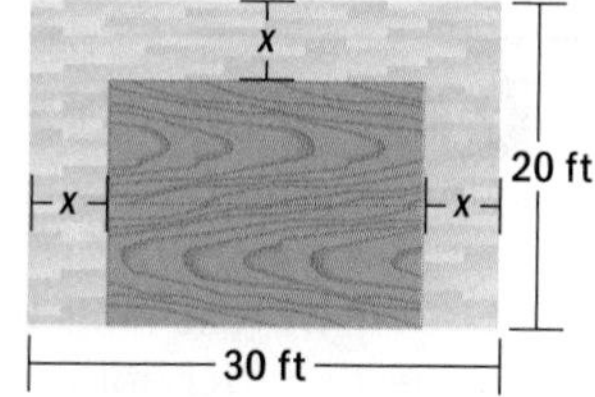

28. Writing Explain why $(x + 3)^2$ does not equal $x^2 + 9$. $(x + 3)^2 = (x + 3)(x + 3) = x^2 + 6x + 9$

C **29. Challenge** Find the product and simplify: $(x + 4)(3x^2 - 2x + 1)$. $3x^3 + 10x^2 - 7x + 4$

30. Savings You put $20 into a savings account with interest compounded annually. The expression $20(1 + r)^3$, where r is the interest rate, gives the account balance after 3 years. Expand this expression and simplify. Find the account balance for $r = 0.05$. $20r^3 + 60r^2 + 60r + 20$; $23.15

31. Work Backward Find the unknown binomial in the equation $x^2 + 8x + 7 = (\underline{\ ?\ })(x + 7)$. $x + 1$

Mixed Review

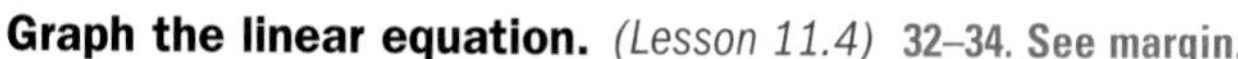

Graph the linear equation. *(Lesson 11.4)* 32–34. See margin.

32. $y = 6x - 4$ **33.** $y = x - 3$ **34.** $y = -2x + 7$

Find the product. *(Lesson 13.3)*

35. $-4r(r + 6)$ $-4r^2 - 24r$

36. $3c(4c^2 + 2c)$ $12c^3 + 6c^2$

37. $-5x(-3x + 2)$ $15x^2 - 10x$

Basic Skills **Plot the point in a coordinate plane.** 38–41. See margin.

38. $(2, -9)$ **39.** $(-7, 6)$ **40.** $(-3, -8)$ **41.** $(0, 4)$

Test-Taking Practice

INTERNET
State Test Practice
CLASSZONE.COM

42. Multiple Choice Find the product $(x + 6)(x - 2)$. D

A. $x^2 - 4x - 12$ **B.** $x^2 - 4x + 4$

C. $x^2 + 4x + 12$ **D.** $x^2 + 4x - 12$

43. Multiple Choice Find the product $(2x + 1)(x - 5)$. F

F. $2x^2 - 9x - 5$ **G.** $x^2 - 9x - 5$

H. $2x^2 + 11x - 5$ **I.** $x^2 + 11x - 5$

4 ASSESS

Assessment Resources

For more assessment resources, see:
- Assessment Book
- Test and Practice Generator

Mini-Quiz

Find the product and simplify.

1. $(x - 7)(2x + 12)$ $2x^2 - 2x - 84$

2. $(10b + 2)(b - 4)$ $10b^2 - 38b - 8$

3. $(2a + 5)(2a + 5)$ $4a^2 + 20a + 25$

4. $(2a + 5)(2a - 5)$ $4a^2 - 25$

5. A circle has a radius of $x + 7$ centimeters. Write an expression that represents the area of the circle. Expand the expression. $\pi(x + 7)^2$; $\pi x^2 + 14\pi x + 49\pi$

5 FOLLOW-UP

Reteaching/Remediation

- Study Guide in Chapter 13 Resource Book, pp. 38-39
- eTutorial Plus Online
- Extra Practice, p. 739
- Lesson Practice in Chapter 13 Resource Book, pp. 35-37

Challenge/Enrichment

- Challenge Practice in Chapter 13 Resource Book, p. 40
- Teacher's Edition, p. 654F

English Learner Support

- Spanish Study Guide
- Multi-Language Glossary
- Chapter Audio Summaries CDs

32-34, 38-41. See Additional Answers beginning on page AA1.

1 PLAN

STRATEGY BACKGROUND

Encourage students to use the strategy Draw a Graph when a visual representation can help solve a problem. A useful graph may be a map grid, a bar graph, a circle graph, or a line graph.

2 TEACH

GUIDING STUDENTS' WORK

In Step 3, suggest that students draw their curves in pencil very lightly and then darken the lines when they feel that the graph is a smooth curve. Make sure students do not connect points with a series of straight lines. You may want to draw the general shape of a sine curve for students and point out how a wave-shaped graph often represents quantities, such as hours of daylight, that repeat over a regular time interval.

EXTRA EXAMPLES

Example The table shows the average high temperature in degrees Fahrenheit (°F) in Forsyth County, North Carolina. Use a graph to estimate the average high temperature in September.

Month	Temp	Month	Temp
Jan	47	Jul	87
Feb	51	Aug	86
Mar	60	Sep	?
Apr	70	Oct	70
May	77	Nov	61
Jun	84	Dec	51

Reasonable estimates would be in the vicinity of 79–81°F.

13.5 Problem Solving Strategies

- Look for a Pattern
- Draw a Diagram
- Act It Out
- Work Backward
- Draw a Graph
- Break into Parts

Draw a Graph

Daylight The table below shows the total hours of daylight, to the nearest quarter hour, in Anchorage, Alaska, on the 20th day of each month. The table is missing data for the month of July. Estimate the total hours of daylight on July 20.

Month	Jan.	Feb.	March	April	May	June	July	Aug.	Sept.	Oct.	Nov.	Dec.
Hours of Daylight	$6\frac{3}{4}$	$9\frac{1}{2}$	$12\frac{1}{4}$	$15\frac{1}{4}$	$17\frac{3}{4}$	$19\frac{1}{4}$	?	$15\frac{1}{2}$	$12\frac{1}{2}$	$9\frac{3}{4}$	7	$5\frac{1}{2}$

1 Read and Understand

Read the problem carefully.

You need to estimate the total hours of daylight on July 20.

2 Make a Plan

Decide on a strategy to use.

You can estimate the hours by drawing a graph. Use the table of values to sketch a curve.

3 Solve the Problem

Reread the problem and draw a graph.

The data in the table are ordered pairs. Let the x-axis show the date (Jan. 20 = 1, Feb. 20 = 2, etc.). Let the y-axis show the hours of daylight. Plot the points in the coordinate plane.

Connect the points with a curve, and use it to estimate the total hours of daylight on July 20.

ANSWER There are about 18 hours of daylight on July 20.

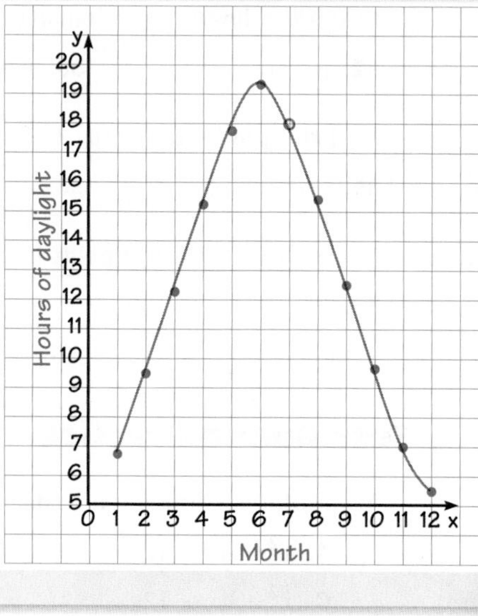

4 Look Back

Because the graph decreases from June to December it is reasonable to say that there are between $19\frac{1}{4}$ and $15\frac{1}{2}$ hours of daylight on July 20. A reasonable estimate is 18 hours.

ILLINOIS Standards and ISAT:
8.D.3a; 8.D.3c, 6.C.3b

Practice the Strategy

Use the strategy *draw a graph.*

1. **E-mail** You e-mail two copies of a joke on January 1. Each recipient e-mails two copies of the joke on the day after receiving it. How many e-mails are sent on January 7? **128 e-mails**
2. **Square Root** Copy and complete the table.

x	1	4	9	16	25	36
$\sqrt{x}$	? 1	? 2	? 3	? 4	? 5	? 6

Estimate the square roots below.

a. $\sqrt{7}$ **2.6** **b.** $\sqrt{30}$ **5.5** **c.** $\sqrt{20}$ **4.5**

3. **Cutting** The area of a poster board is 1000 square inches. You repeatedly cut the poster in half, setting aside one half each time. Estimate how many cuts you will make before the area of the remaining piece is less than 1 square inch. **10 cuts**
4. **Kiwi Bird** A female kiwi bird weighs from 3 to 9 pounds. A kiwi bird's egg weighs about $\frac{1}{5}$ of the mother's body weight. Estimate the weight of a female bird whose egg weighs less than 0.7 pound. **3 lb**
5. **Tutoring** For each hour you spend tutoring after school, you earn 5 extra-credit points. Make a table that shows how many extra-credit points you can earn for hours you spend tutoring. Estimate how many extra-credit points you would earn after tutoring for 1 hour and 45 minutes. **See margin.**

Mixed Problem Solving

Use any strategy to solve the problem.

6. **Peanut Butter** In a poll, 44% of the people said the best thing to eat with peanut butter is jelly. About 23% chose chocolate. Only 15% preferred marshmallow spread with peanut butter. The rest of the people chose bananas. If 2916 people participated in the poll, about how many people choose bananas with peanut butter? **about 525 people**
7. **Draw** Copy the grid. How many squares can you draw by connecting dots? **50 squares**
8. **Encyclopedia** You have a two-volume music encyclopedia. Each volume has 600 pages, and its front and back covers are each 0.4 centimeter thick. If the books sit in the usual order on a shelf, what is the distance, in centimeters, from the first page of Volume 1 to the last page of Volume 2? **0.8 cm**
9. **Solid** Find the volume of the solid shown. The formula for the volume of a sphere is $V = \frac{4}{3}\pi r^3$. Round to the nearest hundredth of a cubic centimeter. **1809.56 cm³**

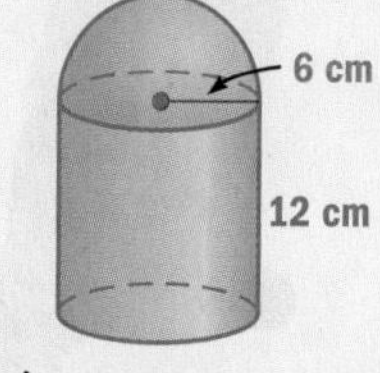

3 APPLY

TRANSPARENCY

Even-numbered answers are available on transparencies.

MATH REASONING

In Exercise 4, students may have difficulty getting started. Point out to them that they need to have information given as ordered pairs to make the graph. Help them to see that they can find ordered pairs in the form (weight of egg, weight of bird), where the weight of the bird is a whole number from 3 to 9, and the weight of the egg is one fifth of the weight of the bird.

TEACHING TIP

In Exercise 7, help students create an organized list of the squares with 1 unit, 2 unit, 3 unit, and 4 unit sides. Then show them the "tipped" square in the figure below and have them find other smaller squares like it.

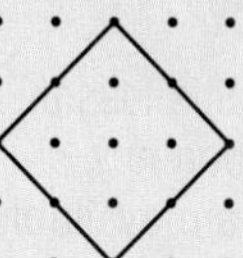

SUGGESTED STRATEGIES

You may wish to suggest the following strategies for the problems in the Mixed Problem Solving:

- Exercise 6: Break into Parts
- Exercise 7: Break into Parts; Draw a Diagram
- Exercise 8: Draw a Diagram
- Exercise 9: Break into Parts

5.

Hours	0.5	1	1.5	2
Points	2.5	5	7.5	10

about 9 points

1 PLAN

SKILL CHECK

Find the value of y for the given value of x.

1. $y = x^2 + 3, x = -2$ **7**
2. $y = 2x^2 + 1, x = 3$ **19**

Lesson Objective

Use function notation and graph non-linear functions.

Pacing

Suggested Number of Days
Basic Course: 2 days
Average Course: 2 days
Advanced Course: 2 days
Block: 1 block

Teaching Resources

For a complete list of Teaching Resources, see page 654B.

Transparency

Warm-Up Exercises for this lesson are available on a transparency. Support transparencies are available for Example 2 and Your turn now Exercises 4-6.

2 TEACH

Motivating the Lesson

Point out that juggling is possible because objects rise and fall in a predictable pattern caused by gravity.

TIPS FOR NEW TEACHERS

Stress that f is not a variable, but represents a function of x. Have students highlight $f(x)$ whenever it occurs to remind them of this fact. See Tips for New Teachers in the *Chapter 13 Resource Book*.

Non-Linear Functions

BEFORE	Now	WHY?
You wrote function rules and graphed linear functions.	You'll use function notation and graph non-linear functions.	So you can find the height of a falling penny, as in Ex. 11.

Word Watch

function notation, p. 680
vertical line test, p. 681

In the Real World

Juggling You are juggling three balls. The height of one ball, in feet, is found with the equation $h = -16t^2 + 20t + 3$, where t is seconds that pass after you let go of the ball. Write the equation in function notation. Use this function to find the height of one ball 0.5 second after you let go of it.

In Lesson 11.1, you wrote functions as equations in x and y. You used x to name the input and y to name the output. Sometimes it is useful to use **function notation** instead.

equation in x and y	function notation
$y = 3x - 4$	$f(x) = 3x - 4$

The symbol $f(x)$ is read as "the function of f at x" or "f of x."

EXAMPLE 1 Using Function Notation

Write a function that models the height of a ball x seconds after you let go of it. Use function notation. Evaluate for $x = 0.5$.

Solution

Let $f(x)$ = height in feet and x = time in seconds.

$f(x) = -16x^2 + 20x + 3$ — Write the height equation above in function notation.

$f(0.5) = -16(0.5)^2 + 20(0.5) + 3$ — Substitute 0.5 for x.

$f(0.5) = -16(0.25) + 10 + 3$ — Evaluate.

$f(0.5) = 9$

ANSWER The function is $f(x) = -16x^2 + 20x + 3$. The height of the ball is 9 feet after 0.5 second.

Your turn now **Rewrite using function notation.**

1. $y = x^2$ $f(x) = x^2$
2. $y = 3x^2 + 4$ $f(x) = 3x^2 + 4$
3. $y = -\frac{1}{2}x^2$ $f(x) = -\frac{1}{2}x^2$

ILLINOIS Standards and ISAT:
8.D.3a

Graphing Functions The function in Example 1 is non-linear. A non-linear function has a graph that is not a straight line. You can graph non-linear functions by first making a table of values.

HELP with Reading

$f(x)$ does not mean "f times x." It means "the value of the function at x."

EXAMPLE 2 Graphing a Non-Linear Function

Graph the function $f(x) = x^2 - 1$.

1. Choose several x-values and make a table of values.

x	−2	−1	0	1	2
$f(x)$	3	0	−1	0	3

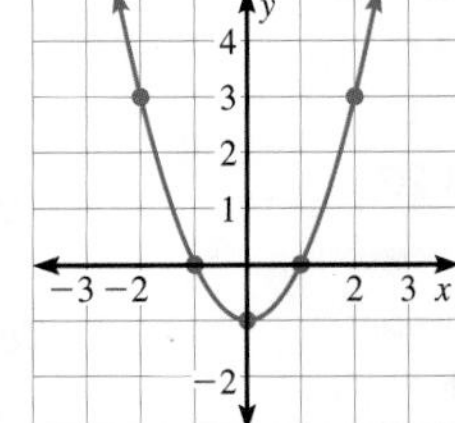

2. List the solutions as ordered pairs.
(−2, 3), (−1, 0), (0, −1), (1, 0), (2, 3)

3. Plot the ordered pairs. Then draw a smooth curve through the points, as shown.

Your turn now **Graph the function using a table of values.**

4–6. See margin.

4. $f(x) = -x^2 + 4$ 5. $f(x) = x^2 + 1$ 6. $f(x) = 2x^2$

Vertical Line Test You can use the **vertical line test** to tell whether a graph represents a function. If a vertical line intersects the graph at more than one point, then the graph does *not* represent a function. Remember, a function has exactly one output value for each input value.

EXAMPLE 3 Using the Vertical Line Test

Tell whether the graph represents a function.

a.

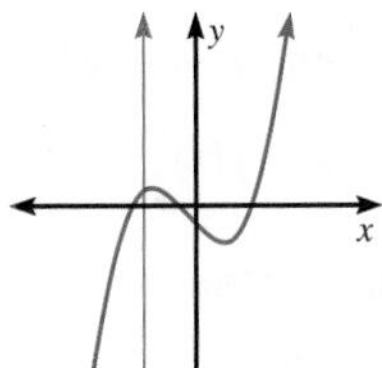

No vertical line intersects the graph at more than one point. So, the graph represents a function.

b.

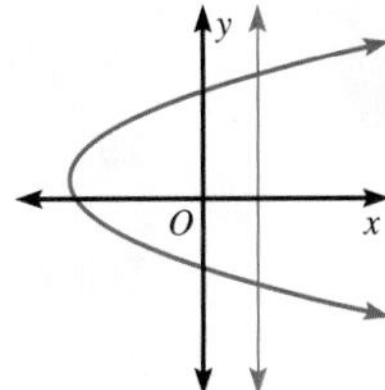

A vertical line intersects the graph at more than one point. So, the graph does *not* represent a function.

EXTRA EXAMPLES

Example 1 The height h, in yards, of a golf ball t seconds after being hit is found by the equation $h = -5.4t^2 + 25t$. Write the equation in function notation. Find the height of the ball 4 seconds after being hit. **$f(x) = -5.4x^2 + 25x$; 13.6 yd**

Example 2 Graph $f(x) = \frac{1}{2}x^2$.

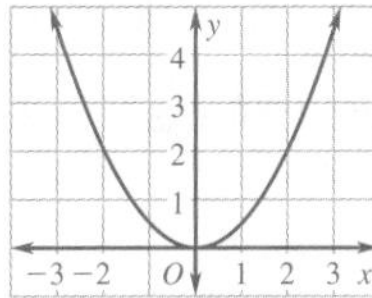

Example 3 Tell whether the graph represents a function.

a. **yes**

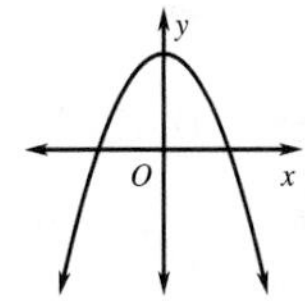

b. **no**

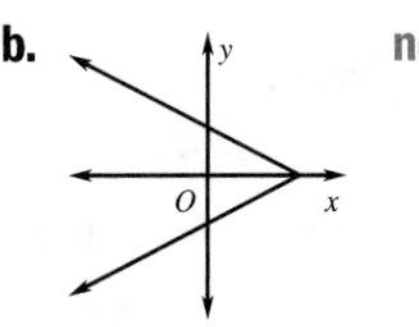

CONCEPT CHECK

Explain how to use the vertical line test. ***Sample answer:*** **If you can draw any vertical line that intersects the graph in more than one point, the graph does not represent a function. Otherwise it does represent a function.**

DAILY PUZZLER

A number enters a "function box," where it is halved, then tripled, multiplied by 6, divided by 10, and multiplied by $1\frac{1}{9}$. What is the result? **the original number**

4–6. See Additional Answers beginning on page AA1.

3 APPLY

ASSIGNMENT GUIDE

Basic Course

Day 1: EP p. 737 Exs. 1, 8–11; pp. 682–684 Exs. 8–14, 23–25, 36–42

Day 2: pp. 682–684 Exs. 15–20, 26–30, 43–49

Average Course

Day 1: pp. 682–684 Exs. 10–13, 23–25, 35–42

Day 2: pp. 682–684 Exs. 18–22, 29–32, 43–49

Advanced Course

Day 1: pp. 682–684 Exs. 10–13, 26–30, 36–42

Day 2: pp. 682–684 Exs. 18–22, 32–35*, 43–49

Block

pp. 682–684 Exs. 10–13, 18–25, 29–32, 35–49

EXTRA PRACTICE

- Student Edition, p. 739
- Chapter 13 Resource Book, pp. 43–45
- Test and Practice Generator

TRANSPARENCY

Even-numbered answers are available on transparencies. Support transparencies are available for Exercises 12–17 and 23–31.

HOMEWORK CHECK

When you review students' homework for this lesson, go over the following exercises to check understanding of key concepts.

Basic: 8, 10, 12, 15, 18

Average: 10, 11, 13, 18, 19

Advanced: 10, 12, 13, 18, 20

12–17. See Additional Answers beginning on page AA1.

13.5 Exercises

More Practice, p. 739

INTERNET eWorkbook Plus CLASSZONE.COM

HELP with Homework

Example	Exercises
1	8–11
2	12–17
3	18–20

Online Resources CLASSZONE.COM

- More Examples
- eTutorial Plus

Getting Ready to Practice

1. Vocabulary Which is written in function notation? B

A. $f = 2x + 4$ **B.** $f(x) = 2x + 4$ **C.** $2(f) + 4$

Evaluate the function for $x = -2, 0,$ and 2.

2. $f(x) = x^2$ 4, 0, 4

3. $f(x) = x^2 - 5$ −1, −5, −1

4. $f(x) = -3x^2$ −12, 0, −12

Tell whether the graph represents a function.

5.

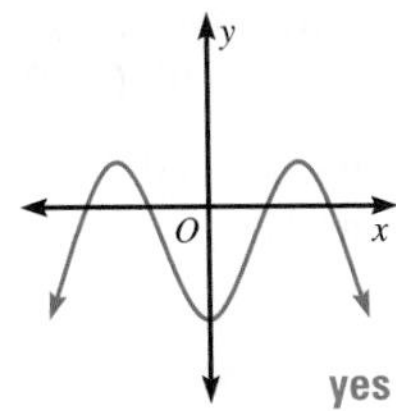

yes

6.

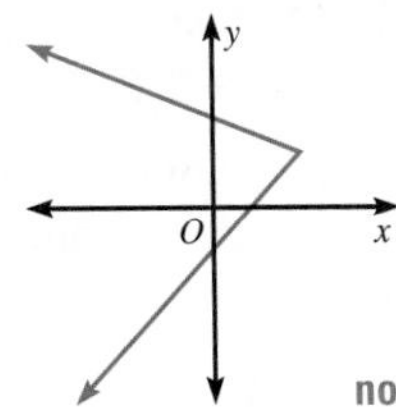

no

7.

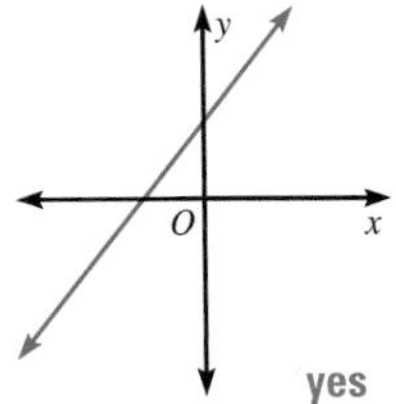

yes

Practice and Problem Solving

A **Rewrite using function notation.**

8. $y = 4x^2$ $f(x) = 4x^2$

9. $y = 2x^2 - x$ $f(x) = 2x^2 - x$

10. $y = -x^2 + 10$ $f(x) = -x^2 + 10$

11. Penny Drop You drop a penny into a well and hear it hit the water after 3 seconds. The function $d = -16t^2 + 4$ gives the elevation of the penny, in feet, after it falls for t seconds. Write this in function notation, and find how far the penny falls before hitting the water. $f(x) = -16x^2 + 4$; −140 ft

Graph the function using a table of values with $x = -3, -2, -1, 0, 1, 2,$ and 3. 12–17. See margin.

12. $f(x) = 4x^2$

13. $f(x) = x^2 + 8$

14. $f(x) = -x^2 + 5$

15. $f(x) = -x^2$

16. $f(x) = 3x^2 - 4$

17. $f(x) = -2x^2 - 1$

Tell whether the graph represents a function.

18.

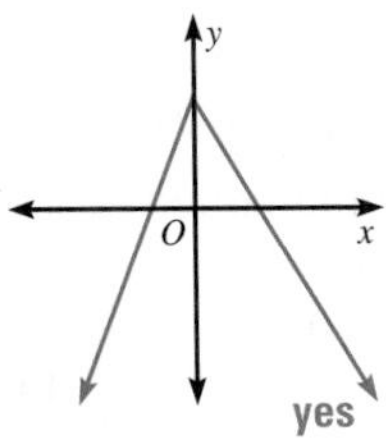

yes

19.

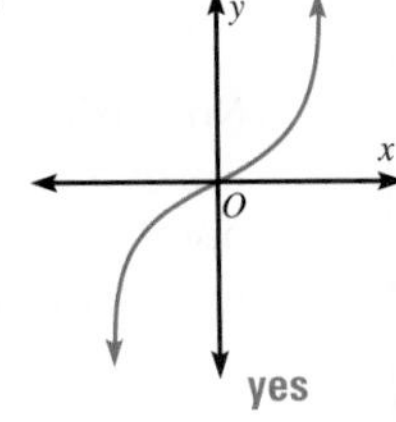

yes

20.

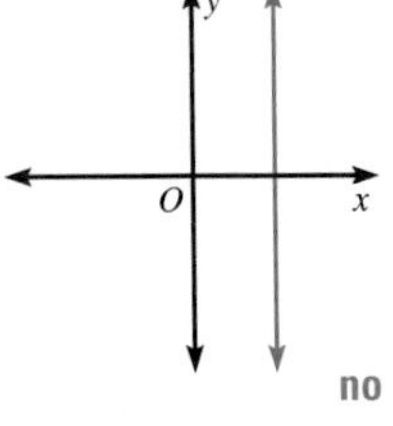

no

21. Reflecting Pool A rectangular reflecting pool is 50 feet long and 30 feet wide, but you do not know how deep the water is. Write a function that you can use to find the volume of water in the pool for different depths. $f(x) = 1500x$

22. Baseball A ball is hit 75 mi/h, or 110 ft/sec, into center field. The height of the ball, in feet, is found with the function $f(x) = -16x^2 + 110x + 3$, where x is the number of seconds after the ball is hit. Graph this function. Use the graph to estimate how many seconds will pass before the ball lands on the ground. See margin for art; about 6.9 sec.

Graph the function using a table of values. 23–28. See margin.

23. $f(x) = -\frac{1}{2}x^2$ **24.** $f(x) = 5 - 5x^2$ **25.** $f(x) = 4x^2 + x$

26. $f(x) = x^2 - 3x$ **27.** $f(x) = (x - 1)^2$ **28.** $f(x) = (x + 2)^2$

29. Make a Table Graph the function $f(x) = x^3$ using a table of values. Describe how the graph of this function is different from the graph of the function $f(x) = x^2$. Be sure to include negative and positive x-values in your table.

B **30. Draw a Graph** Write a function for the area of the triangle. Graph the function using a table of values. Estimate the value of x if the area of the triangle is 30 square inches. See margin.

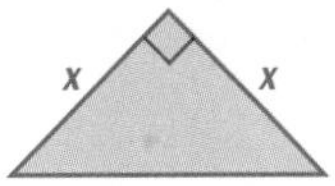

31. Interpret Write a function for the area of the rectangle shown. Graph the function using a table of values, and use it to find the greatest possible area of the rectangle. If the rectangle has the maximum area, what are its length and width? See margin.

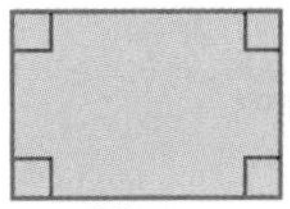
x
10 − x

Work Backward **Write a function in function notation for the values in the table.**

32.

x	−2	−1	0	1	2
$f(x)$	5	2	1	2	5

$f(x) = x^2 + 1$

33.

x	−4	−2	0	2	4
$f(x)$	−64	−8	0	8	64

$f(x) = x^3$

C **34. Challenge** You deposit \$20 into a savings account that earns 2% interest compounded monthly. The expression $20(1.02)^t$ gives the account balance after t months. Write a function for the account balance, and find the balance after 1, 2, and 3 months. $f(x) = 20(1.02)^x$; \$20.40, \$20.81, \$21.22

35. Population In 2001, the United States population was about 2.8×10^8 people and growing 0.8% each year. You can predict the future population with the expression $(2.8 \times 10^8)(1.008)^t$, where t is the number of years after 2001. Write the expression as a function and use it to predict the population of the United States in 2005. $f(t) = (2.8 \times 10^8)(1.008)^t$; about 2.8×10^8

29. See margin for art. *Sample answer:* The graph of $f(x) = x^3$ goes downward from zero as x decreases from zero and upward from zero as x increases from zero, while the graph of $f(x) = x^2$ goes upward from zero both as x decreases from zero and as x increases from zero. The graph of $f(x) = x^2$ has the y-axis as a vertical line of symmetry, while the graph of $f(x) = x^3$ has no vertical line of symmetry.

30. $f(x) = 0.5x^2$; see margin for art; about 7.7 in.

31. $f(x) = 10x - x^2$; see margin for art; 25 square units; 5 and 5.

Teaching Tip

Exercise 22 provides a good opportunity to emphasize to students how a function model must be used with an eye to how it fits into the real world. To start with, students should realize that it makes sense to use the model only for nonnegative values of x. Also, it makes no sense to use the model for values of x greater than that for which $f(x) = 0$, because the model does not take into account the ball being stopped by hitting the ground.

22.

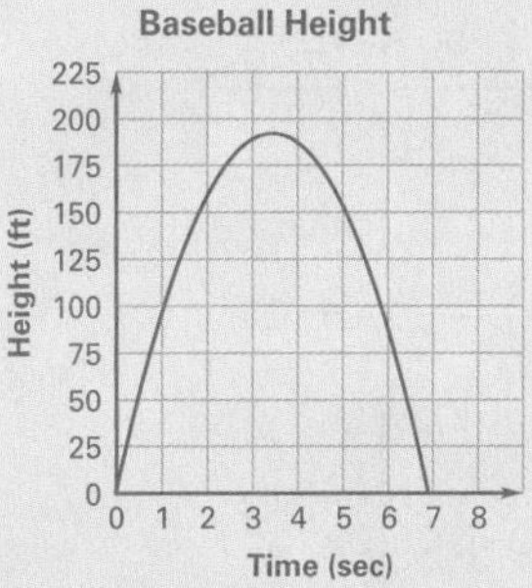

23.

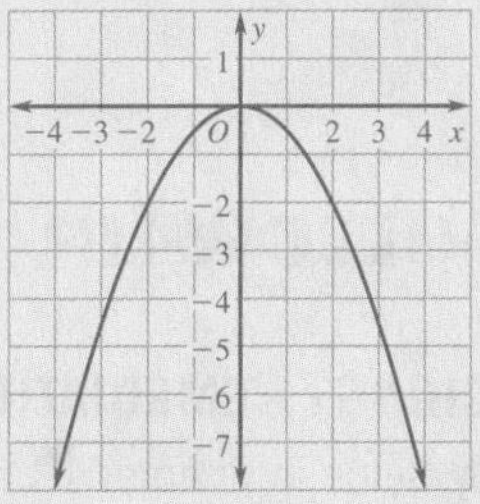

24.

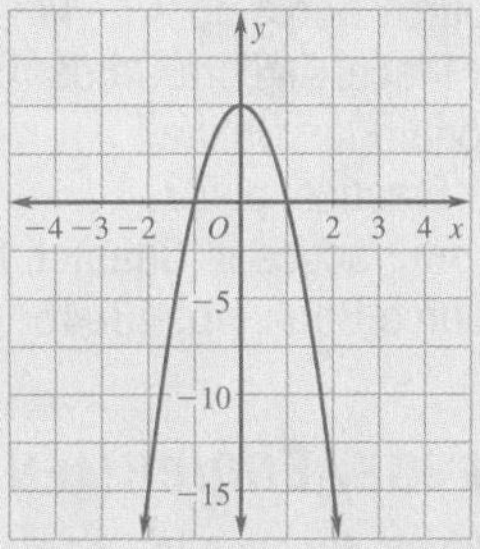

25.

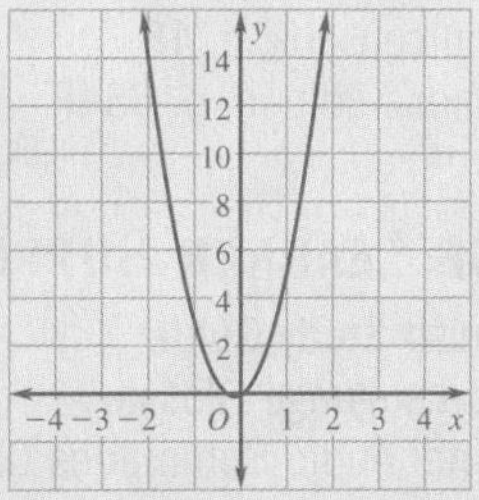

26–31. See Additional Answers beginning on page AA1.

4 ASSESS

Assessment Resources

For more assessment resources, see:

- Assessment Book
- Test and Practice Generator

Mini-Quiz

1. Rewrite $y = 12 + x^2$ using function notation. $f(x) = 12 + x^2$

Graph the function.

2. $f(x) = x^2 - 2$

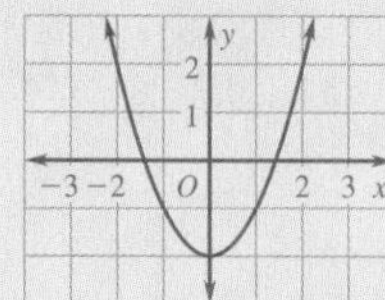

3. $f(x) = \frac{1}{2}x^2 + 1$

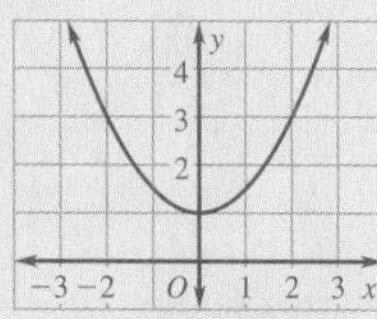

5 FOLLOW-UP

Reteaching/Remediation

- Study Guide in Chapter 13 Resource Book, pp. 46–47
- Tutor Place, Algebra Cards 4, 17
- eTutorial Plus Online
- Extra Practice, p. 739
- Lesson Practice in Chapter 13 Resource Book, pp. 43–45

Challenge/Enrichment

- Challenge Practice in Chapter 13 Resource Book, p. 48
- Teacher's Edition, p. 654F

English Learner Support

- Spanish Study Guide
- Multi-Language Glossary
- Chapter Audio Summaries CDs

49. See Additional Answers beginning on page AA1.

Mixed Review

In Exercises 36–43, solve the equation. *(Lesson 3.3)*

36. $3x + 1 = 7$ **2** **37.** $2x - 3 = 5$ **4** **38.** $-x + 1 = 2$ **−1** **39.** $6x - 1 = -11$ $-1\frac{2}{3}$

40. $2x + 5 = -17$ **−11** **41.** $2x + 4 = 10$ **3** **42.** $-3x - 4 = 11$ **−5** **43.** $5x + 3 = -12$ **−3**

44. List four solutions of the equation $2x + 4y = -12$. *(Lesson 11.3)* ***Sample answer:*** **(−4, −1), (−2, −2), (0, −3) (2, −4)**

Find the product and simplify. *(Lesson 13.4)*

45. $(x + 2)(x + 2)$ $x^2 + 4x + 4$ **46.** $(3z - 2)(2z - 1)$ $6z^2 - 7z + 2$ **47.** $(5a - 1)(a + 3)$ $5a^2 + 14a - 3$

Choose a Strategy Use a strategy from the list to solve the following problem. Explain your choice of strategy.

Problem Solving Strategies
- Draw a Diagram
- Break into Parts
- Solve a Simpler Problem

48. You are saving pennies in a coffee can. On the first day, you put one penny in the can. On the second day, you put two pennies in the can. On the third day, you put three pennies in the can. If you continue this method of saving, how many pennies will be in the can on day 100?

48. 5050 pennies. *Sample answer:* I used the strategy Solve a Simpler Problem to find the sum for the first 10 days. This allowed me to observe a pattern of pairing the first and last terms, the second and next-to-last terms, and so on, which I could then use to find the sum for the first 100 days.

Test-Taking Practice

INTERNET State Test Practice CLASSZONE.COM

49. Extended Response Graph the four functions below using tables of values. Describe the differences in the graphs. Explain the effect of a negative coefficient on a graph.

$f(x) = x^2$ $f(x) = -x^2$ $f(x) = \frac{1}{2}x$ $f(x) = -\frac{1}{2}x$

See margin for art. *Sample answer:* The first two graphs are curves; the second two graphs are lines. The graph in each pair whose function has a negative coefficient is the reflection over the *x*-axis of the graph with the positive coefficient.

Brain Game

Number Crunch

Why was ten afraid of seven? **BECAUSE SEVEN EIGHT NINE**

Use the function $f(x) = 2x^2 - 3x + 7$ to break the code.

$\frac{?}{-3}$ $\frac{?}{5}$ $\frac{?}{0}$ $\frac{?}{3}$ $\frac{?}{-4}$ $\frac{?}{1}$ $\frac{?}{5}$ $\frac{?}{1}$ $\frac{?}{5}$ $\frac{?}{2}$ $\frac{?}{5}$ $\frac{?}{6}$

$\frac{?}{5}$ $\frac{?}{4}$ $\frac{?}{-2}$ $\frac{?}{-1}$ $\frac{?}{-5}$ $\frac{?}{6}$ $\frac{?}{4}$ $\frac{?}{6}$ $\frac{?}{5}$

A	B	C	E	G	H	I	N	S	T	U	V
16	34	7	42	21	12	27	61	6	72	51	9

13.5 Technology Activity

GRAPHING CALCULATOR

Graphing Non-Linear Functions

GOAL Use a graphing calculator to graph non-linear functions.

Example **Use a graphing calculator to compare the functions.**

$y_1 = x^2$ $y_2 = 2x^2$ $y_3 = 3x^2$ $y_4 = 4x^2$

Solution

Use the following keystrokes to enter the functions into a graphing calculator:

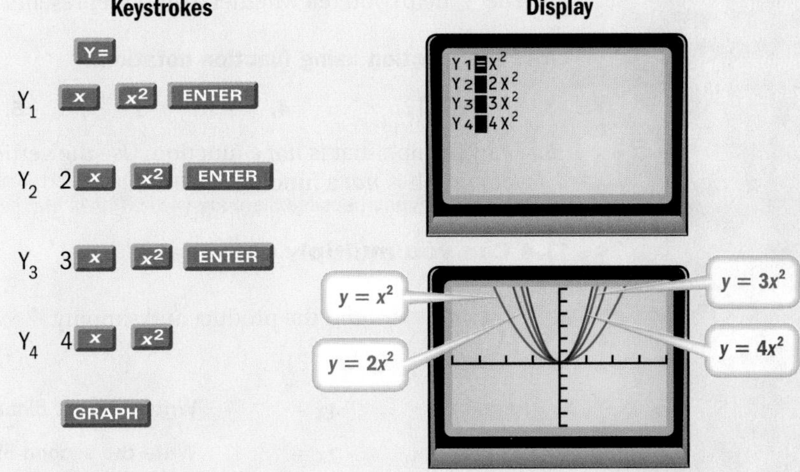

ANSWER The graphs are curves that pass through (0, 0). As the coefficient of x^2 increases, the curve gets narrower.

with Technology

You may need to adjust your viewing window in order to see the graphs.

Your turn now **Graph the functions using a graphing calculator. Describe the pattern in the graphs.**

1. $y = x^2 + 5$ **2.** $y = x^2 - 5$ **3.** $y = x^2 + 7$ **4.** $y = x^2 - 7$

Graph the functions. Describe the pattern in the graphs.

5. $y = -x^2$ **6.** $y = -2x^2$ **7.** $y = -3x^2$ **8.** $y = -4x^2$

1–4. *Sample answer:* The graphs are all parabolas with the same shape and with vertices on the y-axis, but the graph moves up or down compared to the graph of $y = x^2$ by the number of units that are added to or subtracted from x^2. The graph moves up if this number is positive and down if this number is negative.

5–8. *Sample answer:* The graphs are all downward-opening parabolas with vertices at the origin, but opening to different widths. As the absolute value of the coefficient of x^2 gets larger, the parabola becomes narrower (rises more steeply).

ILLINOIS Standards and ISAT: **8.B.3, 8.D.3a**

1 PLAN

LEARN THE METHOD

- Students will use a graphing calculator to graph non-linear functions.
- Students can use the method of this activity to check their work in the Lesson 13.5 exercises.

2 TEACH

DISCUSSION

As students work the Example, ask how to tell which graph corresponds to which function. Students may want to graph the functions one or two at a time in order to observe how the coefficient of the x^2-term relates to the width of the curve.

EXTRA EXAMPLES

Example Graph $y_1 = x^2$, $y_2 = (x - 2)^2$, $y_3 = (x - 4)^2$, and $y_4 = (x - 6)^2$ using a graphing calculator. Describe the pattern in the graphs.

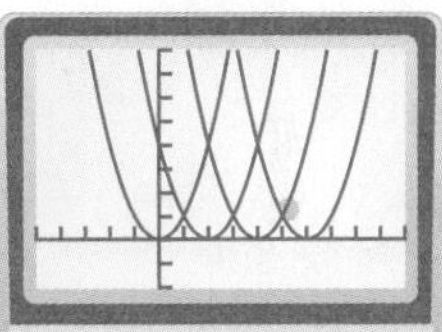

The graphs open upward from the x-axis. The quantity subtracted from x tells how many units to move the graph of $y = x^2$ to the right to obtain the graph.

3 CLOSE

ASSESSMENT

1. How do the graphs of $y = x^2$ and $y = x^2 + 3$ differ? **The second is the first moved up 3 units.**

ADDITIONAL RESOURCES

The following resources are available to help review the materials in Lessons 13.4–13.5.

Chapter 13 Resource Book
- Lesson Practice
- Study Guide

Assessment Book
- Chapter 13 Quiz 2

Technology
- Test and Practice Generator
- eTutorial CD-ROM

Internet
- Classzone
- eWorkbook Plus Online
- eTutorial Plus Online

ENGLISH LEARNER SUPPORT

- Spanish Study Guide
- Multi-Language Glossary
- Chapter Audio Summaries CDs

6. ***Sample:***

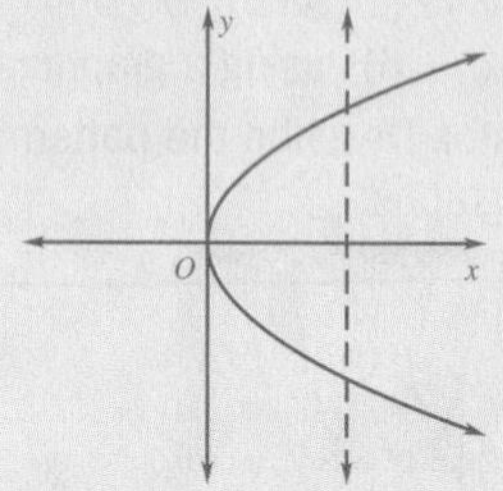

Notebook Review

Review the vocabulary definitions in your notebook.

Copy the review examples in your notebook. Then complete the exercises.

Check Your Definitions

function notation, p. 680 vertical line test, p. 681

Use Your Vocabulary

Copy and complete the statement.

1. The equation $f(x) = 7x - 4$ is written using __?__. **function notation**

2. The __?__ helps you tell whether a graph represents a function. **vertical line test**

Write the function using function notation.

3. $y = 5x - 12$ $f(x) = 5x - 12$

4. $y = 2x^3 + 8$ $f(x) = 2x^3 + 8$

5. $y = x^3 + 3x^2 - 10$ $f(x) = x^3 + 3x^2 - 10$

6. Draw a graph that is *not* a function. Use the vertical line test to show why your graph is *not* a function. **See margin for art.** ***Sample answer:*** **The graph is not that of a function because there are vertical lines that pass through more than one point of the graph.**

13.4 Can you multiply binomials?

EXAMPLE Find the product and simplify.

a. $(4x - 7)(2x + 3)$

$4x - 7$	Write the first binomial.
$\times\quad 2x + 3$	Write the second binomial.
$12x - 21$	Multiply $3(4x - 7)$.
$8x^2 - 14x$	Multiply $2x(4x - 7)$. Line up like terms.
$8x^2 - 2x - 21$	Add $12x - 21$ and $8x^2 - 14x$.

b. $(x + 3)(x + 2)$

$= x(x + 2) + 3(x + 2)$ Distributive property

$= x^2 + 2x + 3x + 6$ Distributive property

$= x^2 + 5x + 6$ Combine like terms.

Find the product and simplify.

7. $(x + 5)(x + 7)$ $x^2 + 12x + 35$

8. $(g + 10)(g - 2)$ $g^2 + 8g - 20$

9. $(y - 4)(3y - 1)$ $3y^2 - 13y + 4$

13.5 Can you graph non-linear functions?

EXAMPLE Graph $f(x) = -2x^2 + 5$.

Choose several x-values and make a table of values.

x	−2	−1	0	1	2
$f(x)$	−3	3	5	3	−3

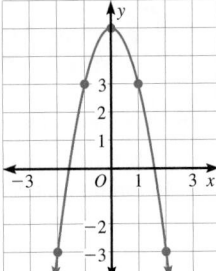

List the solutions as ordered pairs.
(−2, −3), (−1, 3), (0, 5), (1, 3), (2, −3)

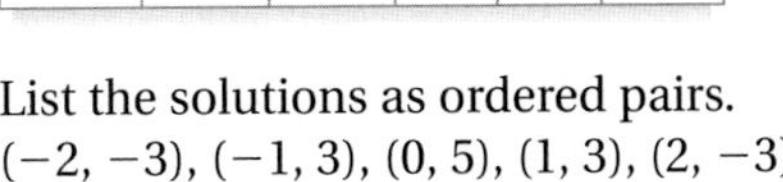

Graph the ordered pairs. Draw a smooth curve through them, as shown.

Graph the function using a table of values. 10–12. See margin.

10. $f(x) = 3x^2$ **11.** $f(x) = -x^2 + 3$ **12.** $f(x) = 2x^2 - 6$

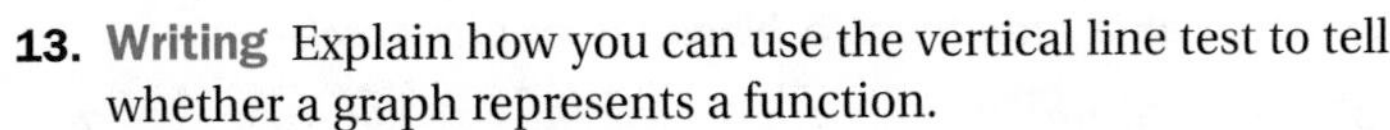

Stop *and* Think about Lessons 13.4–13.5

13. Writing Explain how you can use the vertical line test to tell whether a graph represents a function.

Notebook Review

13. *Sample answer:* If there is any vertical line that intersects a graph at more than one point, then the graph does not represent a function. If every vertical line intersects a graph in at most one point, then the graph does represent a function.

Review Quiz 2

Find the product and simplify.

1. $(x - 1)(x + 9)$ $x^2 + 8x - 9$

2. $(a + 4)(a + 9)$ $a^2 + 13a + 36$

3. $(m - 2)(m - 8)$ $m^2 - 10m + 16$

4. $(4y + 5)(y - 2)$ $4y^2 - 3y - 10$

5. $(b + 3)(4b - 3)$ $4b^2 + 9b - 9$

6. $(3z - 2)(2z - 7)$ $6z^2 - 25z + 14$

Rewrite using function notation.

7. $y = 3x + 9$ $f(x) = 3x + 9$

8. $y = -2x^2 - 4$ $f(x) = -2x^2 - 4$

9. $y = 19 - x + x^2$ $f(x) = 19 - x + x^2$

Evaluate the function for $x = -2, -1, 0, 1$, and 2.

10. $f(x) = 2 - x^2$ −2, 1, 2, 1, −2

11. $f(x) = \frac{1}{2}x^2 - 6$ $-4, -5\frac{1}{2}, -6, -5\frac{1}{2}, -4$

12. $f(x) = x^2 + x$ 2, 0, 0, 2, 6

Graph the function using a table of values. 13–15. See margin.

13. $f(x) = -x^2 + 1$ **14.** $f(x) = \frac{1}{4}x^2$ **15.** $f(x) = -3x^2 - 4$

Notebook Review

10.

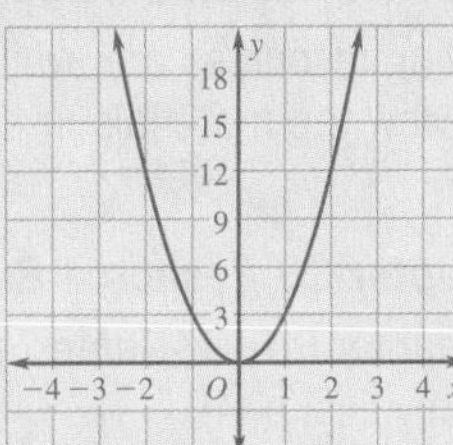

11.

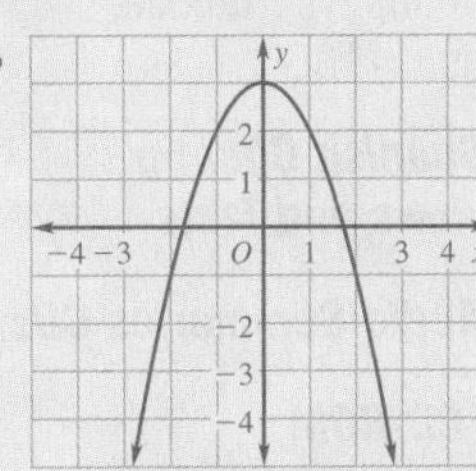

12.

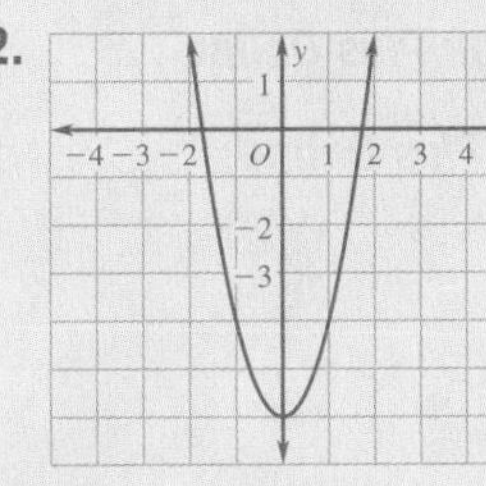

Review Quiz 2

13.

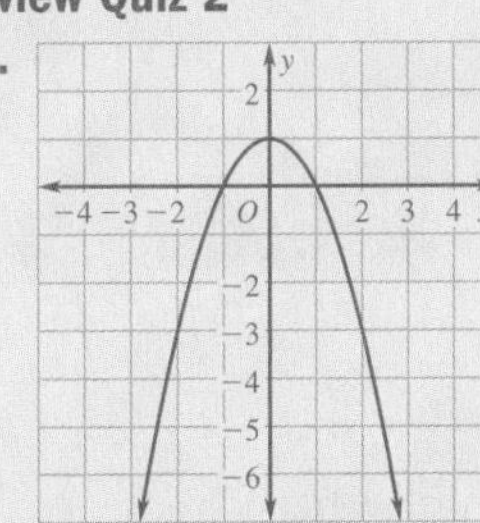

14.

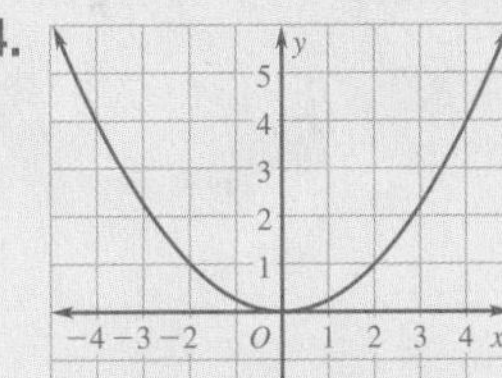

15.

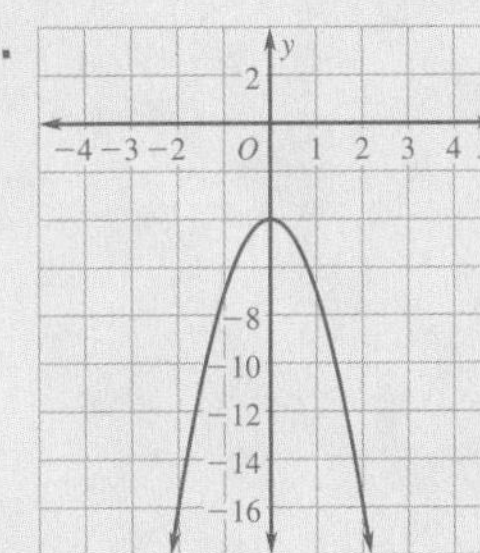

Additional Resources

The following resources are available to help review the materials in this chapter.

Chapter 13 Resource Book

- Chapter Review Games and Activities, p. 49
- Cumulative Practice, Chs. 1–13

English/Spanish Chapter Reviews and Tests

Chapter Audio Summaries CDs

eTutorial CD-ROM

eWorkbook Plus Online

eTutorial Plus Online

Chapter Review

Vocabulary

polynomial, p. 657	trinomial, p. 657	function notation, p. 680
binomial, p. 657	standard form, p. 657	vertical line test, p. 681

Vocabulary Review

Copy and complete the statement.

1. The polynomial $x^3 - 2x + 1$ is a _?_. trinomial
2. A polynomial is written in _?_ if the exponents of the variable decrease from left to right. standard form
3. You can use the _?_ to tell whether a graph represents a function. vertical line test

Classify the polynomial as a *monomial*, a *binomial*, or a *trinomial*.

4. $5x^3 + 2x + 3$ trinomial
5. $5a^3$ monomial
6. $5y + 3$ binomial
7. $-r + 3$ binomial

Review Questions

Write the polynomial in standard form. *(Lesson 13.1)*

8. $7 - 2a^2 + 10a$ $-2a^2 + 10a + 7$
9. $5x - 3x^3 - 4 + x^2$ $-3x^3 + x^2 + 5x - 4$
10. $4 + 7y^2 - 8y^3 + y$ $-8y^3 + 7y^2 + y + 4$
11. $9t + 8 - t^2 + 6t^3$ $6t^3 - t^2 + 9t + 8$
12. $9 + 2m^5 + m^2 - m^4$ $2m^5 - m^4 + m^2 + 9$
13. $25 + n^2 - 3n^4 + 5n$ $-3n^4 + n^2 + 5n + 25$

Simplify the polynomial and write it in standard form. *(Lesson 13.1)*

14. $8k + 1 + 3k + k^2 - 4$ $k^2 + 11k - 3$
15. $5w - 2w + 2w^2 - 8$ $2w^2 + 3w - 8$
16. $6p^2 + 9(2p^3 + 3 + p^2)$ $18p^3 + 15p^2 + 27$
17. $3x^2 + 4(7 - x^2 + 4x)$ $-x^2 + 16x + 28$
18. $-8(2s - 3s^2 + 7) + 4s^3$ $4s^3 + 24s^2 - 16s - 56$
19. $4(5y - 2y^2 + 11) - 2y^2$ $-10y^2 + 20y + 44$

Find the sum or difference. *(Lesson 13.2)*

20. $(10q^2 - 6) + (q^2 + 1)$ $11q^2 - 5$
21. $(2p^2 + 9p) - (5p^2 + 9p)$ $-3p^2$
22. $(3x^2 - x + 7) - (6x^2 + 4x - 11)$ $-3x^2 - 5x + 18$
23. $(7y^2 + y - 4) + (y^2 - y - 1)$ $8y^2 - 5$
24. $4(m^2 - 3m) + 5(2m^2 - m)$ $14m^2 - 17m$
25. $-2(v^3 - v^2 + v) - 3(v^3 + 4v^2)$ $-5v^3 - 10v^2 - 2v$

Review Questions

Simplify the expression. *(Lesson 13.3)*

26. $(3r^2)^3$ $27r^6$

27. $(2xy)^3$ $8x^3y^3$

28. $(7z)(-4z)^2$ $112z^3$

29. $(-6a^2b^4)^3$ $-216a^6b^{12}$

30. $(-c^3)(2c^4)$ $-2c^7$

31. $(-9n)(-7p^2)^4$ $-21{,}609p^8n$

Simplify the expression. *(Lesson 13.3)*

32. $x^2(5x - 7)$ $5x^3 - 7x^2$

33. $-3a(a^2 - 2a)$ $-3a^3 + 6a^2$

34. $4y(6y^2 - 8y)$ $24y^3 - 32y^2$

35. $-y^3(-y^2 + 11y)$ $y^5 - 11y^4$

36. $7b(14 - 6b^2)$ $-42b^3 + 98b$

37. $-6g(3g^2 + 10g)$ $-18g^3 - 60g^2$

Write a polynomial expression for the area of the figure and simplify. *(Lesson 13.3)*

38.

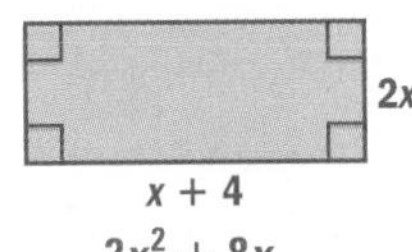

$2x^2 + 8x$

39.

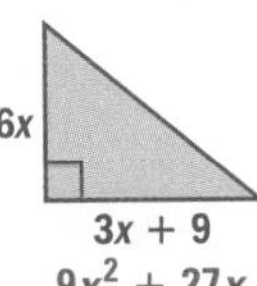

$9x^2 + 27x$

40.

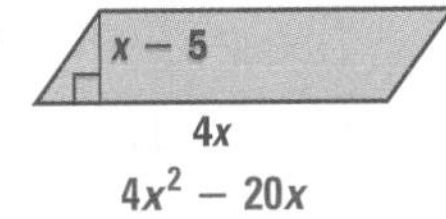

$4x^2 - 20x$

Find the product and simplify. *(Lesson 13.4)*

41. $(t + 3)(t - 4)$ $t^2 - t - 12$

42. $(2x + 3)(x + 5)$ $2x^2 + 13x + 15$

43. $(q - 7)(q - 9)$ $q^2 - 16q + 63$

44. $(m - 4)(m - 5)$ $m^2 - 9m + 20$

45. $(3d + 8)(d - 6)$ $3d^2 - 10d - 48$

46. $(h + 3)(2h - 5)$ $2h^2 + h - 15$

47. $(2k - 9)(-4k - 1)$ $-8k^2 + 34k + 9$

48. $(2n + 6)(3n - 12)$ $6n^2 - 6n - 72$

49. $(-2b + 1)(-b - 4)$ $2b^2 + 7b - 4$

50. Write a polynomial expression for the area of the swimming pool's walkway and simplify. The walkway is x ft wide. *(Lesson 13.4)*

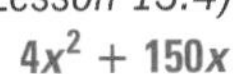

$4x^2 + 150x$

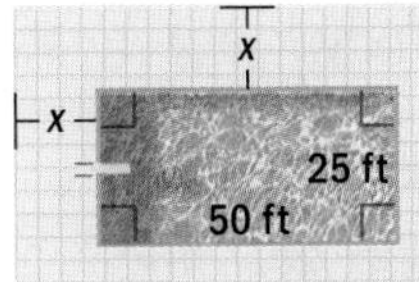

Graph the function using a table of values. *(Lesson 13.5)* **51–54. See margin.**

51. $f(x) = x^2 + 3$

52. $f(x) = 7 - x^2$

53. $f(x) = x^2 - 4$

54. $f(x) = 3x^2 + 1$

Tell whether the graph represents a function. *(Lesson 13.5)*

55. yes

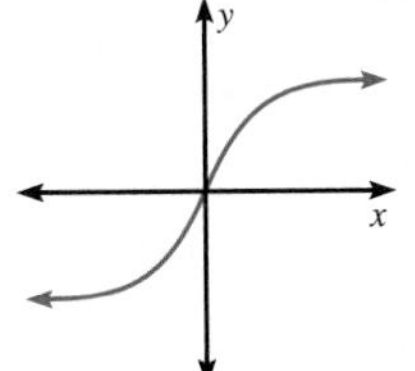

56. no

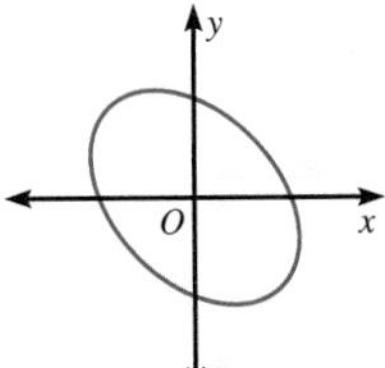

57. yes

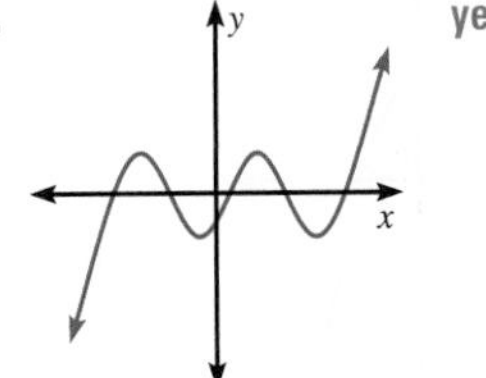

51.

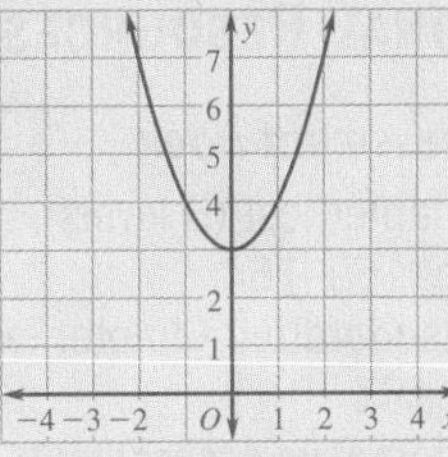

52.

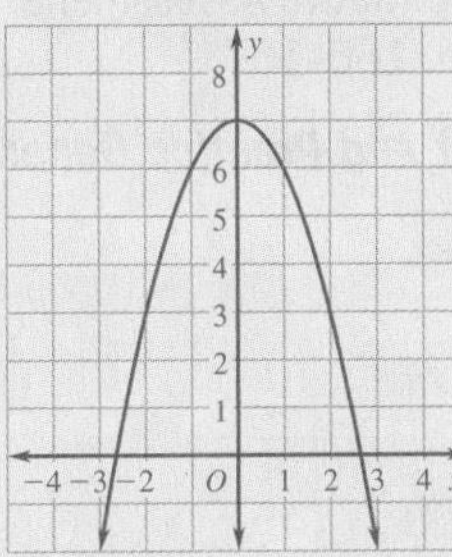

53.

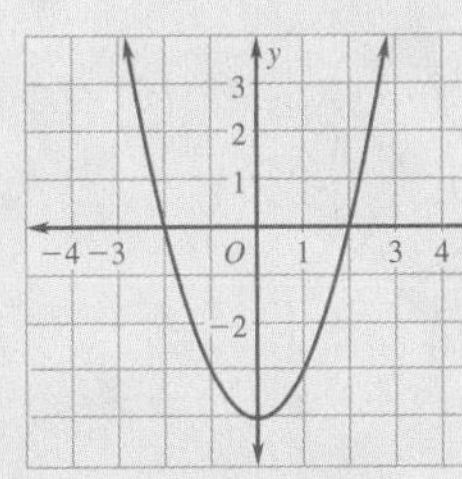

54.

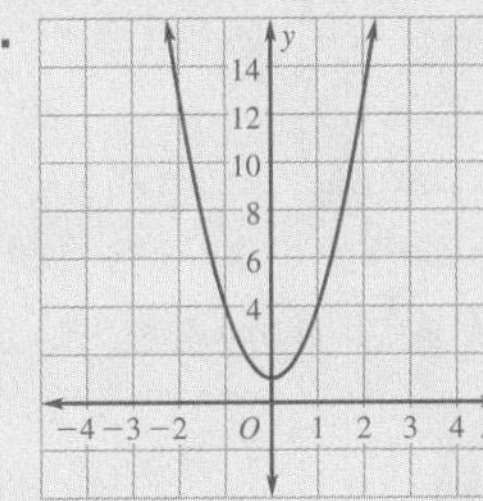

Additional Resources

Assessment Book
- Chapter Test (3 levels), pp. 159–164
- Standardized Chapter Test, p. 165
- Alternative Assessment, pp. 166–167

Test and Practice Generator

25.
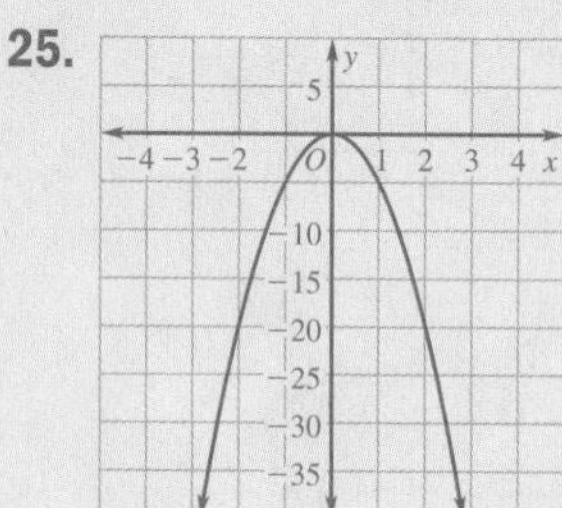

26.
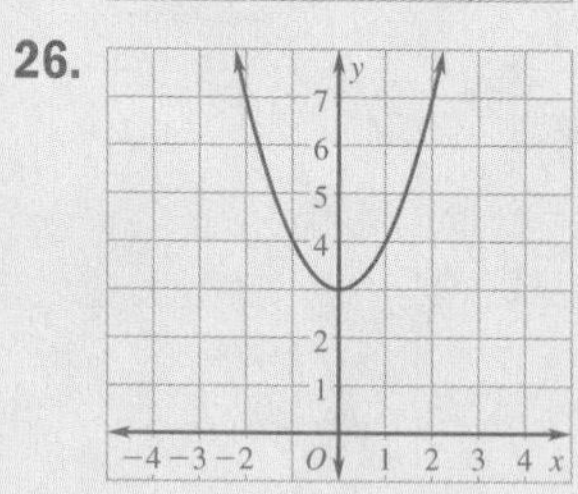

27.
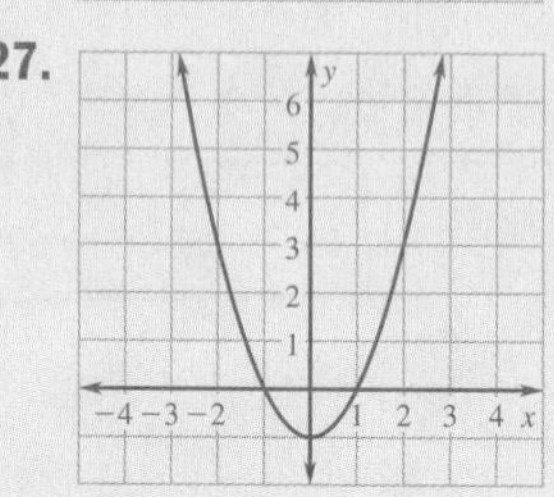

Chapter 13 Chapter Test

Simplify the polynomial and write it in standard form.

1. $10x - 7x + 4 + x^2 - 3x + 4$ $x^2 + 8$

2. $-y + 6(y^2 - y^3 + 1)$ $-6y^3 + 6y^2 - y + 6$

3. Apple Picking An apple falls from a 28 foot tall tree. The height of the apple, in feet, after t seconds of falling, can be found using the polynomial $-16t^2 + 28$. Find the apple's height after 0.5 second. 24 ft

Find the sum or difference.

4. $(3r^2 + 4r - 7) + (-r^2 - r + 11)$ $2r^2 + 3r + 4$

5. $(4s^2 - 11s) - (s^2 - 6s + 21)$ $3s^2 - 5s - 21$

6. $(4a^5 - a) + (-3a^5 + 1)$ $a^5 - a + 1$

7. $(-y^2 + 12) + (8y^2 - 10)$ $7y^2 + 2$

8. $(5x^6 - 3x^2 + x) - (4x^2 + 2x)$ $5x^6 - 7x^2 - x$

9. $(-7z^3 + z^2 - 5) - (z^3 - 3z^2 + 1)$ $-8z^3 + 4z^2 - 6$

10. Perimeter Write a polynomial expression for the perimeter of the triangle. Simplify the polynomial.
$(9x - 5) + (10x - 7) + (x + 2)$; $20x - 10$

$9x - 5$, $10x - 7$, $x + 2$

Simplify the expression.

11. $(3a^2)(5a^2b)$ $15a^4b$

12. $(9z)^2$ $81z^2$

13. $(3d^2)^4$ $81d^8$

14. $(-2w^4)^3$ $-8w^{12}$

15. $(-2p^2)^4$ $16p^8$

16. $(x^4y)^8$ $x^{32}y^8$

17. $(4n^2)(-3n)$ $-12n^3$

18. $(3r)^3(3r)$ $81r^4$

Find the product and simplify.

19. $m^2(3m^2 + 8m)$ $3m^4 + 8m^3$

20. $7n(n^2 - 2n)$ $7n^3 - 14n^2$

21. $3p(2p^2 + 3p)$ $6p^3 + 9p^2$

22. $(2x + 7)(3x + 2)$ $6x^2 + 25x + 14$

23. $(4y + 12)(y - 3)$ $4y^2 - 36$

24. $(z - 9)(5z + 8)$ $5z^2 - 37z - 72$

Graph the function using a table of values. 25–27. See margin.

25. $f(x) = -5x^2$

26. $f(x) = x^2 + 3$

27. $f(x) = x^2 - 1$

Tell whether the graph represents a function.

28. yes

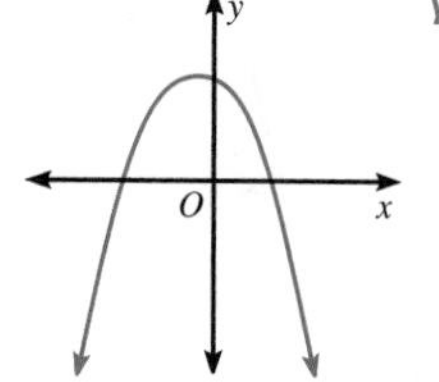

29. no

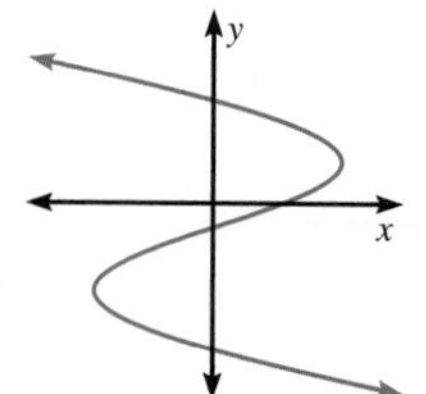

30. yes

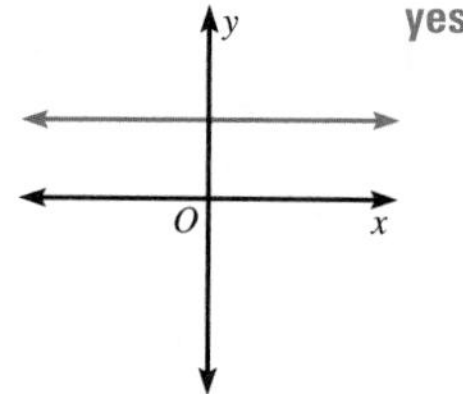

Chapter Standardized Test

Test-Taking Strategy **Think positively during a test. This will help you keep up your confidence and enable you to focus on each question.**

Multiple Choice

1. Simplify the polynomial and write it in standard form. C

$$10 - 5x^2 + 4x^3 + x^2 - 8$$

A. $2 - 4x^2 + 4x^3$ **B.** $4x^3 + 6x^2 + 2$

C. $4x^3 - 4x^2 + 2$ **D.** $2 + 6x^2 + 4x^3$

2. Find the sum. F

$$(4x^2 + 4x - 5) + (5x^2 - x - 8)$$

F. $9x^2 + 3x - 13$ **G.** $9x^2 + 3x - 3$

H. $9x^2 - 3x - 13$ **I.** $9x^2 + 3x + 3$

3. Find the difference. B

$$(2x^2 - 3x + 2) - (x^2 + 3x + 2)$$

A. $x^2 - x$ **B.** $x^2 - 6x$

C. $x^2 + x + 4$ **D.** $x^2 - 6x + 4$

4. Simplify the expression $(2x^2)(x^3y)$. H

F. $2x^6y$ **G.** $2xy^5$ **H.** $2x^5y$ **I.** $2xy^5$

5. Simplify $11x(x^2 - 2x - 8)$. B

A. $11x^3 - 22x^2 + 88$

B. $11x^3 - 22x^2 - 88x$

C. $11x^2 + 22x - 88$

D. $11x^2 + 22x + 88x$

6. Simplify the expression $(5pq)^2$. I

F. $10pq$ **G.** $25pq^2$ **H.** $10pq^2$ **I.** $25p^2q^2$

7. Simplify the expression $(-3n^2)^3$. A

A. $-27n^6$ **B.** $27n^6$ **C.** $-9n^6$ **D.** $9n^6$

8. Find the product $(x + 3)(x - 4)$ and simplify. G

F. $x^2 + 7x - 12$ **G.** $x^2 - x - 12$

H. $x^2 + x - 12$ **I.** $x^2 - x - 7$

9. You deposit $25 into a savings account with interest compounded annually. The account balance after 2 years is given by the expression $25(r + 1)^2$. Expand this expression and simplify. D

A. $25r^2 + 2r + 25$ **B.** $25r^2 + 25r + 1$

C. $25r^2 + 50r + 1$ **D.** $25r^2 + 50r + 25$

10. Find the value of the function for $x = -2$. F

$$f(x) = -3x^2 + 5$$

F. -7 **G.** 7 **H.** 11 **I.** 17

Short Response

11. Write an expression for the area of the rectangle. Simplify the expression, and write it in standard form.
$(3x + 2)(x + 5)$; $3x^2 + 17x + 10$

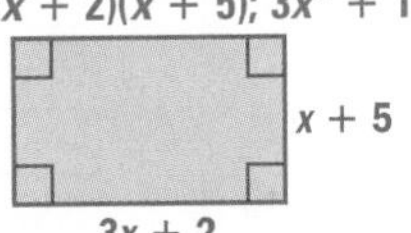

Extended Response

12. Graph each function using a table of values. Explain how the graphs are different. See margin.

$f(x) = x^2$

$f(x) = x^2 + 1$

$f(x) = x^2 + 2$

Describe the graph of the function $f(x) = x^2 + 125$.

ADDITIONAL RESOURCES

Assessment Book
- Standardized Chapter Test, p. 165

Test and Practice Generator

12. $f(x) = x^2$

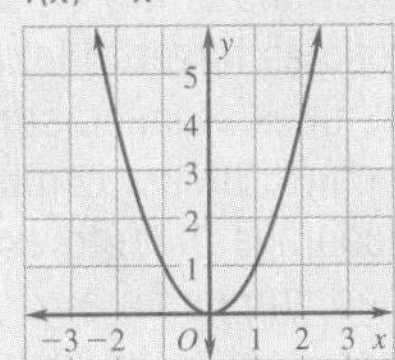

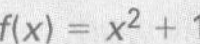

$f(x) = x^2 + 1$

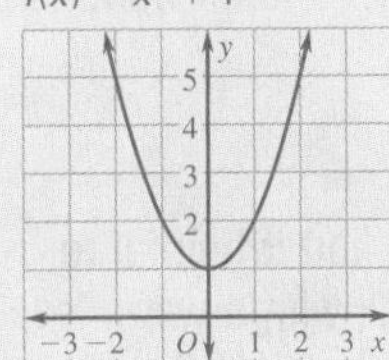

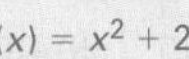

$f(x) = x^2 + 2$

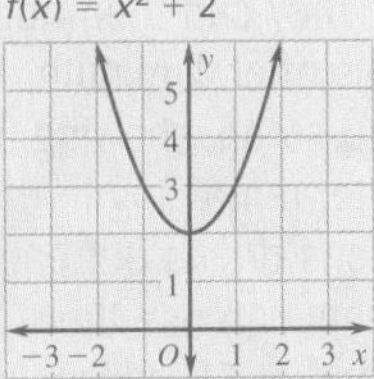

Sample answer: **The graphs of $f(x) = x^2 + 1$ and $f(x) = x^2 + 2$ are the graphs of $f(x) = x^2$ moved up by the number of units added to x^2. The graph of $f(x) = x^2 + 125$ will be the same shape as the graph of $f(x) = x^2$, but will be raised 125 units so that its vertex is at (0, 125).**

USING RUBRICS

The rubric given on the pupil page is a sample of a three-level rubric. Other rubrics may contain four, five, or six levels. For more information on rubrics, see the Professional Development Book.

TEST-TAKING TIP

Encourage students to read the question fully before beginning their work on a solution. Suggest that they take a few moments to organize the steps of the solution process in their mind before starting to write down their work. This approach will help organize their solution into a logical sequence of steps leading to their answer.

COMMON ERROR

When drawing graphs of any type, students sometimes forget to label axes or provide titles. Remind students of what constitutes a complete graph, and encourage them to examine their finished graphs for any missing elements that could result in a loss of credit for their work.

VISUALIZE

Students may find it helpful to sketch the tank with a water level near the top labeled "30 gal", its initial volume. They can then add the water levels after 1 minute, 2 minutes, and so on, showing the amount of water remaining in the tank as 4 gallons drains out each minute. Students can use their sketch to verify that 16 gallons will remain in the tank after the plug has been out for $3\frac{1}{2}$ minutes.

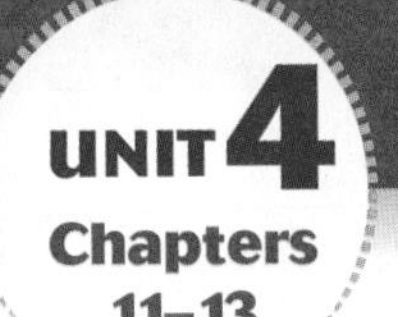

BUILDING **Test-Taking Skills**

Scoring Rubric

Full credit
- answer is correct, *and*
- work or reasoning is included

Partial credit
- answer is correct, but reasoning is incorrect, *or*
- answer is incorrect, but reasoning is correct

No credit
- no answer is given, *or*
- answer makes no sense

Strategies for Answering
Extended Response Questions

Problem

A tank contains 30 gallons of water. You pull out the drain plug, and water begins to flow from the tank at a rate of 4 gallons per minute. Make a table and draw a graph that shows the amount of water in the tank as the water drains. After how much time will the tank contain exactly 16 gallons of water? Give your answer in minutes and seconds. Explain how you found your answer.

Full credit solution

In the graph, the horizontal axis shows minutes after pulling the plug, and the vertical axis shows the gallons of water in the tank.

The table and graph are correct and reflect an understanding of the problem.

minutes	gallons
0	30
1	26
2	22
3	18
4	14
5	10
6	6
7	2

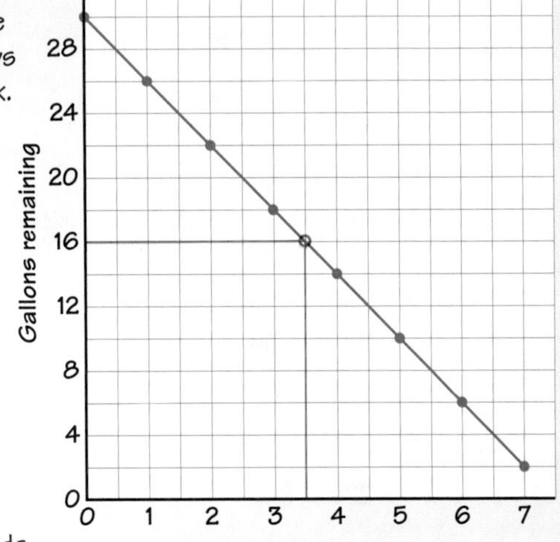

The answer is correct. — After 3 minutes and 30 seconds, the tank will contain 16 gallons of water.

The reasoning behind the answer is explained clearly. — To find my answer, I looked at the graph and saw that the tank will hold 16 gallons at $3\frac{1}{2}$ minutes. Because $\frac{1}{2}$ of a minute equals 30 seconds, I know that the tank will hold 16 gallons of water after 3 minutes and 30 seconds.

Partial credit solution

The table and graph are correct.

minutes	0	1	2	3	4
gallons	30	26	22	18	14

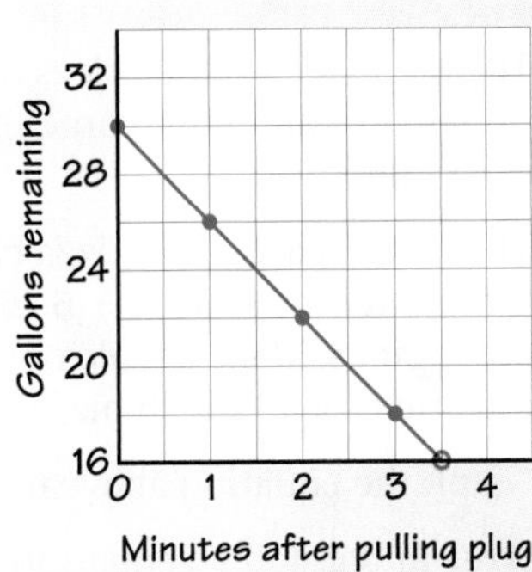

The answer is incorrect.

The tank will hold 16 gallons after 3 minutes and 5 seconds. The graph shows that there are 16 gallons after 3.5 minutes.

No credit solution

The table is correct, but there is no graph.

minutes	0	1	2	3	4
gallons	30	26	22	18	14

The answer is incorrect, and there is no explanation.

The tank will never have exactly 16 gallons in it.

Watch Out!

Scoring is often based on how clearly you explain your reasoning.

Your turn now

1. Score one student's answer to the problem on page 692 as *full credit, partial credit,* or *no credit.* Explain your choice. If you choose *partial credit* or *no credit,* explain how to change the answer so that it earns *full credit.* **Full credit; the answer is correct and the reasoning is correct.**

minutes	0	1	2	3	4
gallons	30	26	22	18	14

The tank will have 16 gallons after 3 minutes and 30 seconds. The table shows that the tank will have 16 gallons between 3 and 4 minutes. 16 is halfway between 14 and 18. So, the tank must have 16 gallons halfway between 3 and 4 minutes. The tank has 16 gallons at 3 minutes and 30 seconds.

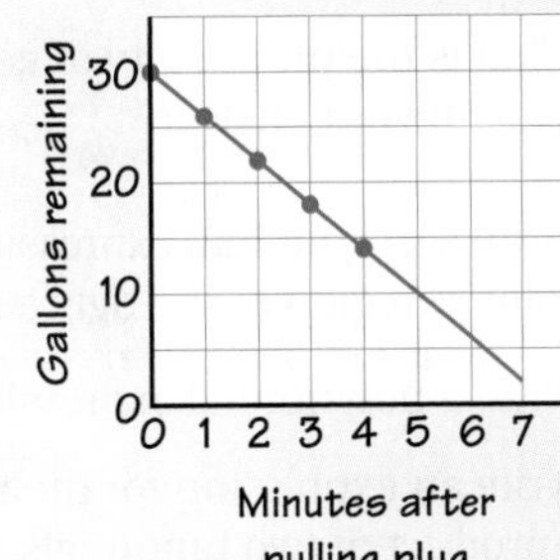

GO ON

693

1.

Toppings, t	Price, p
1	\$7.00
2	\$7.75
3	\$8.50
4	\$9.25
5	\$10.00
6	\$10.75

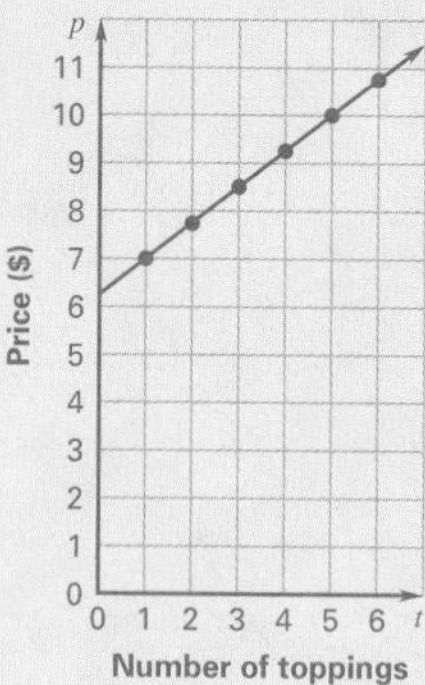

$p = 0.5t + 4.25$;

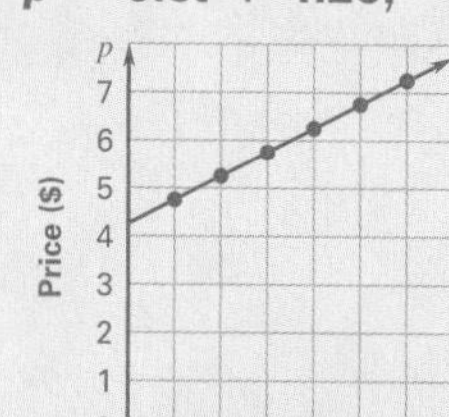

The graph for the price of a 12 inch pizza; its slope is 0.75 while the slope of the 10 inch pizza graph is 0.5, and $0.75 > 0.5$.

2. **Basketball players; there are 6 basketball players but no football players whose heights have a stem of 8 meaning they are at least 80 inches tall, so the basketball players are taller.**

PRACTICING Test-Taking Skills

Extended Response

1. The menu shows the prices of circular cheese pizzas with different diameters and the cost of each topping.

Diameter	Price	Cost of each topping
10 in.	\$4.25	\$.50
12 in.	\$6.25	\$.75
14 in.	\$7.75	\$.75
16 in.	\$8.75	\$1.00
18 in.	\$9.75	\$1.25
24 in.	\$13.00	\$1.75

The price of a 12 inch pizza can be modeled by the equation $p = 0.75t + 6.25$, where t is the number of toppings. Make a table of values that shows the prices of a 12 inch pizza with 1 to 6 toppings.

Graph the equation above using your table of values.

Write and graph an equation for the price of a 10 inch pizza. Which graph has a greater slope? Explain why. **See margin.**

2. The double stem-and-leaf plot shows the heights of 15 football players and 15 basketball players.

Heights of football players (in.)		Heights of basketball players (in.)
9	6	8
3 3 2 2 1 1 0	7	3 5 6 6
8 7 7 6 6 5 4		6 7 8 9
	8	0 0 1 4
		6 7

Key: 0 | 7 | 3 = 70 and 73

What is the height of the tallest football player? **78 in.**

How many basketball players are over 82 inches tall? **3 players**

In general, are the football players or the basketball players taller? Explain how you used the data to draw a conclusion. **See margin.**

3. Players spin the two spinners shown and flip a coin. They earn a point for a 1, a point for blue, a point for tails, and a bonus point for getting all three in one turn.

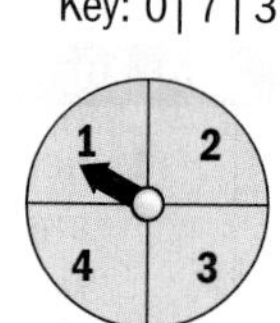

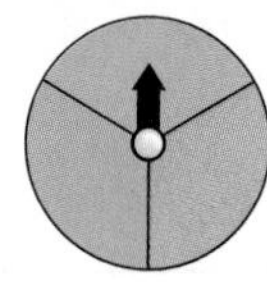

In one turn, what is the probability of spinning a 1? spinning a blue? getting tails? $\frac{1}{4}, \frac{1}{3}, \frac{1}{2}$

What is the probability of getting the bonus point? Explain your answer. $\frac{1}{24}$; **multiply the three probabilities:** $\frac{1}{4} \cdot \frac{1}{3} \cdot \frac{1}{2} = \frac{1}{24}$.

4. Write a polynomial expression for the area of each colored region of the figure shown.
blue: $4x^2$; green: $10x$; red: $2x$; yellow: 5

Write a polynomial expression for the sum of these areas. $4x^2 + 10x + 2x + 5$

Write an expression for the area of the entire figure as a product of two binomials. Explain how you found your answer. $(2x + 1)(2x + 5)$; **the length of the rectangle is $2x + 5$ and the width is $2x + 1$, so its area is $(2x + 1)(2x + 5)$.**

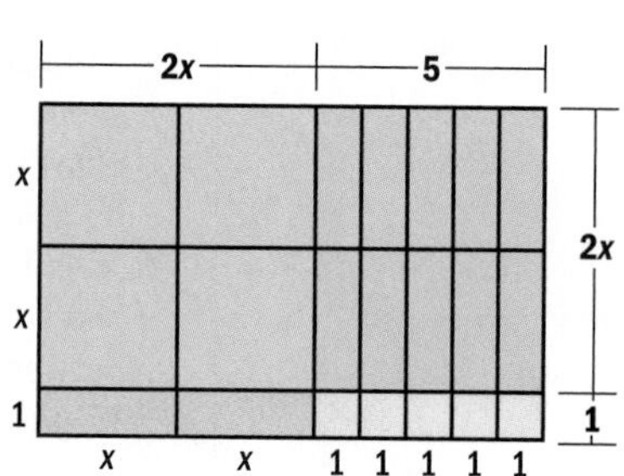

Multiple Choice

5. What is the slope of the line passing through the points $(4, -3)$ and $(-2, 5)$? **A**

   A. $-\frac{4}{3}$ **B.** -1 **C.** $\frac{3}{4}$ **D.** 1

6. Which equation is represented by the graph? **G**

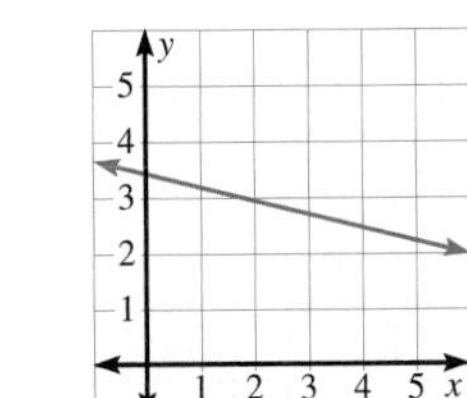

   F. $y = \frac{1}{4}x + 3.5$ **G.** $y = -\frac{1}{4}x + 3.5$

   H. $y = 4x + 3.5$ **I.** $y = -4x + 3.5$

7. Your locker combination has 3 numbers from 0 to 15. Each number must be different. How many locker combinations are possible? **D**

   A. 45 **B.** 48 **C.** 560 **D.** 3360

8. Find the difference. **F**
   $(5x^2 - 2x + 3) - (2x^2 - 2x - 3)$

   F. $3x^2 + 6$ **G.** $3x^2 - 4x$

   H. $3x^2 - 4x + 6$ **I.** $3x^2 + 4x - 6$

9. Find the product $(x - 6)(x + 3)$ and simplify. **C**

   A. $x^2 - 3x + 9$ **B.** $x^2 + 9x - 18$

   C. $x^2 - 3x - 18$ **D.** $x^2 - 9x + 9$

Short Response

10. The table below shows the latitude and a typical minimum temperature in January for each of 6 U.S. cities.

City	Latitude (°N)	Minimum temperature in January (°F)
Anchorage	61	9
Miami	26	60
Helena	47	10
Reno	39	22
Buffalo	43	18
Memphis	35	31

Make a scatter plot of the data. What type of relationship does the scatter plot show between latitude and temperature? Explain. **See margin for art; the scatter plot shows a negative relationship. As the latitude increases, the temperature decreases.**

11. The players of a baseball team hit the following numbers of home runs during one season: 6, 17, 12, 11, 6, 21, 5, 12, 9, 14, 24, 4, 25, 14, 18. Make a box-and-whisker plot of the data. Describe what the plot shows. **See margin.**

12. You roll two number cubes at the same time. What is the probability that the sum of the numbers showing on the two cubes is less than or equal to 5? What is the probability that the sum is greater than 5? Explain how you found your answers. **See margin.**

13. The function $S = 4\pi r^2$ gives the surface area of a sphere with radius r. Write this function in function notation. Graph the function. Estimate the radius of a sphere that has a surface area of 80 square centimeters. Use 3.14 for π. Explain your steps. **See margin.**

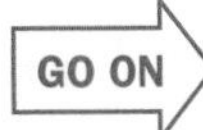

10.

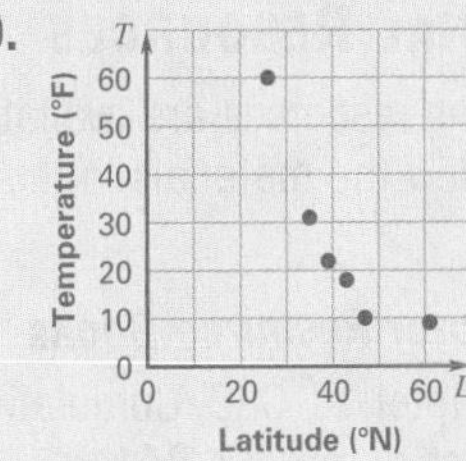

11.

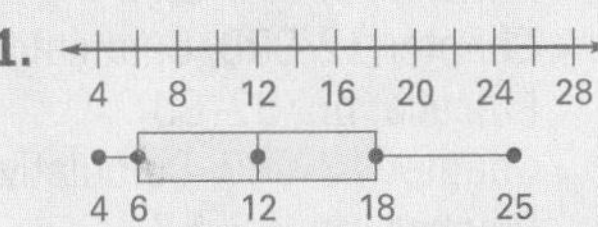

The extremes are 4 home runs and 25 home runs. The median number of home runs hit was 12. 50% of the home runs hits were between 6 and 18.

12. $\frac{5}{18}$, $\frac{13}{18}$; **there are 10 possible sums that are 5 or less, 1 and 1, 1 and 2, 1 and 3, 1 and 4, 2 and 1, 2 and 2, 2 and 3, 3 and 1, 3 and 2, and 4 and 1. So the probability that the sum will be less than or equal to 5 is** $\frac{10}{36} = \frac{5}{18}$. **The probability that the sum will be greater than 5 is the complement of this probability, so the probability is** $1 - \frac{10}{36} = \frac{26}{36}$, **or** $\frac{13}{18}$.

13. $f(x) = 4\pi x^2$;

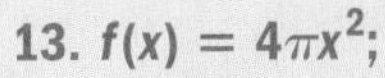

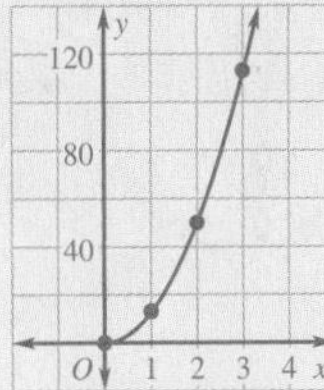

About 2.5 cm; the graph shows $y = 12.56x^2$, where y is the surface area and x is the radius. To find the radius of a sphere with a surface area of 80 square centimeters, look for 80 on the y-axis and find the corresponding x-coordinate to find the radius.

ADDITIONAL RESOURCES

The following resources are available to help review the materials in this unit:

Chapter Resource Books

- Chapter 11 CRB, Cumulative Practice, pp. 83–84
- Chapter 12 CRB, Cumulative Practice, pp. 82–83
- Chapter 13 CRB, Cumulative Practice, pp. 56–57

Assessment Book

- Unit Test, pp. 168–169
- Cumulative Test, pp. 170–173

10a.

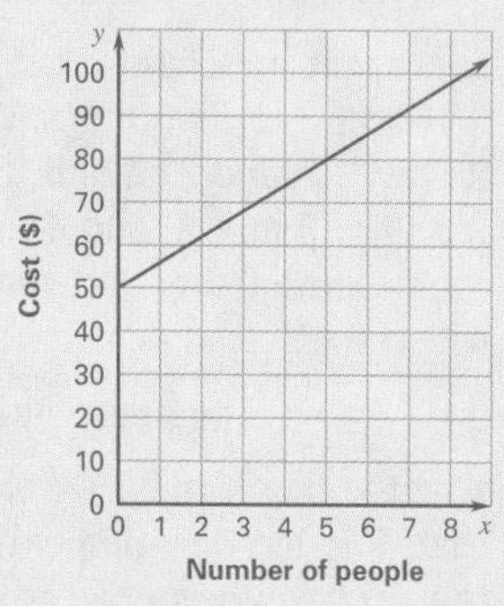

PRACTICING **Test-Taking Skills**

Cumulative Practice for Chapters 11–13

Chapter 11

Multiple Choice In Exercises 1–8, choose the letter of the correct answer.

1. Which of the following relations is *not* a function? *(Lesson 11.1)* **B**

A. (0, −3), (1, −1), (2, 1), (3, 3)

B. (−4, 0), (2, 1), (0, 2), (2, 3)

C. (0, 5), (2, 0), (4, −5), (−1, 3)

D. (6, 5), (0, −1), (3, 6), (−2, −1)

2. The scatter plot shows the amount of money spent on supplies each month. What is the best prediction of the amount of money spent in the eighth month? *(Lesson 11.2)* **I**

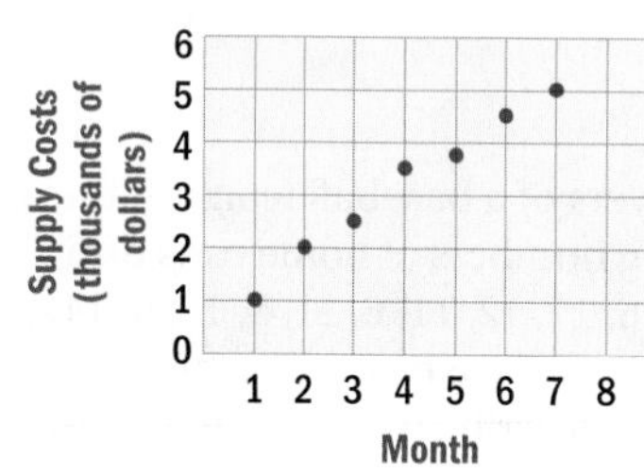

F. \$45 **G.** \$55 **H.** \$4500 **I.** \$5500

3. Which ordered pair is a solution of the equation $y = -2x + 6$? *(Lesson 11.3)* **A**

A. (6, −6) **B.** (−4, 3)

C. (−8, −5) **D.** (7, 7)

4. Which equation is *not* linear? *(Lesson 11.4)* **H**

F. $y = -2x + 4$ **G.** $3x + 4y = 8$

H. $y = x^3 - 8$ **I.** $4x = 8 - 2y$

5. What is the x-intercept of the graph of the equation $2x + 3y = 6$? *(Lesson 11.5)* **D**

A. −3 **B.** −2 **C.** 2 **D.** 3

6. What is the slope of the line? *(Lesson 11.6)* **H**

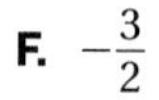

F. $-\frac{3}{2}$

G. 0

H. 1

I. $\frac{3}{2}$

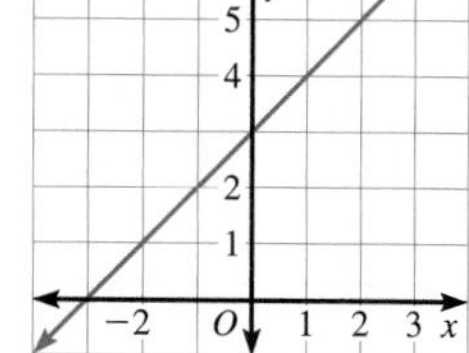

7. A line passes through the points (1, 2) and (2, y) and has a slope of 0. What is the value of y? *(Lesson 11.6)* **B**

A. −1 **B.** 2 **C.** 3 **D.** 5

8. Which ordered pair is a solution of $5x + 9y < 45$? *(Lesson 11.8)* **H**

F. (−3, 8) **G.** (4, 6) **H.** (6, −4) **I.** (−2, 12)

9. Short Response Write a function rule that relates x and y. *(Lesson 11.1)* $y = 2x + 1$

Input x	2	4	6	8
Output y	5	9	13	17

10. Extended Response For a party, you rent a karaoke machine for \$50. Food will cost \$6 per person. *(Lesson 11.7)*

a. Graph the equation $y = 6x + 50$ to see the possible total costs of the party. **See margin.**

b. How much will it cost to invite 11 people? **\$116**

c. You want to spend no more than \$100. How many people can you invite? **no more than 8 people**

Chapter 12

The stem-and-leaf plot shows the number of home runs for each player on a softball team. Use the plot for Exercises 11–12. *(Lesson 12.1)*

0	4 5 7 8
1	2 4 5 6 6 8
2	1 4 5

Key: 2 | 1 = 21

11. What is the greatest number of home runs hit by one player? **B**

A. 4 **B.** 25 **C.** 28 **D.** 52

12. What is the median number of home runs? **G**

F. 12 **G.** 15 **H.** 16 **I.** 21

The box-and-whisker plot shows stereo prices. Use the plot for Exercises 13–14. *(Lesson 12.2)*

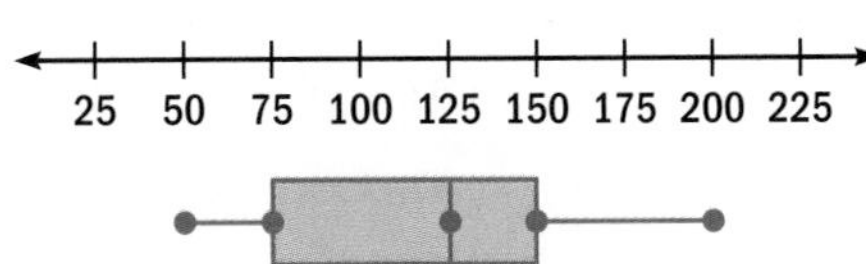

13. What is the lowest stereo price? **B**

A. \$25 **B.** \$50 **C.** \$75 **D.** \$125

14. What is the median price of the stereos? **H**

F. \$75 **G.** \$100 **H.** \$125 **I.** \$150

15. The line graph shows the average number of geese in one area over seven months. Which month had the greatest average number of geese? *(Lesson 12.3)* **C**

A. April

B. May

C. June

D. July

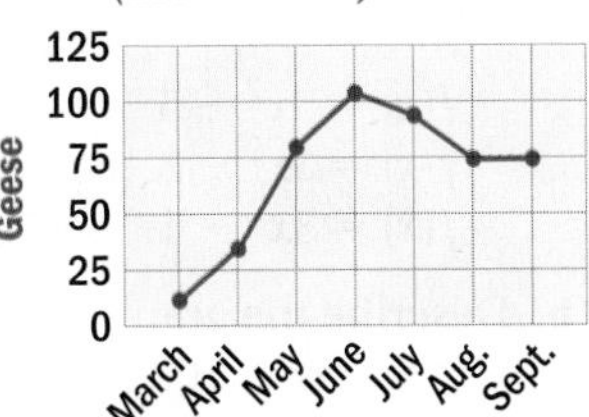

16. You have 3 pairs of shoes, 6 pairs of pants, 4 shirts, and 3 belts. How many different combinations of shoes, pants, shirts, and belts can you make? *(Lesson 12.4)* **H**

F. 16 **G.** 204 **H.** 216 **I.** 313

17. Four cyclists are racing. Trophies are awarded to the people who come in first place and second place. In how many different ways can the trophies be awarded? *(Lesson 12.5)* **C**

A. 2 **B.** 4 **C.** 12 **D.** 24

18. There are 14 pints of rocky road ice cream and 12 pints of fudge almond in a freezer. If Joey chooses a pint at random, what is the probability that he will choose rocky road? *(Lesson 12.7)* **G**

F. $\frac{6}{13}$ **G.** $\frac{7}{13}$ **H.** $\frac{6}{7}$ **I.** $\frac{7}{6}$

19. You roll a number cube once. What are the odds in favor of rolling a four? *(Lesson 12.7)* **B**

A. $\frac{1}{6}$ **B.** $\frac{1}{5}$ **C.** $\frac{1}{4}$ **D.** $\frac{1}{3}$

20. A bag contains 16 red balls and 24 white balls. You draw a ball at random, replace it, and draw a second ball. What is the probability of drawing a red ball and then a white ball? *(Lesson 12.8)* **I**

F. $\frac{1}{384}$ **G.** $\frac{1}{24}$ **H.** $\frac{1}{16}$ **I.** $\frac{6}{25}$

21. A bag contains the letters of the word *Mississippi*. You draw one letter at random, do not replace it, and then draw a second letter. What is the probability of drawing the letter *i* twice? *(Lesson 12.8)* **B**

A. $\frac{12}{121}$ **B.** $\frac{6}{55}$ **C.** $\frac{16}{121}$ **D.** $\frac{8}{55}$

GO ON

22. 252 groups; 252 ways; the answers are the same; either way, you are finding the combination of 10 people taken 5 at a time.

23a.

Lost		Won
8 8 5	0	
8 2 0	1	4 5 6 7 8 9
0	2	0 2 2 2 3 5 6

Key: 0 | 1 | 4 = 10 and 14

b. Since there were two types of related data, a double stem-and-leaf plot is appropriate.

c. *Sample answer:* A circle graph; there is no way to show two different types of data on a circle graph.

32a.

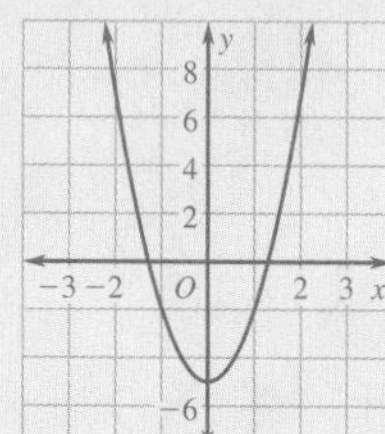

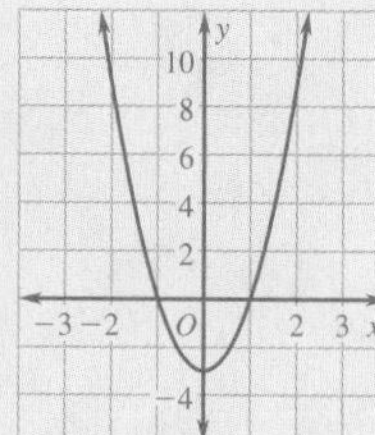

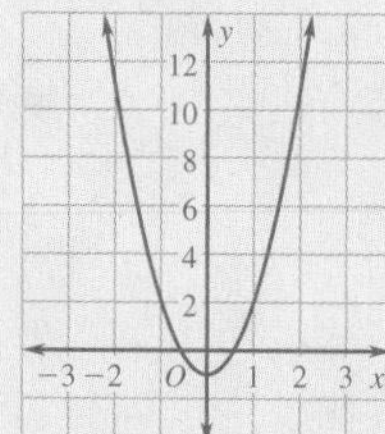

b. The graph will be the same shape as the graph of $f(x) = 3x^2$ but with its vertex at $(0, -100)$.

UNIT 4 Chapters 11–13 PRACTICING Test-Taking Skills

Cumulative Practice continued

22. Short Response A group of 10 people travel in 2 cars with 5 people in each car. How many different groups can go in one car? How many ways can the group split into 2 cars? Explain your answers. *(Lesson 12.6)* **See margin.**

23. Extended Response The points that you scored in each basketball game during the season are given below. Red numbers represent games won, and blue numbers represent games lost. *(Lesson 12.3)*

12, 10, 26, 22, 18, 17, 5, 20, 22, 18,
15, 8, 14, 19, 22, 23, 25, 8, 16, 20

a. Use an appropriate display to represent the data. **See margin.**

b. Explain your choice of display. **See margin.**

c. Identify a type of display that is not a good choice for the data. Explain why it is not a good choice. **See margin.**

Chapter 13

Multiple Choice In Exercises 24–30, choose the letter of the correct answer.

24. Simplify the polynomial. *(Lesson 13.1)*
$4(x^2 - 2x - 4) - 2x^2$ **B**

A. $-2x^2 + 8x + 16$ **B.** $2x^2 - 8x - 16$
C. $-2x^2 - 8x + 16$ **D.** $2x^2 + 8x + 16$

25. What is the value of $-3x^2 - 5x + 8$ for $x = 3$? *(Lesson 13.1)* **F**

F. -34 **G.** -12 **H.** -6 **I.** 34

26. Find the sum $(2x - 6) + (3x - 9)$. *(Lesson 13.2)* **A**

A. $5x - 15$ **B.** $-x - 3$
C. $x + 3$ **D.** $5x + 15$

27. Find the difference. *(Lesson 13.2)* **F**
$(3x^4 - 2x^2 + 3) - (x^4 + 2x^3 + x^2)$

F. $2x^4 - 2x^3 - 3x^2 + 3$
G. $2x^4 - 2x^3 - x^2 + 3$
H. $2x^4 + 2x^3 - x^2 + 3$
I. $2x^4 - 4x^3 - x^2 + 3$

28. Simplify the expression $(3a^2)(4a + 1)$. *(Lesson 13.3)* **C**

A. $7a^2 + 3a$ **B.** $7a^2 + 1$
C. $12a^3 + 3a^2$ **D.** $12a^3 + 3$

29. Simplify the expression $(3y^2)^3$. *(Lesson 13.3)* **H**

F. $27y^5$ **G.** $3y^5$ **H.** $27y^6$ **I.** $3y^6$

30. Find the product and simplify. *(Lesson 13.4)* **B**
$(3x + 3)(2x - 2)$

A. $6x^2 + 6$ **B.** $6x^2 - 6$
C. $6x^2 + 6x - 6$ **D.** $6x^2 - 6x + 6$

31. Short Response A walnut falls from a tree 75 feet off the ground. The polynomial $-16t^2 + 75$ gives the walnut's height, in feet, after t seconds of falling. Find its height after 1 second and 2 seconds. Estimate how many seconds the walnut falls before hitting the ground. *(Lesson 13.1)* **59 ft, 11 ft; about 2.2 sec**

32. Extended Response Use your graphs to look for a pattern. *(Lesson 13.5)* **See margin.**

a. Graph each function in a coordinate plane.

$f(x) = 3x^2 - 5$
$f(x) = 3x^2 - 3$
$f(x) = 3x^2 - 1$

b. Describe the graph of the function $f(x) = 3x^2 - 100$.

End-of-Course Test

Algebra, Integers, and Equation Solving

1. The table shows the number of visits to your Web site for five days. Make a bar graph of the data. See margin.

Days	Mon	Tues	Wed	Thurs	Fri
Visits	12	18	21	25	28

Evaluate the expression.

2. $8 \cdot 4 + 3 \cdot 5$ 47
3. $46 - 25 + 8 \div 2$ 25
4. $(3 + 1)^3 \div 8 - 2$ 6
5. $7a - 4$ when $a = 2$ 10
6. $\frac{9}{2y - 5}$ when $y = 4$ 3
7. x^4 when $x = 5$ 625

Use a number line to order the integers from least to greatest.

8. 65, −13, 19, 61, −19, 34 −19, −13, 19, 34, 61, 65
9. 878, 433, −602, 1074, −1222 −1222, −602, 433, 878, 1074

Find the sum, difference, product, or quotient.

10. $-61 + (-44)$ −105
11. $-13 + 8 + (-6)$ −11
12. $-49 - (-16)$ −33
13. $85 - (-18) - 12$ 91
14. $5(-8)$ −40
15. $-9(-6)(-4)$ −216
16. $\frac{-64}{8}$ −8
17. $\frac{-55}{-11}$ 5

18. In a local school committee election, 250 votes were cast for two candidates. Candidate A won the election by 10 votes. How many votes did Candidate A receive? 130 votes

19. Plot and connect points $A(-10, 12)$, $B(10, 12)$, $C(10, -12)$, and $D(-10, -12)$. Identify the figure. Then find the perimeter and area of the figure. See margin for art; rectangle; 88 units, 480 square units.

Simplify the expression by combining like terms.

20. $6y + 5y$ $11y$
21. $8a - 6b + a$ $9a - 6b$
22. $6(x - 7) + 4x + 3$ $10x - 39$
23. $3(2x + y) - (8 + 5x)$ $x + 3y - 8$

Solve the equation.

24. $49 = d + 12$ 37
25. $b - 18 = 12$ 30
26. $8 = \frac{56}{x}$ 7
27. $15 = \frac{x}{5}$ 75
28. $4b = -64$ −16
29. $-6x = 72$ −12
30. $5b + 9 = 18$ 1.8
31. $-21 = 19 - 4x$ 10

Solve the inequality. Then graph the solution. 32–35. See margin for art.

32. $b + 6 \le 12$ $b \le 6$
33. $6 > 8 + t$ $t < -2$
34. $-\frac{1}{6}a < 24$ $a > -144$
35. $8 \ge -\frac{1}{4}x$ $x \ge -32$

1.
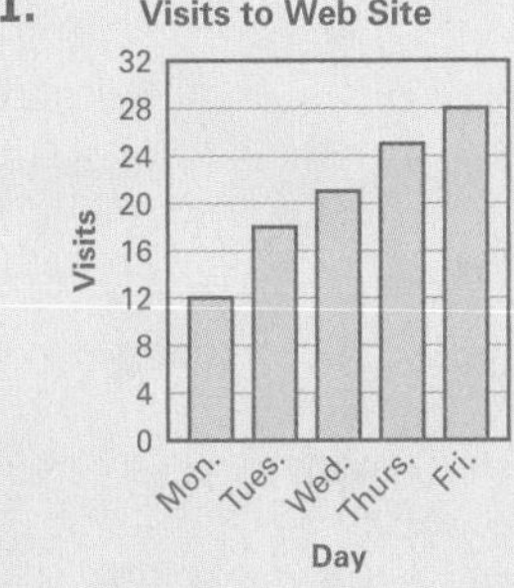

19.
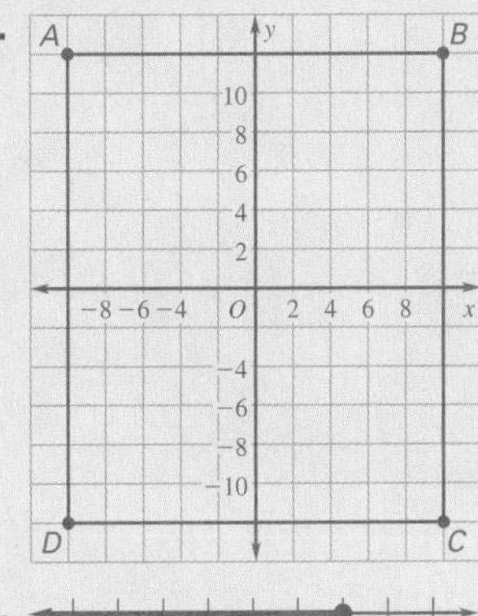

32.
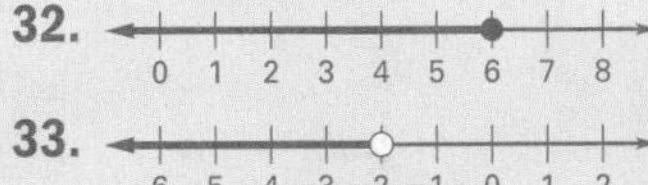

33.

34.
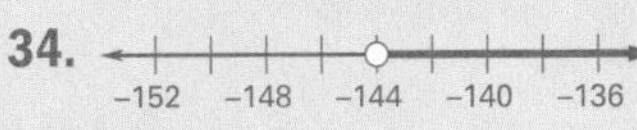

35.
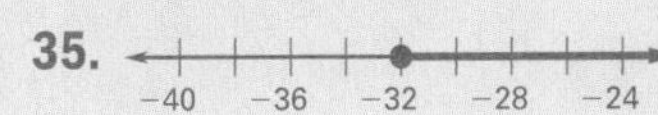

Algebra and Rational Numbers

36. Write the following fractions in simplest form: $\frac{12}{26}, \frac{18}{54}, \frac{16}{82}, \frac{24}{84}$. $\frac{6}{13}, \frac{1}{3}, \frac{8}{41}, \frac{2}{7}$

Find the GCF and LCM of the numbers.

37. 12, 16, 48 GCF: 4, LCM: 48
38. 16, 32, 64 GCF: 16; LCM: 64
39. 45, 90, 180 GCF: 45; LCM: 180
40. 10, 15, 50 GCF: 5; LCM: 150

Simplify. Write the expression using only positive exponents.

41. $y^6 \cdot y^4$ y^{10}
42. $x^{-7} \cdot x^5$ $\frac{1}{x^2}$
43. $\frac{x^{18}}{x^{11}}$ x^7
44. $y^8 \cdot y^{-5}$ y^3

Find the sum, difference, product, or quotient.

45. $\frac{13}{24} + \left(-\frac{7}{24}\right)$ $\frac{1}{4}$
46. $-2\frac{2}{5} - 2\frac{2}{5}$ $-4\frac{4}{5}$
47. $8\frac{1}{2} + 5\frac{1}{4}$ $13\frac{3}{4}$
48. $11\frac{2}{9} - 14\frac{1}{2}$ $-3\frac{5}{18}$
49. $5\frac{1}{4} \cdot \left(-4\frac{1}{5}\right)$ $-22\frac{1}{20}$
50. $-3\frac{1}{3} \cdot \left(-8\frac{4}{5}\right)$ $29\frac{1}{3}$
51. $1\frac{1}{2} \div \left(-3\frac{3}{8}\right)$ $-\frac{4}{9}$
52. $5\frac{1}{9} \div 2\frac{4}{7}$ $1\frac{80}{81}$
53. $7.9 + (-2.344)$ 5.556
54. $-8.1 - (-4.06)$ -4.04
55. $14.66 \cdot 2.1$ 30.786
56. $4.844 \div (-0.56)$ -8.65

57. Order the numbers from least to greatest: $8\frac{2}{3}$, 8.5, 13.35, $7\frac{2}{3}$, $8\frac{9}{20}$, $8.\bar{6}$, 7.7. Then find the mean, median, and mode(s) of the numbers.
$7\frac{2}{3}$, 7.7, $8\frac{9}{20}$, 8.5, $8.\bar{6}$, $8\frac{2}{3}$ 13.35; mean: 9, median: 8.5; mode: $8\frac{2}{3}$, or $8.\bar{6}$

Solve the equation or inequality.

58. $3(b - 9) = -39$ -4
59. $-6 = 11a - 5a$ -1
60. $3x = 9(x - 1)$ $1\frac{1}{2}$
61. $6(y - 4) = 3(y + 9)$ 17
62. $\frac{1}{6}n + \frac{2}{3}n = 1$ $1\frac{1}{5}$
63. $5.9 + c = 3c - 2.1$ 4
64. $5a + 8 \geq 12$ $a \geq \frac{4}{5}$
65. $-2(d + 4) < -4$ $d > -2$
66. $\frac{2}{9} = \frac{10}{a}$ 45
67. $\frac{x}{4} = \frac{21}{12}$ 7
68. $\frac{45}{15} = \frac{y}{1}$ 3
69. $\frac{12}{15} = \frac{p}{100}$ 80

Write the number as a percent, as a decimal, and as a fraction.

70. 22.5% 22.5%, 0.225, $\frac{9}{40}$
71. 0.37 37%, 0.37, $\frac{37}{100}$
72. $\frac{13}{20}$ 65%, 0.65, $\frac{13}{20}$
73. 0.1% 0.1%, 0.001, $\frac{1}{1000}$

74. You buy a stereo for \$74 plus 8% sales tax. What is your total cost? \$79.92

75. What is 0.5% of 65? Five is what percent of 125? 0.325; 4%

76. You draw a tile randomly from a bag that contains 12 B tiles, 6 C tiles, 8 D tiles, and 5 A tiles. What is the probability that you draw a D? $\frac{8}{31}$

81.

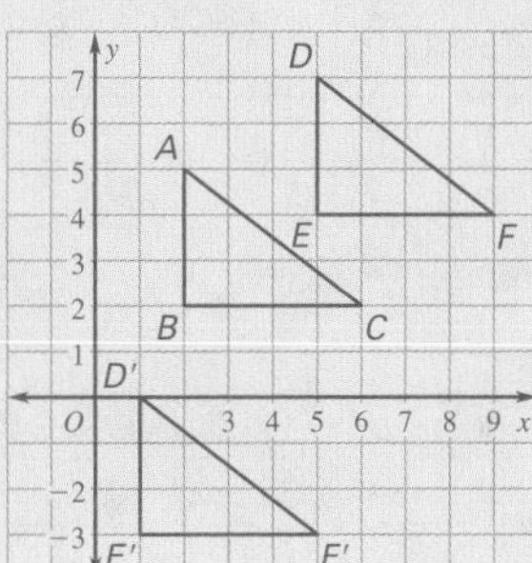

End-of-Course Test

Geometry and Measurement

77. ∠1 and ∠2 are complementary, and $m\angle 1 = 74°$. Find $m\angle 2$. 16°

Find the value of *x*. Then classify the figure.

78.

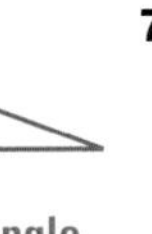

20; right triangle

79.

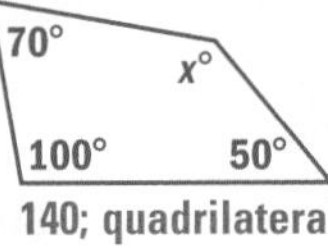

140; quadrilateral

80.

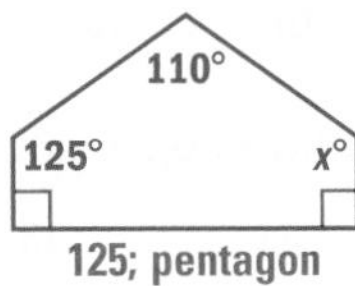

125; pentagon

81. Draw $\triangle ABC$ in the coordinate plane with vertices $A(2, 5)$, $B(2, 2)$, and $C(6, 2)$. Draw $\triangle DEF$ congruent to $\triangle ABC$. Then translate $\triangle DEF$ using $(x, y) \longrightarrow (x - 4, y - 7)$. Identify the coordinates of $\triangle DEF$ and $\triangle D'E'F'$. See margin for art. *Sample answer:* $D(5, 7)$, $E(5, 4)$, $F(9, 4)$, $D'(1, 0)$, $E'(1, -3)$, $F'(5, -3)$

82. Find the following square roots: $-\sqrt{2}$, $\sqrt{121}$, $\sqrt{81}$, $-\sqrt{400}$ −1.414, 11, 9, −20

83. Is $\sqrt{\frac{4}{81}}$ a rational or irrational number? $\sqrt{18}$? Explain. Rational; irrational; the square root of $\frac{4}{81}$ is $\frac{2}{9}$ which is a rational number. The square root of 18 does not terminate or repeat.

A right triangle has leg lengths *a* and *b* and a hypotenuse of length *c*. Find the unknown length. Then find the triangle's area and perimeter.

84. $a = 12$ cm, $b = 5$ cm, $c = ?$
13 cm; 30 cm²; 30 cm

85. $a = 12$ ft, $b = 16$ ft, $c = ?$
20 ft; 96 ft²; 48 ft

Find the value of each variable. Give exact answers.

86.

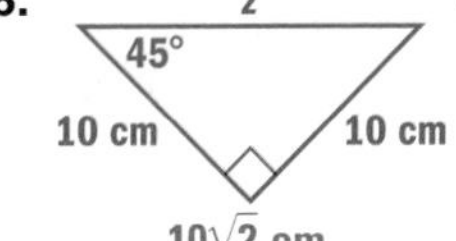

$10\sqrt{2}$ cm

87.

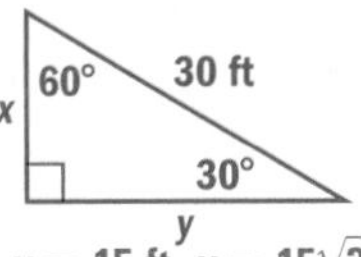

$x = 15$ ft, $y = 15\sqrt{3}$ ft

88.

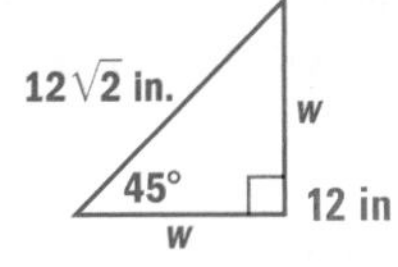

12 in

89. Find the area of a trapezoid with bases of 18 feet and 12 feet and a height of 5 feet. 75 ft²

90. What is the area of a circle with a radius of 5 feet? with a diameter of 12 centimeters? Use 3.14 for π. 78.5 ft²; 113.04 cm²

Find the surface area and volume of the solid. Use 3.14 for π.

91.

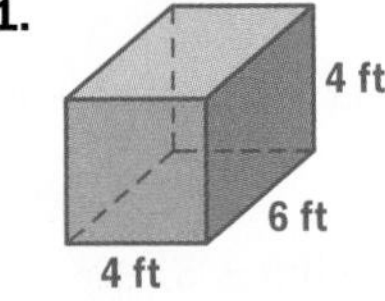

128 ft²; 96 ft³

92.

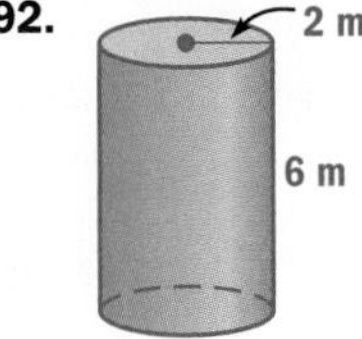
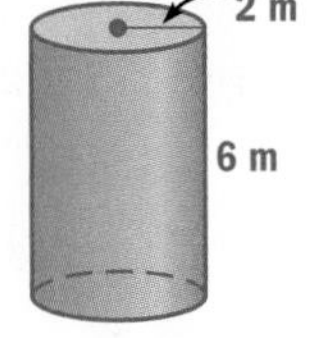

100.48 m²; 75.36 m³

93.

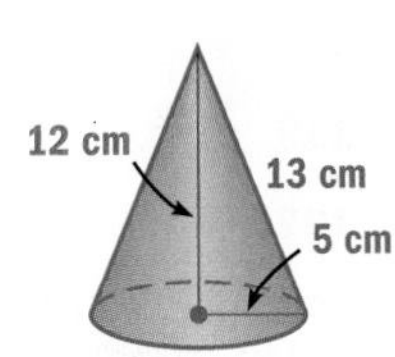

282.6 cm²; 314 cm³

94. $y = 2x$

x	-2	-1	0	1	2
y	-4	-2	0	2	4

range: $-4, -2, 0, 2, 4$

$y = x - 2$

x	-2	-1	0	1	2
y	-4	-3	-2	-1	0

range: $-4, -3, -2, -1, 0$

95.

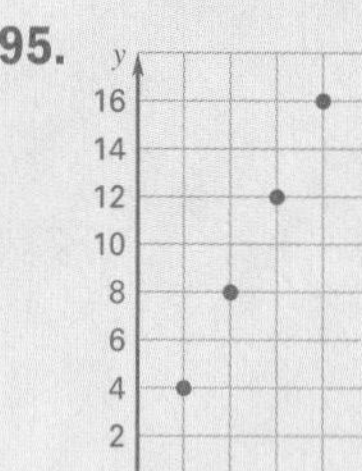

positive relationship; (5, 20)

96.

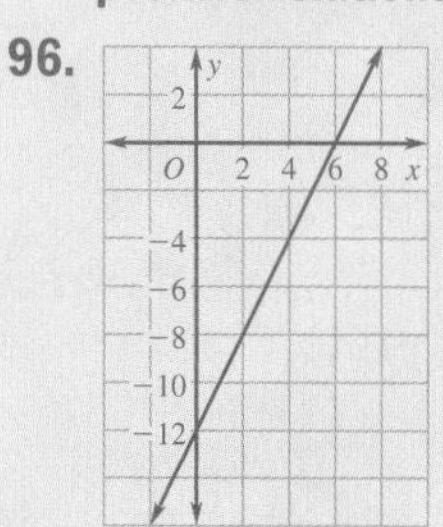

x-intercept: 6, y-intercept: -12

97.

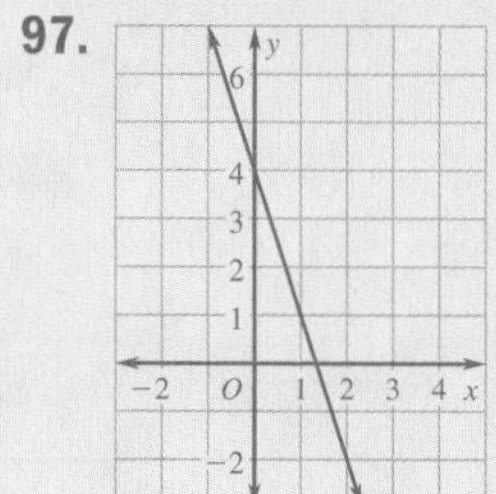

x-intercept: $\frac{4}{3}$, y-intercept: 4

98.

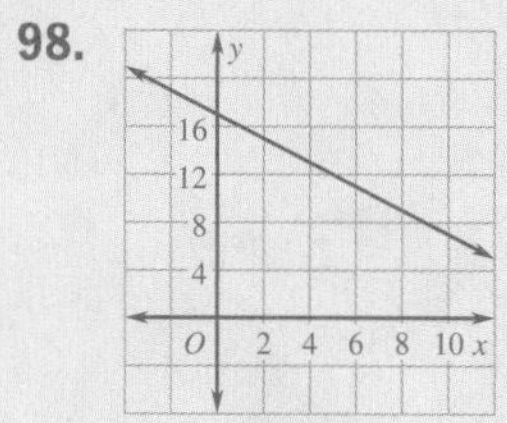

x-intercept: 17,
y-intercept: 17

99–103, 105, 107–109, 127. See Additional Answers beginning on page AA1.

End-of-Course Test

Advanced Algebra Topics

94. Make tables of values for the functions $y = 2x$ and $y = x - 2$. Use a domain of $-2, -1, 0, 1,$ and 2. Identify the range of each function. See margin.

95. Make a scatter plot of (1, 4), (2, 8), (3, 12), and (4, 16). Describe the relationship between the variables. Then find the next ordered pair. See margin.

Graph the equation. Identify the intercepts of the graph. 96–103. See margin.

96. $y = 2x - 12$ **97.** $y = 4 - 3x$ **98.** $y = -x + 17$ **99.** $y = -5x - 6$

100. $y = -\frac{1}{2}x + 5$ **101.** $y = -6x + 8$ **102.** $x + 9y = 18$ **103.** $y = 2x + 4$

104. Find the slope of the line passing through the points (5,8) and (0,5). $\frac{3}{5}$

105. Rewrite $y + 12x = 6$ and $13x - 11y = 12$ in slope-intercept form. Then find the slope and the y-intercept of the graph of each equation. See margin.

106. Tell whether $(-8, -9)$ is a solution of the inequality $12x - 16y \geq 34$. yes

Make a stem-and-leaf plot and a box-and-whisker plot of the data. 107–108. See margin.

107. 46, 49, 66, 51, 68, 83, 78, 64 **108.** \$68, \$63, \$51, \$43, \$53, \$38, \$60, \$66

109. In an election poll, 32% preferred Atkins, 47% preferred Liu, and 21% were undecided. Make a circle graph of the data. See margin.

110. You can choose from 3 sandwiches, 4 drinks, and 2 snacks. How many different sandwich-drink-snack groupings are possible? 24 groupings

Evaluate.

111. ${}_{18}P_2$ 306 **112.** ${}_{14}P_3$ 2184 **113.** ${}_{9}C_6$ 84 **114.** ${}_{8}C_5$ 56

115. You roll a number cube. What are the odds of getting an odd number? $\frac{1}{2}$

Simplify the polynomial and write it in standard form.

116. $4x^2 - 5x - 2x^2 + 7x$ $2x^2 + 2x$ **117.** $-3x^2 + 3x - x + 7$ $-3x^2 + 2x + 7$

Simplify the expression.

118. $(x^2 - 2x + 5) + (x^2 - 4)$ $2x^2 - 2x + 1$ **119.** $(5y^2 - y - 1) - (y^2 + 4y)$ $4y^2 - 5y - 1$ **120.** $(3x^2 - 4x + 2) + (x^2 + 6x - 5)$ $4x^2 + 2x - 3$

121. $(6x)(8x^6)$ $48x^7$ **122.** $(8y)^3$ $512y^3$ **123.** $(x^6)^3$ x^{18}

124. $(n - 3)(n - 3)$ $n^2 - 6n + 9$ **125.** $(4x - 2)(8x - 3)$ $32x^2 - 28x + 6$ **126.** $(12b - 4)(8b + 3)$ $96b^2 + 4b -$

127. Graph $f(x) = x^2 + 6$. Use a table of values with $x = 2, 1, 0, -1,$ and -2. See margin.

Contents of Student Resources

Skills Review Handbook — 704

Number Sense
- Place Value, *704*
- Rounding, *705*
- Divisibility Tests, *706*
- Mixed Numbers and Improper Fractions, *707*
- Ratio and Rate, *708*

Number Operations
- Adding and Subtracting Decimals, *709*
- Adding and Subtracting Fractions, *710*
- Estimation in Addition and Subtraction, *711*
- Solving Problems Using Addition and Subtraction, *712*
- Multiplying Fractions, *713*
- Multiplication of a Decimal by a Whole Number, *714*
- Dividing Decimals, *715*
- Estimation in Multiplication and Division, *716*
- Solving Problems Using Multiplication and Division, *717*

Measurement and Geometry
- Points, Lines, and Planes, *718*
- Angles, *719*
- Using a Ruler, *720*
- Using a Protractor, *721*
- Using a Compass, *722*

Data Analysis
- Reading and Making Line Plots, *723*
- Reading and Making Bar Graphs, *724*
- Reading and Making Line Graphs, *725*
- Venn Diagrams and Logical Reasoning, *726*

Extra Practice — 727

Chapters 1–13

Tables — 740

Symbols, Measures, Formulas, Properties, Squares and Square Roots, Equivalent Fractions, Decimals, and Percents

Glossary — 747

Index — 773

Credits — 796

Selected Answers — SA1

703

Skills Review Handbook

Skills Review

Place Value

The **whole numbers** are the numbers 0, 1, 2, 3, ... A **digit** is any of the numbers 0, 1, 2, 3, 4, 5, 6, 7, 8, or 9. The decimals are numbers such as 121.32, 25.6, and 3.456. For example, the decimal 4.5 has the digits 4 and 5. The place value of each digit in a whole number or a decimal depends on its position within the number. For example, in the number 491,037.892, the 8 has a value of 0.8 or 8×0.1 because it is in the tenths' place.

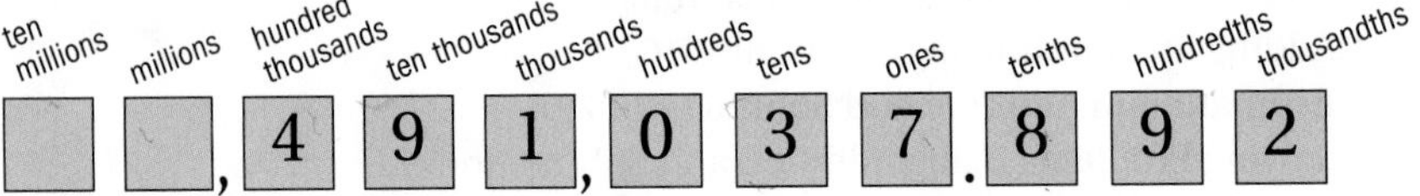

EXAMPLE **Write the number 27,037.6 in expanded form.**

$27{,}037.6 = 20{,}000 + 7000 + 30 + 7 + 0.6$

The zero in the hundreds' position is a placeholder.

$= 2 \times 10{,}000 + 7 \times 1000 + 3 \times 10 + 7 \times 1 + 6 \times 0.1$

EXAMPLE **Write the number in standard form.**

a. $4 \times 1000 + 5 \times 10 + 6 \times 0.1 + 8 \times 0.01$

b. Four million, sixty thousand, five and two thousandths

Solution

a. $4 \times 1000 + 5 \times 10 + 6 \times 0.1 + 8 \times 0.01 = 4000 + 50 + 0.6 + 0.08$

$= 4050.68$

b. Write 4 in the millions' place, 6 in the ten thousands' place, 5 in the ones' place, and the 2 in the thousandths' place. Use zeros as placeholders for the other places. The answer is 4,060,005.002.

Practice

1. $5 \times 10{,}000 + 6 \times 1000 + 8 \times 100 + 9 \times 1$
2. $3 \times 1 + 7 \times 0.01 + 5 \times 0.001$
3. $1 \times 1000 + 2 \times 1 + 3 \times 0.001$
4. $3 \times 100 + 6 \times 1 + 4 \times 0.1 + 5 \times 0.001$

Write the number in expanded form.

1. 56,809 **2.** 3.075 **3.** 1002.003 **4.** 306.405

Write the number in standard form.

5. $5 \times 100{,}000 + 6 \times 10 + 9 \times 1 + 7 \times 0.001$ 500,069.007

6. Five million, ten and thirty-six thousandths 5,000,010.036

Rounding

To **round** a number means to approximate the number to a given place value. When rounding, look at the digit to the right of that place value. If the digit to the right is less than 5 (0, 1, 2, 3, or 4), round down. If the digit to the right is 5 or greater (5, 6, 7, 8, or 9), round up.

EXAMPLE **Round the number to the place value of the red digit.**

a. 6932 **b.** 45.674

Solution

a. Because the 9 is in the hundreds' place, round 6932 to the nearest hundred. Notice that 6932 is between 6900 and 7000, so it will round to one of these two numbers.

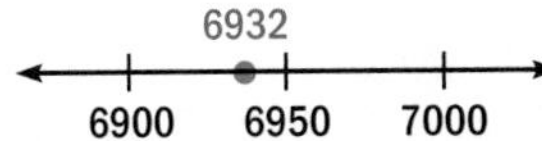

Notice that 6932 is closer to 6900 than to 7000.

The digit to the right of the 9 in the hundreds' place is the 3 in the tens' place. Because 3 is less than 5, round down.

ANSWER 6932 rounded to the nearest hundred is 6900.

b. Because 6 is in the tenths' place, round 45.674 to the nearest tenth. Notice that 45.674 is between 45.6 and 45.7, so it will round to one of these two numbers.

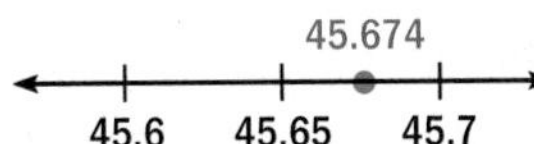

Notice that 45.674 is closer to 45.7 than to 45.6.

The digit to the right of the 6 in the tenths' place is the 7 in the hundredths' place. Because 7 is 5 or greater, round up.

ANSWER 45.674 rounded to the nearest tenth is 45.7.

Practice

Round the number to the place value of the red digit.

1. 1253 1300 **2.** 57,309 57,310 **3.** 8.183 8.2 **4.** 32.76 33 **5.** 44,380 40,000

6. 12.535 12.54 **7.** 452.84 450 **8.** 998,543 1,000,000 **9.** 62.847 62.8 **10.** 640,796 600,000

11. 164.479 164.5 **12.** 1209.4 1209 **13.** 52.961 52.96 **14.** 12,742.5 12,740 **15.** 3,501,652 3,501,700

Divisibility Tests

When two nonzero whole numbers are multiplied together, each number is a **factor** of the product. A number is **divisible** by another number if the second number is a factor of the first. For example, $2 \times 5 = 10$, so 2 and 5 are factors of 10, and 10 is divisible by both 2 and 5.

You can use the following tests to test a whole number for divisibility by 2, 3, 4, 5, 6, 8, 9, and 10.

Divisible by 2: The last digit of the number is 0, 2, 4, 6, or 8.
Divisible by 3: The sum of the digits of the number is divisible by 3.
Divisible by 4: The last two digits of the number are divisible by 4.
Divisible by 5: The last digit of the number is 0 or 5.
Divisible by 6: The number is divisible by both 2 and 3.
Divisible by 8: The last three digits of the number are divisible by 8.
Divisible by 9: The sum of the digits of the number is divisible by 9.
Divisible by 10: The last digit of the number is 0.

EXAMPLE **Test the number for divisibility by 2, 3, 4, 5, 6, 8, 9, and 10.**

a. 2736 **b.** 74,420

Solution

a. The last digit of 2736 is 6, so it is divisible by 2 but not by 5 or 10. The sum of the digits is $2 + 7 + 3 + 6 = 18$, so it is divisible by 3 and 9. The last two digits, 36, are divisible by 4, so 2736 is divisible by 4. Because 2736 is divisible by both 2 and 3, it is divisible by 6. The last three digits, 736, are divisible by 8, so 2736 is divisible by 8.

ANSWER 2736 is divisible by 2, 3, 4, 6, 8, and 9.

b. The last digit of 74,420 is 0, so it is divisible by 2, 5, and 10. The sum of the digits is $7 + 4 + 4 + 2 + 0 = 17$, so it is not divisible by 3 or 9. The last two digits, 20, are divisible by 4, so 74,420 is divisible by 4. Because 74,420 is divisible by 2, but not by 3, it is not divisible by 6. The last three digits, 420, are not divisible by 8, so 74,420 is not divisible by 8.

ANSWER 74,420 is divisible by 2, 4, 5, and 10.

Practice

Test the number for divisibility by 2, 3, 4, 5, 6, 8, 9, and 10.

1. 34 2
2. 84 2, 3, 4, 6
3. 285 3, 5
4. 560 2, 4, 5, 8, 10
5. 972 2, 3, 4, 6, 9
6. 4210 2, 5, 10
7. 2815 5
8. 6390 2, 3, 5, 6, 9, 10
9. 88,004 2, 4
10. 75,432 2, 3, 4, 6, 8

Mixed Numbers and Improper Fractions

A **fraction** is a number of the form $\frac{a}{b}$ $(b \neq 0)$ where a is called the **numerator** and b is called the **denominator**. A number $1\frac{3}{5}$, read as "one and three fifths," is a *mixed number*. A **mixed number** is the sum of a whole number part and a fraction part. An **improper fraction**, such as $\frac{21}{8}$, is any fraction in which the numerator is greater than or equal to the denominator.

EXAMPLE **Write $3\frac{2}{5}$ as an improper fraction.**

$3\frac{2}{5} = \frac{15 + 2}{5}$ 1 whole $= \frac{5}{5}$, so 3 wholes $= \frac{3 \times 5}{5}$, or $\frac{15}{5}$.

$= \frac{17}{5}$ Add.

EXAMPLE **Write $\frac{13}{4}$ as a mixed number.**

1. Divide 13 by 4.

$$\begin{array}{r} 3\text{R}1 \\ 4\overline{)13} \\ \underline{12} \\ 1 \end{array}$$

2. Write the mixed number. $3 + \frac{1}{4} = 3\frac{1}{4}$

Practice

Copy and complete the statement.

1. $7\frac{3}{5} = \frac{?}{5}$ 38 **2.** $3\frac{1}{6} = \frac{?}{6}$ 19 **3.** $\frac{23}{4} = 5\frac{?}{4}$ 3 **4.** $\frac{17}{7} = 2\frac{?}{7}$ 3

Write the mixed number as an improper fraction.

5. $3\frac{1}{2}$ $\frac{7}{2}$ **6.** $1\frac{5}{6}$ $\frac{11}{6}$ **7.** $4\frac{3}{8}$ $\frac{35}{8}$ **8.** $8\frac{5}{7}$ $\frac{61}{7}$ **9.** $10\frac{3}{4}$ $\frac{43}{4}$

Write the improper fraction as a mixed number.

10. $\frac{11}{4}$ $2\frac{3}{4}$ **11.** $\frac{15}{2}$ $7\frac{1}{2}$ **12.** $\frac{25}{6}$ $4\frac{1}{6}$ **13.** $\frac{17}{3}$ $5\frac{2}{3}$ **14.** $\frac{33}{8}$ $4\frac{1}{8}$

Ratio and Rate

One way to compare numbers is to use a ratio. The **ratio** uses division to compare two numbers. You can write the ratio of a to b as $\frac{a}{b}$, as $a : b$, or as "a to b."

EXAMPLE **There are 15 boys and 17 girls in the band. Write the ratio of the number of boys to girls in the band in three ways.**

$$\frac{\text{Number of boys}}{\text{Number of girls}} = \frac{15}{17} = 15 \text{ to } 17 = 15 : 17$$

A **rate** is a ratio of two quantities that have different units, such as $\frac{150 \text{ miles}}{3 \text{ hours}}$. A **unit rate** is a rate with a denominator of 1 unit.

EXAMPLE **Write the rate $\frac{150 \text{ miles}}{3 \text{ hours}}$ as a unit rate.**

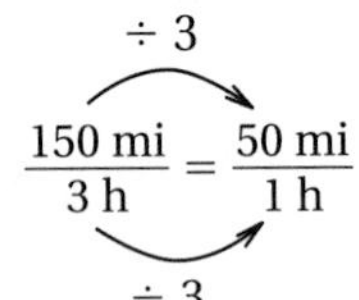

Divide 3 by 3 to get 1, so divide 150 by 3 also.

ANSWER The unit rate is 50 miles per hour.

Practice

The table shows the numbers of boys and girls in Mr. Smith's class and in Ms. Jung's class. Use the table to write the specified ratio.

	Boys	Girls
Mr. Smith's class	13	12
Ms. Jung's class	17	11

1. Boys in Mr. Smith's class to girls in Mr. Smith's class $\frac{13}{12}$, 13 to 12, 13:12
2. Boys in Mr. Smith's class to boys in Ms. Jung's class $\frac{13}{17}$, 13 to 17, 13:17
3. Girls in Ms. Jung's class to all girls $\frac{11}{23}$, 11 to 23, 11:23

Write the rate and unit rate.

4. 8 feet in 2 seconds $\frac{8 \text{ ft}}{2 \text{ sec}} = \frac{4 \text{ ft}}{1 \text{ sec}}$
5. \$24 for 8 pens $\frac{\$24}{8 \text{ pens}} = \frac{\$3}{1 \text{ pen}}$
6. 333 miles in 6 hours $\frac{333 \text{ mi}}{6 \text{ h}} = \frac{55.5 \text{ mi}}{1 \text{ h}}$
7. 280 words in 5 minutes $\frac{280 \text{ words}}{5 \text{ min}} = \frac{56 \text{ words}}{1 \text{ min}}$
8. 3 quarts for \$2.50 $\frac{3 \text{ qt}}{\$2.50} = \frac{1.2 \text{ qt}}{\$1}$
9. 8 inches in 6 days $\frac{8 \text{ in.}}{6 \text{ days}} = 1\frac{1}{3}$ in. per day

708

Adding and Subtracting Decimals

To add and subtract decimals, start with the digits in the place on the right. Moving to the left, add or subtract the digits one place value at a time, regrouping as needed.

EXAMPLE **Find the sum 0.157 + 0.663.**

(1) Add the thousandths. Regroup 10 thousandths as 1 hundredth and 0 thousandths.

$$\begin{array}{r} \scriptstyle 1 \\ 0.157 \\ +\ 0.663 \\ \hline 0 \end{array}$$

(2) Add the hundredths. Regroup 12 hundredths as 1 tenth and 2 hundredths.

$$\begin{array}{r} \scriptstyle 11 \\ 0.157 \\ +\ 0.663 \\ \hline 20 \end{array}$$

(3) Add the tenths. Place the decimal point in the answer.

$$\begin{array}{r} \scriptstyle 11 \\ 0.157 \\ +\ 0.663 \\ \hline 0.820 \end{array}$$

EXAMPLE **Find the difference 30.7 – 3.8.**

(1) Start with the tenths. There are not enough tenths in 30.7 to subtract 8 tenths.

$$\begin{array}{r} 30.7 \\ -\ 3.8 \\ \hline \end{array}$$

(2) Move to the ones. There are no ones in 30.7, so regroup 1 ten as 9 ones and 10 tenths.

$$\begin{array}{r} \scriptstyle 9 \\ \scriptstyle 2\ \not{10}\ 17 \\ \not{3}\not{0}.\not{7} \\ -\ 3.8 \\ \hline \end{array}$$

(3) Subtract. Place the decimal point in the answer.

$$\begin{array}{r} \scriptstyle 9 \\ \scriptstyle 2\ \not{10}\ 17 \\ \not{3}\not{0}.\not{7} \\ -\ 3.8 \\ \hline 26.9 \end{array}$$

✓**Check** Because addition and subtraction are inverse operations, you can check your answer by adding: 26.9 + 3.8 = 30.7.

Practice

Find the sum or difference.

1. 3.56 + 2.74 **6.3**
2. 12.7 + 93.8 **106.5**
3. 27.5 + 3.6 **31.1**
4. 0.923 + 0.179 **1.102**
5. 4.217 + 6.739 **10.956**
6. 9.3 − 2.8 **6.5**
7. 4.56 − 1.65 **2.91**
8. 13.64 − 5.85 **7.79**
9. 38.45 − 19.57 **18.88**
10. 741.52 − 48.66 **692.86**
11. 56.98 + 0.82 **57.8**
12. 100.476 − 4.989 **95.487**
13. 365.57 − 79.38 **286.19**
14. 49.86 + 2.65 **52.51**
15. 97.156 − 9.092 **88.064**
16. 232.543 − 209.692 **22.851**

Adding and Subtracting Fractions

To add two fractions with a common denominator, write the sum of the numerators over the denominator.

Numbers $\frac{2}{5} + \frac{1}{5} = \frac{3}{5}$ **Algebra** $\frac{a}{c} + \frac{b}{c} = \frac{a+b}{c}$ $(c \neq 0)$

EXAMPLE **Find the sum $\frac{4}{7} + \frac{6}{7}$.**

$\frac{4}{7} + \frac{6}{7} = \frac{4+6}{7}$ Write sum of numerators over denominator.

$= \frac{10}{7}$ Add.

$= 1\frac{3}{7}$ Write the improper fraction as a mixed number.

To subtract two fractions with a common denominator, write the difference of the numerators over the denominator.

Numbers $\frac{7}{9} - \frac{2}{9} = \frac{5}{9}$ **Algebra** $\frac{a}{c} - \frac{b}{c} = \frac{a-b}{c}$ $(c \neq 0)$

EXAMPLE **Find the difference $\frac{10}{11} - \frac{4}{11}$.**

$\frac{10}{11} - \frac{4}{11} = \frac{10-4}{11}$ Write difference of numerators over denominator.

$= \frac{6}{11}$ Subtract.

Practice

Find the sum or difference.

1. $\frac{1}{3} + \frac{1}{3}$ $\frac{2}{3}$
2. $\frac{8}{9} + \frac{5}{9}$ $1\frac{4}{9}$
3. $\frac{6}{7} - \frac{3}{7}$ $\frac{3}{7}$
4. $\frac{11}{12} - \frac{4}{12}$ $\frac{7}{12}$
5. $\frac{1}{8} + \frac{7}{8}$ 1

6. $\frac{8}{11} + \frac{7}{11}$ $1\frac{4}{11}$
7. $\frac{13}{15} - \frac{2}{15}$ $\frac{11}{15}$
8. $\frac{5}{6} - \frac{4}{6}$ $\frac{1}{6}$
9. $\frac{1}{9} + \frac{1}{9}$ $\frac{2}{9}$
10. $\frac{10}{11} - \frac{2}{11}$ $\frac{8}{11}$

11. $\frac{11}{12} + \frac{8}{12}$ $1\frac{7}{12}$
12. $\frac{9}{10} - \frac{6}{10}$ $\frac{3}{10}$
13. $\frac{5}{9} - \frac{4}{9}$ $\frac{1}{9}$
14. $\frac{9}{16} + \frac{12}{16}$ $1\frac{5}{16}$
15. $\frac{11}{14} - \frac{2}{14}$ $\frac{9}{14}$

16. $\frac{8}{15} - \frac{8}{15}$ 0
17. $\frac{5}{12} + \frac{2}{12}$ $\frac{7}{12}$
18. $\frac{8}{10} + \frac{1}{10}$ $\frac{9}{10}$
19. $\frac{6}{7} + \frac{5}{7}$ $1\frac{4}{7}$
20. $\frac{5}{8} - \frac{2}{8}$ $\frac{3}{8}$

Estimation in Addition and Subtraction

To **estimate** a solution means to find an approximate answer. When numbers being added have about the same value, you can use *clustering* to estimate their sum. Another way to estimate is to add the digits in the greatest place, then round the remaining parts of the numbers and add. Finally, add the sums together.

EXAMPLE **Estimate the sum 3836 + 4235 + 3982.**

3836	4000	
4235	4000	The numbers all cluster
+ 3982	+ 4000	around the value 4000.
	12,000	

ANSWER The sum 3836 + 4235 + 3982 is *about* 12,000.

To estimate a difference, first subtract the digits in the greatest place. Then round the remaining parts of the numbers and subtract the lesser number from the greater number. Finally, combine the two differences using addition or subtraction as shown below.

EXAMPLE **Estimate the difference 68,453 − 32,792.**

1. First subtract the digits in the ten thousands' place.

   68,453 − 32,792 → 60,000 − 30,000 = 30,000

2. Then round the remaining digits to the nearest thousand. Subtract the lesser number from the greater number.

   8,000 − 3,000 = 5,000

3. Because the greater remaining number was originally on the *top*, you *add* the differences.

   30,000 + 5,000 = 35,000

Note that if the greater remaining number had originally been on the *bottom*, you would *subtract* the differences.

Practice

Estimate the sum or difference. 1–6. Estimates may vary.

1. 935 + 887 + 912 2700 **2.** 4967 + 4802 + 5218 15,000 **3.** 5971 + 6032 + 7865 20,000

4. 8891 − 4932 4000 **5.** 4373 − 2158 2200 **6.** 449,739 − 285,921 160,000

Solving Problems Using Addition and Subtraction

You can use the following guidelines to tell whether to use addition or subtraction to solve a word problem.

- Use addition when you need to combine, join, or find a total.
- Use subtraction when you need to separate, compare, take away, find how many are left, or find how many more are needed.

EXAMPLE **You have 36 stamps in your stamp collection. You want to collect 18 more stamps. How many stamps will you have in all?**

You need to combine, so you need to add.

$36 + 18 = 54$

ANSWER You will have 54 stamps in your stamp collection.

EXAMPLE **Your total bill for lunch is $4.78. You pay with a $5 bill. How much change do you receive?**

You need to take away, so you need to subtract.

$\$5.00 - \$4.78 = \$.22$

ANSWER You receive $.22 in change.

Practice

1. You spend $48 for a coat and $45 for a pair of shoes. How much do you spend in all? **$93**
2. You bought a box of 96 pencils. You gave 28 of the pencils to your friend. How many pencils do you have left? **68 pencils**
3. You have $18. You buy a video for $15.99. How much money do you have left? **$2.01**
4. You have 24 country CDs and 18 pop CDs. How many country and pop CDs do you have in all? **42 CDs**
5. You have 900 minutes a month on your cell phone plan. You have used 652 minutes so far this month. How many minutes do you have left? **248 min**
6. You have $149. You make $24 babysitting. How much money do you have? **$173**

712

Skills Review

Multiplying Fractions

To multiply a fraction by a whole number, multiply the numerator of the fraction by the whole number and write the product over the denominator of the fraction. Simplify if possible.

EXAMPLE **Find the product.**

a. $3 \times \frac{2}{7} = \frac{3 \times 2}{7}$ Write the product of the whole number and the numerator over the denominator.

$= \frac{6}{7}$ Multiply.

b. $\frac{3}{8} \times 5 = \frac{3 \times 5}{8}$ Write the product of the whole number and the numerator over the denominator.

$= \frac{15}{8}$, or $1\frac{7}{8}$ Multiply. Then write as a mixed number.

To multiply two fractions, write the product of the numerators over the product of the denominators. Simplify if possible.

$$\text{product of fractions} = \frac{\text{product of numerators}}{\text{product of denominators}}$$

EXAMPLE **Find the product.**

$\frac{4}{5} \times \frac{2}{3} = \frac{4 \times 2}{5 \times 3}$ Use rule for multiplying fractions.

$= \frac{8}{15}$ Multiply.

Practice

Find the product. Simplify if possible.

1. $6 \times \frac{2}{15}$ $\frac{4}{5}$

2. $2 \times \frac{6}{11}$ $1\frac{1}{11}$

3. $4 \times \frac{5}{9}$ $2\frac{2}{9}$

4. $8 \times \frac{5}{9}$ $4\frac{4}{9}$

5. $\frac{3}{4} \times 7$ $5\frac{1}{4}$

6. $\frac{4}{7} \times 5$ $2\frac{6}{7}$

7. $\frac{6}{7} \times 3$ $2\frac{4}{7}$

8. $\frac{3}{7} \times \frac{6}{11}$ $\frac{18}{77}$

9. $\frac{2}{3} \times \frac{4}{5}$ $\frac{8}{15}$

10. $\frac{3}{4} \times \frac{1}{7}$ $\frac{3}{28}$

11. $\frac{1}{8} \times \frac{3}{5}$ $\frac{3}{40}$

12. $\frac{7}{9} \times \frac{5}{8}$ $\frac{35}{72}$

13. $\frac{5}{9} \times \frac{2}{3}$ $\frac{10}{27}$

14. $\frac{3}{8} \times \frac{4}{5}$ $\frac{3}{10}$

15. $\frac{5}{12} \times \frac{5}{6}$ $\frac{25}{72}$

Skills Review

Multiplication of a Decimal by a Whole Number

To multiply a decimal by a whole number, multiply the entire first number (ignoring the decimal point) by the digit in each place value of the second number to get partial products. Add the partial products. Then place the decimal point in the answer, showing the same number of decimal places as in the decimal.

EXAMPLE **Find the product 31.5 × 206.**

1. Multiply 31.5 by the ones' digit in 206. Ignore the decimal point.

```
   3
  31.5
× 206
  1890
```

2. Skip the 0 in the tens' place, and multiply by the hundreds' digit. Start the partial product in the hundreds' place.

```
   1
  31.5
× 206
  1890
 630
```

3. Add the partial products. The decimal has one decimal place, so show one decimal place in the answer.

```
   31.5
 × 206
   1890
  630
 6489.0
```

Practice

Find the product.

1. 2.3×98 = 225.4
2. 0.62×46 = 28.52
3. 85×7.9 = 671.5
4. 0.56×63 = 35.28
5. 2.08×14 = 29.12
6. 6.52×36 = 234.72
7. 7.24×89 = 644.36
8. 8.35×16 = 133.6
9. 77.6×22 = 1707.2
10. 3.45×105 = 362.25
11. 453×41.2 = 18,663.6
12. 614×6.71 = 4119.94
13. 32.6×463 = 15,093.8
14. 71.8×934 = 67,061.2
15. 90.5×407 = 36,833.5
16. 15.36×123 = 1889.28
17. 3.442×276 = 949.992
18. 93.08×306 = 28,482.48
19. 5.436×682 = 3707.352
20. 60.97×708 = 43,166.76
21. 142.82×35 = 4998.7
22. 25.987×76 = 1975.012
23. 32.903×55 = 1809.665
24. 243.72×38 = 9261.36
25. 75.032×73 = 5477.336
26. 380.07×114 = 43,327.98
27. 508.25×237 = 120,455.25
28. 15.456×591 = 9134.496
29. 36.902×205 = 7564.91
30. 8257.6×459 = 3,790,238.4

Dividing Decimals

In a division problem, the number being divided is called the **dividend** and the number it is being divided by is called the **divisor**. The result of the division is called the **quotient**. To **divide** two numbers, you start with the leftmost digit of the dividend and move to the right. Before you start dividing decimals, place the decimal point in the quotient.

EXAMPLE **Find the quotient 5.2 ÷ 8.**

1. Place the decimal point in the quotient directly above the decimal point in the dividend. Then divide as with whole numbers. Because 8 is greater than 5, place a zero above the 5.

   divisor → $8\overline{)5.2}$ ← dividend, quotient 0.

2. Because 8 × 6 = 48, estimate that 8 divides 52 about 6 times. Multiply 6 and 8. Then subtract 48 from 52. Be sure the difference is less than the divisor: 4 < 8.

   $8\overline{)5.2}$ = 0.6; − 48; 4

3. Add zero as a placeholder. Bring down the zero. Divide 40 by 8 to get 5. Multiply 5 and 8. Subtract 40 from 40. The remainder is zero.

   $8\overline{)5.20}$ = 0.65; − 48; 40; − 40; 0

EXAMPLE **Find the quotient 12 ÷ 2.8.**

1. To multiply the divisor and the dividend by 10, move both decimal points 1 place to the right. Then divide as with whole numbers.

   divisor → $28\overline{)120}$ ← dividend

2. Because 28 × 4 = 112, estimate that 28 divides 120 about 4 times. Multiply 4 and 28. Then subtract 112 from 120.

   $28\overline{)120}$ = 4; − 112; 8

3. Be sure the difference is less than the divisor: 8 < 28. So 12 ÷ 2.8 is equal to $4\frac{8}{28}$, or $4\frac{2}{7}$.

   $28\overline{)120}$ = 4R8; − 112; 8

Practice

Find the quotient.

1. 2.7 ÷ 6 0.45 **2.** 3.8 ÷ 4 0.95 **3.** 6.8 ÷ 8 0.85 **4.** 46.9 ÷ 7 6.7 **5.** 13.71 ÷ 3 4.57

6. 15 ÷ 2.5 6 **7.** 8 ÷ 1.3 6R2 **8.** 32 ÷ 5.46 5R470 **9.** 63 ÷ 7.12 8R604 **10.** 75 ÷ 6.357 11R5073

Estimation in Multiplication and Division

One way to estimate a product or a quotient is to find a range for the product or quotient by finding a low estimate and a high estimate. A low estimate and a high estimate can be found by using *compatible numbers*, which are numbers that make a calculation easier.

EXAMPLE **Find a low and high estimate for the product 56 × 35 using compatible numbers.**

For a low estimate, round both factors *down*. $50 \times 30 = 1500$

For a high estimate, round both factors *up*. $60 \times 40 = 2400$

ANSWER The product 56 × 35 is between 1500 and 2400.

EXAMPLE **Find a low and high estimate for the quotient 23,400 ÷ 45 using compatible numbers.**

When the divisor has more than one digit, round it .

For a *low* estimate, round the divisor *up* and choose a compatible dividend that is *lower* than the original dividend.

$$\begin{array}{r}400\\50\overline{)20,000}\end{array}$$

For a *high* estimate, round the divisor *down* and choose a compatible dividend that is *higher* than the original dividend.

$$\begin{array}{r}600\\40\overline{)24,000}\end{array}$$

ANSWER The quotient 23,400 ÷ 45 is between 400 and 600.

Practice

Find a low and high estimate for the product or quotient using compatible numbers. Estimates may vary.

1. 43 × 16 — 400 and 1000
2. 359 × 28 — 6000 and 12,000
3. 852 × 53 — 40,000 and 54,000
4. 734 × 76 — 49,000 and 64,000
5. 225 ÷ 6 — 30 and 40
6. 2795 ÷ 7 — 300 and 400
7. 17,934 ÷ 77 — 200 and 300
8. 41,042 ÷ 92 — 410 and 500
9. 326 × 48 — 12,000 and 20,000
10. 612 × 273 — 120,000 and 210,000
11. 745 × 158 — 70,000 and 160,000
12. 905 × 657 — 540,000 and 700,000
13. 625 × 28 — 12,000 and 21,000
14. 809 × 97 — 72,000 and 90,000
15. 742 ÷ 8 — 90 and 100
16. 231 ÷ 38 — 5 and 8
17. 5421 ÷ 7 — 700 and 800
18. 4972 ÷ 18 — 240 and 500
19. 1583 ÷ 82 — 10 and 20
20. 43,789 ÷ 64 — 600 and 800

Solving Problems Using Multiplication and Division

You can use the following guidelines to tell whether to use multiplication or division to solve a word problem.

- Use multiplication when you need to find the total number of objects that are in groups of equal size or to find a fractional part of another number.
- Use division when you need to find the number of equal groups or the number in each equal group.

EXAMPLE **You baked 48 muffins. You give $\frac{1}{3}$ of them to your friend. How many muffins did you give to your friend?**

You need to find the fractional part of another number, so you need to multiply.

$$48 \cdot \frac{1}{3} = 16$$

ANSWER You gave 16 muffins to your friend.

EXAMPLE **You bought 4 cans of soup for a total of \$3.56. How much did you pay for each can of soup?**

You need to find the amount in each equal group, so you need to divide.

$$3.56 \div 4 = 0.89$$

ANSWER You paid \$.89 for each can of soup.

Practice

1. You bought 6 notebooks. Each notebook cost \$1.58. How much did you pay for all of the notebooks? **\$9.48**
2. You have 92 baseball cards. You give $\frac{1}{4}$ of your cards to your friend. How many cards did you give your friend? **23 cards**
3. You have 12 flats of flowers. If each flat contains 48 flowers, how many flowers do you have? **576 flowers**
4. You paid \$22.95 for the plates for your party. If you bought 9 packages of plates, how much did you pay for each package? **\$2.55**

Points, Lines, and Planes

In geometry, a **point** is usually labeled with an uppercase letter, such as *A* or *B*. Points are used to name *lines, rays,* and *segments.* A **plane** is a flat surface that extends without end in all directions. You can represent a plane by a figure that looks like a floor or a wall.

Words	Diagram	Symbols
A **line** extends without end in two *opposite* directions.	X Y	$\overleftrightarrow{XY}$ or $\overleftrightarrow{YX}$
A **ray** has one **endpoint** and extends without end in *one* direction.	X Y	$\overrightarrow{XY}$
A **segment** has two endpoints.	X Y	$\overline{XY}$ or $\overline{YX}$

EXAMPLE Identify and name the *line, ray,* or *segment.*

a. A B

b. M N

c.

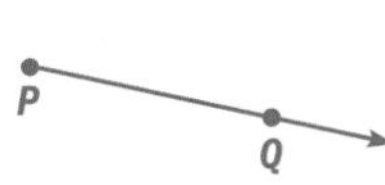

Solution

a. The figure is a segment that can be named $\overline{AB}$.

b. The figure is a line that can be named $\overleftrightarrow{MN}$.

c. The figure is a ray that can be named $\overrightarrow{PQ}$.

Practice

Match the name with the correct figure.

1. $\overline{CD}$ B

2. $\overleftrightarrow{CD}$ C

3. $\overrightarrow{CD}$ A

A.

B.

C.

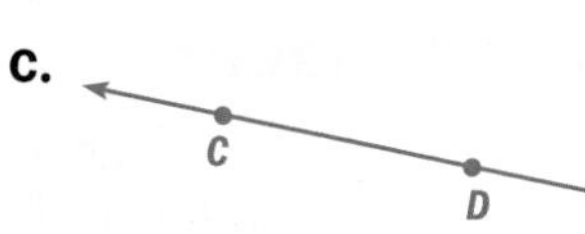

In Exercises 4–7, use the diagram. 4–7. Answers may vary.

4. Name three points. *U, R, V*

5. Name two rays. $\overrightarrow{SR}$ and $\overrightarrow{ST}$

6. Name two lines. $\overleftrightarrow{UV}$ and $\overleftrightarrow{RT}$

7. Name a segment that has *S* as an endpoint. $\overline{SR}$

U S V R T

Angles

An **angle** is formed by two rays with the same endpoint. The endpoint is called the **vertex**. The symbol ∠ is used to represent an angle.

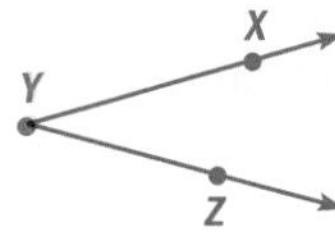

EXAMPLE **Name the angle above in three ways.**

Name the angle by its vertex alone: $\angle Y$

Name the angle by its vertex and two points, with the vertex as the middle point: $\angle XYZ$

Name the angle by its vertex and two points, but reverse the order of the points: $\angle ZYX$

Practice

Match the name with the correct angle.

1. $\angle ABC$ C

2. $\angle RST$ A

3. $\angle MNP$ B

A.

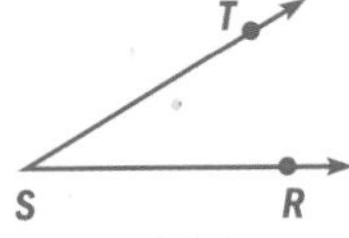

B.

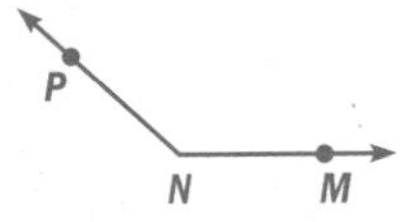

C.

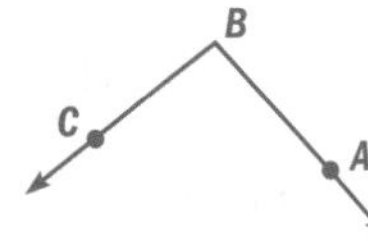

Name the angle in three ways.

4.

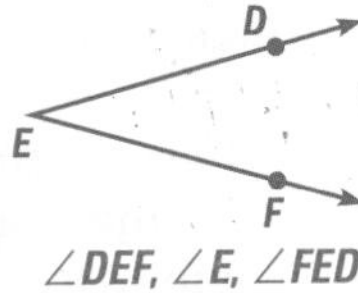

∠DEF, ∠E, ∠FED

5.

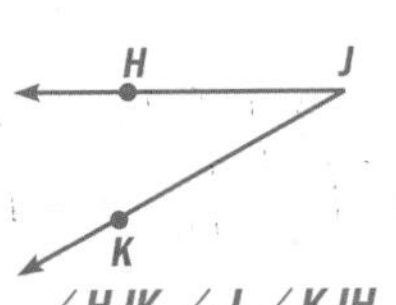

∠HJK, ∠J, ∠KJH

6.

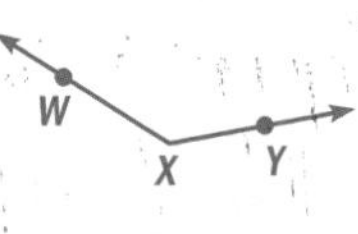

∠WXY, ∠X, ∠YXW

7.

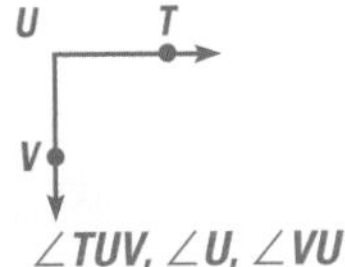

∠TUV, ∠U, ∠VUT

8.

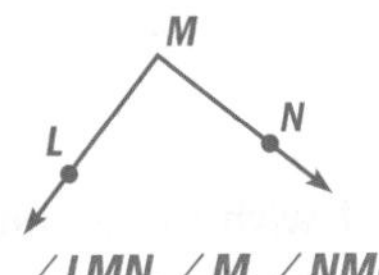

∠LMN, ∠M, ∠NML

9.

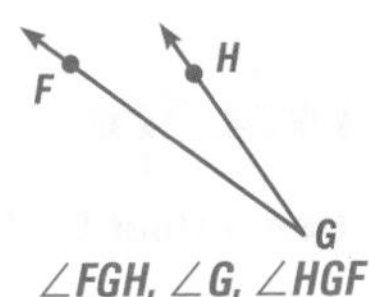

∠FGH, ∠G, ∠HGF

10. Draw a triangle with vertices *P*, *Q*, and *R*. Name each angle of the triangle in three ways. Check drawing; ∠PQR, ∠Q, ∠RQP; ∠QRP, ∠R, ∠PRQ; ∠RPQ, ∠P, ∠QPR.

Using a Ruler

An **inch ruler** has markings for inches, halves of an inch, fourths of an inch, eighths of an inch, and sixteenths of an inch. As the lengths get shorter, so do the markings.

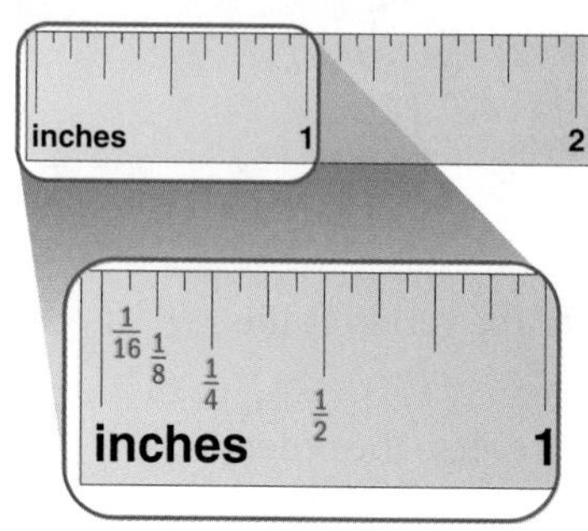

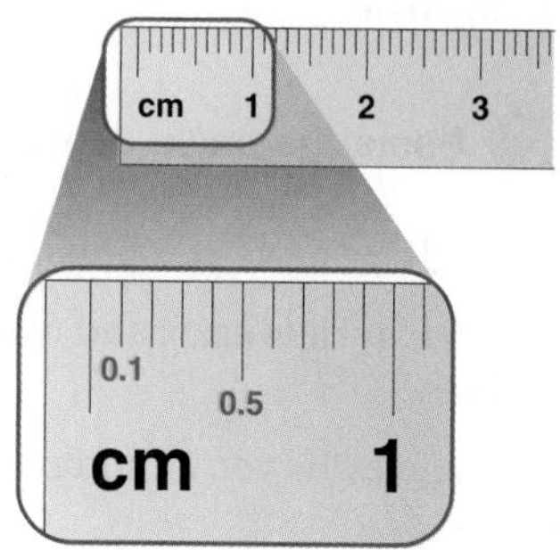

A **centimeter ruler** has markings for centimeters, halves of a centimeter, and tenths of a centimeter (also called *millimeters*). Like an inch ruler, as the lengths get shorter, so do the markings.

EXAMPLE **Use a ruler to draw a segment with the given length.**

a. $2\frac{1}{8}$ inches **b.** 3.8 centimeters

Solution

a. Start at the leftmost mark on the ruler.

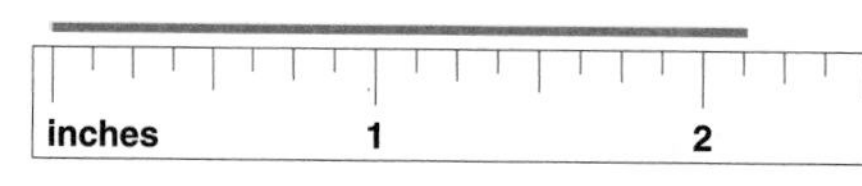

Draw a segment so that the other end is at the first $\frac{1}{8}$ in. mark after 2.

b. Start at the leftmost mark on the ruler.

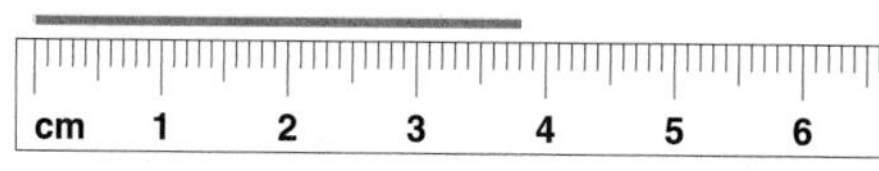

Draw a segment so that the other end is at the 3.8 cm mark.

Practice

Use a ruler to draw a segment with the given length. 1–8. Check drawings.

1. $\frac{7}{16}$ inch **2.** $4\frac{5}{8}$ inches **3.** 4.3 centimeters **4.** 2.7 centimeters

5. $2\frac{5}{16}$ inches **6.** 6.5 centimeters **7.** 2.9 centimeters **8.** $1\frac{1}{4}$ inches

Using a Protractor

A **protractor** is a tool you can use to draw and measure angles. A unit of measure for angles the **degree** (°). To measure an angle, place the center of the protractor on the vertex of the angle and line up one ray with the 0° line. Then read the measure where the other ray crosses the protractor.

The measure of $\angle XYZ$ is 135°. You can write this as $m\angle XYZ = 135°$.

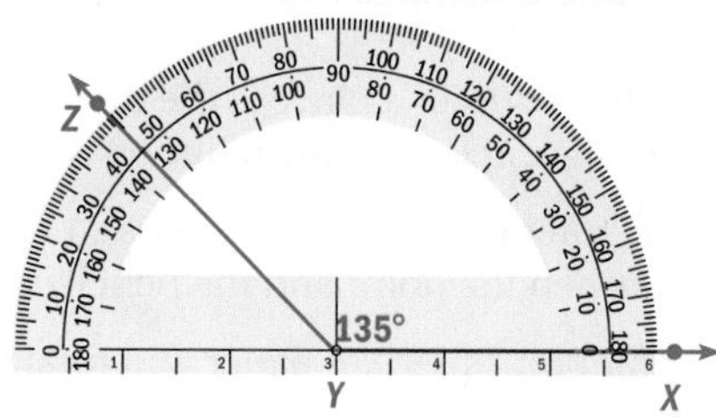

EXAMPLE **Use a protractor to draw an angle that has a measure of 48°.**

1. Draw and label a ray.

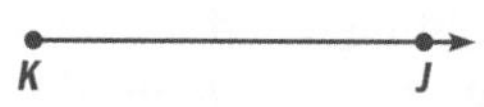

2. Place the center of the protractor at the endpoint of the ray. Line up the ray with the 0° line. Then draw and label a point at the 48° mark on the inner scale.

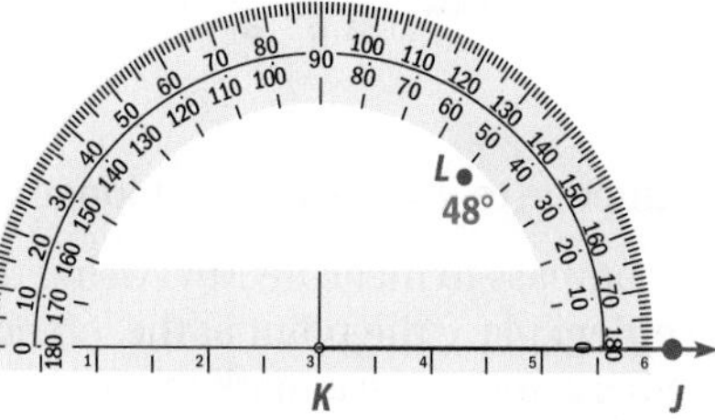

3. Remove the protractor and draw $\overrightarrow{KL}$ to complete the angle.

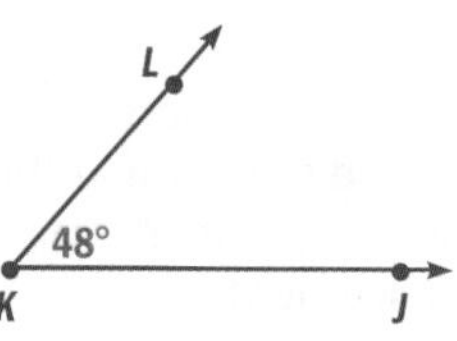

Practice

Use a protractor to measure the angle.

1. 110°

2.

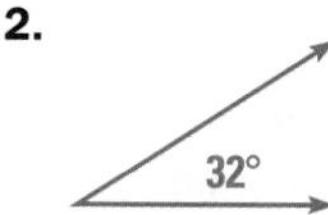

3.

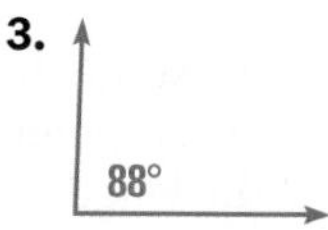

4. Use a protractor to draw angles measuring 46°, 125°, and 73°. **See margin.**

4.

2. Check students' answers. The line should be $3\frac{3}{4}$ in. (or 3.75 in.) long.

3. ________

Skills Review

Using a Compass

A **compass** is an instrument used to draw circles. A **straightedge** is any object that can be used to draw a segment.

EXAMPLE **Use a compass to draw a circle with radius 3 cm.**

Recall that the *radius* of a circle is the distance between the center of the circle and any point on the circle.

Use a metric ruler to open the compass so that the distance between the point and the pencil is 3 cm.

Place the point on a piece of paper and rotate the pencil around the point to draw the circle.

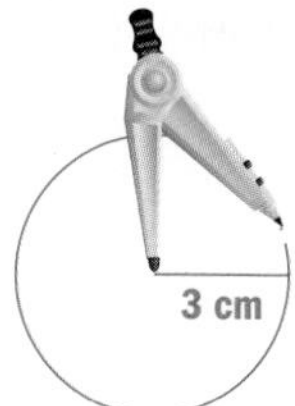

EXAMPLE **Use a straightedge and a compass to draw a segment whose length is the sum of $\overline{MN}$ and $\overline{PQ}$.**

M ________ N P ________ Q

Solution

Use a straightedge to draw a segment longer than both given segments.

Open your compass to measure $\overline{MN}$. Using this compass setting, place the point at the left end of your segment and make a mark that crosses your segment.

Then open your compass to measure $\overline{PQ}$. Using this compass setting, place the point at the first mark you made on your segment and make another mark that crosses your segment.

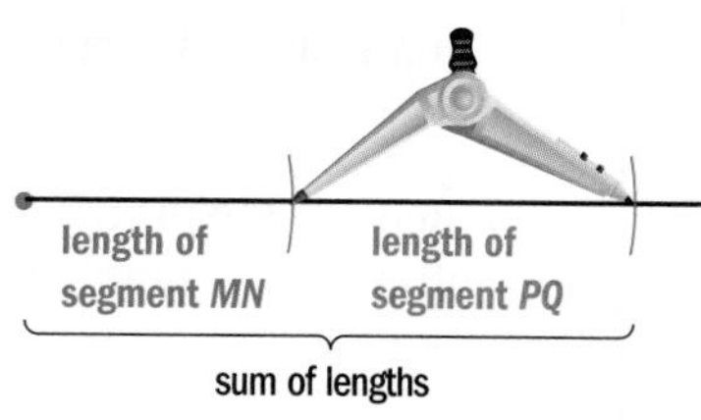

Practice

1. Use a compass to draw a circle with radius 4 cm. **A good answer will show a circle with radius 4 centimeters.**
2. Use a straightedge and a compass to draw a segment whose length is the *sum* of the lengths of the two given segments. **See margin.**

A ________________ B

C ____________ D

3. Use a straightedge and a compass to draw a segment whose length is the *difference* of the lengths of the two given segments in Exercise 2. **See margin.**

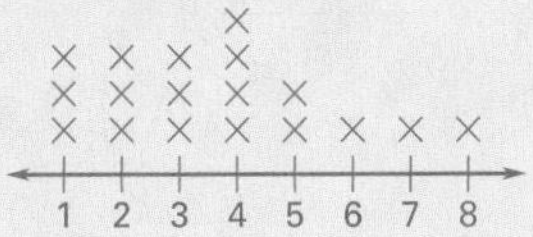

Reading and Making Line Plots

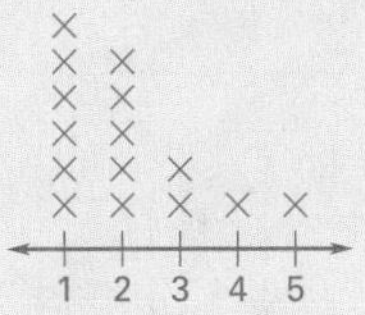

A **line plot** uses a number line to show how often data values occur.

EXAMPLE **You surveyed 20 of your friends and asked them how many pets they have. Their responses were: 6, 2, 3, 1, 5, 0, 2, 4, 1, 1, 6, 2, 0, 3, 1, 4, 3, 2, 1, 1.**

a. Make a line plot of the data. **b.** What was the most frequent response?

Solution

a.

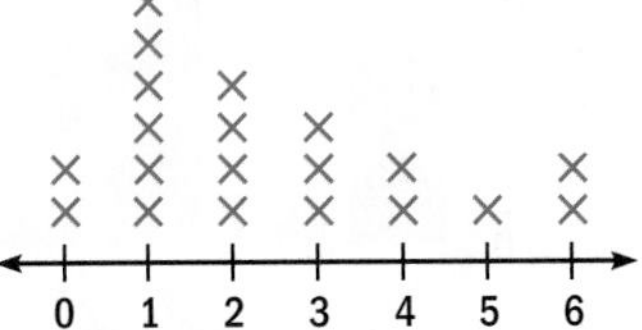

b. The greatest number of $\times$s is above 1, so 1 was the most frequent response.

Practice

Make a line plot of the data. 1–2. See margin.

1. In a survey, 15 people were asked how many TVs they own. Their responses were: 1, 2, 1, 4, 3, 2, 1, 5, 1, 2, 3, 1, 2, 1, 2.
2. In a survey, 18 people were asked how many times they eat out each week. Their responses were: 2, 4, 1, 3, 5, 6, 3, 7, 2, 1, 4, 8, 5, 4, 3, 4, 1, 2.

Use the line plot below. It shows the results of a questionnaire asking people how many hours they exercise each week.

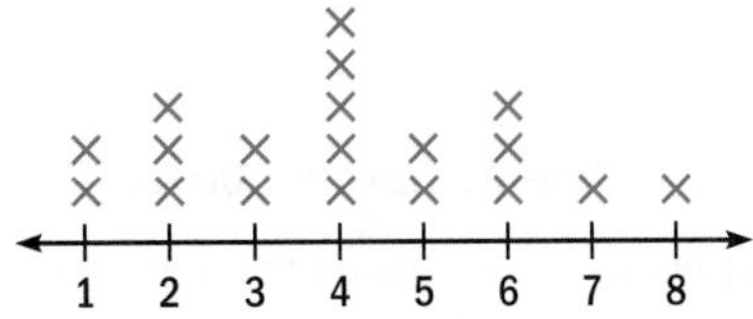

3. How many people completed the questionnaire? 19 people
4. How many more people exercise 4 hours each week than exercise 6 hours each week? 2 more people
5. How many people exercise less than 3 hours each week? 5 people

4.

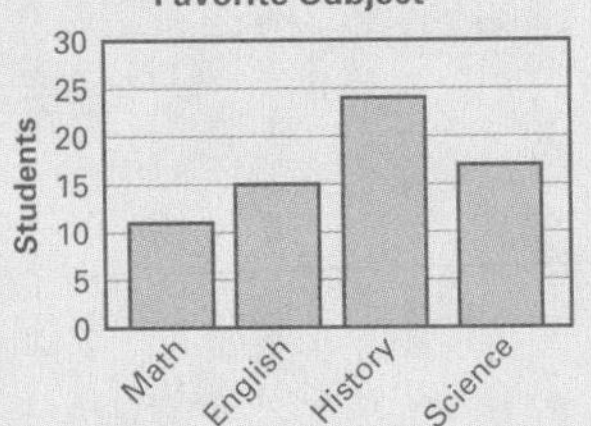

Skills Review

Reading and Making Bar Graphs

Data are numbers or facts. A **bar graph** is one way to display data. A bar graph uses bars to show how quantities in categories compare.

EXAMPLE **The bar graph shows the results of a survey on favorite flavors of ice cream. Which flavor was chosen the most? Which flavor was chosen the least?**

The longest bar on the graph represents the 11 people who chose chocolate. So, chocolate was chosen the most.

The shortest bar represents the 2 students who chose strawberry. So, strawberry was chosen the least.

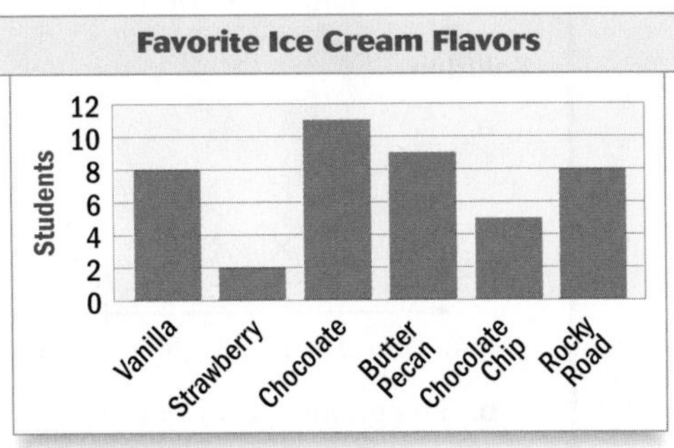

To make a bar graph, choose a title and a scale. Draw and label the axes. Then draw bars to represent the data given.

EXAMPLE **Draw a bar graph for the data given.**

Subject	Number of Students
Math	8
English	15
History	20
Science	16

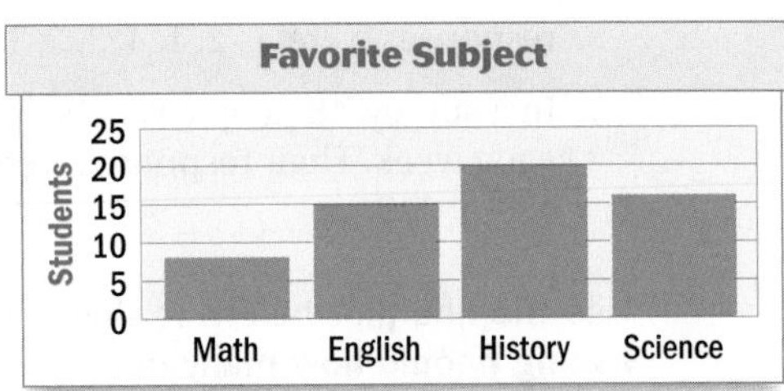

Practice

In Exercises 1–3, use the bar graph of ice cream flavors above.

1. How many students chose butter pecan as a favorite ice cream flavor? **9 students**
2. How many students chose vanilla as a favorite ice cream flavor? **8 students**
3. Which two flavors were chosen by the same number of students? **Vanilla and Rocky Road**
4. Suppose 8 more students took the survey shown in the second example. Draw a new bar graph if 3 of the students chose math, 4 chose history, and 1 chose science. **See margin.**

Reading and Making Line Graphs

Another way to display data is to use a *line graph*. A **line graph** uses line segments to show how a quantity changes over time.

EXAMPLE **The line graph shows plant growth data collected by students every day for 7 days. The greatest increase in growth occurred between what two days? What was the amount of the increase?**

The steepest segment in the line graph is from Monday to Tuesday. The students recorded a height of 1 inch on Monday and a height of 3.5 inches on Tuesday, for an increase of 2.5 inches.

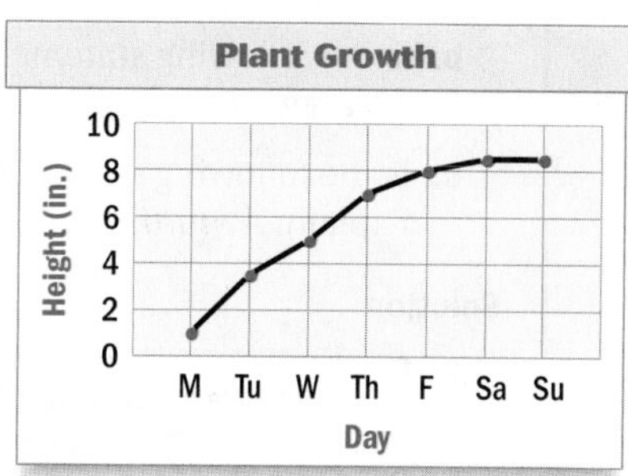

To make a line graph, choose a title and scales. Draw and label the axes. Then plot and connect points to represent the data given.

EXAMPLE **Draw a line graph for the data given.**

Month	Weight of Puppy (pounds)
1	3
2	5.5
3	7
4	11

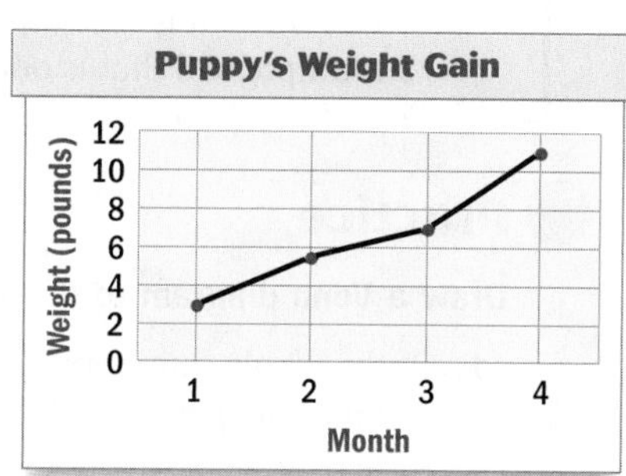

Practice

In Exercises 1 and 2, use the plant growth line graph above.

1. Between which two days was the growth 1 inch? Thursday and Friday
2. Between which two days did the height remain the same? Saturday and Sunday
3. Suppose in month 5 the puppy in the second example weighed 15 pounds. Copy the graph and add this data to it. See margin.

3. Puppy's Weight Gain

Weight (lb)

16 14 12 10 8 6 4 2 0

1 2 3 4 5

Month

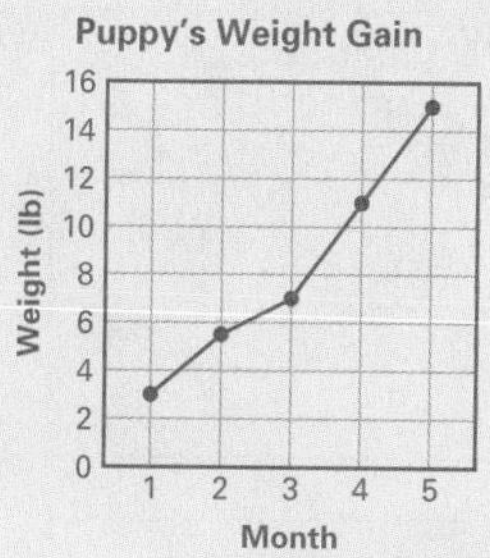

1.

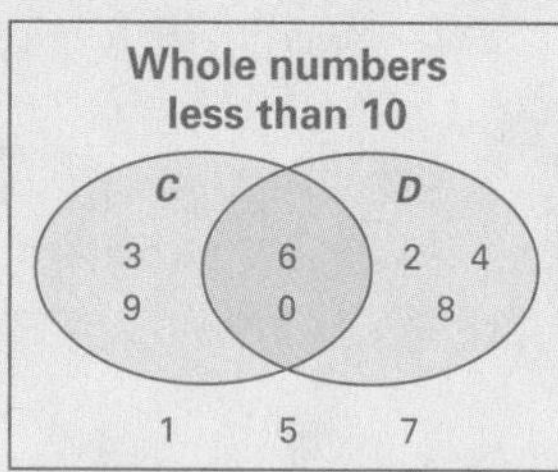

2.

Whole numbers less than 10

C

D

3
9

6
0

2 4
8

1 5 7

Venn Diagrams and Logical Reasoning

A **Venn diagram** uses shapes to show how sets are related.

EXAMPLE **Draw and use a Venn diagram.**

a. Draw a Venn diagram of the whole numbers from 6 through 19 where set *A* consists of even numbers and set *B* consists of multiples of 5.

b. Is the following statement *true* or *false*? Explain.
No even whole number from 6 through 19 is a multiple of 5.

c. Is the following statement *always, sometimes,* or *never* true? Explain. *A multiple of 5 from 6 through 19 is even.*

Solution

a.

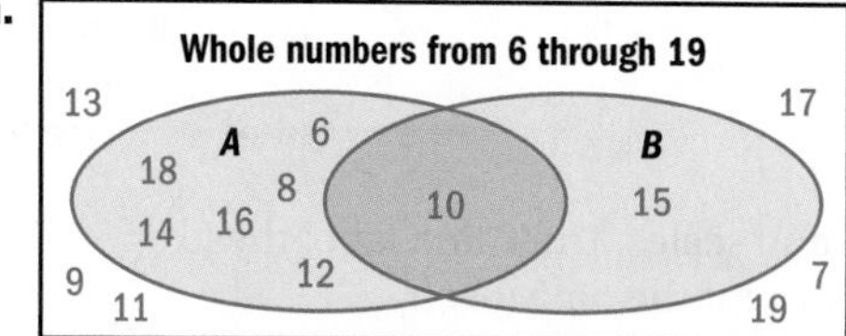

b. False. 10 is an even whole number that is a multiple of 5.

c. Sometimes. It is true that 10 is a multiple of 5 that is even, but 15 is a multiple of 5 that is odd.

Practice

Draw a Venn diagram of the sets described. 1–2. See margin.

1. Of the whole numbers less than 12, set *A* consists of numbers that are greater than 8 and set *B* consists of odd numbers.

2. Of the whole numbers less than 10, set *C* consists of multiples of 3 and set *D* consists of even numbers.

Use the Venn diagrams you drew in Exercises 1 and 2 to answer the question. Explain your reasoning.

3. Is the following statement *true* or *false*?
There is only one odd number greater than 8 and less than 12.
false; both 9 and 11 are odd numbers greater than 8 and less than 12.

4. Is the following statement *always, sometimes,* or *never* true?
A whole number less than 10 is both a multiple of 3 and even.
sometimes; the statement is true for 6 but false for 0-5 and 7-9.

1\. Student Heights

Heights (in.)	54–55.9	56–57.9	58–59.9	60–61.9	62–63.9	64–65.9	66–67.9	68–69.9
Students	1	2	4	5	7	6	3	2

Extra Practice

Chapter 1

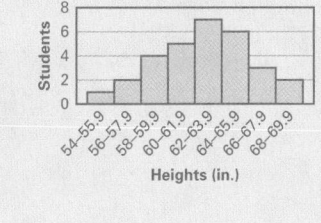

1.1 The frequency table shows the heights of 30 students.

Height (inches)	54-55.9	56-57.9	58-59.9	60-61.9	62-63.9	64-65.9	66-67.9	68-69.9
Frequency	1	2	4	5	7	6	3	2

1. Make a histogram of the data shown in the frequency table. See margin.

2. Which height interval has the greatest number of students? 62–63.9 in.

3. Can you use the histogram to determine the number of students who are between 60 and 69.9 inches tall? Explain.
Yes; you can add the frequencies for the intervals 60–61.9, 62–63.9, 64–65.9, 66–67.9, and 68–69.9.

1.2 Evaluate the expression.

4. $15 - 3 \cdot 2 + 4$ 13

5. $42 \div [(5 - 2) \cdot (1 + 1)]$ 7

6. $2 + \frac{100 - 36}{7 + 9}$ 6

7. $4 \cdot 7 - 8 \cdot 3$ 4

8. $3 + 10 \cdot 5 \div 2$ 28

9. $(11 - 56 \div 8) \cdot 9$ 36

1.3 Evaluate the expression when $r = 1.5$ and $s = 2.4$.

10. $10r + s$ 17.4

11. $\frac{7s}{r + 0.5}$ 8.4

12. $8rs$ 28.8

13. $3(r + s)$ 11.7

1.4 Evaluate the expression.

14. $24 - (2^3 + 1) \cdot 2$ 6

15. $6^3 \div (2 + 1)^2 + 3$ 27

16. $(8 - 5)^4 + 7 \cdot 5^2$ 256

1.5 In Exercises 17–24, solve the equation using mental math.

17. $5n = 35$ 7

18. $\frac{60}{t} = 4$ 15

19. $12 + w = 75$ 63

20. $41 - a = 23$ 18

21. $9 + b = 17$ 8

22. $63 - c = 10$ 53

23. $6x = 54$ 9

24. $\frac{m}{12} = 9$ 108

1.6 **25.** Find the perimeter and area of a rectangular garden with a length of 13 feet and a width of 8 feet. 42 ft; 104 ft^2

1.6 **26.** Ramon jogs at a rate of 5 miles per hour. How far does he jog in 1.5 hours? 7.5 mi

1.6 **27.** Find the side length of a square that has a perimeter of 32 centimeters. 8 cm

1.7 **28.** You do 5 hours of yard work each day for 4 days and earn \$6 per hour. Then you buy 2 concert tickets for \$12 each. Use the problem solving plan to find how much money you have left. \$96

Extra Practice

34–36. See Additional Answers beginning on page AA1.

44–47.

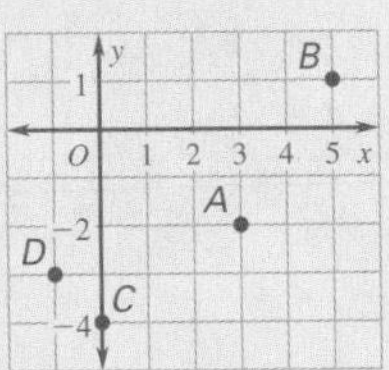

Extra Practice

Chapter 2

2.1 Use a number line to order the integers from least to greatest.

1. 33, −24, −43, 7, 19, −2 −43, −24, −2, 7, 19, 33

2. −230, 157, −68, −146, 5, 94 −230, −146, −68, 5, 94, 157

2.1 Write the opposite and the absolute value of the integer.

3. −25 25; 25 **4.** 467 −467; 467 **5.** 0 0; 0 **6.** $|-2|$ −2; 2

2.2 Find the sum.

7. 342 + (−751) −409 **8.** −147 + 71 −76 **9.** −89 + 268 179

10. −29 + (−51) + 36 −44 **11.** −78 + 65 + 13 0 **12.** 93 + (−57) + (−102) −66

2.3 Find the difference.

13. −12 − 4 −16 **14.** 10 − 13 −3 **15.** 34 − (−17) 51 **16.** −18 − (−17) −1

17. 23 − 38 −15 **18.** 81 − (−16) 97 **19.** −9 − (−77) 68 **20.** −63 − 19 −82

2.4 Find the product.

21. (−7)(−50) 350 **22.** 25(−7) −175 **23.** −4(16) −64 **24.** (−12)(−21) 252

25. −95(0)(−58) 0 **26.** 54(−1)(5) −270 **27.** 8(−2)(−3)(5) 240 **28.** (−14)(4)(6)(9) −3024

2.5 In Exercises 29–32, find the quotient.

29. $\frac{96}{-8}$ −12 **30.** $\frac{-48}{-12}$ 4 **31.** $\frac{0}{4}$ 0 **32.** $\frac{-80}{5}$ −16

2.5 **33.** Find the mean of the data: −8, 6, 3, −20, −9, 4. −4

2.6 Evaluate the expression. Justify each step. 34–36. See margin.

34. $-28 + (74 - 32)$ **35.** $7\left(2 \cdot \frac{3}{7}\right)$ **36.** $(-7.2 + 3.5) + (-3.5)$

2.7 Use the distributive property to evaluate or simplify the expression.

37. −5(−3 + 8) (−5)(−3) + (−5)(8); −25 **38.** $3(m - 4)$ $3m - 12$ **39.** $-1(4 + 9r)$ $-4 - 9r$ **40.** $8(-4j - 3)$ $-32j - 24$

2.7 Simplify the expression by combining like terms.

41. $-x + 3y - 5y + 6x$ $5x - 2y$ **42.** $2(3k - 6) + 4 + 5k$ $11k - 8$ **43.** $5a - 3(2a + b) - 7b$ $-a - 10b$

2.8 Plot the point in a coordinate plane and describe its location. 44–47. See margin for art.

44. $A(3, -2)$ Quadrant IV **45.** $B(5, 1)$ Quadrant I **46.** $C(0, -4)$ on the y-axis **47.** $D(-1, -3)$ Quadrant III

Chapter 3

3.1 **Solve the equation. Check your solution.**

1. $n - 3 = 5$ 8 **2.** $36 = p + 20$ 16 **3.** $-4 = h - 9$ 5 **4.** $27 + z = 51$ 24

3.2 **Solve the equation. Check your solution.**

5. $32 = \frac{x}{2}$ 64 **6.** $11k = -55$ −5 **7.** $76 = 19r$ 4 **8.** $\frac{y}{-1.4} = -5$ 7

3.3 **Solve the equation. Check your solution.**

9. $5a - 2 = 33$ 7 **10.** $\frac{d}{3} + 8 = -6$ −42 **11.** $-1 = 14 - 2h$ 7.5 **12.** $84 - z = 96$ −12

13. $\frac{c}{4} + 7 = 12$ 20 **14.** $47 = -6y + 5$ −7 **15.** $73 = 15 - b$ −58 **16.** $55 = 7t - 8$ 9

3.4 **In Exercises 17 and 18, translate the statement into an equation. Then solve the equation.**

17. Five less than the product of 6 and a number is 13. $6n - 5 = 13$; 3

18. The sum of 5 and the quotient of a number and 3 is -1. $5 + \frac{n}{3} = -1$; −18

3.4 **19.** An auto repair shop charges \$48 per hour for labor plus the cost of parts. Your car needs new parts that cost \$129, and the total cost is \$201. How much time is required to repair the car? 1.5 h

3.5 **Find the area and perimeter of the triangle.**

20.

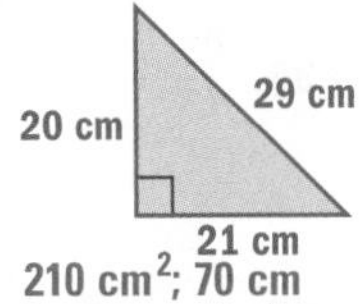

210 cm^2; 70 cm

21.

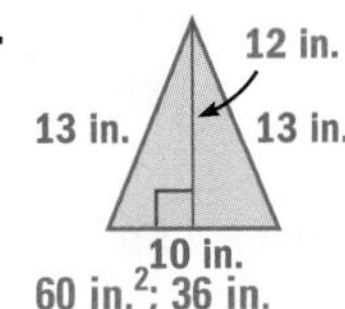

60 in.^{2}; 36 in.

22.

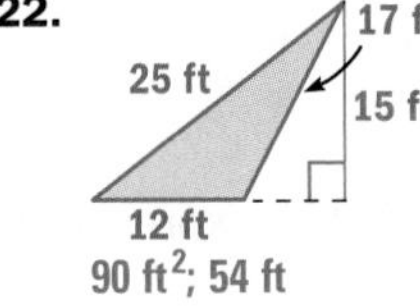

90 ft^2; 54 ft

3.5 **23.** A rectangle has an area of 60 square meters and a length of 12 meters. What is the width of the rectangle? What is the perimeter? 5 m; 34 m

3.5 **24.** A square has an area of 81 square feet. What is the length of each side? 9 ft

3.6 **Solve the inequality. Then graph its solution.** 25–28. See margin for art.

25. $4 + j \geq -1$ $j \geq -5$ **26.** $0 < m - 6$ $m > 6$ **27.** $z + 4.5 \leq 2$ $z \leq -2.5$ **28.** $-38 > t - 46$ $t < 8$

3.7 **Solve the inequality. Then graph its solution.** 29–32. See margin for art.

29. $5x < -25$ $x < -5$ **30.** $3 \leq -\frac{1}{3}y$ $y \leq -9$ **31.** $2 \geq \frac{s}{4}$ $s \leq 8$ **32.** $-13k > -65$ $k < 5$

25. −6 −4 −2 0 2 4

26. −2 0 2 4 6 8 10

27. −4 −3 −2 −1 0 1 2

28. −2 0 2 4 6 8 10

29. −8 −6 −4 −2 0 2 4

30. −12 −10 −8 −6 −4 −2 0

31. −2 0 2 4 6 8 10

32. 0 1 2 3 4 5 6

Extra Practice

Extra Practice

Chapter 4

4.1 Write the prime factorization of the number.

1. 72 $2^3 \cdot 3^2$ **2.** 65 $5 \cdot 13$ **3.** 153 $3^2 \cdot 17$ **4.** 196 $2^2 \cdot 7^2$

4.1 Factor the monomial.

5. $25pq$ $5^2 \cdot p \cdot q$ **6.** $7a^3$ $7 \cdot a \cdot a \cdot a$ **7.** $22xy^2$ $2 \cdot 11 \cdot x \cdot y \cdot y$ **8.** $54s^2t$ $2 \cdot 3^3 \cdot s \cdot s \cdot t$

4.2 Find the greatest common factor of the numbers or monomials.

9. 45, 75 15 **10.** 108, 162 54 **11.** $6bc, 35abc^2$ bc **12.** $4p^2, 18qr$ 2

13. $21mn, 9km^2$ $3m$ **14.** $14x^2y^3, 28xy^2$ $14xy^2$ **15.** $34w^2z^2, 51w^5z^4$ $17w^2z^2$ **16.** $abcdf, a^2d^3gh$ ad

4.3 Write the fraction in simplest form.

17. $\frac{32}{64}$ $\frac{1}{2}$ **18.** $\frac{-15}{39}$ $-\frac{5}{13}$ **19.** $\frac{-22}{77}$ $-\frac{2}{7}$ **20.** $\frac{17}{51}$ $\frac{1}{3}$

21. $\frac{10x}{45xy}$ $\frac{2}{9y}$ **22.** $\frac{-16mn}{40mn}$ $-\frac{2}{5}$ **23.** $\frac{-6ab}{4bc}$ $-\frac{3a}{2c}$ **24.** $\frac{28rs}{7rst}$ $\frac{4}{t}$

4.4 Find the least common multiple of the numbers or monomials.

25. 30, 60 60 **26.** $4x, 18xy^2$ $36xy^2$ **27.** $5ab^2, 3bc^2$ $15ab^2c^2$ **28.** $12x^3y, 8x^2y^4$ $24x^3y^4$

4.5 Copy and complete the statement with <, >, or =.

29. $\frac{7}{8} \underline{?} \frac{9}{11}$ $>$ **30.** $3\frac{3}{5} \underline{?} \frac{11}{3}$ $<$ **31.** $\frac{17}{6} \underline{?} 2\frac{13}{18}$ $>$ **32.** $1\frac{10}{15} \underline{?} \frac{35}{21}$ $=$

33. $\frac{11}{10} \underline{?} 1\frac{1}{8}$ $<$ **34.** $\frac{4}{5} \underline{?} \frac{6}{11}$ $>$ **35.** $\frac{50}{9} \underline{?} 5\frac{2}{7}$ $>$ **36.** $\frac{63}{15} \underline{?} 4\frac{5}{12}$ $<$

4.6 Simplify the expression. Write your answer as a power.

37. $z^5 \cdot z$ z^6 **38.** $5^8 \cdot 5^4$ 5^{12} **39.** $(-7)^6 \cdot (-7)^3$ $(-7)^9$ **40.** $a^2 \cdot a^4$ a^6

41. $\frac{6^9}{6^5}$ 6^4 **42.** $\frac{(-8)^{12}}{(-8)^2}$ $(-8)^{10}$ **43.** $\frac{(-v)^7}{(-v)^4}$ $(-v)^3$ **44.** $\frac{c^9}{c}$ c^8

4.7 Simplify. Write the expression using only positive exponents.

45. $6k^{-1}$ $\frac{6}{k}$ **46.** $a^3 \cdot a^{-3}$ 1 **47.** $\frac{s^{-3}}{s^4}$ $\frac{1}{s^7}$ **48.** $n^{-4} \cdot n^{-2}$ $\frac{1}{n^6}$

4.8 Write the number in scientific notation.

49. 124,000,000 1.24×10^8 **50.** 0.0000005 5×10^{-7} **51.** 0.0000791 7.91×10^{-5} **52.** 32,100 3.21×10^4

4.8 Write the number in standard form.

53. 2.7×10^{-3} 0.0027 **54.** 9.09×10^2 909 **55.** 5.88×10^{11} 588,000,000,000 **56.** 6.2×10^{-8} 0.000000062

Chapter 5

Find the sum or difference.

5.1 **1.** $\frac{7}{8}+\frac{5}{8}$ $1\frac{1}{2}$ **2.** $5\frac{1}{5}-3\frac{4}{5}$ $1\frac{2}{5}$ **3.** $-\frac{11m}{15}+\frac{m}{15}$ $-\frac{2m}{3}$ **4.** $-\frac{5a}{9b}-\frac{4a}{9b}$ $-\frac{a}{b}$

5.2 **5.** $\frac{9}{10}-\frac{5}{6}$ $\frac{1}{15}$ **6.** $\frac{2}{5}-\frac{3}{7}$ $-\frac{1}{35}$ **7.** $4\frac{1}{4}+3\frac{7}{8}$ $8\frac{1}{8}$ **8.** $-\frac{5}{12}+\frac{11}{16}$ $\frac{13}{48}$

5.3 **Find the product.**

9. $\frac{7}{8}\cdot\frac{3}{14}$ $\frac{3}{16}$ **10.** $5\cdot\left(-3\frac{1}{4}\right)$ $-16\frac{1}{4}$ **11.** $-\frac{5}{18}\cdot 1\frac{1}{3}$ $-\frac{10}{27}$ **12.** $-1\frac{3}{5}\cdot\left(-2\frac{1}{4}\right)$ $3\frac{3}{5}$

5.4 **Find the quotient.**

13. $\frac{5}{9}\div 2$ $\frac{5}{18}$ **14.** $-\frac{7}{12}\div\frac{2}{3}$ $-\frac{7}{8}$ **15.** $4\frac{1}{8}\div\left(-1\frac{1}{3}\right)$ $-3\frac{3}{32}$ **16.** $-2\frac{1}{2}\div(-10)$ $\frac{1}{4}$

5.5 **Write the fraction or mixed number as a decimal. Write the decimal as a fraction or mixed number.**

17. $-\frac{48}{125}$ -0.384 **18.** $4\frac{11}{12}$ $4.91\overline{6}$ **19.** -0.28 $-\frac{7}{25}$ **20.** $0.\overline{72}$ $\frac{8}{11}$

21. 0.006 $\frac{3}{500}$ **22.** -8.34 $-8\frac{17}{50}$ **23.** $3\frac{7}{8}$ 3.875 **24.** $-\frac{16}{250}$ -0.064

5.5 **Order the numbers from least to greatest.**

25. $-\frac{7}{3}, -2\frac{5}{12}, -2.43, -2.5, -2\frac{2}{5}$
$-2.5, -2.43, -2\frac{5}{12}, -2\frac{2}{5}, -\frac{7}{3}$

26. $\frac{18}{5}, 3\frac{1}{3}, 3.8, 3.55, 3\frac{7}{12}$ $3\frac{1}{3}, 3.55, 3\frac{7}{12}, \frac{18}{5}, 3.8$

27. $\frac{26}{5}, 5.3, 5\frac{2}{9}, 5.21, 5\frac{3}{8}$ $\frac{26}{5}, 5.21, 5\frac{2}{9}, 5.3, 5\frac{3}{8}$

28. $-4.2, -4\frac{1}{6}, -\frac{59}{14}, -4\frac{3}{7}, -4.04$
$-4\frac{3}{7}, -\frac{59}{14}, -4.2, -4\frac{1}{6}, -4.04$

5.6 **Find the sum or difference.**

29. $7.21+(-3.4)$ 3.81 **30.** $-9.8+(-3.7)$ -13.5 **31.** $0.8-(-12.3)$ 13.1 **32.** $8.217-9.68$ -1.463

33. $-10.2+(-6.35)$ -16.55 **34.** $-8.78+3.9$ -4.88 **35.** $3.28-11.395$ -8.115 **36.** $-0.04-5.789$ -5.829

5.7 **Find the product or quotient.**

37. $-8.32\cdot(-0.47)$ 3.9104 **38.** $-20.51\cdot 3.14$ -64.4014 **39.** $0.435\div 0.29$ 1.5 **40.** $2.072\div(-0.74)$ -2.8

41. $4.7\cdot(-6.78)$ -31.866 **42.** $-0.14\cdot(-9.43)$ 1.3202 **43.** $-19.27\div 2.35$ -8.2 **44.** $0.224\div 5.6$ 0.04

5.8 **Find the mean, median, mode(s), and range of the data.**

45. Finishing times for a race in minutes: 24, 37, 57, 81, 31, 25, 43, 39, 33, 40, 34, 65, 50
43; 39; no mode; 57

46. Daily low temperatures: −6°F, −7°F, −6°F, 5°F, 3°F, 0°F, −3°F
−2; −3; −6; 12

47. Grades on quizzes: 93, 84, 100, 95, 89, 78, 78, 85, 83, 95
88; 87; 78 and 95; 22

Extra Practice

20. Use $\frac{22}{7}$ for π since 14 is divisible by 7.

21. Use $\frac{22}{7}$ for π since 44 is divisible by 22.

22. Use 3.14 for π since 15.7 is divisible by 3.14.

23. −4 −3 −2 −1 0 1 2 3 4 5

24. −16 −12 −8 −4 0

25. −3 −2 −1 0 1 2 3 4 5 6

26. −4 −3 −2 −1 0 1 2 3 4 5

27. −4 0 4 8 12 16

28. −5 −4 −3 −2 −1 0 1 2 3 4

Chapter 6

Solve the equation. Then check the solution.

6.1

1. $6k - 8 - 4k = 6$ 7
2. $16 = 2(s + 9) - 4$ 1
3. $5(n + 7) + 1 = -9$ −9
4. $-8 = -3m + 2 + 5m$ −5
5. $\frac{7a - 2}{3} = 4$ 2
6. $2 = \frac{3 - 4t}{5}$ $-1\frac{3}{4}$

6.2

7. $3a + 2 = 7a + 10$ −2
8. $9y - 8 = 6y + 7$ 5
9. $5x + 7 = 8(x - 1)$ 5
10. $13v = 7(9 - v)$ 3.15
11. $5(w + 3) = -10w$ −1
12. $2(z + 5) = 3z + 14$ −4

6.3

13. $2.8y + 8.6 = 9.12 - 1.2y$ 0.13
14. $7.25p - 3 + p = 14.325$ 2.1
15. $7 - 2.65z = -4.4z$ −4
16. $x - \frac{2}{3}x = \frac{3}{4}$ $2\frac{1}{4}$
17. $\frac{9}{10}n + \frac{1}{5} = \frac{7}{10}n - \frac{3}{5}$ −4
18. $\frac{6}{4}r - \frac{21}{8} = \frac{3}{4}r$ $3\frac{1}{2}$

6.4 **Find the indicated measurement, where *r* = radius, *d* = diameter, and *C* = circumference. Use 3.14 or $\frac{22}{7}$ for π. Explain your choice of value for π.** 20–22. See margin for explanations.

19. $r = \underline{?}$ 4.5 cm
20. $C = \underline{?}$ 88 ft
21. $r = \underline{?}$ 7 yd
22. $d = \underline{?}$ 5 in.

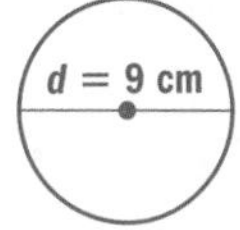

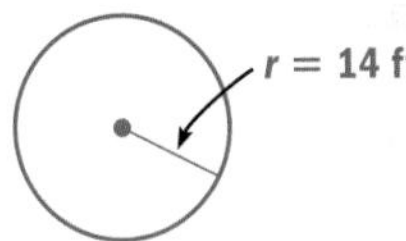

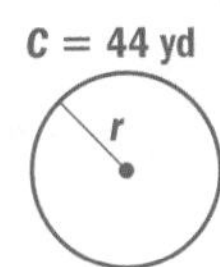

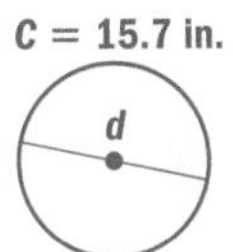

6.5 **Solve the inequality. Then graph the solution.** 23–28. See margin for art.

23. $19 - 8c > 3$ $c < 2$
24. $2(7 + n) \le -10$ $n \le -12$
25. $5s + 3 \ge -7 - 5s$ $s \ge -1$
26. $20 - 11x \ge -2$ $x \le 2$
27. $4(b - 3) > 20$ $b > 8$
28. $-6y - 13 < 11 + 2y$ $y > -3$

6.6 **In Exercises 29–32, write the sentence as an inequality. Let *n* represent the unknown number. Then solve the inequality.**

29. Twelve more than half a number is at most 8. $\frac{1}{2}n + 12 \le 8$; $n \le -8$
30. The difference of 3 times a number and 2 is greater than 7. $3n - 2 > 7$; $n > 3$
31. Four times a number is no less than 16. $4n \ge 16$; $n \ge 4$
32. The quotient of 18 and 6 times a number is less than 3. $\frac{18}{6n} < 3$; $n > 1$

6.6 33. You want to ride your bike for at least 28 miles. You have already biked for 10 miles. If you bike at a speed of 12 miles per hour, how much longer do you need to bike? at least $1\frac{1}{2}$ h

6.6 34. Nathan has $20 to spend at a carnival. The carnival has a $10 entrance fee. Ride tickets cost $.75 each. What number of tickets can Nathan buy? 13 tickets

Extra Practice

Chapter 7

7.1 **A baseball team had 12 wins, 4 losses, and 2 ties in one season. Write the ratio as a fraction in simplest form and two other ways.**

1. wins to losses $\frac{3}{1}$, 3 : 1, 3 to 1
2. losses to games played $\frac{2}{9}$, 2 : 9, 2 to 9
3. wins to games played $\frac{2}{3}$, 2 : 3, 2 to 3

7.1 **Write the equivalent rate.**

4. $\frac{9000 \text{ tickets}}{6 \text{ hours}} = \frac{? \text{ tickets}}{\text{hour}}$ 1500
5. $\frac{240 \text{ tickets}}{\text{hour}} = \frac{? \text{ tickets}}{\text{minute}}$ 4
6. $\frac{7 \text{ meters}}{\text{second}} = \frac{? \text{ meters}}{\text{minute}}$ 420

7.2 **Solve the proportion. Then check your solution.**

7. $\frac{x}{18} = \frac{25}{2}$ 225
8. $\frac{4}{9} = \frac{5}{y}$ 11.25
9. $\frac{3.6}{n} = \frac{4.8}{12.4}$ 9.3
10. $\frac{m}{6} = \frac{35}{42}$ 5

7.3 **Use a percent proportion.**

11. 9 is what percent of 75? 12%
12. 42 is 25% of what number? 168
13. What number is 7% of 128? 8.96
14. 7 is what percent of 56? 12.5%

7.4 **Write the decimal or fraction as a percent.**

15. 0.125 12.5%
16. 1.42 142%
17. $\frac{18}{25}$ 72%
18. $\frac{197}{200}$ 98.5%

7.4 **Write the percent as a decimal and as a fraction.**

19. 31% 0.31; $\frac{31}{100}$
20. 55% 0.55; $\frac{11}{20}$
21. 175% 1.75; $\frac{7}{4}$
22. 1.28% 0.0128; $\frac{8}{625}$

7.5 **In Exercises 23–25, tell whether the change is an *increase* or *decrease*. Then find the percent of change.**

23. Original amount: 25
    New amount: 28
    increase; 12%
24. Original amount: 144
    New amount: 126
    decrease; 12.5%
25. Original amount: 5000
    New amount: 4950
    decrease; 1%

7.6 26. A pair of shoes has a wholesale price of \$28. The percent markup is 110%. What is the retail price? \$58.80

7.6 27. Your food bill at a restaurant is \$18.40. You leave a 15% tip. The sales tax is 5%. Find the total cost of the meal. \$22.08

7.7 **Solve using the percent equation.**

28. What number is 121% of 412? 498.52
29. 13 is 15.6% of what number? $83\frac{1}{3}$
30. 57 is what percent of 76? 75%
31. What number is 0.3% of 28? 0.084

7.8 **A bag contains 12 slips of paper numbered from 1 through 12. A slip of paper is chosen at random. Find the probability of the event.**

32. Drawing a number greater than 4 $\frac{2}{3}$
33. Drawing a number that is divisible by 5 $\frac{1}{6}$

15.
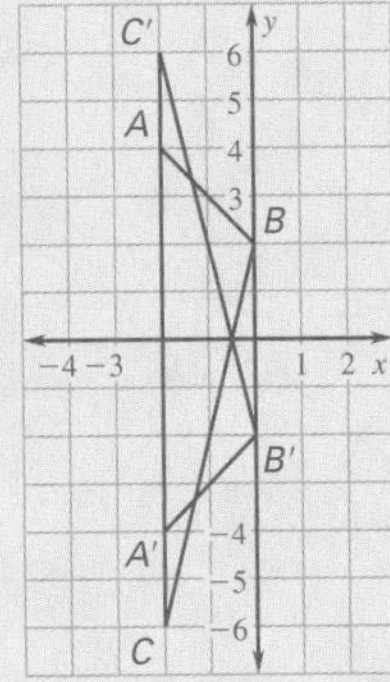

16.
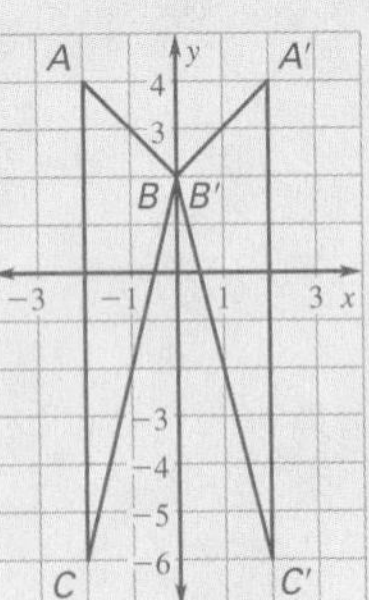

17.
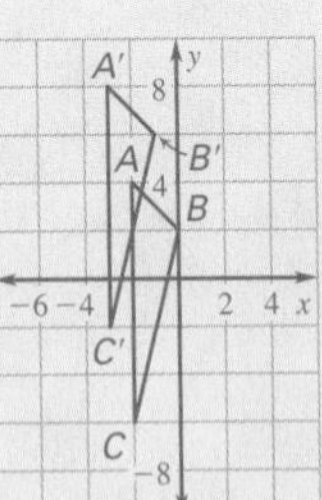

18.
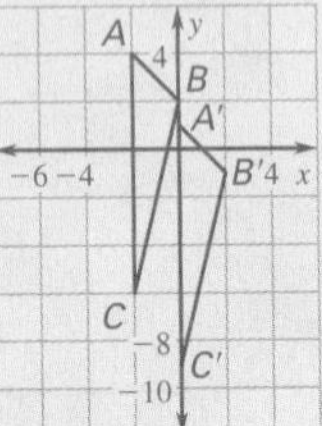

19.
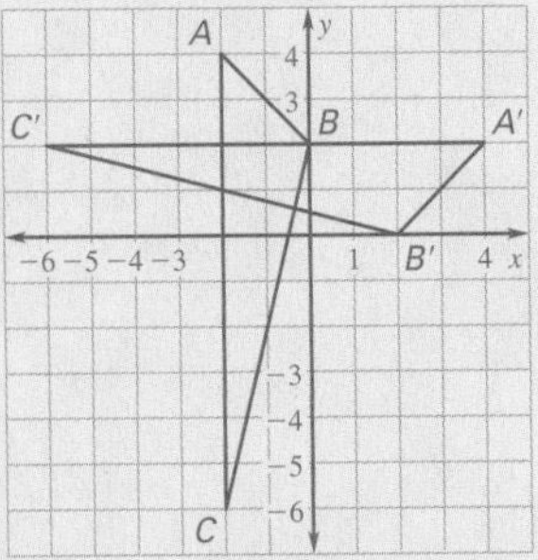

20, 21. See Additional Answers beginning on page AA1.

Chapter 8

8.1 **Find the measure(s) of the numbered angle(s).**

1.
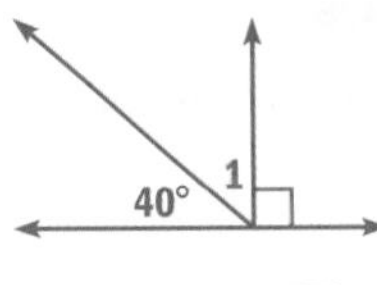

$m\angle 1 = 50°$

2.
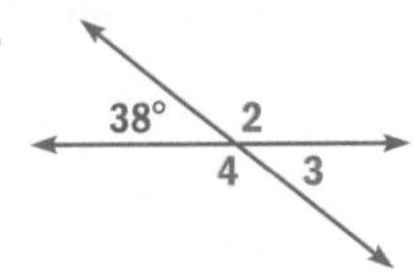

$m\angle 2 = 142°$; $m\angle 3 = 38°$; $m\angle 4 = 142°$

3.
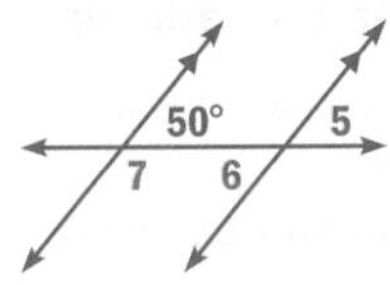

$m\angle 5 = 50°$; $m\angle 6 = 50°$; $m\angle 7 = 130°$

8.2 **Find the value of *x*. Classify the triangle by its angles.**

4.
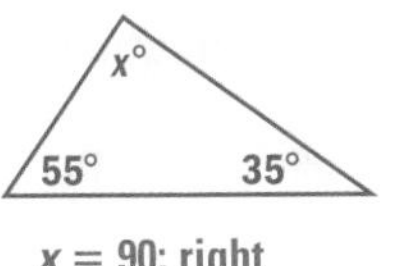

$x = 60$; acute

5.
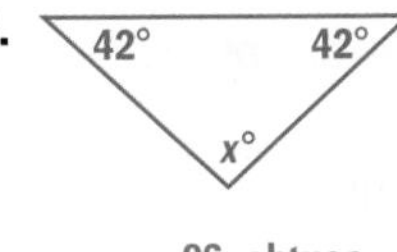

$x = 90$; right

6.
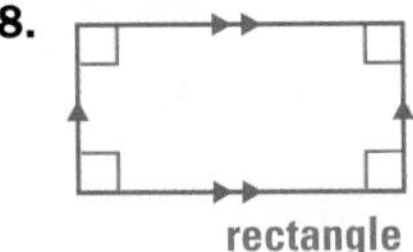

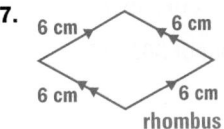

$x = 96$; obtuse

8.3 **In Exercises 7–9, classify the quadrilateral.**

7.
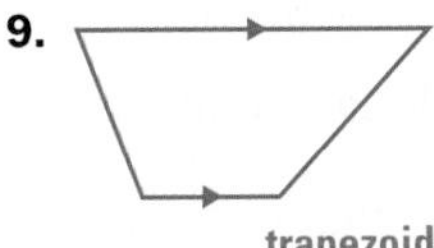

rhombus

8. rectangle

9. trapezoid

8.4 **10.** Find the sum of the angle measures in an 11-gon. 1620°

8.4 **11.** Find the measure of one angle in a regular 18-gon. 160°

8.5 **In Exercises 12–14, use the diagrams.**

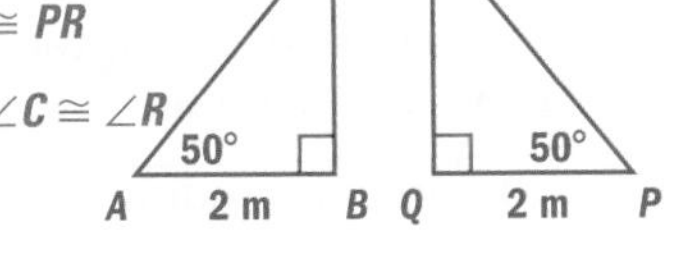

12. Name all pairs of congruent sides. $\overline{AB} \cong \overline{PQ}$; $\overline{BC} \cong \overline{QR}$; $\overline{AC} \cong \overline{PR}$

13. Name all pairs of congruent angles. $\angle A \cong \angle P$; $\angle B \cong \angle Q$; $\angle C \cong \angle R$

14. Explain how you know that $\triangle ABC \cong \triangle PQR$.
$\triangle ABC \cong \triangle PQR$ by Angle-Side-Angle.

Graph $\triangle ABC$ with vertices $A(-2, 4)$, $B(0, 2)$, and $C(-2, -6)$. Then graph its image after the given transformation. 15–21. See margin.

8.6 **15.** Reflect $\triangle ABC$ in the x-axis.

8.6 **16.** Reflect $\triangle ABC$ in the y-axis.

8.7 **17.** Translate $\triangle ABC$ using $(x, y) \to (x - 1, y + 4)$.

8.7 **18.** Translate $\triangle ABC$ using $(x, y) \to (x + 2, y - 3)$.

8.7 **19.** Rotate $\triangle ABC$ 90° clockwise.

8.8 **20.** Dilate $\triangle ABC$ by a scale factor of 2.

8.8 **21.** Dilate $\triangle ABC$ by a scale factor of $\frac{1}{2}$.

Chapter 9

9.1 **Use a calculator to approximate the square root. Round to the nearest tenth.**

1. $\sqrt{52}$ 7.2 **2.** $\sqrt{9.6}$ 3.1 **3.** $-\sqrt{738}$ −27.2 **4.** $-\sqrt{2037}$ −45.1

9.1 **Solve the equation. Check your solutions.**

5. $k^2 = 900$ 30, −30 **6.** $h^2 - 5 = 44$ 7, −7 **7.** $153 + z^2 = 378$ 15, −15 **8.** $168 = v^2 - 1$ 13, −13

9. $a^2 + 7 = 88$ 9, −9 **10.** $m^2 = 3600$ 60, −60 **11.** $x^2 - 11 = 53$ 8, −8 **12.** $w^2 + 78 = 478$ 20, −20

9.2 **In Exercises 13–16, graph the pair of numbers on a number line. Then copy and complete the statement with <, >, or =.**

13. $\sqrt{18}$ _?_ 4 > **14.** $\sqrt{\frac{9}{16}}$ _?_ $\frac{3}{4}$ = **15.** −8 _?_ $-\sqrt{70}$ > **16.** $\frac{2}{3}$ _?_ $\sqrt{\frac{1}{9}}$ >

9.2 **17.** Order the decimals 0.12, $0.\overline{1}$, $0.\overline{12}$, 0.123, and $0.\overline{123}$. $0.\overline{1}$, 0.12, $0.\overline{12}$, 0.123, $0.\overline{123}$

9.2 **18.** Order the decimals 0.34, $0.\overline{3}$, $.\overline{34}$, and 0.334 from least to greatest. $0.\overline{3}$, 0.334, 0.34, $0.\overline{34}$

9.3 **Let *a* and *b* represent the lengths of the legs of a right triangle, and let *c* represent the length of the hypotenuse. Find the unknown length.**

19. $a = 21, b = 28, c =$ _?_ 35 **20.** $a =$ _?_, $b = 63, c = 65$ 16 **21.** $a = 56, b =$ _?_, $c = 65$ 33

22. $a = 1.5, b = 3.6, c =$ _?_ 3.9 **23.** $a =$ _?_, $b = 100, c = 125$ 75 **24.** $a = 32, b =$ _?_, $c = 68$ 60

9.4 **Determine whether the numbers form a Pythagorean triple.**

25. 40, 42, 58 yes **26.** 37, 39, 54 no **27.** 15, 112, 113 yes **28.** 12, 35, 38 no

9.5 **Find the values of the variables. Give exact answers.**

29.

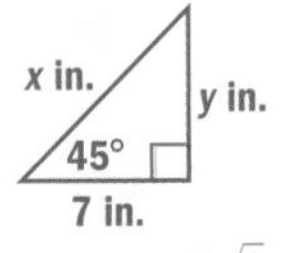

$x = 7\sqrt{2}$; $y = 7$

30. y m, x m, 30°, 18 m

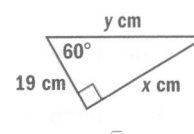

$x = 9$; $y = 9\sqrt{3}$

31. y cm, 60°, 19 cm, x cm

$x = 19\sqrt{3}$; $y = 38$

9.6 **In △*ABC*, write the sine, cosine, and tangent ratios for ∠*A* and ∠*B*.** 32–34. See margin.

32.

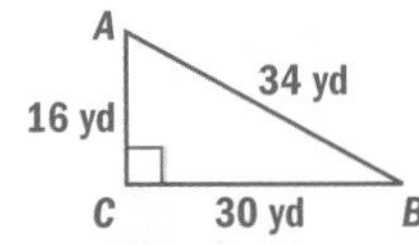

33.

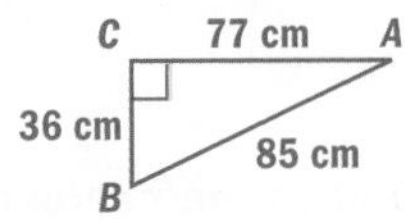

34.

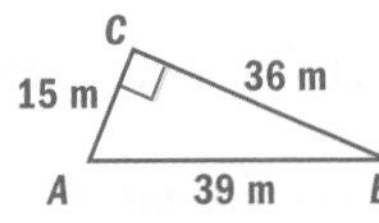

9.6 **35.** Use a calculator to approximate the sine, cosine, and tangent of 62°. Round your answers to four decimal places. sin 62° ≈ 0.8829; cos 62° ≈ 0.4695; tan 62° ≈ 1.8807

32. $\sin A = \frac{15}{17}$; $\cos A = \frac{8}{17}$; $\tan A = \frac{15}{8}$; $\sin B = \frac{8}{17}$; $\cos B = \frac{15}{17}$; $\tan B = \frac{8}{15}$

33. $\sin A = \frac{36}{85}$; $\cos A = \frac{77}{85}$; $\tan A = \frac{36}{77}$; $\sin B = \frac{77}{85}$; $\cos B = \frac{36}{85}$; $\tan B = \frac{77}{36}$

34. $\sin A = \frac{12}{13}$; $\cos A = \frac{5}{13}$; $\tan A = \frac{12}{5}$; $\sin B = \frac{5}{13}$; $\cos B = \frac{12}{13}$; $\tan B = \frac{5}{12}$

Extra Practice

1.

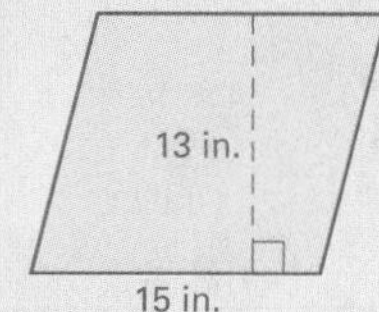

2.

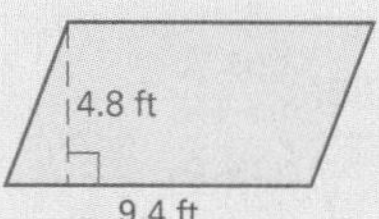

3.

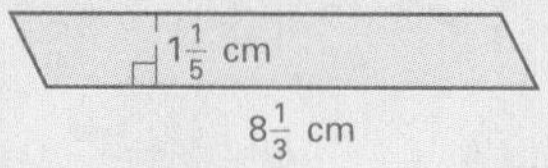

$1\frac{1}{5}$ cm

$8\frac{1}{3}$ cm

4.

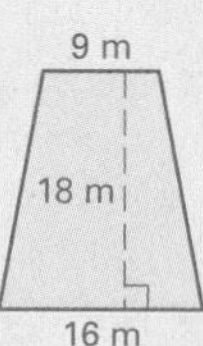

5.

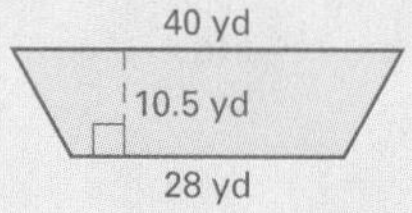

40 yd

10.5 yd

28 yd

15.

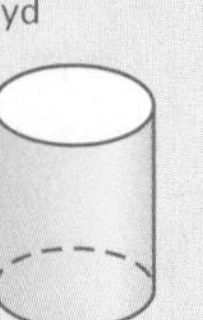

top front side

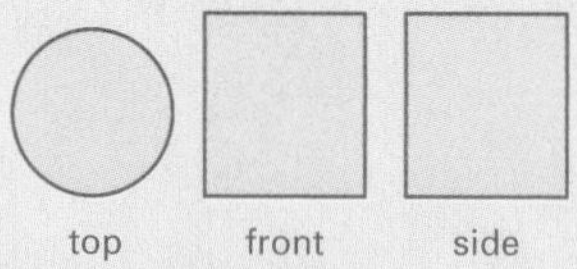

It is not a polyhedron because circles are not polygons.

16.

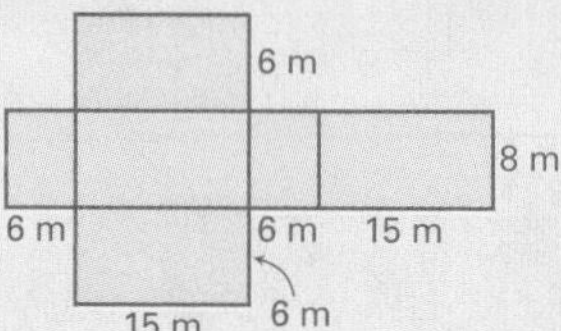

17.

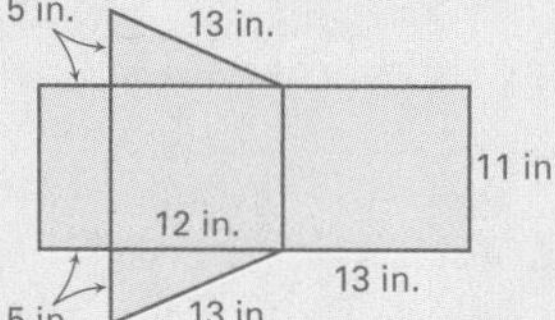

18.

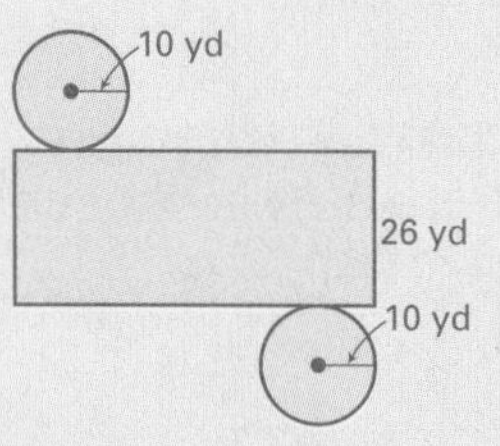

Chapter 10

10.1 Sketch a parallelogram with base *b* and height *h* and find its area. 1–3. See margin for art.

1. $b = 15$ in., $h = 13$ in. 195 in.^{2} **2.** $b = 9.4$ ft, $h = 4.8$ ft 45.12 ft^2 **3.** $b = 8\frac{1}{3}$ cm, $h = 1\frac{1}{5}$ cm 10 cm^2

10.1 Sketch a trapezoid with bases b_1 and b_2 and height *h* and find its area. 4–5. See margin for art.

4. $b_1 = 9$ m, $b_2 = 16$ m, $h = 18$ m 225 m^2 **5.** $b_1 = 40$ yd, $b_2 = 28$ yd, $h = 10.5$ yd 357 yd^2

10.2 In Exercises 6–13, find the area of the circle given its radius *r* or diameter *d*. Use 3.14 for π.

6. $r = 18$ mi 1020 mi^2 **7.** $d = 80$ in. 5020 in.^{2} **8.** $d = 11$ mm 95.0 mm^2 **9.** $r = 2.9$ ft 26.4 ft^2

10. $d = 7.8$ in. 47.8 in.^{2} **11.** $r = 0.3$ cm 0.283 cm^2 **12.** $r = 11$ ft 380 ft^2 **13.** $d = 16$ mi 201 mi^2

10.3 14. How many faces, edges, and vertices does a hexagonal pyramid have? 7 faces; 12 edges; 7 vertices

10.3 15. Show two ways to represent a cylinder. Tell whether it is a polyhedron. See margin.

10.4 Draw a net for the solid. Then find the surface area. Round to the nearest tenth. 16–18. See margin for art.

16.

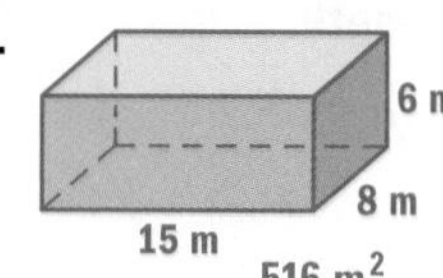

516 m^2

17.

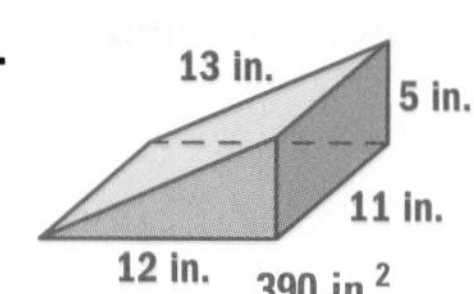

390 in.^{2}

18.

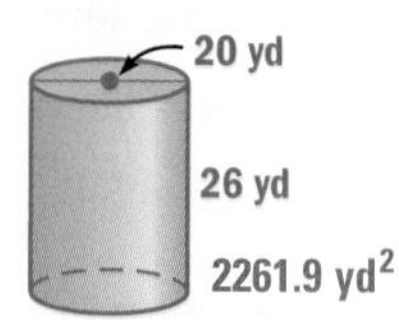

2261.9 yd^2

10.5 Find the surface area of the solid. Round to the nearest tenth.

19. A square pyramid with base side length 12 m and slant height 9 m 360 m^2

20. A cone with radius 8 cm and slant height 9 cm 427.3 cm^2

21. A cone with diameter 15 m and slant height 8.2 m 369.9 m^2

10.6 Find the volume of the solid. Round to the nearest tenth.

22. The prism in Exercise 16 720 m^3

23. The prism in Exercise 17 330 in.^{3}

24. The cylinder in Exercise 18 8168.1 yd^3

10.7 Find the volume of the solid. Round to the nearest tenth.

25. A square pyramid with base side length 10 ft and height 8 ft 266.7 ft^3

26. A cone with radius 18 m and height 6 m 2035.8 m^3

27. The triangular pyramid shown at the right 252 cm^3

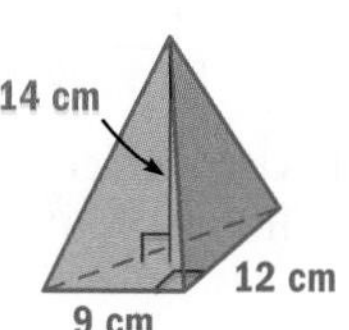

Extra Practice

Chapter 11

11.1 **1.** Decide whether the relation (−3, 3), (−2, 2), (−1, 1), (0, 0), (1, 1) is a function. Explain your answer. **Yes; each input has exactly one output.**

11.1 **2.** Make an input-output table for the function $y = 0.5x$. Use a domain of −4, −2, 0, 2, and 4. Identify the range. **The range is −2, −1, 0, 1, and 2.**

11.1 **3.** Write a function rule that relates x and y. $y = x - 1$

Input x	−5	−3	−1	1
Output y	−6	−4	−2	0

11.2 **4.** Make a scatter plot of the data in Exercise 3. Describe the relationship between x and y. **See margin.**

11.3 **Tell whether the ordered pair is a solution of the equation.**

5. $y = 3x - 7$; (1, 4) **no** **6.** $4x + y = 5$; (2, −1) **no** **7.** $y = \frac{1}{2}x + \frac{1}{2}$; (−3, −1) **yes**

11.3 **List four solutions of the equation.** **8–15. See margin.**

8. $y = -x - 3$ **9.** $y = 7 + 2x$ **10.** $y = -\frac{2}{3}x$ **11.** $y = -x$

12. $-x + y = 1$ **13.** $3x + y = -2$ **14.** $x + 2y = 8$ **15.** $-3y + 4x = 7$

11.4 **Graph the linear equation.** **16–19. See margin.**

16. $y = -3$ **17.** $y = \frac{1}{4}x - 2$ **18.** $x = 4$ **19.** $3x + y = 4$

11.5 **In Exercises 20–23, find the intercepts of the graph of the equation.** **20–23. See margin.**

20. $y = -2x + 4$ **21.** $y = 5x - 1$ **22.** $x + 5y = -5$ **23.** $2x - 3y = 12$

11.5 **24.** Graph the line with an x-intercept of 4 and a y-intercept of −1. **See margin.**

11.5 **25.** Graph the line with an x-intercept of −2 and a y-intercept of 10. **See margin.**

11.6 **Find the slope of the line passing through the points.**

26. (−2, 3), (6, 1) $-\frac{1}{4}$ **27.** (5, 0), (5, −9) **undefined** **28.** (6, −4), (2, −4) **0** **29.** (7, −5), (−2, −14) **1**

30. (−7, 8), (−9, 5) $\frac{3}{2}$ **31.** (−3, −2), (−7, 2) **−1** **32.** (4, 9), (3, 13) **−4** **33.** (0, 7), (−3, −10) $\frac{17}{3}$

11.7 **Find the slope and y-intercept of the graph of the equation.**

34. $y = 3x - 5$ **3; −5** **35.** $y = 2$ **0; −2** **36.** $y = -\frac{1}{3}x + 1$ $-\frac{1}{3}$; **−1** **37.** $2x - y = 8$ **2; −8**

11.8 **Graph the inequality.** **38–41. See margin.**

38. $y > -x - 3$ **39.** $6 \le 3y$ **40.** $5 + 2x > y$ **41.** $4x + 3y \le -12$

Extra Practice

4.

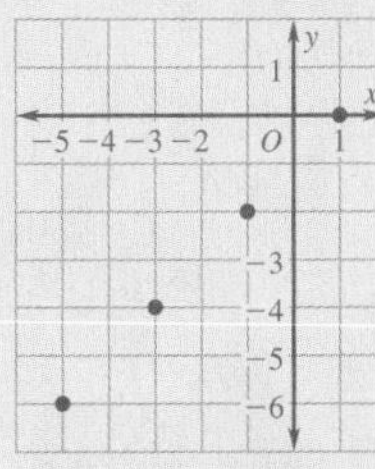

positive relationship

8–15. Sample answers are given.

8. (−1, −2), (0, −3), (1, −4), (2, −5)

9. (−2, 3), (−1, 5), (0, 7), (1, 9)

10. (−3, 2), (0, 0), (3, −2), (6, −4)

11. (−2, 2), (−1, 1), (0, 0), (1, −1)

12. (−1, 0), (0, 1), (1, 2), (2, 3)

13. (−2, 4), (−1, 1), (0, −2), (1, −5)

14. (−2, 5), (0, 4), (2, 3), (4, 2)

15. (−2, −5), (1, −1), (4, 3), (7, 7)

16.

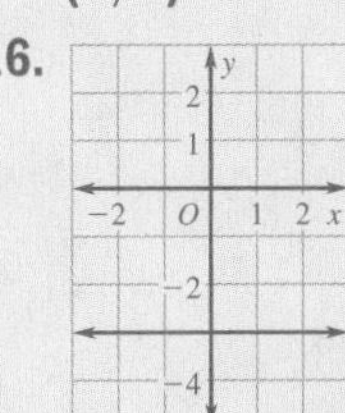

17.

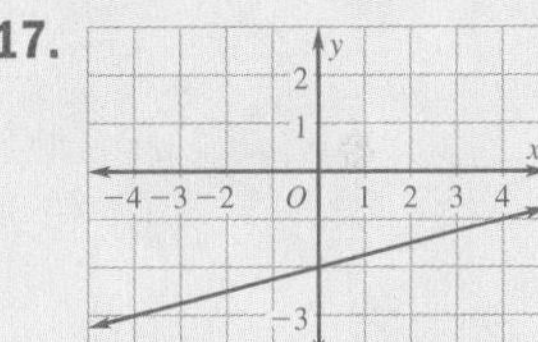

18.

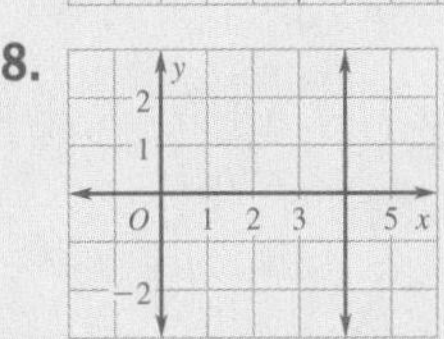

19.

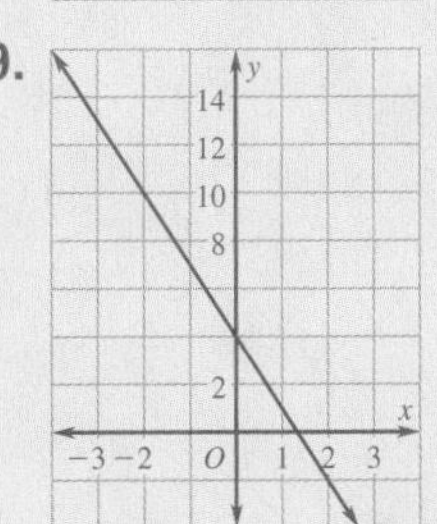

20–25, 38–41. See Additional Answers beginning on page AA1.

1.

9	9
10	0 1 3 5
11	6 7 8
12	7 9
13	0
14	0 0 3

Key: 13 | 0 = 130

3. 100 110 120 130 140

99 103 117.5 130 143

4.

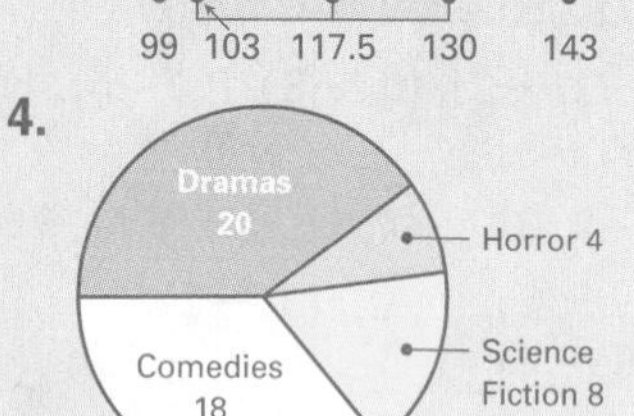

6.

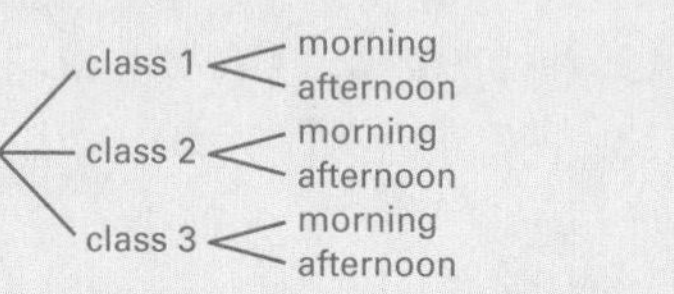

Extra Practice

Chapter 12

In Exercises 1–3, use the following lengths, in inches, of alligators at an alligator farm: 140, 127, 103, 140, 118, 100, 117, 101, 116, 129, 130, 105, 99, 143.

12.1 **1.** Make an ordered stem-and-leaf plot of the data. Identify the interval that includes the most data values. See margin for art; 100–109.

12.1 **2.** Find the median and range of the data. 117.5; 44

12.2 **3.** Make a box-and-whisker plot of the data. What conclusions can you make? See margin for art. *Sample answer*: About 50% of the lengths were between 103 inches and 130 inches.

12.3 **4.** In a survey about favorite kinds of movies, 20 people chose dramas, 4 chose horror movies, 8 chose science fiction, and 18 chose comedies. Represent the data in a circle graph. See margin.

12.3 **5.** You want to display the average monthly price of a stock for each month in 2001. What type of display would you use? Explain. Line graph; a line graph is used to represent data that change over time.

12.4 **6.** You can take one of three different classes in the morning or the afternoon. Make a tree diagram to find the number of choices that are possible. See margin for art; 6 choices.

12.4 **7.** A license plate has 3 digits followed by 3 letters. How many different license plates are possible? 17,576,000 license plates

12.5 **In Exercises 8–11, find the number of permutations.**

8. ${}_7P_2$ 42 **9.** ${}_{11}P_1$ 11 **10.** ${}_8P_5$ 6720 **11.** ${}_{10}P_3$ 720

12.5 **12.** There are 8 students in the school play. How many different ways can the cast be arranged in a row? 40,320 ways

12.6 **In Exercises 13–16, find the number of combinations.**

13. ${}_5C_4$ 5 **14.** ${}_{20}C_2$ 190 **15.** ${}_6C_3$ 20 **16.** ${}_{12}C_9$ 220

12.6 **17.** A CD case holds 30 CDs. How many ways can you select 3 CDs from the case? 4060 ways

12.7 **18.** A telephone number is chosen at random. Find the odds that the last digit is greater than 3. 3 to 2

12.8 **19.** You flip two coins. Find the probability that you do *not* get two heads. $\frac{3}{4}$

12.8 **20.** You and two friends each roll a number cube. What is the probability that all of you roll a 3? $\frac{1}{216}$

12.8 **21.** Ten slips of paper numbered 1 through 10 are placed in a bag. You draw a slip at random and draw another without replacing the first. Find the probability that both numbers are odd. $\frac{2}{9}$

Chapter 13

13.1 In Exercises 1–3, simplify the polynomial and write it in standard form.

1. $3 + 5x - x^2 - 7x + 4$ $-x^2 - 2x + 7$
2. $2t^4 + t^3 - 6 - 3t^3 + t^2$ $2t^4 - 2t^3 + t^2 - 6$
3. $4(5 - k) + 4k - k^2 + 1$ $-k^2 + 21$

13.1 **4.** The height, in feet, of a falling pebble after t seconds of falling from a height of 45 feet can be found using the polynomial $-16t^2 + 45$. Find the pebble's height after 1.5 seconds. 9 ft

13.2 Find the sum or difference.

5. $(3x^2 + 5x - 4) + (-2x^3 + x^2 + 9x)$ $-2x^3 + 4x^2 + 14x - 4$
6. $(-8x^2 - x + 1) - (7x^2 - 5x + 1)$ $-15x^2 + 4x$
7. $(4x^3 - 8x^2 + 2) - (x^3 + x^2 - 6x + 5)$ $3x^3 - 9x^2 + 6x - 3$
8. $(-x^2 - 3x + 7) + (x^2 + 4x - 9)$ $x - 2$
9. $(2x^3 - 2x^2 + 1) + (-x^3 + 9x + 5)$ $x^3 - 2x^2 + 9x + 6$
10. $(3x^2 - 5x - 10) - (5x^3 + x - 2)$ $-5x^3 + 3x^2 - 6x - 8$

13.3 Simplify the expression.

11. $(4z)(-7z^5)$ $-28z^6$
12. $(-r^2)(-3r^2)$ $3r^4$
13. $-3n(2n - 5)$ $-6n^2 + 15n$
14. $q^3(-q + 2)$ $-q^4 + 2q^3$
15. $(5ab)^3$ $125a^3b^3$
16. $(-rst)^4$ $r^4s^4t^4$
17. $(p^6)^4$ p^{24}
18. $(3y^5)^2$ $9y^{10}$

13.4 Find the product and simplify.

19. $(2x + 1)(x - 5)$ $2x^2 - 9x - 5$
20. $(m - 3)(-m + 4)$ $-m^2 + 7m - 12$
21. $(d + 6)(d + 4)$ $d^2 + 10d + 24$
22. $(4y - 3)(4y + 3)$ $16y^2 - 9$
23. $(a - 8)(a - 7)$ $a^2 - 15a + 56$
24. $(5x + 2)(2x - 1)$ $10x^2 - x - 2$

13.5 Rewrite using function notation.

25. $y = 2x - 5$ $f(x) = 2x - 5$
26. $y = 3x^2$ $f(x) = 3x^2$
27. $y = 5x^2 + 1$ $f(x) = 5x^2 + 1$

13.5 Evaluate the function for $x = -2, -1, 0, 1,$ and 2.

28. $f(x) = 2x^2 + x$ 6; 1; 0; 3; 10
29. $f(x) = \frac{1}{4}x^2$ $1; \frac{1}{4}; 0; \frac{1}{4}; 1$
30. $f(x) = \frac{1}{2}x^2 - x$ $4; 1\frac{1}{2}; 0; -\frac{1}{2}; 0$
31. $f(x) = -3x^2 + 2x$ $-16; -5; 0; -1; -8$
32. $f(x) = x^2 + 4x$ $-4; -3; 0; 5; 12$
33. $f(x) = -x^2 - 3$ $-7; -4; -3; -4; -7$

13.5 Graph the function using a table of values. 34–36. See margin.

34. $f(x) = 3x^2$
35. $f(x) = -x^2 + 2$
36. $f(x) = 2x^2 - 4$

13.5 Tell whether the graph represents a function.

37.

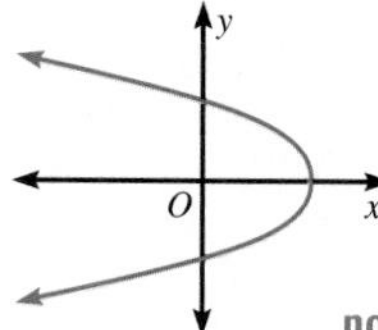

no

38.

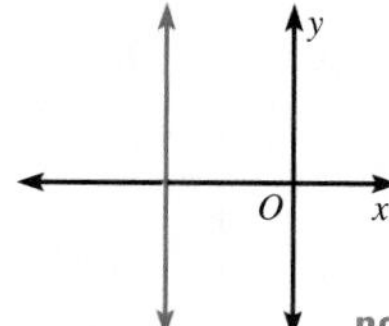

no

39.

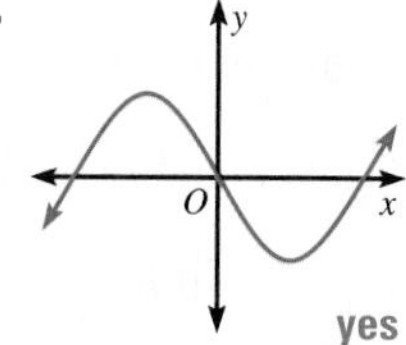

yes

34.

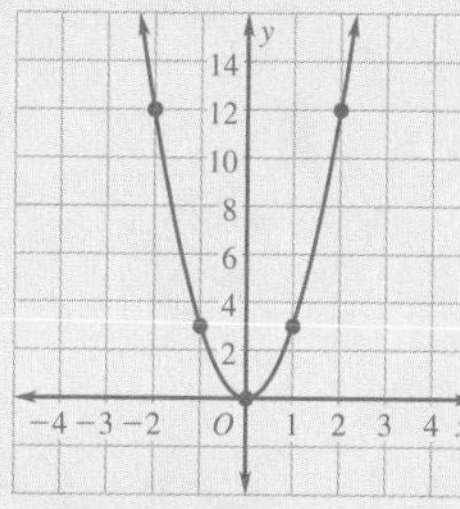

35.

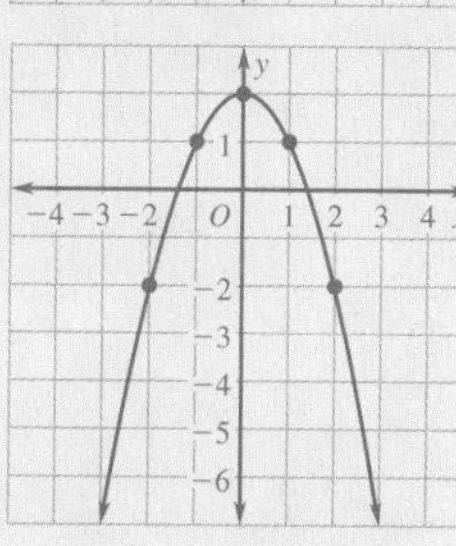

36.

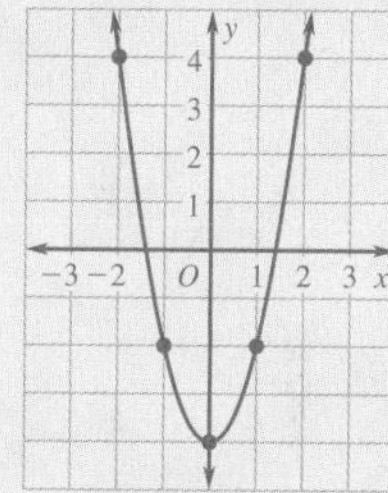

Extra Practice

Table of Symbols

Symbol	Meaning	Page
28.6	decimal point	**4**
$=$	equals, is equal to	**10, 28**
$3 \cdot x$ $3(x)$ $3x$	3 times x	**10, 15**
$\frac{14}{2}$	14 divided by 2	**11**
( )	parentheses—a grouping symbol	**11**
[ ]	brackets—a grouping symbol	**11**
4^3	$4 \cdot 4 \cdot 4$	**20**
$\stackrel{?}{=}$	is equal to?	**26, 29**
$\neq$	is not equal to	**29**
∟	right angle	**33, 375**
$\approx$	is approximately equal to	**39**
. . .	continues on	**53**
-3	negative 3	**53**
-3	the opposite of 3	**54**
$\lvert a \rvert$	the absolute value of a number a	**54**
(x, y)	ordered pair	**91**
$<$	is less than	**141, 302**
$>$	is greater than	**141, 302**
$\leq$	is less than or equal to	**141, 302**
$\geq$	is greater than or equal to	**141, 302**

Symbol	Meaning	Page
$1.1\overline{6}$	repeating decimal 1.16666. . .	**242**
π	pi—a number approximately equal to 3.14	**290**
$a : b, \frac{a}{b}$	ratio of a to b	**317**
%	percent	**327**
$^\circ$	degree(s)	**375, 721**
$\angle A$	angle with vertex point A	**375, 719**
$m\angle B$	the measure of angle B	**375**
$\perp$	is perpendicular to	**376**
$\parallel$	is parallel to	**377**
⇸ ⇸	parallel lines	**377**
$\cong$	is congruent to	**397**
$\overline{AB}$	line segment AB	**397**
$\triangle ABC$	triangle with vertices A, B, and C	**398**
A'	the image of point A	**404**
$\sim$	is similar to	**416**
$\sqrt{a}$	the positive square root of a number a where $a \geq 0$	**431**
$\pm$	plus or minus	**433**
$\not\leq$	is not less than or equal to	**583**
3!	3 factorial, or $3 \cdot 2 \cdot 1$	**623**
$f(x)$	the function of f at x	**680**
$\overleftrightarrow{AB}$	line AB	**718**
$\overrightarrow{AB}$	ray AB	**718**

Table of Symbols

Table of Measures

Time

60 seconds (sec) = 1 minute (min)
60 minutes = 1 hour (h)
24 hours = 1 day (d)
7 days = 1 week (wk)
4 weeks (approx.) = 1 month

365 days, 52 weeks (approx.), 12 months = 1 year
10 years = 1 decade
100 years = 1 century

METRIC

Length

10 millimeters (mm) = 1 centimeter (cm)
100 cm, 1000 mm = 1 meter (m)
1000 m = 1 kilometer (km)

Area

100 square millimeters (mm^2) = 1 square centimeter (cm^2)
10,000 cm^2 = 1 square meter (m^2)
10,000 m^2 = 1 hectare (ha)

Volume

1000 cubic millimeters (mm^3) = 1 cubic centimeter (cm^3)
1,000,000 cm^3 = 1 cubic meter (m^3)

Liquid Capacity

1000 milliliters (mL), 1000 cubic centimeters (cm^3) = 1 liter (L)
1000 L = 1 kiloliter (kL)

Mass

1000 milligrams (mg) = 1 gram (g)
1000 g = 1 kilogram (kg)
1000 kg = 1 metric ton (t)

Temperature Degrees Celsius (°C)

0°C = freezing point of water
37°C = normal body temperature
100°C = boiling point of water

UNITED STATES CUSTOMARY

Length

12 inches (in.) = 1 foot (ft)
36 in., 3 ft = 1 yard (yd)
5280 ft, 1760 yd = 1 mile (mi)

Area

144 square inches ($in.^2$) = 1 square foot (ft^2)
9 ft^2 = 1 square yard (yd^2)
43,560 ft^2, 4840 yd^2 = 1 acre (A)

Volume

1728 cubic inches ($in.^3$) = 1 cubic foot (ft^3)
27 ft^3 = 1 cubic yard (yd^3)

Liquid Capacity

8 fluid ounces (fl oz) = 1 cup (c)
2 c = 1 pint (pt)
2 pt = 1 quart (qt)
4 qt = 1 gallon (gal)

Weight

16 ounces (oz) = 1 pound (lb)
2000 lb = 1 ton

Temperature Degrees Fahrenheit (°F)

32°F = freezing point of water
98.6°F = normal body temperature
212°F = boiling point of water

Table of Formulas

Geometric Formulas

Rectangle (p. 33)

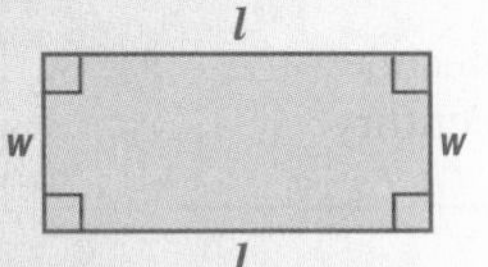

Area
$A = lw$

Perimeter
$P = 2l + 2w$

Square (p. 33)

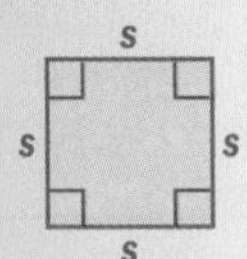

Area
$A = s^2$

Perimeter
$P = 4s$

Triangle (p. 134)

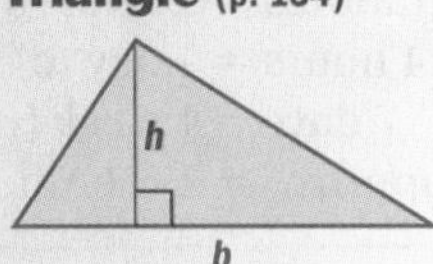

Area
$A = \frac{1}{2}bh$

Parallelogram (p. 481)

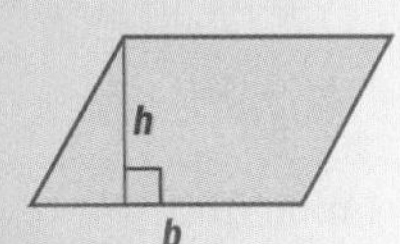

Area
$A = bh$

Trapezoid (p. 482)

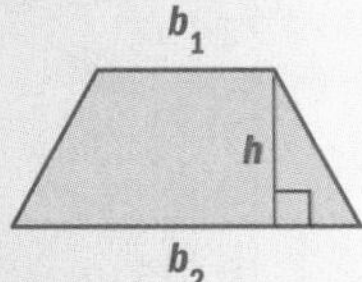

Area
$A = \frac{1}{2}(b_1 + b_2)h$

Circle (pp. 290, 486)

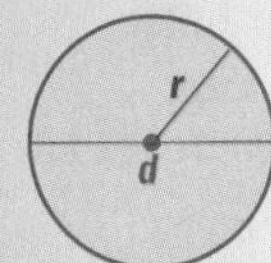

Area
$A = \pi r^2$

Circumference
$C = \pi d$ or
$C = 2\pi r$

Prism (pp. 503, 513)

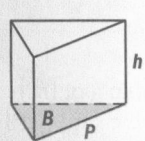

Surface Area
$S = 2B + Ph$

Volume
$V = Bh$

Cylinder (pp. 504, 514)

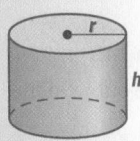

Surface Area
$S = 2\pi r^2 + 2\pi rh$

Volume
$V = \pi r^2 h$

Pyramid (pp. 507, 519)

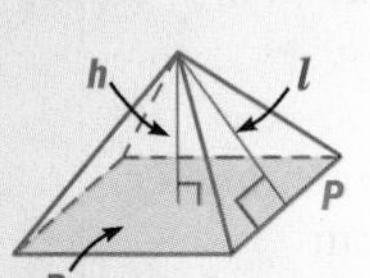
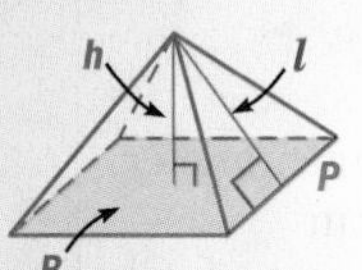

Surface Area
$S = B + \frac{1}{2}Pl$

Volume
$V = \frac{1}{3}Bh$

Cone (pp. 508, 520)

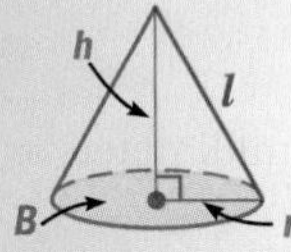

Surface Area
$S = \pi r^2 + \pi rl$

Volume
$V = \frac{1}{3}Bh = \frac{1}{3}\pi r^2 h$

Other Formulas

Distance traveled (p. 34)	$d = rt$ where d = distance, r = rate, and t = time
Simple interest (p. 348)	$I = Prt$ where I = simple interest, P = principal, r = annual interest rate, and t = time in years
Pythagorean theorem (p. 443)	In a right triangle, $a^2 + b^2 = c^2$ where a and b are the lengths of the legs, and c is the length of the hypotenuse.

742

Table of Properties

Identity Properties (pp. 59, 71)

Addition The sum of a number and the additive identity, 0, is the number.

Numbers $7 + 0 = 7$
Algebra $a + 0 = a$

Multiplication The product of a number and the multiplicative identity, 1, is the number.

Numbers $3 \cdot 1 = 3$
Algebra $a \cdot 1 = a$

Inverse Properties (pp. 61, 73, 234)

Addition The sum of a number and its additive inverse, or opposite, is 0.

Numbers $4 + (-4) = 0$
Algebra $a + (-a) = 0$

Multiplication The product of a nonzero number and its multiplicative inverse, or reciprocal, is 1.

Numbers $\frac{2}{3} \cdot \frac{3}{2} = 1$
Algebra $\frac{a}{b} \cdot \frac{b}{a} = 1 \ (a, b \neq 0)$

Commutative Property (p. 80)

Addition In a sum, you can add terms in any order.

Numbers $-2 + 5 = 5 + (-2)$
Algebra $a + b = b + a$

Multiplication In a product, you can multiply factors in any order.

Numbers $3(-6) = -6(3)$
Algebra $ab = ba$

Associative Property (p. 81)

Addition Changing the grouping of terms in a sum will not change the sum.

Numbers $(2 + 4) + 6 = 2 + (4 + 6)$
Algebra $(a + b) + c = a + (b + c)$

Multiplication Changing the grouping of factors in a product will not change the product.

Numbers $(6 \times 2.5) \times 4 = 6 \times (2.5 \times 4)$
Algebra $(ab)c = a(bc)$

Distributive Property (p. 85)

You can multiply a number and a sum by multiplying each term of the sum by the number and then adding these products. The same property applies to subtraction.

Numbers $3(4 + 6) = 3(4) + 3(6)$ $\quad 2(8 - 5) = 2(8) - 2(5)$
Algebra $a(b + c) = a(b) + a(c)$ $\quad a(b - c) = a(b) - a(c)$

Properties of Exponents (pp. 196, 197)

To find the *product of powers* with the same base, add their exponents.

Numbers $5^2 \cdot 5^3 = 5^{2+3} = 5^5$
Algebra $a^b \cdot a^c = a^{b+c}$

To find the *quotient of powers* with the same nonzero base, subtract the denominator's exponent from the numerator's exponent.

Numbers $\frac{7^4}{7^2} = 7^{4-2} = 7^2$ **Algebra** $\frac{a^b}{a^c} = a^{b-c}$

Cross Products Property (p. 323)

The cross products of a proportion are equal.

Numbers Because $\frac{3}{4} = \frac{6}{8}$, $3 \cdot 8 = 4 \cdot 6$. **Algebra** If $\frac{a}{b} = \frac{c}{d}$, then $ad = bc$, $b, d \neq 0$.

Finding Squares and Square Roots

EXAMPLE 1 **Finding a Square**

Find 54^2.

Find 54 in the column labeled *No.* (an abbreviation for *Number*). Read across to the column labeled *Square*.

No.	Square	Sq. Root
51	2601	7.141
52	2704	7.211
53	2809	7.280
54	2916	7.348
55	3025	7.416

ANSWER So, $54^2 = 2916$.

EXAMPLE 2 **Finding a Square Root**

Find a decimal approximation of $\sqrt{54}$.

Find 54 in the column labeled *No.* Read across to the column labeled *Sq. Root*.

No.	Square	Sq. Root
51	2601	7.141
52	2704	7.211
53	2809	7.280
54	2916	7.348
55	3025	7.416

ANSWER So, to the nearest thousandth, $\sqrt{54} \approx 7.348$.

EXAMPLE 3 **Finding a Square Root**

Find a decimal approximation of $\sqrt{3000}$.

Find the two numbers in the *Square* column that 3000 is between. Read across to the column labeled *No.*; $\sqrt{3000}$ is between 54 and 55, but closer to 55.

No.	Square	Sq. Root
51	2601	7.141
52	2704	7.211
53	2809	7.280
54	2916	7.348
55	3025	7.416

ANSWER So, $\sqrt{3000} \approx 55$. A more accurate approximation can be found using a calculator: 54.772256.

Squares and Square Roots

744

Table of Squares and Square Roots

No.	Square	Sq. Root	No.	Square	Sq. Root	No.	Square	Sq. Root
1	1	1.000	**51**	2601	7.141	**101**	10,201	10.050
2	4	1.414	**52**	2704	7.211	**102**	10,404	10.100
3	9	1.732	**53**	2809	7.280	**103**	10,609	10.149
4	16	2.000	**54**	2916	7.348	**104**	10,816	10.198
5	25	2.236	**55**	3025	7.416	**105**	11,025	10.247
6	36	2.449	**56**	3136	7.483	**106**	11,236	10.296
7	49	2.646	**57**	3249	7.550	**107**	11,449	10.344
8	64	2.828	**58**	3364	7.616	**108**	11,664	10.392
9	81	3.000	**59**	3481	7.681	**109**	11,881	10.440
10	100	3.162	**60**	3600	7.746	**110**	12,100	10.488
11	121	3.317	**61**	3721	7.810	**111**	12,321	10.536
12	144	3.464	**62**	3844	7.874	**112**	12,544	10.583
13	169	3.606	**63**	3969	7.937	**113**	12,769	10.630
14	196	3.742	**64**	4096	8.000	**114**	12,996	10.677
15	225	3.873	**65**	4225	8.062	**115**	13,225	10.724
16	256	4.000	**66**	4356	8.124	**116**	13,456	10.770
17	289	4.123	**67**	4489	8.185	**117**	13,689	10.817
18	324	4.243	**68**	4624	8.246	**118**	13,924	10.863
19	361	4.359	**69**	4761	8.307	**119**	14,161	10.909
20	400	4.472	**70**	4900	8.367	**120**	14,400	10.954
21	441	4.583	**71**	5041	8.426	**121**	14,641	11.000
22	484	4.690	**72**	5184	8.485	**122**	14,884	11.045
23	529	4.796	**73**	5329	8.544	**123**	15,129	11.091
24	576	4.899	**74**	5476	8.602	**124**	15,376	11.136
25	625	5.000	**75**	5625	8.660	**125**	15,625	11.180
26	676	5.099	**76**	5776	8.718	**126**	15,876	11.225
27	729	5.196	**77**	5929	8.775	**127**	16,129	11.269
28	784	5.292	**78**	6084	8.832	**128**	16,384	11.314
29	841	5.385	**79**	6241	8.888	**129**	16,641	11.358
30	900	5.477	**80**	6400	8.944	**130**	16,900	11.402
31	961	5.568	**81**	6561	9.000	**131**	17,161	11.446
32	1024	5.657	**82**	6724	9.055	**132**	17,424	11.489
33	1089	5.745	**83**	6889	9.110	**133**	17,689	11.533
34	1156	5.831	**84**	7056	9.165	**134**	17,956	11.576
35	1225	5.916	**85**	7225	9.220	**135**	18,225	11.619
36	1296	6.000	**86**	7396	9.274	**136**	18,496	11.662
37	1369	6.083	**87**	7569	9.327	**137**	18,769	11.705
38	1444	6.164	**88**	7744	9.381	**138**	19,044	11.747
39	1521	6.245	**89**	7921	9.434	**139**	19,321	11.790
40	1600	6.325	**90**	8100	9.487	**140**	19,600	11.832
41	1681	6.403	**91**	8281	9.539	**141**	19,881	11.874
42	1764	6.481	**92**	8464	9.592	**142**	20,164	11.916
43	1849	6.557	**93**	8649	9.644	**143**	20,449	11.958
44	1936	6.633	**94**	8836	9.695	**144**	20,736	12.000
45	2025	6.708	**95**	9025	9.747	**145**	21,025	12.042
46	2116	6.782	**96**	9216	9.798	**146**	21,316	12.083
47	2209	6.856	**97**	9409	9.849	**147**	21,609	12.124
48	2304	6.928	**98**	9604	9.899	**148**	21,904	12.166
49	2401	7.000	**99**	9801	9.950	**149**	22,201	12.207
50	2500	7.071	**100**	10,000	10.000	**150**	22,500	12.247

Equivalent Fractions, Decimals, and Percents

Fraction	Decimal	Percent
$\frac{1}{10}$	0.1	10%
$\frac{1}{8}$	0.125	$12\frac{1}{2}\%$
$\frac{1}{5}$	0.2	20%
$\frac{1}{4}$	0.25	25%
$\frac{3}{10}$	0.3	30%
$\frac{1}{3}$	$0.\overline{3}$	$33\frac{1}{3}\%$
$\frac{3}{8}$	0.375	$37\frac{1}{2}\%$
$\frac{2}{5}$	0.4	40%
$\frac{1}{2}$	0.5	50%
$\frac{3}{5}$	0.6	60%
$\frac{5}{8}$	0.625	$62\frac{1}{2}\%$
$\frac{2}{3}$	$0.\overline{6}$	$66\frac{2}{3}\%$
$\frac{7}{10}$	0.7	70%
$\frac{3}{4}$	0.75	75%
$\frac{4}{5}$	0.8	80%
$\frac{7}{8}$	0.875	$87\frac{1}{2}\%$
$\frac{9}{10}$	0.9	90%
1	1	100%

Glossary

a	Example
absolute value (p. 54) The absolute value of a number a is the distance between a and 0 on a number line. The absolute value of a is written $\|a\|$.	$\|4\| = 4$ $\|-7\| = 7$ $\|0\| = 0$
acute angle (p. 382) An angle whose measure is less than 90°.	
acute triangle (p. 382) A triangle with three acute angles.	60° 50° 70°
addition property of equality (p. 110) Adding the same number to each side of an equation produces an equivalent equation.	If $x - 5 = 2$, then $x - 5 + 5 = 2 + 5$, so $x = 7$. If $x - a = b$, then $x - a + a = b + a$.
additive identity (p. 59) The number 0 is the additive identity because the sum of any number and 0 is the original number.	$-7 + 0 = -7$ $a + 0 = a$
additive inverse (p. 61) The additive inverse of a number a is the opposite of the number, or $-a$. The sum of a number and its additive inverse is 0.	The additive inverse of 6 is -6, so $6 + (-6) = 0$.
angle (p. 719) A figure formed by two rays that begin at a common point, called the vertex.	vertex, ray, ray
angle of rotation (p. 410) In a rotation, the angle formed by two rays drawn from the center of rotation through corresponding points on the original figure and its image.	*See* rotation.
annual interest rate (p. 348) In simple interest, the percent of the principal earned or paid per year.	*See* simple interest.
area (p. 33) The number of square units covered by a figure.	2 units, 7 units; *Area* = 14 square units
associative property of addition (p. 81) Changing the grouping of terms in a sum does not change the sum.	$(9 + 4) + 6 = 9 + (4 + 6)$ $(a + b) + c = a + (b + c)$
associative property of multiplication (p. 81) Changing the grouping of factors in a product does not change the product.	$(2 \cdot 5) \cdot 3 = 2 \cdot (5 \cdot 3)$ $(ab)c = a(bc)$

Glossary

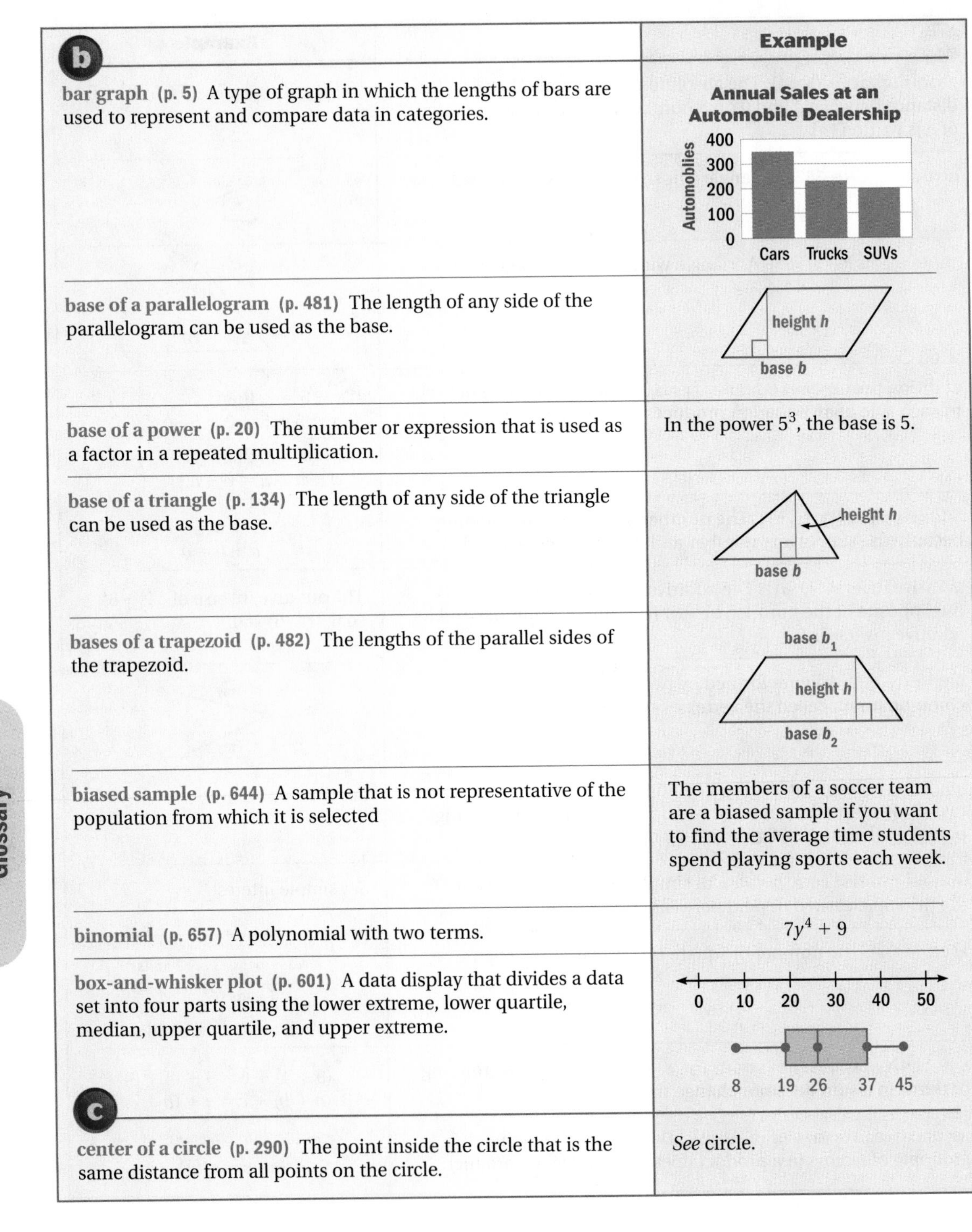

b	**Example**
bar graph **(p. 5)** A type of graph in which the lengths of bars are used to represent and compare data in categories.	**Annual Sales at an Automobile Dealership** Automobiles: 0, 100, 200, 300, 400 Cars, Trucks, SUVs
base of a parallelogram **(p. 481)** The length of any side of the parallelogram can be used as the base.	height h base b
base of a power **(p. 20)** The number or expression that is used as a factor in a repeated multiplication.	In the power 5^3, the base is 5.
base of a triangle **(p. 134)** The length of any side of the triangle can be used as the base.	height h base b
bases of a trapezoid **(p. 482)** The lengths of the parallel sides of the trapezoid.	base b_1 height h base b_2
biased sample **(p. 644)** A sample that is not representative of the population from which it is selected	The members of a soccer team are a biased sample if you want to find the average time students spend playing sports each week.
binomial **(p. 657)** A polynomial with two terms.	$7y^4 + 9$
box-and-whisker plot **(p. 601)** A data display that divides a data set into four parts using the lower extreme, lower quartile, median, upper quartile, and upper extreme.	0, 10, 20, 30, 40, 50 8, 19, 26, 37, 45
c	
center of a circle **(p. 290)** The point inside the circle that is the same distance from all points on the circle.	*See* circle.

Glossary

	Example
center of rotation (p. 410) The point about which a figure is turned when the figure undergoes a rotation.	*See* rotation.
circle (p. 290) The set of all points in a plane that are the same distance, called the radius, from a fixed point, called the center.	
circle graph (p. 331, 605) A circle graph displays data as sections of a circle. The entire circle represents all the data. Each section is labeled using the actual data or using data expressed as fractions, decimals, or percents of the sum of the data.	
circumference (p. 290) The distance around a circle.	*See* circle.
coefficient (p. 86) The number part of a term that includes a variable.	The coefficient of $7x$ is 7.
combination (p. 627) A grouping of objects in which the order is not important.	There are 6 combinations of 2 letters chosen from VASE: VA VS VE AS AE SE
common factor (p. 173) A whole number that is a factor of two or more nonzero whole numbers.	The common factors of 8 and 12 are 1, 2, and 4.
common multiple (p. 186) A multiple that is shared by two or more numbers.	The common multiples of 4 and 6 are 12, 24, 36, ...
commutative property of addition (p. 80) In a sum, you can add terms in any order.	$4 + 7 = 7 + 4$ $a + b = b + a$
commutative property of multiplication (p. 80) In a product, you can multiply factors in any order.	$5(-8) = -8(5)$ $ab = ba$
complementary angles (p. 375) Two angles whose measures have a sum of 90°.	
complementary events (p. 632) Two events are complementary when one event or the other (but not both) must occur.	When rolling a number cube, the events "getting an odd number" and "getting an even number" are complementary events.

	Example
composite number (p. 169) A whole number greater than 1 that has positive factors other than 1 and itself.	6 is a composite number because its factors are 1, 2, 3, and 6.
cone (p. 492) A solid with one circular base.	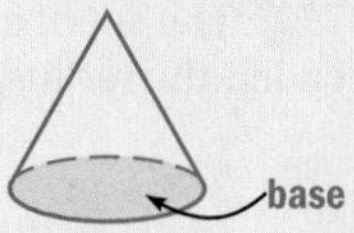 base
congruent angles (p. 397) Angles that have the same measure.	*See* congruent polygons.
congruent polygons (p. 397) Similar polygons that have the same size. For congruent polygons, corresponding angles are congruent and corresponding sides are congruent. The symbol ≅ indicates congruence and is read "is congruent to."	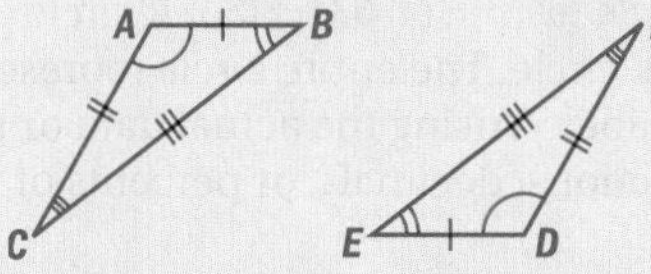 A B C E F D $\triangle ABC \cong \triangle DEF$
congruent sides (p. 397) Sides that have the same length.	*See* congruent polygons.
constant term (p. 86) A term that has a number but no variable.	In the expression $5y + 9$, the term 9 is a constant term.
converse (p. 444) An if-then statement where the hypothesis and conclusion of the original statement have been reversed.	Original: If you clean your room, then it will be neat. Converse: If your room is neat, then you cleaned it.
coordinate plane (p. 91) A coordinate system formed by the intersection of a horizontal number line, called the x-axis, and a vertical number line, called the y-axis.	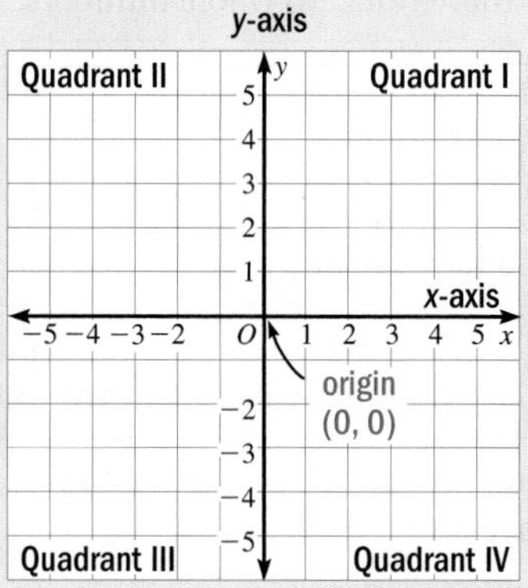 y-axis Quadrant II Quadrant I x-axis origin (0, 0) Quadrant III Quadrant IV

	Example
corresponding angles **(p. 377)** Angles that occupy corresponding positions when a line intersects two other lines.	1 2 ∠1 and ∠2 are corresponding angles.
corresponding parts **(p. 397)** Pairs of sides and angles of polygons that are in the same relative position.	B D A C E F ∠A and ∠E are corresponding angles. $\overline{AB}$ and $\overline{ED}$ are corresponding sides.
cosine **(p. 463)** The cosine of any acute angle A of a right triangle is the ratio of the adjacent leg to the hypotenuse.	B hypotenuse side opposite ∠A a c C b A side adjacent to ∠A $\cos A = \frac{b}{c}$
counting principle **(p. 619)** If one event can occur in m ways, and for each of these a second event can occur in n ways, then the number of ways that the two events can occur together is $m \cdot n$. The counting principle can be extended to three or more events.	If a T-shirt is made in 5 sizes and in 7 colors, then the number of different T-shirts that are possible is $5 \cdot 7 = 35$.
cross products **(p. 323)** In a proportion $\frac{a}{b} = \frac{c}{d}$ where $b \neq 0$ and $d \neq 0$, the cross products are ad and bc.	The cross products of the proportion $\frac{2}{3} = \frac{4}{6}$ are $2 \cdot 6$ and $3 \cdot 4$.
cylinder **(p. 492)** A solid with two congruent circular bases that lie in parallel planes.	bases
d	
data **(p. 5)** Information, facts, or numbers that describe something.	Numbers of cars sold annually at a dealership: 340, 350, 345, 347, 352, 360, 365
degrees **(p. 721)** Unit of measure for angles. The symbol for degrees is °. There are 360° in a circle.	A 58°

Glossary

	Example
dependent events **(p. 639)** Two events such that the occurrence of one affects the likelihood that the other will occur.	A bag contains 5 red and 8 blue marbles. You randomly choose a marble, do not replace it, then randomly choose another marble. The events "first marble is red" and "second marble is red" are dependent events.
diameter of a circle **(p. 290)** The distance across the circle through the center.	*See* circle.
dilation **(p. 418)** A transformation that stretches or shrinks a figure.	The scale factor is $\frac{1}{2}$.
discount **(p. 342)** A decrease in the price of an item.	The original price of a pair of jeans is $42 but the store sells it for $29.99. The discount is $12.01.
distributive property **(p. 85)** For all numbers a, b, and c, $a(b + c) = ab + ac$ and $a(b - c) = ab - ac$.	$8(10 + 4) = 8(10) + 8(4)$ $3(4 - 2) = 3(4) - 3(2)$
division property of equality **(p. 114)** Dividing each side of an equation by the same nonzero number produces an equivalent equation.	If $6x = 54$, then $\frac{6x}{6} = \frac{54}{6}$, so $x = 9$. If $ax = b$ and $a \neq 0$, then $\frac{ax}{a} = \frac{b}{a}$.
domain of a function **(p. 542)** The set of all possible input values for the function.	*See* function.

e

edge of a polyhedron **(p. 492)** A line segment where two faces of the polyhedron meet.	

Glossary

	Example
equation (p. 28) A mathematical sentence formed by setting two expressions equal.	$3 \cdot 6 = 18$ and $x + 7 = 12$ are equations.
equilateral triangle (p. 382) A triangle with three congruent sides.	
equivalent equations (p. 109) Equations that have the same solution(s).	$2x - 6 = 0$ and $2x = 6$ are equivalent equations because the solution of both equations is 3.
equivalent fractions (p. 179) Fractions that represent the same part-to-whole relationship. Equivalent fractions have the same simplest form.	$\frac{6}{8}$ and $\frac{9}{12}$ are equivalent fractions that both represent $\frac{3}{4}$.
equivalent inequalities (p. 141) Inequalities that have the same solution.	$3x \le 12$ and $x \le 4$ are equivalent inequalities because the solution of both inequalities is all numbers less than or equal to 4.
equivalent ratios (p. 317) Ratios that have the same value.	$\frac{15}{12}$ and $\frac{25}{20}$ are equivalent ratios because $\frac{15}{12} = 1.25$ and $\frac{25}{20} = 1.25$.
evaluate (p. 10) To find the value of an expression with one or more operations.	$4(3) + 6 \div 2 = 15$
event (p. 354) A collection of outcomes of an experiment.	An event for rolling a number cube is "getting a number divisible by 3."
experimental probability (p. 355) A probability based on a sample or repeated trials of an experiment. The experimental probability of an event is given by: $P(\text{event}) = \frac{\text{Number of favorable outcomes}}{\text{Number of trials or items in sample}}$	During one month, your school bus is on time 17 out of 22 school days. The experimental probability that the bus is on time is: $P(\text{bus is on time}) = \frac{17}{22} \approx 0.773$
exponent (p. 20) A number or expression that represents how many times a base is used as a factor in a repeated multiplication.	In the power 5^3, the exponent is 3.

Glossary

f

Example

face of a polyhedron (p. 492) A polygon that is a side of the polyhedron.

See edge of a polyhedron.

factor tree (p. 169) A diagram that can be used to write the prime factorization of a number.

54
6 × 9
2 × 3 × 3 × 3

factorial (p. 623) The expression $n!$ is read "n factorial" and represents the product of all integers from 1 to n.

$4! = 4 \cdot 3 \cdot 2 \cdot 1 = 24$

favorable outcomes (p. 354) Outcomes corresponding to a specified event.

When rolling a number cube, the favorable outcomes for the event "getting a number greater than 4" are 5 and 6.

formula (p. 33) An equation that relates two or more quantities such as perimeter, length, and width.

$P = 2l + 2w$

fraction (p. 179) A number of the form $\frac{a}{b}$ $(b \neq 0)$ where a is called the numerator and b is called the denominator.

$\frac{5}{7}$ and $\frac{18}{10}$ are fractions.

frequency (p. 6) The number of data values that lie in an interval of a frequency table or histogram.

See frequency table *and* histogram.

frequency table (p. 6) A table used to group data values into intervals.

Interval	Tally	Frequency
0–9	II	2
10–19	IIII	4
20–29	𝍸	5

front-end estimation (p. 248) A method for estimating the sum of two or more numbers. In this method, you add the front-end digits, estimate the sum of the remaining digits, and then add the results.

To estimate $3.81 + 1.32 + 5.74$, first add the front-end digits: $3 + 1 + 5 = 9$. Then estimate the sum of the remaining digits: $0.81 + (0.32 + 0.74) \approx 1 + 1 = 2$. The sum is about $9 + 2 = 11$.

function (p. 541) A pairing of each number in a given set with exactly one number in another set. Starting with a number called an input, the function associates with it exactly one number called an output.

Input x	1	2	3	4
Output y	2	4	6	8

The input-output table above represents a function.

Glossary

	Example
function notation (p. 680) An equation that uses $f(x)$ to represent the output of the function f for an input of x.	$f(x) = 5x + 13$ is written using function notation.
g	
graph of an inequality (p. 140) On a number line, the set of points that represents the solution of the inequality. (*See* half-plane.)	The graph of the inequality $x < 2$ is shown below.
greatest common factor (GCF) (p. 173) The greatest whole number that is a factor of two or more nonzero whole numbers.	The GCF of 18 and 27 is 9. The GCF of 48, 24, and 36 is 12.
h	
half-plane (p. 584) The graph of a linear inequality in two variables.	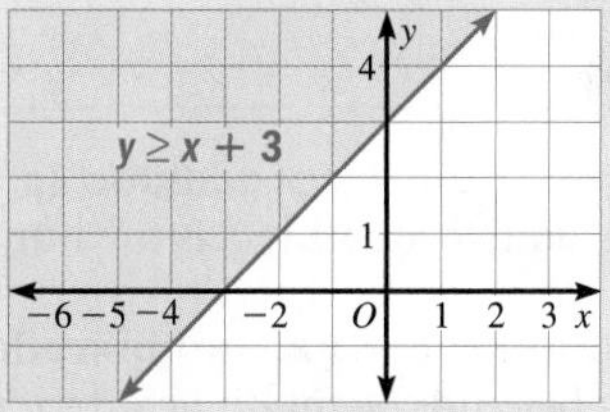 $y \geq x + 3$
height of a parallelogram (p. 481) The perpendicular distance between a side whose length is the base and the opposite side.	*See* base of a parallelogram.
height of a trapezoid (p. 482) The perpendicular distance between the bases of the trapezoid.	*See* bases of a trapezoid.
height of a triangle (p. 134) The perpendicular distance between a side whose length is the base and the vertex opposite that side.	*See* base of a triangle.
heptagon (p. 390) A polygon with seven sides.	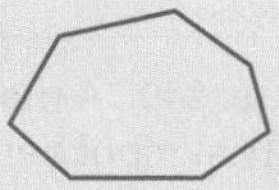
hexagon (p. 390) A polygon with six sides.	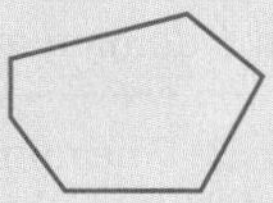

	Example
histogram (p. 6) A graph that displays data from a frequency table. A histogram has one bar for each interval of the frequency table. The height of the bar indicates the frequency for the interval.	**Library Visitors on a Saturday** Frequency: 0–9: 2; 10–19: 4; 20–29: 5; 30–39: 3; 40–49: 4 Age (years)
hypotenuse (p. 443) The side of a right triangle that is opposite the right angle.	hypotenuse, leg, leg
identity property of addition (p. 59) The sum of a number and the additive identity, 0, is the number.	$8 + 0 = 8$ $a + 0 = a$
identity property of multiplication (p. 71) The product of a number and the multiplicative identity, 1, is the number.	$4 \cdot 1 = 4$ $a \cdot 1 = a$
image (p. 404) The new figure formed by a transformation.	*See* reflection, rotation, *and* translation.
improper fraction (p. 707) A fraction whose numerator is greater than or equal to its denominator.	$\frac{8}{7}$ is an improper fraction.
independent events (p. 639) Two events such that the occurrence of one does not affect the likelihood that the other will occur.	You toss a coin and roll a number cube. The events "getting heads" and "getting a 6" are independent events.
inequality (p. 140) A mathematical sentence formed by placing an inequality symbol between two expressions.	$3 < 5$ and $x + 2 \geq -4$ are inequalities.
input (p. 541) A number on which a function operates. An input value is in the domain of the function.	*See* function.
integers (p. 53) The numbers . . . , −4, −3, −2, −1, 0, 1, 2, 3, 4, . . . consisting of the negative integers, zero, and the positive integers.	−8 and 14 are integers. $-8\frac{1}{3}$ and 14.5 are *not* integers.

Glossary

756

	Example
interest (p. 348) The amount earned or paid for the use of money.	*See* simple interest.
inverse operations (p. 109) Operations that "undo" each other.	Addition and subtraction are inverse operations. Multiplication and division are also inverse operations.
inverse property of addition (p. 61) The sum of a number and its additive inverse, or opposite, is 0.	$5 + (-5) = 0$ $a + (-a) = 0$
inverse property of multiplication (pp. 73, 234) The product of a nonzero number and its multiplicative inverse, or reciprocal, is 1.	$\frac{3}{4} \cdot \frac{4}{3} = 1$ $\frac{a}{b} \cdot \frac{b}{a} = 1 \quad (a, b \neq 0)$
irrational number (p. 437) A real number that cannot be written as a quotient of two integers. The decimal form of an irrational number neither terminates nor repeats.	$\sqrt{2}$ and 0.313113111. . . are irrational numbers.
isosceles triangle (p. 382) A triangle with at least two congruent sides.	
L	
leading digit (p. 251) The first nonzero digit in a number.	The leading digit of 725 is 7. The leading digit of 0.002638 is 2.
least common denominator (LCD) (p. 192) The least common multiple of the denominators of two or more fractions.	The LCD of $\frac{7}{10}$ and $\frac{3}{4}$ is 20, the least common multiple of 10 and 4.
least common multiple (LCM) (p. 186) The least number that is a common multiple of two or more whole numbers.	The LCM of 4 and 6 is 12. The LCM of 3, 5, and 10 is 30.
legs of a right triangle (p. 443) The two sides of a right triangle that form the right angle.	*See* hypotenuse.
like terms (p. 86) Terms that have identical variable parts raised to the same power. (Two or more constant terms are considered like terms.)	In the expression $x + 4 - 2x + 1$, x and $-2x$ are like terms, and 4 and 1 are like terms.
linear equation (p. 556) An equation in which the variables appear in separate terms and each variable occurs only to the first power.	$7y = 14x + 21$ is a linear equation.

Glossary

	Example
linear function **(pp. 556, 681)** A function whose graph is a line or part of a line.	$y = -x + 1$
linear inequality **(p. 583)** An inequality in which the variables appear in separate terms and each variable occurs only to the first power.	$y \leq 2x + 5$ is a linear inequality
line graph **(pp. 606, 725)** A type of graph in which points representing data pairs are connected by line segments. A line graph is used to show how a quantity changes over time.	Average Price of Gold
line of reflection **(p. 404)** The line over which a figure is flipped when the figure undergoes a reflection.	*See* reflection.
line of symmetry **(p. 406)** A line that divides a figure into two parts that are mirror images of each other.	*See* line symmetry.
line symmetry **(p. 406)** A figure has line symmetry if it can be divided by a line, called a line of symmetry, into two parts that are mirror images of each other.	A square has 4 lines of symmetry.
lower extreme **(p. 601)** The least value in a data set.	*See* box-and-whisker plot.
lower quartile **(p. 601)** The median of the lower half of a data set.	*See* box-and-whisker plot.
m	
markup **(p. 342)** The increase in the wholesale price of an item.	The wholesale price of a loaf of bread is \$1 but the store sells it for \$1.59. The markup is \$.59.

	Example
mean **(pp. 75, 257)** The sum of the values in a data set divided by the number of values.	The mean of the data set 85, 59, 97, 71 is $\frac{85 + 59 + 97 + 71}{4} = \frac{312}{4} = 78$.
median **(p. 257)** The middle value in a data set when the values are written in numerical order. If the data set has an even number of values, the median is the mean of the two middle values.	The median of the data set 8, 17, 21, 23, 26, 29, 34, 40, 45 is the middle value, 26.
mixed number **(p. 707)** A number that has a whole number part and a fraction part.	$3\frac{2}{5}$ is a mixed number.
mode **(p. 257)** The value in a data set that occurs most often. A data set can have no mode, one mode, or more than one mode.	The mode of the data set 73, 42, 55, 77, 61, 55, 68 is 55 because it occurs most often.
monomial **(p. 170, 657)** A number, a variable, or a product of a number and one or more variables.	$3xy$, $8x^2$, x, and 14 are monomials.
multiple **(p. 186)** A multiple of a number is the product of the number and any nonzero whole number.	The multiples of 3 are 3, 6, 9, ...
multiplication property of equality **(p. 113)** Multiplying each side of an equation by the same nonzero number produces an equivalent equation.	If $\frac{x}{3} = 7$, then $3 \cdot \frac{x}{3} = 3 \cdot 7$, so $x = 21$. If $\frac{x}{a} = b$ and $a \neq 0$, then $a \cdot \frac{x}{a} = a \cdot b$.
multiplication property of zero **(p. 71)** The product of a number and 0 is 0.	$-4 \cdot 0 = 0$ $a \cdot 0 = 0$
multiplicative identity **(p. 71)** The number 1 is the multiplicative identity because the product of any number and 1 is the original number.	$9 \cdot 1 = 9$ $a \cdot 1 = a$
multiplicative inverse **(p. 73, 234)** The multiplicative inverse of a number $\frac{a}{b}$ $(a, b \neq 0)$ is the reciprocal of the number, or $\frac{b}{a}$. The product of a number and its multiplicative inverse is 1.	The multiplicative inverse of $\frac{3}{2}$ is $\frac{2}{3}$, so $\frac{3}{2} \cdot \frac{2}{3} = 1$.

Glossary

n	Example
negative integers (p. 53) The integers that are less than zero.	The negative integers are −1, −2, −3, −4, ...
net (p. 502) A two-dimensional representation of a solid. This pattern forms a solid when it is folded.	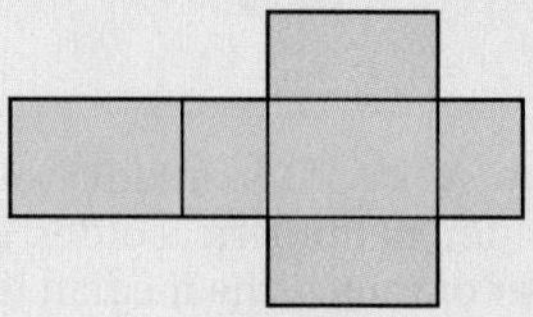
numerical expression (p. 10) An expression consisting of numbers and operations.	$4(3) + 24 \div 2$

o	
obtuse angle (p. 382) An angle whose measure is greater than 90° and less than 180°.	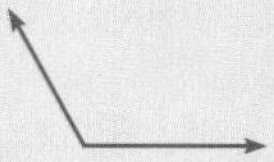
obtuse triangle (p. 382) A triangle with one obtuse angle.	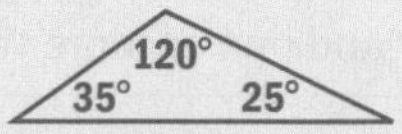 120° 35° 25°
octagon (p. 390) A polygon with eight sides.	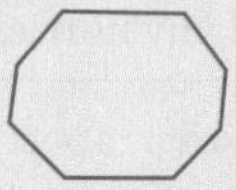
odds in favor of an event (p. 633) The ratio of favorable outcomes to unfavorable outcomes.	The odds of rolling an even number on a six sided number cube is $\frac{3}{3}$, or 1.
opposites (p. 54) Two numbers that are the same distance from 0 on a number line but are on opposite sides of 0.	−3 and 3 are opposites.
order of operations (p. 10) A set of rules for evaluating an expression involving more than one operation.	To evaluate $3 + 2 \cdot 4$, you perform the multiplication before the addition: $3 + 2 \cdot 4 = 3 + 8 = 11$
ordered pair (p. 91) A pair of numbers (x, y) that can be used to represent a point in a coordinate plane. The first number is the x-coordinate, and the second number is the y-coordinate.	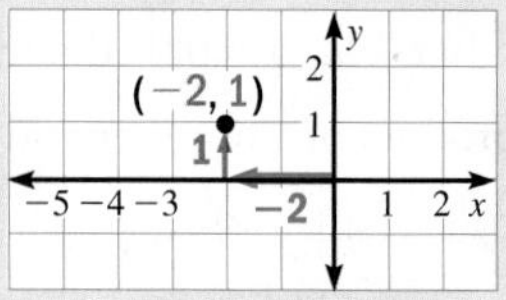 (−2, 1) 1 −2 −5 −4 −3 1 2 x y 2 1

Glossary

	Example
origin (p. 91) The point (0, 0) where the x-axis and the y-axis meet in a coordinate plane.	*See* coordinate plane.
outcomes (p. 354) The possible results when an experiment is performed.	When tossing a coin, the outcomes are heads and tails.
output (p. 541) A number produced by evaluating a function using a given input. An output value is in the range of the function.	*See* function.
p	
parallel lines (p. 377) Two lines in the same plane that do not intersect. The symbol ∥ is used to indicate parallel lines.	a, b, $a \parallel b$
parallelogram (p. 386) A quadrilateral with both pairs of opposite sides parallel.	
pentagon (p. 390) A polygon with five sides.	
percent (p. 327) A ratio whose denominator is 100. The symbol for percent is %.	$\frac{17}{20} = \frac{17 \cdot 5}{20 \cdot 5} = \frac{85}{100} = 85\%$
percent of change (p. 338) A percent that shows how much a quantity has increased or decreased in comparison with the original amount: Percent of change $p = \frac{\text{Amount of increase or decrease}}{\text{Original amount}}$	The percent of change p from 15 to 19 is: $p = \frac{19 - 15}{15} = \frac{4}{15} \approx 0.267 = 26.7\%$
percent of decrease (p. 338) The percent of change in a quantity when the new amount of the quantity is less than the original amount.	*See* percent of change.
percent of increase (p. 338) The percent of change in a quantity when the new amount of the quantity is greater than the original amount.	*See* percent of change.
perfect square (p. 432) A number that is the square of an integer.	49 is a perfect square because $49 = (\pm 7)^2$.

	Example
perimeter (p. 33) The distance around a figure. For a figure with straight sides, the perimeter is the sum of the lengths of the sides.	7 ft, 4 ft, 4 ft, 7 ft *Perimeter* = 22 ft
permutation (p. 623) An arrangement of a group of objects in a particular order.	There are 6 permutations of the 3 letters in the word CAT: CAT ACT TCA CTA ATC TAC
perpendicular lines (p. 376) Two lines that intersect to form a right angle. The symbol ⊥ is used to indicate perpendicular lines.	a, b $a \perp b$
pi (π) (p. 290) The ratio of the circumference of a circle to its diameter.	You can use 3.14 or $\frac{22}{7}$ to approximate π.
plane (p. 718) A plane can be thought of as a flat surface that extends without end.	
polygon (p. 390) A closed geometric figure made up of three or more line segments that intersect only at their endpoints.	Polygon Not a polygon
polyhedron (p. 492) A solid that is enclosed by polygons.	
polynomial (p. 657) A monomial or a sum of monomials.	*See* binomial, trinomial, monomial.
population (p. 644) In statistics, the entire group of people or objects about which you want information.	If a biologist wants to determine the average age of the elephants in a wildlife refuge, the population consists of every elephant in the refuge.
positive integers (p. 53) The integers that are greater than zero.	The positive integers are 1, 2, 3, 4, ...

	Example
power (p. 20) A product formed from repeated multiplication by the same number or expression. A power consists of a base and an exponent.	2^4 is a power with base 2 and exponent 4. $2^4 = 2 \cdot 2 \cdot 2 \cdot 2 = 16$
prime factorization (p. 169) Expressing a whole number as a product of prime numbers.	The prime factorization of 54 is $2 \times 3 \times 3 \times 3 = 2 \times 3^3$.
prime number (p. 169) A whole number greater than 1 whose only positive factors are 1 and itself.	5 is a prime number because its only positive factors are 1 and 5.
principal (p. 348) An amount of money that is deposited or borrowed.	*See* simple interest.
prism (p. 492) A solid, formed by polygons, that has two congruent bases lying in parallel planes.	
probability of an event (p. 354) A number from 0 to 1 that measures the likelihood that the event will occur.	*See* experimental probability *and* theoretical probability.
proportion (p. 322) An equation stating that two ratios are equivalent.	$\frac{3}{5} = \frac{6}{10}$ and $\frac{x}{12} = \frac{25}{30}$ are proportions.
pyramid (p. 492) A solid, formed by polygons, that has one base. The base can be any polygon, and the other faces are triangles.	
Pythagorean theorem (p. 443) For any right triangle, the sum of the squares of the lengths a and b of the legs equals the square of the length c of the hypotenuse: $a^2 + b^2 = c^2$.	$15^2 + 20^2 = 25^2$
Pythagorean triple (p. 451) A set of three positive integers a, b, and c such that $a^2 + b^2 = c^2$.	5, 12, and 13 is a Pythagorean triple.

Glossary

	Example
q	
quadrant **(p. 91)** One of the four regions that a coordinate plane is divided into by the x-axis and the y-axis.	*See* coordinate plane.
quadrilateral **(p. 386)** A closed geometric figure made up of four line segments, called sides, that intersect only at their endpoints; a polygon with four sides.	
r	
radical expression **(p. 431)** An expression involving a radical sign, $\sqrt{\ }$.	$\sqrt{3(22+5)}$ is a radical expression.
radius of a circle **(p. 290)** The distance between the center and any point on the circle.	*See* circle.
random sample **(p. 644)** A sample selected in such a way that each member of the population has an equally likely chance to be part of the sample.	A random sample of 5 eighth graders can be selected by putting the names of all eighth graders in a hat and drawing 5 names without looking.
range of a data set **(p. 258)** The difference of the greatest and least values in the data set.	The range of the data set 60, 35, 22, 46, 81, 39 is $81 - 22 = 59$.
range of a function **(p. 542)** The set of all possible output values for the function.	*See* function.
rate **(p. 318)** A ratio of two quantities measured in different units.	An airplane climbs 18,000 feet in 12 minutes. The airplane's rate of climb is $\frac{18{,}000 \text{ ft}}{12 \text{ min}} = 1500$ ft/min.
ratio **(p. 317)** A comparison of two numbers using division. The ratio of a to b (where $b \neq 0$) can be written as a to b, as $\frac{a}{b}$, or as $a : b$.	The ratio of 17 to 12 can be written as 17 to 12, as $\frac{17}{12}$, or as 17 : 12.
rational number **(p. 242)** A number that can be written as $\frac{a}{b}$ where a and b are integers and $b \neq 0$.	$6 = \frac{6}{1}$, $-\frac{3}{5} = \frac{-3}{5}$, $0.75 = \frac{3}{4}$, and $2\frac{1}{3} = \frac{7}{3}$ are all rational numbers.
real numbers **(p. 437)** The set of all rational numbers and irrational numbers.	0, $-\frac{5}{9}$, 2.75, and $\sqrt{3}$ are all real numbers.

Glossary

	Example
reciprocals (p. 234) Two nonzero numbers whose product is 1.	$\frac{2}{3}$ and $\frac{3}{2}$ are reciprocals.
reflection (p. 404) A transformation that creates a mirror image of each point of a figure; also known as a *flip*.	flip Reflection in the y-axis.
regular polygon (p. 390) A polygon with all sides equal in length and all angles equal in measure.	Regular pentagon
relation (p. 541) A set of ordered pairs.	(5, 7), (6, 5), (0, 5), (6, 0) is a relation
relatively prime numbers (p. 174) Two or more nonzero whole numbers whose greatest common factor is 1.	9 and 16 are relatively prime because their GCF is 1.
repeating decimal (p. 242) A decimal that has one or more digits that repeat without end.	0.7777. . . and $1.\overline{29}$ are repeating decimals.
rhombus (p. 386) A parallelogram with four congruent sides.	
right angle (p. 375) An angle whose measure is exactly 90°.	
right triangle (p. 382) A triangle with one right angle.	50° 40°
rise (p. 570) The vertical change between two points on a line.	*See* slope.

Glossary

	Example
rotation (p. 410) A transformation that rotates a figure through a given angle, called the angle of rotation, and in a given direction about a fixed point, called the center of rotation; also known as a *turn*.	
rotational symmetry (p. 410) A figure has rotational symmetry if a turn of 180° or less produces an image that fits exactly on the original figure.	 A square has rotational symmetry.
run (p. 570) The horizontal change between two points on a line.	*See* slope.

S

sample (p. 644) A part of a population.	To predict the results of an election, a survey is given to a sample of voters.
scale (p. 324) In a scale drawing, the scale gives the relationship between the drawing's dimensions and the actual dimensions.	The scale "1 in. : 10 ft" means that 1 inch in the scale drawing represents an actual distance of 10 feet.
scale drawing (p. 321) A diagram of an object in which the dimensions are in proportion to the actual dimensions of the object.	
scale factor (p. 418) The ratio of corresponding side lengths of a figure and its image after dilation.	*See* dilation.

Glossary

	Example
scale model **(p. 324)** A model of an object in which the dimensions are in proportion to the actual dimensions of the object.	A scale model of the White House appears in Tobu World Square in Japan. The scale used is 1 : 25.
scalene triangle **(p. 382)** A triangle with no congruent sides.	
scatter plot **(p. 545)** The graph of a set of data pairs (x, y), which is a collection of points in a coordinate plane.	
scientific notation **(p. 205)** A number is written in scientific notation if it has the form $c \times 10^n$ where c is greater than or equal to 1 and less than 10, and n is an integer.	In scientific notation, 328,000 is written as 3.28×10^5, and 0.00061 is written as 6.1×10^{-4}.
similar polygons **(p. 416)** Polygons that have the same shape but not necessarily the same size. Corresponding angles of similar polygons are congruent, and the ratios of the lengths of corresponding sides are equal. The symbol ~ is used to indicate that two polygons are similar.	 $\triangle LMN \sim \triangle PQR$
simple interest **(p. 348)** Interest that is earned or paid only on the principal. The simple interest I is the product of the principal P, the annual interest rate r written as a decimal, and the time t in years: $I = Prt$.	You deposit \$700 in a savings account that pays a 3% simple annual interest rate. After 5 years, the interest is $I = Prt = (700)(0.03)(5) = \$105$, and your account balance is $\$700 + \$105 = \$805$.
simplest form of a fraction **(p. 179)** A fraction is in simplest form if its numerator and denominator have a greatest common factor of 1.	The simplest form of the fraction $\frac{6}{8}$ is $\frac{3}{4}$.

	Example
sine (p. 463) The sine of any acute angle A of a right triangle is the ratio of the opposite leg to the hypotenuse.	side opposite $\angle A$; hypotenuse; side adjacent to $\angle A$; B, C, A, a, b, c $\sin A = \frac{a}{c}$
slant height (p. 507) The height of any face that is not the base of a regular pyramid.	slant height
slope (p. 570) The slope of a nonvertical line is the ratio of the rise (vertical change) to the run (horizontal change) between any two points on the line.	run = 5; rise = −2 The slope of the line above is: $\text{slope} = \frac{\text{rise}}{\text{run}} = \frac{-2}{5} = -\frac{2}{5}.$
slope-intercept form (p. 577) The form of a linear equation $y = mx + b$ where m is the slope and b is the y-intercept.	$y = 6x + 8$ is in slope-intercept form.
solid (p. 492) A three-dimensional figure that encloses a part of space.	*See* cone, cylinder, prism, pyramid, *and* sphere.
solution of an equation (p. 28) A number that makes the equation true when substituted for the variable in the equation.	The solution of the equation $n - 3 = 4$ is 7.
solution of an equation in two variables (p. 549) An ordered pair (x, y) that makes the equation true when the values of x and y are substituted into the equation.	$(3, 8)$ is a solution of $y = 3x - 1$.
solution of an inequality (p. 140) The set of all numbers that make the inequality true when substituted for the variable in the inequality.	The solution of the inequality $y + 2 > 5$ is $y > 3$.
solution of a linear inequality (p. 583) An ordered pair (x, y) that makes the inequality true when the values of x and y are substituted into the inequality.	A solution of $y \geq 2x - 9$ is $(5, 1)$.

Glossary

	Example
solving an equation **(p. 28)** Finding all solutions of the equation by using mental math or the properties of equality.	To solve the equation $4x = 20$, find the number that can be multiplied by 4 to equal 20; $4(5) = 20$, so the solution is 5.
sphere **(p. 492)** A solid formed by all points in space that are the same distance from a fixed point called the center.	center
square root **(p. 431)** A square root of a number n is a number m which, when multiplied by itself, equals n.	The square roots of 81 are 9 and -9 because $9^2 = 81$ and $(-9)^2 = 81$.
standard form **(p. 657)** A polynomial written with the exponents of the variable decreasing from left to right.	$3x^5 - 8x^3 + 5x^2 + x - 2$ is in standard form.
stem-and-leaf plot **(p. 597)** A data display that helps you see how data values are distributed. Each data value is separated into a leaf (the last digit) and a stem (the remaining digits). In an ordered stem-and-leaf plot, the leaves for each stem are listed in order from least to greatest.	stems leaves 10 | 8 11 | 2 2 5 12 | 1 3 Key: 10 | 8 = 108
straight angle **(p. 375)** An angle whose measure is exactly 180°.	
subtraction property of equality **(p. 109)** Subtracting the same number from each side of an equation produces an equivalent equation.	If $x + 7 = 9$, then $x + 7 - 7 = 9 - 7$, so $x = 2$. If $x + a = b$, then $x + a - a = b - a$.
supplementary angles **(p. 375)** Two angles whose measures have a sum of 180°.	79° 101°
surface area of a polyhedron **(p. 503)** The sum of the areas of the faces of the polyhedron.	3 in. 4 in. 6 in. *Surface area* $= 2(6)(4) + 2(6)(3) + 2(4)(3)$ $= 108 \text{ in.}^2$

Glossary

t	Example
tangent (p. 463) The tangent of any acute angle A of a right triangle is the ratio of the opposite leg to the adjacent leg.	side opposite $\angle A$; hypotenuse; side adjacent to $\angle A$; B, C, A, a, b, c $\tan A = \frac{a}{b}$
terminating decimal (p. 242) A decimal that has a final digit.	0.4 and 3.6125 are terminating decimals.
terms of an expression (p. 86) The parts of an expression that are added together.	The terms of $2x + 3$ are $2x$ and 3.
tessellation (p. 414) A covering of a plane with congruent copies of the same pattern so that there are no gaps or overlaps.	
theoretical probability (p. 354) When all outcomes are equally likely, the theoretical probability of an event is the ratio of the number of favorable outcomes to the number of possible outcomes.	A bag of 20 marbles contains 7 red marbles. The theoretical probability of randomly choosing a red marble is: $P(\text{red}) = \frac{7}{20} = 0.35.$
transformation (p. 404) An operation that changes a figure into another figure, called the image.	*See* translation, reflection, *and* rotation.
translation (p. 409) A transformation that moves each point of a figure the same distance in the same direction; also known as a *slide*.	slide; y; O; x
trapezoid (p. 386) A quadrilateral with exactly one pair of parallel sides.	

Glossary

	Example
tree diagram (p. 618) A branching diagram that shows all the possible choices or outcomes of a process carried out in several stages.	H: H, T; T: H, T Outcomes: HH, HT, TH, TT
trigonometric ratio (p. 463) A ratio of the lengths of two sides of a right triangle.	*See* sine, cosine, and tangent.
trinomial (p. 657) A polynomial with three terms.	$3x^2 + 2x - 4$

u

unfavorable outcome (p. 633) An outcome that is not a favorable outcome.	*See* favorable outcome.
unit rate (p. 318) A rate that has a denominator of 1 unit.	\$9 per hour is a unit rate.
upper extreme (p. 601) The greatest value in a data set.	*See* box-and-whisker plot.
upper quartile (p. 601) The median of the upper half of a data set.	*See* box-and-whisker plot.

v

variable (p. 15) A symbol, usually a letter, that is used to represent one or more numbers.	In the expression $m + 5$, the letter m is the variable.
variable expression (p. 15) An expression that consists of numbers, variables, and operations.	$n - 3$, $\frac{2s}{t}$, and $x + 4yz + 1$ are variable expressions.
verbal model (p. 11) A word equation that represents a real-world situation.	Distance traveled = Speed of car • Time traveled
vertex of a polyhedron (p. 492) A point where three or more edges of the polyhedron meet.	*See* edge of a polyhedron.
vertical angles (p. 376) A pair of opposite angles formed when two lines meet at a point.	1 2 3 4 $\angle 1$ and $\angle 3$ are vertical angles. $\angle 2$ and $\angle 4$ are also vertical angles.

Glossary

	Example
vertical line test **(p. 681)** If a vertical line intersects a graph at more than one point, then the graph does not represent a function.	Function / Not a function
volume of a solid **(p. 513)** The amount of space the solid occupies.	2 m, 3 m *Volume* = $\pi r^2 h$ $\approx (3.14)(2)^2(3)$ $\approx 37.7 \text{ m}^3$

X

***x*-axis** **(p. 91)** The horizontal number line in a coordinate plane.	*See* coordinate plane.
***x*-coordinate** **(p. 91)** The first number in an ordered pair representing a point in a coordinate plane.	The *x*-coordinate of the ordered pair (−2, 1) is −2.
***x*-intercept** **(p. 564)** The *x*-coordinate of the point where the graph intersects the *x*-axis.	The *x*-intercept is 4.

Y

***y*-axis** **(p. 91)** The vertical number line in a coordinate plane.	*See* coordinate plane.
***y*-coordinate** **(p. 91)** The second number in an ordered pair representing a point in a coordinate plane.	The *y*-coordinate of the ordered pair (−2, 1) is 1.
***y*-intercept** **(p. 564)** The *y*-coordinate of the point where the graph intersects the *y*-axis.	The *y*-intercept is 2.

Teacher's Edition Credits

Photography

T42 SW Productions/Getty Images; **T44** Frank Siteman; **T48** Ghislain & Marie David de Lossy/Getty Images; **T50** Graeme Harris/Getty Images; **T54** SW Productions/Getty Images

Credits

Photography

iii *top to bottom* Meridian Creative Group, RMIP/Richard Haynes, Michael Girard, Jerry Head Jr.; **vi** *br* Anup Shah/Getty Images; Copyright © AFP/Corbis; **vii** *br* Kwame; Jim Schwabel/Index Stock; **viii** Bobby Model/National Geographic/Getty Images; **ix** Copyright © Tom Stewart/Corbis; **x** Copyright © Reuters NewMedia/Corbis; **xi** Charles Krupa/AP Wide World Photos; **xii** *left* PhotoDisc; *right* Lee Celano/AP Wide World Photos; **xiii** Frank Siteman; **xiv** Paul Sancya/AP Wide World Photos; **xv** Kevin Bartram/The Galveston County Daily News/AP Wide World Photos; **xvi** Scott Spiker/ImageState; **xvii** West Rock/Stone/Getty Images; **xviii** Matthias Clamer/Stone/Getty Images; **1** John Warden/Getty Images; **2** Copyright © Corbis; **3** *left* Copyright © Joseph Sohm; Chromosohm, Inc./Corbis; *right* Copyright © Royalty-Free/Corbis; **5** Diaphor Agency/ Index Stock; **6** Copyright © Alan Schein/ CorbisStockMarket; **7** Copyright © Corbis; **8** Silvia Flores,The Press-Enterprise/AP Wide World Photos; **9** PhotoDisc; **10** Copyright © Mark Richards/PhotoEdit/PictureQuest; **11** Copyright © Galen Rowell/ Corbis; **12** Jerry Trafford; **13** *left* Julie Blum/Columbus Telegram/AP Wide World Photos; *right* Copyright © Becky Luigart-Stayner/Corbis; **15** *top* Copyright © PunchStock; *bottom* Zefa Visual Media-Germany/Index Stock; **17** *top* Greer & Associates, Inc/SuperStock; *bottom left* Stockbyte; *bottom right* PhotoDisc; **18** *left* James Meyer/The Image Bank/Getty Images; *right* Copyright © Comstock; **20** Copyright © Ron Watts/Corbis; **22** PhotoDisc; **23** Eric Wessman/ Photonica; **26** Frank Siteman; **27** Syracuse Newspapers/The Image Works; **29** *both* Copyright © Reuters NewMedia, Inc./Corbis; **31** Copyright © AFP/Corbis; **34** Barbara Strnadova/Photo Researchers, Inc.; **35** Larry West/Photo Researchers, Inc.; **36** Ken Osburn/ Index Stock; **37** Johner/ Photonica; **38** Ted S. Warren/AP Wide World Photos; **42** Kevork Djansezian/AP Wide World Photos; **47** Copyright © Stephen Frink/Corbis; **48** PhotoDisc; **53** Artville; **54** *top left* Copyright © Comstock; *bottom left* Photo by Jerry Trafford, Courtesy of Vintage IWear; *right* Artville; **56** *left* NASA; *right* Ken O'Donoghue; **61** *both* The Picture Desk; **62** Copyright © Bob Daemmrich/PictureQuest; **64** Jeff Hunter/The Image Bank/Getty Images; **66** Tim Haske/Index Stock; **68** Frank Siteman; **69** Copyright © Kwame Zikomo/SuperStock; **70** *top* Shinoda/Photonica; *bottom* Copyright © Stephen Frink/Corbis; **73** *left* Copyright © Corbis; *right, both* PhotoDisc; **75** Copyright © Dean Conger/Corbis; **76** PhotoDisc; **77** Copyright © Paul A. Souders/Corbis; **80** *top* School Division, Houghton Mifflin Company; *bottom* Steve Casimiro/Getty Images; **83** Steven Senne/AP Wide World Photos; **84** *left* Ken O'Donoghue, *right* PhotoDisc; **85** SuperStock; **87**, **88** *all* Ken O'Donoghue; **89** Jim Schwabel/Index Stock; **93** Copyright © Bill Ross/Corbis; **94** *top left* Copyright © PhotoDisc/Getty Images; *top right* EyeWire Collection/Getty Images; **99** School Division, Houghton Mifflin Company; **102** *top* Copyright © Galen Rowell/Corbis; *bottom* Copyright © Darrell Gulin/Corbis; **103** *top* Copyright ©Bjorn Backe; Papilio/Corbis; *bottom* Copyright © Richard Hamilton Smith/ Corbis; **104** *all* NASA; **105** *left* NASA; *right* Copyright © NASA/Corbis; **110** Bobby Model/National Geographic/Getty Images; **111** Ken O'Donoghue; **112** Darryl Torckler/Getty Images; **114** Steve Hix/Getty Images; **115** G.D.T./Getty Images; **119** *top* Stockbyte; *bottom* Frank Siteman; **121** Ken O'Donoghue; **123** Dennis O'Clair/Getty Images; **124** Mitchell Funk/Getty Images; **127** *left* Copyright © Image 100/Royalty-Free/Corbis; *right* Ken O'Donoghue; **132** Frank Siteman; **133** Antonio Mo/Getty Images; **135** Copyright © Cosmo Condina; **136** John Warden/ Getty Images; **138** Brand X Pictures; **139** RubberBall Productions/CorbisStockMarket; **140** *left* Ken O'Donoghue; *right* Copyright © Kurt Wittman/Corbis; **143** Adrian Weinbrecht/Getty Images; **144** Copyright © Reuters NewMedia Inc./ Corbis; **147** Art Wolfe/Getty Images; **148** Brand X Pictures; **149** Dale Durfee/Stone/Getty Images; **154** Ryan McVay/PhotoDisc/Getty Images; **163** David Young-Wolff/Stone/Getty Images; **164** Alistair Cowin/Index Stock; **165** *background* Benelux Press/Index Stock; *top left* Stephen Simpson/Taxi/Getty Images; *top right* Copyright © Tom Stewart/Corbis; *bottom left* Benelux Press/Index Stock; **168** *both* Ken O'Donoghue; **170** School Division, Houghton Mifflin Company; **171** National Park Service Historic Photograph Collection; **172** Ken O'Donoghue; **175** *top* School Division, Houghton Mifflin Company; *bottom* Bob Torrez/Stone/Getty Images; **176** *both* PhotoDisc; **177** Courtesy of Jonathan Wheeler; **179** *top* Copyright © Erich Lessing/Art Resource, NY; *center three images* Christie's Images; *bottom image* Eric Kamp/Index Stock; **180** *both* Christie's Images; **181** PhotoDisc; **181** Copyright © PhotoDisc; **182** Claus Meyer/Minden Pictures; **184** Frank Siteman; **185** David Davis/Index Stock; **186** *left* Copyright © Guy Cali/Picturequest; *right* Copyright © Comstock; **188** Copyright © Corbis; **193** Konrad Wothe/Minden Pictures; **194** Copyright © Tom Stewart/Corbis; **195** Steve Miller/AP Wide World Photos; **199** Copyright © NASA/Corbis; **201** *top* Copyright © Roger Holden/Index Stock/PictureQuest; *bottom* Copyright © M. Hans/Vandystadt/Photo Researchers, Inc.; **203** Copyright © MICROFIELD SCIENTIFIC LTD/Photo Researchers, Inc.; **204** *left* Artville; *right* Pho/AP Wide World Photos; **205** *top* Courtesy of Fan Yang; The Science of Bubbles; *center* International Stock/ImageState; **207** NASA; **208** Artville; **213** Robb Helfrick/Index Stock; **214** G.K. & Vikki Hart/The Image Bank/Getty Images; **216** © David Brooks/Corbis; **217** *left* Don Mason/Corbis; *right* School Division, Houghton Mifflin Company; **220** Photo by Shawn Lockhart, courtesy of Southwest Wisconsin Reptiles; **222** David Madison/Stone/Getty Images; **223** David Young-Wolff/Stone/Getty Images; **224** Ryan McVay/PhotoDisc/ PictureQuest; **225** Ken O'Donoghue; **226** Copyright © Reuters NewMedia Inc./Corbis; **228** Frank Siteman; **229** Donna Day/Stone/Getty Images; **230** EyeWire Collection/Getty Images; **231** *top* F. Schussler/Photolink/ Getty Images; *bottom* PunchStock; **232** Ken O'Donoghue; **233** Gianni Cigolini/Image Bank/Getty Images; **236** Copyright © Image 100/Royalty-Free/Corbis; **243** Steve Maslowski/Photo Researchers, Inc.; **244** G.K. & Vikki Hart/The Image Bank/Getty Images; **245** Frank Siteman; **246** Tom Bean/Stone/Getty Images; **247** Frank Siteman; **248** Ken O'Donoghue; **250** Copyright © Peter Adams/Index Stock/PictureQuest; **251** Bruce Leighty/Index Stock; **253** Michael K. Nichols/National Geographic/Getty Images; **254** Brad Lewis/Adventure Photography/ImageState; **257** Copyright © Ralph White/Corbis; **258** Copyright © Tom Stewart/Corbis; **259** PhotoDisc; **260** Copyright © Jon Feingersh/Corbis; **265** Kevin Schafer/The Image Bank/Getty Images; **266** Copyright © Comstock; **269** Ken O'Donoghue; **271** *both* Ken O'Donoghue; **273** Neo Vision/Photonica; **274** Copyright © Chuck Savage/CorbisStockMarket; **275** Ken O'Donoghue; **276** Copyright © Rob Lewine/CorbisStockMarket; **277** Volo Pictures/ Photonica; **278** Stockbyte; **281** Tony Anderson/Taxi/Getty Images; **282** *top* Gary Bell/Taxi/Getty Images; *bottom* Georgette Douwma/Taxi/Getty Images; **285**, **288** Ken O'Donoghue; **289** *top row: left, center* Ken O'Donoghue; *right* PhotoDisc; *bottom row: left, right* Ken O'Donoghue; *center* Comstock; **291** Copyright © Alan Schein Photography/Corbis; **294** Frank Siteman; Copyright © Anthony Nex/Corbis; **296** *left* Antonio Mo/Getty Images; *right* Copyright © Comstock; **298** Charles Krupa/AP Wide World Photos; **301** *top* Copyright © Duomo/Corbis; *bottom* Frank Siteman; **303** Ken O'Donoghue; **304** Josef Peter Fankhauser/Getty Images; **312** *left* Copyright © Tony Freeman/Photo Edit; *type background* Copyright © Corbis; **313** Zefa Visual Media Germany/Index Stock; **315** Ken O'Donoghue; **317** Copyright © Marc Muench/Corbis; **318** Copyright © J Silver/SuperStock Images; **319** Frank Siteman; **321** PhotoDisc; **322** Copyright © Wolfgang Kaehler/Corbis; **324** Courtesy of the city of Strawberry Point, Iowa; **325** Copyright © Paul A. Souders/ Corbis; **326** School Division, Houghton Mifflin Company; **327** *top* PhotoDisc; *bottom* Lee Celano/AP Wide World Photos; **328** *left* Ian Shaw/ Stone/Getty Images; *right: inset top* Stockbyte; *inset bottom* Photospin; **329** Stuart Cohen/The Image Works; **330** Ken O'Donoghue; **331** Philip Lee Harvey/Getty Images; **334** C Squared Studios/PhotoDisc/Getty Images; **335** Ken O'Donoghue; **338** PhotoDisc; **339** Copyright © Nik Wheeler/ Corbis; **340** *left* Copyright © Patrik Giardino/Corbis; *right* Corbis; **341** Getty Images; **342** *top* Darrell Gulin/Stone/Getty Images; *bottom* Nick Daly/Stone/Getty Images; **344** Ken O'Donoghue; **345** Copyright © Stockbyte/PunchStock; **346** PhotoDisc; **347** *top* PhotoDisc; *bottom* Copyright © Ariel Skelley/Corbis; **348** PhotoDisc; **349** James L. Stanfield/ National Geographic Image Collection; **350** Inga Spence/Index Stock; **352** Frank Siteman; **353** Daniel Allan/Taxi/Getty Images; **355** Ken O'Donoghue; **357** Don Smetzer/Stone/Getty Images; **361**, **362** PhotoDisc; **371** Copyright © Royalty-Free/Corbis; **373** Ken O'Donoghue; **376** Copyright © Mike Chew/Corbis; **379**, **380** Ken O'Donoghue; **385**

Copyright © Lee Snider/Corbis; **391** *top* Ken O'Donoghue; *bottom* PhotoDisc; **393** Lionel Glyn Coates/www.bciusa.com; **397** *top* David Young-Wolff/Stone/Getty Images; *bottom* Stockbyte/PunchStock; *frames*: Ken O'Donoghue; **399** Copyright © Richard Cummins/Corbis; **400** Courtesy of Michigan State University, Department of Crop and Soil Sciences; **401** *both* Sanford Ponder www.thepod.net; **402** Frank Siteman; **403** Copyright © Tim Pannell/Corbis; **404** Frank Siteman; **406** *all* PhotoDisc; **412** *top left, right* Ken O'Donoghue; *center left* Copyright © SuperStock Images; **414, 415** Ken O'Donoghue; **416** Frank Siteman; *televisions*: PhotoDisc; **428** *background* PhotoDisc; *top left* ImageState; *center, both* Ken O'Donoghue; **429** *top left* Joe McBride/Stone/Getty Images; *top right* PhotoDisc/Getty Images; *bottom right* Copyright © Royalty-Free/Corbis; *background insets* PhotoDisc; **432** Ian Shaw/Getty Images; **433** Eunice Harris/Photo Researchers, Inc.; **434** Frank Siteman; **435** Ed Elberfeld/Index Stock; **436** Benelux Press/Index Stock; **439** *left* Rex Ziak/Stone/Getty Images; *right* AP Photo/Goran Stenberg; **440** Ken O'Donoghue; **441** Frank Siteman; **444** Copyright © Royalty-Free/Corbis; **446** Arthur Tilley/Stone/Getty Images; **447** *top* Alan Carey/Photo Researchers, Inc.; *left* Copyright © George Lepp/Corbis; **448** *background* Ken O'Donoghue; *center* Frank Siteman; **449** Sentinel-Tribune, J.D. Pooley/AP Wide World Photos; **450** *left* Copyright © Tony Freeman/ PhotoEdit, Inc.; *right* School Division, Houghton Mifflin Company; **453** *left* Copyright © Royalty-Free/Corbis; *center* Jeffrey Sylvester/Taxi/ Getty Images; *center right* Ken O'Donoghue; *right* PhotoDisc; **456** *top* Ken O'Donoghue; *bottom* Copyright © Cleve Bryant/PhotoEdit, Inc.; **458** Telegraph Herald, David Raoyal/AP Wide World Photos; **459** Copyright © SuperStock Images; **463** Copyright © Jeff Greenberg/eStock Photography/ PictureQuest; **465** Paul Sancya/AP Wide World Photos; **466** Harvey Lloyd/ Taxi/Getty Images; **468** Greg Kiger/Index Stock; **473** Copyright © Tony Freeman/PhotoEdit, Inc.; **474** Christophe Ratier/Photo Researchers, Inc.; **476** *top left* courtesy of The Planetarium, Armagh, Northern Ireland; *bottom left* Ken Wardius/Index Stock; *type background* Digital Vision Getty Images; **477** *top right* courtesy of The Planetarium, Armagh, Northern Ireland; *top inset* Copyright © Corbis; *bottom* Copyright © Roger Ressmeyer/Corbis; **482** Copyright © Thomas A. Heinz/Corbis; **485** Stockbyte; **487** Mike Powell/Allsport Concepts/Getty Images; **488** David Lees/Taxi/Getty Images; **489** Copyright © Australian Picture Library/ Corbis; **494** *all* Ken O'Donoghue; **495** Copyright © Philip Gould/Corbis; **500** Frank Siteman; **501** Moggy/Stone/Getty Images; **502** courtesy of Kerry Cashman, photo by Ken O'Donoghue; **505** Ken O'Donoghue; **506** Copyright © Dave G. Houser/Corbis; **509** Copyright © Greer & Associates, Inc./SuperStock Images; **510** *left* PhotoDisc; *right, both* Copyright © Corbis; **511** Copyright © Royalty-Free/Corbis; **513** Copyright © Mark Gibson/Corbis; **516** PhotoDisc; **517** David Hanover/ Stone/Getty Images; **519** Kevin Bartram/The Galveston County Daily News/AP Wide World Photos; **521** EyeWire Collection/Getty Images; **537** Copyright © Royalty-Free/Corbis; **539** *left* Jason Hindley/Stone/Getty Images; *right* Ken O'Donoghue; **541, 542** Frank Siteman; **543** Sea World/ AP Wide World Photos; **544** Copyright © Peter Beck/Corbis; **545** NASA/AP Wide World Photos; **548** Copyright © Royalty-Free/Corbis; **549** *top* Copyright © Brooklyn Productions/Royalty-Free/Corbis; *bottom* Copyright © Merritt Vincent/PhotoEdit, Inc.; **551** Ken O'Donoghue; **552** Copyright © Mark Garten/Corbis; **554** Frank Siteman; **555** Copyright © Corbis; **557** Donna Day/Stone/Getty Images; **559** Antonio Mo/Taxi/Getty Images; **565** Copyright © Kevin Radford/SuperStock; **566** Copyright © Tom Stewart/ Corbis; **570** Jim Schwabel/Index Stock; **572** Nancy R. Cohen/PhotoDisc/ Getty Images; **574** Glyn Kirk/Stone/Getty Images; **577** RO-MA Stock/Index Stock; **578** Copyright © Larry Prosor/SuperStock; **579** Ken O'Donoghue; **580** Copyright © J. H. Robinson/Photo Researchers, Inc.; **585** Ken O'Donoghue; **586** Scott Spiker/ImageState; **591** WEST ROCK/Taxi/Getty Images; **592** Stewart Cohen/Index Stock; **594–595** *background* Tui De Roy/Minden Pictures; **595** *left* Tui De Roy/Minden Pictures; *center* Michio Hoshino/Minden Pictures; *right* Franz Lanting/Minden Pictures; **597** *top* David Young-Wolff/PhotoEdit, Inc.; *bottom* Rubberball/PunchStock; **600** Ron Schwane/AP Wide World Photos; **601** Paul Nicklen/National Geographic/Getty Images; **602** Jason Homa/The Image Bank/Getty Images; **604** The Time Herald, Tony Pitts/ AP Wide World Photos; **606** A. H. Rider/Photo Researchers, Inc.; **607** *top* Stuart Hughs/Stone/Getty Images; *bottom* School Division, Houghton Mifflin Company; **609** Antonio Mo/ Taxi/Getty Images; **616** Frank Siteman; **617** Copyright © Lisette Le Bon/SuperStock; **618** Frank Siteman; **619** Copyright © Roger Allyn Lee/SuperStock Images; **622** Billy Hustace/Stone/Getty Images; **624** Myrleen Cate/Index Stock; **625** *all* PhotoDisc *except 4th from right*: Photospin; **626** Rubberball/PunchStock; **627** *top, both* Ken O'Donoghue; *center left* West Rock/Stone/Getty Images; **629** Ken O'Donoghue; **631** Marc Romanelli/The Image Bank/ Getty Images; **634** Photo by David Gray, Copyright © Reuters 1998; **635** Ken O'Donoghue; **636** Stephen Simpson/ Taxi/Getty Images; **639** School Division, Houghton Mifflin Company; **644** Ken O'Donoghue; **645** Marvin E. Newman/The Image Bank/Getty Images; **648** Dorling Kindersley; **649** Zbigniew Bzdak/The Times of Northwest Indiana/AP Wide World Photos; **652** *left* Copyright © Eric and David Hosking/Corbis; *right* Copyright © Gary W. Carter/Corbis; **653** *top right* PhotoDisc; *bottom right* Copyright © Arthur Morris/Corbis; **654, 655** *all* Ken O'Donoghue, *except* **655** *bottom row, far right*: Comstock; **658** Matthias Clamer/Stone/ Getty Images; **660** Copyright © Royalty-Free/ Corbis; **663** PhotoDisc/ Getty Images; **664** Ken O'Donoghue; **667** Ken O'Donoghue; **669** Ken O'Donoghue; *inset* Stockbyte; **670** Copyright © NASA/Corbis; **676** PhotoDisc; **677** PhotoDisc/ Getty Images; **678** Frank Siteman; **679** Copyright © Royalty-Free/Corbis; **680** Frank Siteman; **683** Copyright © M.Dillon/Corbis

Illustration

Brian White
19, 30, 43, 60, 67, 72, 95, 116, 128, 145, 177, 189, 200, 221, 237, 238, 261, 280, 287, 299, 320, 326, 333, 346, 389, 408, 420, 436, 445, 467, 471, 522, 546, 553, 582, 599, 615, 620, 642, 643, 665, 682, 684

Rob Dunlavey
268, 269 372, 373, 478, 479

Sam Ward
122

Credits

Selected Answers

Chapter 1

1.1 Getting Ready to Practice (p. 7) **1.** intervals **3.** 3 times **5.** Step 1: histogram; Steps 2–3:

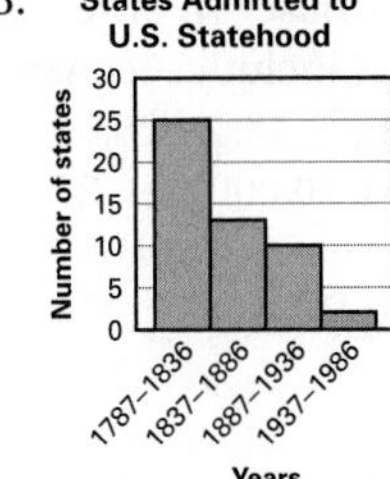

1.1 Practice and Problem Solving (pp. 7–9)
7. department stores **9.** No. *Sample answer:* The category with the most stores might not have the most floor space if each store is small, while a category with fewer stores might have the most floor space if each store is large. **11.** Table; exact amounts are given in a table but may be difficult to read from a bar graph.

13.

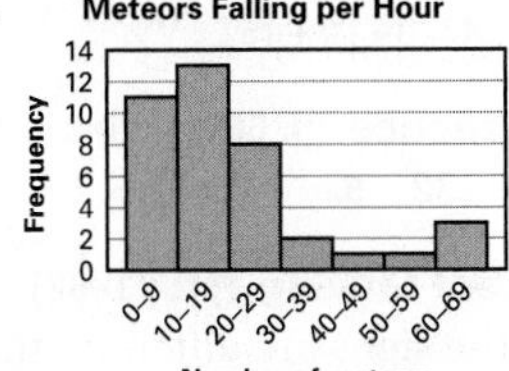

15. 52 hurricanes **17.** No; there does not appear to be a pattern in the data.

19.

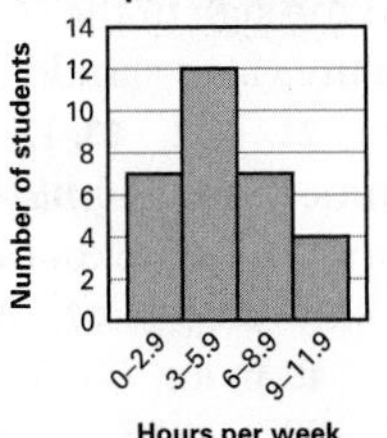

21. about 4000 schools **25.** 136 **27.** 7 **29.** 45.44 **31.** 58.78

1.2 Getting Ready to Practice (p. 12) **1.** Multiply 2 by 5. Add the result (10) to 8. Subtract 4 from this sum (18) to obtain the final result (14). **3.** Multiply 5 by 15; 25. **5.** Subtract 7 from 15; 18. **7.** Subtract 2 from 5; 30. **9.** In the second step, 63 must be divided by 9 before being added to 9: $3 \times 3 + 63 \div 9 = 9 + 63 \div 9 = 9 + 7 = 16$.

1.2 Practice and Problem Solving (pp. 12–13)
11. 29 **13.** 24 **15.** 15 **17.** 5 **19.** \$250 **21.** $\frac{3}{4}$ **23.** 12 **25.** 10.1 **27.** 54.6 **29.** 7 **31.** $12 \div (6 + 4 - 7) = 4$ **33.** 372 cookies **35.** $\times$; $12 \times (4 + 2) = 72$ **37.** 32 students **39.** 4 **41.** 6

1.2 Technology Activity (p. 14) **1.** 106.8 **3.** 7 **5.** 5 **7.** 2 **9.** \$10.44

1.3 Getting Ready to Practice (p. 17) **1.** variable; numerical **7.** 44 **9.** 5

1.3 Practice and Problem Solving (pp. 18–19)
11. 23 **13.** 39.5 **15.** 5 **17.** 6 **19.** $\frac{2}{5}x$ **21.** $12 + x$ **23.** 18 mi **25.** *Sample answer:* Serena is saving to buy a gift for her sister. She starts with \$2 and saves an additional \$8 per week. **27.** $4 + 17n$; \$106 **29.** 32.8 **31.** 96 **33.** 1.6 **35.** 10 **37.** A good answer will include an expression that can only be evaluated correctly by using the order of operations. The explanation of the correct order to use will follow the rules for the order of operations. **39.** $2.75p + 1.25d$; \$13.25 **41.** 50 **43.** 18 **45.** 4095 **47.** 42

1.4 Getting Ready to Practice (p. 22) **1.** *Sample answer:* base $\rightarrow 3^{2} \leftarrow$ exponent **3.** 1331 **5.** 64 **7.** 0 **9.** 6 **11.** 7^2 means 7×7; $7^2 = 7 \times 7 = 49$.

1.4 Practice and Problem Solving (pp. 22–23)
13. 3^3; 3 to the third power, or 3 cubed **15.** 6 **17.** 128 **19.** 1 **21.** 109 **23.** 12 **25.** 3 **27.** 16 **29.** 119 **31.** $1000 \cdot 2^3$ **33.** < **35.** 17.17 **37.** 1030.301 **39.** No; $16 \cdot 2^2 = 64$, so the divers have fallen 64 feet after 2 seconds. **41.** 302 **45.** 9 **47.** 6 outfits. *Sample answer:* I used Draw a Diagram because a tree diagram allowed me to find the total number of outfits in an organized way.

1.1–1.4 Notebook Review (pp. 24–25) **1.** Evaluate expressions inside grouping symbols. **2.** The question cannot be answered using the bar graph because the depth does not determine the area of the lake. **3.** Erie **4.** 18 **5.** 3 **6.** 7 **7.** 57 **8.** 1000 **9.** 370 **10.** The number of zeros is the same as the exponent.

1.5 Problem Solving Strategies (p. 27) **1.** 106, 107 **3.** 17 blue chips; 3 green chips **5.** *Sample:*

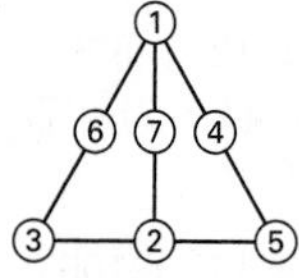

7. twice **9.** Bob, Kelly, Justin, Tim, Michelle

1.5 Getting Ready to Practice (p. 30) **1.** *Sample answer:* $4 + x = 7$; use mental math and ask "4 plus what number is 7?" The answer is 3. **3.** 44 **5.** 7 **7.** yes **9.** no

1.5 Practice and Problem Solving (pp. 30–31) **15.** yes **17.** no **19.** 11 **21.** 29 **23.** 2 **25.** 15 **27.** $14 + r = 43$; 29 in. **29.** $5033 + b = 5396$; 363 lb **31.** $4p = 60$; 15 invitations **37.** $x + 220 = 245$; 25 min **39.** 96 **41.** 6000 **43.** 1000

1.6 Getting Ready to Practice (p. 35) **1.** Area is the surface a figure covers, while perimeter is the distance around the figure. **3.** $P = 30$ in., $A = 56$ in.^{2} **5.** 159 cm

1.6 Practice and Problem Solving (pp. 36–37) **7.** $P = 22$ cm, $A = 24$ cm^2 **9.** $P = 40$ ft, $A = 100$ ft^2 **11.** $P = 72$ in., $A = 324$ in.^{2} **13.** $P = 54$ cm, $A = 182$ cm^2 **15.** 6 m **17.** 9 km/h **19.** 10.5 mi **21.** 225 mi **23.** 90 mi/h **25.** about 4 h **27.** 1560 ft **29.** 2 bags **33.** 9 **35.** 30 **37.** 15.54

1.7 Getting Ready to Practice (p. 41) **1.** Step 1. Read and Understand, Step 2. Make a Plan, Step 3. Solve the Problem, Step 4. Look Back **3.** Step 1: Trains in one hour = people in one hour ÷ people per train, so trains in one hour = people in one hour ÷ (cars per train • passengers per car); Step 2: 45 trains; Step 3: $45 \cdot 20 = 900$

1.7 Practice and Problem Solving (pp. 41–43) **5.** 15 h **7.** 16 h **9.** 12 oz **11.** 3, 1 **13.** 9, 5 **15.** $5060 **17.** $8x$, $10x$ **19.** $31x^2$, $39x^2$ **21.** 7 ft; 49 ft^2 **23.** 5 **25.** 4 **29.** 0 **31.** $P = 38$ in., $A = 48$ in.^{2} **33.** > **35.** >

1.5–1.7 Notebook Review (pp. 44–45) **1.** $P = 2l + 2w$ **2.** 13 **3.** 12 **4.** 3 **5.** 18 **6.** $P = 22$ m, $A = 28$ m^2 **7.** 9 teaspoons **8.** Yes; perimeter is measured in linear units and area is measured in square units.

Chapter Review (pp. 46–47) **1.** histogram **3.** order of operations **5.** base **7.** false **9.** true **11.** No; the age group that includes teenagers also includes other ages. **13.** 1 **15.** $2 \cdot 28.5 - 20$; $37 **17.** 4 **19.** 72 **21.** 225 **23.** 10,000 **25.** 27 **27.** 261 **29.** 7 **31.** $P = 32$ m, $A = 60$ m^2 **33.** $P = 32$ in., $A = 64$ in.^{2} **35.** B, C, and D

Chapter 2

2.1 Getting Ready to Practice (p. 55) **1.** opposites **3.** −130, −56, 0, 62, 74, 120 **5.** 8, 8 **7.** −1327, 1327

2.1 Practice and Problem Solving (pp. 55–56) **9.** > **11.** < **13.** > **15.** > **17.** −20, −12, 18, 44, 59, 64 **23.** Gieselmann Lake **25.** 32 **27.** −29 **29.** 81 **31.** −3 **33.** = **35.** < **37.** Flight crew departs for launch pad. Pilot starts auxiliary power units. Main engine starts. Liftoff. Shuttle clears launch tower, and control switches to the Mission Control Center. **41.** 19 **43.** 34 pages

2.2 Getting Ready to Practice (p. 60) **1.** absolute values **3.** −12 **5.** 0 **7.** −32 **9.** −34 **11.** −17

2.2 Practice and Problem Solving (pp. 61–62) **13.** −3 **15.** 4 **17.** Since the signs are different, the lesser absolute value should be subtracted from the greater absolute value and the sign of the number with the greater absolute value should be used; $-8 + 5 = -3$. **19.** −109 **21.** −82 **23.** 12 **25.** −3 **27.** always **29.** sometimes **31.** *Sample answer:* when you are balancing your checkbook **33.** $-1200 + 800 = -400$; 400 B.C. **35.** 90 **37.** 146 **39.** −1207 **41.** −999 **43.** 0; at **45.** 0; no **47.** 5 **49.** −19 **51.** 122 **53.** 512 **55.** −921, −346, −125, 128, 724

2.3 Getting Ready to Practice (p. 65) **1.** $-2 - 6$ **3.** −7 **5.** −4 **7.** −10 **9.** −23 **11.** Step 1: 55 ft, 0 ft, −35 ft; Step 2: $55 - 0 = 55$ ft, $0 - (-35) = 35$ ft, $55 - (-35) = 90$ ft; Step 3: 55, 35, 90

2.3 Practice and Problem Solving (pp. 65–67) **13.** 0 **15.** −8 **17.** −27 **19.** 44 **21.** −1000 points **23.** 5 **25.** Subtract −137 from 123. **27.** 42°F

29. -259 **31.** 1802 **33.** -10 **35.** -18 **37.** 12 **39.** -71 **41.** Triassic Period: 37 million yr; Jurassic Period: 64 million yr; Cretaceous Period: 79 million yr **43.** 5 **45.** -31 **49.** 8 **51.** 3 **53.** 2 **55.** 168 **57.** 5649

2.4 Problem Solving Strategies (p. 69) **1.** 55 dots **3.** 144 blue tiles **5.** Scott: 12 yr old, Ben: 15 yr old, Kelly: 9 yr old **7.** \$40 **9.** 19 ways

2.4 Getting Ready to Practice (p. 72) **1.** negative **3.** 0 **5.** -6 **7.** 270 **9.** The product of two negative integers is positive; $-8(-12) = 96$.

2.4 Practice and Problem Solving (pp. 72–73) **11.** 17 **13.** 44 **15.** -15 **17.** 32 **19.** -288 **21.** 0 **23.** 70 **25.** -133 **27.** -132 **29.** -4 **31.** -4 **33.** The power is positive when the exponent is even and negative when the exponent is odd. **35.** 64 **37.** 9216 **39.** $-\$81.70$ **41.** $-104{,}832$ **43.** -682 **45.** 17 ft **47.** -23 **49.** 15 **51.** 2

2.5 Getting Ready to Practice (p. 76) **1.** mean **3.** 0 **5.** -5 **7.** -3 **9.** -3

2.5 Practice and Problem Solving (pp. 76–77) **11.** 7 **13.** -9 **15.** 7 **17.** 0 **19.** 1 **21.** Always. *Sample answer:* The mean of -3, -5, and -1 is $\frac{-9}{3} = -3$. **23.** 4 **25.** -4 **27.** -1.5 **29.** 0.8 **31.** -29.2°F **35.** 5^5 **37.** b^4 **39.** -72

2.1–2.5 Notebook Review (pp. 78–79)
1. 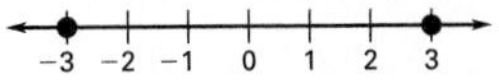

2. $-15, -5, 1, 4, 8, 16$ **3.** $-85, -60, -6, 40, 42, 98$ **4.** 38 **5.** -55 **6.** -119 **7.** -66 **8.** -65 **9.** -15 **10.** 312 **11.** -62 **12.** -6 **13.** 4 **14.** Yes. *Sample answer:* The opposite of the sum can be written as $-1(a + b)$. Using the distributive property you get $-a + (-b)$ which is the sum of the opposites.

2.6 Getting Ready to Practice (p. 82) **7.** 45; commutative and associative properties of addition **9.** -290; commutative and associative properties of multiplication **11.** -36; associative property of addition **13.** 15 in.^{3}

2.6 Practice and Problem Solving (pp. 83–84) **15.** 54; commutative property of multiplication **17.** 9; associative property of addition **19.** 69 **21.** 21 **23.** -700 **25.** -900 **27.** $70x$ **29.** $70 + x$ **31.** No. *Sample answer:* $20 \div 4 = 5$, but $4 \div 20 = 0.2$. **33.** 5.7 **35.** 35 **37.** 420 **39.** \$60 **41.** The student grouped the first and last numbers, the second and next to last numbers, and so on, to make 10, and then all of the 10s and the 5 were added to find the sum; 190. **45.** 26 in. and 34 in. *Sample answer:* I used Guess, Check, and Revise because I decided to choose two numbers whose sum was 60 and then check to see if the difference was 8. I revised my guess until it was correct. **47.** $1.35 < 1.53$

2.7 Getting Ready to Practice (p. 87) **1.** like terms: $7x$ and x, $-3y$ and $-6y$; coefficients: 7, -3, -6, 1 **3.** $-7(3) + (-7)(2)$ **5.** $9y$ **7.** $6m + n - 4b$

2.7 Practice and Problem Solving (pp. 88–89) **13.** $9x - 27$ **15.** 56 **17.** $-34z + 884$ **19.** $4r + 2s$ **21.** $5a + 6b$ **23.** $-3x - 9y$ **25.** Add \$2.35 and \$.65 to get \$3.00. Multiply \$3.00 by 6 to find the total, \$18. **27.** $7y - 14$ **29.** $2x + 2$ **31.** $12d$ **33.** \$786.24 **35.** $3x - 5$ **37.** $1.7y - 6.7$ **39.** *Sample answer:* $4(30 + 4) = 120 + 16 = 136$; mental math can be used to multiply and then add. **41.** *Sample answer:* $24(10 + 2) = 240 + 48 = 288$; mental math can be used to multiply and then add. **43.** Yes; by the commutative property of multiplication, $xy = yx$. **47.** $-100, -90, -20, 0, 70$ **49.** -21 **51.** -700

2.7 Technology Activity (p. 90) **1.** $-28{,}546$ **3.** 11,009 **5.** $-2{,}105{,}804$ **7.** $-262{,}890{,}144$ **9.** -101 **11.** about 13,904 km; about 10,428 km

2.8 Getting Ready to Practice (p. 93)
1. 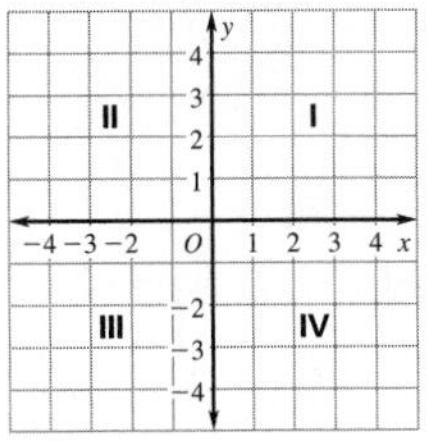

3. (0, 1) **5.** (1, -2)

SA3

6–9.

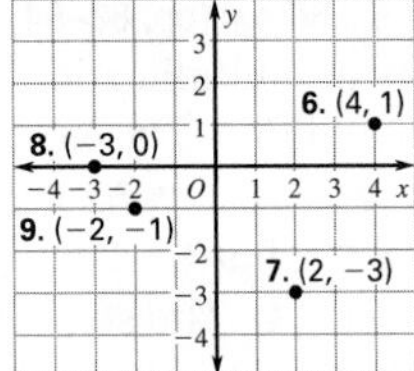

2.8 Practice and Problem Solving (pp. 93–95)
11. $(-3, 3)$ **13.** $(-5, 0)$ **15.** $(0, -2)$

17–20. 17. (−2, 3); 18. (3, −1); 20. (−3, −4); 19. (0, −5)

17. Quadrant II
19. y-axis

21.

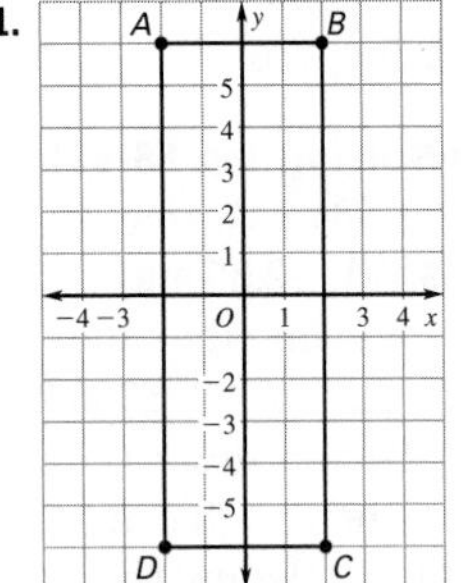

rectangle; 32 units

23.

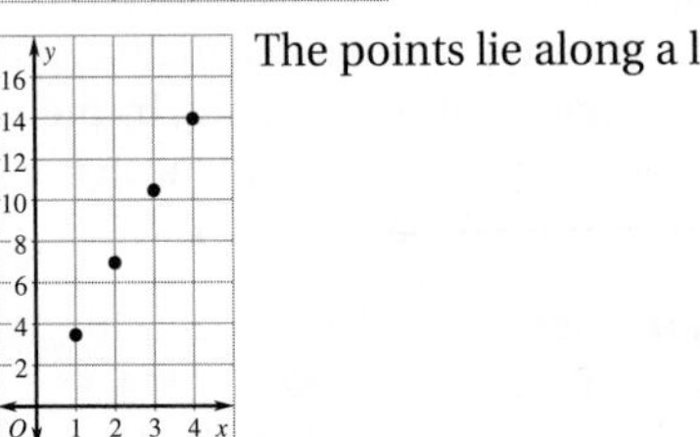

The points lie along a line; \$8.75.

25.

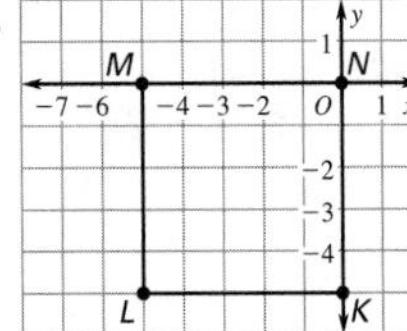

20 units; 25 square units

27. \$.70, \$1.40, \$2.10 **29.** \$4.20

31.

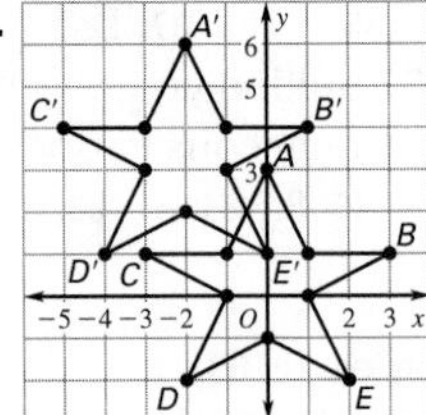

$A(-2, 6)$, $B(1, 4)$, $C(-5, 4)$, $D(-4, 1)$, $E(0, 1)$

33. -1 **35.** $4x + 36$ **37.** $-9z + 18$

2.6–2.8 Notebook Review (pp. 96–97) **1.** -5
2. -190 **3.** -1300 **4.** -83 **5.** $27a + 95$
6. $76b + 36$ **7.** $-70c + 40$

8–11.

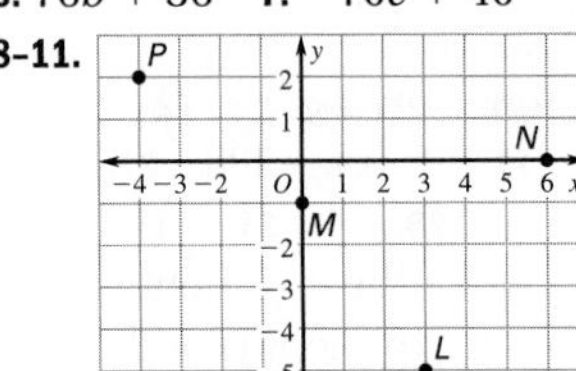

8. Quadrant IV
9. y-axis
10. x-axis
11. Quadrant II

12. Use $4(6 + 0.11) = 4(6) + 4(0.11) = 24 + 0.44 = 24.44$.

Chapter Review (pp. 98–99) **1.** 2; 15, -15
3. 4;

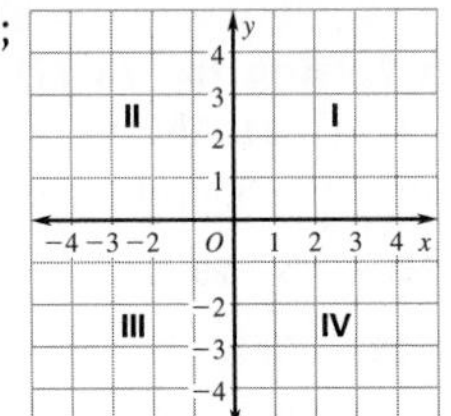

5. coordinate plane **7.** $-42, -31, -5, 8, 11, 53$
9. $-22, 22$ **11.** 512, 512 **13.** -172 **15.** 176
17. -86 **19.** 79 **21.** -54 **23.** 0 **25.** -192
27. -140 **29.** 152 ft **31.** 14 **33.** -9 **35.** 1
37. 97; commutative and associative properties of addition **39.** 1900; commutative and associative properties of multiplication **41.** 0; multiplication property of zero **43.** $63 + 77y$ **45.** $7x - 2y$
47. \$38.70 **49.** $(-4, 3)$ **51.** $(-2, -3)$

Chapter 3

3.1 Getting Ready to Practice (p. 111) **1.** inverse
3. 20 **5.** Step 1: Sales tax; Step 2: $54.99 + x = 58.29$; Step 3: \$3.30

3.1 Practice and Problem Solving (pp. 111–112)
7. subtracting 4.5 **9.** 5 **11.** 13 **13.** 2 **15.** 24 **17.** -28 **19.** 64 **21.** yes **23.** no; $t = 29 - 3$
25. *Sample answer:* There are 55 cats at the shelter. There are 13 more cats than dogs. How many dogs are at the shelter? **27.** 0 **29.** 1 **31.** 4.7 **33.** 8
35. -31 **39.** \$3.52

40–43.

41. Quadrant IV
43. Quadrant I

45. *Sample answer:* 130, 220 **47.** *Sample answer:* 2800, 4000

3.2 Getting Ready to Practice (p. 115) **1.** divide
3. $\frac{y}{9} = -3$ [original equation]; $\frac{y}{9} \cdot 9 = (-3) \cdot 9$ [Multiply each side by 9.]; $y = -27$ [Simplify.]

3.2 Practice and Problem Solving (pp. 115–116)
5. 18 **7.** 70 **9.** 3 **11.** 105 **13.** 216 **15.** 2.5
19. dividing by 5 **21.** subtracting -6, or adding 6
23. -216 **25.** 10 **27.** 29.9 **29.** 30 **31.** 3 **33.** -2.1
35. *Sample answer:* $3x = 18$, $\frac{x}{2} = 3$ **37.** about 17 eggs; about 4 eggs **39.** < **41.** > **43.** sixteen and two hundredths **45.** seven million, five hundred forty thousand, six hundred eighty-eight

3.3 Getting Ready to Practice (p. 121)
1. addition, division; 3 **3.** 3 **5.** 1 **7.** -4

3.3 Practice and Problem Solving (pp. 121–123)
11. 4 **13.** 7 **15.** $\frac{1}{4}$, or 0.25 **17.** 3 **19.** 9 **21.** $-\frac{1}{2}$, or -0.5 **23.** $2\frac{2}{3}$; because 3 miles is an estimate, $3h$ is an estimate for the number of miles of trail cleaned per hour, so the number of hours will also be an estimate. **25.** 7 **27.** $-1\frac{2}{3}$ **29.** 40 **31.** 55
33. -7 **35.** 24 **37.** 19 min **39.** Divide each side by 2; simplify; subtract 3 from each side; simplify.
41. -15 **45.** 132; the summer pass would be cheaper than paying for 40 day passes.

47. *Sample answer:* Choose the summer pass if you go to the pool more than 29 days because it is cheaper. Choose the day pass if you go to the pool 29 days or less because it is cheaper. **49.** 19
51. 48 **53.** 50% **55.** 20%

3.4 Practice and Problem Solving (pp. 126–128)
7. $4 + 5n = 9$; 1 **9.** 16 sandwiches on rye bread
11. *Sample answer:* You buy 5 boxes of your favorite cereal at the store. With the store's double-coupon policy, you save \$6 with your coupons. You pay \$9 for the cereal. What was the original price of each box? **13.** \$7 **15.** $2x + 5 = 12$; 3.5 **17.** $-2n + 3.5 = 7.5$; -2 **19.** 85 people **21.** the number of hours worked **27.** $P = 30$ ft; $A = 36$ ft^2 **29.** $P = 84$ m; $A = 432$ m^2 **31.** 35

3.4 Technology Activity (p. 129) **1.** *Sample answer:* $35(4) + 10x = 190$; 5 adults

3.1–3.4 Notebook Review (pp. 130–131)
1. addition and subtraction; multiplication and division **2.** -11 **3.** 42 **4.** 12 **5.** 47 **6.** -11
7. -9 **8.** 27 **9.** -40 **10.** 55 **11.** -4 **12.** 0 **13.** 2
14. 105 envelopes per hour **15.** It uses inverse operations in reverse order to their corresponding operations.

3.5 Problem Solving Strategies (p. 133) **1.** 672 ft^2
3. \$118,125 **5.** the room where students share tables **7.** The total number of students is greater than 1238.

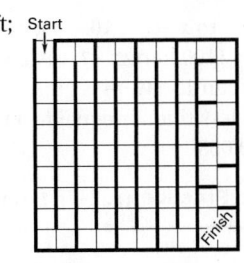

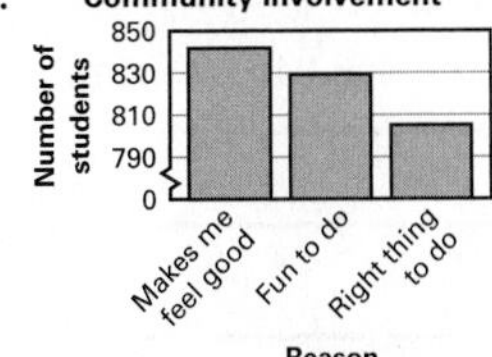

9. 96 ft; *Sample answer:* I tried drawing other mazes.

SA5

3.5 Getting Ready to Practice (p. 137) **1.** base, height **3.** $A = 4\text{ cm}^2$; $P = 8$ cm **5.** Step 1: 42 yd^2; Step 2: 9 yd^2; Step 3: 51 yd^2

3.5 Practice and Problem Solving (pp. 137–139)
7. $A = 24\text{ in.}^2$; $P = 32$ in. **9.** 3 ft **11.** 4 cm **13.** 20 m **15.** Area is given in square units; $A = 10\text{ in.}^2$ **17.** 24 in. **19.** $\frac{5}{x}$ m **21.** 16 m^2 **23.** 180 ft^2 **25.** *Sample answer:* about 3 ft by 6 ft; 18 ft^2 **27.** Doubles the area. **29.** Quadruples the area. **31.** No; Kate has 121 square feet and the room has an area of 252 square feet, so Kate has less than half the area of the room. **33.** 37.5 m^2 **35.** −60 **37.** 21 **39.** −32 **41.** 7 **43.** 35 **45.** > **47.** <

3.6 Getting Ready to Practice (p. 142)
1. equivalent inequalities
7. $t < -2$; −3 −2 −1 0 1 2 3
9. Step 1: 360; Step 2: $360 + x \geq 425$, $x \geq 65$; Step 3: 60 70 80 90

3.6 Practice and Problem Solving (pp. 143–145)
11. $x \geq -5$ **13.** $x < 6$ **15.** no **17.** yes **19.** j is greater than −4. **21.** n is less than 0.
23. $t > -3$; −4 −3 −2 −1 0 1 2
25. $r \geq 8$; −2 0 2 4 6 8 10
27. $p > 7$; 2 3 4 5 6 7 8
29. $m \leq 11$; 6 7 8 9 10 11 12
31. $33.96 + x \geq 50$; $x \geq \$16.04$ **33.** 20 min
35. $r < 7.5$; 5 6 7 8
37. $p \geq 3$; −1 0 1 2 3 4 5
39. $t > 4\frac{3}{4}$; 4 5
41. $x \geq 13$ is the solution to $x - 3 \geq 10$. **43.** no **45.** $x > 81$ hertz and $x < 1100$ hertz **47.** y is greater than −2 and y is less than 1. **49.** m is greater than or equal to 4 and m is less than or equal to 11. **53.** −53 **55.** −7 **57.** 9.053

3.7 Getting Ready to Practice (p. 148) **1.** reverse **3.** yes **5.** $m \leq -42$; −50 −46 −42 −38
7. $p > -5$; −6 −5 −4 −3 −2 −1 0

3.7 Practice and Problem Solving (pp. 148–149)
13. $x > 4$; −1 0 1 2 3 4 5
15. $b \leq -360$; −360 −120 0 120 240
17. $g < 6$; −2 0 2 4 6 8 10
19. $c \geq -6$; −8 −6 −4 −2 0 2 4
25. No; there are infinitely many solutions. **33.** You undo the operations in the same way. If you multiply or divide by a negative number in an inequality, you must reverse the direction of the inequality. **35.** $x \geq 80$ **37.** $x \geq \frac{1}{2}$ **41.** 12 cm by 16 cm **43.** 1 **45.** $c \leq 4$; 0 1 2 3 4 5 6
47. $x > 29$; 25 26 27 28 29 30 31 **49.** 72

3.5–3.7 Notebook Review (pp. 150–151)
1. *Sample:* height base **2.** 10 cm **3.** 9 ft
4. $h > 24$; 21 22 23 24 25 26 27
5. $k \leq 10$; 0 2 4 6 8 10 12
6. $p > -8$; −10 −8 −6 −4 −2 0 2
7. $d \geq -6$; −10 −8 −6 −4 −2 0 2
8. $d \leq 204$ **9.** $x \leq -100$ **10.** $c > 5$ **11.** $b > -4$ **12.** $c \geq 54$ **13.** 7; the solution to the inequality is $x < 8$ and the greatest integer that is less than 8 is 7.

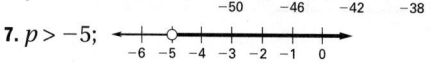

Chapter Review (pp. 152–153) **1.** Addition and subtraction, multiplication and division; one operation undoes the other. **3.** equivalent equations **5.** 32 **7.** 15 **9.** 40 **11.** 1288 **13.** −3 **15.** 2.4 **17.** Fuel in tank − Fuel used = Fuel left; $\frac{5}{8} - x = \frac{3}{8}$; $x = \frac{2}{8} = \frac{1}{4}$ **19.** 9 **21.** −5 **23.** 27 **25.** −115 **27.** −45 **29.** 18 baskets **31.** 8 m **33.** 20 in.^2 **35.** 60 yd^2
37. $c \leq 108$; −72 −36 0 36 72 108 144
39. $h > -4$; −5 −4 −3 −2 −1 0 1
41. The inequality sign should not be reversed when subtracting; $x < 10$.

Chapter 4

4.1 Getting Ready to Practice (p. 170) **1.** prime **3.** 1, 3, 9, 27 **5.** 1, 2, 3, 6, 11, 22, 33, 66 **7.** $5 \cdot 11$ **9.** $2^5 \cdot 3$

4.1 Practice and Problem Solving (pp. 171–172) **11.** 1, 2, 17, 34 **13.** 1, 2, 3, 4, 6, 9, 12, 18, 27, 35, 54, 108 **15.** composite **17.** prime **19.** $2^3 \cdot 7$ **21.** $2 \cdot 3 \cdot 17$ **23.** second row: 8; fourth row: 2, 2, 2, 11; $2^3 \cdot 11$ **25.** second row: 2; third row: 2, 21; fourth row: 5, 3, 7; $2 \cdot 3 \cdot 5 \cdot 7$ **27.** $3 \cdot 5 \cdot c \cdot d$ **29.** $3 \cdot 3 \cdot a \cdot a \cdot b \cdot b \cdot b \cdot b$ **31.** 3 stars by 5 stars **33.** 5 stars by 6 stars (or 3 stars by 10 stars, or 2 stars by 15 stars) **35.** 1, 13, 23, 299 **37.** 1, 2, 4, 5, 8, 10, 16, 20, 25, 40, 50, 80, 100, 200, 400 **39.** $2^3 \cdot 5 \cdot 7$ **41.** $3^2 \cdot 5^3$ **43.** *Sample answer:* $3 + 7$ **45.** *Sample answer:* $11 + 17$ **47.** No; 40 is not a factor of 140. **49.** 2 and 3 **53.** $-4a + 4b + 2$ **55.** $y \geq 40$ **57.** 850 ft^2. *Sample answer:* I used Draw a Diagram to draw the spaces and find the area. **59.** *Sample answer:* 7000; 9000 **61.** *Sample answer:* 13; 20

4.2 Getting Ready to Practice (p. 175) **1.** greatest common factor, or GCF **7.** Step 1: $56 = 2 \cdot 2 \cdot 2 \cdot 7$, $68 = 2 \cdot 2 \cdot 17$; Step 2: 2 and 2; Step 3: 4; the greatest number of teams that can be formed is 4, where each has 14 girls and 17 boys.

4.2 Practice and Problem Solving (pp. 176–177) **9.** 7 **11.** 12 **13.** no; 5 **15.** yes **17.** no; 18 **19.** yes **21.** 30 baskets; 2 cans of cranberry sauce, 4 cans of fruit, 3 cans of corn, 2 boxes of muffin mix **23.** $2z^2$ **25.** $4xy^2$ **27.** $15bc$ **29.** always **31.** *Sample answer:* 6 and 25 **33.** 90 bouquets **35.** 12 ft **37.** -8 **39.** $2^2 \cdot 3 \cdot 7$

4.3 Getting Ready to Practice (p. 181) **1.** yes **3.** yes **5.** $\frac{2}{3}$ **7.** $\frac{5}{8}$ **9.** *Sample answer:* $\frac{2}{10}, \frac{3}{15}$ **11.** 64

4.3 Practice and Problem Solving (pp. 182–183) **13.** $\frac{3}{4}$ **15.** $\frac{-1}{8}$, or $-\frac{1}{8}$ **17.** $\frac{b}{2}$ **19.** $\frac{-3t}{10}$, or $-\frac{3t}{10}$ **21.** yes **23.** yes **25.** *Sample answer:* $\frac{1}{2}, \frac{2}{4}$ **27.** *Sample answer:* $\frac{2}{5}, \frac{4}{10}$ **29.** $\frac{1}{3}$ **31.** 1 **33.** $\frac{9}{50}$ **35.** $\frac{8}{25}$ **37.** $\frac{1}{10}$ **39.** For birds, about $\frac{60}{1500} = \frac{1}{25}$ are threatened; a greater fraction of mammals is threatened than birds; $\frac{1}{40}$ (reptiles), $\frac{64}{1541}$ (birds), $\frac{1}{10}$ (mammals). **41.** $\frac{3}{5}, \frac{3}{5}$; yes **43.** $\frac{3}{4}, \frac{5}{8}$; no **45.** $\frac{5}{6}, \frac{5}{6}$; yes **47.** $\frac{3}{4}, \frac{7}{8}$; no **49.** y^2 **51.** $\frac{-4z}{x^2y}$, or $-\frac{4z}{x^2y}$ **53.** no **55.** yes

61.

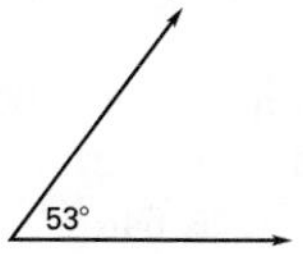

63.

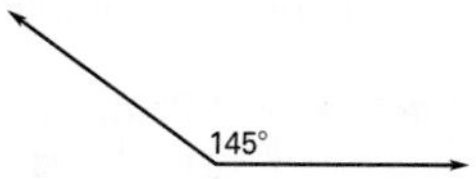

4.4 Problem Solving Strategies (p. 185) **1.** 10 ways **5.** 16 choices **7.** 44 posts **9.** 168 in., or 14 ft

4.4 Getting Ready to Practice (p. 188) **1.** common multiple **7.** 4 is the GCF of 12 and 24. The LCM is $2 \cdot 2 \cdot 2 \cdot 3$, or 24.

4.4 Practice and Problem Solving (pp. 188–189) **9.** multiples of 6: 6, 12, 18, 24, 30, 36, 42; multiples of 21: 21, 42; LCM: 42 **11.** multiples of 10: 10, 20, 30; multiples of 15: 15, 30; LCM: 30 **13.** $17 = 17$, $57 = 3 \cdot 19$; 969 **15.** $125 = 5^3$, $500 = 2^2 \cdot 5^3$; 500 **17.** $8 = 2^3$, $16 = 2^4$, $32 = 2^5$; 32 **19.** $20 = 2^2 \cdot 5$, $24 = 2^3 \cdot 3$, $60 = 2^2 \cdot 3 \cdot 5$; 120 **21.** $49s^3t^2$ **23.** $120c^2d^6$ **25.** 180 sec **27.** 4320 **29.** 4788 **31.** 300 **33.** 60 **35.** $120x^4y^7$ **37.** $495g^4h^5k^3$ **39.** 24 min **43.** $19x + 20 + 2y$ **45.** 73.7 **47.** 134.77

4.1–4.4 Notebook Review (pp. 190–191) **1.** prime factorization **2.** $2^3 \cdot 5$ **3.** 7 **4.** $5 \cdot 17$ **5.** $2^3 \cdot 3 \cdot 5$ **6.** 16 **7.** 20 **8.** $7a$ **9.** $20y^4$ **10.** $\frac{1}{3}$ **11.** $\frac{3}{20}$ **12.** $\frac{b}{3}$ **13.** $\frac{n^2}{3}$ **14.** 84 **15.** 270 **16.** $50c^2d$ **17.** $36n^3$ **18.** *Sample answer:* When you list the factors of a number, you list all numbers by which the number is divisible, including 1, composite numbers, and the number itself. When you find the prime factorization of a number, you write the number as a product only of its prime factors.

4.5 Getting Ready to Practice (p. 194) **1.** least common multiple or LCM **3.** 20 **5.** 36 **7.** < **9.** >

SA7

4.5 Practice and Problem Solving (pp. 194–195)
11. > **13.** < **15.** > **17.** $\frac{1}{8}, \frac{5}{16}, \frac{1}{2}, \frac{3}{4}$ **19.** $\frac{15}{16}, \frac{5}{3}, \frac{35}{15}, 2\frac{2}{5}$
23. $\frac{-47}{4}, -11\frac{7}{12}, \frac{-23}{2}, -11\frac{17}{48}, \frac{-34}{3}$ **25.** >
31. $2^4 \cdot 3 \cdot 7$

4.6 Getting Ready to Practice (p. 198) **1.** base **3.** yes **5.** no **7.** 4^6 **9.** a^{12} **11.** c **13.** 8^5 **15.** The bases should not be multiplied;. $2^2 \cdot 2^4 = 2^{2+4} = 2^6$.

4.6 Practice and Problem Solving (pp. 199–200)
17. v^{12} **19.** m^{19} **21.** x^4 **23.** y^2 **25.** $(-4)^5$ **27.** 7^4 **29.** 2^{10} **31.** 9^4 **33.** 5 **35.** 9 **37.** $4y^5$ **39.** $64a^7b^{10}$ **41.** z^5 **43.** $25n^3$ **45.** 10^{12} **47.** 10^{12} **49.** 2^2 **55.** 157 **57.** 18 **59.** >

4.7 Getting Ready to Practice (p. 203) **1.** true **3.** $\frac{1}{81}$ **5.** $\frac{1}{16}$ **7.** 5^{-3} means $\frac{1}{5^3}$; $5^{-3} = \frac{1}{5^3} = \frac{1}{5 \cdot 5 \cdot 5} = \frac{1}{125}$.

4.7 Practice and Problem Solving (pp. 203–204)
9. $\frac{1}{36}$ **11.** $\frac{1}{625}$ **13.** $\frac{1}{m^4}$ **15.** $\frac{9}{n^3}$ **17.** $\frac{1}{b^6}$ **19.** $\frac{1}{d^{13}}$ **21.** $\frac{kg}{m \cdot s^2}$ **23.** −8 **25.** 10 **27.** 10^{11} **29.** 10^8 **31.** 10^7 **33.** never **35.** −25 **37.** 52 **39.** 90 **41.** −17

4.8 Getting Ready to Practice (p. 207) **1.** yes **3.** yes **5.** 4.68×10^{-1} **7.** 4,350,000 **9.** 96,200,000

4.8 Practice and Problem Solving (pp. 207–208)
11. 7.9×10^3 **13.** 2.13×10^6 **15.** 4.15×10^{-7} **17.** 0.0871 **19.** 0.00000000176 **21.** 2,830,000,000,000 **23.** 6×10^8 **25.** 6.552×10^{14} **27.** 1.5×10^7 **31.** > **33.** 1.066×10^5 **35.** 1.944×10^{-13} **37.** 3.5×10^{11} **39.** 1.19×10^8; 6.205×10^9 **41.** 1.2×10^{-13} cm **43.** 6 **45.** $\frac{2}{3m}$

4.8 Technology Activity (p. 209) **1.** 2.7115×10^{14} **3.** 1.584×10^{-11} **5.** 2.682119205×10^7 **7.** $1.365853659 \times 10^{-7}$ **9.** about 2.3×10^2

4.5–4.8 Notebook Review (pp. 210–211)
1. scientific notation **2.** > **3.** < **4.** < **5.** = **6.** n^{13} **7.** y^{16} **8.** x^2 **9.** c^4 **10.** $\frac{12}{a^5}$ **11.** $\frac{1}{n^3}$ **12.** $\frac{1}{m^{11}}$ **13.** $\frac{1}{c^{13}}$ **14.** 3.46×10^{10} **15.** 9×10^{-7} **16.** 5.02×10^{-10}

17. *Sample answer:* Use the commutative and associative properties to rewrite the product as $(5 \times 4) \times (10^9 \times 10^{15})$. Use multiplication and the product of powers property to simplify this to 20×10^{24}. Move the decimal point to write the product in scientific notation as 2.0×10^{25}.

Chapter Review (pp. 212–213) **1.** The greatest common factor is the greatest number that is a factor of both numbers. The least common multiple is the smallest number that is a multiple of both numbers. **3.** *Sample answer:* $3x$, $4s^2$, $7ab^3$ **5.** simplest form **7.** prime factorization **9.** $2 \cdot 3^3$ **11.** $2 \cdot 3 \cdot 5^2$ **13.** $19 \cdot a \cdot a \cdot b$ **15.** $2 \cdot 2 \cdot 2 \cdot 7 \cdot u \cdot u \cdot v \cdot v$ **17.** 10 **19.** 3 **21.** $9xy$ **23.** $\frac{1}{3}$ **25.** $-\frac{16}{51}$ **27.** $\frac{c}{3}$ **29.** $\frac{4}{n}$ **31.** 105 **33.** $25m^2n^4$ **35.** 24 sec **37.** < **39.** > **41.** 8^4 **43.** 7^2 **45.** $\frac{7}{x^4}$ **47.** $\frac{1}{3w^8}$ **49.** 0.000658 **51.** 6×10^6 ft³/min; 3.6×10^8 ft³/h

Chapter 5

5.1 Getting Ready to Practice (p. 221)
1. denominator, numerator **3.** $\frac{2}{3}$ **5.** $\frac{1}{5}$ **7.** $1\frac{3}{7}$ **9.** c **11.** $18\frac{3}{4}$ in.

5.1 Practice and Problem Solving (pp. 222–223)
13. $\frac{1}{9}$ **15.** $-\frac{11}{12}$ **17.** $\frac{1}{5}$ **19.** $-\frac{1}{2}$ **21.** $\frac{8}{15}$ **23.** $-8\frac{2}{5}$ **25.** $-\frac{n}{7}$ **27.** $-\frac{q}{p}$ **29.** 15 h; $2\frac{2}{3}$ h **31.** $1\frac{11}{18}$ **33.** $\frac{8}{25}$ **35.** $\frac{15}{16}$ **37.** $-8\frac{1}{5}$ **39.** $3\frac{1}{12}$ **41.** $\frac{1}{4}$ **43.** $1\frac{1}{3}$ **47.** 5 **49.** −42 **51.** 105 **53.** 1850 **55.** 9 **57.** 24 **59.** 16 **61.** 1.25

5.2 Getting Ready to Practice (p. 226) **1.** least common denominator or LCD **3.** $1\frac{23}{24}$ **5.** $\frac{36 + x}{9x}$

5.2 Practice and Problem Solving (pp. 226–227)
7. $\frac{5}{8}$ **9.** $\frac{13}{18}$ **11.** $-\frac{1}{32}$ **13.** $-\frac{33}{40}$ **15.** $11\frac{19}{36}$ **17.** $13\frac{8}{35}$ **19.** $8\frac{1}{3}$ ft **21.** true **23.** false **25.** $\frac{17s}{20}$ **27.** $\frac{77}{50n}$

29. West; traveling east is $\frac{27}{50}$ of the way around the equator, while traveling west is $1 - \frac{27}{50} = \frac{23}{50}$ of the way. Since $\frac{23}{50} < \frac{27}{50}$, traveling west is shorter.

31. $1\frac{11}{72}$ **35.** 0 **37.** -126 **39.** $<$ **41.** $<$

5.3 Problem Solving Strategies (p. 229)
1. 7 students. *Sample answer:* Choose 18 classmates. Let 2 classmates represent the students that have both a dog and a cat. Six more classmates are needed to represent the students that have a dog and 3 more to represent those that have a cat. There are 7 classmates left over. **3.** 3 bows. *Sample answer:* Let one floor tile represent $\frac{1}{6}$ of a yard. Mark off $13 \cdot 5 = 65$ tiles to represent the amount of ribbon needed to decorate 5 gifts. Mark off 120 tiles to represent the amount of ribbon you have. The difference, 55 tiles, represents the length of ribbon left from which to make bows. Since 15 tiles represent the amount of ribbon needed to make a bow and $55 \div 15 = 3\frac{2}{3}$, 3 bows can be made with the remaining ribbon.
5. 16 students; eighth. *Sample answer:* I had 4 classmates stand in front of me and 6 stand behind me. Then I had another classmate stand in front of me, and then two more classmates stood behind her but in front of me. Then I had 2 more classmates join the end of the line. Counting showed 16 classmates in line, of which I was eighth.
7. 5 sweatshirts and 12 T-shirts

5.3 Getting Ready to Practice (p. 232)
1. numerators, denominators **3.** $-1\frac{7}{8}$ **5.** $\frac{23}{32}$

5.3 Practice and Problem Solving (pp. 232–233)
7. $\frac{7}{66}$ **9.** $\frac{1}{6}$ **11.** $4\frac{1}{2}$ **13.** $8\frac{3}{4}$ **15.** $27\frac{2}{9}$ **17.** $14\frac{2}{5}$ **19.** $1\frac{2}{5}$ km **21.** $-1\frac{3}{4}$ **23.** $-\frac{35}{48}$ **25.** 35 ft. *Sample answer:* Let one floor tile represent $\frac{1}{4}$ foot. Mark off 7 tiles to represent $1\frac{3}{4}$ feet. Mark off 7 tiles 19 more times to get 140 total tiles. Since 140 tiles times $\frac{1}{4}$ foot per tile equals 35, the answer is 35 feet.

27. $\frac{2}{3}$ ft^2 **29.** $-\frac{9}{100}$ **31.** $-9\frac{3}{4}$ **33.** $3\frac{19}{120}$ **35.** $4\frac{3}{4}$ **37.** 7^5 **39.** 8^2 **41.** $1\frac{1}{2}$ **43.** $\frac{29}{60}$

5.4 Getting Ready to Practice (p. 236) **1.** The multiplicative inverse, or reciprocal, of a number is the number that when multiplied by the original number equals 1. **3.** 6 **5.** $1\frac{1}{3}$ **7.** $\frac{2}{9}$ **9.** $-1\frac{2}{3}$ **11.** Step 1: Number of pounds of hamburger = Pounds per hamburger • Number of hamburgers; Step 2: $5 = \frac{1}{4}h$; Step 3: 20 hamburgers

5.4 Practice and Problem Solving (pp. 237–238)
13. $-\frac{9}{14}$ **15.** $1\frac{1}{2}$ **17.** $-\frac{3}{40}$ **19.** $-\frac{7}{8}$ **21.** $-3\frac{1}{2}$ **23.** $-7\frac{1}{12}$ **25.** $-\frac{2}{7}$ **27.** $2\frac{11}{35}$ **29.** $\frac{1}{6}$ **31.** $1\frac{3}{4}$ **33.** about $8\frac{1}{3}$ days **35.** Yes. *Sample answer:* When the two fractions are written with the same denominator c, then they can be represented as $\frac{a}{c}$ and $\frac{b}{c}$. Then $\frac{a}{c} \div \frac{b}{c} = \frac{a}{c} \cdot \frac{c}{b} = \frac{a}{b}$, so Juan's method works. **37.** 40 **39.** $1\frac{1}{5}$ **41.** 875 people. *Sample answer:* I solved the equation $\frac{2}{5}p = 350$. **43.** $\frac{2}{5}$ **45.** $\frac{3}{14}$ **47.** $\frac{x}{3}$ **49.** $\frac{7x^2}{9y^2}$ **51.** $1\frac{8}{9}$ **53.** $9\frac{1}{3}$

5.4 Technology Activity (p. 239) **1.** $\frac{47}{55}$ **3.** $\frac{2}{3}$ **5.** $1\frac{1}{27}$ **7.** $11\frac{1}{5}$ **9.** $1\frac{1}{16}$ qt

5.1–5.4 Notebook Review (pp. 240–241) **1.** 1 **2.** $\frac{1}{2}$ **3.** $-1\frac{1}{8}$ **4.** $1\frac{7}{8}$ **5.** $\frac{22x}{15}$ **6.** $\frac{5}{14}$ **7.** 2 **8.** $-8\frac{1}{2}$ **9.** $10\frac{5}{6}$ **10.** 9 **11.** $-1\frac{3}{7}$ **12.** $1\frac{3}{4}$ **13.** Multiply the answer by the divisor. The answer should be the dividend. *Sample answer:* $\frac{2}{5} \div \frac{5}{6} = \frac{12}{25}$ and $\frac{12}{25} \cdot \frac{5}{6} = \frac{2}{5}$
14. Greater than. *Sample answer:* Since dividing by a number is the same as multiplying by its reciprocal, and the reciprocal of a fraction between 0 and 1 will be greater than 1, the quotient will be greater than the original number.

SA9

5.5 Getting Ready to Practice (p. 244)

1. rational number, integer, whole number **3.** rational number, integer **5.** 0.8 **7.** $0.\overline{3}$ **9.** $\frac{3}{5}$ **11.** $\frac{8}{9}$ **13.** 1.8 in., $1\frac{7}{8}$ in., 2.1 in., $2\frac{1}{9}$ in.

5.5 Practice and Problem Solving (pp. 245–246)

15. $-0.\overline{1}$ **17.** $0.58\overline{3}$ **19.** 0.54 **21.** -0.4125 **23.** $-14.\overline{63}$ **25.** $0.6\overline{136}$ **27.** $-\frac{14}{25}$ **29.** $2\frac{79}{100}$ **31.** $7\frac{253}{1000}$ **33.** $-5\frac{2}{625}$ **35.** $\frac{8}{9}$ **37.** $\frac{5}{33}$ **39.** $\frac{14}{333}$ **41.** $20\frac{41}{198}$ **43.** $9\frac{9}{13}$, $9\frac{5}{7}$, 9.72, 9.74, $9\frac{3}{4}$ **45.** $0.\overline{09}$, $0.\overline{18}$, $0.\overline{27}$; $0.\overline{36}$, $0.\overline{45}$ **47.** 200 students **49.** 0.049; $\frac{1}{20}$ **53.** 17 **55.** 13 **57.** *Sample answer:* 170 **59.** *Sample answer:* 60

5.6 Getting Ready to Practice (p. 249)

1. 13, 11, 25 **3.** 7.37 **5.** 2.4 **7.** 5.61 **9.** 32

5.6 Practice and Problem Solving (pp. 249–250)

11. 38.103 **13.** -3.419 **15.** 4.988 **17.** -1.63 **19.** -7.71 **21.** 22.1 **23.** 18.985 **25.** -5.027 **27.** 7.31 **29.** -0.17 **31.** -6.347 **33.** 60 **35.** $300 + 40 + 5 + 0.6 + 0.09 + 0.002$ **37.** 67.75 ft **39.** 26.42 m **45.** -1 **47.** $\frac{1}{b^{14}}$ **49.** $\frac{40}{63}$ **51.** $7\frac{1}{2}$

5.7 Getting Ready to Practice (p. 253)

1. divisor → $9\overline{)7.2}$ ← dividend, 0.8 ← quotient **3.** 1.5; $4 \cdot 0.4 = 1.6$ **5.** 0.4; $0.5 \div 1 = 0.5$

5.7 Practice and Problem Solving (pp. 253–254)

7. 5 **9.** -5.74 **11.** 4 **13.** -50 **15.** 1.8935 **17.** 8.65 **19.** 8.7 **21.** 290.405 **23.** The answer should have $2 + 1 = 3$ decimal places; 33.252. **27.** -8.1 **29.** 0.2675 **31.** 37.414 **33.** If you multiply both 4.6 and 0.23 by 100, you get 460 and 23; yes; because you have multiplied $\frac{4.6}{0.23}$ by $\frac{100}{100} = 1$ to get $\frac{460}{23}$. **37.** 6,890,000,000 **39.** 0.000007405 **41.** -0.46, $-\frac{9}{20}$, $-\frac{5}{12}$, -0.4, $-\frac{3}{8}$ **43.** 25 R2 **45.** 204 R39

5.8 Getting Ready to Practice (p. 259)

1. mean **3.** range **5.** -56; -56; -56; 27 **7.** Step 1: 1365 sec, 1316 sec, 1263 sec, 1233 sec, 1228 sec; Step 2: 6405 sec; 1281 sec; Step 3: 21:21

5.8 Practice and Problem Solving (pp. 259–261)

9. 191; 185; 185; 174 **11.** $181.1\overline{6}$ ft; 87 ft; none; 531 ft **13.** $9\frac{3}{4}$ in.; 10 in.; $10\frac{1}{2}$ in.; $2\frac{3}{8}$ in. **15.** Isaac: 9.375, Carl: 9.6, Kurt, 9.425; Carl's **17.** *Sample answer:* The median; there are equally many salaries above and below it, so it should reflect the most likely salary for me in each career. **19.** $\frac{7b}{6}$ **21.** Yes. *Sample answer:* I prefer Roberta's method because it is shorter and can be used for any value of *a*. **25.** -5 **27.** 0 **29.** -16 **31.** 66 **33.** -16

5.5–5.8 Notebook Review (pp. 262–263)

1. mean, median, mode **2.** $6\frac{3}{8}$, 6.4, $6\frac{5}{12}$, $6\frac{4}{9}$ **3.** 1.87 **4.** 42.598 **5.** 1.315 **6.** 98.11 **7.** 2.34 **8.** 3.0132 **9.** -24.8 **10.** 2 **11.** 24; 24; 24; 10 **12.** 7.45; 7.4; 7.2 and 7.7; 0.8 **13.** *Sample answer:* 3, 4, 12, 12 **14.** They both can be written as ratios. *Sample answer:* $0.2 = \frac{1}{5}$ and $0.\overline{2} = \frac{2}{9}$.

Chapter Review (pp. 264–265)

1. reciprocals **3.** front-end estimation **5.** mean **7.** $1\frac{1}{3}$ **9.** $-1\frac{1}{5}$ **11.** $\frac{17}{20}$ **13.** $-\frac{47}{56}$ **15.** $-\frac{4n}{3}$ **17.** $-\frac{1}{2c}$ **19.** $\frac{1}{4}$ in. **21.** $-\frac{1}{4}$ **23.** $-16\frac{1}{14}$ **25.** $\frac{3}{35}$ **27.** $-7\frac{7}{11}$ **29.** 30 **31.** $-7\frac{1}{7}$ **33.** 2, $\frac{11}{5}$, 2.25, $2\frac{3}{10}$, 2.32, $\frac{5}{2}$ **35.** 25.88 **37.** 6.045 **39.** -53.44 **41.** 0.425 **43.** 92.79 lb **45.** 238.05 mi^2 **47.** 0.125°C; 1°C; -7°C and 2°C; 15°C **49.** $3\frac{1}{10}$ in.; $3\frac{1}{8}$ in.; no mode; $\frac{3}{4}$ in.

Chapter 6

6.1 Getting Ready to Practice (p. 273)

1. $5x$ and $-9x$, 6 and -2 **3.** -15, 1, and -20 **5.** 5 **7.** 7 **9.** 82

6.1 Practice and Problem Solving (pp. 274–275)

11. no; -6 **13.** no; 3 **15.** -2 **17.** -4 **19.** -5 **21.** -5 **23.** 37 **25.** length: 40 mm, width: 17 mm, perimeter: 114 mm; 46 **27.** $-1\frac{1}{3}$ **29.** -4 **31.** $\frac{2}{3}$ **33.** 167 **35.** $\frac{19(x + 11)}{2} = 228$; 13 in.

37. Yes. *Sample answer:* If you divide each side by 3, you get $x + 2 = 3$, so $x = 1$. This is the same answer you get using the distributive property. **39.** $x = 5, y = 8$; 34 **41.** > **43.** 34, 34, 32, 7 **45.** 28,800

6.2 Problem Solving Strategies (p. 277)
1. 18,320 mi **3.** 60 min **5.** 60 pages **7.** 165, 167, 169 **9.** 2012

6.2 Getting Ready to Practice (p. 280) **1.** the sum of the lengths of the sides, or twice the length plus twice the width **3.** 5 **5.** $-1\frac{2}{3}$

6.2 Practice and Problem Solving (pp. 280–281)
7. 3 **9.** 5 **11.** 3 **13.** 41 **15.** -2 **17.** 132 **19.** 12 wk **21.** $-\frac{4}{5}$ **23.** $\frac{3}{4}$ **25.** $1\frac{1}{2}$ **27.** \$.80; \$60 **29.** $\frac{3}{8}$ **31.** -21 **33.** 17 **37.** 36 **39.** 9.558 **41.** 21.038 **43.** 14 **45.** 7 **47.** 47

6.3 Getting Ready to Practice (p. 284) **1.** least common denominator or LCD **3.** 100; 4 **5.** 8; $\frac{7}{13}$ **7.** 20; 20

6.3 Practice and Problem Solving (pp. 284–285)
9. -12 **11.** $3.\overline{63}$ **13.** $-1\frac{2}{5}$ **15.** $1\frac{1}{5}$ **17.** $7x - 2 = 2x + 3$; 1; it is about 1; about 1.0097; the answers are very close. **19.** -5.36 **21.** $-1\frac{14}{17}$ **23.** \$3 on red, \$10 on purple, and \$3.50 on blue **25.** Yes. *Sample answer:* The extra factor(s) will divide out, so the simplified result will be the same. **27.** 18.439 **29.** 33.7635 **31.** -3 **33.** 2.25 **35.** $-15y + 60$

6.1–6.3 Notebook Review (pp. 286–287)
1. *Sample answer:* To combine like terms, find the terms with the same variable part, including exponents, and add or subtract the coefficients. The result is the coefficient of the term with that same variable part. Constants are like terms. **2.** -4 **3.** -6 **4.** $\frac{3}{4}$ **5.** 4.8 **6.** $\frac{1}{5}$ **7.** Multiply each side by 1000.

6.4 Getting Ready to Practice (p. 292)
1. 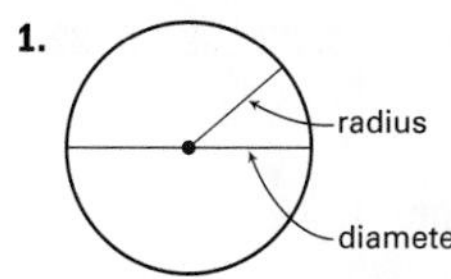

3. 10.5 in.; I used $\frac{22}{7}$ because 66 is divisible by 22. **5.** 34.5 cm; I used 3.14 because 11 is not divisible by 7. **7.** 105 yd; I used $\frac{22}{7}$ because 330 is divisible by 22.

6.4 Practice and Problem Solving (pp. 293–294)
9. 2; 6.28 cm **11.** 7; 44.0 mm **13.** 25 yd **15.** 62.8 mm **17.** 44 in. **19.** 10.5 km **21.** Ex. 9: 6 cm; Ex. 10: 2.25 in.; Ex. 11: 42 mm; the actual answers should be close to these estimates. **23.** about 301 ft **25.** about 24,900 mi **27.** about 4620 mi **29.** 7.64 in. **37.** $x \le 23$ **39.** $a \le 2$ **41.** 3 **43.** $4\frac{1}{2}$

6.5 Getting Ready to Practice (p. 297) **1.** less than; greater than; less than or equal to; greater than or equal to
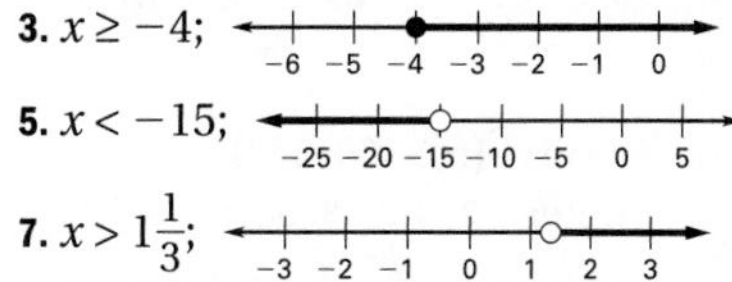
3. $x \ge -4$;

5. $x < -15$;

7. $x > 1\frac{1}{3}$;

6.5 Practice and Problem Solving (pp. 297–299)
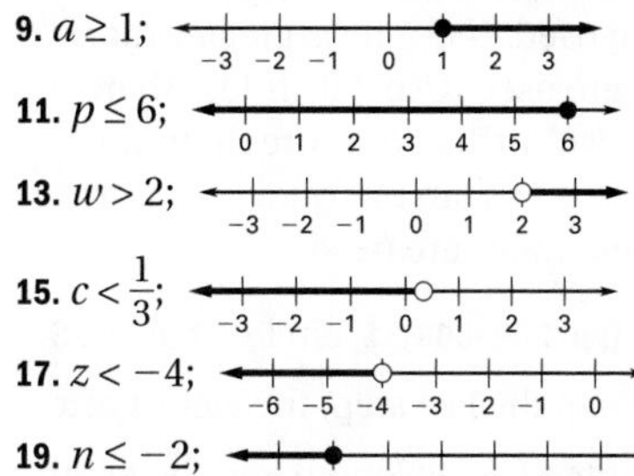
9. $a \ge 1$;

11. $p \le 6$;

13. $w > 2$;

15. $c < \frac{1}{3}$;

17. $z < -4$;

19. $n \le -2$;

21. $x \ge 750$; the salesperson must sell at least \$750 in clothes in that week to make at least \$500 for the week. **23.** at least 23 pledges; $925 + 25p \ge 1500$; $p \ge 23$ **25.** $k \le 9$ **27.** $d \ge -20$ **29.** $x > 4.8$ **31.** $z \le 4.9$ **33.** $3.95m - 1.2m \ge 25{,}000$; $m \ge 9090.\overline{90}$; the publisher must sell at least 9091 magazines each month to make a profit. **39.** *Sample answer:* You cannot buy a negative number of soft drinks.

41. 18 sandwiches. *Sample answer:* I used Make a List to list all of the possibilities. **43.** $22\frac{1}{3}$, 22.5, 22 **45.** 3.4

6.5 Technology Activity (p. 300) **1.** $y < 13$ **3.** $n \leq -1$ **5.** $t > -3$ **7.** 16 pencils

6.6 Getting Ready to Practice (p. 303) **1.** $x \geq 5$ **3.** $8 - x \leq 6$ **5.** Step 1: $32m + 50$; Step 2: $32m + 50 \leq 200$; Step 3: $m \leq 4.6875$; you can be a member up to 4 months without spending more than $200.

6.6 Practice and Problem Solving (pp. 304–305) **7.** $9 < x + 1$; $x > 8$ **9.** $8x \geq 40$; $x \geq 5$ **15.** "3 less than a number" is equivalent to the expression $n - 3$, while "3 is less than a number" is equivalent to the inequality $3 < n$. **17.** more than 15 dances **19.** $2 + 0.5n \geq 6$; 3 A.M.; no. *Sample answer:* If there are 6 inches of snow at 3 A.M., and it keeps snowing at the same rate, then there will be 7.5 inches of snow at 6 A.M. **21.** $2 + 0.4 \cdot 5 \cdot m$; $2.50 + 0.25 \cdot 7 \cdot m$ **23.** $m < 2$ mi **25.** 213.52 in. **27.** 89 **29.** 25

6.4–6.6 Notebook Review (pp. 306–307) **1.** circumference; diameter **2.** 44 **3.** 38.5 **4.** 50 **5.** $b < 42$ **6.** $j > 6$ **7.** $y \leq 9$ **8.** $8\frac{1}{3}$ min **9.** *Sample answer:* Use < if the expressions "is less than" or "is fewer than" are used. Use > if "is greater than" or "is more than" are used. Use ≤ if "is less than or equal to," "is at most," or "is not more than" are used. Use ≥ if "is greater than or equal to," "is at least," or "is not less than" are used.

Chapter Review (pp. 308–309) **1.** circle **7.** 6 **9.** 9 **11.** 7 **13.** $-\frac{5}{12}$ **15.** In the last step, the values of x and y were substituted for the length and the width to find the perimeter. Instead, the values of x and y must first be substituted into the expressions for the length and width of the rectangle. The length is $4x + 2 = 4(3) + 2 = 14$. The width is $2y = 2(4) = 8$. So, $P = 2(14) + 2(8) = 44$. **17.** $2w + 50 = 3w - 87$; 137 teams **19.** $1\frac{1}{2}$ mi **21.** 25.1 mm **23.** 1.91 in. **25.** $x > -7$;

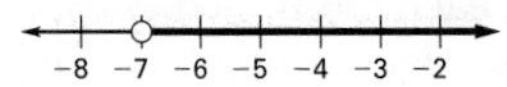

27. $a < 10$;

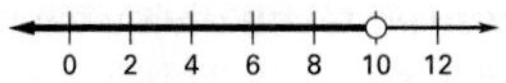

29. $g \leq -1$;

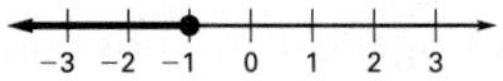

31. $14 - 3x \leq 11$; $x \geq 1$ **33.** $7(15 - x) \geq 56$; $x \leq 7$

Chapter 7

7.1 Getting Ready to Practice (p. 319) **1.** rates **3.** $\frac{3}{2}$, 3 to 2, 3 : 2 **5.** yes **7.** yes **9.** Multiply by $\frac{7 \text{ days}}{1 \text{ week}}$: $\frac{14 \text{ times}}{1 \text{ day}} \cdot \frac{7 \text{ days}}{1 \text{ week}} = \frac{98 \text{ times}}{1 \text{ week}}$.

7.1 Practice and Problem Solving (pp. 319–320) **11.** $\frac{4}{5}$, 4 to 5, 4 : 5 **13.** $\frac{5}{7}$, 5 to 7, 5 : 7 **15.** $\frac{2}{3}$, 2 to 3, 2 : 3 **17.** $\frac{-3}{1}$, −3 to 1, −3 : 1 **19.** 2 **21.** 4.32 **23.** $\frac{4 \text{ adults}}{1 \text{ car}}$ **25.** $\frac{1.5 \text{ lb}}{1 \text{ dollar}}$ **27.** $\frac{5}{5} = \frac{1}{1}$ **29.** 2 **31.** 25 **33.** Check work; $\frac{1}{10}$ of the people in the class are left-handed, so divide the number of people by 10. **35.** 1134 people/mi^2 **37.** 6.25 ft **39.** 6 **41.** −8

7.2 Getting Ready to Practice (p. 324) **1.** Find the cross products and solve the resulting equation to solve the proportion. **3.** 6 **5.** 6 **7.** 2640 ft

7.2 Practice and Problem Solving (pp. 325–326) **9.** no **11.** yes **13.** 9 **15.** 9 **17.** 38.5 **19.** 1513 **21.** 12 in. **23.** 27.25 in. **25.** $90 **27.** 34,375 mi **29.** 1 **31.** 23 **35.** length: 5 in.; width: 1.75 in.; height: 1.25 in. **37.** $\frac{3 \text{ people}}{1 \text{ taxi}}$ **39.** $\frac{2 \text{ dogs}}{1 \text{ household}}$

7.3 Getting Ready to Practice (p. 329) **1.** percent **3.** 25% **5.** 550

7.3 Practice and Problem Solving (pp. 329–330) **7.** 4% **9.** 90% **11.** 110.25 **13.** 589 **15.** 560 **17.** 925 **19.** 40.08 ft **21.** 135% **23.** 2860 **25.** 540 **27.** 60% **29.** $4y$ **31.** 28.6% **35.** $1\frac{43}{50}$ **37.** $\frac{78}{125}$ **39.** 45.216

7.4 Getting Ready to Practice (p. 333) **1.** 100%; 1 **3.** 9% **5.** 150% **7.** 0.125, $\frac{1}{8}$ **9.** 1.1, $1\frac{1}{10}$ **11.** The numerator of the fraction should be 0.1; $0.001 = \frac{0.1}{100} = 0.1\%$.

7.4 Practice and Problem Solving (pp. 334–335)
13. 5.7% **15.** 0.4% **17.** 15% **19.** 0.5% **21.** 105.6% **23.** 52.5% **25.** $85\frac{1}{3}$% **27.** 70% **29.** 0.87, $\frac{87}{100}$ **31.** 1.01, $1\frac{1}{100}$ **33.** 0.042, $\frac{21}{500}$ **35.** 1.24, $1\frac{6}{25}$ **37.** 0.004, $\frac{1}{250}$ **39.** 0.4455, $\frac{891}{2000}$ **41.** 0.6%, $\frac{3}{50}$, 0.0606, 6.6%, 0.606 **43.** $\frac{21}{100}$, 0.212, $\frac{21}{20}$, 212%, 21.2 **45.** Spanish **47.** 23% **49.** $<$ **51.** $>$ **53.** $=$ **55.** *Sample answer:* when referring to part or all of a group of people **59.** $13 + 4x \le 9$; $x \le -1$ **61.** \$6. *Sample answer:* I used Work Backward because it allowed me to start with the known final amount and then "undo" each of the steps one at a time. **63.** 3.5 **65.** 11.88

7.1–7.4 Notebook Review (pp. 336–337)
1. proportion **2.** $\frac{7.5 \text{ ft}}{1 \text{ sec}}$ **3.** $\frac{\$1.68}{1 \text{ gal}}$ **4.** 6% **5.** 24.7 **6.** 0.74, $\frac{37}{50}$ **7.** 0.038, $\frac{19}{500}$ **8.** 0.168, $\frac{21}{125}$ **9.** 1.3, $1\frac{3}{10}$ **10.** If the cross products are equal, then the ratios form a proportion.

7.5 Getting Ready to Practice (p. 340)
1. increase **3.** decrease; 20% **5.** 23.1

7.5 Practice and Problem Solving (pp. 340–341)
7. increase; 60% **9.** decrease; $6.\overline{6}$% **11.** decrease; 10% **13.** 1144 **15.** 12.8 **17.** 77,393.75 **19.** about 15,390 tons **21.** 50% increase **23.** 50% decrease **25.** False; multiplying by 5 gives a 400% increase. **27.** True; to find an 80% decrease, multiply by 80% and subtract. The final result is 20% of the original number, and finding 20% of a number is the same as dividing by 5. **29.** 9.9% **31.** 9 in. by 6 in.; 125% **33.** -5.36 **35.** -14 **37.** 26 **39.** 12

7.6 Getting Ready to Practice (p. 344) **1.** markup **3.** \$11.40 **5.** \$34.80 **7.** \$37.80

7.6 Practice and Problem Solving (pp. 345–346)
9. \$39.90 **11.** \$16.80 **13.** \$101.37 **15.** \$61.61 **17.** \$22.50 **21.** discount; 10% **23.** markup; 120% **25.** discount; about 40% **27.** 19% **29.** 40% **33.** 3 **35.** 28 **37.** 45 **39.** 40

7.7 Getting Ready to Practice (p. 349)
1. principal **3.** 82% **5.** 399

7.7 Practice and Problem Solving (pp. 349–350)
7. 208 **9.** 66 **11.** 250 **13.** 78 **15.** 0.5% **17.** \$15 **19.** 31% **21.** $=$ **23.** Row 1: 1.1, 3.3; Row 2: 2.5, 5, 7.5; Row 3: 3.8, 7.6, 11.4; for 22, the number increased by 1.1 each time; for 50, the number increased by 2.5 each time; for 76, the number increased by 3.8 each time. **25.** \$142.50; \$1342.50 **29.** $\frac{5}{6}$ **31.** -3 **33.** $n \le 11\frac{3}{8}$

7.7 Technology Activity (p. 351) **1.** \$7577.03 **3.** \$3744.89

7.8 Problem Solving Strategies (p. 353) **1.** 62 red, 38 blue. *Sample answer:* In the 5 trials, 31 red marbles were chosen and 19 blue marbles were chosen. So $\frac{31}{50} = \frac{x}{100}$, or $x = 62$, and $\frac{19}{50} = \frac{y}{100}$, or $y = 38$. **3.** *Sample answer:* Draw and then replace a letter 20 times and record the results. Write a proportion comparing the ratio of the number of consonants drawn in the experiment to the ratio that would be drawn in 60 trials. Solve the proportion to find the predicted number of consonants drawn. **5.** \$20; \$34 **7.** 27 triangles

7.8 Getting Ready to Practice (p. 356) **1.** 2, 4, 6 **3.** The experimental probability is the ratio of favorable outcomes to total outcomes, not to unfavorable outcomes as shown. The number of total outcomes is 20, so the experimental probability of spinning red is $\frac{7}{20}$.

7.8 Practice and Problem Solving (pp. 356–357)
5. $\frac{1}{5}$ **7.** $\frac{3}{10}$ **9.** 1 **11.** 16.8% **13.** 49.2% **15.** 24 **17.** 56 **19.** about 46% **21.** $\frac{3}{4}$ **25.** *Sample answer:* Each time she rolls the number cube has no effect on any other time she rolls the number cube. **27.** 10% **29.** -28 **31.** -32

7.5–7.8 Notebook Review (pp. 358–359) **1.** Find the ratio of the number of favorable outcomes to the number of possible outcomes. **2.** \$51 **3.** \$59.04 **4.** 96 **5.** 291.04 **6.** red: $\frac{8}{17}$; yellow: $\frac{5}{17}$; blue: $\frac{4}{17}$ **7.** \$525

SA13

Chapter Review (pp. 360–361) **1.** unit rate **3.** favorable outcomes; possible outcomes **7.** 4.78 **9.** 360 **11.** 8 **13.** 10 **15.** 308 **17.** 0.5% **19.** 0.3% **21.** 145% **23.** $\frac{7}{20}$ **25.** 23% **27.** \$14.45 **29.** \$127.05 **31.** $\frac{1}{2}$ **33.** $\frac{3}{4}$

Chapter 8

8.1 Getting Ready to Practice (p. 378)
1. supplementary **3.** supplementary **5.** Vertical angles have the same measure, so $m\angle 2 = 112°$.

8.1 Practice and Problem Solving (pp. 378–379)
7. 109° **9.** $m\angle 6 = 45°$, $m\angle 5 = m\angle 7 = 135°$
11. 105° 75° 75° 105°

13. *Sample answer:* Together, the angles form a straight angle, so the sum of their measures is 180°. So, $135° + m\angle 2 = 180°$, and $m\angle 2 = 180° - 135° = 45°$. **17.** $y = 2$; $m\angle 6 = 90°$, $m\angle 3 = 90°$ **19.** $\frac{113}{500}$ **21.** $\frac{9}{2000}$ **23.** 3 in.^{2} **25.** 32.5 ft^2

Special Topic Exercises (p. 381) **1–7.** Sample answers are given.

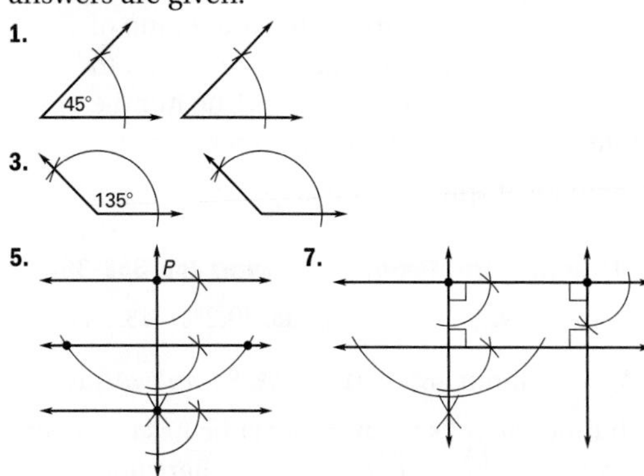

8.2 Getting Ready to Practice (p. 384) **1.** scalene **3.** equilateral **5.** The triangle has one right angle, so it is a right triangle.

8.2 Practice and Problem Solving (pp. 384–385)
7. right **9.** scalene **11.** isosceles **13.** 24; right **15.** Isosceles; an isosceles triangle has two sides of equal length. **17.** Yes; the sum of the measures of the angles is 180°. **19.** 20°, 70°, 90° **21.** 60°, 60°, 60° **23.** $m\angle 1 = 75°$, $m\angle 2 = 35°$, $m\angle 3 = 70°$ **25.** 5.2 yd, 1.2 yd^2 **27.** 148,941,024 km^2

8.3 Getting Ready to Practice (p. 387)
1. parallelogram **3.** rectangle **5.** parallelogram, rectangle **7.** 91

8.3 Practice and Problem Solving (pp. 388–389)
9. 1.6 cm; parallelogram, rhombus **11.** 109 **13.** 65 **15.** $x = 65$, $y = 115$ **17.** dark blue rectangle, red square, green trapezoid, light blue parallelogram, purple parallelogram, yellow trapezoid **19.** sometimes **21.** never **23.** 5; $m\angle E = 121°$, $m\angle H = 119°$ **27.** 5 **29.** 1 **31.** never **33.** sometimes

8.4 Getting Ready to Practice (p. 392)
1. polygon **3.** not a polygon **5.** 1440° **7.** 1620° **9.** 128.6°

8.4 Practice and Problem Solving (pp. 392–393)
11. yes **13.** yes **15.** about 154° **17.** about 176.9° **19.** 78 **21.** $x = 72$; $m\angle R = m\angle N = 72°$; $m\angle L = m\angle M = m\angle P = m\angle Q = 144°$ **23.** $x = 45$; $m\angle B = m\angle E = 135°$ **27.** 360°; 360°; 360° **29.** $\frac{49}{50}$ **31.** $\frac{7}{5000}$ **33.** about 103.5%

8.1–8.4 Notebook Review (pp. 394–395) **1.** one **2.** 122; obtuse **3.** 26; right **4.** 52° **5.** 720°
6. Yes;

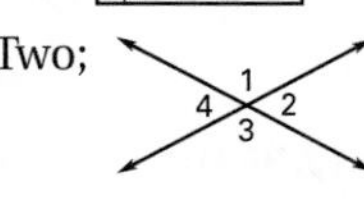

Sample answer: The sum of the other four angles just needs to be 540°.

7. Two; 1 2 3 4 *Sample answer:* There are two pairs of angles that do not share a side: $\angle 1$ and $\angle 3$, and $\angle 2$ and $\angle 4$.

8.5 Getting Ready to Practice (p. 399)
1. congruent **3.** $\angle K$ and $\angle S$, $\angle L$ and $\angle P$, $\angle M$ and $\angle Q$, $\angle N$ and $\angle R$ **5.** 12 in. **7.** The corresponding vertices are not listed in the correct order; $\triangle ABC \cong \triangle DFE$ by Side-Angle-Side.

SA14

8.5 Practice and Problem Solving (pp. 400–401)
9. 80° **11.** 100° **13.** Side-Angle-Side **15.** Side-Side-Side; $x - 6 = 4$; 10 **17.** Angle-Side-Angle; $2x - 24 = x$; 24 **19.** 127.5° **23.** 59.15 **25.** 103
27–30.

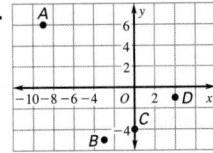

8.6 Problem Solving Strategies (p. 403)
1. *Sample:* mirror images: 1 and 2, 3 and 4, 5 and 6, 1 and 6, 2 and 3, 4 and 5, 1 and 4, 2 and 5, 3 and 6

3. Scott, Alan, David, Mary, Peter; Scott, Alan, Peter, Mary, David **5.** 96 oz **7.** 92

8.6 Getting Ready to Practice (p. 406)
1. reflection **3.** no **5.** no **7.** none

8.6 Practice and Problem Solving (pp. 407–408)
11.
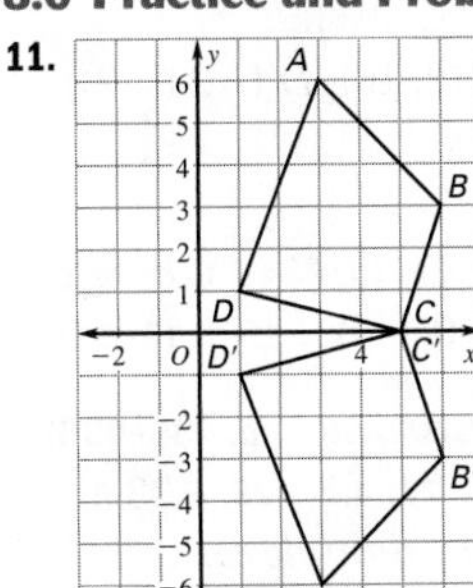

13.
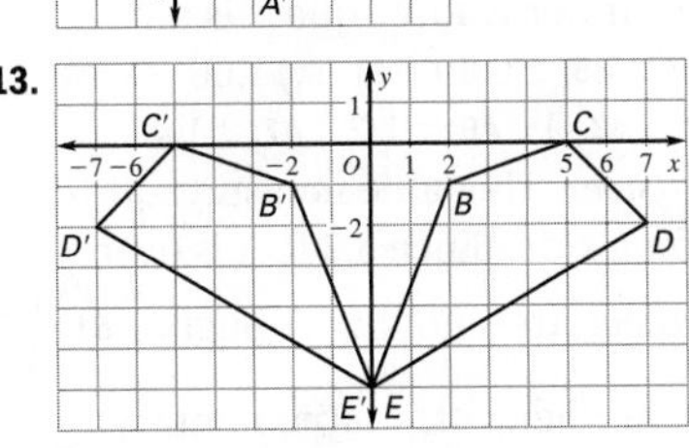
15. two

17.
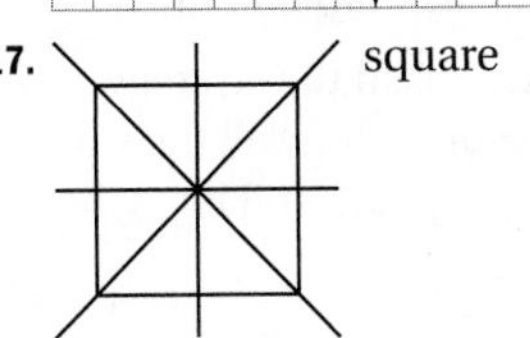
square

19. Lines of Symmetry entries in table: 3, 4, 5, 6, 8 **21.** A good answer will include a clearly drawn reflection. **25.** 280% **27.** 150°

8.7 Getting Ready to Practice (p. 411)
1. reflection **3.** rotation

8.7 Practice and Problem Solving (pp. 412–413)
5. reflection **7.** translation **9.** reflection **11.** rotation **13.** rotation **15.** $(x + 5, y + 4)$
17. $P'(-5, 0)$, $Q'(-2, 0)$, $R'(0, -2)$
19.
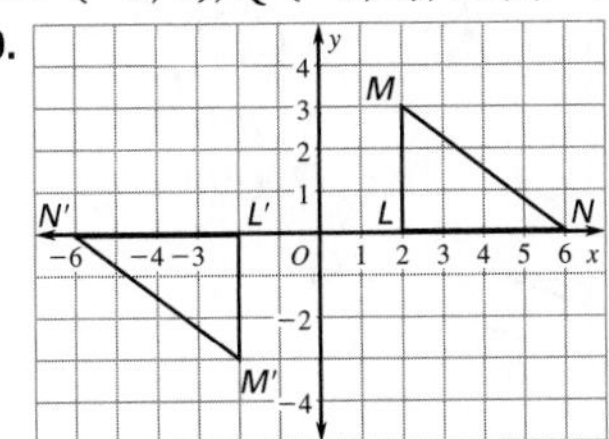

21.
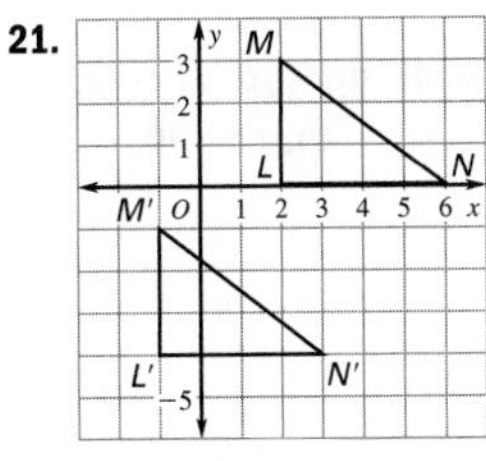

23.
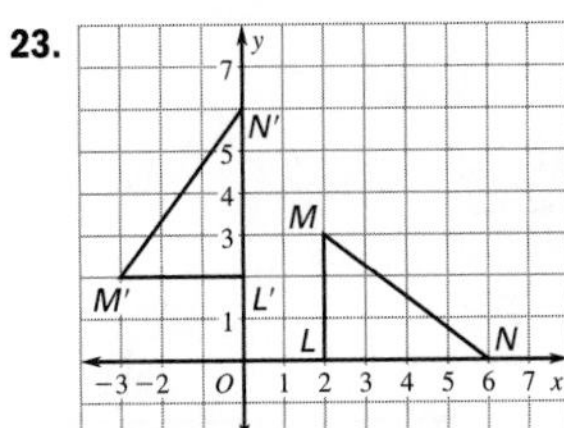

27. *Sample answer:* Reflect in the y-axis and then the x-axis; make two 90° clockwise rotations; make two 90° counterclockwise rotations; reflect in the x-axis and then the y-axis. **29.** 384
31. 49.5; right **33.** 74.8; acute **35.** 110.2, 110, 110

Special Topic Exercises (p. 415) **1.** no **3.** no
5. Check work.
7. *Sample:*
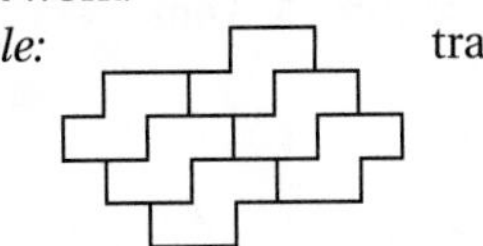
translation

SA15

9. A good answer will include a rectangle with a piece cut from one side and slid to another side. The translation of that figure forms a tessellation. **11.** *Sample:*

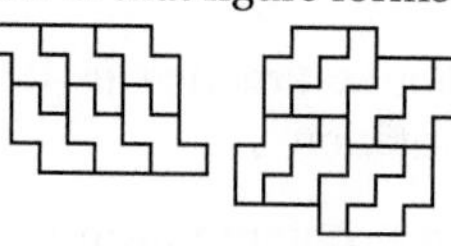

8.8 Getting Ready to Practice (p. 418) **1.** scale factor **3.** $\triangle MNL \sim \triangle PQR$

5. Steps 1, 3:

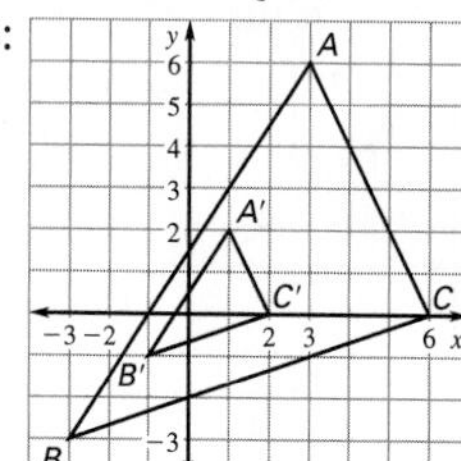

Step 2: $A'(1, 2)$, $B'(-1, -1)$, $C'(2, 0)$

8.8 Practice and Problem Solving (pp. 419–421)
7. $ABCD \sim EDGF$ **9.** 40 **11.** 3 in. **13.** $x = 90$, $y = 6.75$ cm

15.

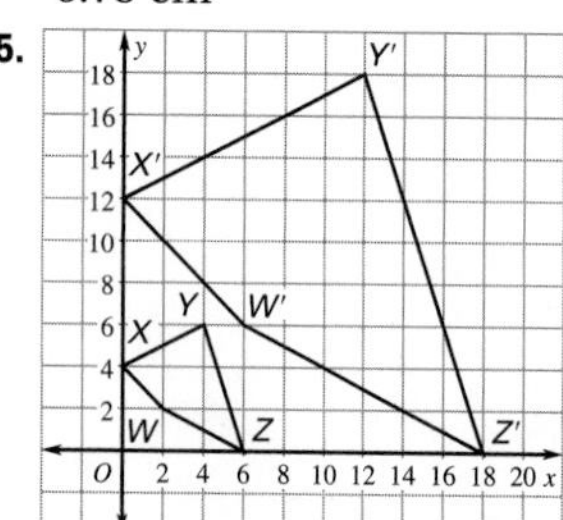

17.

19.

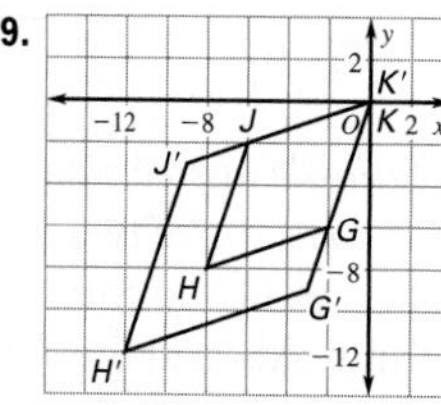

21. 4 in. by 8 in. **23.** $x = 44$, $y = 136$ **27.** $27.50

8.5–8.8 Notebook Review (pp. 422–423)
1. reflection **2.** translation **3.** 3 cm

4.

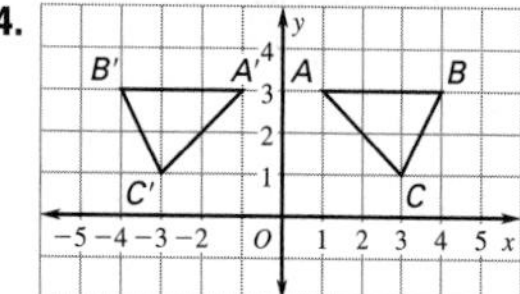

5.

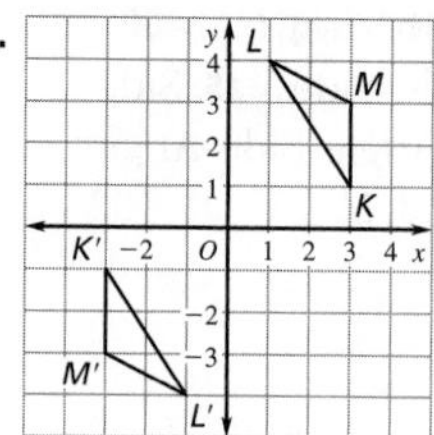

6. 25 m **7.** *Sample answer:* The perimeter of the image is the product of the scale factor and the perimeter of the original figure. **8.** *Sample answer:* A person turning around to face the opposite way

Chapter Review (pp. 424–425) **9.** 109° **11.** 25° **13.** rectangle **15.** 900° **17.** $\angle A \cong \angle P$, $\angle B \cong \angle Q$, $\angle C \cong \angle R$, $\angle D \cong \angle S$, $\angle E \cong \angle T$ **19.** $\triangle ABC \cong \triangle GFH$; two sides and the included angle of one triangle are congruent to two sides and the included angle of the other triangle, so the triangles are congruent by Side-Angle-Side. **21.** no **23.** no

25.

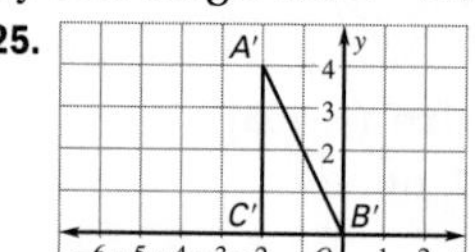

27.

29. $A'(-4, 0)$, $B'(-4, 8)$, $C'(-12, 16)$, $D'(-24, 12)$

Chapter 9

9.1 Getting Ready to Practice (p. 434) **1.** $b^2 = c$ **3.** ± 4 **5.** ± 11 **7.** -22.0 **9.** 49.4 **11.** ± 7 **13.** ± 9

9.1 Practice and Problem Solving (pp. 434–436)
15. -1 **17.** 12 **19.** 6 **21.** 11 **23.** 4.7 **25.** -38.4 **27.** 0 **29.** ± 13 **31.** ± 6 **33.** No. *Sample answer:* There is no real number whose square is a negative number. **35.** ± 6.40 **37.** ± 11.66 **39.** ± 14.14 **41.** 4 **43.** 9 **45.** ± 1.2 **47.** ± 1.4 **49.** No. *Sample answer:* The table measures $\sqrt{34.5} \approx 5.9$ feet on a side. Since 5.9 feet is over 70 inches, the tablecloth is not big enough. **51.** $\frac{1}{2}$ **53.** $\frac{7}{8}$ **55.** $\frac{12}{13}$ **59.** neither **61.** supplementary **63.** 6 ways. *Sample answer:* I used the strategy Draw a Diagram so that I could draw all the ways that 3 stamps can be arranged and still be attached. **65.** $5\frac{7}{20}$ **67.** $-9\frac{1}{20}$

9.2 Getting Ready to Practice (p. 439)
1. irrational **3.** Irrational. *Sample answer:* 5 is not a perfect square. **5.** Rational. *Sample answer:* $\sqrt{\frac{25}{49}} = \frac{5}{7}$ which is a quotient of two integers.

7. 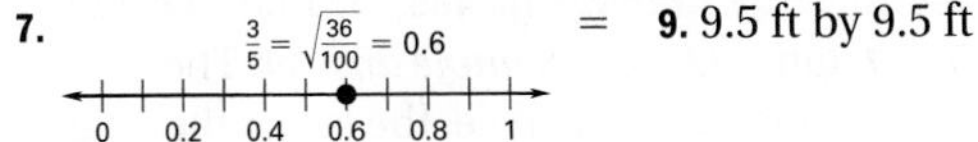

= **9.** 9.5 ft by 9.5 ft

9.3 Practice and Problem Solving (pp. 440–441)
11. Rational. *Sample answer:* $\frac{9}{46}$ is a quotient of two integers. **13.** Irrational. *Sample answer:* neither 3 nor 5 is a perfect square.

15. 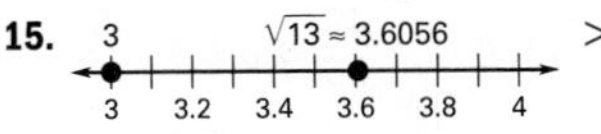

>

17. $-5 = -\sqrt{25}$ =

−5.5 −5.3 −5.1 −4.9 −4.7 −4.5

19. $0.\overline{262}, 0.2\overline{6}, 0.266, 0.\overline{26}$ **21.** $\sqrt{4} = 2$; rational **23.** $\sqrt{20}$; irrational

25. 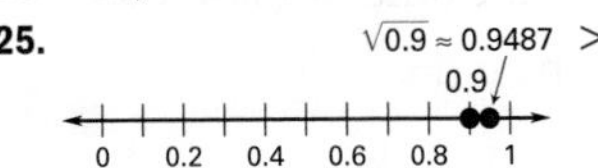

>

27. $\sqrt{2.25} = \frac{3.6}{2.4} = 1.5$ =

1 1.2 1.4 1.6 1.8 2

29. $-4, -3.75, 1.5, \sqrt{8}$ **31.** $-3.5, -\sqrt{12}, -\frac{3}{4}, -\sqrt{\frac{1}{4}}$

33. Yes; too small. *Sample answer:* Because $\sqrt{110} \approx 10.5$, the piece of carpet should about fit the 10.5 foot dimension, but will be about 0.7 foot too short in the other dimension. **37.** $30a^{11}$ **39.** -5

41. c^4 **43.** $-\frac{2}{3n^4}$ **45.** rotation; $(x, y) \to (y, -x)$

47. translation; $(x, y) \to (x - 3, y + 1)$

9.3 Getting Ready to Practice (p. 445)
1. hypotenuse **3.** 15 **5.** 25 **7.** yes **9.** no

9.3 Practice and Problem Solving (pp. 446–447)
11. 34 ft **13.** 19.6 ft **15.** 24.5 in. **17.** no **19.** yes **21.** 8.9 ft **23.** 9 m **25.** 4.24 ft **27.** no **29.** yes **31.** 2 **33.** 5.3 **35.** 3

39. 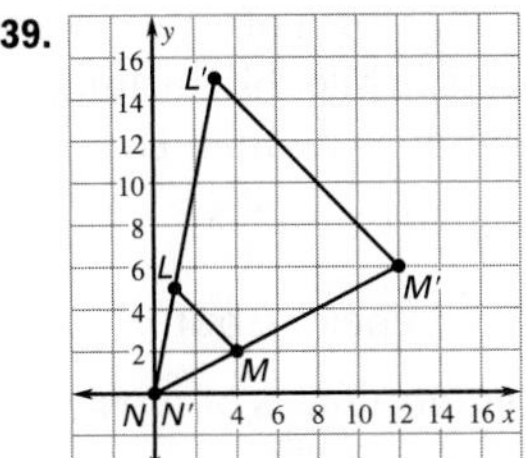

9.4 Problem Solving Strategies (p. 449) **1.** 7.1 m **3.** 37 ft **5.** yes **7.** \$140 **9.** 6 possibilities

9.4 Getting Ready to Practice (p. 452)
1. Pythagorean triple **3.** 96 ft

5. Steps 1–2: 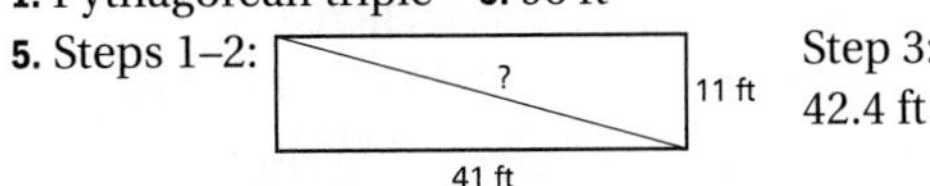

Step 3: 42.4 ft

9.4 Practice and Problem Solving (pp. 452–453)
7. 15 ft; 60 ft², 40 ft **9.** 6 in.; 8.64 in.², 14.4 in. **11.** 44 m; 2574 m², 286 m **13.** yes **15.** no **17.** 30 in. **19.** 18 in. **21.** 24 m **23.** 182 cm

25. 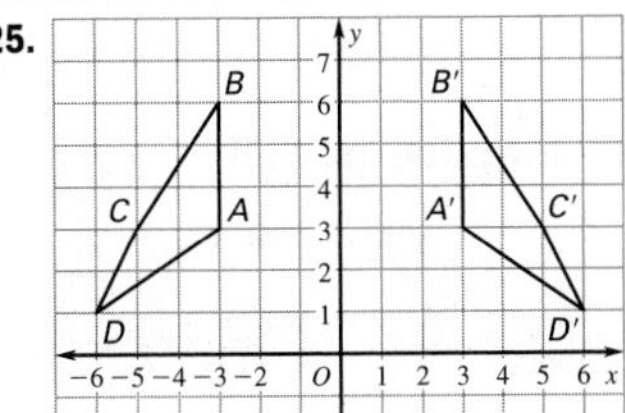

27. -12 **29.** 8.5

9.1–9.4 Notebook Review (pp. 454–455) **1.** real numbers **2.** ±13 **3.** ±11 **4.** ±8

5. 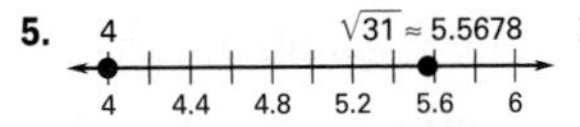

>

6. 7 $\sqrt{59} \approx 7.6811$ <

7 7.2 7.4 7.6 7.8 8

7. $-9 = -\sqrt{81}$ =

−9.5 −9.3 −9.1 −8.9 −8.7 −8.5

8. 6.3 $\sqrt{48} \approx 6.9282$ >

6 6.2 6.4 6.6 6.8 7

9. 15 **10.** 32 **11.** 2.5

SA17

12. *Sample answer:* The decimal form of a rational number terminates or repeats, while the decimal form of an irrational number does neither. For example, $\frac{3}{4}$ and $\frac{1}{3}$ are rational because $\frac{3}{4} =$ 0.75 (terminates) and $\frac{1}{3} = 0.\overline{3}$ (repeats), but $\pi \approx$ 3.1415926535..., which never terminates or repeats.

9.5 Getting Ready to Practice (p. 458) **1.** The length of the hypotenuse is $\sqrt{2}$ times the length of a leg. **3.** 50 ft **5.** Step 1: $\frac{5\sqrt{3}}{2}$ in.; Step 2: 7.5 in.

9.5 Practice and Problem Solving (pp. 459–460) **7.** 28 cm **9.** $x = 11$ in., $y = 11\sqrt{3}$ in. **11.** $y = 36\sqrt{3}$ m, $z = 72$ m **13.** 115 ft **15.** 10 in. **17.** $x = 8$ m, $y = 8\sqrt{3}$ m **19.** $x = 32\frac{1}{2}$ cm, $y = \frac{65\sqrt{3}}{2}$ cm **21.** $x^2 + (x\sqrt{3})^2 \stackrel{?}{=} (2x)^2, x^2 + 3x^2 \stackrel{?}{=} 4x^2, 4x^2 = 4x^2$. *Sample answer:* $3^2 + (3\sqrt{3})^2 \stackrel{?}{=} 6^2$, $9 + 27 \stackrel{?}{=} 36, 36 = 36$. **25.** $1\frac{1}{2}$ **27.** $\frac{7 \text{ people}}{1 \text{ team}}$ **29.** $\frac{61 \text{ rotations}}{1 \text{ min}}$ **31.** 10

9.6 Getting Ready to Practice (p. 466)

5. Step 1:

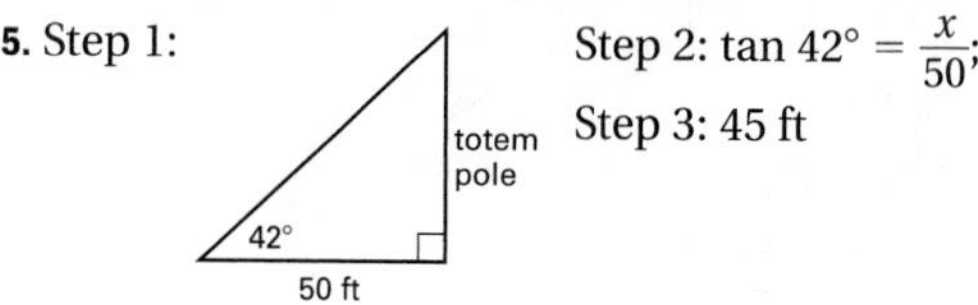

Step 2: $\tan 42° = \frac{x}{50}$; Step 3: 45 ft

9.6 Practice and Problem Solving (pp. 466–468) **7.** $\sin P = \frac{11}{61}, \cos P = \frac{60}{61}, \tan P = \frac{11}{60}, \sin R = \frac{60}{61}, \cos R = \frac{11}{61}, \tan R = \frac{60}{11}$ **9.** 1.2349 **11.** 0.5878 **13.** 3.441 in. **15.** 20.796 m **19.** The tangent ratio is the length of the opposite side over the length of the adjacent side, not over the length of the hypotenuse. So $\tan 25° = \frac{x}{13}$, and $x \approx 6$ cm. **21.** $m\angle C = 60°, AC = 10$ in.; $\sin A = \frac{1}{2}, \cos A = \frac{8.7}{10}, \tan A = \frac{5}{8.7}$ **23.** $m\angle A = 20°, BC \approx 17.2$ cm; $\sin A = \frac{17.2}{51}, \cos A = \frac{48}{51}, \tan A = \frac{17.2}{48}$ **25.** about 1813 m **27.** 84.4 in. **29.** 119 ft

33. 10.73 **35.** Rational. *Sample answer:* 484 is a perfect square, $22^2 = 484$. **37.** Irrational. *Sample answer:* Neither 17 nor 29 is a perfect square. **39.** 3.625 mi/h

9.6 Technology Activity (p. 469) **1.** 14.0° **3.** 42.6° **5.** 87.7° **7.** $\tan^{-1}(32.46)$. *Sample answer:* The greater the tangent of an angle, the larger the angle.

9.5–9.6 Notebook Review (pp. 470–471) **1.** opposite; hypotenuse **2.** $8\sqrt{2}$ in. **3.** 20 cm **4.** $x = 6$ m, $y = 6\sqrt{3}$ m **5.** $\sin A = \frac{3}{5}, \cos A = \frac{4}{5}, \tan A = \frac{3}{4}, \sin B = \frac{4}{5}, \cos B = \frac{3}{5}, \tan B = \frac{4}{3}$ **6.** $\sin A = \frac{48}{73}, \cos A = \frac{55}{73}, \tan A = \frac{48}{55}, \sin B = \frac{55}{73}, \cos B = \frac{48}{73}, \tan B = \frac{55}{48}$ **7.** $\sin A = \frac{36}{85}, \cos A = \frac{77}{85}, \tan A = \frac{36}{77}, \sin B = \frac{77}{85}, \cos B = \frac{36}{85}, \tan B = \frac{77}{36}$ **8.** *Sample answer:* Use the Pythagorean theorem to find that the length of the other leg is 4. Use this fact to find the cosine ratio, $\frac{4}{5}$.

Chapter Review (pp. 472–473) **1.** *Sample answer:* A rational number can be written as a quotient of two integers, while an irrational number cannot. A rational number has a decimal representation that either terminates or repeats, while an irrational number does not. **3.** *Sample answer:* $\sqrt{2}, \pi, \sqrt{7}$ **5.** perfect square **7.** shorter **9.** 9.7 **11.** −46.02 **13.** ±14 **15.** ±8 **17.** Rational. *Sample answer:* 100 is a perfect square, since $10^2 = 100$. **19.** Rational. *Sample answer:* $\frac{16}{25}$ is the quotient of two integers. **21.** $0.\overline{181}, 0.\overline{18}, 0.188, 0.1\overline{8}$ **23.** 11 in. **25.** no **27.** yes **29.** 679.23 m **31.** $x = 15\sqrt{3}$ m, $y = 30$ m **33.** $\sin P = \frac{21}{29}, \cos P = \frac{20}{29}, \tan P = \frac{21}{20}, \sin Q = \frac{20}{29}, \cos Q = \frac{21}{29}, \tan Q = \frac{20}{21}$ **35.** $\sin P = \frac{21}{29}, \cos P = \frac{20}{29}, \tan P = \frac{21}{20}, \sin Q = \frac{20}{29}, \cos Q = \frac{21}{29}, \tan Q = \frac{20}{21}$ **37.** 0.3346 **39.** 0.8391

Chapter 10

10.1 Getting Ready to Practice (p. 483) **1.** $A = bh$ **3.** $A = \frac{1}{2}(b_1 + b_2)h$ **5.** 56 in.^{2}

7. Step 1:

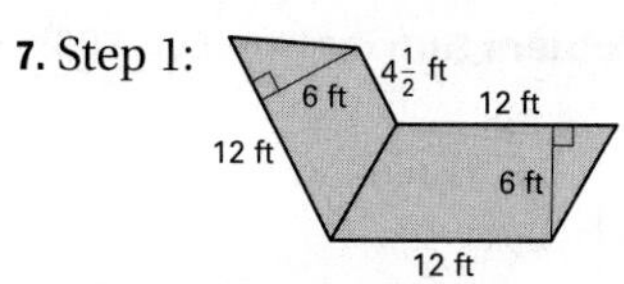

Step 2: trapezoid: $49\frac{1}{2}$ ft^2; parallelogram: 72 ft^2;

Step 3: $121\frac{1}{2}$ ft^2

10.1 Practice and Problem Solving (pp. 483–485)

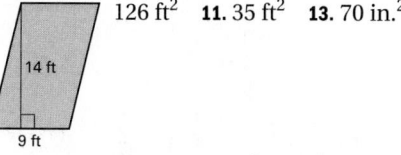

9. 126 ft^2 **11.** 35 ft^2 **13.** 70 in.^{2}

15.

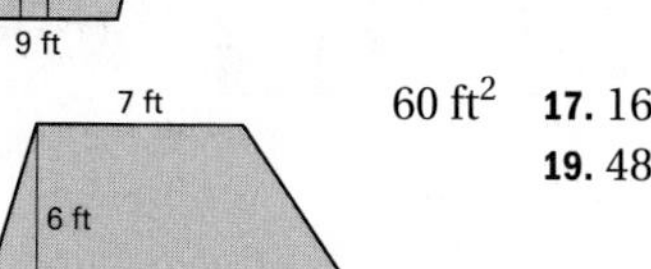

60 ft^2 **17.** 162 in.^{2} **19.** 480 m^2

21.

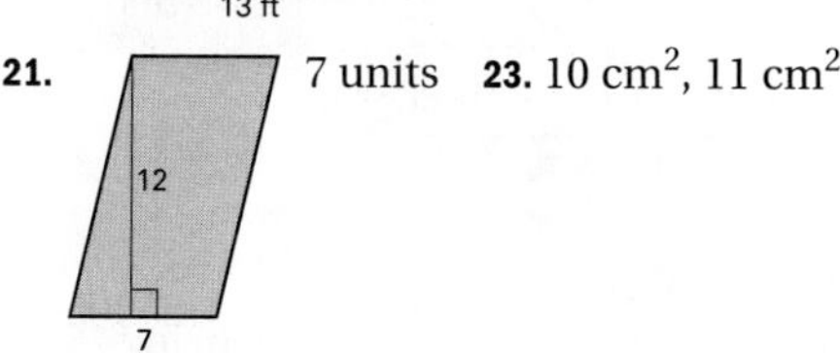

7 units **23.** 10 cm^2, 11 cm^2

25. 90 cm^2, 99 cm^2; the new areas are nine times the original areas. **27.** *Sample answer:* about 112,500 mi^2 **29.** 79.85 in.^{2} **31.** 162 m^2 **33.** 360 ft^2

35.

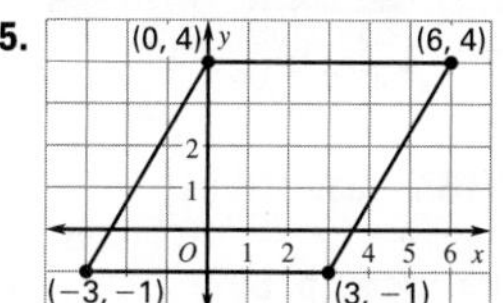

30 units^2

41. $11\frac{2}{3}$ **43.** $\sin P = \frac{8}{17}$, $\cos P = \frac{15}{17}$, $\tan P = \frac{8}{15}$, $\sin R = \frac{15}{17}$, $\cos R = \frac{8}{17}$, $\tan R = \frac{15}{8}$

10.2 Getting Ready to Practice (p. 488) **1.** radius **3.** 314 cm^2 **5.** about 7 m

10.2 Practice and Problem Solving (pp. 488–490)

7. 555 m^2 **9.** 340 cm^2 **11.** 314 ft^2 **13.** 615 mm^2 **15.** 1260 in.^{2} **17.** 1 m **19.** 6 in. **21.** 9 cm **23.** 10 mm; 314 mm^2 **25.** 239 in.^{2} **27.** 5 ft **29.** $18.84 = 2(3.14)r$; 3 ft; 28.3 ft^2 **31.** $37.68 = 2(3.14)r$; 6 cm; 113 cm^2

33. Larger square: 400 mm^2, smaller square: 200 mm^2, estimate: 300 mm^2; actual: 314 mm^2. *Sample answer:* The estimate is close to the actual area of the circle. **37.** no

10.2 Technology Activity (p. 491) **1.** multiplied by 3 **3.** multiplied by 5 **5.** Multiplied by $\sqrt{2}$; multiplied by $\sqrt{3}$. *Sample answer:* If the area of a circle is multiplied by n, then the radius is multiplied by $\sqrt{n}$.

10.3 Getting Ready to Practice (p. 494)

1. cylinder; no **3.** sphere; no

5.

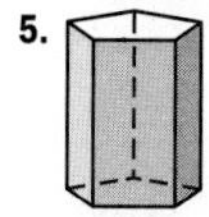

7 faces, 15 edges, 10 vertices

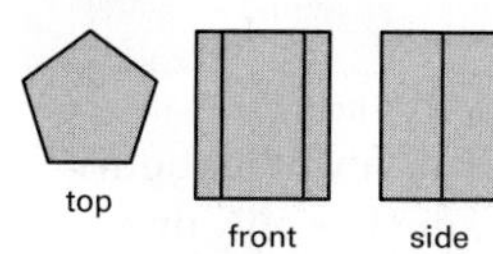

10.3 Practice and Problem Solving (pp. 494–495)

7. sphere; no **9.** cylinder; no

11.

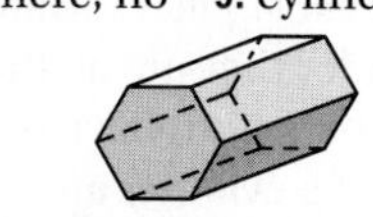

4 faces, 6 edges, 4 vertices

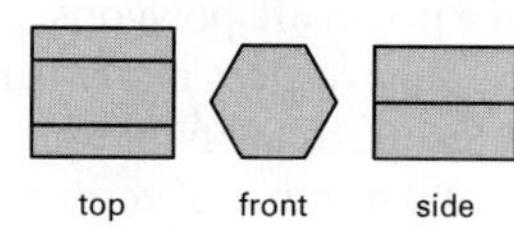

19. pentagonal prisms **21.** cylinder and cone

23.

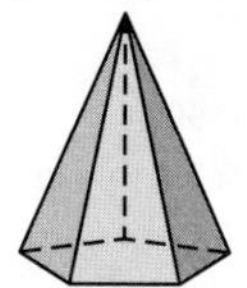

25. 346 in.^{2}

Special Topic Exercises (p. 497)

1. **3.**

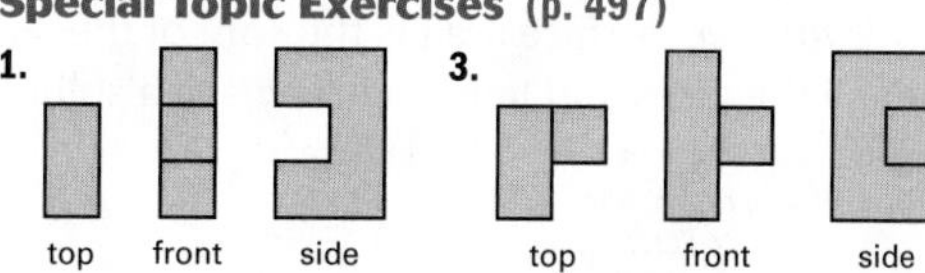

Selected Answers

5.

7.

9.

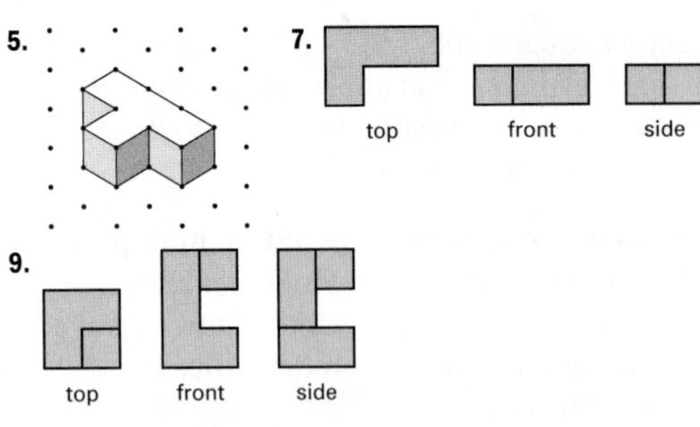

10.1–10.3 Notebook Review (pp. 498–499)

1. polyhedron **2.** 160 ft^2 **3.** 1810 in.^{2} **4.** 50.2 mm^2
5. 254 yd^2 **6.** *Sample:*

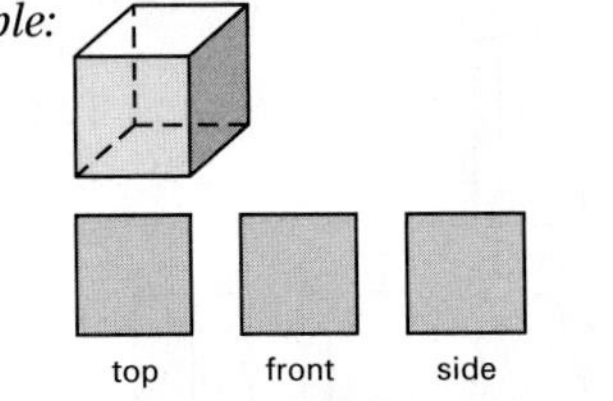

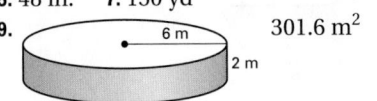

7. *Sample answer:* A cone and a cylinder both have circular bases, but a cone has only one circular base while a cylinder has two. A cross-section of either solid parallel to a base is a circle, but for the cone these circles get smaller toward the vertex, while for the cylinder they are all the same size. A cylinder and a prism both have two parallel bases, but the bases of a cylinder are circles, while the bases of a prism are polygons.
8. No. *Sample answer:* The only vertices of a prism are on its bases. Because the bases are two congruent polygons, the total number of vertices is twice the number on one base, so it is an even number.

10.4 Problem Solving Strategies (p. 501)

1. 396 in.^{2} **3.** 11 0's, 21 1's, 20 of each of the digits 2–9 **5.** 12 sandwiches **7.** 4 and 13

10.4 Getting Ready to Practice (p. 505)

1. *Sample answer:* Surface area is the sum of the areas of all the faces and lateral surfaces of a solid.
3. *Sample:* 184 m^2

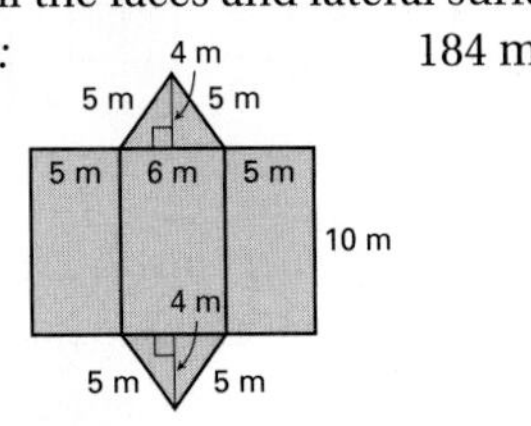

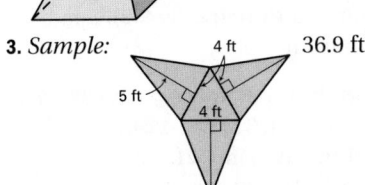

10.4 Practice and Problem Solving (pp. 505–506)

5. 48 in.^{2} **7.** 150 yd^2
9. 301.6 m^2

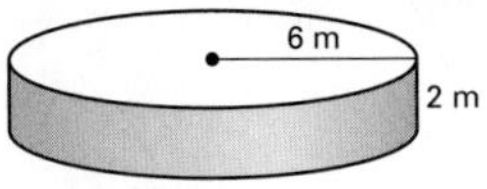

6 m
2 m

11. 1885.0 cm^2

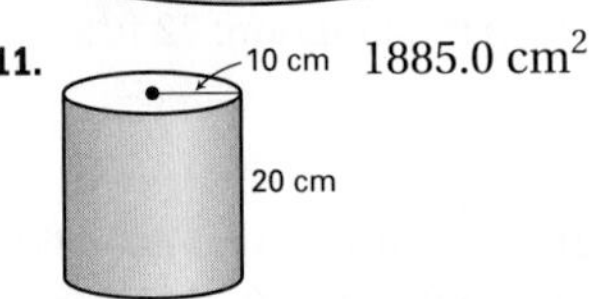

13. triangular prism; 680 in.^{2}
15. *Sample:* 600 in.^{2}

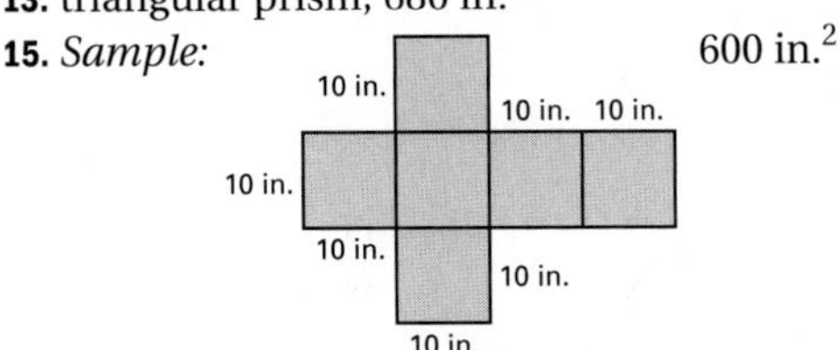

17. *Sample:* 88 m^2

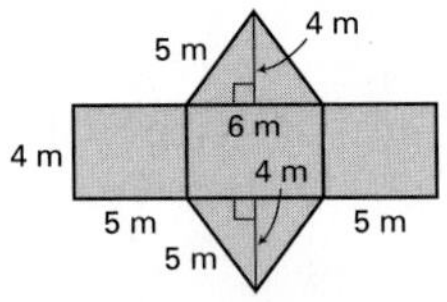

5 m, 4 m, 6 m, 4 m, 4 m, 5 m, 5 m, 5 m

19. 1062 ft^2 **21.** 76 cm^2
23. *Sample:* 46 in.^{2}

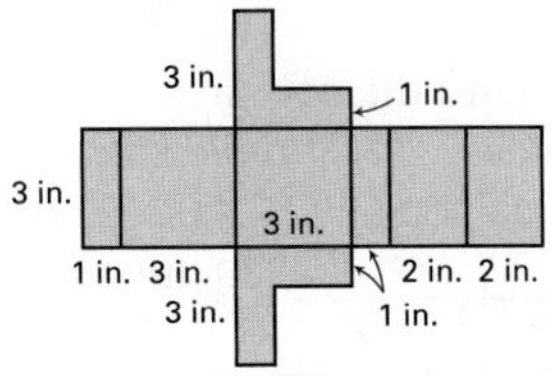

3 in., 1 in., 3 in., 3 in., 1 in., 3 in., 3 in., 2 in., 2 in., 1 in.

27. yes **29.** 0.4245 **31.** 0.9135 **33.** 216 in.^{2}

10.5 Getting Ready to Practice (p. 509)

1.

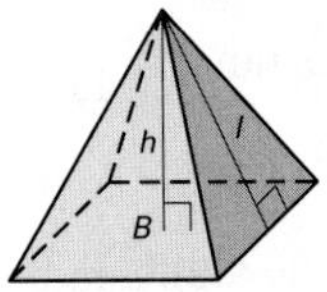

h, l, B

3. *Sample:* 36.9 ft^2

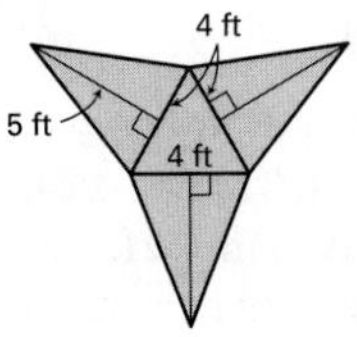

4 ft, 5 ft, 4 ft

5. Step 1: $(\pi r^2 + \pi rl) - \pi r^2 = \pi rl$; Step 2: $\pi(1)\left(4\frac{1}{4}\right)$; Step 3: 13.4 in.^{2}

10.5 Practice and Problem Solving (pp. 510–511)
7. 144 m^2 **9.** 525 yd^2 **11.** 138.2 in.^{2} **13.** 119.4 mm^2
15. *Sample:*

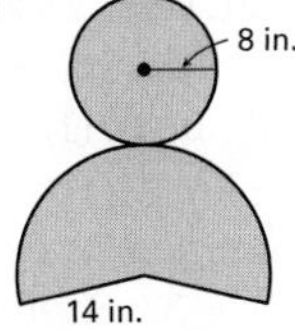

552.9 in.^{2}

17. 261 in.^{2} **19.** 1508.0 m^2 **21.** 373.8 ft^2
23. 243.3 in.^{2} **25.** 6π in.^{2} **27.** 54π in.^{2}
29. $S = B + \frac{1}{2}Pl = \pi r^2 + \frac{1}{2}(2\pi r)l = \pi r^2 + \pi rl$; the simplified expression is the same as the formula for the surface area of a cone. **33.** rational **35.** irrational

10.6 Getting Ready to Practice (p. 515)
1. *Sample answer:* Area is the measure of the region inside a two-dimensional shape, while volume is the measure of the space inside a solid. **3.** 200 in.^{3} **5.** The area of the base is πr^2, not $2\pi r$; $V = Bh = \pi r^2 h = \pi(4^2)5 \approx 251.3$.

10.6 Practice and Problem Solving (pp. 516–517)
7. 343 in.^{3} **9.** 120 ft^3 **11.** 254.5 cm^3 **13.** 64 yd^3
15. 1260 m^3 **17.** 25,446.9 mm^3 **19.** surface area
21. volume **23.** 3820.2 cm^3 **25.** 8.6 mm^3
27. 336 m^3 **29.** 11 times **31.** They would have the same effect. *Sample answer:* Since $V = lwh$, if any dimension is doubled, the volume is doubled.
33. 36 **35.** 192 in.^{2} **37.** 75.4 ft^2

10.7 Getting Ready to Practice (p. 521)
5. 96 cm^3 **7.** 3141.6 ft^3

10.7 Practice and Problem Solving (pp. 522–523)
9. 60 ft^3 **11.** 2560 m^3 **13.** 247.5 ft^3 **15.** 144 yd^3
17. 3421.2 cm^3 **19.** 5399.6 ft^3 **21.** 506.8 ft^3
23. 134.0 m^3 **25.** 70.7 ft^3 **27.** 0.2 cm^3 **29.** Doubling the radius. *Sample answer:* The radius is squared in the volume formula, but the height is not. **31.** Find the volume of the rectangular pyramid and the volume of the rectangular prism and add; $V = \frac{1}{3}lwh_1 + lwh_2$. **33.** 28.8 ft; 36.7 ft **37.** 2770.9 in.^{3}

10.4–10.7 Notebook Review (pp. 524–525) **1.** It is the height of a lateral face. **2.** 471.24 m^2
3. 146 in.^{2} **4.** 105 m^2 **5.** 785.40 ft^2 **6.** 126 m^3
7. *Sample answer:* Area is the measure of the region inside a two-dimensional figure, while surface area is the sum of the areas of all faces or surfaces of a solid.

Chapter Review (pp. 526–527)
5. *Sample:*

7. $S = 2\pi r^2 + 2\pi rh$; $V = \pi r^2 h$ **9.** $S = B + \frac{1}{2}Pl$; $V = \frac{1}{3}Bh$ **11.** 112 ft^2 **13.** $53\frac{1}{4}$ in.^{2} **15.** 90 yd^2
17. 707 yd^2 **19.** 1.77 m^2
21. *Sample:*

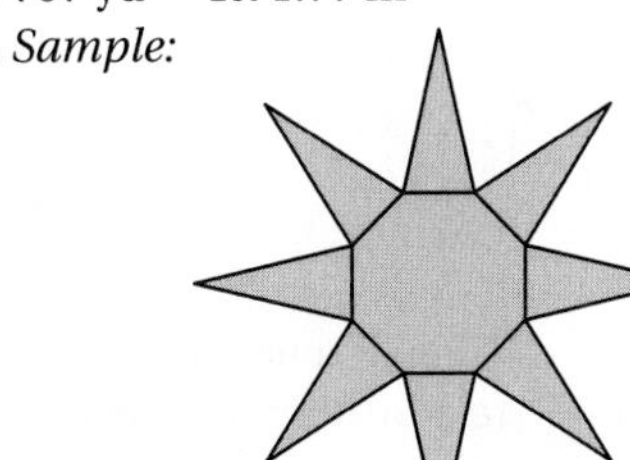

9 faces, 16 edges, 9 vertices

23. 2921.7 yd^2 **25.** 785.4 ft^2 **27.** 144 in.^{2}
29. 103.8 mm^3 **31.** 20 in.^{3} **33.** 314.2 ft^3 **35.** No. *Sample answer:* The volume of the pyramid is 15 cubic inches, which is greater than the 12 cubic inches of candle wax.

Chapter 11

11.1 Getting Ready to Practice (p. 543)
1. function **3.** yes **5.** 18, 13, 8, 3 **7.** $y = -5x$

11.1 Practice and Problem Solving (pp. 543–544)
9. No; one input, 4, has two output values.
11. Yes; each input has exactly one output value.
13.

Input *x*	−2	−1	0	1	2
Output *y*	−3	−2	−1	0	1

range: −3, −2, −1, 0, 1

SA21

15.

Input x	-2	-1	0	1	2
Output y	-10	-5	0	5	10

range: $-10, -5, 0, 5, 10$

17. $y = 5x$ **19.** No; the weight of the cans that Stanley recycles is a function of the amount of money. **21.** $t = 3r - 2$ **23.** Yes; each input has exactly one output value. **25.** 113.5 m^2 **27.** 6670 ft^2

11.2 Getting Ready to Practice (p. 547)

1. scatter plot

11.2 Practice and Problem Solving (pp. 547–548)

3. no relationship **5.** negative relationship

7.

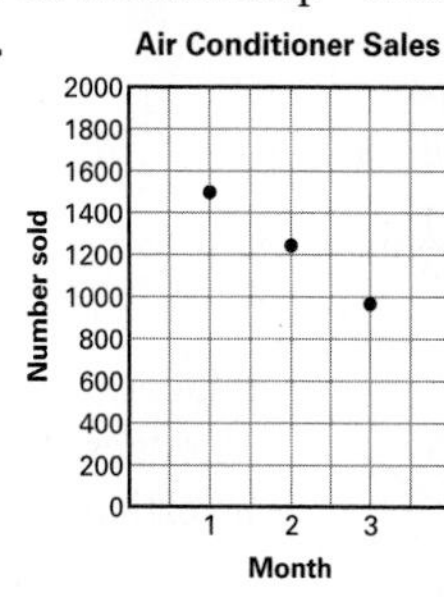

There is a negative relationship. As the summer turns fall, sales of air conditioners decrease.

9.

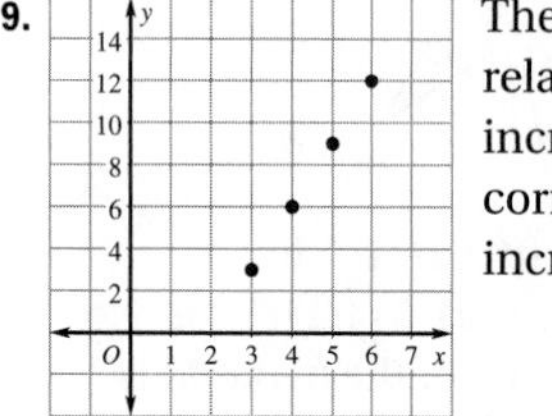

There is a positive relationship, with each increase of 1 in x corresponding to an increase of 3 in y; (7, 15).

11. positive relationship **13.** *Sample answer:* When the weather is nicer, more people will vote; no, because it would be hard to find a single measure that would accurately indicate how "nice" the weather is. **15.** 90 m^2

17.

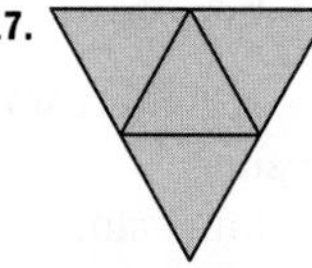

21. 19 **23.** 19

11.3 Getting Ready to Practice (p. 551)

1. solution **3.** $y = 2x + 4$ **5.** The x value was substituted for y and the y value was substituted for x. The second step should be $2(-5) + 3(4) \stackrel{?}{=} -7$, followed by $-10 + 12 \stackrel{?}{=} -7$ and $2 \neq -7$. So, $(-5, 4)$ is not a solution.

11.3 Practice and Problem Solving (pp. 551–553)

7. y values in the table: 3, 8, 13, 18 **9.** y values in the table: $-25, -20, -15, -10$ **11.** no **13.** yes **15.** yes **17.** *Sample answer:* $(-1, -6)$, $(0, -10)$, $(1, -14)$, $(2, -18)$ **19.** no **21.** yes **23–27.** Sample answers are given. **23.** $(-1, -15)$, $(0, -13)$, $(1, -11)$, $(2, -9)$ **25.** $(-1, 8)$, $(0, 3)$, $(1, -2)$, $(2, -7)$ **27.** $(-1, -45)$, $(0, -51)$, $(1, -57)$, $(2, -63)$ **29.** 20 wk **31.** $y = -x + 8$. *Sample answer:* $(-1, 9)$, $(0, 8)$, $(1, 7)$, $(2, 6)$ **33.** $y = 3x + 33$. *Sample answer:* $(-1, 30)$, $(0, 33)$, $(1, 36)$, $(2, 39)$ **35.** $y = 2 - 3x$. *Sample answer:* $(-1, 5)$, $(0, 2)$, $(1, -1)$, $(2, -4)$ **37.** $y = 2x + 4$ **39.** *Sample answer:* $9x = 24$ and $8y \approx -6$, so $9x + 8y \approx 18$, which is greater than 16. **41.** $(2, -1)$ **43.**

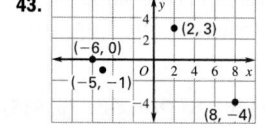

45.

Input x	-2	-1	0	1	2
Output y	3	2.5	2	1.5	1

range: 1, 1.5, 2, 2.5, 3

47.

Input x	-2	-1	0	1	2
Output y	12	10	8	6	4

range: 4, 6, 8, 10, 12 **49.** -8.75

11.4 Problem Solving Strategies (p. 555)

1. 2nd row: 140, 120, 100, 80 **3.** 60 ft **5.** Krystal **7.** 27 rectangles; 81 rectangles **9.** Leslie

11.4 Getting Ready to Practice (p. 558)

1. line

3. *Sample:*

Input x	-2	-1	0	1	2
Output y	-4	-4	-4	-4	-4

11.4 Practice and Problem Solving (pp. 559–560)

9. yes **11.** *Sample answer:* $(-1, -3)$, $(0, -2)$, $(1, -1)$ **13.** *Sample answer:* $(-1, 6)$, $(0, 6)$, $(1, 6)$

15.

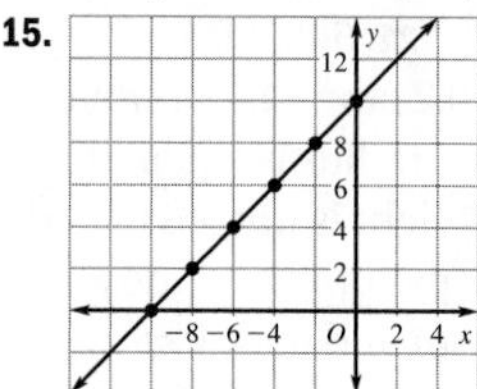

17.

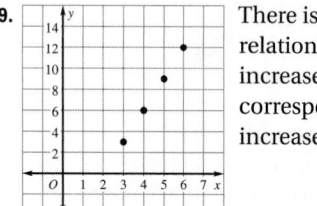

19.

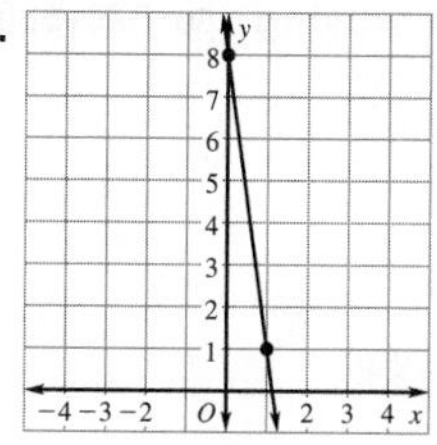

23.

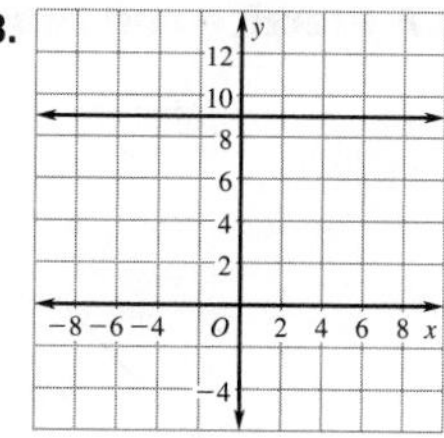

27. $x = 5$

29.

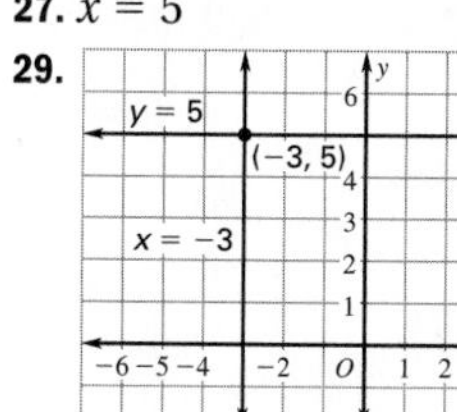

$(-3, 5)$. *Sample answer:* Since $x = -3$ and $y = 5$, $(-3, 5)$ will be the coordinates of the point of intersection.

37. $y = 2$ **39.** *Sample answer:* The line must be horizontal and contain all points with a y-coordinate of -8.6, so the equation of the line is $y = -8.6$. **41.** 140 square units **43.** 1056 square units **45.** y values in table: $-14, -8, 1, 4, 13$ **47.** -252

11.4 Technology Activity (p. 561)

1.

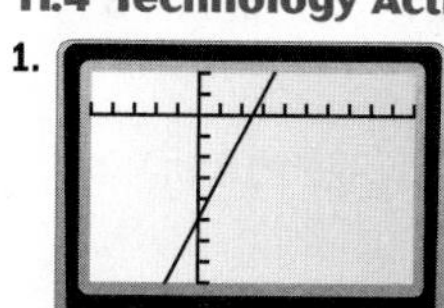

3.

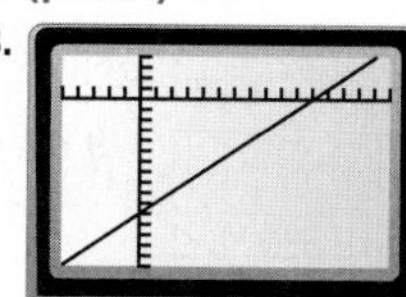

5. yes

11.1–11.4 Notebook Review (pp. 562–563)

1. input-output table **2.** $y = -4x$ **3.** $y = x + 3$

4.

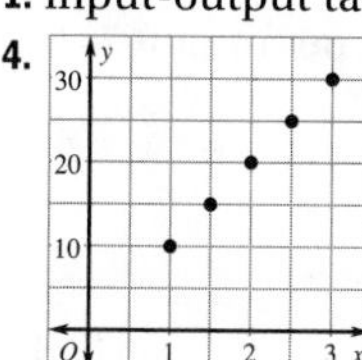

The data have a positive relationship, with every increase of 0.5 in x there is a corresponding increase of 5 in y.

5–7. Sample solutions are given.

5. $(0, 5), (1, 3), (2, 1)$

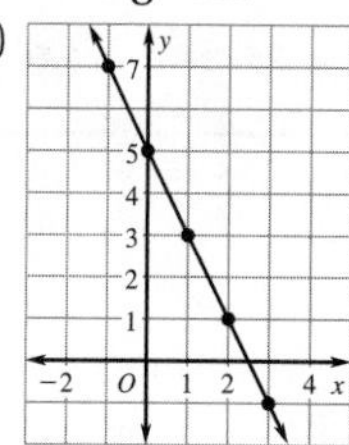

6. $(0, -6), (1, -3)\ (2, 0)$

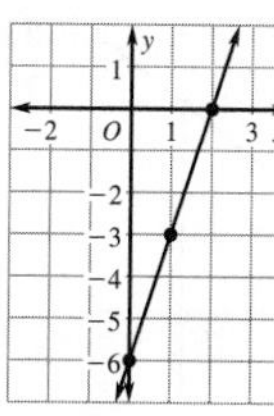

7. $(0, 4), (4, 5), (8, 6)$

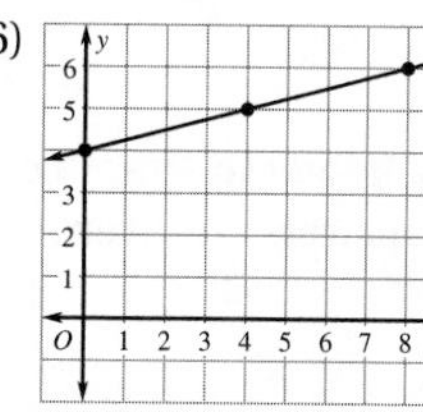

8. *Sample answer:* $4y = -2x + 16$ can be rewritten as $16 = 2x + 4y$, or $8 = x + 2y$, so the equations are equivalent and have the same solutions.

11.5 Getting Ready to Practice (p. 566)

1. y-intercept, x-intercept **3.** x-intercept: 3, y-intercept: -1

11.5 Practice and Problem Solving (pp. 566–567)

5. x-intercept: $\frac{1}{2}$, y-intercept: -3 **7.** x-intercept: -2, y-intercept: 10 **9.** x-intercept: 5, y-intercept: 4

11.

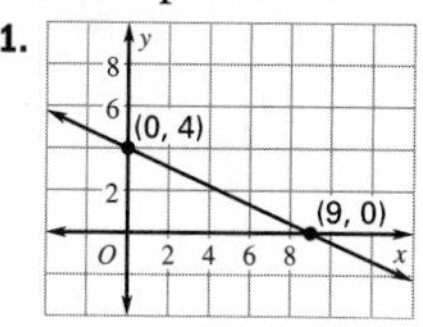

13. 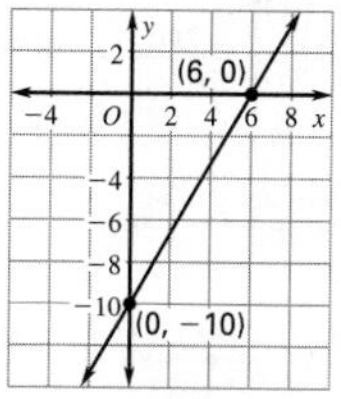 (6, 0) (0, −10)

15. Up. *Sample answer:* The x-intercept will be on the positive side of the x-axis and the y-intercept will be on the negative side of the y-axis, so the line will slant up from left to right. **17.** x-intercept: none, y-intercept: 14

19.

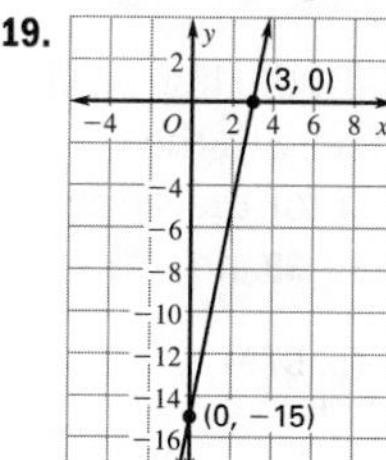

21.

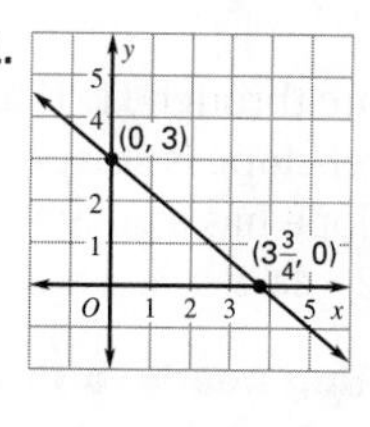

25. x-intercept: 1.71, y-intercept: 3.65

27. x-intercept: -3.64, y-intercept: -15.01

SA23

31. 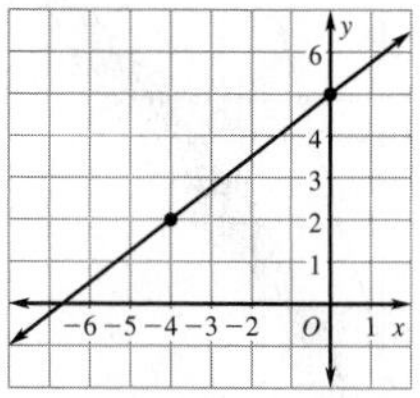

33. 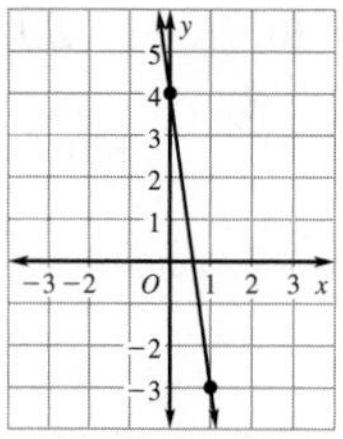

35. 60 km/h

11.6 Getting Ready to Practice (p. 572) **1.** rise **3, 5.** Sample answers are given.

3. 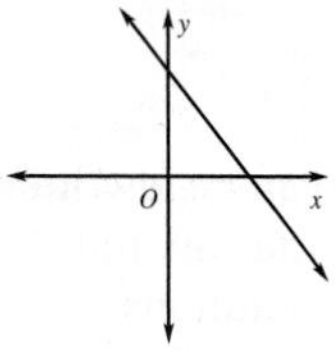

5. 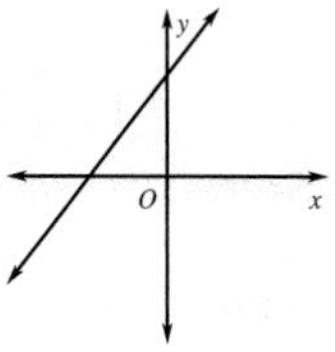

7. 3 **9.** 1

11.6 Practice and Problem Solving (pp. 573–574)

11. (1, 0), (−2, 6); −2 **13.** $-\frac{1}{5}$ **15.** 1 **17.** $\frac{3}{5}$ **19.** $-\frac{5}{12}$ **21.** $\frac{3}{32}$

23. 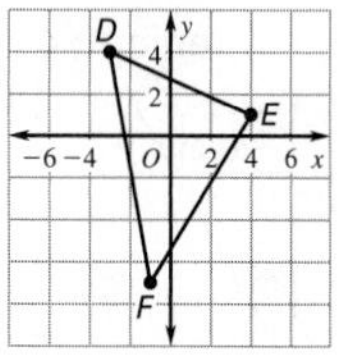

slope of $\overline{DE} = -\frac{3}{7}$, slope of $\overline{EF} = \frac{8}{5}$, slope of $\overline{FD} = -\frac{11}{2}$

25. 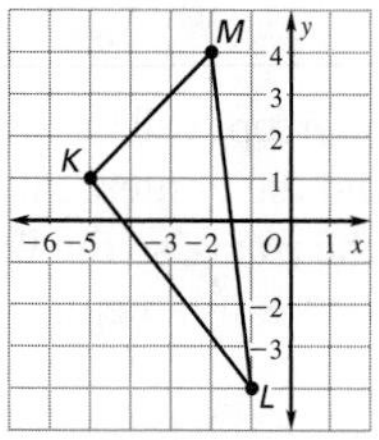

slope of $\overline{KL} = -\frac{5}{4}$, slope of $\overline{LM} = -8$, slope of $\overline{MK} = 1$

27. The line through (1, 1) and (3, 4); the line with the greater slope is steeper; the line with the greater slope has a greater number for the slope. **31.** $x = 12$ **33.** $x = 4, y = 3$ **37.** yes **39.** no **41.** 63

11.7 Getting Ready to Practice (p. 579) **1.** −5, 7 **3.** $y = 2x - 5$ **5.** 1, 3 **7.** 2, −1

11.7 Practice and Problem Solving (pp. 579–580)

9. 1, −8; 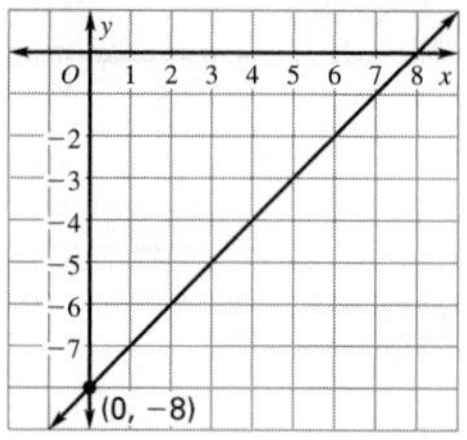

11. −1, 7; 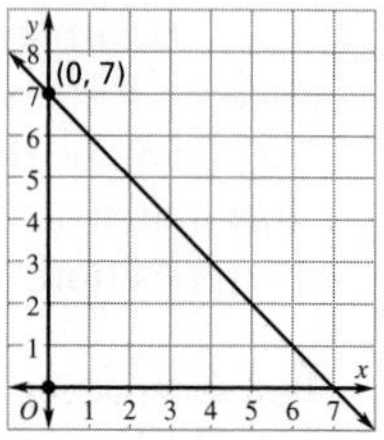

13. $\frac{2}{3}$, −4; 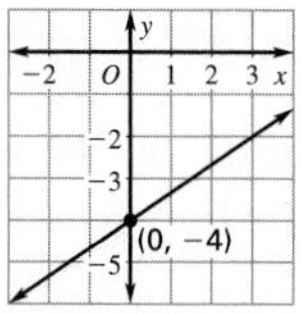

15. $y = -6x + 10$; −6, 10 **17.** $y = \frac{2}{3}x - 3$; $\frac{2}{3}$, −3 **19.** $y = -12x$; −12, 0

21. 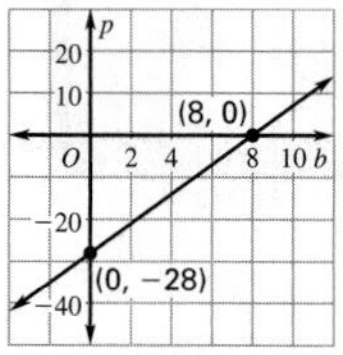

9 bracelets **23.** $y = -\frac{3}{2}x - 3$

25. 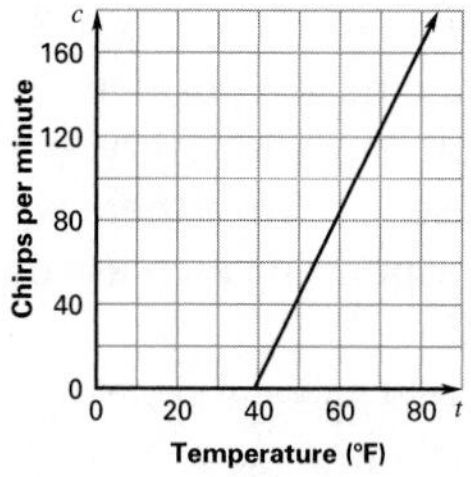

At 39°F, the number of chirps per minute is 0.

27. $y = -\frac{a}{b}x - \frac{c}{b}$ **29.** $5x \geq 35$; $x \geq 7$ **31.** 75 ft^3

33. $t > 6$; 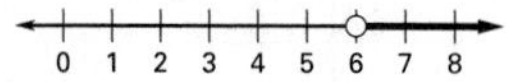

Special Topic Exercises (p. 582)

1. (1, 2)

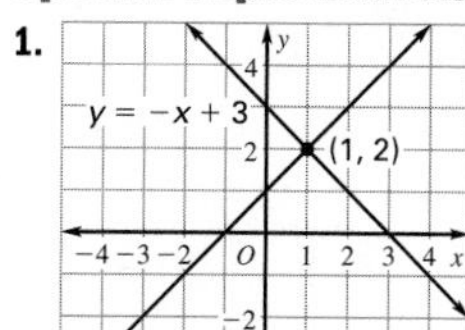

3. (6, −3) **5.** (−1, 5)

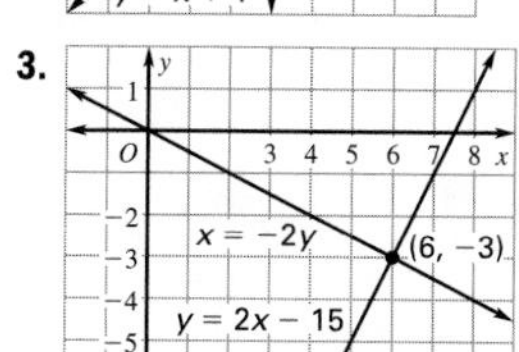

7. in 40 days

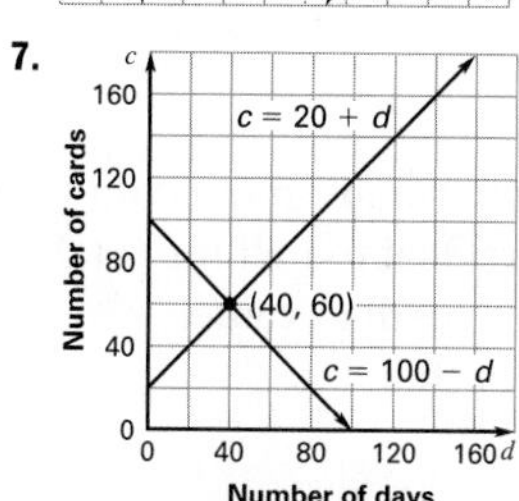
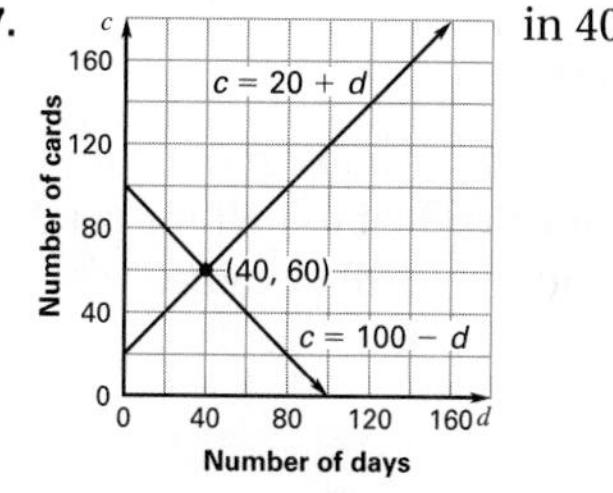

11.8 Getting Ready to Practice (p. 585)

1. half-planes **3.** yes **5.** no

7.

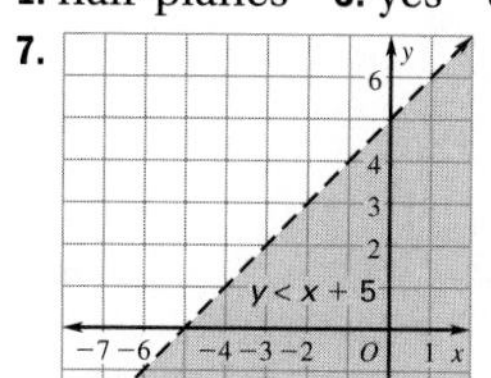

9.

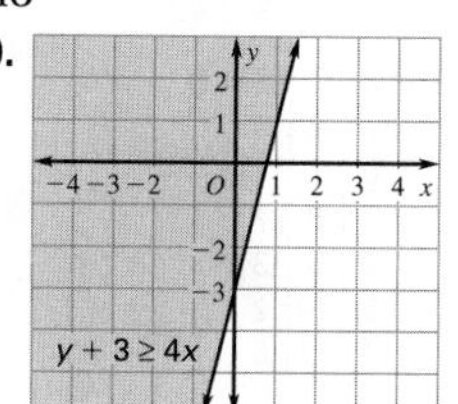

11.8 Practice and Problem Solving (pp. 586–587)

11. yes **13.** no **15.** Use a dashed line when the inequality symbol is < or >. Use a solid line when the inequality symbol is ≤ or ≥.

21.

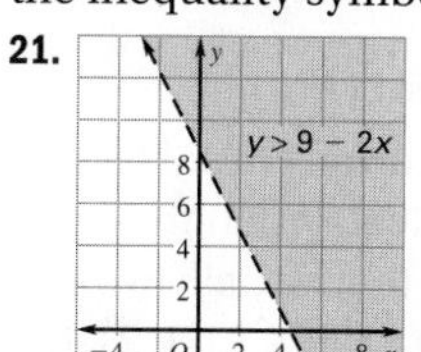

23.

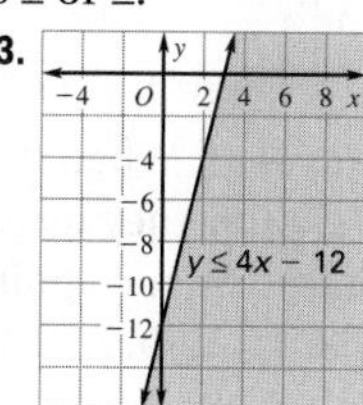

27.

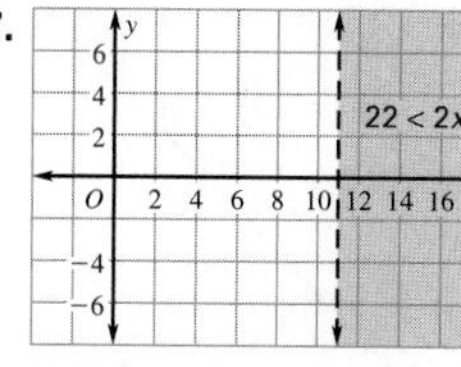

29.

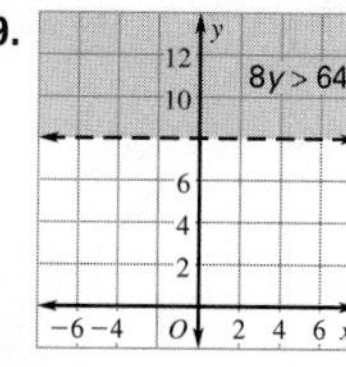

31.

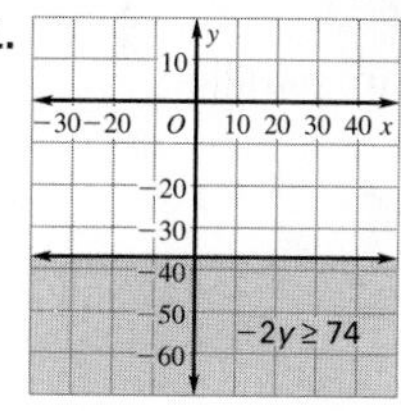

33.

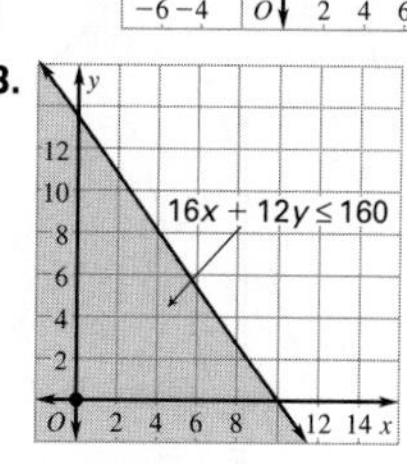

37. $y < -\frac{1}{3}x + 5$; $y > \frac{1}{3}x - 5$; $y > \frac{2}{3}x - 6$; $y < -\frac{2}{3}x + 6$

39. $\frac{6}{5}$ **41.** $3\frac{3}{4}$ **43.** $7\frac{41}{250}$

11.5–11.8 Notebook Review (pp. 588–589)

1. slope; y-intercept **2.** $\frac{4}{3}$ **3.** $\frac{2}{5}$ **4.** $-\frac{5}{3}$

5. 5, 20;

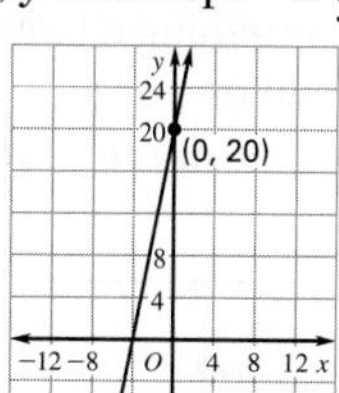

6. $\frac{2}{3}$, 4;

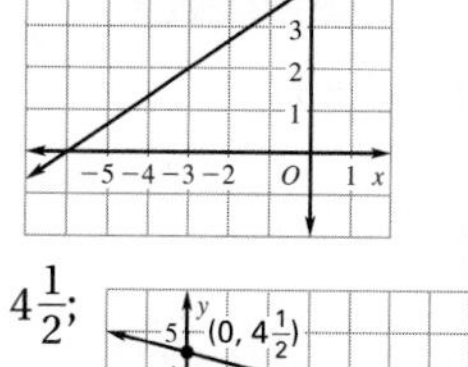

7. $-\frac{1}{4}$, $4\frac{1}{2}$;

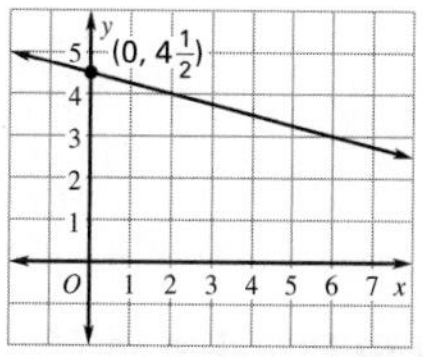

8.

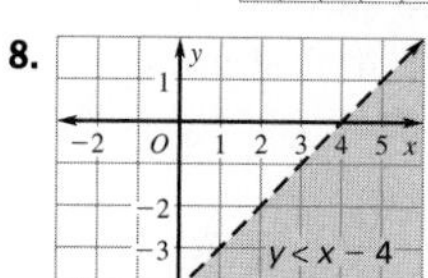

9.

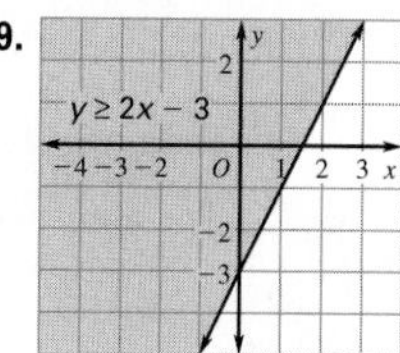

SA25

10. 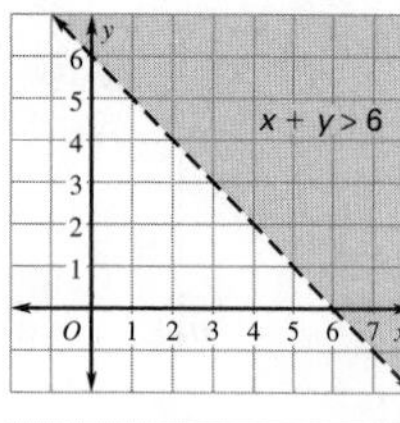

11. 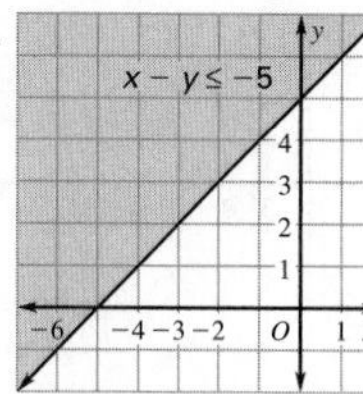

12. 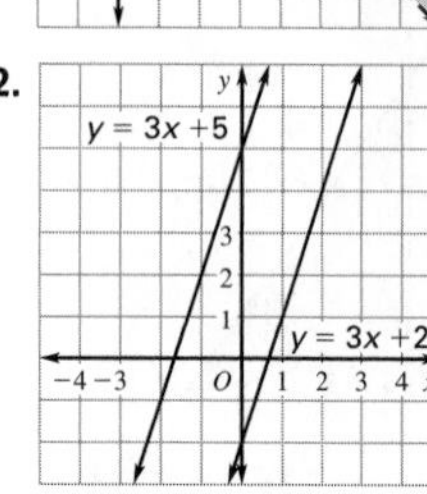

They are parallel.

Chapter Review (pp. 590–591) **1.** half-plane **3.** rise, run **5.** A good answer will include a situation that changes over time, such as time and distance traveled, and an explanation that the slope tells you how quickly something changes. **7.** No; each input has more than one output. **9.** Yes; each input has exactly one output. **11.** \$141

15. 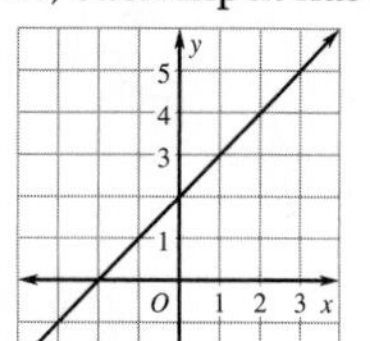

17. 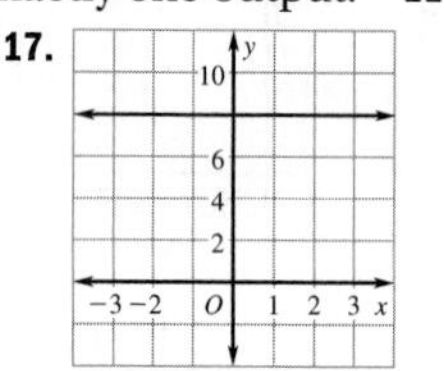

19. *Sample answer:* $(-2, 3)$, $(2, 3)$; 0 **21.** $y = 4x + 10$; 4, 10 **23.** $y = -\frac{3}{7}x - 3$; $-\frac{3}{7}$, -3

25. 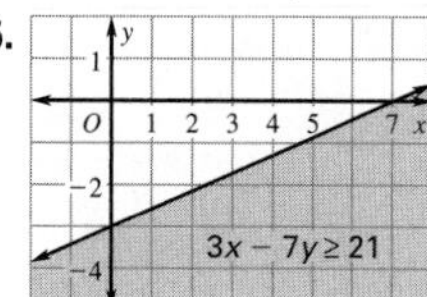

Chapter 12

12.1 Getting Ready to Practice (p. 599) **1.** stem, leaf **3.** 11 | 7; stem: 11, leaf: 7 **5.** 4 | 6; stem: 4, leaf: 6

12.1 Practice and Problem Solving (pp. 599–600)

7.

Stem	Leaves
4	5 8
5	0
6	3 5 7
7	4
8	2

Key: 5 | 0 = 50

60–69

9.

Stem	Leaves
8	9
9	4 5
10	3 8 9
11	2

Key: 10 | 3 = 103

100–109

11.

Stem	Leaves
18	1 3 7
19	
20	2
21	
22	5 6

Key: 18 | 1 = 18.1

18.0–18.9

13. Count the total number of values in the data set. Then count from the first leaf to half the total number of values to find the median value.

15.

Stem	Leaves
4	3 7
5	5 8 9
6	5
7	2 8
8	4 4
9	5 6

Key: 4 | 3 = 43

53; greater than

17.

Set C	Stem	Set D
	6	5
7 0	7	
	8	7 8
8 2	9	3 5
2	10	2
8 1	11	5

Key: 2 | 9 | 3 = 92 and 93

19.

Wins	Stem	Losses
7	0	6 7
8	1	0 2 4 5 6
7 4 4 3 0	2	1
	3	
1	4	

Key: 0 | 2 | 1 = 20 and 21

Sample answer: When the Browns scored less than 20 points, they usually lost. When they scored more than 20 points, they usually won.

21. 13.8, 14.2, 14.4, 15.6, 17.1, 18.7, 20.6, 21.4, 21.1, 19.3, 16.4, 13.8 **23.** 3.5, 6, 6 and 14, 42

12.2 Getting Ready to Practice (p. 603)

1. lower quartile; upper quartile

12.2 Practice and Problem Solving (pp. 603–604)

3. 25 30 35 40 45 50 55 60 65 70

28 37 52.5 61.5 70

5.

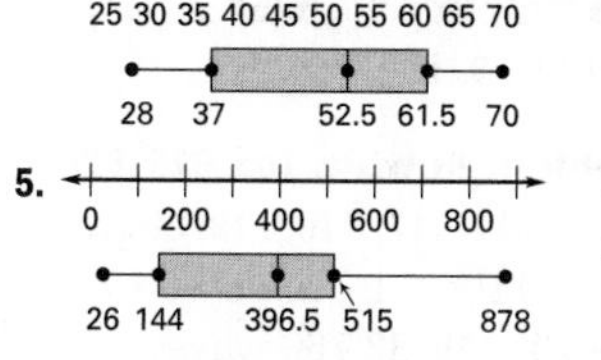

7. 15 in. **9.** 22 in. **11.** 28 in.

13.

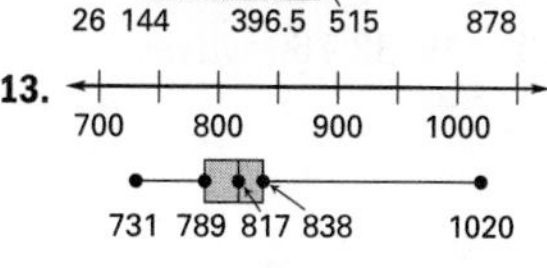

Sample answer: The middle half of the pumpkin weights clustered within about a 50 pound range, from 789 pounds to 838 pounds, but the range was much wider, nearly 300 pounds.

17.

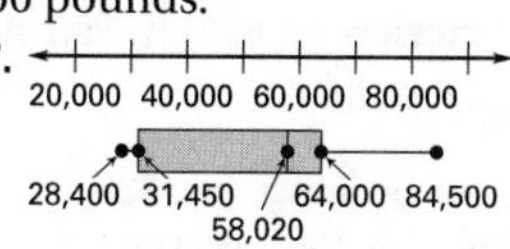

Sample answer: The outlier does not have much of an effect on the quartiles, but it makes a whisker very long and thus greatly increases the range.

19.

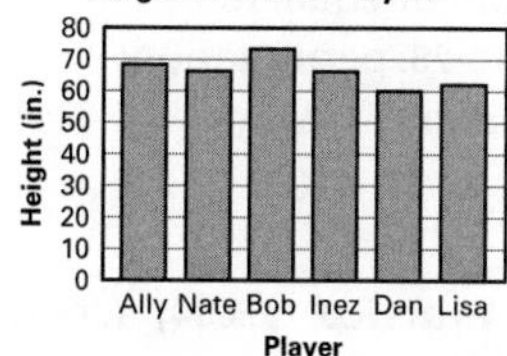

21. x-intercept: 10, y-intercept: -6, slope: $\frac{3}{5}$

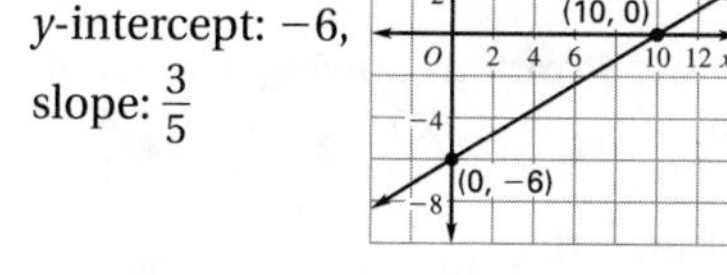

12.3 Getting Ready to Practice (p. 607) **1.** circle graph **3.** 112° **5.** 50° **7.**

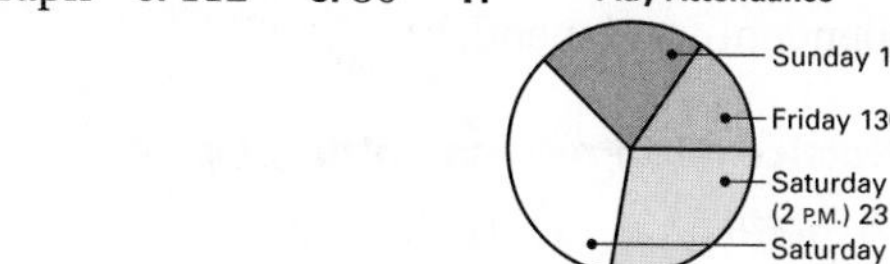

12.3 Practice and Problem Solving (pp. 608–609)

9.

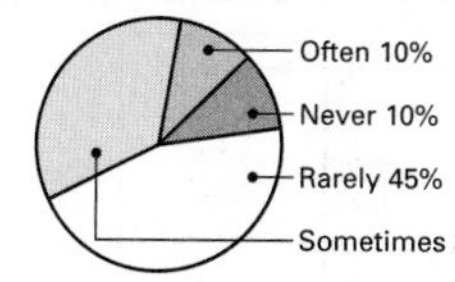

11.

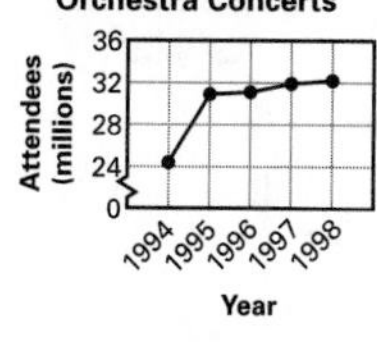

Sample answer: The number of people who attend symphony orchestra concerts increased rapidly from 1994 to 1995, and then at a slower rate from 1995 to 1998.

13.

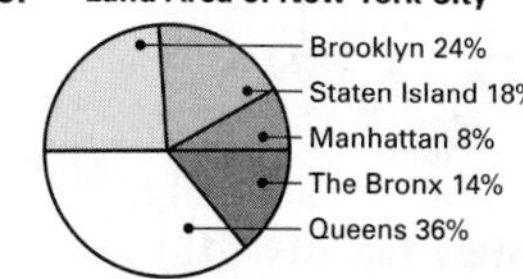

15. *Sample answer:* Line graph; the data is collected over time. **17.** *Sample answer:* Histogram; the data is the frequency of occurrence in equal intervals for a certain range. **19.** red; dark blue **21.** No; it does not show a change in data over time; yes; it shows data in distinct categories.

23.

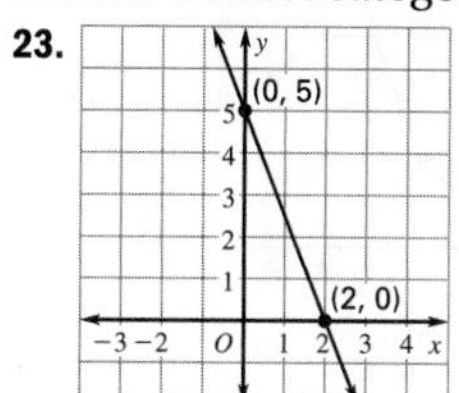

25.

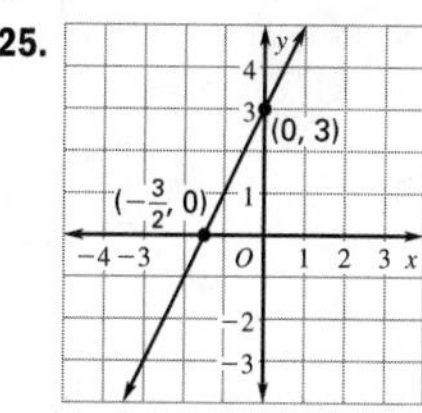

12.3 Technology Activity (pp. 610–611)

1.

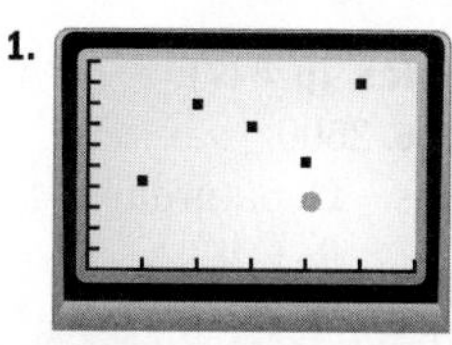

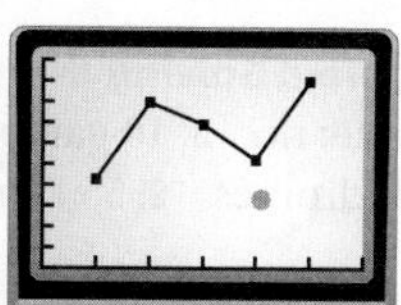

3.

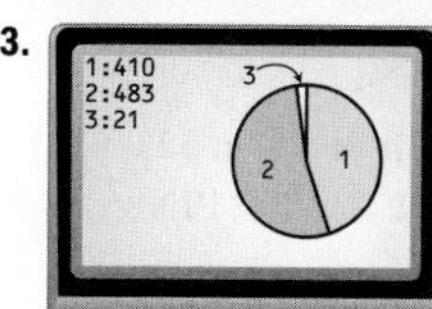

SA27

Special Topic Exercises (p. 613)

1. No. *Sample answer:* There is a break in the vertical scale, so the relative change is smaller than it appears.

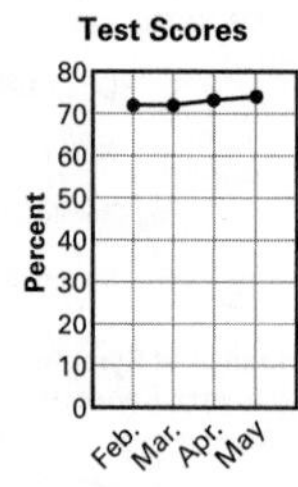

3.

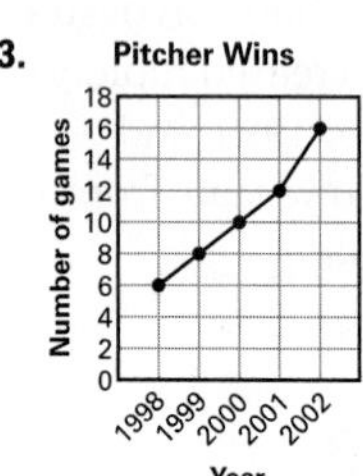

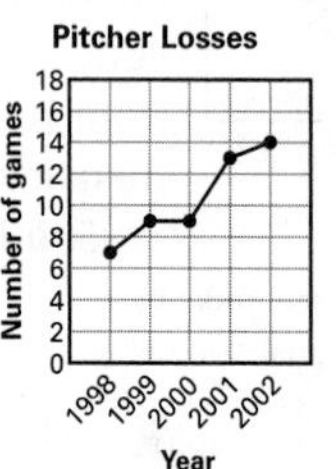

12.1–12.3 Notebook Review (pp. 614–615)

1. lower extreme, upper extreme

2.

0	7 8 9
1	1 1 4 5 8 9
2	4

Key: 1 | 4 = 14

6 8 10 12 14 16 18 20 22 24 26

7 9 12.5 18 24

3.

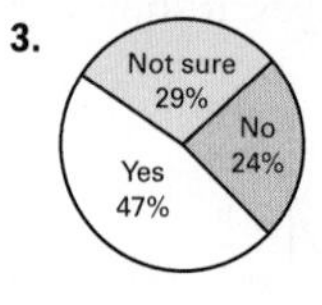

4.

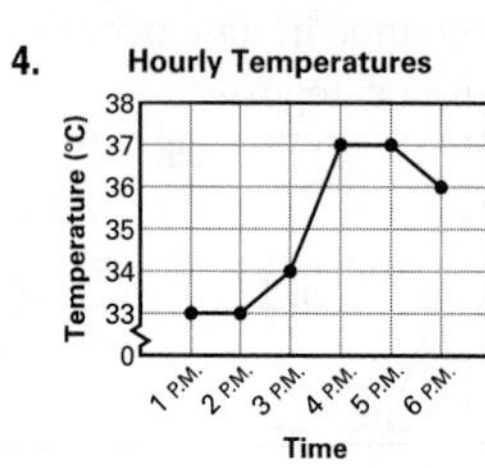

5. *Sample answer:* movie attendance each night for two weeks **6.** No. *Sample answer:* It does not show data that vary over time; bar graph.

12.4 Problem Solving Strategies (p. 617)

1. 60 people; no **3.** 10 games **5.** 2500 **7.** 58 palindromes **9.** 55 squares **11.** Saturday

12.4 Getting Ready to Practice (p. 620) **1.** $m \cdot n$ **3.** 9 choices **5.** 6 choices **7.** $\frac{1}{64}$

12.4 Practice and Problem Solving (pp. 621–622)

9. 24 choices **11.** 16 choices **13.** 26,000 PINs **15.** $\frac{1}{64}$ **21.** 3 desserts **25.** $\frac{1}{2}$

27.

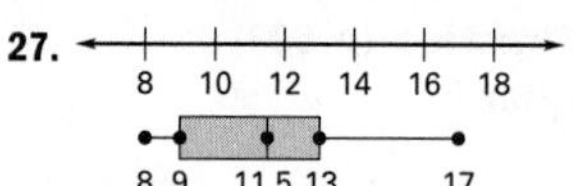

12.5 Getting Ready to Practice (p. 625) **1.** ${}_{15}P_7$ **3.** 1 **5.** 362,880 **7.** 60,480 **9.** 120

12.5 Practice and Problem Solving (pp. 625–626)

11. 24 orders **13.** 20 **15.** 504 **17.** 840 **19.** 6840 **21.** 360,360 ways **23.** yes; $11! = 11 \cdot 10 \cdot 9 \cdot 8 \cdot 7 \cdot 6 \cdot 5 \cdot 4 \cdot 3 \cdot 2 \cdot 1 = 11 \cdot 10!$ **25.** 32,760 ways

29.

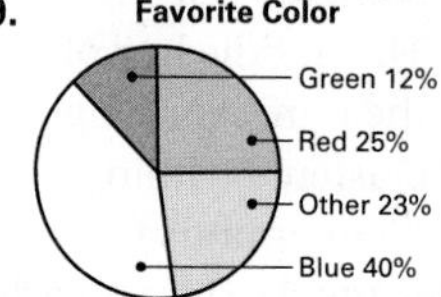

12.6 Getting Ready to Practice (p. 629) **1.** 9; 5 **3.** 4 **5.** 7 **7.** combination; 6 pairs

12.6 Practice and Problem Solving (pp. 630–631)

11. 1 **13.** 70 **15.** 8 **17.** 126 **19.** 78 **21.** 100 **23.** 792 teams **25.** No. *Sample answer:* You cannot choose more items than you have to start with, that is, r must be less than or equal to n. **27.** combination; 10 sets **29.** permutation; 1,814,400 ways; combination, 45 ways **31.** 4845 **35.** 30,240 **37.** 4896 **39.** $\frac{2}{3}$

12.7 Getting Ready to Practice (p. 634) **1.** odds in favor **3.** $\frac{3}{5}$ **5.** $\frac{1}{10}$ **7.** $\frac{1}{3}$ **9.** $\frac{3}{7}$

12.7 Practice and Problem Solving (pp. 635–636)

11. $\frac{4}{13}; \frac{9}{4}$ **13.** $\frac{3}{7}; \frac{5}{9}$ **15.** $\frac{5}{1}$ **17.** $\frac{1}{2}$ **21.** $\frac{7}{25}$ **23.** $\frac{4}{1}$ **27.** 0.04 **29.** 51 in. **31.** $-\frac{1}{10}$ **33.** $\frac{7}{15}$ **35.** $\frac{3}{56}$

12.8 Getting Ready to Practice (p. 641)

1. independent **3.** dependent; $\frac{1}{506}$

12.8 Practice and Problem Solving (pp. 642–643)

5. 0.1 **7.** 0.375 **9.** 0.13 **11.** dependent; $\frac{2}{21}$ **13.** $\frac{1}{17{,}018}$

17. 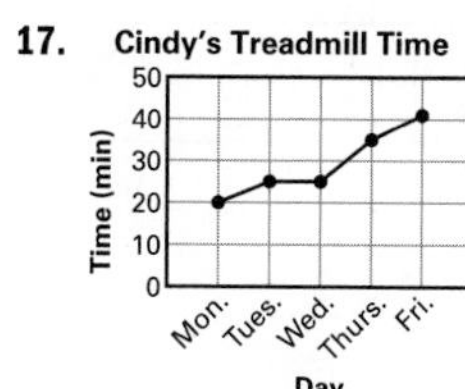

Sample answer: About 46 min; if you extend the graph, it passes through 46 on Saturday.

19. 57 **21.** 5

Special Topic Exercises (p. 645) **1.** Yes; people who call in to a sports talk show are likely to favor sports. **3.** Yes; people who enter a sporting goods store are likely to favor sports. **5.** *Sample answer:* Yes; this question suggests the mall is noisy and crowded. It encourages respondents to favor staying at home. So, the question could lead to biased results. **7.** *Sample answer:* No; this question is straight forward with no suggestions. It is not likely to lead to biased results.

12.4–12.8 Notebook Review (pp. 646–647)
1. permutation **2.** 20 birdhouses **3.** 210 ways
4. $\frac{3}{11}$ **5.** $\frac{2}{121}$ **6.** *Sample answer:* Ordering toppings on a pizza

Chapter Review (pp. 648–649)
7. 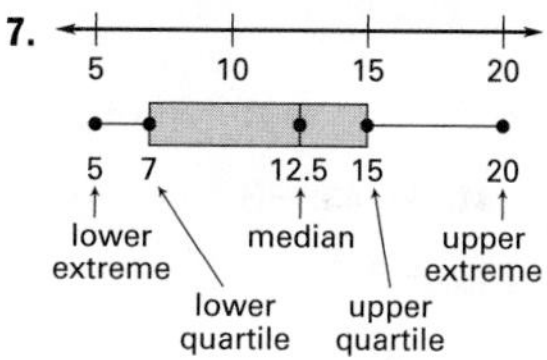

9.

Stem	Leaves
6	7
7	5
8	
9	
10	
11	2 3
12	
13	
14	
15	0 1 7

Key: 7 | 5 = 7.5

15.0–15.9

11. Favorite Summer Treat

Ice cream 50%
Frozen fruit 25%
Other 15%
Ices 10%

13. 1680 **15.** 36 **17.** 5040 ways **19.** permutation; 120 ways **21.** $\frac{7}{13}$ **23.** $\frac{1}{380}$

Chapter 13

13.1 Getting Ready to Practice (p. 659)
1. trinomial **3.** monomial **5.** $3m + 7$
7. $6b^3 + 4b - 4$ **9.** $5y - 1$ **11.** $-3x^2$ and $-20x$ are not like terms and cannot be combined. The expression $-3x^2 - 20x - 4$ cannot be simplified.

13.1 Practice and Problem Solving (pp. 659–660)
13. $4x^{10} - 13x^3$; binomial **15.** $4x - 4$ **17.** $-7q^5 + 3q^3 + 3q$ **19.** $-3b + 17$ **21.** $2(2x + 3) + 4x$; $8x + 6$ **23.** $12m^2 + m - 6$ **25.** $8x^2 - 15x + 30$ **27.** 98 ft **29.** 122 ft **31.** $18t^2 + 12t - 37$ **33.** always **35.** never
41. $\frac{1}{4}$ **43.**

Stem	Leaves
34	2
35	8
36	2 3 4 6
37	5 6
38	6 6

Key: 35 | 8 = 35.8

45. -21 **47.** 60

13.2 Getting Ready to Practice (p. 663) **1.** like terms **3.** $6x + 12$ **5.** $3p + 8$ **7.** $-a + 6$

13.2 Practice and Problem Solving (pp. 664–665)
9. $5x + 4$ **11.** $7n - 2$ **13.** $6g^2 + g + 3$
15. $-10d - 7$ **17.** $-11h^2 + 10h$ **19.** $3r^2 + 2r + 4$
21. $(x + 7) + (3x - 2) + (4x - 1)$; $8x + 4$ **23.** $6k^2$
25. $6x^3 + 8x^2 - 12x - 3$ **27.** $12n + 3$
29. $16r^2 - 4(\pi r^2)$; $3.44r^2$; yes; one coaster needs $3.14r^2$ of clay, which is less than what is left over.
31. $-7s^2 + 5s - 9$ **33.** $-14t^3 - 10t^2 + 22t$
35. $-14v^4 + 15v^3 - 21v^2 + 37$ **39.** b^{10}
41. m^4n^3 **43.** 10,000 passwords

13.3 Getting Ready to Practice (p. 668)
5. $2x^3 - 2x$ **7.** z^{16}

13.3 Practice and Problem Solving (pp. 669–670)
9. $-20x^4$ **11.** $3x^3$ **13.** b^{11} **15.** $m^2 + 4m$
17. $-t^3 + 4t$ **19.** $-2w^3 - w^2$ **21.** $\frac{1}{2}(b - 6)(3b + b)$; $2b^2 - 12b$ **23.** $x^5y^5z^5$ **25.** $-216z^3$ **27.** $9r^2s^2$
29. $100{,}000b^5h^5$ **31.** y^4 **33.** x^{20} **35.** x^6y^6 **37.** $8r^9$
39. $(2w^2 + 4w)$ in.^{2} **41.** $-3a^{26}b^8c^4$ **43.** $\frac{\pi r^2}{(2r)^2}$; $\frac{\pi}{4}$
45. 2.7×10^{13} **47.** 6.25×10^{30} **49.** about 7.35×10^8 km^3 **55.** $\frac{71}{100}$ **57.** $\frac{9}{50}$ **59.** $\frac{1}{36}$

SA29

13.1–13.3 Notebook Review (pp. 671–672)
1. monomial **2.** polynomial **3.** $a^2 + 18$ **4.** $2z^2 - 3z + 1$ **5.** $2n^3 + 5n^2 - 2n - 3$ **6.** $-5x^2 + 4x + 4$ **7.** $48x^{10}$ **8.** $36n^6m^2$ **9.** $16a^4b^4$ **10.** $4r^3 - 20r^2$ **11.** *Sample answer:* By the associative property of multiplication, $(2x)(x^2y) = 2(x \cdot x^2)y$. By the product of powers property, $2(x \cdot x^2)y = 2x^3y$. So $(2x)(x^2y) = 2x^3y$. **12.** $24\pi h^2$

13.4 Getting Ready to Practice (p. 676)
1. binomial **3.** $6m^2 + 2m$ **5.** $y^2 - 3y - 4$ **7.** $z^2 + 2z - 8$

13.4 Practice and Problem Solving (pp. 676–677)
9. $x^2 + 7x - 18$ **11.** $a^2 + 6a - 40$ **13.** $3q^2 - 4q + 1$ **15.** $6r^2 + r - 7$ **17.** $-11x^2 - 43x + 60$ **19.** $x^2 - 16$ **23.** $4\pi(0.6875 + x)^2 = 4\pi(0.4727 + 1.375x + x^2) = 1.8908\pi + 5.5\pi x + 4\pi x^2$ **25.** $3b^2 - 58b + 72$ **27.** $(30 - 2x)(20 - x) = 600 - 70x + 2x^2$; 300 ft^2 **31.** $x + 1$

33.

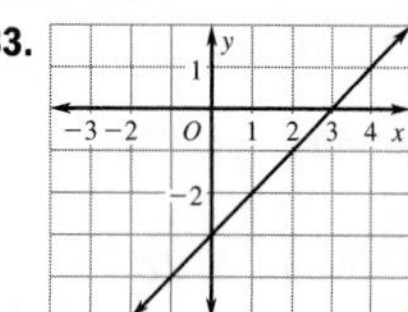

35. $-4r^2 - 24r$ **37.** $15x^2 - 10x$

38–41.

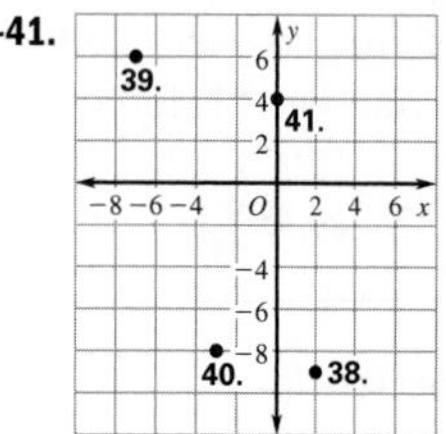

13.5 Problem Solving Strategies (p. 679)
1. 128 e-mails **3.** 10 cuts

5.

Hours	0.5	1	1.5	2
Points	2.5	5	7.5	10

about 9 points

7. 50 squares **9.** 1809.56 cm^3

13.5 Getting Ready to Practice (p. 682) **3.** -1, -5, -1 **5.** yes **7.** yes

13.5 Practice and Problem Solving (pp. 682–684)
9. $f(x) = 2x^2 - x$ **11.** $f(t) = -16t^2 + 4$; -140 ft

13.

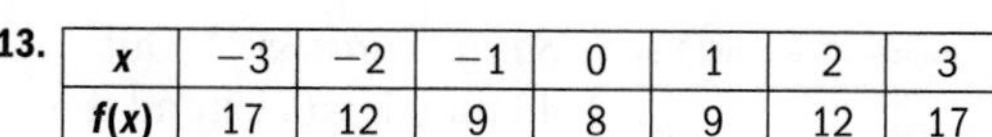

x	−3	−2	−1	0	1	2	3
f(x)	17	12	9	8	9	12	17

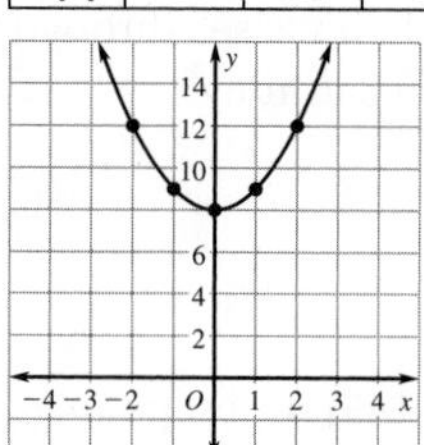

15.

x	−3	−2	−1	0	1	2	3
f(x)	−9	−4	−1	0	−1	−4	−9

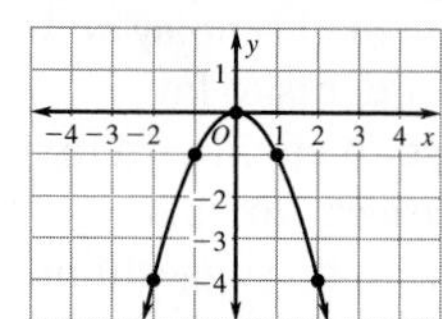

19. yes **21.** $f(x) = 1500x$

23.

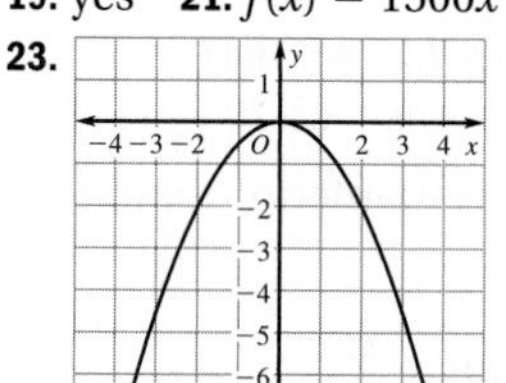

27.

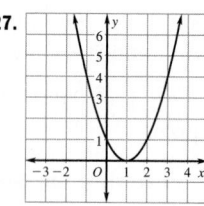

33. $f(x) = x^3$ **35.** $f(t) = (2.8 \times 10^8)(1.008)^t$; about 2.8×10^8 **37.** 4 **39.** $-1\frac{2}{3}$ **41.** 3 **43.** -3 **45.** $x^2 + 4x + 4$ **47.** $5a^2 + 14a - 3$

13.5 Technology Activity (p. 685) **1–4.** *Sample answer:* The graphs are all parabolas with the same shape and with vertices on the *y*-axis, but the graph moves up or down compared to the graph of $y = x^2$ by the number of units that are added to or subtracted from x^2. The graph moves up if this number is positive and down if this number is negative. **5–8.** *Sample answer:* The graphs are all downward-opening parabolas with vertices at the origin, but opening to different widths. As the absolute value of the coefficient of x^2 gets larger, the parabola becomes narrower (rises more steeply).

13.4–3.5 Notebook Review (pp. 686–687)
1. function notation **2.** vertical line test **3.** $f(x) = 5x - 12$ **4.** $f(x) = 2x^3 + 8$ **5.** $f(x) = x^3 + 3x^2 - 10$

6. 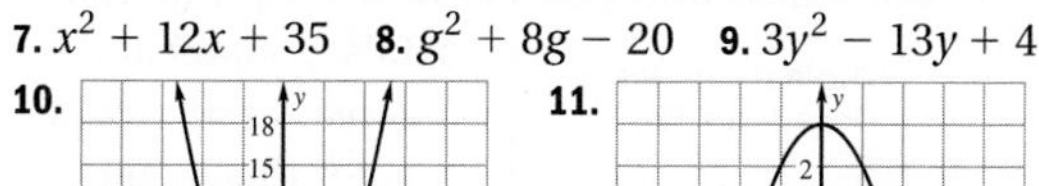 *Sample answer:* The graph is not that of a function because there are vertical lines that pass through more than one point of the graph.

7. $x^2 + 12x + 35$ **8.** $g^2 + 8g - 20$ **9.** $3y^2 - 13y + 4$

10. **11.** 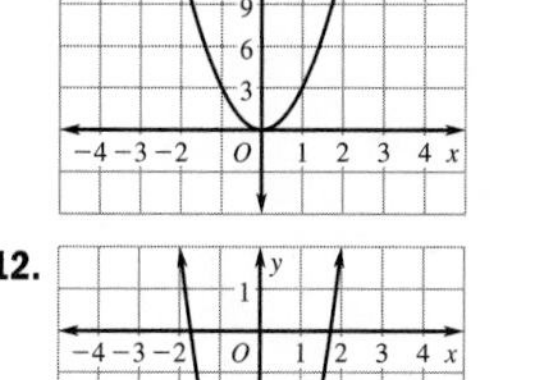

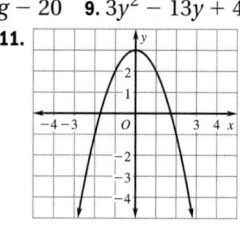

12. 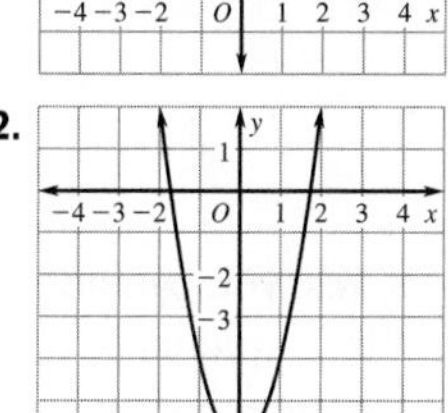

13. *Sample answer:* If there is any vertical line that intersects a graph at more than one point, then the graph does not represent a function. If every vertical line intersects a graph in at most one point, then the graph does represent a function.

Chapter Review (pp. 688–689) **1.** trinomial **3.** vertical line test **5.** monomial **7.** binomial **9.** $-3x^3 + x^2 + 5x - 4$ **11.** $6t^3 - t^2 + 9t + 8$ **13.** $-3n^4 + n^2 + 5n + 25$ **15.** $2w^2 + 3w - 8$ **17.** $-x^2 + 16x + 28$ **19.** $-10y^2 + 20y + 44$ **21.** $-3p^2$ **23.** $8y^2 - 5$ **25.** $-5v^3 - 10v^2 - 2v$ **27.** $8x^3y^3$ **29.** $-216a^6b^{12}$ **31.** $-21{,}609p^8n$ **33.** $-3a^3 + 6a^2$ **35.** $y^5 - 11y^4$ **37.** $-18g^3 - 60g^2$ **39.** $9x^2 + 27x$ **41.** $t^2 - t - 12$ **43.** $q^2 - 16q + 63$ **45.** $3d^2 - 10d - 48$ **47.** $-8k^2 + 34k + 9$ **49.** $2b^2 + 7b - 4$

51. 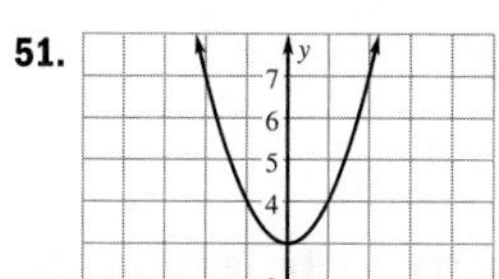 **53.** 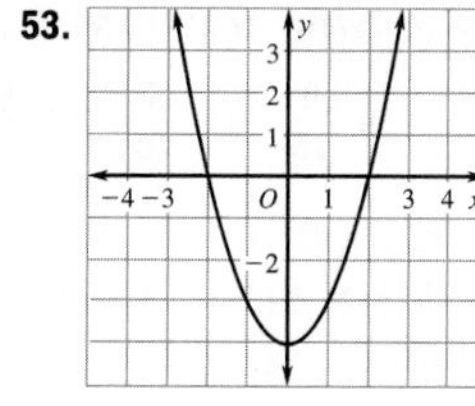

55. yes **57.** yes

Skills Review Handbook

Place Value (p. 704) **1.** $5 \times 10{,}000 + 6 \times 1000 + 8 \times 100 + 9$ **3.** $1 \times 1000 + 2 \times 1 + 3 \times 0.001$ **5.** 500,069.007

Rounding (p. 705) **1.** 1300 **3.** 8.2 **5.** 40,000 **7.** 450 **9.** 62.8 **11.** 164.5 **13.** 52.96 **15.** 3,501,700

Divisibility Tests (p. 706) **1.** 2 **3.** 3, 5 **5.** 2, 3, 4, 6, 9 **7.** 5 **9.** 2, 4

Mixed Numbers and Improper Fractions (p. 707)
1. 38 **3.** 3 **5.** $\frac{7}{2}$ **7.** $\frac{35}{8}$ **9.** $\frac{43}{4}$ **11.** $7\frac{1}{2}$ **13.** $5\frac{2}{3}$

Ratio and Rate (p. 708) **1.** $\frac{13}{12}$; 13 to 12; 13 : 12 **3.** $\frac{11}{23}$; 11 to 23; 11 : 23 **5.** $\frac{\$24}{8 \text{ pens}} = \frac{\$3}{1 \text{ pen}}$ **7.** $\frac{280 \text{ words}}{5 \text{ min}} = \frac{56 \text{ words}}{1 \text{ min}}$ **9.** $\frac{8 \text{ in.}}{6 \text{ days}} = 1\frac{1}{3}$ in. per day

Adding and Subtracting Decimals (p. 709) **1.** 6.3 **3.** 31.1 **5.** 10.956 **7.** 2.91 **9.** 18.88 **11.** 57.8 **13.** 286.19 **15.** 88.064

Adding and Subtracting Fractions (p. 710) **1.** $\frac{2}{3}$ **3.** $\frac{3}{7}$ **5.** 1 **7.** $\frac{11}{15}$ **9.** $\frac{2}{9}$ **11.** $1\frac{7}{12}$ **13.** $\frac{1}{9}$ **15.** $\frac{9}{14}$ **17.** $\frac{7}{12}$ **19.** $1\frac{4}{7}$

Estimation in Addition and Subtraction (p. 711)
1-5. Estimates may vary. **1.** 2700 **3.** 20,000 **5.** 2200

Solving Problems Using Addition and Subtraction (p. 712) **1.** $93 **3.** $2.01 **5.** 248 min

SA31

Multiplying Fractions (p. 713) **1.** $\frac{4}{5}$ **3.** $2\frac{2}{9}$ **5.** $5\frac{1}{4}$ **7.** $2\frac{4}{7}$ **9.** $\frac{8}{15}$ **11.** $\frac{3}{40}$ **13.** $\frac{10}{27}$ **15.** $\frac{25}{72}$

Multiplication of a Decimal by a Whole Number (p. 714) **1.** 225.4 **3.** 671.5 **5.** 35.28 **7.** 644.36 **9.** 1707.2 **11.** 18,663.6 **13.** 15,093.8 **15.** 36,833.5 **17.** 949.992 **19.** 3707.352 **21.** 4998.7 **23.** 1809.665 **25.** 5477.336 **27.** 120,455.25 **29.** 7564.91

Dividing Decimals (p. 715) **1.** 0.45 **3.** 0.85 **5.** 4.57 **7.** 6R2 **9.** 8R604

Estimation in Multiplication and Division (p. 716) **1–19.** Estimates may vary. **1.** 400 and 1000 **3.** 40,000 and 54,000 **5.** 30 and 40 **7.** 200 and 300 **9.** 12,000 and 20,000 **11.** 70,000 and 160,000 **13.** 12,000 and 21,000 **15.** 90 and 100 **17.** 700 and 800 **19.** 10 and 20

Solving Problems Using Multiplication and Division (p. 717) **1.** \$9.48 **3.** 576 flowers

Points, Lines, and Planes (p. 718) **5.** *Sample answer:* $\overrightarrow{SR}$ and $\overrightarrow{ST}$ **7.** *Sample answer:* $\overline{SR}$

Angles (p. 719) **5.** $\angle HJK$, $\angle J$, $\angle KJH$ **7.** $\angle TUV$, $\angle U$, $\angle VUT$ **9.** $\angle FGH$, $\angle G$, $\angle HGF$

Using a Ruler (p. 720) **1–7.** Check drawings.

Using a Protractor (p. 721) **1.** 110° **3.** 88°

Using a Compass (p. 722) **1.** A good answer will show a circle with radius 4 centimeters.

3. ____________

Reading and Making Line Plots (p. 723)

1.

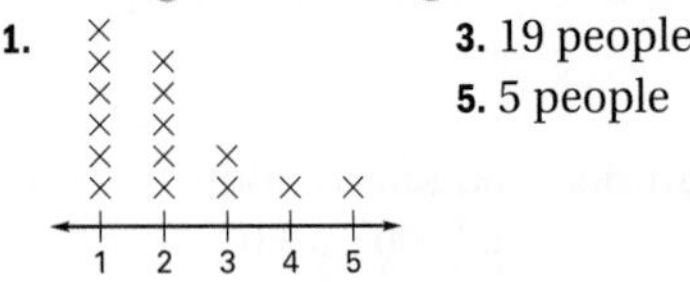

3. 19 people **5.** 5 people

Reading and Making Bar Graphs (p. 724) **1.** 9 students **3.** Vanilla and Rocky Road

Reading and Making Line Graphs (p. 725) **1.** Thursday and Friday **3.**

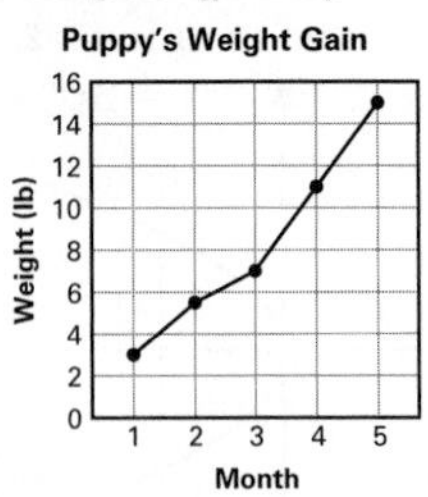

Venn Diagrams and Logical Reasoning (p. 726)

1.

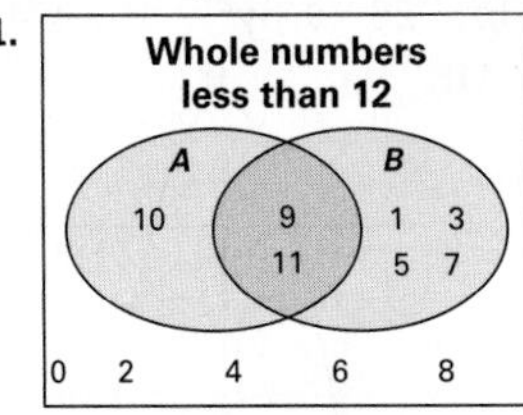

3. false; both 9 and 11 are odd numbers greater than 8 and less than 12

Extra Practice

Chapter 1 (p. 727)

1.

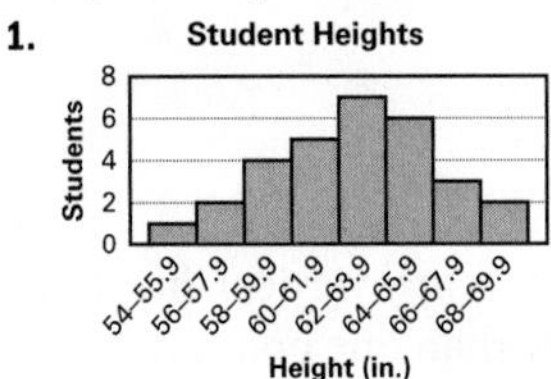

3. Yes; you can add the frequencies for the intervals 60–61.9, 62–63.9, 64–65.9, 66–67.9, and 68–69.9.

5. 7 **7.** 4 **9.** 36 **11.** 8.4 **13.** 11.7 **15.** 27 **17.** 7 **19.** 63 **21.** 8 **23.** 9 **25.** 42 ft; 104 ft^2 **27.** 8 cm

Chapter 2 (p. 728) **1.** $-43, -24, -2, 7, 19, 33$ **3.** 25; 25 **5.** 0; 0 **7.** -409 **9.** 179 **11.** 0 **13.** -16 **15.** 51 **17.** -15 **19.** 68 **21.** 350 **23.** -64 **25.** 0 **27.** 240 **29.** -12 **31.** 0 **33.** -4

35. $7\left(2 \cdot \frac{3}{7}\right)$ [original expression]

$= 7\left(\frac{3}{7} \cdot 2\right)$ [commutative property of multiplication]

$= \left(7 \cdot \frac{3}{7}\right) \cdot 2$ [associative property of multiplication]

$= 3 \cdot 2$ [Multiply 7 and $\frac{3}{7}$.]

$= 6$ [Multiply 3 and 2.]

37. $(-5)(-3) + (-5)(8); -25$ **39.** $-4 - 9r$ **41.** $5x - 2y$ **43.** $-a - 10b$

44–47. 45. Quadrant I 47. Quadrant III

Chapter 3 (p. 729) **1.** 8 **3.** 5 **5.** 64 **7.** 4 **9.** 7 **11.** 7.5 **13.** 20 **15.** −58 **17.** $6n - 5 = 13$; 3 **19.** 1.5 h **21.** 60 in.^{2}; 36 in. **23.** 5 m; 34 m **25.** $j \geq -5$; **27.** $z \leq -2.5$; **29.** $x < -5$; **31.** $s \leq 8$;

Chapter 4 (p. 730) **1.** $2^3 \cdot 3^2$ **3.** $3^2 \cdot 17$ **5.** $5^2 \cdot p \cdot q$ **7.** $2 \cdot 11 \cdot x \cdot y \cdot y$ **9.** 15 **11.** bc **13.** $3m$ **15.** $17w^2z^2$ **17.** $\frac{1}{2}$ **19.** $-\frac{2}{7}$ **21.** $\frac{2}{9y}$ **23.** $-\frac{3a}{2c}$ **25.** 60 **27.** $15ab^2c^2$ **29.** > **31.** > **33.** < **35.** > **37.** z^6 **39.** $(-7)^9$ **41.** 6^4 **43.** $(-v)^3$ **45.** $\frac{6}{k}$ **47.** $\frac{1}{s^7}$ **49.** 1.24×10^8 **51.** 7.91×10^{-5} **53.** 0.0027 **55.** 588,000,000,000

Chapter 5 (p. 731) **1.** $1\frac{1}{2}$ **3.** $-\frac{2m}{3}$ **5.** $\frac{1}{15}$ **7.** $8\frac{1}{8}$ **9.** $\frac{3}{16}$ **11.** $-\frac{10}{27}$ **13.** $\frac{5}{18}$ **15.** $-3\frac{3}{32}$ **17.** −0.384 **19.** $-\frac{7}{25}$ **21.** $\frac{3}{500}$ **23.** 3.875 **25.** −2.5, −2.43, $-2\frac{5}{12}$, $-2\frac{2}{5}$, $-\frac{7}{3}$ **27.** $\frac{26}{5}$, 5.21, $5\frac{2}{9}$, 5.3, $5\frac{3}{8}$ **29.** 3.81 **31.** 13.1 **33.** −16.55 **35.** −8.115 **37.** 3.9104 **39.** 1.5 **41.** −31.866 **43.** −8.2 **45.** 43; 39; no mode; 57 **47.** 88; 87; 78 and 95; 22

Chapter 6 (p. 732) **1.** 7 **3.** −9 **5.** 2 **7.** −2 **9.** 5 **11.** −1 **13.** 0.13 **15.** −4 **17.** −4 **19.** 4.5 cm **21.** 7 yd; use $\frac{22}{7}$ for π since 44 is divisible by 22. **23.** $c < 2$; **25.** $s \geq -1$; **27.** $b > 8$; **29.** $\frac{1}{2}n + 12 \leq 8$; $n \leq -8$ **31.** $4n \geq 16$; $n \geq 4$ **33.** at least $1\frac{1}{2}$ h

Chapter 7 (p. 733) **1.** $\frac{3}{1}$, 3 : 1, 3 to 1 **3.** $\frac{2}{3}$, 2 : 3, 2 to 3 **5.** 4 **7.** 225 **9.** 9.3 **11.** 12% **13.** 8.96 **15.** 12.5% **17.** 72% **19.** 0.31; $\frac{31}{100}$ **21.** 1.75; $\frac{7}{4}$ **23.** increase; 12% **25.** decrease; 1% **27.** $22.08 **29.** $83\frac{1}{3}$ **31.** 0.084 **33.** $\frac{1}{6}$

Chapter 8 (p. 734) **1.** $m\angle 1 = 50°$ **3.** $m\angle 5 = 50°$; $m\angle 6 = 50°$; $m\angle 7 = 130°$ **5.** $x = 90$; right **7.** rhombus **9.** trapezoid **11.** 160° **13.** $\angle A \cong \angle P$; $\angle B \cong \angle Q$; $\angle C \cong \angle R$

15.

17.

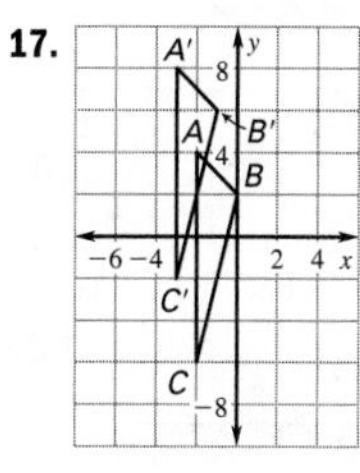

19.

21.

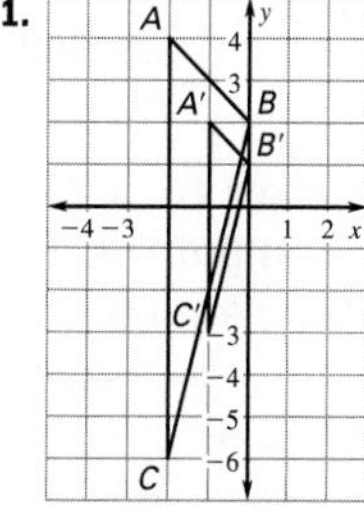

Chapter 9 (p. 735) **1.** 7.2 **3.** −27.2 **5.** 30, −30 **7.** 15, −15 **9.** 9, −9 **11.** 8, −8 **13.** > **15.** > **17.** $0.\overline{1}$, 0.12, $0.\overline{12}$, 0.123, $0.\overline{123}$ **19.** 35 **21.** 33 **23.** 75 **25.** yes **27.** yes **29.** $x = 7\sqrt{2}$; $y = 7$ **31.** $x = 19\sqrt{3}$; $y = 38$ **33.** $\sin A = \frac{36}{85}$; $\cos A = \frac{77}{85}$; $\tan A = \frac{36}{77}$; $\sin B = \frac{77}{85}$; $\cos B = \frac{36}{85}$; $\tan B = \frac{77}{36}$ **35.** $\sin 62° \approx 0.8829$; $\cos 62° \approx 0.4695$; $\tan 62° \approx 1.8807$

Chapter 10 (p. 736) **1.**

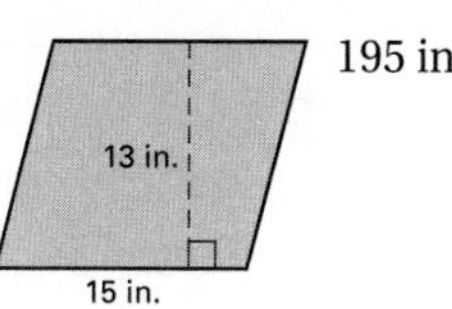

195 in.^{2}

SA33

3. 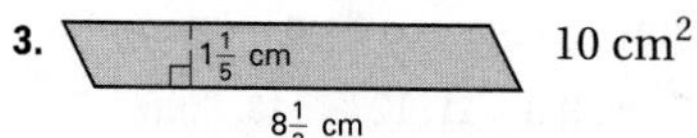

10 cm^2

5. 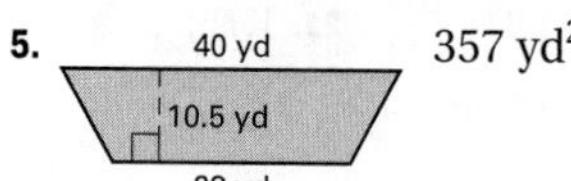

357 yd^2

7. 5020 in.^{2} **9.** 26.4 ft^2 **11.** 0.283 cm^2 **13.** 201 mi^2

15. 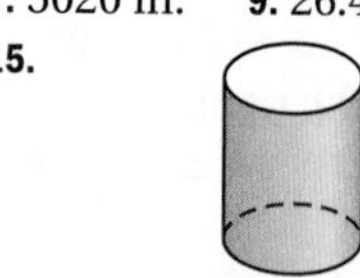 no

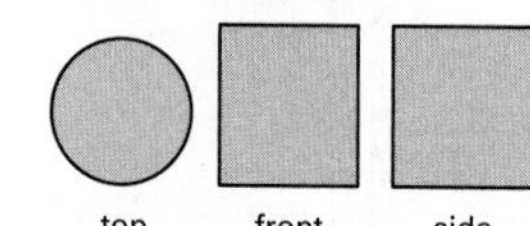

17. 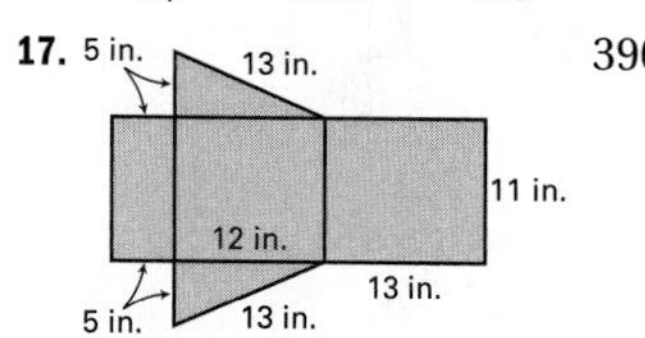

390 in.^{2}

19. 360 m^2 **21.** 369.9 m^2 **23.** 330 in.^{3} **25.** 266.7 ft^3 **27.** 252 cm^3

Chapter 11 (p. 737) **1.** Yes; each input has exactly one output. **3.** $y = x - 1$ **5.** no **7.** yes **9.** *Sample answer:* (−2, 3), (−1, 5), (0, 7), (1, 9) **11.** *Sample answer:* (−2, 2), (−1, 1), (0, 0), (1, −1) **13.** (−2, 4), (−1, 1), (0, −2), (1, −5) **15.** (−2, −5), (1, −1), (4, 3), (7, 7)

17. 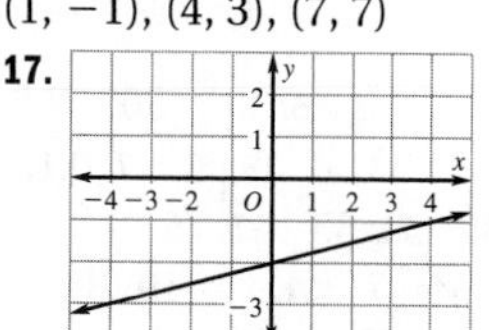

19.

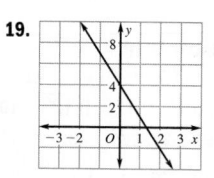

21. x-intercept, $\frac{1}{5}$; y-intercept, −1 **23.** x-intercept, 6; y-intercept, −4

25. 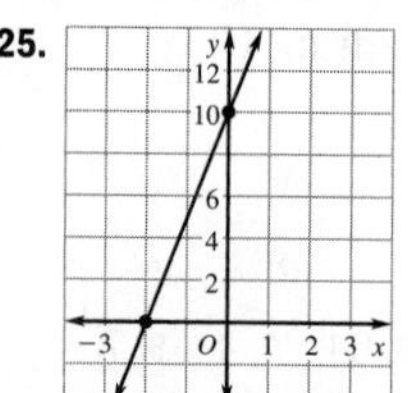

27. undefined **29.** 1 **31.** −1 **33.** $\frac{17}{3}$ **35.** 0; 2 **37.** 2; −8

39. 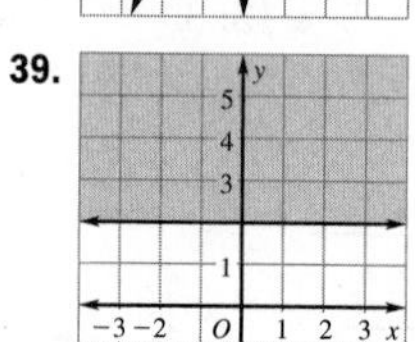

41.

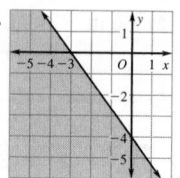

Chapter 12 (p. 738)

1. 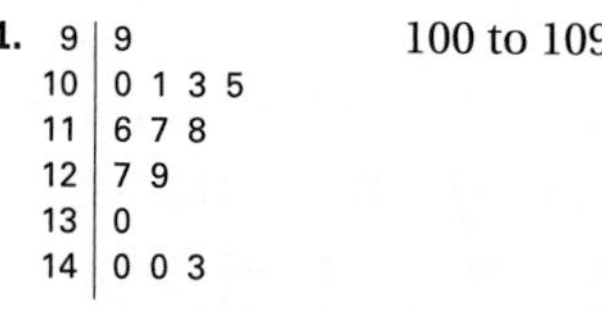

9	9
10	0 1 3 5
11	6 7 8
12	7 9
13	0
14	0 0 3

Key: 13 | 0 = 130

100 to 109

3. 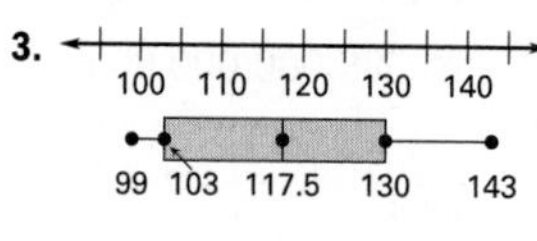

Sample answer: About 50% of the lengths were between 103 inches and 130 inches.

5. Line graph; a line graph is used to represent data that change over time. **7.** 17,576,000 license plates **9.** 11 **11.** 720 **13.** 5 **15.** 20 **17.** 4060 ways **19.** $\frac{3}{4}$ **21.** $\frac{2}{9}$

Chapter 13 (p. 739) **1.** $-x^2 - 2x + 7$ **3.** $-k^2 + 21$ **5.** $-2x^3 + 4x^2 + 14x - 4$ **7.** $3x^3 - 9x^2 + 6x - 3$ **9.** $x^3 - 2x^2 + 9x + 6$ **11.** $-28z^6$ **13.** $-6n^2 + 15n$ **15.** $125a^3b^3$ **17.** p^{24} **19.** $2x^2 - 9x - 5$ **21.** $d^2 + 10d + 24$ **23.** $a^2 - 15a + 56$ **25.** $f(x) = 2x - 5$ **27.** $f(x) = 5x^2 + 1$ **29.** 1; $\frac{1}{4}$; 0; $\frac{1}{4}$; 1 **31.** −16; −5; 0; −1; −8 **33.** −7; −4; −3; −4; −7

35. 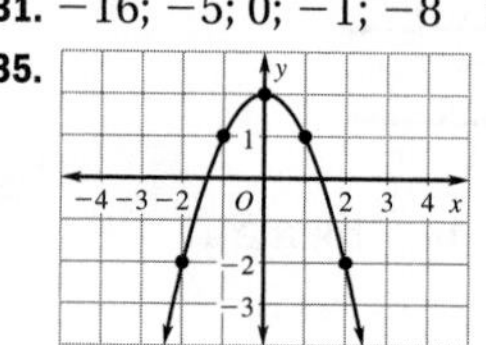

37. no **39.** yes

Teacher's Edition Index

Pupil's Edition in black
Teacher's Edition in blue

Absolute value, 54–56
length on the coordinate plane and, 92–95
modeling on a number line, 54
opposites and, 54–56
Accuracy of a measurement
angle, 721
length
customary, 720
metric, 720
Act it out, problem solving strategy, 228–229, 232
Activities, *See also* Games
algebra
adding polynomials, 661
binomial multiplication, 673
division equations, 113
graphs of linear inequalities, 583
monomials and powers, 666
multi-step inequalities, 295
one-step equations, 107–108
slope-intercept form, 575–576
solving equations, 28
solving equations with variables on both sides, 278
two-step equations, 117–118
data
collecting and analyzing, 255–256
counting choices, 618
fractions
dividing, 234
equivalent, 178
geometry
copying a triangle, 396
modeling the Pythagorean theorem, 442
graphing
a linear function, 556
line slope, 568–569
integer
addition, 57
subtraction, 63
measurement
angle sums for polygons, 390
area of a circle, 486
area of a rectangle, 32
area of a triangle, 134
comparing volumes, 518
diameter and circumference, 288–289
side length to perimeter ratios for squares, 317
volume of a rectangular prism, 512
number
investigating factors, 167
using patterns to multiply powers, 196
square root, 431
probability
complementary events, 632
perform an experiment, 354
simulations, 637–638
ratio, making a scale drawing, 321
trigonometry, exploring trigonometric ratios, 461–462
Activity Notes
Hands-on, 26–27, 32–33, 57, 107–108, 117–118, 167, 178, 255–256, 288–289, 321, 396, 442, 461–462, 512, 518, 575–576, 637–638, 673
In-lesson, 28, 63, 113, 134, 173, 196, 235, 278, 295, 317, 354, 390, 410, 431, 486, 556, 583, 618, 632, 661, 666
Technology, 14, 90, 129, 209, 239, 300, 351, 469, 561, 610–611, 685
Acute angle, 375, 382
Acute triangle, 382
Addition
to check subtraction, 709
decimal, 247–250, 709
estimating sums, 248, 711
equations, 107–112
modeling, 107–108, 109
of exponents to multiply powers, 196–200
of fractions
with common denominators, 219–223, 710
with different denominators, 224–227
integer, 57–62
modeling, 57–59
multiple addends, 59–62
rules for, 59
as inverse of subtraction, 109
of mixed numbers
with common denominators, 219–223
with different denominators, 225–227
order of operations and, 10–14
polynomial, 661–665
game, 665
properties
associative, 81
commutative, 80
equality, 110
identity, 59
inequality, 141
to solve inequalities, 140–145
words indicating, 16
Addition property of equality, 110
Addition property of inequality, 141
Additive identity property, 59
Additive inverse, 61
Adjacent side, of a right triangle, 463
Algebra
equations
addition, 107–112, 219
checking solutions, 29
decimal, 282–285
division, 113–116, 234
with fractions, 219, 230, 234, 282–285
graphing, 556–561
integer, 57–67
linear, 556–561, 564–580
using mental math to solve, 28–31
multiplication, 113–116, 230
multi-step, 271–275
percent, 327, 327–330, 347–350
percent of change, 338
probability of an event, 354
square root, 433–435
subtraction, 107–112, 219
two-step, 117–128
in two variables, 549–553
variables on both sides, 278–281
exercises, 83, 171, 176, 222, 227, 232, 237, 249, 254, 260, 266, 379, 385, 392, 421, 426, 467, 484, 489, 573
expressions
evaluating, 221–222, 239
numerical, 10–14
polynomial, 658–660
simplifying, 225–227
variable, 15–19, 64–67, 180–183, 225–227
writing, 16–19
formulas
area of a circle, 486
area of a parallelogram, 481
area of a rectangle, 33
area of a square, 33
area of a trapezoid, 482
area of a triangle, 134
circumference, 289, 290–294
for combinations, 628

energy, 312
percent of change, 338
perimeter of a triangle, 134
for permutations, 624
probability, 354
Pythagorean theorem, 443
simple interest, 348
slope of a line, 568, 570
surface area of a cone, 508
surface area of a cylinder, 504
surface area of a prism, 503
surface area of a pyramid, 507
surface area of a sphere, 510
volume of a cone, 520
volume of a cylinder, 514
volume of a prism, 513
volume of a pyramid, 519
functions
evaluating, 542–544
graphing, 556–561
non-linear, 680–685
games, 19, 104, 238, 268–269, 287, 299, 314, 326, 538, 553, 654, 665, 684
inequalities, 140–149
multi-step, 295–300
monomials
multiplying, 666–670
powers and, 666–670
negative exponents, 201
order of operations, 10–14, 21, 221
polynomials
adding, 661–665
evaluating, 658–660
simplifying, 658–660
subtracting, 662–665
powers and exponents, 20–23
properties
addition property of equality, 110
addition property of inequality, 141
additive identity, 59
associative, 81
commutative, 80
cross product, 323
distributive, 85
division property of equality, 114
division property of inequality, 147
multiplication property of equality, 113
multiplication property of inequality, 146
multiplicative identity, 71
power of a power, 668
power of a product, 667
product of powers, 196
quotient of powers, 197
subtraction property of equality, 109
subtraction property of inequality, 141
proportion, 322–326
variable, definition of, 15
Algebra tiles, 28, 107–108, 117–118, 278, 661, 673
Alternate exterior angles, 377
Alternate interior angles, 377
Alternative assessment, *See* Activities; Extended response questions; Games; Projects; Short response questions; Test-taking skills
Analyze, exercises, 245, 293, 305, 421
Angle(s)
acute, 382
alternate exterior, 377
alternate interior, 377
in circle graphs, 605–609
classifying, 382–385
classifying triangles by, 382–385
complementary, 375
congruent, 397–401
constructions
copying, 380
copying a triangle, 396
corresponding, 377, 397–401
definition of, 719
of elevation, 476
included, 398
inverse trigonometric ratios and, 469
measures
of a polygon, 391
of quadrilaterals, 387
of a triangle, 383
measuring with a protractor, 382–383, 461–462, 605–609, 721
naming, 719
obtuse, 382
pairs of, 375–379
polygons and, 390–393
right, 375, 382
symbol for, 33
of rotation, 410–411
straight, 375
sums
for polygons, 390–393
for a quadrilateral, 387, 390–393
for a triangle, 383
supplementary, 375
trigonometric ratios and, 461–469
vertex of, 719
vertical, 376
Angle-side-angle congruence, 398–401
Annual interest rate, 348
Applications
advertising, 145, 449
agriculture, 340, 350, 435
airplanes, 143, 468, 471, 535
amusement parks, 6, 159, 213, 266, 291, 433, 463, 465, 552
animals, 31, 34, 35, 47, 48, 64, 66, 77, 102–103, 112, 116, 124, 136, 144, 146, 147, 157, 161, 177, 186, 193, 229, 237, 244, 253, 263, 265, 320, 322, 329, 359, 474, 543, 580, 594–595, 603, 623, 650, 652–653, 679, 697, 723, 725, 738
apparel, 14, 23, 47, 54, 99, 160, 259, 267, 325, 337, 345, 353, 356, 400, 555, 579, 618, 620, 630, 635, 647, 697, 712, 733
aquarium, 10, 11
architecture, 85, 385, 482, 519
art, 61, 89, 168, 285, 324, 412, 585, 664
astronomy, 8, 90, 199, 207, 232, 476–477, 670
banking, 143, 158, 250, 449, 567, 621, 675, 676, 677, 683, 691
baseball, 12, 25, 185, 195, 259, 357, 366, 367, 407, 456, 534, 574, 613, 625, 645, 649, 660, 676, 683, 695, 697, 717, 733
basketball, 42, 69, 97, 114, 129, 260, 312–313, 634, 698
bicycling, 18, 41, 80, 126, 131, 158, 164–165, 265, 370, 450, 697, 732
biology, 102–103, 209, 220, 243, 257, 598
bowling, 296, 305, 403
boxes, 82, 403
Braille, 622
business, 7, 42, 116, 126, 191, 298, 303, 612
chemistry, 62
climbing, 110
clubs, 304, 330, 403, 617, 630
community service, 42, 46, 176, 215, 222
computers, 23, 133, 149, 199, 233, 679
construction, 69, 155, 176, 224, 225, 453, 467, 489, 500, 501
consumer, 12, 14, 17, 27, 41, 84, 88, 100, 111, 122, 127, 145, 151, 154, 155, 159, 160, 185, 253, 258, 266, 287, 298, 300, 303, 304, 307, 310, 311, 344, 345, 346, 353, 358, 359, 361, 363, 366, 367, 370, 546, 551, 559, 566, 585, 591, 599, 603, 613, 697, 700, 712, 717, 729
containers, 504, 513, 516, 517, 523, 527, 529
culture, 61, 294, 334, 521, 533, 654
currency, 208, 222, 264, 341
dance, 149, 158, 247, 261, 304, 644, 650

decorating, 440
design, 379, 403
distance, 15, 160, 324, 435, 449, 682
diving, 23, 70, 158, 555
earth science, 5, 8, 20, 106, 161, 213, 254, 265, 439, 536, 594–595
employment, 83, 115, 121, 122, 126, 144, 162, 185, 237, 260, 274, 275, 284, 297, 319, 335, 364, 727
entertainment, 612, 620, 680, 732
environment, 282, 327, 606
exercise, 45
fabric arts, 84, 170, 221, 285, 369, 378, 434, 459, 475, 625, 646, 669
fairs, 60, 68, 127, 132, 273, 305, 627, 631, 640, 665
fashion, 294
fireworks, 30
flags, 171
food, 13, 27, 48, 69, 94, 115, 151, 153, 181, 189, 211, 213, 214, 223, 232, 241, 258, 266, 344, 362, 369, 421, 501, 505, 528, 585, 602, 615, 620, 622, 626, 633, 635, 642, 645, 649, 651, 679, 694, 697, 702, 717, 724, 733
football, 22, 83, 335, 600, 694
fund raising, 12, 27, 126, 148, 229, 274, 309, 361, 541, 542, 563, 593, 640
games, 27, 45, 65, 72, 133, 162, 172, 185, 297, 307, 352, 353, 603, 617, 631, 641, 648, 649, 694
gardening, 139, 156, 160, 185, 267, 337, 488, 530, 532, 603, 625, 630, 690, 717, 727
geography, 182, 227, 385, 630
geometry, 45, 69, 99, 172, 250, 274, 275, 280, 287, 353, 548, 636, 664, 679
gifts, 229, 592, 632
Global Positioning System (GPS), 53
golf, 62, 140, 142, 201, 259, 368, 650
gymnastics, 260
hiking, 154, 159, 228, 403, 449, 577
history, 179, 215, 535
hockey, 301, 487, 630, 635, 647
home improvement, 37, 159, 229, 502, 528
hot air balloon, 15, 99, 555
kites, 400, 441, 448
maps, 277, 362, 366, 608, 630
measurement, 31, 88, 94, 121, 133, 151, 172, 199, 204, 260, 274, 293, 305, 319, 335, 388, 439, 440, 445, 447, 449, 455, 459, 484, 488, 501, 516, 529, 533, 659
models, 325, 326, 330, 363, 591
money, 27, 41, 48, 69, 72, 139, 149, 156, 158, 159, 229, 277, 280, 348, 349, 350, 351, 361, 366, 367, 421, 449, 552, 559, 567, 617, 712
movies, 8, 19, 544, 620, 625, 650, 738
music, 14, 18, 41, 76, 119, 144, 151, 237, 277, 335, 342, 343, 345, 608, 623, 630, 708, 712
newspapers, 310, 328
nutrition, 18
parks, 207
parties, 281, 629, 696, 717
passwords, 619, 622, 626, 651
photography, 201, 236, 341, 420, 534, 649, 669
physics, 79, 203, 208
physiology, 17, 27, 241, 265, 329, 333, 357
plants, 25, 73, 176, 267, 271, 725
poetry, 624
population, 208, 277, 320, 341, 683
postcards, 230, 231
recreation, 122, 133, 216, 217, 227, 251, 282, 310, 586, 647
recycling, 309, 362, 515, 544
robots, 264
running, 31, 123, 162, 189, 233, 259, 309, 320, 330, 555, 565, 727
schedule, 186, 188, 277, 307
school, 9, 60, 101, 125, 133, 158, 175, 189, 229, 266, 276, 277, 328, 348, 353, 366, 367, 403, 593, 614, 629, 630, 649, 679, 708, 724
skateboarding, 428–429, 619
skating, 154, 549
soccer, 7, 175, 400, 510, 619, 698
space exploration, 56, 208, 545
sports, 9, 13, 17, 38, 48, 152, 158, 222, 226, 260, 298, 309, 317, 400, 444, 446, 465, 574, 651
stock market, 69, 73, 245, 738
structures, 61, 293, 309, 311, 393, 401, 425, 447, 449, 453, 473, 474, 475, 489, 506, 517, 519, 525, 529, 532, 533, 535, 552, 572, 573, 646, 663, 683, 689, 692
survey, 133, 159, 237, 347, 361, 370, 605, 607, 608, 609, 611, 615, 633, 644, 645, 679, 723, 724, 738
swimming, 36, 123, 189, 449, 554, 629
tax, 249, 591
telephone, 277, 305, 367, 369, 560, 712, 738
television, 18, 65, 194, 319
temperature, 36, 66, 74, 75, 77, 84, 100, 101, 157, 265, 523, 592, 613, 615, 650, 695
tennis, 185, 340, 489, 510
theater, 27, 115, 153, 248, 607, 677
time, 158, 162, 259, 267, 330, 366, 368, 501, 566, 589, 599, 643
toys, 204, 215, 592, 649
track, 69, 77, 222, 250, 265, 597, 629
trains, 36, 570
travel, 36, 45, 47, 116, 277, 501
vacation, 229, 607
vehicles, 49, 135, 152, 185, 222, 239, 365, 533, 545, 592, 609, 620, 698
walking, 194, 531, 617
water, 207, 209
weather, 30, 67, 75, 158, 249, 263, 304, 318, 349, 634, 647, 649
Approximately equal to, 39
Approximation, *See also* Estimation
of angle measures, 469
of square root, 432–436
with a calculator, 432, 434, 435
Arc, 380
Arc notation, to show equal angle measures, 383
Area, *See also* Surface area
of a circle, 486–491
of a composite figure, 37, 85, 86, 89, 132, 133, 136, 138, 139, 485, 489, 500, 501
definition of, 33
geometric probability and, 652–653
of a parallelogram, 481, 483–485
modeling, 481
of a rectangle, 32–37, 136–139
modeling, 32
of a right triangle, 451–453
of a square, 33–37
of a trapezoid, 482–485
modeling, 482
of a triangle, 134–139
modeling, 134
Area models
to compare fractions, 192
geometric probability and, 652–653
to show addition of fractions, 219
to show area
of a circle, 486
of a parallelogram, 481
of a rectangle, 32
of a trapezoid, 482
of a triangle, 134
to show division by fractions, 234

to show equivalent fractions, 178
to show fractions, 166
to show percent, 331, 334
to show square root, 431
to show surface area, 503–505, 507–508, 510, 511

Arrangement(s)
combinations, 627–631
permutations, 623–626, 629–631

Assessment, *See also* Internet; Review
Chapter Standardized Test, 49, 101, 155, 215, 267, 311, 363, 427, 475, 529, 593, 651, 691
Chapter Test, 48, 100, 154, 214, 266, 310, 362, 426, 474, 528, 592, 650, 690
Cumulative Practice, 160–162, 368–370, 534–536, 696–698
End-of-Course Test, 699–702
Pre-Course Practice, xxviii–xxxi
Pre-Course Test, xxvi–xxvii
Review Quiz, 25, 45, 79, 97, 131, 151, 191, 211, 241, 263, 287, 307, 337, 359, 395, 423, 455, 471, 499, 525, 563, 589, 615, 647, 672, 687
Test-Taking Practice, 9, 13, 19, 23, 31, 37, 43, 56, 62, 67, 73, 77, 84, 89, 95, 112, 116, 123, 128, 139, 145, 149, 172, 177, 189, 195, 200, 204, 208, 223, 227, 233, 238, 246, 250, 254, 261, 275, 281, 285, 294, 299, 305, 320, 326, 330, 335, 341, 346, 350, 357, 379, 385, 389, 393, 401, 408, 413, 421, 436, 441, 447, 453, 460, 468, 485, 490, 495, 506, 511, 517, 544, 548, 553, 560, 567, 574, 587, 600, 604, 609, 622, 626, 631, 636, 643, 660, 665, 670, 677, 684
Test-Taking Skills
building, 156–157, 364–365, 530–531, 692–693
practicing, 158–162, 366–370, 532–536, 694–698
Test-Taking Strategies, 49, 101, 155, 215, 267, 311, 363, 427, 475, 529, 593, 651, 691

Assignment Guide, *Occurs at the beginning of each exercise set*

Associative property
for addition, 81
for multiplication, 81

Average, 257, *See also* Mean; Median; Mode
game, 261
representative, 258–261

Axis (axes), coordinate, 91

Bar graph, *See also* Histogram
choosing a data display, 606, 608–609
definition of, 5, 724
double, 9
interpreting, 5–9, 24, 724
game, 594–595
making, 8, 724
misleading, 612

Bar notation, for repeating decimals, 242

Base(s)
of a cone, 492
of a cylinder, 492
of a parallelogram, 481
in a percent equation, 327, 328, 347, 348
of a power, 20
of a prism, 492
of a pyramid, 492
of a trapezoid, 482
of a triangle, 134

Biased question, 645

Biased sample, 644–645

Binomial(s), 657
multiplying, 673–677
FOIL method, 675
using models, 673, 674

Box-and-whisker plot, 601–604
choosing a data display, 606, 608–609
comparing data on, 602
extremes, 601
interpreting, 602–604
making, 601–604
outliers and, 604
quartiles, 601

Brain Games, *See* Games

Break into parts, problem solving strategy, 500–501, 502

Calculator, *See also* Technology activities
2nd key, 239, 432, 464, 469
approximating square root with, 432–435
EE key, 209
exercises, 23, 73, 77, 116, 246, 259, 298, 330, 341, 392, 420, 434, 435, 466, 489, 552, 567, 670, 683
FracMode, 239
inverse tangent feature, 469
order of operations and, 14
pi key, 290, 504
random integer function, 638
sign key, 90
square root key, 432
TRIG key, 464, 469
trigonometric ratios of angles, 464, 466
Unit key, 239

Careers
in animal behavior, 653
astronomer, 477
biologist, 103
carpenter, 224
salesperson, 297
in scientific research, 313
veterinarian, 186

Cartesian plane, *See* Coordinate plane

Center
of a circle, 290
of rotation, 410
of a sphere, 492

Centimeter ruler, measuring with, 720

Challenge, exercises, 9, 13, 19, 23, 31, 37, 42, 56, 62, 66, 73, 77, 84, 89, 94, 112, 116, 122, 127, 139, 144, 149, 172, 177, 183, 189, 195, 200, 204, 208, 223, 227, 233, 238, 246, 250, 260, 275, 281, 285, 294, 298, 313, 320, 326, 330, 335, 341, 346, 350, 357, 385, 389, 393, 401, 408, 413, 421, 435, 441, 447, 453, 460, 468, 485, 489, 506, 511, 517, 523, 544, 552, 560, 569, 574, 580, 587, 604, 609, 621, 626, 631, 635, 642, 660, 664, 670, 677, 683

Challenge Problems, 2F, 50F, 104F, 164F, 216F, 268F, 314F, 372F, 428F, 478F, 538F, 594F, 654F

Change, percent of, 338–341

Chapter Test, *See* Assessment

Checking
using the counting principle, 621
equations using substitution, 29, 113, 114, 119, 120, 124, 276, 296, 323, 542, 550, 581
using estimation, 156, 235, 251
inequalities using substitution, 583–587
integer addition, 59, 60
by measuring, 380
problem solving and, 39–42
using rounding, 318
subtraction by adding, 709
whether two ratios form a proportion, 323–326

Choose a strategy, 23, 27, 69, 84, 123, 133, 172, 185, 229, 246, 277, 299, 335, 353, 403, 421, 436, 449, 490, 501, 555, 617, 631, 679, 684, *See also* Test-taking skills

Circle
area of, 486–491
game, 490
center of, 290
circumference of, 288, 290
equations involving, 290–294
comparing circumference and diameter, 288–289
definition of, 290
diameter of, 288, 290
radius of, 290
Circle graph
choosing a data display, 606–609
examples, 223, 331, 337, 361
on a graphing calculator, 611
interpreting, 331, 334, 605, 607–609, 611
game, 594–595
making, 605–609, 611
percent and, 331, 334
Circumference
comparing with diameter, 288–289
definition of, 288, 290
equations involving, 290–294
Classifying
angles, 382–385
polynomials, 657, 659
quadrilaterals, 386-389, 426, 492–494
real numbers, 437, 439, 440
solids, 492, 494
triangles, 382–385, 426
Clustering, 711
Coefficient
of a variable, 86
negative, 120
Combination notation, 628
Combinations, 627–631
permutations and, 629–631
Combining like terms, 86–89, 272–275
inequalities and, 296–300
Common denominator(s)
adding fractions with, 219–223
adding mixed numbers with, 219–223
subtracting fractions with, 219–223
subtracting mixed numbers with, 219–223
Common Error, 7, 16, 18, 22, 29, 42, 55, 59, 66, 69, 88, 115, 127, 133, 144, 156, 169, 174, 188, 197, 203, 277, 284, 304, 325, 329, 343, 364, 381, 392, 400, 403, 440, 446, 488, 497, 505, 510, 530, 542, 550, 582, 617, 635, 640, 645, 659, 664, 669, 692
Common factor, 173
Common multiple, 186
Communication, *See* Error analysis; Reading mathematics; Writing mathematics
Commutative property
of addition, 80
of multiplication, 80
Comparing
data
using box-and-whisker plots, 602
using double stem-and-leaf plots, 598
diameter and circumference, 288–289
exercises, 8, 55, 83, 122, 123, 245, 260, 293, 305, 467, 484, 499, 600, 626, 635, 669
fractions, 192–195, 216
misleading comparisons, 613–615
radii of circles, 491
using ratio, 708
real numbers, 438–441
volumes, 518
Compass, 380–381, 396, 722
Compatible numbers, estimation and, 716
Complementary angles, 375
Complementary events, 632–636
Composite figure
area of, 37, 85, 86, 89, 132, 133, 136, 138, 139, 485, 489
perimeter of, 37
Composite number, 167, 169
Composite solid, 495, 496–497
surface area of, 506, 555
volume of, 516, 517
Compound interest, 350, 351, 675
Computer, *See also* Internet; Technology activities
spreadsheet, 300, 491
truth function, 300
Concept Check, *Occurs in each lesson*
Concept grid, 480
Concept map, 374, 386
Conclusions
drawing
choosing a representative average, 258–261
from an experiment, 352–353, 653
from graphs, 334, 546, 547, 548, 612–613
from plots, 598–600, 602–604
supporting, 83, 151, 183
Cone, 492
base of, 492
height of, 520
slant height of, 508
surface area of, 508–511
formula, 508
volume of, 520–523
formula, 520
Congruence
angle-side-angle, 398–401
side-angle-side, 398–401
side-side-side, 398–401
Congruent angles, 397–401
Congruent figures
symmetry and, 406
tessellation and, 414–415
Congruent polygons, 397–401
naming, 397, 399
Congruent sides, 397–401
Congruent triangles, 398–401
Conjecture, *See also* Critical thinking; Prediction
examples, 583
Connections to other disciplines
art, 324
astronomy, 199
biology, 136, 147, 193, 203, 557
geography, 246, 350, 604
history, 171, 521
science, 64, 66, 102–103, 214, 291, 312–313, 339, 393, 476–477, 602, 652–653, 670
Connections to real world, *See* Applications
Consecutive numbers, 26, 27
Constant term, 86
Constructions
combining segments, 722
copying an angle, 380
copying a line segment, 722
copying a triangle, 396
parallel lines, 381
perpendicular lines, 381
Converse, of a statement, 444
Converse of the Pythagorean theorem, 444–447
Converting
decimals, fractions, and percents, 331–335
fractions and decimals, 242–246
improper fractions and mixed numbers, 193–195, 707
Coordinate notation
to describe reflection, 404–408
to describe rotation, 410–411
to describe translation, 409
Coordinate plane
definition of, 91
dilation in, 418, 420

distance on, 92–95
graphing functions on, 556–561
graphing linear equations on, 556–561
using intercepts, 564–567
using slope-intercept form, 578–580
graphing linear inequalities, 583–587
graphing non-linear functions, 681–685
half plane, 584
parts of, 91
plotting points on, 91–95
game, 95, 372–373, 539
reflection in, 404–408
rotation in, 410–413
scatter plots, 545–548
translation in, 409, 411–413
Copying
an angle, 380
a line segment, 722
a triangle, 396
Corresponding angles, 377, 397–401
Corresponding sides, 377, 397–401
Cosine ratio, 462–468
Counting methods, 618–622
Counting principle, 619–622
definition of, 619
permutations and, 623–626
Critical thinking
describe, 100
exercises, 3, 9, 13, 22, 32, 37, 42, 51, 56, 57, 61, 83, 103, 112, 116, 127, 131, 138, 143, 151, 171, 172, 176, 183, 195, 199, 204, 208, 237, 241, 246, 250, 254, 263, 275, 281, 285, 293, 308, 315, 321, 334, 335, 359, 393, 423, 444, 446, 460, 462, 469, 484, 489, 495, 511, 512, 516, 552, 559, 567, 580, 589, 600, 622, 642, 653, 655, 660, 664, 669, 672, 676
explain, 8, 45, 66, 73, 79, 84, 89, 102, 108, 138, 148, 165, 217, 232, 237, 241, 254, 256, 269, 275, 285, 304, 312, 313, 330, 345, 373, 388, 396, 400, 429, 434, 440, 452, 459, 468, 476, 477, 491, 499, 520, 523, 559, 567, 573, 587, 595, 603, 608, 609, 615, 625, 638
Cross-Curriculum, 40, 180, 291, 406, 464
Cross products
distributive property and, 325
proportions and, 323–326
Cross products property, 323
Cubic units, 512, 513, 515
Cylinder, 492
bases of, 492
height of, 504
radius of, 504
surface area of, 504–506
formula, 504
volume of, 514–518
formula, 514

d

Daily Puzzler, *Occurs in each lesson*
Data
analyzing, 255–256
biased question, 645
biased sample, 644–645
choosing a display, 606–609
choosing a representative average, 258–261
collecting, 255–256
definition of, 5, 724
displays, 606
bar graph, 5–9, 24, 724
circle graph, 605–609, 611
line graph, 606–609, 725
misleading, 612–613
grouping into intervals, 6–9
lower extreme, 601
lower quartile, 601
mean, 255–261
median, 255–261
mode, 255–261
organizing
box-and-whisker plot, 601–604
frequency table, 6–9
line plot, 723
stem-and-leaf plot, 597–600
tree diagram, 618–622
outlier, 604
prediction from, 352, 353, 355, 356
random sample, 644
range of, 258–261
samples, 644–645
survey
biased questions, 645
results, 331
samples and, 644–645
upper extreme, 601
upper quartile, 601
Decimal(s)
adding, 247–250, 709
clearing to solve equations, 283–285
dividing, 251–254, 715
zero as placeholder, 252
equivalent fractions, percents, and, 746
estimating sums, 248
fractions and, 242–246, 331–335
mixed numbers and, 243–246
multiplying, 251–254
by a whole number, 714
ordering, 438–441
ordering fractions, percents, and, 333–334
percent and, 331–335
repeating, 242–246
rounding, 705
subtracting, 247–250, 709
terminating, 242–246
Decimal form, of a real number, 437
Decision making, *See also* Choose a strategy
choosing a representative average, 258–261
identifying biased samples, 644–645
supporting conclusions, 83, 151, 183
Decrease, percent of, 338–341
Deductive reasoning, *See* Activities; Critical thinking
Denominator, 707
least common, 192
Dependent event(s), 639–643
definition of, 639
game, 643
Diagram(s)
to check answers, 40
concept grid, 480
concept map, 374, 386
tree, 618–622
Venn, 242, 437, 726
Diameter
of a circle
circumference and, 288–294
comparing with circumference, 288–289
definition of, 288, 290
Differentiating Instruction
side column notes, 16, 35, 39, 59, 82, 120, 142, 169, 174, 197, 202, 220, 225, 243, 298, 303, 318, 328, 339, 377, 398, 433, 444, 457, 504, 509, 514, 520, 557, 640, 662, 667
Strategies for Underachievers, English Learners, Advanced Learners, 2E–F, 50E–F, 104E–F, 164E–F, 216E–F, 268E–F, 314E–F, 372E–F, 428E–F, 478E–F, 538E–F, 594E–F, 654E–F
Technology, 2G–H, 50G–H, 104G–H, 164G–H, 216G–H, 268G–H, 314G–H, 372G–H, 428G–H, 478G–H, 538G–H, 594G–H, 654G–H

Digit, 704
Dilation, 418–421
in the coordinate plane, 418, 420
Discount, 342–346
Discrete mathematics
combinations, 501
counting faces, edges, and vertices, 493, 495
counting principle, 619–622
divisibility tests, 706
Euler's formula, 495
factorials, 623–626
functions, 541–544
outlier, 604
perfect squares, 432
permutations, 623–626
Pythagorean triples, 451–452
Sieve of Eratosthenes, 167
tree diagrams, 169, 171, 618–622
triangular numbers, 617
Venn diagrams, 242, 437, 726
Distance
on the coordinate plane, 92–95
formula, 34
forms of, 35
using, 34–37, 70
Distributive property, 85–89
cross products and, 325
equations with variables on both sides and, 279–281
to multiply a monomial and binomial, 667–670
multi-step equations and, 272–275
Dividend, 715
Divisibility tests, 706
Division
checking, using estimation, 252
decimal, 251–254, 715
zero as placeholder, 252
divisibility tests, 706
equations, 113–116
estimating quotients, 716
to find equivalent fractions, 192
to find mean, 255–261
with fractions, 234–238
multiplicative inverse and, 234
integer, 74–77
as inverse of multiplication, 113
with mixed numbers, 235–238
order of operations and, 10–14
properties
equality, 114
inequality, 147
quotient of power, 197–200
to solve inequalities, 146–151
words indicating, 16
to write a fraction as a decimal, 242–246
by zero, 74
Division property of equality, 114
Division property of inequality, 147
Divisor, 715
Domain, of a function, 542
Double bar graph, 9
Double stem-and-leaf plot, 598–600
Draw a diagram, problem solving strategy, 132–133, 134, 448–449, 453, 467
Draw a graph, problem solving strategy, 678–679, 681
Drawing, *See also* Constructions; Graphs
to add fractions, 219
to enlarge a picture, 321
to find patterns, 68, 69
isometric, 496–497
to model fractions, 192
nets, 502–506
to show division by a fraction, 234
to show equivalent fractions, 178
solids, 493–497

e

Edge(s), of a polyhedron, 492–493
Elevation, angle of, 476
Eliminate possibilities, 157, *See also* Problem Solving
Endpoint, definition of, 718
Enlargement, drawing, 321
Equality
addition property of, 110
division property of, 114
multiplication property of, 113
subtraction property of, 109
Equation(s), *See also* Linear equation
addition, 107–112
checking solutions, 29, 113, 114, 119, 120, 124, 276, 296, 323, 542, 550, 581
circumference, 290–294
decimal, 248–250, 282–285
definition of, 28
division, 113–116
equivalent, 109
formulas as, 33–37
with fractions, 220–223, 236–237, 273–275, 282–285
in function form, 550
game, 314
mental math, 28–31
with mixed numbers, 220–223
modeling
addition and subtraction, 28, 107–108, 109
two step, 117–118
variables on both sides, 278
multiplication, 113–116
multi-step, 271–275
game, 287
percent, 327–330, 347–350
percent of change, 338–341
proportion, 322–326
simple interest, 348
slope of a line, 570
solution of, 28
square root, 433–435
subtraction, 107–112
two step
solving, 117–123
writing, 124–128
in two variables, 549–553
game, 553
variable, 248–250
game, 538
with variables on both sides, 278–281
distributive property and, 279–281
writing, 114
two-step, 124–128
Equiangular triangle, 385
Equilateral triangle, 382
Equivalent equations, 109
Equivalent fractions, 179–183
decimals, percents, and, 746
modeling, 178
negative, 220
Equivalent inequalities, 141
Equivalent ratios, 317–320
Erathosthenes, sieve of, 167
Error analysis, 12, 22, 35, 41, 55, 61, 72, 88, 121, 138, 153, 175, 188, 198, 203, 221, 249, 253, 259, 284, 292, 297, 308, 319, 324, 333, 356, 378, 384, 392, 446, 458, 467, 483, 515, 551, 579, 629, 659, 663, 676
Estimation
angle measures, 469
to answer multiple choice questions, 156
to check answers are reasonable, 235, 251, 252
using clustering, 711
using compatible numbers, 716
definition of, 711
differences, 711

exercises, 18, 36, 94, 138, 284, 293, 346, 484, 489, 552, 582, 670
front-end, 248–250, 711
using graphs, 546, 581–582
high and low estimates, 716
using leading digits, 251
products, 716
quotients, 716
using rounding, 711, 716
square root, 432–436
sums, 248, 711
value of pi, 288–289, 290
Euler's formula, 495
Event(s), 354, *See also* Outcome
complementary, 632–636
dependent, 639–643
independent, 639–643
multiple, 640
odds of, 633–636
probability of, 354–357
Expanded form
expression, 196
number, 704
Experiment
conducting, 352–353, 354
designing, 313
Experimental probability, 352–357, 652–653, *See also* Probability
simulation, 637–638
Exploring Math in Science, 102–103, 312–313, 476–477, 652–653
Exponent(s)
adding to multiply powers, 196–200
game, 200, 654
negative, 201–204
patterns for multiply powers, 196
powers and, 20–23
prime factorization and, 169–172
rules of, 196–200
scientific notation and, 205–209
standard form of a polynomial and, 657
subtracting to divide powers, 197–200
zero, 202
Expression(s)
combining like terms, 86–89
distributive property and, 85–89
monomial, 666–670
numerical, 10–14
evaluating, 10–14, 81, 82, 83, 90, 202–204, 221–222, 239
order of operations and, 10–14
polynomial, 658–660
terms of, 86
variable, 15–19
evaluating, 16–19, 64–67, 71–73, 75–77, 86–89, 90, 181–183
simplifying, 87–89, 180–183
writing, 16–19
Extended problem solving, *See* Problem solving
Extended response questions, *See* Problem solving
Extra Examples, *Occur in each lesson*

f

Face(s), of a polyhedron, 492–493
Factor(s), 167–172
common, 173
definition of, 706
divisibility tests and, 706
factor tree, 169, 171
greatest common, 173–177
powers and, 196–200
prime factorization, 169–172
relatively prime numbers and, 174
Sieve of Eratosthenes, 167
writing, 168–172
Factor tree, 169, 171
Factorial notation, 623
Factorial(s), 623–626
Factoring
a monomial, 170–172
a number, 167–172
Favorable outcome, 354, 633
FOIL method, for multiplying binomials, 675
Formula(s)
applying, 134–139
area
of a circle, 486
of a parallelogram, 481
of a rectangle, 33
of a square, 33
of a trapezoid, 482
of a triangle, 134
circumference, 289, 290
combination, 628
definition of, 33
distance, 34
energy, 312
inverse tangent, 469
mean, 75
odds, 633, 634
percent of change, 338
perimeter
of a rectangle, 33
of a square, 33
permutation, 624
probability, 354
Pythagorean theorem, 443
simple interest, 348
slope, 568
spreadsheet, 300
surface area
of a cone, 508
of a cylinder, 504
of a prism, 503
of a pyramid, 507
of a sphere, 510
table of, 742
volume
of a cone, 520
of a cylinder, 514
of a prism, 513
of a pyramid, 519
45°-45°-90° right triangle, 456, 458–460
Fraction(s), *See also* Mixed numbers; Proportion; Rate; Ratio
adding
common denominators, 219–223, 710
different denominators, 224–227
clearing to solve equations, 273–275
comparing, 192–195
game, 216
decimals and, 242–246, 331–335, 746
definition of, 179, 707
denominator, 707
dividing, 234–238
game, 238
equivalent, 179–183
game, 217
modeling, 178
improper, 193–195
modeling, 192
multiplying, 230–233
by a whole number, 713
negative, 195
numerator, 707
ordering decimals, percents, and, 333–334
percent and, 331–335, 746
repeating decimals and, 242–246
simplest form, 179
simplifying, 179–183
by combining like terms, 220–223
using powers properties, 198
slope and, 568–574

square root of, 435
subtracting
common denominators, 219–223, 710
different denominators, 224–227
Fraction bar, evaluating expressions containing, 11
Frequency table
definition of, 6
intervals for, 6
making, 6–9, 256
scale, 6
Front-end estimation, 248–250, 711
Front view
of a solid, 493, 496–497
drawing, 496–497
Function(s)
definition of, 541
domain, 542
evaluating, 542–544
graphing, 556–561
identifying, 541, 543
input-output tables and, 541–544
non-linear, 680–685
game, 684
graphing, 681–685
range, 542
relations and, 541, 543
truth, 300
vertical lines and, 558
vertical line test and, 681
writing rules for, 542–544
Function form, 550
Function notation, 680–684
Function rule, 542
writing, 542–544

g

Games
algebra
combining like terms, 655
dividing fractions, 238
equations in one variable, 538
equations in two variables, 553
mental math equations, 104
multi-step equations, 287
multi-step inequalities, 299
non-linear functions, 684
one- and two-step equations, 268–269
polynomial addition, 665
proportions, 326
solving equations, 314
variable expressions, 19
writing expressions, 128
coordinate, plotting points, 95, 372–373, 539
data, interpreting plots, 615
fractions
comparing, 216
equivalent, 217
geometry
identifying angles in triangles, 429
reflections, 408
vocabulary, 389
graphing
interpret bar graphs, 594–595
interpret circle graphs, 594–595
integer, sums and differences of, 67
measurement
area of a circle, 490
perimeter, area, circumference, 478–479
number
evaluating powers, 428
exponents, 200
greatest common factor, 177
place value, 3
properties of exponents, 654
rounding, 3
square root, 436
operations
decimal operations, 315
integer operations, 105
multiplying whole numbers, 50–51
whole number and decimal sums, 2
whole number division, 164–165
percent, enlarging and reducing, 346
probability, dependent events, 643
reasoning, logic, 43, 145
statistics, averages, 261
trigonometry, trigonometric ratios, 471
Geometric probability, 652–653
Geometry, *See also* Applications; Area; Connections to math strands; Coordinate plane; Geometry; Measurement; Perimeter; Surface area; Volume
angles
acute, 382
alternate exterior, 377
alternate interior, 377
classifying, 382–385
complementary, 375
congruent, 397–401
corresponding, 377
obtuse, 382
right, 33, 375, 382
straight, 375
supplementary, 375
arc, 380
circle, 290–294, 486–491
circumference, 288–289, 290–294
classification
angle, 382–385
quadrilateral, 386–389
solids, 492, 494
triangle, 382–385
compass use, 380–381, 396, 722
constructions, 380–381, 396, 722
corresponding parts, 397–401
endpoint, 718
half plane, 584
intersecting lines, 376
line, 718
parallel lines, 377
parallelogram, 386, 481, 483–485
perpendicular lines, 376
plane, 718
point, 718
polygon, 382–385, 386–389, 390–393, 416–421
protractor use, 396, 461–462
Pythagorean theorem, 442–447, 450–453
quadrilateral, 386–389
ray, 718
rhombus, 386
segment, 718
sides
adjacent, 463
congruent, 397–401
corresponding, 377, 397–401
hypotenuse, 463
opposite, 463
similarity, 416–421
solids
classifying, 492, 494
cone, 492, 508–511, 520–523
cylinder, 492, 504–506, 514–518
drawing, 493–497
prism, 492, 502–506, 512–518
pyramid, 492, 507–511, 519–523
sphere, 492, 510, 679
square, 33–37, 386
symmetry, 406–408
tessellation, 414–415
three-dimensional figure, 492–495
transformations
reflection, 404–408
rotation, 410–413
translation, 409, 411–413
trapezoid, 386, 482–485

triangles
acute, 382
classifying, 382–385
equilateral, 382
isosceles, 382
obtuse, 382
right, 382
scalene, 382
sum of angle measures, 383
trigonometric ratios, 461–468
Graphing
functions, 556–561
non-linear, 681–685
inequalities, 140–145, 295, 297, 298
linear, 583–587
integers on a number line, 53
linear equations, 556–561
using the slope-intercept form, 578–580
systems of, 581–582
reflections on the coordinate plane, 404–408
Graphing calculator, *See also* Calculator; Technology activities
graphing linear functions, 561
graphing non-linear functions, 685
making data displays, 610–611
Graphs, *See also* Plots
bar, 5–9, 724
choosing a data display, 606–609
circle, 331, 334, 605, 607–609, 611
coordinate
non-linear functions, 681–685
plotting points, 91–95
transformations, 404–415, 418, 420
double bar, 9
histogram, 6–9
line, 606–609
linear, 556–561
of horizontal lines, 558–560
using intercepts, 564–567
line slope, 568–574
using the slope-intercept form, 578–580
systems of equations, 581–582
of vertical lines, 558–560
misleading, 612–613
Greatest common divisor (GCD), 173
Greatest common factor (GCF), 173–177
game, 177
of monomials, 174–177
Grouping symbols, 11
order of operations and, 11–14
Guess, check, and revise, problem solving strategy, 26–27, 31
Guided problem solving, *See* Problem solving

h

Half plane, 584
Hands-on activities, *See* Activities; Games; Math in Science; Technology activities
Height
of a cone, 520
of a cylinder, 504
of a parallelogram, 481
of a prism, 503
of a pyramid, 507
of a trapezoid, 482
of a triangle, 134
Heptagon, 390
Hexagon, 390
Histogram
choosing a data display, 606, 608–609
interpreting, 6–9
making, 6–9
scale, 6
Homework, *See* Student help
Homework Check, *Occurs at the beginning of each exercise set*
Horizontal line, graph of, 558–560
Hypotenuse, 442, 443, 463
Hypothesis, *See* Critical thinking; Prediction

i

Identity property
of addition, 59
of multiplication, 71
Image, 404
Improper fraction(s)
mixed numbers and, 193–195, 707
ordering, 193–195
Inch ruler, measuring with, 720
Included angle, 398
Included side, 398
Increase, percent of, 338–341
Independent events, 639–643
definition of, 639
Indirect measurement, 417, 420, 421
Pythagorean theorem and, 450, 452–453
Inductive reasoning, *See* Activities; Critical thinking; Reasoning
Inequality (inequalities)
combining like terms in, 296–300
definition of, 140
equivalent, 141
graphing, 140–145, 295, 297, 298
linear, 583–587
multi-step, 295–300
game, 299
problem solving and, 301–305
solution of, definition, 140
solving
using addition or subtraction, 140–145
using multiplication or division, 146–149
symbols, 141
writing, 296–300, 301–305
Input, 541
Input-output table, 541–544
Integer(s)
absolute value and, 54–56
adding, 57–62
game, 67
multiple addends, 59–62
on a number line, 57–59
rules for, 59
additive identity, 59
definition of, 53
dividing, 74–77
mean, 257, 259, 260
modeling on a number line, 53–54
multiplying, 70–73
negative, 53
opposite, 54–56
ordering, 53, 55–56
on a number line, 53
positive, 53
subtracting, 63–67
game, 67
using patterns, 63
zero, 53
Intercept(s)
definition of, 564
finding, 564–567
using to graph a line, 565–567
Interdisciplinary, *See* Applications; Connections to other disciplines; Math in science
Interest
compound, 350, 351
simple, 348
Internet, *See also* Student help
eTutorial Plus, 7, 12, 22, 30, 36, 41, 55, 61, 65, 72, 76, 83, 88, 93, 111, 115, 121, 126,

137, 143, 148, 171, 176, 182, 188, 194, 199, 203, 207, 222, 226, 232, 237, 245, 249, 253, 259, 274, 280, 284, 293, 297, 304, 319, 325, 329, 334, 340, 345, 349, 356, 378, 384, 388, 392, 400, 407, 412, 419, 434, 440, 446, 452, 459, 466, 483, 488, 494, 505, 510, 516, 522, 543, 547, 551, 559, 566, 573, 579, 586, 599, 603, 608, 621, 625, 630, 635, 642, 659, 664, 669, 676, 682
eWorkbook Plus, 7, 12, 17, 22, 30, 35, 41, 55, 60, 65, 72, 76, 82, 93, 111, 115, 121, 126, 137, 142, 148, 170, 175, 181, 188, 194, 198, 203, 207, 221, 226, 232, 236, 244, 249, 253, 259, 273, 280, 284, 292, 297, 303, 319, 324, 329, 333, 340, 344, 349, 356, 378, 384, 387, 392, 399, 406, 411, 419, 434, 439, 445, 452, 458, 466, 483, 488, 494, 505, 509, 515, 521, 543, 547, 551, 558, 566, 572, 579, 585, 599, 603, 607, 620, 625, 629, 634, 641, 659, 663, 668, 676, 682
project support, 103, 313, 477, 653
searching for information, 129
state test practice, 9, 13, 19, 23, 31, 37, 43, 56, 62, 67, 73, 77, 84, 89, 95, 112, 116, 123, 128, 139, 145, 149, 172, 177, 183, 189, 195, 200, 204, 208, 223, 227, 233, 238, 246, 250, 254, 261, 275, 281, 285, 294, 299, 305, 320, 326, 330, 335, 341, 346, 350, 357, 379, 385, 389, 393, 401, 408, 413, 421, 436, 441, 447, 453, 468, 485, 495, 506, 511, 517, 523, 544, 548, 553, 560, 567, 574, 580, 587, 600, 604, 609, 622, 626, 631, 636, 643, 660, 665, 670, 677, 684
Intersecting lines, 376
Interval, 6
Inverse
additive, 61
multiplicative, 234
Inverse operations
addition and subtraction, 109–112
definition of, 109
multiplication and division, 113–116
Inverse tangent, 469
Investigations, *See* Activities; Math in Science; Technology activities
Irrational number, 437, 439–441
definition of, 437
Isometric drawing, 496–497
Isosceles triangle, 382

Journal, *See* Notebook; Notebook review; Note taking; Writing in mathematics

Labs, *See* Activities; Technology Activities
Leading digit(s), estimation and, 251
Leaf, in a stem-and-leaf plot, 597
Least common denominator (LCD), 192
adding fractions, 224–227
comparing fractions, 192–195
subtracting fractions, 224–227
Least common multiple (LCM), 186–189
of monomials, 187–189
Legs, of a right triangle, 442, 443–444
Length, on the coordinate plane, 92–95
Like terms, 86
collecting on one side of an equation, 278–281
combining, 86–89
to add polynomials, 661–665
game, 655
to simplify fractions, 220–222
to solve equations, 272–275
Linear equation(s)
graphing, 556–561
using a graphing calculator, 561
horizontal lines, 558–560
using intercepts, 564–567
using slope-intercept form, 578–580
vertical lines, 558–560
slope of graph, 568–574
slope-intercept form, 575–580
systems of, 581–582
Linear function, *See* Linear equation
Linear graph, 556–561
using intercepts, 564–567
using slope-intercept form, 578–580
slope of a line, 568–574
Linear inequality (inequalities), graph of, 583–587
Line graph
choosing a data display, 606, 608–609
interpreting, 606–609, 725
making, 606–609, 725
misleading, 612–613
Line plot
making, 723
reading, 723
Line(s)
definition of, 718
intersecting, 376
parallel, 377
perpendicular, 376
Line of symmetry, 406–408
List, make a, problem solving strategy, 184–185, 186, 618, 627
Logical reasoning, *See also* Classification; Critical thinking; Error analysis; Games, Number sense; Problem solving
concept grid, 48
concept map, 374, 386
converse of a statement, 444
tree diagram, 169, 171, 618–622
truth function, 300
unit analysis, 40
Venn diagrams, 242, 437, 726
Look for a pattern, problem solving strategy, 68–69
Lower extreme, 601
Lower quartile, 601

Make a list, problem solving strategy, 184–185, 186, 618, 627
Make a model, problem solving strategy, 402–403, 407
Make a table, problem solving strategy, 554–555, 556, 683
Manipulatives, *See also* Calculator; Mathematical tools; Modeling; Technology activities
algebra tiles, 28, 107–108, 117–118, 278, 661, 673
cards, 50, 200, 478, 637
compass, 380–381, 396, 722
markers, 50, 268
number cube, 255–256, 268, 352
real world objects, 518
ruler, 321, 461–462, 518, 720
square tiles, 32
straightedge, 380–381, 396, 722
unit cubes, 512
Mathematical reasoning, *See* Reasoning
Mathematical techniques, *See* Estimation; Mental math; Number sense; Problem solving

Mathematical tools, *See also* Calculator; Estimation; Manipulatives; Mental math
balance scale, 109
compass, 380–381, 396, 722
protractor, 396, 461–462, 721
ruler, 321, 461–462, 518, 720
straightedge, 380–381, 396, 722
Math Background and Teaching Strategies, 2C–D, 50C–D, 104C–D, 164C–D, 216C–D, 268C–D, 314C–D, 372C–D, 428C–D, 478C–D, 538C–D, 594C–D, 654C–D
Math in Science
aiming a telescope, 476–477
geometric probability, 652–653
hibernating in the Arctic, 102–103
the physics of basketball, 312–313
Math Reasoning, 27, 36, 87, 133, 147, 176, 185, 323, 348, 353, 387, 433, 449, 482, 484, 501, 555, 572, 662, 679
Mean, 75, 255–261
choosing a representative average, 258–261
definition of, 75, 257
Measurement, *See also* Area; Measurement tools; Perimeter; Surface area; Volume
accuracy of measurement, 720, 721
angle, 382–383, 461–462, 605–609, 721
of a polygon, 391
of a quadrilateral, 387
of a triangle, 383
circumference of a circle, 288–294
comparing diameter and circumference, 288–289
exercises, 36, 384, 385, 388, 400, 484
indirect, 417, 420, 421, 450, 452–453
using a ruler, 321, 461–462, 518, 720
scale drawing, 321
similar figures and, 416–421
Measurement tools
balance scale, 109
compass, 380–381, 396, 605–609
how to use, 722
protractor, 382–383, 461–462, 605–609
how to use, 721
ruler, 321, 461–462, 518, 720
how to use, 720
Measures, table of, 741
Measures of dispersion, *See* Range
Median, 255–261
box-and-whisker plots and, 601
choosing a representative average, 258–261
definition of, 257
Mental math
exercises, 36, 62, 72, 82, 89, 99, 149, 237, 325, 385, 489
integer subtraction and, 63
to solve equations, 28–31
Mini-Quiz, *Occurs at the end of each exercise set*
Misleading graph, 612–613
Mixed number(s)
adding
common denominators, 219–223
different denominators, 224–227
decimals and, 243–246
definition of, 707
dividing, 235–238
improper fractions and, 193–195, 707
multiplying, 231–233
ordering, 193–195
subtracting
common denominators, 219–223
different denominators, 224–227
Mode, 255–261
choosing a representative average, 258–261
definition of, 257
Model
make a, problem solving strategy, 402–403, 407
scale, 324, 325
Modeling
addition
of fractions, 219
integer, 57–59
area
of a circle, 486
of a parallelogram, 481
of a rectangle, 32
of a trapezoid, 482
of a triangle, 134
binomial multiplication, 673, 674
equations
using algebra tiles, 28, 107–108, 117–118, 278
using a balance scale, 109
two-step, 117–118
fractions, 192
division, 234
equivalent, 178
integers, 53–54
linear inequalities, 583–587
patterns, 68
percent on a circle graph, 331, 334
polynomial addition, 661
the Pythagorean theorem, 442
rational numbers, 242
real numbers, 438
rounding, 705
square root, 432
surface area
of a cone, 508, 510
of a cylinder, 504, 505
of a prism, 502, 503, 505
of a pyramid, 507, 510
volume, 512, 518
Monomial(s), 657
definition of, 170
factoring, 170–172
greatest common factor of, 174–177
least common multiple of, 187–189
multiplying, 666–670
powers and, 666–670
Multiple(s), 186
common, 186
least common, 186–189
Multiple choice questions, *See* Problem solving
Multiple events, 640
Multiple representations, *See* Representation
Multiple Representations notes, 34, 81, 114, 193, 235, 348, 398, 457, 508, 584, 619
Multiplication
binomial, 673–677
checking, using estimation, 251
cross products, 323–326
decimal, 251–254
by a whole number, 714
equations, 113–116
equivalent fractions and, 179–183, 192
estimating products, 716
exponents and, 20–23
of fractions, 230–233, 713
by a whole number, 713
integer, 70–73
as inverse of division, 113
mixed number, 231–233
monomial, 666–670
order of operations and, 10–14
percent equation and, 347–350
properties
associative, 81
commutative, 80
equality, 113

identity, 71
inequality, 146
product of powers, 196–200
zero, 71
in scientific notation, 206–209
to solve inequalities, 146–149
words indicating, 16
Multiplication property of equality, 113
for clearing decimals, 283–285
for clearing fractions, 273–275, 283–285
Multiplication property of inequality, 146
Multiplicative identity, 71
Multiplicative inverse, 234
Multi-step equation, 271–275
Multi-step inequality (inequalities)
problem-solving and, 301–305
solving, 295–300
writing, 296–300, 301–305
Multi-step problem, *See* Problem solving; Test-taking skills

Negative exponent, 201–204
Negative integer, 53
Negative slope, 571, 572
Negative square root, 431
Net, 502–505, 507, 508, 510, 518
Nonexamples, 215, 325, 335, 375, 390, 391, 392, 404, 681
Non-linear function(s), 680–685
game, 684
graphing, 681–685
using a graphing calculator, 685
Non-routine problem *See* Problem solving strategies; Test-taking skills
Non-standard form, of a polynomial, 657
Notation
arc, to show equal angle measures, 383
combination, 628
factorial, 623
fraction bar, 11
function, 680–684
permutation, 624
rotation in the coordinate plane, 410–411
Notebook
entries
adding and subtracting fractions, 219
addition property of equality, 110
addition and subtraction properties of inequality, 141
additive identity property, 59
angle measures in a polygon, 391
angles and parallel lines, 377
using appropriate data displays, 606
area of a circle, 486
area of a parallelogram, 481
area and perimeter of a triangle, 134
area of a trapezoid, 482
the associative property, 81
average, 257
circumference of a circle, 290
classifying triangles, 382
combination notation, 628
the commutative property, 80
counting principle, 619
cross products property, 323
dilation, 418
distance formula, 34
dividing decimals, 252
dividing fractions, 234
dividing integers, 74
division property of equality, 114
division property of inequality, 147
finding intercepts, 564
45°-45°-90° triangle, 456
graphing linear inequalities, 584
multiplication property of equality, 113
multiplication property of inequality, 146
multiplying decimals, 251
multiplying fractions, 230
multiplying integers, 70
negative exponents, 201
90° rotation, 410
180° rotation, 411
order of operations, 10, 21
percent of change, 338
the percent equation, 347
perimeter and area formulas, 33
permutation, 624
power of a power property, 668
power of a product property, 667
probability of an event, 354
probability of dependent events, 640
probability of independent events, 640
problem-solving plan, 39
product of powers property, 196
Pythagorean theorem, 443
quotient of powers property, 197
reflection, 405
using scientific notation, 205
similar polygons, 416
simple interest, 348
slope-intercept form, 577
slope of a line, 570
solving a percent problem, 327
solving a two-step equation, 120
subtracting integers, 63
subtraction property of equality, 109
summary of percent problems, 328
summary of slope, 572
surface area of a cone, 508
surface area of a cylinder, 504
surface area of a prism, 503
surface area of a pyramid, 507
30°-60°-90° triangle, 457
trigonometric ratios, 463
volume of a cone, 520
volume of a cylinder, 514
volume of a prism, 513
volume of a pyramid, 519
zero exponents, 202
how to take notes
using a concept grid, 480
contrasting terms, 596
illustrating with examples, 430
keeping a notebook, 4
making a concept map, 374
noting vocabulary, 52
organizing information, 106
preview the chapter, 166
recording the process, 270
summarizing material, 656
taking notes in class, 316
write questions about homework, 540
writing helpful hints, 218
Notebook review, 24–25, 44–45, 78–79, 96–97, 130–131, 150–151, 190–191, 210–211, 240–241, 262–263, 286–287, 306–307, 336–337, 358–359, 394–395, 422–423, 454–455, 470–471, 498–499, 524–525, 562–563, 588–589, 614–615, 646–647, 671–672, 686–687
Notetaking, student help with, 21, 86, 146, 219, 244, 282, 328, 386, 443, 486, 565, 629, 674
side column notes, 34, 64, 135, 174, 220, 243, 272, 323, 391, 439, 503, 578, 628, 675
Number line
to approximate square root, 432
for comparing real numbers, 438
for graphing, inequalities, 140–145
integer addition on, 57–59
for line plots, 723
for modeling absolute value, 54
for modeling opposites, 54

for ordering
fractions, decimals, and percents, 333
integers, 53, 78
rational numbers, 243
for rounding
decimals, 705
whole numbers, 705
time line, 66
Number sense, *See also* Comparing; Estimation; Ordering; Properties
absolute value, 54–56
circumference, diameter, and pi, 288–289, 290
common factor, 173
common multiple, 186
comparing radii of circles, 491
composite number, 167, 169
consecutive numbers, 26, 27
digits, 704
divisibility tests, 706
exercises, 13, 42, 182, 208, 260, 275, 277, 298, 330, 511, 517
expanded form, 704
factorials, 623–626
factors, 167–172
front-end estimation, 248–250
greatest common divisor (GCD), 173
greatest common factor (GCF), 173–177
irrational numbers, 437, 439–441
leading digit, 251
least common denominator (LCD), 192
least common multiple (LCM), 186–189
multiple choice questions and, 157
multiplicative inverse, 234
negative exponents, 201–204
number relationships, 242
opposite integers, 54–56
percent
discount, 342, 344–346
increase and decrease, 338–341
markup, 342–346
sale price, 342, 344–346
perfect square, 432
prediction from experiments, 352, 353, 355, 356
prime factorization, 169–172
prime number, 167, 169
product form, 205–206
Pythagorean triple, 451, 452
rational numbers, 242, 437–441
real numbers, 437
reciprocals, 234
relatively prime numbers, 174
repeating decimal, 242–246
rules of exponents, 196–200
scientific notation, 205–209
selecting a representative average, 258–261
Sieve of Eratosthenes, 167
square root, 431–436
standard form, 205–207, 704
terminating decimal, 242–246
triangular number, 617
whole number, 704
Numerator, 707

Obtuse angle, 382
Obtuse triangle, 382
Octagon, 390
Odds, 632–636
Opposite(s), 54–56
of a polynomial, 662
Opposite side, of a right triangle, 463
Ordered pair
definition of, 91
plotting, 91–95
relations and, 541, 543
as solution to an equation in two variables, 549
as solution to a linear inequality, 583
Ordering
data
in a box-and-whisker plot, 601–604
to find median, 255–261
in a stem-and-leaf plot, 597–600
decimals, 438–441
exercises, 55, 245, 265
fractions, decimals, and percents, 333–334
improper fractions, 193–195
integers, 53, 55–56
mixed numbers, 193–195
rational numbers, 242–246
Order of operations, 10–14
for evaluating expressions, 221–222
Origin, coordinate plane, 91
Outcome(s), 354, *See also* Event
using counting methods to find, 618–622
favorable, 354, 633
odds of, 633–636
unfavorable, 633
Outlier, 604
Output, 541

Pacing, *Including Regular and Block,* 2A, 50A, 104A, 164A, 216A, 268A, 314A, 372A, 428A, 478A, 538A, 594A, 654A, *Also occurs in each lesson*
Palindrome(s), 617
Parallel lines, 377
constructing, 381
Parallelogram, 386
area of, 481, 483–485
base of, 481
height of, 481
Patterns
exercises, 41, 72, 245, 253, 350, 393, 407, 435, 631, 676, 685
exponent, 156, 666
geometric, 68, 69, 495
integer, 63
number, 68, 69, 616, 617
tessellation, 414–415
in trigonometric ratios, 461–462
writing function rules from, 542–544
Pentagon, 390
Percent
applications, 342–346
discount, 342, 344–346
interest, 348–351
markup, 342–346
sale price, 342, 344–346
sales tax, 343–346
tip, 344–346
of change, 338–341
circle graphs and, 331, 334
decimals and, 331–335
decrease, 338–341
definition of, 327
equation, 347–350
equivalent fractions, decimals and, 746
fractions and, 331–335
game, 346
greater than 100%, 332–335
increase, 338–341
proportion and, 327–330
summary of types of percent problems, 328
Perfect square, 432
Perform an experiment, problem solving strategy, 352–353, 354
Perimeter
of a composite figure, 37
in the coordinate plane, 92–95
of a rectangle, 33–37, 136–139
of a right triangle, 451–453

of a square, 33–37
ratio of side length to, 317
of a triangle, 134, 136–139, 279
Permutation notation, 624
Permutations, 623–626
combinations and, 629–631
definition of, 623
Perpendicular lines, 376
constructing, 381
Pi
circumference, diameter and, 288–289
definition of, 290
estimating the value of, 288–289
Place value, 704
game, 3
rounding to, 705
Plane figures, *See* Geometry
Plane, *See* Coordinate plane
Plot(s)
box-and-whisker, 601–604
choosing a data display, 606–609
line, 723
scatter plot, 545–548
stem-and-leaf, 597–600
double, 598–600
Point(s)
in the coordinate plane, 91–95
definition of, 718
Polygon(s), 390–393
angle sums for, 390–393
congruent, 397–401
dilating, 418–421
quadrilaterals, 386–389
regular, 390–391
similar, 416–421
tessellation and, 414–415
triangles, 382–385
Polyhedron, *See also* Solids, 492
edges of, 492–493, 495
faces of, 492–493, 495
vertices of, 492–493, 495
Polynomial(s)
adding, 661–665
game, 665
binomial, 657
classifying, 657, 659
definition of, 657
evaluating, 658–660
monomial, 657
monomials and powers, 666–670
multiplying
binomials, 673–677
monomials, 666–670
non-standard form, 657
opposite of, 662
simplifying, 658–660
standard form, 657–660
subtracting, 662–665
trinomial, 657
Population, 644
Positive integer, 53
Positive slope, 571, 572
Positive square root, 431
Power of a power property, 668
Power of a product property, 667
Powers
base, 20
dividing, 197–200
evaluating, 20–23
game, 428
exponents and, 20–23
monomials and, 666–670
multiplying, 196–200
negative, 201–209
order of operations and, 21
of powers, 668–670
of products, 667–670
reading, 20
scientific notation and, 205–209
of ten, 205-209
writing products as, 20–23
zero, 202
Precision, *See also* Error analysis
front-end estimation and, 248–250
Precision measurement tools, *See* Measurement tools
Prediction
exercises, 8, 103, 359, 363, 617, 683
from an experiment, 352, 353, 355, 356
from a graph, 103
from a table, 42
using geometric probability, 652–653
using a pattern, 616, 617
Prime factorization, 169–172
factor tree, 169, 171
greatest common factor and, 173–177
Prime factor(s), 169
Prime number, 167, 169
relatively prime, 174
Principal, interest and, 348
Prism, 492
bases of, 492
height of, 503
sketching, 493
surface area of, 502–506
formula, 503
volume of, 512–518
formula, 513
Probability
of an event, 354–357
complementary events, 632–636
counting methods and, 618–622
dependent events, 639–643
experimental, 352–357, 652–653
formula, 354
geometric, 652–653
independent events, 639–643
multiple events, 640
odds and, 633–636
outcome, 354
favorable, 354, 633
unfavorable, 633
prediction from an experiment, 352, 353, 355, 356
simulations, 637–638
theoretical, 354, 355–357
tree diagrams and, 618–622
Problem solving, *See also* Error analysis
choose a method, exercises, 122
choose a strategy, 23, 27, 69, 84, 123, 133, 172, 185, 229, 246, 277, 299, 335, 353, 403, 421, 436, 449, 490, 501, 555, 617, 631, 679, 684
eliminate possibilities, 157
extended problem solving, 8, 13, 94, 123, 138, 182, 245, 293, 305, 325, 393, 407, 467, 484, 586, 600, 621, 626, 636, 670
extended response questions, 9, 49, 89, 101, 128, 155, 159, 160, 162, 172, 215, 261, 267, 294, 311, 341, 363, 367, 368, 369, 370, 413, 427, 453, 475, 529, 533, 534, 535, 536, 580, 593, 604, 651, 684, 691, 694, 696–698
guided problem solving, 7, 17, 41, 65, 76, 87, 111, 121, 126, 137, 142, 170, 175, 194, 207, 226, 236, 253, 259, 273, 303, 329, 349, 411, 419, 434, 452, 458, 466, 483, 494, 509, 547, 566, 599, 603, 668
inequalities and, 301–305
multiple choice questions, 13, 19, 23, 31, 37, 43, 56, 62, 67, 77, 84, 95, 112, 116, 123, 128, 139, 145, 155, 156–157, 158–162, 172, 177, 189, 195, 200, 204, 208, 223, 227, 233, 238, 246, 250, 254, 275, 281, 285, 299, 305, 311, 320, 326, 330, 335, 346, 350, 357, 363, 366–370, 379, 385, 389, 393, 401, 408, 421, 436, 441, 447, 460, 468, 485, 490, 495, 506, 511, 523, 530–531, 532–536, 544, 548, 553, 560, 567, 574, 587, 593, 600, 604, 609, 622, 626, 631, 636, 643, 660, 665, 670, 677, 695–698

short response questions, 19, 31, 37, 49, 77, 84, 95, 101, 116, 123, 145, 149, 155, 159, 160, 161, 162, 189, 208, 215, 227, 233, 250, 254, 267, 275, 305, 311, 320, 330, 350, 363, 364–365, 366, 368, 369, 370, 379, 401, 408, 427, 447, 475, 485, 490, 506, 511, 517, 529, 533, 534, 535, 536, 553, 560, 567, 593, 609, 622, 626, 631, 643, 651, 691, 695–698
Problem-solving plan, 38–42
Problem-solving strategies, *See also* Test-taking skills; Test-taking strategies
act it out, 228–229
exercises, 232
break into parts, 500–501, 502
exercises, 506
draw a diagram, 132–133, 134, 448–449
exercises, 453, 467
draw a graph, 678–679, 681
exercises, 683
guess, check, and revise, 26–27
exercises, 31
look for a pattern, 68–69
make a list, 184–185, 186, 618, 627
make a model, 402–403
exercises, 407
make a table, 554–555, 556
exercises, 683
perform an experiment, 352–353, 354
solve a simpler problem, 616–617
exercises, 622
work backward, 276–277,
exercises, 280, 677, 683
Product form, 205–206
Product of powers property, 196
Project ideas, 103, 313, 477, 653, *See also* Math in Science
Properties
associative
addition, 81
multiplication, 81
commutative
addition, 80
multiplication, 80
cross product, 323–326
distributive, 85–89
equations with variables on both sides and, 279–281
multi-step equations and, 272–275
of equality
addition, 110
division, 114
multiplication, 113
subtraction, 109
identity
additive, 59
multiplicative, 71
of inequality
addition, 141
division, 147
multiplication, 146
subtraction, 141
power of a power, 668
power of a product, 667
product of powers, 196
quotient of powers, 197
table of, 743
zero, multiplication, 71
Proportion
cross products and, 323–326
definition of, 322
dilation and, 418–421
for finding angles in circle graphs, 605, 607–609, 611
game, 326
indirect measurement and, 417, 420, 421
percent and, 327–330
prediction and, 352, 353, 355, 356
scale and, 324–326
similarity and, 416–421
writing and solving, 322–326
Proportional reasoning
comparing radii of circles, 491
cross products and, 323–326
diameter and circumference, 288–289
equivalent fractions, 179–183
making a circle graph, 605, 607–609, 611
percent and, 327–330
rates and, 318–320
ratios and, 317–320
scale and, 324–326
scale drawing, 321
similarity and, 416–421
unit rate and, 318–320
Protractor, 382–383, 396, 461–462, 605, 607–609, 721
how to use, 721
Pyramid, 492
base of, 492
height of, 507
slant height of, 507
surface area of, 507–511
formula, 507
volume of, 519–521
formula, 519
Pythagorean theorem, 442–447, 450–453
converse of, 444–447
formula for, 443
indirect measurement and, 450, 452–453
modeling, 442
Pythagorean triple, 451, 452

q

Quadrant(s), coordinate, 91
Quadrilateral(s), 386–389
classifying, 386–389
congruent, 397–401
definition of, 386
dilating, 418, 420
parallelogram, 386
rectangle, 386
rhombus, 386
square, 386
sum of the angle measures of, 390–391
trapezoid, 386
Quotient, 715
Quotient of powers property, 197

r

Radical sign, 431
Radius
of a circle, 290
circumference and, 290–294
of a cylinder, 504
Random sample, 644
Range
of data, 258–261
of a function, 542
Rate(s), 318–320, 708
definition of, 318, 708
equivalent, 318–320
unit, 318–320, 708
Ratio(s), *See also* Proportion; Rate; Scale
circumference and diameter, 288–289
comparison and, 708
cosine, 462–468
definition of, 317, 708
equivalent, 317–320
percent and, 327–330
probability and, 352–357, 632–636
proportion and, 322–326
rates and, 317–320, 708
scale factor and, 418–421
sine, 462–468
slope, 568–574
tangent, 462–468
inverse, 469
trigonometric, 461–468

Rational number(s), 437–441, *See also* Fractions
definition of, 242, 437
ordering, 243–246
Ray, definition of, 718
Reading mathematics
identifying points, lines, and planes, 718
naming angles, 719
reading angle markings, 383
reading bar graphs, 5–9, 24, 724
reading box-and-whisker plots, 601–604
reading circle graphs, 605, 607–609
reading coordinate notation, 404–405, 409–411
reading double bar graphs, 9
reading histograms, 6–9
reading integer values, 54
reading line graphs, 606–609, 725
reading misleading graphs, 612–614
reading powers, 20
reading scatter plots, 545–548
reading stem-and-leaf plots, 598–600
scientific notation, 205–209
student help with, 16, 29, 33, 39, 54, 302, 351, 383, 390, 398, 410, 433, 482, 515, 633, 681
translating verbal phrases, 16
translating verbal sentences, 302–305
Real number(s)
classifying, 437, 439, 440
comparing, 438–441
definition of, 437
Venn diagram of, 437
Reasoning, *See also* Critical thinking; Decision making; Error analysis; Extended response questions; Patterns; Proportional reasoning; Short response questions; Thinking skills
concept grid, 480
concept map, 374, 386
converse of a statement, 444
games, 43
problem-solving plan, 38–42
Pythagorean theorem, 444
tree diagram, 169, 171, 618–622
truth function, 300
unit analysis, 40
Venn diagram, 242, 437, 726
Reciprocal(s), 234
Rectangle, 386
area of, 32–37, 136–139
modeling, 32
perimeter of, 33–37, 136–139
Rectangular prism, *See* Prism
Reflection, 404–408
in the x-axis, 405
in the y-axis, 405
tessellation and, 414–415
Regular polygon, 390–391
Relation(s)
definition of, 541
functions and, 541, 543
Relatively prime numbers, 174
Repeating decimal(s), 242–246
fractions and, 242–246
irrational numbers and, 437
rational numbers and, 437
Report, project, 313
Representation, *See also* Graphs; Modeling; Number line; Plots
of the additive identity property, 59
of area, 32–33
area of a circle as area of a parallelogram, 486
area of a parallelogram as area of a rectangle, 481
of data, averages, 255–261
of equations using algebra tiles, 28
expressions in expanded form, 196
forms of a fraction, 166
fractions as percents, 331–335
functions in tables, 541–544
improper fractions as mixed numbers, 193–195, 707
mixed numbers as improper fractions, 193–195, 707
of number sets in a Venn diagram, 242, 437, 726
numbers in expanded form, 704
numbers in standard form, 704
percents as decimals, 332–335
percents as fractions, 332–335
of perimeter, 33
of points, lines, and planes, 718
of polynomials with algebra tiles, 661
of the Pythagorean Theorem, 442
of real numbers with a Venn diagram, 437
verbal model, 11
verbal phrases as expressions, 16–19
Research, project, 103, 313, 477, 653
Review, *See also* Assessment; Internet; Notebook Review; Skills Review Handbook
basic skills, 9, 13, 19, 31, 37, 43, 67, 73, 84, 95, 112, 116, 123, 139, 145, 149, 172, 177, 183, 189, 195, 204, 208, 223, 238, 246, 254, 275, 285, 305, 320, 335, 341, 346, 357, 379, 401, 413, 436, 460, 468, 523, 548, 553, 560, 567, 574, 580, 587, 631, 636, 643, 660, 677
Chapter Review, 46–47, 98–99, 152–153, 212–213, 264–265, 308–309, 360–361, 424–425, 472–473, 526–527, 590–591, 648–649, 688–689
extra practice, 727–739
mixed review, 9, 13, 19, 23, 31, 37, 43, 56, 62, 67, 73, 77, 84, 89, 95, 112, 116, 123, 128, 139, 145, 149, 172, 177, 183, 189, 195, 200, 204, 208, 223, 227, 233, 238, 246, 250, 254, 261, 275, 281, 285, 294, 299, 305, 320, 326, 330, 335, 341, 346, 350, 357, 379, 385, 389, 393, 401, 408, 413, 421, 436, 441, 447, 453, 460, 468, 485, 490, 495, 506, 511, 517, 523, 544, 548, 553, 560, 567, 574, 580, 587, 600, 604, 609, 622, 626, 631, 636, 643, 660, 665, 670, 677, 684
student help with, 6, 81, 120, 135, 169, 193, 224, 230, 272, 292, 295, 318, 338, 413, 417, 437, 451, 571, 577, 620, 658, 665
Rhombus, 386
Right angle, 375, 382
symbol for, 33, 375
Right triangle, 382
area of, 451–453
converse of the Pythagorean theorem and, 444–447
45°-45°-90°, 456–460
hypotenuse of, 442, 443
indirect measurement and, 450, 452–453
legs of, 442, 443
perimeter of, 451–453
Pythagorean theorem and, 442–447, 450–453
Pythagorean triple and, 451, 452
30°-60°-90°, 457–460
trigonometric ratios and, 461–469
Rise, vertical change, 568, 570
Rotation, 410–413
coordinate notation for, 410–411
in the coordinate plane, 410–413
tessellation and, 414–415
Rounding
to approximate square root, 432–436
to check answers are reasonable, 251, 252
definition of, 705
to estimate, 711, 716
game, 3
to a place value, 705

Rule(s)
for adding integers, 59
of exponents, 196–200
Ruler, using, 720
Run, horizontal change, 568, 570

S

Sales tax, 343–346
Sample(s), 644–645
biased, 644–645
random, 644
Scaffolding, *See* Problem solving
Scale
definition of, 324
for a drawing, 321
misleading graphs and, 612–613
for a model, 324, 325
proportion and, 324–326
Scale drawing, making, 321
Scale factor, 418–421
Scale model, 324, 325
Scalene triangle, 382
Scatter plot
on a graphing calculator, 610
interpreting, 545–548
making, 545–548
Scientific notation, 205–209
multiplying numbers in, 206–209
standard form numbers and, 205–209
Segment
definition of, 718
drawing with a compass, 722
length on the coordinate plane, 92–95
Sequences, *See* Patterns
Short response questions, *See* Problem solving
Side(s)
congruent, 397–401
corresponding, 377, 397–401
included, 398
of a polygon, 390
of a right triangle
adjacent, 463
hypotenuse, 442, 443, 463
opposite, 463
of a triangle, classifying by, 382–383
Side-angle-side congruence, 398–401
Side-side-side congruence, 398–401
Side view
of a solid, 493, 496–497
drawing, 496–497
Sieve of Eratosthenes, 167
Similarity, 416–421
Similar polygons, 416–421
Simple interest, 348–350
Simplifying fractions, 179–183, 198, 220–222
Simulation, 637–638
Sine ratio, 462–468
Skill Check, *Occurs at the beginning of each lesson*
Skills Review Handbook, 704–726
data displays
bar graphs, 724
line graphs, 725
line plots, 723
decimals
adding, 709
dividing, 715
multiplication by a whole number, 714
rounding, 705
subtracting, 709
estimation
differences, 711
products, 716
quotients, 716
sums, 711
fractions
adding, 710
multiplying, 713
subtracting, 710
geometry
angles, 719
lines, 718
planes, 718
points, 718
improper fractions, mixed numbers and, 707
logical reasoning, 726
measurement
using a compass, 722
using a protractor, 721
using a ruler, 720
mixed numbers, improper fractions and, 707
number sense
divisibility tests, 706
place value, 704
rounding, 705
problem solving
using addition and subtraction, 712
using multiplication and division, 717
rate, 708
ratio, 708
Venn diagrams, 726
Slant height
of a cone, 508
of a pyramid, 507
Slope
line, 568–574
definition of, 570
negative, 571, 572
positive, 571, 572
undefined, 571, 572
zero, 571, 572
Slope-intercept form, 575–580
Solid(s), *See also* specific solids; Surface area; Volume
bases of, 492
classifying, 492, 494
composite, 495, 496–497, 506
definition of, 492
drawing, 493–497
edges of, 492–493
faces of, 492–493
vertices of, 492–493
views of, 493, 496–497
Solution
of an equation, 28
in two variables, 549
of a linear inequality, 583
of a system of linear equations, 581
Solve a related/simpler problem, problem solving strategy, 616–617, 622
Solving equations, *See* Equations
Spatial reasoning, *See also* Drawing; Graphs; Modeling
algebra tiles, 28, 107–108, 117–118, 278, 661, 673
area of a circle, 486
area of a parallelogram, 481
area of a trapezoid, 482
classifying angles, 382–385
classifying triangles, 382–385
diameter and circumference, 288–289
drawing, solids, 493–497
geometric probability, 652–653
nets, 502–505, 507, 508, 510, 518
reflection, 404–408
similarity, 416–421
stem-and-leaf plots, 597–600
surface area, 502–511
tessellation, 414–415
translation, 409, 411–413
tree diagram, 618–622
Venn diagram, 242, 437, 726
vertical line test, 681

volume
of a cone, 520
of a cylinder, 514
of a pyramid, 519
of a rectangular prism, 513
Sphere, 492
center of, 492
surface area of, 510
volume of, 679
Spreadsheet
for comparing radii of circles, 491
for solving inequalities, 300
Square, 386
area of, 33–37
perimeter of, 33–37
ratio of side length to perimeter, 317
square root and side length, 431
Square root, 431–436
approximating, 432–436
definition of, 431
equation, 433–435
finding, 744
of a fraction, 435
game, 436
negative, 431
perfect square and, 432
positive, 431
radical sign, 431
table of, 745
Squares
finding, 744
table of, 745
Standard form
of a number, 205–207, 704
of a polynomial, 657–660
Standardized test practice, *See* Assessment; Test-taking skills; Test-taking strategies
Statistics, *See also* Graphs; Plots
analyzing data, 255–256
choosing a representative average, 258–261
game, 261
collecting data, 255–256
lower extreme, 601
lower quartile, 601
mean, 75, 255–261
median, 255–261
mode, 255–261
outliers, 604
range, 258–261
upper extreme, 601
upper quartile, 601
Stem(s), in a stem-and-leaf plot, 597
Stem-and-leaf plot, 597–600
choosing a data display, 606, 608–609
double, 598–600
interpreting, 598–600
making, 597–600
Stop and Think exercises, *See* Thinking skills
Straight angle, 375
Straightedge, 380–381, 396, 722
Strategies, *See* Problem-solving strategies; Test-taking strategies
Student help
with homework, 7, 12, 18, 22, 30, 36, 41, 55, 61, 65, 72, 76, 83, 88, 93, 111, 115, 121, 126, 137, 143, 148, 171, 176, 182, 188, 199, 203, 207, 222, 226, 232, 237, 245, 249, 253, 259, 274, 280, 284, 293, 297, 304, 319, 325, 329, 334, 340, 345, 349, 356, 378, 384, 388, 392, 400, 407, 412, 419, 434, 440, 446, 452, 459, 466, 483, 488, 494, 505, 510, 516, 522, 543, 547, 551, 559, 566, 573, 579, 599, 603, 608, 621, 625, 630, 635, 642, 659, 664, 669, 676, 682
with notetaking, 21, 86, 146, 219, 244, 282, 328, 386, 443, 486, 565, 629, 674
with reading, 16, 29, 33, 39, 54, 302, 351, 383, 390, 398, 410, 433, 482, 515, 633, 681
with review, 6, 81, 120, 135, 169, 193, 224, 230, 272, 292, 295, 318, 338, 413, 417, 437, 451, 571, 577, 620, 658, 665
with solving problems, 10, 56, 71, 81, 87, 92, 113, 120, 125, 141, 180, 192, 195, 205, 220, 235, 283, 291, 292, 322, 332, 343, 355, 377, 381, 431, 444, 457, 463, 497, 507, 514, 542, 550, 557, 582, 583, 584, 585, 598, 601, 605, 612, 623, 624, 632
with technology, 14, 209, 300, 464, 469, 504, 685
with vocabulary, 34, 82, 173, 348, 411, 492, 493, 570, 675
Substitution
to check equations, 29, 113, 114, 119, 120, 124, 276, 296, 323, 542, 550, 581
to solve linear systems, 582
Subtraction
checking with addition, 709
decimal, 247–250, 709
equations, 108–112
modeling, 108
estimating differences, 711
of exponents to divide powers, 197–200
of fractions
common denominators, 219–223, 710
different denominators, 224–227
integer, 63–67
as inverse of addition, 109
of mixed numbers
common denominators, 219–223
different denominators, 225–227
order of operations and, 10–14
polynomial, 662–665
properties
equality, 109
inequality, 141
to solve inequalities, 141–145
words indicating, 16
Subtraction property of equality, 109
Subtraction property of inequality, 141
Supplementary angles, 375
Support Materials, 2B, 50B, 104B, 164B, 216B, 268B, 314B, 372B, 428B, 478B, 538B, 594B, 654B
Surface area
of a cone, 508–511
of a cylinder, 504–506
of a prism, 502–506
of a pyramid, 507–511
of a sphere, 510
Survey
questions, 644–645
biased, 645
samples and, 644–645
Symbols, table of, 740
Symmetry, 406–408
line of, 406
System of linear equations, 581–582
solution of, 581

t

Table(s)
data, 32, 199, 243, 260, 288, 390, 545–548
frequency, 6–9, 256
for graphing linear equations, 556–561
input-output, 541–544
patterns and, 68, 69
representing functions, 541–544
Table of formulas, 742
Table of measures, 741
Table of properties, 743
Table of squares and square roots, 745

Table of symbols, 740
Tally chart, *See* Frequency table
Tally mark, 6
Tangent ratio, 462–468
inverse, 469
Teaching Tip, 12, 21, 27, 30, 34, 55, 61, 69, 76, 83, 86, 93, 122, 133, 137, 138, 144, 148, 180, 182, 194, 222, 229, 237, 245, 249, 259, 277, 283, 319, 324, 328, 332, 334, 340, 343, 345, 349, 353, 377, 380, 381, 384, 403, 407, 411, 415, 418, 435, 438, 444, 449, 452, 459, 466, 467, 497, 501, 514, 516, 522, 552, 555, 566, 579, 582, 608, 613, 617, 624, 642, 645, 667, 679, 683
Technology, *See also* Calculator; Graphing calculator; Technology activities
student help with, 14, 209, 300, 464, 469, 504, 685
Technology activities
calculator
compound interest, 351
finding an angle measure, 469
integer operations, 90
operations with fractions, 239
using order of operations, 14
using scientific notation, 209
simulation using the random function, 638
computer
comparing radii of circles, 491
solving inequalities, 300
graphing calculator
graphing linear functions, 561
graphing non-linear functions, 685
making data displays, 610, 611
internet, searching for information, 129
Terminating decimal(s), 242–246
irrational numbers and, 437
rational numbers and, 437
Term(s)
of an expression, 86
constant, 86
like, 86
Tessellation, 414–415
Test practice, *See* Assessment; Review; Test-taking strategies
Test-taking skills
building, 156–157, 364–365, 530–531, 692–693
practicing, 158–162, 366–370, 532–536, 694–698
strategies for extended response questions, 692–693
strategies for multiple choice questions, 156–157
context based, 530–531
strategies for short response questions, 364–365
Test-taking strategies, 49, 101, 155, 215, 267, 311, 363, 427, 475, 529, 593, 651, 691
Theoretical probability, 354, 355–357, *See also* Probability
Thinking skills, *See also* Critical thinking; Error analysis
Stop and Think, 3, 25, 32, 45, 51, 79, 97, 105, 108, 118, 131, 151, 165, 167, 178, 191, 211, 217, 241, 256, 263, 269, 287, 289, 307, 315, 321, 337, 359, 373, 395, 396, 423, 429, 442, 455, 462, 471, 479, 499, 512, 518, 525, 539, 563, 569, 576, 589, 595, 615, 638, 647, 655, 672, 673, 687
30°-60°-90° right triangle, 457–460
Three-dimensional figure, 492–495, *See also* Solids
Tiling patterns, *See* Tessellation
Tip, percent, 344–346
Tips for New Teachers, *Occurs in each lesson*
Top view
of a solid, 493, 496–497
drawing, 496–497
Transformations
reflection, 404–408
rotation, 410–413
tessellation and, 414–415
translation, 409, 411–413
Translating
verbal phrases, 16
verbal sentences, 302–305
Translation, 409, 411–413
coordinate notation for, 409
in the coordinate plane, 94, 409, 411–413
tessellation and, 414–415
Trapezoid, 386
area of, 482–485
bases of, 482
height of, 482
Tree diagram
as a counting method, 618–622
factor tree, 169, 171
Triangle(s), *See also* Right triangle
acute, 382
angle-side-angle congruence, 398–401
area of, 134–139
base of, 134
classifying, 382–385
congruent, 397–401
copying, 396
equiangular, 385
equilateral, 382
height of, 134
isosceles, 382
obtuse, 382
perimeter of, 134, 136–139, 279
right, 382
scalene, 382
side-angle-side congruence, 398–401
side-side-side congruence, 398–401
sum of angle measures, 383
game, 429
Triangular numbers, 617
Trigonometric ratio, 461–469
cosine, 462–468
game, 471
inverse of, 469
sine, 462–468
tangent, 462–468
Trinomial, 657
Truth function, 300
Two-dimensional figures, *See* Geometry
Two-step equations
modeling, 117–118
solving, 117–123
writing, 124–128

Undefined slope, 571, 572
Unfavorable outcome, 633
Unit analysis, 40, 80
Unit rate, 318–320
definition of, 318
Upper extreme, 601
Upper quartile, 601

Variable(s)
on both sides of an equation, 278–281
coefficient of, 86
definition of, 15
equations in two, 549–553
in formulas, 33–37
Variable equation, *See also* Equations
solution of, 28

Variable expression(s), 15–19
definition of, 15
evaluating, 16–19, 64–67, 71–73, 75–77, 86–89, 181–183, 231–233
integer, 64–67
game, 19
simplifying, 180–183, 202–204, 225–227
writing, 16–19
Venn diagram
definition of, 726
drawing, 726
real number, 437
to show number relationships, 242, 726
Verbal model
definition of, 11
examples, 14, 38, 39, 75, 92, 111, 112, 126, 132, 179, 236, 253, 274, 275, 276, 304
writing to solve problems, 11, 29, 80, 110, 114, 115, 119, 124, 125, 129, 131, 136, 142, 147, 225, 236, 271, 273, 278, 282, 296, 297, 301, 303, 307, 324, 342, 507, 578, 663
Verbal phrases
indicating inequality, 302
translating, 16, 28
Verbal sentences, translating, 302–305
Vertex (vertices)
of an angle, 719
of a polyhedron, 492–495
Vertical angles, 376
Vertical line, graph of, 558–560
Vertical line test, 681
Views of a solid, 493, 496–497
Visualize, 16, 81, 110, 187, 272, 333, 364, 376, 432, 489, 572, 628, 658, 692
Volume
comparing, 518
of a cone, 520–523
formula, 520
of a cylinder, 514–517
formula, 514
of a prism, 512–518
formula, 513
of a pyramid, 519–523
formula, 519
of a sphere, 679
formula, 679

What do you think?, 17, 29, 36, 42, 64, 66, 75, 123, 136, 147, 171, 193, 222, 246, 291, 298, 324, 339, 350, 393, 400, 447, 489, 521, 557, 602, 604, 660, 670
Whole number
definition of, 704
place value, 704
rounding, 705
Work backward
problem solving strategy, 276–277
exercises, 116, 280, 677, 683
Writing
using coordinate notation, 404–405
decimals
as fractions, 243–246
as percents, 332–335
equations, 114, 124–128, 578–580
equivalent fractions, 180–183
equivalent ratios, 317–320
formula for circumference, 289
fractions
as decimals, 242–246
with different denominators, 224–227
as percents, 331
a function rule, 542–544
improper fractions as mixed numbers, 193–195, 707
inequalities, 296–300, 301–305
mixed numbers as improper fractions, 193–195, 707
multi-step equations, 271–275
multi-step inequalities, 296–300, 301–305
a number
in expanded form, 704
in scientific notation, 205–209
in standard form, 704
percents
as decimals, 332–335
as fractions, 332–335
products as powers, 20–23
proportions, 322–326
rates, 318–320, 708
ratios, 317–320, 708
repeating decimals as fractions, 224
scientific notation in standard form, 206–209
two-step equations, 124–128
unbiased survey questions, 645
variable expressions, 16–19
Writing in Mathematics, exercises, 3, 7, 18, 23, 31, 42, 57, 61, 76, 83, 89, 97, 105, 108, 112, 118, 127, 144, 149, 151, 165, 167, 171, 176, 178, 188, 189, 194, 203, 211, 217, 223, 227, 237, 241, 246, 254, 256, 260, 263, 287, 289, 293, 304, 307, 312, 315, 320, 337, 345, 349, 357, 373, 378, 385, 395, 396, 413, 420, 423, 429, 455, 460, 466, 471, 479, 494, 523, 525, 539, 544, 548, 560, 563, 573, 586, 587, 595, 599, 615, 621, 630, 638, 647, 655, 672, 677, 687

***x*-axis,** 91
reflection in, 405
***x*-coordinate,** 91
***x*-intercept,** 564

***y*-axis,** 91
reflection in, 405
***y*-coordinate,** 91
***y*-intercept,** 564

Zero
as an exponent, 202
as an integer, 53
division by, 74
multiplication property of, 71
as a place holder, 247, 252
slope, 571, 572
square root for, 431

Additional Answers

Chapter 1

1.1 Getting Ready to Practice (p. 7)

5. Steps 2–3:

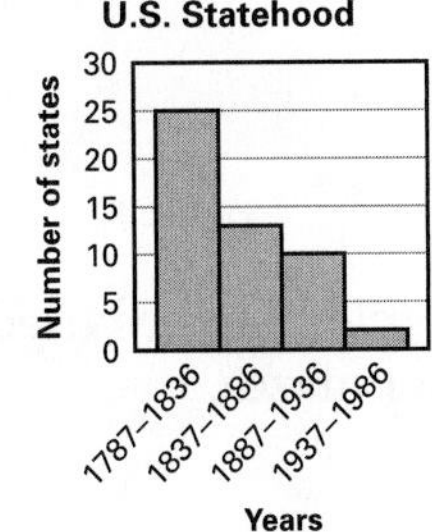

1.1 Test-Taking Practice (p. 9)

32.

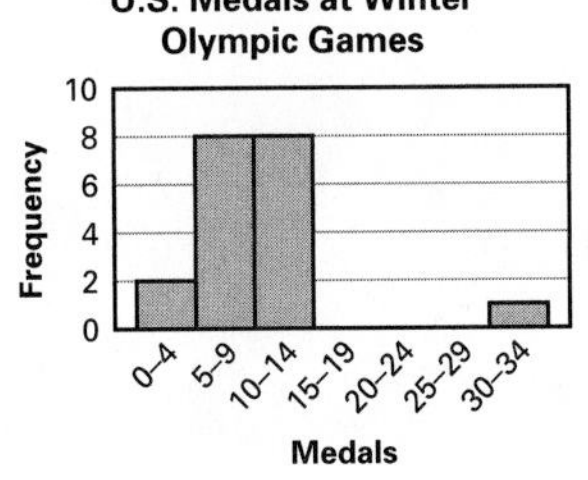

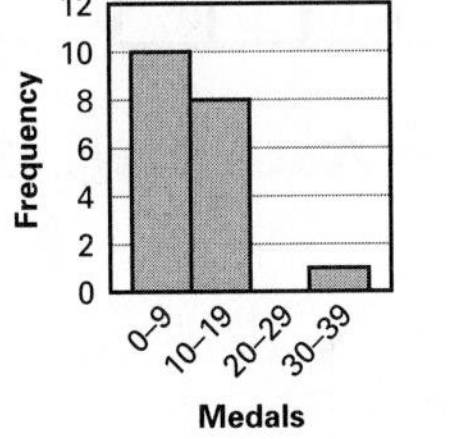

1.5 In-lesson Activity (p. 28)

1. **2.** **3.**

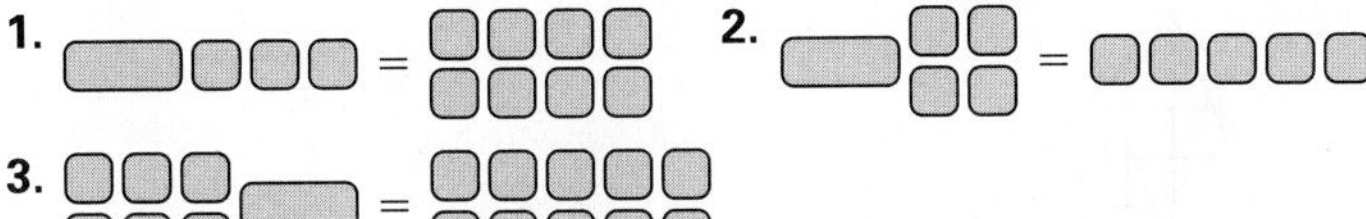

1.7 Practice and Problem Solving (pp. 41–42)

6.

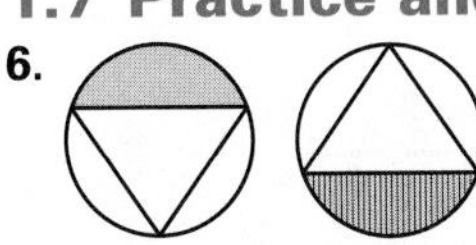

Chapter 2

2.2 Hands-on Activity (p. 57)

11. Negative. *Sample answer:* A negative number lies to the left of 0 on the number line. As shown in the number line below, which illustrates $-5 + (-4) = -9$, adding a second negative number moves the result even farther to the left, so the sum is negative.

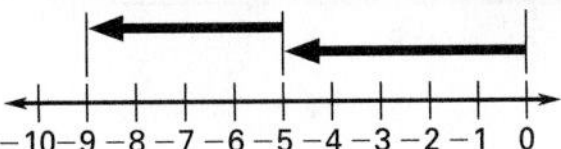

2.5 Practice and Problem Solving (pp. 83–84)

30. *Sample answer:* Reorder the numbers, then group together pairs of numbers that are easy to add. For example, group 52 with 38, and group 99 with 11. Add these sums together, and add 65 to the result. The result is $(90 + 110) + 65 = 200 + 65 = 265$.

2.7 Test-Taking Practice (p. 89)

52. 25 ft; $200 - 2(60) = 80$, so each missing side is $0.5 \cdot 80$ ft $= 40$ feet. Then $10 + 5 + x = 40$, or $15 + x = 40$, and $x = 25$ feet. To find the area, multiply the length by the width, which gives $40(60) = 2400$, or multiply each section of the length by the width and add the results: $10(60) + 25(60) + 5(60) = 600 + 1500 + 300 = 2400$. The area is 2400 square feet.

2.8 Your turn now (p. 92)

4–7.

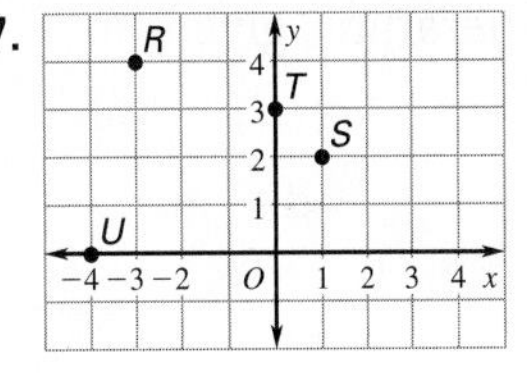

8. A, B, C, D

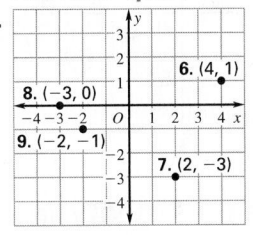

2.8 Getting Ready to Practice (p. 93)

1.

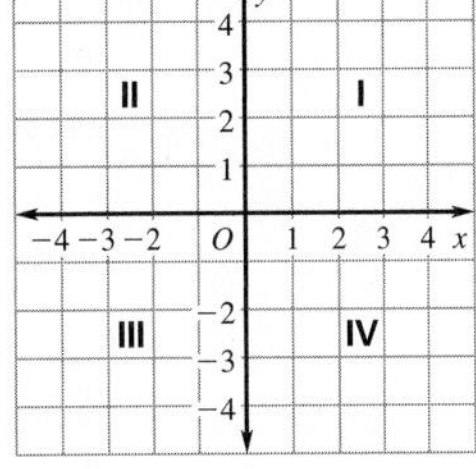

6–9. 6. (4, 1) 7. (2, −3) 8. (−3, 0) 9. (−2, −1)

2.8 Practice and Problem Solving (pp. 93–94)

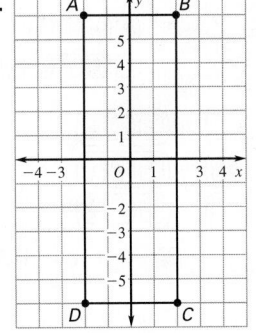

17–20.

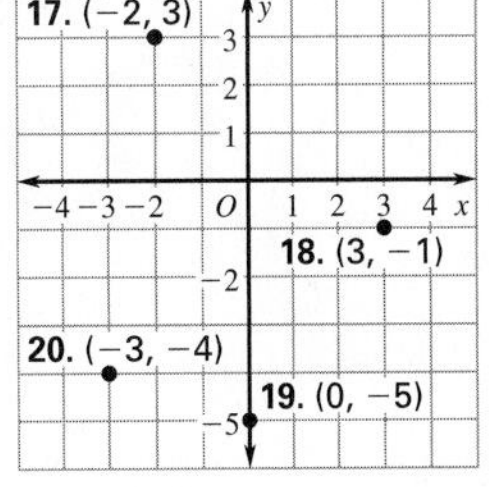

21. A, B, C, D

22.

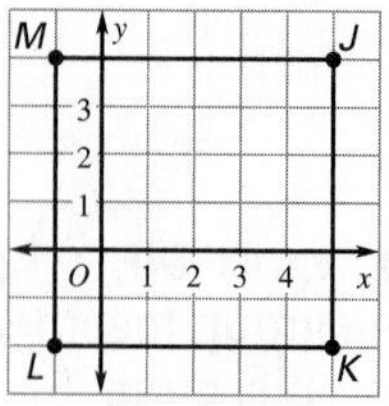

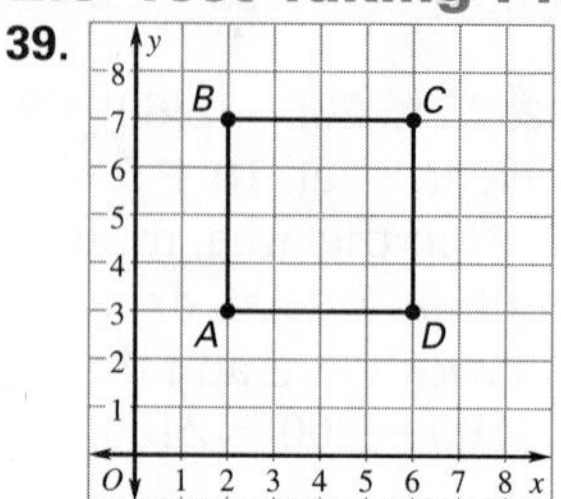

2.8 Test-Taking Practice (p. 95)

39.

Exploring Math in Science (pp. 102–103)

4. No; 36°C is much greater than all of the other temperatures given, so it distorts the mean.

Chapter 3

3.1 Mixed Review (p. 112)

40–43.

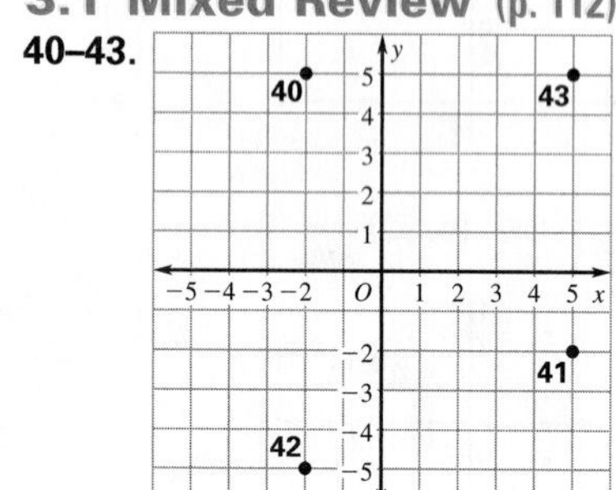

3.3 Hands-on Activity (pp. 117–118)

1. Step 1:

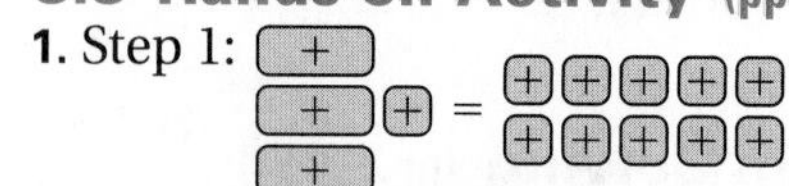

Step 2:

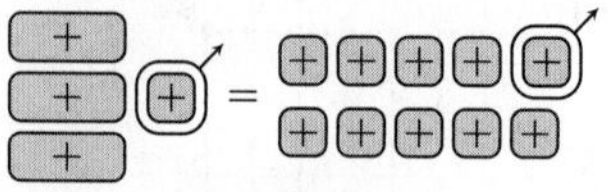

Step 3:

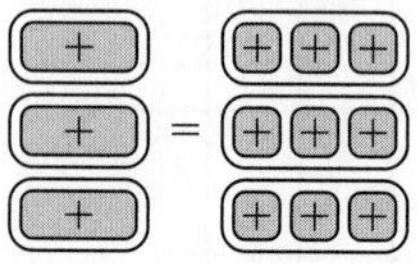

Step 4: 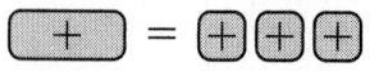 $x = 3$; $3(3) + 1 = 9 + 1 = 10$ ✓

3.5 Problem Solving Strategies (p. 133)

4. The available area is 1000 square feet greater when the bleachers are closed (6200 ft^2 closed versus 5200 ft^2 open). **5.** the room where students share tables

7.

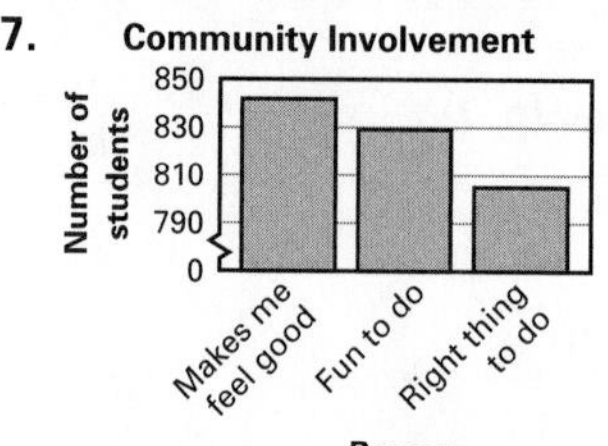

9. 96 ft;

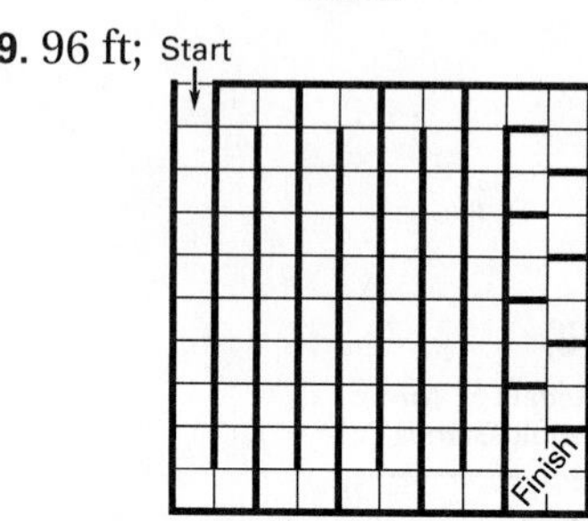

Sample answer: I tried drawing other mazes.

3.5 In-lesson Activity (p. 134)

Step 3.

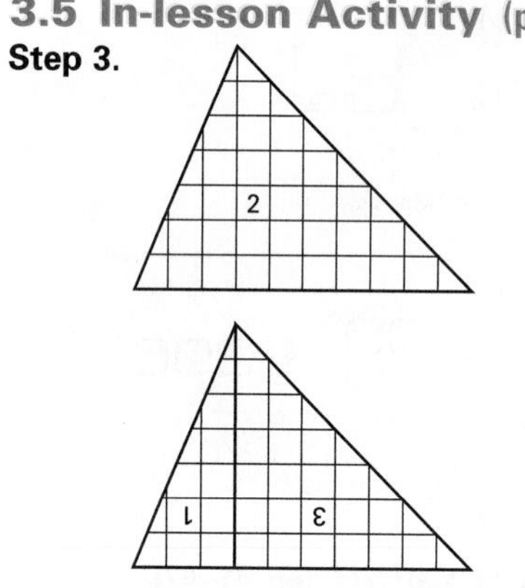

3.6 Your turn now (p. 140)

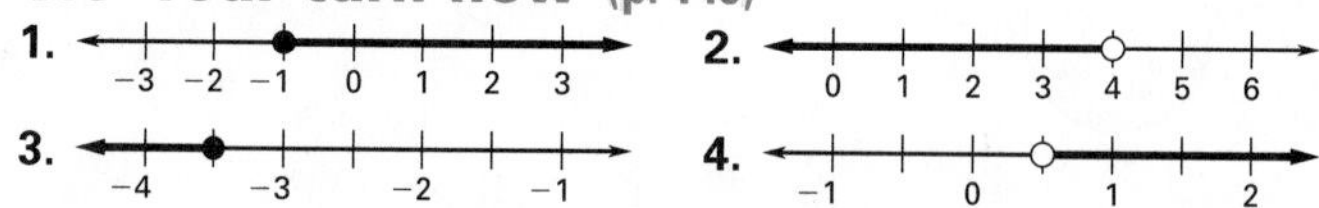

1. **2.** **3.** **4.**

3.6 Practice and Problem Solving (pp. 143–145)

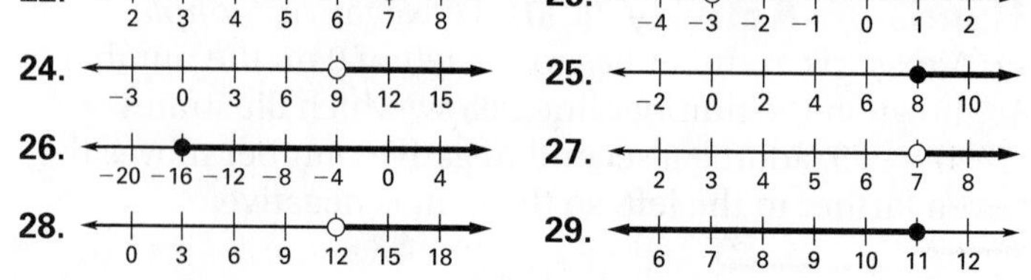

22. 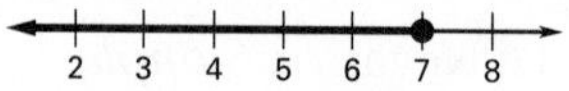 **23.** 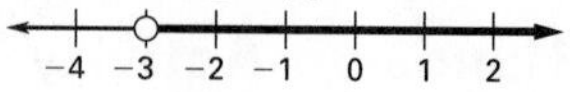 **24.** **25.** **26.** **27.** **28.** **29.**

30. 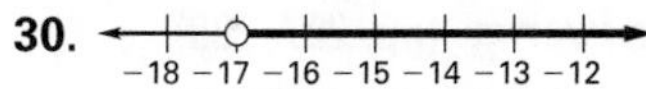

34. 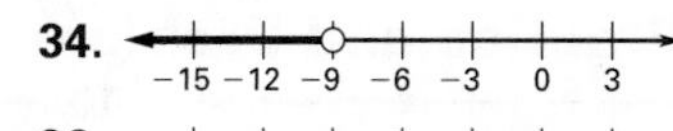

35. 5 6 7 8

36. 4 5 6 7

37. −1 0 1 2 3 4 5

38. −3 −2 −1 0

39. 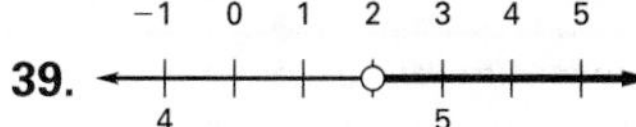

3.7 Getting Ready to Practice (p. 148)

4. 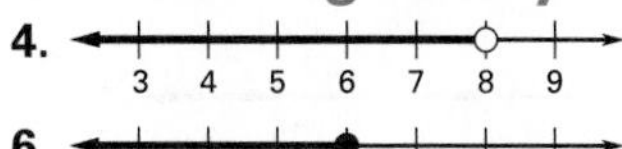

5. 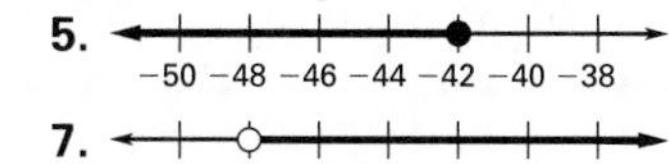

6. −6 −5 −4 −3 −2 −1 0

7. −6 −5 −4 −3 −2 −1 0

3.7 Practice and Problem Solving (pp. 148–149)

13. 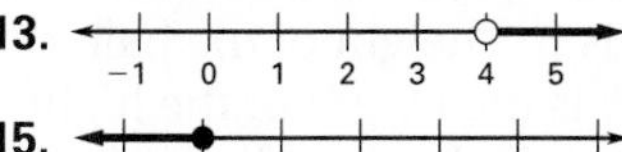

14. 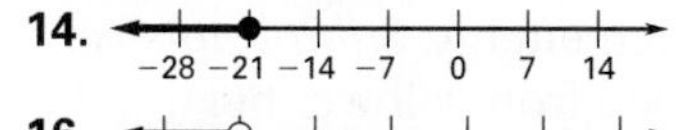

15. −480 −360 −240 −120 0 120 240

16. −132 −99 −66 −33 0 33 66

17. 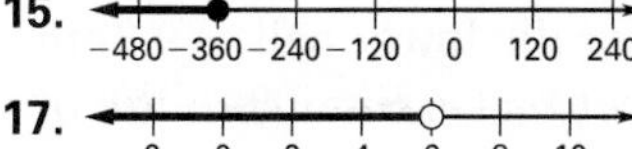

18. −6 −5 −4 −3 −2 −1 0

19. 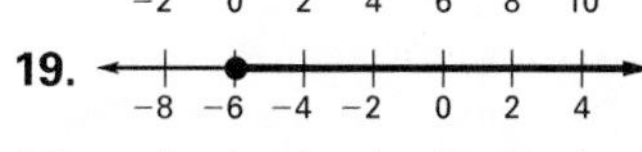

20. −5 −4 −3 −2 −1 0 1

21. −70 −56 −42 −28 −14 0 14

22. −8 −6 −4 −2 0 2 4

23. −2 −1 0 1 2 3 4

24. −378 −374 −370

27. −5 −4 −3 −2 −1 0 1

28. −6 −3 0 3 6 9 12

29. −2 −1 0 1 2 3 4

30. −8 −7 −6 −5 −4 −3 −2

31. −12 −11 −10 −9 −8 −7 −6

32. −4 −3 −2 −1 0 1 2

3.7 Mixed Review (p. 149)

45. 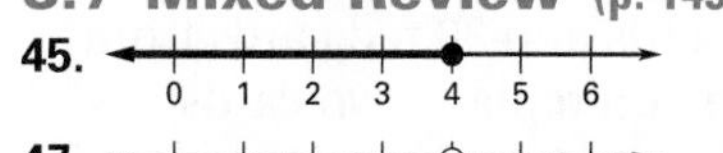

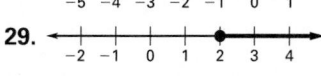

46. 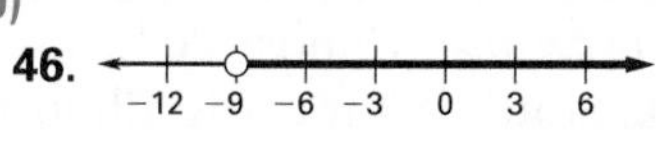

47. 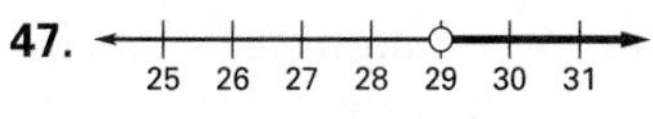

Chapter 4

4.1 Hands-on Activity (p. 167)

Steps 4–5. 1 (2) (3) ~~4~~ (5) ~~6~~ (7) ~~8~~ ~~9~~ ~~10~~
(11) ~~12~~ (13) ~~14~~ ~~15~~ ~~16~~ (17) ~~18~~ (19) ~~20~~
~~21~~ ~~22~~ (23) ~~24~~ ~~25~~ ~~26~~ ~~27~~ ~~28~~ (29) ~~30~~
(31) ~~32~~ ~~33~~ ~~34~~ ~~35~~ ~~36~~ (37) ~~38~~ ~~39~~ ~~40~~
(41) ~~42~~ (43) ~~44~~ ~~45~~ ~~46~~ (47) ~~48~~ ~~49~~ ~~50~~
~~51~~ ~~52~~ (53) ~~54~~ ~~55~~ ~~56~~ ~~57~~ ~~58~~ (59) ~~60~~

3. Prime. *Sample answer:* All composite numbers will be crossed out because they are multiples of smaller whole numbers.

4.3 Hands-on Activity (p. 178)

1. 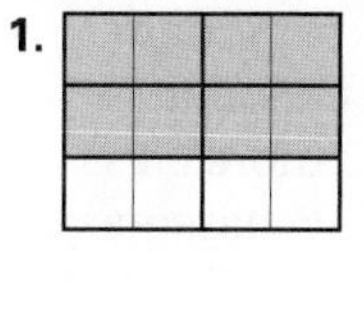

2. 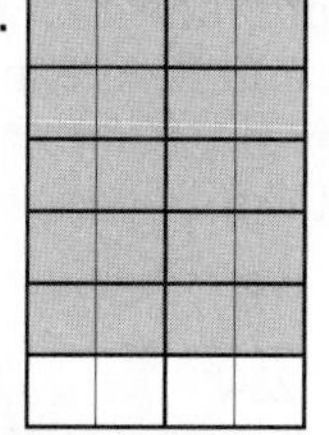

3. 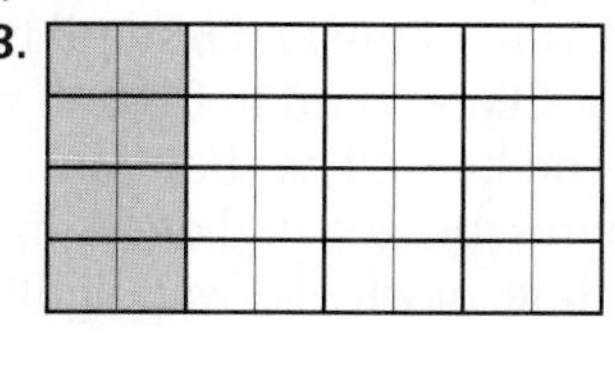

4. 

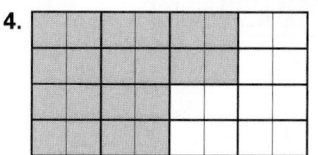

4.3 Mixed Review (p. 183)

61. **62.** **63.**

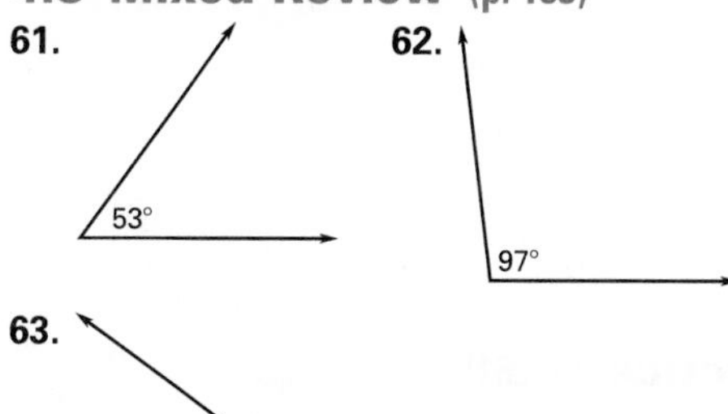

4.4 Practice and Problem Solving (pp. 188–189)

8. multiples of 4: 4, 8, 12; multiples of 6: 6, 12; LCM: 12
9. multiples of 6: 6, 12, 18, 24, 30, 36, 42; multiples of 21: 21, 42; LCM: 42 **10.** multiples of 8: 8, 16, 24, 32, 40; multiples of 10: 10, 20, 30, 40; LCM: 40 **11.** multiples of 10: 10, 20, 30; multiples of 15: 15, 30; LCM: 30

Chapter 5

5.3 Problem Solving Strategies (p. 229)

3. 3 bows. *Sample answer:* Let one floor tile represent $\frac{1}{6}$ of a yard. Mark off $13 \cdot 5 = 65$ tiles to represent the amount of ribbon needed to decorate 5 gifts. Mark off 120 tiles to represent the amount of ribbon you have. The difference, 55 tiles, represents the length of ribbon left from which to make bows. Since 15 tiles represent the amount of ribbon needed to make a bow and $55 \div 15 = 3\frac{2}{3}$, 3 bows can be made with the remaining ribbon.

4. 7 beads. *Sample answer:* Put 24 items in a bowl. Since $\frac{1}{6}$ of 24 is 4, count out 4 for Anna, and then count out 2 more for John. There are 18 items left, so count out $\frac{1}{9}$ of these, or 2, for Lena. There are 16 items remaining. Since $\frac{1}{4}$ of 16 is 4, count out 4 for Dawn, and then count out 5 for Jamal. There are 7 items left.

5. 16 students; eighth. *Sample answer:* I had 4 classmates stand in front of me and 6 stand behind me. Then I had another classmate stand in front of me, and then 2 more classmates stood behind her but in front of me. Then I had 2 more classmates join the end of the line. Counting showed 16 classmates in line, of which I was eighth.

5.4 In-lesson Activity (p. 234)

Step 3.

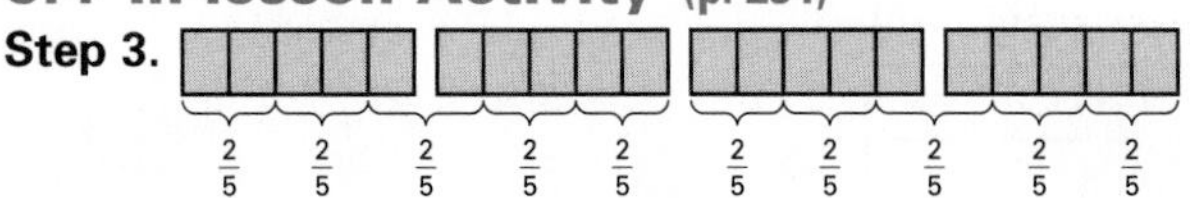

5.6 Test-Taking Practice (p. 250)

54.

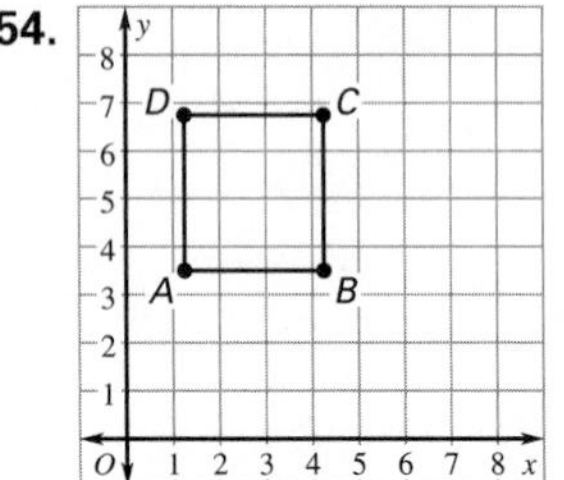

12.5 units

5.8 Test-Taking Practice (p. 261)

34.

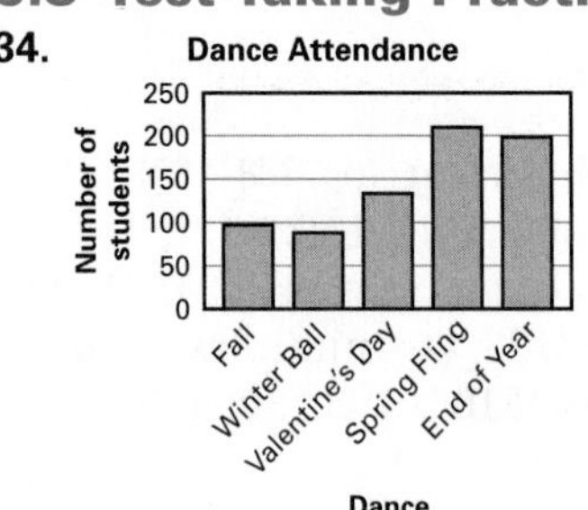

Chapter 6

6.4 Mixed Review (p. 294)

33–36.

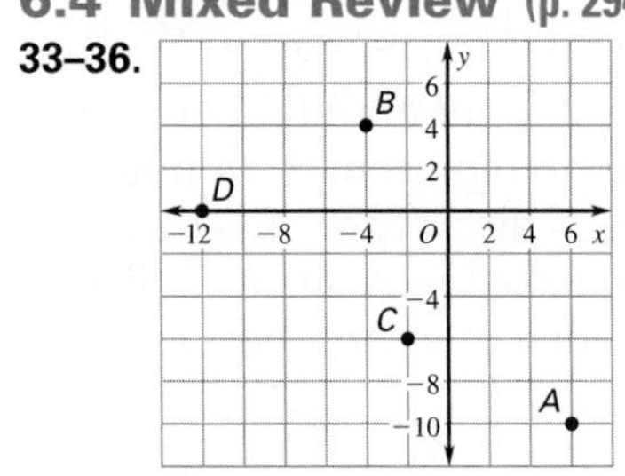

6.5 Getting Ready to Practice (p. 297)

6. **7.**

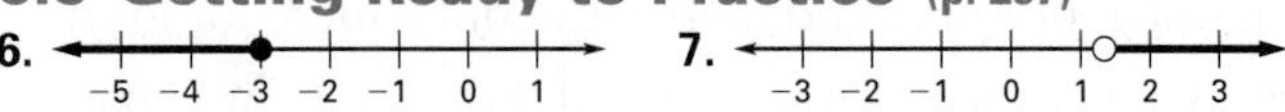

6.5 Practice and Problem Solving (pp. 297–298)

9.–**20.**

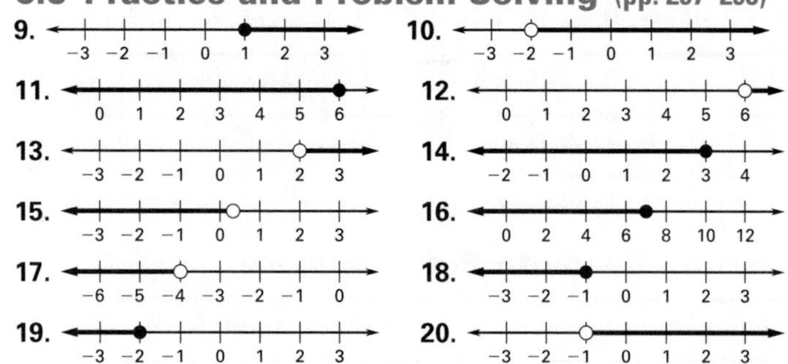

Exploring Math in Science (pp. 312–313)

5. The basketball dropped from twice as high will hit the ground with twice as much energy. *Sample answer:* If h is the height of the ball dropped from a lower height, then $2h$ is the height of the higher ball. The formula gives the energy E for the lower ball as $9.8mh$ while the energy formula for the higher ball is $E = 9.8m(2h)$, or $E = 2(9.8mh)$.

Chapter 7

7.4 Practice and Problem Solving (pp. 334–335)

57.

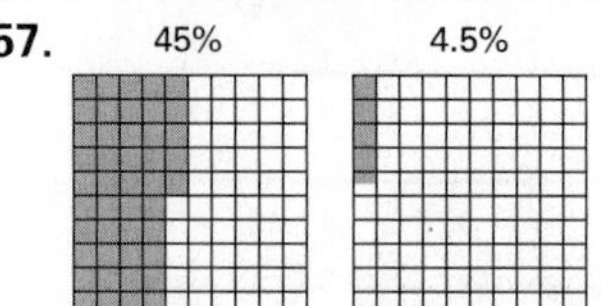

7.8 Problem Solving Strategies (p. 353)

4. 49 times. *Sample answer:* Choose 20 black cards and 20 red cards from a deck. Shuffle your cards. Choose and replace two cards 20 times and record the results. The ratio of matching colors in the experiment should match the ratio in the original situation of 100 drawings. Use this fact to write and solve a proportion.

Chapter 8

Special Topic Exercises (p. 381)

1–7. Sample answers are given.

1. **2.** **3.** **4.**

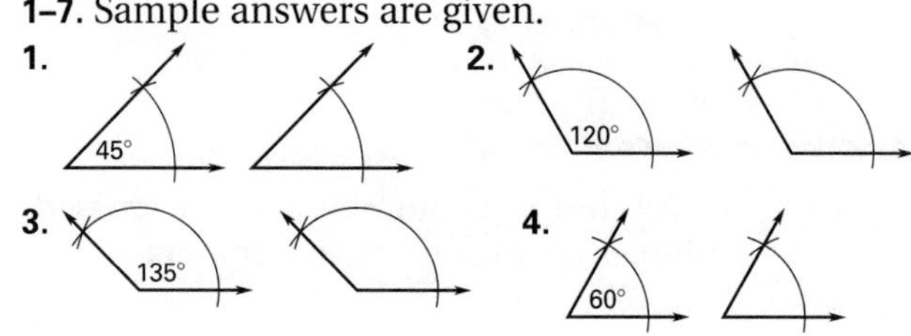

5. 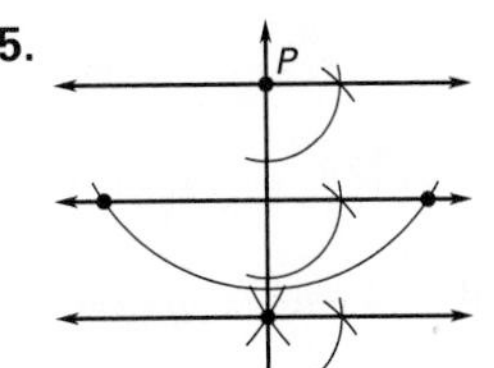

6. 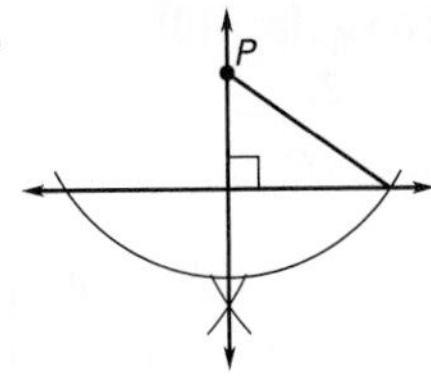

7. 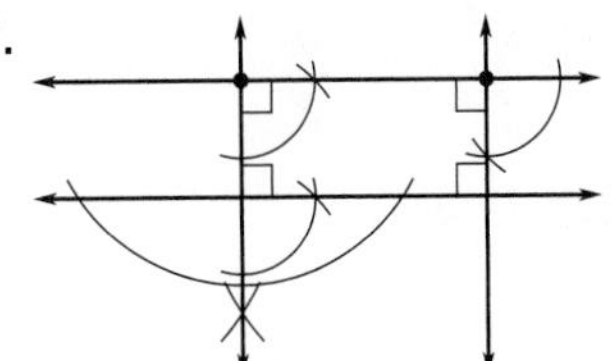

8.3 Mixed Review (p. 389)

30. 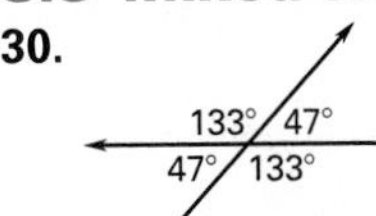

8.4 Practice and Problem Solving (pp. 392–393)

24. 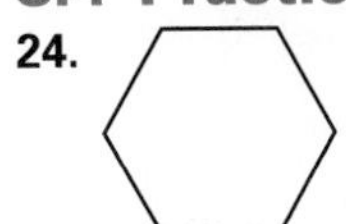

8.5 Hands-on Activity (p. 396)

1.–3. 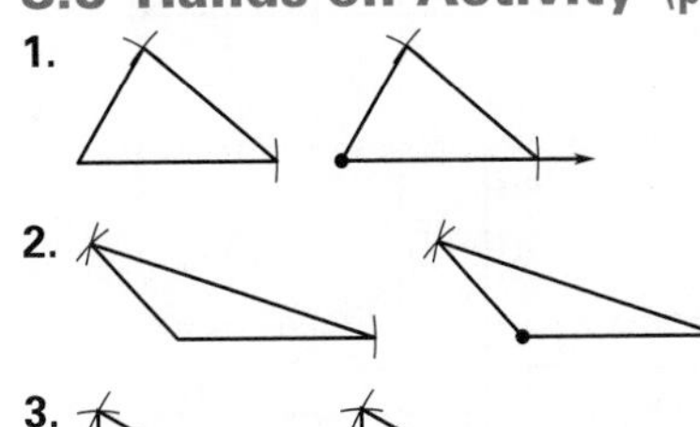

4. The measures of each angle of the triangle and its copy are the same. *Sample answer:* Each copy has the same side lengths as the original triangle, so the measures of its angles must also be the same.

8.5 Practice and Problem Solving (pp. 400–401)

18. *Sample answer:* Since the hexagons share a side and are regular, all of their sides are congruent. The angles are all congruent because the hexagons are regular. So, the hexagons are congruent.

8.5 Mixed Review (p. 401)

27–30. 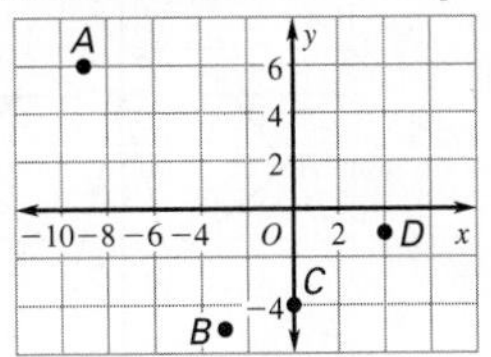

8.6 Problem Solving Strategies (p. 403)

4. *Sample answer:* Call the smallest box A, the next B, the next C, and the largest D. Call the tables 1, 2, and 3. (1) Move A to 3. (2) Move B to 2. (3) Move A to 2. (4) Move C to 3. (5) Move A to 1. (6) Move B to 3. (7) Move A to 3. (8) Move D to 2. (9) Move A to 2. (10) Move B to 1. (11) Move A to 1. (12) Move C to 2. (13) Move A to 3. (14) Move B to 2. (15) Move A to 2. 8. The problem is $271 + 546 = 817$.

8.6 Your turn now (p. 405)

1. 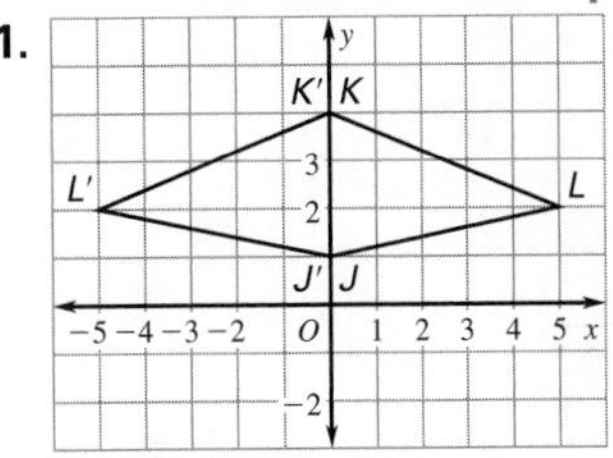

2. 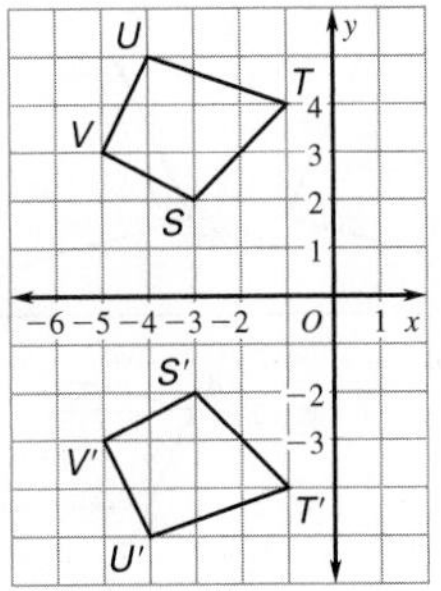

8.6 Getting Ready to Practice (p. 406)

10. 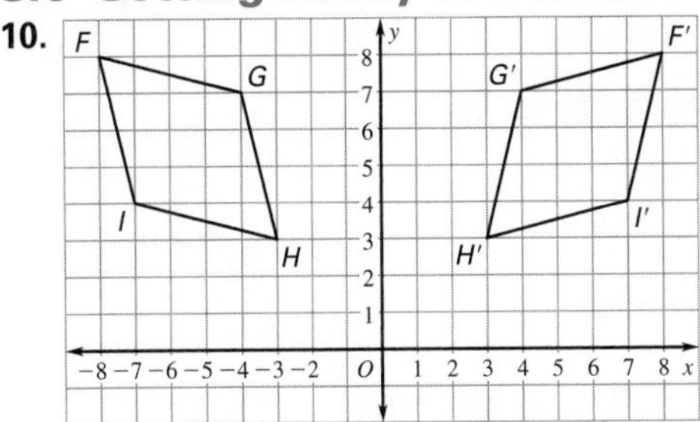

8.6 Practice and Problem Solving (pp. 407–408)

11. 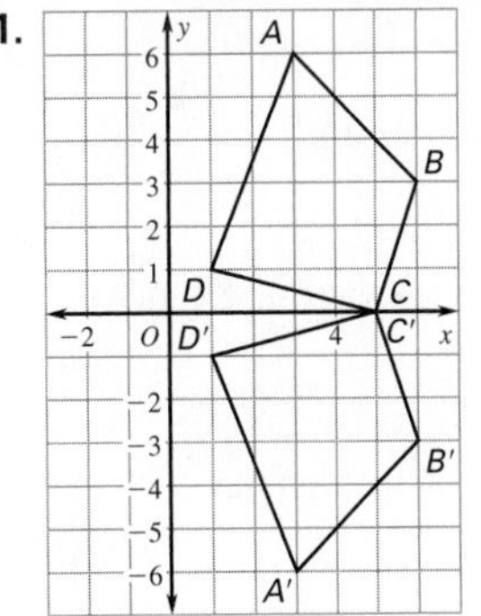

12. 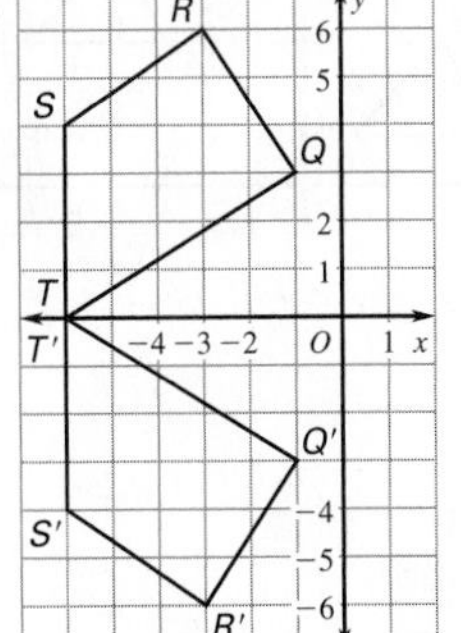

Additional Answers

13.

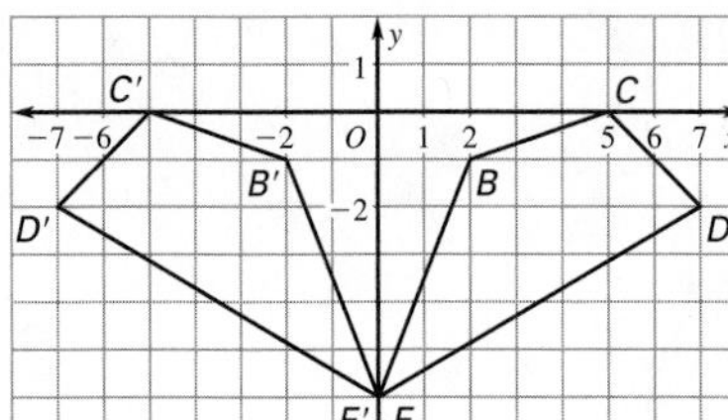

14.

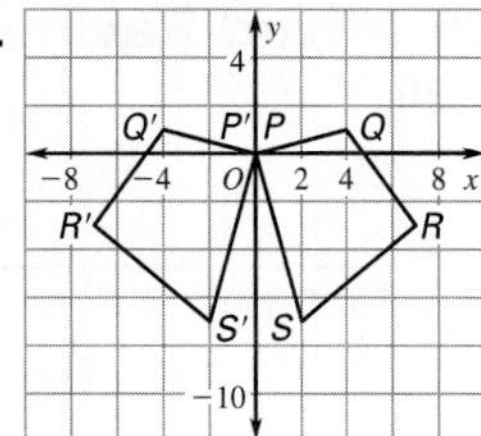

17.

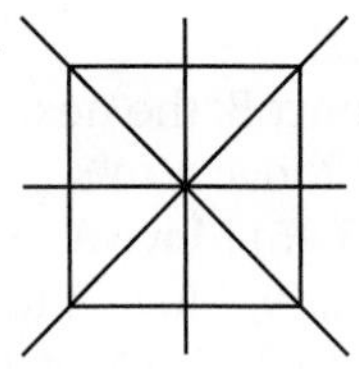

22.

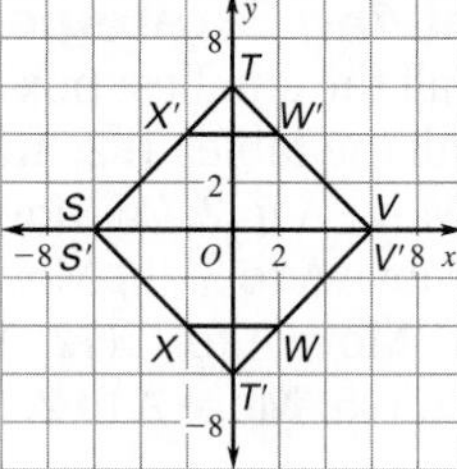

23.

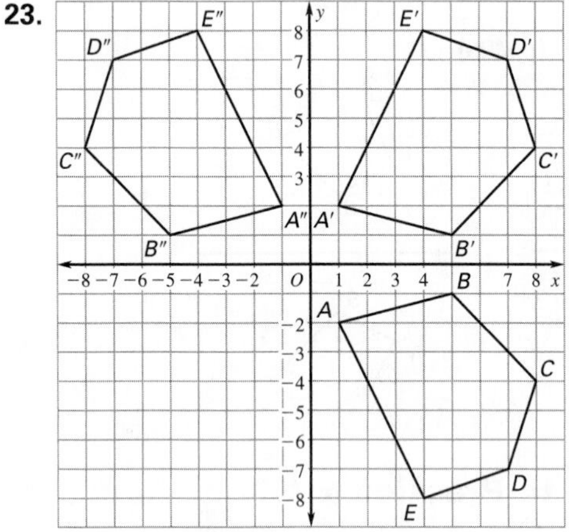

8.6 Test-Taking Practice (p. 408)

29.

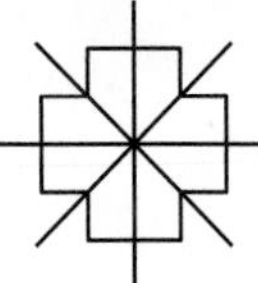

8.7 In-lesson Activity (p. 409)

Steps 1–2.

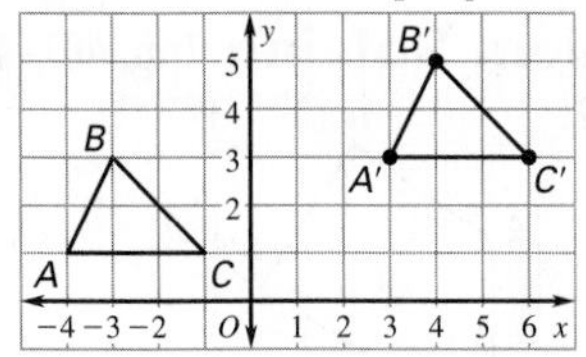

8.7 Your turn now (p. 410)

1.

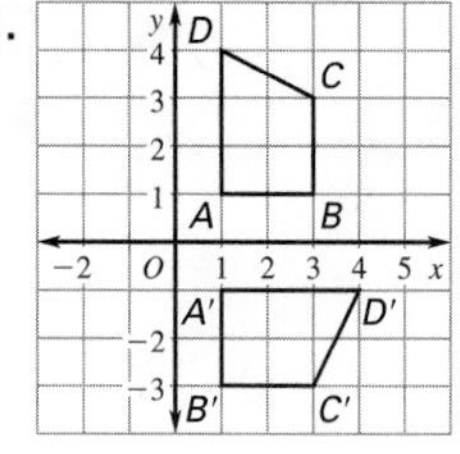

2.

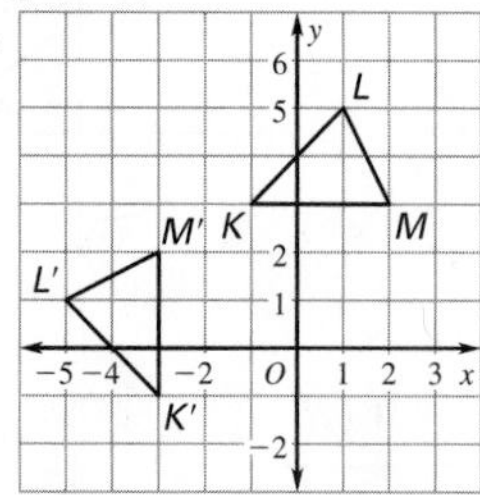

8.7 Getting Ready to Practice (p. 411)

4. Steps 1, 3:

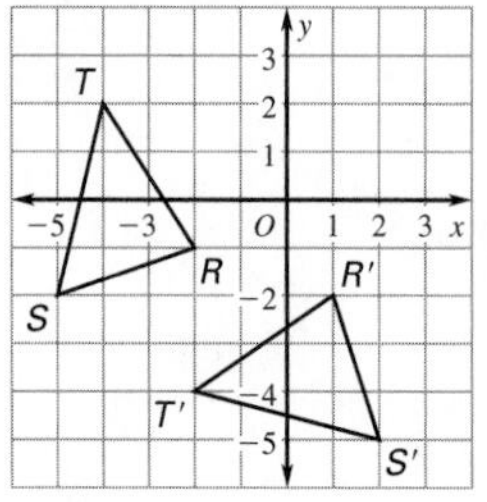

8.7 Practice and Problem Solving (pp. 412–413)

19.

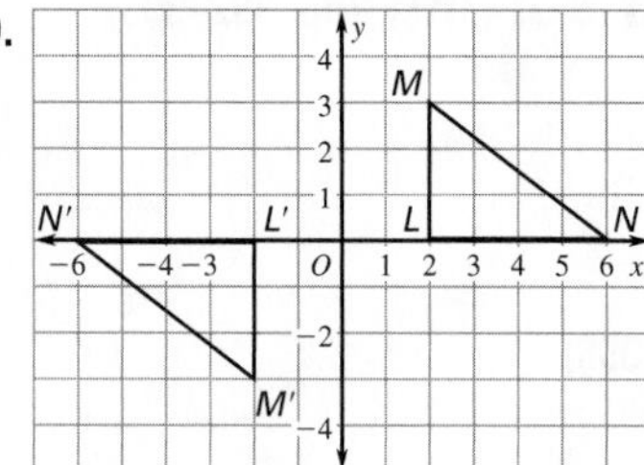

20.

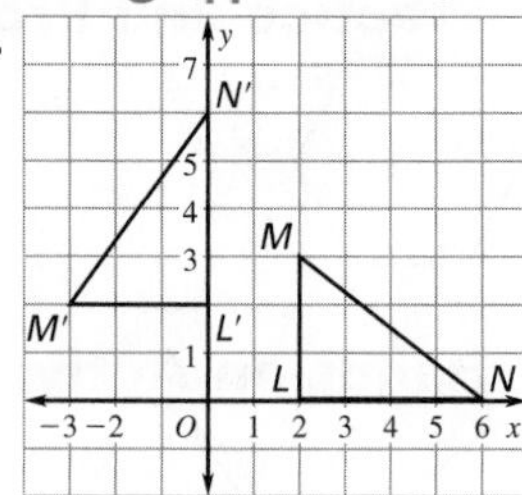

21.

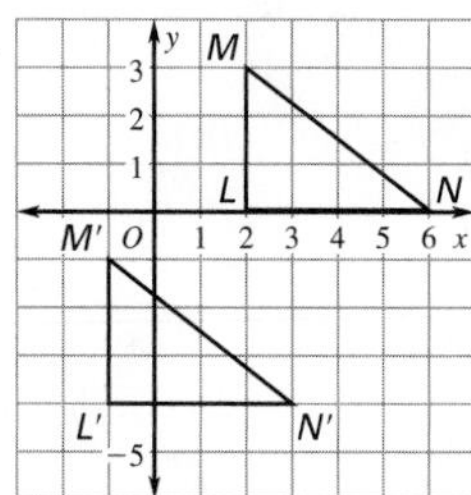

22.

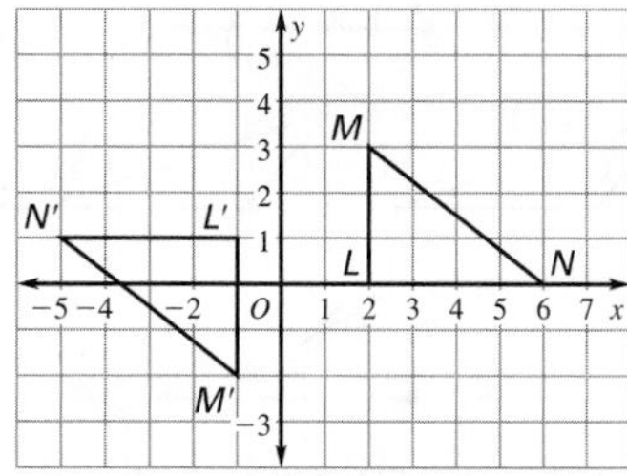

23.

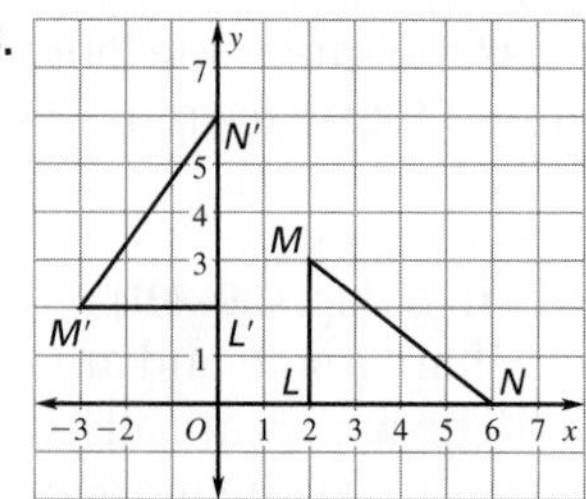

24.

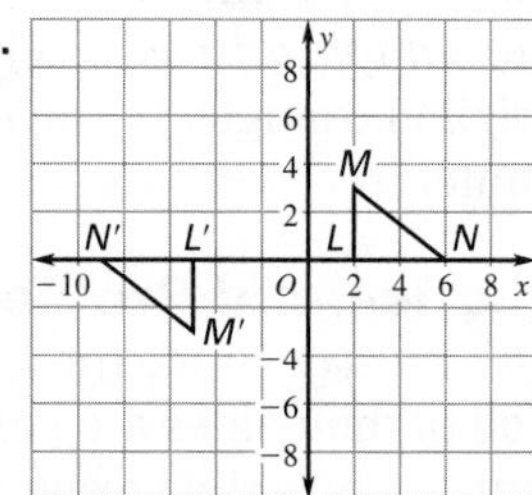

26.

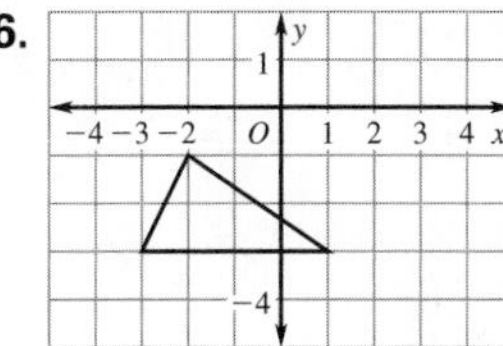

8.7 Test-Taking Practice (p. 413)

36.

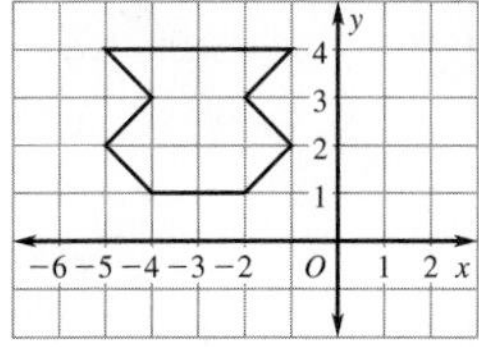

Sample answer: The coordinates are switched and the opposites are taken. This is because the rotation is $(x, y) \rightarrow (y, -x)$, and then the reflection is $(y, -x) \rightarrow (-y, -x)$.

Special Topic Exercises (p. 415)

6.

7. *Sample:*

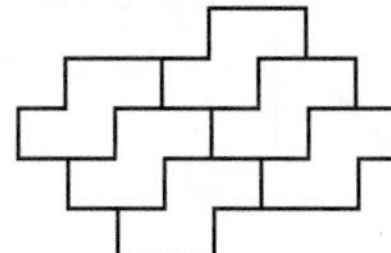

8. *Sample:*

11. *Sample:*

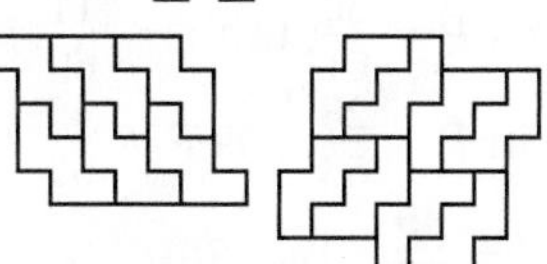

8.8 Your turn now (p. 418)

2.

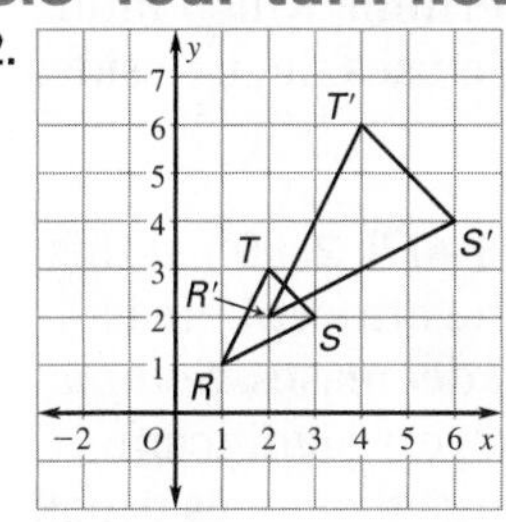

3.

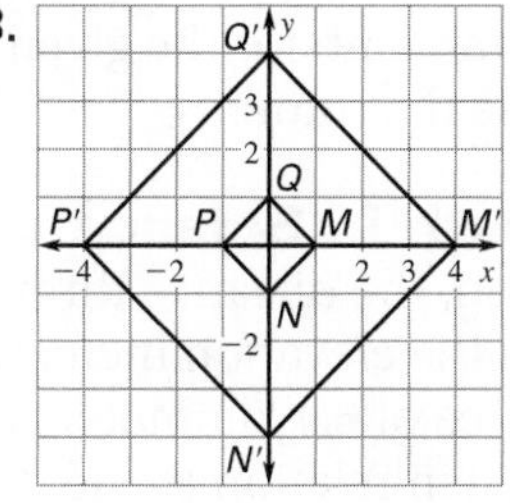

4.

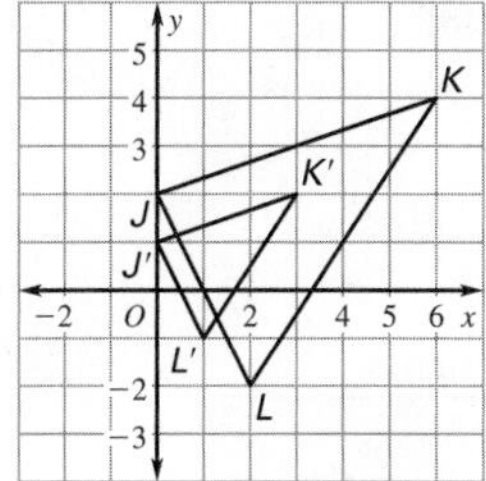

5.

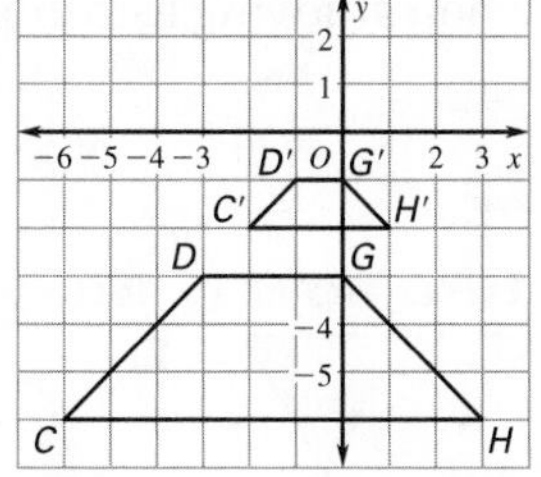

8.8 Getting Ready to Practice (p. 419)

5. Steps 1, 3:

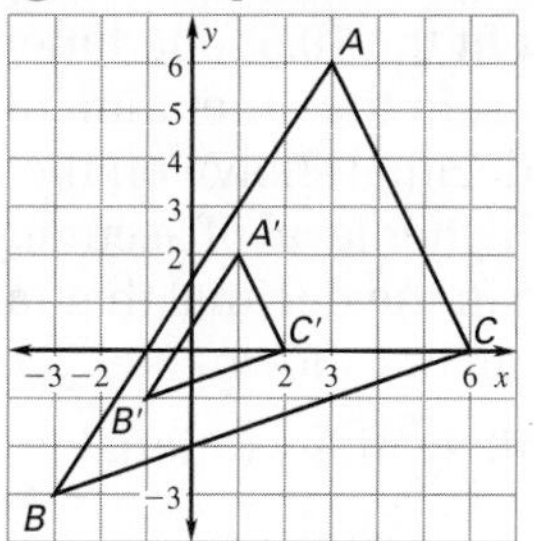

8.8 Practice and Problem Solving (pp. 419–421)

18.

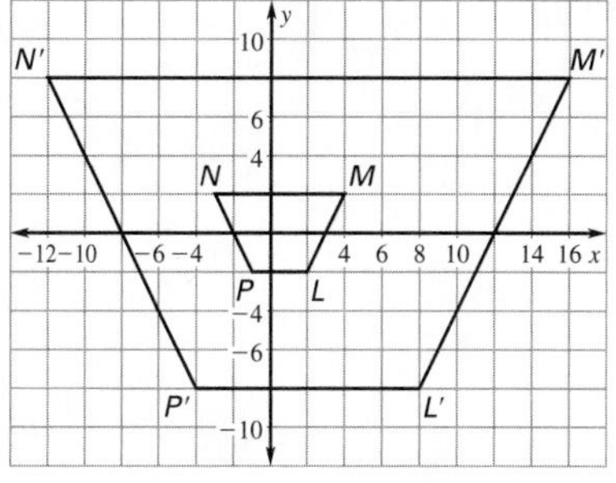

8.8 Mixed Review (p. 421)

28.

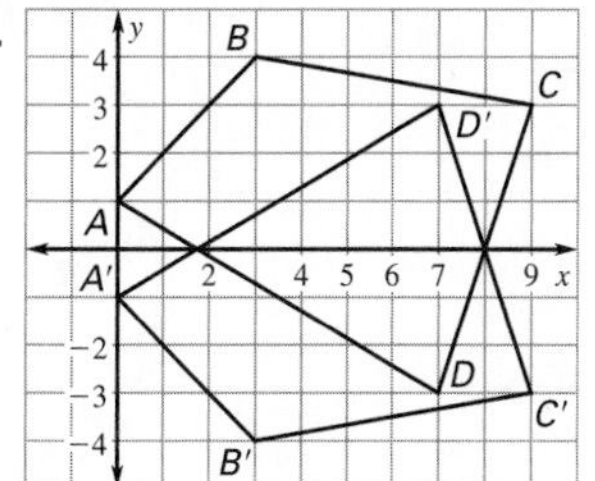

Chapter 9

9.2 Practice and Problem Solving (pp. 440–441)

14.

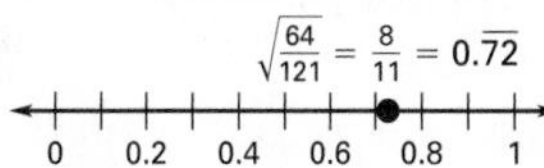

15.

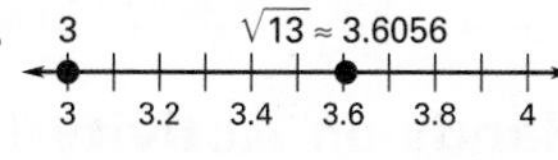

16.

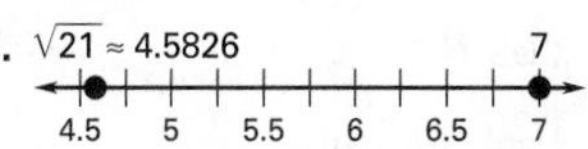

17.

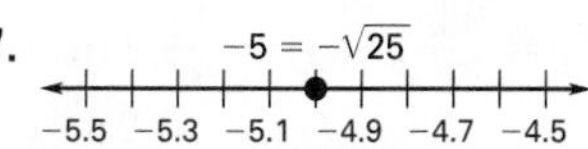

25.

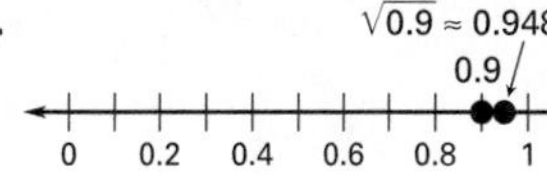

26.

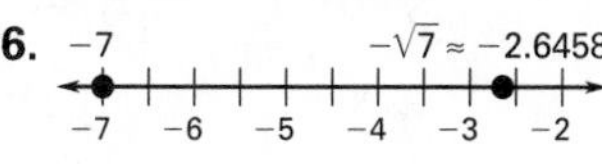

27.

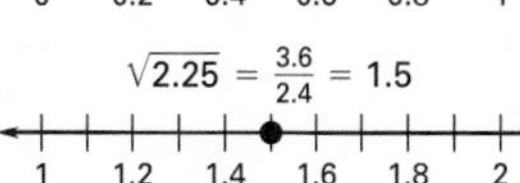

28.

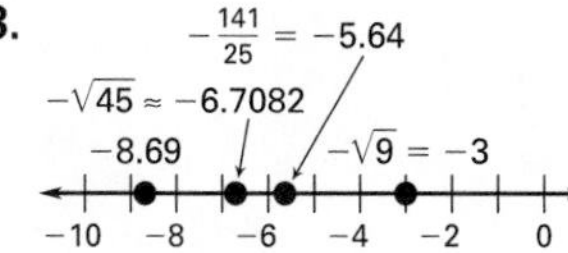

33. Yes; too small. *Sample answer:* Because $\sqrt{110} \approx 10.5$, the piece of carpet should about fit the 10.5 foot dimension, but will be about 0.7 foot too short in the other dimension. **34.** No. *Sample answer:* The decimal shown on the calculator screen could terminate at a higher level of accuracy, or there might be a repeating pattern in the decimal that takes more decimal places to identify than are shown. **35.** *Sample answer:* $\frac{17}{25}, \frac{7}{10}, \frac{18}{25}$; no; there are infinitely many rational numbers between $\frac{2}{3}$ and $\frac{3}{4}$.

9.3 Mixed Review (p. 447)

39.

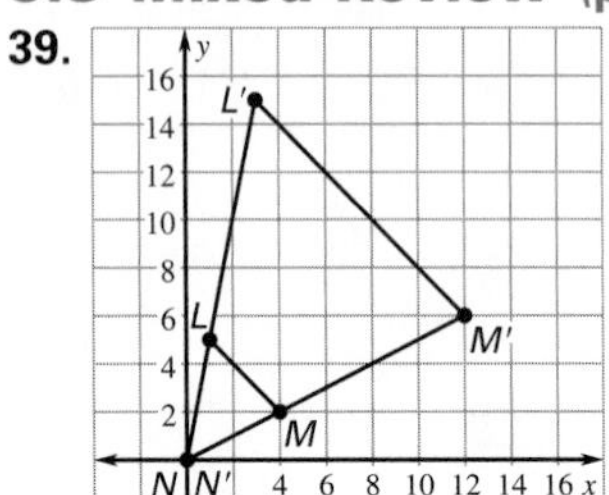

9.4 Getting Ready to Practice (p. 452)

5. Steps 1–2:

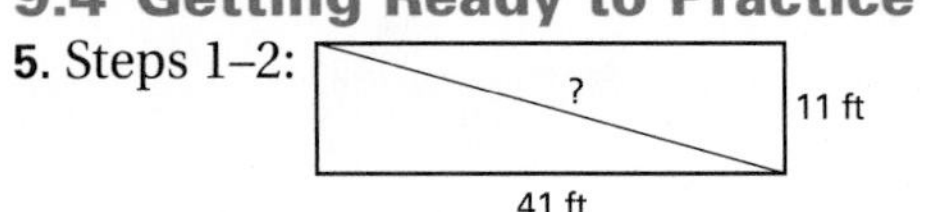

9.4 Mixed Review (p. 453)

25.

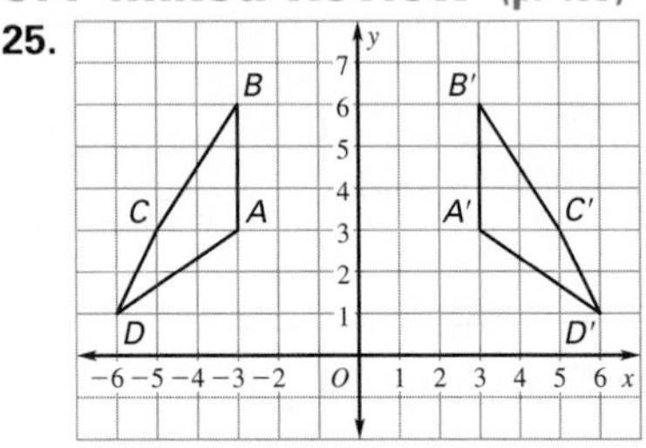

9.6 Hands-on Activity (p. 462)

5. $\sin A = \frac{35}{37}$, $\cos A = \frac{12}{37}$, $\sin B = \frac{12}{37}$, $\cos B = \frac{35}{37}$
6. $\sin A = \frac{3}{3.25}$, $\cos A = \frac{1.25}{3.25}$, $\sin B = \frac{1.25}{3.25}$, $\cos B = \frac{3}{3.25}$

7.

$m\angle A$	sin A	cos A
37°	$\frac{6}{10} = 0.6$	$\frac{8}{10} = 0.8$
53°	$\frac{12}{15} = 0.8$	$\frac{9}{15} = 0.6$
62°	$\frac{15}{17} \approx 0.88$	$\frac{8}{17} \approx 0.47$
67°	$\frac{3}{3.25} \approx 0.92$	$\frac{1.25}{3.25} \approx 0.38$
71°	$\frac{35}{37} \approx 0.95$	$\frac{12}{37} \approx 0.32$
74°	$\frac{24}{25} = 0.96$	$\frac{7}{25} = 0.28$

9.6 Getting Ready to Practice (p. 466)

5. Step 1:

totem pole
42°
50 ft

9.6 Practice and Problem Solving (pp. 466–468)

6. $\sin P = \frac{40}{41}$, $\cos P = \frac{9}{41}$, $\tan P = \frac{40}{9}$, $\sin R = \frac{9}{41}$, $\cos R = \frac{40}{41}$, $\tan R = \frac{9}{40}$ **7.** $\sin P = \frac{11}{61}$, $\cos P = \frac{60}{61}$, $\tan P = \frac{11}{60}$, $\sin R = \frac{60}{61}$, $\cos R = \frac{11}{61}$, $\tan R = \frac{60}{11}$ **8.** $\sin P = \frac{28}{53}$, $\cos P = \frac{45}{53}$, $\tan P = \frac{28}{45}$, $\sin R = \frac{45}{53}$, $\cos R = \frac{28}{53}$, $\tan R = \frac{45}{28}$ **16.** *Sample answer:* Look at which angle measure is given, which side length is given, and which side length needs to be found. Determine which ratio, sine, cosine, or tangent, for the given angle uses the two sides involved and use that ratio.

Exploring Math in Science (pp. 476–477) **2.** 90°; at this angle of elevation, the distance through the atmosphere is the least. **4.** As the elevation increases, d decreases. *Sample answer:* A distance of 6.4 kilometers is not very significant when considered in relation to the very large distances usually encountered when studying astronomy.

Chapter 10

10.1 Your turn now (p. 482)

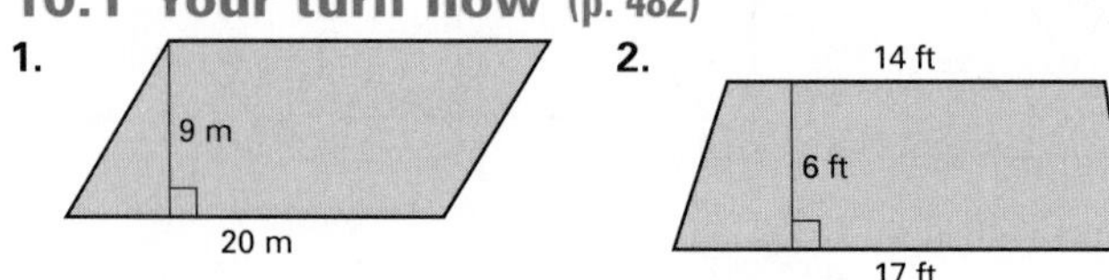

10.1 Getting Ready to Practice (p. 483)

7. Step 1:

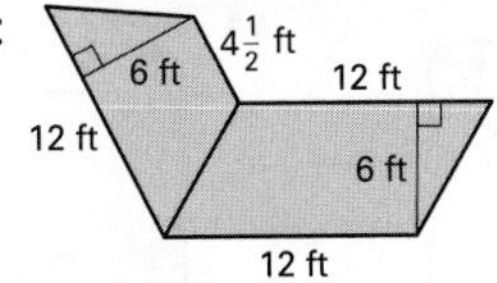

10.1 Practice and Problem Solving (pp. 483–485)

8.

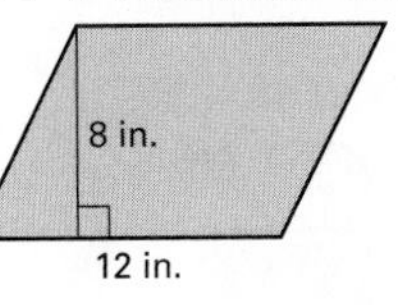

9.

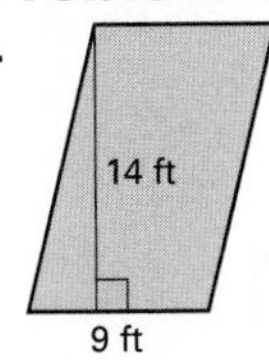

10.

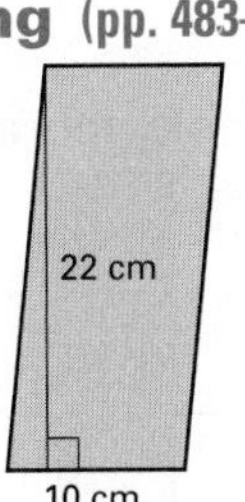

15.

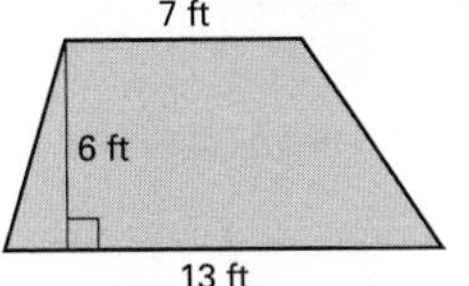

16.

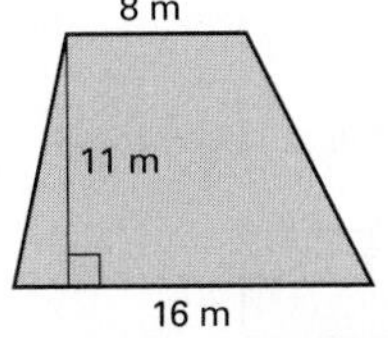

35.

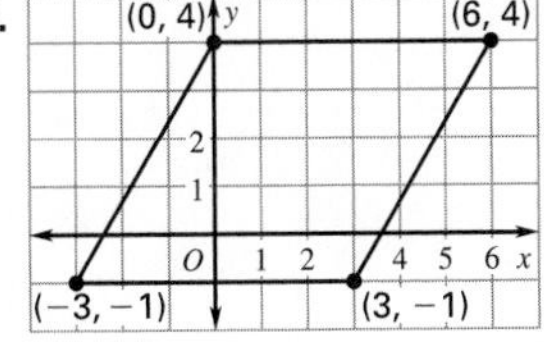

36.

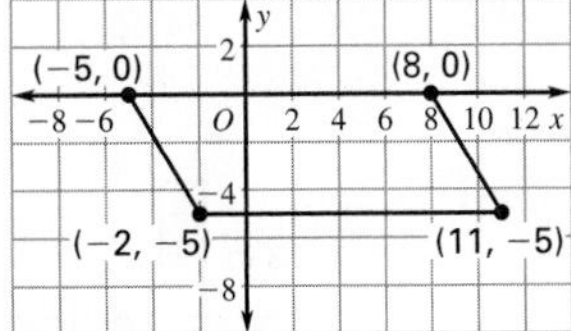

10.1 Test-Taking Practice (p. 485)

45. *Sample:*

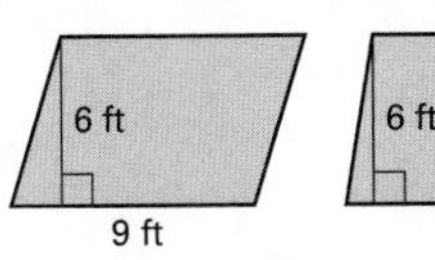

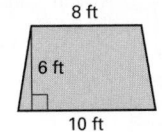

10.2 Technology Activity (p. 491)

6. *Sample answer:* The formula for the area of a circle is $A = \pi r^2$. Dividing both sides of this equation by π gives $\frac{A}{\pi} = r^2$, and taking the square root of both sides yields $\pm\sqrt{\frac{A}{\pi}} = r \left(\text{or } r = \pm\sqrt{\frac{A}{\pi}}\right)$. Since the radius must be a positive number, the formula for the radius r of a circle can be written as just $r = \sqrt{\frac{A}{\pi}}$.

10.3 Your turn now (p. 493)

4. *Sample:*

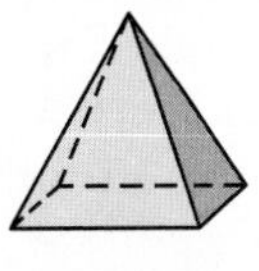

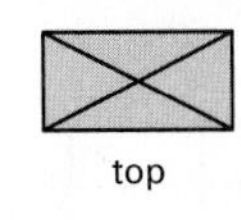
top

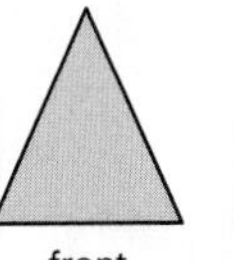
front

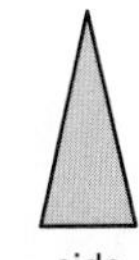
side

10.3 Getting Ready to Practice (p. 494)

5.

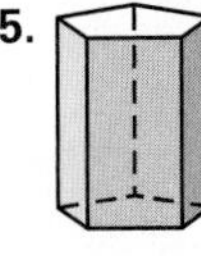

top

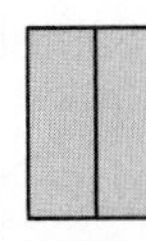
front

side

6. Steps 1–3:

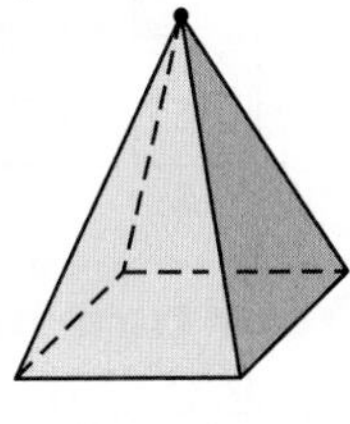

10.3 Practice and Problem Solving (pp. 494–495)

10.

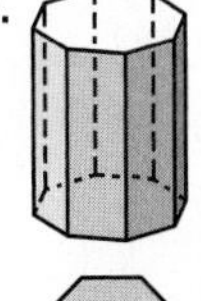

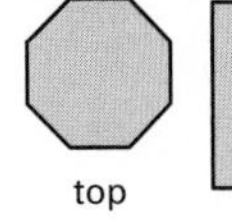
top

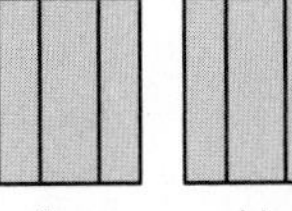
front

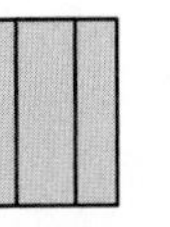
side

11.

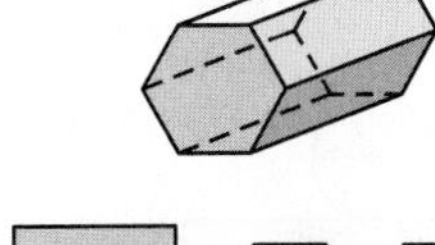

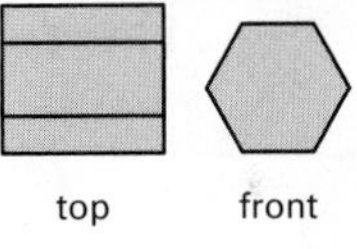
top

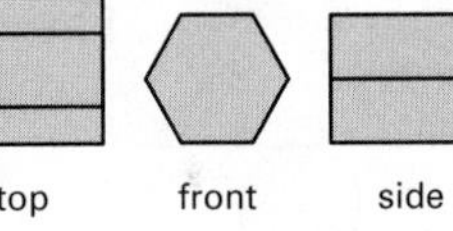
front

side

22.

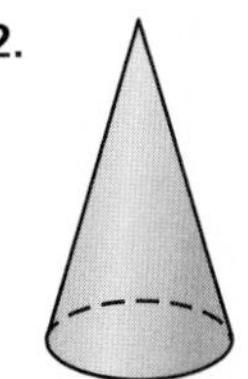

23.

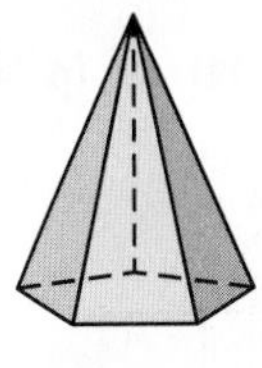

Special Topic Exercises (p. 497)

1.

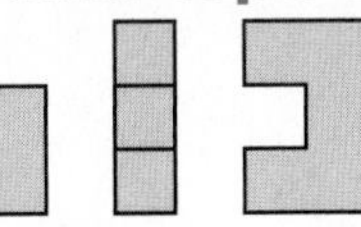
top front side

2.

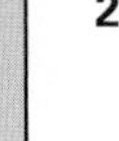

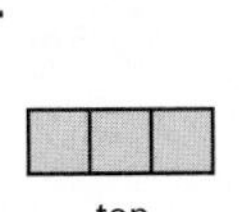
top

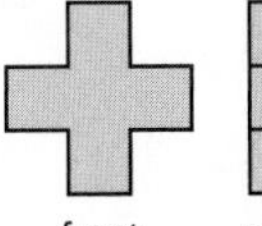
front

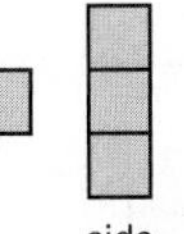
side

3.

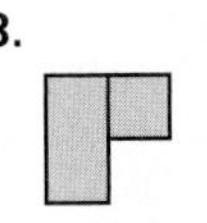
top

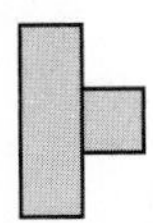
front

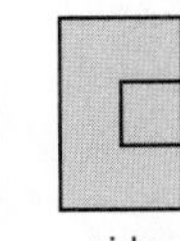
side

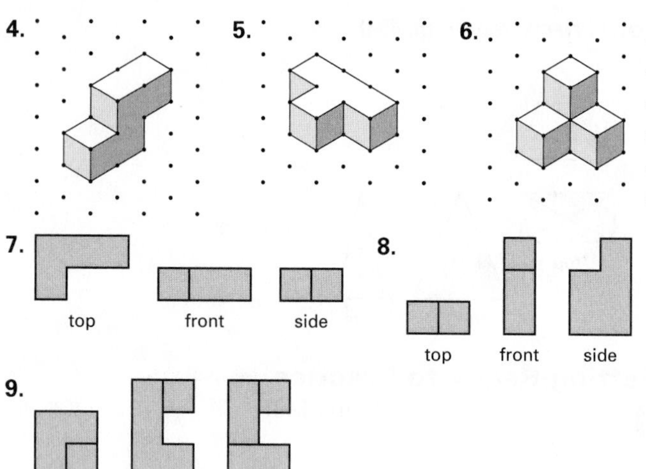

10.4 Your turn now (p. 504) 1–3. Sample nets are shown.

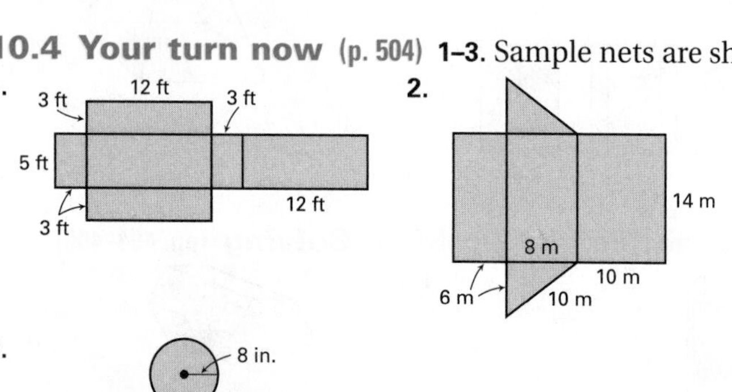

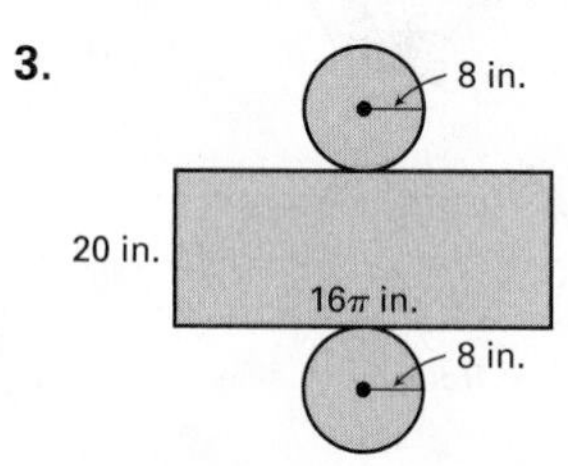

10.4 Getting Ready to Practice (p. 505)

2–4. Sample nets are shown.

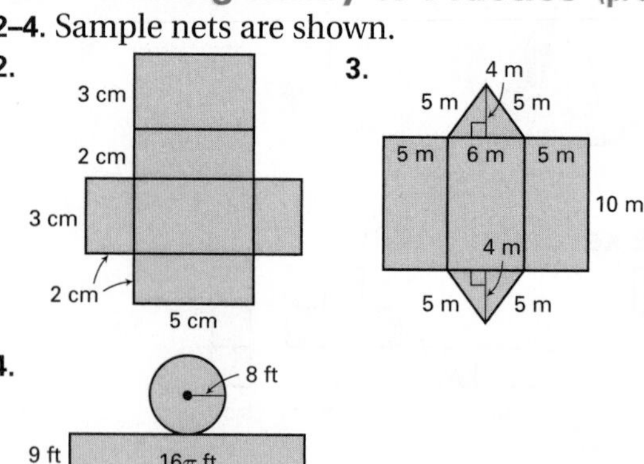

10.4 Practice and Problem Solving (pp. 505–506)

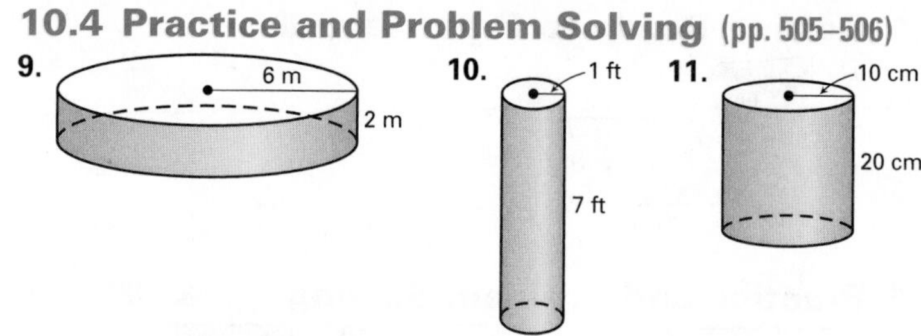

15–17. Sample nets are shown.

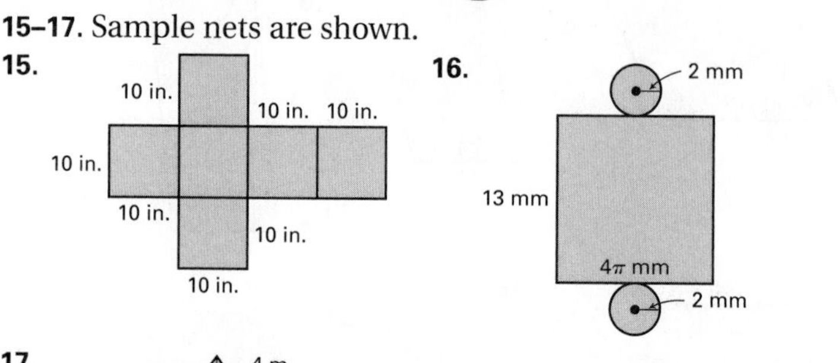

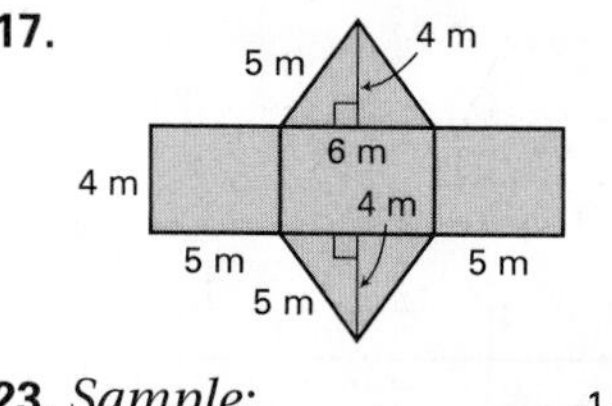

23. *Sample:*

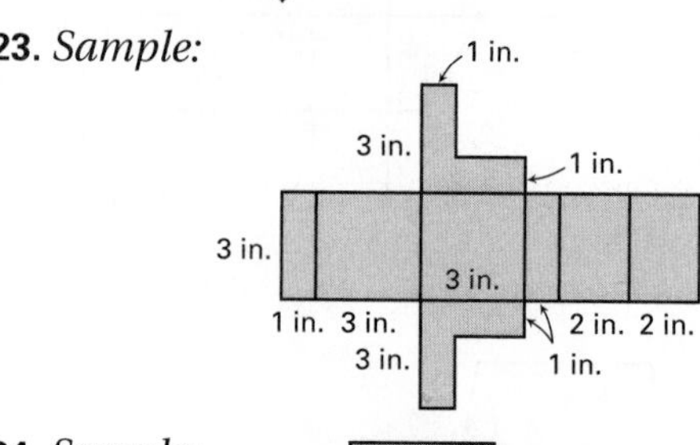

24. *Sample:*

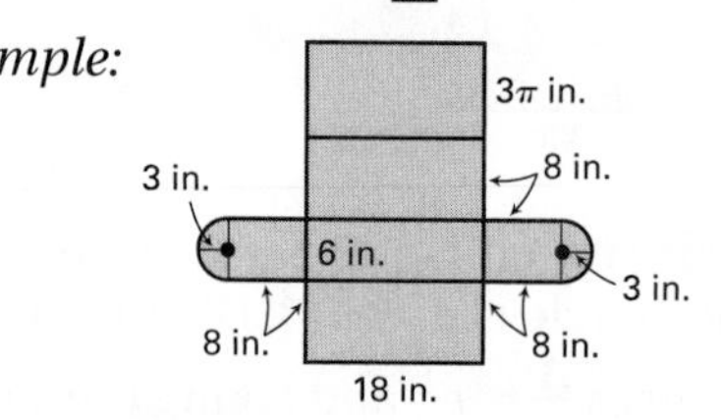

10.4 Test-Taking Practice (p. 506)

34. *Sample:*

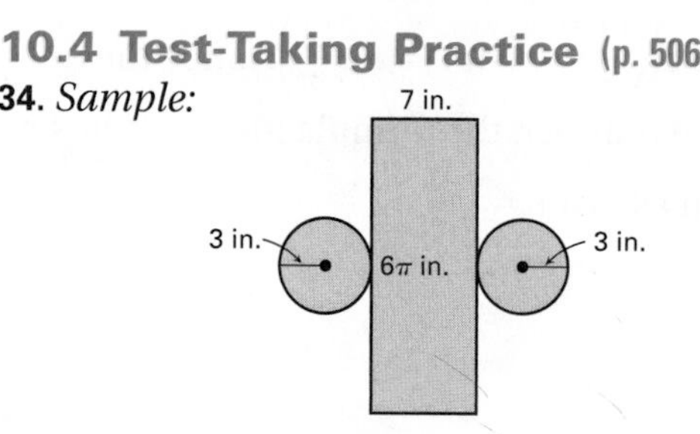

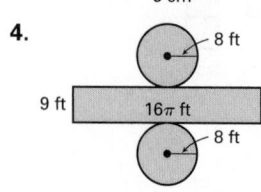

10.5 Getting Ready to Practice (p. 509)

1.

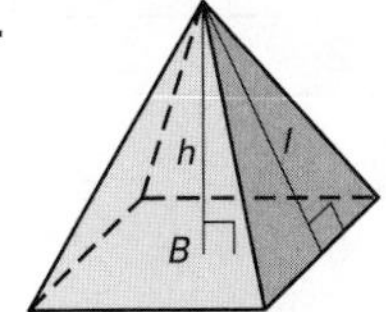

2–4. Sample nets are shown.

2.

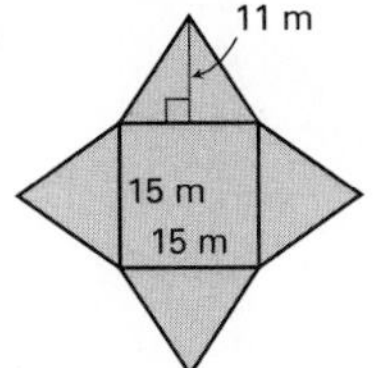

3.

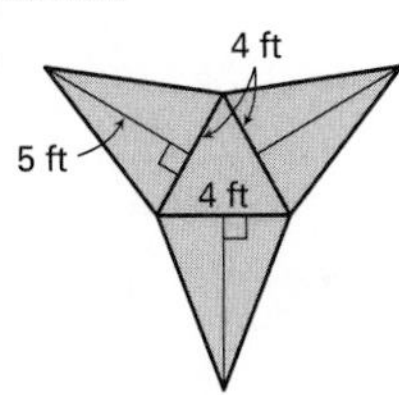

4.

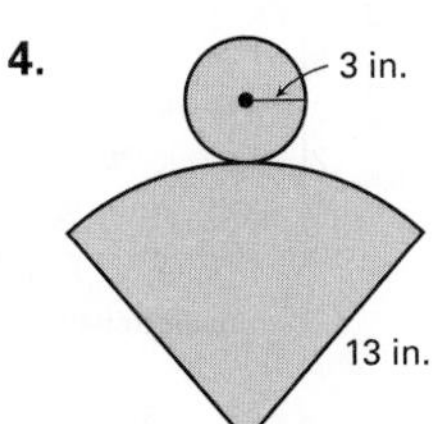

10.5 Practice and Problem Solving (pp. 510–511)

14–16. Sample nets are shown.

14.

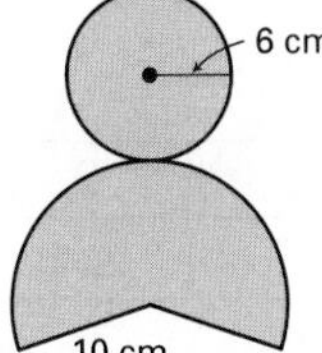

15.

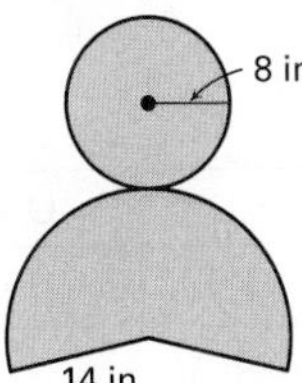

16.

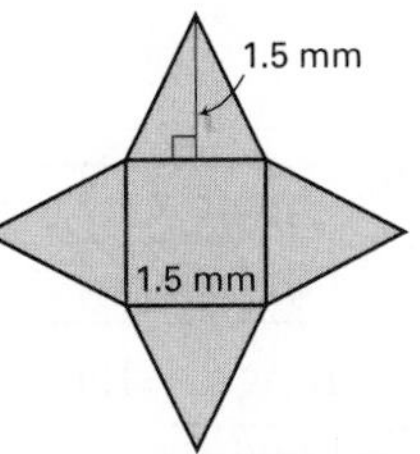

10.5 Practice and Problem Solving (pp. 522–523)

34.

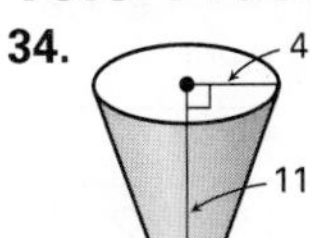
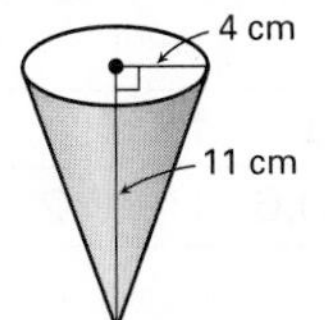

10.5 Mixed Review (p. 523)

35–36. Sample answers are given.

35.

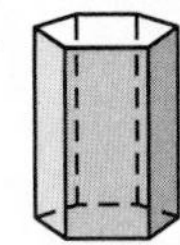
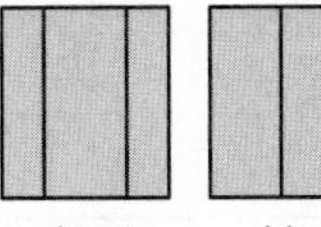

36.

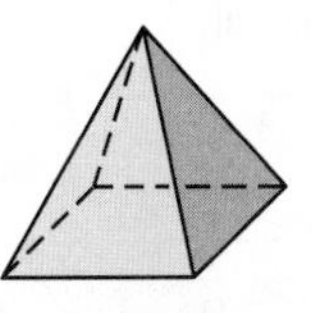
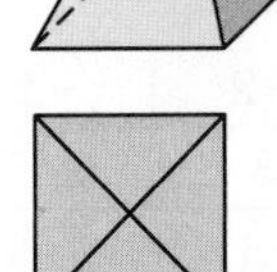
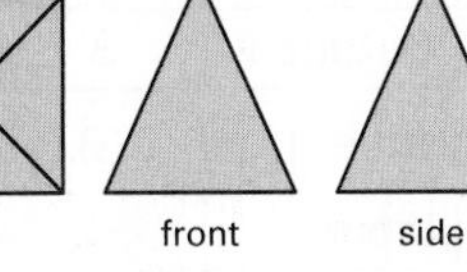

38.

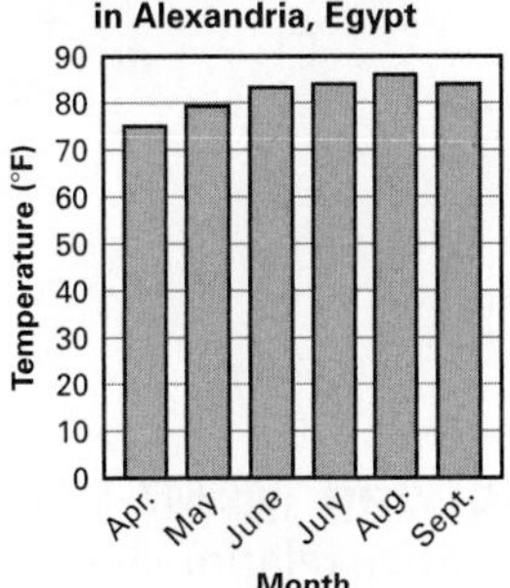

Chapter 11

Chapter Opener (pp. 538–539)

Brain Game:

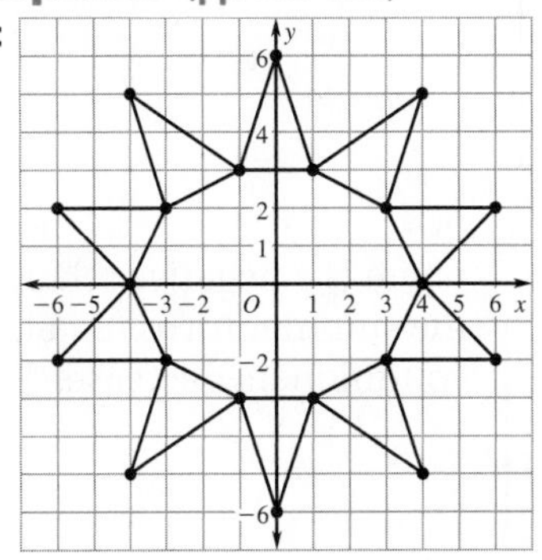

11.1 Practice and Problem Solving (pp. 543–544)

13.

Input *x*	−2	−1	0	1	2
Output *y*	−3	−2	−1	0	1

range: −3, −2, −1, 0, 1

14.

Input *x*	−2	−1	0	1	2
Output *y*	$\frac{1}{2}$	$\frac{1}{4}$	0	$-\frac{1}{4}$	$-\frac{1}{2}$

range: $-\frac{1}{2}, -\frac{1}{4}, 0, \frac{1}{4}, \frac{1}{2}$

15.

Input *x*	−2	−1	0	1	2
Output *y*	−10	−5	0	5	10

range: −10, −5, 0, 5, 10

16.

Input *x*	−2	−1	0	1	2
Output *y*	4	1	0	1	4

range: 0, 1, 4

Additional Answers

11.2 Your turn now (p. 545)

1. 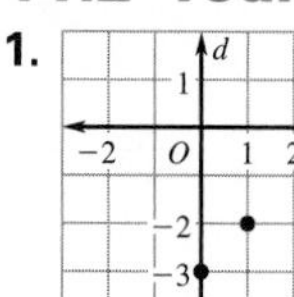 

2. 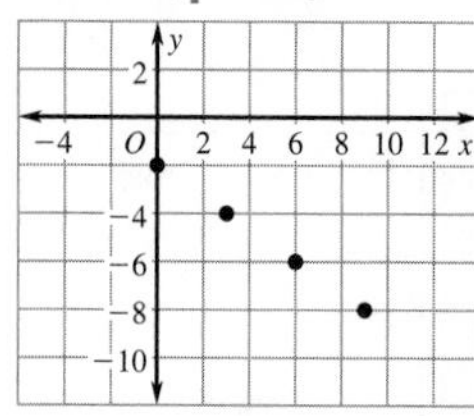

11.2 Practice and Problem Solving (pp. 547–548)

6. 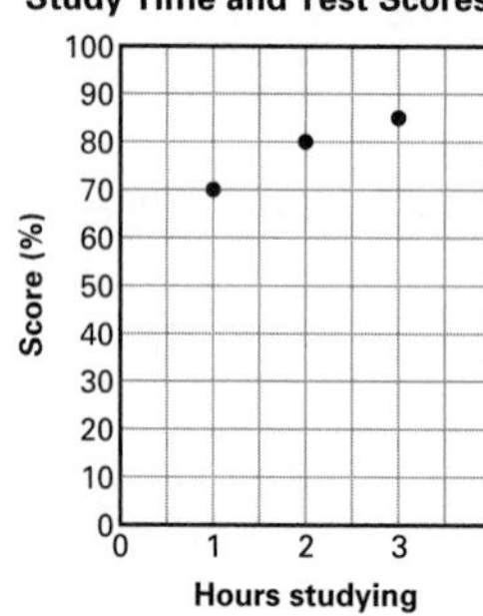

There is a positive relationship. As study time increases, test scores increase.

7. 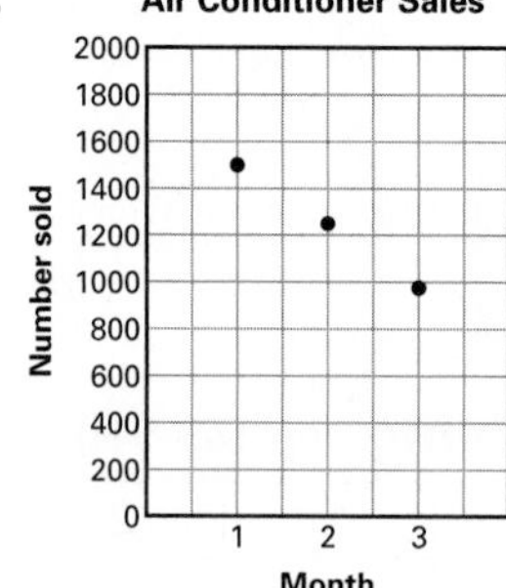

There is a negative relationship. As the summer turns to fall, sales of air conditioners decrease.

8. 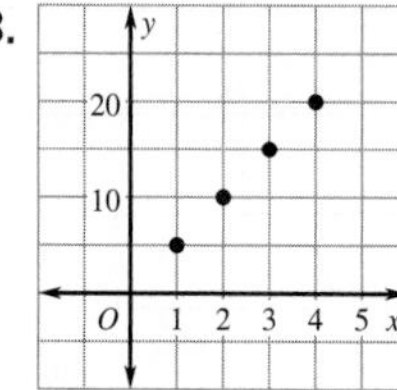

There is a positive relationship, with each increase of 1 in x corresponding to an increase of 5 in y; (5, 25).

9. 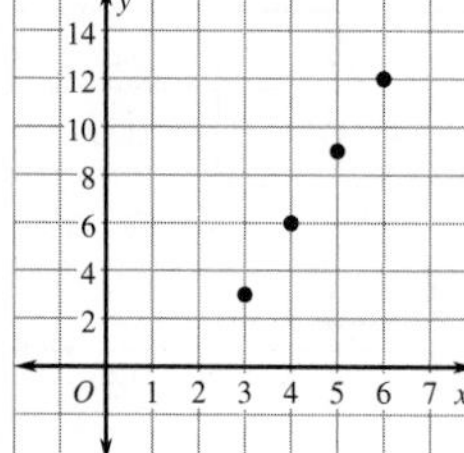

There is a positive relationship, with each increase of 1 in x corresponding to an increase of 3 in y; (7, 15).

14.

Length l	1	2	3	4	5
Width w	5	4	3	2	1

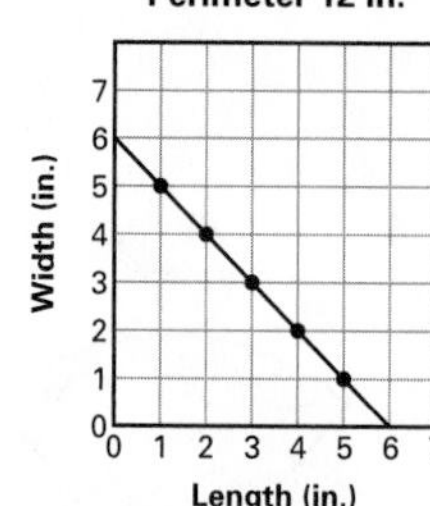

2.5 in.

11.2 Mixed Review (p. 548)

17. *Sample:* 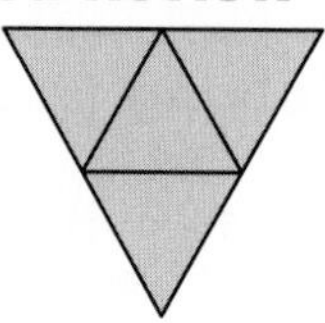

18.

Input x	−2	−1	0	1	2
Output y	−1.4	−0.7	0	0.7	1.4

range: −1.4, −0.7, 0, 0.7, 1.4

19.

Input x	−2	−1	0	1	2
Output y	−2	1	4	7	10

range: −2, 1, 4, 7, 10

20.

Input x	−2	−1	0	1	2
Output y	−1.8	−1.4	−1	−0.6	−0.2

range: −1.8, −1.4, −1, −0.6, −0.2

11.3 Mixed Review (p. 553)

43.

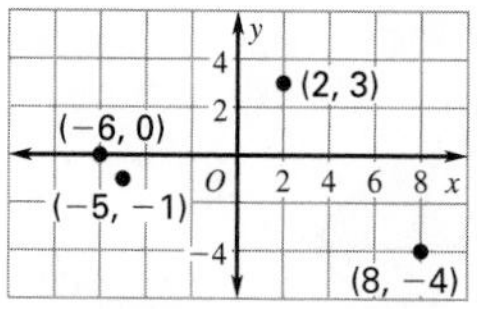

(2, 3)
(−6, 0)
(−5, −1)
(8, −4)

45.

Input x	−2	−1	0	1	2
Output y	3	2.5	2	1.5	1

range: 1, 1.5, 2, 2.5, 3

46.

Input x	−2	−1	0	1	2
Output y	16	14	12	10	8

range: 8, 10, 12, 14, 16

47.

Input x	−2	−1	0	1	2
Output y	12	10	8	6	4

range: 4, 6, 8, 10, 12

11.4 In-lesson Activity (p. 556)

Step 2.

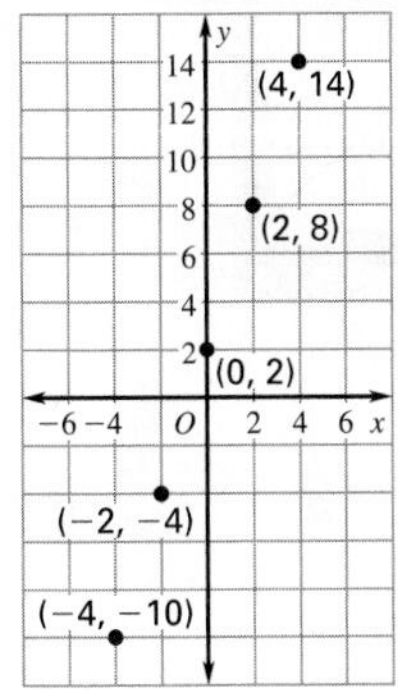

11.4 Your turn now (p. 557)

1.

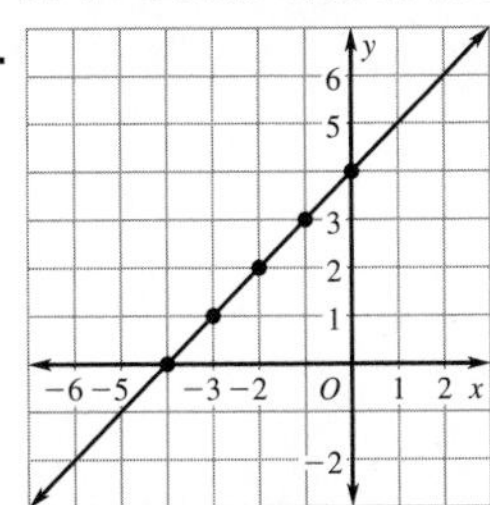

2.

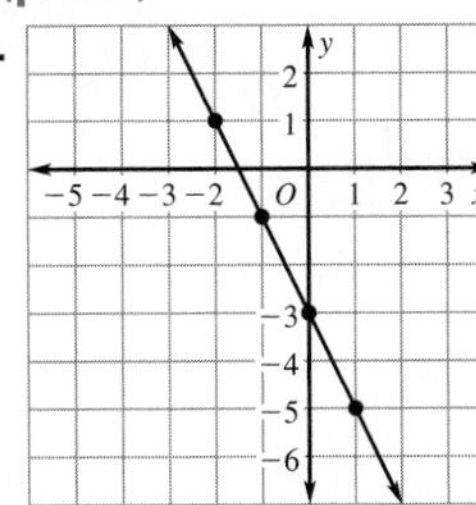

3.

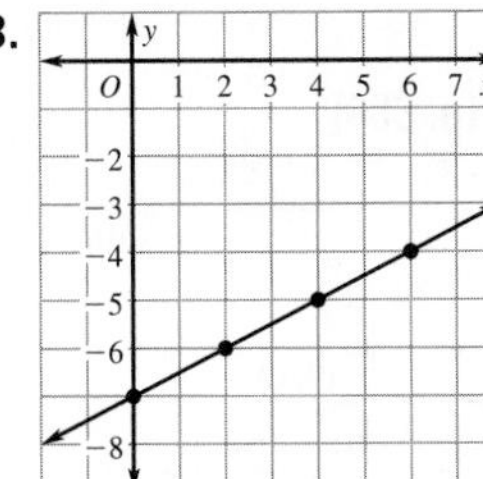

4.

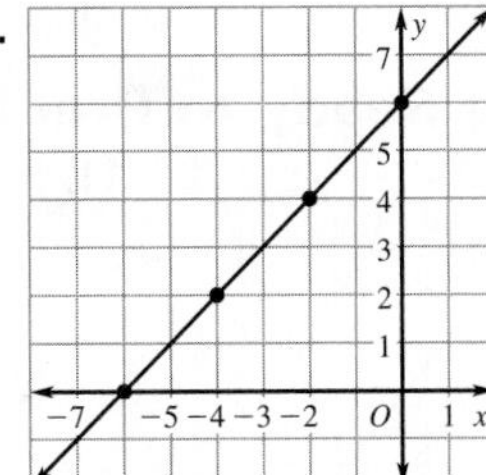

11.4 Practice and Problem Solving (pp. 559–560)

14.

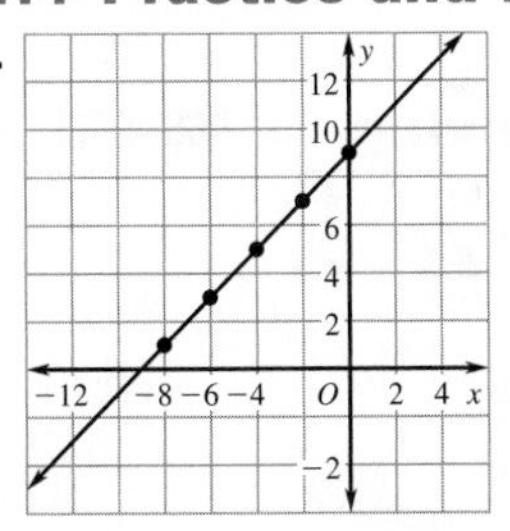

15.

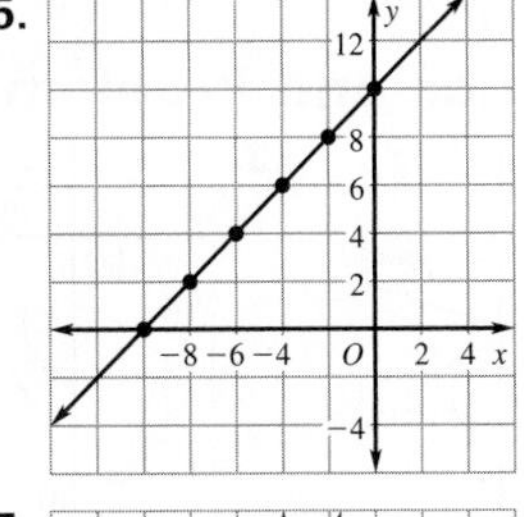

16.

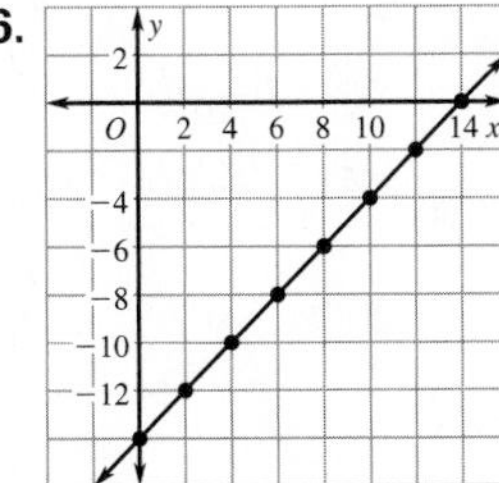

17.

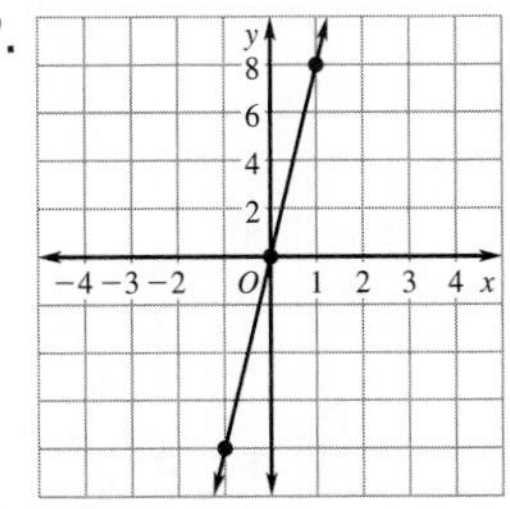

18.

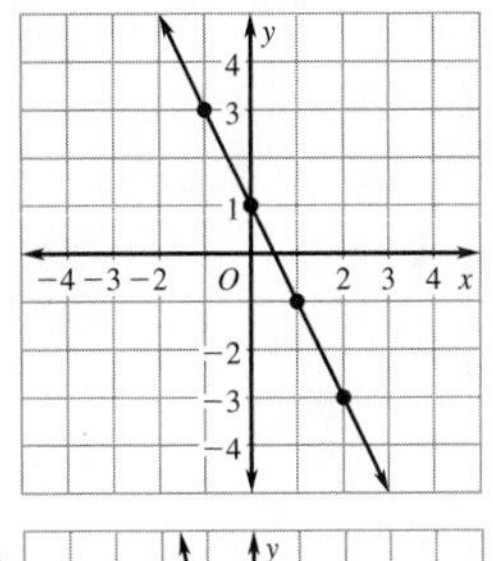

19.

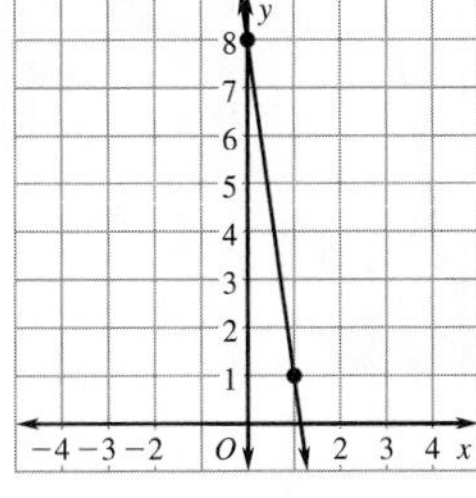

20.

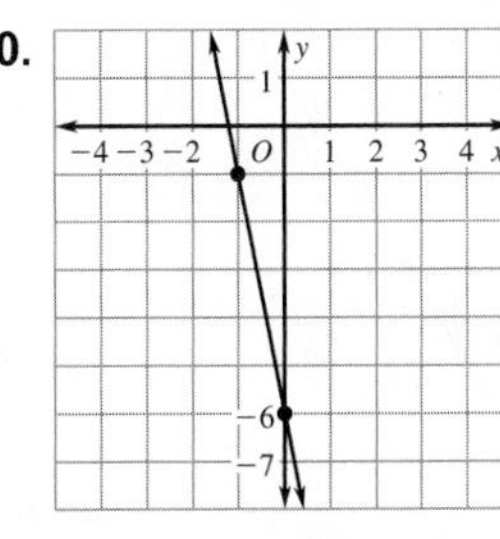

21.

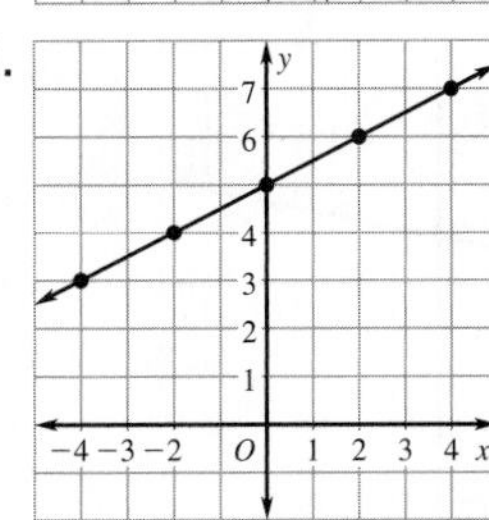

22.

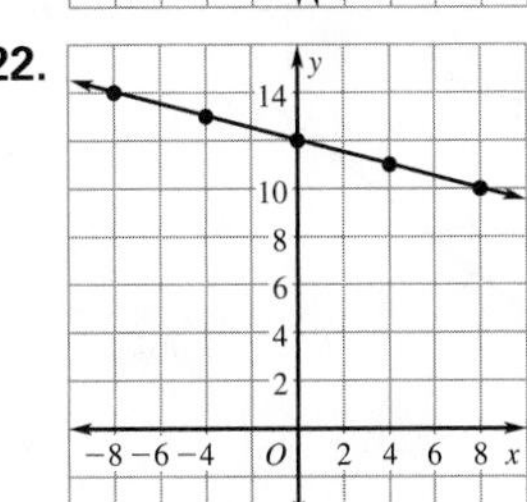

23.

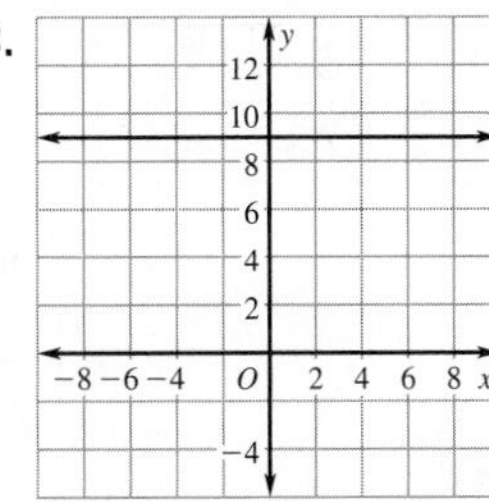

24.

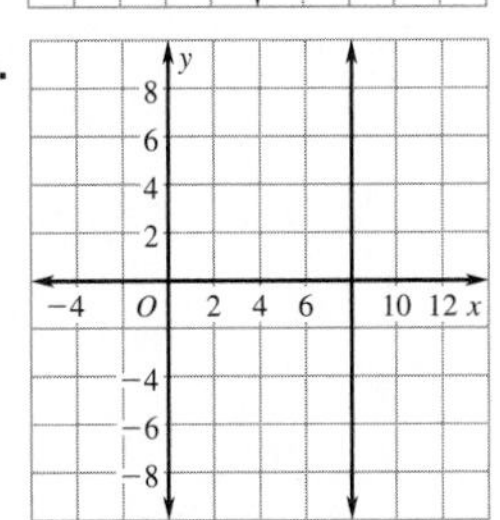

25.

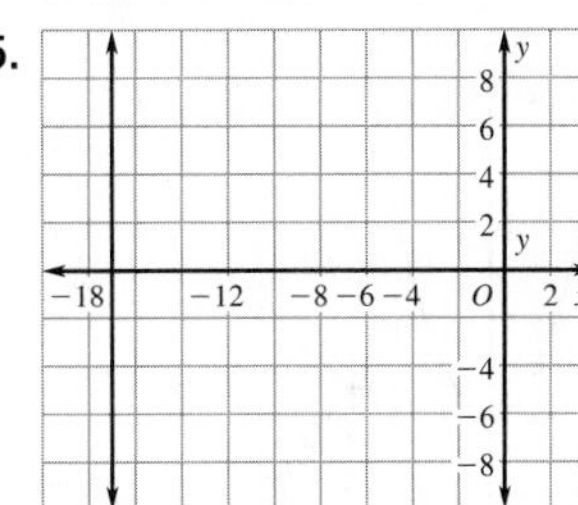

28.

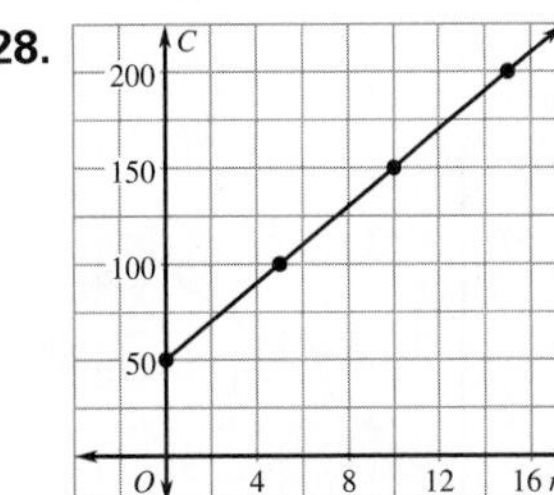

29.

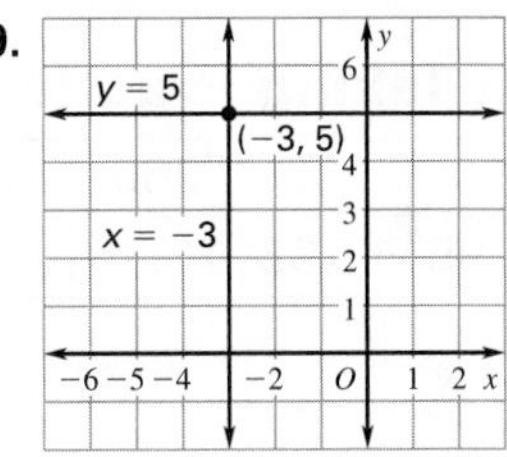

30.

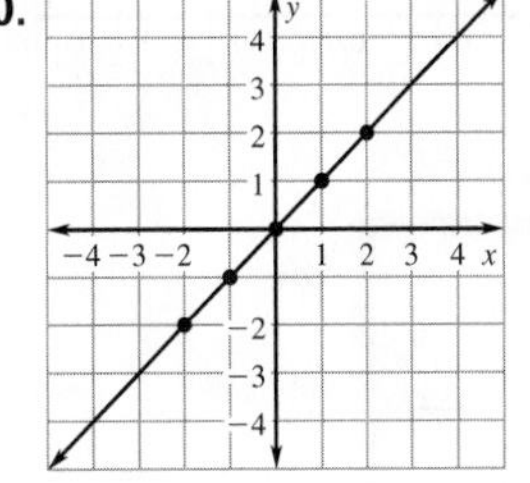

31.

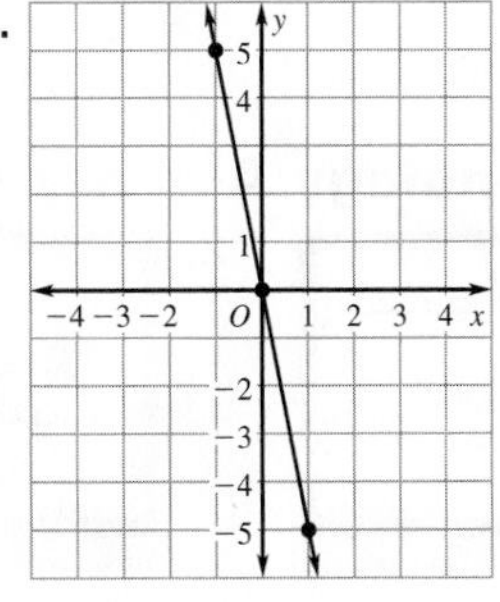

Additional Answers

32.

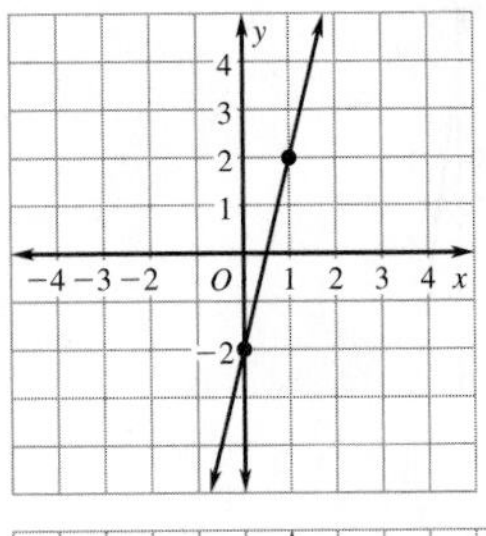

33.

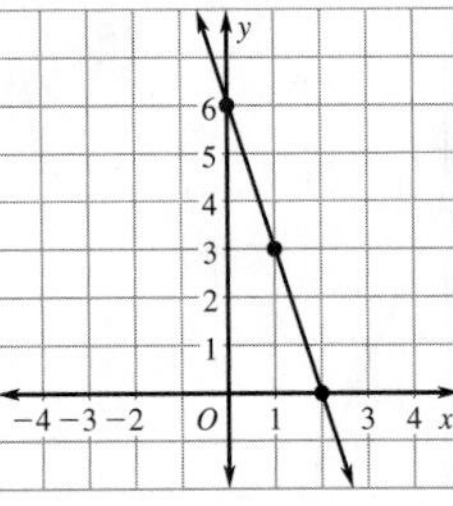

34.

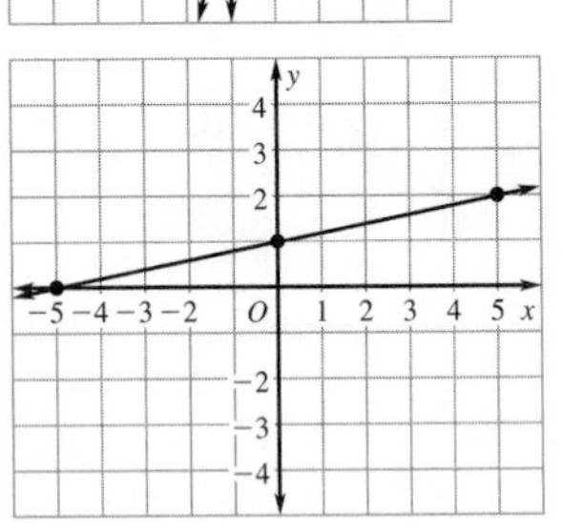

35.

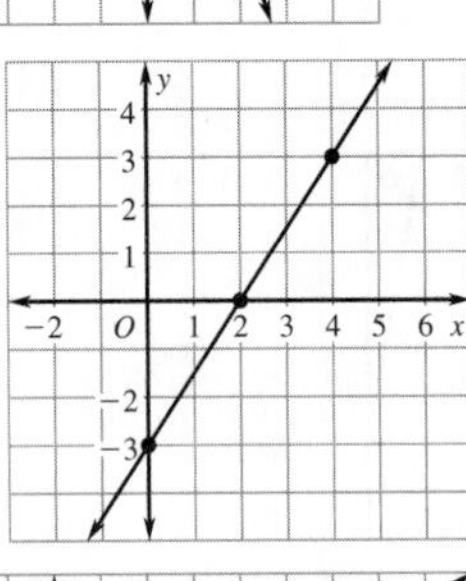

36.

x	0	6	12
y	80	173	266

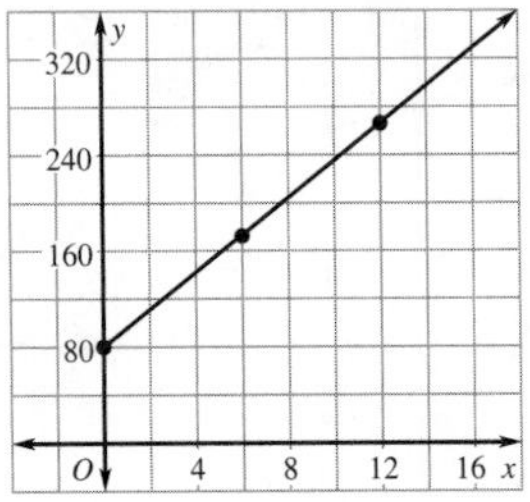

40.

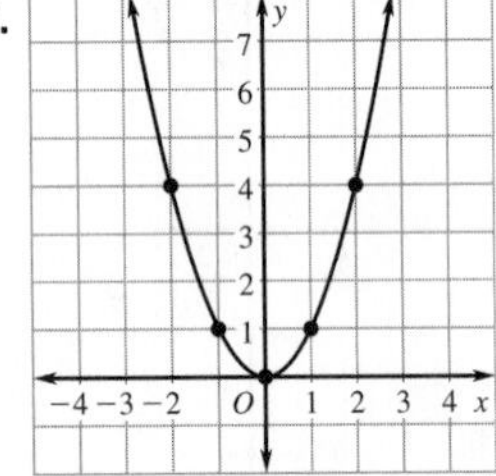

11.4 Test-Taking Practice (p. 560)

50.

t	120	240	360	480
c	11.95	17.95	23.95	29.95

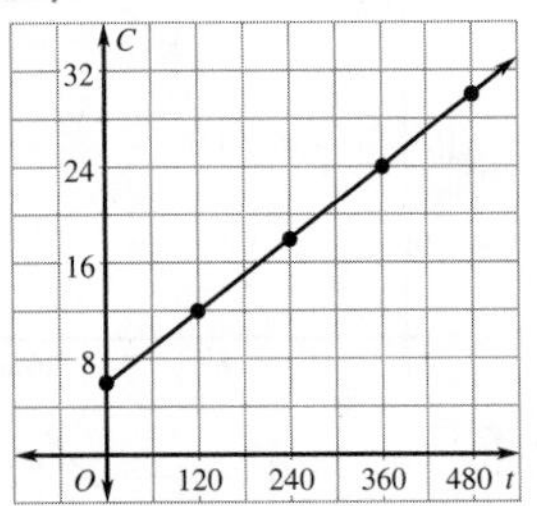

11.4 Technology Activity (p. 561)

1.

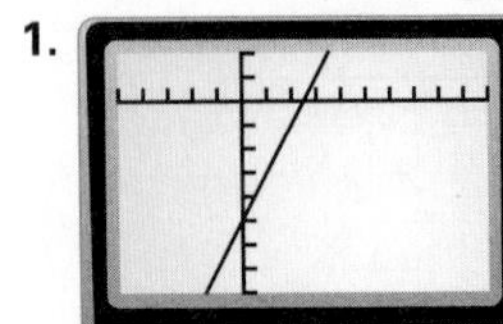

2.

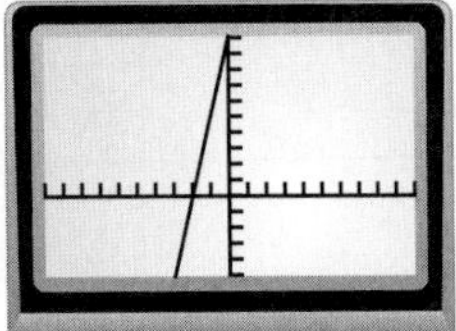

3.

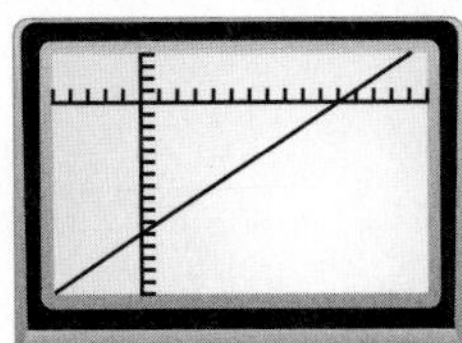

4.

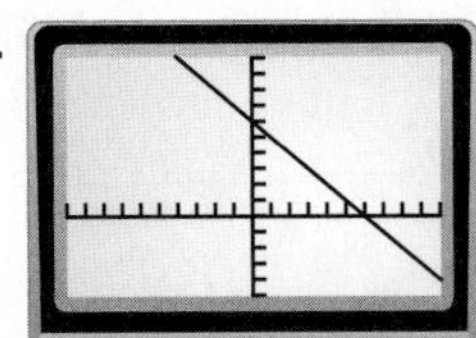

11.5 Your turn now (p. 565)

1.

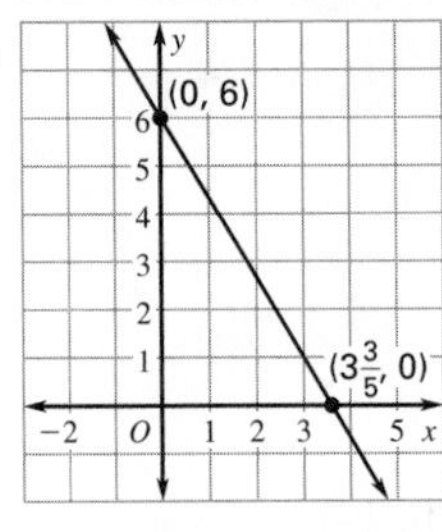

2.

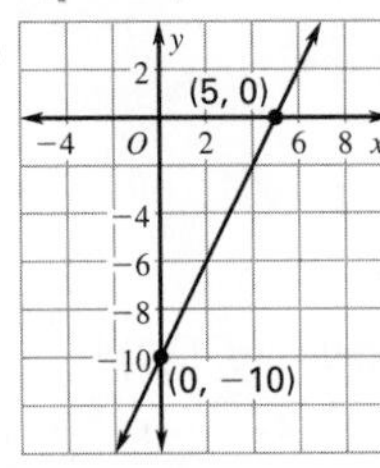

3.

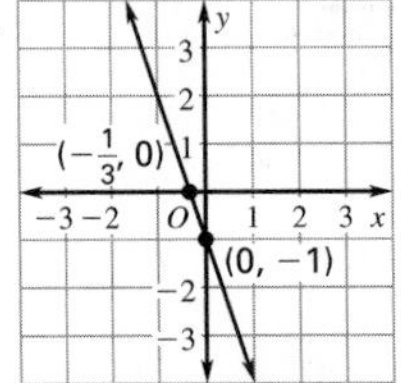

11.5 Getting Ready to Practice (p. 566)

4. Step 2:

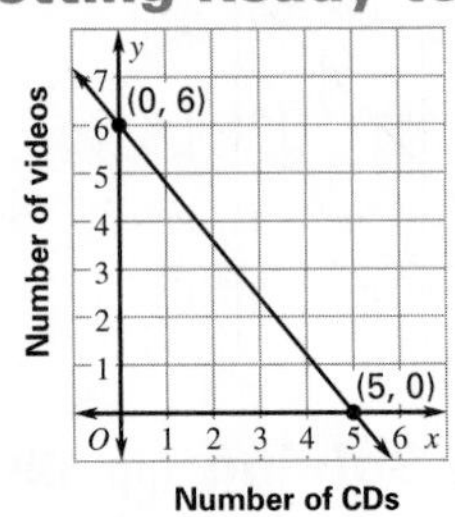

11.

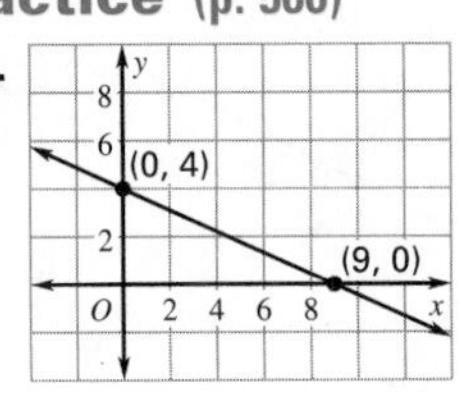

11.5 Practice and Problem Solving (pp. 566–567)

12.

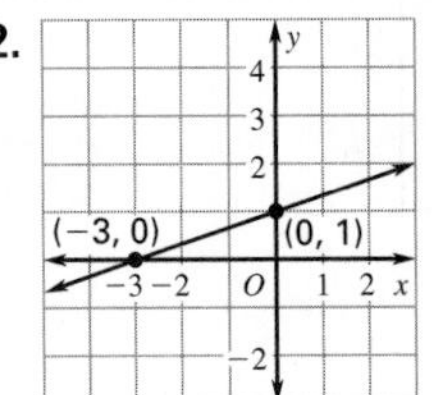

13.

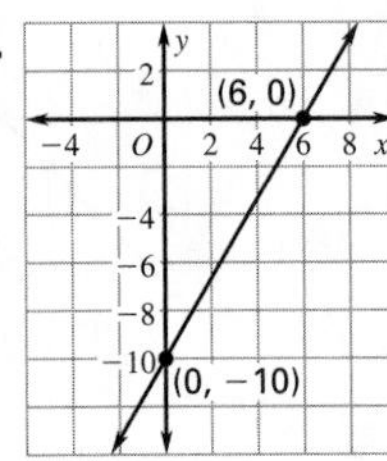

14.

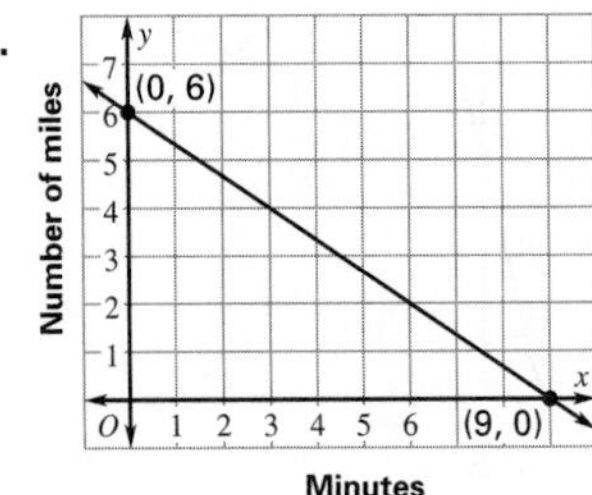

19. 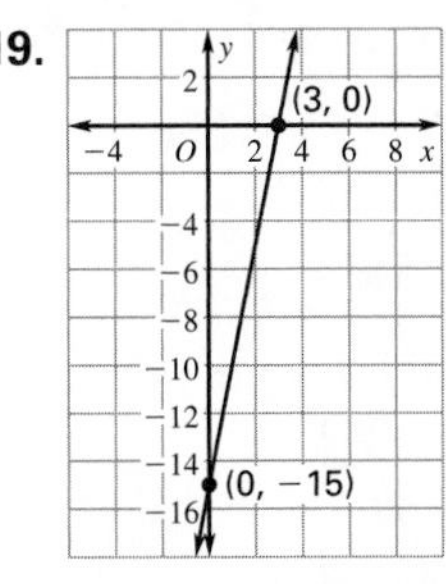

20. 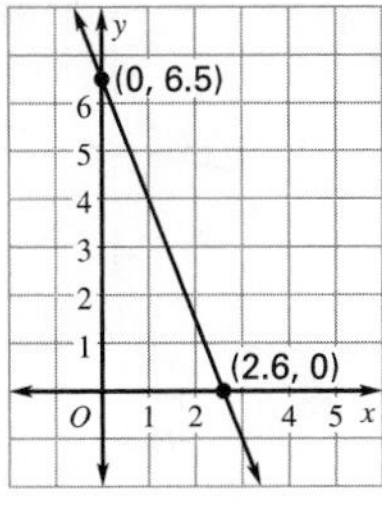

21. 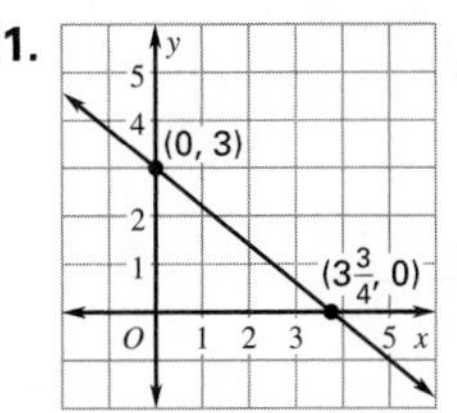

22. 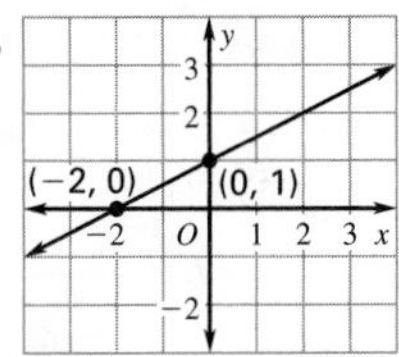

23. 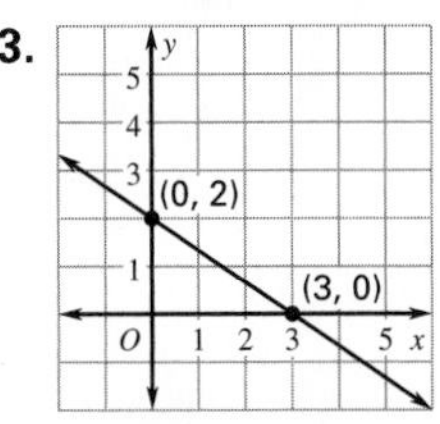

24. 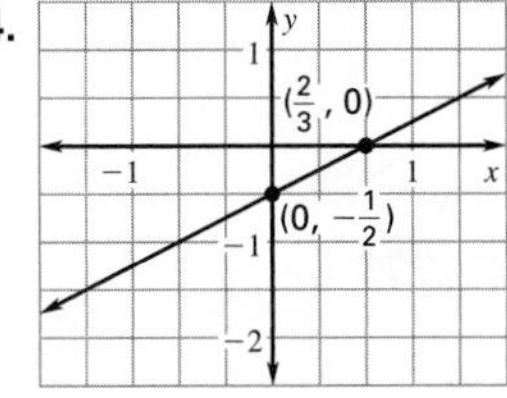

11.5 Mixed Review (p. 567)

31. 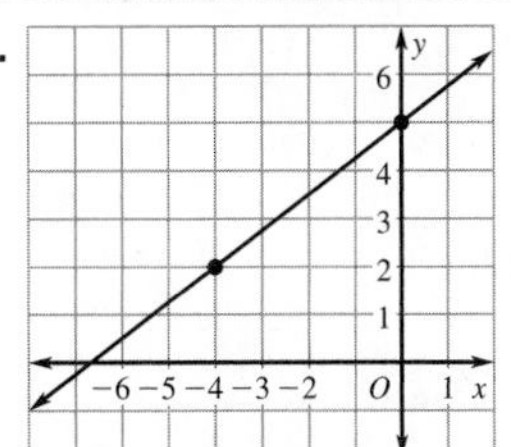

32. 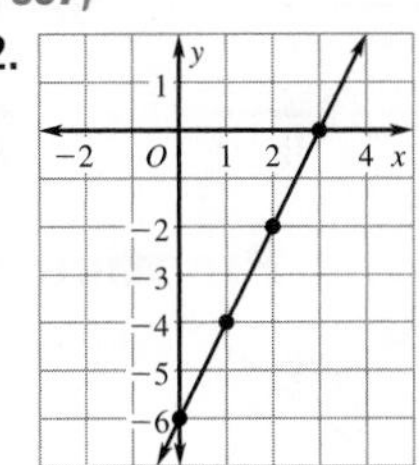

33. 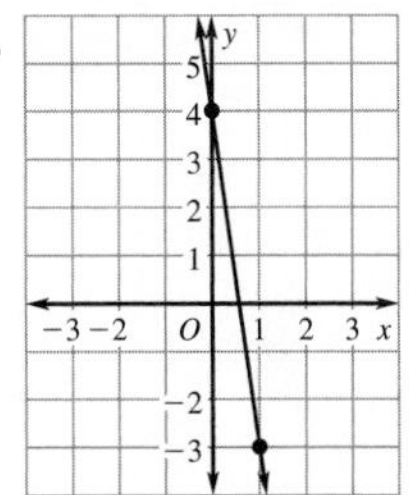

11.6 Getting Ready to Practice (p. 572)

3–6. Sample graphs are shown.

3. 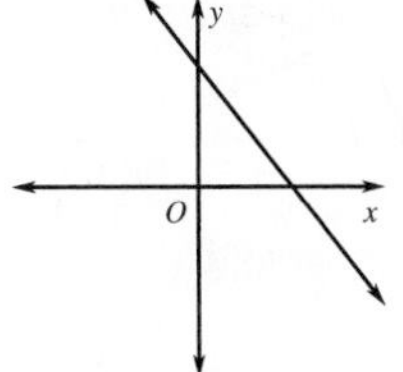

4. 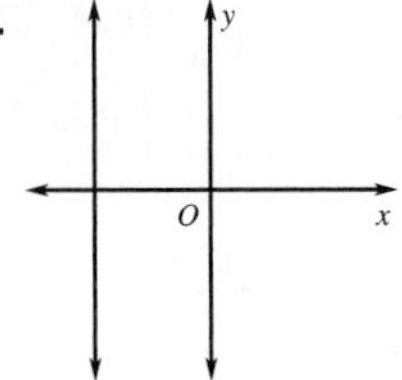

5. 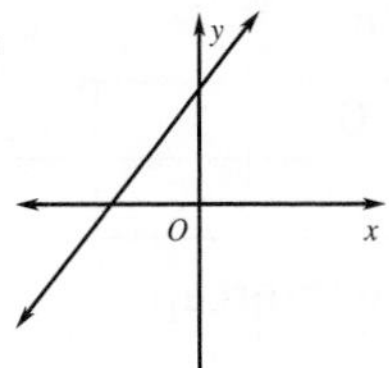

6. 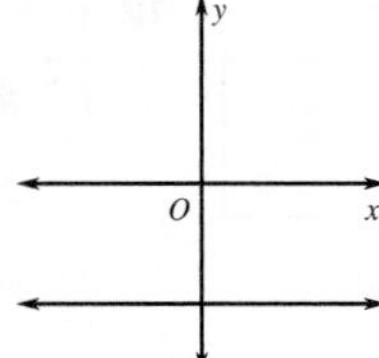

11.6 Practice and Problem Solving (pp. 573–574)

22. 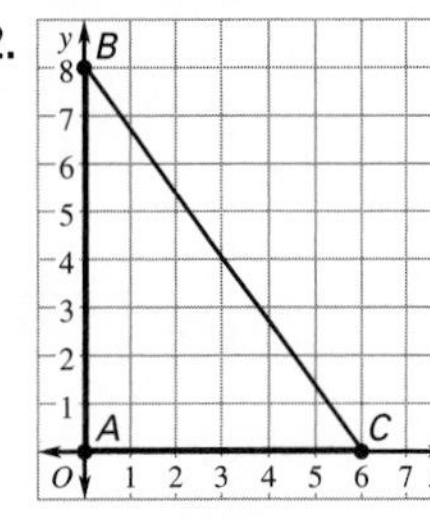

23. 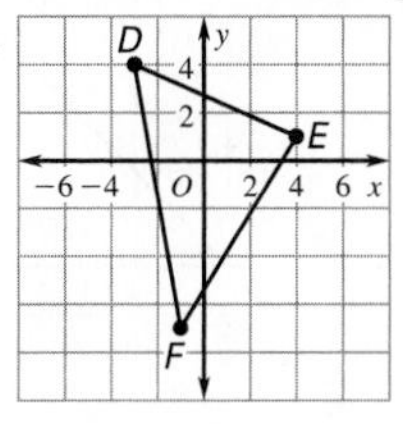

24. 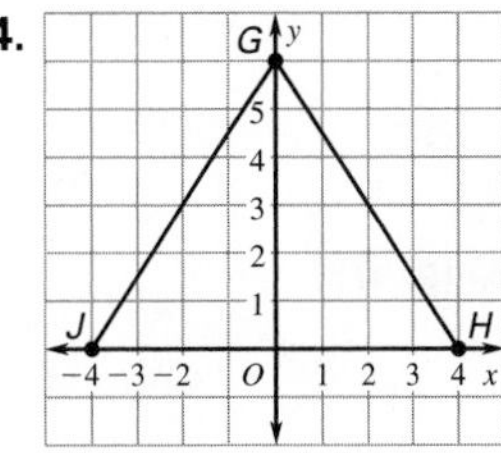

25. 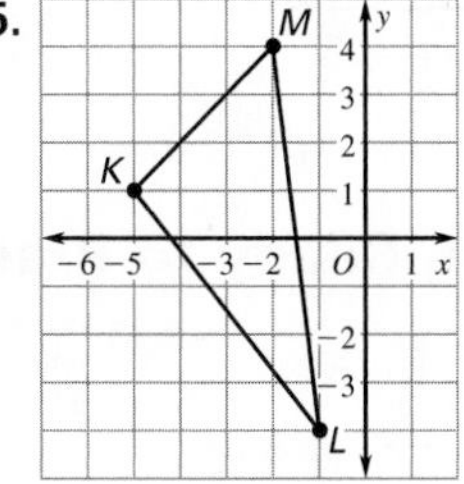

11.6 Mixed Review (p. 574)

35. 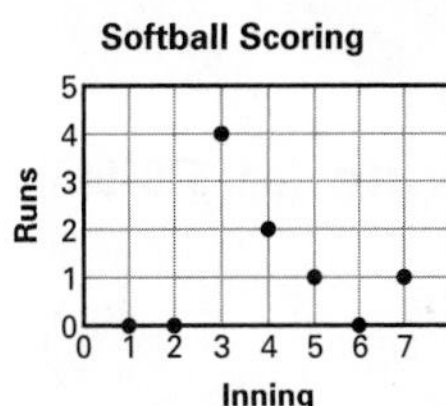

11.7 Hands-on Activity (pp. 575–576)

2. 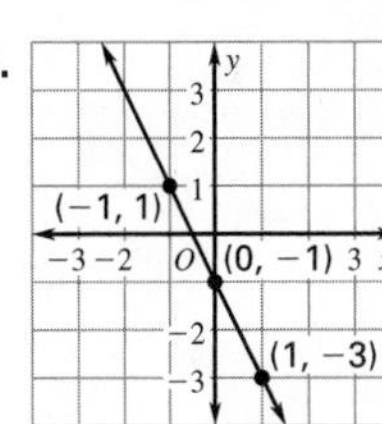

8. 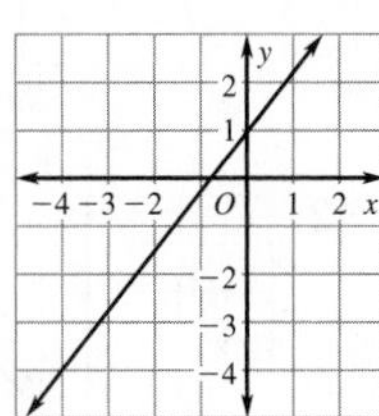

slope: $\frac{5}{4}$, y-intercept: 1

9–12. Sample tables are given.

9. $y = \frac{1}{2}x - 2$

x	−2	0	2
y	−3	−2	−1

slope: $\frac{1}{2}$, y-intercept: −2

10. $y = -\frac{2}{3}x + 3$

x	−3	0	3
y	5	3	1

slope: $-\frac{2}{3}$, y-intercept: 3

11. $y = -4x - 5$

x	0	1	2
y	−5	−9	−13

slope: −4, y-intercept: −5

12. $y = 3x - 5$

x	0	1	2
y	−5	−2	1

slope: 3, y-intercept: −5

13.

14.

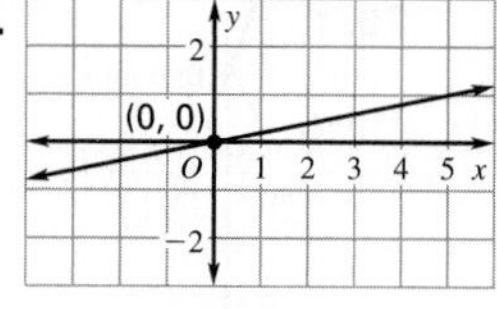

11.7 Your turn now (p. 578)

1.

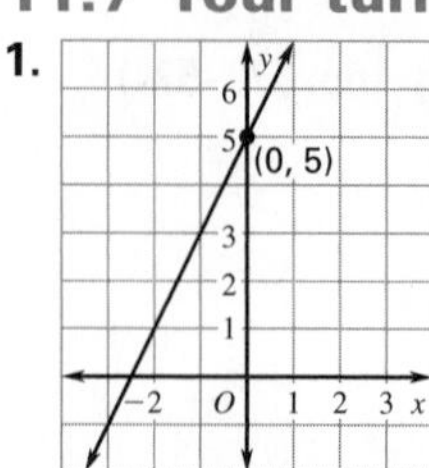

2.

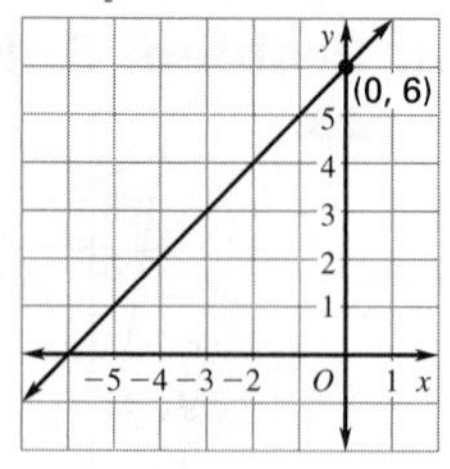

3.

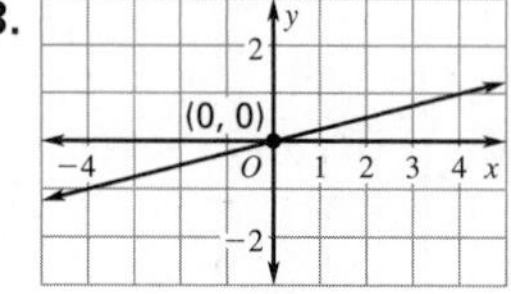

11.7 Getting Ready to Practice (p. 579)

8.

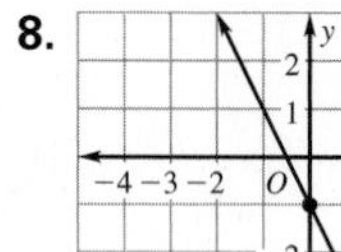

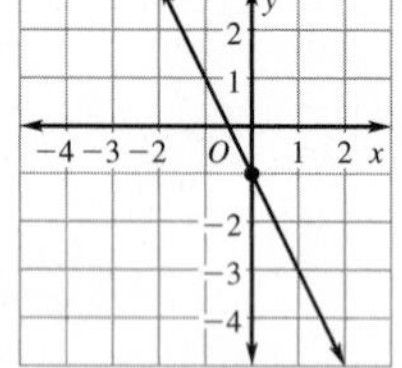

11.7 Practice and Problem Solving (pp. 579–580)

9.

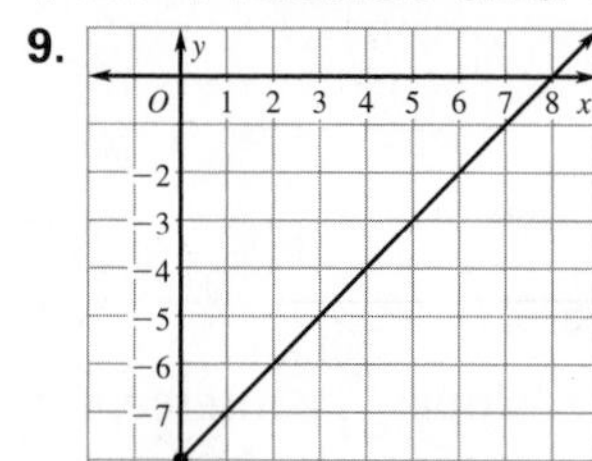

10.

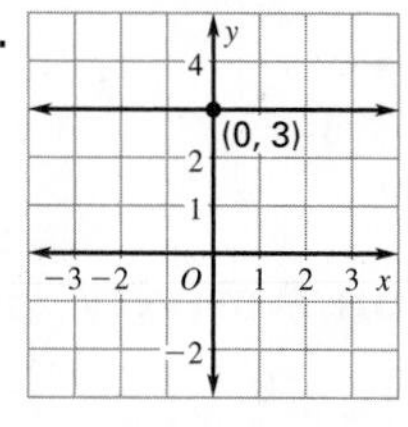

11.

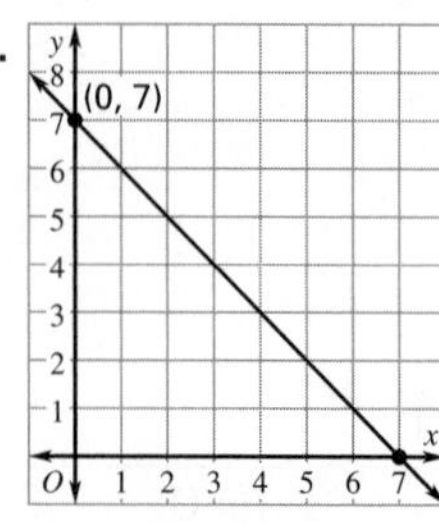

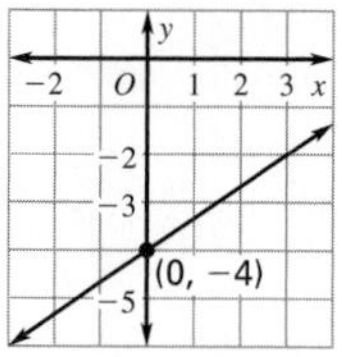

12.

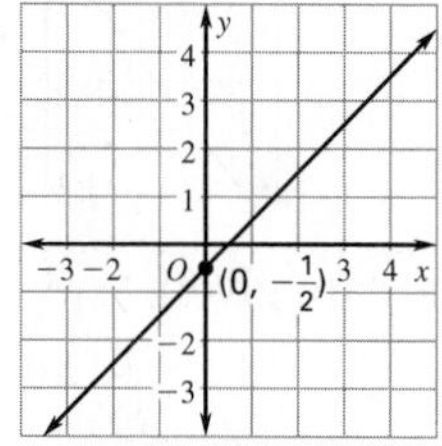

21.

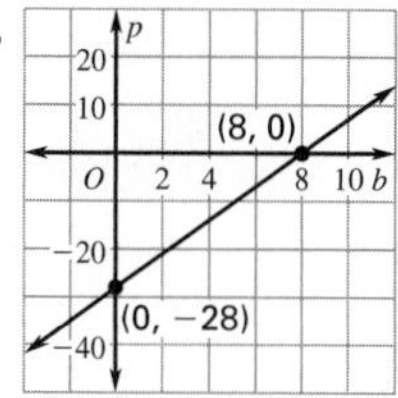

25.

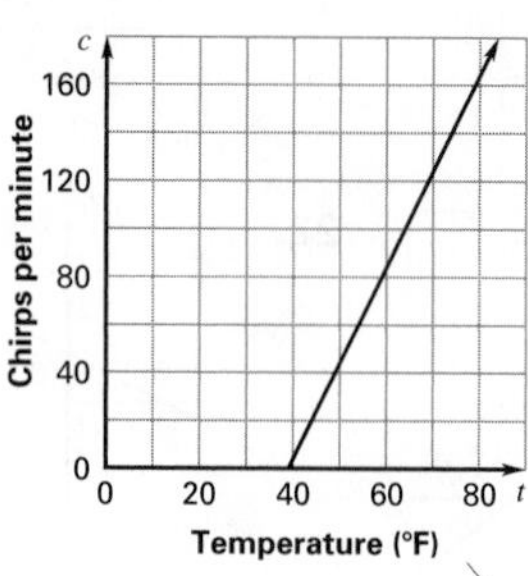

26.

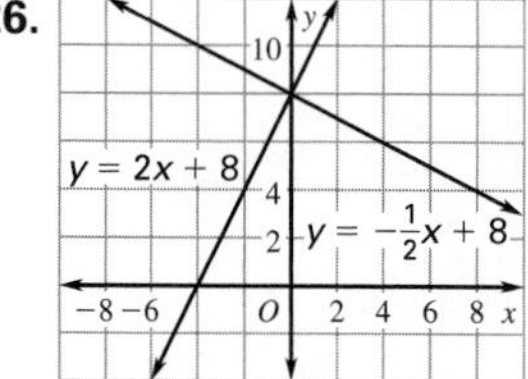

11.7 Mixed Review (p. 580)

32.

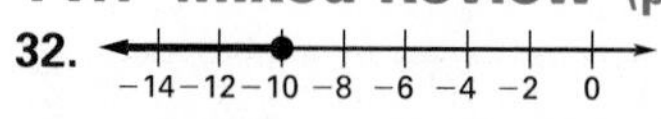

33.

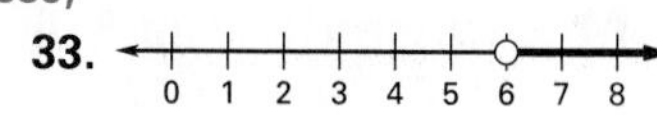

34.

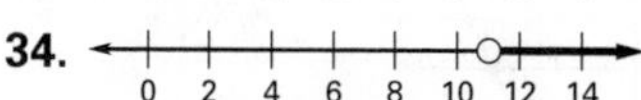

11.7 Test-Taking Practice (p. 580)

35.

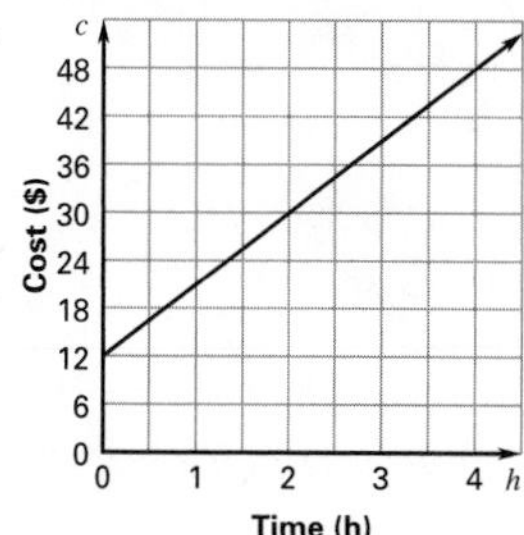

Special Topic Exercises (p. 582)

2.

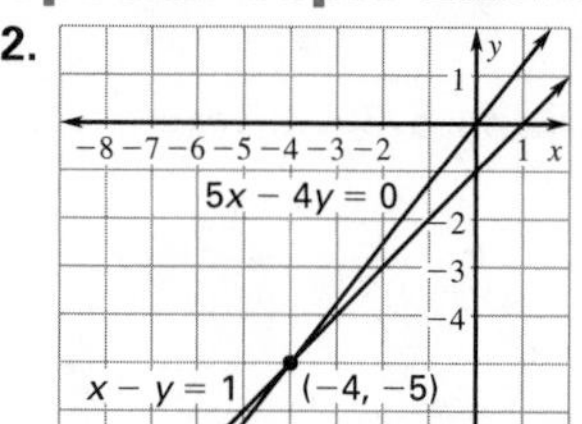

3.

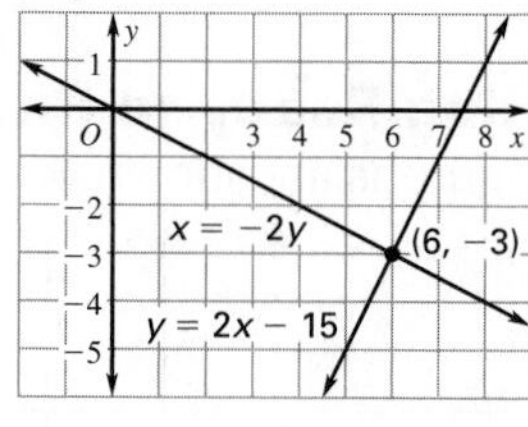

7.

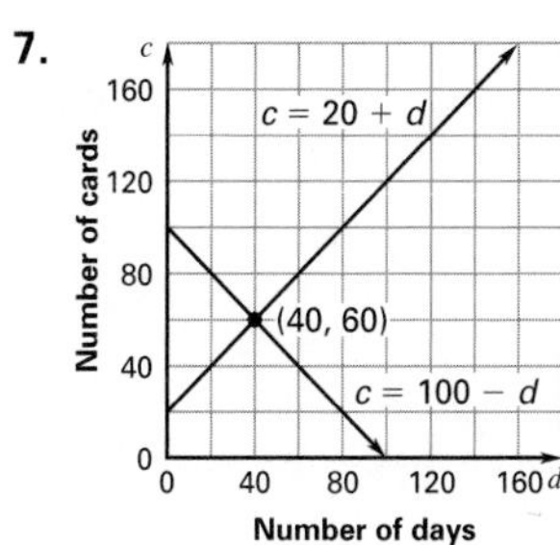

11.8 In-lesson Activity (p. 583)

Steps 3–4.

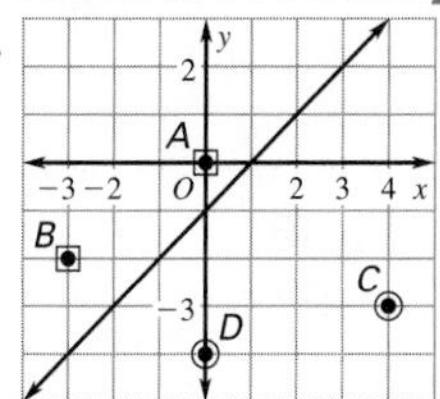

11.8 Your turn now (p. 584)

5.

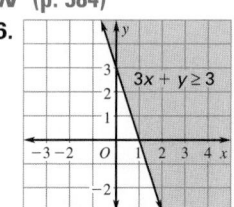

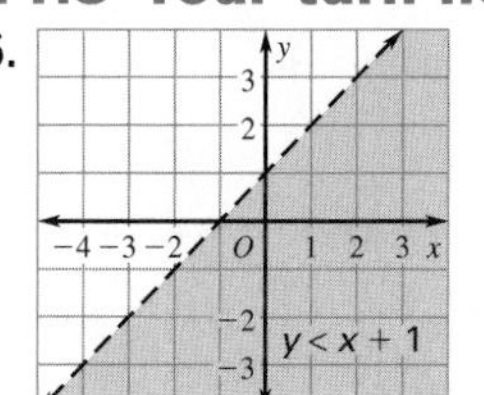

6. $3x + y \geq 3$

7. $x - 2y \geq -1$

8.

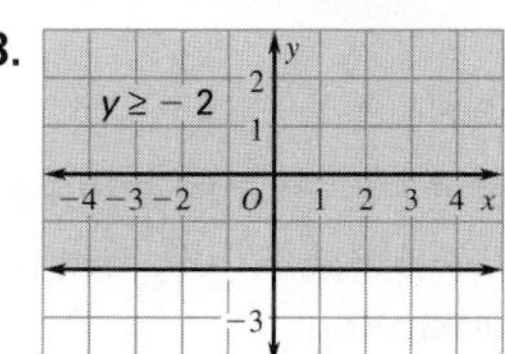

11.8 Getting Ready to Practice (p. 585)

6.

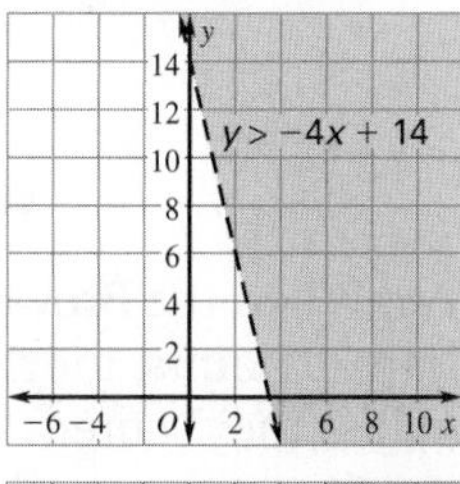

7. $y < x + 5$

8.

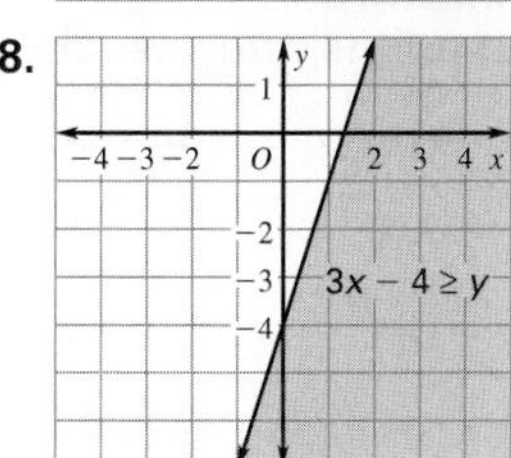

9.

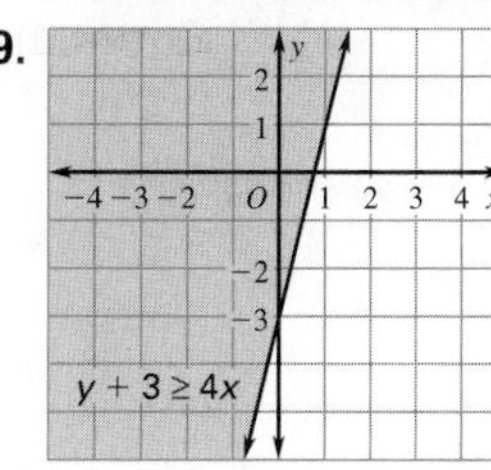

10.

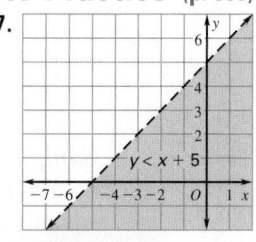

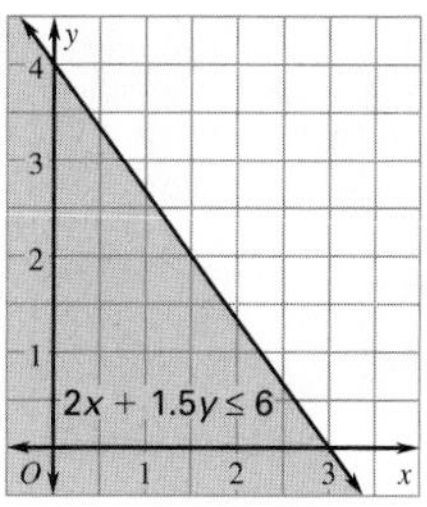

11.8 Practice and Problem Solving (pp. 586–587)

20.

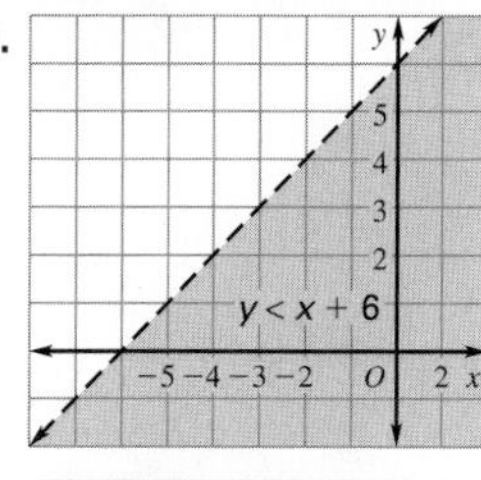

21.

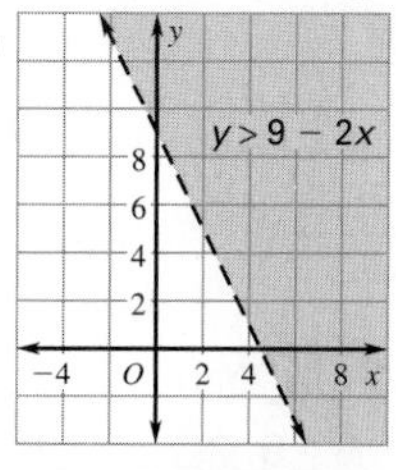

22.

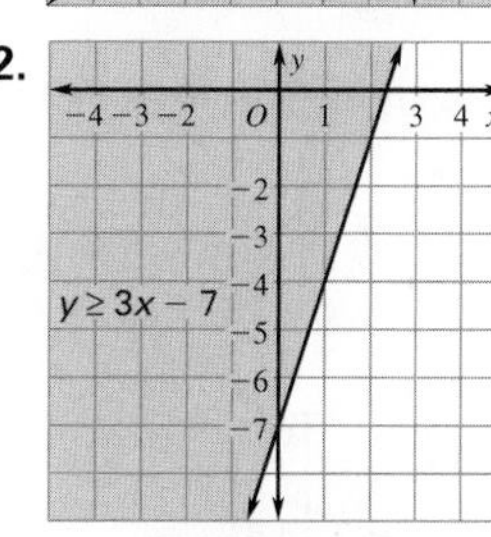

23.

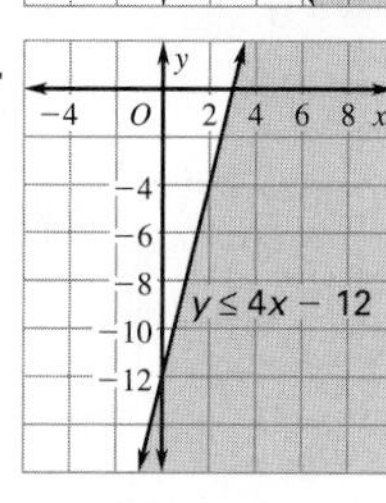

24.

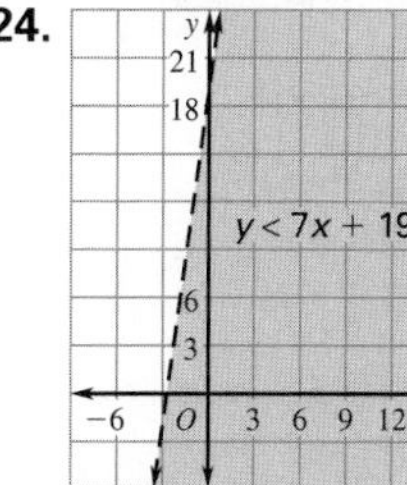

25.

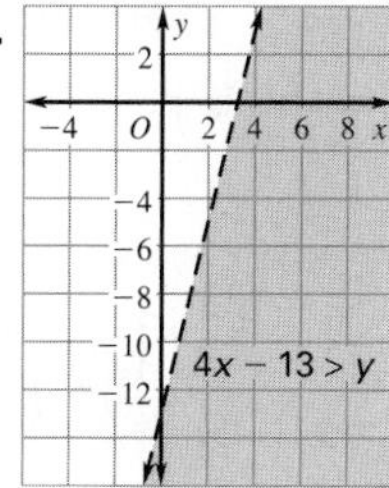

26. $5x \leq 45$

27.

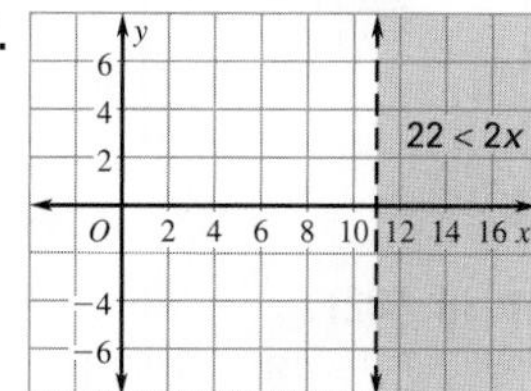

28.

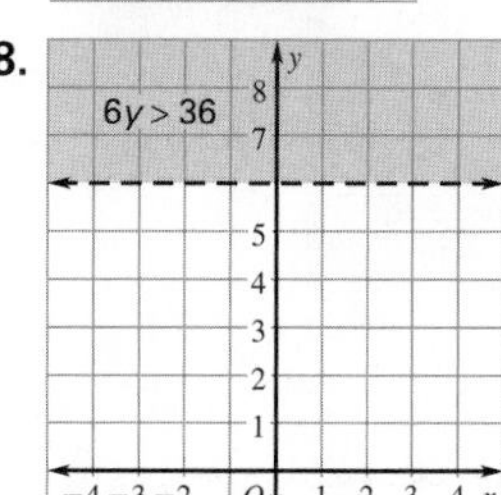

29.

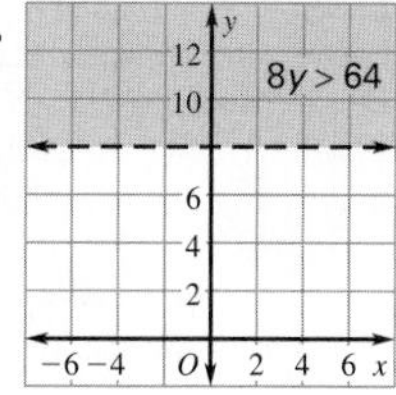

30.

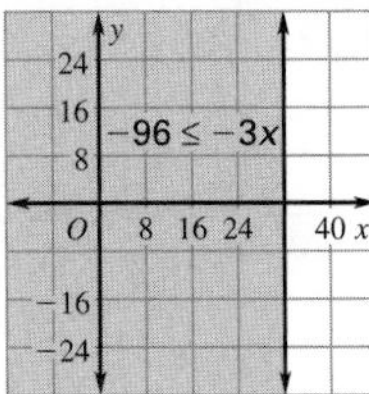

31. $-2y \ge 74$

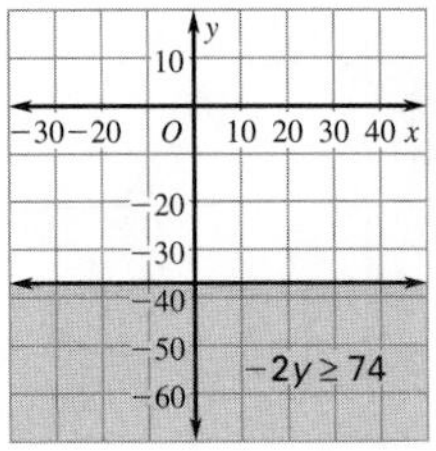

33.

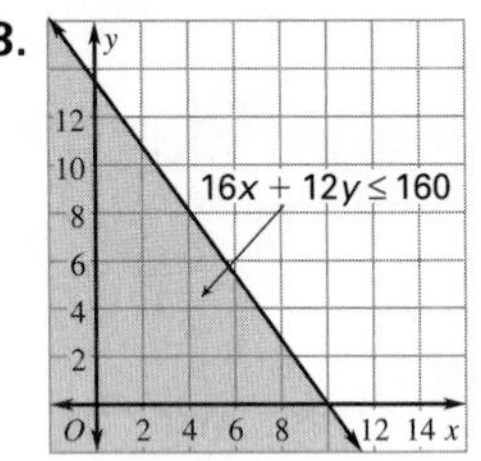

Review Quiz 2 (p. 589)

8.

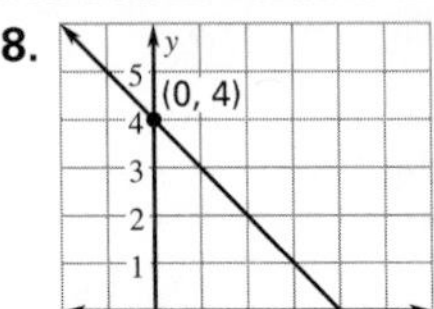

9.

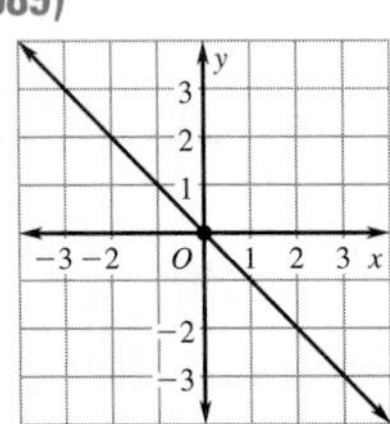

10.

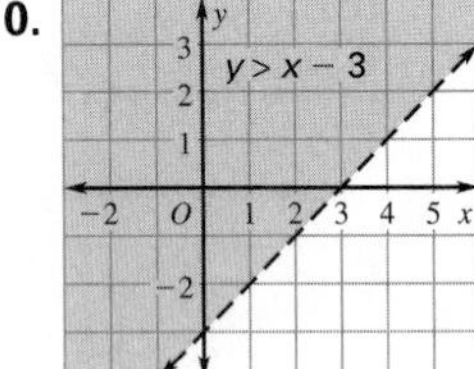

11.

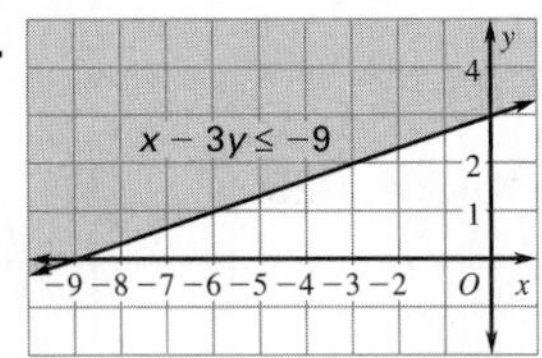

12.

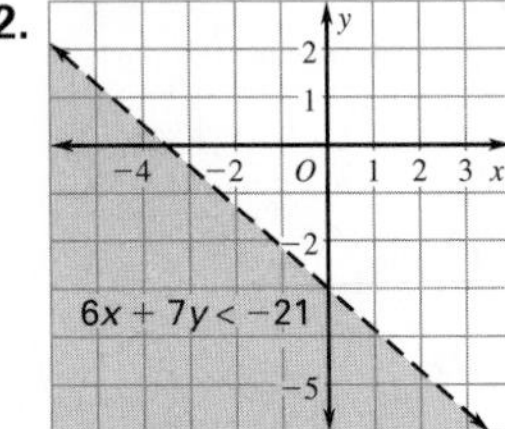

13.

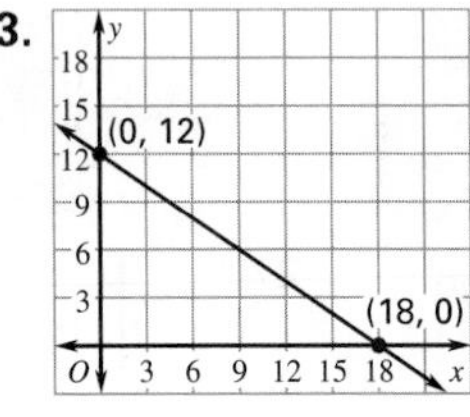

Chapter Test (p. 592)

17.

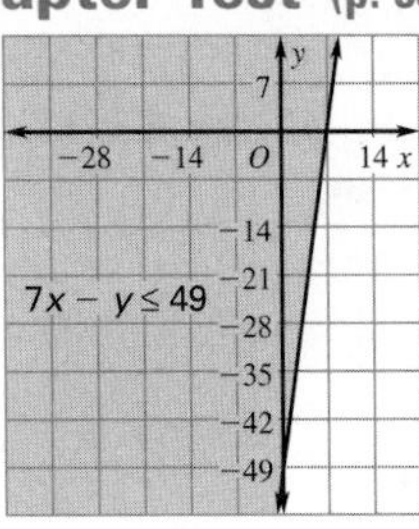

18.

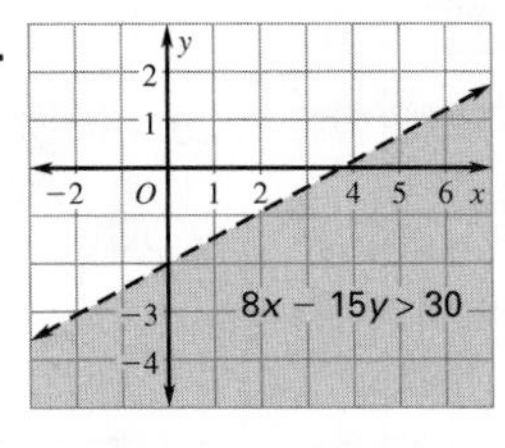

19.

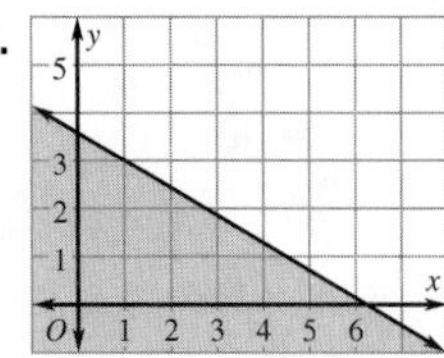

Chapter 12

12.1 Practice and Problem Solving (pp. 599–600)

8. 0–9

Stem	Leaves
0	4 6 8 9
1	2 4
2	6
3	3 5 7

Key: 1 | 2 = 12

9. 100–109

Stem	Leaves
8	9
9	4 5
10	3 8 9
11	2

Key: 10 | 3 = 103

10. 460–469

Stem	Leaves
43	9
44	
45	
46	1 7
47	
48	5
49	2
50	1

Key: 43 | 9 = 439

11. 18.0–18.9

Stem	Leaves
18	1 3 7
19	
20	2
21	
22	5 6

Key: 18 | 1 = 18.1

12. 5.0–5.9

Stem	Leaves
3	2
4	0
5	1 3 3 7
6	9

Key: 3 | 2 = 3.2

13. Count the total number of values in the data set. Then count from the first leaf to half the total number of values to find the median value.

15. 53; greater than

Stem	Leaves
4	3 7
5	5 8 9
6	5
7	2 8
8	4 4
9	5 6

Key: 4 | 3 = 43

19.

Wins		Losses
	0	6 7 7
8	1	0 2 4 5 6
7 4 4 3 0	2	1
	3	
1	4	

Key: 0 | 2 | 1 = 20 and 21

Sample answer: When the Browns scored less than 20 points, they usually lost. When they scored more than 20 points, they usually won.

20.

56	8 9
57	6
58	0
59	
60	1
61	6
62	7
63	
64	
65	7
66	8
67	
68	
69	1 9
70	5

Key: 56 | 8 = 56.8

22.

13	8 8
14	2 4
15	6
16	4
17	1
18	7
19	3
20	6
21	1 4

Key: 14 | 2 = 14.2

Sample answer: The temperatures in degrees Celsius are lower than the temperatures in degrees Fahrenheit, and distributed over a smaller range. This is because as temperatures change by 1 degree Celsius, they change by 1.8 degrees Fahrenheit.

12.2 Your turn now (p. 602)

1. 15 20 25 30 35 40 45

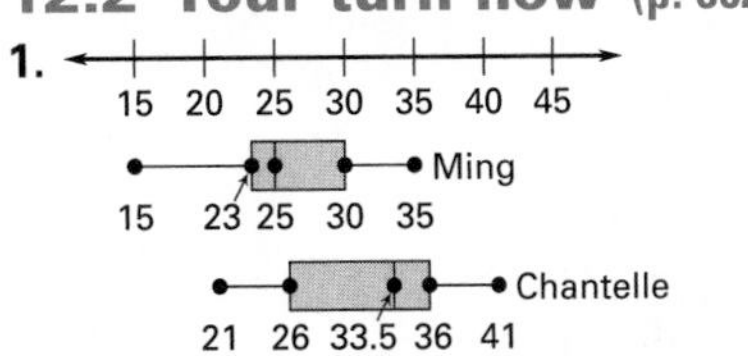

12.2 Getting Ready to Practice (p. 603)

2. Step 1: 100 150 200 250 300 350

Step 3: 100 150 200 250 300 350

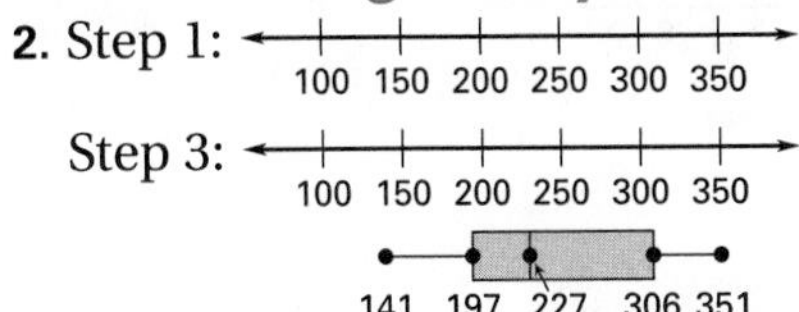

12.2 Practice and Problem Solving (pp. 603–604)

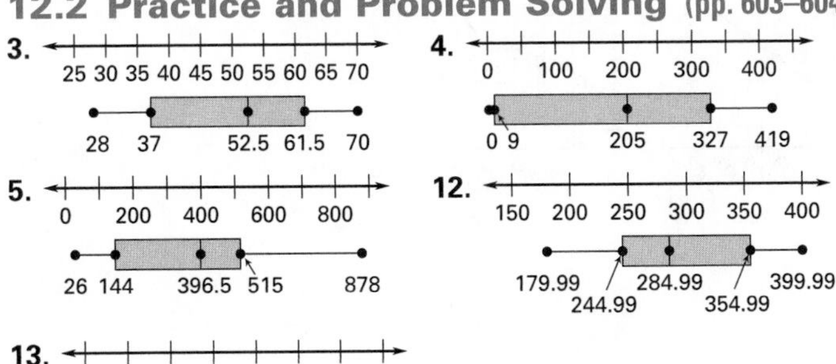

13. 700 800 900 1000

731 789 817 838 1020

15. *Sample answer:* Karen has a higher median score than Tasha, 11 points versus 9 points, but her performance is much more variable. For Karen, it took an interval of 7, from 7 to 14, to contain half of her point totals, but for Tasha, it took only an interval of 4, from 8 to 12, to contain half of her point totals, so Tasha's scoring is more consistent. This is also shown by the fact that the extremes for Tasha are between the extremes for Karen, and the range for Tasha is only 8 points, but 15 points for Karen.

16.

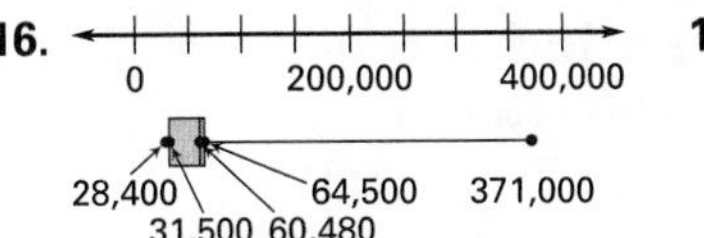

17.

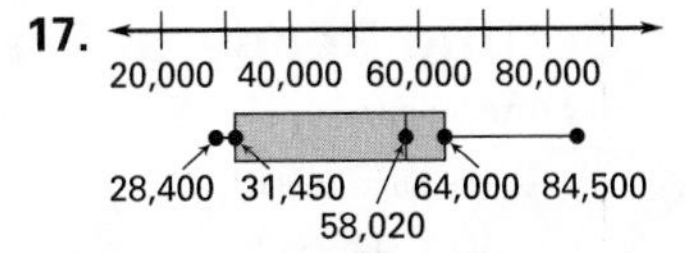

18. *Sample answer:* Change 5 to 14. Because the desired median and lower quartile were above the actual ones, I wanted to change a data value from the first quartile to a greater value. To keep the upper quartile the same, I wanted the new value to lie in the new third quartile, where the values are from 14 to 17.

12.2 Mixed Review (p. 604)

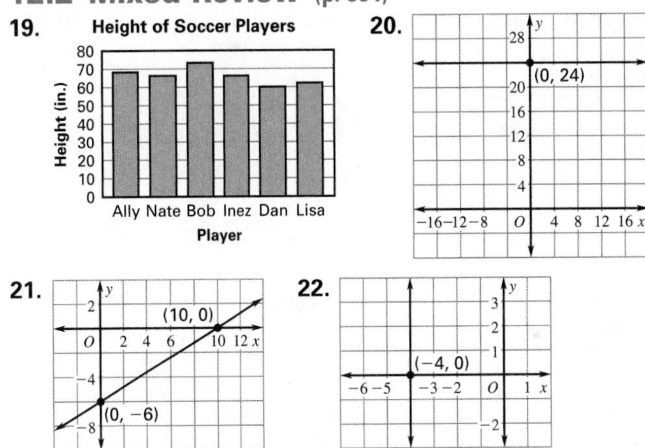

12.2 Test-Taking Practice (p. 604)

23.

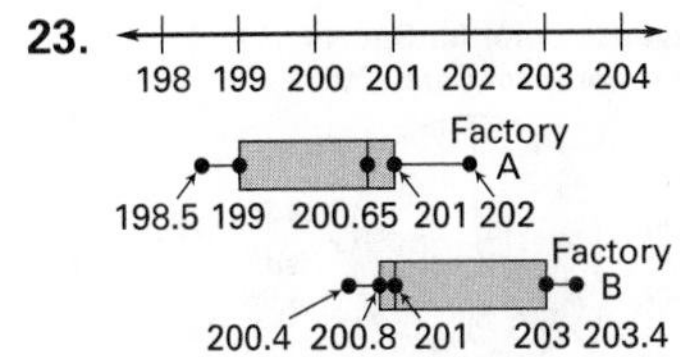

Sample answer: All of Factory A's bolts were within the desired range, and more than half but less than three quarters of Factory B's bolts were within the desired range, with the rest above the desired range. The masses of half of Factory B's bolts were at or above the upper quartile for Factory A, and the lower extreme for Factory B was nearly as high as the median for Factory A. So in general, the masses of Factory B's bolts were greater.

12.3 Your turn now (p. 606)

1. Who Will You Vote For?

2. Votes for Ben

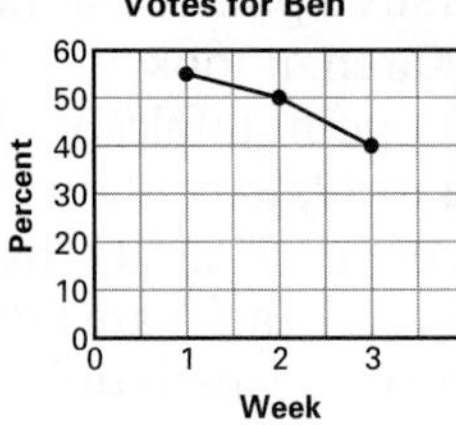

12.3 Getting Ready to Practice (p. 607)

7. Play Attendance

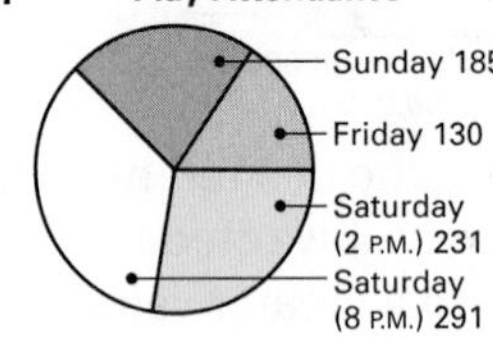

8. Money Collected

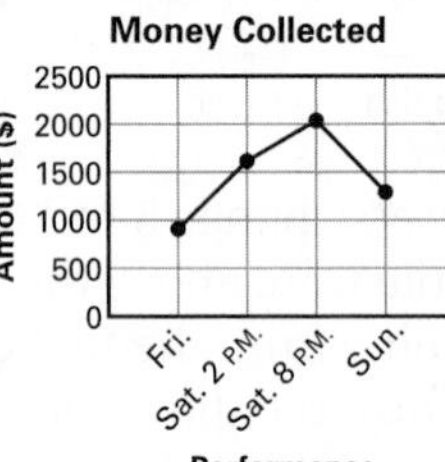

12.3 Practice and Problem Solving (pp. 608–609)

9. How Often Do You Snack?

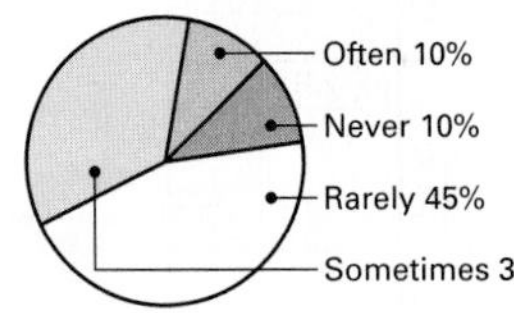

10. New Single-Family House Sales

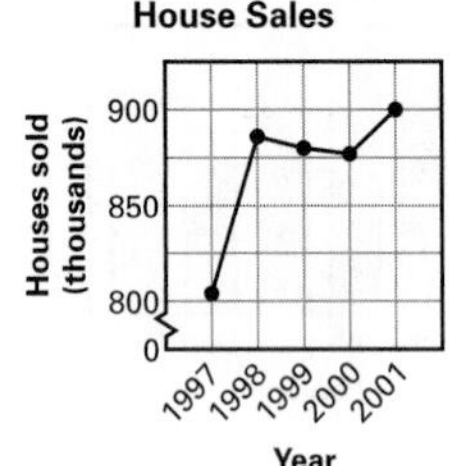

11. Attendance at Symphony Orchestra Concerts

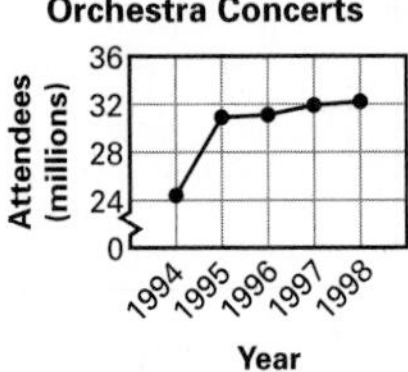

13. Land Area of New York City

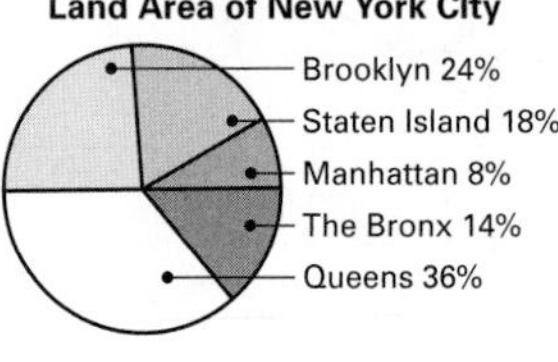

18. Favorite Color for Sports and Compact Cars 2000

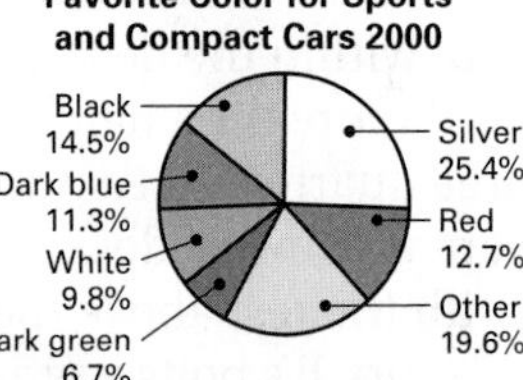

Favorite Color for Sports and Compact Cars 2001

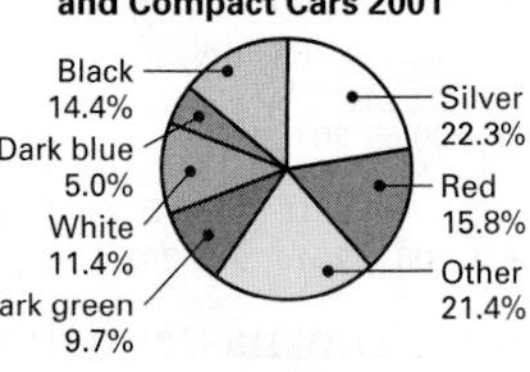

22. *Sample answer:* Temperatures collected at the same time every day for a month could be shown in a stem-and-leaf plot, a box-and-whisker plot, or a histogram. For the stem-and-leaf plot, just order the data and group it into the plot. For the box-and-whisker plot, find the extremes, the upper quartile, the median, and the lower quartile, and draw the plot. For the histogram, count the number of temperatures in each of several adjoining intervals and draw the graph.

12.3 Mixed Review (p. 609)

23.

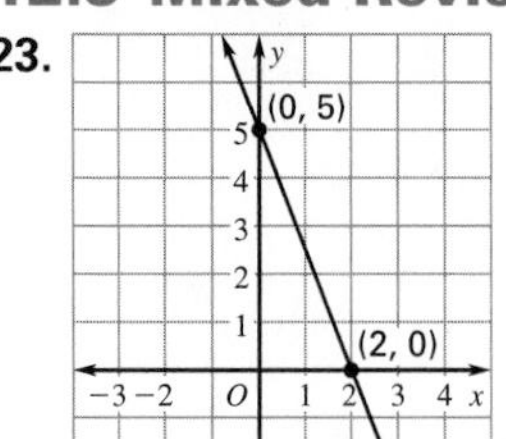

24.

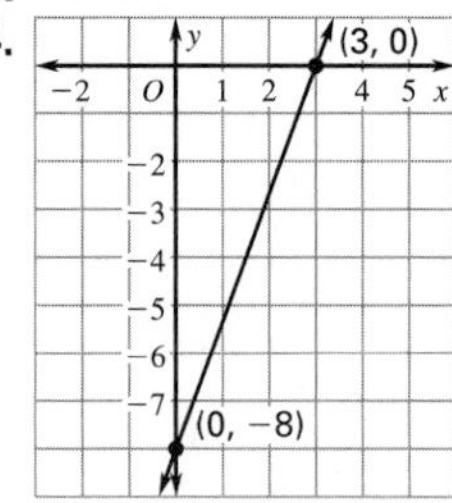

25.

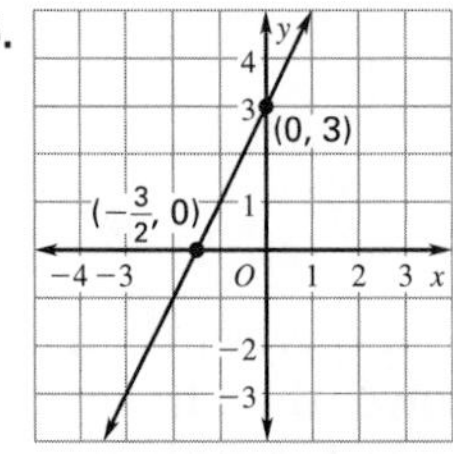

12.3 Technology Activity (p. 610)

1.

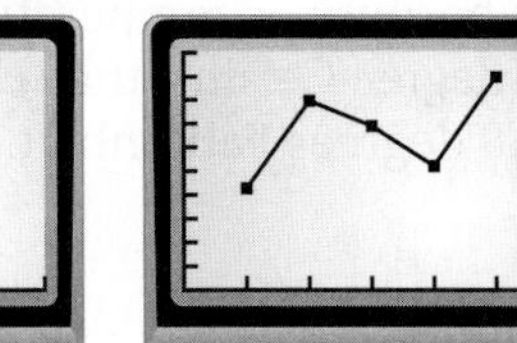

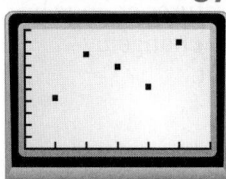

Special Topic Exercises (p. 613)

1. Test Scores

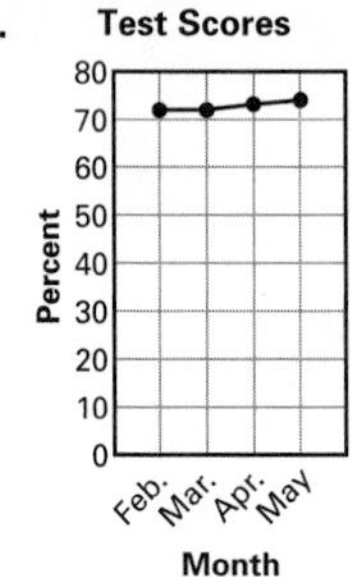

2. CD Prices

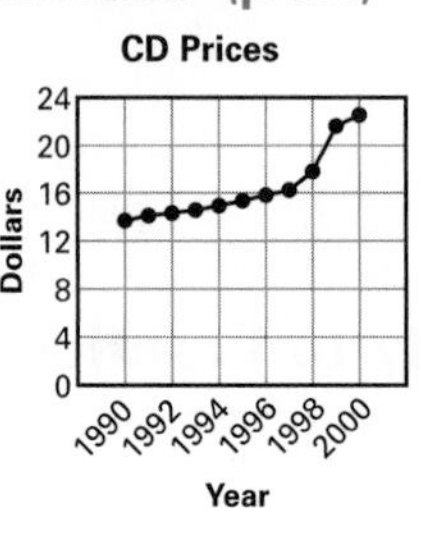

3. Pitcher Wins

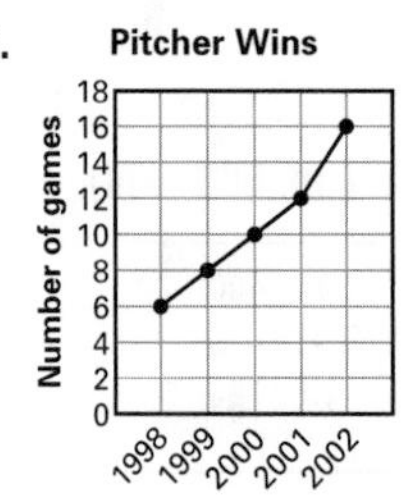

Pitcher Losses

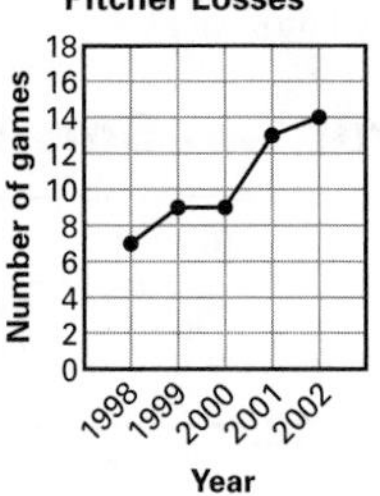

Review Quiz 1 (p. 615)

2. 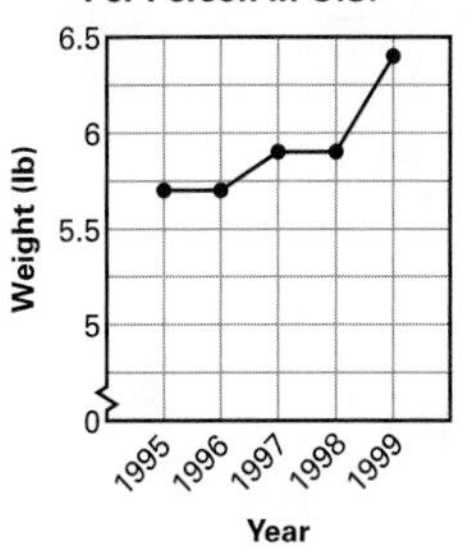

Sample answer: I used a line graph because the data varied over time.

12.4 Mixed Review (p. 622)

27. 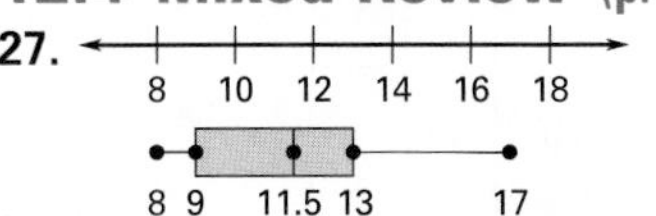

12.4 Test-Taking Practice (p. 622)

29. 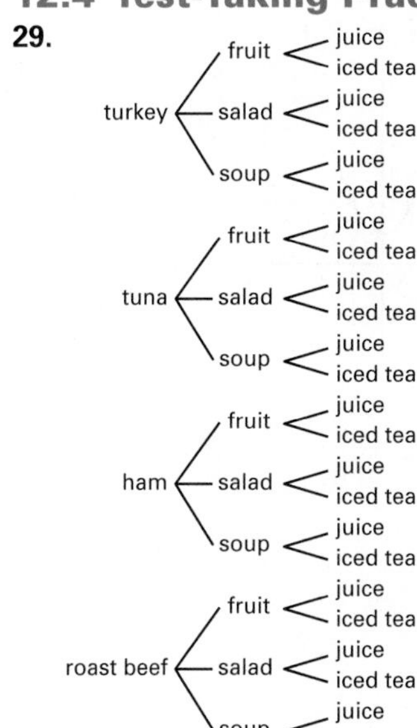

12.5 Mixed Review (p. 626)

29. Favorite Color

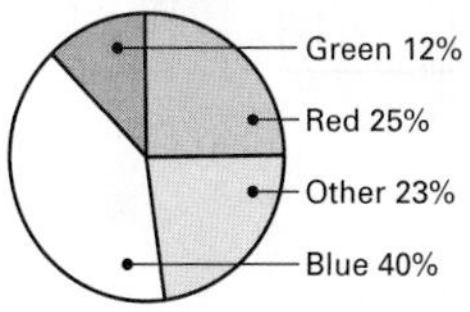

Green 12%

Red 25%

Other 23%

Blue 40%

30. 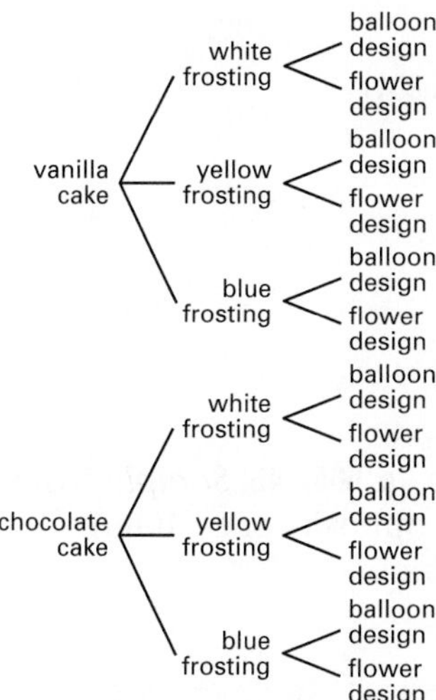

12.6 Getting Ready to Practice (p. 629)

2. The answer given is the number of permutations of the projects because it considers order. To find the number of combinations, divide the given answer by 3!: $\frac{6 \cdot 5 \cdot 4}{3 \cdot 2 \cdot 1} = 5 \cdot 4 = 20$ ways to choose.

12.8 Mixed Review (p. 643)

17. 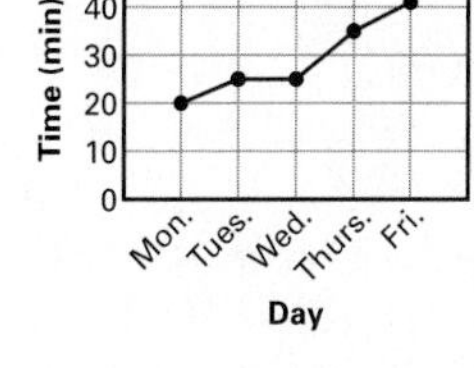

Chapter Test (p. 650)

4. 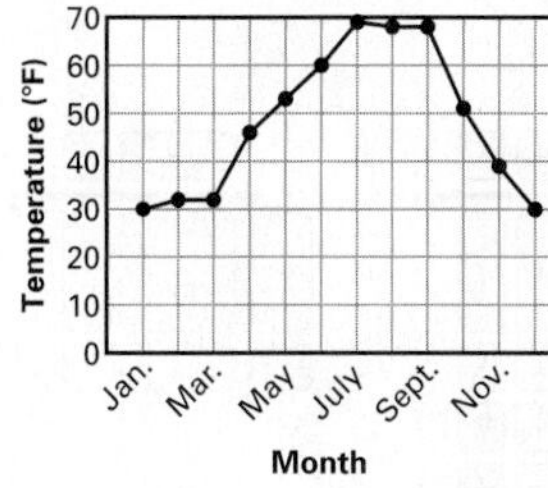

6. 24 orders; 1, 2, 3, 4; 1, 2, 4, 3; 1, 3, 2, 4; 1, 3, 4, 2; 1, 4, 2, 3; 1, 4, 3, 2; 2, 1, 3, 4; 2, 1, 4, 3; 2, 3, 1, 4; 2, 3, 4, 1; 2, 4, 1, 3; 2, 4, 3, 1; 3, 1, 2, 4; 3, 1, 4, 2; 3, 2, 1, 4; 3, 2, 4, 1; 3, 4, 1, 2; 3, 4, 2, 1; 4, 1, 2, 3; 4, 1, 3, 2; 4, 2, 1, 3; 4, 2, 3, 1; 4, 3, 1, 2; 4, 3, 2, 1

Exploring Math in Science (pp. 652–653)

4. In each condition listed, the robins did much better than geometric probability predicts for random results. **5.** The results suggest robins use their senses to find worms. They did best when all senses were available. They did much better than expected by chance when sight or sound was available.

Chapter 13

13.2 In-lesson Activity (p. 661)

Step 2.

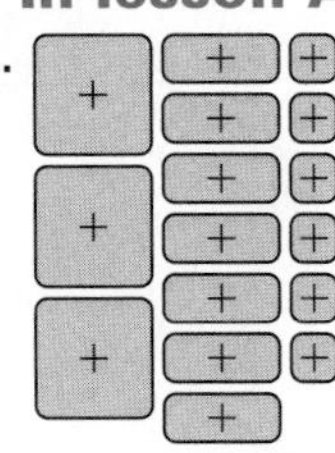

13.2 Test-Taking Practice (p. 665)

45. *Sample answer:* Use a vertical format, adding the opposite of each term of the second expression to the first expression:

$$\begin{array}{r} x^4 - 3x^3 \qquad\quad + 5x + 3 \\ -x^4 - 2x^3 + 9x^2 \qquad\qquad \\ \hline -5x^3 + 9x^2 + 5x + 3 \end{array}$$

Use a horizontal format and the distributive property: $(x^4 - 3x^3 + 5x + 3) - (x^4 + 2x^3 - 9x^2) = x^4 - 3x^3 + 5x + 3 - x^4 - 2x^3 + 9x^2 = (x^4 - x^4) + (-3x^3 - 2x^3) + 9x^2 + 5x + 3 = -5x^3 + 9x^2 + 5x + 3$.

13.3 In-lesson Activity (p. 666)

Step 1. second row: $(-2) \cdot x \cdot 5 \cdot x \cdot x \cdot x \cdot x$, $(-2) \cdot 5 \cdot x \cdot x \cdot x \cdot x \cdot x$, $-10x^5$; fourth row: $4x \cdot 4x$, $4 \cdot 4 \cdot x \cdot x$, $16x^2$; fifth row: $(-3x) \cdot (-3x) \cdot (-3x)$, $(-3) \cdot (-3) \cdot (-3) \cdot x \cdot x \cdot x$, $-27x^3$

13.4 Hands-on Activity (p. 673)

1.

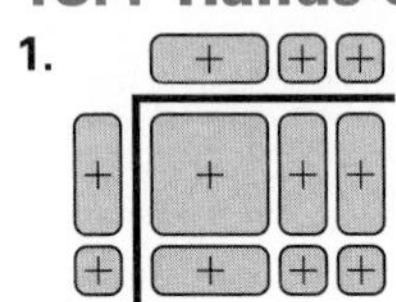

2.

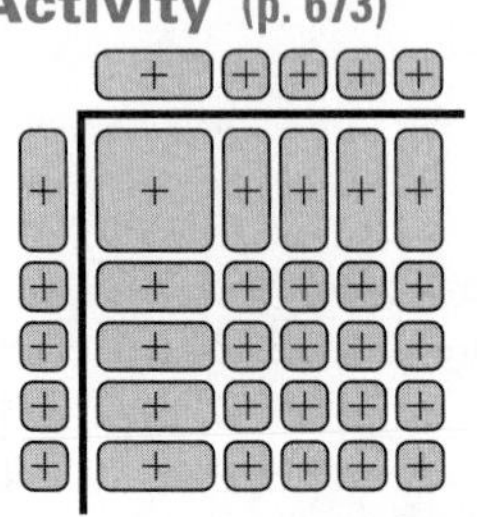

3.

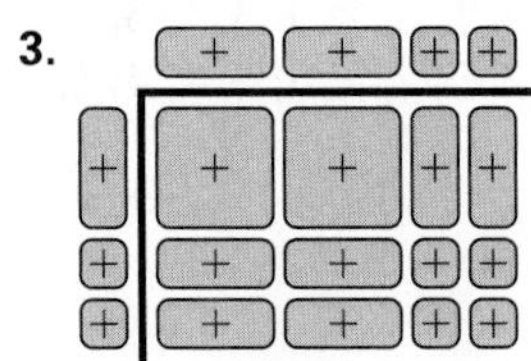

4.

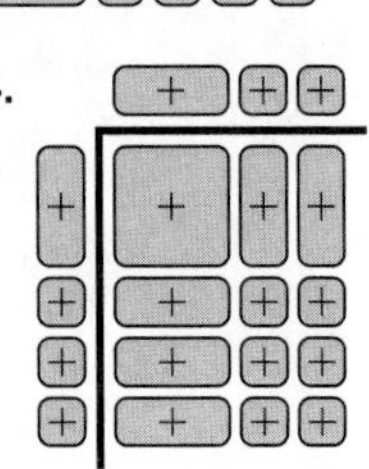

5.

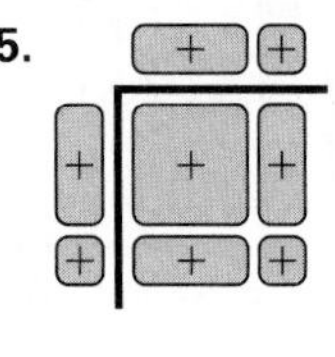

6.

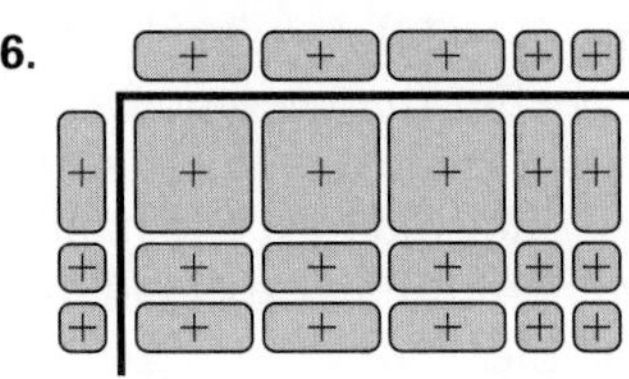

13.4 Mixed Review (p. 677)

32.

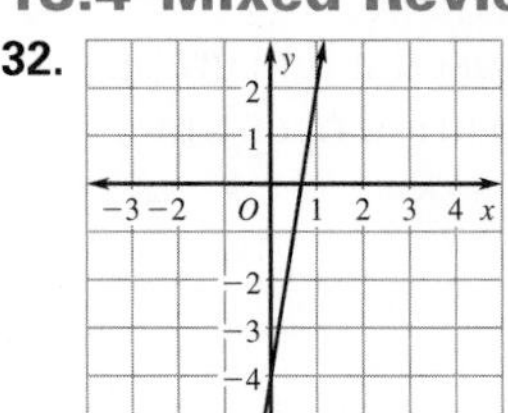

33.

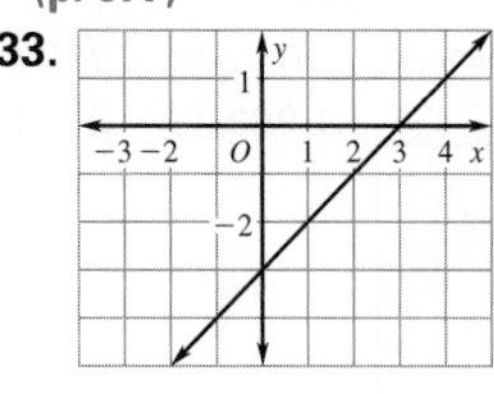

34.

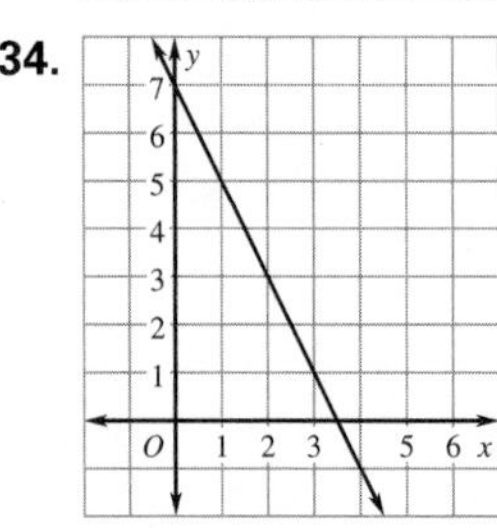

38–41.

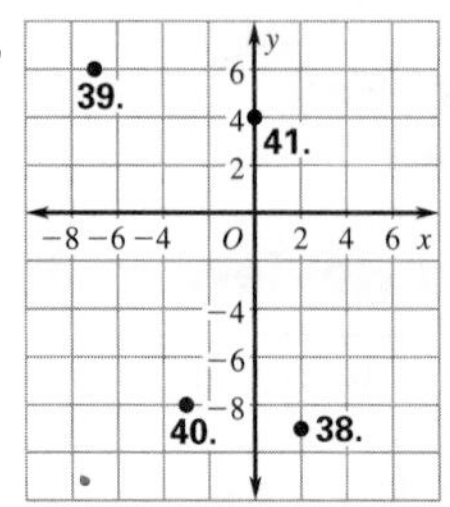

13.5 Your turn now (p. 681)

4.

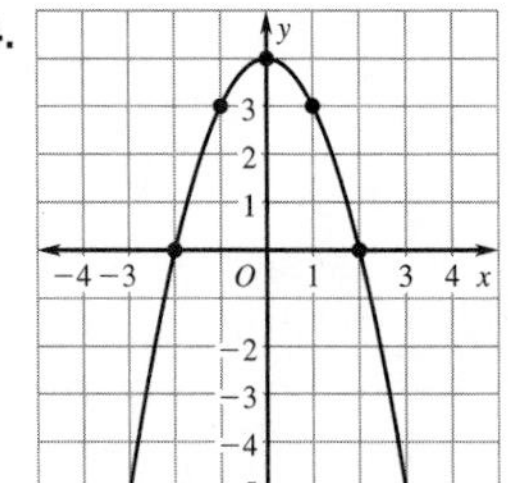

5.

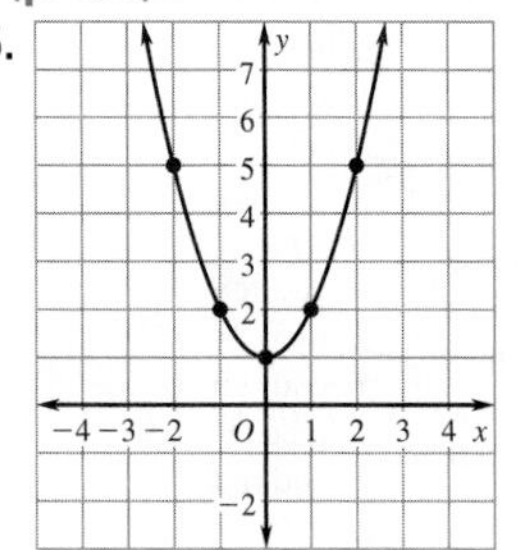

6.

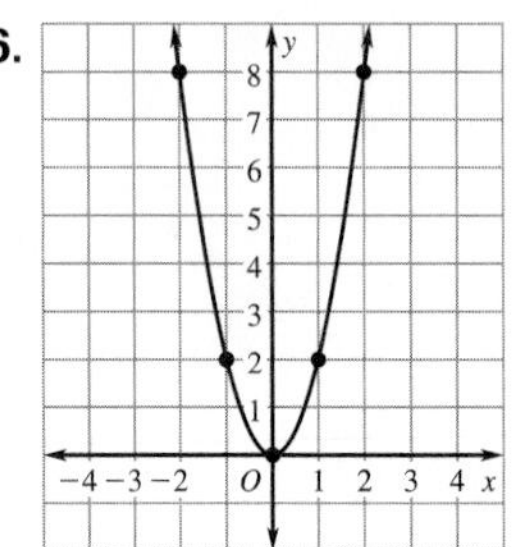

13.5 Practice and Problem Solving (pp. 682–683)

12.

x	−3	−2	−1	0	1	2	3
$f(x)$	36	16	4	0	4	16	36

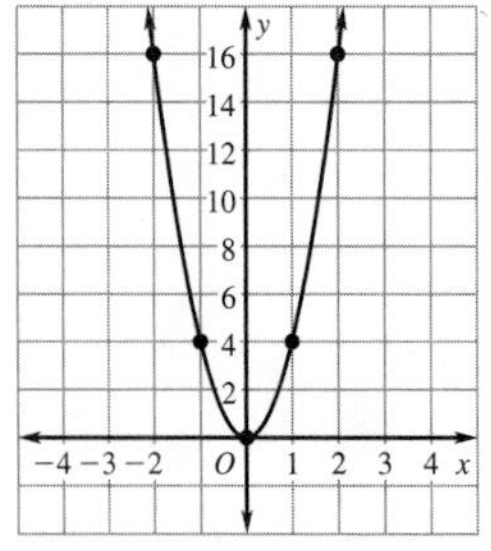

13.

x	−3	−2	−1	0	1	2	3
f(x)	17	12	9	8	9	12	17

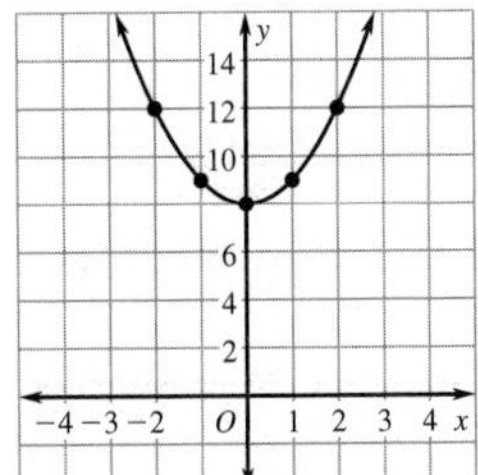

14.

x	−3	−2	−1	0	1	2	3
f(x)	−4	1	4	5	4	1	−4

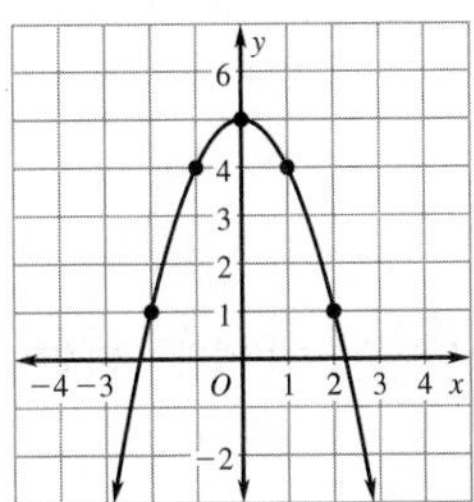

15.

x	−3	−2	−1	0	1	2	3
f(x)	−9	−4	−1	0	−1	−4	−9

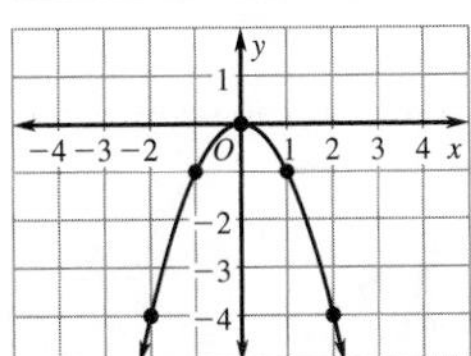

16.

x	−3	−2	−1	0	1	2	3
f(x)	23	8	−1	−4	−1	8	23

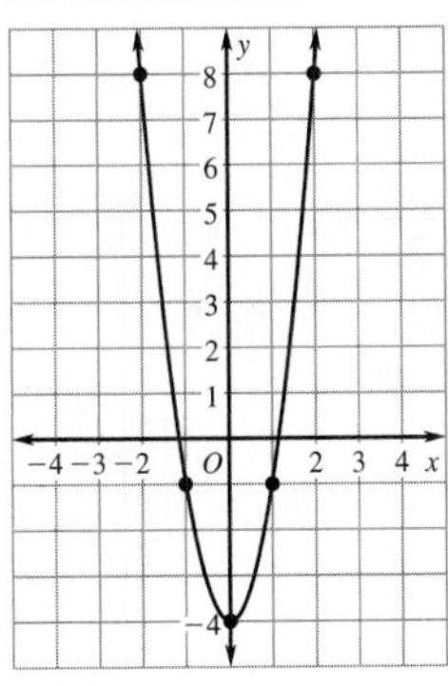

17.

x	−3	−2	−1	0	1	2	3
f(x)	−19	−9	−3	−1	−3	−9	−19

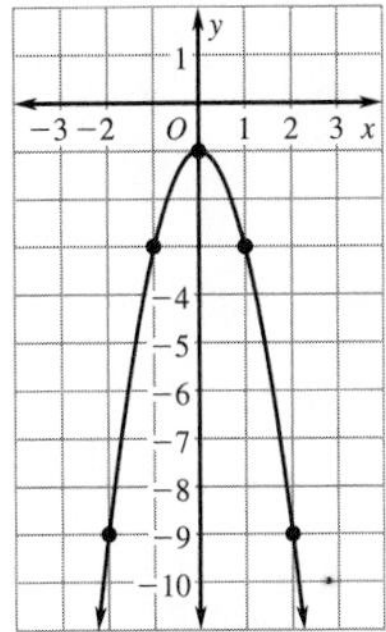

26.

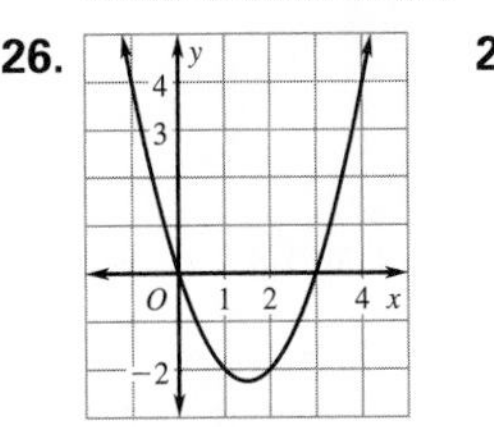

27.

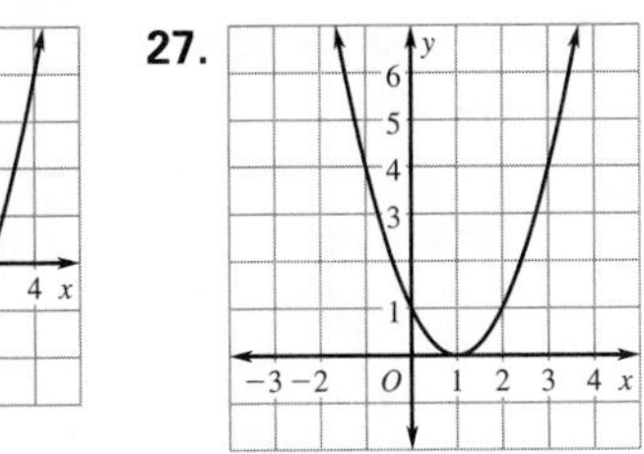

28.

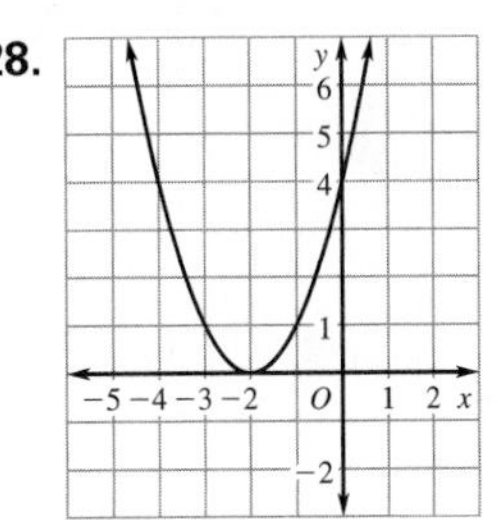

29.

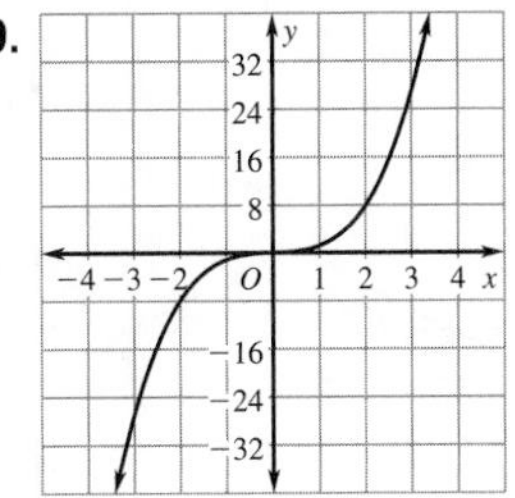

30.

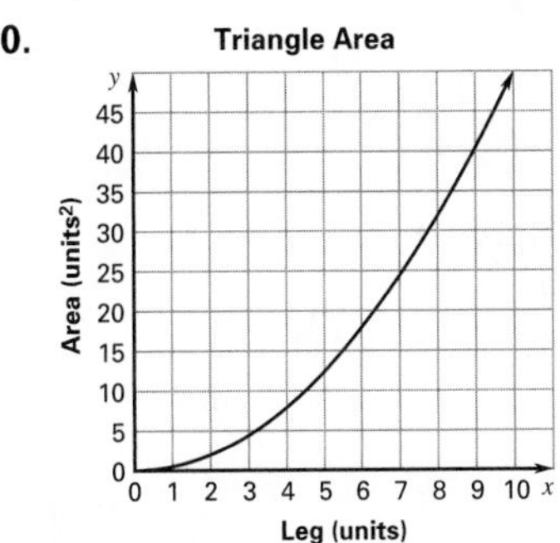

31.

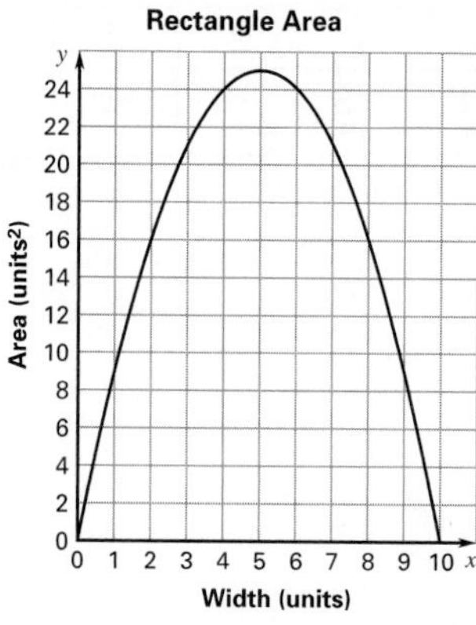

13.5 Test-Taking Practice (p. 684)

49. $f(x) = x^2$ $\quad$ $f(x) = -x^2$

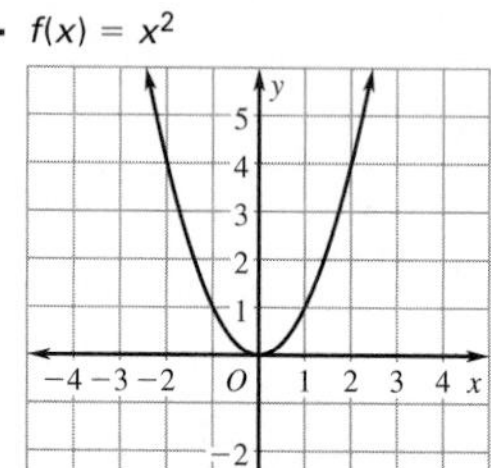

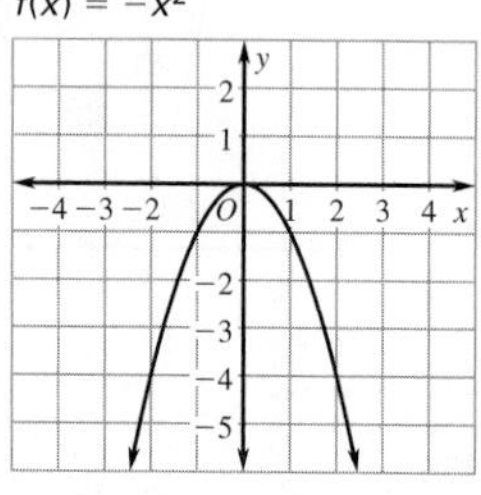

$f(x) = \frac{1}{2}x$ $\quad$ $f(x) = -\frac{1}{2}x$

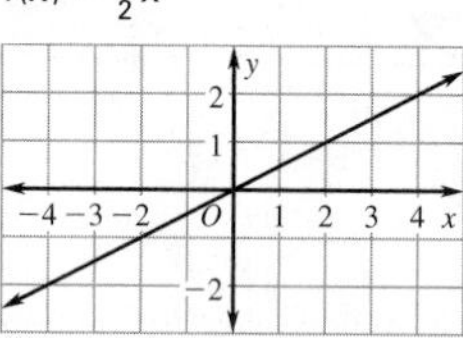

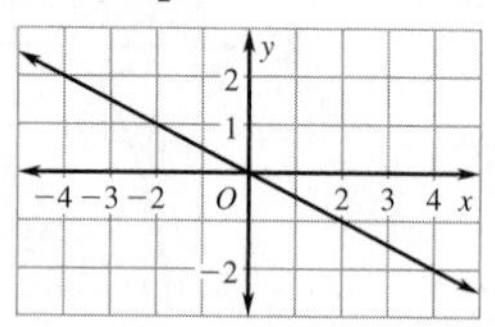

End-of-Course Test

Advanced Algebra Topics (p. 702)

99. 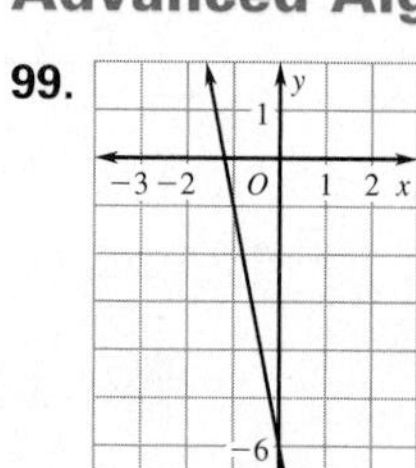 x-intercept: $-\frac{6}{5}$, y-intercept: -6

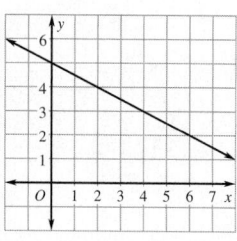

100. x-intercept: 10, y-intercept: 5

101. 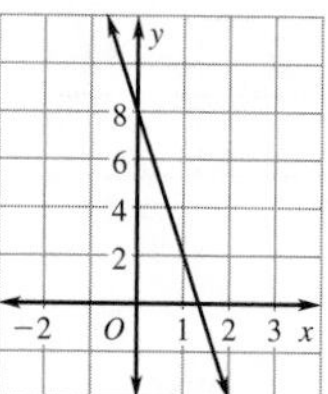 x-intercept: $\frac{4}{3}$, y-intercept: 8

102. 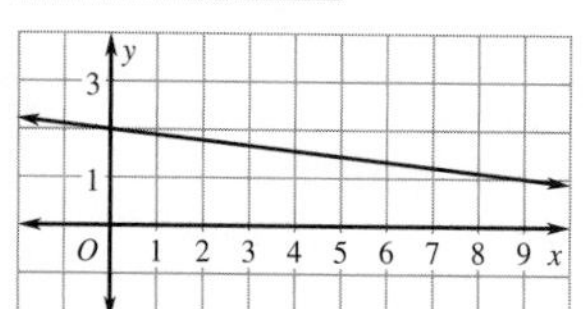 x-intercept: 18, y-intercept: 2

103. 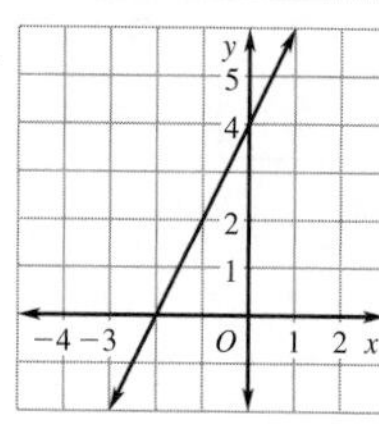 x-intercept: -2, y-intercept: 4

105. $y = -12x + 6$, slope: -12, y-intercept: 6; $y = \frac{13}{11}x - \frac{12}{11}$, slope: $\frac{13}{11}$, y-intercept: $-\frac{12}{11}$

107.

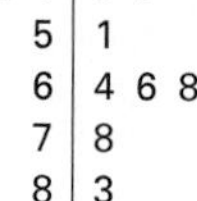

Stem	Leaves
4	6 9
5	1
6	4 6 8
7	8
8	3

Key: 5 | 1 = 51

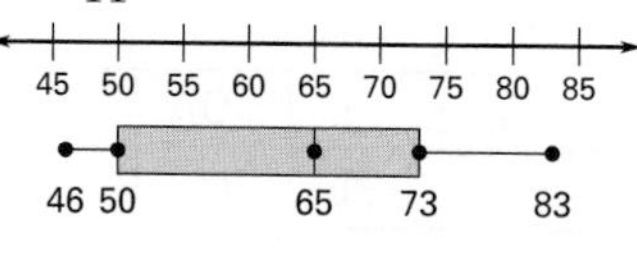

108.

Stem	Leaves
3	8
4	3
5	1 3
6	0 3 6 8

Key: 3 | 8 = $38

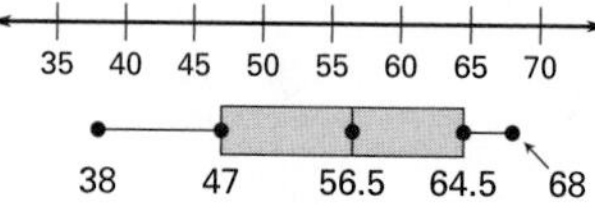

109.

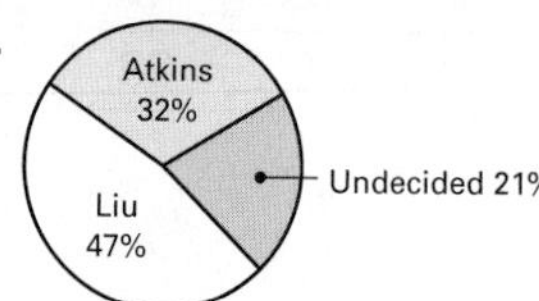

127.

x	-2	-1	0	1	2
y	10	7	6	7	10

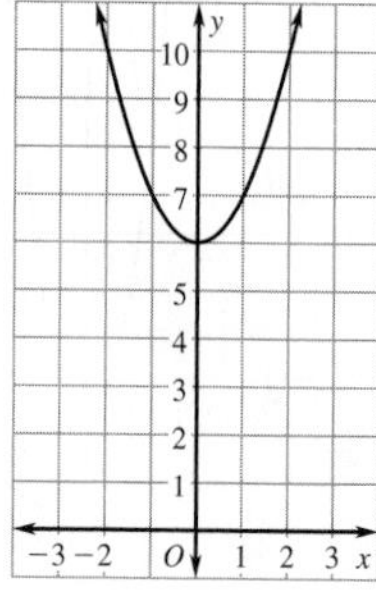

Extra Practice

Chapter 2 (p. 728)

34. $-28 + (74 - 32)$ [original expression]
$= -28 + 42$ [Subtract 32 from 74.]
$= 42 + (-28)$ [commutative property of addition]
$= 42 - 28$ [Change addition to subtraction.]
$= 14$ [Subtract 28 from 42.]

35. $7\left(2 \cdot \frac{3}{7}\right)$ [original expression]
$= 7\left(\frac{3}{7} \cdot 2\right)$ [commutative property of multiplication]
$= \left(7 \cdot \frac{3}{7}\right) \cdot 2$ [associative property of multiplication]
$= 3 \cdot 2$ $\left[\text{Multiply 7 and } \frac{3}{7}.\right]$
$= 6$ [Multiply 3 and 2.]

36. $(-7.2 + 3.5) + (-3.5)$ [original expression]
$= -7.2 + [3.5 + (-3.5)]$ [associative property of addition]
$= -7.2 + 0$ [additive inverse property]
$= -7.2$ [additive identity property]

Chapter 8 (p. 734)

20.

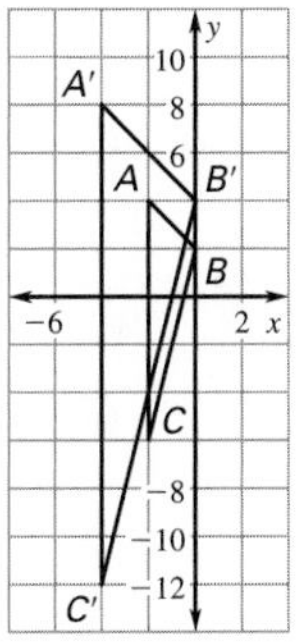

21.

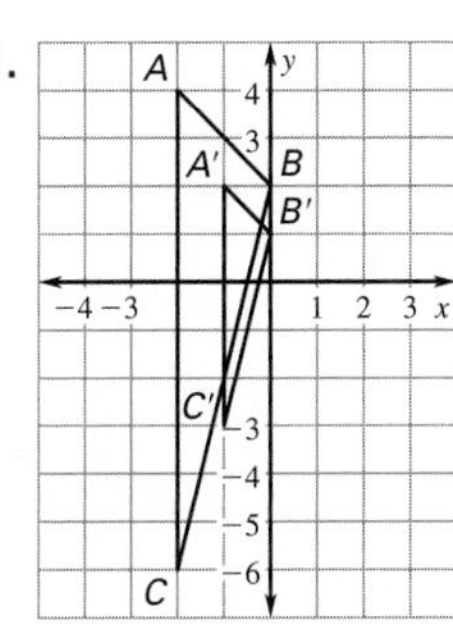

Chapter 11 (p. 737)

20. x-intercept, 2; y-intercept, 4 **21.** x-intercept, $\frac{1}{5}$; y-intercept, -1 **22.** x-intercept, -5; y-intercept, -1 **23.** x-intercept, 6; y-intercept, -4

24.

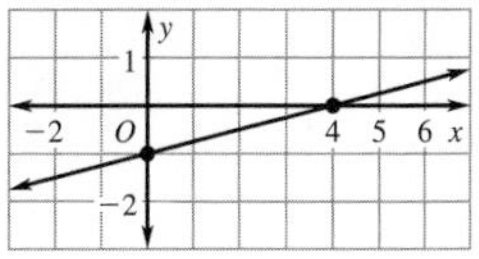

25.

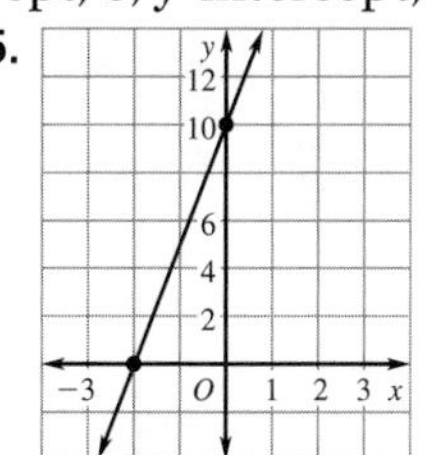

38.

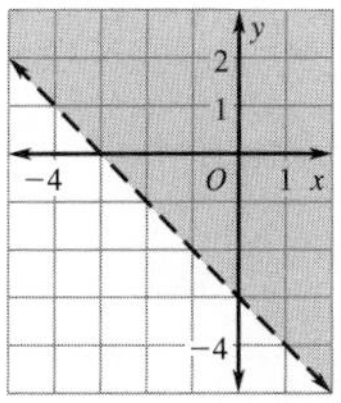

39.

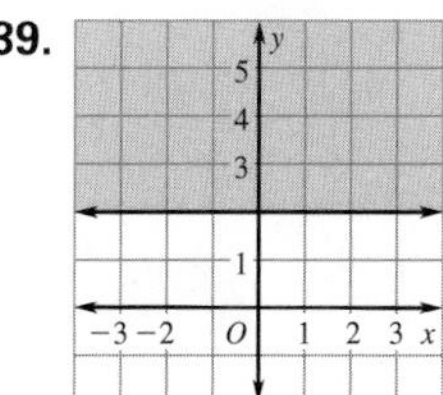

40.

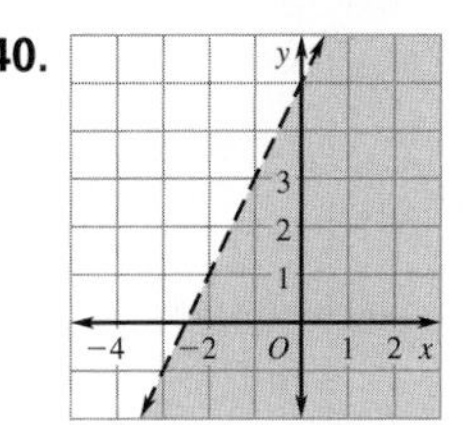

41.

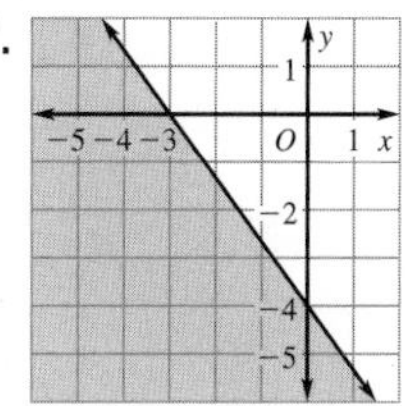

McDougal Littell Middle School Math, Course 3

This middle school math program provides the math your students need to know in a way they can understand. Fully integrated problem solving, notetaking, and assessment strategies help your students succeed.

Features	Benefits
Chapter Warm-Up Games See pp. 2–3, 268–269, 594–595.	These quick, easy-to-play games review skills needed for the upcoming chapter. The *Stop and Think* questions lead students to reflect on key mathematical ideas.
Before, Now, Why? See pp. 372–373, 375.	At the start of each chapter and lesson, this feature makes a connection to prior knowledge and answers the question, "Why should I learn this?"
Word Watch, Vocabulary Questions See pp. 270, 271, 273, 286, 308.	*Word Watch* alerts students to the key review words and new words they should know. Questions that help students understand and review vocabulary occur throughout each chapter.
Notetaking Strand See pp. 106, 109, 110, 130–131.	*Know How to Take Notes* strategies appear at the beginning of each chapter. Additional help with notetaking is integrated throughout each chapter.
Algebra Preparation See pp. 15, 28, 33, 92, 114, 119, 283, 323, 410, 504, 542, 564, 577, 674.	Through work with variables and expressions, one-step, two-step, and multi-step equations and inequalities, proportions and formulas, functions, polynomials, and graphing in the coordinate plane, this course helps students prepare for future mathematics courses.
Stepped-Out Examples See pp. 71, 125, 220, 302, 487, 564.	Clear, step-by-step examples, with explanations for each step and color coding to show relationships, help make the math clear and accessible to students.
Problem Solving Strategies See pp. 68, 228, 352, 616.	These strategies are taught and practiced in each chapter so that students are continually extending and reinforcing their skills.
Developing Problem Solving Skills See pp. 17, 41, 123, 207, 305, 452, 586, 670.	*Guided Problem Solving* and *Extended Problem Solving* exercises help students work through real-world problems and prepare students for multi-step problems that appear on high-stakes assessments.
Hands-On Activities See pp. 32, 107–108, 255–256, 321, 637–638.	These optional activities help students develop conceptual understanding through exploration, reflection, and critical thinking.
Building Test-Taking Skills See pp. 156, 364, 530, 692.	This unique feature helps students learn how to analyze and respond to multiple choice, short response, and extended response questions.
Exploring Math in Science See pp. 102, 312, 476, 652.	These cross-curricular extensions offer opportunities for projects and cooperative learning.